MW00651444

Modern Biology®

ANNOTATED TEACHER'S EDITION • ALBERT TOWLE

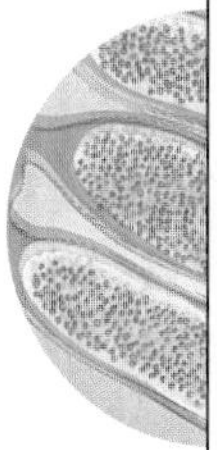

Building on a long tradition of excellence

Holt, Rinehart and Winston
Harcourt Brace Jovanovich HBJ
Austin • Orlando • San Diego • Chicago • Dallas • Toronto

Acknowledgments

Reviewers and Consultants

Byron Asakawa
San Diego High School
San Diego, CA

Jocelyn Baker
Windsor Forest High School
Savannah, GA

Wayne Becker, Ph.D.
Dept. of Botany
University of Wisconsin
Madison, WI

Bassem Bejjani, M.D.
Center for Human Genetics
Boston University School of Medicine
Boston, MA

Santanu Bhattacharya, Ph.D.
Dept. of Chemistry
Massachusetts Institute of Technology
Cambridge, MA

Mark Bierner, Ph.D.
Southwest Texas State University
San Marcos, TX

Mary Davis
Glenelg High School
Glenelg, MD

Jeffrey L. Doering, Ph.D.
Associate Professor of Biology
Loyola University
Chicago, IL

Jody Lee Duek
Granada Hills High School
Granada Hills, CA

Susan E. Eichhorn, M.S.
Dept. of Botany
University of Wisconsin
Madison, WI

John Einset, Ph.D.
EniChem Americas
Monmouth Junction, NJ

Barbara Foots
Science Director
Houston Independent School District
Houston, TX

Jerry Franklin, Ph.D.
Bloedel Professor of Forest Ecosystems Analysis
University of Washington
Seattle, WA

Joyce Gellhorn, Ph.D.
Boulder High School
Boulder, CO

Bob Gomprecht
Assistant Headmaster
Fordham Prep School, Bronx, NY

Jerald Halpern, Ph.D.
Rudolf Steiner School
New York, NY

Carl Helms, Ph.D.
Dept. of Biological Sciences
Clemson University
Clemson, SC

Andrea Huvard, Ph.D.
California Lutheran
Thousand Oaks, CA

Jerry E. Ivins, Ph.D.
Northwest Local School District
Cincinnati, OH

Garland E. Johnson
Science Coordinator
Fresno Unified School District
Fresno, CA

Jack Kelley
El Camino High School
Sacramento, CA

Burt C. Kessler
Skyline High School
Oakland, CA

Ted King
R. Nelson Snider High School
Ft. Wayne, IN

David Largent, Ph.D.
Dept. of Biology
Humboldt State University
Arcata, CA

Ruben A. Leal
J. W. Nixon High School
Laredo, TX

Daniel Leary
Apple Valley High School
Apple Valley CA

Welton L. Lee, Ph.D.
6600 Mokelumne Avenue
Oakland, CA

Christine Lekutis
New England Primate Center
Harvard University
Southborough, MA

Jamie Marantz
Skyline High School
Oakland, CA

David Moury, Ph.D.
East Tennessee State University
Johnson City, TN

Linda Barrett Phelps
Camden Central High School
Camden, TN

John Roller
Science Math Coordinator
Tulsa Public Schools
Tulsa, OK

Front cover: Great horned owl, *Bubo virginianus*

Page T1: Rainbow grasshopper, *Dactylotum bicolor*

Copyright © 1993 by Holt, Rinehart and Winston, Inc.

All rights reserved. No part of this publication may be reproduced or transmitted in any form or by any means, electronic or mechanical, including photocopy, recording, or any information storage and retrieval system, without permission in writing from the publisher.

Requests for permission to make copies of any part of the work should be mailed to: Permissions Department, Holt, Rinehart and Winston, Inc., 8th floor, Orlando, Florida 32887

Material from earlier editions copyright © 1991, 1989, 1985, 1981, 1977, 1973, 1969 by Holt, Rinehart and Winston, Inc. All rights reserved.

Printed in the United States of America

ISBN 0-03-074883-6

6 041 97

MODERN BIOLOGY is a registered trademark of Harcourt Brace & Company.

John Smarrelli, Jr., Ph.D.
Associate Professor of Biology
Loyola University
Chicago, IL

Terry Snell
Rubidoux High School
Riverside, CA

Annice Steadman
Chairperson of Science Dept.
Little Rock Central High School
Little Rock, AR

James K. Stringfield, Ph.D.
Harnett Central High School
Angier, NC

Aleta Sullivan
Hattiesburg High School
Hattiesburg, MS

Nina Surawicz, M.D.
Student Health Service
Arizona State University
Tempe, AZ

David Sutton
Chairperson of Science Dept.
Wauwatosa West High School
Wauwatosa, WI

Lyn Swan
John Marshall High School
Los Angeles, CA

Bradley Switzer
Tates Creek Senior High School
Lexington, KY

Linda Thayer
Jeremiah Burke High School
Dorchester, MA

James Thomas
Grove City High School
Grove City, Ohio

Salvatore Tocci
Chairperson of Science Dept.
East Hampton High School
East Hampton, NY

George Tong
Northgate High School
Walnut Creek, CA

Betty Tumminello
Chairperson of Science Dept.
Pineville High School
Pineville, LA

Marge Tunnell
Gregory Middle School
Naperville, IL

Robert Vasconcellos
Gunderson High School
San Jose, CA

Contributors

Beth M. Atkin, Ph.D.
Dept. of Medicine
University of Chicago
Chicago, IL

Judy Berlfein
Encinitas, CA

Ronnee Bernberg-Yashon
Lakeview High School
Chicago, IL

Professor Steven Gilbert
Biology Dept.
Ball State University
Muncie, IN

Deborah L. Jensen
Oak Ridge High School
Conroe, TX

Maureen Lemke
Goodnight Junior High School
San Marcos, TX

Glenn K. Leto
Barrington High School
Barrington, IL

Violetta Lien, Ph.D.
Division of Education
University of Texas at San Antonio
San Antonio, TX

Jennifer Matos, Ph.D.
Professor of Biology
Washington University
St. Louis, MO

Janice Moore
Associate Professor of Biology
Colorado State University
Ft. Collins, CO

Randy Moore, Ph.D.
Chairperson of Biology
Wright State University
Dayton, OH

Carl Reed
Barrington High School
Barrington, IL

Carol Savonen
Oregon State University
Corvallis, OR

Richard Strickland
Washington Sea Grant Program
University of Washington
Seattle, WA

National Advisory Panel

Vernon Ahmadjian, Ph.D.
Professor of Botany
Clark University
Worcester, MA

Karen Arms, Ph.D.
Savannah, GA

Mildred Berry, Ed.D.
Director, General Education
Dade County Public Schools
Miami, FL

Ray Evert, Ph.D.
Professor of Botany
University of Wisconsin
Madison, WI

Maura C. Flannery, Ph.D.
Associate Professor of Biology
St. John's University
Jamaica, NY

Gerald Garner
Secondary Science Specialist
Los Angeles Unified School District
Los Angeles, CA

Mary Alice Garza-Gonzales
Jefferson High School
San Antonio, TX

Jerry Ivins, Ph.D.
Science Coordinator
Northwest Local School District
Cincinnati, OH

Donald Johnson
Science Dept. Chairperson
Mumford High School
Detroit, MI

Jane Matthews
B. C. Rain High School
Mobile, AL

Harold Slavkin, Ph.D.
Director, Center for Craniofacial Molecular Biology
University of Southern California
Los Angeles, CA

Paul Sugg
Secondary Science Specialist
3700 Ross Avenue
Dallas, TX

Herbert Vitale
Director, Programs for Exceptional Children
Lynchburg City Schools
Lynchburg, VA

Dan Walker, Ph.D.
Dept. of Biological Sciences
San Jose State University
San Jose, CA

Contents

Teacher's Guide

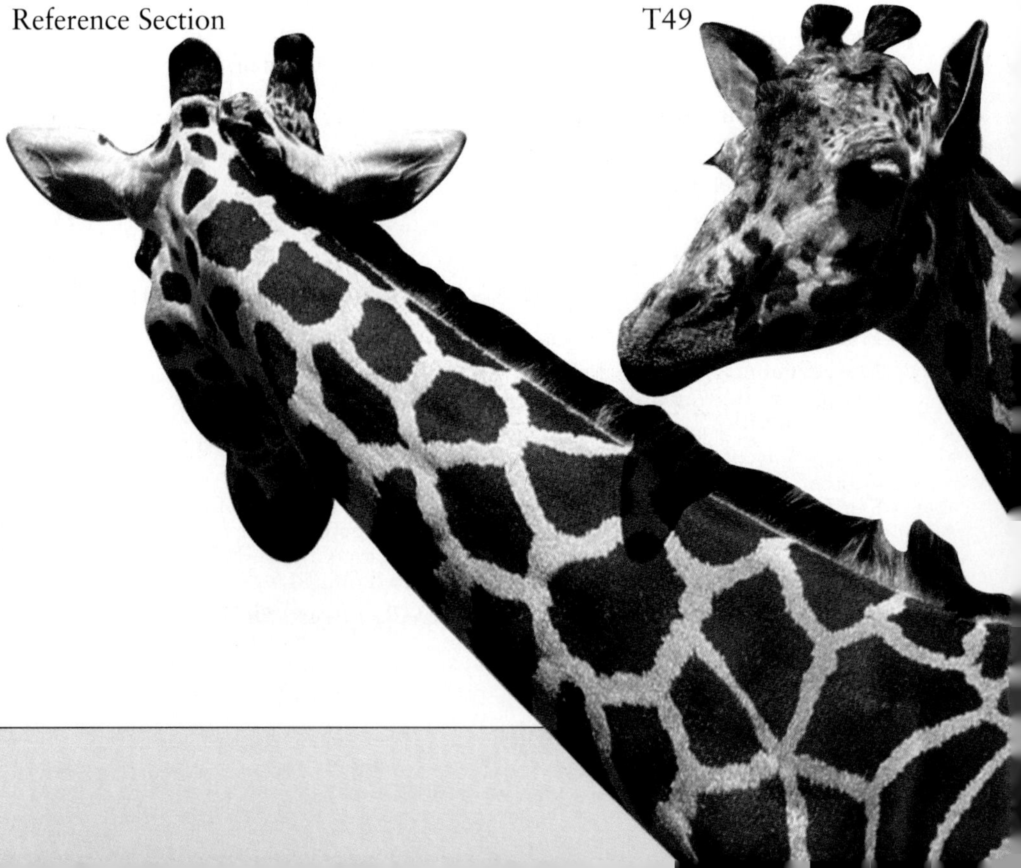

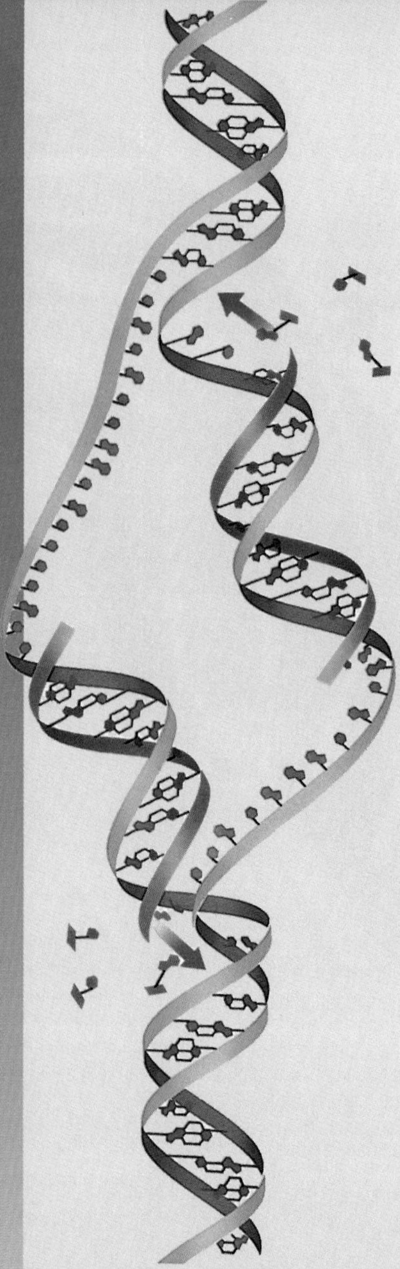

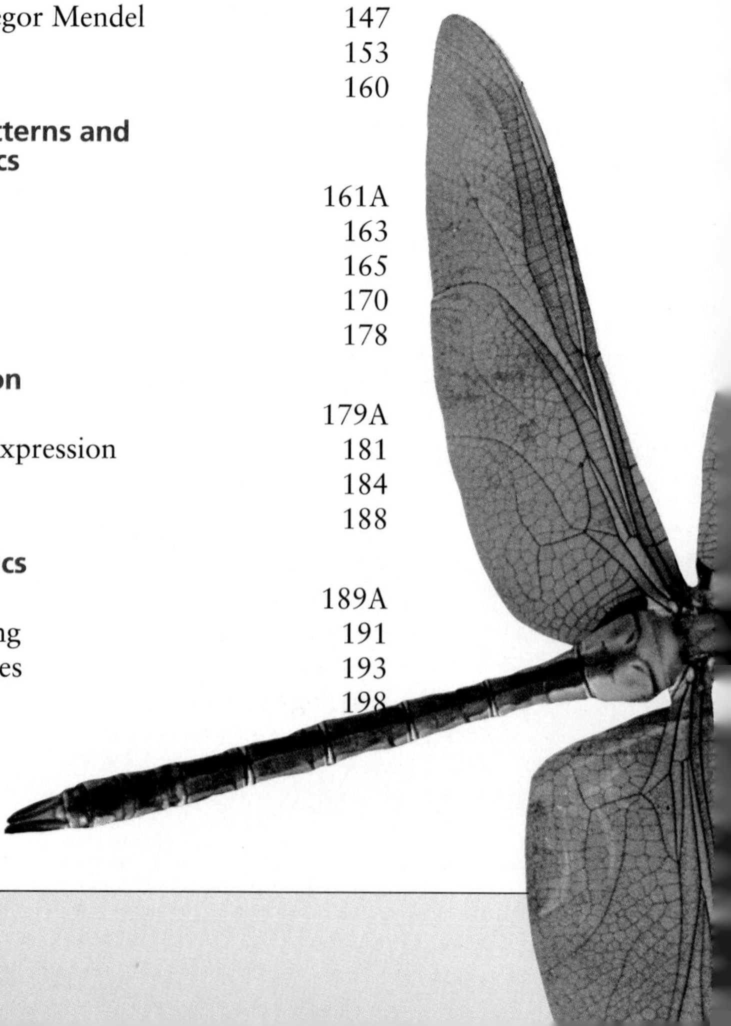

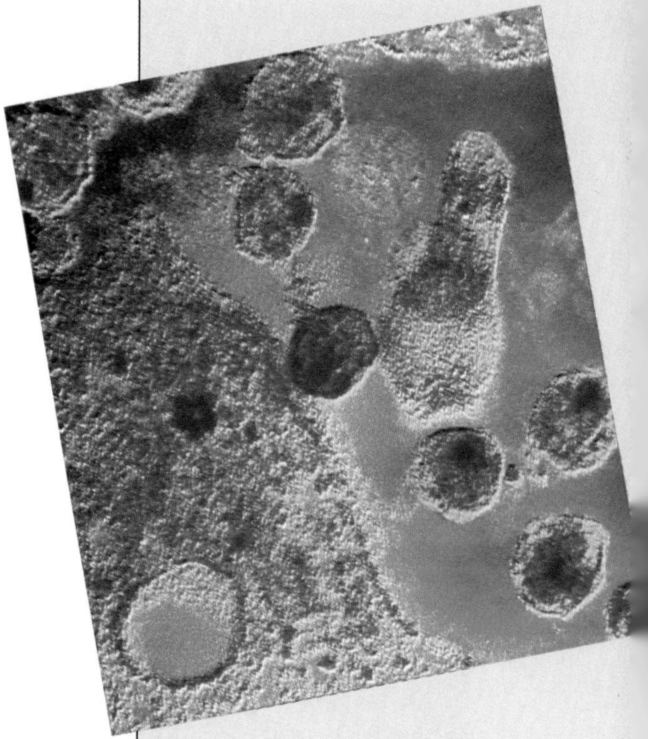

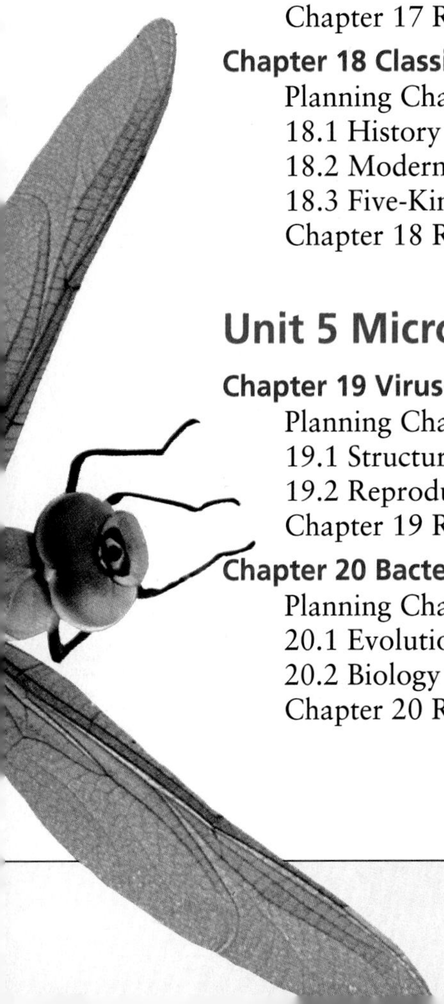

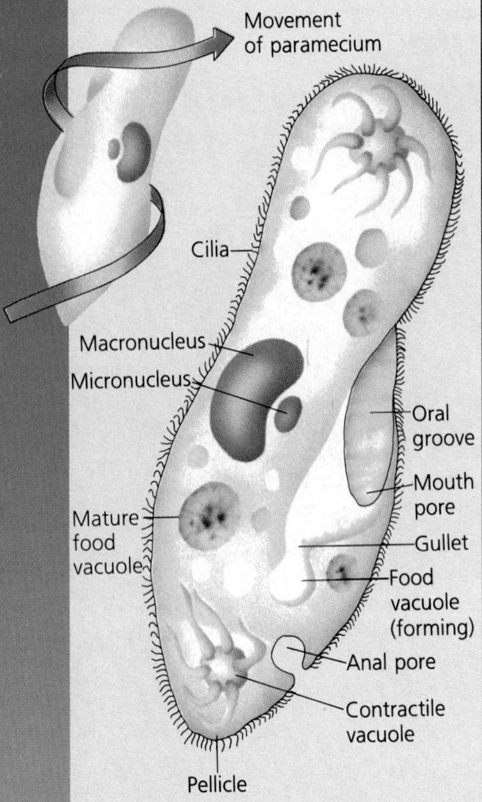
Movement
of paramecium
Cilia
Macronucleus
Micronucleus
Oral
groove
Mouth
pore
Mature
food
vacuole
Gullet
Food
vacuole
(forming)
Anal pore
Contractile
vacuole
Pellicle

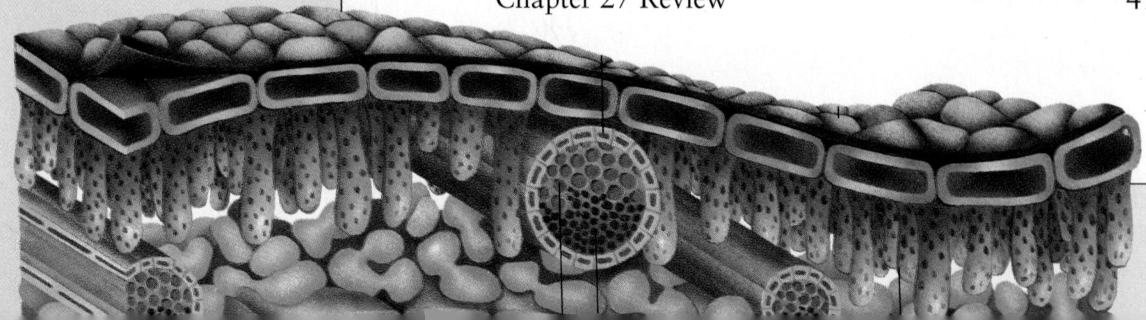

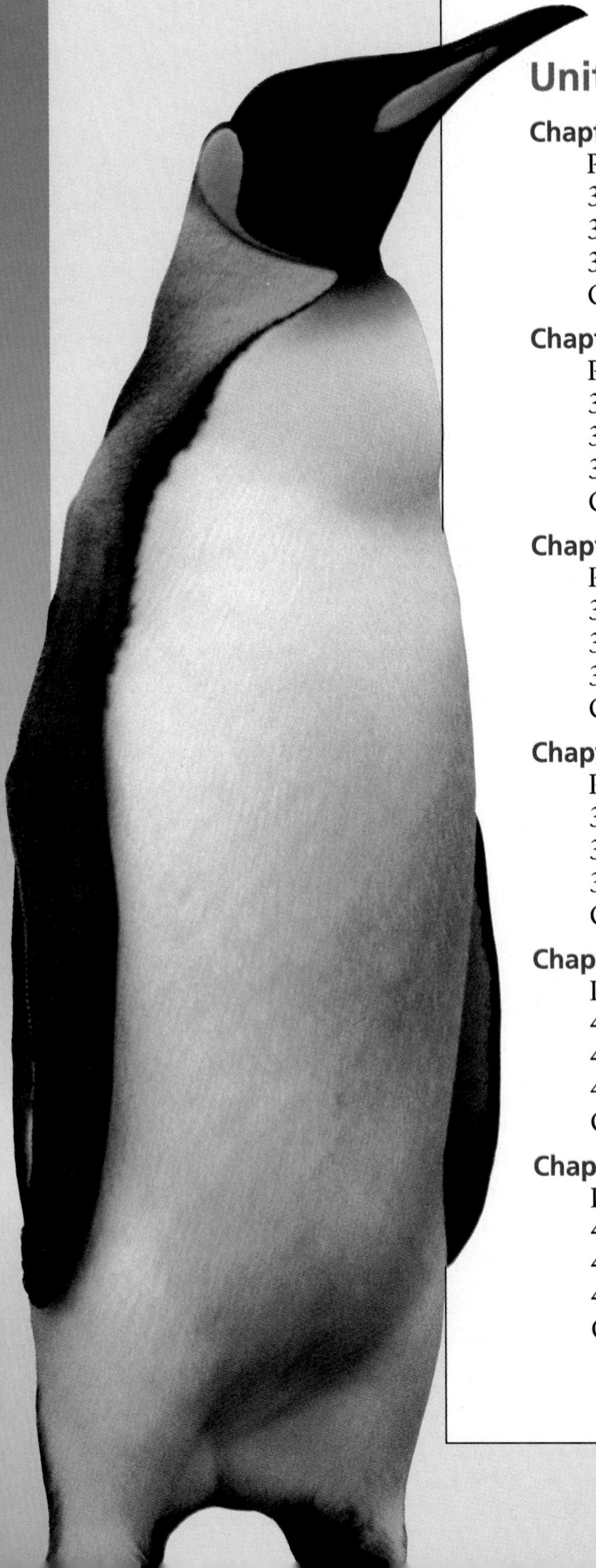

Unit 9 Human Biology 633A

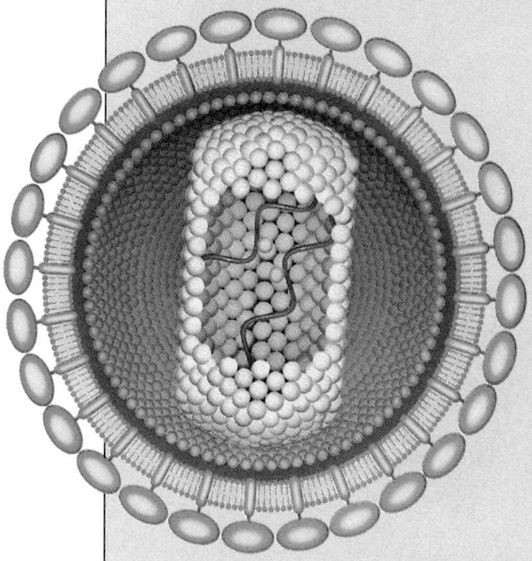

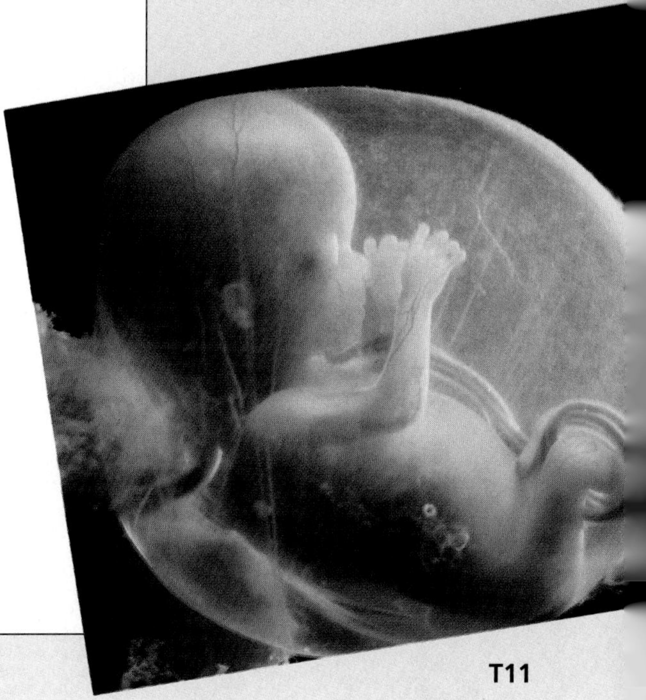

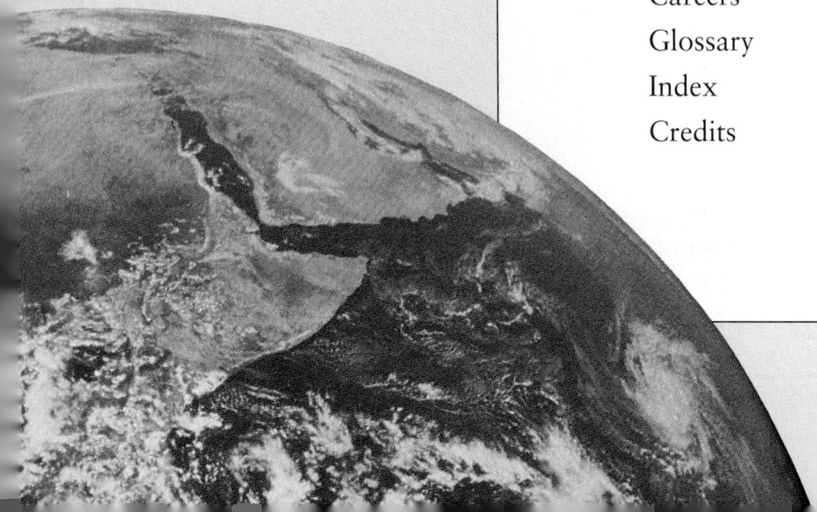

Features

Biology in Process

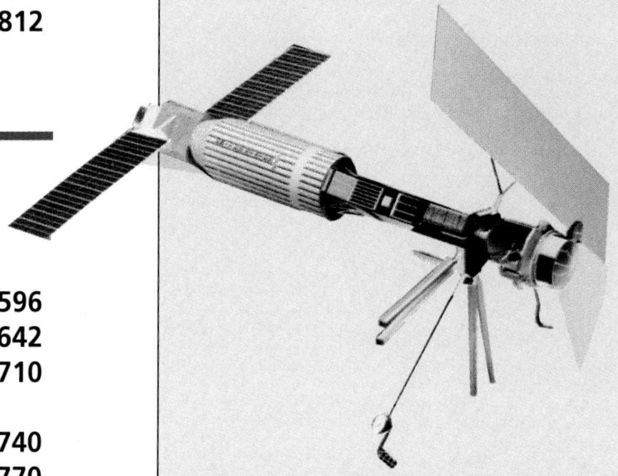

Biotechnology

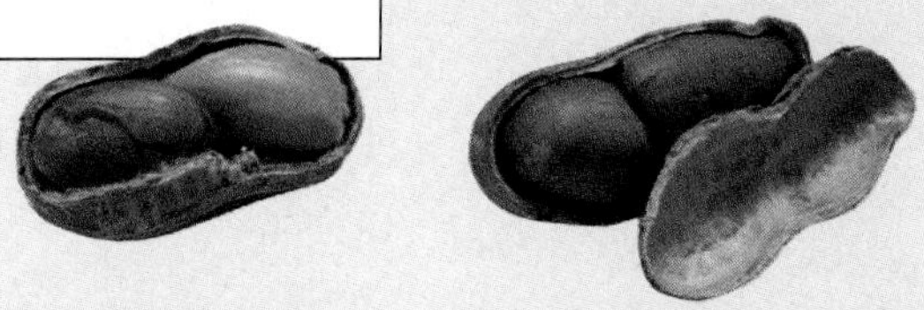

Laboratory Investigations

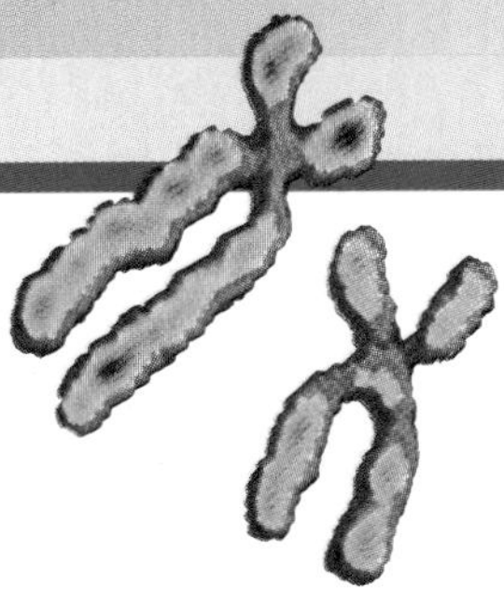

Writing About Biology

Intra-Science

Modern Biology

The Thorough Coverage You Need to Teach Thematically

The Modern Biology Course

Nowhere has the explosion of knowledge and the impact of modern technology on human lives been more apparent than in the field of biology. New discoveries are announced with increasing frequency; students, as well as adults, are confronted with new social, political, and ethical choices. Modern Biology *stresses the vital connection between biological principles and the processes of science. Students are given the solid foundation they need to understand the expanding role of biology in modern society and the skills to excel in future courses in science.*

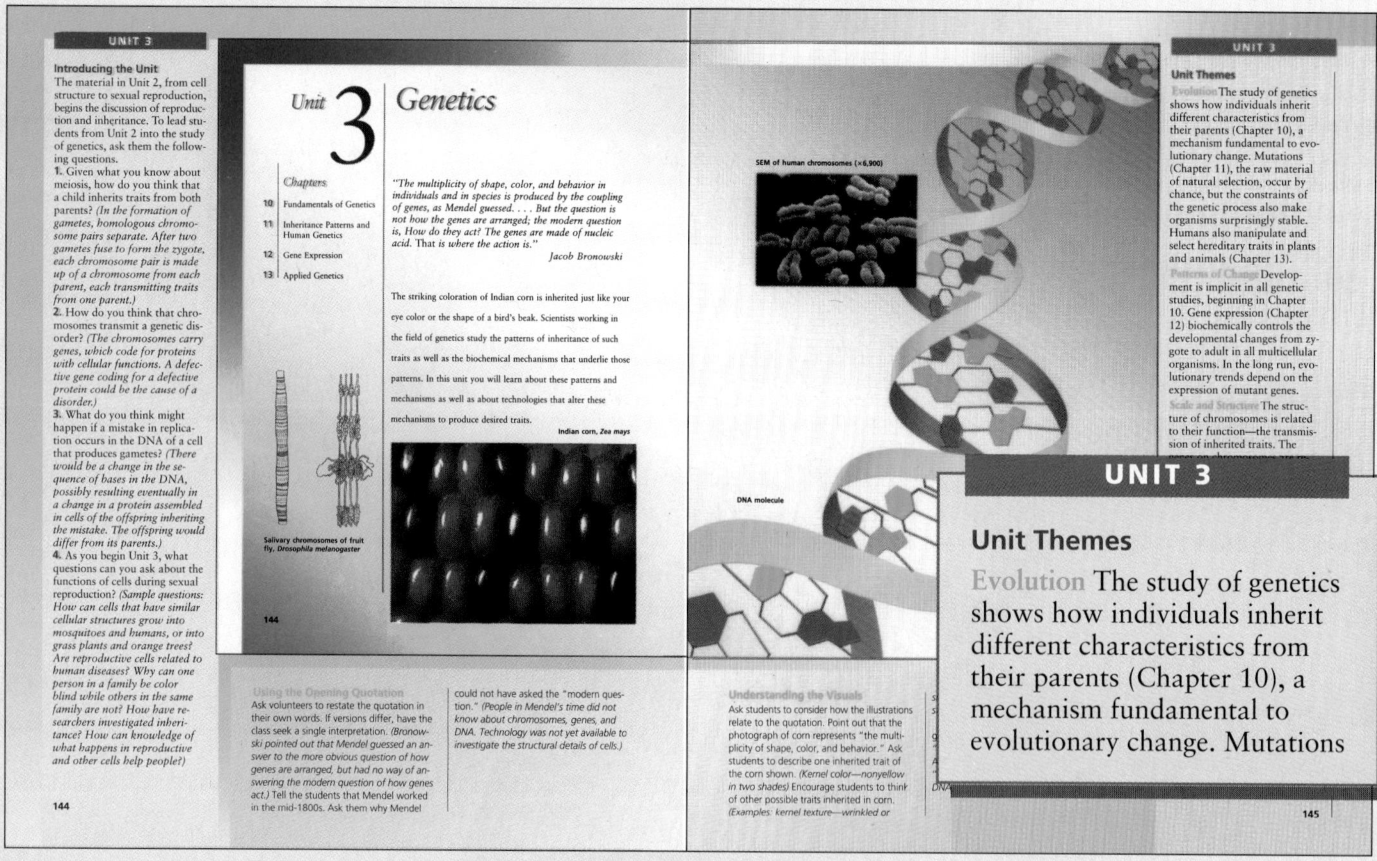

UNIT 3

Introducing the Unit

The material in Unit 2, from cell structure to sexual reproduction, begins the discussion of reproduction and inheritance. To lead students from Unit 2 into the study of genetics, ask them the following questions.

1. Given what you know about meiosis, how do you think that a child inherits traits from both parents? *(In the formation of gametes, homologous chromosome pairs separate. After two gametes fuse to form the zygote, each chromosome pair is made up of a chromosome from each parent, each transmitting traits from one parent.)*

2. How do you think that chromosomes transmit a genetic disorder? *(The chromosomes carry genes, which code for proteins with cellular functions. A defective gene coding for a defective protein could be the cause of a disorder.)*

3. What do you think might happen if a mistake in replication occurs in the DNA of a cell that produces gametes? *(There would be a change in the sequence of bases in the DNA, possibly resulting eventually in a change in a protein assembled in cells of the offspring inheriting the mistake. The offspring would differ from its parents.)*

4. As you begin Unit 3, what questions can you ask about the functions of cells during sexual reproduction? *(Sample questions: How can cells that have similar cellular structures grow into mosquitoes and humans, or into grass plants and orange trees? Are reproductive cells related to human diseases? Why can one person in a family be color blind while others in the same family are not? How have researchers investigated inheritance? How can knowledge of what happens in reproductive and other cells help people?)*

144

Unit 3 **Genetics**

Chapters

10 Fundamentals of Genetics

11 Inheritance Patterns and Human Genetics

12 Gene Expression

13 Applied Genetics

"The multiplicity of shape, color, and behavior in individuals and in species is produced by the coupling of genes, as Mendel guessed. . . . But the question is not how the genes are arranged; the modern question is, How do they act? The genes are made of nucleic acid. That is where the action is."

Jacob Bronowski

The striking coloration of Indian corn is inherited just like your eye color or the shape of a bird's beak. Scientists working in the field of genetics study the patterns of inheritance of such traits as well as the biochemical mechanisms that underlie those patterns. In this unit you will learn about these patterns and mechanisms as well as about technologies that alter these mechanisms to produce desired traits.

Indian corn, *Zea mays*

Salivary chromosomes of fruit fly, *Drosophila melanogaster*

144

Using the Opening Quotation

Ask volunteers to restate the quotation in their own words. If versions differ, have the class seek a single interpretation. *(Bronowski pointed out that Mendel guessed an answer to the more obvious question of how genes are arranged, but had no way of answering the modern question of how genes act.)* Tell the students that Mendel worked in the mid-1800s. Ask them why Mendel could not have asked the "modern question." *(People in Mendel's time did not know about chromosomes, genes, and DNA. Technology was not yet available to investigate the structural details of cells.)*

SEM of human chromosomes (×6,900)

DNA molecule

Understanding the Visuals

Ask students to consider how the illustrations relate to the quotation. Point out that the photograph of corn represents "the multiplicity of shape, color, and behavior." Ask students to describe one inherited trait of the corn shown. *(Kernel color—nonyellow in two shades)* Encourage students to think of other possible traits inherited in corn. *(Examples: kernel texture—wrinkled or*

UNIT 3

Unit Themes

Evolution The study of genetics shows how individuals inherit different characteristics from their parents (Chapter 10), a mechanism fundamental to evolutionary change. Mutations (Chapter 11), the raw material of natural selection, occur by chance, but the constraints of the genetic process also make organisms surprisingly stable. Humans also manipulate and select hereditary traits in plants and animals (Chapter 13).

Patterns of Change Development is implicit in all genetic studies, beginning in Chapter 10. Gene expression (Chapter 12) biochemically controls the developmental changes from zygote to adult in all multicellular organisms. In the long run, evolutionary trends depend on the expression of mutant genes.

Scale and Structure The structure of chromosomes is related to their function—the transmission of inherited traits. The

145

UNIT 3

Unit Themes

Evolution The study of genetics shows how individuals inherit different characteristics from their parents (Chapter 10), a mechanism fundamental to evolutionary change. Mutations

Unifying Themes

Modern Biology helps you focus your teaching on developing a deeper understanding of basic biological principles through the use of unifying themes. Chapter 1 of the student text lists the seven biological themes that have been chosen to unify the content.

They are:

- Evolution
- Reproduction and Inheritance
- Development
- Structure and Function
- Energy Relationships
- Ecology
- Science and Society

Your Teacher's Edition is organized around six scientific themes that unify all sciences.

- Energy
- Evolution
- Patterns of Change
- Scale and Structure
- Stability
- Systems and Interactions

In Chapter 1 on page 5, you will see an explanation of these six themes and a graphic organizer that shows how the biological themes in the student text relate to the broader scientific themes stressed in your Teacher's Edition. Presenting the scientific themes in the Teacher's Edition helps you show students how the biology they are learning connects with what they've learned in other science courses. For example, students see how energy flow relates not only to physical and chemical systems, but to biological systems as well. In this way, students get a broader, but connected view of science. You'll find the important themes for the unit highlighted on the right column of the unit opener page. The specific themes covered in each chapter are found in the left column of the chapter opener. The material in each section is also linked to themes that are highlighted as part of the Lesson Plan for that section.

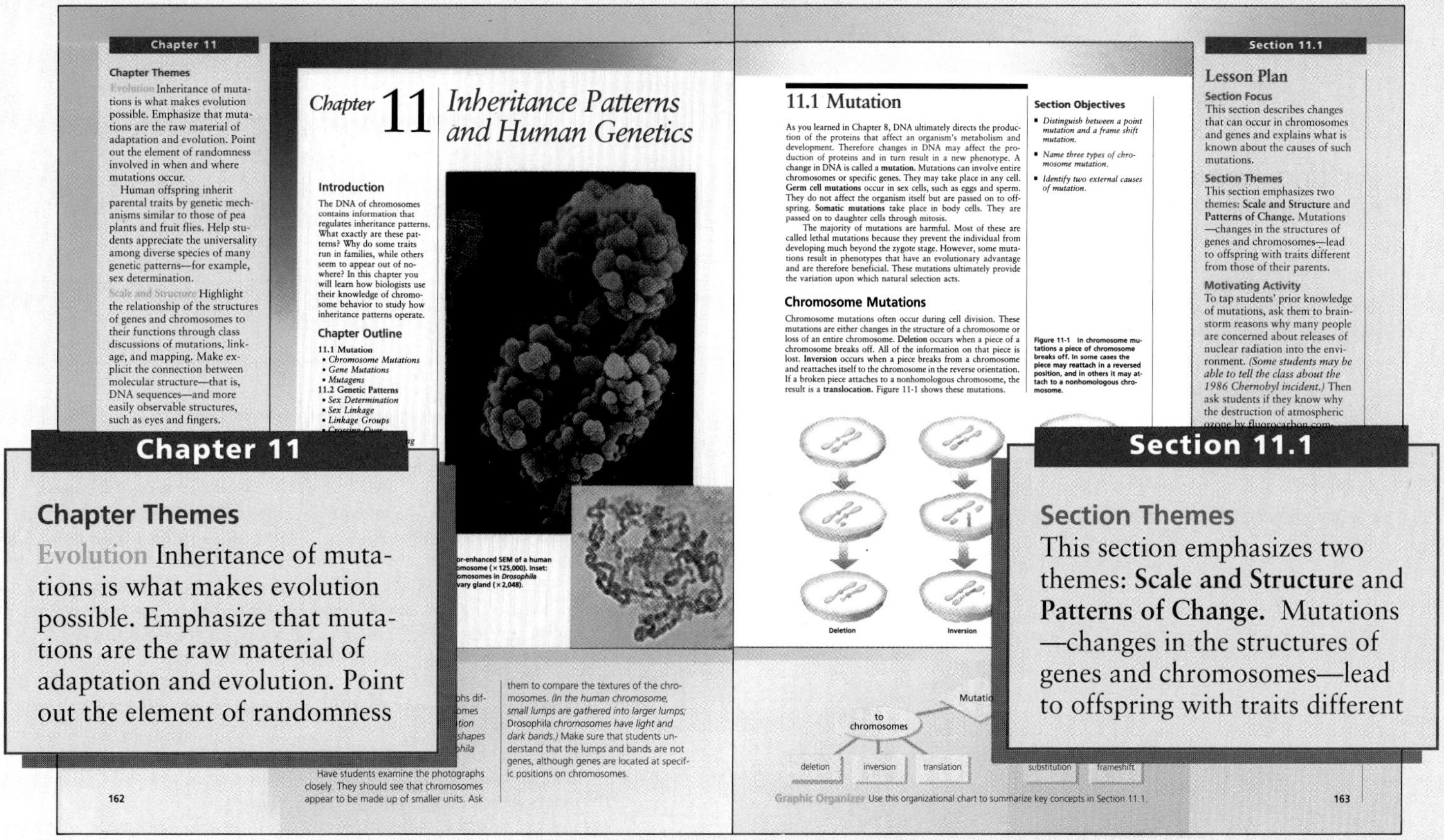

Thorough Coverage for Developing Scientific Literacy

Developing scientific literacy while engaging students with relevant issues helps them see the societal implications of scientific endeavors. It also means that students understand the nature of scientific reasoning and recognize the importance of a rational approach to solving problems, which includes the ability to apply critical thinking skills to evaluating an issue or problem. Modern Biology *provides many avenues to further this goal.*

Writing About Biology

Wyoming Reverie

This excerpt is from The Dinosaur Heresies *by Robert Bakker.*

From my Field Book, 1981 . . . July 3, 6:35 A.M. Como Bluff, Wyoming. 7,020 feet above sea level. No human being or human structure visible. Air clear, dry, cool. . . .

I'm still excited by the first dinosaur of the summer. I sit here on the crest of a little sandstone hogback, remnant of a stream that flowed a hundred million years ago, and look down on my crew's work of the last four days. It's becoming a sizeable hole, a proper dinosaur dig, twenty-five feet across, dug by pickax, army-surplus trenching shovel, ice-pick, and fingernails.

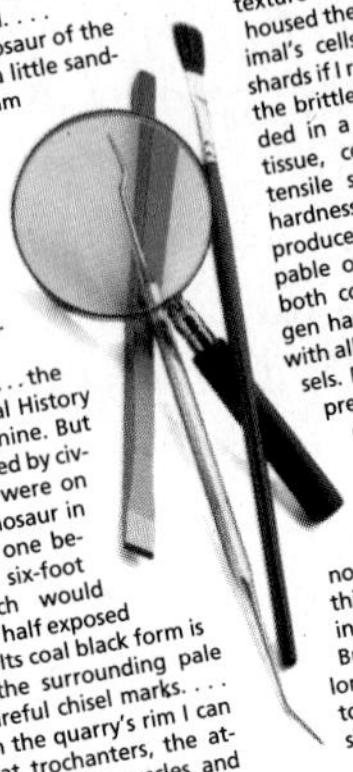

I saw my first dinosaur in . . . the American Museum of Natural History in New York, at the age of nine. But those skeletons seemed tamed by civilization, mounted as they were on steel and plaster. . . . A dinosaur in the rock is different. This one before me is huge, and its six-foot long thigh bone, which would dwarf any elephant's, lies half exposed to the Wyoming sunrise. Its coal black form is clearly etched against the surrounding pale rock by thousands of careful chisel marks. . . .

From where I sit on the quarry's rim I can see the dinosaur's great trochanters, the attachment site of the immense hip muscles, and the bone surface pitted and rough where tendons and ligaments were anchored to the femur. A hundred thousand millenia ago, those tendons and muscles were full of dinosaur blood coursing through capillary beds, bringing oxygen to the cells that powered the stride of this ten-ton giant. Muscles pulsed in cycles of contraction and release, and the hind limb, from hip to toenails, swung through its stroke covering six feet with every pace.

Broken chips of bone lie under my boots, wretched fragments from now unidentifiable bones which had eroded long before we found the site. . . . Some of the broken bits are incredibly delicate bubbles of bone, a frothy texture of holes and vesicles that housed the living substance of the animal's cells. These bits crumble into shards if I rub them too hard, but in life the brittle bone crystals were embedded in a fabric of tough connective tissue, collagen fibers whose great tensile strength combined with the hardness of the bone crystals to produce a living bony architecture capable of resisting enormous loads of both compression and tension. Collagen has long since rotted away, along with all the muscle fibers and blood vessels. But the fossilized bone faithfully preserves the canals left by every capillary that made its passage through it to serve the dinosaur in life. . . .

Reverie is normal in Wyoming at sunrise. I suppose a no-nonsense laboratory scientist might think I was wasting my time communing with the spirit of the fossil beast. But scientists need reverie. We need long walks and quiet times at the quarry to let the whole pattern of fossil history sink into our consciousness.

Write

- **Write a short essay explaining why you think scientists may need reverie. In what way might it help them find answers to their questions? Does Bakker's line of reasoning here have anything to do with the concern that Lewis Thomas expressed in the beginning of his essay on p. 28?**

... Robert Bakker. Reprinted by **227**

Writing About Biology

Writing About Biology features expose students to the thought-provoking perspectives of scientists through their writings. Students are then given the opportunity to do their own writings on an issue related to the subject of the article.

Biology in Process

Biology in Process features show the ways in which biologists have used basic scientific processes to expand our knowledge of the world. Students are asked to give their evaluations of the validity of the scientists' methods.

Northern Bahamas

Biology in Process

Classifying Cerion

The snails shown are members of a group of Bahamian land snails of the genus *Cerion (SIR-EE-on)*. Scientists have observed variation in the snails' shell size, structure, and color.

Nineteenth-century scientists, using the morphological species concept, classified up to 600 species.

This long list of snail species discouraged scientific study of *Cerion*. Under the morphological species concept members of different species could be distinguished only by minute differences in their shells. The American scientist Stephen Jay Gould studied *Cerion* by using both the biological and the morphological concepts of species.

Gould observed *Cerion* in the northern Bahamas, a group of islands formed from two submerged landmasses, or banks. Little Bahama Bank and Great Bahama Bank, shown on the map, are separated by a deep channel.

Each island of the northern Bahamas has one coast facing the open ocean and one coast facing the interior of its bank. Gould observed that *Cerion* on the ocean coasts of both banks had thick, ribbed shells and a uniform color. Those on the interior coasts of both banks had

238 *Chapter 16*

Issues in Biology

Use your discretion in introducing the following to[pic] for class discussion, and be sensitive to family a[nd] community values.

In pregnancies that appear to be at risk, techni[ques] such as amniocentesis and chorion villi sampling spot chromosomal abnormalities as well as ce[rtain] mutati[ons] ...reening s... that th... ...rder, the p...

Issues in Biology

Issues in Biology topics appear at the opening of each unit in your Teacher's Edition. Valuable background information is provided to help you in monitoring a discussion of these controversial issues in the classroom.

Intra-Science
How the Sciences Work Together

The Question in Biology: Will Earth's Forests Vanish?

Scientists estimate that every year an expanse of tropical rain forest the size of Pennsylvania is destroyed. Already, almost half the rain forests that once encircled the earth have vanished. According to Thomas Lovejoy of the Smithsonian Institution, "The rain forest will be won or lost in the 1990s." If the battle is lost, the rain forests may be gone by the middle of the twenty-first century.

Although tropical rain forests cover only about 6 percent of the earth's surface, they are home to 50 percent of the earth's plants and animals. A rain forest the size of a city park may contain 1,500 different flowering plants, 750 species of trees, and hundreds of kinds of mammals, birds, reptiles, amphibians, and insects.

Why are these forests being destroyed? The reasons involve complex social and economic problems in many nations. The government policies of some Southeast Asian nations, for example, permit the harvest and export of mahogany, teak, and other hardwoods to help reduce national debt. International banks loan money to build new industries that involve destroying the rain forests in Central America and South America. Government subsidies and tax breaks to Brazilian cattle ranchers also make it profitable to clear huge tracts of rain forest. Poor farmers often "slash and burn" the rain forest to quickly create pastureland for sale to wealthy cattle ranchers.

As a result of these policies and activities, the rate of deforestation has rapidly increased. In the ten years between 1979 and 1989, the rate of rain forest deforestation nearly doubled. Since 1989, about 2 percent of remaining rain forest vanishes each year.

Deforestation is not limited just to tropical rain forests, however. From the early 1600s to the 1900s, settlers in North America cut down temperate forests to create farmland. According to Ken Andrasko of the Environmental Protection Agency (EPA), "The people in the tropics are do- ing now..."

...im- ...ithout ...s. ...and ...dige- ...of re- ...uts, ...zoolo- ...ms. ...o mon- ...col- ...For ...e bio-

Intra-Science

Intra-Science features show students how scientists with different backgrounds collaborate in attempting to solve a world problem. These issues are organized to engage students in expressing their own thoughts on the problem.

The motions ... are analyzed by c... produce a three-d... map of the speci... The image presen... monitor represen... tion of approxim... lion times the spe...

At first the S... to study samples ... as gold and nicke... STMs were being ... ture images of vi... (p. 26). The DNA ... double-helix shap... ten compared to ... der. The images c... molecule that an ... are so fine that t... the narrow space...

Biotechnology

Scanning Tunneling Microscope

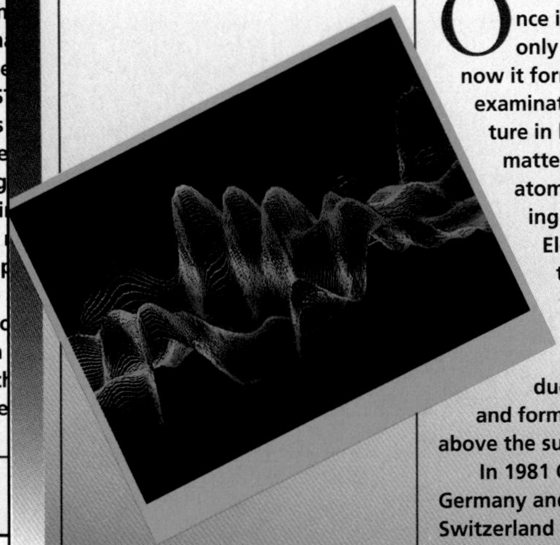

Once it was considered only a curious theory; now it forms the basis for the examination of atomic structure in living and nonliving matter. Around every atomic nucleus is a moving cloud of energy. Electrons leak, or tunnel, from the surface of all matter—especially matter that conducts electricity well—and form electron clouds just above the surface.

In 1981 Gerd Binnig of West Germany and Heinrich Rohrer of Switzerland designed a microscope that could make use of these electron clouds to map the surface of an object, atom by atom. The scanning tunneling microscope (STM) has no lenses and doesn't need a focused beam of light or electrons to produce an image. Instead, the STM searches the surface of the specimen, using a sensor to detect the motion of tunneling electro[ns] ...

The... with a ... an ato[m] ... detect ... the de[n]... cloud (... the sur[face] ... tours at ... from the specimen.

Biotechnology

Biotechnology features expose students to the tools and techniques that scientists use in developing new products and technologies.

26 *Chapter 2*

Thorough Coverage for Developing Process and Inquiry Skills

The pursuit of knowledge through scientific inquiry involves emulating the processes that scientists use to build theories. The laboratory program in *Modern Biology* provides several ways to show students that scientific processes are ways of going about learning things.

Goals of the Laboratory Program

The laboratories are designed for students to engage in inquiry, which includes formulating hypotheses and designing experiments to test those hypotheses. Students are challenged to think about what they are doing in lab while actively involved in the discovery of ideas and the development of problem-solving skills. The process skills developed in this program are highlighted below.

The best way to teach process skills is to place students in a laboratory setting where they perform a scientific investigation. The 53 Laboratory pages in the text combined with the 59 additional investigations in the *Laboratories* manual provide a wide range of options for you to give students hands-on experiences. Each lab in the student text and the lab manual lists the process skills that are developed within that experience.

In-Text Laboratories

Traditional Inquiry The procedure steps are outlined specifically in the lab. Students make observations or collect data and then form conclusions.

Guided Inquiry Questions are provided to initiate student thought before students begin the procedure. More questions are embedded in the investigation itself in order to encourage students to think scientifically about procedure and results while they work.

Student Designed Inquiry In these laboratories, students consider a problem and formulate a hypothesis. Then they adapt the technique given in the lab and design their own experiment to test this hypothesis.

Laboratory Investigations in the *Teacher's Resource Binder*

Laboratory investigations in *Modern Biology* help students learn to solve scientific problems using critical thinking skills, process skills, and creativity. Students are asked a variety of inquiry questions throughout each Procedure. The questions get students thinking about the procedure as well as the results of the Investigation. Because the inquiry questions are part of the Procedure, students will be doing the thinking in the lab.

Each Investigation incorporates at least two of the process skills highlighted in Chapter 2. Students report their findings on separate report sheets that are organized for easy grading. For

Chapter Laboratories

Process Skill	1	2	3	4	5	6	7	8	9	10	11	12	13	14	15	16	17	18	19	20	21	22	23	24	25	26	27	28	29	30
observing			•	•	•	•					•	•		•				•		•	•		•	•	•	•	•		•	•
collecting data		•							•	•					•													•		
measuring															•															
organizing data									•																	•				
classifying	•				•				•								•	•				•		•	•		•			
hypothesizing		•			•		•	•				•		•					•	•	•	•						•	•	•
predicting										•			•			•														
experimenting		•	•	•		•	•	•											•	•	•							•	•	•
analyzing data		•							•				•		•	•										•	•	•		
inferring	•							•		•	•	•	•		•		•					•	•	•	•		•			
modeling																•														
communicating	•										•																			

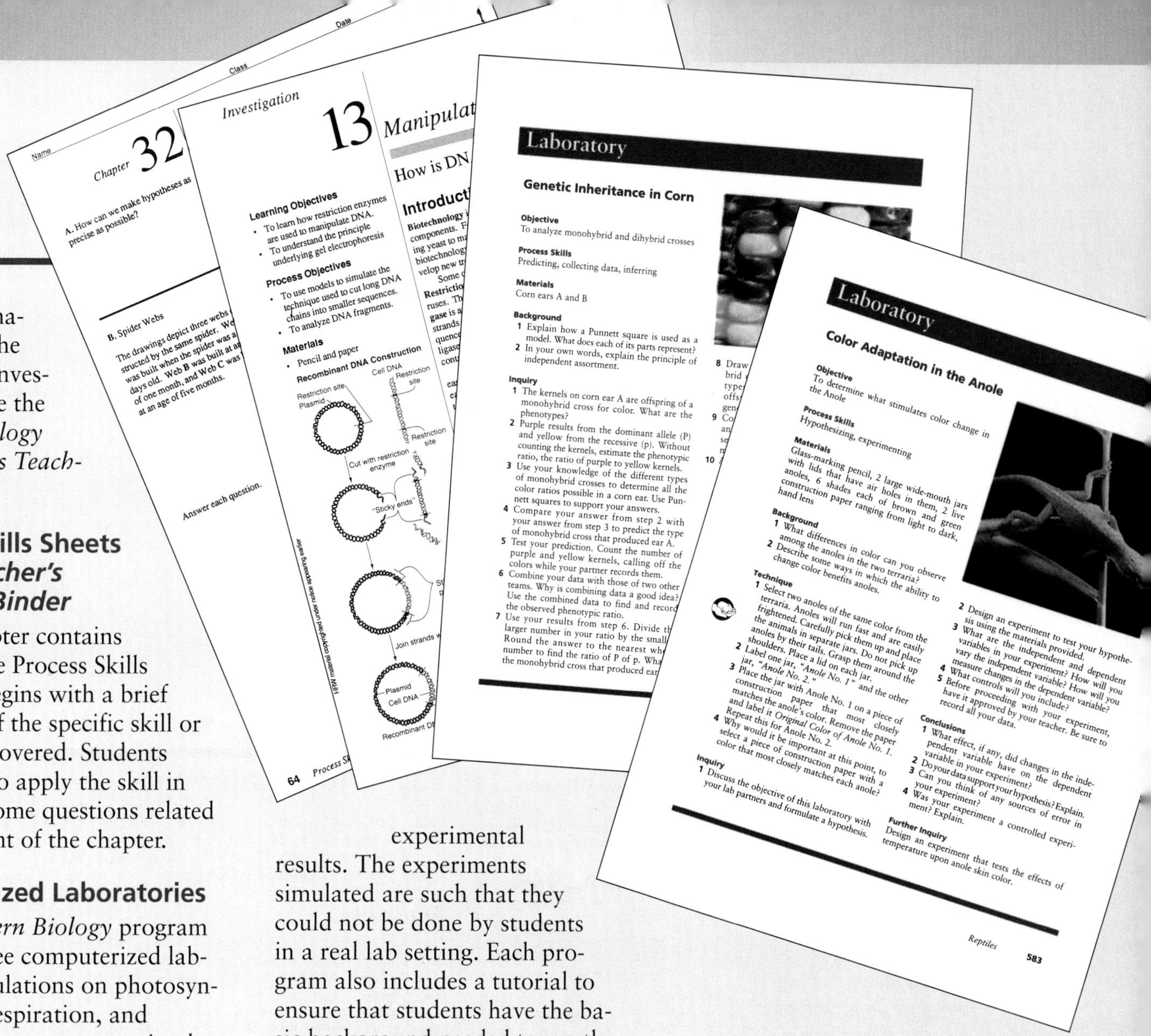

more information about the laboratory investigations, see the *Modern Biology Laboratories Teacher's Edition.*

Process Skills Sheets in the *Teacher's Resource Binder*

Each chapter contains one full-page Process Skills sheet that begins with a brief discussion of the specific skill or skills to be covered. Students then go on to apply the skill in answering some questions related to the content of the chapter.

Computerized Laboratories

The *Modern Biology* program includes three computerized laboratory simulations on photosynthesis, cell respiration, and genetics. These computer simulations are designed to give students the opportunity to apply scientific processes in analyzing experimental results. The experiments simulated are such that they could not be done by students in a real lab setting. Each program also includes a tutorial to ensure that students have the basic background needed to use the simulations. Laboratory worksheets are included to help guide students through the simulations.

Chapter Laboratories

31	32	33	34	35	36	37	38	39	40	41	42	43	44	45	46	47	48	49	50	51	52	53	Process Skill
		•	•	•		•		•	•	•	•		•	•			•		•	•			observing
															•								collecting data
																		•					measuring
																							organizing data
				•	•								•						•				classifying
•	•					•	•	•	•			•			•	•					•	•	hypothesizing
														•				•					predicting
•	•						•					•			•	•		•			•	•	experimenting
		•	•												•								analyzing data
	•	•		•		•		•	•	•	•		•	•			•		•	•		•	inferring
														•			•						modeling
					•																		communicating

Well-Crafted Lessons Promote Student Success

The logical organization and clear lesson design in Modern Biology *make the relationships between ideas and their relative importance immediately apparent to students. The innovative visual program that accompanies the written text helps to clarify the content and amplify meaning. This solid, working relationship between the text and the visuals gives* Modern Biology *a distinctive, motivating approach to instruction.*

Section Objectives
Each lesson begins with a list of three to five objectives that preview the major concepts and focus students' attention on essential content.

Section Headings
A numbered main heading signals the beginning of each lesson.

Subheads
Two levels of boldfaced subheadings outline the major topics and subtopics, clarifying relationships and helping students relate information.

State-of-the-Art Photography
Close-up, dramatic views of the living world capture students' interest and attention.

Section Objectives

- *Name the three main groups of arachnids, and list their distinguishing structural differences.*
- *Explain the adaptations arachnids have for predatory life on land.*
- *List similarities and differences between millipedes and centipedes.*

32.3 Other Arthropods

Unlike crustaceans, nearly all members of Chelicerata and Uniramia are terrestrial. In this section we will examine the major class of chelicerates, Arachnida, as well as two classes of the Subphylum Uniramia, Diplopoda and Chilopoda.

Arachnida

The Class Arachnida *(uh-RACK-nuh-duh)* is a group of more than 100,000 species, including spiders, scorpions, and mites. Most arachnids are adapted to kill prey with poison glands, stingers, or fangs.

Like crustaceans, arachnids have a body that is divided into a cephalothorax and an abdomen. Attached to the cephalothorax are four pairs of legs, a pair of chelicerae, and a pair of appendages called pedipalps. The **pedipalps** aid in chewing; in some species pedipalps are specialized to perform other functions.

Diversity

Spiders range in length from less than 0.5 mm to 9 cm in some tropical tarantula species. Spiders feed mainly on insects. Various species are adapted to capture prey in different ways. Some chase after prey, some catch prey in "trapdoors" in the ground, and some snare prey in elaborate webs.

Most scorpions live in tropical or semitropical areas; others live in dry temperate or desert regions. Scorpions differ from spiders in two ways. Scorpions have greatly enlarged pedipalps, which they hold in a forward position. They also have a large stinger on the last segment of the abdomen. Most scorpions hide during the day and hunt at night. Scorpions seize their prey with their pincerlike pedipalps. Then the fang injects paralyzing venom, the chelicerae tear the prey, the animal is ingested, and digestion begins. Only a few species have a sting that may be fatal to humans.

Unlike other a
lothorax and abdo
and most specializ
millimeters to 3 cm
Some mites ar
der mites damage f
Many parasitic tick
the process they ca
Lyme disease and

Structure and F

Arachnids share m
ple, the nervous, di
are structurally sir
therefore have a
through openings
Air passes through
both. **Book lungs,**
ponents, provide a
Tracheae *(TRAY-k*
The excretory
main excretory or
bules, are hollow
body fluids, remo
Most of the water
the body. Some s
remove wastes and
of the leg.
Spiders have
Many spiders also
contains three pair
microscopic tubes.
and hardens into a
used to build nests
use a long thread

Figure 32-7 The Kenya giant scorpion, *Pandinus* sp. (left, ×0.25), and the Australian black widow spider, *Latrodectus seville* (center, ×4), are deadly arachnids. The red spider mite (right, ×43) is a parasite.

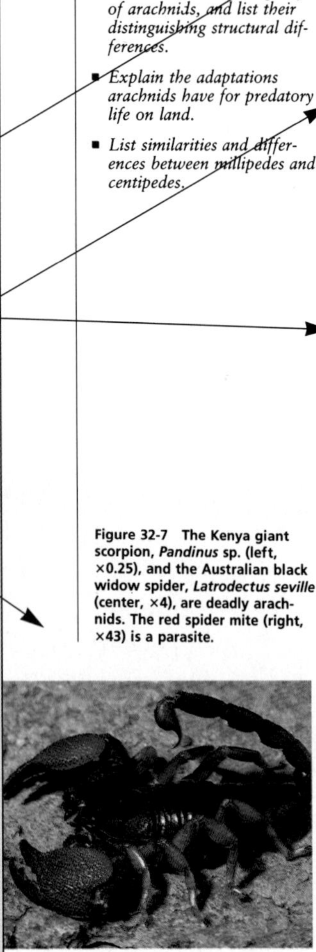

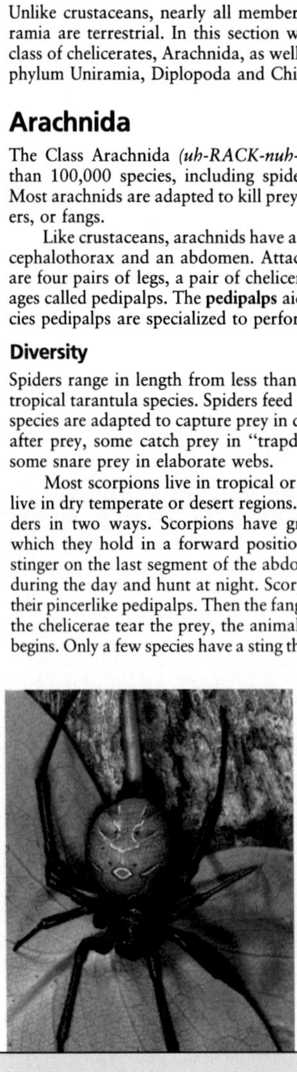

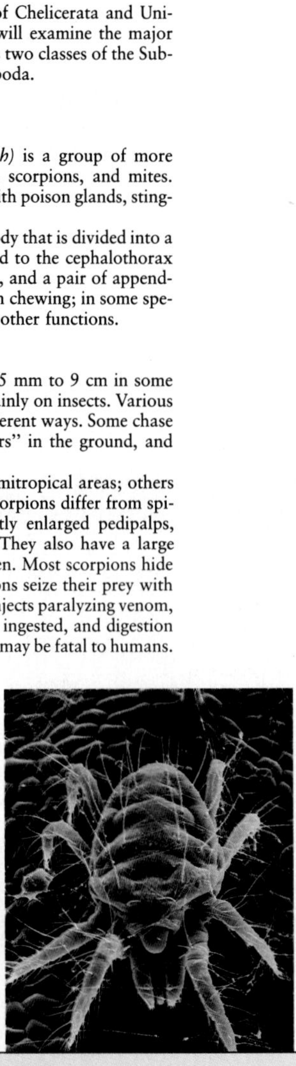

Internal anatomy of th

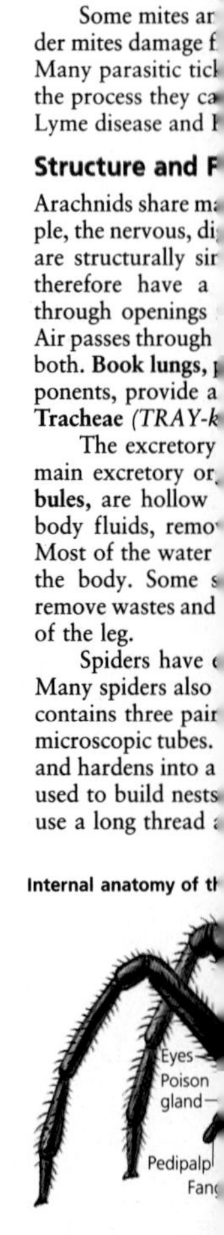

486

Think

At least once in each chapter a feature called "Think" challenges students to think critically about a concept related to the topic they are studying.

mites and ticks have a fused cepha-
s and ticks are the most abundant
ds. Ticks range in size from a few
tes are less than a millimeter long.
pests; others transmit diseases. Spi-
hen they suck fluid from the leaves.
eir host's skin to feed on blood. In
organisms such as those that cause
untain spotted fever.

teristics with crustaceans. For exam-
d circulatory systems of both groups
vever, arachnids are terrestrial and
espiratory system. Spiders respire
cle called **spiracles** *(SPIR-uh-kulz)*.
es to the book lungs, the tracheae, or
in the abdomen with pagelike com-
ace area for the exchange of gases.
y air directly to the tissues.
also modified for life on land. The
d **Malpighian** *(MAL-PIG-ee-un)* **tu-**
s of the digestive tract that collect
and carry wastes to the intestine.
bsorbed, and the solid wastes leave
o have **coxal glands,** organs that
them through an opening at the base

e eyes rather than compound eyes.
The posterior tip of their abdomen
erets, each made up of hundreds of
silk glands passes through the tubes
t can be spun into webs. Silk is also
ocoons. The young of some species
n to ride the wind to new habitats.

Think

These arachnids, called pseudoscorpions, use their pedipalps to attach themselves to beetles. Why might they do this? What trait seems to distinguish pseudoscorpions from scorpions?

Figure 32-8 Note the structures of the respiratory system that make it possible for a spider to live on land.

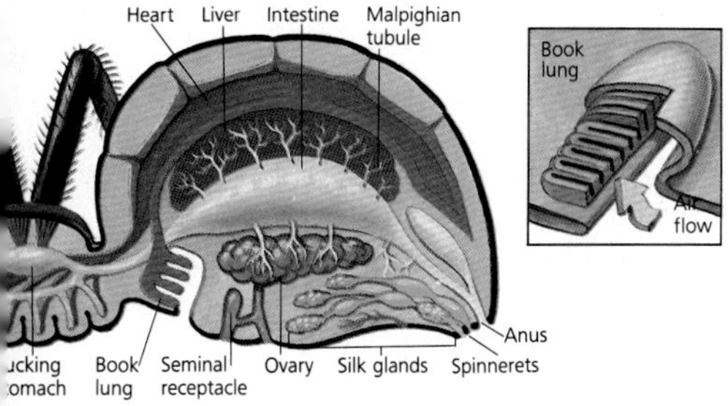

Arthropods **487**

Figure 32-9 The millipede (top) of Southern Ontario is from the Class Diplopoda, while the giant centipede, *Scolopendra heros* (bottom), found in Texas, is from the Class Chilopoda.

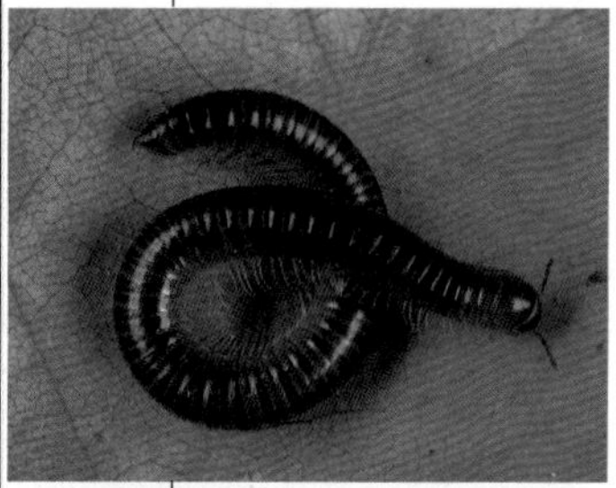

In reproduction, a male spider gathers sperm in special sacs in the tips of his pedipalps. He places the sperm in the seminal receptacle of the female. Later the female lays eggs, which are fertilized by the stored sperm as they pass through the genital pore. The female then seals the eggs in a case of silk. The young spiders go through their first molt inside the case.

Myriapods

Centipedes and millipedes are collectively called **myriapods,** which means "many feet." Myriapods, along with insects, are members of the Subphylum Uniramia. All centipedes and millipedes are terrestrial. Centipedes and millipedes do not have a waxy cuticle. They retain moisture through behavioral adaptations, such as living in damp environments to prevent desiccation.

Millipedes

Millipedes are members of the Class Diplopoda. The term *millipede* means "thousand feet." Millipedes have two pairs of legs on each body segment except the last two. Although millipedes have many legs, they have far fewer than a thousand. The legs of a millipede are strong and well adapted for burrowing through humus and soil. However, these legs are also short, which makes them slow. When threatened, a millipede rolls its body into a coil and may also spray a noxious chemical that contains cyanide.

In cross section the bodies of millipedes are rounded. They live in soil, in logs, and under objects. Many have a strong sense of smell but poor vision. Millipedes are herbivores adapted for chewing plants and decayed matter in the soil.

Centipedes

Centipedes are members of the Class Chilopoda. The term *centipede* means "hundred legs." Centipedes differ from millipedes by having the body flattened in cross section. They also have only one pair of legs per segment, except the first one and the last two. They can also move faster because their legs are longer. Many coil up for defense. Centipedes may have anywhere from 15 to 175 pairs of legs. Voracious predators, centipedes feed on earthworms and on insects such as cockroaches. The first body segment has a pair of clawlike appendages that can inject venom into prey.

Section Review

1. Define *pedipalps,* and explain their function.
2. Name two ways in which scorpions differ from spiders.
3. How is the arachnid excretory system adapted for life on land?
4. How are millipedes and centipedes different?
5. How might the feeding habits of spiders benefit humans?

488 *Chapter 32*

Vocabulary

Vocabulary terms appear in boldfaced type and are clearly defined in context. Phonetic respellings help students pronounce difficult terms.

Illustrations

Carefully executed, detailed illustrations present complex information in an effective visual format.

Section Review

Five questions at the end of each lesson help students' evaluate their progress. Question 1 checks students' understanding of new vocabulary. Questions 2–4 test their recall of facts. Question 5 requires students to think critically about a new concept.

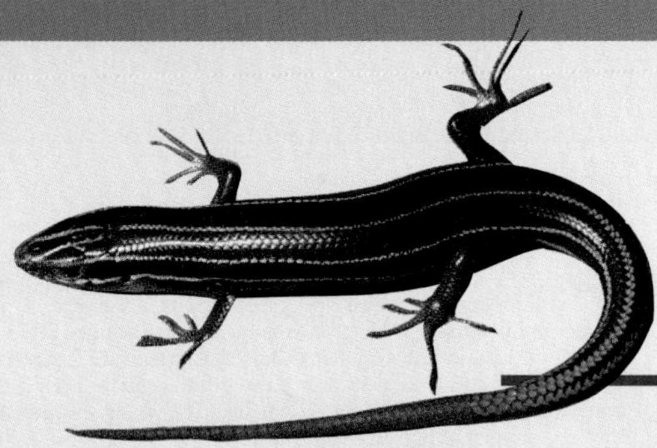

Efficient Planning Ensures Effective Teaching

34.2 Structure and Function

This discussion of anatomy and behavior will focus on the sea star as a representative echinoderm. The anatomy and behavior of sea stars illustrates the relationship between structure and function in many echinoderms. Also note that the structure and movement of echinoderms is unique among invertebrates.

Body Plan

The sea star's mouth is located on the underside of the body, called the **oral surface.** The top of the body is called the **aboral surface.** While some invertebrates have an external skeleton, a sea star, like all echinoderms, has an endoskeleton—a skeleton found within the body. The sharp, protective spines on the aboral surface form from calcium plates called **ossicles,** which are covered with a thin epidermal layer of cells. Groups of **pedicellariae** surround the spines. Pedicellariae, which resemble tiny forceps, help protect and clean the surface of the body.

Water-Vascular System

While most invertebrates swim, wiggle, or use appendages for movement, sea stars use a water-vascular system. This is a network of canals in which muscle contractions create hydrostatic pressure, which in turn permits movement. Water enters the **sieve plate,** a small opening on the aboral surface. It passes through the madreporite and down the **stone canal.** Use Figure 34-6 to trace the path of water from the **ring canal** encircling the mouth to the five **radial canals** that extend into each arm.

The radial canals carry water to hundreds of paired, hollow tube feet. The upper end of each foot connects to a bulblike sac called an **ampulla.** Muscles in the tube feet contract, forcing water into the ampullae and creating suction, which causes suckers at the tip of the feet to grip the surface. When the ampullae contract, water enters the feet, releasing the suction and causing the feet to

Section Objectives

- *Describe the general body plan of the sea star.*
- *Explain how the water-vascular system aids in movement and feeding.*
- *Describe sexual and asexual reproduction in the sea star.*

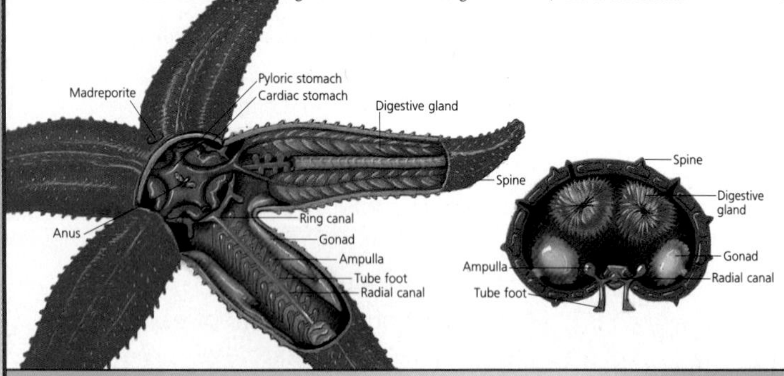

Figure 34-6 Trace the path of water in the water-vascular system of the sea star.

Water-Vascular System

water enters sieve plate → water passes through canal network → water reaches tube feet → muscle contractions create hydrostatic pressure → movement is permitted

Graphic Organizer Use this sequential diagram in Guided Practice on p. 516.

Section 34.2

Lesson Plan

Section Focus
This section focuses on the structure and function of a representative echinoderm—the sea star. Students will learn about its body plan, its water-vascular system, and the ways in which it lives and reproduces.

Section Themes
This section emphasizes the theme of **Scale and Structure** by describing how various structures are related to their functions. For example, the sea star uses its tube feet to move and grasp prey.

Motivating Activity
Show students a photograph of a sea star and remind them that it is also called a starfish. How does this name illustrate some problems biologists face? *(First, different names cause confusion in communication. Second, the word* fish *suggests a close evolutionary tie to the vertebrate fish, but no such relationship exists.)* How can these problems be avoided? *(By using scientific names)*
■ *See* Laboratories, *Investigation 34.*

Teaching Strategies
Interpreting the Visuals Ask students to explain how the cross section (on the right) in Figure 34-6, p. 515, relates to the drawing of the sea star's aboral surface. *(The cross section shows the interior of an arm and the detailed structure of tube feet.)*
■ *See* Overhead Transparency *T34 and* Blackline Master *70.*

Videodiscs
■ *1229–1233, Asteroidea: Sea Stars (s)*
■ *1739–1758, Starfish Development (s)*
■ *1759–1785, Sea Urchin Development (s)*

515

Section Focus
This overview of the lesson identifies the major instructional focus.

Section Themes
Teachers are alerted to the major themes that are interwoven in the lesson.

Motivating Activity
These opening activities focus the lesson by tapping students' prior knowledge or relating the topic to their personal experiences. The activities stress demonstrations and discussions that stimulate interest and promote involvement.

Teaching Strategies
Each lesson offers a bank of strategies that makes it possible for teachers to customize instruction based on individual preferences and students' needs. The suggested activities cover a range of modalities and cultural learning styles.

Videodiscs
Images and film clips from Optical Data's *Life Science* videodisc are correlated to appropriate lessons. Bar codes that allow quick access to these images are available in a separate package.

Graphic Organizers
Graphic organizers in every Lesson Plan offer creative strategies that help students to unify key concepts and visually portray relationships.

The all-new Annotated Teacher's Edition *offers more support than ever before—more classroom-tested strategies, more creative reinforcement, more thought-provoking extensions. With* Modern Biology, *teacher choice becomes a powerful factor in the shape and flow of lessons.*

Guided Practice

Each lesson includes an opportunity for students to explore their developing understanding of the concept while still working in a sheltered situation.

Independent Practice

After students have refined their understanding through Guided Practice, they are ready to work independently. These suggestions help the teacher to use the Section Reviews effectively and also suggest additional alternative strategies.

Check Your Understanding

For each lesson, these quick quizzes provide an informal measure of students' comprehension and progress.

Reteaching

These alternative strategies provide for students who may need a varied approach to the content.

Enrichment

These suggestions encourage students to work beyond the text, developing new interests and expanding their perceptions of science and its links to society and technology.

Section 34.2

Guided Practice
Help students create a sequential diagram that shows how the sea star's water-vascular system aids in movement. A sample diagram appears on p. 515.

Independent Practice
- Have students write answers to the Section Review.
- Direct students to write a script for a nature film describing a sea star attacking and eating a clam.

Answer to Think
There is a good chance that some eggs will be fertilized even if predators eat many eggs and others are washed away unfertilized.

Check Your Understanding
1. What is unusual about the sea star's digestive system? *(The sea star can extrude its stomach through its mouth, then insert it into a partly opened bivalve.)*
2. How does suction develop at the tip of tube feet? *(Muscle contractions in the tube feet act on the water-vascular system.)*

Reteaching
Ask students to compare the diagram of a sea star in Figure 34-6, p. 515, with that of a sea urchin in Figure 34-4, p. 514. Have them identify similar structures and compare the body plans of the two organisms.
- *See* Section Reviews *worksheet, Section 34.2.*

Enrichment
Have students research and report on the impact of sea stars on shellfish beds and the economic effects on the seafood industry. Suggest that students use nature and popular science magazines.

Closure
Point out that sea stars are slow-moving organisms that are often easy to see. Ask students to suggest what characteristics help sea stars survive against predators.

516

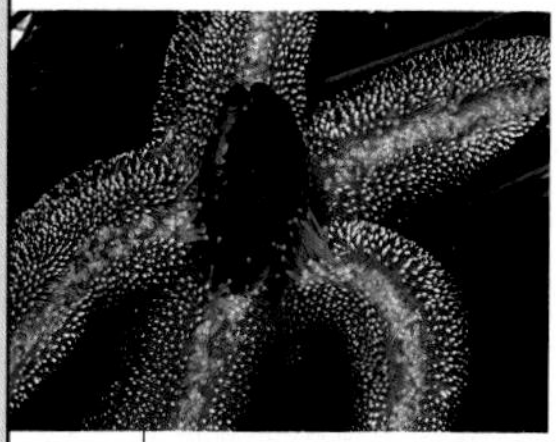

Figure 34-7 This ochre sea star is feeding on a California mussel along the Pacific coast.

Think

Why is it an adaptive advantage for aquatic, externally fertilizing organisms to produce millions of eggs?

extend. These coordinated muscle contractions enable the sea star to climb slippery rocks or to capture prey.

Feeding and Digestion

Sea stars use their tube feet to obtain food—usually mollusks, worms, and other slow-moving animals. The sea star attaches the suckers of its tube feet to both halves of a clamshell and pulls until the shell opens a crack. The sea star then turns its stomach inside out through its mouth and inserts its stomach into the clam.

Enzymes secreted by the sea star's stomach digest the clam's soft parts while they are still in the shell. The sea star then withdraws the stomach, containing the partially digested food, back into its body, where the digestive process is completed.

Other Body Systems

The sea star has no circulatory, excretory, or respiratory systems. Fluid in the coelom bathes the organs and distributes nutrients and oxygen. Gas exchange and waste excretion take place by diffusion through the thin walls of the tube feet and through the **skin gills,** hollow tubes that project from the coelom lining.

The sea star has no head or brain. A **nerve ring** surrounds the mouth and branches off into nerve cords that extend into each arm. Each arm has an eyespot that responds to light and a tentacle that responds to touch. The tube feet also respond to touch.

Reproduction

Each arm of the sea star has two gonads, which produce eggs in females and sperm in males. Fertilization occurs externally. Females produce up to 200 million eggs in one season. Each fertilized egg develops into a bilaterally symmetrical, free-swimming larva called a **bipinnaria.** After about two months the larva settles to the bottom, and metamorphosis begins. During metamorphosis the sea star develops into a pentaradially symmetrical adult.

Sea stars can also reproduce asexually by regenerating lost parts. In fact, a completely new sea star may grow from a segment of an arm as long as part of the central disk is still attached.

Section Review

1. Distinguish between the *oral surface* and the *aboral surface.*
2. Trace the path of water through the water-vascular system.
3. Describe the way a sea star grips and digests a clam.
4. How are gas exchange, distribution of nutrients, and excretion of wastes accomplished in the sea star?
5. Was the former practice of breaking the arms off of sea stars to prevent them from feeding on clams and oysters a good idea?

516 *Chapter 34*

Answers to Section Review
1. The oral surface is the side where the mouth is; the aboral surface is the opposite side. In sea stars the oral surface faces the sea bottom.
2. Water enters through the sieve plate and then goes through the stone canal, ring canal, radial canals, and tube feet.
3. After opening the shell with its tube feet, the sea star inserts its stomach into the shell, partially digests the clam and then withdraws the stomach and completes digestion in its body.
4. Fluid in the coelom distributes oxygen and nutrients. Excretion and gas exchange take place by diffusion through the tube feet and skin gills.
5. No, because a segment of an arm could regenerate into a new sea star

Closure

Individual, team, or cooperative learning activities help students to summarize the lesson and "lock in" major concepts.

Answers to Section Review

Answers appear at the bottom of the page.

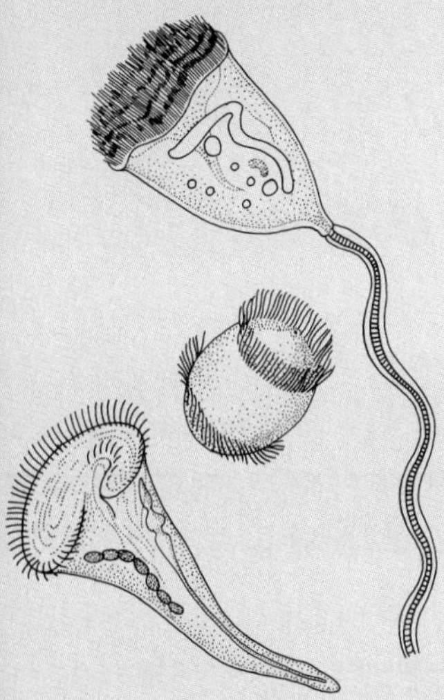

A Complete Program Responsive to Classroom Needs

The wide variety of ancillary materials available with Modern Biology *helps you to meet the needs of a diverse student population. With* Modern Biology, *you have options for approaches to thorough instruction and reinforcement that tap all learning modalities and are suitable for a variety of learning styles.*

Core Materials

- Pupil's Edition
- Annotated Teachers' Edition
- Teachers' Resource Binder
  (includes the following blackline masters organized by chapter)
  - Daily Lesson Plans
  - Process and Vocabulary Skills
  - Laboratories
  - Section Reviews
  - Chapter Tests
  - Answer Keys

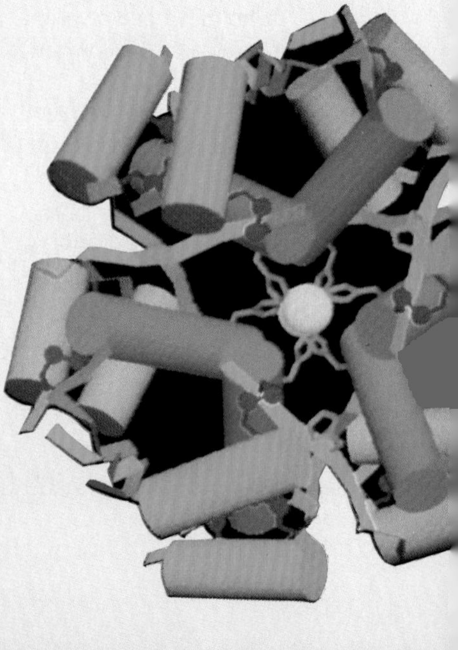

Laboratory Resources

- Laboratories *(consumable edition)*
- Laboratories *(nonconsumable edition)*
- Computerized Laboratories
  - Photosynthesis *(Apple® II series)*
  - Cellular Respiration *(Apple® II series)*
  - Genetics *(Apple® II series)*

Audiovisual Resources

- Teaching Transparencies
- Transparency Review Worksheets with Critical Thinking Questions
- Science in Action Video Series
  - Laboratory Safety, Equipment, and Technique/The Process of Science
  - The Atoms and Molecules of Life/DNA and Protein Synthesis
  - Cell Structure and Function/ Cell Division
  - Photosynthesis and Cellular Respiration
  - Alternatives to Dissection: The Earthworm and the Frog
- Correlation Chart and Barcode Stickers for Use with Optical Data's *Life Science* Videodiscs
- Posters
- Directed Reading Audio Program

Additional Resources

- Alternate Tests
- Test Generator *(IBM®, Apple®)*
- Spanish Glossary

Thorough Coverage For Reaching Visual Learners

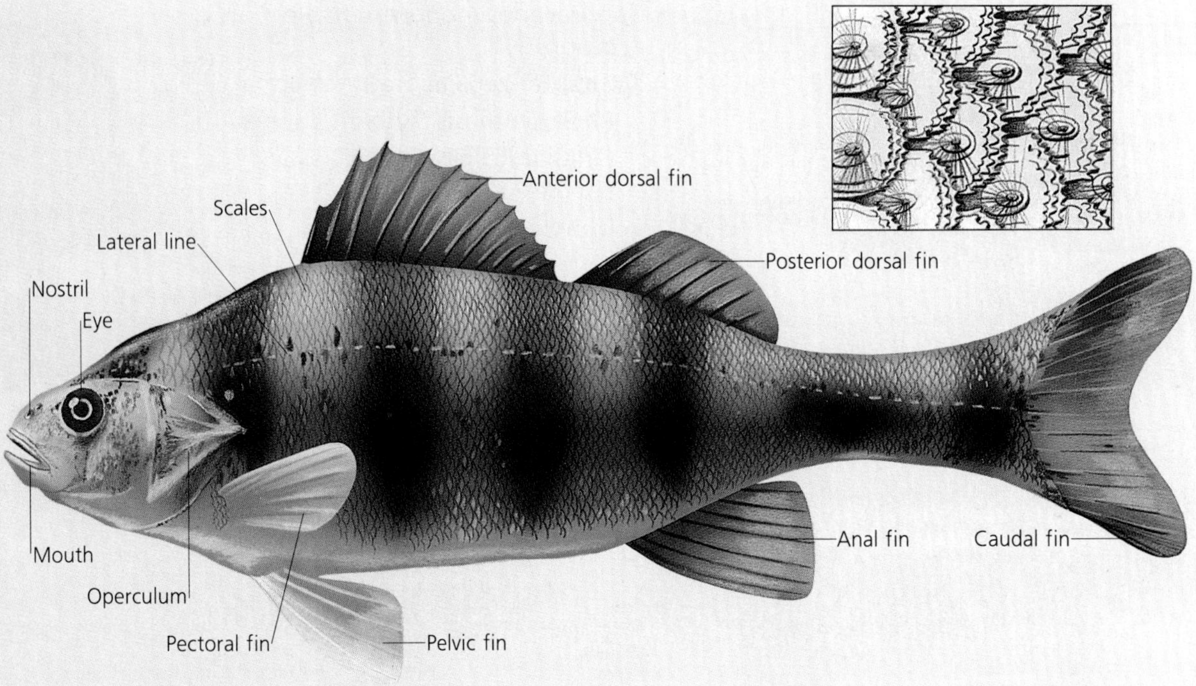

Graphic Organizers

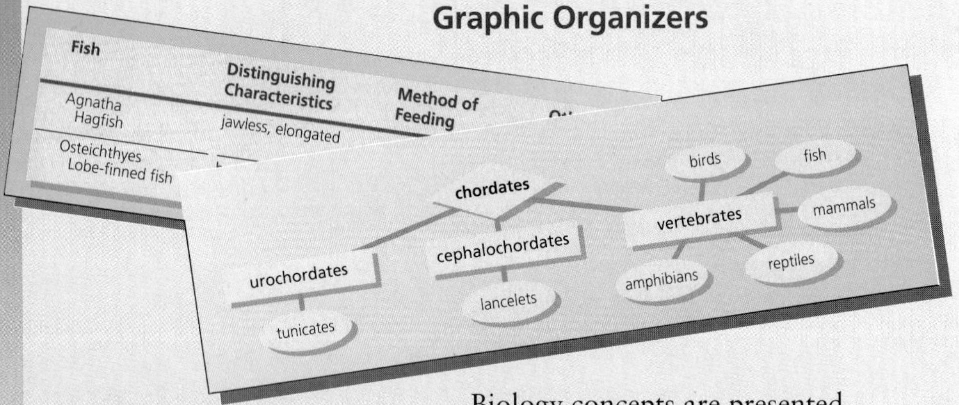

Biology concepts are presented through a variety of visual/textual media. Tables and photo/art combinations provide the visual links students need to form mental images of a concept, process, idea, or structure. The uniquely illustrated tables, throughout the program, show information at a glance with the added benefit of a visual link to aid students in comparing and contrasting information. Detail diagrams are constructed such that students can make the link between very small or microscopic structures and the whole organism or process. True understanding stems from the ability to associate an image or series of images with a term.

Your Teacher's Edition presents a variety of graphic organizers to show relationships among various ideas in a section. It is strongly recommended that you use these organizers so students get in the habit of looking at material displayed graphically.

Use of Videodiscs in The Biology Classroom

Modern Biology is correlated to Optical Data's *Life Science* videodiscs. Using the *Life Science* videodisc offers some exciting possibilities for enhancing instruction. You can show the diversity of life in a particular kingdom using the thousands of still images found in the series. Text diagrams of abstract processes, such as protein synthesis, come alive with the video clips. There is the added advantage of freezing a video image without the distortion you get with videotape. You can access images from anywhere on the disc almost instantaneously. The bar code or frame number takes you directly to the image. There is no hunting for the exact stopping place as on videotape.

Your Teacher's Edition provides a reference and frame number for those images to be used when teaching a particular section. If you have a barcode reader, you will want the separate package of barcode stickers. The barcode stickers can be placed right in your Teacher's Edition. The barcode sticker package also contains a command card which allows you to process various commands, like forward and reverse, through your barcode reader.

Science in Action Video Series

The *Science in Action Video* series focuses on ten areas identified by teachers as "trouble spots" in instruction. Each tape contains two topics and a discussion guide to be used in helping students with the information on the tapes. The following subjects are available.

- Laboratory Safety, Equipment, and Technique/The Process of Science
- The Atoms and Molecules of Life/DNA and Protein Synthesis
- Cell Structure and Function/Cell Division
- Photosynthesis and Respiration
- Alternatives to Dissection: The Earthworm and The Frog

Additional AV Resources

In your Teacher's Edition, you will find listings of audiovisual materials and software for each unit on the unit opening pages. An example can be found on page 1B. Suppliers for the resources listed for each unit can be found on page T49 of this Teacher's Edition.

Thorough Coverage for Reaching All Students

Planning for Different Ability Levels

Modern Biology is organized to meet your needs for using one text to satisfy the curricular needs of classes tracked by ability level. The Chapter Planning Chart that leads off each chapter in the Teacher's Edition codes each section of the chapter for its appropriateness for use with Basic, Standard, and Advanced level classes.

Basic Level The Basic Level curriculum is set up to aid teachers of students who are academically below average in reading comprehension and general scholastic ability. The idea behind this curriculum is not to teach at a lower level but to cover fewer topics at a slower pace. The planning charts provide the suggestions for material to leave out of the Basic course.

Standard Level The Standard curriculum is designed for average students. These students are able to read and comprehend the text with relative ease. They should be able to master all but the more advanced topics. The planning charts provide guidance as to what advanced material can be skipped.

Advanced Level The Advanced Level curriculum includes suggestions for teaching the most academically talented students. These advanced students quickly comprehend the text. They are moving or have moved from the concrete to formal operational stage, and they can deal with the more abstract ideas in biology.

Chapter Planning Chart

B	S	A	Sections and Subsections	Page	Features	Page	Resources
•	•	•	**7.1 The Need for Energy**				
			Energy for Life Processes Adenosine Triphosphate ATP-ADP Cycle	93 94 95	Section Review	95	Videodiscs Blackline Master 13 Overhead Transparency T7 Blackline Master 14 Section Reviews Worksheet
	•	•	**7.2 Photosynthesis**				
			Light Absorption by Chlorophyll Light-Dependent Reactions Light-Independent Reactions	96 97 99	Biology in Process Laboratory Section Review	100 109 102	Videodiscs Science in Action Videotape: Photosynthesis and Cellular Respiration Process Skills: Experimental Controls Laboratories: Chromatography Section Reviews Worksheet
	•	•	**7.3 Respiration**				
			Glycolysis Fermentation Aerobic Respiration	103 104 105	Think Section Review	105 108	Videodiscs Blackline Master 15 Blackline Master 16 Blackline Master 17 Laboratories: Fermentation Section Reviews Worksheet
			End of Chapter Activities				
					Chapter Review	110	Vocabulary Skills Chapter Test Computer Test Generator

B *The Basic Level curriculum presents the most fundamental knowledge offered in the course.*
S *The Standard Level curriculum is designed for the average student who is able to master most topics.*
A *The Advanced Level curriculum includes suggestions for teaching the most academically able students.*

Pacing for Different Ability Levels

The pacing recommendations that follow are based on a 180-day curriculum and an extended study curriculum. The 180-day curriculum is based on a national average for the length of the school year. The extended study curriculum considers the time necessary for in-depth coverage of the topic. This curriculum represents the ideal time necessary to teach the subject. To suit your district requirements, you can alter the charts as needed.

Pacing Chart

Chapter	Basic Curriculum: Recom-mended sections	Basic Curriculum: 180-day curriculum	Basic Curriculum: Extended study	Standard Curriculum: Recom-mended sections	Standard Curriculum: 180-day curriculum	Standard Curriculum: Extended study	Advanced Curriculum: Recom-mended sections	Advanced Curriculum: 180-day curriculum	Advanced Curriculum: Extended study
1	A	4	5	A	4	5	A	3	4
2	A	4	5	A	5	5	A	3	4
3	A	4	5	A	5	5	A	4	4
4	A	5	5	A	5	5	A	4	4
5	A	5	5	A	5	5	A	4	7
6	A	3	5	A	4	5	A	4	5
7	1	3	5	A	8	10	A	4	10
8	A	5	8	A	5	8	A	4	10
9	A	5	8	A	5	8	A	4	10
10	A	5	10	A	5	10	A	4	10
11	3	3	5	1,3	3	5	A	4	5
12	■	■	■	■	■	■	A	4	5
13	■	■	■	1	2	2	A	3	4
14	1,2	3	5	A	4	5	A	3	4
15	A	5	5	A	4	5	A	4	5
16	■	■	■	1	3	4	A	4	10
17	A	4	7	A	4	5	A	4	5
18	A	3	3	A	4	7	A	3	5
19	A	4	5	A	4	5	A	4	5
20	A	4	5	A	4	5	A	4	5
21	A	4	5	A	4	5	A	4	5
22	1	3	5	A	3	5	A	4	5
23	1	3	5	1	3	5	A	4	5
24	1	2	3	A	3	3	A	3	3
25	A	4	7	A	4	6	A	4	5
26	A	4	7	A	4	6	A	4	5
27	2, 3, 4	4	7	A	4	6	A	4	5
28	■	■	■	A	3	5	A	3	5
29	A	4	5	A	3	5	A	3	5
30	A	4	5	A	3	5	A	3	5
31	A	4	5	A	3	5	A	3	5
32	A	4	5	A	3	5	A	3	5
33	A	4	5	A	4	6	A	3	5
34	1	2	3	A	3	5	A	3	5
35	■	■	■	■	■	■	A	4	5
36	A	5	5	A	3	5	A	3	5
37	A	4	5	A	3	5	A	3	5
38	A	4	5	A	3	5	A	3	5
39	A	4	5	A	3	5	A	3	5
40	A	4	5	A	3	5	A	3	5
41	■	■	■	■	■	■	A	4	5
42	A	5	7	A	3	7	A	3	7
43	A	5	7	A	4	7	A	3	7
44	A	5	7	A	3	7	A	4	7
45	A	5	7	A	4	7	A	4	7
46	1, 3	4	7	A	3	7	A	4	7
47	A	5	7	A	3	7	A	4	7
48	A	5	5	A	3	5	A	2	5
49	A	4	5	A	3	5	A	2	5
50	1, 2	3	4	A	3	5	A	2	5
51	■	■	■	1	2	3	A	2	5
52	■	■	■	A	3	4	A	2	5
53	A	3	4	A	2	4	A	2	4

Key

■ = not recommended as part of curriculum

A = all sections recommended

Varying Instruction to Use Different Learning Modalities

The Lesson Plan in your Teacher's Edition is rich with strategies that take advantage of different learning modalities.

Visual Learners

The various kinds of graphic organizers in *Modern Biology* provide a framework for visual learning. The visual learner is also supported when you use the following.

- Teaching Transparencies
- Blackline Masters
- Graphic Organizers
- Concept Maps
- Videodisc materials
- Audio Tapes
- *Science in Action Video* series

Auditory Learners

The auditory learner is supported when you use the *Modern Biology Directed Reading Audio Tapes*. This series of 12 tapes guides students through every chapter in the textbook page by page. The content on each page is presented in a simpler, more informal manner using examples from everyday life. The tape begins by guiding students through the outline of the chapter to give them an idea how the content will unfold as they move through the chapter.

The tapes use the visual images in the text as the main vehicle for conveying information. They help students by walking through biological processes and cycles. They help students locate various parts of organisms by pointing out their colors or shapes. The tapes use fewer vocabulary terms to cover the topics than you will find in the student text. This series is an excellent resource for Basic Level students to help them through any reading difficulties.

The audio program may be particularly useful in the following situations:

- with Limited English Proficiency students and reluctant readers
- with auditory learners
- with visual learners
- as a home study option
- as an independent preview or review of a chapter

Teaching Students with Special Needs

Modifications in instructional methods are often necessary to reach all students effectively. General strategies are given in the Lesson Plans in your Teacher's Edition.

Limited English Proficiency Students

It is now common to work with students with limited proficiency in English.

LEP students are highly motivated and sensitive to the teacher. And as such, their needs can be summarized as follows:

- They want to adjust to U.S. society.
- They want to speak and understand English.
- They want to succeed in school.
- They need a warm and accepting environment to accomplish the above goals.

These needs must all be taken into consideration when working with LEP students. They are not mutually exclusive. Teachers should also be aware of the following.

- Be aware of the discrepancies between the student's home culture and American culture.
- Recognize that these students need constant encouragement; focus on the positive— what they are getting right and not what they are getting wrong.
- Provide opportunities for students to use English.
- Determine a student's reading and writing proficiency in the first language. Use an interpreter to find out about the student's prior science education. Deficiencies in the first language will hamper a student's ability to learn English.
- "Take students from where they are to where you want them to be."
- Recognize that you cannot provide all the individual attention a student needs.
- LEP students are not learning disabled; they just do not know English.

Basic Methods for LEP Students

Oral Language Approach Select the ten most important ideas of a chapter and re-inforce them through repetition and recitation. Use your objectives as a guide to the main ideas.

Total Physical Response Reinforce the main ideas by physically acting them out using hand and arm motions.

Cooperative Groups Use group work as much as possible. Students are then put into situations for social interaction, which can increase their confidence. Students learn from peers.

Mistakes to Avoid with LEP Student Speaking louder and slower to LEP students has no effect and may even make students self-conscious and intimidated.

Make sentences simple, but do not use the Tarzan technique: "Jane like Tarzan. Tarzan like Jane." Avoid idioms and slang.

Evaluating Responses Focus on the meaning of what is said and not on the correctness of pronunciation.

Teaching Physically Impaired Students

If the student is in a wheelchair, check the room to make sure that equipment and materials are accessible and that aisles are wide enough to accommodate the wheelchair. For students who have difficulty writing, taped lectures and computers can help with note taking. Consider oral exams. The *Modern Biology Directed Reading Audio Tapes* can be useful for these students.

Teaching Visually Impaired Students

Seat the student in the front of the room. The *Modern Biology Directed Reading Audio Tapes* are useful for these students.

Teaching Hearing Impaired Students

Make sure always to face the class when speaking. During discussions, periodically summarize what students have said. Repeat questions students ask before answering them. Use visual media as much as possible. See the information on visual learners, page T28, for specific information on visual media in the *Modern Biology* program.

Teaching Students with Speech Impairments

The most important quality to exhibit when teaching speech-impaired students is patience. Resist the temptation to finish sentences for a student who stutters. Use cooperative grouping strategies for oral reports.

Thorough Coverage For Creating a Cooperative Learning Environment

Allowing students to share ideas with peers while learning is a strategy that has been used since the days of the one-room schoolhouse. The use of this strategy is now formalized in the *Modern Biology Teacher's Edition*. Each chapter in your Teacher's Edition opens with a cooperative learning activity. Additional cooperative learning suggestions can be found throughout the Lesson Plan sections.

Laboratories are also excellent opportunities for students to work cooperatively. The student-designed inquiry labs, in the text, challenge students to organize their ideas to build an experimental design.

Consider the following guidelines in facilitating cooperative groups.

Group Size The size of the group should depend on the number of tasks that can be assigned. If groups become too large, some students may have nothing to do.

Assign Outcomes Students need to know what will be expected of them. Identify the group goal and the materials students will be expected to create by the end of the session (tables, charts, recommendations, and so on).

Individual Accountability Each group member should know what his or her responsibility is for the assigned material. In addition, each group member is responsible for the learning of the other group members.

Positive Interdependence All members of the group must realize that their success depends on the success of each member. Therefore students must work with one another and depend upon one another to reach their goals. Positive interdependence may be achieved through a division of labor, resources, or roles in the group. Rewards for the group, such as the same grade for every group member, may be an additional incentive.

Running a Safe Laboratory Program

You can shape and reinforce proper student attitudes toward the laboratory by setting a good example. Maintain strict adherence to safety rules and procedures to avoid accidents. Some general guidelines are provided here. For more thorough information write the National Science Teachers Association, 1742 Connecticut Avenue, N.W., Washington, D.C., 20009.

Your state may have specific guidelines concerning eye protection, lab aprons, storage of combustible materials, fire safety, availability of first aid supplies, and the disposal of chemical waste. Contact your state science supervisor for information. In addition to local regulations, the following general precautions should be followed.

Classroom/Laboratory

Your classroom should have two fire exits and adequate ventilation. Review evacuation procedures with students in case of fire. Make a list of instructions along with a diagram of the fire exits to be posted in the room at all times.

- Never permit students to eat in the laboratory.
- Never permit students to conduct experiments without teacher supervision.
- Students should wash their hands at the beginning and end of each lab period.

Safety Equipment

Safety equipment commonly found in school biology laboratories should include fire extinguishers, fire blankets, sand buckets, eyewash fountains, emergency showers, safety goggles, laboratory aprons, gloves, tongs, respirators, and a first aid kit. All of this equipment must meet federal standards.

- Students must be familiar with the location and use of all safety equipment in the laboratory.
- Call the school nurse or a physician immediately if an injury occurs.

Post the telephone number of the local poison-control center.

Materials/Chemicals

When teaching large classes, set up materials stations in several parts of the room to minimize the distance that students will have to carry materials. Be sure you can adequately supervise these stations.

- Material Safety Data Sheets should be available for all chemicals in use. These sheets are your guide to the handling of all chemicals. All chemicals should be clearly labeled with hazard precautions.
- Volatile, combustible liquids such as ether and alcohol should be used only in ventilated areas and never near an open flame. A hot plate or water bath/burner setup should always be used when a procedure calls for warming these substances.
- Chemicals should be stored in a well-ventilated area that is kept locked at all times. This area should be clean, orderly, and well lit. Flammable chemicals should be stored in a fire-resistant cabinet or refrigerator that is specifically marked explosion proof.

animal care

animal safety

caustic substances

chemical safety

clothing protection

electrical safety

explosion danger

eye safety

fire safety

gas precaution

glassware safety

hand safety

heating safety

plant safety

hygenic care

proper waste disposal

water safety

Association of Biology Teachers, 11250 Roger Bacon Drive, Reston, VA 22090.

Dissections

- Rinse preserved specimens before use. Provide adequate ventilation to dispel fumes from preservatives. Wear gloves to avoid contact with preservatives.
- Refrigerate or preserve any unpreserved specimens. Do not use any unpreserved specimen that has decayed.

Live Animals

- Before bringing any animal into the classroom, have a complete plan for the care and feeding of the animal.
- Confirm that all mammals have been inoculated against rabies, unless purchased from a reliable biological supply house.
- Potentially dangerous animals should never be brought into the classroom.
- Experiments with animals should not involve drugs, toxic substances, anesthetics, surgery, carcinogens, or radiation.
- Make certain that any student who has been scratched or bitten by an animal receives immediate attention.
- Animals should not be teased or handled unnecessarily.
- Students should wash their hands thoroughly after handling any animal.
- Animals taken from their natural environment should be returned to it when they are no longer needed.
- In addition to these guidelines, consult the NABT Guidelines for the Use of Live Animals, available from the National

Plants

- Because some plants are poisonous, never allow students to put any part of a plant into their mouths or near their eyes.
- Students should wash their hands thoroughly after working with plants in the laboratory.

Bacteriological Procedures

- Pathogenic bacteria should never be used in the laboratory. If you suspect that a culture has been contaminated with a pathogen, autoclave the culture before discarding it. If you cannot autoclave the culture, flood it with disinfectant.
- Petri dishes that contain bacterial cultures should be sealed with tape.
- Cleanliness of the work area is especially important in bacteriological investigations. Containers of disinfectant should be available at each laboratory station. Lab tables should be wiped with the disinfectant at the beginning and end of the laboratory period. If a culture is spilled, the affected area should be covered with disinfectant and wiped clean immediately.
- Wire loops that are used to transfer microorganisms should be "flamed" before and after the organisms are transferred.
- Students should use a suction bulb to pipette any liquid medium or bacterial solution.

Lab Equipment

- Keep microscopes, hot plates, and other electrical equipment in good working order.
- Electric outlets should have ground fault protectors in areas where liquids will be used.
- Make sure that students understand that they should never touch electrical equipment with wet hands.
- Never permit students to operate an autoclave or pressure cooker. Conduct all sterilization procedures yourself.

Glassware

- Before each laboratory session, have students examine glassware for cracks and chips.
- Never allow students to force glass tubing into rubber stoppers.
- Glass containers that will be heated should be made of borosilicate glass or some other heat-resistant material.

Fire Safety

- Students should tie back long hair and confine loose clothing.
- Materials should be located in such a way that students never reach over an open flame.
- Dispose of all extinguished matches properly.
- Extinguish all open flames and turn off all hot plates when not in use.

Safety Symbols

- The instructions in the in-text laboratories will include safety symbols where necessary. An explanation of the safety symbols used in *Modern Biology* is found on page 841. Review this page before the first lab experience. Students should be tested on their recognition of the symbols and their meanings.

Safety Video

The *Science in Action Video* series includes Laboratory Safety, Equipment, and Technique. This tape emphasizes the importance of safety in the laboratory and acquaints students with the equipment they will be expected to use.

Clean Up/Laboratory Waste

The regional office of the Environmental Protection Agency (EPA) or the proper state authority should be consulted for specific disposal instructions. Guidelines vary by state, so you will want to use procedures that apply to your area.

- Students should always wash their hands before leaving the laboratory.
- Lab tables and floor should be wiped dry.

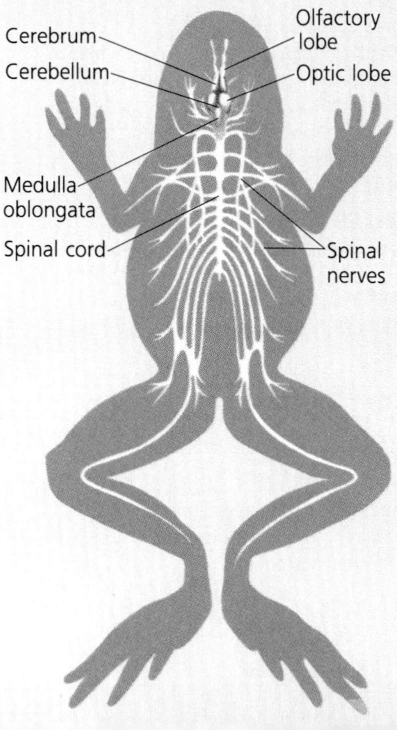

Equipment and Materials

Biological equipment and materials can be obtained from a variety of sources. In addition to the suppliers listed, many of the materials may also be purchased from other scientific supply houses.

Cambridge Instruments
Optical Systems Division
P.O. Box 123
Buffalo, NY 14240

Carolina Biological Supply Co.
2700 York Road
Burlington, NC 27215

Connecticut Valley Biological Supply
82 Valley Road P.O. Box 326
Southhampton, MA 01073

Delta Biologicals
P.O. Box 26666
Tucson, AZ 85726

Denoyer-Geppert Science Co.
5215 N. Ravenswood Avenue
Chicago, IL 60640

Difco Laboratories
P.O. Box 331058
Detroit, MI 48232-7058

Edmund Scientific Co.
1010 E. Gloucester Pike
Barrington, NJ 08007

Fisher Scientific Co.
Education Materials Division
4901 W. Lemoyne Avenue
Chicago, IL 60651

Frey Scientific Company
905 Hickory Lane
Mansfield, OH 44905

Hubbard Scientific Company
1946 Raymond Drive
or P.O. Box 104
Northbrook, IL 60065

LaPine Scientific Company
P.O. Box 780
Blue Island, IL 60406-0780

Nasco
901 Janesville
Fort Atkinson, WI 55538

Nasco
1524 Princeton Avenue
Modesto, CA 95352-3837

Sargeant-Welch Scientific Co.
7400 N. Linder Avenue
Skokie, IL 60076

Science Kit and Boreal Laboratories, Inc.
777 East Park Drive
Tonawanda, NY 14150

VWR Scientific
Rose Tree Corporate Center
1400 N. Providence Road
Suite 100
Media, PA 19063

Ward's Natural Science Establishment, Inc.
P.O. Box 92912
Rochester, NY 14962-9012

Ward's Natural Science Establishment, Inc.
P.O. Box 2567
Santa Fe Springs, CA 90670-0567

Master Materials List

The materials needed for each in-text Laboratory *are listed at the beginning of each laboratory exercise. A complete listing of materials is presented here for your convenience. This list is organized by chapter so that you can determine the materials you might have to order in advance. Refer to* Laboratory Preparation *in this* Teacher's Guide *for hints on preparing specimens and solutions and on ordering supplies. Remember to allow time in your planning to obtain the materials and the live specimens you cannot store ahead.*

Quantities of various items are given in parentheses. Quantities are based on the quantity needed for one student or pair of students to do one Laboratory. *If no quantity is given for an item, the quantity needed per student or pair of students is one. Be sure to take into account the size of your class when assembling materials. No quantities are listed for readily available items such as water.*

See the particular Laboratory *for more specific information. The page number where the* Laboratory *appears in the text is listed after the chapter number for your reference.*

Chapter 1 (p. 13)
compound microscope; cotton batting; coverslip; medicine dropper; microscope slide; unlined paper; pond water

Chapter 2 (p. 29)
paper; watch with second hand

Chapter 3 (p. 43)
household ammonia; 30-mL beakers (2); lemon juice; medicine dropper; fresh skim milk; paper towels; narrow-range pH paper; wide-range pH paper; glass stirring rods (2)

Chapter 4 (p. 55)
1-L beaker; Benedict's solution; 0.5% copper sulfate solution; cornstarch; food substance; glucose; hot plate; iodine-potassium iodide solution; lard; medicine droppers (4); nonfat dry milk; 10% aqueous sodium hydroxide solution; glass stirring rod; Sudan III solution;
test tube rack; test tube stoppers (2); test tubes (8); tongs; distilled water

Chapter 5 (p. 77)
compound microscope; coverslip; *Elodea* plant; human cheek cells, prepared slide; medicine dropper; microscope slide

Chapter 6 (p. 89)
clock or watch; coverslip; plastic fork; medicine droppers (2); microscope; microscope slide; red onion; paper towel; petri dishes (2); fresh potato; blunt probe; scalpel; 10% sodium chloride solution

Chapter 7 (p. 109)
balance; 250-mL beaker; 200-watt bulb; graduated 250-mL cylinder; 15-cm-long *Elodea* springs (4); 1,000-mL Erlenmeyer flask (2); meter stick; glass-marking pencil; pH paper; sodium bicarbonate; glass stirring rod; timer; distilled water

Chapter 8 (p. 125)
400-mL beaker; diphenylamine; DNA solution; hot plate; medicine droppers; glass-marking pencil; RNA solution; test tube holder; test tubes (3); tongs; water

Chapter 9 (p. 139)
Allium root tip, longitudinal section; microscope

Chapter 10 (p. 159)
corn ears A and B

Chapter 11 (p. 177)
paper; pencil

Chapter 12 (p. 187)
4-L aerator; aquariums with 1.5% salt solution (2); brine shrimp eggs; compound microscope; depression slides; dip net; dissecting microscope; measuring spoon; medicine dropper; unlined paper; dry baker's yeast

Chapter 13 (p. 197)
paper; pencil

Chapter 14 (p. 215)
aspartic acid; metric balance; 500-mL beaker; clock or timer; compound microscope; coverslip; 50-mL graduated cylinder; 125-mL Erlenmeyer flask (2); glutamic acid; glycine; hot plate; medicine dropper; microscope slides; ring stand with clamp; 1% sodium chloride solution; glass stirring rod; tongs

Chapter 15 (p. 233)
graph paper; peanuts in shell; metric ruler

Chapter 16 (p. 251)
200 black and 200 white beads (400); containers (3)

Chapter 17 (p. 263) paper; pencil

Chapter 18 (p. 275) living or preserved invertebrate specimens (11)

Chapter 19 (p. 291)
100-mL beaker; 400-grit carborundum powder; cotton swabs; 10-mL, 0.1 M disbasic potassium phosphate solution; mortar and pestle; glass-marking pencil; tobacco from several brands of cigarettes; tobacco plants (4)

Chapter 20 (p. 305)
glass-marking pens; petri dish with nutrient agar; 3/4 inch transparent tape

Chapter 21 (p. 317)
coverslips; *Euglena* culture; medicine droppers; methyl cellulose; microscope; microscope slides; paper towel; *Paramecium* culture; vinegar; distilled water; salt water

Chapter 22 (p. 331)
Chlamydomonas culture; mixed culture of *Chlamydomonas, Eudorina, Gonium, Pandorina, Hydrodictyon,* and *Volvox;* compound microscope; coverslips; depression slides; green plants; medicine dropper

Chapter 23 (p. 345)
dissecting microscope; unlined paper; petri dishes (2); probe; *Rhizopus stolonifer* culture, plus and minus strains; single-strain *Rhizopus stolonifer* culture

Chapter 24 (p. 361)
culture dish; dissecting microscope; variety of food plants; scalpel

Chapter 25 (p. 377)
centimeter graph paper; representative conifer, monocot, and dicot plant specimens; scalpel

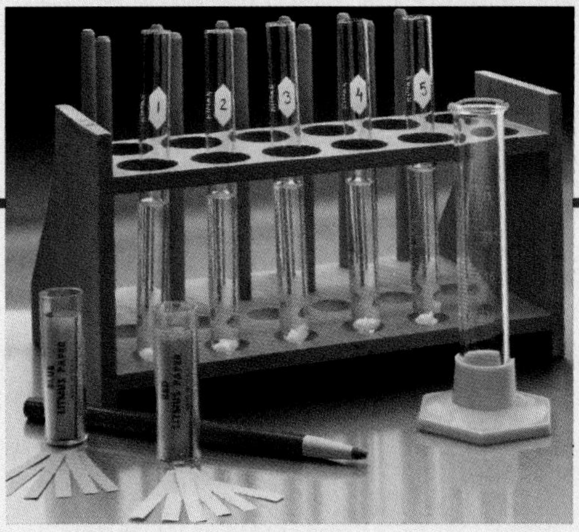

Chapter 26 (p. 397)
balance; cord; corn seeds (3); lima bean seeds (3); paper; 7-cm pots (6); potting soil; ruler; scissors; spring scale; adhesive tape; water

Chapter 27 (p. 417)
bean and corn seedlings 1, 2, 3 and 10 days old; soaked bean seed; soaked corn kernel; dissecting tray; hand lens; scalpel or single-edge razor blade

Chapter 28 (p. 429)
3 cm or taller bean seedlings; cotton swabs; 20 cm or larger flower pots; gibberellic acid solution; glass-marking pencil; potting mixture; ruler; wetting agent

Chapter 29 (p. 449)
50-mL beaker; brine shrimp culture; compound microscope; culture dishes (2); depression slide; dissecting microscope; glutathione; *Hydra* culture; methylene blue; probe; glass rod; vinegar; pasteurized spring water

Chapter 30 (p. 461)
culture dish; dissecting microscope; *Dugesia;* small flashlight; raw liver; glass medicine dropper; plastic medicine dropper with tip cut off; pond water; blunt probe

Chapter 31 (p. 475)
3% aqueous, ammonium hydroxide solution; book; cotton swabs; earthworm; lamp; shallow pan; black paper or cardboard; paper towel; blunt probe

Chapter 32 (p. 489)
aluminum foil; filter paper (2); bright lamp or flashlight; paper towels; petri dish with cover; live pill bugs (5)

Chapter 33 (p. 507)
culture dish; forceps; hand lens or dissecting microscope; unlined paper; preserved *Polistes;* blunt probe

Chapter 34 (p. 517)
brittle star; dissecting microscope; dissecting pan; forceps; sea star; sea urchin; sea urchin test

Chapter 35 (p. 529)
annelid; arthropod; coelenterate; dissecting microscope; echinoderm; flatworm; mollusk; roundworm

Chapter 36 (p. 551)
paper; pencil

Chapter 37 (p. 567)
5-gallon aquarium; cardboard box; cricket or mealworm; frog; large jar

Chapter 38 (p. 583)
anoles (2); large, wide-mouth beakers or jars (2); brown and green construction paper; hand lens; glass-marking pencil

Chapter 39 (p. 599)
prepared contour feather slide; prepared down feather slide; down, contour, and quill feathers, 1 of each; microscope; unlined paper

Chapter 40 (p. 615)
compound microscope; hand lens; mammalian skin, microscope slide; mirror; photographs of male and female fetal pigs; selection of vertebrate skulls or skeletons

Chapter 41 (p. 629)
large aquarium; live fish; live lizard; live salamander; live snake; large terrarium

Chapter 42 (p. 651)
chicken wing; dissecting pan; forceps; paper towel; unlined paper; scalpel; scissors

Chapter 43 (p. 669)
metal or plastic basin; 250-mL graduated cylinder; 1-gallon jug; glass-marking pencil; soda straw; cellophane tape; rubber tubing; water

Chapter 44 (p. 683)
compound microscope; prepared slides of *Clostridium botulinum, Histoplasma capsulatum, Treponema pallidum,* and red blood cells infected with *Escherichia coli,* malarial *Plasmodium,* and tapeworm

Chapter 45 (p. 703)
10-mL graduated cylinder; cooked egg white; 0.2% hydrochloric acid; red and blue litmus paper; notebook paper; glass-marking pencil; 1% pepsin solution; scalpel; 1% sodium bicarbonate; test tube rack; test tubes with stoppers (5); distilled water

Chapter 46 (p. 723)
bottles (5); sterile cotton swabs (10); paper cups (6); paper towels; marking pencil; tap water

Chapter 47 (p. 745)
600-mL beakers (3); 50-mL graduated cylinder; 8-1/4-inch culture dish; small fish net; 1-mm graph paper; glass-marking pencil; different colored pencils (3); petri dish; pond water; strained spinach; tadpoles with hind legs showing (9); 0.01% thyroxine stock solution

Chapter 48 (p. 757)
aspirator; rubber bulb from medicine dropper; burette clamp; cigarettes; matches; ring stand; scissors; rubber tubing; tubing-cork system

Chapter 49 (p. 777)
Elodea in 2 bottles of water; 25% manganous sulfate solution; medicine droppers (2); 1-mL and 2-mL pipettes; 40% potassium hydroxide-potassium iodide solution; safety goggles; 0.003% sodium thiosulfate solution; concentrated sulfuric acid

Chapter 50 (p. 793)
coverslips; eyedroppers; keys to freshwater organisms; microscope; microscope slides; pond water

Chapter 51 (p. 807)
prepared legume nodules slides, cross-section; microscope; plants (2), one infected with symbiotic *Rhizobium,* the other without *Rhizobium* infection; scalpel

Chapter 52 (p. 817)
alcohol lamp; medium culture tube with screw cap; medicine dropper; microscope; microscope slides; graph paper; Pasteur pipette; test tube rack; *Tetrahymena* culture; tongs

Chapter 53 (p. 827)
125-mL beaker; 400-mL beakers (2); dissecting microscope; ice; *Paramecium* culture; pond water; thermometer; 12 cm glass tubing, U-shaped with end corks

Thorough Coverage for Developing Critical Thinking

There is no universally accepted definition for critical thinking. In *Modern Biology*, critical thinking requires the validation of facts and decision making.

Validating Facts

Many critical thinking items in the text involve judging the validity of facts by collecting evidence that either supports the facts or refutes them. Sometimes judging the validity of facts involves direct observation. The Laboratories in *Modern Biology* allow students to observe organisms and to conduct experiments. As students become more proficient in applying the methods of science, they are better able to judge the validity of information and determine the sources of error that lead to invalid conclusions.

Making Decisions

Two essential results of applying critical thinking are the ability to make decisions and make value judgments. Making workable, ethical decisions means mastering the background knowledge of the subject.

Critical Thinking in the Chapter Review

These items require students to validate facts through analyzing concepts, synthesizing concepts, and drawing inferences.

▼

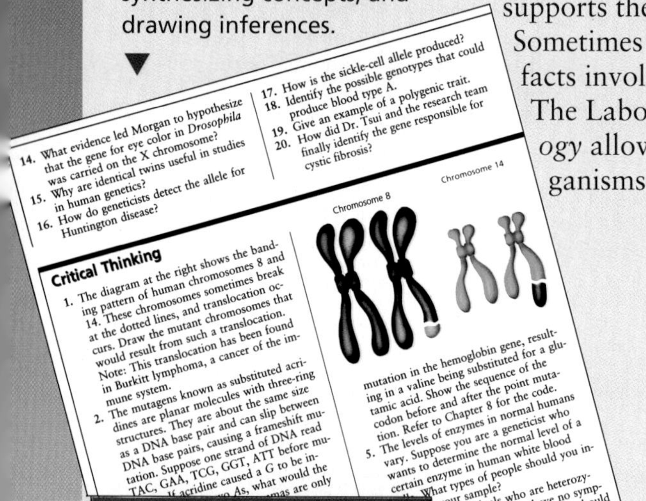

Think

Name five adaptations of the song sparrow, *Melospiza melodia*, that you infer are the result of natural selection.

▲

Think

These items require students to judge the validity of information or make a decision about some given information.

Intra-Science

These features include questions where students make value judgments regarding a biological issue

▼

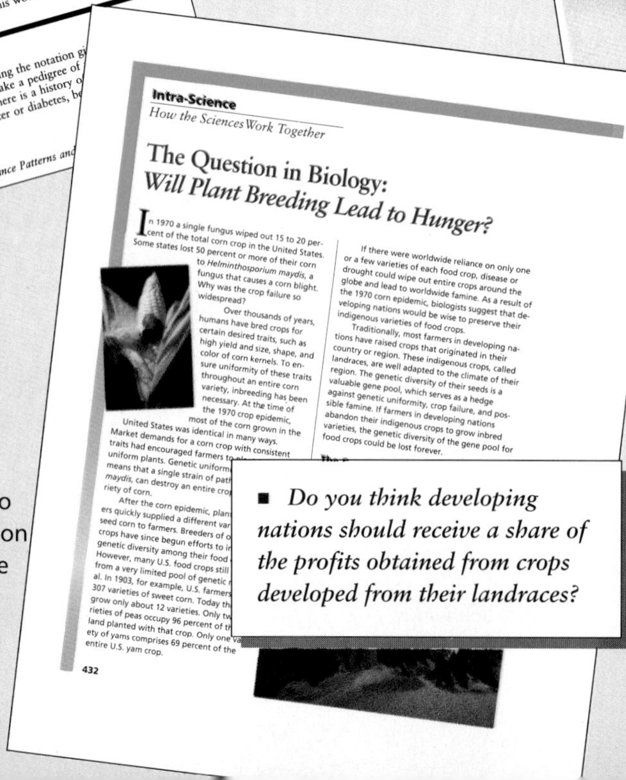

■ *Do you think developing nations should receive a share of the profits obtained from crops developed from their landraces?*

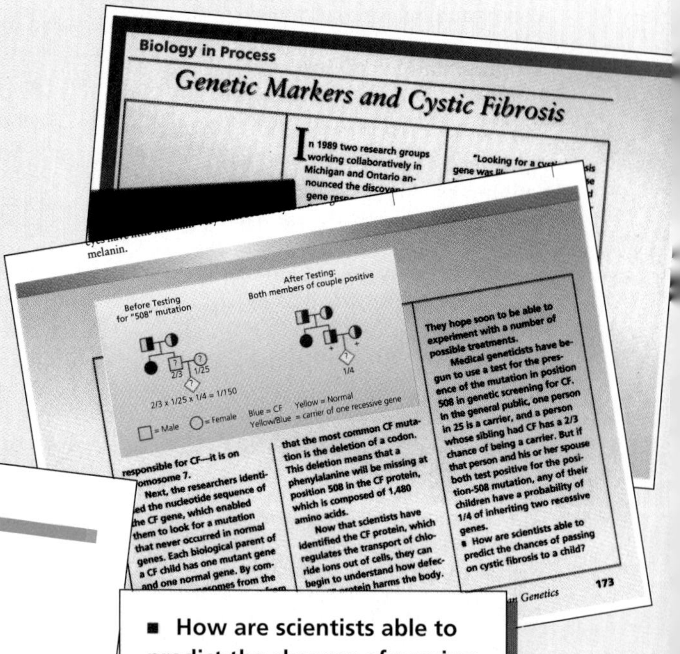

■ **How are scientists able to predict the chances of passing on cystic fibrosis to a child?**

▲

Biology in Process

Each feature closes with a question which has students analyze the scientists' methodology to determine its validity.

Thorough Coverage for Developing Writing Skills

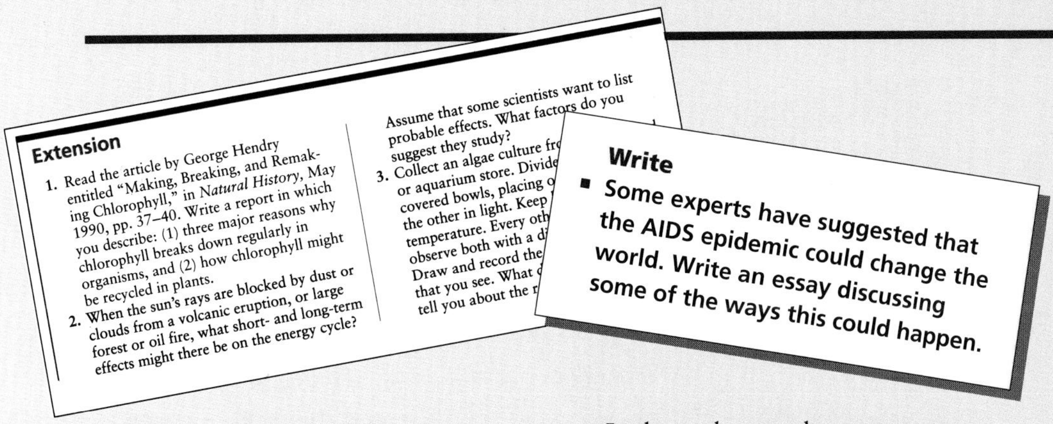

Writing Skills

Written laboratory reports, Extensions in the Chapter Review, and Writing About Biology features are three parts of the *Modern Biology* program that provide the practice students need to communicate ideas on paper in a clear and organized manner.

Writing A Laboratory Research Report

A complete laboratory research report should include the following components:

1. Title page
2. Introduction
3. Any prelab research on the experiment
4. Hypothesis
5. Materials and methods
6. Observations and data collected
7. Conclusions
8. Footnotes
9. Bibliography

Evaluating Laboratory Research Reports

Look for the following in grading reports.

- Is the hypothesis clearly stated?
- Is there thorough coverage of the experimental procedure?
- Is there an organized presentation of data collected?
- How valid are the conclusions?
- Are reasons for possible discrepencies in data stated clearly?

Components of The Research Paper

The standard research paper should contain the following components.

1. Title page
2. Introduction
3. Outline
4. Body of the report
5. Conclusions
6. Footnotes
7. Bibliography

Writing A Research Paper

Writing a research paper is a sequential process. Here are some guidelines you can use with students.

1. Start by having students choose broad topic areas.
2. Have students write several specific questions they will want to answer as a result of their research.
3. Have students do some preliminary reading about the topic.
4. Students should then narrow their topics and find specific references using the card catalog and the *Readers' Guide to Periodical Literature.*
5. Notes from these specific references should be placed on index cards.
6. Students will now need to make an outline for the paper. The outline should contain the following.
   a. Introduction — Stating the topic and the kind of information found in the paper.
   b. Three or more paragraphs, each telling interesting or important facts or ideas about the topic.
   c. Summary/commentary — Why is the topic interesting? Why is it important? What did the student learn? What questions remain?
7. Students may now proceed to write the first draft. It is essential that you provide feedback to students during the first-draft stage.
8. Based on first draft comments, students should then revise and proofread their papers.

Evaluating Research Papers

Look for the following in grading papers.

- Is the topic clearly stated or defined?
- Is the working outline thorough and in the proper form?
- Are the reference materials cited appropriate?
- Are the references cited in the body of the report accurate?
- Are the conclusions stated valid?

Thorough Coverage for Developing Reading Comprehension Skills

Parts of the Textbook

As an assignment the first week of school, students should become acquainted with the parts of their textbook. Students will get far more out of the textbook if they understand how it is organized and how it can help them in preparing for exams. Students should be familiar with the Table of Contents, Appendix, Glossary, and Index. They should know how to use these sections to find information and definitions of terms from previous courses.

Take part of a class session to review the pedagogical aids in the text with students. The chapter introductions and section objectives direct students as to what they will be expected to learn. The headings within a chapter provide an outline of the chapter content. Each section of a chapter contains one main idea, stated first or last. Supporting details follow or precede the main idea in a recognizable pattern.

Prereading Strategies

Building on Prior Knowledge The amount of prior knowledge that students have about a topic directly influences their comprehension. The more students know about a topic, the easier it will be for them to grasp new information.

Related research also strongly suggests that students tend to maintain misconceptions they may have about a topic. If the text information seems to conflict with their preconceptions,

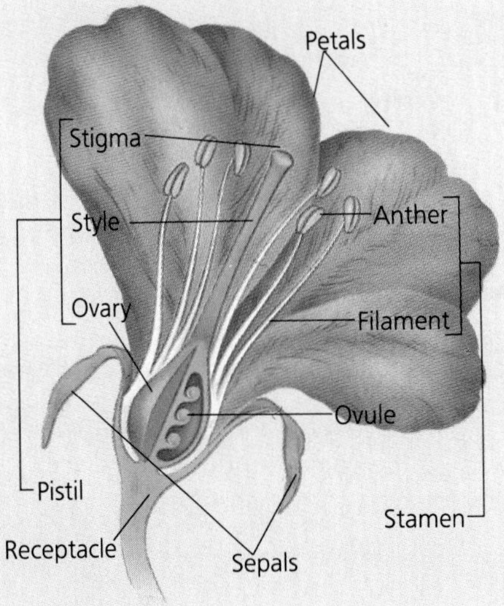

students may ignore or reject new information. Students will discard or modify misconceptions, however, when the teacher provides direct instruction before reading that clarifies and corrects their misconceptions.

Helping students identify information they already know about a topic before reading helps in at least three ways:

1. When students read the text, they can relate the new information to existing knowledge.

2. It helps you identify class awareness of a particular topic. You can plan instructional time accordingly.

3. It gives you the opportunity to identify misconceptions students may have. You can plan lectures, demonstrations, or other experiences to help students confront and correct their misconceptions prior to reading.

Strategies for Building on Prior Knowledge The side column material in your Teacher's Edition for the chapter opener pages includes may specific strategies for establishing students' prior knowledge about a topic. Motivating Activities and the Teaching Strategies help students prepare for what they are about to read.

The Teaching Strategies often suggest brainstorming sessions to determine what students already know about the topic. During brainstorming sessions, write all responses on the chalkboard or on an overhead transparency. Ask key questions to probe relationships among the concepts students have identified. Ask how related terms are alike and how they are different. Those questions that cannot be answered should be used to guide the reading assignment.

Establishing a Purpose for Reading Model effective reading and study practices for students. Teach them to preview a chapter by looking at all the chapter headings, illustrations, and boldface terms and phrases before actually reading the text. This technique helps students gain a feel for the chapter and build a basic structure of the information. Later, when they read the chapter, students can fill in the details on the basic structures they have built. The *Modern Biology Directed Reading Audio Tapes* provide the strategies that help students with comprehension problems. For more information on the tapes, see p. T32.

Vocabulary Development

Scientific concepts are conveyed by words. Students need

to understand the vocabulary used in biology. In *Modern Biology*, new terms are printed in boldface and defined when they are first introduced. New terms for each chapter are listed in the Chapter Review with a page reference for where the term is defined. All boldface terms are defined again in the Glossary.

Use class discussions to build a common vocabulary. Since many terms have multiple meanings, some of which are scientific, provide a context for these terms to help students develop their meanings.

Vocabulary mastery and comprehension are measured in a variety of ways in the *Modern Biology* program.

- Section Reviews
- Chapter Reviews
- Concept mapping activities suggested in the Teacher's Edition
- Graphic organizer activities suggested in the Teacher's Edition
- Vocabulary Skill sheets in the *Teacher's Resource Binder*

Interpreting Illustrations

The illustrations in this book are designed as instructional tools. Students will not get the full value of their importance if they are not expected to interpret illustrations. You can help students develop this skill using the following steps.

1. Read the caption that accompanies the diagram.
2. Review the symbols or terms used in the diagram.
3. Think about what the diagram illustrates and why the diagram is effective.
4. Read the text surrounding the diagram and see how it relates to the information.

Making Generalizations

The ability to make generalizations about new data or observations places this new information in context and enhances its meaning. Throughout your teaching, you should be asking students to make generalizations relating to the themes presented in Chapter 1.

For example, the relationship between structure and function in living things is emphasized in *Modern Biology*. Making students aware of such a relationship will help them understand the significance of the structure of the cell membrane. It will also encourage students to look at familiar objects in new ways, as when they observe variations in the beaks and feet of birds.

Sequencing

Scientific processes, such as mitosis, meiosis, and embryonic development, occur in an exact, predictable sequence. Throughout *Modern Biology*, students are exposed to the logic process scientists use in attacking a problem. Evaluating students' understanding of these processes should involve appropriate sequencing of events.

Comparing and Contrasting

One way for students to improve reading comprehension is to compare and contrast the material they are reading with what they already know.

For example, as students read about plant reproduction, they should look for key similarities and differences in the reproductive cycles of members of the different plant divisions. This process of comparing and contrasting sets of information will enhance student's appreciation of the various adaptations of plants.

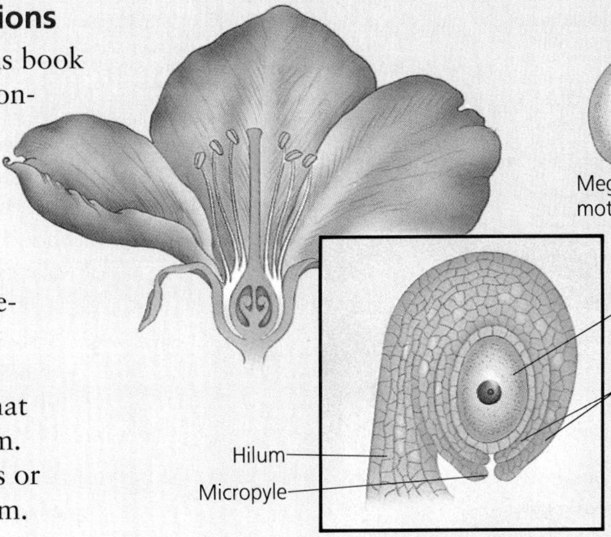

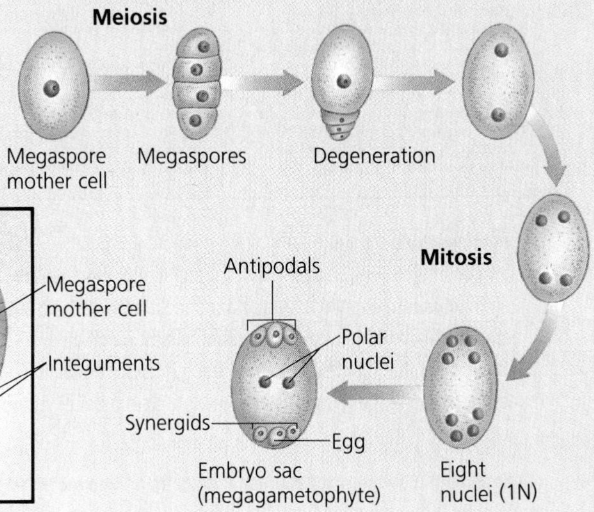

Thorough Coverage for Evaluating Student Progress

Review Materials in the Student Text

Student understanding of the text material is measured at various levels of comprehension. The Section Reviews include items that evaluate the recall of important facts. The Chapter Reviews are more comprehensive. Each Chapter Review consists of the following.

Vocabulary

A listing of the boldface terms from the chapter followed by a short exercise to determine students' understanding of important terms.

Critical Thinking

These items require that students compare, contrast, form relationships, make generalizations, determine the validity of claims, and cite evidence for their answers. As students move into the Critical Thinking portion of the Chapter Review, their ability to apply ideas to new situations is evaluated. One item is specifically designed to evaluate students' understanding of a picture, chart, or diagram.

Chapter 25 Review

Vocabulary

alternation of generations (368)
angiosperm (367)
capsule (369)
cotyledon (375)
cuticle (365)
dicot (375)
fiddlehead (373)
frond (373)
gametophyte (368)
gymnosperm (367)
monocot (375)
multicellular gametangia (365)
nonvascular pl
(367)
phloem (371)
rhizoid (369)
rhizome (373)
seed (373)
sporangium (368)
vascular plant (367)
vascular tissue (365)
xylem (371)

Explain the difference between each of the following pairs of terms.
1. rhizoid and rhizome
2. gametophyte and sporophyte
3. angiosperm and gymnosperm
4. monocot and dicot
5. xylem and phloem

Review

1. The Division Bryophyta includes (a) mosses and club mosses (b) hornworts and liverworts (c) liverworts and cycads (d) conifers and ginkgos.
2. Mosses help start new biological communities by (a) detecting air pollution (b) forming new soil (c) producing spores (d) slowing decomposition.
3. Phloem conducts (a) air (b) sugars (c) chlorophyll (d) soil.
4. The presence of silicon dioxide in the outer cells of the plant is a characteristic of (a) ferns (b) mosses (c) horsetails (d) club mosses.
5. Flowering plants are in the Division (a) Psilophyta (b) Anthophyta (c) Gnetophyta (d) Sphenophyta.
6. Seedless vascular plants include all of the following *except* (a) ferns (b) horsetails (c) cycads (d) club mosses.
7. Gymnosperms include all of the following *except* (a) cycads (b) gnetophytes (c) ginkgos (d) quillworts.
8. The great success of angiosperms is due in part to (a) highly efficient vascular systems (b) seeds protected inside fruits (c) coevolution with insects (d) all of the

(b) two seed leaves (c) four-part flowers (d) five-part flowers.

10. The distinguishing feature of all plants is the presence of (a) vascular tissue (b) pollen grains (c) multicellular gametangia (d) rhizoids.
11. When did the first land plants appear?
12. Which division of organisms is believed to represent the ancestors of land plants? Why?
13. What is the genetic difference between the gametophyte and the sporophyte?
14. How is alternation of generations different in nonvascular plants and vascular plants?
15. Why were microtechniques for analyzing fossils necessary before the details of the evolution of land plants could be revealed?
16. What factors limit the size of nonvascular plants?
17. Why must nonvascular plants live in damp environments?
18. What is the principal distinguishing feature of vascular plants?
19. List the structural features of vascular plants that nonvascular plants lack.

placed

Critical Thinking

1. The water lily, illustrated at the rig vascular plant that lives in aquatic tats. Do you think its cuticle would thicker on the upper surface of the on the lower surface? Explain.
2. Fossils of trees are easier to find th sils of small plants. Give two possib planations for this fact.
3. Luminous moss (*Schistostega penna* cells shaped like lenses, with chloro spread out behind the curving cell brane. In what sort of environment you expect to find this moss?
4. Cactuses are vascular plants that a adapted to dry environments. What cific adaptations might have been s for over the course of their evolutio
5. Explain whether or not you would to find mosses growing in open fiel

Extension

1. Read the article by Julie Ann Miller entitled "Plant Phylogeny Aided by Ants and Hummingbirds" in *BioScience*, November 1990, p. 714. Prepare an oral report in which you discuss how *Centropogon's* interactions with ants and hummingbirds are proving useful for clarifying evolutionary trends. Concentrate on the relationship that appears to exist between pollinator and plant structure. What evidence suggests a lowland origin for *Centropogon*? How do *Centropogon* and sicklebills reveal coevolutionary trends in structure and geographic distribution?
2. Go to your local florist or garden sho and get a handful of *Sphagnum* moss. it dry overnight in a warm place. Wei the moss to the nearest 0.1 g, and rec the weight. Then place the moss in w and weight it down. Let the moss sit night. Remove the moss, let the exces water drain off, and weigh the moss again. Calculate the percentage increa weight as follows:
   (a) Wet weight − dry weight = weight due to water
   (b) Weight due to water/dry weight × 100 = percentage increase due to water
3. Collect leaves from five different types of plants growing in deep shade (such as under a porch, in a forest, or in the shadow of a tall building). Also collect leaves from five different types of plants growing in full sun. Examine the leaves with a hand lens or dissecting microscope, and create a chart using the following col-

Review

This section includes multiple choice and short answer items that demonstrate students' ability to recall important facts and ideas in the chapter. As students progress through this section, the responses require a deeper level of understanding.

Extensions

These items include additional readings, research projects, and hands-on activities. The readings are especially useful because prereading questions are included to guide students in reading the article. These items give students additional exposure to scientific writings in popular magazines and science journals.

Review Components in the *Teacher's Resource Binder*

Section Reviews For every section of the text, you will find two pages of review items that can be used as quizzes or homework assignments to prepare students for their Chapter Test.

Vocabulary Skills These sheets provide extra practice in developing the vocabulary of the chapter.

Process Skills Sheets These sheets provide situations for students to use process skills and organize their observations to obtain meaningful conclusions.

Testing in *Modern Biology*

There are three testing components available for the *Modern Biology* program.

Chapter Tests This component is found in copymaster form in the *Teacher's Resource Binder*. Each Chapter Test contains 35 questions in true/false, multiple choice, short answer, and essay formats. All test items are correlated to the objectives in the student text. Test items increase in difficulty from true/false through to essay items. Because illustrations are an important part of the *Modern Biology* program, each test will contain a series of items that require the interpretation of an illustration.

Alternate Tests Available as a separate component in copymaster form, the Alternate Tests are similar in organization and style to the Chapter Tests. They are provided to increase your flexibility in testing. You can use the Alternate Tests for every other student if you have concerns about students copying answers from each other and as make-up exams for students who have been absent or are being retested after going through a reteaching phase.

Computer Test Generator A software package (for both IBM and Apple) enables you to create tests for each chapter of *Modern Biology* using a bank of 3,800 items stored on disks. Each test item is correlated to an objective from the text. Items are classified by level of difficulty and they come in five formats: true/false, multiple choice, short answer, essay, and critical thinking. The software allows you to edit any item or write your own items to supplement those provided. A booklet of blackline diagrams is included in the package so that you can add illustrations to your chapter tests.

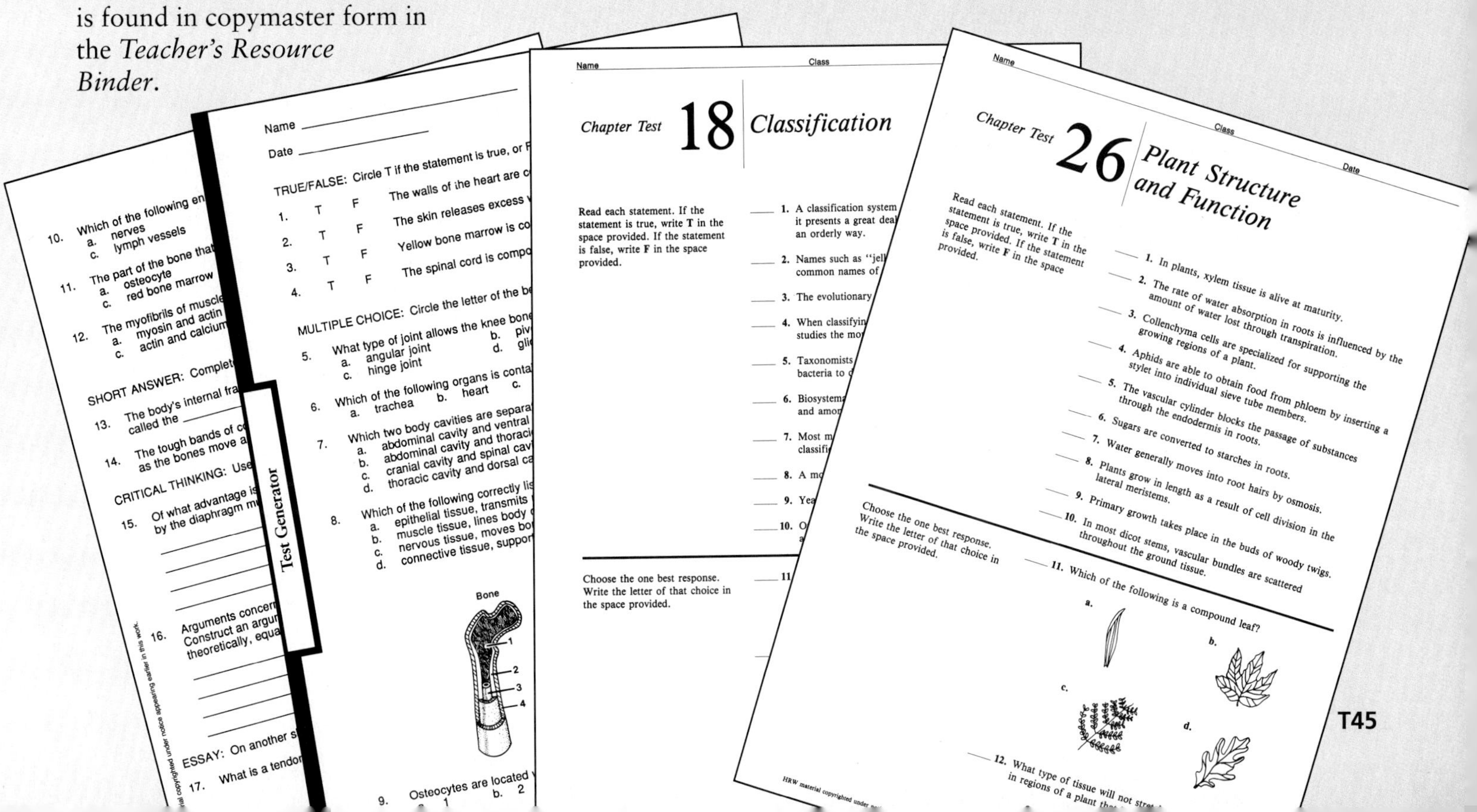

Thorough Coverage That is Easily Adapted to Alternative Approaches

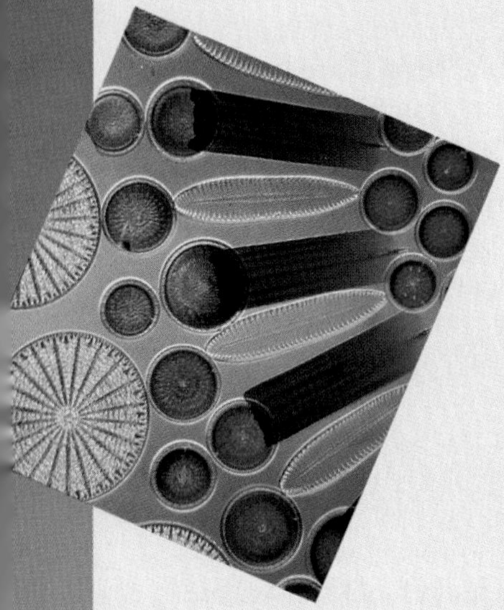

The diversity of high school biology classrooms makes it almost impossible for a single textbook to meet the needs of all teachers. Teachers vary greatly in backgrounds, interests, and teaching philosophies. In addition, state and local requirements often mandate a specific curriculum.

The organization of *Modern Biology* is phylogenetic. This organization appears to be preferred by teachers because it places the diversity of life in an evolutionary context. It also teaches students about whole organisms and allows teachers to emphasize the increasing complexity and adaptations of the earth's inhabitants.

The first portion of the text covers the basic principles and vocabulary students need for further study of the different phylogenetic groups. Once the introductory material is mastered, the remaining units of the text can be treated as independent teaching blocks.

Because *Modern Biology* is such a comprehensive text, it offers flexibility in organization. Based on your teaching philosophy, you may want to reorganize the material to suit personal or district requirements. The explanations and charts that follow are suggestions for helping you vary the approach of the text.

Using the Alternative Approaches Charts

For each approach, you are given a Topic Sequence that is broken down into the chapter sequence that you would use to teach that topic. Refer to the Pacing Chart on page T31 for the time allotments to be used for each chapter. Use the Chapter Planning Charts to organize the material for each chapter for Basic, Standard, or Advanced classes.

Systems Approach

Topic	Chapters
Biological Principles	1–4
Human Body Systems	42–48
Invertebrate Systems	35, 29, 30–34 Relevant sections
Vertebrate Systems	41, 36–40 Relevant sections
Microorganism Systems	19–23 Relevant sections
Plant Systems	24–28
Cell Systems	5–9
Genetic Systems	10–13
Evolution	14–18
Ecology	49–53

◀ *Systems Approach*

This approach involves presenting basic principles using systems as the organizational scheme. For example, a teacher might spend two weeks discussing digestion and the digestive systems of organisms, and another two weeks on excretion and excretory systems of a variety of organisms.

Modern Biology is easily adapted to a systems approach because the chapters are organized into sections that can be taught as independent units. By using this chart, you can easily adapt your class to a systems approach.

Process Approach	
Topic	**Chapters**
Process and Principles	1–4
The Cell	5–9
Genetics	10–13
Evolution	14–18
Ecology	49–53
Microorganisms	19–23
Plants	24–28
Invertebrates	29–35
Vertebrates	36–41
Human Biology	42–48

◀ *Process Approach*

This approach emphasizes the activities of science and tries to place scientific knowledge in the context of its discoveries. As such, teachers who prefer this approach have a greater emphasis on laboratory work in their courses. They try to get students to experience a phenomenon before they read about it in the text. The inquiry orientation of the Laboratories in the student text along with all the Investigations in the *Laboratories* manual provides ample opportunities for students to practice applying process skills. In addition, special emphasis should be placed on using the Biology in Process, Biotechnology, Intra-Science, and Writing About Biology features to give students a greater appreciation for the work of scientists.

Cellular/Molecular Approach	
Topic	**Chapters**
Biological Principles	1–4
The Cell	5–9
Genetics	10–13
Human Biology	42–48
Microorganisms	19–23
Invertebrates	29–35
Vertebrates	36–41
Plants	24–28
Ecology	49–53
Evolution	14–18

◀ *Cellular/Molecular Approach*

If you wish to place an emphasis on cell biology and biochemistry in your course, *Modern Biology* is organized to fit this need. These topics are thoroughly covered in the first part of the text. You can then emphasize molecular biology throughout the year.

Ecological Approach ▶

You may prefer to teach ecology first to take advantage of fall weather for outdoor study. You can then discuss the other topics in the book using an ecological context, which emphasizes the organism's role in the environment.

Ecological Approach	
Topic	**Chapters**
Biological Principles	1–4
Ecology	49–53
Plants	24–28
Microorganisms	19–23
Invertebrates	29–35
Vertebrates	36–41
Genetics	10–13
Evolution	14–18
The Cell	5–9
Human Biology	42–48

Evolutionary Approach ▶

Modern Biology is well suited to presenting the subject using an evolutionary approach. Students are introduced to the concepts of evolution, phylogeny, and adaptation on page 6, and most chapters reflect the evolutionary theme. With slight modifications is scope and sequence, *Modern Biology* can easily be used for this approach.

Evolutionary Approach	
Topic	**Chapters**
Biological Principles	1–4
DNA and Genetics	9–13
Principles of Evolution	14–18
Evolution of Microorganisms	19–23
Evolution of Invertebrates	29–35
Evolution of Vertebrates	36–41
Evolution of Plants	24–28
Ecology and Evolution	49–53
The Cell	5–8
Adaptations	42–48

Concept Maps

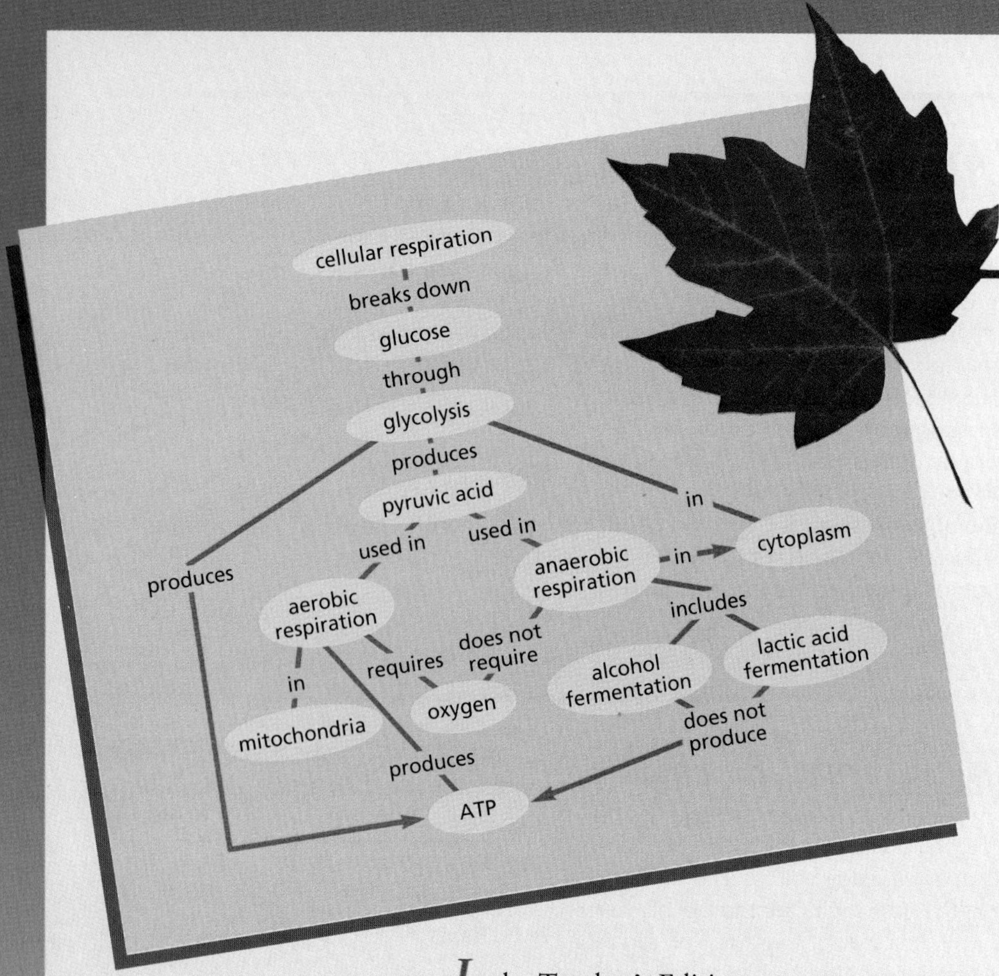

*I*n the Teacher's Edition concept maps will be suggested as instructional strategies. Concept maps help students visualize the cognitive relationships among major topics and supporting ideas in the text. Drawing concept maps forces students to examine relationships among concepts and is an excellent reteaching strategy. Drawing concepts maps involves the following steps.

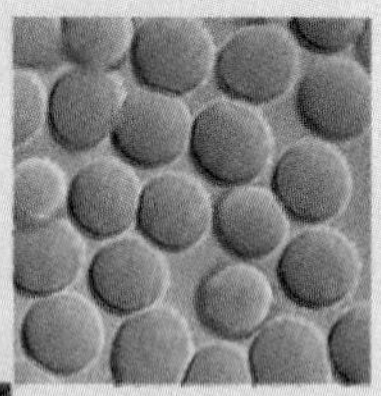

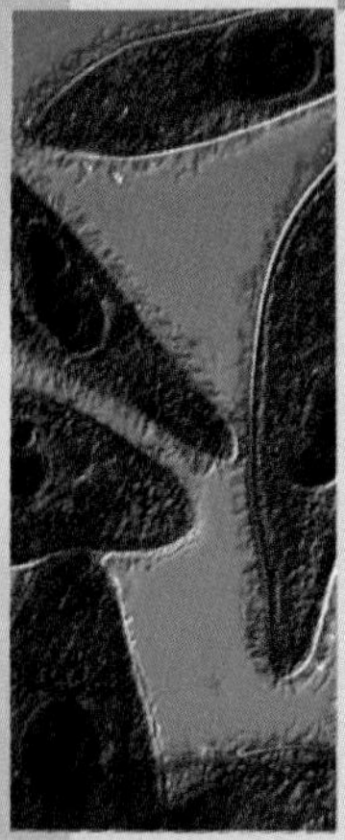

1. Start with a list of the concepts or ideas to be mapped. This list does not have to be complete, but it should be complete enough to allow you to choose the main idea of the map.

2. Look through the list to identify the concept words that directly relate to the main idea. Place these below the main idea. Continue this procedure with all the words in your list and any supporting ideas until they are all placed in order of priority under the main idea.

3. Use lines to connect the concepts based on relationships that link them.

4. Use connecting words to label the linking lines so that the relationship between the two concepts is a clear, complete thought.

5. Finally, look for all possibilities to add cross links to your map. Cross links show how deeply you understand the relationships among concepts.

When working with students and evaluating maps emphasize that there is no single correct concept map for an idea. Each map should be evaluated on the following:

1. Adequate branching
Students' first maps generally look similar to outlines. And as such they tend to lack adequate branching. Provide incentives for students to turn in highly branched maps. They will work hard on developing this skill.

2. Accurate links
Is the link between concepts meaningful? Does it correctly represent the relationship? Can complete ideas be traced through several links? Are there sufficient cross links? Here again, provide incentives for students to turn in maps that show good cross linking.

3. Concept selection
Concepts should be succinctly represented. They should not be longer than three words. Concepts should not be repeated in a map. A repeating concept is best represented by cross links.

A-V and Software Suppliers

The codes for the audiovisual and software suppliers' names used in the Resources section of the Teacher's Guide appear below in bold face type. The full name and mailing address of each company or distributor follow.

AIMS
AIMS Media
6901 Woodley Ave.
Van Nuys, CA 91406-4878

Bill Mokin
Arthur Mokin Productions, Inc.
P.O. Box 1866
Santa Rosa, CA 95402-1866

Barr
Barr Films
12801 Schabarum Ave.
P.O. Box 7878
Irwindale, CA 91706-7878

Benchmark
Benchmark Films, Inc.
145 Scarborough Rd.
Briarcliff Manor, NY 10510

Bio. Learning
Biological Learning
Distributed by Carolina Biological

Biology Media
Distributed by Carolina Biological

Britannica
Encyclopedia Britannica
310 S. Michigan Ave.
Chicago, IL 60604

Bullfrog
Bullfrog Films, Inc.
P.O. Box 149
Oley, PA 19547

Centre
Centre Communications
1800 30th St., Suite 207
Boulder, CO 80301

Churchill
Churchill Farms
12210 Nebraska Avenue
Los Angeles, CA 90025

COMPress
Distributed by Carolina Biological

Conduit
Distributed by Carolina Biological

Coronet
Coronet Films and Video
108 Wilmot Rd.
Deerfield, IL 60015

Cross
Distributed by Carolina Biological

Educational Images
Educational Images Ltd.
P.O. Box 3456
West Side Station
Elmira, NY 14905

Fanlight
Fanlight Productions
47 Halifax Street
Jamaica Plain, MA 02130

Filmakers
Filmaker's Library, Inc.
124 E. 40th St. Suite 901
New York, NY 10016

Films
Films, Inc.
5547 N. Ravenswood Avenue
Chicago, IL 60640

Focus
Distributed by Carolina Biological

Hagemann
Distributed by Carolina Biological

Hawkhill
Hawkhill Associates, Inc.
125 E. Gilman St.
Madison, WI 53703

Helix
Distributed by Carolina Biological

Humanities and Sciences
Films for Humanities and Sciences
Box 2053
Princeton, NJ 08543

Human Relations
Human Relations Media
175 Thompkins Ave.
Pleasantville, NY 10570

IFB
International Film Bureau, Inc.
332 S. Michigan Ave.
Chicago, IL 60604

J & S Software
J & S Software, Inc.
135 Haven
Port Washington, NY 11050

Knowledge
Knowledge, Unlimited
Box 52
Madison, WI 53701

Lucerne
Lucerne Films, Inc.
37 Ground Pine Rd.
Morris Plains, NJ 07950

Media Guild
The Media Guild
11722 Sorrento Valley Rd. Suite E
San Diego, CA 92121

Nasco
Nasco
901 Janesville Ave.
Fort Atkinson, WI 55538

National Geographic
National Geographic Society
Educational Services
P.O. Box 90
Washington, D.C. 20036

New Dimension
New Dimension Media, Inc.
85895 Lorane Hwy.
Eugene, OR 97405

Oxford
Oxford Scientific Films, Ltd.
Distributed by Carolina Biological

Pleasantville
Pleasantville Media
P.O. Box 415
Pleasantville, NY 10570

Pyramid
Pyramid Film and Video
Box 1048
Santa Monica, CA 90406-1048

Scholastic
Scholastic Software
2931 East McCarty St.
P.O. Box 7502
Jefferson City, MO 65102

Science & Mankind
Science & Mankind, Inc.
Communications Park
Box 1000
Mt. Kisco, NY 10549

Sunburst
Sunburst Communications, Inc.
101 Castleton Street
Pleasantville, NY 10570

Time-Life
Time-Life Films
1271 Avenue of the Americas
New York, NY 10020

U. of I.
University of Illinois Film Center
1325 S. Oak
Champaign, IL 61820

Using Media Resources with Modern Biology

The following products are available through Holt, Rinehart and Winston.

Videodiscs

Modern Biology is correlated to the Life Science Videodisc series from Optical Data Corporation as described on page T29. *Modern Biology* Videodisc Correlation Chart and Bar Code Stickers is available to facilitate instant access to a videodisc.

Videotapes

The *Science in Action Video* series is described on page T29.

Computer Software

Modern Biology Computer Test Generator is described on page T45. It can be purchased from Holt, Rinehart and Winston.

- Computerized Laboratories are described on page T21.
- Audiovisual/Software References in this Teacher's Edition

The pages that open each unit in your Teacher's Edition provide information on films, videos, and software that correlate to the topics for each chapter in the unit. A list of suppliers for the audiovisual and software references is on page T49.

Resources for Teachers

Unit Resource Lists The two pages preceding every unit opener in your Teacher's Edition provide a listing of resources for you and your students. The resources are categorized as Print or Audiovisual/Software.

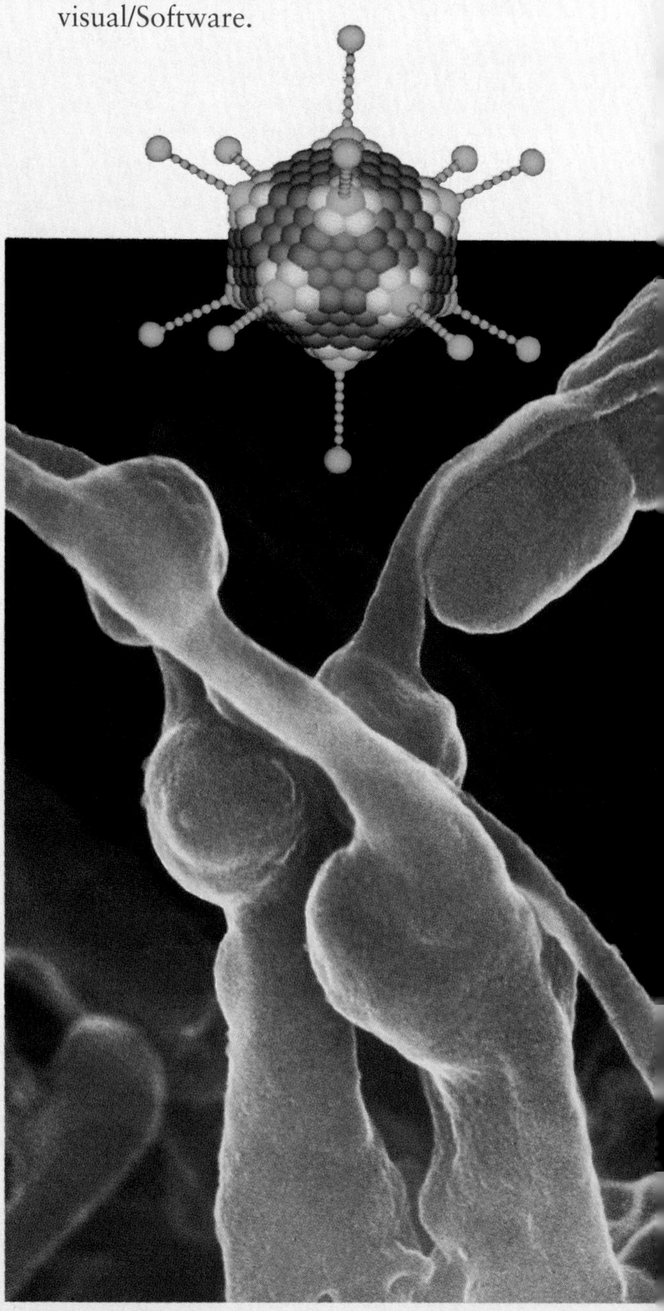

Directory of Organizations

Many government agencies, business and professional organizations, and nonprofit organizations are useful sources for pamphlets and other teaching materials. In addition to those listed below, check your telephone directory for local or regional offices of the organizations listed.

Alcoholics Anonymous
General Service Board
P.O. Box 459
Grand Central Station
New York, NY 10017

American Association for the Advancement of Science
1333 H Street, N.W.
Washington, DC 20005

American Cancer Society
1599 Clifton Road N.E.
Atlanta, GA 30329

American Dental Association
Bureau of Dental Health Education
211 East Chicago Avenue
Chicago, IL 60611

American Heart Association
The National Center
7320 Greenville Avenue
Dallas, TX 75231

American Hospital Association
840 North Lake Shore Drive
Chicago, IL 60611

American Institute of Biological Sciences
3900 Wisconsin Avenue, N.W.
Washington, DC 20016

American Lung Association
1740 Broadway
New York, NY 10019

American Medical Association
Department of Health Education
535 North Dearborn Street
Chicago, IL 60610

American National Red Cross
17th and D Streets, N.W.
Washington, DC 20006

American Public Health Association
1015 15th Street, N.W.
Washington, DC 20005

Centers for Disease Control
1600 Clifton Road N.E.
Atlanta, GA 30333

Department for Health and Human Services
200 Independence Avenue, S.W.
Washington, DC 20201

Narcotics Anonymous
Box 9999
Van Nuys, CA 91409

National Academy of Sciences
2101 Constitution Avenue, N.W.
Washington, DC 20418

National Association of Biology Teachers
11250 Roger Bacon Drive
Reston, VA 22090

National Coordinating Council on Drug Abuse
P.O. Box 19400
Washington, DC 20036

National Health Council
1740 Broadway
New York, NY 10019

National Institute of Mental Health
Barlow Building
Chevy Chase, MD 20015

National Interagency Council on Smoking and Health
P.O. Box 3654
Central Station
Arlington, VA 22203

National Kidney Foundation
30 East 33rd Street
New York, NY 10016

National Science Foundation
1880 G Street, N.W.
Washington, DC 20550

National Science Teachers Association
1742 Connecticut Avenue, N.W.
Washington, DC 20009

National Sickle Cell Disease Program
Building 31, Room 4A-27, NIH
Bethesda, MD 20041

Society for Nutrition Education
Suite 300
1700 Broadway
Oakland, CA 94612

Society for Public Health Education
655 Sutter Street
San Francisco, CA 94102

Superintendent of Documents
U.S. Government Printing Office
Washington, DC 20460

U.S. Environmental Protection Agency
Office of Public Affairs
Washington, DC 20460

U.S. Public Health Service
Department of Health and Human Services
200 Independence Avenue, S.W.
Washington, DC 20201

Unit 1 Biological Principles

Chapters

Unit Overview

Unit 1 provides the foundation necessary for students to understand the wide array of biological topics presented in subsequent units. Chapter 1 introduces themes central to biological science. These themes help show unity in the diversity of life and serve as a base to which students can attach and extend new material. Chapter 2 describes the use of various scientific processes and methods to better understand nature. Students will learn that different investigations warrant different approaches. Chapter 3 introduces basic chemical principles and stresses how life is governed by chemical properties and energy relationships. In Chapter 4 basic compounds necessary for biological life are presented. Students examine how chemical structures and biological functions of these compounds are related.

Issues in Biology

As scientists learn more about chemical properties of genes, more questions about our role in determining characteristics of life-forms will arise. A few cases in point: it is possible to genetically alter bacteria to digest oil from spills; to inject cows with genetically altered bacteria to increase milk production; and to isolate the controlling gene to increase the size of fish. Research is being conducted on how to slow the aging process in humans.

Ask students to consider some ramifications of these cases by asking questions such as: Is it ethical to alter the genetic composition of animals? Is it wise to release new species of bacteria, plants, or animals into the world? Can a person own a patent on another life-form? Given the choice, would you want to live for two centuries? What would longevity do to the job market, medical costs, and food demands?

Research in Progress

Scientists are only now coming to understand how significant is the link between biology and chemistry. Using techniques from cellular and molecular biology, neuroscientists are discovering the genetic and chemical origins of basic emotions, instincts, and learning. As a result, new drugs are being synthesized to treat neurochemical disorders such as schizophrenia, depression, and obesity. Knowledge of brain chemistry helps develop drugs that can mimic the action of natural neurotransmitters. Individuals are born with their own genetically determined brain chemistry that results in their predisposition to anxiety and fearfulness, cognitive and affective learning, and memory. Nonetheless, scientists are discovering how to intervene and effect changes in behavior. The fields of biology, chemistry, and psychology are united in ways that were unthinkable 20 years ago.

Interdisciplinary Activity

Social Studies Scientific process skills provide a method of inquiry about the world around us. Because these skills form a fundamental strategy to raise questions and analyze known and new information, these processes may be applied to many areas outside science. Ask students to suggest possible uses of these scientific processes in other disciplines. After students have reviewed Chapter 2, challenge them to provide specific examples of scientific processes that were used to investigate issues in current events. Encourage students to bring in examples from newspaper or magazine articles, textbooks, or radio or television broadcasts. *(Examples may include collecting and organizing data for criminal investigations and analyzing economic news based on reports of various indicators such as unemployment and factory production.)*

Resources

Chapter	Print: For the Teacher	Print: For the Student	Audiovisual/Software
1	■ Isaac Asimov, *Frontiers,* Nightfall, Inc., 1989. ■ Helena Curtis and N. Sue Barnes, *Biology,* 5th ed., Worth Publishers, Inc., 1989.	■ Marguerite Holloway, "Profile: Vive La Différence," *Scientific American,* October 1990, 40–42. ■ Jack McClintock, "Piracy on the High Seas," *Discover,* February 1991, 26. ■ Stefi Weisburd, "The Spark: Personal Testimonies of Creativity," *Science News,* November 7, 1987, 298–300.	■ *Basic Biology*. 2 disks. Apple II, 32K; IBM PC, 128K. Media Materials, Inc., 1986. ■ *Living or Nonliving.* Film, 16 min. National Geographic, 1986. ■ *Life Science and Ecosystem Series: A Season in the Sun*. Video, 55 min. Benchmark Films, 1985.
2	■ David Pepi, *Thoreau's Method: A Handbook for Nature Study,* Prentice-Hall, 1985. ■ H. Kumar Wickramasinghe, "Scanned-Probe Microscopes," *Scientific American,* October 1989, 98–105.	■ James Trefil, "Seeing Atoms," *Discover,* June 1990, 54–60. ■ Tom Waters, "Cretaceous Splashdown," *Discover,* September 1990, 32–33.	■ *Laboratory of Life.* Film or video, 21 min. National Geographic, 1985. ■ *Problem Solving in Science.* Video, 40 min. Educational Activities. ■ *Science Toolkit-Master Module*. Disk. Apple 64K. User's manual and guide. Scholastic, 1986.
3	■ David W. Oxtoby and Norman H. Nachtrieb, *Principles of Modern Chemistry,* 2nd ed., Saunders College Publishing, 1990. ■ Steven S. Zumdahl, *Chemistry,* D.C. Heath and Company, 1989.	■ Elizabeth Pennisi, "Buckyballs Still Charm," *Science News,* August 24, 1991, 120–123. ■ Janet Raloff, "Lime for Your Drink? Here's a New Twist," *Science News,* February 24, 1990, 27.	■ *Atomic Theory and Chemistry*. Film or video, 19 min. Encyclopædia Britannica, 1985. ■ *Elements, Compounds and Mixtures,* 2nd ed. Film or video, 20 min. Coronet, 1985.
4	■ Frank B. Armstrong, *Biochemistry,* 3rd ed., Oxford University Press, 1989. ■ Christopher K. Matthews and K. E. Van Holde, *Biochemistry,* Benjamin/Cummings Publishing, 1990.	■ Liz Applegate, "Carbohydration," *Runner's World,* October 1990, 24. ■ Robert Pool, "101 Uses for Tiny Tubules," *Science,* March 23, 1990, 1410–1411.	■ *Biology Programs for the Apple II.* 8 diskettes. J & S Software. ■ *Functional Chemistry in Living Cells.* Filmstrips or slides with cassettes. Human Relations, 1984. ■ *Organic Chemistry, Vol. 2: Industrial Applications.* Video, 60 min. TVOntario, 1988.

Science in Action Video Series

In teaching Unit 1, you may wish to use both segments of the videotape *Laboratory Safety, Equipment, and Technique/The Process of Science,* from the Science in Action Video Series. The first segment demonstrates safe laboratory techniques—use of a Bunsen burner, electrical equipment, and dissecting instruments; aseptic technique; and use of a microscope. The second segment discusses the nature of science and follows scientists as they use the steps of a scientific method.

Introducing the Unit

Topics presented in Unit 1 provide background and organizational structure necessary to effectively integrate material presented in the rest of this text. Ask students to suggest possible answers to the following questions and reflect on them as they study material in this unit.

1. Name as many different areas of biology as you can. What do these areas have in common; are any themes tied together? *(Accept a wide array of responses, such as zoology, botany, ecology, pathology, or anatomy. All of these branches of biology present how organisms live, explore their life cycles, identify what threatens life, and describe what is necessary to life.)*

2. What do you think distinguishes living things from nonliving things? *(Answers may include biological functions such as reproduction, locomotion, growth, and eating.)*

3. How is science different from other areas of study, such as philosophy or religion, when you are seeking answers to questions? *(Students' answers may include observing and scientific experimenting, or they may include physical rather than spiritual realms of inquiry. Students may also mention the scientific method.)*

4. Given what you may already know about biology and chemistry, how do you think that they may be related? *(Cells have chemicals in them: reactions are necessary for life. Knowledge of chemistry is fundamental to understanding biological processes.)*

Unit 1 Biological Principles

Chapters

"Our life is a faint tracing on the surface of mystery, like the idle, curved tunnels of leaf miners on the face of a leaf. We must somehow take a wider view, look at the whole landscape, really see it, and describe what's going on here."

Annie Dillard

Answering questions about nature involves processes of investigation and discovery that are at the heart of biology. As biologists go about their work, they use scientific processes, special tools and techniques, and their knowledge of basic principles of biology and chemistry. This unit will introduce you to the themes, processes, tools, techniques, and principles of biology. Before you begin to study the unit, look at the illustrations on these two pages to see some of the types of questions that biologists seek to answer.

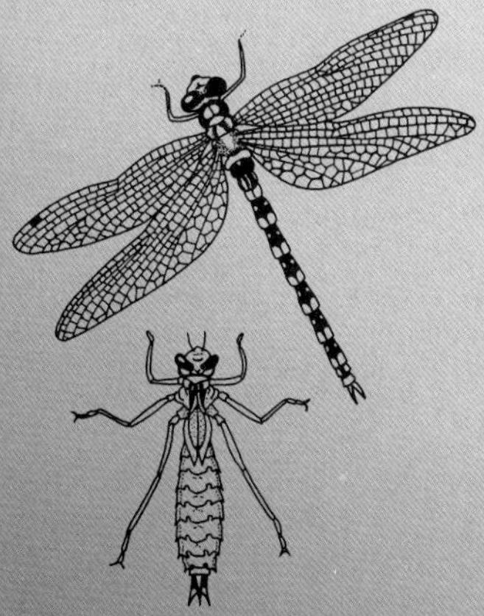

What developmental changes convert a larval dragonfly, *Anax junius,* into an adult?

How do a clownfish, *Amphiprion percula,* and a sea anemone depend on each other?

2

Using the Opening Quotation

Ask students if they have ever walked or driven from one place to another without realizing what they saw or passed along the way. Ask them to describe an example. *(Students may allude to "daydreaming" or walking someplace automatically without realizing what they passed along the way.)* Have students discuss how much occurs around us of which we remain unconscious. *(The discussion may roam from simple physical changes in one's environment to more complex awareness of consequences of one's actions.)* Ask students if they think that it is possible to become aware of the path they make on "the surface of mystery."

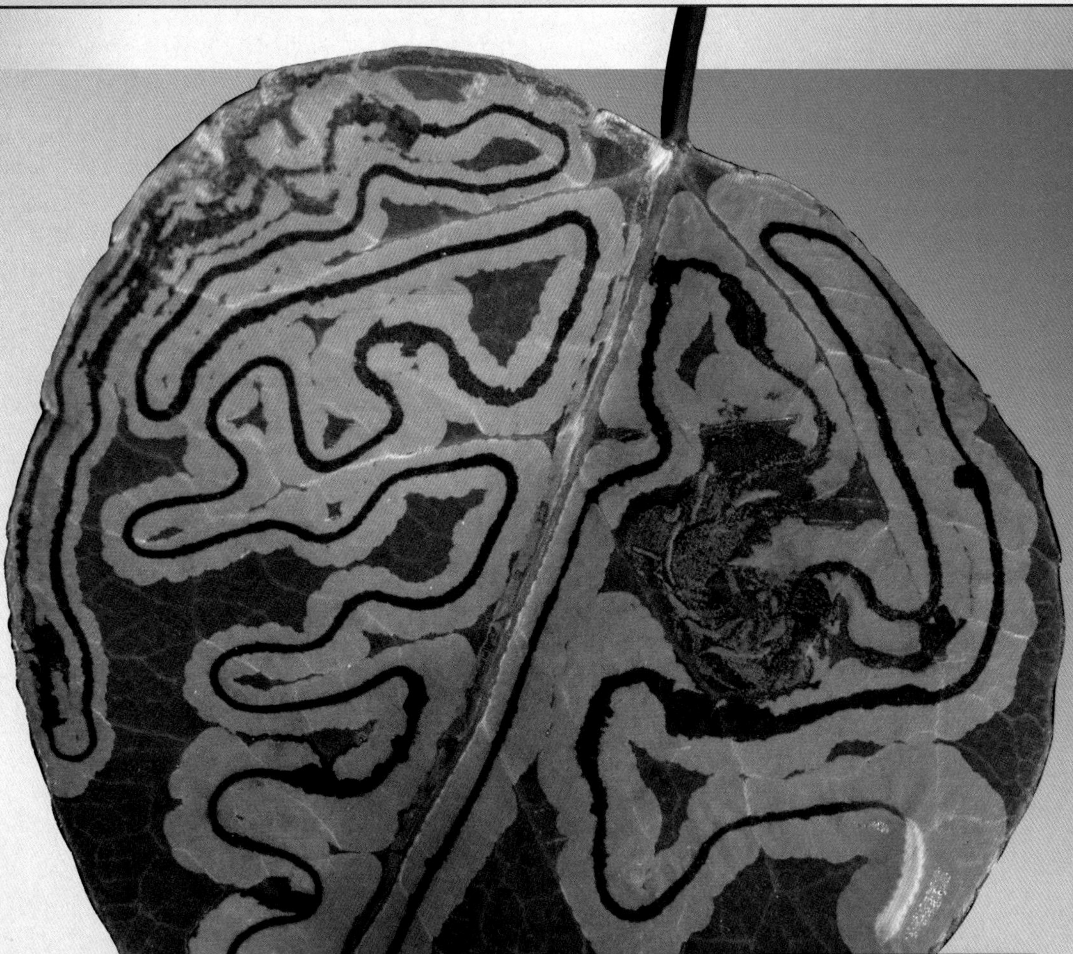

What do you think has produced the unusual pattern on this aspen, *Populus tremuloides,* leaf?

How is the structure of the beak of the broadbilled hummingbird, *Cynanthus latirostris,* related to its function?

Unit Themes

Energy All organisms require energy to drive cellular metabolic processes for growth, reproduction, and maintenance. They must obtain, store, and release energy (Chapter 3).

Evolution Differences in organisms permit some populations to adapt to specific environmental changes. Scientists use a variety of tools and methods to explore how organisms differ and what these differences might mean (Chapter 2).

Patterns of Change Continuities, trends, and dynamic changes exist in biochemical processes and traits of individuals over generations. These patterns characterize what scientists call life (Chapter 1).

Scale and Structure The morphological structure of an organism from molecular to cellular to structural is related to biological functions as well as to chemistry concepts (Chapters 3, 4). Biological structure and function are related particularly to four major types of organic compounds (Chapter 4).

Stability Interactions of a cell or an organism require consistent balance between the cell and its environment so that cell composition remains stable (Chapter 4).

Systems and Interactions No organism exists separately from all other living or nonliving things but is an integral part of a larger network of ecological factors. Unifying themes of biology encompass the "web of life" (Chapter 1).

Understanding the Visuals

Refer students to the photo of the leaf and ask them to consider how it relates to the quotation on the opposite page. *(It shows the meandering path of a leaf miner taking in nutrients it needs to survive. Like the leaf miner, we too carry out life processes. However, we can also reflect on ourselves and the world around us, seeking the principles that regulate all living things.)*

Explain to students that the needlelike beak of the hummingbird enables it to suck nectar from flowers. This is just one example of the way that structure and function relate. Throughout this unit and this year, students will observe the marvelous organization of the landscape of living things.

Chapter 1 Biological Themes

Chapter Overview

Chapter 1 introduces topics that are central to all subsequent chapters of this text. Section 1.1 presents seven unifying themes of biology. The application of these themes to the study of life reveals patterns that link all organisms despite their diversity in life-form and habitat. In Section 1.2 students begin to study characteristics common to all life.

Chapter Planning Chart

B	S	A	Sections and Subsections	Page	Features	Page	Resources
•	•	•	**1.1 Themes in Biology**				
			Evolution	6	Biology in Process	8	Videodiscs
			Reproduction and Inheritance	7	Think	10	Process Skills: The Metric System
			Development	7	Section Review	10	Blackline Master 1
			Structure and Function	8			Overhead Transparency T1
			Energy Relationships	9			Section Reviews Worksheet
			Ecology	10			
			Science and Society	10			
•	•	•	**1.2 The World of Biology**				
			Characteristics of Life	11	Laboratory	13	Videodiscs
			The Living World	12	Section Review	12	Laboratories: What Is Life?
							Section Reviews Worksheet
			End of Chapter Activities				
					Chapter Review	14	Vocabulary Skills
							Chapter Test
							Computer Test Generator

B *The Basic Level curriculum presents the most fundamental knowledge offered in the course.*
S *The Standard Level curriculum is designed for the average student who is able to master most topics.*
A *The Advanced Level curriculum includes suggestions for teaching the most academically able students.*

Cooperative Learning

Group Activity: Defining Life

- **Group Size:** *4–5 students*
- **Outcome:** *Students will construct a group list of characteristics common to all life.*
- **Individual Accountability:** *Each student will contribute three to five suggested criteria for* living *or* nonliving *to the group based on his or her own observations of objects.*
- **Positive Interdependence:** *The group will evaluate the criteria suggested by group members and establish a comprehensive list of criteria for life.*

Present an array of living and nonliving objects (for example, insects, a radio, a mouse, a piece of wood), and challenge the groups to develop a list of criteria that will classify each thing as living or nonliving. Tell each group member to examine the objects and write three to five suggested criteria. Each student must justify his or her suggestion.

Tell each group to construct one comprehensive list of criteria for life and explain how each object meets the group's criteria. *(A sample student criterion might be using own power for movement. The student might justify that criterion by stating that the mouse can move using its own power, but the toy car moves only when supplied with power externally.)* Have the entire class compare and discuss the groups' lists.

Concept Map

The following is one possible solution to the concept mapping activity in Relating Concepts on p. 6.

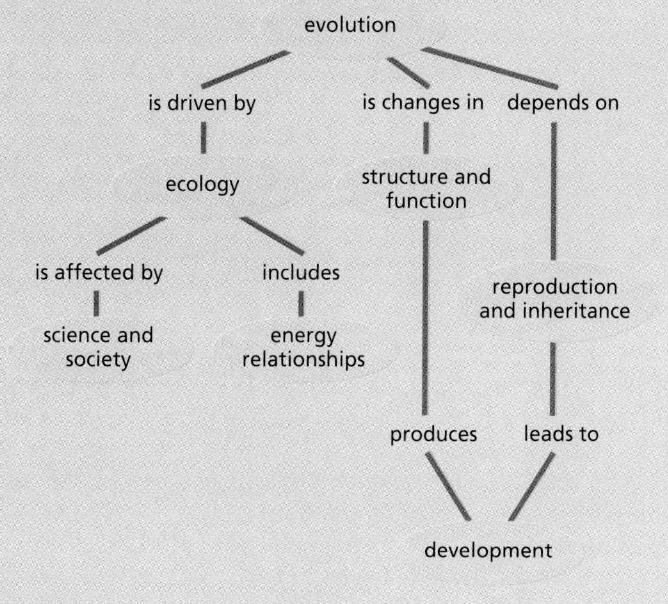

Laboratory Preparation

Overview *(See p. 13.)*

In this lab students examine a sample of pond water through a microscope to look for evidence of life. They relate the characteristics of life (as described in Section 1.2) to the microscopic specimens they observe in the pond water. Students discover that although some characteristics of life may be readily observable in some pond water organisms, other characteristics, such as reproduction and growth, are not. Students speculate on what methods could be used to collect further evidence that pond water organisms display the characteristics of all other living things.

Preparation

If pond water is not available, mixed cultures of protozoa can be ordered from a biological supply house. These organisms can be placed in tap water that has been set out overnight in open containers.

Teaching Tips

To train students in the proper use of a microscope and the preparation of a wet mount, have them do Investigation 2 *(Introduction to the Microscope)* in the *Laboratories* manual before they do this lab. Remind students to clean the microscope lenses only with the special lens paper provided in class. Whenever students carry microscopes, make sure they place one hand under the base and one hand on the arm. Also remind students not to squint or use one eye when viewing specimens through a microscope. Both eyes should remain open to reduce eye fatigue.

For Conclusions, point out that some common pond water organisms show little or no observable evidence of life. For example, diatoms appear glassy and crystalline and do not move.

Safety

Have all students wash their hands after this activity.

Chapter Themes

Evolution The tremendous diversity in life is the direct result of evolution. Emphasize that evolution has enabled living things to occupy nearly all areas on earth.

Patterns of Change Explain that change is universal among living things—within individuals, among groups, and at the species level. Point out that individuals change during development and growth and as they respond to their environment. Natural selection leads to changes in species.

Energy The existence of all forms of life on earth depends entirely upon energy. Emphasize that without energy, no organism would be able to develop, grow, respond, reproduce, or even maintain its structure.

Systems and Interactions Life is organized into systems from the cellular to the ecological level, and interactions occur within and among these systems. Show the relationship between systems and interactions in several examples: stomach cells interact during digestion, muscles and bones interact during movement, and a flower and a bee interact during pollination.

Chapter Motivating Activity

To introduce the idea of themes as unifying concepts, ask students to list examples of different societies or cultures, both past and present. *(Japanese, ancient Egyptian, Canadian, Haitian, American Indian, ancient Ghanaian, Eskimo)* Next, ask students to list concepts or "themes" that some of these societies or cultures have in common. *(Religion, traditions, government, education)* Ask students how some themes on the second list may unify several examples on the first list. *(Religion may be common to several otherwise diverse cultures.)*

Chapter 1 Biological Themes

Introduction

Earth is probably the only planet in our solar system where life occurs. Scientists estimate that 40 million species of organisms exist on earth. Of these, only about a million have been named, and few have been studied in detail. Thus much of the world of biology is uncharted territory. However, this fascinating world is not without guideposts. In this chapter you will read about the unifying themes of biology that allow scientists to study the diversity of life.

Chapter Outline

Chapter Concept

As you read, notice the recurring themes of biology and the characteristics common to all organisms.

Waterfall with plants, Cascade Mountains, Oregon. Inset: Scientist in laboratory.

Understanding the Visuals

Ask students to list examples of living things *(plants)* and nonliving things *(water, rocks)* that are visible in the large photo. Next, have students list examples of living and nonliving things that are likely to be present in the scene but are not visible in the photo. *(Fish, bacteria, birds, frogs, insects, mammals, air, decaying wood, soil)*

Ask students in what ways using only our senses in biological research could lead to incomplete observations. *(Eyes cannot see all sizes of objects or perceive all wavelengths of light; ears cannot hear all wavelengths of sound; the nose cannot smell all chemicals.)* Then ask how the inset photo relates to the larger one. *(Using laboratory equipment extends our senses.)*

1.1 Themes in Biology

Life arose on earth over 3.5 billion years ago. The first **organism**—or living thing—was composed of a single cell. For millions of years single-celled organisms floating in the seas were the only life on earth. No fishes swam in the ocean, no birds flew through the air, no snakes slithered across the ground.

In time organisms diversified, became more complex, and came to inhabit almost every region of the earth. Today brilliant tropical birds glide through the trees of lush rain forests. Strange fish living in the dark depths of the ocean emit eerie red light that helps them locate their prey. Giant sequoia trees tower hundreds of feet above the ferns on forest floors. Colonies of green algae populate the tips of a polar bear's hollow hair.

These and millions of other types of organisms form the diverse citizenry of earth. **Biology**—the science of life—includes the study of every one of these organisms. It includes the study of the microscopic structure of a single organism as well as the study of the global interactions of millions of organisms. It includes the study of an organism's individual life history as well as the collective history of all organisms.

The science of biology is as varied as the organisms that are its subjects. However, biology is unified by certain themes. Seven major themes recur throughout this book: (1) evolution, (2) reproduction and inheritance, (3) development, (4) structure and function, (5) energy relationships, (6) ecology, and (7) science and society. The paragraphs below will give you a brief introduction to each theme. By reflecting on these themes as you study biology, you will recognize larger patterns in the study of life.

Section Objectives

- *List seven themes important in biology.*
- *Discuss the relationship between adaptation and evolution.*
- *Explain how genes play a role in determining the developmental stages of an organism.*
- *Tell why the study of ecology is important in biology.*
- *Evaluate George Washington Carver's contributions to science and society.*

Figure 1-1 Many organisms exhibit similarities, such as the similar patterns found on the zebra, *Equus* sp., and the zebra moth, *Heliconius charitonius*. Yet these two organisms differ in many fundamental ways. The questions that biologists ask about similarities and differences of organisms are the basis of biological inquiry.

Lesson Plan

Section Focus

Six general scientific themes unify all the sciences, not just biology, and tie biology to the other sciences. Seven themes of biology are presented in Section 1.1 to introduce students to the specific field of biology. The table below correlates the seven biological themes described in Section 1.1 with the six general scientific themes.

Section Themes

The theme of **Energy** is evident in the ways in which all organisms acquire, store, use, and transfer energy.

The theme of **Evolution** encompasses the inheritance of adaptations during reproduction, which leads to natural selection.

The **Patterns of Change** theme is evident in each interaction of an organism with other organisms and with its environment, in the development of a zygote into a mature individual, and in the changes in organisms that occur through reproduction and inheritance.

The theme of **Scale and Structure** is reflected at all levels of biological organization, from the molecule to the ecosystem. For example, the processes of reproduction and inheritance depend upon the molecular structure of genetic material.

The interdependence of organisms and their environment directly affects the **Stability** of an ecosystem. The theme of **Systems and Interactions** is reflected in the interactions of organisms with one another and with their environment, in the interactions of structures within individual organisms, and in the relationship between science and society.

Videodiscs

- *Side 3 3302, A Drop of Water (m)*

Teacher's Edition Themes

Energy	Evolution	Patterns of Change	Scale and Structure	Stability	Systems and Interactions
Themes in Section 1.1					
▪ Energy Relationships	▪ Evolution ▪ Reproduction & Inheritance	▪ Ecology ▪ Reproduction & Inheritance ▪ Development	▪ Structure & Function ▪ Reproduction & Inheritance ▪ Development	▪ Ecology ▪ Structure & Function	▪ Ecology ▪ Structure & Function ▪ Science & Society

Graphic Organizer Use this table to relate the six scientific themes to the seven biology themes.

Motivating Activity

Display an empty can, a newspaper, a garbage bag, a disposable diaper, and photos of air and water pollution. Ask what these things have in common. *(They are examples of society's waste.)* To show that students already understand some biological themes, ask them what they know about ecology. *(Answers may include pollution and recycling.)*

Teaching Strategies

Interpreting the Visuals Point out that the smallest groups in Figure 1-2 are at the ends of the branches, and that groups splitting from the same branch are related. Explain that the point where branches connect indicates common ancestors, with the oldest ancestors represented along the trunk.

Give students the option of constructing a "phylogenetic tree" of their own families. Be sensitive to students who do not live with their biological parents or family. Stress that closely related individuals should appear near the ends of branches.

■ *See* **Overhead Transparency** *T1 and* **Blackline Master** *1.*

Relating Concepts Show students how to construct a concept map according to the five steps presented under *Thorough Coverage for Reaching Visual Learners* on p. T28. Let them practice drawing concept maps of nonbiological ideas. Then ask students to draw a concept map illustrating how the seven biological themes presented in Section 1.1 relate to one another. An example of a completed concept map is shown on p. 3B.

Ask volunteers to put their concept maps on the board and explain them. Ask students why a variety of maps are valid. *(There are many interrelationships among the themes.)*

Evolution

Evolution—the theory that species change over time—is the unifying theme of biology. The theory of evolution helps explain how all the kinds of organisms came into existence. It helps us understand why organisms look the way they do and how organisms of the past are related to organisms alive today. It also helps explain relationships among various groups of living organisms.

Scientists suggest that evolution occurs by a process called natural selection. According to the theory of evolution by natural selection, organisms that have certain inheritable traits are better able to survive in specific environments than organisms that lack those traits. Such favorable traits are called **adaptations.** In most circumstances organisms having adaptations are more likely to live to reproduce than organisms lacking the adaptations. In time organisms lacking the adaptations will die out. Individuals with adaptations live, and thus species change over time.

As you study biology, you will learn about evolution by examining adaptations of different organisms to various environments. For example, the cactus plant is adapted to a desert environment. Cactuses have thick, waxy coverings that reduce water loss. Their leaves are reduced to thin spines that further prevent evaporation and keep predators from eating the plant. In your study of biology, you will also learn about **phylogeny** *(fie-LAHJ-uh-nee)*—the evolutionary history of groups of organisms. The phylogeny of birds is shown in Figure 1-2.

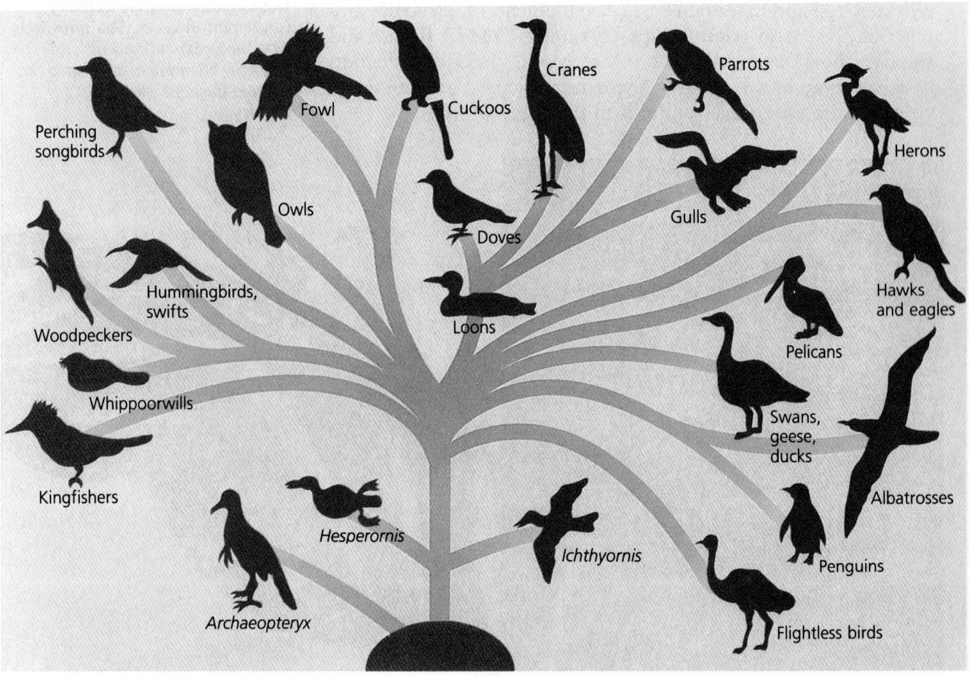

Figure 1-2 Scientists developed phylogenetic trees, such as this phylogenetic tree of birds, to illustrate the probable evolutionary history of a group of organisms.

Cooperative Learning

Bioethics To help students understand the application of ethics to biology, have them debate one bioethical question, such as "Should products be tested on animals?" Divide the class into small "pro" and "con" groups. (Explain that students do not have to endorse a position personally to advocate it in a debate.) Instruct the groups to define ethics first and then write down arguments supporting their assigned position. Ask volunteers to present their group's position to the whole class. Have the class discuss the merits of the two positions, considering costs *versus* benefits (harming animals *versus* ensuring human safety, for example) and whether the merits depend on the circumstances (testing cosmetics *versus* testing vaccines).

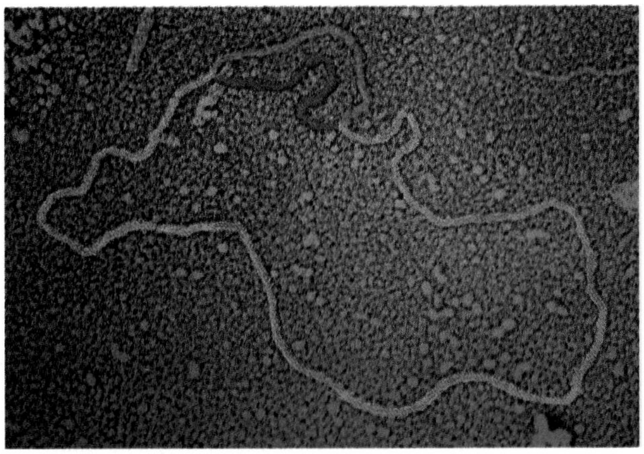

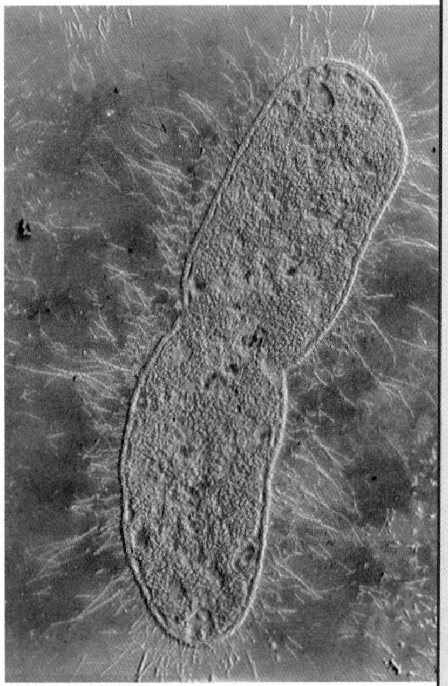

Figure 1-3 The strand of DNA (left, × 140,300) contains the genetic information of a bacterium. A single gene on this strand has been marked blue. The bacterial cell (right, × 17,650) is dividing, or undergoing asexual reproduction.

Reproduction and Inheritance

All organisms come from preexisting organisms by the process of reproduction. Reproduction involves the transfer of genetic information from parent to offspring. This information is contained in the structure of a molecule called **deoxyribonucleic acid,** or **DNA.** A short segment of DNA that contains a chemical message coding for the development of a certain trait is called a **gene.** The acquisition of traits from parents is **inheritance.**

Reproduction can be asexual or sexual. In **asexual reproduction** genetic information from different organisms is not combined. For example, when a bacterium reproduces asexually, it splits in two. The resulting bacteria usually contain identical genes. In **sexual reproduction** genetic information from different organisms is combined. For example, when an egg of a female leopard frog is fertilized by sperm of the male leopard frog, the egg and sperm fuse, forming a zygote *(ZIE-GOTE)*. The zygote contains genetic information from both the female and the male. The zygote divides, and the resulting cells divide repeatedly and develop into a new individual that contains genes from both of its parents.

Development

All organisms are composed of and develop from cells. Some organisms are composed of only one cell. These organisms are called **unicellular organisms.** Most of the living things you see around you are composed of more than one cell. Such organisms are called **multicellular organisms.** Multicellular organisms usually arise from a zygote. The process by which a zygote becomes a mature individual is called **development.**

Consider the life cycle of a salamander, for example. An egg, a larva, and an adult salamander each represent a stage in this cycle. How can an egg, a larval salamander, and an adult salamander, whose cells contain the same genes, look so different

Applying Concepts To emphasize that the seven biological themes are woven through the book, have students turn to the parts of their texts that further develop the theme of **Evolution** *(Chapters 14–18, pp. 204–277, especially Table 15-1, Figure 17-4, and Figure 17-7).* Challenge students to scan the text for additional phylogenetic trees. *(Figures 18-4, 29-3, 32-3, 35-5, 36-4, 38-3, 40-4, and 41-1)*

Discussing the Issues To increase students' awareness of the interaction between science and society, point out that since 1980 the U.S. Supreme Court has allowed patents for genetically altered microorganisms. A ruling in 1988 allowed patents for higher life forms, such as fishes and cattle, as well.

Ask students what they think about the idea of "owning" a life form and about the introduction of new, gene-altered plants and animals into the environment. Encourage students to explain whatever opinion they express. Next, ask whether students know anyone who has bred animals and what kinds of animals they were. *(Responses may include dogs, horses, cats, and cattle.)* To help put into perspective ethical issues pertaining to genetic engineering, point out that people have been breeding plants and animals for thousands of years, thereby altering adaptations in these organisms.

Videodiscs

- *2590–2592, Classification Systems (s)*
- *2593, Evolutionary Relationships (s)*
- *Side 1 33499, Cell Structure: General Functional Anatomy (m)*
- *Side 1 25971, DNA Replication (m)*

Interdisciplinary Activity

Social Studies To show how themes can contribute to the understanding of broad topics, suggest that human societies can be analyzed based on different themes, including religious, philosophical, and political themes. To use the political theme, ask students how the electoral process can be applied to the study of human societies. *(How people organize, persuade, and manipulate to be elected or appointed to office tells us something about a society's beliefs and ideologies.)* Ask students how applying this theme helps unify the study of human societies. *(Different societies can be compared according to their electoral processes.)*

Interpreting the Visuals To assist students in answering the caption question for Figure 1-4, explain that crinoids are ocean-dwelling animals that usually live attached to rocks or the ocean bottom. The mouth is located in the center, and the ends of each tiny arm are "sticky." *(The crinoid gathers food by capturing it with its arms.)*

Guided Practice

Ask small groups of students to list examples of the seven biological themes presented in Section 1.1 and to share their results during class discussion. *(Sample answers: Evolution—polar bears are adapted to the Arctic; Reproduction and Inheritance—dimples run in a family; Development—a tadpole becomes a frog; Structure and Function—a whale's flippers allow it to swim; Energy Relationships—a bird gets energy from the worm it eats; Ecology—some tree species depend on the wind to spread their seeds; Science and Society—some terminally ill people can be kept alive only with expensive technology they cannot afford.)*

Independent Practice

- Have students write answers to the Section Review.
- Give students pairs of themes and ask them to write a sentence expressing the relationship between the themes in each pair. For example, pair Evolution with Reproduction and Inheritance. *(The inheritance of adaptations during reproduction leads to natural selection and, thus, to evolution.)* Share some of the results with the class.

Figure 1-4 How does the structure of this crinoid enable it to gather food?

from one another? At each stage of the salamander's development, only some of the genes are active. When a gene is active, scientists say that it is expressed. In the salamander's egg some genes are expressed and others are not. The same is true for the larva and for the adult salamander. As any organism develops, different genes are expressed at different times.

Structure and Function

Biologists use the term **morphology** *(mor-FAHL-uh-jee)* to refer to the structure and form of an organism or any of its parts. **Anatomy** is a branch of morphology that deals with the internal structure of organisms.

In biology structure is almost always related to function. A relationship between structure and function exists at all levels of biological organization. For example, a starch molecule consists of a long chain of sugar molecules. Its structure corresponds to its function—storage of sugar. The structure of the beak of the great horned owl shown on the cover of this book is related to the beak's function. The sharp, curved point allows the owl to tear the flesh of its prey.

Biology in Process

Developing the Peanut as a Food Crop

The development of new food crops is one of the most important ways that scientists work to benefit society. With his work on the peanut American scientist George Washington Carver made an enormous contribution to American agriculture.

During the 1800s and into the 1900s cotton was the chief cash crop grown in the southern part of the United States. However, cotton robs the soil of nutrients when it is planted in the same field year after year. Thus southern farmers, especially those who farmed small plots, made little money growing this crop.

George Washington Carver wanted to help the southern farmer. After receiving his master's degree in agriculture in 1896, Carver became head of the newly formed Agriculture Department at the Tuskegee Institute in Tuskegee, Alabama.

Carver set up a laboratory and experimental plots for agricultural research. He employed students to help carry out experiments on different crops and on products that could be made from those crops. Carver was especially interested in the peanut and the sweet potato, crops that harbor

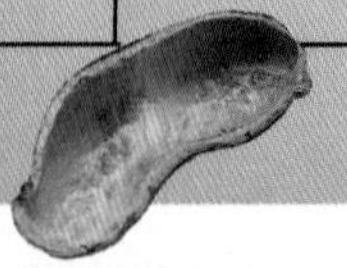

LEP Activity

Divide the class into seven groups. Assign each group one of the themes presented in Section 1.1. Ask each group to design a large colored sketch or collage, made of magazine pictures, that illustrates the assigned theme. Alternatively, individuals could make posters illustrating one theme. Students may base their work on pp. 6–10 of the text and might add examples illustrating the themes based on their own observations. Help students combine their sketches or collages to construct a mural that illustrates all seven biological themes. Arrange for students to display their work in a hallway of the school.

Energy Relationships

All organisms use energy. How organisms get, use, and transfer energy is a major topic of study in biology. The sun supplies almost all of the energy for life on earth. Through the process of photosynthesis plants and certain unicellular organisms capture solar energy and convert it into a form of energy that can be used by living things.

Organisms that acquire energy by making their own food are called **autotrophs.** Plants and certain unicellular organisms are autotrophs. Organisms that gain energy by eating other organisms are called **heterotrophs.** Some unicellular organisms, as well as all animals and fungi, are heterotrophs. In studying biology you will learn about how energy flows from the sun to autotrophs and finally to heterotrophs.

How energy is converted, stored, and used within a single organism is also an important subject of study in biology. Most organisms on earth and every cell within these organisms use similar chemical processes to release energy from food. They all use this energy for growth and maintenance, as well as for carrying out essential life functions.

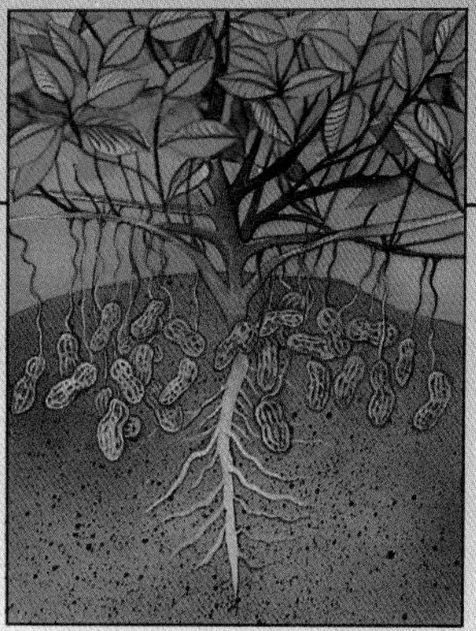

bacteria on their roots that add nutrients to the soil. Carver discovered about 300 products that could be made from peanuts and over 100 products that could be made from sweet potatoes. These products included flour, cheese, milk, cosmetics, dyes, rubber, and peanut butter.

Carver's impressive list of products established the importance of the peanut and the sweet potato. Southern farmers began to grow these crops, which were especially suited to the warm weather and the sandy soil of that region.

In 1921 Carver went to Washington, D.C., to testify before Congress about the importance of the peanut. Because of Carver's testimony Congress acted to promote the growth of peanuts in the United States. In time the soil-enriching peanut became the second largest crop in the South. By 1950 it had become the sixth leading crop in the nation.

Carver continued his agricultural research. He published articles on practical matters such as improved farm techniques and food preservation. His work was especially appreciated during the Great Depression of the 1930s, when many people were out of work and had little money to buy food. Carver was also an influential teacher, inspiring young people to find ways to make science work for the betterment of all.

■ What are two ways in which Carver's work on the peanut benefited society?

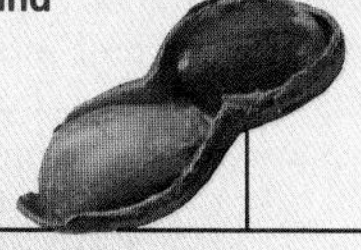

More Information

Aristotle Modern taxonomists use morphology, physiology, embryology, genetics, and biochemistry to infer phylogenetic relationships and devise classification systems. Aristotle (382–322 B.C.) proposed perhaps the earliest known classification scheme. He proposed a hierarchical system of being, placing all nonliving things on the bottom rungs of a ladder, followed by plants, animals, and humans on the top rung. Although the model seems simplistic, Aristotle paid close attention to the characteristics of organisms. For example, he was the first to group whales and dolphins with mammals, which he did based on his observations that they breathe air and suckle their young.

Biology in Process

Using the Feature

To provide a preview of the scientific processes that will be introduced in Chapter 2, ask students to cite examples of the following process skills in this feature: experimenting *(Carver directed experiments on crops and their products)*, collecting data *(Carver compiled a list of products that could be made from peanuts and sweet potatoes)*, and communicating *(Carver published his findings)*.

Explain to students that the specific problem addressed by Carver was nitrogen depletion in the soil by the cotton crop. Nitrogen is necessary for plant growth. Although nitrogen is abundant in the atmosphere (as N_2), it is not in a usable form for plants. Certain bacteria live in nodules on the roots of the peanut plant (and other legumes). The bacteria convert N_2 to nitrogen compounds that are released into the soil in a form that plants can use. This process is called nitrogen fixation. Ask students to infer what the long-term effect might be if nitrogen fixation did not exist. *(Plants would not survive because the soil would become depleted of certain nutrients that they need.)*

Answer to the Feature

Student answers could include: Carver discovered more than 300 products that could be made from peanuts; he popularized a soil-enriching crop from which farmers could make money; and he inspired young people to use science to benefit humankind.

Videodiscs

- ***2540, Photosynthetic Prokaryote (s)***
- ***2541, Photosynthetic Eukaryote (s)***
- ***Side 4 34768, Interactions: Rhinoceros and Birds (m)***

Section 1.1

Check Your Understanding

1. What is the value of considering themes in biology? *(Considering themes helps us recognize patterns among living things.)*
2. How does the theme of Evolution relate to the theme of Ecology? *(Evolution has resulted in many diverse species having adaptations to many different environments.)*
3. How do genes relate to adaptations? *(Adaptations are favorable traits coded for by genes.)*

Answer to Think

The deer depends on the egret for removal of external parasites and on plants around it for food. Both animals depend on the environment for water and oxygen.

Reteaching

List the seven biological themes across the board. Have students volunteer examples of how each theme relates to their own lives. *(Sample answers: Ecology—people's waste products pollute the environment; Structure and Function—a thumb and fingers allow us to perform precise motor tasks)* List student suggestions under each heading for class discussion.

■ *See* Section Reviews *worksheet, Section 1.1.*

Enrichment

To further develop the Science and Society theme, have students research and report to the class on ways in which biotechnology has benefited society and has created problems for society.

Closure

Have students apply themes to other scientific disciplines. For example, ask students to construct a short list of ways evolution can be applied to geology. *(Landmasses and oceans have not always been the same but have evolved into different formations over time.)*

Think

The egret, *Ardeola ibis,* and the sambar deer, *Cervus unicolor,* shown in the picture are dependent on each other. The egret feeds on organisms that live on the deer's skin and on insects stirred up when the deer passes. How might the deer be dependent on the egret? In what ways are both animals dependent on the environment?

Ecology

The study of individual organisms is an important part of biology. However, to understand fully the biological world, scientists study interactions of organisms with each other and with the environment. This branch of biology is called **ecology.**

By studying ecology, biologists have come to recognize the interdependence of organisms. Even solitary spiders that spend most of their lives away from other members of their species depend on other animals for food. By studying ecology, biologists have also come to recognize the interdependence of organisms and the physical environment. To survive, all organisms need substances such as nutrients, water, and gases from the environment. The stability of the environment in turn depends to some extent on the healthy functioning of organisms in that environment. For example, the oxygen in the atmosphere is largely a product of plant life. When vast areas of forest are cut down, less oxygen is released. In time a great reduction of forests could alter the composition of the atmosphere. Such a change in the physical environment could eventually affect all life on earth.

Science and Society

Knowledge from biological science can be applied to specific problems in society to improve human life. For example, the development of the polio vaccine in the 1950s was a significant scientific breakthrough that had a large impact on society. By producing the polio vaccine in bulk and distributing it throughout the world, scientists, business leaders, and governments have worked together to reduce the threat of polio.

How biological knowledge should be used involves decisions based on **ethics**—the study of what is right and wrong and of our moral choices. **Bioethics** is the application of ethics to biological concerns. One biological issue involves genetic engineering—making new forms of life by placing genes from one organism into another. A second issue involves AIDS, a viral disruption of the immune system, which has profoundly affected our society. Understanding biology can help people responsibly answer ethical questions, such as, whether restrictions should be placed on genetic engineering, or whether AIDS test results should be publicized. Sound decisions will ensure a healthy future for society.

Section Review

1. What is *morphology?*
2. What is the relationship between adaptation and phylogeny?
3. Explain development in terms of gene expression.
4. Why is the study of ecology important in biology?
5. What bioethical questions does society face in deciding how to deal with species threatened with extinction?

Answers to Section Review

1. The internal or external structure of an organism or any of its parts
2. Phylogeny reflects evolutionary relationships among groups of organisms based on adaptations that each group acquired as it evolved.
3. Different genes are expressed at different developmental stages.
4. By studying ecology, biologists have come to recognize the interdependence of organisms.
5. Possible questions: Should people try to save species threatened with extinction, or would that be "interfering" with nature? Should people try to prevent the endangerment of species in the first place?

1.2 The World of Biology

Our world abounds with a great variety of life. Giant tube worms thrive at the bottom of the ocean near bubbling volcanic vents. Red algae grow, covering the surface of arctic glaciers like a carpet. Bacteria find shelter even in the pores of your skin. Tube worms, algae, and bacteria and all other organisms—no matter how diverse they may be—share certain features characteristic of all living things.

Section Objectives

- *List seven characteristics of life.*
- *State how living things are organized.*
- *Differentiate between a response and a behavior.*

Characteristics of Life

Although it is difficult to define life, biologists have formulated a list of characteristics by which we recognize living things. These characteristics are elaborated in the paragraphs below.

- **Cells** All living things are composed of cells. In multicellular organisms some cells are highly specialized, each having a unique role in the function of the organism.
- **Organization** All organisms are organized at both molecular and cellular levels. They take in substances from the environment and organize them in complex ways. Cells have an internal organization in which specific cell structures carry out particular functions. In multicellular organisms cells are organized into tissues, tissues are organized into organs, and organs are organized into systems.
- **Energy Use** As you learned in Section 1.1, all organisms use energy for growth and maintenance.
- **Response to the Environment** All organisms respond to the environment. A **response** is a reaction to a stimulus. For example, if a lion charges a gazelle, the gazelle may respond by running away. Responses may be simple or complex. A complex set of responses is called **behavior.** The annual migration of a bird is a behavioral response to changes in the seasons.

Figure 1-5 Life-forms vary greatly. The fluorescent coral (left) appears inanimate, while the gazelle, *Litocranius walleri* (right), is very swift. Yet both are classified as living things because they have the characteristics of life.

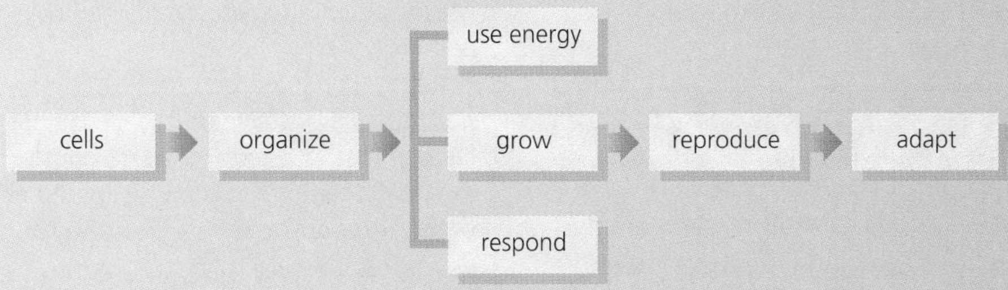

Graphic Organizer Use this chart in Guided Practice on p. 12.

Lesson Plan

Section Focus

This section explains that no single criterion defines life. All living things exhibit the following characteristics: cells, organization, energy use, response to the environment, growth, reproduction, and adaptation.

Section Themes

In this section the theme of **Energy** is expressed as a defining characteristic of life—energy use; **Evolution** is expressed as another characteristic—adaptation. The **Patterns of Change** theme is evident in organisms' responses, reproduction, and growth. **Scale and Structure** and **Stability** are reflected in organisms' cells and organization. The theme of **Systems and Interactions** is evident in an organism's organization and responses.

Motivating Activity

Have students watch a toy bumper car respond to obstacles by changing directions. Ask them why the car is not alive, since it responds to the environment and uses energy.

■ *See* Laboratories, ***Investigation 1.***

Teaching Strategies

Contrasting Concepts To emphasize that all seven characteristics of life must be present for something to be alive, ask students to identify inanimate objects that have some but not all the characteristics. *(Water moves but is not made of cells, a television set uses energy but does not grow, a computer responds but does not adapt.)*

Videodiscs

■ ***Side 4 3461, Pufferfish: Behavior (m)***
■ ***Side 4 45808, Camouflage: Ptarmigan (m)***
■ ***Side 4 19464, Butterfly: Time-lapse Photography (m)***

Guided Practice
Ask students to illustrate how the seven characteristics of life are interrelated. Use the chart on p. 11 as a model.

Independent Practice
- Have students write answers to the Section Review.
- Give students pairs of life characteristics and ask them to describe the relationship between each pair. For example, pair *energy use* with *reproduction. (Living things need energy to reproduce.)*

Check Your Understanding
1. What is the difference between growth in living things and in nonliving things? *(Living things: result of cell enlargement and cell division; nonliving things, such as crystals: usually the result of accumulation of matter.)*
2. How do living and nonliving things use energy differently? *(Living things use energy for all life functions; nonliving things use energy only for functions for which they were designed.)*

Reteaching
Write *computer* and *grasshopper* on the board. Ask students to identify all the characteristics of life exhibited by each thing. Have students explain why the grasshopper is living but the computer is not. *(Computer: only some of the characteristics of life; grasshopper: all of them.)*
- *See* Section Reviews *worksheet, Section 1.2.*

Enrichment
Have students research and write a summary of the Gaia hypothesis.

Closure
To show how the seven characteristics of life relate to students' own lives, ask them for personal examples of each characteristic. *(Sample answer: Energy use—my body uses energy from food)*

Figure 1-6 A lizard extending its frill, *Chlamydosaurus kingii* (left), and sky pointing by a blue-footed booby, *Sula nebouxii* (right), are two examples of behavior by animals.

- **Growth** All living things grow. Growth occurs through cell division and cell enlargement. **Cell division** is the orderly formation of new cells from a parent cell. **Cell enlargement** is the increase in cell size. In multicellular organisms, cell division and cell enlargement together result in growth.
- **Reproduction** All species of organisms have the ability to reproduce. Reproduction is not essential for the survival of an individual organism. It is essential for the continuity of life, because no organism lives forever.
- **Adaptation** Organisms have adaptations. These adaptations are traits that give an organism an advantage in an environment. Variations of adaptations are essential for the continuity of life, because they confer an advantage on some members of a species in a changing environment.

The Living World

The world of biology is so rich that scientists have yet to explore all of it. New discoveries, like the algae population inside the polar bear's fur and the underwater vent community, are found every year. The wide variety of organisms in these communities shows us how much is still to be learned about organisms. Wherever you may live, the world around you teems with life. This book will help you appreciate this living world.

Section Review

1. What is the relationship between a *response* and a *behavior?*
2. List five characteristics of all organisms.
3. Describe three ways in which living things are organized.
4. Why is reproduction an important characteristic of life?
5. What kind of test might a scientist devise to figure out whether something is alive?

Answers to Section Review
1. A behavior is a complex set of responses.
2. Accept any five of the following: cells, organization, energy use, response to the environment, growth, reproduction, and adaptation.
3. Organisms take in substances from the environment and organize them into more complex molecules; cells have internal organization; in multicellular organisms, cells are organized into tissues, tissues into organs, and organs into systems.
4. Reproduction perpetuates life.
5. A test for evidence of all seven characteristics of life: for example, the scientist should create a stimulus to see whether the object responds to it.

Laboratory

Life in a Drop of Water

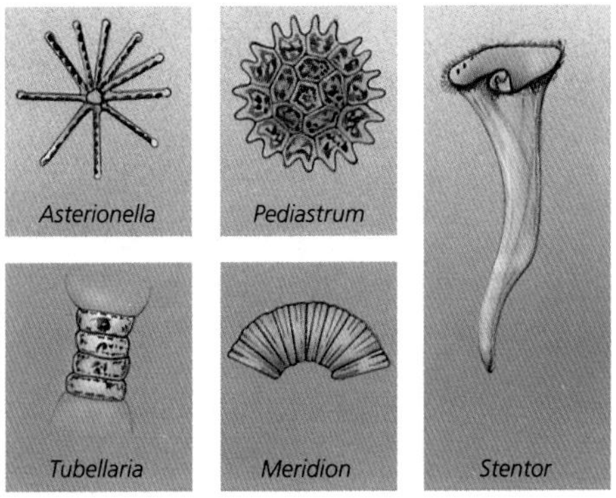

Objective
To examine the variety of living organisms found in a drop of pond water

Process Skills
Classifying, inferring, communicating

Materials
Strands of cotton from a ball of cotton batting, microscope slide, medicine dropper, pond water, coverslip, compound microscope, unlined paper

Inquiry
1 Place two or three strands of cotton on a microscope slide. Use a medicine dropper to apply one drop of pond water to the cotton strands on the slide. Place a coverslip over the drop of water, using the wet mount technique.
2 Place the slide on the microscope stage and observe the drop of water under low power. Record your observations. Center the microscope on an interesting organism, then shift to high power. Why is it necessary to begin your observation by using the low power objective of your microscope?
3 Try to distinguish between the nonliving objects and the living organisms you see in the water sample. What are some guidelines for distinguishing between living and nonliving matter? Make a sketch of each structure you identify as a living organism.
4 Under each sketch write a brief description of the organism's color, shape, and relative size. Be sure to record any other distinguishing physical features, such as cilia. Cilia are the organism's hairlike structures that aid in movement.
5 Observe whether or not the organism moves under its own power. If it is motile, try to determine its means of locomotion. What effect do the cotton strands have on the movement of the organisms through the water?
6 For each organism look for evidence that it responds to stimuli—such as light, obstacles, and movement—in its environment.
7 Look for evidence that the organism is capable of reproduction.
8 Compare your observations with those of your classmates.
9 Work as a class to compile a list of generalizations about organisms found in pond water.

Conclusions
1 What characteristics did you observe in living organisms in pond water?
2 From what observation can you infer that pond water organisms expend energy?
3 What characteristics of the pond water organisms are difficult to observe in this type of investigation?
4 What characteristics might be used to distinguish between plantlike and animallike organisms?

Further Inquiry
Think of an investigation that would reveal the characteristics of living organisms that you found difficult to observe in this investigation.

Laboratory

(For an overview of evidence of life and preparatory information related to the laboratory, see p. 3B.)

Inquiry
2. It is easier to locate an object using the low-power objective than the high-power objective.
3. Guidelines include presence of cells or cellular structures, movement, and structures that could be adaptations.
4. Point out that cilia are adaptations to an aquatic environment.
5. The strands interfere with the organism's movement, and it may respond to them by changing the direction of its movement.

Conclusions
1. Answers will vary but may include cells or cellular organization, locomotion, responses to stimuli, and structural adaptations.
2. The movement of these organisms indicates that they use energy.
3. Reproduction and growth are difficult to observe.
4. A plantlike organism might be distinguished by green coloration.

Further Inquiry
Students may think of ways to observe reproduction and growth, such as a long-range study that measures population changes among a limited number of organisms.

Vocabulary

1. Phylogeny reflects the history of a species' evolution, which occurred through the natural selection of individuals with certain adaptations.
2. Sexual reproduction involves the combining of genetic material from different individuals, whereas asexual reproduction does not.
3. Heterotrophs and autotrophs both use energy; heterotrophs acquire energy from other organisms, but autotrophs acquire energy by making their own food.
4. A response is a single reaction to a stimulus, whereas a behavior is a complex set of responses.
5. Cell division contributes to growth through formation of new cells, and cell enlargement through increase in cell size.

Review

1. c	**6.** c
2. b	**7.** a
3. a	**8.** d
4. d	**9.** c
5. c	**10.** b

11. Seven important themes in biology are Evolution, Reproduction and Inheritance, Development, Structure and Function, Energy Relationships, Ecology, and Science and Society.
12. Organisms having adaptations are better able to survive and reproduce than are organisms lacking these adaptations. In time, organisms lacking the adaptations die out, leaving no offspring; species thus change over time.
13. At each developmental stage, only some of the salamander's genes are expressed. As the salamander develops, different genes are expressed at different times.
14. Answers will vary. Accept examples such as: The shape of the owl's beak allows it to kill prey.

Chapter 1 Review

Vocabulary

adaptation (6)	biology (5)	evolution (6)	organism (5)
anatomy (8)	cell division (12)	gene (7)	phylogeny (6)
asexual reproduction (7)	cell enlargement (12)	heterotroph (9)	response (11)
autotroph (9)	development (7)	inheritance (7)	sexual reproduction (7)
behavior (11)	deoxyribonucleic acid (DNA) (7)	morphology (8)	unicellular organism (7)
bioethics (10)	ecology (10)	multicellular organism (7)	
	ethics (10)		

1. What is the relationship between adaptation, phylogeny, and evolution?
2. What is the difference between asexual reproduction and sexual reproduction?
3. Compare heterotrophs and autotrophs.
4. What is the difference between a response and a behavior?
5. How do cell division and cell enlargement contribute to growth?

Review

1. Evolution helps explain how complex organisms came into existence, why organisms of the past differ from those alive today, and (a) how various groups of living organisms develop (b) how various groups of living organisms reproduce (c) how various groups of living organisms are related to each other (d) how various groups of living organisms obtain energy.
2. Reproduction involves the transfer of genetic information from (a) male to female (b) parents to offspring (c) unicellular organism to multicellular organism (d) egg to zygote.
3. When a gene is active, scientists say that it is (a) expressed (b) inherited (c) functional (d) interdependent.
4. In biology structure is almost always related to (a) evolution (b) adaptation (c) development (d) function.
5. The branch of science that includes the study of the interactions of organisms with one another and with the environment is called (a) biology (b) morphology (c) ecology (d) phylogeny.
6. All organisms are composed of (a) DNA (b) genes (c) cells (d) energy.
7. A response is a reaction to (a) a stimulus (b) a behavior (c) an adaptation (d) a developmental stage.
8. Growth occurs through (a) organization and reproduction (b) adaptation and evolution (c) stimulus and response (d) cell division and cell enlargement.
9. Reproduction is essential for the continuity of life because (a) organisms must reproduce to survive (b) organisms must reproduce to adapt to their environment (c) no organism lives forever (d) no organism is totally independent of other organisms.
10. The science of life is referred to as (a) phylogeny (b) biology (c) ecology (d) anatomy.
11. List seven themes that are important in biology.
12. What is the theory of evolution by natural selection?
13. How do genes play a role in the developmental stages of an organism such as a salamander?
14. Give an example of how structure is related to function in biology.
15. How does energy flow from the sun to autotrophs and then to heterotrophs?

15. Autotrophs convert solar energy into energy stored in food during photosynthesis. Heterotrophs that eat autotrophs gain the energy stored in food made by autotrophs.
16. Scientists have learned that organisms are dependent on one another and on the environment.
17. Answers will vary. Accept answers showing that students recognize several different sides of the issue they select.
18. Carver conducted agricultural research to identify crops that could be grown successfully in the South and from which a large number of products could be made, and to improve farming and food preservation techniques. He also promoted the growth of peanuts by testifying before Congress and he

16. What have scientists learned by studying ecology?
17. Explain the ethical implications involved in a biological issue, such as genetic engineering.
18. How did George Washington Carver work to benefit science and society?
19. List seven characteristics of all life-forms.
20. What do biologists mean when they say that organisms are organized?

Critical Thinking

1. One of the first branches of biology to be developed was taxonomy, the naming of organisms. Why might it be important for taxonomy to develop before the other branches of biology?
2. The branch of biology known as ecology has developed only fairly recently. Why might this be so? What sort of biological knowledge would be necessary before the study of ecology could begin?
3. Examine the photograph of the puffin at right. This animal, like all organisms, has adaptations that enable it to survive in its particular environment. Judging from the appearance of the puffin, what type of environment does it inhabit? Using the photograph, name two adaptations of the puffin that enable it to survive in its environment.
4. The first law of thermodynamics states that energy can be neither created nor destroyed during a process; only the form of the energy can be changed. How does the biology of a plant or an animal reflect this law? Give an example.

Extension

1. Read the article by Jack McClintock entitled "Piracy on the High Seas" in *Discover,* February 1991, p. 26. Make an oral report in which you include: (1) a description of the relationship between the amphipod and the sea butterfly, (2) an explanation of what the amphipod gained from the sea butterfly, and (3) an account of how McClintock investigated the reason for the amphipod's behavior. Researchers observed that about 75 percent of the amphipods near the surface of water demonstrated their unusual behavior; only 10 percent of the amphipods deeper down demonstrated the behavior. Explain why the amphipod behavior was observed more often near the surface of water.
2. A hiker in the Wisconsin woods suddenly sees a brown bear. The bear runs in one direction and the hiker in the other. Later in the summer the hiker meets a mother bear with two cubs. The bear chases the hiker. Make a table in which you list the stimulus and response for the bear and the hiker in each situation. Why did the bear respond differently in the second situation?

inspired young people to work in science to help society.

19. All living things are made of cells, are organized, use energy, respond to the environment, grow, reproduce, and have adaptations.

20. At the molecular level, organisms take in substances from the environment and organize them into more complex molecules. At the cellular level, organisms' cells are organized internally. In multicellular organisms, cells are organized into tissues, tissues into organs, and organs into systems.

Critical Thinking

1. It was necessary to describe and name organisms so that different scientists studying them independently could accurately compare their results.

2. Biologists needed a lot of information about specific organisms and their environments in order to study their interrelationships. This information has taken many years to obtain.

3. The puffin, *Lunda cirrhata,* lives in arctic regions of the Pacific and along Alaska's coast. Its thick body is adapted to the cold climate. The coloration of its feathers and bill may help attract a mate. The puffin's webbed feet are adapted for swimming.

4. A plant converts solar energy into energy stored in food and releases some of this energy for its own use. An animal releases the food energy of plants or other animals that it eats.

Extension

1. Encourage students to consider what biological themes and characteristics of life are demonstrated by the organisms described in the article.

2. A sample table appears below. In the second situation, the bear perceived the hiker as a threat to her cubs and reacted to remove the threat, whereas in the first situation, the bear perceived the hiker as a threat to itself and reacted to avoid the threat. Animals that raise their young often protect their young in response to perceived threats.

Situation 1		
Organism	Stimulus	Response
Bear	Hiker	Runs from hiker
Hiker	Bear	Runs from bear

Situation 2		
Organism	Stimulus	Response
Bear	Hiker	Chases hiker
Hiker	Bear	Runs from bear

Chapter 2 Biological Processes

Chapter Overview

Chapter 2 introduces the activities of scientists in general and the tools and techniques of biologists in particular. In Section 2.1 students learn how scientific processes and scientific methods are used in research projects. Section 2.2 presents an overview of how biologists use microscopes, laboratory and field techniques, and computers.

Chapter Planning Chart

B	S	A	Sections and Subsections	Page	Features	Page	Resources
•	•	•	**2.1 Scientific Processes and Methods**				
			Scientific Processes	17	Think	23	Videodiscs
			Scientific Methods	23	Writing About Biology	24	Science in Action Videotape: The Process of Science
					Laboratory	29	Process Skills: Owls, Mice, and Bees
					Section Review	23	Blackline Master 2
							Overhead Transparency T2
							Section Reviews Worksheet
•	•	•	**2.2 Biological Tools and Techniques**				
			Microscopes	25	Biotechnology	26	Videodiscs
			Laboratory Techniques	27	Section Review	28	Science in Action Videotape: Laboratory Safety, Equipment, and Technique
			Field Techniques	28			Blackline Master 3
			Computers	28			Laboratories: Introduction to the Microscope
							Section Reviews Worksheet
			End of Chapter Activities				
					Chapter Review	30	Vocabulary Skills
							Chapter Test
							Computer Test Generator

B *The Basic Level curriculum presents the most fundamental knowledge offered in the course.*
S *The Standard Level curriculum is designed for the average student who is able to master most topics.*
A *The Advanced Level curriculum includes suggestions for teaching the most academically able students.*

Cooperative Learning

Group Activity: Using Scientific Processes

- **Group Size:** *2–3 students*
- **Outcome:** *Students will design and conduct controlled experiments on plant growth using various scientific processes and will produce summary reports.*
- **Individual Accountability:** *Each student will organize and write an individual report.*
- **Positive Interdependence:** *The group will confirm the observations of each group member, and each group will collaborate with one other group to merge their data.*

This activity will be most effective if conducted beyond the time that the class studies Chapter 2. Tell the class that some groups will investigate the effect of soil type on plant growth; other groups will investigate the effect of light exposure. Assign one type of experiment to each group. Stress the importance of sharing information.

Provide students with: seeds (preferably lima bean seeds), potting soil, sand, small pots, boxes with lids, and water, and let them decide how to conduct controlled experiments. Tell each group that they will collect the results of a group that investigated a different question and that each student will write a summary of the conclusions for both questions. Students' reports should identify the scientific processes they used.

Concept Map

The following is one possible solution to the concept mapping activity in Guided Practice on p. 22.

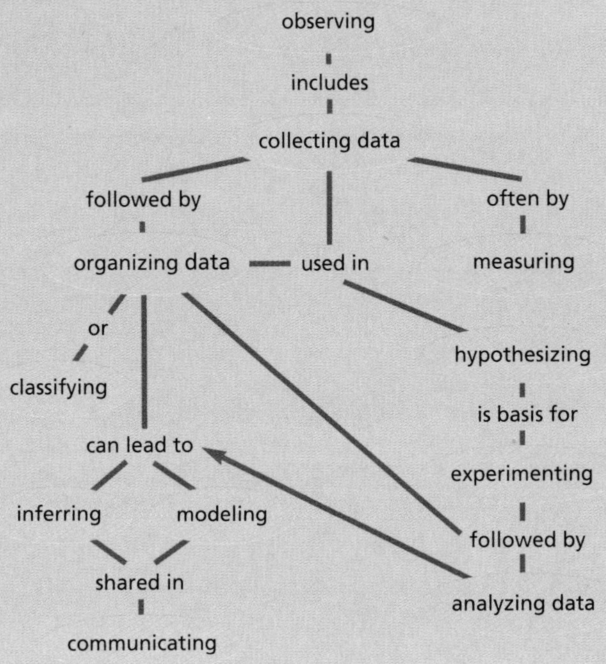

Laboratory Preparation

Overview *(See p. 29.)*

This lab introduces students to designing and carrying out an experiment, which they will do in several subsequent labs. William Harvey's pioneering work on circulation is presented in the Background as a historical example of the collection and analysis of quantitative data to form a hypothesis.

Investigating the effect of exertion on pulse rate is a good introduction to the process of inquiry because pulse rate is easy to examine quantitatively and physical exertion is an easily controlled variable. This lab offers an excellent opportunity for collecting and analyzing group data if time permits.

Preparation

This lab requires no preparation.

Teaching Tips

Have students read the Technique section of the lab before they design their inquiry.

Demonstrate to students the correct way to find their pulse. Instruct them to place the index and middle fingers of their right hand on the palm side of their left wrist, "off center" near the the base of the hand, on either the thumb side (ulnar artery) or the little-finger side (radial artery). Tell students to use the very tips of their fingers and to apply slight pressure. Remind them not to use their thumb to find their pulse.

Students should not begin counting until they can clearly feel their pulse. If time is limited or if students find it difficult to count their pulse for a full minute, you can have them count for 30 seconds and then double the result.

Make sure that, in designing and conducting their experiments, students choose a safe form of exertion that does not disturb other students. Walking or jogging in place are probably the most suitable exercises for a classroom.

To extend this lab, you may wish to ask students to suggest other factors that might affect pulse rate. *(Answers could include pleasant or terrifying experiences or fantasies.)*

Safety

Students with injuries or medical conditions that preclude exertion, and any student who has a medical excuse from physical education class, should not perform the physical activity portion of this lab. These individuals can still count their pulse, form a hypothesis, and design an experiment, and then serve as "recorders" for other participants.

Chapter Themes

Stability The premise of all scientific investigation is that nature is predictable. For example, when scientists repeat an experiment they expect to reproduce their initial results. Emphasize that biologists employ various scientific methods, tools, and techniques in their efforts to develop testable predictions about living things.

Patterns of Change Help students understand that scientists are constantly alert to changes as they investigate nature. Changes in data are incorporated into conclusions and, if confirmed repeatedly, are incorporated ultimately into new or revised scientific theories.

Explain that the theme of **Stability** and the themes of **Evolution** and **Patterns of Change** only appear to contradict each other. Different themes may be appropriate to different aspects of the same natural system.

Chapter Motivating Activity

Hold up a large rubber or plastic ball and tell students that it represents a newly discovered planet. Tell them to imagine that they are leading an expedition to search for life on this planet. Have the class brainstorm a set of questions they would need to answer to determine whether life exists on the planet and, if so, in what forms. *(Students' questions should focus on the seven characteristics of life introduced in Chapter 1.)* List their questions on the board and explain that what scientists do is pose questions and gather data to answer them. Biologists use a variety of processes and tools to obtain the information they seek.

Chapter 2 Biological Processes

House dust mite, *Dermato phaggides*, on a piece of dust (×380). Inset: Electron microscope.

Introduction

The science of biology has been built on the observations of many scientists over thousands of years. Their curiosity about the natural world has led to a body of knowledge that grows larger every day. In this chapter you will learn about the processes, tools, and techniques biologists use to add to the body of knowledge we call biology.

Chapter Outline

Chapter Concept

As you read this chapter, notice how scientific processes, tools, and techniques are used by biologists in their scientific methods.

Understanding the Visuals

Direct students' attention to the large scanning electron micrograph of a dust mite. Ask students whether they have ever seen an organism like this in dust and whether they know that such a creature lives in all homes. (This will be a surprise to most students.) Explain how the magnification of this image is presented. (The magnification, ×380, is shown in parentheses.) Dust mites are not visible to the unaided eye. Ask students how the inset photo relates to the SEM of the dust mite. *(Students may suggest that the scientist is viewing the mite through the electron microscope.)* Explain that the inset photo shows one of many instruments used by biologists.

2.1 Scientific Processes and Methods

Science is a body of knowledge. Science is also a way of learning about the natural world. One of the best introductions to science comes from watching scientists in action. Dr. Luis Baptista is a biologist who studies birds that live in the rain forests of South America. These equatorial forests are home to thousands of bird species, many of which have not even been named, much less studied in detail. Simply finding out what's there is one of Dr. Baptista's primary aims. To do this he does a series of field studies. A field study involves spending several weeks or months at one site, observing and collecting birds.

Each day Dr. Baptista puts in long hours of intense observation. Carrying a portable tape recorder to record unusual bird calls, he spends the day hiking through the rain forest, visiting different habitats, such as a river edge, a rocky ledge, or a clearing, to observe and identify birds. He may also spend part of the day identifying birds that have been caught in collecting nets. In the evening, when most birds are inactive, he records information on what he observed that day. Such records of his observations enable Dr. Baptista to communicate with his colleagues about what he observed. They also can help other biologists classify the birds and learn more about their behavior.

Dr. Baptista is just one of thousands working to add to our knowledge of the rain forest. Not all of these biologists are field biologists—scientists who work outdoors. Some biologists work in laboratories doing research on plants or animals brought back from the rain forest. Others use information collected by field and laboratory scientists to develop computer models of interactions between organisms and their resources in the complex environment of the rain forest.

The ecology of the rain forest is just one of many broad topics that biologists study. Whatever they study, all biologists, in fact all scientists, use certain processes to obtain knowledge about nature. Understanding scientific processes will help you further appreciate how scientists work.

Scientific Processes

All areas of science involve posing questions about nature and discovering facts that can help answer those questions. The work of Dr. Baptista centers on the question, "What species of birds live in a particular area of the South American rain forest?" His field study is an attempt to discover facts that can help answer that question. As you read about the scientific processes, note how each process contributes to the formulation of questions or the discovery of facts that can help answer those questions.

Section Objectives

- *Define and give examples of observing, measuring, organizing and analyzing data, classifying, inferring, and modeling.*
- *Explain the relationship between hypothesizing, predicting, and experimenting.*
- *Tell why communicating is an important process in science.*
- *List some similarities and some differences in the ways that scientists work.*

Figure 2-1 Studying the tropical rain forest requires the use of many scientific processes.

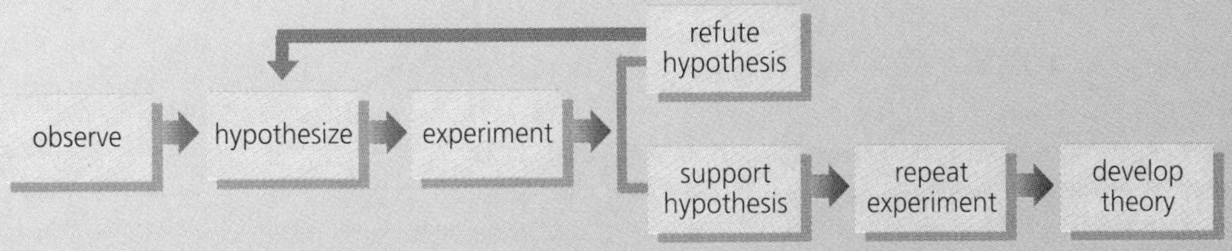

Graphic Organizer Use this sequential diagram in the LEP Activity on p. 22.

Lesson Plan

Section Focus

This section presents scientific processes used by scientists in their work. These processes are observing and collecting data, measuring, organizing data, classifying, hypothesizing, predicting, experimenting, analyzing data, inferring, modeling, and communicating. Scientific processes are combined in a variety of ways to meet the needs of each investigation.

Section Themes

The theme of **Stability** is reflected in the way scientists base scientific theories on consistent evidence. The **Patterns of Change** theme encompasses the changes in data observed by scientists in both natural settings and controlled experiments.

Motivating Activity

Tell students to imagine that they are scientists addressing this question: Do high school students learn at slower or faster rates than elementary school students? Ask them first to propose a testable answer. *(Accept both "slower" and "faster.")* Then have students brainstorm procedures for gathering information to support or refute their answers. *(Answers should include sampling of representatives of the two student populations.)* Summarize the suggestions on the board and then ask whether any of the procedures would allow them to "prove" their answer beyond doubt. *(Probably not. For irrefutable proof, they would have to test every elementary and high school student in the world.)*

Videodiscs

- ***Side 1 3301, History of Diabetes Research (m)***

Teaching Strategies

Interpreting the Visuals Refer students to Figure 2-2 and ask what similarities they notice between the tanager and the tropical rain forest. *(The colors of the bird and the colors of its habitat are virtually identical.)* Ask students to describe a procedure they might use to determine whether this bird's coloration is an advantage in its habitat. *(Sample answer: Release some tanagers in a habitat where their coloration does not match the surroundings and study how well they evade predators and capture food.)*

Organizing Data Ask students what is the value of quantitative data. *(Such data can be compared by scientists who are repeating or extending the experiments of their colleagues.)* Direct students' attention to Figure 2-3 and ask them to describe other ways to quantify and organize data about rain forest birds on a graph. *(Sample answers: number of birds of one species at different levels of a tree at one time, or at one level at different times of day; number of species with certain colors of feathers)* Point out that valuable data are not always quantitative; tape recordings of bird calls and descriptions of feeding behavior, for example, also are important.

Figure 2-2 The green-headed tanager, *Tangara seledon* (left), can be found in a habitat such as the tropical rain forest (right).

Figure 2-3 Biologists use graphs to organize quantitative information in a visual format.

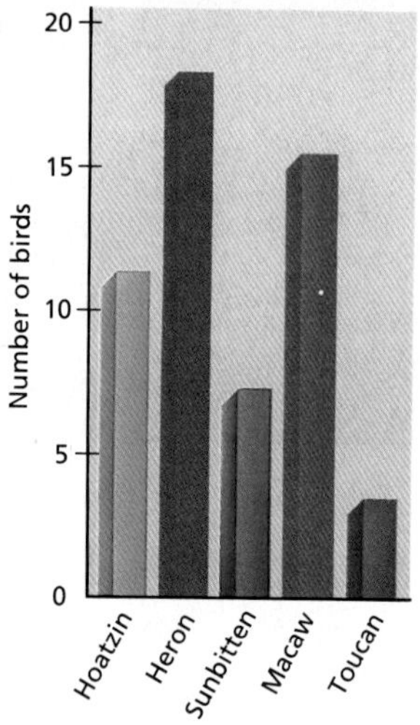

Observing and Collecting Data

All scientific understanding of the natural world ultimately is based on observations. **Observing** is the use of one or more of the five senses to perceive objects or events. For example, in the rain forest Dr. Baptista uses his senses of sight and hearing to perceive the location of birds in different habitats. Scientists use various tools to aid in making observations. Dr. Baptista uses binoculars to help him see birds at a distance, for example. Scientists use other tools such as microscopes to help them perceive objects or events that would otherwise go unobserved.

While making observations, scientists often collect data. **Collecting data** is the gathering and recording of specific information based on observations. For example, Dr. Baptista might tape a bird call and then record the time, location, habitat, and weather conditions where he made the specific observation.

Measuring

Observations are most useful when they involve quantitative data—data that can be measured in numbers. **Measuring** is the process of determining the dimensions of an object, the number of objects in a group, the duration of an event, or other characteristics in precise units. For example, when Dr. Baptista counts the number of birds of different species collected in a particular habitat, he is making measurements that may be useful in understanding the behavior of the species. Most scientific measurements throughout the world are made using the metric system. Refer to Measurement on p. 840 to review this system.

Organizing Data

Data are of little use unless they are organized. **Organizing data** involves placing observations and measurements in some kind of logical order, such as in a graph, chart, table, or map. Dr. Baptista might organize his quantitative data as shown in Figure 2-3. This bar graph shows the number of birds of various species collected at a particular location on a specific date.

Cooperative Learning

Gender Differences in Pulse Rate Without revealing the process skills to be used in this activity, divide the class into groups composed of both girls and boys. Ask each group to collect data on the one-minute resting pulse rates for all its members and to organize the data according to girls' rates and boys' rates. (Refer to the laboratory Teaching Tips on p. 15B for proper pulse-taking procedure.)

Pool the groups' data on the board, compute the average pulse rates of male and female students, and compare the two averages. If the average pulse rates for male and female students differ, ask students to suggest a testable hypothesis to explain the difference. *(Although females usually have a faster average pulse rate than males do, scientists have not reached a conclusion as to the reason why. One possible explanation is*

Classifying

Classifying is the process of grouping objects, organisms, or phenomena into an established organizational scheme, or developing new organizational schemes. In biology classifying is most often used to organize living things into groups that share morphological traits. Dr. Baptista might collect many birds in the rain forest. Some he will be able to classify immediately because their anatomy, behavior, and habitats are similar to those of known species. Others may not have been studied by scientists before. To classify these birds, biologists will study the anatomy, behavior, and habitats of the unidentified birds to find out how the birds might be related to known species.

Hypothesizing

The scientific processes discussed so far often lead to the formulation of questions. For example, after collecting and organizing his data, Dr. Baptista might notice that one species of bird is usually found in a riverbank habitat early in the day and in a thicket habitat during midday. He might wonder why this would be so. To help answer this question, he might think of possible explanations for this behavior. For example, insects the birds feed on could be more prevalent near the riverbank early in the day and more prevalent in the thicket during midday. Or predators might be less common near the riverbank early in the day and less common in the thicket during midday.

Dr. Baptista might put a possible explanation into the form of a testable statement—or **hypothesis.** His hypothesis might be: The birds avoid predation by moving from the riverbank to the thicket during the middle of the day.

Hypothesizing, the process of forming testable statements about observable phenomena, is often one of the first steps in a scientific investigation. A statement is testable if evidence can be collected that either supports the hypothesis or refutes it. For example, the above hypothesis could be shown to be false if the predators of the birds were observed to be equally common in both habitats in the early morning and in the middle of the day.

Although a hypothesis may be refuted, it can never be proved true beyond all doubt. It can only be supported by evidence. At any time new data might be collected that indicate a previously accepted hypothesis does not hold true in all instances. Good scientists look for ways to refine and revise their hypotheses as they uncover new evidence.

Predicting

To test a hypothesis, a scientist usually makes a prediction that follows from the hypothesis. **Predicting** is stating in advance the result that will be obtained from testing a hypothesis. A prediction often takes the form of an "if–then" statement. The biologist might make the following prediction based on the hypothesis that

Figure 2-4 After observing this great egret, *Egretta alba,* in its water biome, a biologist might formulate questions about the behavior of the bird and then form a hypothesis that answers those questions.

Relating Terms Explain that biologists classify organisms based on many criteria, including morphology, biochemistry, development, behavior, and habitat. Ask students to recall the definitions of *morphology* and *phylogeny* in Chapter 1. (*Morphology—the structure and form of an organism; phylogeny—the evolutionary history of groups of organisms)* Ask them to suggest how morphology relates both to phylogeny and to the scientific process of classifying. *(Morphology is one of the criteria used by biologists both in classifying organisms and in inferring their phylogeny.)*

Distinguishing Terms Ask whether any students have ever heard the term *hypothesis* defined as a guess. *(Many probably have.)* Ask what the noun *guess* means. *(A judgment based on little or no evidence)* Have students explain why this definition does not reflect the meaning of *hypothesis* in the context of scientific processes. *(The formation of a hypothesis arises from careful consideration of observations, both new and historical. In hypothesizing, therefore, a scientist does not make "guesses" but instead constructs testable statements based on collected data.)*

that females have a higher metabolic rate than males.) Ask students to suggest possible explanations for differences in pulse rate between individuals. *(Answers may include differences in weight, health of lungs, health of heart, and blood pressure.)*

Have students identify the process skills that they used in this activity. *(Observing and collecting data, measuring, organizing data, analyzing data, hypothesizing)*

Interpreting the Visuals Ask students to identify the experimental part of the controlled experiment shown in Figure 2-5. *(The vine growing up the cord)* Next, have students look at Figure 2-6 on p. 21. Explain that, in designing a controlled experiment, scientists should try to anticipate possible sources of experimental error—also called uncontrolled variables. Challenge students to identify possible uncontrolled variables in Figure 2-6. *(Sample answers: possibly diseased vines, possible differences in the textures or other surface properties of the real and artificial trees, possible misrecording of data)*

Point out that all experiments contain some degree of experimental error because people and their instruments are not perfect. Similar results from repeat experiments, however, do increase scientists' confidence in their conclusions.

■ *See* **Overhead Transparency T2** *and* **Blackline Master 2.**

Making Predictions Refer students to Figure 2-7 on p. 21. Ask them what conclusion they would have drawn if the experiment had ended after only one day. *(The average growth rate for the experimental plants was greater than that of the control plants.)* Next, ask students how they could predict what the difference in the average heights of the experimental and control groups would be if the experiment continued for five more days. *(The curve for each group could be extended, or extrapolated, at the present slope for five more days. This assumes that the plants do not reach a terminal height or slow their growth rate.)*

is discussed on the last page: *If* it is true that the birds move from riverbank habitats to thicket habitats to avoid predators, *then* I will observe fewer predators in the riverbank habitat in the morning than during midday, and I will observe fewer predators in the thicket habitat during midday than in the morning. Showing this prediction to be false refutes the hypothesis; showing this prediction to be true supports the hypothesis.

Experimenting

Some hypotheses or predictions can best be tested through careful observations in a natural setting, such as a field study. Others can be tested through experiments. **Experimenting** is the process of testing a hypothesis or prediction by carrying out data-gathering procedures under controlled conditions. Such conditions eliminate extraneous influences and allow close observations to be made.

Most experiments in biology are controlled experiments. A **controlled experiment** is based on a comparison of a control group or phase with an experimental group or phase. The control group and the experimental group are designed to be identical except for one factor. This factor is called the **independent variable** or the manipulated variable. During the course of a controlled experiment, a scientist observes or measures one main factor in both the control group and the experimental group. This factor is called the **dependent variable** or the responding variable.

The following example shows how a controlled experiment works. Suppose that a biologist collects cuttings from a species of vine that grows up trunks of small trees in the rain forest. The biologist might hypothesize that the vine depends on the tree only for support. From this hypothesis the biologist might make the following prediction: If the vine depends on the tree only for support, then a vine transplanted onto an artificial tree should grow as rapidly as a vine transplanted onto a real tree.

Figure 2-5 The vine growing up this tree in a tropical rain forest is the control in an experiment conducted to see if the vine depends on the tree only for support.

To test this prediction, the biologist might design the controlled experiment shown in Figure 2-6. The control group consists of vine cuttings transplanted onto small trees similar to those in the rain forest. The experimental group consists of vine cuttings transplanted onto plastic models of the trees in the control group. The vines in the control group, and those in the experimental group would be treated identically except for the independent variable. Each group would be in the same type of soil, at the same temperature, and receive the same amount of sunlight and water. In other words, variables such as type of soil, temperature, and amount of sunlight and water would be held constant. The type of tree, real or artificial, is the independent variable; the rate of growth of the vines is the dependent variable.

Analyzing Data

After a scientist has collected and organized data from a field study or an experiment, the data must be analyzed. **Analyzing data** is the process of determining whether data are reliable and

Interdisciplinary Activity

Language Arts Have students compare the scientific definitions and everyday, common meanings of the following terms: *fact, observing, hypothesizing, predicting, experimenting, theory,* and *law.* Assign different sets of three or four words to small groups and have the groups brainstorm the common meanings of the words. (For example, the everyday usage of *theory* is often equivalent to the scientific term *hypothesis.*) Do not allow students to use a dictionary. Instruct the groups to write down a definition that they agree upon for each assigned word. Tell each group to pool its results with those of another group so that they have common meanings for all seven terms.

Have each student write a report contrasting the common meanings agreed upon by the groups with the scientific

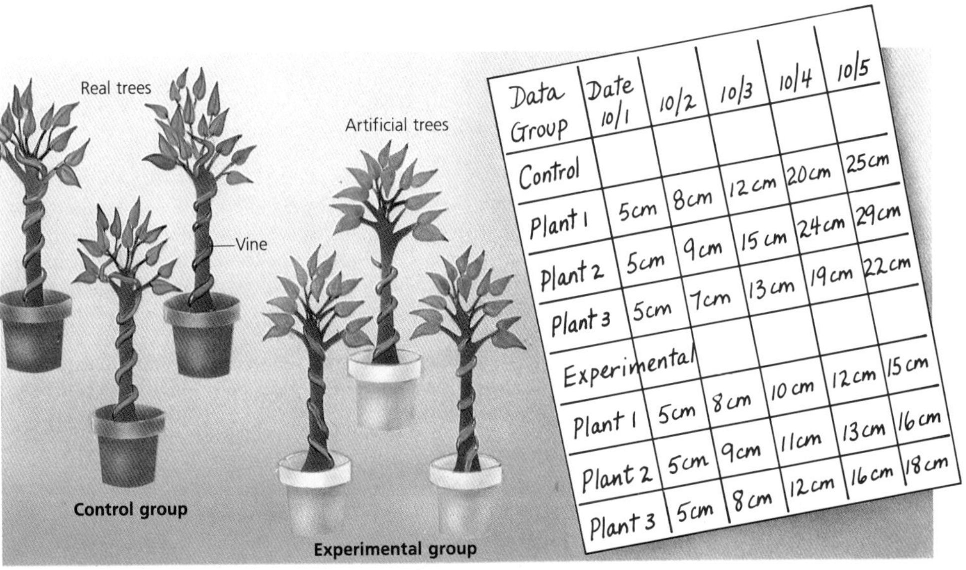

Data Group	Date 10/1	10/2	10/3	10/4	10/5
Control					
Plant 1	5cm	8cm	12 cm	20cm	25cm
Plant 2	5cm	9cm	15 cm	24cm	29cm
Plant 3	5cm	7cm	13cm	19cm	22cm
Experimental					
Plant 1	5cm	8 cm	10 cm	12cm	15 cm
Plant 2	5cm	9cm	11cm	13cm	16cm
Plant 3	5cm	8 cm	12cm	16cm	18cm

Figure 2-6 The control and experimental groups initially differ only in the independent variable.

whether they support or refute a given prediction or hypothesis. Scientists analyze data in many ways, including using statistics, interpreting graphs, determining relationships between variables, comparing the data to those obtained from other studies, and determining possible sources of experimental error.

For example, suppose that the biologist who conducted the experiment on vines obtained the data charted in Figure 2-6. In analyzing the data, the biologist might first average the heights of the plants in each group for every set of measurements. Figure 2-7 shows a graph of these averages. It indicates that the plants in the experimental group grew slower than did the plants in the control group. Further analysis would determine whether the data refute the hypothesis and whether the data are reliable.

Inferring

Inferring is the process of drawing conclusions on the basis of facts or premises instead of direct perception. Facts might include data gathered during a field study or an experiment; premises might include conclusions drawn from previous knowledge or from past experience. Based on the data gathered in the experiment discussed above, the biologist might infer that all vines obtain nutrients from the trees on which they grow.

Some inferences, such as the one discussed above, are theoretically testable. However, other inferences are not testable. For example, suppose a biologist notices that two species of fossil horses show many similarities in structure. Further analysis might indicate that one fossil is 30 million years old and the other is 20 million years old. Based on knowledge of evolution, the biologist might infer that the older species is ancestral to the younger species. Even though this may be true, the inference is not testable

Figure 2-7 After four days the control and experimental groups differ in the dependent variable.

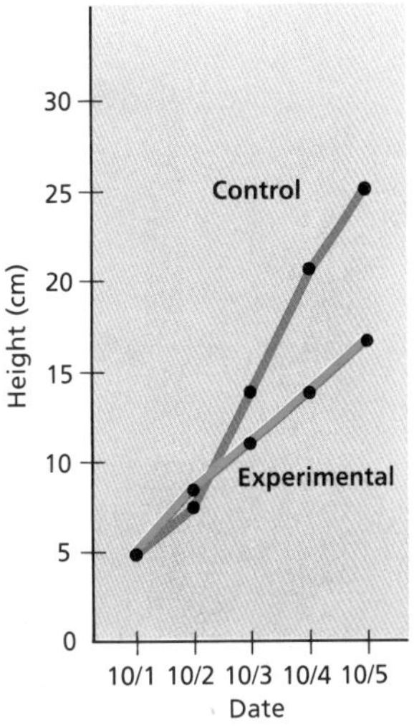

definitions presented in the text. Give students the following scientific definition of *fact:* A fact is a confirmed or repeatable observation; facts can be measurements recorded during a field study, for example. Make sure students understand the distinction between *fact* and *inference* in scientific usage.

Students can present their reports to the class for discussion. Stress the importance of using precise language in scientific matters.

Designing an Experiment Ask small groups of students to plan and conduct an experiment to test the hypothesis that mold grows slower on bread containing preservatives than on bread containing no preservatives. Have students list the process skills they would use. *(Sample experimental design: Obtain two loaves of bread made from the same ingredients and under the same conditions, except that one loaf contains preservatives and the other does not. Place the same amount of each kind of bread on different plates and store the two plates side by side so that they are exposed to the same environmental conditions. Record the number and sizes of mold colonies on each kind of bread each day and graph the results. The process skills used would be observing and collecting data, measuring, organizing data, experimenting, analyzing data.)*

- *See* Process Skills, *Chapter 2.*

Exploring Careers Ongoing rapid developments in science create a continuing need for many kinds of laboratory technicians, research assistants, and research scientists. Call students' attention to the list of national organizations on p. 842 that they may contact for further information. Explain that these careers generally require associate's, bachelor's, or master's degrees in science-related fields. Point out that work in all scientific fields relies on the scientific processes presented in this chapter to achieve advances in scientific knowledge. Invite speakers to your classroom to describe their work in science.

Videodiscs

- ***Side 1 12217, Barnacle Molting: Testing a Hormone (m)***

Guided Practice
To emphasize that there is no single "scientific method" and that scientists combine different scientific processes in different methods of investigation, ask each student to draw a concept map that illustrates the relationships among scientific processes. Have students compare their concept maps. An example of a completed concept map is shown on p. 15B.

Independent Practice
- Have students write answers to the Section Review.
- Use the following activity to reinforce the concept that scientific processes are skills people can use every day. Tell students to select two products that claim to do the same thing and to analyze data to determine which size of each product is the most economical. Point out that students need not purchase the products but can record the necessary data in the store. *(Answers should compare the products' unit prices.)* Ask students how they could scientifically determine the more effective product. *(By using the products—that is, observing and then comparing their effectiveness)*

Check Your Understanding
1. Explain whether the following statement describes an observation or an inference: Acid rain has killed the fish in the lake. *(Inference—this is one possible conclusion that could be drawn from an observation.)*
2. Develop a prediction based on the following hypothesis: My test scores reflect the amount of time I spend studying. *(If I spend more time studying, then my test scores will improve.)*
3. Why is it possible to have more than one scientific method? *(Different investigations may require different approaches, or combinations of scientific processes.)*

because it is based on events that would have occurred millions of years ago and that therefore are not directly observable.

Modeling
Modeling involves constructing a representation of an object, a system, or a process that helps show relationships between data. A model may be visual, verbal, or mathematical. A biologist might create a mathematical model to show how environmental factors, such as sunlight, temperature, rainfall, and humidity, affect the growth of plants in the rain forest. Figure 2-8 shows a visual model of the feeding relationships between many animals in the rain forest. Scientists sometimes use models to help generate new predictions or hypotheses.

Communicating
Scientists do not work in isolation. Often they work in groups. In many cases they publish results of their experiments in scientific journals or present them at scientific meetings. Sharing information, or **communicating,** is essential to progress in science. Communication allows scientists to build on the work of others. For instance, when scientists find out about the results of the vine growth experiment, they may form hypotheses about how vines get nutrients from trees. This will lead to further experiments and greater understanding of the relationship between vines and trees.

To avoid confusion, scientists often define terms using **operational definitions,** or definitions that are limited to repeatable and observable phenomena. For instance, in the vine experiment, an operational definition of *growth rate* is the rate at which the height of the vine changes. This definition makes it clear to other scientists how vine growth was measured.

Figure 2-8 This model represents how various plants are food for animals. These animals, in turn, are food for other animals.

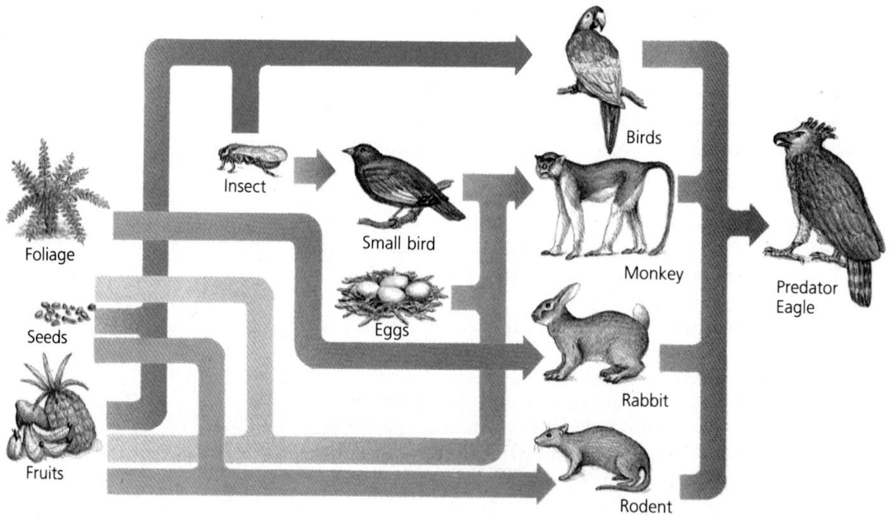

LEP Activity
Use the sequential diagram on p. 17 to help students understand the relationship between key scientific processes and theory building. Draw the diagram on the board and ask students to suggest what Dr. Baptista could do (or did) for each part of the diagram. *(For example, tape bird calls—observing)* Point out that although this diagram omits several processes, they could be incorporated into the sequence. Emphasize that hypotheses are based on prior observations, experiments can support or refute hypotheses, and theories are developed and modified after repeated experiments, or testing of hypotheses. Explain that theories may change as a result of the development of new scientific tools and techniques.

Scientific Methods

Science does not prescribe one single method for asking and seeking answers to questions. Scientists combine some or all the processes you have read about in a logical way to devise a **scientific method** best suited for a particular research project.

For example, in his field study of birds of the rain forest, Dr. Baptista might use a scientific method that combines observing, collecting data, measuring, organizing and analyzing data, and communicating. The biologist doing the experiment on vines might use a scientific method that combines all the science processes. A biologist making a mathematical model of environmental factors affecting plant growth in the rain forest might use a scientific method that combines organizing and analyzing data, predicting, inferring, modeling, and communicating.

Some scientists use less complex methods. For instance, by observing animals over long periods, scientists can uncover individual and societal patterns of behavior. The processes of observing, organizing data, and communicating are integrated into one kind of scientific method.

Scientists use different scientific methods, but they share certain ways of reasoning. For instance, if a hypothesis describes *how* things happen and continues to be supported by evidence gathered from many different experiments, it may come to be called a law. A **law** is a general statement that describes a wide variety of phenomena. If a hypothesis explains *why* things happen and continues to be supported by evidence gathered from many different experiments, it may come to be called a theory. A **theory** is the most probable explanation for a set of data based on the best available evidence. Theories and laws can not only be used to explain and describe existing data respectively, they can be used to make predictions about new data.

If new data, or a fresh look at existing data, contradict a law or theory, the law or theory may have to be modified or discarded. The tentative nature of scientific theories and laws leads scientists to constantly weigh evidence, examine inferences, and modify hypotheses.

Think

Suppose a biologist does a month-long field study on eagles nesting in the mountains. What scientific processes might the biologist use while working in the field? What processes might the biologist use on returning to the laboratory?

Section Review

1. How does a *hypothesis* differ from a *theory?*
2. Define each of the following processes: observing, measuring, organizing and analyzing data, classifying, inferring, and modeling.
3. What is the relationship between hypothesizing, predicting, and experimenting in science?
4. Why is communicating an important process in science?
5. It is sometimes said that science is based on *probabilistic* rather than *absolute* truth. Based on what you have read about scientific processes and methods, what do you think this statement means?

Answer to Think

Scientific processes used in the field might include observing and collecting data, measuring, organizing data, classifying, hypothesizing, and predicting; processes used in the lab include analyzing data, inferring, modeling, and communicating.

Reteaching

Ask students to read through the laboratory investigation on p. 567 and to explain how each process skill listed is used in the lab. Also ask them to identify at least one other process skill that is not listed and to explain how it is used. *(Sample answers: observing—watching the frog swim, breathe, and eat; inferring—suggesting an advantage of the frog's coloration; hypothesizing—explaining what might happen to the air in the frog's mouth. Not listed: analyzing data—contrasting the frog's swimming style with that of a fish)*

■ ***See* Section Reviews *worksheet, Section 2.1.***

Enrichment

Have students research and write a report summarizing Pavlov's use of scientific processes in his work on the conditioned reflex in dogs.

Closure

Ask students to cite examples of the use of scientific processes in their lives. *(Sample answers: measuring—weighing myself; organizing data—charting my weight over time; classifying—sorting glass for recycling; analyzing data—comparing batting averages; inferring—deciding that my pet prefers one kind of food because of its texture; modeling—mapping the best route from school to my home)*

Videodiscs

■ ***Side 4 42212, Stickleback: Experiment with Models (m)***

Answers to Section Review

1. A hypothesis is a testable statement, whereas a theory is a likely explanation that is supported by evidence gathered from many different experiments.
2. Accept student wording of glossary definitions.
3. Hypothesizing is forming a testable statement about observable phenomena; predicting is stating in advance the result of testing a hypothesis; experimenting is testing a hypothesis or a prediction by gathering data under controlled conditions.
4. Communicating enables scientists to build on each other's work.
5. Accept answers showing understanding that scientific theories are tentative because they cannot be proved beyond doubt, and that scientists constantly weigh evidence, examine inferences, and modify theories.

Background

Lewis Thomas was constantly exposed to science as a boy. His mother was a nurse, his father a physician. Throughout his career, Thomas experienced the rigors of scientific research and took an analytic approach to both pure and applied biological sciences. In this excerpt, Thomas realizes that while immersed in the processes of science, he had become unable to "see the forest for the trees."

Discussion

After students have read "The Tucson Zoo," ask them to discuss the following questions.

1. What does Thomas mean when he states that, in science, we may overlook the whole by being preoccupied with the parts? *(Scientists often break down a complex system into many isolated parts to study their structure and function. In so doing, scientists may lose sight of the wonderful entity formed by those parts.)*

2. What is the message to science students in this excerpt? *(Be careful not to lose your sense of wonder and appreciation for the beauty in nature.)*

3. What kind of friendship is Thomas referring to in this excerpt? *(We are an integral part of nature; human beings need to feel "friendship" with other creatures.)*

Extension

To help students appreciate Thomas's concerns, have them write an anonymous short essay on a part of the natural world that they may have taken for granted. Students should attempt to describe the emotions they experience as they reconsider their part in the natural world. Post students' essays around the room to encourage further discussion.

Writing About Biology

The Tucson Zoo

This excerpt is from an essay in Lewis Thomas' book, The Medusa and the Snail.

Much of today's public anxiety about science is the apprehension that we may forever be overlooking the whole by an endless, obsessive preoccupation with the parts. I had a brief, personal experience of this misgiving one afternoon in Tucson, where I had time on my hands and visited the zoo, just outside the city. The designers there have cut a deep pathway between two small artificial ponds, walled by clear glass, so when you stand in the center of the path you can look into the depths of each pool, and at the same time you can regard the surface. In one pool, on the right side of the path, is a family of otters; on the other side, a family of beavers. Within just a few feet from your face, on either side, beavers and otters are at play, underwater and on the surface, swimming toward your face and then away, more filled with life than any creatures I have ever seen before. . . .

I was transfixed. As I now recall it, there was only one sensation in my head: pure elation mixed with amazement at such perfection. Swept off my feet, I floated from one side to the other, swiveling my brain, staring astounded at the beavers, then at the otters. . . . I remember thinking, with what was left in charge of my consciousness, that I wanted . . . never to know how they performed their marvels; I wished for no news about the physiology of their breathing, the coordination of their muscles, their vision, their endocrine systems, their digestive tracts. . . . All I asked for was the full hairy complexity, then in front of my eyes, of whole, intact beavers and otters in motion.

It lasted, . . . for only a few minutes, and then I was back . . . wondering about the details by force of habit, but not, this time, the details of otters and beavers. Instead, me. Something worth remembering had happened in my mind. . . . I became a behavioral scientist, an experimental psychologist, an ethologist, and in the instant I lost all the wonder and the sense of being overwhelmed.

But I came away from the zoo with something, a piece of news about myself: I am coded, somehow, for otters and beavers. I exhibit instinctive behavior in their presence, ... Beavers and otters possess a "releaser" for me, . . . What was released? Behavior. What behavior? Standing, swiveling flabbergasted, feeling exultation and a rush of friendship. I could not, as the result of the transaction, tell you anything more about beavers and otters than you already know. I learned nothing new about them. Only about me, and I suspect also about you, maybe about human beings at large. . . . Left to ourselves, . . . we hanker for friends.

- **Think of a special animal you have observed and enjoyed—at home, at the zoo, on television. Write a journal entry describing your feelings about the animal.**

24 *From* The Medusa and the Snail *by Lewis Thomas. Copyright © 1974, 1975, 1976, 1977, 1978, 1979 by Lewis Thomas. All rights reserved. Reprinted by permission of Viking Penguin Inc.*

About the Author

Lewis Thomas received his M.D. degree from Harvard University and made significant contributions in the fields of microbiology and immunology. Thomas has held posts at several universities and has been president of the Memorial Sloan-Kettering Cancer Center of New York.

He is known for his humanistic insights into a variety of scientific subjects, which are expressed in *The Medusa and the Snail, Lives of a Cell,* and other writings. His recognition of the humanistic side of science has helped him to better understand the impact on society of emerging technologies and the responsibility that scientists and physicians have to society.

2.2 Biological Tools and Techniques

To study the living world, biologists need to observe cells and cell parts, analyze chemical reactions, and determine relationships between organisms. Biological tools and techniques aid them in their study. As you read this section, notice the uses of tools and techniques in various scientific processes.

Section Objectives

- *Compare light microscopes with transmission and scanning electron microscopes in terms of magnification and resolution.*
- *Define and discuss three techniques scientists use in the laboratory.*
- *Explain why scientific sampling is an important technique in field studies.*
- *List ways scientists might use computers.*
- *Describe how a scanning tunneling microscope works and list its advantages over light and electron microscopes.*

Microscopes

Among the most widely used tools in biology are microscopes. A **microscope** is an instrument that can form an enlarged image of an object. Biologists use microscopes to study organisms or objects too small to be seen with the naked eye. The **magnification** of a microscope refers to its power to increase an object's apparent size. The **resolution** of a microscope refers to its power to show detail clearly. Several kinds of microscopes are discussed below. They vary in magnification, resolution, and usage.

Light Microscope

In a light microscope, a beam of light passing through one or more lenses produces an enlarged image of the object or specimen being viewed. Use Figure 2-9 to follow the path of light through a typical light microscope. Notice that the specimen is illuminated by an electric light bulb. The light passes through two lenses. The lens closest to the specimen is called the **objective lens.** Most microscopes have a series of interchangeable objective lenses that can be rotated into place. The objective lens directs light to the **ocular** *(AHK-yuh-lur)* **lens** in the eyepiece. The magnification of a light microscope is determined by the power of its lenses. The objective lens of a typical light microscope can magnify an object so that it appears to be 40 times (×40) its actual size. The ocular lens can magnify an object ten times (×10). When an object is viewed through both lenses, the magnification is 400 times (×400). The most powerful light microscopes can magnify an object about 2,000 times (×2,000). Scientists use light microscopes to observe living organisms and preserved cells.

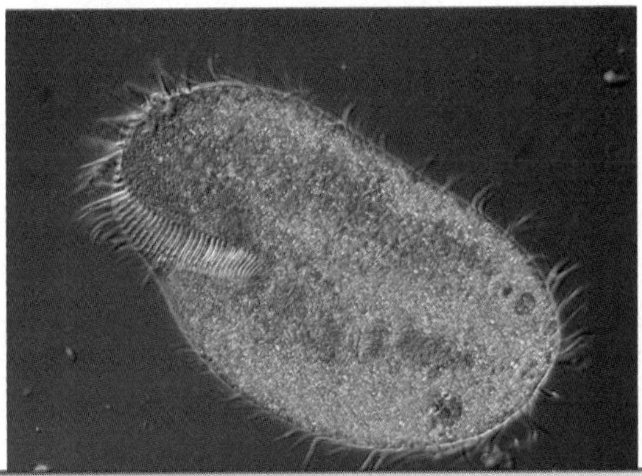

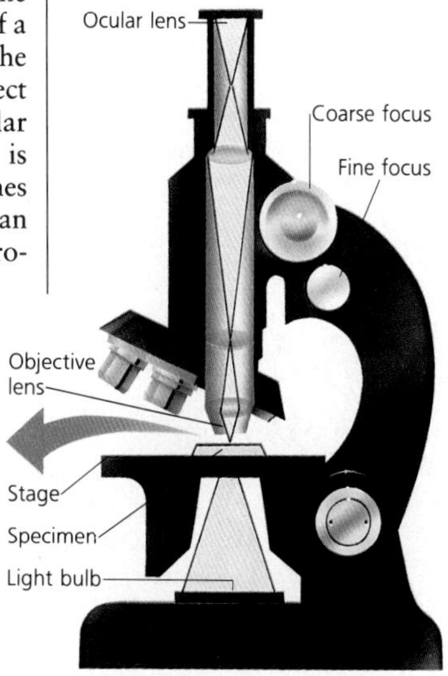

Figure 2-9 The lenses in a light microscope (right) can magnify objects up to 2,000 times. The ciliate (left) was viewed at a magnification of 100.

Biological Tools		Biological Techniques	
▪ light microscope	▪ scanning tunneling microscope	▪ cell culture	▪ electrophoresis
▪ transmission electron microscope	▪ computer	▪ fractionation	▪ scientific sampling
▪ scanning electron microscope		▪ centrifugation	▪ collecting organisms
		▪ chromatography	

Graphic Organizer Use this table in Reteaching on p. 28.

Lesson Plan

Section Focus

This section introduces several tools and techniques used in biological investigation. These tools and techniques allow biologists to observe cells and cell parts, analyze substances, and study relationships within and among organisms. As the level of sophistication increases in biotechnology, so does our understanding of living things.

Section Themes

The theme of **Scale and Structure** encompasses the structures observed and substances analyzed with the aid of biological tools and techniques. The **Systems and Interactions** theme is reflected in the information about biological interrelationships that is gained through laboratory and field techniques.

Motivating Activity

Ask students to imagine what it would be like if their eyesight were powerful enough to see the minute structures within their skin cells, if they could hear people speak on the other side of the earth, or if they could run 50 miles per hour. Ask how common tools and instruments, such as microscopes, radios, and cars, extend our biological capacities. *(They enable us to see, hear, and move beyond our normal capacities.)* Ask students to name other things that extend our senses and capabilities. *(Sample answers: sight—television, telescopes, X-ray machines; hearing—stereos, telephones, hearing aids; smell—air pollution monitors, smoke detectors; movement—trains, airplanes, satellites)*

▪ ***See* Laboratories, *Investigation 2.***

Videodiscs

▪ ***Side 1 14497, How Microscopes Work (m)***

Teaching Strategies

Interpreting the Visuals Refer students to Figure 2-9 on p. 25 and review the parts and uses of the light microscope. To demonstrate how instruments such as the light microscope and centrifuge can extend our senses, remove a sample of pond water from an aquarium containing a lot of debris. Centrifuge the water and have students use a microscope to examine a sample taken from the bottom of the centrifuge tube. Next, ask them to examine an uncentrifuged sample through a microscope and compare the two samples. *(The centrifuged sample should contain a greater density of debris than the uncentrifuged sample.)* Have students share their observations with the class.

■ *See* Blackline Master *3.*

Applying Concepts Allow students to examine photographs from magazines or newspapers, first through a magnifying glass and then through the low-power objective of a light microscope. Have them describe what they see. *(Tiny dots; an inverted image for the microscope)* Point out that the unaided eye can barely resolve, or discriminate, the tiny dots that make up the photograph because the distances between dots are so small. The eye's inability to resolve the dots makes the photograph appear to be a clear, unified image. The magnifying glass and microscope both enlarge and resolve the dots, but lose the overall image in the photograph.

Guided Practice

Set up opportunities for students to use laboratory instruments or products (such as an electron micrograph) of instruments described in this section. Create labels for the instruments or products and have students place the labels next to the correct items.

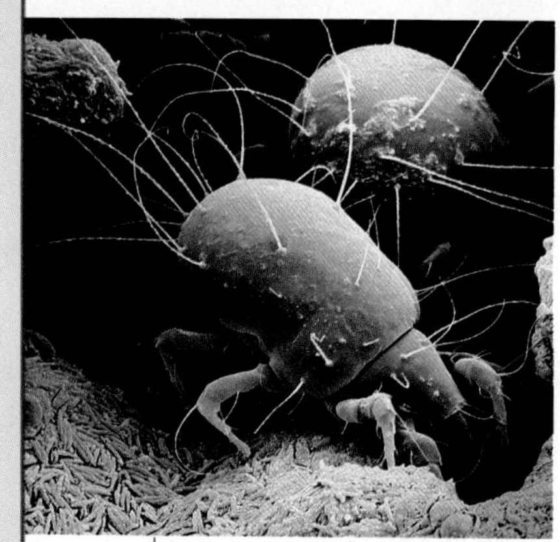

Figure 2-10 The term *SEM* refers both to the scanning electron microscope and to the image it produces, which is a scanning electron micrograph. This SEM shows a soft-bodied mite, *Acarus siro* (×37).

Electron Microscopes

In an electron microscope, a beam of electrons focused by magnets produces an enlarged image of an object. Electron microscopes are more powerful than light microscopes. However, an electron microscope cannot be used to observe living organisms, which cannot survive the necessary preparation techniques.

A **transmission electron microscope**, called a TEM, transmits a beam of electrons through a very thinly sliced specimen. Magnetic lenses enlarge the image and focus it on a fluorescent screen or photographic plate, producing a visible image. Transmission electron microscopes can magnify objects up to 2,000,000 times.

A **scanning electron microscope,** called an SEM, scans the surface of an object with a beam of electrons. In preparation for scanning the surface of the object is sprayed with a fine metallic mist. The electron beams bounce off the surface of the object and are projected onto a fluorescent screen or photographic plate. This produces a three-dimensional image of the object. Scanning electron microscopes can magnify objects up to 50,000 times. However, the importance of the SEM is its ability to produce a clear, striking image of the surfaces of an object.

Biotechnology

Scanning Tunneling Microscope

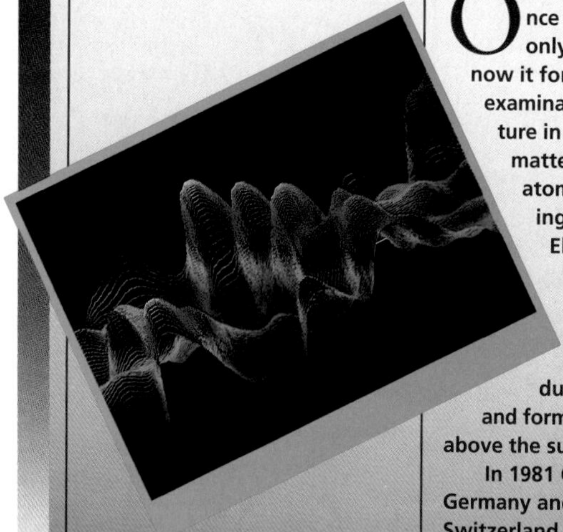

Once it was considered only a curious theory; now it forms the basis for the examination of atomic structure in living and nonliving matter. Around every atomic nucleus is a moving cloud of energy. Electrons leak, or tunnel, from the surface of all matter—especially matter that conducts electricity well—and form electron clouds just above the surface.

In 1981 Gerd Binnig of West Germany and Heinrich Rohrer of Switzerland designed a microscope that could make use of these electron clouds to map the surface of an object, atom by atom. The scanning tunneling microscope (STM) has no lenses and doesn't need a focused beam of light or electrons to produce an image. Instead, the STM searches the surface of the specimen, using a sensor to detect the motion of tunneling electrons as they escape.

The STM sensor is a needle with a point about the size of an atom, sensitive enough to detect even slight variations in the density of the electron cloud (p. 27). The sensor scans the surface and follows the contours at a constant distance from the specimen.

More Information

Resolution Students may find it interesting to contrast the size-range detection capabilities of various optical tools. The unaided human eye can detect organisms as small as 0.01 cm wide (ameba). Most light microscopes can pick up organisms with a width as small as 0.0001 cm—or 1 micrometer or micron—(bacterium). Scanning electron microscopes can pick up cell organelles approximately 0.000001 cm wide (plasma membrane). Transmission electron microscopes can pick up molecules somewhat smaller than 0.0000001 cm—or 1 nanometer—in width (molecular distances within the DNA molecule).

Laboratory Techniques

The study of living organisms hinges on gaining a deeper knowledge of cells and how they work. Laboratory techniques enable biologists to experiment with cells and analyze substances cells produce. Scientists can then model the workings of cells and the organisms they compose. Several laboratory techniques are discussed below.

Cell Cultures

The ability to grow cells in the laboratory has allowed biologists to study cell growth, interaction between cells, and cells' response to substances in the environment. A population of identical cells grown in the laboratory is referred to as a **cell culture.** A biologist can isolate one type of cell, such as a heart muscle cell, and grow a population of these cells in a cell culture. The biologist then can use the cell culture in controlled experiments in order to study the effects of certain nutrients on these cells. The use of a cell culture allows biologists to determine how specific types of cells react without having the data obscured by the presence of other types of cells.

The motions of the needle are analyzed by computer to produce a three-dimensional map of the specimen's surface. The image presented on the monitor represents a magnification of approximately 100 million times the specimen's size.

At first the STM was used to study samples of metals, such as gold and nickel. By 1988 STMs were being used to capture images of viruses and DNA (p. 26). The DNA molecule has a double-helix shape, which is often compared to a twisted ladder. The images of a single DNA molecule that an STM produces are so fine that they can reveal the narrow space between the two sides of the ladder and the wider step between each two turns of the spiral. Because the STM searches only the surface, there is no need to slice a specimen or coat it with metal. Therefore, it can be used to study living organisms.

Moreover, the STM is being miniaturized. Research teams are working on ways to make the microscope smaller in order to develop complete STMs with a diameter equal to a single human hair. Although the sensor is already tiny, the mechanism that controls the sensor is larger than a shoe box. Once the STM becomes microscopic, a miniaturized STM could be implanted in a human heart to serve as a monitor, or be used to hold detailed maps for the guidance systems of spacecraft.

Independent Practice

- Have students write answers to the Section Review.
- Have each student design an experiment that would demonstrate scientific sampling. *(Possible experiments: sampling the coins in a bag, the plants in a garden, or the cars in a neighborhood. Designs should include strategies for obtaining representative samples.)*

Biotechnology

Using the Feature

Students may think that this microscope tunnels through the specimen or that a beam of light tunnels through it. Be sure they understand that the word *tunneling* refers to the electrons that are detected, not to the action of the detector.

Point out to students that the STM has applications other than making an image. STMs have also been used to rearrange the atoms on the surface of materials. Encourage students to suggest other areas in which fine-resolution control is important. *(Answers may include medical devices, computer chips, integrated microcircuitry, and information storage and retrieval technologies.)*

One of the teams working to miniaturize the STM is at Cornell University. This team also hopes to find ways to make STMs that are sensitive to such factors as light and motion. With miniaturization, several sensors might be combined in a single unit. Have students suggest uses for these tiny multiple sensors.

Videodiscs

- ***1555–1568, Various Objects Under the Microscope (s)***
- ***2255–2299, Scanning and Transmission Electron Microscopy (s)***
- ***1586–1597, Staining (s)***

Interdisciplinary Activity

Social Studies Discuss some of the techniques used in sampling. Use an election opinion poll or the A. C. Nielsen television survey as an example. Ask students what steps the surveyor must take so that valid generalizations can be made from the survey data. *(Sample answer: a cross section of people of different ages, incomes, and locations should be interviewed.)*

Ask students why samples are used. *(It would not be feasible, for example, for Nielsen to ask the entire population about its television-watching habits to make sure that the information obtained was absolutely accurate.)* Point out the importance of the estimated probable error that should accompany such reports.

Section 2.2

Check Your Understanding

1. A market research firm wants to identify the most popular foods among high school students in North America and intends to interview only your class. Will the results of this sample be valid? Why or why not? *(No; the sample is probably not representative of all high school students in North America.)*

2. If electron microscopes provide far greater magnification and resolution than light microscopes do, why not use them exclusively? *(Cost aside, electron microscopes can be used to examine only prepared specimens, not living organisms.)*

Reteaching

Write the topics listed in the Graphic Organizer on p. 25 in random order on the board and have students classify each as either a tool or a technique. Ask students why these tools and techniques are important in biology. *(They permit biologists to study the structural and chemical components of cells.)*

■ *See* **Section Reviews** *worksheet, Section 2.2.*

Enrichment

Have students research and write a report on biological tools and techniques that have been developed in the last 25 years.

Closure

Tell students that you have an unidentified microorganism and you want to identify its components and compare it with other living things. Ask how the laboratory techniques described in Section 2.2 might help in this task. *(Cell culture—to observe its growth, interactions, and responses; fractionation—to see what cell components could be released; centrifugation—to separate cell parts; chromatography and electrophoresis—to see whether the chemical components match those found in other living cells)*

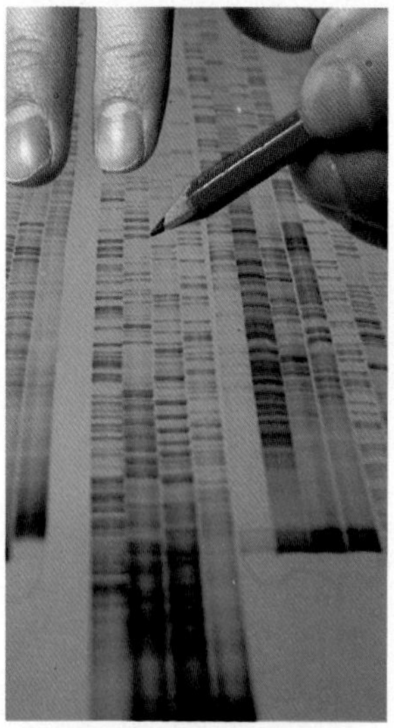

Figure 2-11 In gel electrophoresis, some molecules move faster along the gel than others do. Radioactive labels and fluorescent stains help researchers detect the invisible bands of molecules in the gel.

Fractionation, Centrifugation, and Chromatography

Cell **fractionation** is a technique used to release the components of a cell. Cells can be fractionated in a blender. The grinding action breaks open cells, releasing the cell parts.

Centrifugation is a technique used to separate cell parts by type by spinning fractionated cells at high speeds. The spinning action causes heavier components to settle to the bottom of a tube while the lighter components remain near the top.

Chromatography is the separation of the chemical components of a substance by passing the components in liquid up a piece of paper or a column of beads. **Electrophoresis** is a process that separates fragments of large molecules, such as proteins and DNA, on the basis of their electrical charge and size. In Figure 2-11, an electric current flows through a gel to cause the separation.

Field Techniques

Working in a natural environment such as a rain forest, a biologist has little control over variables. However, certain field techniques aid the biologist in collecting accurate data.

Scientific sampling is a technique in which a small sample is used to represent an entire population. A biologist studying one region of the rain forest might identify and count the plants in one acre. From this sample the biologist could estimate the total number of plants of different species in the region. However, the biologist's estimate will be accurate only if the acre is representative of the entire region being studied.

Field biologists often collect organisms. Such collections are most useful when the biologist keeps careful records of location and conditions. Scientists can use such information to classify the organisms and learn about their behavior.

Computers

Many biologists collect data that can best be organized and analyzed through the use of computers. A biologist studying the rain forest might collect data on factors affecting plant growth. Using a computer, the biologist can construct a model showing the effect of environmental factors on plant growth.

Section Review

1. Compare cell *fractionation* and *centrifugation*.
2. How do microscopes differ in magnification and use?
3. Why is scientific sampling necessary in field research?
4. How might computers be used in biology?
5. How might a cell culture allow for greater control of variables in an experiment on cell growth?

Answers to Section Review

1. Fractionation releases cell components; centrifugation separates cell components.
2. Light microscope—up to ×2,000; used for both living and preserved cells. TEM—up to ×2,000,000; used for thin slices of nonliving specimens. SEM—up to ×50,000; used for the surfaces of nonliving specimens.
3. A scientific sample can be used to represent an entire population that could not be studied as a whole.
4. Computers can be used to organize and analyze data and to make models of biological interactions.
5. Because the cells in a cell culture are identical, they eliminate the variable of differences among cells in the experiment.

Laboratory

Scientific Methods

Objective

To understand how scientists approach and solve problems

Process Skills

Hypothesizing, experimenting, collecting and analyzing data

Materials

Watch with second hand, paper

Background

1 One of the most important characteristics of modern science is its quantitative approach to solving problems. One of the first scientists to use quantitative methods was William Harvey, who discovered that blood circulated through the body. At the time Harvey began his work, anatomists believed that the liver produced blood from the food that the body consumed. The blood was then carried by veins to the heart, purified in the lungs, and then pumped to the various organs of the body, where it was consumed. Harvey measured that the left ventricle of the heart held roughly 100 mL of blood. He also measured that the heart beats an average of 64 times per minute. Assuming that 1 mL of blood weighs 1 g, how much blood would the body need to produce per hour to replace the blood consumed by the organs? Roughly how much food, do you think, would the body need to consume to produce this much blood? Harvey hypothesized that the same blood must circulate continuously throughout the body. Keeping Harvey's measurements in mind, can you determine how he formed this hypothesis?

Technique

1 While sitting quietly at your desk, find the pulse in your wrist and count the beats for one minute. The number of beats per minute is your pulse rate. Record your result.
2 Repeat step 1 twice. Calculate your average pulse rate and record your result.

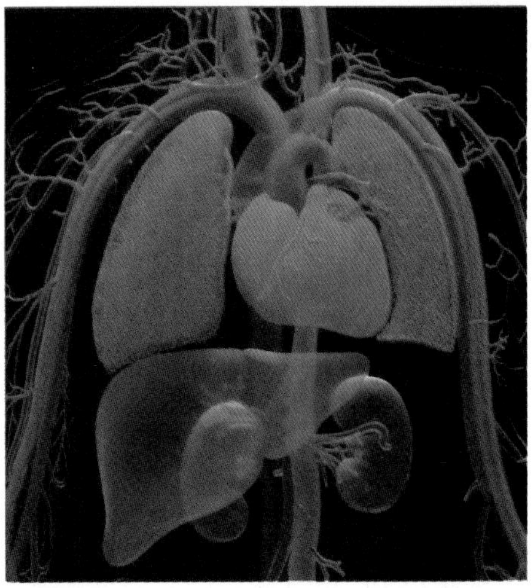

Inquiry

1 Formulate a hypothesis about the effect of exertion, such as walking or jogging, on pulse rate. Design an experiment to test your hypothesis.
2 What is the independent variable in your experiment? What is the dependent variable? How will you vary the independent variable? How will you measure the dependent variable?
3 Proceed with your experiment once it has been approved by your teacher.

Conclusions

1 What effect, if any, did changes in the independent variable have on the dependent variable?
2 Do the data support your hypothesis? Explain.
3 What control did you use in your experiment?
4 Based on the results of your experiment, formulate an operational definition of exertion.

Further Inquiry

What are some possible sources of error in this experiment?

Laboratory

(For an overview of measuring pulse rate and preparatory information related to the laboratory, see p. 15B.)

Background

1. Harvey's data indicate that the body would need to produce 384,000 g (384 kg) of blood per hour to replace the blood consumed by the organs. Accept student answers indicating that no human being could consume the amount of food necessary to produce blood at this rate. Harvey probably formed his hypothesis on the basis of the conclusions stated above.

Inquiry

1. One possible hypothesis: Jogging in place increases pulse rate from its average resting rate. One way to test this hypothesis is to jog in place for two minutes and then measure the pulse rate for one minute immediately afterward. This procedure could be repeated five minutes later and the results averaged. Compare the average jogging pulse rate with the average resting rate. Students might suggest that several people conduct the same experiment and then pool their results to calculate their average pulse rates.
2. In the experiment suggested above, the independent variable is the subject's level of exertion before measuring the pulse rate. The dependent variable is the pulse rate. The independent variable is varied by changing from a resting state to a jogging state. The dependent variable is measured by counting the pulse in the wrist.

Conclusions

1. Answers will vary depending on the experiment, but exertion probably increased the subject's pulse rate.
2. Students' data support their hypothesis only if the subject's pulse rate was higher immediately after exertion.
3. Students may have used a partner who continued to rest before measuring the pulse rate for the second time.
4. Sample answer: Exertion is physical activity that increases the pulse rate from its average resting rate.

Further Inquiry

Sources of errors: inaccurate measurement; inadequate exertion or rest; unperceived, uncontrolled variables, such as food, medication, emotional state, room temperature, and time of day

Chapter 2 Review

Vocabulary

1. Measuring is a type of observing, but observing can be done without measuring.
2. Collecting data is simply gathering and recording specific information; organizing data is placing them in a logical order; analyzing data is determining whether the data are reliable and whether they support or refute a specific prediction or hypothesis.
3. Hypothesizing is forming a testable statement about observable phenomena; experimenting is gathering data under controlled conditions to test a hypothesis; inferring is drawing conclusions based on facts, such as those gathered during an experiment.
4. Classifying is grouping into an established or new organizational scheme; modeling is constructing a visual, verbal, or mathematical representation that helps show relationships.
5. A TEM transmits electrons through a thinly sliced specimen and magnifies the image of the slice up to x2,000,000; an SEM scans the surface of an object with a beam of electrons and magnifies the image of the surface up to x50,000.

Review

1. a	**6.** d
2. b	**7.** b
3. c	**8.** a
4. c	**9.** c
5. d	**10.** d

11. Accept examples that include a stated hypothesis or prediction, a control group and an experimental group differing only in one factor, and measurement of the dependent variable in both groups.
12. Accept answers indicating that an inference is testable only if directly observable evidence that either supports or refutes the inference can be collected.

Chapter 2 Review

Vocabulary

analyzing data (20)
cell culture (27)
centrifugation (28)
chromatography (28)
classifying (19)
collecting data (18)
communicating (22)
controlled experiment (20)
dependent variable (20)
electrophoresis (28)
experimenting (20)
fractionation (28)
hypothesis (19)
hypothesizing (19)
independent variable (20)
inferring (21)
law (23)
magnification (25)
measuring (18)
microscope (25)
modeling (22)
objective lens (25)
observing (18)
ocular lens (25)
operational definitions (22)
organizing data (18)
predicting (19)
resolution (25)
scanning electron microscope (26)
scientific method (23)
scientific sampling (28)
theory (23)
transmission electron microscope (26)

Explain the difference between each set of related terms.

1. observing, measuring
2. collecting data, organizing data, analyzing data
3. hypothesizing, experimenting, inferring
4. classifying, modeling
5. transmission electron microscope, scanning electron microscope

Review

1. Scientific knowledge is ultimately based on (a) observations (b) hypotheses (c) experiments (d) models.
2. Data that is quantitative can be (a) described in words (b) measured in numbers (c) recorded on a tape recorder (d) seen through a microscope.
3. A hypothesis is a testable statement that (a) can help a biologist classify organisms (b) can be supported in all circumstances (c) can be demonstrated false through experimentation (d) is the first step in every research project.
4. "If–then" statements are used in (a) collecting data (b) organizing data (c) predicting (d) inferring.
5. Scientists analyze data to (a) gather and record specific information based on observations (b) place observations and measurements in a logical order (c) group objects, organisms, or phenomena into an established organizational scheme (d) determine whether data are reliable and whether they support or refute a given hypothesis.
6. A theory is defined as the most probable explanation for a set of data based on (a) a testable hypothesis (b) dependent and independent variables (c) a visual, verbal, or mathematical model (d) the best available evidence.
7. The resolution of a microscope refers to (a) its power to increase an object's apparent size (b) its power to show detail clearly (c) its series of interchangeable objective lenses (d) its power to scan the surface of an object.
8. Cell cultures allow a biologist to (a) observe cells in a controlled environment (b) release cell parts (c) isolate cell parts (d) separate dissolved substances.
9. In scientific sampling researchers use a sample to represent (a) a control group (b) an experimental group (c) an entire population (d) an entire field study.
10. The scanning tunneling microscope magnifies objects up to (a) 1,000 times (b) 100,000 times (c) 500,000 times (d) 100,000,000 times.
11. Describe a controlled experiment.

13. The purpose of a scientific model is to help show relationships between data and, sometimes, to help generate new predictions or hypotheses.
14. Communicating enables scientists to build on each other's work.
15. Sample similarity: All scientists pose questions about nature and seek facts that can help answer those questions. Sample difference: Scientists combine scientific processes in different ways to devise methods tailored to particular research projects.
16. A specimen is illuminated by a source of light; the light passes through the lenses, producing an enlarged image of the specimen.
17. Advantages: Electron microscopes are more powerful than light microscopes, and SEMs can produce clear,

12. Give an example of a testable inference and an untestable inference.
13. What is the purpose of a scientific model?
14. How do scientists benefit by communicating with each other?
15. What are some similarities and differences in the ways that scientists work?
16. How does a light microscope work?
17. What are some advantages and disadvantages of electron microscopes in biology?
18. Describe three techniques a biologist might use in the laboratory.
19. How might a biologist use a computer?
20. For a biologist, what advantages does a scanning tunneling microscope have over a scanning electron microscope?

Critical Thinking

1. Scientists often try to repeat, or replicate, the results of other scientists' experiments. Why do you think this is an important part of the scientific process?
2. One of the most important parts of any scientific publication is the part called "Methods and Materials," in which the scientist describes the procedure used in the experiment. Why do you think such details are so important?
3. Why do scientists prefer to use the metric system of measurement?
4. Cell culture has the advantage of being controllable. What might be one disadvantage of using a cell culture in a scientific experiment?

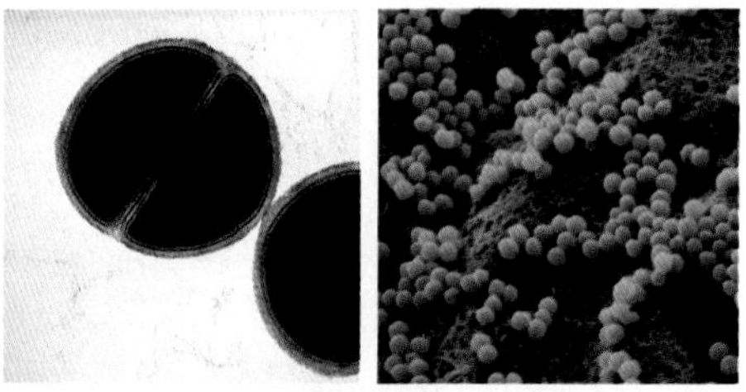

5. Look at the photographs above. The TEM (left, ×33,000) is of *Staphylococcus aureus.* The SEM (right, ×2,500) is also of *S. aureus.* Compare and contrast what each electron micrograph tells you about this organism.

Extension

1. Read the article by Tom Waters entitled "Cretaceous Splashdown," *Discover,* September 1990, pp. 32–33. Make an oral report to the class in which you include answers to the following questions:
(1) What is the best evidence so far to support the asteroid-impact explanation of the extinction of dinosaurs? (2) How do paleontologists use the chemical composition of the layer of clay to support the asteroid-impact explanation? (3) How does the distribution of the layer of clay support this? (4) How does the location of coarse deposits in North America, Mexico, Cuba, and the Caribbean Sea support it? (5) What important piece of evidence is missing to support the asteroid-impact explanation?
2. Go to your local supermarket or grocery store and observe the fresh, frozen, and canned vegetable sections and the people in them. Note ten customers in each area and estimate their age. Make a bar graph of your data. Record the ages of individuals on the *x*-axis of the graph. Group the ages as follows: (1) under 20, (2) 20–40, (3) 40–60, and (4) over 60. Record the number of individuals in each age group in the *y*-axis. Remember that you will need a separate bar for each of the three vegetable sections. Can you draw any conclusions as to whether fresh vegetables are bought by a certain age group? What are some of the possible sources of error in this experiment?

three-dimensional images of the surfaces of objects. Disadvantages: Electron microscopes cannot be used to observe live organisms.
18. Answers may include descriptions of the following techniques: cell culture, fractionation, centrifugation, chromatography, and electrophoresis.
19. Students might mention the use of computers to organize data, analyze data, and construct models.
20. The scanning tunneling microscope can be used to study live organisms.

Critical Thinking

1. The more times an observation can be repeated, the greater the probability that it is valid and the greater the confidence scientists have in it.
2. Such details enable scientists to evaluate the reliability of the experimental procedure and thus of the conclusions, to understand the conditions to which the conclusions apply, and to try to repeat the experiment.
3. Using the metric system is convenient because its units are multiples of 10. Also, its use aids scientific communication because it is understood by scientists all over the world.
4. Answers will vary, but some students might suggest that the cells in a culture may not behave exactly as they do in the body.
5. Both photographs show that the organism is round. The SEM also shows that the organism is spherical and can be found in clumps. But the TEM shows that the organism is single-celled, appears to have a cell wall, and can grow a new cell wall across the middle of the cell.

Extension

1. Make sure students answer all five questions. Encourage students to focus on the scientific processes chosen by the scientists and described in the article.
2. As students attempt to draw conclusions, ask them to consider whether their samples are representative. *(A sample size of ten customers per section is not representative of the entire grocery-shopping population.)* Possible sources of experimental error include not seeing age groups that may typically shop at other times of day, counting individuals who are passing through the section but not purchasing from it, counting individuals who are shopping for other people, and incorrectly estimating a person's age.

Chapter 3 Chemistry

Chapter Overview

This chapter presents an overview of basic principles of chemistry—properties of matter and energy relationships—and their importance in biology. Section 3.1 introduces atoms, elements, and compounds, and explains ionic and covalent bonding. In Section 3.2, students study types of mixtures—solutions, suspensions, colloids—and learn about acidic and basic solutions. Section 3.3 describes forms of energy and the role of energy in chemical reactions.

Chapter Planning Chart

B	S	A	Sections and Subsections	Page	Features	Page	Resources
•	•	•	**3.1 Composition of Matter**				
			Atoms	33	Biology in Process	34	Videodiscs
			Elements	34	Think	36	Blackline Master 4
			Compounds	35	Section Review	37	Overhead Transparency T3
							Process Skills: Modeling Water
							Section Reviews Worksheet
•	•	•	**3.2 Mixtures**				
			Solutions	38	Laboratory	43	Videodiscs
			Suspensions	38	Section Review	40	Blackline Master 5
			Colloids	39			Laboratories: Acids and Bases
			Acids and Bases	39			Section Reviews Worksheet
•	•	•	**3.3 Energy**				
			Forms of Energy	41	Section Review	42	Videodiscs
			Chemical Reactions	42			Laboratories: Calorimetry
			Energy and Chemical Reactions	42			Section Reviews Worksheet
			End of Chapter Activities				
					Chapter Review	44	Vocabulary Skills
							Chapter Test
							Computer Test Generator

B *The Basic Level curriculum presents the most fundamental knowledge offered in the course.*
S *The Standard Level curriculum is designed for the average student who is able to master most topics.*
A *The Advanced Level curriculum includes suggestions for teaching the most academically able students.*

Cooperative Learning

Group Activity: Energy Changes

- **Group Size:** *2–4 students*
- **Outcome:** *Students will compare temperature changes during endothermic and exothermic reactions.*
- **Individual Accountability:** *Each student will measure temperature changes during reactions of dissolving.*
- **Positive Interdependence:** *The groups will share and organize experimental data.*

Use this activity to introduce students to the release and absorption of energy in biological processes. **CAUTION:** Have students wear goggles, gloves, and an apron. Conduct this activity in a well-ventilated room.

Tell each group to place 100 mL of water and a thermometer in a 250-mL beaker and to record the starting water temperature. Tell half the groups to dissolve 10 g of calcium chloride in their water, and the other half 10 g of ammonium nitrate, stirring with a glass rod and taking care not to spatter. Instruct them to record the temperature in their beakers every ten seconds for one minute after adding the powder, while a group member feels the outside of the beaker.

Have groups share their data with a group that used a different chemical and graph the temperature readings for both reactions. Ask: Which reaction is endothermic; exothermic? *(Calcium chloride—solution turns warm: exothermic reaction; ammonium nitrate—solution turns cold: endothermic reaction)*

Concept Map

The following is one possible solution to the concept mapping activity in Reteaching on p. 37.

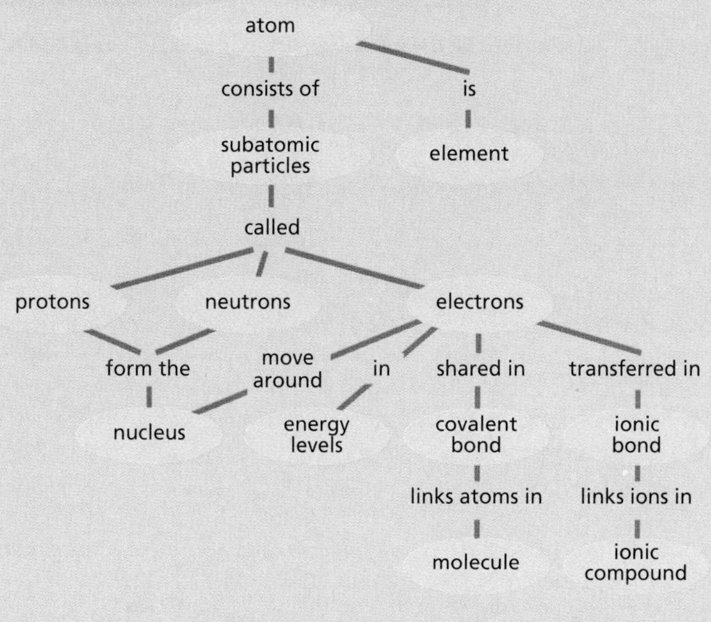

Laboratory Preparation

Overview *(See p. 43.)*

In this lab students study the effects of acids and bases on organic molecules. The activities of biological molecules are greatly affected by pH; the cells and fluids of most organisms contain buffers that limit the effects of changes in the concentration of hydronium and hydroxide ions by reacting with these ions.

Preparation

Most of the materials needed for this lab can be purchased at a grocery store or brought in from home. The skim milk should be fresh. Use distilled water in Inquiry step 2.

This lab requires two kinds of pH paper: wide-range and narrow-range. Sometimes, pH paper that has not been used for a long period loses its ability to detect pH. Before setting up the lab, check to make sure that your pH paper is functioning properly by testing it with drops of known acids and bases. Cut each pH paper strip into squares the width of the strip, and make enough squares so that students can repeat the measurements if they question their results.

Teaching Tips

Before students begin the lab, give them the following definition of *organic molecules:* Organic molecules are those particles that either make up or are produced by living things. (This definition is sufficient for the purposes of this lab; in Chapter 4, students will learn that organic compounds contain carbon.)

During discussion of the students' conclusions, explain that the shapes of organic molecules are important to their functions, and that changes in pH can alter the shapes of these molecules. Ask students what they would expect, therefore, if the pH within a cell or of the fluid surrounding a cell changed. *(The organic molecules within or outside the cell might not be able to function properly.)* Ask students why many people are concerned about acid rain. *(Acid rain can decrease the pH of bodies of water and soil, on which living things depend.)*

Safety

Ammonia solutions can be dangerous. Conduct this lab in a well-ventilated room. Caution students to take care not to spill household ammonia and to avoid breathing in the fumes. If solution is spilled on skin, flush the affected area with water immediately. Also, tell students to wash their hands after the lab.

Chapter Themes

Scale and Structure Scientists have produced models that help explain the structure and behavior of matter. Show students how the chemical properties of matter depend on its organization at various levels: subatomic, atomic, and molecular. Stress that biology is intricately tied to chemistry because chemical structure and reactions are central to all biological processes.

Energy All the activities carried out by living things—maintenance, growth, response, and reproduction—hinge on the ability of cells to convert energy from one form to another and to use energy. Emphasize that understanding the role of energy in chemical reactions is necessary to understand how organisms function.

Chapter Motivating Activity

Tell students that you have obtained some raisins with "supernatural powers." To demonstrate, fill a small plastic cup (or glass beaker) with about 200 mL of cold water. Stir 1 rounded teaspoon of baking soda (sodium bicarbonate) and 6 or 7 mL of vinegar (acetic acid) into the water. Now add several raisins and ask students to describe what happens to the raisins. *(They eventually rise and fall repeatedly.)*

Ask what the source of the raisins' "supernatural powers" might be. *(Gas bubbles collect on the raisins and carry them to the surface; there the gas is released into the air and, no longer buoyed, the raisins sink.)* Ask students to try to infer what caused the bubbles. *(Gas [CO_2] formed as the result of a chemical reaction between the baking soda and vinegar.)* Point out that, in the past, only mysticism could explain events such as the one students just observed.

Chapter 3 Chemistry

Introduction

The earth supports a variety of living organisms. However, as different as they appear, all organisms share certain characteristics, which you learned about in Chapter 1. All these characteristics are governed by the laws of chemistry. In this chapter you will learn some of the fundamental principles of chemistry. They will give you a better understanding of living organisms and how they function.

Chapter Outline

3.1 Composition of Matter
- *Atoms*
- *Elements*
- *Compounds*

3.2 Mixtures
- *Solutions*
- *Suspensions*
- *Colloids*
- *Acids and Bases*

3.3 Energy
- *Forms of Energy*
- *Chemical Reactions*
- *Energy and Chemical Reactions*

Chapter Concept

As you read, notice how a knowledge of chemistry helps you understand and explain biological phenomena.

Raindrops on a tamarack tree, *Larix laricina*. Inset: *Paramecium bursaria* surrounded by phytoplankton (×50).

Understanding the Visuals

Ask students what similarity they see in the organisms in the two photographs. *(The only apparent similarity is green color.)* Have students brainstorm what causes the green color. *(A certain chemical within these organisms appears green.)*

Point out that phytoplankton are single-celled aquatic algae. Phytoplankton and plants store solar energy in food with the aid of the "green chemical" (called chlorophyll), which absorbs energy from sunlight. Ask students whether the tamarack tree and phytoplankton are autotrophs or heterotrophs. *(Both are autotrophs.)* Point out that the *Paramecium* is a single-celled heterotroph, and ask students to speculate on why it also appears green in the photograph. *(It has ingested phytoplankton.)*

3.1 Composition of Matter

Everything in the universe is made up of matter. This includes all living things, from amebas to whales, from bacteria to giant sequoias. **Matter** is anything that occupies space and has mass. **Mass** is the quantity of matter an object has. The pull of gravity on the mass of an object gives the object the property of weight.

Changes in matter are essential to all life processes. For example, when an organism takes in food, it alters the physical and chemical properties of the food. Such changes allow the organism to make use of the nutrients in the food. By learning how changes in matter occur you will gain an understanding of organisms and how they adapt to the environment.

Section Objectives

- *Draw a model of the structure of the atom.*
- *Define* element, isotope, *and* radioisotope.
- *Define* compound, *and list two properties of compounds.*
- *Contrast two types of chemical bonds.*
- *Describe the experimental data on which Rutherford formulated his model of the atom.*

Atoms

The **atom** is the fundamental unit of matter. The nature and properties of atoms determine the structure and behavior of matter. Atoms are about 10 nm in diameter. Thus they can be observed only with a very powerful electron microscope, and even then the internal structure cannot be observed. However, through experimentation, scientists have developed models that describe the structure and behavior of the atom.

Figure 3-1 shows a simplified model of the atom. The various components that make up an atom are called subatomic particles. The central core, or **nucleus**, consists of two kinds of subatomic particles. One, the **proton**, has a positive electrical charge. The other, the **neutron**, has no electrical charge. Most of the mass of the atom is concentrated in the nucleus. **Electrons** are particles with a negative electrical charge that move about the nucleus at tremendous speeds. An atom has an equal number of protons and electrons. The electrical charges of these particles offset one another, so that the net electrical charge of the atom is zero.

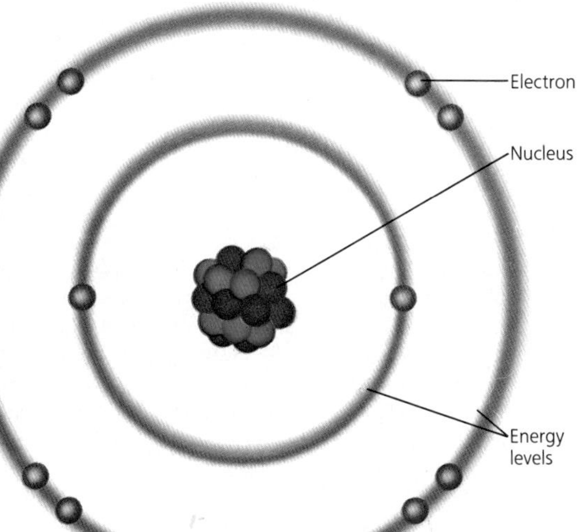

Figure 3-1 The electrons in this model of a neon atom are distributed into two energy levels. The innermost level holds a maximum of two electrons. The second level has a maximum of eight electrons.

Lesson Plan

Section Focus

This section introduces basic properties of matter to give students a foundation for understanding biological structures and processes at the cellular level. Students learn the structure of the atom and the relationships among the subatomic particles—electrons, protons, and neutrons. The section also introduces the formation of compounds through ionic and covalent bonding.

Section Themes

The theme of **Scale and Structure** encompasses the properties of subatomic particles, and the arrangement of atoms and their bonds in various molecules and compounds. The chemical behavior of matter relates directly to its structure at these different levels. The **Stability** theme is reflected in the similarity of structure of all matter at the atomic level.

Motivating Activity

Have students pass around and examine a vial containing sulfur and another vial containing iron filings. Ask them to describe each substance. *(Sulfur—yellow powder; iron filings—dark fibers)* Pass a magnet along each vial to demonstrate the magnetism of the iron filings.

Mix equal amounts of each element (between 0.5 g and 1.0 g) and heat the mixture in a test tube over a Bunsen burner flame in a well-ventilated area. Ask students to describe the test tube contents after heating. *(Gray, lumpy, nonmagnetic)* Explain that a chemical change (reaction) just occurred and produced a substance (iron sulfide) with properties that are completely different from those of the two original substances.

Videodiscs

- ***2625, Hydrogen Atom (s)***
- ***2627, Oxygen Atoms (s)***

Subatomic Particle	Location in Atom	Charge	Number Determines
proton	nucleus	+	identity of element (atomic number)
electron	energy level	–	stability of atom; type of bond formed
neutron	nucleus	o	isotope of element (mass number)

Graphic Organizer Use this table to summarize concepts in Section 3.1.

Teaching Strategies

Using Analogies Most students find the scale and structure of atoms unimaginable without concrete comparisons. Ask students to examine the thickness of a hair on their heads. Tell them that the thickness of that hair approximates more than one million atoms stacked one on top of another. Ask how one million of anything can fit into the thickness of a human hair. *(The particles or atoms must be extremely small.)*

Use the following analogy to show that an atom consists mostly of empty space. Hold up a marble (or similar-sized object) and state that it represents the nucleus of an atom. Ask students how far away they would have to stand to represent the first electron energy level. *(Students will probably underestimate the distance—the first level would be approximately 1/2 mile away.)* Point out that an electron would be roughly the size of a grain of sand relative to a marble-sized nucleus.

To help students understand that energy levels are not flat rings, have them suggest a three-dimensional analogy for energy levels. *(Balls fitting one inside another, with electrons moving along the surface of each "ball")*

Interpreting the Visuals Call students' attention to the caption questions for Figure 3-2 on p. 34. *(The mass number of Na is 23 on p. 34. Na has 12 neutrons.)* Point out that the number of neutrons is found by subtracting the atomic number from the mass number. Have students repeat this for the other five elements in the figure. *(H = 0 neutrons; C = 6 neutrons; N = 7 neutrons; O = 8 neutrons; Ne = 10 neutrons; Cl = 18 neutrons.)*

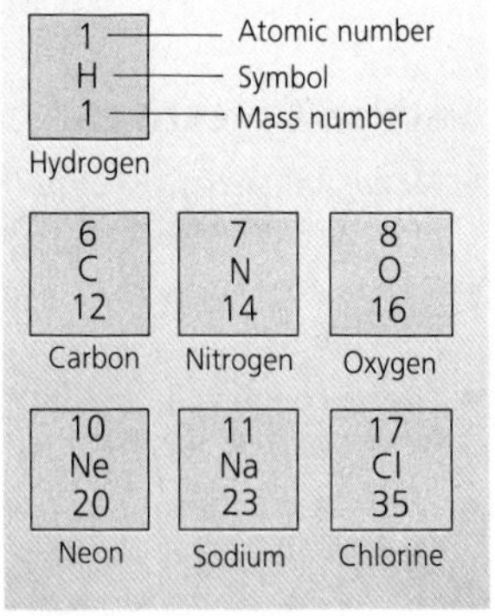

Figure 3-2 The chemical symbol, atomic number, and mass number of six common elements are shown here. What is the mass number of sodium? How many neutrons does sodium have?

Elements

Elements are substances that cannot be broken down chemically into simpler kinds of matter. Each element has a unique chemical symbol. More than 100 elements have been identified. Ninety-two elements occur in nature. The rest have been synthesized in physics laboratories.

Each atom of any element has the same number of protons. The number of protons in an atom is called the **atomic number** of the element. For example, since each atom of the element carbon has six protons, the atomic number of carbon is 6.

Isotopes

Although in any given element the number of protons in each atom is the same, the number of neutrons can vary. Atoms of the same element that differ in the number of neutrons they contain are called **isotopes.** Most elements have two or more isotopes. The **mass number** is the sum of the protons and neutrons in an atom. For each element shown in Figure 3-2 the mass number for the most common isotope is given just below the chemical symbol.

Biology in Process

Developing a Model of the Atom

By the late 1800s the electron had been identified as a subatomic particle. However, at the time scientists had little idea of where electrons were located in the atom or even of what the structure of the atom was.

The British scientist J. J. Thomson proposed a model of the atom in which electrons were embedded in positive matter of the atom like "raisins in a plum pudding." This model was accepted until scientist Ernest Rutherford produced data that did not fit the "plum pudding" model.

In the early 1900s Rutherford, who was born in New Zealand, conducted several experiments in which he directed a beam of fast-moving positively charged particles called alpha particles toward thin sheets of gold. He used both photographic plates and a Geiger counter to detect the paths of the alpha particles after they hit the gold sheets.

Most of the alpha particles passed directly through the gold as would be expected from the plum pudding model. However, Rutherford was shocked to observe that a few of the particles bounded back. Rutherford used this observa-

Cooperative Learning

Atomic Modeling Give each pair of students a bag containing large metal washers. Tell them to mark a "P" (for proton) on half the washers and an "N" (for neutron) on the other half by either using a felt pen or writing on masking tape. Next, give each pair a separate bag containing smaller-sized washers to represent electrons. Tell one student in each pair to refer to a periodic table and select an element from the first ten atomic numbers. Have each student's partner use the washers to construct a model showing the arrangement of the particles in the nucleus and in the electron energy levels of the element selected. Have the students check their partners' work and then switch roles and repeat the activity. Suggest that interested students also model different isotopes of their elements.

Radioisotopes

Some isotopes have unstable nuclei—that is, their nuclei tend to release particles or radiant energy or both. Such isotopes are called radioactive isotopes or **radioisotopes.** When the nucleus of a radioisotope emits radiation, the number of protons or neutrons in the nucleus is reduced.

Radioisotopes are useful in certain types of biological experiments because the radiation can be detected. A botanist, for example, can add a radioisotope of phosphorus to the soil. The botanist can trace the movement of phosphorus through the plant by measuring the radiation present in various parts of the plant at various times.

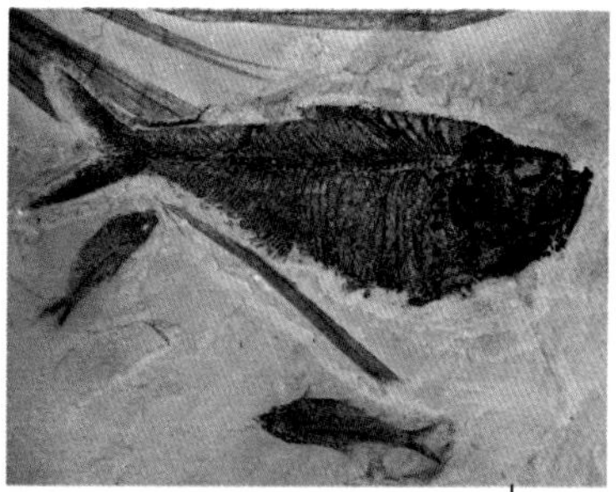

Figure 3-3 By studying the proportion of certain radioactive isotopes in a fossil, scientists can determine its age. A commonly used isotope for dating organisms is carbon-14.

Compounds

Compounds consist of atoms of two or more elements that are joined by chemical bonds. In a compound the proportions of individual atoms are fixed. For example, in the compound water the atoms of hydrogen (H) and oxygen (O) are always in a proportion

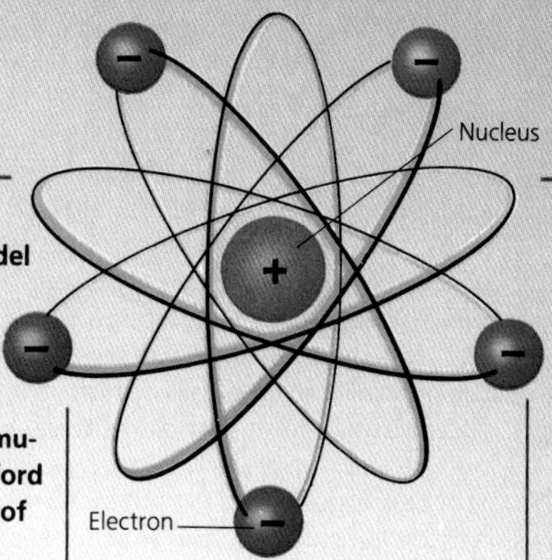

tion to formulate a new model of the atom, and he presented this model in 1911.

Study the picture of the Rutherford atom as you read about Rutherford's formulation of this model. Rutherford reasoned that because most of the alpha particles passed through the gold sheets undeflected, the atoms, of which the gold sheets were composed, must consist mainly of empty space.

From the scattering of the alpha particles Rutherford inferred that only a concentrated mass of positively charged material could repel the alpha particles, which were also positively charged. Only a large, concentrated mass could deflect them at the large angles he detected in his experiment. From these observations, he inferred the existence of the nucleus—a dense, central, positively charged core.

Rutherford then speculated that electrons were arranged around this positive core in the way that rings are arranged around Saturn. He also realized, however, that compared to the entire atom, the nucleus must be relatively very small.

Since Rutherford's time scientists have modified the model of the atom. Experiments have revealed more about the nature of the nucleus and about the arrangement of electrons around the nucleus. Yet Rutherford's experiments and model were a crucial stage in the process of modeling the atom.

- **How did Rutherford use inferring and modeling to formulate his concept of the atom?**

Biology in Process

Using the Feature

Rutherford's work, conducted at McGill University in Montreal, exemplifies the use of the scientific processes of experimenting, collecting data, analyzing data, inferring, and modeling. Explain that the experiments that led him to formulate his "new" model of the atom in 1911 were made possible by experiments he had conducted in 1899. Point out that Rutherford's model of the atom did not include neutrons, which were discovered by James Chadwick in 1932. Use this information to reinforce the benefit of communication between scientists.

Answer to the Feature

Rutherford inferred the structure of the atom based on his analysis of data, and he used his inferences to devise a model representing the structure of the atom.

Videodiscs

- ***2535–2537, Atomic and Molecular Structures (s)***

LEP Activity

To reinforce the relationships among subatomic particles, atomic number, and mass number, draw on the board a chart that allows students conceptually to break down the atom into its parts. Write the following column headings across the top of the chart: *Chemical Symbol, Atomic Number, Protons, Electrons, Neutrons, Mass Number.* Along the left side of the chart write the names of the elements shown in Figure 3-2 on p. 34. Have students complete the chart while they consult Figure 3-2. Remind students that mass number = protons + neutrons and atomic number = protons = electrons.

Interpreting the Visuals Ask students to use Figure 3-4 on p. 37 to make a statement about which electrons bond. *(Only those in the outer energy level)* Explain that bonding does not always result in a compound. For example, in hydrogen gas, two hydrogen atoms share a pair of electrons in a covalent bond, forming a hydrogen molecule (H_2) in which the two atoms are stable. Each has two electrons in its outer energy level. Point out that a chemical formula, such as CO_2, shows the number of atoms of each element in a molecule.

■ *See* **Overhead Transparency T3** *and* **Blackline Master 4.**

Guided Practice

Write on the board the following formulas: CH_4 (methane); $(NH_4)_2SO_4$ (ammonium sulfate); and the amino acid glycine: $(NH_2)CH_2(COOH)$. Have students determine how many atoms of which elements are in one molecule of each compound. *(Methane = 1 C, 4 H; ammonium sulfate = 2 N, 8 H, 1 S, 4 O; glycine = 1 N, 5 H, 2 C, 2 O)*

■ *See* **Process Skills, *Chapter 3*.**

Independent Practice

■ Have students write answers to the Section Review.

■ Tell students that in a neutral atom the number of electrons equals the number of protons. Have them list the number of protons, electrons, and neutrons in atoms of each element in Figure 3-2, p. 34. *(H = 1, 1, 0; C = 6, 6, 6; N = 7, 7, 7; O = 8, 8, 8; Ne = 10, 10, 10; Na = 11, 11, 12; Cl = 17, 17, 18)*

Answer to Think

This binding keeps these ions from leaching out of the topsoil. Point out to students that in cases of topsoil erosion, the ions are washed out with the soil.

of 2 to 1. A chemical formula shows the kind and proportion of atoms that form a particular compound. The chemical formula for water is H_2O. A compound differs in physical and chemical properties from the elements that compose it. For example, in nature the element oxygen is usually found as a gas (O_2) and the element hydrogen is usually found as a gas (H_2). However, when oxygen gas and hydrogen gas combine, they form the compound water (H_2O), a liquid.

How elements combine to form compounds depends on the number and arrangement of the electrons in the atoms. Experiments show that higher-energy electrons are located at a greater distance from the nucleus than lower-energy electrons are. Thus scientists have developed a model of the atom in which electrons occupy discrete energy levels at varying distances from the nucleus. Figure 3-1 illustrates this model.

According to the model each energy level can hold only a certain number of electrons. For example, the level nearest the nucleus can hold only two electrons. The next level can hold up to eight electrons. Most elements are most stable when the outermost energy level contains eight electrons. An important exception relevant to biology is hydrogen, which is most stable when its outer energy level contains two electrons. Aside from helium, neon, and a few other elements, most elements do not have such a stable configuration of electrons in their atoms. Hence most elements undergo reactions that cause their atoms to become stable. These reactions involve forming bonds with other atoms.

Ionic Bonds

Figure 3-4 shows how sodium and chlorine bond to form table salt. Note that the sodium atom has one electron in its outer energy level and that the chlorine atom has seven electrons in its outer energy level. Remember that most atoms are stable when their outer energy level contains eight electrons.

The diagram shows that when sodium and chlorine interact, the outer electron of the sodium atom moves to the chlorine atom. Afterward sodium and chlorine each have eight electrons in their outer energy level. In this process each atom becomes an **ion**—an atom or a polyatomic particle with an electrical charge. Sodium has lost an electron, and thus it becomes a positively charged ion, abbreviated as Na^+. Chlorine has gained an electron. Thus it becomes a negatively charged ion, chloride, abbreviated as Cl^-.

Because positive and negative charges attract each other, the sodium ion and the chloride ion attract each other and form a bond based on this attraction. Such a bond is an **ionic bond.** The resultant compound, in this case NaCl, is an ionic compound.

Ions are important in a number of biological processes. The elements that plants absorb from the soil—such as magnesium, nitrogen, iron, phosphorus, potassium, and calcium—are all in ionic form. Sodium and potassium ions play a major role in the transmission of nerve impulses in the human body.

Think

Many minerals needed by plants can be washed away by rain. Calcium, potassium, and sodium compounds are nutrients essential for the growth of plants. These nutrients occur as positively charged ions, which allows them to bind to negatively charged particles in the soil. Why is it important that calcium, potassium, and sodium ions can bind to soil?

Interdisciplinary Activity

Health/Physical Education To demonstrate the role of chemistry in health, have students investigate the effects of using chemicals to improve athletic performance. Suggest that students research the use of anabolic steroids, protein supplements, glucose pills, pain-killing drugs, and vitamins. Have students write a report that describes the effects of these chemicals on the body and contrasts various viewpoints regarding the use of these chemicals. Suggest that students solicit opinions from other students, athletes, coaches, science teachers, and parents to identify different viewpoints.

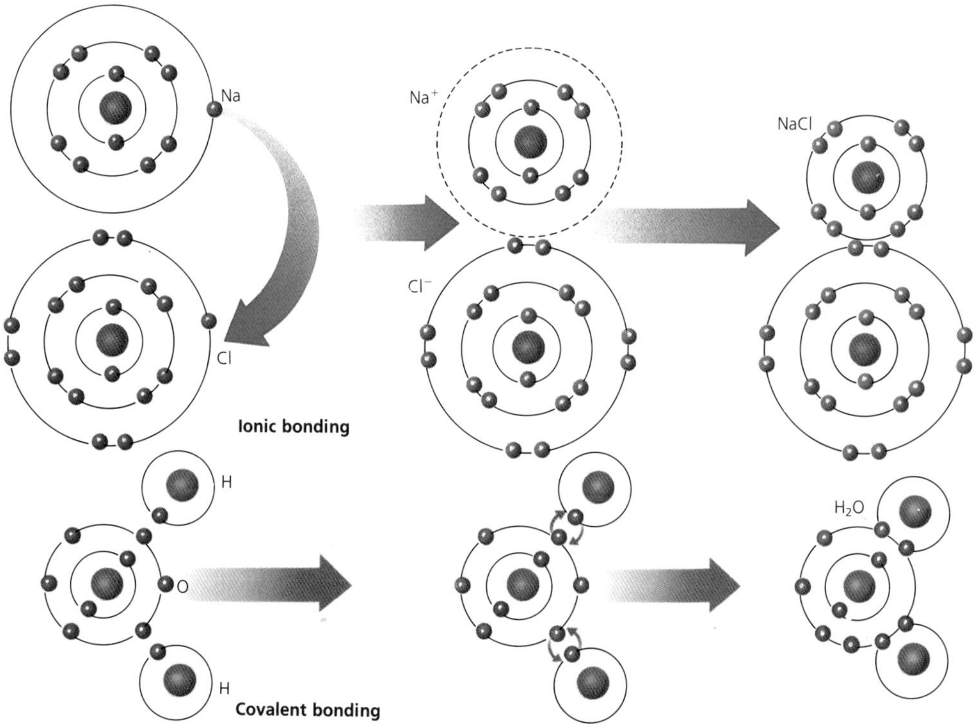

Figure 3-4 Table salt forms through the ionic bonding of sodium ions and chlorine ions (top). Water forms through the covalent bonding of hydrogen atoms and oxygen atoms (bottom).

Covalent Bonds

A **covalent bond** forms when two atoms share one or more pairs of electrons. Water is made up of one oxygen atom and two hydrogen atoms held together by covalent bonds. Since hydrogen has one electron, it needs another to give it the stable arrangement of two electrons in its outer energy level. Since oxygen has six electrons in its outer energy level, it needs two more electrons to give it the stable arrangement of eight electrons. The hydrogen and oxygen atoms gain stability by sharing pairs of electrons.

A **molecule** is a group of atoms held together by covalent bonds. Many substances important in biology are molecules, including carbon dioxide (CO_2) and water. A molecule can be represented either by a chemical formula, such as H_2O, or by a structural formula, such as H—O—H. The structural formula shows the arrangement of atoms in the molecule.

Section Review

1. Define *element, isotope,* and *radioisotope.*
2. How are subatomic particles arranged in the atom?
3. What are two properties of compounds?
4. How does an ionic bond differ from a covalent bond?
5. How would medical researchers use radioactive substances to trace the movement of substances in the body?

Section 3.1

Check Your Understanding

1. How are compounds and molecules related? *(Compounds formed by covalent bonding are molecules. Molecules composed of atoms of two or more elements are compounds.)*
2. How many protons, electrons, and neutrons are in an atom of an element having the atomic number 19 and the mass number 39? *(Protons—19; electrons—19; neutrons—20 [potassium])*
3. What makes a compound different from an element? *(An element cannot be chemically broken down into other substances, but a compound can be chemically broken down into elements.)*
4. How are chemical bonds between atoms formed? *(Either an outer electron moves from one atom to another and the resultant ions with opposite charges are attracted to each other [ionic], or one or more pairs of electrons are shared by two atoms [covalent].)*

Reteaching

Ask students to draw a concept map illustrating the relationships among the components of matter. An example of a completed concept map is shown on p. 31B.
■ *See* **Section Reviews** *worksheet, Section 3.1.*

Enrichment

Have students research and write a report on the use of radioisotopes in medicine, agriculture, paleontology, or power generation. Ask them to include safety issues in their reports.

Closure

Ask students to explain why current scientific models of the atom and of chemical bonding could still be modified. *(No one has actually observed the components of an atom or the structure of a chemical bond.)*

Videodiscs

■ *Side 1 29807, Molecular Dynamics (m)*

Answers to Section Review

1. Elements are substances that cannot be broken down chemically into simpler kinds of matter. Isotopes are atoms of the same element that differ in the number of neutrons they contain. Radioisotopes have nuclei that emit radiation.
2. Protons and neutrons make up the nucleus of the atom, and electrons move around the nucleus.
3. In a compound, atoms of two or more elements are joined by either ionic or covalent bonds; a compound differs in physical and chemical properties from the elements that compose it.
4. Ionic bond: ions with opposite electrical charges attract each other; covalent bond: atoms share electrons.
5. Radioisotopes injected into the blood can be traced by detecting the radiation.

Lesson Plan

Section Focus

This section presents the properties of three basic types of mixtures—solutions, suspensions, and colloids—and provides examples of these types of mixtures in living things. The section also introduces the concepts of acidity and alkalinity and the importance of pH control in living systems.

Section Themes

The theme of **Scale and Structure** is reflected in the distinctions scientists make between the sizes, types, and arrangements of particles in different mixtures. The **Systems and Interactions** theme encompasses the behavior and interactions of the particles in mixtures.

Motivating Activity

Prepare dilute mixtures in test tubes (approximately 1 g in 20 mL) of sugar and water, plaster of paris and water, and milk and water. Tell students to shine a flashlight into each mixture; ask in which mixtures they can see the flashlight beam. *(In the plaster of paris mixture and milk mixture, but not the sugar mixture)* Have students label the mixtures according to type and allow them to sit overnight. *(Sugar/water—solution; plaster of paris/water—suspension; milk/water—colloid)* Ask students to predict which mixtures will separate and which will not. *(Only the suspension—plaster of paris/water—will settle out.)*

Section Objectives

- *Compare and contrast mixtures and compounds.*
- *List some characteristics that distinguish solutions from other mixtures.*
- *Define* suspension, *and give an example of one.*
- *Compare the sol state and the gel state of a colloid.*
- *Contrast properties of acids and bases.*

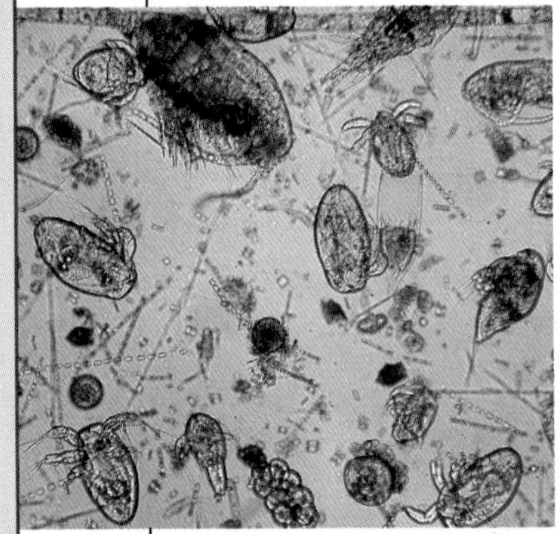

Figure 3-5 Marine microorganisms, such as these zooplanktons and phytoplanktons, live in aqueous solutions.

3.2 Mixtures

In a compound the combined substances do not retain their original chemical properties. In a **mixture,** however, the combined substances do retain their original chemical properties. For example, if sand and salt are mixed, neither changes chemically. How are the different types of mixtures important in biology?

Solutions

A **solution** is a mixture in which one or more substances are uniformly distributed in another substance. The **solute** is the substance being dissolved in the solution; the particles that compose a solute may be ions, atoms, or small molecules. The **solvent** is the substance in which the solute is dissolved. When sugar, a solute, and water, a solvent, are mixed, a solution of sugar water results. Though the sugar dissolves in the water, neither the sugar molecules nor the water molecules are altered chemically.

Solutions can be composed of various proportions of a given solute in a given solvent. Thus solutions can vary in concentration. The **concentration** of a solution is a measurement of the amount of solute dissolved in a fixed amount of solution. The more solute dissolved, the greater the concentration of the solution. For example, sugar can be added to a glass of water, spoonful by spoonful, increasing the concentration of the solution. At some point, however, sugar will no longer dissolve in the solution. The solution is then said to be saturated.

Solutions can be mixtures of liquids, solids, or gases. Brass, for example, is a solid solution, formed by cooling a mixture of liquid zinc and liquid copper. Most biologically important solutions, however, are those in which gases, liquids, or solids are dissolved in water. **Aqueous solutions**—solutions in which water is the solvent—are universally important to living organisms. Marine microorganisms spend their lives immersed in the sea, an aqueous solution. Most nutrients that plants need are in aqueous solution in moist soil. Plasma, the liquid part of the blood, is an aqueous solution containing dissolved nutrients and gases. Body cells exist in an aqueous solution of intercellular fluid.

Suspensions

A **suspension** is a mixture in which particles spread through a liquid or a gas but settle out over time. Waves on a beach can form a suspension of sand and water. The whipping of the wind can form a suspension of dust particles in the air. The particles in a suspension are larger than solute particles in a solution.

One suspension of importance in biology is blood. Red corpuscles and white blood cells are suspended in the plasma. The motion of blood coursing through blood vessels keeps these blood

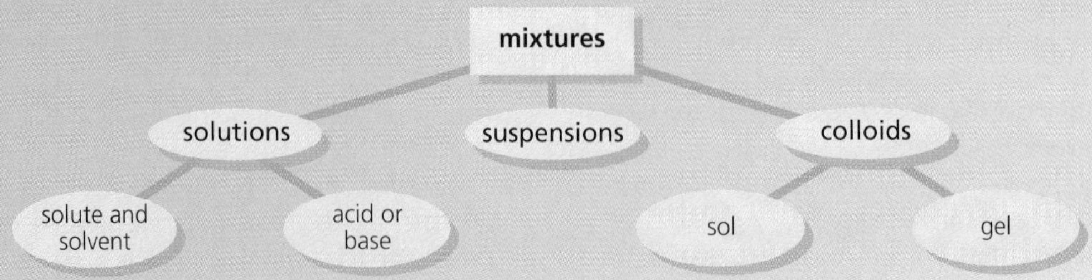

Graphic Organizer Use organizational chart in Guided Practice on p. 39.

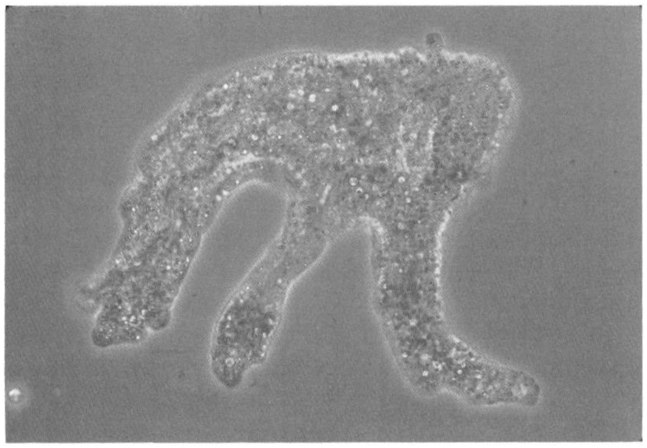

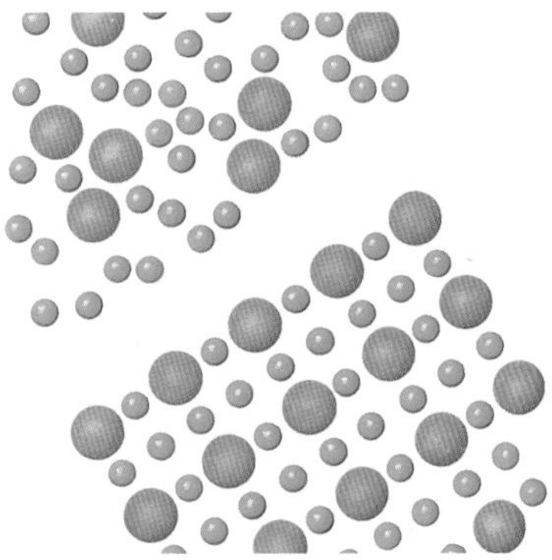

Figure 3-6 An ameba (left) moves as the cytoplasm near the membrane changes from a gel to a sol. The sol changes back to a gel as the molecules become arranged in a loose network (right).

cells distributed throughout the plasma. However, blood in an undisturbed test tube soon becomes separated into layers, with the blood cells settling to the bottom of the test tube.

Colloids

Colloids *(KAHL-OIDZ)*, also called colloidal suspensions, are mixtures in which, like solutions, particles do not settle out over time. However, particles in a colloid are intermediate in size between particles in a solution and those in a suspension.

Colloids can exist in a sol state or a gel state. For example, a colloid is formed when warm water and gelatin powder are mixed. The colloid is first a liquid called a **sol.** When the mixture cools, the gelatin molecules become arranged in a way that forms a loose network, and the colloid becomes a **gel,** a semisolid colloid. A colloid can change from a sol to a gel and back to a sol.

Cytoplasm, the material inside of cells, is an example of a colloid important in biology. Cytoplasm in the gel state helps maintain cell shape. For example, in an ameba the cytoplasm away from the cell membrane is in a gel state and helps maintain the shape of the organism. Cytoplasm near the membrane is often in a sol state. The change from sol to gel and back causes locomotion in amebas, as shown in Figure 3-6.

Acids and Bases

The health and functioning of a living thing depend on the chemical makeup both of the organism's internal environment and of the external environment. One of the most important aspects of an environment is the degree of its acidity or alkalinity.

Acidity or alkalinity is a measure of the relative amounts of hydronium ions (H_3O^+) and hydroxide ions (OH^-) dissolved in a solution. In water these ions form naturally: water molecules break up, or dissociate, to form hydrogen ions (H^+) and hydroxide ions (OH^-). The hydrogen ions spontaneously recombine with water molecules to form hydronium ions (H_3O^+). Pure water contains equal numbers of hydronium ions and hydroxide ions; thus water is a neutral solution.

Teaching Strategies

Interpreting the Visuals Ask students to explain which part of the right side of Figure 3-6 represents a sol state and which represents a gel state. *(The upper part represents the less orderly sol state, the lower part a gel state, in which the molecules are arranged in a loose network.)* If possible, provide ameba specimens so that students can observe the changing sol-gel states and their effect on an ameba's locomotion and shape.

Refer students to Figure 3-7 on p. 40 and explain that a pH change of one unit represents a tenfold change in concentration of either hydronium ions or hydroxide ions. Ask students how much more concentrated hydronium ions are in stomach acid than in vinegar. *(10 times)* Emphasize that acidity and alkalinity are properties of solutions. Have students use Figure 3-7 to identify the pH range that normally exists in the human body. *(From 2 to 8)* Ask what are the approximate pH's of blood and urine. *(Blood, 7.5; urine, 6)*

- *See* **Blackline Master 5.**

Guided Practice

Have students create an organizational chart illustrating the relationships among the main concepts in this section. A sample chart is shown on p. 38.

Independent Practice

- Have students write answers to the Section Review.
- Ask students to write a statement explaining why acids and bases are important to living things. *(Many chemical reactions in living things occur only within certain pH ranges.)*
- *See* **Laboratories, *Investigation 3.1.***

Videodiscs

- ***2518, pH Values of Common Solutions (s)***

LEP Activity

Set out labeled beakers containing: lemon juice, household ammonia, vinegar, milk, black coffee, chlorine bleach, baking soda solution, cola, and milk of magnesia. Give students strips of wide-range pH paper and have them test and record the pH of each solution. *(Approximate pH values: lemon juice, 2; ammonia, 12; vinegar, 3; milk, 7; black coffee, 5; chlorine bleach, 13; baking soda solution, 8.5; cola, 3; milk of magnesia, 10.5)* Have students write the name of each solution at the correct position on a pH scale like the one in Figure 3-7. Ask them why vinegar and lemon juice taste sour. *(They are acids.)* Ask why a baking soda solution tastes bitter. *(It is alkaline.)* Then ask why milk tastes neither sour nor bitter. *(It is a neutral solution.)* **CAUTION:** Warn students not to taste solutions.

Check Your Understanding

1. How could you decrease the concentration of a solution? *(Increase the amount of solvent.)*
2. How could you tell whether a mixture is a solution or a suspension? *(Let it remain still and, over time, particles will settle out if it is a suspension.)*
3. Why would drinking a baking soda solution, which is alkaline, relieve the symptoms of excess stomach acid? *(The alkaline solution neutralizes the acid.)*

Reteaching

To clarify the differences among solutions, suspensions, and colloids, have students label drawings that you put on the board or in handouts. Use the sketches here to guide your drawing. Ask students to explain why they labeled the drawings as they did.

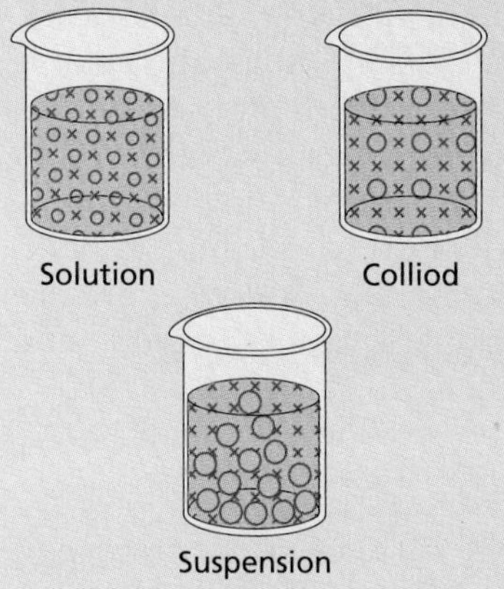

■ *See* Section Reviews *worksheet, Section 3-2.*

Enrichment

Have students research acid rain. Tell them to find out where ponds and lakes have become more acidic over the past few years, how the pH is monitored, and what have been the effects of increased acidity.

Closure

Ask students to list examples of the three types of mixtures in living things. *(Solution—intracellular fluid, blood plasma; suspension—whole blood; colloid—cytoplasm)*

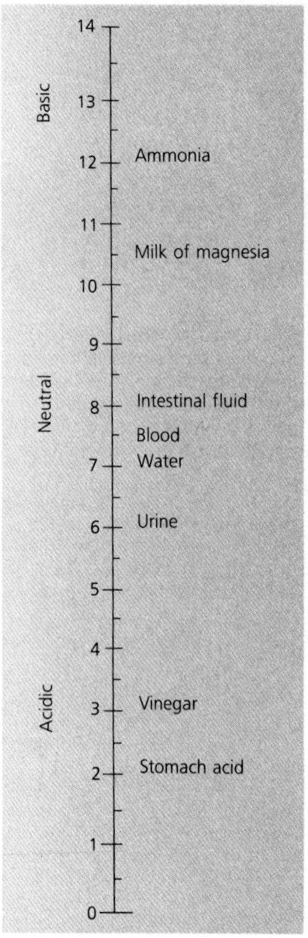

Figure 3-7 The pH scale indicates the relative concentrations of hydroxide ions and hydronium ions in a solution. Some litmus paper turns red in acidic solutions and blue in alkaline solutions.

Acids

If hydrogen chloride (HCl) is dissolved in water, some of its molecules dissociate to form hydrogen ions (H^+) and chloride ions (Cl^-). The hydrogen ions combine with water molecules to form hydronium ions. Such an aqueous solution then contains many more hydronium ions than hydroxide ions and is therefore defined as an **acid solution.** Acid solutions are often just called acids. Acids tend to have a sour taste; they produce a tingling or burning sensation if they come into contact with the skin. In concentrated forms they are highly corrosive. Citric acid, found in oranges, lemons, and grapefruit, is an example of a common acid of biological significance.

Bases

If sodium hydroxide (NaOH) is dissolved in water, some of its molecules dissociate to form sodium ions (Na^+) and hydroxide ions (OH^-). Such a solution contains many more hydroxide ions than hydronium ions and is therefore defined as a **base solution.** Base solutions are often called bases. The adjective *alkaline* refers to bases. Bases have a bitter taste; they tend to feel slippery. Ammonium hydroxide (NH_4OH), a waste product given off by many living organisms, is an example of a base found in nature.

pH

Scientists have developed a scale for measuring the relative concentrations of hydronium ions and hydroxide ions in a solution. It is called the **pH scale** and ranges from 0 to 14, as shown in Figure 3-7. A solution with a pH of 0 is very acidic; a solution with a pH of 7 is neutral; a solution with a pH of 14 is very basic. The pH of a solution can be measured electronically or with litmus paper, a treated paper that changes color at various pH levels.

The control of pH is important for living systems. For example, the chemicals that digest nutrients in the stomach can work only in an acidic environment. Glands in the stomach secrete acids that lower the pH of the food as it enters the stomach. These acids have a pH of about 2. The chemicals that digest nutrients in the intestine, on the other hand, can function only in a more basic environment. Glands that empty into the intestine secrete bases to raise the pH of the fluid that enters the intestines. These bases have a pH of about 8.

Section Review

1. How do mixtures differ from compounds?
2. What is a solution?
3. Why is blood considered an example of a suspension?
4. How do the compositions of an acid and a base differ?
5. If all the cytoplasm in a cell changed permanently to a gel, the cell would die. Explain why this is true.

Answers to Section Review

1. In mixtures, the combined substances retain their original chemical properties. In compounds, the combined elements lose their original chemical properties.
2. A solution is a mixture in which one or more substances are uniformly distributed in another substance.
3. In an undisturbed test tube, blood separates into layers, with the blood cells settling to the bottom of the test tube.
4. An acid contains more hydronium ions than hydroxide ions; a base contains more hydroxide ions than hydronium ions.
5. Nutrients and waste products would not be able to move through the thick material.

3.3 Energy

One characteristic of living organisms is that they use energy. To understand how organisms function, you need to learn some basic facts about energy.

Forms of Energy

Scientists define **energy** as the ability to do work. Work is defined as the movement of a mass. Energy occurs in various forms, including light energy, heat energy, electrical energy, chemical energy, and mechanical energy. Energy can be converted from one form to another. For example, when plants manufacture glucose during photosynthesis, they transform light energy from the sun into chemical energy.

Energy of any form can be classified as either potential or kinetic. **Potential energy** is stored energy or energy of position. A boulder at rest at the top of a hill or the water at the top of a waterfall has potential energy. If the boulder begins to roll down the hill or the water passes over the waterfall, their potential energy will change to **kinetic energy**—energy of motion.

All the atoms and molecules in any substance are in constant motion; thus they have kinetic energy. The kinetic energy of the atoms or molecules of a substance determines its state: solid, liquid, or gas. Particles of a solid are tightly bound together in a definite shape. Though the particles vibrate, they have relatively little kinetic energy. Particles of a liquid are not as tightly bound as those in a solid. They have greater kinetic energy and move more freely, giving a liquid its ability to flow and to conform to the shape of any container. Particles of a gas have even greater kinetic energy than particles of a liquid or a solid. Gas particles move rapidly and fill the volume of any container. With the addition of sufficient energy matter changes from solid to liquid to gas.

Section Objectives

- *Contrast potential energy with kinetic energy.*
- *Describe the relationship between the states of matter and the kinetic energy of molecules, atoms, or ions that compose matter.*
- *Describe how chemical reactions are illustrated by chemical equations.*
- *Explain how every chemical reaction involves either a net absorption or a net release of energy.*

Figure 3-8 The energy in the boulder at the top of the incline is potential energy. The energy in the waterfall is kinetic energy. If the boulder moves, its energy will become kinetic energy.

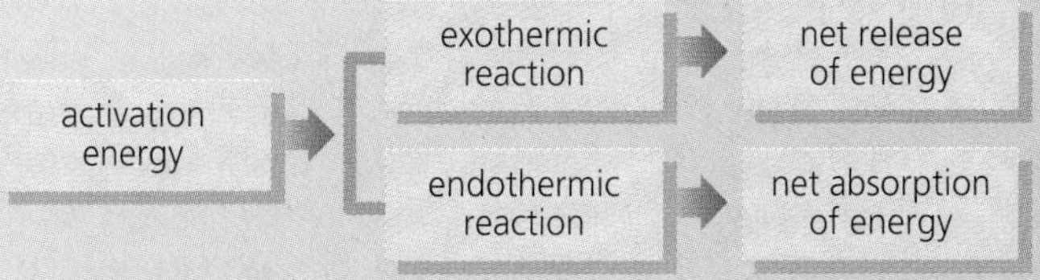

Graphic Organizer Use this sequential diagram to review concepts in Section 3.3.

Lesson Plan

Section Focus

This section introduces the concepts of potential and kinetic energy and describes the relationship between the kinetic energy of atoms and states of matter. Students also learn the role of energy in chemical reactions, particularly reactions in cells.

Section Themes

This section emphasizes the themes of **Energy** and **Patterns of Change.** Energy is either potential or kinetic and is either released or absorbed in chemical reactions. Molecules and forms of energy change during chemical reactions.

Motivating Activity

Heat a hot plate to a high temperature, turn off room lights, and shine a projector beam over the plate. **CAUTION:** *Tell students to stay clear.* Clap two chalk erasers together near the plate so chalk dust can be seen rising in the column of hot air.

Ask students: Where did the energy to lift the chalk particles come from? *(From the electricity, the moving air, and heat from the hot plate)* What form of energy moves the air around the particles? *(Heat)* What would happen if the erasers were clapped near a cold plate? *(Dust would fall over the plate.)*

Teaching Strategies

Analyzing Concepts Explain that atoms are never created or destroyed during chemical reactions. Have students count the atoms of each element on both sides of the chemical equations in Table 3-1 on p. 42 to see that equations follow this concept.

Videodiscs

- ***Side 1 40704, Bioluminescence in Marine and Other Organisms (m)***

Guided Practice
Ask students to identify the following as exothermic or endothermic: burning wood, green plants using sunlight, breakdown of nutrients in cells. *(Burning—exothermic; plants using sunlight—endothermic; food breakdown—exothermic)*
■ *See* **Laboratories, *Investigation 3.2*.**

Independent Practice
■ Have students write answers to the Section Review.
■ Ask students to describe examples of potential energy, kinetic energy, and activation energy in their homes. *(Potential: heating fuel; kinetic: a food processor blending; activation: pilot light in a gas stove)*

Check Your Understanding
1. How does the kinetic energy of the molecules in a substance change as the substance changes from a solid to a liquid to a gas? *(The kinetic energy increases.)*
2. What is the role of activation energy in a chemical reaction? *(It starts the reaction.)*

Reteaching
Have a student gently push a book off a table. Ask what type of energy change took place. *(The book's potential energy changed to kinetic energy.)* Lift the book back onto the table and ask what energy change this represents. *(Kinetic energy changing to potential energy)*
■ *See* **Section Reviews *worksheet, Section 3.3.***

Enrichment
Have students develop a chart of energy pathways among living things, fuels, the sun, machines, and other environmental factors.

Closure
To show that energy is never destroyed, ask students what happens to the stored energy in wood that burns. *(Conversion to heat and light)*

Table 3-1
Chemical Equations

Reactants		Products
$2Na + Cl_2$	$\longrightarrow$	$2NaCl$
$2H_2O$	$\longrightarrow$	$2H_2 + O_2$
$6CO_2 + 6H_2O$	$\longrightarrow$	$C_6H_{12}O_6 + 6O_2$

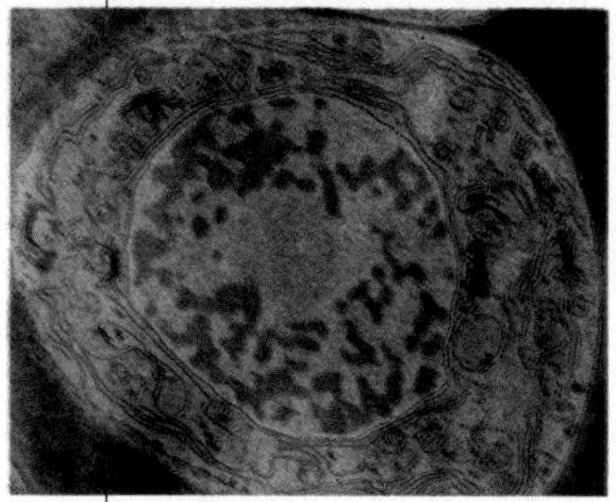

Figure 3-9 A cell in the corn root tip must be supplied continuously with nutrients to get the energy it needs.

Chemical Reactions

A **chemical reaction** is the process of breaking chemical bonds or of forming new bonds or both. In a chemical reaction the atoms of the reactants combine to form the products of the reaction. For example, the reactants Na^+ and Cl^- combine in a chemical reaction to form the product NaCl.

Chemical equations show how reactants change during chemical reactions. The reactants are shown on the left side of the equation; the products of the reaction are shown on the right side. The number of each kind of atom must be the same on either side of the arrow. Identify the products and reactants in the chemical equations shown in Table 3-1.

Energy and Chemical Reactions

For most chemical reactions to occur at an observable rate, energy must be added to the reactants. The **activation energy** is the amount of energy required for the reaction to begin. Touching a burning match to a piece of paper supplies the activation energy necessary for the molecules in the paper to react with oxygen—that is, to burn. Once started, every chemical reaction involves either a net release of energy or a net absorption of energy. Chemical reactions that involve a net release of energy are called **exothermic** *(ECK-suh-THUR-mick)* **reactions.** Reactions that involve a net absorption of energy are called **endothermic** *(EN-duh-THUR-mick)* **reactions.** Many reactions that occur in cells are endothermic. Because these reactions use energy, cells need to be continually replenished with nutrients that can supply energy.

Exothermic reactions often release energy quickly. A rapid release of energy in living things, however, would damage the organism's cells. Therefore living things have **intermediary metabolism,** a series of chemical reactions by which energy is released slowly in controlled amounts that will not damage cells. When sugar is broken down in a cell, its chemical energy is released in a complex series of chemical reactions. This slow release of energy prevents damage to the cell.

Section Review

1. Define *chemical reaction,* and write a chemical equation for a common chemical reaction.
2. How does potential energy differ from kinetic energy?
3. How does the kinetic energy of the atoms or molecules of a substance determine its state?
4. State the difference between endothermic and exothermic reactions.
5. Burning oil causes an exothermic reaction in which energy is released as a hot flame. The body can also use oil as a source of energy. How do these two processes differ?

Answers to Section Review
1. A chemical reaction is the process of breaking chemical bonds or forming new bonds, or both. Accept any of the chemical equations given in the chapter.
2. Potential energy is stored energy, or energy of position, whereas kinetic energy is energy of motion.
3. The greater the kinetic energy of atoms and molecules, the faster and more freely they move and the less tightly bound together they are.
4. An endothermic reaction involves a net absorption of energy, whereas an exothermic reaction involves a net release of energy.
5. Burning oil releases energy quickly, but the body releases energy from oil slowly, through intermediary metabolism.

Laboratory

pH and Living Systems

Objective
To study the effect of acids and bases on organic molecules

Process Skills
Experimenting, observing

Materials
Small squares of wide-range pH paper, paper towels, medicine dropper, household ammonia, lemon juice, fresh skim milk, 2 30-mL beakers, small squares of narrow-range pH paper, 2 stirring rods

Inquiry

1 Line up four squares of wide-range pH paper 1 cm apart on a paper towel.
2 Use a medicine dropper to put one drop of water on a pH paper square. Determine the pH and then record it.
3 Use a clean dropper to place a small drop of ammonia on another square of the pH paper. Determine the pH of the ammonia and record your result.
4 Repeat step 3 with lemon juice and then repeat it again with milk.
5 Compare your results for the four substances that you have tested. Which substance is the most acidic? Which substance is the most basic? Is one of these substances neither acidic nor basic?
6 Molecules that make up, or are produced by, living organisms usually can function only within a very narrow pH range. To show how a biological molecule is affected by pH, place 100 drops of milk in a beaker. Measure the pH of the milk by transferring a drop of milk from the stirring rod to a square of narrow-range pH paper placed on a paper towel. Record the result. Why should you remeasure the pH of the milk with the narrow-range pH paper?
7 Add a drop of lemon juice to the milk in the beaker. Stir the mixture thoroughly. Measure the pH of the solution with the narrow-range pH paper.
8 Repeat step 7 until you notice an obvious change in the appearance of the milk. What is the pH of the milk at the point of change? The milk changes appearance because the acid in the lemon juice has changed the shape of the proteins in the milk, causing the proteins to precipitate out of solution. What evidence do you see of this?
9 Repeat step 7 until you no longer note a change in the pH of the milk. Record the pH at this point. Compare this figure with your initial result in step 6.
10 Repeat steps 6 and 7 using a clean beaker and fresh milk, and substitute ammonia for the lemon juice. Add ammonia to the milk until the change in pH of the milk is equal to the change in pH you measured in step 9. Does the appearance of the milk change after this point?

Conclusions

1 Was the pH of the milk when you stopped adding lemon juice the same as when you stopped adding ammonia?
2 Why do you think lemon juice curdled the milk but ammonia did not?

Further Inquiry
Design an experiment investigating whether milk or water is more easily made acidic.

(For an overview of acids and bases and preparatory information related to the laboratory, *see p. 31B.)*

Inquiry

2. Have students use distilled water in this step. Tap water varies in pH. Even distilled water is not neutral (pH: 5–6) because of dissolved carbon dioxide forming carbonic acid.
4. Remind students to rinse their medicine droppers with distilled water before they test each new substance.
5. The most acidic substance is the lemon juice (approximate pH: 2). The most basic is the ammonia solution (approximate pH: 12). Both the milk and the distilled water are closer to neutral (pH: 7). Point out that tap water may not be neutral because it may be treated with chemicals.
6. The narrow-range pH paper gives a more precise reading.
8. The curdling of the milk occurs gradually, and it is impossible to say what the exact point of change is. The approximate pH of the milk at the change of appearance is 5. The evidence of the precipitation of the proteins is the formation of curds in the milk.
10. When a drop of ammonia hits the milk, it makes a "hole" in the milk, that is, the area around the drop becomes clear. As more ammonia is added, the milk becomes less white and less opaque. By the time the change in pH is equal to the change measured in step 9, the maximum change in appearance has already occurred. There is no change in the appearance of the milk after this point.

Conclusions

1. No. The milk became acidic with lemon juice and became basic with ammonia.
2. The acid in the lemon juice changed the shape of the protein molecules in the milk, whereas the ammonia, a base, did not change its shape. (Instead, the ammonia dissolved some of the protein in the milk.)

Further Inquiry
Students may design the following experiment. Compare the amount of an acid that must be added to a given amount of milk with the amount of the same acid that must be added to the same amount of distilled water in order to lower the pH to a certain value. Students can infer whether the milk or water is more easily made acidic.

Chapter 3 Review

Vocabulary

acid solution (40)
activation energy (42)
aqueous solution (38)
atom (33)
atomic number (34)
base solution (40)
chemical equation (42)
chemical reaction (42)
colloid (39)
compound (35)
concentration (38)
covalent bond (37)
electron (33)
element (34)
endothermic reaction (42)
energy (41)
exothermic reaction (42)
gel (39)
intermediary metabolism (42)
ion (36)
ionic bond (36)
isotope (34)
kinetic energy (41)
mass (33)
mass number (34)
matter (33)
mixture (38)
molecule (37)
neutron (33)
nucleus (33)
pH scale (40)
potential energy (41)
proton (33)
radioisotope (35)
sol (39)
solute (38)
solution (38)
solvent (38)
suspension (38)

Explain the difference between the terms in each of the following sets.

1. electron, neutron, proton
2. element, compound
3. solution, suspension, colloid
4. acid, base
5. endothermic reaction, exothermic reaction

Review

1. The nucleus of the atom is made up of (a) protons and neutrons (b) protons and electrons (c) elements and compounds (d) sols and gels.
2. Isotopes are atoms of the same element that differ in their number of (a) ions (b) molecules (c) formulas (d) neutrons.
3. How elements bond to form compounds depends on the (a) activation energy of the compound (b) dissociation of the ions in the compound (c) number and arrangement of electrons in the component atoms (d) model of the atom.
4. The results of Rutherford's experiment were surprising because after hitting the gold foil, some alpha particles (a) passed through the foil (b) bounced back from the foil (c) became radioactive (d) were stripped from the atoms.
5. When sugar dissolves in water, (a) ionic bonds break (b) covalent bonds break (c) the sugar molecules and water molecules are altered (d) the sugar molecules and water molecules are not altered.
6. Particles in a suspension (a) will settle over time (b) will not settle over time (c) are always acidic (d) are neutral.
7. Particles in a colloid are larger than those in a (a) solution (b) suspension (c) sol (d) gel.
8. Atoms in a solid have (a) more kinetic energy than those in a gas (b) less kinetic energy than those in a gas (c) more kinetic energy than those in a liquid (d) less potential energy than those in a gas.
9. The amount of energy required for a chemical reaction to get started is called (a) potential energy (b) kinetic energy (c) electrical energy (d) activation energy.
10. Intermediary metabolism (a) releases more energy than it uses (b) releases less energy than it uses (c) releases energy slowly in controlled amounts that will not damage cells (d) releases smoke, heat, and light as products of the reactions.
11. How do radioisotopes differ from nonradioactive isotopes, and how are radioisotopes useful in certain experiments?
12. Contrast the properties of compounds with those of mixtures.

Chapter 3 Review

Vocabulary

1. An electron is negatively charged and moves around the nucleus; a neutron has no charge and is part of the nucleus; a proton is positively charged and is part of the nucleus.
2. An element cannot be broken down chemically into simpler substances with the same properties, whereas a compound, which is two or more elements joined by chemical bonds, can be broken down.
3. In a solution, one or more substances are uniformly distributed in another substance; in a suspension, particles spread through a liquid or a gas but settle out over time; in a colloid, particles are intermediate in size between particles in a solution and those in a suspension.
4. An acid contains more hydronium ions than hydroxide ions, whereas a base contains more hydroxide ions.
5. An endothermic reaction involves a net absorption of energy, whereas an exothermic reaction involves a net release of energy.

Review

1. a	**6.** a
2. d	**7.** a
3. c	**8.** b
4. b	**9.** d
5. d	**10.** c

11. The nucleus of a radioisotope emits radiation. Radioisotopes mixed with nonradioactive isotopes of a substance are useful for tracing the movement of this substance through an organism because the movement of the radiation can be detected.
12. In compounds, the combined elements do not retain their original chemical properties and combine only in fixed proportions, but in mixtures, the combined substances do retain their original chemical properties and can combine in various proportions.
13. An ion is an atom or a molecule with an electrical charge.
14. In a covalent bond, one or more pairs of electrons are shared by two atoms.
15. Rutherford inferred that the atom consists mainly of empty space and has a dense, central, positively charged core (nucleus).
16. The sol phase is a liquid state, whereas the gel phase is a semisolid state in which the molecules are arranged in a loose network.
17. An acid solution is a solution containing more hydronium ions than hydroxide ions; a base solution is a solution containing more hydroxide ions than hydronium ions. Stomach chemicals can digest nutrients only in an acidic environment; intestinal chemicals can digest nutrients only in a more basic environment.

13. What is an ion?
14. How are electrons distributed in a covalent bond?
15. What inferences did Rutherford use to formulate his model of the atom?
16. How does the sol phase of a colloid differ from its gel phase?
17. Define the terms *acid solution* and *base solution,* and give an example of how the control of pH is important in biology.
18. What is the difference between potential energy and kinetic energy?
19. Write the chemical equation for the formation of water from hydrogen and oxygen, and identify both the reactants and the products.
20. Most reactions in the cell are endothermic. How does this explain why cells need a continual supply of nutrients?

Critical Thinking

1. A carbon atom has six electrons. How many protons does it have?
2. Phosphorus-32 is a radioisotope of phosphorus commonly used by scientists studying DNA. Ordinary phosphorus has 15 protons and a mass number of 31. How many protons does phosphorus-32 have?
3. Common sulfur has 16 electrons and a mass number of 32. How many neutrons does it have?
4. Sulfur-35 is a radioisotope of sulfur used by scientists studying gene expression. How many neutrons does it have? (See information in question 3.)
5. If a scientist adds NaCl and HCl to pure water, what ions will be in the resulting solution?
6. A scientist mixes salt, sugar, and sand in water. Will the result be a suspension, a solution, or both? What will the result be after the water sits for an hour?

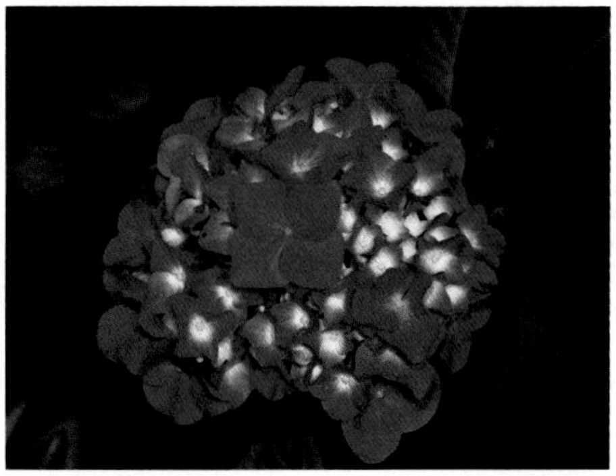

7. The plant in the photograph has blue flowers, as shown, when the soil is alkaline but pinkish flowers when the soil is acidic. Explain.
8. A dam that is located on a fast-flowing mountain stream generates electricity. What is the source of energy for the electricity?

Extension

1. Read the article by Elizabeth Pennisi entitled "Buckyballs Still Charm" in *Science News,* August 24, 1991, pp. 120–123. Make an oral report in which you describe some of the surprising properties of the C_{60} spheres commonly known as buckyballs.
2. Dissolve table salt or sugar in water at room temperature until it is saturated. The solution will be saturated when excess salt or sugar stays at the bottom of the container. Remove the clear solution at the top with a spoon. Place the remaining saturated solution in the refrigerator and leave it for two hours. Observe the results. What do your observations tell you about the effect of temperature on molecules in solution inside a living cell?

18. Potential energy is stored energy, or energy of position, whereas kinetic energy is energy of motion.
19. $2H_2 + O_2 \longrightarrow 2H_2O$. Reactants are $2H_2$, O_2; products are $2H_2O$. (This is the reverse of the second reaction in Table 3-1.)
20. The energy used during endothermic reactions in cells comes from the breakdown of nutrients.

Critical Thinking
1. six
2. 15
3. 16
4. 19
5. Na^+, Cl^-, H_3O^+, and OH^-
6. Both—the salt and sugar will dissolve in the water, forming a solution; the sand will spread through the water, forming a suspension. After an hour the sand will settle to the bottom of the container.
7. The flowers contain a chemical (pigment) that becomes blue when the plant absorbs a basic (alkaline) solution from the soil; the chemical becomes pink when the plant absorbs an acidic solution from the soil. (This plant is the hydrangea.)
8. The energy source is the kinetic energy of the water falling over the dam.

Extension
1. "Buckyballs Still Charm" is a challenging article that would be good for advanced students, to stimulate their interest in chemistry and biology.
2. Students will observe more salt or sugar at the bottom of the container after it is left in the refrigerator. Based on this, students may infer that the amount of solute that can dissolve in a solution decreases as temperature decreases. Students may then conclude that the higher the temperature, the more nutrients and gases that dissolve in solution in living cells. Ask students what would happen if they placed the spooned-off clear liquid in the refrigerator instead. *(Salt or sugar would appear at the bottom of the container.)*

Chapter 4 Biochemistry

Chapter Overview

This chapter introduces the basic biochemical compounds that are essential for all life. Section 4.1 describes the structure and behavior of the water molecule and of the carbon atom. Section 4.2 explains the structure and function of the four essential types of organic compounds: carbohydrates, lipids, proteins, and nucleic acids.

Chapter Planning Chart

B	S	A	Sections and Subsections	Page	Features	Page	Resources
•	•	•	**4.1 Compounds Important to Life**				
			Water	47	Section Review	48	Videodiscs
			Carbon Compounds	48			Section Reviews Worksheet
•	•	•	**4.2 Organic Compounds**				
			Carbohydrates	49	Think	50	Videodiscs
			Lipids	50	Biology in Process	52	Blackline Master 6
			Proteins	52	Laboratory	55	Overhead Transparency T4
			Nucleic Acids	54	Section Review	54	Blackline Master 7
							Process Skills: Enzymes and pH
							Laboratories: Catalase
							Section Reviews Worksheet
			End of Chapter Activities				
					Chapter Review	56	Vocabulary Skills
							Chapter Test
							Computer Test Generator

B *The Basic Level curriculum presents the most fundamental knowledge offered in the course.*
S *The Standard Level curriculum is designed for the average student who is able to master most topics.*
A *The Advanced Level curriculum includes suggestions for teaching the most academically able students.*

Cooperative Learning

Group Activity: Biochemistry Crossword Puzzle

- **Group Size:** *2 students*
- **Outcome:** *Students will identify key terms in Chapter 4 that match a given set of "clues."*
- **Individual Accountability:** *Each student will construct a crossword puzzle and will solve another crossword puzzle constructed by his or her partner.*
- **Positive Interdependence:** *Each partner will evaluate the other's solution to the crossword puzzle and will help the partner solve the puzzle.*

This chapter presents 34 key terms (in boldface type) related to basic biochemistry. Knowledge of these terms is necessary to understanding concepts introduced in later chapters, particularly those in units 2 and 3. This activity is designed to help students master the key terms in the chapter.

Using the list of key terms in Vocabulary, p. 56, randomly assign 17 terms to one member of a pair and the remaining 17 terms to the other member. Create different combinations of terms for each pair. Instruct each student to use graph paper to construct a crossword puzzle for the 17 assigned terms, using clues derived from the definitions given in the text. Have students do this part outside class.

Have partners exchange puzzles and, without referring to the text, attempt to solve each other's puzzle. Tell each "author" to check his or her partner's solution and, if necessary, provide hints to help the partner complete the puzzle.

Concept Map

The following is one possible solution to the concept mapping activity in Independent Practice on p. 52.

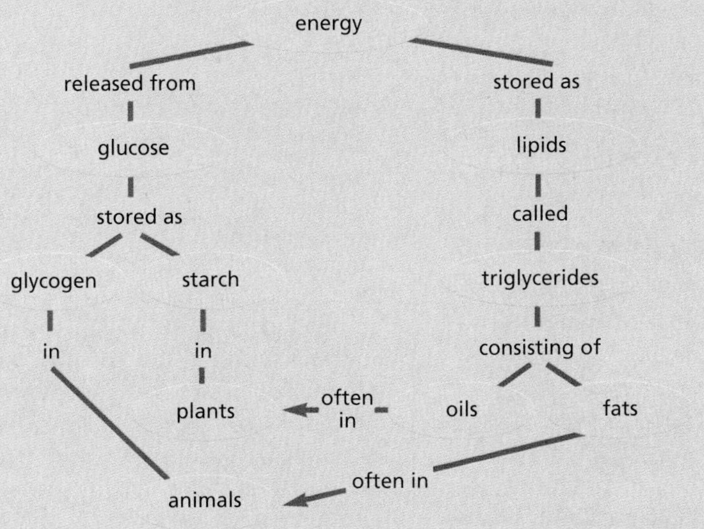

Laboratory Preparation

Overview *(See p. 55.)*

In this lab, students test for carbohydrates, proteins, and lipids in "known" foods and in an unidentified sample, chosen because their light colors do not mask color changes produced in the tests.

Benedict's solution tests for presence of simple sugars such as glucose. Iodine-potassium iodide solution tests for presence of starch. A 10% sodium hydroxide solution with 0.5% copper (II) sulfate solution tests for presence of proteins. Sudan III solution tests for presence of lipids.

Preparation

Use lowfat cottage cheese as the unidentified food. Purchase glucose in powder form and Benedict's solution from a biological supply house.

To prepare iodine–potassium iodide solution, add 10 g of potassium iodide to 50 mL of distilled water. Stir until dissolved. Add 5 g of iodine and stir again. Add enough distilled water to bring the total volume to 100 mL. Store the solution in brown bottles away from strong light.

Prepare a 10% sodium hydroxide solution (10 g in a final volume of 100 mL of water) and 0.5% copper (II) sulfate solution (0.5 g in a final volume of 100 mL of water) separately. Alternatively, purchase Biuret reagent from a biological supply house.

To prepare a 2% stock solution of Sudan III, add 2 g and dilute to a final volume of 100 mL with undiluted ethyl alcohol. Just before using, mix the stock solution with an equal amount of 45% ethyl alcohol.

Teaching Tips

Do not reveal that the unidentified food is lowfat cottage cheese until students have completed the lab.

You may wish to have each team test only one of the four known foods, as well as the unknown, then have teams share their data to draw conclusions.

Extend this lab by having students test additional unidentified foods such as corn syrup for glucose, crushed saltine crackers or raw white potato for starch, raw egg white for protein, and vegetable oil for lipids.

Safety

Caution students not to spatter the chemical reagents because they can injure skin and eyes or stain skin and clothing. Have students wear goggles, aprons, and gloves. Pour solutions into dropper bottles for student use.

If the iodine–potassium iodide solution or sodium hydroxide solution comes in contact with skin, flush affected areas immediately with water.

Chapter Themes

Scale and Structure The structure of the carbon atom, with its four outer electrons, enables it to form four covalent bonds in various ways and leads to many types of carbon chains and rings. Help students understand that the great variety of organic compounds results from carbon's ability to bond in varied ways.

Systems and Interactions Emphasize that all compounds, both inorganic and organic, within living systems interact with other compounds within and outside these systems. Water interacts with ionic and polar compounds that it dissolves and with other molecules when it undergoes adhesion or cohesion. Reactions among organic compounds within organisms are the basis for metabolism, growth, and reproduction.

Chapter Motivating Activity

Have students use medicine droppers to investigate the behavior of drops of water, liquid detergent, vegetable oil, and rubbing alcohol on various surfaces: aluminum foil, waxed paper, and plastic wrap. Ask students: What are the "splash patterns" of different liquids when dropped onto a surface from different heights? How easily do the drops roll when the surface is tilted? How close can two drops of the same liquid be pushed together before they "join" to form one drop? *(When dropped onto a surface, oil or detergent droplets tend to stay together, but water or alcohol droplets tend to disperse because their polar molecules adhere to other charged surfaces; liquids roll more slowly on waxed paper than on foil.)* Use this activity as a lead-in to Section 4.1.

Chapter 4 Biochemistry

Introduction

Carbon, hydrogen, oxygen, and nitrogen make up 99 percent of all living things. These elements join in various combinations and arrangements to form four major types of compounds: carbohydrates, proteins, lipids, and nucleic acids. In this chapter you will learn about the structure of these four types of compounds and about the function of the compounds in living organisms.

Chapter Outline

Chapter Concept

As you read, notice how structure relates to function in each of the four organic compounds.

Crystallized amino acid. Inset: Three-dimensional model of a protein molecule.

Understanding the Visuals

Ask students how the photograph of the amino acid crystal and the model of a protein molecule on this page differ from the illustrations of amino acid molecules in Figures 4-6 and 4-7, pp. 52–53. *(The drawings of the molecules in Figures 4-6 and 4-7 are models that represent only the arrangements of the component atoms of the amino acids, whereas the pictures on this page show either an actual compound [amino acid crystal] or represent the appearance of a molecule of a compound [protein model].)* Point out that the visuals serve as a reminder that molecular formulas and structural models that the students will learn throughout their study of biology represent substances with three-dimensional shapes, and that this shape affects the physical and chemical properties of the substance.

4.1 Compounds Important to Life

Biologists classify compounds into organic compounds and inorganic compounds. **Organic compounds** are generally derived from living things and contain carbon. **Inorganic compounds** are generally derived from nonliving things. Both organic and inorganic compounds are important to life. In this section you will learn about water and carbon compounds, both of which are essential to living things.

Section Objectives

- *Define* organic, inorganic, *and* polar compounds.
- *Summarize the way in which polarity in the water molecule gives water its unique properties and makes it essential for life.*
- *Describe why carbon readily combines with other elements, and discuss its significance in living things.*
- *Compare condensation reactions and hydrolysis.*

Water

Water, an inorganic molecule, has unique properties that make it one of the most important compounds for living things. In the water molecule (H_2O) the hydrogen and oxygen atoms bond so that the electrical charge is unevenly distributed. The area of the molecule containing oxygen has a slightly negative charge, and the areas containing hydrogen have slightly positive ones. Because of this uneven charge, water is called a **polar compound.**

Because water is a polar compound, it is an effective solvent. For example, when ionic compounds interact with water, the compounds often break apart, or dissociate into ions. This splitting or breaking up of an ionic compound frees ions to participate in biological reactions. Most polar molecules also tend to dissolve in water.

Water molecules and the molecules of solid surfaces are attracted to each other. This phenomenon, called adhesion, gives water its property of **capillarity**—the ability to spread through fine pores or to move upward through narrow tubes against the force of gravity.

Figure 4-1 Attraction between water molecules and the molecules of a solid surface can result in capillarity, which allows water to flow against the force of gravity.

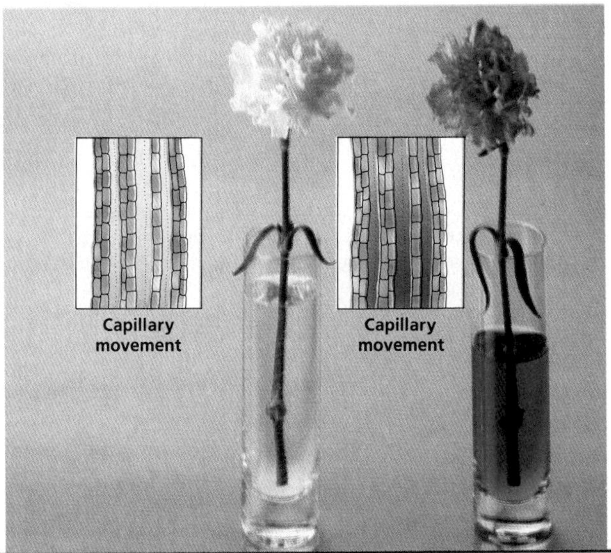

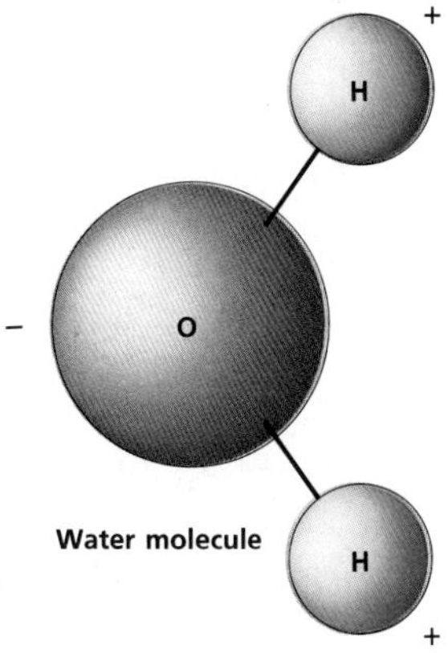

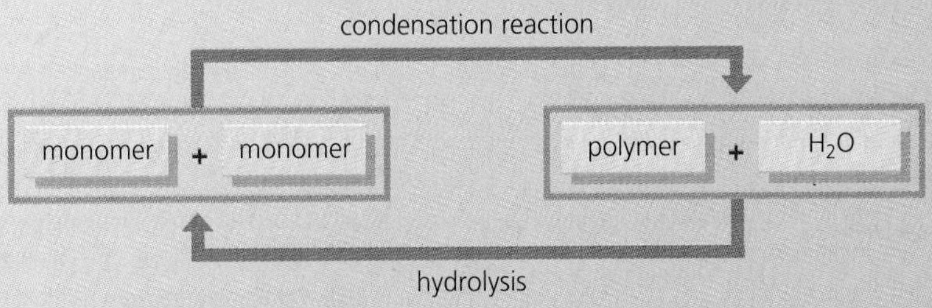

Graphic Organizer Use this diagram in Reteaching, p. 48 and Applying Concepts, p. 51.

Lesson Plan

Section Focus

Section 4.1 explains how the polarity of water makes it important to life and how the structure of carbon is the source of great variation among living things.

Section Themes

This section emphasizes the theme of **Scale and Structure**—the behavior of a compound is determined by its molecular structure.

Motivating Activity

Use silk to charge a glass rod, and use fur to charge a rubber rod. Demonstrate that an electrically charged rod can move other charged objects such as tiny pieces of metal foil. Explain that students will learn how some molecules, such as water, have charged areas that greatly affect their properties.

Teaching Strategies

Observing Properties Run a thin stream of water from a sink. Rub a glass rod with a silk cloth, explaining that this rubbing gives the rod a positive charge. Then place the rod next to the stream and ask students to explain what happens. *(Although a water molecule is neutral, its charge is not evenly distributed. The hydrogen atoms are slightly positive, while the oxygen atom is slightly negative. The positive charge on the glass rod attracts the negatively charged oxygen in the water molecules, bending the stream toward the rod.)*

Videodiscs

- *2528, Water Molecule (s)*

Section 4.1

Guided Practice
Have students use Styrofoam balls and toothpicks to build models of a water molecule and simple carbon chains. Ask what the balls and toothpicks represent. *(Balls—atoms; toothpicks—covalent bonds)* Use markers to show charges on water molecules.

Independent Practice
- Have students write answers to the Section Review.
- Give students pairs of concepts and ask them to write a sentence expressing the relationship between the two concepts. For example, pair *macromolecule* with *condensation reaction. (Macromolecules are formed through condensation reactions.)*

Check Your Understanding
1. How is adhesion different from cohesion? *(Adhesion is attraction between unlike molecules; cohesion is attraction between like molecules.)*
2. What causes cohesion? *(The uneven electric charge in polar molecules)*

Reteaching
Draw on the board the diagram on p. 47 (Graphic Organizer) without labels for the boxes, and ask students to label each box with one of the following: *monomer, polymer,* or H_2O. Emphasize that hydrolysis is the reverse of condensation.
- *See* **Section Reviews** *worksheet, Section 4.1.*

Enrichment
Have students research and write a report on why oil is not soluble in water.

Closure
Ask students to write a list of ten living organisms that are as different from one another as possible. Stress that all the differences that these organisms exhibit, as well as their similarities, can be explained by the carbon compounds each possesses.

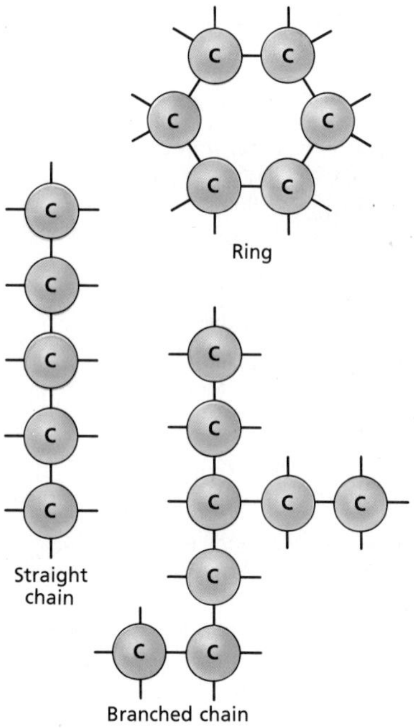

Figure 4-2 A carbon atom, with only four electrons in its outer energy level, readily bonds with other carbon atoms in various formations.

The uneven electrical charge in the water molecule causes the molecules to bond with one another. This phenomenon, called **cohesion,** explains why water heats up and cools down slowly in comparison with other substances. When water is heated, most of the heat energy goes into breaking the bonds between the molecules. Only after the bonds have been broken will the heat energy increase the motion of the molecules and thus raise the temperature of the water. In organisms, the cohesive property of water helps keep cells at an even temperature despite temperature fluctuations in the environment.

Carbon Compounds

As you learned in Chapter 3, the carbon atom has four electrons in its outer energy level. Remember that atoms become stable when their outer energy level contains eight electrons. Carbon, therefore, readily forms four covalent bonds with other elements. As shown in Figure 4-2 carbon also bonds to other carbon molecules, forming straight chains, branched chains, or rings. Because carbon can bond in such a variety of ways, organic compounds exhibit great variability. This variability is responsible for the great variation among living things. Among the most familiar organic compounds are sugars, fats, and proteins. Each of these kinds of organic compounds results from the unique bonding properties of carbon.

Many carbon compounds that are essential for life are **polymers,** compounds consisting of repeated linked units. Each unit in a polymer is called a **monomer** and consists of a simple molecule. Large polymers are called **macromolecules.**

Monomers link together, often forming polymers through a chemical reaction called a condensation reaction. In a **condensation reaction,** also called dehydration synthesis, the reactants give off a hydrogen ion (H^+) and a hydroxide ion (OH^-), which in turn combine to produce a water molecule (H_2O). Conversely, the breakdown of some polymers into monomers occurs through a reversal of this process, called hydrolysis. In **hydrolysis** *(hie-DRAHL-uh-suss)* a water molecule splits into a hydrogen ion and a hydroxide ion. As the polymer breaks apart, the hydrogen and hydroxide ions each combine with one of the monomers.

Section Review

1. Distinguish between *organic* and *inorganic compounds.*
2. What properties make water essential for living things?
3. What property allows carbon compounds to exist in a number of forms?
4. How does the reactive process by which polymers bond differ from the process by which they dissociate?
5. The cohesion between water molecules gives water a high boiling point. Why might this be important for living things?

Answers to Section Review
1. Organic compounds contain carbon and are generally derived from living things. Most inorganic compounds are derived from nonliving things.
2. Very effective solvent, capillarity, cohesion, slowness to change temperature
3. The ability of a carbon atom to readily form four covalent bonds
4. When a polymer forms, water molecules are given off. When a polymer breaks down, a hydrogen ion and hydroxide ion from a water molecule replace the sides of the two broken bonds at each site joining two monomers.
5. Large amounts of heat are needed to break the bonds between polar molecules, so the water in organisms resists drastic temperature changes that could destroy cells.

4.2 Organic Compounds

For all living organisms four types of organic compounds are essential: carbohydrates, lipids, proteins, and nucleic acids. As you read, study the structure of each organic compound shown in Figure 4-3 and note its function in the cell.

Carbohydrates

Carbohydrates are organic compounds composed of carbon, hydrogen, and oxygen in a ratio of two hydrogen atoms to one oxygen atom. The number of carbon atoms varies. Carbohydrates exist as monosaccharides, disaccharides, or polysaccharides.

Monosaccharides

A **monosaccharide** *(MAHN-uh-SACK-uh-ride)*—or simple sugar—contains carbon, hydrogen, and oxygen in a ratio of one to two to one. The most common monosaccharides are glucose, fructose, and galactose. Glucose is manufactured by plants during photosynthesis. It is the main source of energy for both plants and animals and is metabolized during the process called cellular respiration. Fructose is found in fruits and is the sweetest of the monosaccharides. Galactose is found in milk and is usually in

Section Objectives

- *Define* monosaccharide, disaccharide, *and* polysaccharide, *and discuss their significance to organisms.*
- *Relate the structure of lipids to their functions.*
- *Compare the structures of the various types of proteins.*
- *List two essential functions of nucleic acids.*
- *Outline Sanger's experiment for deciphering the structure of insulin.*

Figure 4-3 The four major kinds of organic compounds are proteins, carbohydrates, nucleic acids, and lipids.

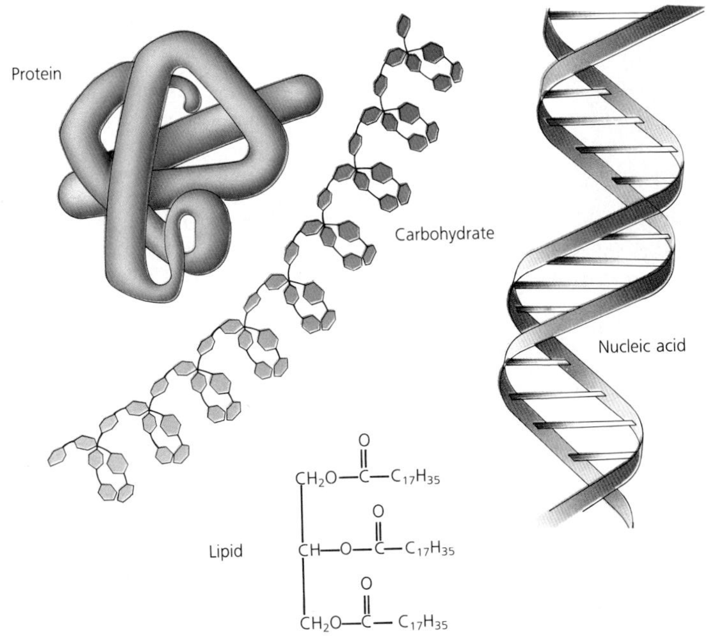

Lesson Plan

Section Focus

This section presents the four major kinds of organic compounds: carbohydrates, lipids, proteins, and nucleic acids. The section describes structures of molecules representative of the four kinds of compounds and explains their functions in living things.

Section Themes

The theme of **Scale and Structure** encompasses the relationship between bonding patterns and structures of monomers and polymers. The **Systems and Interactions** theme is reflected in reactions through which monomers link to form polymers, and polymers break down to form monomers.

Motivating Activity

Ask students if they or members of their families have ever dieted. Have them brainstorm a list of the kinds of diets that are or have been fashionable. *(High-protein diets; low-fat, high-carbohydrate diets; starvation diets; vegetarian diets; high-fruit, high-fiber diets)* Point out that this section explains what proteins, fats, and carbohydrates are, what they do, and how they differ.

Teaching Strategies

Drawing Analogies Students are already familiar with structures composed of many small, repeating units. Have them make a list of these structures. *(Sample answers: walls made of bricks, jewelry made of beads, mosaics made of tiles)* Ask students how polymers are analogous to these structures. *(Polymers are composed of many small, repeating units.)*

Videodiscs

- ***2532–2533, Glucose, Fructose (s)***

Organic Compound	Monomers	Polymers
carbohydrates	monosaccharides (ex. glucose)	polysaccharides (ex. cellulose)
lipids	fatty acids, carbon rings, alcohols	triglycerides, steroids, waxes
proteins	amino acids (ex. serine, alanine)	enzymes
nucleic acids	nucleotides	DNA, RNA

Graphic Organizer Use this table in Reteaching on p. 54.

Interpreting the Visuals Stress that compounds shown in Figure 4-3 on p. 49 are all polymers, or macromolecules. Ask students what types of monomers make up these polymers. *(Protein—amino acids; carbohydrate—monosaccharides; lipid—fatty acids or carbon rings; nucleic acid—nucleotides)*

Have students describe the shapes of the protein, carbohydrate, and nucleic acid shown in Figure 4-3. *(The protein is bent and folded on itself many times; the carbohydrate is a chain of hexagonal rings arranged in loops; the nucleic acid looks like a spiral or coiled ladder, or a double helix.)* Point out that these types of compounds exist in other shapes as well.

- *See* **Overhead Transparency T4** *and* **Blackline Master 6.**

Interpreting the Visuals Ask students what similarity they see in the structures of the three monosaccharides shown in Figure 4-4, p. 50. *(Their central structures are rings made of one oxygen atom and several carbon atoms.)* Have students count the total number of carbon, oxygen, and hydrogen atoms in each molecule. *(All three have the same molecular formula—$C_6H_{12}O_6$.)* Emphasize that the arrangement of atoms in a molecule determines its properties. Thus, molecules with the same number and kinds of atoms but different atom configurations (isomers) exhibit different properties.

- *See* **Blackline Master 7.**

Answer to Think

Bonds in lipids store more energy than bonds in carbohydrates. Birds use a large amount of energy during long, migratory flights. If a bird stored energy as carbohydrates, it might be too heavy to fly.

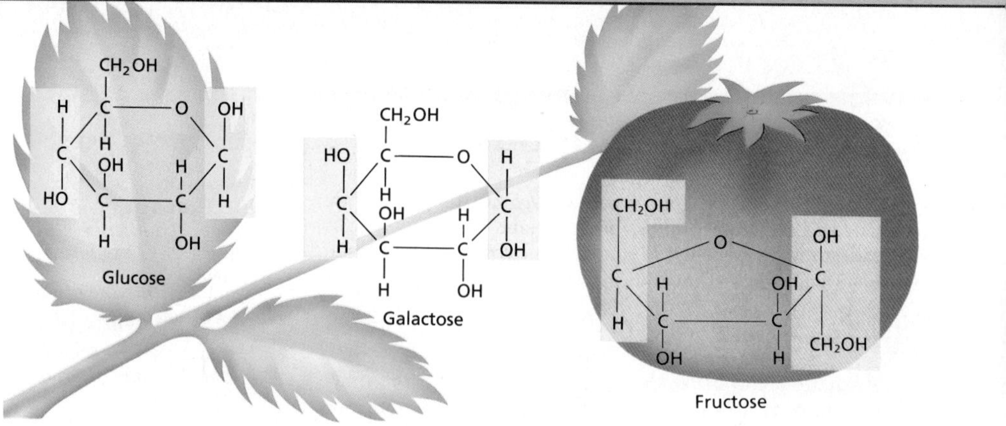

Figure 4-4 The monosaccharides—glucose, galactose, and fructose—all have the same molecular formula although their structures vary.

combination with glucose or fructose. Glucose, fructose, and galactose all have the identical molecular formula, $C_6H_{12}O_6$, but not the same structural formulas. Therefore glucose, fructose, and galactose are **isomers**—compounds that differ in structure but not in molecular composition. Look at the isomers in Figure 4-4.

Disaccharides and Polysaccharides

In organisms two monosaccharides combine in a condensation reaction forming a double sugar—or **disaccharide** *(die-SACK-uh-ride)*. Sucrose, a diasaccharide found in sugarcane and sugar beets, is composed of fructose and glucose. Lactose, a diasaccharide found in milk, is composed of glucose and galactose.

A **polysaccharide** *(PAHL-ih-SACK-uh-ride)* is a complex molecule composed of three or more monosaccharides. Like disaccharides, polysaccharides form through the linking of monosaccharides in condensation reactions. The most important polysaccharides found in living organisms are glycogen, starch, and cellulose.

Animals store glucose in the form of a polysaccharide called glycogen *(GLIE-kuh-jun)*. Glycogen, sometimes called animal starch, consists of hundreds of glucose molecules strung together in a highly branched chain. Plants store glucose in the form of a polysaccharide called starch. Starch molecules have two basic forms—highly-branched chains that are similar to glycogen and long unbranched chains that coil like a telephone cord. Cellulose is a polysaccharide that gives strength and rigidity to the plant cell. In a cellulose molecule thousands of glucose monomers are linked in long, straight chains, which help support plants.

Think

Why would it be to the advantage of an animal, such as a migratory bird, to store energy in the form of lipids rather than in the form of carbohydrates?

Lipids

A **lipid** is a fatty compound made up of carbon, hydrogen, and oxygen. A lipid molecule has a larger number of carbon and hydrogen atoms and a smaller number of oxygen atoms than carbohydrates do. Fats, oil, and waxes are lipids. Unlike the other organic compounds, lipids do not dissolve in water.

Cooperative Learning

Modeling Monomers Have pairs of students use kits or toothpicks with gumdrops or colored marshmallows to build models of the three monosaccharides in Figure 4-4. Have two pairs check each other's models for accuracy. Ask how fructose differs from the other two monomers. *(Its ring has only four carbon atoms.)* How do glucose and galactose differ? *(In the orientations of two H's and two –OH groups)* Have students use their models to show how the total number of atoms in fructose and glucose would change if linked in a condensation reaction to form sucrose. *(Two hydrogen atoms and one oxygen atom would be lost to the water molecule formed during the reaction.)* Then have students use the models to perform hydrolysis on sucrose.

The cell membrane is composed mostly of lipids. The insolubility of the lipids in water allows the membrane to form a barrier between the aqueous environments inside and outside the cell. Lipids also store energy efficiently. The lipid molecule has a relatively large number of carbon–hydrogen bonds, which store more energy than the carbon–oxygen bonds more common in the molecules of other organic compounds.

Fatty Acids

Fatty acids are the monomers that make up most lipids. Figure 4-5 shows that a **fatty acid** is composed of a long, straight hydrocarbon chain with a carboxyl (COOH) group attached at one end.

The contrasting properties of the two ends of the fatty acid molecule account for the characteristics of lipids. The carboxyl end of the fatty acid molecule is polar. Thus it is attracted to water molecules, which are also polar. Because of this attraction the carboxyl end of the fatty acid molecule is said to be **hydrophilic** *(HIE-druh-FIL-ick),* which means that it is "water loving."

In contrast, the hydrocarbon end of the fatty acid molecule is nonpolar. It tends not to interact with water molecules and in effect repels water. The hydrocarbon end of the fatty acid molecule is said to be **hydrophobic** *(HIE-druh-FOE-bick),* or "water fearing." In cell membranes the hydrophilic ends of the fatty acid molecules are oriented to the aqueous side of the membrane and the hydrophobic ends are oriented to the center of the membrane.

Triglycerides, Waxes, and Steroids

Three kinds of lipids exist: triglycerides, waxes, and steroids. A **triglyceride** *(trie-GLISS-uh-ride)* is a type of lipid in which the macromolecule is composed of three molecules of fatty acids joined to one molecule of glycerol. Each fatty acid molecule combines with the glycerol molecule through a condensation reaction. There are two main types of triglycerides. Triglycerides that are liquid at room temperature are called **oils.** The triglycerides found in plants are usually oils. These are often found in seeds, where they serve as an energy source for sprouting plants. Triglycerides that are solid at room temperature are called **fats.** The triglycerides found in animals are usually fats.

A **wax** is a type of lipid in which the molecule consists of a long fatty acid chain joined to a long alcohol chain. These long chains make waxes highly waterproof. In plants, wax forms a protective coating on the outer surfaces. In animals, wax forms protective layers, too. For example, earwax forms a barrier that keeps microorganisms from entering the middle ear.

In contrast with most other lipid polymers, which are composed of fatty acids, a **steroid** *(STIR-OID)* is a lipid in which the molecule is composed of four carbon rings. Steroids are considered lipids because they do not dissolve in water. Steroids are found in substances as varied as hormones, nerve tissue, toad venoms, and plant poisons.

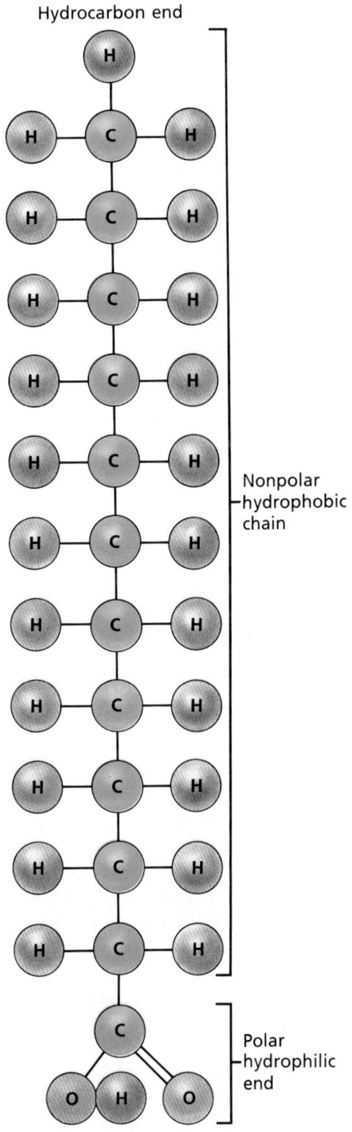

Figure 4-5 A fatty acid consists of a chain of carbon atoms. At the "head" end of each fatty acid is a carboxyl group; this end is polar. The hydrocarbon, nonpolar, end is the "tail."

Applying Concepts Redraw the diagram on p. 47 (Graphic Organizer) on the board or on overhead acetates. Ask students what process produces sucrose from fructose and glucose. *(By condensation reaction)* Next, ask how lactose forms from glucose and galactose. *(Also by condensation reaction)* Ask what other molecule is formed during each reaction that produces a disaccharide. *(H_2O)* Finally, by what process is a disaccharide broken down into its component monosaccharides? *(By hydrolysis)*

Remind students that hydrolysis is the reverse of condensation. Put the following diagram on the board to illustrate this idea for sucrose and its component monosaccharides.

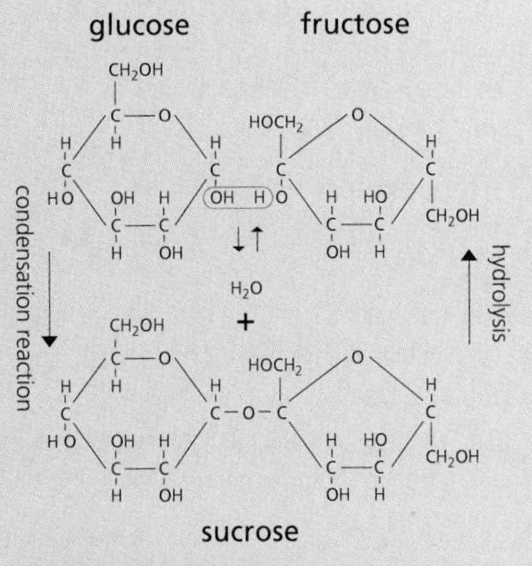

Emphasize that polysaccharides, such as glycogen, starch, and cellulose, also form by condensation reactions and are broken down by hydrolysis. Point out that these molecules are usually hundreds to thousands of units long.

Interpreting the Visuals Have students examine the nonpolar portions of the fatty acid in Figure 4-5, p. 51. Explain that the cell membrane is formed of two layers of such molecules, with the nonpolar portions forming a barrier insoluble to many molecules.

Interdisciplinary Activity

Health Have students explore questions about health and organic compounds—for example, what organic compounds are essential to a healthy diet, what is the effect of deficiency of an essential organic compound, and what are the dangers of fad diets and eating disorders. Encourage students to consult a variety of resources to gather information: the library, textbooks, physicians, nutritionists, and health teachers. Students can also refer to brochures on diet published by organizations such as the American Heart Association. Have students write reports summarizing their findings. Tell them to include an explanation of the different meanings of "organic" in science and in popular use.

Reviewing Concepts

Review the pH scale in Figure 3-7, p. 40, and tell students that stomach "chemicals," which are enzymes, require a specific pH and other conditions in order to function.

- *See* Process Skills, *Chapter 4, and* Laboratories, *Investigation 4.*

Guided Practice

Ask students to give examples of the functions of each of the four types of organic compounds in living things. *(Carbohydrates—source of energy for both plants and animals, strength and rigidity in plant cells; lipids—barrier between aqueous environments inside and outside cells, energy storage, protective coatings or layers; proteins—structure of skin and muscles, catalysts in intermediary metabolism [enzymes]; nucleic acids—storage and transfer of information essential to cell activities)*

Independent Practice

- Have students write answers to the Section Review.
- Have students draw a concept map illustrating relationships between organic compounds and energy. An example of a completed concept map is shown on p. 45B.

Check Your Understanding

1. How do a dipeptide and disaccharide differ? *(Dipeptide: two amino acids bonded together; disaccharide: two monosaccharides bonded together.)*
2. Why are enzymes essential to life? *(They are catalysts, proteins that enable essential reactions to occur in cells at body temperature.)*
3. Compare oils and fats. *(Both triglycerides; oils liquid at room temperature, usually found in plants; fats solid at room temperature, usually found in animals.)*

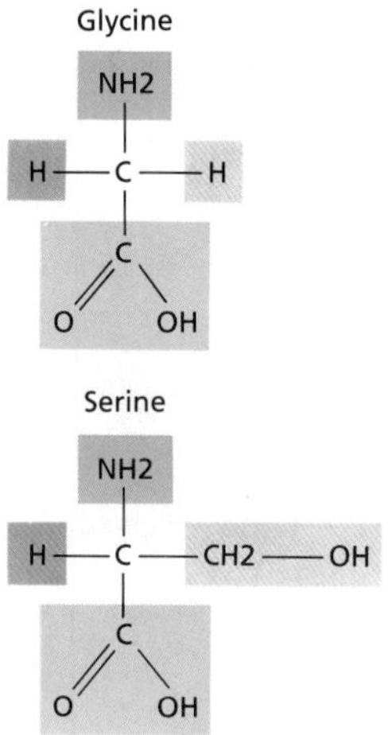

Figure 4-6 Glycine and serine contain the same elements but in different amounts. How does the structure of glycine differ from that of serine?

Proteins

Proteins are organic compounds composed mainly of hydrogen, oxygen, carbon, and nitrogen. Formed from the linkage of monomers called amino acids, which you will read about below, **proteins** are structural and functional compounds of universal importance in cells and thus in organisms. The skin and muscles of animals are made up mostly of proteins, as are the chemicals that are essential for the life processes in both plants and animals. Each species of organism has thousands of unique proteins.

Amino Acids

The 20 **amino acids**—monomers that form proteins—share the same basic structure. As Figure 4-6 shows, each amino acid contains a central carbon atom to which four other atoms or groups of atoms bond covalently. A single hydrogen atom, shown in orange, bonds at one site. A carboxyl group (COOH), shown in green, bonds at a second site. An amine group (NH_2), shown in blue, bonds at the third site. A group of atoms called the R group, shown in yellow, bonds at the fourth site. The differences between kinds of amino acids result from different R groups.

Biology in Process

Analyzing the Structure of a Protein

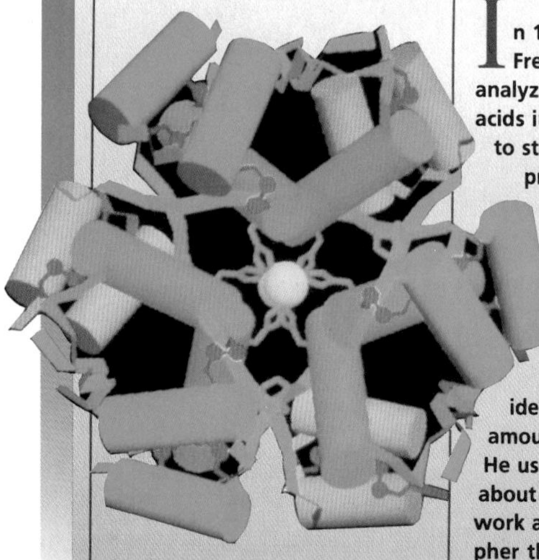

In 1943 the British scientist Frederick Sanger set out to analyze the sequence of amino acids in a protein. Sanger chose to study a relatively small protein, insulin—a protein hormone that helps control the amount of blood sugar.

First Sanger broke insulin into its constituent amino acids. Using chromatography, he identified the kinds and amounts of the amino acids. He used this information about insulin to verify his work as he proceeded to decipher the sequence of amino acids in the insulin molecule.

When amino acids bond together, the amino group of one amino acid attaches to the carboxyl group of the next amino acid. Thus at one end of any polypeptide chain is a free amino group, and at the other end is a free carboxyl group. Sanger used this knowledge to figure the number of polypeptide chains in insulin. He used a chemical that bonded only with free amino groups to show that insulin was composed of two free amino groups and thus consisted of two polypeptide chains.

Next Sanger had to determine the order of the amino acids in each of the two chains.

LEP Activity

To help students visualize how a condensation reaction links monomers and how hydrolysis breaks down polymers, have student groups make models of the amino acids glycine and alanine. Tell students to use Figure 4-7 as a guide, and let them use metal washers, building blocks, Styrofoam balls and toothpicks, or chemistry model kits to make their models. First have students "perform" a condensation reaction by removing an H and an OH from the two molecules to form a dipeptide and H_2O molecule, as shown in Figure 4-7. Then have them do the reverse to "perform" hydrolysis of the dipeptide.

Dipeptides and Polypeptides

Two amino acids bond together to form a **dipeptide** *(die-PEP-TIDE)*. Bonding occurs by a condensation reaction in which the amino group of one amino acid releases a hydrogen ion (H^+) and the carboxyl group of the second amino acid releases a hydroxide ion (OH^-). Then the nitrogen atom from the amino group and the carbon atom from the carboxyl group bond covalently. A covalent bond between the amino group of one amino acid and the carboxyl group of another forms a **peptide bond.**

A long chain of amino acids is called a **polypeptide.** Proteins are composed of two or more polypeptides. The amino acid sequence of the proteins determines how each protein bends and folds on itself and how the proteins intertwine.

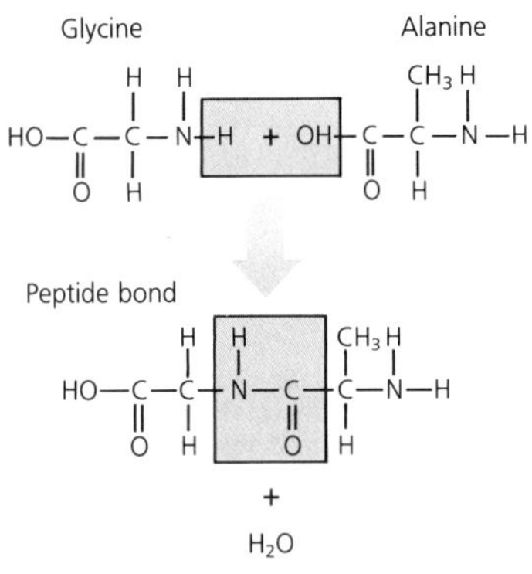

Figure 4-7 When amino acids such as glycine and alanine bond, a dipeptide forms. The covalent bond that joins a nitrogen atom and a carbon atom is a peptide bond.

Enzymes

Intermediary metabolism in living things usually involves catalysts—substances that speed up chemical reactions without being affected by the reactions themselves. **Enzymes**—proteins that act as catalysts in intermediary metabolism—are essential for the functioning of any cell. An enzyme speeds up a chemical reaction

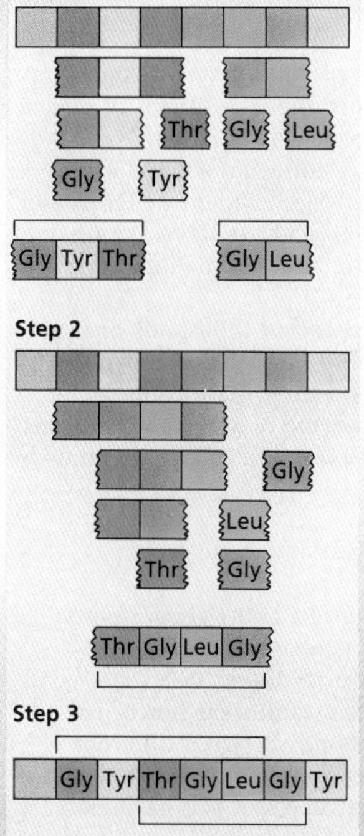

The diagram shows the steps in the complex procedure he followed. In step 1 he used chemicals that broke the bonds between specific amino acids to split the chains into smaller fragments. Then he treated these fragments with chemicals that broke off amino acids one at a time. Using chromatography he then identified the individual amino acids. Sanger checked his results with the results of his first experiment, which had revealed the composition of insulin.

Finally Sanger had to determine how the fragments fit together. In step 2 he repeated the fragmentation of insulin, using a different chemical, which cleaved the polypeptide chains at different sites. He analyzed the amino acid sequences in this set of fragments and compared them with the sequences from the first set of fragments. By comparing the two sets of fragments Sanger could determine the order of the amino acids in insulin (step 3). Sanger's painstaking labor paid off. In 1953 he deciphered the amino acid sequence of insulin. In 1958 he won the Nobel Prize in chemistry for his achievement.

▪ What was the process Sanger used to discover the sequence of amino acids in insulin?

More Information

Models of Enzyme Action Although Figure 4-8 on p. 54 does not specifically name the "lock-and-key" model of enzyme activity, it does illustrate an "exact fit" model. Recent research, however, has produced evidence that although some enzymes have a specific three-dimensional structure that fits a substrate precisely, most enzymes are "flexible molecules" that can change shape when they bind to a substrate. The substrate appears to induce structural change in the shape of the enzyme molecule, allowing that enzyme, once released, to continue mediating chemical reactions of similar substrates. This phenomenon is called the Induced Fit Hypothesis.

Biology in Process

Using the Feature

Sanger's efforts to discover the structure of insulin focused on the scientific processes of collecting data, experimenting, analyzing data, and inferring. Explain to students that in the diagram on p. 53, step 3 shows how he combined data from step 1 (upper brackets) and step 2 (lower bracket) to infer the amino acid sequence in insulin.

Explain that the computer model of insulin on p. 52 shows two polypeptide chains—one in yellow and green, the other in blue. The "ribbons" represent sulfur bonds that hold the polypeptide chains together. The white "ball" represents a zinc atom at the center of the molecule.

Point out that insulin had been isolated in 1922 by two scientists (Banting and Best) in Canada. Ask students why Sanger was the one to receive the Nobel Prize. *(The procedures he developed could be used to analyze the structure of other essential proteins.)* Explain that Sanger also paved the way for development of synthetic insulin, which could be produced in large amounts to treat diabetes. Other proteins have since been synthesized for use by individuals unable to produce essential proteins themselves.

Answer to the Feature

He first used chromatography to identify amino acids in insulin. Next, he used chemicals that bond with amine groups to identify the number of polypeptide chains, and then other chemicals to cleave the polypeptide chains and, ultimately, to break off individual amino acids. By comparing different polypeptide fragments, he inferred the amino acid sequence.

Section 4.2

Reteaching

To help students organize the four types of organic compounds as monomers or polymers, write across the board the column headings of the table on p. 49, and ask students to fill in the table text. An example of a completed table appears on p. 49.

■ *See* Section Reviews *worksheet, Section 4.2.*

Enrichment

Have students plan a one-day vegetarian diet that includes all the essential nutrients needed by a human. Tell them to identify and include essential organic compounds that the human body cannot make itself, as well as vitamins and minerals. Encourage them to consult a nutritionist to gather data.

Closure

Have students review the relationship between structure and function by asking them to draw analogies between organic molecules and the following everyday objects: a chain, spring, and lock and key. *(The structure of a fatty acid or a cellulose molecule is analogous to a chain; one kind of starch molecule coils like a spring; the structure and function of an enzyme and a substrate are analogous to those of a lock and key.)*

Videodiscs

- *2535–2537, Amino Acids (s)*
- *Side 1 25971, DNA Replication (m)*
- *Side 1 27255, DNA and Ethidium (m)*

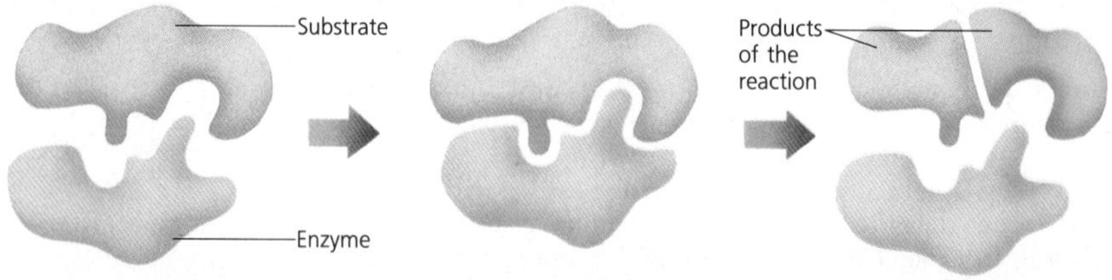

Figure 4-8 An enzyme, which is the essential catalyst in cell metabolism, binds in an exact fit to a specific site on a molecule, or substrate.

by using an alternate way to change reactant to product. The reaction catalyzed by the enzyme has a lower activation energy than the reaction without the enzyme.

Figure 4-8 shows one model of enzyme action. Notice that the shape of a particular enzyme allows it to hook up with a specific molecule. This molecule, called the **substrate,** is the reactant in a chemical reaction that is catalyzed by the enzyme. The linkage of the enzyme and the substrate probably weakens some chemical bonds in the substrate. This weakening might explain why the enzyme reaction has its low activation energy. After the reaction, the enzyme releases the products. Like any catalyst, the enzyme itself is regenerated to speed up other chemical reactions.

Nucleic Acids

Nucleic acids are complex organic molecules that store important information in the cell. The two most important types of nucleic acids are DNA and RNA. Deoxyribonucleic *(DEE-AHK-sih-RIE-boe-noo-KLEE-ick)* acid, or DNA, stores information that is essential for almost all cell activities, including cell division. **Ribonucleic** *(RIE-boe-noo-KLEE-ick)* acid, or **RNA,** stores and transfers information that is essential for the manufacturing of proteins.

Both DNA and RNA are composed of thousands of monomers called **nucleotides** *(NOO-klee-uh-TIDEZ)*. As shown in Figure 4-9, each nucleotide is made up of three main components: a phosphate group, a five-carbon sugar, and a ring-shaped nitrogen base. You will learn more about these important compounds in Chapter 8.

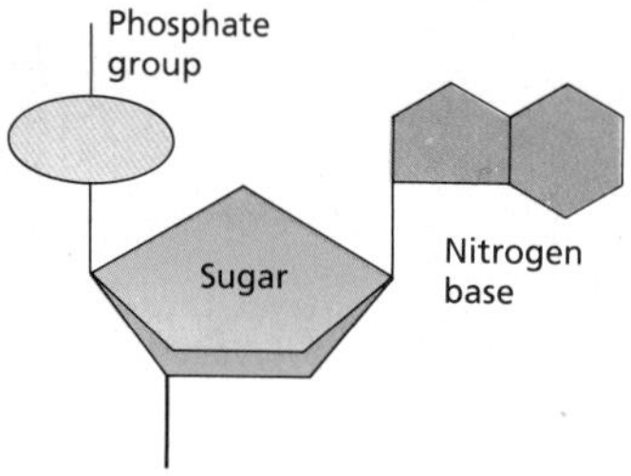

Figure 4-9 Each nucleotide in RNA and DNA consists of a phosphate group, a five-carbon sugar, and a ring-shaped nitrogen base.

Section Review

1. Define *monosaccharide, disaccharide,* and *polysaccharide.*
2. Describe the structure of amino acids and proteins.
3. How do the two ends of a fatty acid differ?
4. What are two types of nucleic acids and their functions?
5. High temperatures can weaken bonds between different parts of a protein molecule, thus changing its shape. How might this change alter the effectiveness of an enzyme?

Answers to Section Review

1. A monosaccharide is a simple sugar. A disaccharide is a double sugar formed from two monosaccharides. A polysaccharide is a complex carbohydrate composed of three or more monosaccharides.
2. Amino acids: a central carbon atom bonded to one hydrogen atom, carboxyl group, amine group, and variable R group. Proteins: one or more polypeptides.
3. The carboxyl end is hydrophilic; the hydrocarbon end is hydrophobic.
4. DNA stores information essential for almost all cell activities; RNA stores and transfers information essential for the manufacture of proteins.
5. If the shape of an enzyme were altered, its substrate might not "fit" into it, and thus the enzyme might lose its effectiveness.

Laboratory

Testing Food for Nutrients

Objective
To evaluate the nutrient content of an unidentified food

Process Skills
Experimenting, observing

Materials
1-L beaker, hot plate, glucose, unknown substance, 8 test tubes, 4 medicine droppers, distilled water, Benedict's solution, glass stirring rod, tongs, test tube rack, cornstarch, iodine–potassium iodide solution, nonfat dry milk, 10% aqueous sodium hydroxide solution, 0.5% copper sulfate solution, test tube stopper, lard, Sudan III solution

Inquiry

1 Fill a 1-L beaker half full with water and heat it on the hot plate.
2 Place pea-sized portions of glucose and the unknown substance in separate test tubes. What type of nutrient is glucose? Use a dropper to add about 2.5 cm of distilled water and 10 drops of Benedict's solution to each test tube. Mix with a stirring rod.
3 When the water boils, use tongs to place the test tubes in the water bath. Leave the test tubes in the water bath for 10 minutes.
4 Remove the test tubes with tongs and place the tubes in a test tube rack. When the tubes cool, an orange or red precipitate will form if large amounts of glucose are present. Small amounts of glucose will form a yellow or green precipitate. Record your observations.
5 You will use chemical reagents to test the unknown for specific nutrients. By comparing the color change a reagent produces in the unknown with the change it produces in the known nutrient, you can estimate the amount of that nutrient. Use small samples. Record all observations.

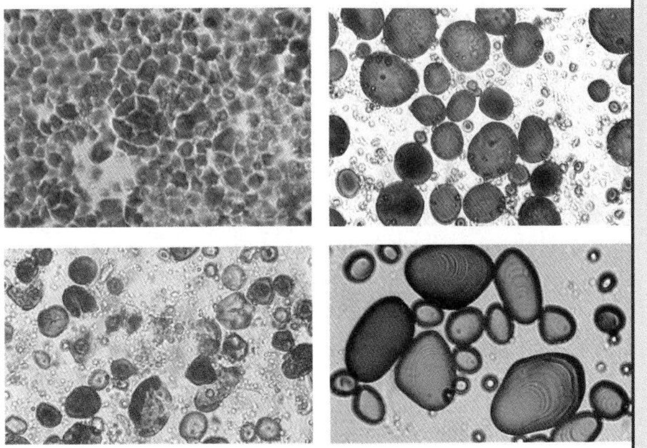

6 Place cornstarch in a clean test tube and some of the unknown substance in another. What type of nutrient is cornstarch?
7 Use a clean dropper to add 10 drops of iodine–potassium iodide solution to each test tube. Observe the results.
8 Place nonfat dry milk in a clean test tube and some of the unknown substance in another. What is the main nutrient in milk?
9 With a clean dropper slowly add an amount of sodium hydroxide solution about equal to the amount of the milk sample, and mix carefully. Then add 10 drops of copper sulfate solution one drop at a time. Stopper and gently shake the tube between drops.
10 Repeat step 9 with the unknown substance.
11 Place a small piece of lard in a clean test tube and some of the unknown substance in another. What type of nutrient is lard?
12 Use a clean dropper to add 10 drops of Sudan III solution to each test tube. Mix with a stirring rod, and observe.

Conclusions

1 What is the main nutrient in the unknown?
2 What are the controls in this investigation?

Further Inquiry
What are sources of error in this investigation?

(For an overview of nutrient testing and preparatory information related to the laboratory, see p. 45B.)

Inquiry

2. Have students rinse their medicine droppers with distilled water after using them for Benedict's solution. Glucose is a carbohydrate—specifically, a monosaccharide (simple sugar).
6. Cornstarch is a carbohydrate—specifically, a polysaccharide.
7. Remind students to rinse their medicine droppers with distilled water before they use each new reagent. Students should observe a blue-black color in the cornstarch after adding the iodine–potassium iodide solution.
8. Students may infer that the main nutrient in milk is protein.
10. Both nonfat dry milk and lowfat cottage cheese will show a positive test for protein—a purple or pink-purple color.
11. Students may infer that lard is a lipid—specifically, a fat.
12. Lard will show a positive test for lipids—a pink color. Students can perform an alternative test for presence of fat simply by rubbing a food sample on brown paper. Fats produce a translucent spot that is visible in the paper when it is held up to a light source.

Conclusions

1. The main nutrient in the unknown is protein, evidenced by the purple color in the protein test. Small amounts of sugars and lipids in lowfat cottage cheese may produce weak positive color changes.
2. The four known foods—glucose, cornstarch, nonfat dry milk, and lard—are the controls.

Further Inquiry

Possible sources of error are not measuring solutions accurately, impurities in foods tested, using unwashed equipment, and, in the glucose test, not heating or cooling substances long enough.

Chapter 4 Review

Vocabulary

1. Monomers are the units that make up polymers.
2. Amino acids are joined by peptide bonds to form proteins.
3. Two monosaccharides combine to form a disaccharide; polysaccharides are composed of three or more monosaccharides.
4. The terms have opposite meanings: *hydrophilic* means "attracted to water"; *hydrophobic* means "repels water."
5. Nucleotides make up nucleic acids; RNA is one type of nucleic acid.

Review

1. c	**6.** a
2. b	**7.** b
3. c	**8.** b
4. a	**9.** d
5. d	**10.** c

11. Water readily dissolves ionic compounds, freeing ions to participate in biological reactions. Adhesion of water molecules to solid surfaces enables water to spread through pores and to move upward through narrow tubes against the force of gravity. Cohesion of water molecules makes water heat up and cool down relatively slowly and thus keeps cells at an even temperature despite temperature fluctuations in the environment.
12. Each reaction is the reverse of the other. In a condensation reaction, two monomers link to form a polymer, releasing a water molecule; in hydrolysis, a water molecule splits, and a polymer breaks down into two monomers.
13. A disaccharide is a double sugar composed of two monosaccharides. Examples are sucrose and lactose.
14. The sequence of amino acids determines a protein's shape.
15. Accept diagrams that show steps similar to those shown in Figure 4-8.
16. Lipids have more carbon-hydrogen bonds than do most other organic molecules. These bonds store more energy than do the carbon-oxygen bonds common in other organic molecules.
17. The carboxyl end is polar and thus is hydrophilic; the hydrocarbon end is nonpolar and thus is hydrophobic.
18. All three are lipids—they contain carbon, hydrogen, and oxygen in proportions different from those in carbohydrates, and they do not dissolve in water. Triglycerides are composed of three fatty acids joined to one glycerol molecule. Waxes consist of a long, fatty acid chain joined to a long alcohol chain. Steroids are composed of four carbon rings.

Chapter 4 Review

Vocabulary

amino acid (52)
capillarity (47)
carbohydrate (49)
cohesion (48)
condensation reaction (48)
dipeptide (53)
disaccharide (50)
enzyme (53)
fat (51)
fatty acid (51)
hydrolysis (48)
hydrophilic (51)
hydrophobic (51)
inorganic compound (47)
isomer (50)
lipid (50)
macromolecule (48)
monomer (48)
monosaccharide (49)
nucleic acid (54)
nucleotide (54)
oil (51)
organic compound (47)
peptide bond (53)
polar compound (47)
polymer (48)
polypeptide (53)
polysaccharide (50)
protein (52)
ribonucleic acid (RNA) (54)
steroid (51)
substrate (54)
triglyceride (51)
wax (51)

Explain the relationship between the terms in each of the following sets.

1. monomer, polymer
2. amino acid, peptide bond, protein
3. monosaccharide, disaccharide, polysaccharide
4. hydrophilic, hydrophobic
5. nucleotide, nucleic acid, RNA

Review

1. Most organic compounds contain carbon and are (a) hydrophobic (b) not important to life (c) made by living organisms (d) not made by organisms.
2. The distinguishing feature of a polar compound is its (a) even distribution of electrical charge (b) uneven distribution of electrical charge (c) even temperature (d) uneven temperature.
3. Because the carbon atom has four electrons in its outer energy level carbon (a) participates in condensation reactions (b) participates in hydrolysis (c) bonds easily to itself and to other elements (d) adheres to solid surfaces.
4. The main source from which plants and animals get their energy is the monosaccharide (a) glucose (b) fructose (c) galactose (d) glycogen.
5. Plants store glucose in a polysaccharide called (a) cellulose (b) maltose (c) lactose (d) starch.
6. When two amino acids bond, (a) the carboxyl group of one amino acid joins to the amine group of the other in a condensation reaction (b) the carboxyl group of one amino acid joins to the amino group of the other during hydrolysis (c) a dipeptide is formed through intermediary metabolism (d) a polypeptide is formed through intermediary metabolism.
7. Enzymes speed up chemical reactions in the cell by (a) raising the activation energy (b) lowering the activation energy (c) releasing the products of the reaction (d) emerging from the reaction unaltered.
8. Lipids are distinguished from other organic molecules because they (a) contain carbon, hydrogen, and oxygen in a ratio of 1:2:1 (b) do not dissolve in water (c) store energy (d) form structural and functional compounds of universal importance in cells.
9. Steroids differ from other lipid polymers in that steroids (a) do not occur in varied substances (b) are not hydrophilic (c) are not hydrophobic (d) are not composed of fatty acid monomers.
10. A nucleotide is composed of a phosphate group, a five-carbon sugar, and a (a) substrate (b) triglyceride (c) nitrogen base (d) macromolecule.

11. How does the polarity in the water molecule give water unique properties that make it essential to life?
12. Compare and contrast a condensation reaction with hydrolysis.
13. Define *disaccharide* and give examples.
14. What factor determines the shape of a protein?
15. Diagram a model of one of the ways scientists think that enzymes might work.
16. How do lipids store energy efficiently?
17. How does the carboxyl end of the fatty acid molecule differ from the hydrocarbon end of the molecule?
18. Compare and contrast triglycerides, waxes, and steroids.
19. What are two nucleic acids and their functions?
20. How did Sanger use his knowledge of the structure of amino acids to discover the number of polypeptide chains in insulin?

Critical Thinking

1. Examine the shape of the water droplets on the leaf in the photograph at the right. What property of water molecules might give them that shape?
2. When we sweat, our bodies are cooled as the water evaporates. Explain how the polarity of the water molecules makes this an efficient way of cooling.
3. As you learned in the chapter, the triglycerides in animals are usually fats, and those in plants are usually oils. However, in many animals of the Arctic and Antarctic, the triglycerides are proportionately oils. What adaptive advantage would the storage of body fat as oil instead of fat be to animals that live in freezing climates?

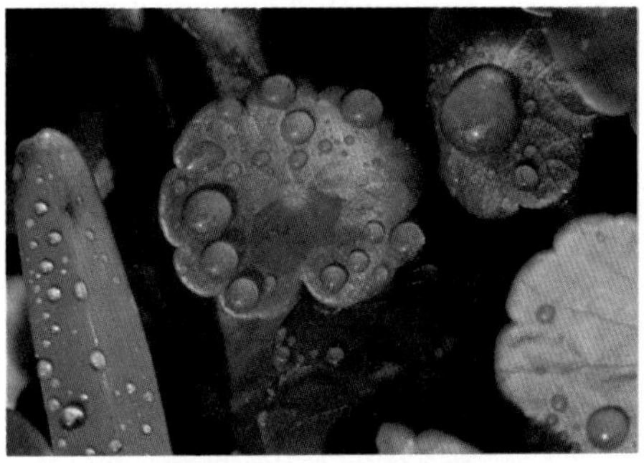

4. Meat tenderizers contain papain, an enzyme that digests proteins. These tenderizers are derived from unripe papayas. How might a tenderizer make meat tender?

Extension

1. Read the article by Liz Applegate entitled "Carbo-hydration" in *Runner's World,* October 1990, p. 24. Give an oral report in which you explain what carbohydrate loading is and why athletes use it. What precautions should a marathon runner or other athlete take when planning a carbohydrate-loading regimen?
2. Cut fibrous meat into four one-inch cubes. Sprinkle three of the cubes with equal amounts of meat tenderizer. Place one cube in the refrigerator, leave one at room temperature, and place the other in an incubator at 32°C. For the fourth cube, place the same amount of meat tenderizer and a few tablespoons of water in a container, boil for three minutes, and place on the meat. After three hours observe the texture of all four meat cubes. What do you conclude about the effect of temperature on the enzyme in meat tenderizer? Write a report in which you explain the method used, give the temperatures, and compare your observations of the meat before and after the incubation with the enzyme.

19. DNA stores information essential for almost all cell activities, including cell division; RNA stores and transfers information essential for manufacture of proteins.

20. Sanger knew that the amine group of one amino acid attaches to the carboxyl group of another when two amino acids bond. Thus, every polypeptide chain has a free amine group at one end and a free carboxyl group at the other end. Based on this knowledge, Sanger used a chemical that bonded only with free amine groups to show the number of free amine groups, and therefore the number of polypeptide chains, in insulin.

Critical Thinking

1. The cohesion of water molecules, caused by their polarity, gives water droplets their bubblelike shape.

2. Because the polarity of water molecules makes them cohesive, water molecules evaporate only after a large amount of heat energy breaks the bonds between them; during sweating, this heat energy comes from the body, thus cooling it.

3. Oil solidifies at a lower temperature than fat does; storing body fat as oil is adaptive in freezing climates because oil is less likely than fat to solidify in these climates.

4. The papain in the tenderizer breaks some peptide bonds of the proteins in meat, thus weakening the muscle fiber of meat, or making it "tender."

Extension

1. Students can also investigate whether different types of athletes tend to follow different diets that correspond to requirements of their sport.

2. Students should conclude that the rate of enzyme action depends on temperature, within limits. The higher the temperature, the faster the enzyme reaction occurs. However, extreme heat, such as heat from boiling, alters the enzyme, rendering it inactive. Have students use their results to infer the approximate temperature at which enzymes are most effective in catalyzing cellular chemical reactions.

Discussion

Guide the discussion by posing the following questions.

1. How can the rapid destruction of forests contribute to global warming? *(Trees help reduce the amount of carbon dioxide in the atmosphere. The more carbon dioxide in the air, the warmer the atmosphere. Carbon dioxide insulates the earth.)*

2. Compare the similarities and differences between the destruction of rain forests in tropical regions today and the destruction of temperate forests in North America centuries ago. *(Students should point out that like the settlers of North America, the peoples of tropical regions cut down trees to gain land for their survival and economic development. However, the rate of rain forest destruction in tropical regions today is much more rapid than the rate of destruction in temperate North America many years ago.)*

3. Explain how the rapid destruction of rain forests in another country can affect your own future. *(Students should identify and explain some of the long-term and global consequences of destroying rain forests at a rapid rate: global warming, mass extinction of species, pollution of water supplies and waterways, and the loss of opportunities to develop new uses of rain forest organisms for medical or other responsible purposes.)*

4. Describe some ways you might make a living in the rain forest without destroying it. *(Students may name a variety of careers that involve a responsible use of the forest, a renewable resource. For example, students may mention the vocation of farmer raising fruit or nut trees; forest or national park ranger; tree surgeon; agronomist.)*

Intra-Science

How the Sciences Work Together

The Question in Biology: *Will Earth's Forests Vanish?*

Scientists estimate that every year an expanse of tropical rain forest the size of Pennsylvania is destroyed. Already, almost half the rain forests that once encircled the earth have vanished. According to Thomas Lovejoy of the Smithsonian Institution, "The rain forest will be won or lost in the 1990s." If the battle is lost, the rain forests may be gone by the middle of the twenty-first century.

Although tropical rain forests cover only about 6 percent of the earth's surface, they are home to 50 percent of the earth's plants and animals. A rain forest the size of a city park may contain 1,500 different flowering plants, 750 species of trees, and hundreds of kinds of mammals, birds, reptiles, amphibians, and insects.

Why are these forests being destroyed? The reasons involve complex social and economic problems in many nations. The government policies of some Southeast Asian nations, for example, permit the harvest and export of mahogany, teak, and other hardwoods to help reduce national debt. International banks loan money to build new industries that involve destroying the rain forests in Central America and South America. Government subsidies and tax breaks to Brazilian cattle ranchers also make it profitable to clear huge tracts of rain forest. Poor farmers often "slash and burn" the rain forest to quickly create pastureland for sale to wealthy cattle ranchers.

As a result of these policies and activities, the rate of deforestation has rapidly increased. In the ten years between 1979 and 1989, the rate of rain forest deforestation nearly doubled. Since 1989, about 2 percent of remaining rain forest vanishes each year.

Deforestation is not limited just to tropical rain forests, however. From the early 1600s to the 1900s, settlers in North America cut down temperate forests to create farmland. According to Ken Andrasko of the Environmental Protection Agency (EPA), "The people in the tropics are doing now in a very short period of time what we did over hundreds of years." Once densely covered in forest, much of North America is now farmland or urban and suburban communities.

Connections to Other Disciplines

Social Studies Today, the people of most nations realize the dangers of destroying their forests. In the history of some nations, students may find a connection between the destruction of rain forests and nationwide upheaval. Using Ethiopia as an example, have students research and describe how deforestation there may have led to political and economic instability and social unrest.

Home Economics Certain consumer items, such as facial tissues and paper towels, are recycled paper products. Such recycling helps conserve trees. Encourage small groups of students to visit a supermarket and compile a list of products for which manufacturers could find ways to help conserve trees. Each group should share its list of products and suggestions with the class during class discussion.

The acid rain caused by tons of air pollution from thriving industrial centers may further destroy the remaining forests in North America and Europe.

Connection to Chemistry

When trees are destroyed by the slash-and-burn method, tons of carbon dioxide are released quickly into the atmosphere. Carbon dioxide acts as a greenhouse around the earth, trapping heat. As the number of trees decreases, the carbon dioxide once absorbed by these trees builds up in the atmosphere. For this reason, scientists estimate that deforestation can contribute to global warming.

■ *Why does deforestation decrease the amount of oxygen in the atmosphere?*

Connection to Earth Science

The destruction of rain forests damages the environment in several ways. In a rain forest most of the nutrients from the soil have been absorbed by the trees. When the trees are burned, the poor soil that remains can only support rice, grass for grazing livestock, or other crops—for three to five years. Once the soil is depleted, the land is abandoned and becomes a scrub desert.

Heavy rainfall in the tropics erodes acres of cleared land each year. The soil that is washed away pollutes rivers, forcing fisheries and hydroelectric power plants to close. Silt has even threatened the closing of the Panama Canal.

Deforestation also can affect local climates. In the Amazon River region, 50 percent of the water that falls as rain evaporates from the ocean. The other 50 percent comes from water given off by trees and other plants. Thus, as the size of the forest dwindles, annual rainfall declines.

■ *Describe several ways deforestation affects the environment.*

Connections to Other Sciences

The field of medicine may soon feel the effects of deforestation. Many medicines have been derived from plants that grow only in tropical rain forests. Today, researchers are working with about 3,000 plants that may produce medicines to fight cancer.

■ *How may the destruction of rain forests affect opportunities to discover new medicines?*

Connections to Careers

A variety of people are looking for ways to improve the economies of tropical countries without destroying the rain forests or local ecologies. Government officials, international bankers, and forest rangers are working together with indigenous peoples to promote the responsible use of renewable resources, such as trees for fruits, nuts, and rubber, as well as for lumber. Botanists, zoologists, and ecologists study the forest ecosystems. Various scientists use satellite photographs to monitor fires in rain forests. Air quality specialists collect and analyze data about global warming. For more information about related careers in the biological sciences, turn to page 842.

Intra-Science

5. What efforts could help to reverse the pollution caused by the destruction of rain forests? *(Answers will vary but should indicate that planting trees will increase the amount of oxygen in the air and decrease the amount of carbon dioxide.)*

6. Why is agriculture not a good way to use rain forest land? *(The soil is poor and can support crops for only a few years, after which the land becomes a virtual desert.)*

7. Why is deforestation likely to affect regional climates? *(Half the water that falls as rain in tropical regions is given off by the trees. Without the trees, rainfall in the region will decrease.)*

8. How can nonscientists help slow the destruction of rain forests? *(Students may suggest that citizens encourage governments of tropical regions to establish conservation policies for rain forests. Local people can use traditional and sustainable farming and forestry methods, which can assure the long-term survival of rain forests.)*

Answers to

Chemistry Remind students that trees release oxygen into the atmosphere. As deforestation increases, the amount of oxygen in the air decreases.

Earth Science When trees are burned, tons of nutrients are lost to the atmosphere; the remaining soil lacks nutrients and will support farming for only a few years. Also, without trees, soil is likely to erode during annual rainfall. Abandoned lands become scrub deserts.

Other Sciences About 25 percent of all medicines have come from rain forest plants. As destruction of rain forests continues, opportunities to discover new medicines from rain forest plants will be lost.

Enrichment

Hawaii, Puerto Rico, the U.S. Virgin Islands, and American Samoa are parts of the United States that contain rain forests. Encourage students to research and report on the status and management of these forests.

Unit 2 Cells

Chapters

Unit Overview

Unit 2 expands the coverage of biochemistry begun in Unit 1. Chapters 5, 6, 7, 8, and 9 further show how scientific processes are used to study biological structures and processes. Chapter 5, which introduces multicellular organization, describes shapes and functions of cells, organelles, and tissues in multicellular organisms. Chapter 6 shows physical and chemical processes that move ions and larger molecules in and out of cells, by active transport using energy or by passive concentration gradients. Chapter 7 details how solar energy is captured by chloroplasts and then stored. Chapter 8 describes the discovery of DNA and explains how its structure was modeled. Chapter 9 discusses the structure of chromosomes and their actions during mitosis and meiosis.

Issues in Biology

Use your discretion in introducing the following topic for class discussion, and be sensitive to family and community values.

Some cancers can be treated with medicinal products developed from tissue cultures derived from human cells. However, strong ethical and legal issues surround the use of human cells or tissues to establish cell lines for these new medicinal treatments. What ownership rights do patients have to medical products developed from their cells or tissues? Ask students to consider the points of view of the doctor or manufacturer who develops a cell line and the patient whose cells are used. Should a doctor or manufacturer obtain the patient's permission before developing a cell line from the patient's cells? Should a patient share in the profits from these products?

Research in Progress

Cell cycle research, once a relatively narrow field, is currently expanding at a remarkable rate. In recent years it has grown to include oncogene and tumor suppressor gene research. Insights into the normal regulation of a cell's cycle have provided clues to the abnormal and uncontrolled growth of cancer cells.

Researchers have found that cell division is driven by two proteins: kinase, an enzyme, and cyclin, which serves to activate kinase. Scientists at laboratories such as the Cold Spring Harbor Laboratory are discovering many more of these proteins than were first known to exist. Studies of cyclins and kinases isolated from yeast and mammalian cells show the possibility that their abnormal activity may contribute to cancer development. About a dozen cyclins and ten different kinases have already been identified, and this may only be the beginning.

Interdisciplinary Activity

Visual Arts Before the development of photography, all biological illustrations were drawn by hand. Have students do library research to locate examples of hand-drawn illustrations of cells or organelles. Old books on botany, comparative anatomy, or invertebrate zoology can be a good source of these illustrations. During class presentations, use an overhead projector to have students compare the hand-drawn illustrations with modern photo- or electron micrographs of cells or organelles. Encourage students to describe similarities and differences between the old and new types of cell illustrations.

Resources

Chapter	Print: For the Teacher	Print: For the Student	Audiovisual/Software
5	■ James Darnell, Harvey Lodish, and David Baltimore, *Molecular Cell Biology,* 2nd ed., Scientific American Books, 1990. ■ J. M. Lackie and J. A. T. Dow, eds., *The Dictionary of Cell Biology,* Academic Press, 1989.	■ Mary Murray, "Life on the Move," *Discover,* March 1991, 72–75. ■ Robert Pool, "Making Light Work of Cell Surgery," *Science,* April 6, 1990, 29–31.	■ *Cell Biology—Living Cell.* Video, 14 min. Coronet, 1988. ■ *Cell Structure and Function.* Video filmstrip, 25 minutes. Biology Media.
6	■ W. Jonathan Lederer, Ernst Niggli, and Robert W. Hadley, "Sodium-Calcium Exchange in Excitable Cells: Fuzzy Space," *Science,* April 20, 1990, 283. ■ Howard Rasmussen, "The Cycling of Calcium as an Intracellular Messenger," *Scientific American,* October 1989, 66–73.	■ I. Amato, "Mapping Chemical Microscapes of Cells," *Science News,* March 17, 1990, 167. ■ Richard J. Margolis, "Make Me Whole," *The New Leader,* August 6–20, 1990, 9–10.	■ *Biology: The Cell.* Apple 48K. 2 disks. Scholastic, 1986. ■ *Cell Biology—Plasma Membrane.* Video, 15 min. Coronet, 1988. ■ *Diffusion and Osmosis,* 2nd ed. Film, 14 min. Encyclopædia Britannica.
7	■ Govindjee and William J. Coleman, "How Plants Make Oxygen," *Scientific American,* February 1990, 50–58. ■ R. P. F. Gregory, *Biochemistry of Photosynthesis,* 3rd ed., Blackie and Son Ltd., 1989.	■ George Hendry, "Making, Breaking, and Remaking Chlorophyll," *Natural History,* May 1990, 37–40. ■ R. Weiss, "Green Genes Blasted into Chloroplasts," *Science News,* November 10, 1990, 295.	■ *Biology Concepts: Cellular Respiration.* Video, 39 min. Educational Activities. ■ *How Green Plants Make and Use Food,* revised. Film or video, 12 min. Coronet, 1986. ■ *Photosynthesis: Unlocking the Power of the Sun.* 2 disks. Apple, 128K. IBM PC, 128K. Scholastic, 1986.
8	■ James D. Watson, *The Double Helix,* 1968, NAL-Dutton, reprinted 1991. ■ Harold M. Weintraub, "Antisense RNA and DNA," *Scientific American,* January 1990, 40–46.	■ Elizabeth Pennisi, "Dancing DNA," *Science News,* August 3, 1991, 74–75. ■ Peter Radetsky, "Genetic Heretic," *Discover,* November 1990, 79–84. ■ John Rennie, "Down for the Count," *Scientific American,* March 1991, 27–30.	■ *Beyond the Double Helix.* Video, 25 min. BBC/Coronet, 1987. ■ *Protein Synthesis.* Apple II, 48K. Helix. Distributed by Carolina Biological. ■ *Translating the Code: Protein Synthesis.* Video, 30 min. Human Relations Media.
9	■ Robert K. Moyzis, "The Human Telomere," *Scientific American,* August 1991, 48–55. ■ Peter J. Russell, *Essential Genetics,* 2nd ed., Blackwell Scientific Publications, 1987.	■ Rick Weiss, "Uneven Inheritance," *Science News,* July 7, 1990, 8–11. ■ "No Bad Eggs," *Discover,* April 1990, 14.	■ *Cell Division and the Life Cycle.* 2 filmstrips and cassettes, 15 min. each. Human Relations Media, 1985. ■ *Mitosis and Meiosis: How Cells Divide.* Video or 4 filmstrips with cassettes, 10–13 min. each. Teacher's guide. Science and Mankind.

Science in Action Video Series

In teaching Unit 2, you may wish to use the videotapes *Cell Structure and Function/Cell Division* and *Photosynthesis and Respiration,* both from the Science in Action Video Series. Details of cell structures and life processes are shown using microphotography and graphic animation.

Introducing the Unit

Unit 2 places the biological and biochemical principles of Unit 1 inside the basic building block of life, the cell. To lead students into the study of cell structure, metabolism, and reproduction, ask the following questions.

1. In Unit 1 you learned that organisms contain ions, molecules, and organic macromolecules. Where do you think that these can be found in cells and tissues of your body? *(The whole body is chemical. Structures such as bones, cell membranes, and genes are made of organic molecules. Ions, small molecules, and water diffuse in and out of cells.)*

2. Scientists claim that all life is made of small units called cells, which organize into tissues and organs. How would you verify or search for exceptions to this claim? *(Look at a lot of life forms; devise some way to fix, stain, and slice them to look at internal structure.)*

3. Life requires energy. What is the original source for most life forms? *(Sunlight)* How is energy stored in and released from food? *(Nutrients enter intermediary metabolism to release energy from chemical bonds.)*

4. Cells experience considerable wear-and-tear. Are they replaced? How? (*Yes, new cells replace old cells in some active tissues.)*

5. The information for all life processes is carried in genes and transferred to the next generation by meiosis and fertilization. What substance carries this information? *(DNA)* What do you know about the code? *(Answers will vary.)*

Unit 2 | Cells

Chapters

"With the cell, biology discovered its atom."
François Jacob

Just as atoms are the basic structural and functional units of all matter, cells are the basic structural and functional units of living things. In Unit 1 you learned how a knowledge of atoms helps scientists understand and predict the behavior of chemical substances. In this unit you will gain a knowledge of cell structure and function that will help you better understand the processes that take place within living things.

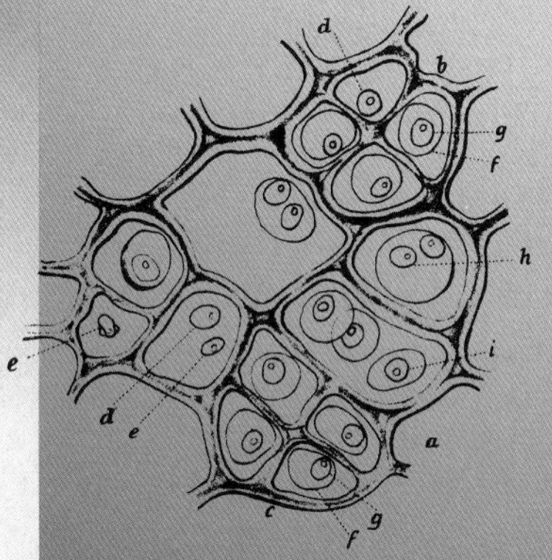

Sketch of animal cells, after Theodor Schwann (1839)

Spirogyra sp. cells (×140)

60

Using the Opening Quotation

Ask students to offer their own explanation for why François Jacob, a biochemist, thought that cells are analogous to atoms. In other words, for Jacob: a cell is to biology as an atom is to physics. *(Help students comprehend that in Jacob's analogy, as the atom is the basic building unit of most physical structures, a cell is the basic building unit of most biological structures.)* Reviewing Unit 1, ask students what are the building blocks of proteins. *(Amino acids)* Ask how biologists discovered the cell. *(Many people looked with hand lenses and microscopes at a great variety of living materials.)*

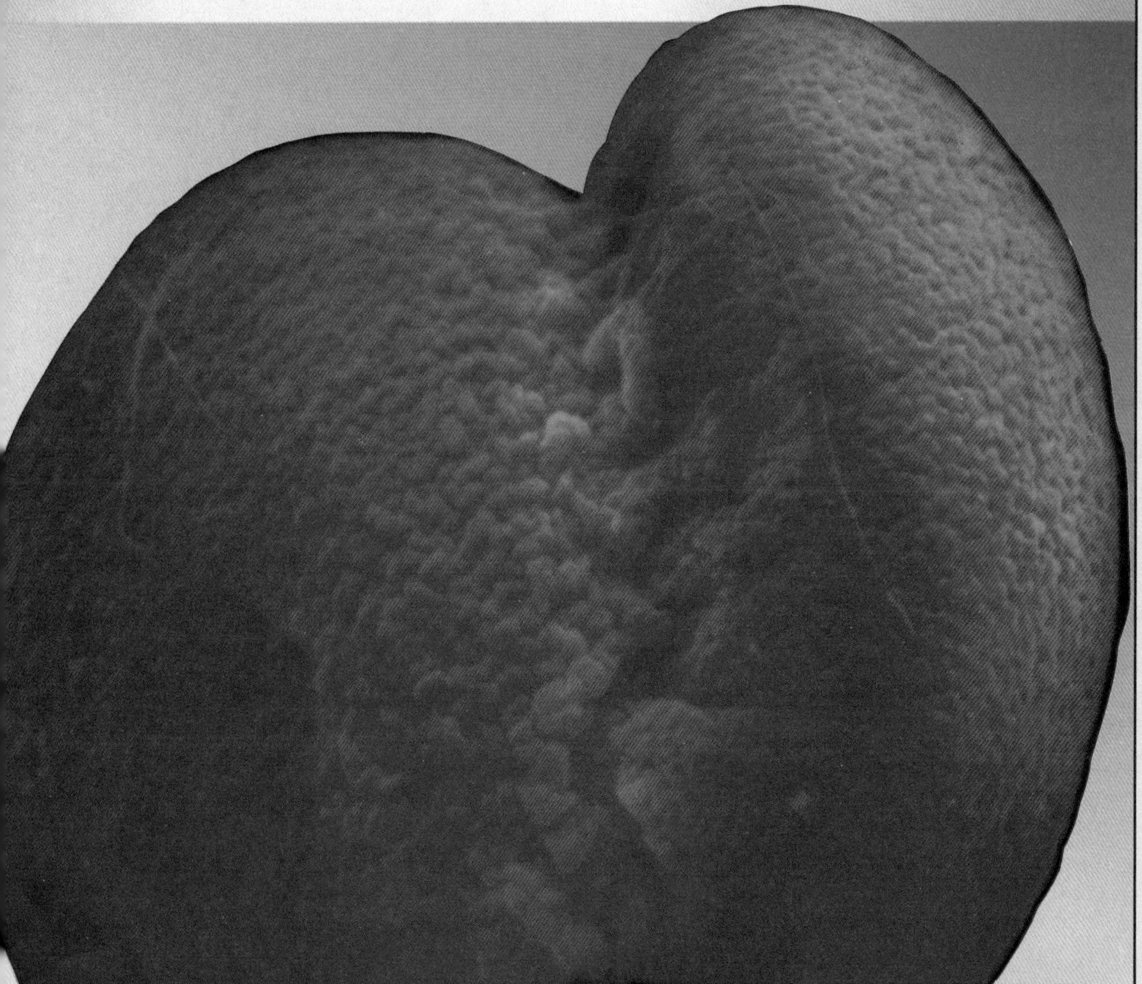

SEM of human cell dividing (×1,800)

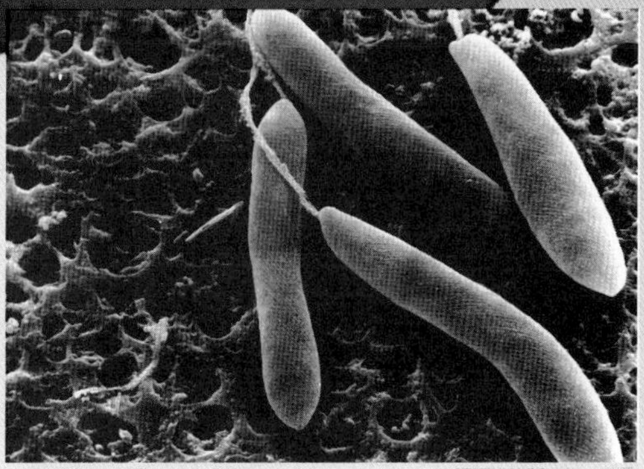

SEM of *Euglena gracilis* cells

Understanding the Visuals

Ask students to identify the types of cells shown. *(Animal cells: the cells in Schwann's drawing and the human cells; algal cells:* Spirogyra *and* Euglena*)* Ask students how the assortment of cells indicates the diversity of cellular organization found in nature. *(Help students recognize that the animal cells are part of larger organisms, while the* Euglena *are individual organisms.)*

Unit Themes

Scale and Structure Each level of organisms has characteristic sizes and appearances: ultramicroscopic (DNA models or electron microscope images of organelle compartments for various metabolic pathways, Chapters 5, 8), microscopic (stained cells in tissues or in cell division, Chapters 5, 9), and visible (organs and organisms, plant and animal cells).

Stability Organelles, cells, genes of DNA, and cell division stages all stay remarkably stable and recognizable for many generations. Homeostasis readjusts the internal environment during many biochemical changes.

Energy Energy flows through living forms. Solar energy is converted to chemical energy in photosynthesis (Chapter 7), and respiration and storage of ATP provides energy for cell activities such as protein synthesis (Chapter 8) and growth and cell division (Chapter 9). Concentration gradients cause motion of ions and molecules that changes potential energy to kinetic energy (Chapter 6).

Systems and Interactions Continuous input and output go on across the cell membrane, moving food and wastes in and out of a cell (Chapter 6). Cells communicate with one another.

Patterns of Change The cell cycle of metabolic activity (in interphase) and cell division (in mitosis, Chapter 9) alternates throughout the life of many cells.

Evolution The DNA code is almost universal (Chapter 8). It also provides a mechanism for mutations, which are redistributed during meiosis (Chapter 9).

Chapter 5 Structure and Function of the Cell

Chapter Overview

Chapter 5 discusses cells, the basic units of life. Section 5.1 explains the cell theory, relationships among cell size, shape, and function, and differences between prokaryotes and eukaryotes. Section 5.2 relates the structures of cell parts, or organelles, to their specialized functions. Section 5.3 discusses how cells with specific functions operate as organized tissues in multicellular plants and animals.

Chapter Planning Chart

B	S	A	Sections and Subsections	Page	Features	Page	Resources
•	•	•	**5.1 Introduction to the Cell**				
			Discovery of the Cell	63	Section Review	65	Videodiscs
			Cell Diversity	64			Section Reviews Worksheet
•	•	•	**5.2 Parts of the Cell**				
			Cell Membrane	66	Biotechnology	70	Videodiscs
			Cytoplasm and Organelles	67	Think	74	Science in Action Videotape: Cell Structure and Function
			Cell Nucleus	72	Laboratory	77	Blackline Master 8
			Plant Cells	72	Section Review	74	Overhead Transparency T5
							Blackline Master 9
							Blackline Master 10
							Process Skills: The Structure of Cells
							Laboratories: Cells
							Section Reviews Worksheet
•	•	•	**5.3 Multicellular Organization**				
			Tissues, Organs, and Organ Systems	75	Section Review	76	Videodiscs
			Organisms	76			Section Reviews Worksheet
			End of Chapter Activities				
					Chapter Review	78	Vocabulary Skills
							Chapter Test
							Computer Test Generator

B *The Basic Level curriculum presents the most fundamental knowledge offered in the course.*
S *The Standard Level curriculum is designed for the average student who is able to master most topics.*
A *The Advanced Level curriculum includes suggestions for teaching the most academically able students.*

Cooperative Learning

Group Activity: Discovering Kinds of Cells

- **Group size:** *3–4 students*
- **Outcome:** *Students will be able to recognize cell diversity and understand the historical context of the cell theory.*
- **Individual Accountability:** *Each student takes the role of an early scientist.*
- **Positive Interdependence:** *Students will share observations and make comparisons with each other's interpretations.*

Use this activity to introduce Section 5.1. Have each student use the library to research one of the early scientists described on pp. 63 and 64. Then have each student take his or her scientist's role, describing to the rest of the group Hooke's observations of cork and a plant stem, van Leeuwenhoek's observations of pond water and material from his teeth, or Schleiden's, Schwann's, or Virchow's observations.

Ask students to discuss how scientists make reproducible observations and how their curiosity leads to observation of more specimens. Point out that many of the text figures are EMs and SEMs, using much greater magnifications than those used by early scientists.

Concept Map

The following is one possible solution to the concept mapping activity in Closure on p. 65.

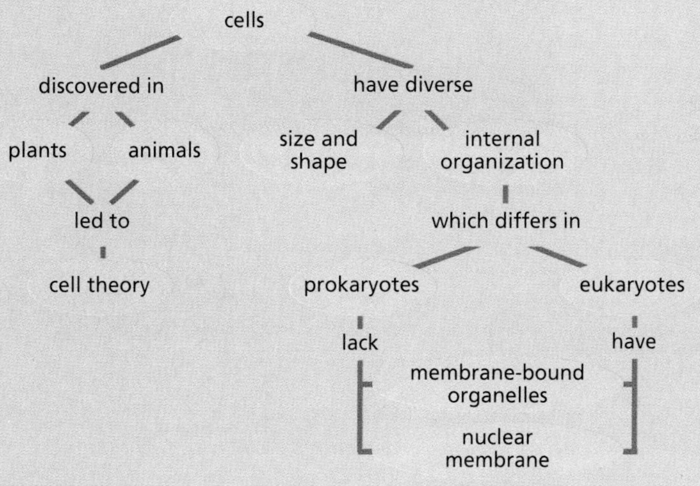

Laboratory Preparation

Overview *(See p. 77.)*

In this lab, students compare plant and animal cells. They should understand that *Elodea* cells are bounded by cell walls arranged like stacked boxes. Animal cheek cells may be single or in ragged sheets of cells.

Students will discover that plant cell structures such as cell walls, a central vacuole, and chloroplasts are absent in animal cells. The vacuole has several functions. It takes up space, reducing the area of cell activity and thus reducing a cell's energy requirements. It also stores waste products. The fluid-filled vacuole pressing the cell contents against the cell wall provides support for plants. In contrast, most animals have an external or internal skeletal system for support.

Preparation

Elodea, sometimes called *Anacharis,* may be obtained from aquarium stores and grown in tap water that has stood 24 hours to remove excess chlorination. Order cheek slides from a supply house, or prepare some. Have students gently scrape the inside of their cheek with a toothpick, reminding them not to gouge. Add a drop of methylene blue to a smear of cheek cells on a slide, then cover with a coverslip.

Teaching Tips

Help students to imagine what makes a leaf green and stiff or what makes the cheek soft and flexible. Emphasize, through work with the microscope, that cells are three-dimensional.

Recall that the fine structure of cell organelles is seen only under the electron microscope. Students can be disappointed at cell appearance unless the minuteness and complexity of submicroscopic features is explained.

Discourage students' tendency to draw idealized cells from the book. Explain that they will learn much more if they draw only what they see and then ask themselves why certain cell structures do not appear as expected.

You may wish to obtain slides or drawings of cells stained with hematoxylin and eosin (blue and red) or other colorful stains.

Safety

Caution students not to cut themselves when handling glass slides. If students are preparing slides of their own cheek cells, remind them not to share toothpicks. Tell students never to taste stains and to avoid getting any stains on their skin or clothing.

Chapter Themes

Scale and Structure Most students intuitively grasp that they are made of cells, yet have difficulty visualizing the tiny scale of cells. Point out that although our planet seems huge to us, it is but one tiny part of the much larger solar system. Stress that the internal structure of many cells is similar; metabolic pathways occur at specific locations and structures. Differences of structure and function define plant vs. animal cells, and multicellular tissues.

Evolution The structure of organelles is similar in many different kinds of cells. Help students understand the reasonable conclusion that all sorts of cells must be related through evolution.

Chapter Motivating Activity

Show students a hen's egg or a variety of eggs without identifying them. Use eggs or pictures of eggs, including chicken, goose, turkey, lizard, snake, or turtle eggs. Ask students to identify and define the object that they are being shown. *(Students may say it is an egg, a baby bird or reptile, or a means of making more birds or reptiles.)* Explain that the yolk of an unfertilized bird or reptile egg is considered a single cell. Ask students what other types of cells they have seen. (*Some students have used microscopes and made drawings for previous classes or science projects. Many PBS TV programs show cells and their internal structure. Students may name the human egg or sperm, skin cells, cancer cells, or blood cells.)* You may prefer having students make a list or bring in pictures to display.

Chapter 5 Structure and Function of the Cell

Introduction

Living things, like nonliving things, are composed of chemicals—chemical compounds and ultimately chemical elements such as carbon, hydrogen, oxygen, and nitrogen. It is the organization of these elements into cells that distinguishes living things from all other matter. In this chapter you will learn about the characteristics of cells and the organization of specialized cells into larger organisms. You will also learn how structural variations within cells relate to specialized functions.

Chapter Outline

5.1 Introduction to the Cell
- *Discovery of the Cell*
- *Cell Diversity*

5.2 Parts of the Cell
- *Cell Membrane*
- *Cytoplasm and Organelles*
- *Cell Nucleus*
- *Plant Cells*

5.3 Multicellular Organization
- *Tissues, Organs, and Organ Systems*
- *Organisms*

Chapter Concept

As you read, look for examples of how cell structures vary with their functions.

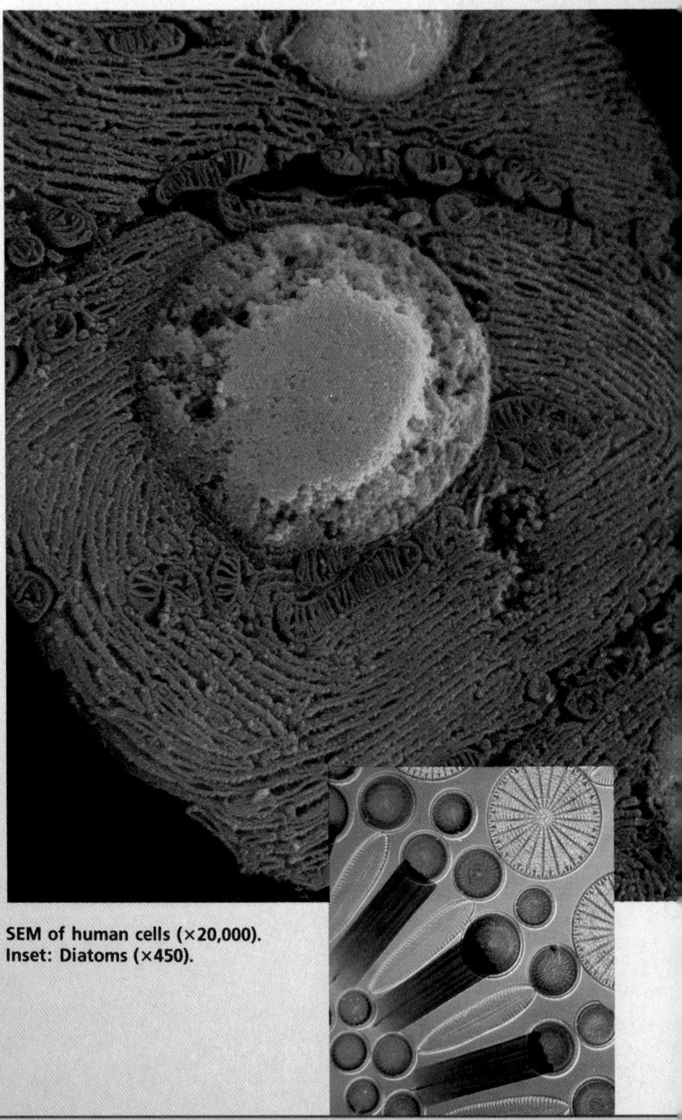

SEM of human cells (×20,000). Inset: Diatoms (×450).

Understanding the Visuals

Have students examine the photographs after having read the chapter. Ask students to identify the structures in the large photograph. *(The large yellow mass is the nucleus; the small brown shapes with crossbars are mitochondria; the numerous large folds are endoplasmic reticulum.)* Ask students to identify the functions of each structure. *(The nucleus is the site of nucleic acid synthesis, directing cell activities. The mitochondria are the sites of cellular respiration, where ATP—the compound that provides the chemical energy for a cell's chemical reactions—is formed. The endoplasmic reticulum functions as a transport system or as a protein storage area.)* Identify the inset as a variety of unicellular organism that makes a glasslike shell.

5.1 Introduction to the Cell

A **cell** is the smallest unit that can carry on all the processes of life. Every living thing—from the tiniest bacterium floating in a drop of water to the largest elephant—is made up of one or more cells. A complete living thing that consists of only one cell is called a **unicellular organism.** Though small in size, unicellular organisms, such as the *Paramecium caudatum* shown in Figure 5-1, are the most numerous of all life-forms. A living thing consisting of more than one cell is called a **multicellular organism.** Figure 5-2 shows that the buttercup, a multicellular organism, is made up of individual cells.

Discovery of the Cell

Only a few cells are large enough to be seen by the unaided eye. How, then, did scientists come to recognize that all forms of life are made up of cells? Our knowledge of cells began with the invention of the lens in the 1600s and grew along with advances in microscope technology. The light microscope allows us to view specimens magnified only up to about 2,000 times. At such magnifications plant and animal cells are visible, and many cell structures can be seen. The transmission electron microscope (TEM) is 1,000 times stronger than the light microscope. The scanning electron microscope (SEM) produces three-dimensional images. With these advances the smallest cells can be seen in clear detail.

Hooke and van Leeuwenhoek

Imagine the puzzlement of the English scientist Robert Hooke (1635–1703) when in 1665 he cut a thin slice of cork and observed it with a microscope. "I could exceedingly plainly perceive it to be all perforated and porous," he wrote, and further described it as consisting of "a great many little Boxes." Hooke used a microscope to observe the stems of elder trees, carrots, and ferns. He observed that each showed a similar formation. These "little Boxes" reminded him of the small rooms in which monks lived, so he called them cells.

What Hooke had observed were actually dead plant cells. The first person to observe living cells was a Dutch microscope maker, Anton van Leeuwenhoek (1632–1723), in 1675.

Section Objectives

- *Outline the discoveries that led to the development of the cell theory.*
- *State the cell theory.*
- *Identify a limitation in the size of cells.*
- *Describe the relationship between cell shape and cell function.*
- *Distinguish between prokaryotes and eukaryotes.*

Figure 5-1 All the life activities of a paramecium, *Paramecium caudatum,* shown here in color-enhanced magnification, occur within a single cell (×140).

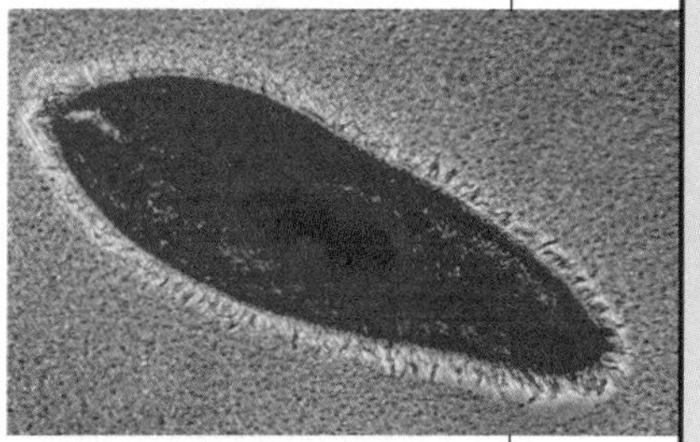

Figure 5-2 A buttercup, *Ranunculus* sp. (left), a multicellular organism, is composed of individual cells like those in the root tip (right, ×60).

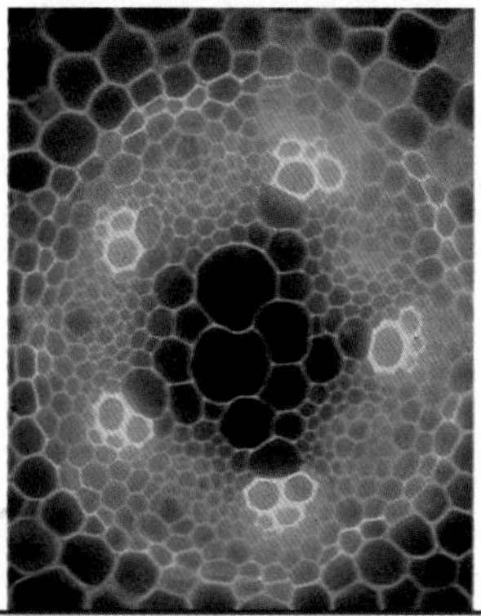

Scientist	Nationality	Observed
Hooke	English	dead plant cells and cells of trees, carrot, fern
van Leeuwenhoek	Dutch	living cells
Schleiden	German	plant cells
Schwann	German	animal cells
Virchow	German	disease-causing cells

Graphic Organizer Use this table to summarize historical information in Section 5.1.

Lesson Plan

Section Focus

Cells are the basic units of life, a conclusion based on observations made using microscopes of increasing magnification. This section also discusses cell structure and function—for example, the differences between prokaryotic and eukaryotic cells, and the relationship of cell size to surface-area-to-volume ratios.

Section Themes

This section emphasizes the theme of **Scale and Structure** in two ways: magnification is necessary in order to see cells; and surface-area-to-volume ratios are necessary in order to understand limits on cell size.

Motivating Activity

Bring in several objects that have lenses—camera, binoculars, prescription glasses—and ask students what feature they share. *(All use lenses.)* Have students list other uses for lenses. *(Telescope, microscope)* Ask students what lenses do *(Magnify objects)* and how they relate to the discovery of cells. *(Most cells can't be seen unaided; the invention of lenses was necessary to allow cell observations.)*

Teaching Strategies

Recognizing Scientific Processes

Observations of many organisms are repeated by many people. Ask how many years it took to develop the cell theory and why it took that long. *(1665 to 1838, 173 years; scientists worked in isolation, often as a hobby; communication between researchers was infrequent or slow.)* Within 17 years (by 1855) key concepts were established. Have students make a time line that can be used in later chapters; they can incorporate the discoveries of Mendel, Darwin, and others.

Making Observations Remind students of the laboratory in Chapter 1, or provide fresh slides and pictures of pond water. Ask students to infer which things are alive (*Those that move, exhibit characteristics of life*), were alive *(Cell debris)*, or are inorganic. Ask if shape helps in the decision. *(Often, living materials appear roughly square or round and have some depth [cuboidal or spherical]; inorganic minerals often have highly regular shapes.)* Then ask students to draw cell outlines and to infer which cells contain nuclei. *(Living eukaryotic cells)*

Interpreting the Visuals Have students use Figure 5-5 on p. 65 to compare eukaryotic and prokaryotic cells. Which specific features of the alga and bacterium lead to their classification? *(An alga has a large nucleus and nucleolus (right); a bacterium has no similar structures. Algal cytoplasm has large inclusions.)* Point out that the bacterium is dividing; a wall is forming across the cell center.

Guided Practice

Have students hypothesize how a cell might grow large despite the surface-area-to-volume ratio limitation. *(Specialized cells evolved. Examples are highly elongated and tenuous nerve extensions and broad, flat skin cells. The largest cell, an ostrich egg, is supported by its firm external shell.)*

Independent Practice

- Have students write answers to the Section Review.
- Have students search the section for evidence that a unicellular organism can be a eukaryote. *(Figure 5-1 shows a paramecium, a unicellular organism with a nucleus.)*

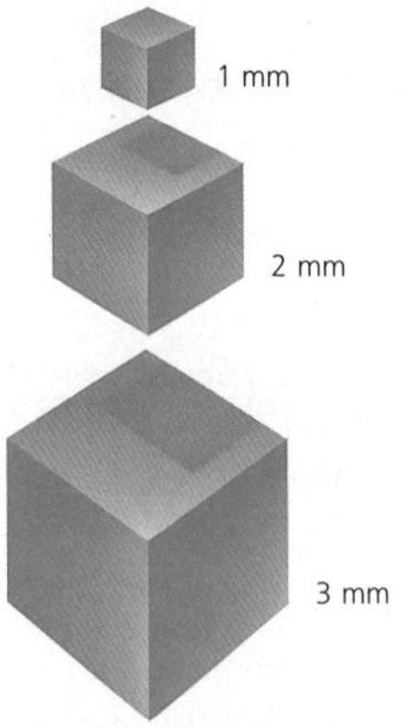

Figure 5-3 A 1-mm cube has a surface area of 6 mm² and a volume of 1 mm³, giving a surface-to-volume (S/V) ratio of 6 : 1. For a 2-mm cube, surface area and volume are 24 mm² and 8 mm³ respectively, a 3 : 1 S/V ratio. For a 3-mm cube, surface area and volume are 54 mm² and 27 mm³ respectively, and the S/V is 2 : 1.

Figure 5-4 SEMs of human cells with structure-related functions include nerve (left), skin (center, ×750), and white blood (right, ×250).

The Cell Theory

About 150 years passed before scientists began to organize the observations of Hooke and van Leeuwenhoek into a unified theory. In 1838 a German botanist, Matthias Schleiden (1804–1881), concluded that all plants were composed of cells. A year later the German zoologist Theodor Schwann (1810–1882) came to the same conclusion about animals. In 1855 a German physician, Rudolph Virchow (1821–1902), while studying how disease affects living things, determined that cells come only from other cells. The observations of these three scientists, taken together, are known as the **cell theory.** This theory has three parts:

1. All living things are composed of one or more cells.
2. Cells are organisms' basic units of structure and function.
3. Cells come only from existing cells.

Cell Diversity

Although all living things are composed of cells, not all cells are alike. Even cells within the same organism may show enormous diversity in size, shape, and internal organization.

Size

Cells range in size from 2 m long, as in the thin nerve cells that extend down a giraffe's leg, to .2 micrometers (μm) in diameter, as in some bacteria. Most plant and animal cells are about 10 to 50 μm in diameter and are visible only with a microscope.

Many cells are roughly cuboidal or spherical. A cell with such a shape is limited in size by the ratio between its volume and its outer surface area. The food, oxygen, and other materials a cell requires must enter through its surface. Likewise, waste products must leave through its surface. The larger the cell, the larger the surface area required to maintain it. As a cell grows, its volume increases more rapidly than its surface area does. Figure 5-3

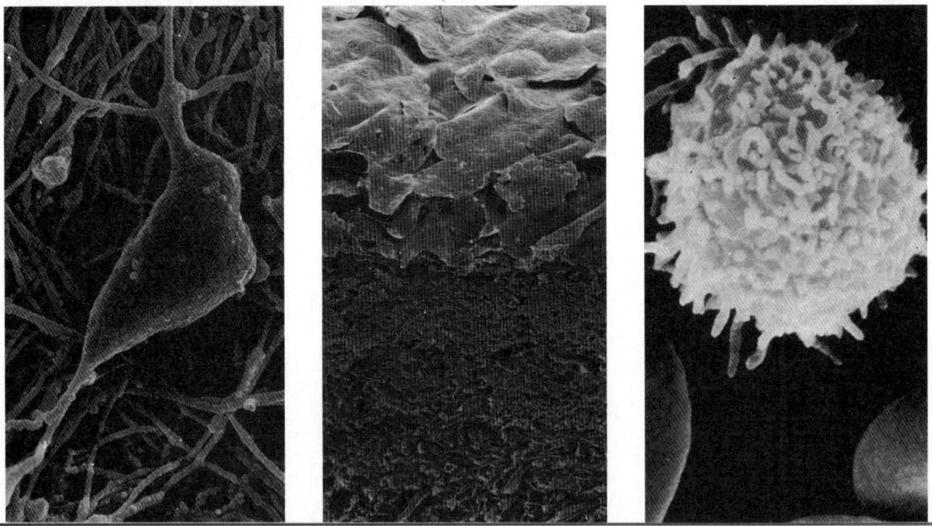

Interdisciplinary Activity

Mathematics Help students review some basic geometry formulas and have them calculate the surface area and volume for a sphere as it increases from 1 unit to 3 units to 5 units in radius. Use the following:

$\pi = 3.1$
Area = $4 \pi r^2$
Volume = $4/3 \pi r^3$

(For r = 1, A = 12.4, V = 4.1; for r = 3, A = 111.6, V = 111.6; for r = 5, A = 310, V = 516.7) Be sure students comprehend that the surface area increases at a smaller rate than the volume. Have students compare ratios of volume to surface area by dividing area by volume. *(When r = 1: A/V = 3.0; when r = 3: A/V = 1; when r = 5: A/V = 0.6. As r increases, the ratio of surface area to volume decreases.)*

shows how growth affects the ratio between surface area and volume. Volume increases by the cube, while surface area increases by the square. This suggests that as a cell grows large, its surface area becomes too small to maintain life functions.

Shape

We have said that most cells are roughly cuboidal or spherical. Many plant cells, for example, are shaped like triskaidekahedrons; that is, they are roughly round but have 13 flat sides. However, cells differ widely in shape. This diversity of form reflects a diversity of function. Look at the three human cells in Figure 5-4. The long extensions that reach out in various directions from the nerve cell body allow the cell to receive and transmit nerve impulses. In contrast, the flat shape of dead skin cells is well suited to their function of covering the body surface. White blood cells have the ability to change shape. This allows them to move through narrow openings and to surround and isolate bacteria that invade the body.

Internal Organization

Cells also differ in their internal organization. Look at the photomicrograph of an algal cell in Figure 5-5 (top). Note the large structure near the center of the cell. This structure is the **nucleus,** which directs the activities of the cell. It contains DNA, the hereditary information that passes from one cell to another during cell division. DNA directs the formation of the proteins that carry out cell activities. Look again at Figure 5-5 (top), and notice the other smaller structures in addition to the nucleus. These are the cell organelles, many of them enclosed by membranes. An **organelle** is a cell component that performs specific functions in the cell. Cells that contain a nucleus and membrane-bound organelles are called **eukaryotes** *(yoo-KAR-ee-OTES).* The cells of plants, animals, fungi, protozoa, and algae are all eukaryotes.

Note the bacterium in Figure 5-5 (bottom). Do you observe a nucleus or organelles? Cells that lack nuclei and membrane-bound organelles are called **prokaryotes** *(proe-KAR-ee-OTES).* Bacteria and related microorganisms are prokaryotes.

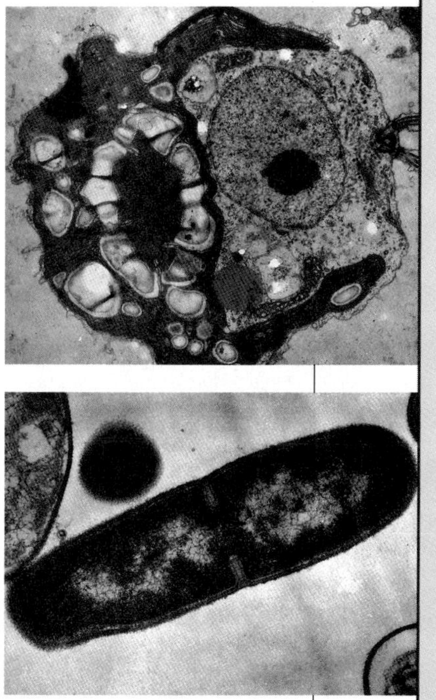

Figure 5-5 Two TEMs contrast the unicellular alga (top), a eukaryote, with the bacterium *Bacillus licheniformis,* a prokaryote (bottom, ×136,000). Note the nucleus (the area within the dark circle) in the eukaryote.

Section Review

1. Define *nucleus,* and describe the structure and function of the cell nucleus.
2. What is the cell theory?
3. What single factor limits the size that most cells are able to attain?
4. How would you determine whether a unicellular organism was a prokaryote or a eukaryote?
5. How do you account for the fact that three different scientists made major contributions to the cell theory within a 17-year period?

Check Your Understanding

1. Which are more numerous, uni- or multicellular organisms? *(Unicellular)*
2. Give the size range of cells. *(0.2 micrometer diameter to 2 meters in length)*
3. List five types of eukaryotes. *(Plants, animals, fungi, protozoa, algae)*

Reteaching

Clarify the importance of surface-area-to-volume ratios. Have students imagine a spherical cell and a flat cell. Through which cell would materials have the farthest to travel? Why? *(Spherical cell; it would have a smaller surface-area-to-volume ratio than a flat cell.)*

■ *See* Section Reviews *worksheet, Section 5.1.*

Enrichment

Have students make wet mount slides of apple skin and pulp, and compare the large, thin-walled pulp cells with the small, thick-walled skin cells. Ask students to infer how these cells' structures might be related to their function. *(Skin cell walls are protective and waterproof; pulp cell surface area and thin walls facilitate diffusion of materials in and out of the cell.)*

Closure

Have students map the key concepts of cells in this section. An example of a completed concept map is shown on p. 61B.

Videodiscs

■ *1955–1956, Plant Tissue Structures (s)*
■ *1561–1563, Cheek Cells Under Microscopes (s)*
■ *Side 1 39272, Paramecium (m)*
■ *Side 1 31819, Bacterial Cells and Cell Membrane (m)*

Answers to Section Review

1. A nucleus is large, rounded, and located near the cell center. It directs cell activities.
2. The cell theory says all living things are made of one or more cells; cells are the basic units of structure and function; cells come only from preexisting cells.
3. The ratio between volume and surface area limits cell size.
4. Look for a nucleus and organelles.
5. By the mid-1800s, many observations were made with the light microscope. Scientists could use previous observations and interpretations to interpret their own data.

Lesson Plan

Section Focus

This section details the three main parts of cells: membrane, cytoplasm with organelles, and nucleus. Organelle structure is related to function. Plant cells contain more types of organelles than do animal cells.

Section Themes

This section emphasizes two themes: **Scale and Structure** and **Systems and Interactions**. The size and shape of organelles vary little among diverse organisms, and organelle structure is essential to organelle function. For example, the surface cavities of ribosomes read the code of a linear message (mRNA) during protein synthesis. In addition, all cell parts work together to perform the cell's life activities.

Motivating Activity

Suggest to students that a cell resembles a house or apartment building. Daily life requires many activities; have students contribute to a list of examples on the board. Then begin a list of where such activities occur in a typical animal cell, using the labels in Figure 5-6. Add activities as students complete this section. Note that a human body has 10^{23} cells, each carrying out these functions. *(Daily activities may include: prepare and eat meals, dispose of wastes, make rules. Lysosomes located in the cytoplasm digest food or dispose of wastes; nucleus directs cell activities.)* Remind students that this analogy aids in understanding a cell but is not the same as a cell.

Section Objectives

- *Describe the structure, composition, and function of the cell membrane.*
- *Name the major organelles found in the cell and describe their functions.*
- *Describe the structure and functions of the cell nucleus.*
- *Compare and contrast animal and plant cells.*
- *Describe how VEC microscopy is useful in observing microtubules.*

5.2 Parts of the Cell

Each living cell carries out the tasks of taking in food, transforming food into energy, getting rid of wastes, and reproducing. In this section you will learn about the structures of eukaryotic cells that help perform these functions. Prokaryotic cells will be discussed in Chapter 20.

Although there is no typical eukaryotic cell, most have three main components:

1. The **cell membrane** is the outer boundary of the cell and separates the cell from its surroundings and other cells.
2. The **cytoplasm** *(SITE-uh-PLAZZ-um)* lies inside the cell membrane, contains water and salts, and surrounds organelles.
3. The nucleus contains DNA and directs the activities of the cell.

Cell Membrane

The cell membrane, sometimes called the plasma membrane, is the structure that separates the cell from its external environment. It gives shape and flexibility to the cell. The cell membrane is a complex barrier that keeps out some molecules but allows others to permeate, or pass, into the inside of the cell. The cell membrane is therefore called a **selectively permeable membrane.** Some scientists use the term *semipermeable membrane.* The membrane is about 7.5 to 10 nanometers (nm) thick.

The cell membrane is composed of two layers of molecules. Each layer is made up of a sheet of lipids. Recall from Chapter 4 that a lipid molecule has a carboxyl group as a "head" and a

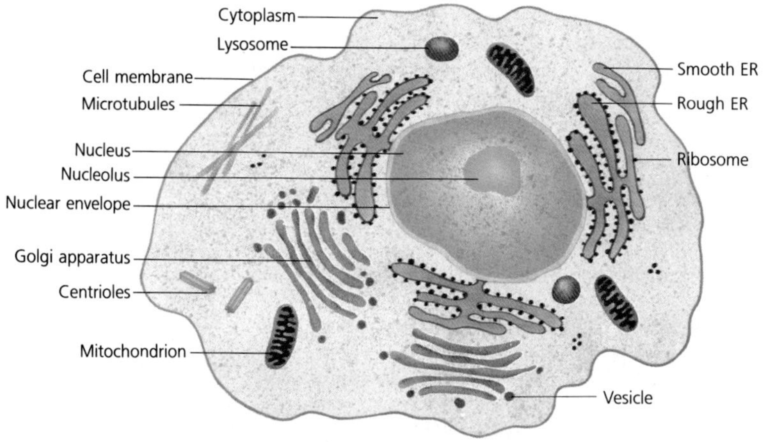

Figure 5-6 A typical animal cell contains many organelles within a cell membrane.

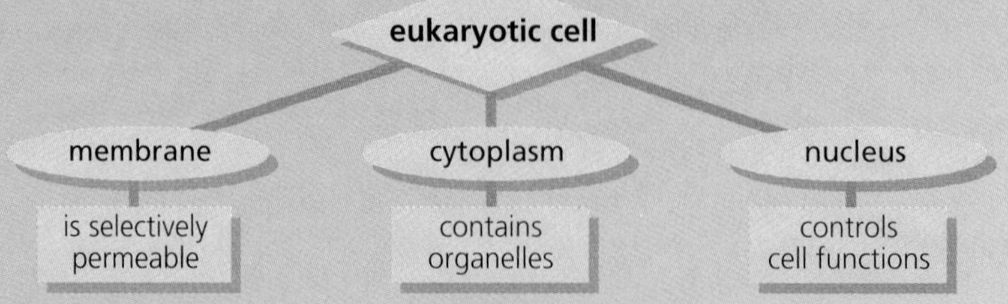

Graphic Organizer Use this chart to summarize the main concepts of Section 5.2.

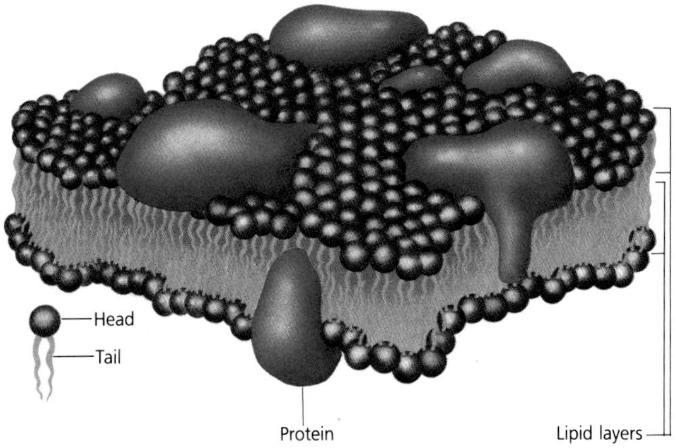

Figure 5-7 Lipids and proteins can move in relation to one another in the fluid mosaic model of the cell membrane. Why does this two-layer model look as though it is composed of three layers?

hydrocarbon chain as a "tail." As Figure 5-7 shows, the lipid molecules in membranes are arranged so that their heads form the outside of the membrane and their tails form the inside of the membrane. In addition, protein molecules are embedded in the lipid layers. Some are associated with only one layer, while others penetrate the entire membrane. You will learn more about how this structure affects transport of materials in Chapter 6.

The lipid molecules that form the membrane are fluid. They can move about relative to one another in a fluid manner. Some of the proteins are also free to move about, so that the mosaic, or pattern, of lipids and proteins changes. Because of these characteristics, scientists call their model of the dynamic cell membrane the **fluid mosaic model.**

Cytoplasm and Organelles

The cytoplasm is the jellylike material found inside the cell membrane. It surrounds organelles and contains water, salts, and organic molecules. The cytoplasm is in constant motion as particles and organelles move around. This motion, called **cytoplasmic streaming,** is most apparent in some plant cells and in protozoa.

Cytoplasm surrounds organelles. The word *organelle* means "little organ." Like the organs of the body, each organelle performs a specific activity.

Ribosomes

The most numerous of the cell's organelles are **ribosomes** *(RIE-buh-SOMEZ)*, the organelles where proteins are made. As you can see in Figure 5-8, each ribosome is a spherical structure of about 15 to 20 nm in diameter. It is composed of three nucleic acid molecules and over 50 proteins. The ribosome is the site of protein

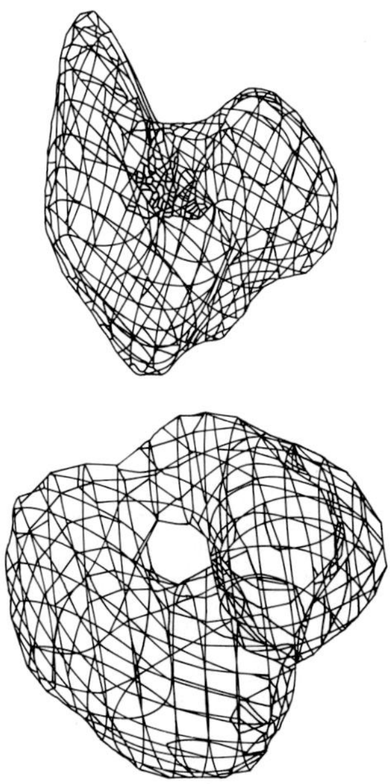

Figure 5-8 Ribosomes are formed from RNA and proteins. They support mRNA, the template for protein synthesis. Note their three-dimensional structure in top (top) and side (bottom) views.

Teaching Strategies

Applying Concepts Review Chapter 4 and Figures 4-3 and 4-5 (pp. 49 and 51) on lipids. Explain to students that carboxyl groups can have a charge, which is attracted to water (is hydrophilic) and that the hydrocarbon chain tails attract each other and are hydrophobic, forming the inner layer of the membrane. Point out that Figure 5-7 (two layers) looks like three layers because each part of the molecule is colored.

Making Models Have students make a fluid mosaic model by floating a thin layer of vegetable oil on water. Have them sprinkle on top a small amount of an herb, such as oregano, which should float and change position often. Tell students that in a cell membrane, tiny drops of protein in the lipid move in a similar way. (An oil slick is another example.) Also point out that some materials cannot get through the oil layer; like the cell membrane, the oil is only semipermeable.

Videodiscs

- *Side 1 33499, Cell Structure and Functional Anatomy (m)*
- *Side 2 3302, Cytoplasmic Streaming in* Elodea *and* Nitella *(m)*
- *2286–2299, Cell Parts (s)*

Cooperative Learning

Model Organelles Have students, in pairs or groups of four, form organelles with modeling clay. Assign each student a specific organelle to model and to explain to others in the group. After all the models have been created and each group is familiar with the organelles, have each group present their models before the class. Each group will discuss the structural and functional relationships of their model organelles to the organelles made by the other groups. Save these models for use in Section 8.3 (protein synthesis) and Section 9.2 (mitosis). As an alternative to the clay models, have students create an edible cell using gelatin as cytoplasm, noodles as ER, and so on.

Making Observations Cytoplasmic streaming, such as students observe in *Elodea,* also can be seen in an animal cell. Provide students with a culture of live amebas. Visible as tiny white dots on the bottom of the culture jar, they can be transferred with an eyedropper. Have students use a microscope to watch the organelles flow with the cytoplasm as the amebas move. Ask students to draw and label all the structures. *(Small spicules and spheres are in the central cytoplasm, which appears to have a thinner consistency.)* Ask students to locate the nucleus. *(Near the center of the cell)* Tell them that most organelles are too small to see.

Interpreting the Visuals Have students use Figure 5-6 on p. 66, a typical animal cell, to learn the organelles responsible for different functions, for example, protein synthesis. *(Protein synthesis: ribosomes, ER, Golgi apparatus)* Give each student a photocopy of Blackline Master 8 and have them study it as a group. Have students check off and color each organelle as they learn it.

■ *See* **Overhead Transparency** *T5 and* **Blackline Master** *8.*

Understanding Scale The animal cells shown in Section 5.2 are either photographs taken with a transmission electron microscope (TEM) or models of such photographs. The magnification is 10,000 to 100,000,000—most often around 100,000. Help students interpret this scale through analogy. *(If 1 cm, about 125 pages of this textbook, represents the diameter of one unmagnified cell, then the distance from El Paso to Houston, nearly 1,000 km, would represent the diameter of a cell magnified 100,000,000 times.)*

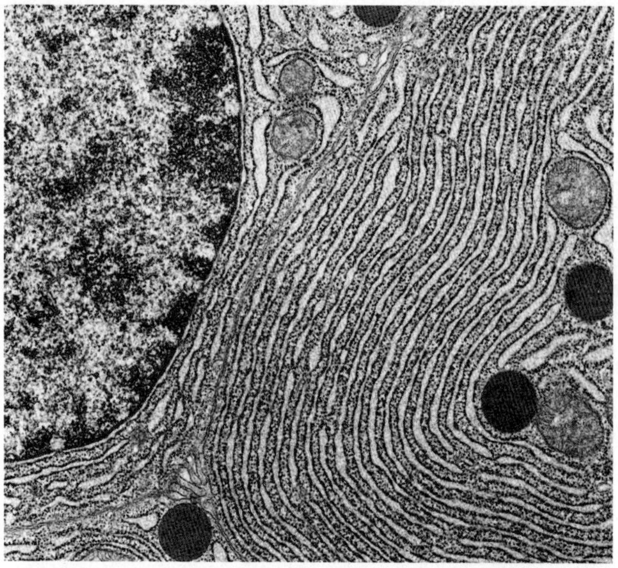

Figure 5-9 Rough ER in cells of the human pancreas are covered with ribosomes. These cells produce and export enzymes used in the digestive process.

synthesis, a process that you will learn more about in Chapter 8. The distribution of the ribosomes within the cell depends on how the proteins they produce will be used. Proteins used within the cell are produced by ribosomes that float freely in the cytoplasm. Proteins that will be exported for use outside the cell are produced by ribosomes attached to a system of membranes called the endoplasmic reticulum.

Endoplasmic Reticulum

The **endoplasmic reticulum** *(EN-duh-PLAZZ-mick ree-TICK-yuh-lum)* is a membrane system of folded sacs and tunnels. It is called ER for short. Endoplasmic reticulum that is covered with ribosomes, as shown in Figure 5-9, is known as rough ER; ER with few or no ribosomes is called smooth ER. The relative amounts of rough and smooth ER vary from one type of cell to another. Cells that make a lot of proteins that will be exported contain a lot of rough ER. For example, rough ER predominates in those cells of the pancreas that produce and export digestive enzymes. Smooth ER functions primarily as an intracellular highway, a path along which molecules move from one part of the cell to another. In addition, smooth ER can serve as a storage area for proteins that will later be exported from the cell.

Golgi Apparatus

The **Golgi apparatus** is the processing, packaging, and secreting organelle of the cell. It consists of a stack of membranes or sacs filled with fluid and dissolved or suspended substances. To understand how the Golgi apparatus works, follow the process in Figure 5-10. The Golgi apparatus operates like a production line in a factory, where a product is assembled at one end, then packaged,

Figure 5-10 An ingenious system moves a protein from its point of synthesis to the cell exterior.

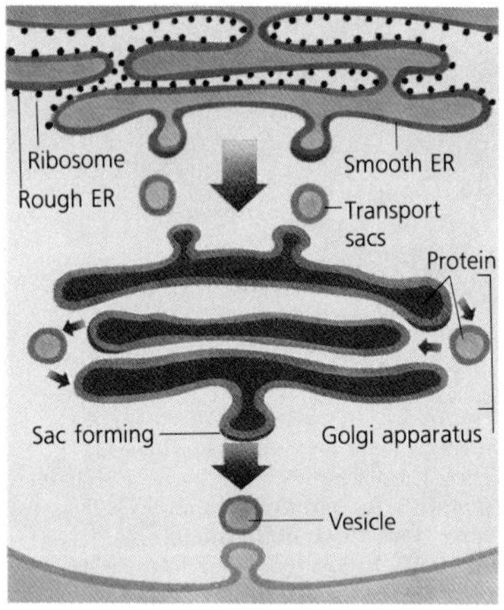

More Information

Cellular Recycling Lysosomes may contain at least 40 different enzymes packaged by the Golgi apparatus. If these enzymes were free in the cell, they could digest necessary structures and wastefully degrade newly synthesized macromolecules. A particularly good example of building-block recycling is the reuse of components from worn red blood cells (RBC). After about 40 days in circulation, the lipoprotein membrane of human RBC wears out. The cells are then degraded in the spleen and the basic building blocks are carried in the blood to the liver for resynthesis.

and finally put into a mail bag at the other end. After protein is synthesized on a ribosome, the protein passes into the interior of the ER membrane. Then it moves through the interior of the membrane to an area of smooth ER. There the protein is enclosed in a vesicle, or membranous pouch, that buds off from smooth ER. The vesicle migrates to and fuses with a Golgi sac. The contents of the vesicle are then modified as they pass from sac to sac. Finally a new vesicle is formed from the last Golgi sac, which moves to the cell membrane and discharges its contents outside the cell.

Mitochondria

Scattered throughout the cytoplasm are large organelles that can grow, divide, or fuse with one another. These are the **mitochondria** *(MITE-uh-KAHN-dree-uh),* the respiration centers of the cell. Chemical reactions within mitochondria release the energy from the nutrients taken into the cell. As Figure 5-12 shows, a mitochondrion has two membranes. The smooth outer membrane serves as the boundary between the mitochondrion and the cytoplasm. The inner membrane has many long folds, called cristae, that enlarge the internal surface area, providing more space for the reactions of cell respiration that take place there.

The mitochondrion is the place where adenosine triphosphate (ATP) is formed. You will learn more about this process in Chapter 7. ATP provides the chemical energy that drives the chemical reactions of the cell. Mitochondria are therefore most numerous in cells that use a lot of energy, such as muscle cells. A liver cell, which uses energy to carry out a host of biochemical activities, may contain as many as 2,500 mitochondria.

Mitochondria have their own DNA, and new mitochondria arise only when existing ones divide. These facts have led to the theory, discussed further in Chapter 14, that mitochondria developed from prokaryotic cells that came to live inside eukaryotic cells. The prokaryotes, according to the theory, may have sought protection by living inside the eukaryotes, supplying energy for the eukaryotes in turn.

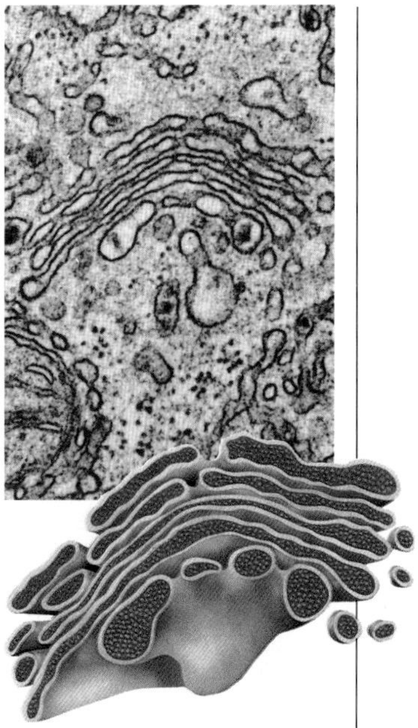

Figure 5-11 TEM of a Golgi apparatus from a rat liver cell (top, ×34,000) is shown in greater detail in an artist's rendering (bottom).

Figure 5-12 TEM of a mitochondrion in a bat pancreas (left, ×79,000) is diagrammed in detail at right.

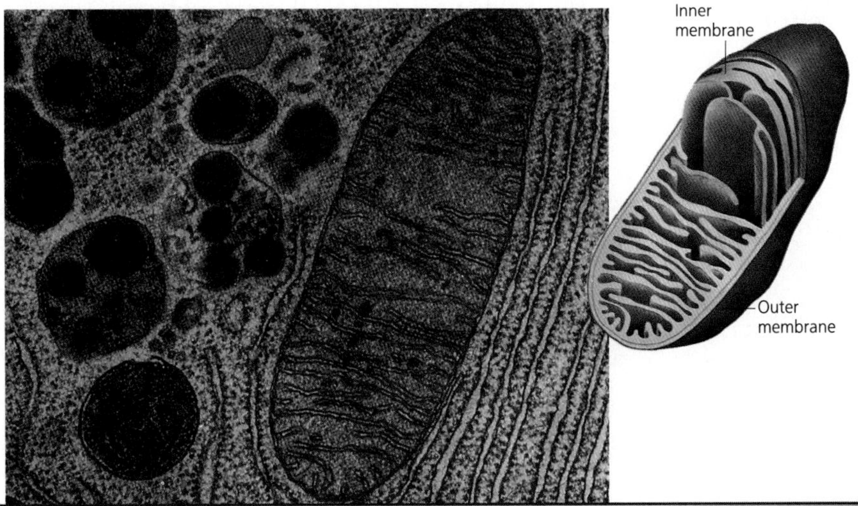

Interpreting the Visuals When students use light microscopes to observe prepared slides of cells, they will not see the detail visible in EM views of organelles. With high power (× 450) and stain, the ribosomes and ER appear intensely colored. This indicates an area of protein synthesis, but no line- or dotlike structures are visible. Ask students how scientists might use photographs, such as Figures 5-9 and 5-11, to assemble models of the location of stages of protein synthesis and packaging, such as Figure 5-10. *(Scientists take many photographs over time of cells at different stages and then interpret the sequence of events.)*

■ *See* **Process Skills,** ***Chapter 5.***

Inferring Relationships The structure of mitochondria can be used to help students practice interpreting models and biochemical statements. Figure 5-12 shows an EM of the cristae and outer membrane of a mitochondrion, and a three-dimensional cutaway drawing. The three-dimensional shape is evident when using a microtome with a diamond knife to cut many serial sections. When the sections are viewed and photographed in order, the shape can be reconstructed. Tell students that the location of enzymes on the cristae reflects the order in which they are needed in a cell's reactions.

Drawing Conclusions Ask students what a cell must do to be "successful." *(Survive; efficiently use energy)* Explain that a cell or organism that lives, grows, and reproduces has an adaptive advantage over another that "wastes energy."

Videodiscs

■ ***Side 1 22695, Protein Synthesis (m)***

Applying Concepts Ask students to name macromolecules that cells must make. *(Proteins, lipids, carbohydrates)* Have students work in small groups to find the three sites of molecule synthesis in the text. *(Free ribosome, rough ER, and smooth ER)* Stress that each macromolecule is made at a specific site and has specific functions. Suggest that students apply their knowledge by matching the functions of a macromolecule to its site of origin and ultimate destination. *(Proteins such as intracellular enzymes or muscle and skin proteins work inside the cell; others, such as digestive enzymes and hormones, travel outside and go to other cells. Some are attached to lipids, making lipoproteins, or to carbohydrate groups as glycoproteins. Complex carbohydrates are synthesized in the soluble cytoplasm. The other two are made by ribosomes or ER. As a general rule, free ribosomes make intracellular structural proteins; rough ER makes intracellular enzymes and extracellular proteins such as hormones. Smooth ER synthesizes lipids.)*

Lysosomes

Organelles that contain digestive enzymes are called **lysosomes** *(LIE-suh-SOMEZ)*. These small, spherical organelles are surrounded by a single membrane. They exist primarily in animal and fungal cells and contain some 40 kinds of enzymes. These enzymes digest food particles, disease-causing bacteria captured by the white blood cells, and worn-out and broken parts of cells. Lysosomes also play a role in early development. For example, the embryonic human hand begins as a solid stump. Then lysosomal enzymes selectively destroy tissue and form fingers.

Microtubules and Microfilaments

Long, slender protein tubes called **microtubules** and fine protein threads called **microfilaments** help shape and support cells. Collectively, they form the **cytoskeleton**, the framework of the cell. They are assembled as needed and are then broken down and reassembled to form new structures. Specialized microtubules, called **spindle fibers,** aid in movement of chromosomes during cell division. Microfilaments, which lie just under the cell membrane, help move cellular materials and play a role in cytoplasmic streaming.

Biotechnology

Video–Enhanced Contrast Microscopy

In 1879 scientists observed a strange phenomenon—particles moving in different directions in the unicellular organism *Gromia*. The particles also seemed to move along extensions from the organism at constantly varying speeds. For the next 100 years, microscopy was able to capture the motions of these particles within the cell, called intracellular transport, but not show exactly how it was possible.

In the late 1970s, three investigators—Robert Day Allen, Nina Allen (p. 71), and Shinya Inoué, visiting scientists at the Marine Biological Laboratory (MBL) at Woods Hole, Massachusetts—were independently developing video-enhanced contrast microscopy. Inoué had been modifying and improving optical microscopes since the 1960s. When he coupled video cameras with microscopes, he discovered that he could adjust the contrast to enhance desired features.

The Allens made their initial discovery accidentally while teaching an optical microscopy course at the MBL. They attached a video camera and a monitor to the microscope so that the whole class could view a specimen simultaneously. When the

More Information

Microtubules Microtubules occur in all eukaryotic cells. Many originate near the nucleus and form the cytoskeleton. Just inside the cell membrane, microtubules form a dense, elastic network. In cells like the ameba or white blood cells, these microtubules aid in cell movement.

Both cilia and flagella arise from a basal body, a bundle of microtubules. A cilium, too, is essentially a bundle of microtubules. Cilia are usually arranged in orderly rows. Each row beats, or bends over and returns, in synchrony. The mechanism for this synchrony is still not clear.

Cilia and Flagella

Cilia *(SILL-ee-uh)* and **flagella** *(fluh-JELL-uh)* are two kinds of structures that extend out from the surface of the cell and function in movement. Cilia are short, hairlike extensions that occur in large numbers on the surface of some cells. A unicellular paramecium, for example, moves forward by beating the 17,000 cilia that cover its surface. In many animals cilia also line the surface of organs, where they function to move fluids and mucus. The cilia in the human respiratory tract, for example, move mucus that traps dust and bacteria.

Flagella are whiplike, longer than cilia, and occur singly or in pairs. By whipping back and forth, flagella swiftly move unicellular organisms, such as *Euglena,* or cells in multicellular organisms. A sperm cell is rapidly propelled toward the egg by the power of its single flagellum.

Cilia and flagella are internally similar. The cross section in Figure 5-13 reveals that each is composed of nine pairs of microtubules located around its circumference and one pair of microtubules running down its center. Biologists refer to this as the "9 + 2" structure. Each cilium or flagellum is anchored to the cell by a cylindrical structure called a basal body.

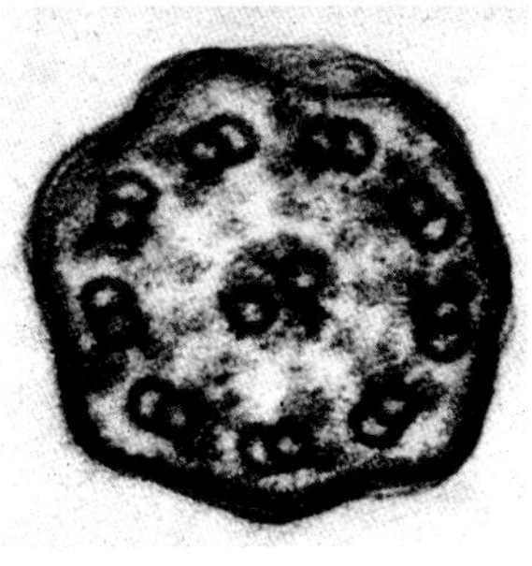

Figure 5-13 This TEM of the cross section of a single cilium shows the typical 9 + 2 structure (×70,000).

image contrast was adjusted, they were startled to see that background structures one-tenth the size of the smallest structures visible under an optical microscope were suddenly revealed. Organelles could be seen moving in both directions along filaments, almost like vehicles along a network of highways.

The Allens showed this accidental discovery to other workers at the MBL, and the investigation of the 100-year-old mystery of intracellular transport began. Using video-enhanced contrast (VEC) microscopy, the investigators discovered that movement proceeded along filaments, which were later shown to be microtubules (p. 70).

Since then video cameras have been made even more light sensitive. This feature allows researchers, working under low light conditions, to observe and record processes in living cells that would have been killed by standard fluorescent labeling techniques. Other improvements in VEC technology offer better image resolution, allowing more details of a specimen to be seen.

These improvements and the use of computers for digital enhancement of video images mean that video cameras are rapidly becoming standard equipment for many scientists working on living tissues or entire organisms. Researchers can create permanent, inexpensive records of biological events and capture the processes being observed as they happen.

More Information

Cell Mobility An ameba moves by cytoplasmic streaming. The nature of cytoplasm and sol-gel transformations has been discussed on p. 39. Other organisms may move by means of cilia or flagella.

Although cilia and flagella appear to be extensions on the surface of the cell, they are actually out-pockets of the cell covered by the cell membrane. Examples of cilia can be found throughout the book by using the index. *(Figure 21-4, p. 312,* Paramecium *cilia)*

Some cells move by means of one or two flagella, which are much longer than cilia. The word *flagellum* comes from the Latin word meaning "little whip." *(SEM of* Euglena gracilis *cells, p. 61)*

Interpreting the Visuals Point out that in Figure 5-13 on p. 71 microtubules appear in cross section as dense rings around a light center; in long section they look like straws made of globular spherical proteins. Ask students to suggest analogous structures they could create using common household objects. *(Students may compare the TEM with a cross section of a tomato or pomegranate. The microtubules may be compared to ziti pasta noodles or straws.)*

Biotechnology

Using the Feature

The main technique used in the observations of microtubules is video-enhanced contrast (VEC) microscopy. Point out to students that prior to the use of video, scientists relied upon electron microscopy for imaging small structures in the nanometer range. While electron microscopy does reveal striking detail, it requires the drying and fixation of specimens, so that all the images are of dead tissue.

Tell students that only one journal, *Cell Motility,* has tried, thus far unsuccessfully, to publish videos. Other scientists suggest creating electronic journals that could be received by computer terminals, with both a printed article and an accompanying video. Discuss the pros and cons of such technology with students.

You can demonstrate the effect of video-enhanced contrast by adjusting the contrast levels of a computer screen or a television set. If possible, contact a local university to see if any of its biology faculty uses video cameras in their research and would be willing to show one of their videotapes to the class.

Interpreting the Visuals Have students answer the caption question for Figure 5-15 on p. 73. *(Plastids—chloroplasts and leucoplasts—are found in plant cells only, as are cell walls and large central vacuoles.)* Refer students to Figure 5-6 on p. 66 as necessary.

■ *See* **Blackline Master 9.**

Guided Practice

Use Figure 5-14 to help students understand the nucleus. Have them identify the domed structure, the nuclear envelope. Ask students to speculate as to the function of the nuclear pores. *(Allow passage of large molecules; some evidence indicates the pores connect directly to the ER.)* Point out that the nuclear membrane is visible because the cell is not dividing.

■ *See* **Laboratories, *Investigation 5.***

Independent Practice

■ Have students write answers to the Section Review.

■ Tell students to list all the places where membranes are found in cells. What are the exceptions? *(Membranes are found at the cytoplasm, nucleus, Golgi apparatus, mitochondria, and lysosomes; as endoplasmic reticulum; over cilia and flagella. Ribosomes lack a membrane.)*

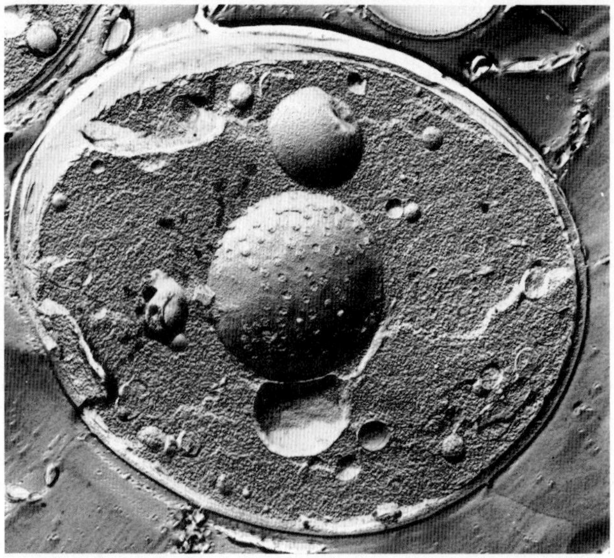

Figure 5-14 This SEM of a yeast cell prepared by the freeze-fracture technique shows the nuclear pores. In the freeze-fracture technique, cells are quick frozen and fractured along a line that splits membranes down the middle of the lipid layer, exposing the inner membrane.

Cell Nucleus

The nucleus is the site where nucleic acids are synthesized and it therefore directs the activities of the cell. It is surrounded by a double membrane called the **nuclear envelope.** Substances enter and leave the nucleus through holes in this envelope called nuclear pores. The pores form channels that allow large molecules, such as nucleic acids, to pass back and forth from the interior of the nucleus to the cytoplasm.

Inside the nuclear envelope is a dense, protein-rich substance called nucleoplasm. The nucleoplasm contains fine strands of **chromatin,** a combination of DNA and proteins. When a cell is dividing, a strand of chromatin coils up and condenses and can be seen under a microscope as a **chromosome.** Chromosomes thus are mostly DNA, the genetic information of the cell.

Most nuclei also contain at least one spherical body called the **nucleolus.** Ribosomes are synthesized and partially assembled in the nucleolus. After assembly they migrate to the cytoplasm.

Plant Cells

Most of the parts of the cell just described are common to all eukaryotic cells. Fungal cells and cells of protozoa and algae have some modifications, which will be discussed in the chapters on those organisms. Plant cells possess some structures in addition to those just described. In plants, a **cell wall** surrounds the cell membrane and helps support and protect the cell. The cell wall is one characteristic that distinguishes a plant cell from an animal cell. Two others are fluid-filled cavities or sacs called **vacuoles** and large organelles called **plastids,** which store food or pigments.

More Information

Cellular Packaging An analogy can be made between cell organelles and a manufacturing and packaging operation. The microtubule and microfilament skeleton resembles the infrastructure of the building. The channels of the ER and Golgi complex make production of a protein, such as an enzyme or a hormone, somewhat like factory assembly lines. Each protein is synthesized on a ribosome in the ER. Next, each product moves to the Golgi complex to be coated with a membrane and form a vesicle, somewhat like a boxing and sealing department. An enzyme entering the digestive tract or a hormone entering the blood is comparable to product delivery.

Cell Wall

A cell wall is the rigid covering of a plant cell. It is made primarily of long chains of cellulose embedded in hardening compounds such as pectin and lignin. Pores in the cell wall allow ions and molecules to pass to and from the cell membrane. Cell walls are of two types. Primary cell walls are formed during cell growth. Secondary cell walls are formed after growth has ceased. Each type of wall aids in strengthening the cell.

When a plant cell divides, a middle lamella is first formed between the new cells. The **middle lamella** is an intercellular glue made of pectin, the substance that makes jelly gel. Next, the primary wall is formed between the middle lamella and the cell membrane. Its cellulose fibers are laid down in layers. Each layer has all of the fibers oriented in one direction. The growing cell is thus able to expand sequentially at a right angle to the most recent fiber layer. This structure functions both to protect the cell and simultaneously to allow the cell to grow.

After growth ceases, a secondary cell wall is formed. This wall is made of cellulose and lignin fibers interwoven so that no further expansion of the cell is possible. The secondary wall functions to strengthen the mature cell. A compound called lignin in secondary walls makes them woody. When you pick up a piece of wood, you hold in your hand secondary cell walls.

Vacuoles

Vacuoles are organelles often found in plant cells. Like lysosomes in animal cells, vacuoles store enzymes and waste products. In a mature plant cell, a vacuole typically takes up as much as 90 percent of the volume, crowding the other structures into the

Figure 5-15 Most organelles of a plant cell (below left) are also found in animal cells. Which organelles are not common to both? The elements that make up a cell wall appear at the right.

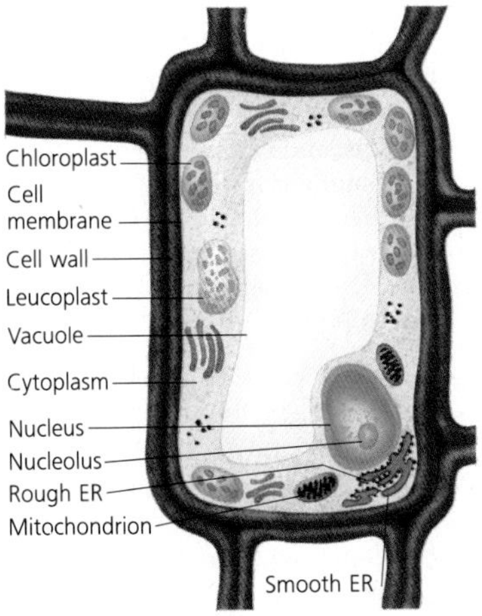

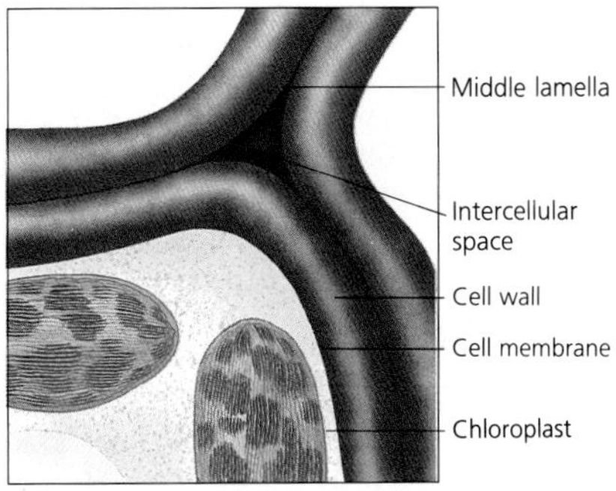

Check Your Understanding

1. Name three structures found in plant but not in animal cells. *(Cell wall, chloroplast, and vacuole)*

2. Explain in your own words the fluid mosaic model of the cell membrane. *(The mosaic or pattern of protein location in the two layers of lipids keeps moving around.)*

3. Compare ribosomes to mitochondria. *(Ribosomes are smaller and are made of nucleic acid and protein. They are the sites of protein synthesis. Mitochondria are large organelles with two membranes. The inner membrane has many folds, where ATP is formed.)*

Reteaching

Use Table 5-1 on p. 74 to help students compare prokaryotes and eukaryotes. As you move down the list of features, ask students to sketch three typical cells, showing the shape of each organelle present in prokaryote, animal, or plant cells.

- *See* Blackline Master *10.*
- *See* Section Reviews *worksheet, Section 5.2.*

Videodiscs

- *1611-1612, Leucoplasts (s)*
- *1935-1937, Chloroplasts in* Elodea *Leaf (s)*
- *2538-2551, Plant and Animal Cells (s)*

LEP Activity

Have students use a dictionary to find the origins and meanings of organelle names. Point out that a name can describe function or structure and can be used as a memory aid. For example, the word origins for *leucoplast*, a colorless plant plastid, are *leucos-*, meaning "white, clear," and *plast-*, meaning "something molded" (both from the Greek). *Nucleus* is from the Latin for kernel and is related to *nucula*, meaning "little nut." *Mitochondrion* is from the Greek *mitos* meaning "thread" and *chondrion*, meaning "small grain," thus describing the mitochondrion's appearance under a light microscope. Have students share their findings in small groups, then with the class.

Section 5.2

Enrichment
Have students use library resources to research current cell work. Possible topics include cell transport mechanisms or Lynn Margulis's endosymbiosis hypothesis. Ask students to focus their research on the role of organelles.

Answer to THINK
The pressure of the vacuole against the cell walls may also provide support for plant cells. Have students visualize a balloon filled with water vs. one filled with sand. Both keep their shape, but materials diffuse more easily through the liquid medium than through the solid sand.

Closure
Have students draw an analogy between the structure of a cell and the human body. On the board, write the column head *Cell* and ask students to list the major organelles under that head. Write the second column head *Human Body* and ask students to list an analogous part of the body. *(Nucleus = brain; mitochondria = cells, sites of cellular respiration; endoplasmic reticulum = circulatory system; cytoplasm = muscles; vacuoles = fat deposits; cell membrane = skin; microtubules = skeleton)* Have students speculate on what would happen if a body part, or an organelle, were missing. *(For example, without the nucleus or brain, there is no direction or control.)*

Think

In many plant cells the vacuole takes up a large space. As the above photograph of a spinach leaf cell shows, this crowds the other organelles to the edge of the cell. In addition to providing a storage area for nutrients and wastes, how else might the large area occupied by a vacuole function to benefit the cell?

Table 5-1 Comparison of Prokaryotes and Eukaryotes

		Eukaryotes	
Feature	**Prokaryotes**	**Animals**	**Plants**
Average size (diameter)	1–10 μm	10–20 μm	30–50 μm
Cell membrane	Yes	Yes	Yes
Cell wall	Yes	No	Yes
Nucleus	No	Yes	Yes
Ribosomes	Yes	Yes	Yes
Endoplasmic reticulum	No	Yes	Yes
Golgi complex	No	Yes	Yes
Mitochondria	No	Yes	Yes
Vacuoles	No	Small or absent	Usually a single large one per cell
Lysosomes	No	Often present	Rare
Microtubules	No	Yes	Yes
Cilia and flagella	Yes	Often present	Mostly absent except for sperm

space that's left. Some of the waste products stored by vacuoles are toxic materials that need to be kept away from the rest of the cell. Some acacia trees store cyanides in their vacuoles as a poisonous defense against plant-eating animals.

Plastids
Plants depend on light as a source of energy. Solar energy must be converted into chemical energy and then be stored. In plants plastids carry out these functions. **Chloroplasts** contain a green pigment called chlorophyll that absorbs sunlight as the first step in the conversion process. You will learn more about chloroplasts in Chapter 7. **Chromoplasts** synthesize and store pigments such as orange carotenes, yellow xanthophylls, and various red pigments, some of which function in trapping sunlight for energy. Chromoplasts are what give certain plants their distinctive colors. **Leucoplasts** *(LOO-kuh-PLASTS)* store food such as starches, proteins, and lipids. Present in most plant cells, leucoplasts are especially prominent in storage organs such as potato tubers.

Section Review
1. Name the three main parts of the eukaryotic cell.
2. Summarize the fluid mosaic model of the cell membrane.
3. Compare and contrast the vacuole and the lysosome.
4. Distinguish between the nucleus and the nucleolus.
5. Why do you think plant, and not animal, cells have walls?

Section Review
1. Cell membrane, cytoplasm, and nucleus
2. The protein molecules form patterns, or mosaics, in and on the lipid surfaces of the membrane. Lipids and some proteins move relative to each other, so patterns change.
3. Both are containers for stored enzymes or wastes. The small lysosomes are found more often in animal cells; the large central vacuole is found in plant cells.
4. The nucleolus is in the nucleus. Chromosomes in the nucleus contain DNA, the genes that direct cell activities. The nucleolus is the site of ribosome synthesis and partial assembly.
5. Plant cell walls may add strength and stability to plants, which do not move. All but a few animals require motility to get food.

5.3 Multicellular Organization

Biologists suggest that the earliest cells on earth were simple prokaryotic cells similar to some present-day bacteria. Like most bacteria they lacked the internal structures to synthesize their own food; they depended on organic nutrients in the environment. As they reproduced and their numbers increased, however, they began to compete for limited natural resources. With increasing competition cells with adaptations evolved. Some of these cells were eukaryotic. These unicellular eukaryotes may have existed in temporary groups, or colonies, with other cells, with some cells acting as special energy producers. Eventually, such temporary colonies may have evolved into multicellular organisms in which groups of cells became specialized for various functions. You will learn more about the evolution of prokaryotes and eukaryotes in Chapter 14.

Tissues, Organs, and Organ Systems

You have learned how the organelles within a cell perform specific functions that contribute to cell maintenance. Division of labor is also carried out by the individual cells that compose a multicellular organism. Each cell depends on other cells to perform one or more of the functions that keep the entire organism alive. The division of labor among cell types is called cell specialization.

In most multicellular organisms, cells are organized into tissues. A **tissue** is a group of similar cells that carry out a common function. Epithelial tissue, for example, consists of sheets of closely packed cells that form surface coverings, such as the outermost living layer of the skin and the lining of the nose. Cells that pull against one another make up muscle tissue. Cells that are specialized for transmitting messages make up nervous tissue.

Several types of tissue that interact to perform a specific function form an **organ**. The stomach, for example, is an organ. In the

Section Objectives

- *Distinguish between tissues, organs, and organ systems.*
- *Describe the way in which cells are organized in multicellular organisms.*

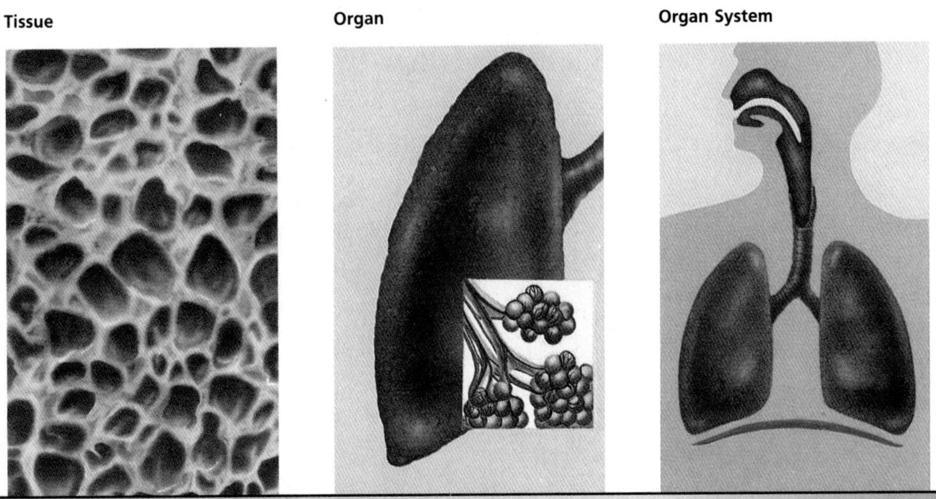

Figure 5-16 Spongy tissue (left) is the foundation for the tiny branching tubes and air sacs that form the lungs, an organ (center). The lungs, in turn, are part of the respiratory system (right).

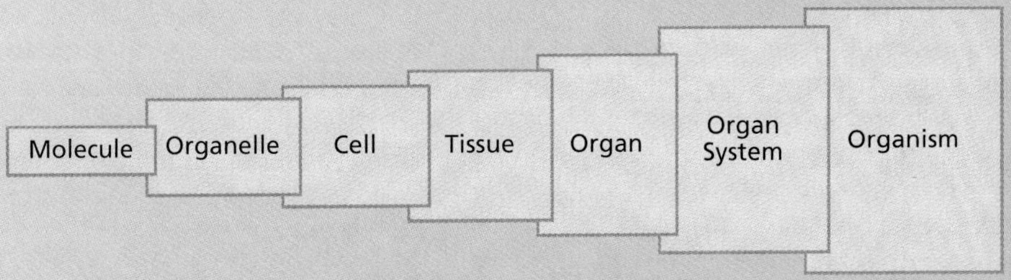

Graphic Organizer Use this hierarchical diagram in Reteaching on p. 76.

Section 5.3

Lesson Plan

Section Focus

Cells, which contain the same organelles, have different appearances depending upon the cells' specialized functions. Cells are organized into multicellular tissues within organs. An animal's organs are grouped into systems. Plant tissue systems and organs are classified differently.

Section Themes

This section illustrates the theme of **Systems and Interactions.** Within a cell, organelles function to maintain the systems necessary for life. Stress to students that all the systems of a plant or animal body work together to form a functioning whole organism.

Motivating Activity

Use an overhead projector to show students a picture of a cutaway car. Compare human body systems to the fuel, electrical, and exhaust systems of the car. Have students tell how each part is needed for the car to function. *(Fuel system supplies the power needed for work)* Point out that tissue organization and organ systems function in a similar manner.

Teaching Strategies

Organizing a Hierarchy Provide students terms (for example, kidney, epithelial tissue, nervous system) and have students show hierarchical relationships by telling what level each term represents. *(Organ, tissue, system)*

Guided Practice

Use a slide projector to show students color slides of human skin and plant stem cross sections. Ask how many layers or tissues they observe. *(Skin: 2 layers [epidermis and dermis], 4 tissues; Stem: 3 tissues [dermal, vascular, ground])*

Section 5.3

Independent Practice

- Have students write answers to the Section Review.
- Have students make an illustrated guide to multicellular organization, such as was done in Figure 5-16, p. 75. Student illustrations should include "cell."

Check Your Understanding

1. Which of the following is a tissue: stomach, muscle, or nervous system? *(Muscle)*
2. Which of the following isn't a plant tissue: ground, leaf, vascular? What is it? *(Leaf; an organ)*

Reteaching

Copy on the board the diagram on p. 75. Draw an analogy between multicellular organization and a school. A student represents a cell; grade levels represent tissues; a school represents an organ; all schools in the district represent an organ system. Have students give other examples. (*House, town, state, country*)

- *See* **Section Reviews** ***worksheet, Section 5.3.***

Enrichment

Assign students a human organ system. Have them refer to Unit 9 to identify its tissues and organs. Stress that all systems contain the four tissue types.

Closure

Have students name the basic unit of life. *(Cell)* Ask them to describe and relate cellular organization to multicellular organization. *(Cells contain organelles having specific structures and functions. Cells also have specific structures and functions and are organized into tissues.)*

Videodiscs

- *2650, Human Skin (s)*
- *Side 3 3302, A Drop of Fresh Water: Volvox (m)*

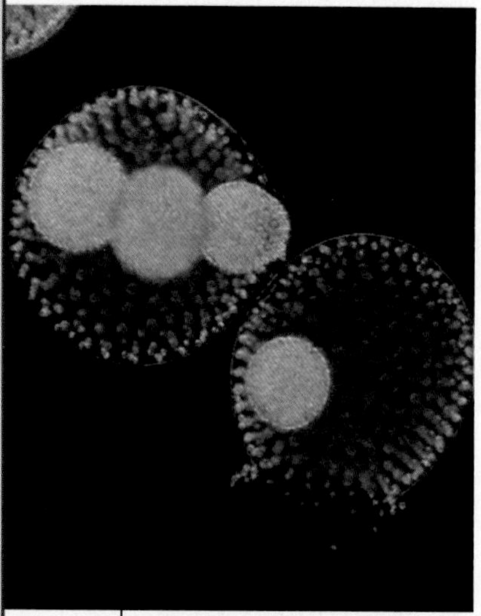

Figure 5-17 New *Volvox* colonies are formed in the interior of other colonies and are released when the old colony ruptures.

stomach, muscle tissue causes movement, epithelial tissue secretes enzymes, and nervous tissue transmits messages back and forth between the stomach and the brain.

An **organ system** is made up of a group of organs that work together to perform a set of related tasks. For example, the mouth, esophagus, stomach, intestines, and several other organs make up the digestive system. Each of these organs performs a specific aspect of the complex process we refer to as digestion.

Plants have tissue systems and organs. These are organized somewhat differently from those in animals. A dermal tissue system forms the outer layer of a plant. A ground tissue system makes up the bulk of roots and stems. A vascular tissue system is the water transport system of the plant. The three plant organs are roots, stems, and leaves.

Organisms

In a unicellular organism one cell carries out all the functions of life. Some life-forms, called colonial organisms, appear to be neither unicellular nor multicellular. A **colonial organism** is a group of more or less similar cells that live together in closely connected groups. An example is *Volvox,* a green alga that can be seen in Figure 5-17.

The organization of *Volvox* may give a clue to how multicellular organisms evolved. In *Volvox* each cell maintains its own individual existence. Sometimes, however, individual cells carry out specialized functions, such as reproduction or movement, for the whole colony. Each hollow *Volvox* sphere contains 500 to 60,000 cells. The spheres move in the water by the combined beating of the flagella of the specialized outer cells. A few of the cells are specialized for reproduction. They produce daughter colonies, which you can see as the darker spheres floating within the main sphere.

The same principle of specialization found in *Volvox* is found within all multicellular organisms. However, in multicellular organisms cells are so specialized that they are dependent on the function of other cells of the organism.

Section Review

1. Explain how a cell, a tissue, and an organ are related.
2. Give an example of an organ system, and name some of the parts that form it.
3. Name the plant tissue systems and organs.
4. To what extent are the individual cells within a *Volvox* colony independent of one another?
5. Green algae, such as *Codium,* enlarge by dividing the nucleus but do not form cell walls between the parent and the daughter cells. Would you call *Codium* a unicellular or a multicellular organism? Explain your answer.

Answers to Section Review

1. A tissue consists of one or more types of cells that perform a specialized function. An organ consists of one or more types of tissue that perform a specialized function.
2. The digestive system: mouth, esophagus, stomach, intestines
3. Plant tissue systems: dermal, ground, vascular; plant organs: root, stem, leaf
4. Each *Volvox* cell independently maintains its own life, but some cells depend on others for reproduction and movement.
5. Scientists classify *Codium* as multicellular but lacking walls. However, multinucleate-unicellular would be a reasonable answer.

Laboratory

Comparing Plant and Animal Cells

Objective
To examine similarities and differences in the structure of plant and animal cells

Process Skills
Hypothesizing, classifying, observing

Materials
Elodea plant, microscope slide, medicine dropper, coverslip, compound microscope, prepared slide of human cheek cells

Background
1 Name at least two ways in which plants and animals differ.
2 Based on the chapter text, what differences might you expect to observe between plant and animal cells?

Inquiry
1 Create a data table with two columns, *Plant Cell* and *Animal Cell.* What overall cell characteristics and specific features will you record?
2 Remove a young *Elodea* leaf from the plant tip. Place the leaf in a drop of water on a slide and cover with a coverslip.
3 Observe the outermost cell layer under low power. Draw several cell shapes. Label the cell walls. Record your observations.
4 Select a cell. Draw it and record its contents. Find and label the green, oval chloroplasts. Are they moving or stationary? If moving, use arrows to show the direction. If you do not observe cytoplasmic streaming, gently warm the slide and observe again.
5 Gently raise or lower the objective to focus on the cell's center. At what level do you see the fewest chloroplasts? Infer why chloroplasts might be scarce at this level.

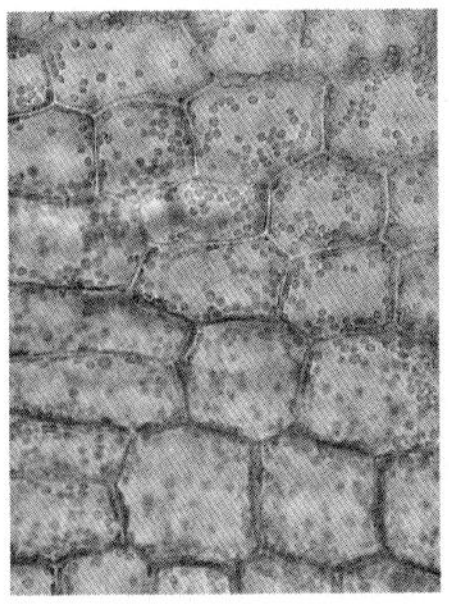

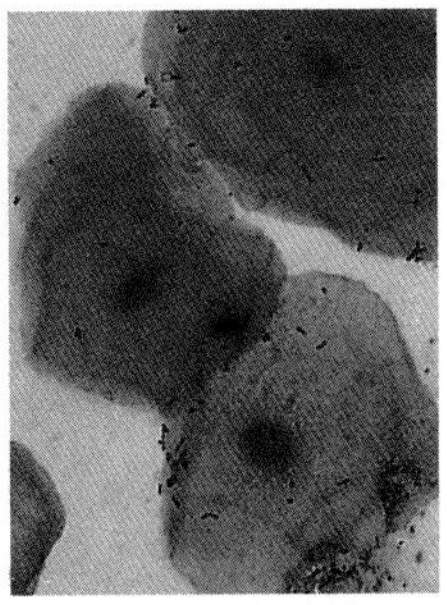

6 The vacuole at the cell's center resembles a clear, water-filled balloon inside a box. What observable evidence indicates the presence of a vacuole? Label the vacuole.
7 Find the small, dark nucleus. How do your observations relate to the vacuole's location? Label the nucleus on your drawing and record your observations.
8 Observe the prepared slide of human cheek cells under low power of your microscope. Draw several cells and record the shapes. Label the cell membrane. In the mouth, cheek cells are joined as a sheet. Why are they scattered here?
9 Select a cell and draw its contents. Locate its nucleus and observe it under high power. Label the nucleus in your drawing. Record your observations.

Conclusions
1 Review your data table. What observable characteristics can be used to classify a cell as a plant cell? an animal cell?
2 What characteristics that you observed are common to both *Elodea* and cheek cells? What characteristics are unique to each?
3 Which organelles described in Chapter 5 did you not see in this lab? Why not?

Further Inquiry
What might you observe if you stained an *Elodea* leaf? Place a drop of methylene blue on a plant cell slide. Record your observations.

(For an overview of plant and animal cells and preparatory information related to the laboratory, see p. 61B.)

Background
1. Plants are autotrophs. Most are green and immobile. Animals are heterotrophs. They vary in color and can move freely.
2. If students have read Chapter 5 before doing this laboratory, they will list plant and animal cell characteristics as given in the text (see Table 5-1, p. 74).

Inquiry
1. Overall characteristics include cell color and shape. Specific features include the cell wall, nucleus, and organelles.
4. Chloroplasts are seen, still or streaming, around the outer edge of the cell.
5. Fewer chloroplasts are located at the cell center. Students may infer that chloroplasts exist only in cytoplasm, not in the vacuole at the cell center. Alternatively, students may infer that chloroplasts are located at the area of maximum light intensity where they can efficiently function to make food.
6. The vacuole's edge may be seen as a thin line. Also, the cytoplasm and its organelles rim the cell's outer edge; the vacuole must push the cytoplasm there.
7. The nucleus is located within the cytoplasm; the nucleus, too, is displaced by the large, central vacuole.
8. The cheek cells were separated when scraped from the surface of the inner cheek where they only loosely adhere to one another.

Conclusions
1. Plant: green, box-shaped; have a cell wall, chloroplasts, a vacuole. Animal: irregularly shaped or roughly spherical and flattened; visible cell membrane.
2. Similarities: nucleus, cytoplasm, cell membrane. Unique to *Elodea:* cell wall, chloroplasts, central vacuole; cell shape regular and angular. Unique to cheek cells: shape rounded or irregular.
3. Answers will vary. The nucleus, chloroplasts, and cell wall are usually the most clearly visible. Stain used in the prepared slides may not color all samples equally.

Further Inquiry
Students may predict that the nucleus will stain darkly. Methylene blue will also tint the cytoplasm.

Vocabulary

1. *Eu-* means "true," *pro-* means "before," and *kary-* means "kernel" or "nucleus." Eukaryotes have a *true* nucleus. The name *prokaryote* suggests these cells evolved before a nucleus existed.
2. A cell membrane is two layers of lipid molecules embedded with proteins. The membrane functions to hold in the cell contents and regulate molecule movement in and out of the cell. The cell wall is located between cell membranes of adjacent cells and functions to support the cell and the organism.
3. *Cyto-* means "cell." Thus, cytoplasm is cell plasma, or fluid. Cytoskeleton is the framework of the cell.
4. Microtubules are hollow protein tubes that form the internal structure of cilia and flagella. Both make a cell motile; flagella are longer.
5. Chromatin does not belong in the group, being a nuclear material. The other three terms refer to membrane-bound cytoplasmic organelles.

Review

1. b	**6.** d
2. a	**7.** c
3. d	**8.** d
4. c	**9.** b
5. b	**10.** b

11. Each advance in microscope technology enabled teams of scientists to observe more of the structure and workings of cells.
12. Size is limited by the ratio of cell volume to surface area.
13. The cell membrane is called selectively permeable because it allows some materials to pass through and excludes others.

Chapter 5 Review

Vocabulary

cell (63)
cell membrane (66)
cell theory (64)
cell wall (72)
chloroplast (74)
chromatin (72)
chromoplast (74)
chromosome (72)
cilia (71)
colonial organism (76)
cytoplasm (66)
cytoplasmic streaming (67)
cytoskeleton (70)
endoplasmic reticulum (68)
eukaryote (65)
flagella (71)
fluid mosaic model (67)
Golgi apparatus (68)
leucoplast (74)
lysosome (70)
microfilament (70)
microtubule (70)
middle lamella (73)
mitochondria (69)
multicellular organism (63)
nuclear envelope (72)
nucleolus (72)
nucleus (65)
organ (75)
organelle (65)
organ system (76)
plastid (72)
prokaryote (65)
ribosome (67)
selectively permeable membrane (66)
spindle fibers (70)
tissue (75)
unicellular organism (63)
vacuole (72)

1. Look up in a dictionary the meaning of the word parts *eu-*, *pro-*, and *kary-*. Explain why the words *prokaryote* and *eukaryote* are good terms for the organisms they describe. What do the terms suggest about the evolution of these organisms?
2. Describe the structure and function of a cell membrane, and compare it with the structure and function of a cell wall.
3. Look up in a dictionary the meaning of the word part *cyto-*. Use what you have learned to explain the meaning of the terms *cytoplasm* and *cytoskeleton*.
4. Explain the relationship between microtubules, cilia, and flagella.
5. Choose the term that does not belong in the following group, and explain why: Golgi apparatus, endoplasmic reticulum, chromatin, and mitochondria.

Review

1. A prokaryote has (a) a cell nucleus (b) a cell membrane (c) organelles (d) all of the above.
2. The growth of cells is limited by the ratio between (a) volume and surface area (b) organelles and surface area (c) organelles and cytoplasm (d) nucleus and cytoplasm.
3. A cell membrane is composed of (a) lipids (b) proteins (c) nucleic acids (d) lipids and proteins.
4. The function of the Golgi apparatus is to (a) synthesize proteins (b) release energy (c) process and package proteins (d) synthesize lipids.
5. Mitochondria (a) transport materials (b) release energy (c) make proteins (d) control cell division.
6. Lysosomes function in cells to (a) recycle cell parts (b) destroy disease-causing agents (c) shape developing body parts (d) all of the above.
7. The nucleolus is (a) the control center of the cell (b) the storehouse of genetic information (c) the site where ribosomes are synthesized (d) none of the above.
8. Plant cells differ from animal cells in having (a) fluid-filled vacuoles (b) cell walls surrounding the cell membrane (c) chromoplasts (d) all of the above.
9. Leucoplasts (a) synthesize proteins (b) store food (c) synthesize pigments (d) store pigments.
10. The stomach is an example of (a) a tissue (b) an organ (c) an organ system (d) none of the above.

14. Proteins are synthesized on the ribosomes, some in rough ER, some in smooth ER. Packaging of proteins that will leave the cell occurs in the Golgi apparatus.
15. Rough ER contains many ribosomes; smooth ER has few or none visible.
16. Cristae, the folds of the inner membrane, provide a large surface area where energy is released from bonds of organic molecules and stored in ATP for use by the cell.
17. VEC technology enabled scientists to observe the particles moving along microtubules.
18. Chromatin is fine threads of genetic material, which coil up and become visible during cell division. The thickened coils of chromatin are the chromosomes.

11. How have microscopes been helpful in the study of cells? Explain.
12. What limits the size of cells?
13. Why is the cell membrane called a selectively permeable membrane?
14. Explain how the ribosomes, the endoplasmic reticulum, and the Golgi apparatus function together in protein synthesis.
15. Distinguish between the structure of rough ER and that of smooth ER.
16. Describe the inner structure of mitochondria, and explain their function.
17. How has VEC technology enhanced our understanding of the structure and function of microtubules?
18. What is the difference between chromatin and chromosomes?
19. How are cell walls formed?
20. What is cell specialization? Give an example of cell specialization.

Critical Thinking

1. A mature human red blood "cell" is simply a membrane surrounding hemoglobin, the protein molecule that carries oxygen. Suggest an advantage for the simple organization of human red blood cells.
2. The coils of a radiator provide a large surface area from which heat is radiated into a room. Which cell organelles have a structure similar to that of a radiator? How is this structure related to their function?
3. Children who are born with Tay-Sachs disease are unable to carry out the normal breakdown of lipids in the brain because of a defect in a cell organelle. Based on this information, which cell organelle do you think may be defective in Tay-Sachs victims? Explain.
4. Livestock in the western United States often die after eating a locoweed, such as *Astragalus toanus*. The chemical the plant contains is also poisonous to plants. How does locoweed keep from poisoning itself?

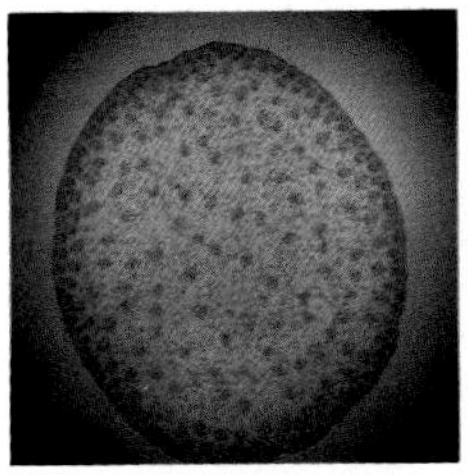
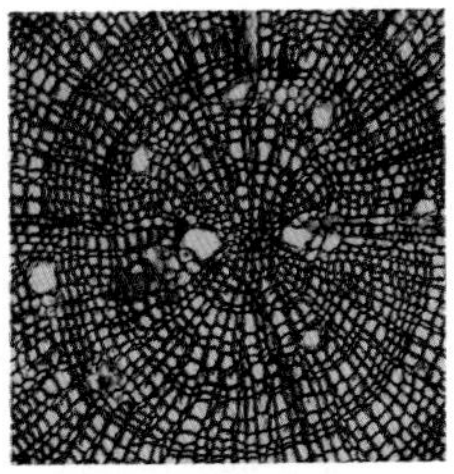

5. Compare the two photos above. One shows cells from a grass stem, and the other shows cells from the trunk of a conifer tree. Which photo do you think shows the tree cells? Why do you think so?
6. What characteristic of eukaryotic cells gives them a greater capacity for specialization than prokaryotic cells have? Explain your answer.

Extension

1. Read the article by Mary Murray entitled "Life on the Move," in *Discover,* March 1991, pp. 73–75. Prepare an oral report for the class on how a new video technique has enhanced cell biologists' understanding of the movement of particles within a cell.
2. Use the resources in your school or public library to learn more about the work of Schleiden, Schwann, or Virchow. Write a brief report summarizing the processes that the researcher used to arrive at his conclusions about cells.
3. Place a sprig of the aquarium plant *Elodea* in water, and shine a bright light on it for an hour. Then examine a leaf under the microscope and make a drawing, noting the direction of chloroplast movement. How do you think the movement of cell organelles helps the cell to function?

19. First, a middle lamella forms between two cells. Then, the cell on each side forms a primary wall. Some plants have an additional secondary wall.
20. The division of labor among cell types within an organism. *Volvox* colonies have cells specialized for reproduction and motion.

Critical Thinking

1. An RBC is specialized to perform one function. Without any organelles, an RBC can carry more hemoglobin and, therefore, more oxygen.
2. The ER and cristae of mitochondria have large surface areas similar to radiator coils. This gives more area for biochemical reactions.
3. The lysosomes, which contain enzymes that digest lipids, are probably lacking in children with Tay-Sachs disease.
4. The poisonous chemical is stored in a vacuole, isolating it from the rest of the cell.
5. The tree trunk cells (right photo) have secondary thickening in a regular pattern, suggesting a strong structure necessary to support a tree.
6. The presence of organelles and more membranes in eukaryotic cells makes possible a greater specialization of function and more variety for selection by evolutionary factors.

Extension

1. The student's oral report on "Life on the Move" should describe how Robert Allen accidentally discovered the video technique used to study intracellular movement.
2. All three were Germans of the mid-1800s who made numerous microscopic observations of a variety of subjects. Also, the development of organic stains made it possible to study specific cell structures.
3. Cytoplasmic streaming moves the chloroplasts, increasing their chances of being exposed to light. Also, movement ensures that reactants and products of photosynthesis are distributed as needed.

Chapter 6 Homeostasis and Transport

Chapter Overview

Chapter 6 focuses on the transport of materials into and out of the cell through the cell membrane. Section 6.1 differentiates between diffusion and osmosis and discusses the role of osmosis in homeostasis, the maintenance of a cell's stable inner environment. Section 6.2 discusses the difference between passive and active transport and explores the relationship between the structure of the cell membrane and its function in transport.

Chapter Planning Chart

B	S	A	Sections and Subsections	Page	Features	Page	Resources
•	•	•	**6.1 Diffusion and Osmosis**				
			Diffusion	81	Think	82	Videodiscs
			Osmosis	82	Laboratory	89	Process Skills: Osmosis Experiment
					Section Review	83	Laboratories: Osmosis
							Section Reviews Worksheet
•	•	•	**6.2 Other Kinds of Transport**				
			Carrier Transport	84	Biology in Process	86	Videodiscs
			Gated Channels	86	Section Review	88	Blackline Master 11
			Endocytosis and Exocytosis	87			Overhead Transparency T6
							Blackline Master 12
							Section Reviews Worksheet
			End of Chapter Activities				
					Chapter Review	90	Vocabulary Skills
							Chapter Test
							Computer Test Generator

B *The Basic Level curriculum presents the most fundamental knowledge offered in the course.*
S *The Standard Level curriculum is designed for the average student who is able to master most topics.*
A *The Advanced Level curriculum includes suggestions for teaching the most academically able students.*

Cooperative Learning

Group Activity: Cell Membrane Function

- **Group Size:** *2–4*
- **Outcome:** *Students will recognize and understand the role of the cell membrane in cellular transport.*
- **Individual Accountability:** *Each student prepares microscopic slides and records his or her observations.*
- **Positive Interdependence:** *Group members discuss their observations and explain their results.*

At least 24 hours before class, prepare an active yeast culture by dissolving a packet of dry yeast in a 10% molasses solution. Provide each group with two test tubes, each containing 5 mL of the yeast culture. Have students put one tube in boiling water for 10 minutes, let it cool, then label it. Ask what boiling will do to the single-celled yeast organisms. *(Yeasts will die; the cell membrane's integrity will be disrupted.)*

Have students add 10 drops of Congo red dye to each tube. Next, have each student prepare and label slides of each culture, add coverslips, examine them under a compound microscope, and record observations. Then have the group members compare their observations, agree on an explanation of their observations and present it to the class. Emphasize that a cell membrane keeps a cell whole and is a selective barrier against materials; in this case, against the red dye.

Concept Map

The following is one possible solution to the concept mapping activity in Reteaching on p. 83.

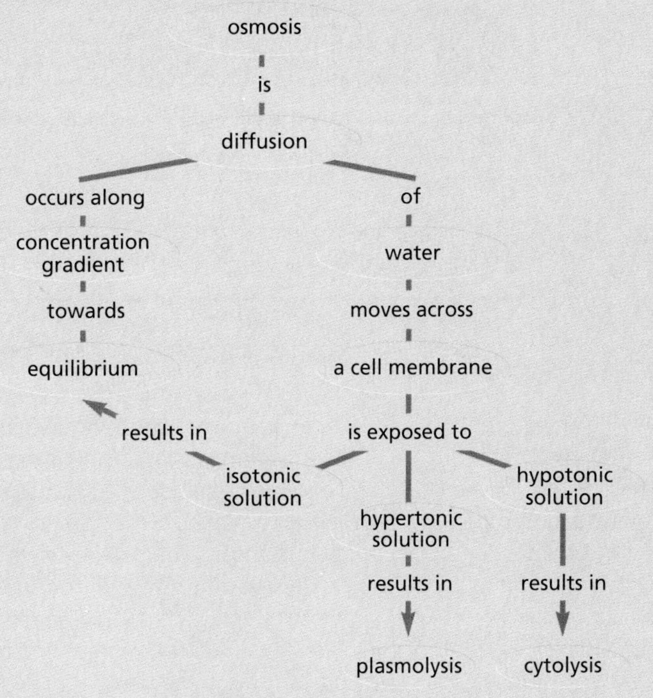

Laboratory Preparation

Overview *(See p. 89.)*

In this investigation students observe the results of osmosis on plant tissue. They will understand that osmosis causes turgor pressure which keeps a cell firm and therefore supports a plant. Students can relate this information to their study of plant cell structure and their observation of *Elodea* in Chapter 5.

Preparation

To make 10% salt solution, dissolve 10 g of NaCl in distilled water to a final volume of 100 mL.

The color in red onions facilitates cell observation, making dyes unnecessary. Onion cells are slow to demonstrate changes in osmotic pressure. Consider using *Nitella* or *Elodea* cells, which show more rapid cytoplasmic changes.

Teaching Tips

Have students cut the potato sticks "regular french fry" size. Thin sticks ("julienne" fries) will bend too readily to show an increase of osmotic pressure. Very thick sticks ("beefsteak" fries) will not bend enough to demonstrate a loss of turgor.

Have students make quantitative measurements, for example, by using a protractor to measure the angle of bending. Students should use the same holes each time they pick up the stick.

Tell students to use only a thin layer of onion cells. Caution them to make careful observation because onion cells respond slowly to changes in osmotic pressure. Tell students to focus on one clear area of normal cells and caution them not to move the slide. Tell them to observe these cells at 2, 5, 10, and 20 minutes.

Emphasize that a hypertonic salt solution causes water to leave a cell by osmosis because the solute concentration (salt ions) outside the cell is greater than the concentration within. In other words, water moves from a lower to a higher solute concentration, and turgor pressure decreases, resulting in plasmolysis. Distilled water, a hypotonic solution, causes water to enter the cell, increasing the internal turgor pressure, resulting in cytolysis.

Safety

Remind students to use scalpels carefully and to hold the potato or onion far from the blade. Remind them to wash their hands at the end of the investigation.

Chapter Themes

Stability Cells tend to remain stable—that is, they demonstrate homeostasis. Emphasize to students that continuous metabolic processes cause imbalances that must be constantly corrected. Without this dynamic balance, life activities could not go on.

Energy Remind students that all life requires energy. Point out that in some cases the movement of molecules into and out of cells requires biochemical energy.

Systems and Interactions A cell responds to its environment and interacts with other cells. Stress that materials continuously cross the cell membrane during normal life activities, moving food and wastes into and out of the cell. Point out that tissue consists of cells that can respond or react to each other through connecting gaps in the cell membrane.

Chapter Motivating Activity

Have students handle a wilted lettuce leaf or celery stick and a normal one. Ask them what they might do to wilt a vegetable. *(Students may suggest leaving vegetables unrefrigerated or applying heat.)* Ask students why a salad is dressed just before being served, why fresh vegetables on a salad bar or a produce counter are sprayed with water and not with salt water, and what happens when a concentrated solution of ions contacts plant cells. *(Contact with a concentrated solution of ions, such as salt water, causes water to leave the cells, making vegetables wilt. They are not as appealing to buy or eat when wilted.)* Ask students to infer what prevents wilting in growing plants. *(The cell membrane excludes or pushes out excess salt.)* Tell students that some of the water and ion movement is passive, some active.

Chapter 6 *Homeostasis and Transport*

Introduction

A cell exists in a constantly changing environment. By adjusting to changes, a cell maintains a balance with its environment. In the previous chapter you learned that the cell membrane is the boundary of the cell. In this chapter you will learn how the cell membrane functions to regulate the passage of materials into and out of the cell, maintaining a balance between the cell and its environment.

Chapter Outline

Chapter Concept

As you read, look for the ways in which a cell regulates the movement of materials and maintains homeostasis.

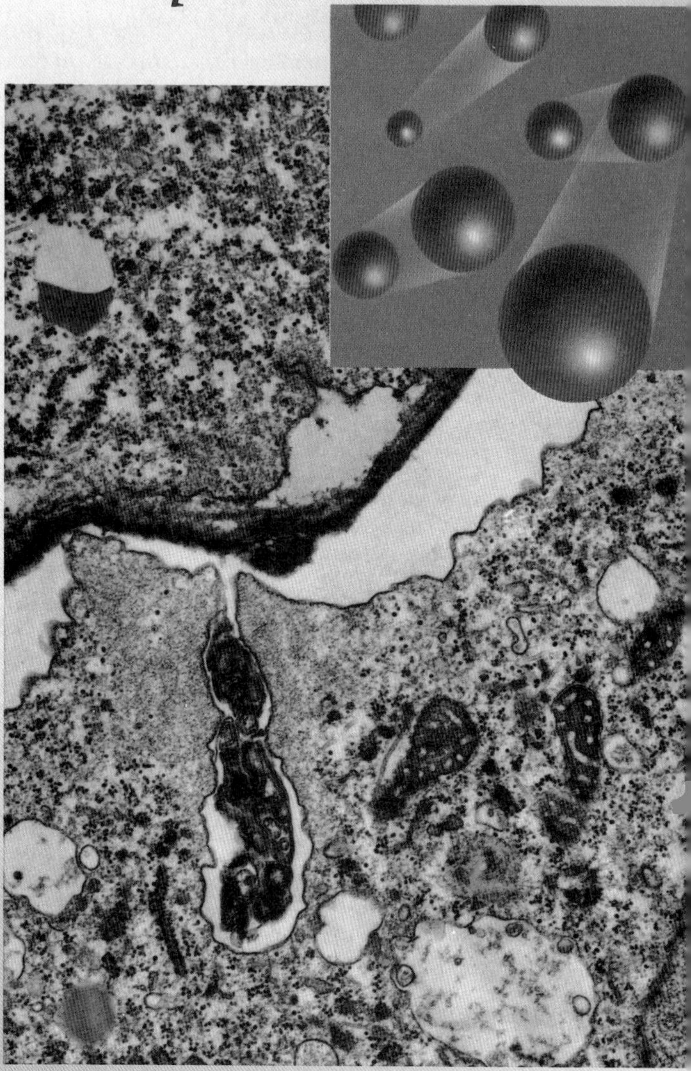

TEM of endocytosis (×80,000). Inset: Artist's representation of atoms in motion.

Understanding the Visuals

Ask students to locate the cell membranes of the top and bottom cells in the electron micrograph. *(The thin irregular lines, clearest in the bottom cell)* Have students compare the membranes to visuals in Chapter 5: Figure 5-7, p. 67, Figure 5-5, p. 65, and Figure 5-14, p. 72. Point out the pocket in the bottom cell in the TEM above. The food particle is enclosed by a membrane that will form a tiny packet inside the cell. Ask students to infer what endocytosis is, based on these guided observations. *(It is the process by which cells enclose a large substance with a fold of the cell membrane.)* Point out that endocytosis requires the cell to use energy. Certain other types of transport do not require energy; they involve random molecular movement, represented by the colored atoms in the inset.

6.1 Diffusion and Osmosis

To remain alive and function optimally, cells, tissues, organs, and organisms must maintain a biological balance with their immediate environment. Cells maintain this biological balance, or **homeostasis,** by controlling and regulating what gets into and out of the cell. Though cells can exist within a range of environmental states, there is a limit to how much they can adjust.

Diffusion

To understand how cells maintain homeostasis, you must understand how molecules move. Molecules are in constant motion. They travel in straight lines until they hit something, then rebound, still traveling in a straight line but in a different direction. They rebound again, and so on. As the net effect of their random motion, molecules tend to move into those areas where they are less concentrated. This tendency results in an overall direction of movement among the molecules. **Diffusion** is the process by which molecules spread from an area of greater concentration to an area of lesser concentration.

Equilibrium

An example of diffusion occurs when you put a cube of sugar in water. The sugar molecules diffuse away from the cube into the water. At first the molecules are more concentrated near the sugar cube and less concentrated farther from the cube. This difference in concentrations of a substance across space is called a **concentration gradient.** Eventually the sugar molecules diffuse throughout the water so that they are equally distributed. When the concentration of the molecules of a substance is the same throughout a space, a state called **equilibrium** exists. Once equilibrium is established the random movement of molecules continues, and equilibrium is maintained.

Section Objectives

- *Define homeostasis.*
- *Describe the movement of molecules to achieve equilibrium.*
- *Explain the process by which water molecules move across a membrane.*
- *Differentiate between diffusion and osmosis.*

Figure 6-1 Ink dropped into a beaker of water (left) diffuses from areas of high concentration to areas of lower concentration. Over time the ink diffuses evenly throughout the water (center and right). Eventually equilibrium is established.

Cell Solution	Environment	Water Movement	Results
hypertonic	hypotonic	into cell	cytolysis
hypotonic	hypertonic	out of cell	plasmolysis
isotonic	isotonic	balanced	equilibrium

Graphic Organizer Use this table to summarize key concepts in Section 6.1.

Lesson Plan

Section Focus

Diffusion and osmosis are physical processes by which an organism maintains homeostasis. Homeostasis is the biological balance an organism maintains with its immediate environment.

Section Themes

This section emphasizes the theme of **Stability.** The cell membrane maintains a stable internal environment—homeostasis—during metabolic activities.

The theme of **Energy** is illustrated indirectly. Transport by diffusion and osmosis do not use cellular energy.

Motivating Activity

If possible, have students eat a handful of salted nuts or similar food, then ask what happens after they eat salted or spicy food. *(They get thirsty.)* Tell students that such foods tend to have highly concentrated particles and lower water content, which causes water to leave the cells of the mouth. Ask how to remedy the condition. *(Drinking water replaces water lost by the cells.)* Point out that students will learn how this process occurs.

Teaching Strategies

Making Generalizations Point out to students that they breathe continuously. Ask what other processes must occur for life to continue. *(Students may suggest eating, eliminating wastes, using energy.)* Stress that in a cell, organic and inorganic compounds and ions must also be constantly transported into and out of cells, across the cell membrane.

Videodiscs

- *2515–2517, Diffusion Process (s)*

Answer to Think

The bottom photo shows swollen red blood cells. Have students use Table 6-1 to determine what type of solution caused this condition. *(Hypotonic solution)* Explain that distilled water is made by heating water and collecting the pure water vapor. Ask students which of the two solutions has more solute, the salt solution or the distilled water. *(Salt solution)* Ask students to conclude which solution caused the cells to swell and why. *(The distilled water; it has a lower solute concentration than the cell's inner environment. Water diffused into the cells, down a concentration gradient.)*

Illustrating Scientific Processes

Have students create posters illustrating the effects of osmosis on a cell. Have them color code or label the cell membrane, water molecules, and solute particles, and use arrows to indicate water movement. Have students show a cell in a hypotonic, a hypertonic, and an isotonic solution. *(Hypotonic: lower concentration of solute particles outside the cell than within; water moves into cell. Hypertonic: higher concentration of solute particles outside the cell than within; water leaves cell. Isotonic: equal concentrations of solute particles in the cell and the environment; water moves in and out of cell at equal rates.)*

■ *See* Laboratories, *Investigation 6.*

Guided Practice

Have students think of environmental conditions that represent the conditions in Table 6-1, p. 82. For example, a pond under normal conditions, isotonic solution; a pond whose level has dropped due to summer heat, hypertonic solution; a flooded pond, hypotonic solution.

■ *See* Process Skills, *Chapter 6.*

Think

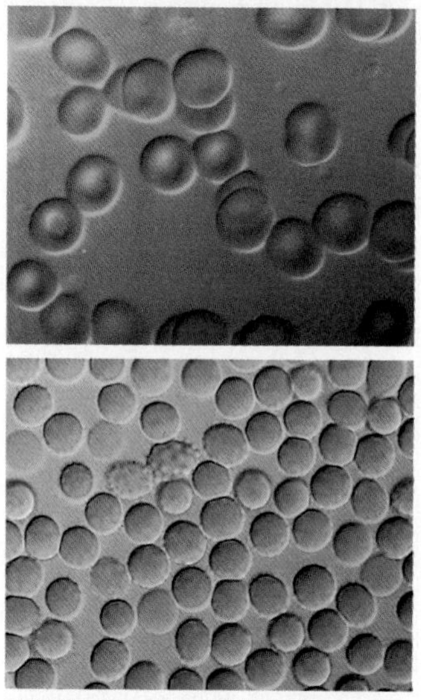

The normal red blood corpuscles in the top photo are in a plasma solution. Now look at the red blood corpuscles in the bottom photo. Do you think they are in a salty solution or in distilled water? Why? The micrograph of red corpuscles appears green because a red blood cell *in vivo* is straw-colored, almost transparent. The cells appear reddish only when they are in a large grouping, or when the cell is nonliving and stained. Without the blue-green background color, the cell would not be visible.

Diffusion Across Membranes

Some kinds of molecules can also diffuse across a membrane. They do this by moving between the molecules that make up the membrane. If a substance can pass through a membrane, the membrane is **permeable** to it. As with all diffusion, molecules diffuse from an area of greater concentration on one side of the membrane to one of lesser concentration on the other.

Not all molecules can diffuse through all membranes. The ability of a molecule to pass through a membrane depends on the size and type of molecule and the molecular structure of the membrane. Membranes that let only some substances through are called selectively permeable membranes, or semipermeable membranes. Cell membranes are semipermeable; thus they regulate what gets into and out of a cell. Monosaccharides, for example, enter by diffusion, but large molecules like starch do not.

Osmosis

Recall from Chapter 3 that a solution is composed of a solute dissolved in a solvent. In the example cited on the previous page sugar is the solute and water is the solvent. In organisms the solvent is water and the solutes are inorganic and organic compounds. In the sugar example the solute diffused. However, it is also possible for the solvent to diffuse. The process by which water molecules diffuse through a membrane from an area of greater concentration to an area of lesser concentration is called **osmosis** *(ahz-MOE-suss)*. Note that in biology osmosis refers only to the diffusion of water.

Direction of Osmosis

What determines the net direction in which the water molecules diffuse across a cell membrane? The direction depends on the concentrations of water and solutes dissolved in the solutions. Study Table 6-1. If the concentration of solute molecules in the

Table 6-1 Direction of Osmosis

Conditions	Environment solution is	Cell solution is	Water will move
If solute concentration in the environment is lower than in the cell	Hypotonic	Hypertonic	Into the cell
If solute concentration in the environment is higher than in the cell	Hypertonic	Hypotonic	Out of the cell
If solute concentration in the environment is equal to that in the cell	Isotonic	Isotonic	Water will not move

Cooperative Learning

Moving Particles Have students work in pairs to observe Brownian motion, the random, continuous activity of atoms, visible as the motion of impacted particles. Have each pair place a drop of India ink or of nonhomogenized (raw) milk on a slide and cover with a coverslip. As one student observes the slide under low power, have the second student record the first student's description of one particle's movements over several minutes. Then let the students exchange places so that each student makes and records observations. Stress that the movement of the small ink or milk particles is constant and random. Have each pair present their description to the class.

environment outside the cell is lower than that in the cell, the solution outside is **hypotonic** relative to its environment. The prefix *hypo-* means "lower." Water will move into the cell until equilibrium is established. When the concentration of solute molecules outside the cell is greater than that inside, the solution outside is **hypertonic** relative to its environment. The prefix *hyper-* means "higher." Water will diffuse out of the cell until equilibrium is established. When the concentration of solutes outside and inside the cell are equal, the solution is **isotonic** relative to its environment. The prefix *iso-* means "equal." Water will diffuse into and out of the cell at equal rates, establishing osmotic balance.

Notice that the prefixes *hypo-, hyper-,* and *iso-* refer to the relative concentration of solute. Remember that a hypotonic solution exists in relation to a coexisting hypertonic solution. A hypertonic solution exists in relation to a coexisting hypotonic solution. An isotonic solution has an adjacent isotonic solution.

Role of Osmosis

A plant cell swells as it fills with water. It does not swell endlessly because it is restricted by cell walls. As water diffuses into the cell, pressure—called **turgor pressure**—increases. The pressure forces the cytoplasm and cell membrane against the cell wall and the cell becomes rigid. Such a cell has high turgor pressure.

Turgor pressure is maintained while the cells are in a hypotonic environment. If the environment loses water or gains solutes, the concentration of solutes outside the cell may become greater than that inside. Water then leaves the cell, turgor pressure is lost, and the cell wilts. This condition is called **plasmolysis** *(plazz-MAHL-uh-suss)*. The reverse condition, in which cells take in so much water that they burst, is called **cytolysis.**

Unicellular freshwater organisms exist in a hypotonic environment and are thus hypertonic relative to their environment. Water will therefore diffuse into the cell. Since these organisms need to maintain a relatively lower concentration of water inside the cell to function normally, they must rid themselves of the excess water that enters the cell by osmosis. Some organisms do this with **contractile vacuoles,** organelles that remove water. The contractile vacuoles collect the excess water and then contract, squeezing the water out of the cell.

Figure 6-2 The plant cell at the top is in osmotic balance since conditions are such that water is leaving and entering the cell in equal amounts. In the plant cell at the bottom, a hypertonic solution outside the cell has caused plasmolysis.

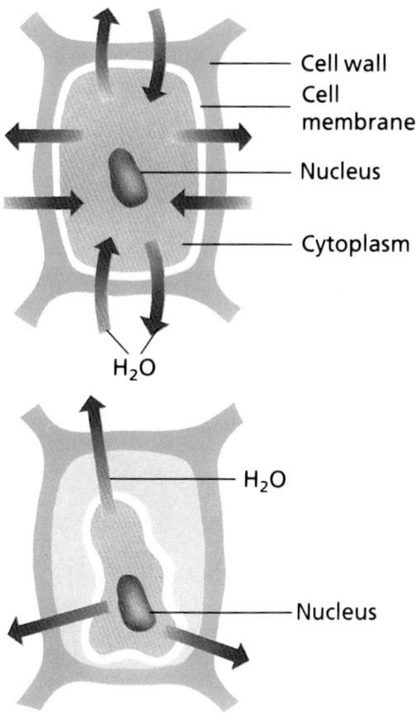

Section Review

1. Distinguish between *diffusion* and *osmosis.*
2. How does the cell membrane help maintain homeostasis?
3. What is one factor that determines the direction in which molecules move across a membrane?
4. When the turgor pressure of a plant cell increases, does that indicate that the cell is hypotonic, hypertonic, or isotonic relative to its environment? Explain your answer.
5. Why would drinking sea water be dangerous for humans?

Independent Practice

- Have students write answers to the Section Review.
- Have students infer the effect of a hypotonic solution on plant and animal cells. How does each cell maintain homeostasis? *(Both swell as water diffuses in, but the cell wall of a plant cell protects it from cytolysis. Unicellular freshwater organisms often have contractile vacuoles.)*

Check Your Understanding

1. Why is it incorrect to say that oxygen enters a cell by osmosis? *(Osmosis is diffusion of water.)*
2. Why is it incorrect to say that there is no movement during a state of equilibrium? *(Molecules are in a constant state of random movement, even at equilibrium.)*

Reteaching

Have small groups of students draw a concept map of the key concepts of osmosis and diffusion. An example of a completed map is shown on p. 79B.

- *See* **Section Reviews** ***worksheet, Section 6.1.***

Enrichment

Ask students to research applications of osmosis, such as dialysis (which purifies the blood of patients with impaired kidneys) and water purification systems that use membranes.

Closure

Grass wilts if too much fertilizer is applied. Ask students to relate the concept of osmosis to this event. (*High salt concentration in water around roots or leaves causes an osmotic flow of water out of cells.)*

Videodiscs

- ***Side 2 5406, Osmosis in Leaves (m)***
- ***Side 2 6646, Osmosis: Forces (m)***
- ***Side 2 8002, Plants Use Osmosis (m)***

Answers to Section Review

1. Diffusion is the movement of molecules from an area of higher to an area of lower concentration. Osmosis is the diffusion of water molecules through a membrane.
2. The cell membrane is semipermeable, regulating what enters and leaves the cell.
3. The concentration gradient determines the direction of molecular movement.
4. The cell is hypertonic relative to its environment; water is moving into the cell.
5. Seawater has a higher concentration of solutes than human body cells. Water would diffuse out of the body cells, which would shrink and possibly die.

Lesson Plan

Section Focus

In addition to simple diffusion and osmosis, chemical processes of the cell membrane regulate the passage of materials into and out of the cell.

Section Themes

The theme of **Energy** is evident in the requirement for ATP and other sources of chemical energy by some forms of cell transport. Facilitated diffusion and active transport across the membrane depend upon carrier molecules and biochemical processes.

Transport mechanisms are a part of homeostasis, illustrating the theme of **Stability.** Homeostasis maintains the stable internal environment of the cell and organism.

Motivating Activity

Make an analogy between the proteins in the cell membrane and gatekeeper jobs. Have students list jobs in which passage of people or objects is regulated. *(Museum guard, toll booth attendant, parking lot attendant, elevator operator)* Compare a carrier molecule to an admission ticket; the ticket taker at an event permits entry only to those with tickets.

Teaching Strategies

Organizing Information Have students make a table of the transport mechanisms discussed in Section 6.2 and the materials they transport. *(The table will list facilitated diffusion, transporting specific molecules such as glucose; active transport, transporting sodium and potassium ions; gated channels, transporting molecules that cannot cross the cell membrane; endocytosis, transporting large amounts of fluids or nutrients; and exocytosis, exporting proteins or wastes.)*

Section Objectives

- *Describe how carrier molecules transport materials across the cell membrane.*
- *Distinguish between facilitated diffusion and active transport.*
- *Explain how protein channels function in transport.*
- *Compare and contrast endocytosis and exocytosis.*
- *Describe the process that led researchers to hypothesize that communication between cells occurred.*

6.2 Other Kinds of Transport

Diffusion and osmosis are forms of passive transport. **Passive transport** is the movement of any substance across a membrane without the use of chemical energy. **Active transport** is the movement of any substance across a cell membrane with the use of chemical energy. Materials cross the cell membrane by either passive or active transport, depending on the size and chemical makeup of the material. The structure of the cell membrane also plays an important role in both types of transport.

As you recall from Chapter 5, the cell membrane consists of two layers, each containing lipid molecules. The carboxyl, hydrophilic ends of the lipid molecules are on the outside surface of the membrane. The glycerol, hydrophobic ends of the lipid molecules form the inside. This structure ensures that molecules that dissolve in water do not automatically pass through the membranes. A layer of lipids separates the two aquatic environments, that of the cell and that of the surrounding environment. The lipid layer thus forms a chemical barrier to the free movement of molecules into and out of the cell. However, many mechanisms serve to ensure the passage of biologically important materials across a membrane.

Carrier Transport

The cell membrane has proteins associated with the lipid layers. Some of these proteins extend across the membrane and others are embedded in it. Each of these two types of proteins aids in the transport of molecules across the membrane. Proteins that function in transport are called **carrier molecules.** These proteins are also called permeases. The carrier molecules and solute molecules move across the membrane. Generally, each carrier molecule is specialized to allow the movement of only one type of molecule across a membrane.

Figure 6-3 Unlike active transport, none of the several types of passive transport requires the expenditure of chemical energy. Gated channels are explained on p. 86.

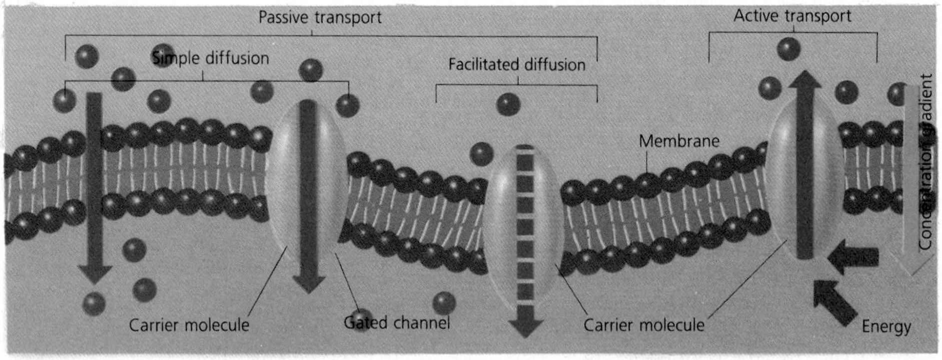

Type of Transport	Transport Aid	Chemical Energy Used	Examples
passive	carrier, gate, or none	no	diffusion, facilitated diffusion, gated channels
active	carrier	yes	sodium-potassium pump, endocytosis, exocytosis

Graphic Organizer Use this table in Independent Practice on p. 88.

Facilitated Diffusion

Some carrier molecules transport solute molecules through a membrane without expending energy. This passive form of carrier transport is called **facilitated diffusion.** In this type of diffusion carrier molecules speed up the diffusion. Glucose molecules, for example, are too large to diffuse quickly across a cell membrane. Sometimes the cell needs glucose in large quantities as a source of energy. If the glucose level within the cell falls too low, carrier molecules accelerate the transport of glucose molecules across the membrane. Facilitated diffusion also operates when the level of glucose is too high inside the cell and must be lowered. The carrier molecules speed the rate of diffusion out of the cell.

Active Transport

Carrier molecules also function in the active transport of solute molecules across cell membranes. One common active transport system is the **sodium–potassium pump,** a chemical mechanism that moves sodium ions (Na^+) out of the cell and forces potassium ions (K^+) in. Movement in both cases is against the respective concentration gradients. The process depends on the ability of the protein carrier molecule to change shape. Three sodium ions fit into the carrier molecule. A chemical reaction using high-energy ATP molecules changes the shape of the carrier molecule, which causes the sodium to be released outside the cell. The carrier molecule can accept two potassium ions. The loss of phosphate from ATP causes a second shape change and the release of the potassium inside the cell.

The pump moves three sodium ions in one direction for every two potassium ions moved in the opposite direction. The change in their distribution on either side of the membrane results in a buildup of a positive charge outside the cell and creates a gradient of electrical charge across the membrane.

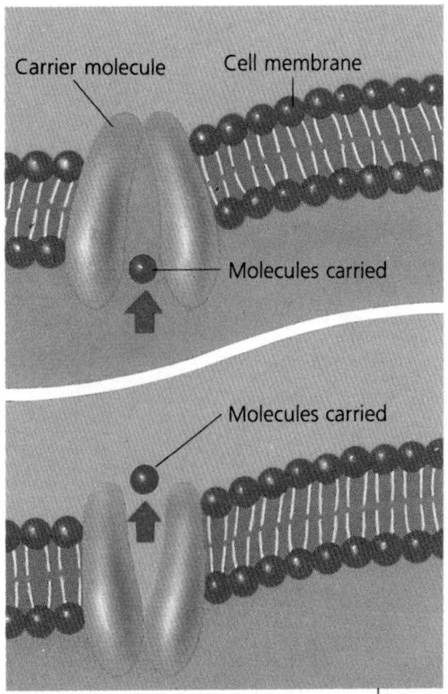

Figure 6-4 In facilitated diffusion carrier molecules speed up diffusion without expending energy.

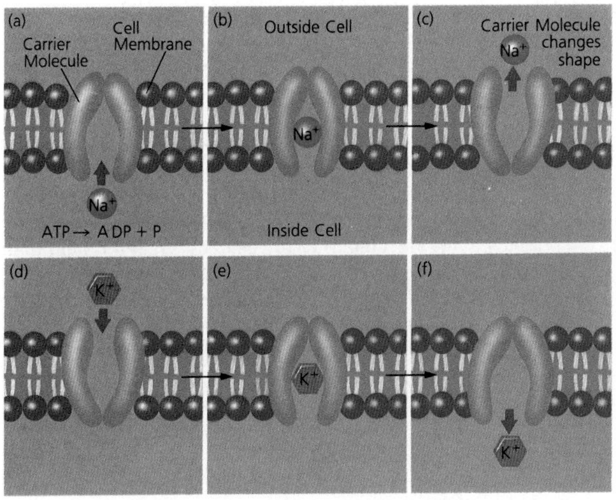

Figure 6-5 The sodium–potassium pump moves sodium ions out of the cell and potassium ions into the cell. In both cases the pump works against the concentration gradients.

Interpreting the Visuals Figures 6-3, 6-4, and 6-5, pp. 84–85, are models of the cell membrane. Ask students how a protein carrier molecule is represented. *(Large, light blue oval)* How is the cell membrane represented? *(Double layer of orange balls and yellow lines)* What do the orange balls represent? (Review Figure 5-7, p. 67, if necessary.) *(Hydrophilic ends of lipid molecules)* How are ions and molecules such as glucose modeled? *(Figures 6-3 and 6-4 portray them identically. In Figure 6-5, Na^+ is a green ball, and K^+ is a pink hexagon.)* Have students use Figure 6-3 to compare active and passive transport.

- *See* **Overhead Transparency** ***T6 and*** **Blackline Masters** ***11 and 12.***

Inferring Relationships Point out that a cell membrane separates two water environments. Review the structure of the membrane (Figure 5-7, p. 67). Ask students to describe the two water environments. *(Inside the cell are water and the molecules and ions necessary for and resulting from metabolism. The external environment may be tissue fluid similar to the cell's internal environment, or, in the case of a unicellular organism, an aquatic environment. In either case, the external environment may be hypertonic, hypotonic, or isotonic.)* Do glucose and most salts, soluble in water, easily cross the cell membrane? *(Yes, but not quickly enough to meet the cell's needs)* How does a cell get the important sugars and salts needed for metabolic activities? *(Through facilitated diffusion and active transport, using cell energy)*

Videodiscs

- *Side 1 29807, Molecular Dynamics (m)*
- *2532, Glucose (s)*

LEP Activity

Help students to remember difficult polysyllabic terms by associating each term with a memorable mental picture. For example, students might associate *carrier molecule* with the image of an automobile or truck carrying an important medical shipment across a border. They might associate *osmosis* with the image of rainwater oozing through a tent roof, and *diffusion* with the experience of detecting cooking odors, smoke, perfume, or cologne as they enter a room.

Summarizing Functions Have students review pp. 84–86. Then have them contribute to a list on the board of the functions of membrane proteins in transport. *(P. 84: specialized carrier molecules, or permeases, move across the membrane with the solute molecules; p. 85: glucose carriers accelerate the rate at which sugar moves passively into or out of the cell; p. 85: proteins carry 3 Na^+ or 2 K^+ across the membrane, using ATP; p. 86: other carriers of sugars and amino acids; p. 86: protein-controlled gated channels alter membrane permeability by remaining open or by opening and closing rapidly.)*

Making Inferences Ask students to recall how much energy is used to maintain the sodium-potassium pump. *(One-third of all energy expenditure maintains the pump.)* In a resting animal, where is the pump active? *(Nerve and muscle cells)* What can students infer about activities that occur during "rest"? *(Even when resting, the body is active; it exports and imports materials, produces materials needed elsewhere, and carries on other activities of metabolism.)*

Applying Concepts Have students apply their knowledge of active transport. Give each student a photocopy of Blackline Masters 11 and 12. Have them label the cell membrane and the cell's interior and exterior, then draw 9 sodium ions (Na^+) and 12 potassium ions (K^+) inside the cell. Tell them to draw 18 Na^+s and 6 K^+s outside the cell. Next, have students draw the situation after ATP activates the sodium-potassium pump once. *(Inside: 6 Na^+s, 14 K^+s; outside: 21 Na^+s, 4 K^+s)*

The sodium–potassium pump is crucial to many physiological processes in animals, including the conduction of nerve impulses and the contraction of muscles. One-third of the energy expended by an animal at rest goes to power this pump.

The sodium–potassium pump is only one example of an active transport system. Other systems work in similar ways to provide the energy for transporting sugars, amino acids, and other important metabolic materials across cell membranes.

Gated Channels

Another form of passive transport occurs when proteins in the membrane form a gated channel across the lipid membrane. A **gated channel** is a protein-controlled passage that permits the cell membrane to be permeable as needed. Molecules that for some reason cannot cross the membrane can diffuse through these channels. Some channels are permanently open. Others open in response to environmental stimuli. For example when an impulse travels down a nerve, stimulates a muscle, and causes it to contract, at least four types of gated channels open and close in the neuromuscular junction in less than one second.

Biology in Process

Connections Between Cells

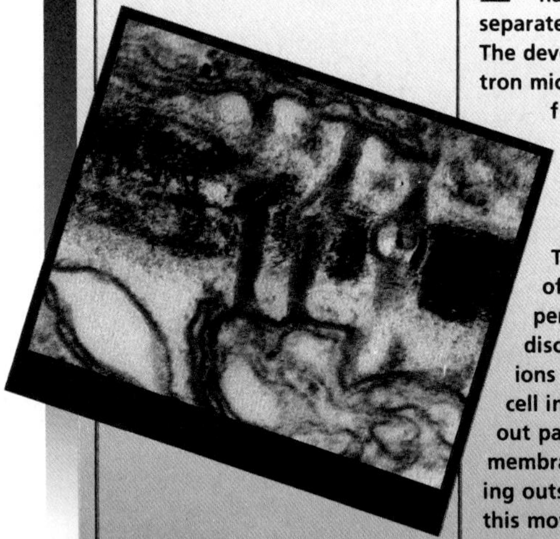

For 150 years scientists had thought of cells as separate, autonomous units. The development of the electron microscope seemed to confirm this view. The electron microscope allowed researchers to see that cell membranes enclosed cells. Then in 1962 two teams of U.S. researchers independently made startling discoveries. They detected ions that moved from one cell interior to another without passing through the cell membrane and without moving outside the cells. How did this movement occur?

Werner Loewenstein and Yoshinobu Kanno asked this question while they were engaged in a study of cells from the salivary gland of the fruit fly larva. As part of their study they caused the nucleus of one cell to carry an electric charge. To their surprise they found that an electric charge was soon evident in adjacent cells but not in the external environment. This discovery indicated to Loewenstein and Kanno that ions must have passed from one cell to another. At about the same time two other researchers, Stephen W. Kuffler and David D. Potter, made a similar observation while studying leech cells.

Interdisciplinary Activity

Health A disinfectant is a substance that destroys disease-causing organisms on nonliving objects. Disinfectants such as alcohols, quaternary ammonium compounds, mercurials, oligodynamic metals (silver, copper, mercury), acids, and coal-tar derivatives kill pathogens by denaturing proteins and destroying or damaging the pathogen's cell membrane or cell wall.

Have each student or group of students use the library to prepare a brief report describing one of the disinfectants listed above. If possible, they should include the disinfectant's mode of action. Encourage students to speculate about how protein damage to a bacterial cell's membrane would affect various transport processes.

Endocytosis and Exocytosis

Some molecules, such as food particles and waste materials, are too large to pass through the cell membrane. However, the processes called endocytosis and exocytosis enable these large molecules and particles to enter and exit the cell without passing through the cell membrane. These processes are part of the cell's maintenance of homeostasis. Cells use endocytosis and exocytosis to stay in balance with their environment by taking in nutrients, exporting proteins, and excreting wastes. Such transfers are made possible by the dynamic nature of the cell membrane.

Endocytosis

Endocytosis *(EN-duh-sie-TOE-suss)* is the process by which cells engulf substances that are much too large to enter the cell by passing through the cell membrane. These large materials outside the cell are enclosed by a portion of the cell, which folds into itself and forms a pouch. The pouch, called a vesicle, then pinches off from the cell membrane and enters the cytoplasm. Once inside the cytoplasm the contents of the vesicle are digested by cellular enzymes.

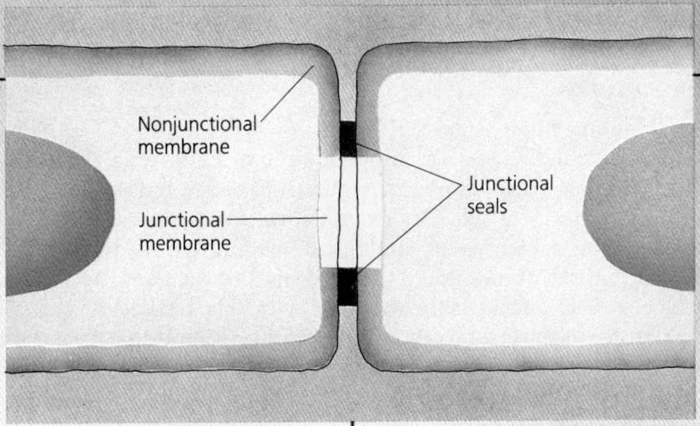

Electrical measurements and detailed examinations of electron photomicrographs suggested to the researchers that a passage existed between the cell membranes of the two cells. Such passages have since become known as "gap junctions" (left).

Loewenstein and Kanno then decided to determine whether or not particles larger than ions could pass through a gap junction. The researchers injected fluorescent tracer molecules into the interior of one cell. These tracer molecules later showed up in adjacent cells as well. By using tracer molecules of different sizes, the researchers determined the size range of molecules that were able to pass through a gap junction.

The team then set out to find the role that various ions played in affecting the permeability of the gap junctions.

The researchers injected calcium ions in the cytoplasm. They determined that an increase in calcium ions lowered the permeability of the gap junctions.

- **What was the significance of the observation that the tracer molecules injected into the cell pass only to adjacent cells?**

Guided Practice

Show students a film or video of amebas engulfing food such as paramecia. Have students identify the process. *(Endocytosis—specifically, phagocytosis)* Ask students to name the second type of endocytosis and explain how it differs from phagocytosis. *(Pinocytosis; it is the movement of solutes or fluids into a cell.)*

Biology in Process

Using the Feature

The feature focuses on the process skills of observation and data interpretation. Emphasize to students that the researchers made many observations and considered much evidence before concluding that ions and molecules could pass from cell to cell without passing through the cell membrane. Ask students who observed similar evidence in leech cells. *(Kuffler and Potter)* Ask students what was used to confirm the existence of gap junctions and the size of the molecules that pass through them. *(Electrical measurements, electron photomicrographs, fluorescent tracer molecules)* Researchers hypothesized that different ions affected gap junction permeability differently. Ask how the role of calcium ions in gap junction permeability was tested. *(By injecting calcium ions into the cytoplasm; an increase in calcium ions increases the molecular movement between cells.)*

Answer to the Feature

The tracer molecules must have passed into the cells through junctions between adjacent cells.

Videodiscs

- *Side 1 33499, Cell Function (m)*
- *532, Paramecium Engulfed by Ameba (s)*

More Information

Active Transport Gap junctions connect one cell to another. Viewed on end with an electron microscope, gap junctions in animal embryonic cells appear as a donut-shaped patch of proteins. Called a connexon, they resemble six-pointed flowers and project from the cell membrane enough to cause a gap of 2–4 nanometers (nm) between cells. Their pores can open to a width of about 1.5 nm, allowing the passage of sugars, amino acids, vitamins, and inorganic ions between cells. Plasmodesmata are openings in the cell wall of plant cells. The opening is 20–40 nm wide, and cytoplasmic strands have been seen connecting one cell to another through the plasmodesmata.

Independent Practice
- Have students write answers to the Section Review.
- Have students create a table comparing passive and active transport. An example of a completed table appears on p. 84.

Check Your Understanding
1. How does active transport differ from passive transport? *(Active transport requires chemical energy.)*
2. How are facilitated diffusion and gated channels similar? *(Both are passive transport.)*
3. How do large molecules leave the cell? *(Via exocytosis.)*

Reteaching
Ask students if the cytoplasm is on the left or right in each picture in Figure 6-6, p. 88. *(Left)* Ask how food enters a cell by endocytosis and wastes leave by exocytosis. *(Left: membrane buds into the cytoplasm, enclosing food. Right: a vacuole fuses with the membrane, releasing wastes.)*
- *See* Section Reviews *worksheet, Section 6.2.*

Enrichment
Have students use the library to write a brief report on the history of cell membrane research, then present their reports for class discussion. *(Under a light microscope, the cell membrane was just an edge. Staining, early EMs, and physical measurements suggested a structure of two lipid layers. Fluid mosaics and gap junctions weren't understood until the 1960s and 1970s.)*

Closure
Stress the importance of cell membranes in maintaining cell integrity. Ask students to list functions of the cell membrane. *(A chemical barrier against free passage of any molecules in and out of the cell; allows passage of biologically important materials)*

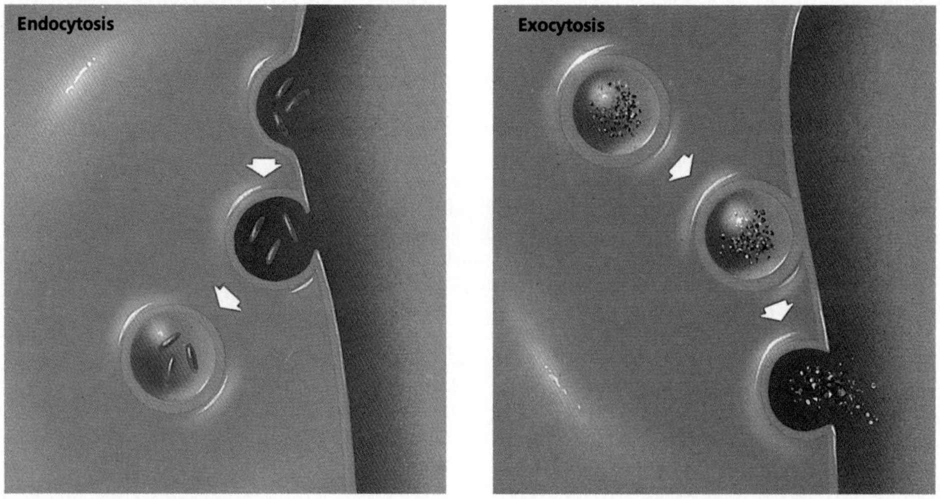

Figure 6-6 In endocytosis (left) cells engulf fluids or food particles that are too large to diffuse or be carried through the membrane. In exocytosis (right) cells excrete wastes or export proteins that cannot exit through the cell membrane.

Biologists distinguish two kinds of endocytosis on the basis of the materials enclosed. **Pinocytosis** *(PIN-uh-sie-TOE-suss)* is the movement of solutes or fluids into the cell, while **phagocytosis** *(FAG-uh-sie-TOE-suss)* is the movement of large food particles or whole microorganisms into the cell. Amebas feed by phagocytosis. In mammals white blood cells called phagocytes engulf and digest bacteria. Review the process of endocytosis by studying Figure 6-6.

Exocytosis
Maintaining homeostasis within a cell often involves exporting large molecules as well as importing them. **Exocytosis** *(ECK-soe-sie-TOE-suss),* also shown in Figure 6-6, is the passage of large molecules out of a cell. For example, cells manufacture proteins necessary for various physiological reactions outside the cell. Recall that ribosomes make the proteins and the Golgi apparatus processes and packages them into vesicles. The packaged proteins then move to the cell membrane. The vesicle membrane fuses with the cell membrane and dumps its contents out of the cell.

Section Review
1. Explain the difference between *facilitated diffusion* and *active transport.*
2. How does the structure of the cell membrane facilitate transport by carrier molecules?
3. How does the sodium–potassium pump work?
4. Describe the process of endocytosis.
5. How might carrier molecules help maintain homeostasis during exercise, when extra energy is needed quickly?

Answers to Section Review
1. Both involve carrier molecules, but facilitated diffusion does not need cell energy.
2. Proteins embedded in the lipid bilayer act as carrier molecules. Substances bound to the carrier on one side of the membrane are released on the other side.
3. A chemical reaction using the energy of ATP causes carrier molecules to pass sodium ions out of the cell and bring in potassium ions in a ratio of 3:2. Both move against a concentration gradient.
4. The cell membrane surrounds a food particle and pinches off to form a sac.
5. Carrier molecules speed up the passage of glucose, depleted during exercise, into the muscle cells.

Laboratory

Osmosis and Turgor Pressure

Objective
To examine the osmotic behavior of cells and to understand the concept of turgor pressure

Process Skills
Observing, experimenting

Materials
Fresh potato, scalpel, plastic fork, 2 petri dishes, 10% salt solution, clock or watch, piece of red onion, 2 medicine droppers, microscope slide, coverslip, blunt probe, microscope, paper towel

Inquiry
1 In this investigation you will study potato and onion cells in order to observe the relationship between osmosis and turgor pressure. Cut a potato in half lengthwise. Cut a 3-mm-thick slice along the length of one of the halves. Cut four sticks 3 mm wide along the length of the slice.
2 Holding a fork in one hand, place a potato stick across the middle of the tines so that equal amounts overhang each side. Observe how much the potato stick bends. What does the amount of bend tell you about the turgor pressure inside the potato cells? How might this observation serve as a control for later observations?
3 Fill a petri dish about half full with water. Place an equal amount of 10% salt solution in another petri dish. Add two potato sticks to each dish.
4 Once each minute, use the fork to pick up each stick by its center to test it for bend. Test each stick until you no longer notice any difference in how much it bends. Compare your observations about the sticks placed in water and the sticks placed in salt solution with your observations in step 2. What inference can you draw from your observations? How might you test your inference directly?
5 Take a small piece of onion and peel off a sheet of the purple skin. With a scalpel cut a piece of skin about 6 mm^2.
6 Use a medicine dropper to place a drop of 10% salt solution on a microscope slide. Place the piece of onion skin over the drop and cover the slide with a coverslip.
7 Examine the slide under low power of a microscope. What do you observe? How do these observations relate to those in step 4?
8 Use a clean dropper to add water to one side of the coverslip and paper towel to absorb the salt solution on the other side. What happens to the onion cells? What can you infer about the movement of water between cells and their external environment?

Conclusions
1 What effect did the salt solution have on the potato and onion cells?
2 Which caused greater turgor pressure inside the cell—water or salt solution?

Further Inquiry
How can you use what you have learned about the flexibility of the potato sticks to determine the salt concentration naturally present in the cells of a freshly cut stick?

Laboratory

(For an overview of osmosis and turgor pressure and preparatory information related to the laboratory, see p. 79B.)

Inquiry
2. The stick bends little or not at all, indicating a normal—that is, high—turgor pressure. Drawing or measuring the amount of bend sets the standard control for comparison.
4. The sticks in water bend less than those in the salt solution and less than the fresh-cut stick; student infers that due to osmosis, water moved into the potato cells, increasing turgor pressure; water is hypotonic to cytoplasm, so turgor pressure is high. Sticks in salt solution become limp and bend more; student infers that the salt solution is hypertonic; turgor pressure decreases and the cell wilts. Comparing the solute concentrations of the water and the salt solution would directly test the inferences.
7. Onion cells in salt solution show plasmolysis; their cytoplasm is rounded and pulls away from the cell wall. As in step 4, turgor pressure decreased in a salt solution.
8. Water diffuses into the cells. The cytoplasm expands as turgor pressure rises. Student may infer that water diffuses either way across the membrane; cells respond to their environment.

Conclusions
1. The salt solution caused water to leave the cells because the solute concentration outside the cell was greater than the concentration inside the cell.
2. Water caused increased turgor pressure because water diffused into the cell, swelling the cytoplasm and increasing its pressure against the cell wall. The cell became rigid.

Further Inquiry
Students can use potato sticks to test which percentages of salt solutions produce neither swelling nor limpness. Parallel observations with onion cells conserve solutions but take a little longer.

Chapter 6 Review

Vocabulary

1. In both processes, molecules move from an area of higher to an area of lower concentration. In facilitated diffusion, however, carrier molecules increase the rate of diffusion.
2. A selectively permeable membrane allows the passage of some substances, but not others. The cell membrane is an example.
3. As turgor pressure decreases, a plant cell's cytoplasm shrinks. This is called plasmolysis.
4. A contractile vacuole is an organelle that collects water from the cytoplasm of an animal cell. Contraction of the vacuole forces the water outside the cell.
5. *Pino-* means "drink," *phago-* means "eat," and *cyto-* means "cell." In pinocytosis the cell membrane of a "drinking cell" surrounds and takes in liquids or small particles. In phagocytosis, the "eating cell" surrounds and ingests food with its membrane.

Review

1. c
2. d
3. c
4. a
5. b
6. c
7. b
8. c
9. c
10. b

11. Equilibrium is the even distribution of randomly moving molecules within a space.
12. No. Some molecules are too large or of an incompatible charge or type to pass through some membranes. Selectively permeable membranes can prohibit—by pore size, charge, and carrier molecule—the passage of some substances.
13. Cytolysis may occur. Water would diffuse down a concentration gradient into the organism, which would have no means of getting rid of excess water.
14. The direction of water movement into or out of a cell depends on the concentration of water and of solutes in the internal and external environments.
15. The lipid layer is hydrophobic, preventing passage of most water-soluble or charged ions and molecules.
16. A carrier molecule binds to a particular substance, transports it across the cell membrane, and releases it inside.
17. Glucose is carried by facilitated diffusion.
18. ATP provides energy required for the sodium-potassium pump.
19. Endocytosis brings in particles too large to pass through the pores in the cell membrane. Exocytosis releases large molecules, such as protein products, from the cell.

Chapter 6 Review

Vocabulary

active transport (84)
carrier molecules (84)
concentration gradient (81)
contractile vacuole (83)
cytolysis (83)
diffusion (81)
endocytosis (87)
equilibrium (81)
exocytosis (88)
facilitated diffusion (85)
gated channels (86)
homeostasis (81)
hypertonic (83)
hypotonic (83)
isotonic (83)
osmosis (82)
passive transport (84)
permeable (82)
phagocytosis (88)
pinocytosis (88)
plasmolysis (83)
sodium–potassium pump (85)
turgor pressure (83)

1. Distinguish between diffusion and facilitated diffusion.
2. Explain what is meant by a selectively permeable membrane. Give an example of a biological system that employs a semipermeable membrane.
3. How is plasmolysis related to turgor pressure?
4. What is a contractile vacuole, and how does it function?
5. Use a dictionary to find the meaning of the word parts *pino-*, *phago-*, and *cyto-*. Why are the terms *pinocytosis* and *phagocytosis* good names for the processes they describe?

Review

1. Homeostasis is (a) the movement of materials into and out of a cell (b) the transport of proteins against the concentration gradiant (c) a state of biological balance (d) the process of molecules spreading out evenly across an environment.
2. The part of the cell that functions to maintain homeostasis relative to the cell's environment is the (a) cytoplasm (b) Golgi apparatus (c) nucleus (d) cell membrane.
3. Gap junctions aid the (a) movement of molecules against a concentration gradient (b) movement of particles in response to random movement of molecules (c) movement of molecules from one cell to another (d) paired movement of sodium and potassium ions.
4. Glucose enters a cell by (a) diffusion (b) pinocytosis (c) phagocytosis (d) active transport.
5. When the solution inside the cell is hypertonic relative to its environment, (a) water will move from inside the cell to outside the cell (b) water will move from outside the cell to inside the cell (c) the water balance will be maintained (d) the cell will burst.
6. When the turgor pressure of a cell is high, a plant (a) wilts (b) dies (c) is rigid (d) explodes.
7. Plasmolysis refers to a cell's (a) taking in too much water (b) shriveling (c) consuming dangerous bacteria (d) maintaining a fluid balance.
8. Gated channels function to (a) export proteins out of the cell (b) transport proteins against the concentration gradient (c) transport molecules by diffusion through the channel (d) import proteins into the cell.
9. The cell must expend energy to transport substances using (a) a protein channel (b) facilitated diffusion (c) a sodium–potassium pump (d) osmosis.
10. As part of the immune system, a white blood cell engulfs, digests, and destroys an invading bacterium through the process of (a) facilitated diffusion (b) phagocytosis (c) pinocytosis (d) osmosis.
11. Explain equilibrium.

12. Can all molecules diffuse through all membranes? Explain your answer.
13. What would happen to a freshwater unicellular organism if its contractile vacuole stopped functioning? Explain your answer.
14. What determines the direction of movement of water across a cell membrane?
15. How does the lipid layer of a membrane form a barrier to molecules?
16. How does a carrier molecule transport materials across a cell membrane?
17. What form of transport is used by the cell membrane to speed up the intake of glucose when needed?
18. What energy source does the cell use to work the sodium–potassium pump?
19. Distinguish between endocytosis and exocytosis.
20. What did researchers observe that led them to hypothesize that a connection existed between cells?

Critical Thinking

1. In an inflated ballon there is a higher concentration of air molecules inside than there is in the air outside. Because of their constant random motion these molecules push against the balloon and keep it taut. In what way is this pressure similar to turgor pressure? In what way is it different?
2. Sometimes water seeps through the concrete wall of a basement after a heavy rain, and the homeowner removes it with a sump pump. How can this situation be compared with the action of a unicellular organism that lives in a pond?
3. When a cell like the one pictured on the right takes in substances through endocytosis, the cell membrane forms an inside-out pouch. The outside of the cell membrane becomes the inside of the vesicle. What might this suggest about the structure of the cell membrane?

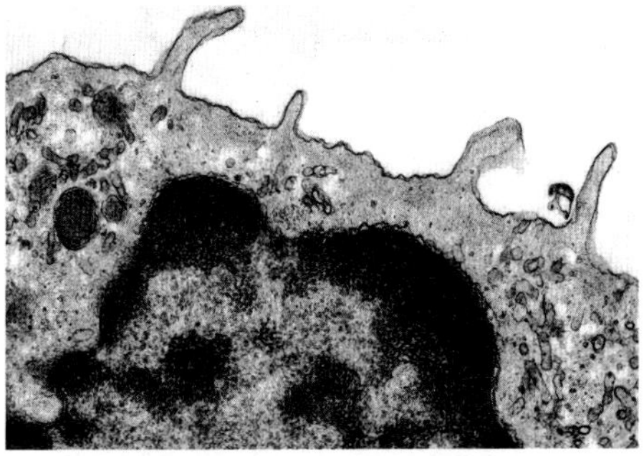

Extension

1. Read the article by I. Amato entitled "Mapping Chemical Microscapes of Cells," in *Science News,* March 17, 1990, p. 167. Make an oral report in which you explain some advantages of ion microscopy, including how the new technique helps chemists track the absorption of calcium into different cells.
2. Kidney dialysis is the artificial filtering of a patient's blood to remove wastes when the patient's kidneys can no longer function well. Selectively permeable membranes are used in kidney dialysis and in other areas of medicine. Consult your local hospital, and obtain information on how kidney dialysis is performed and on whom. You may wish to read the article by Richard J. Margolis entitled "Make Me Whole," in *New Leader,* August 6, 1990, pp. 9–10.
3. Examine a number of food items at a grocery store. List at least four foods in which salt is used as a preservative. Keeping in mind what you have learned about osmosis, explain why salt is used so commmonly to preserve food.

20. Researchers observed that electrically charged ions moved from cell to cell without appearing outside the cells. The hypothesis was confirmed when the researchers observed that fluorescent-tagged tracer molecules of various sizes also moved from cell to cell.

Critical Thinking

1. The air pressure in a balloon resembles turgor pressure in that random molecular motion keeps the outer membrane taut. A difference is that the cell membrane is more permeable to water than the balloon is to air. Also, air is forced into the balloon through a single opening. Water diffuses across the cell membrane by osmosis.

2. A selectively permeable membrane can be compared to the concrete wall; water crosses both barriers. The sump pump removes water using electrical energy. A cell vacuole removes water using chemical energy from ATP.

3. It suggests that the structure of the cell membrane's inner and outer layers are interchangeable, essentially the same. This reflects the dynamic, flexible nature of the cell membrane.

Extension

1. Students' reports should include a description of the ion microscope and its capabilities. Encourage students to quote the researchers or author to emphasize how the instrument functions and its impact on biological research.

2. Students may find more information on the techniques used in hemodialysis if their local hospital does not perform or has little information on peritoneal dialysis. Encourage students to research the emotional impact of dialysis as discussed in Margolis's article.

3. Salt can be used to preserve pickles, eggs, and meats. Through osmosis, a salt solution pulls water from the food tissues and prevents lysosomes and cell enzymes from digesting the food. Also, salt can kill some bacteria through cytolysis.

Chapter 7 Photosynthesis and Respiration

Chapter Overview

Chapter 7 elaborates on the discussion of energy relationships introduced in Chapter 1. Section 7.1 discusses metabolic pathways of autotrophs and heterotrophs—photosynthesis and respiration—and the energy on which all life depends. Section 7.2 focuses on photosynthesis, the use of light energy to produce food in the form of carbohydrates. Section 7.3 examines respiration, how glucose is broken down to produce energy for life activities.

Chapter Planning Chart

B	S	A	Sections and Subsections	Page	Features	Page	Resources
•	•	•	**7.1 The Need for Energy**				
			Energy for Life Processes	93	Section Review	95	Videodiscs
			Adenosine Triphosphate	94			Blackline Master 13
			ATP-ADP Cycle	95			Overhead Transparency T7
							Blackline Master 14
							Section Reviews Worksheet
	•	•	**7.2 Photosynthesis**				
			Light Absorption by Chlorophyll	96	Biology in Process	100	Videodiscs
			Light-Dependent Reactions	97	Laboratory	109	Science in Action Videotape: Photosynthesis and Cellular Respiration
			Light-Independent Reactions	99	Section Review	102	Process Skills: Experimental Controls
							Laboratories: Chromatography
							Section Reviews Worksheet
	•	•	**7.3 Respiration**				
			Glycolysis	103	Think	105	Videodiscs
			Fermentation	104	Section Review	108	Blackline Master 15
			Aerobic Respiration	105			Blackline Master 16
							Blackline Master 17
							Laboratories: Fermentation
							Section Reviews Worksheet
			End of Chapter Activities				
					Chapter Review	110	Vocabulary Skills
							Chapter Test
							Computer Test Generator

B *The Basic Level curriculum presents the most fundamental knowledge offered in the course.*
S *The Standard Level curriculum is designed for the average student who is able to master most topics.*
A *The Advanced Level curriculum includes suggestions for teaching the most academically able students.*

Cooperative Learning

Group Activity: Molecular Models

- **Group Size:** *4 students*
- **Outcome:** *Students will visualize the reactants and overall products of photosynthesis and respiration.*
- **Individual Accountability:** *Each student will build a molecular model.*
- **Positive Interdependence:** *Each group will model the overall processes of photosynthesis or respiration.*

Assign each group a process—*Photosynthesis* or *Respiration*. Provide each group with materials to build molecular models—gumdrops and toothpicks will work. Have *Photosynthesis* group members build six models each of carbon dioxide (CO_2) and water (H_2O). Have *Respiration* group members build a glucose molecule ($C_6H_{12}O_6$) and six oxygens (O_2).

Next, have *Photosynthesis* groups use parts of their CO_2 and H_2O models to produce models of O_2 and glucose. Have *Respiration* group members use their glucose and O_2 models to build H_2O and CO_2 molecules.

Have a *Photosynthesis* group and a *Respiration* group explain their model-building process to each other. Ask students to suggest possible origins of the oxygen atoms in the carbohydrate product of photosynthesis *(H_2O or CO_2)* and in the respiration product, CO_2 *(glucose or O_2)*. Tell students they will learn the correct answers in the chapter.

Concept Map

The following is one possible solution to the concept mapping activity in Reteaching on p. 108.

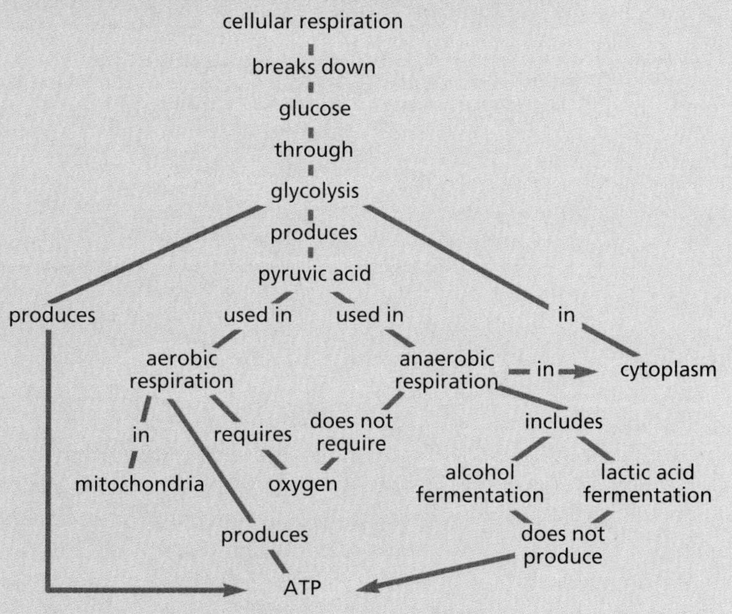

Laboratory Preparation

Overview *(See p. 109.)*

In this lab students investigate the relationship between light intensity and the rate of photosynthesis. Be sure students understand that oxygen and carbohydrates are products of photosynthesis; they can infer that the bubbles observed in the lab are bubbles of oxygen. Students will infer that a change in the oxygen production rate reflects a change in the rate of photosynthesis. They will also infer that an increase in light intensity increases the rate of photosynthesis.

Other factors affecting the rate of photosynthesis include the availability of carbon dioxide and water. On land, temperature and humidity are important factors.

Preparation

Elodea, also called *Anacharis,* may be obtained from aquarium stores or a local pond. Place *Elodea* in tap water that has stood for 24 hours to remove excess chlorine. Store the plants in dim light until needed.

Teaching Tips

Have students complete the Background questions; review the answers prior to the lab. Have students read the Technique section before they design an experiment.

Have students make the bicarbonate solution a day in advance to avoid the chance of their mistaking air bubbles for oxygen bubbles. Caution students to make careful observations, as the oxygen bubbles are small. To keep *Elodea* upright in the beaker, have students tie each end of the sprig to each end of the stirring rod.

Use the lab to discuss the greenhouse effect and increased atmospheric CO_2, explained in Chapter 50. Have students speculate as to whether an unlimited CO_2 supply means unlimited O_2 production by photosynthesis. *(Under field conditions, the CO_2 concentration is the rate-limiting factor, but an unlimited CO_2 supply does not mean an unlimited rate of photosynthesis and O_2 production. Light intensity and temperature are also factors. At a high light intensity, a temperature increase increases the rate of photosynthesis. At a low light intensity, a temperature increase does not increase the rate of photosynthesis.)*

Safety

Caution students to avoid touching hot lamp bulbs and remind them of electrical safety. Remind them to use a hotpad to support the bottom of the Erlenmeyer flasks when they empty the flask of warmed water.

Chapter Themes

Energy Point out that the total amount of energy in a system is constant, but that its form can change. Autotrophs convert solar energy to chemical energy through photosynthesis. Respiration, the breakdown of glucose to provide chemical energy, occurs in both heterotrophs and autotrophs.

Patterns of Change Complex biochemical pathways often include series of cyclic reactions. Give an example of a cycle that regenerates its starting compound, such as oxaloacetic acid of the Krebs cycle.

Scale and Structure Relate the structures of the chloroplast and mitochondrion—double lipid layers and enzymes—to similarities in their functions—diffusion of materials, electron transport, and chemiosmosis.

Chapter Motivating Activity

Encourage students to bring in potted plants. Ask them to list ways in which such plants could be beneficial or harmful. *(Benefits include the psychological well-being they can impart or their decorative beauty. However, some people are allergic to plant pollen; some plants are poisonous on contact or through ingestion.)* Tell students that some people keep plants in their home or office, believing that the plants use CO_2 and provide additional O_2. Ask students if this belief is reasonable. *(Photosynthesis uses CO_2 to produce O_2, but respiration, which produces CO_2, also occurs in plants. Also, the amounts of CO_2 and O_2 used and produced by a single potted plant probably do not significantly affect the levels of those gases in a room.)* Tell the class this chapter examines the importance of such compounds in both plants and animals.

Chapter 7 *Photosynthesis and Respiration*

Introduction

In Chapters 1 and 3 you learned that all living organisms use energy. In this chapter you will learn of the importance of energy to living organisms and how cells transfer energy as packets in chemical bonds. Cycles of energy and matter are of crucial importance in cell metabolism.

Chapter Outline

Chapter Concept

As you read about the complex biochemical pathways cells use to transfer energy, keep in mind that carbohydrates that are made in photosynthesis are broken down in respiration.

Leaf of a tulip tree, *Liriodendron tulipifera*. Inset (left): TEM of mitochondrion in a bat pancreas (×6,000). Inset (right): Color-enhanced TEM of a chloroplast in the moss *Physcomitrella potens* (×5,700).

Understanding the Visuals

Point out to students that two of the three photographs are magnified beyond the capability of their class microscopes. Ask students to identify the organelles shown and to recall where in the textbook they were first shown. *(Mitochondrion and chloroplast, Chapter 5)* Have students speculate as to similarities and differences of structure and function between the two organelles. *(Students may say the organelles have similar oval shapes; both have internal lines. Students may use their knowledge of mitochondria to infer that chloroplasts also have internal membranes. Students may speculate that the products of one process are utilized in the other.)* Point out that the chapter will provide details on the roles of these organelles in photosynthesis and respiration.

7.1 The Need for Energy

All living cells use energy for life processes. Cells use energy to digest food, grow, or build macromolecules. Where do cells get this energy? If you said, "from food," you were right. However, the original energy source for most organisms is light.

Energy for Life Processes

Radiant energy of sunlight must be changed by several complex reactions before a cell can use sunlight for life processes. Figure 7-1 traces the path of energy from sun to cell. The first stage is called photosynthesis. The process of **photosynthesis** converts radiant solar energy into chemical energy stored in the bonds of organic compounds, usually carbohydrates. As you read in Chapter 4, carbohydrates, including sugars and starches, are forms of stored energy important to many organisms.

The second stage in the passage of energy from sun to cell is the release of energy from food. The release of chemical energy for cellular use is called **respiration,** which occurs in all cells. Respiration is a type of intermediary metabolism. As you read in Chapter 3, intermediary metabolism causes a series of small changes to a molecule, each change releasing a small amount of chemical energy. Most organisms depend on respiration and photosynthesis to provide energy directly or indirectly.

Recall from Chapter 1 that organisms can be classified according to the origin of their food energy. Plants and certain other organisms can make their own food. Organisms that use energy, such as light, to build organic molecules from inorganic substances are called **autotrophs** (*AWT-uh-TROFES*). Plants are autotrophs because they convert the sun's energy into chemical energy by photosynthesis. Therefore, a unicellular alga in the ocean and a 10-story-high redwood tree are both autotrophs.

Animals and other organisms that cannot make their own food are called **heterotrophs** *(HET-uh-ruh-TROFES)*. Heterotrophs feed on autotrophs or on other heterotrophs that feed on autotrophs. For example, a cow and the water buffalo shown in Figure 7-2 are heterotrophs that feed directly on an autotroph, grass. A human that eats the meat of a cow feeds indirectly on autotrophs. Therefore, both the human and the cow are heterotrophs. Ultimately, all life depends on autotrophs.

Section Objectives

- *Explain the importance of energy to living organisms.*
- *Distinguish between autotrophs and heterotrophs.*
- *Compare and contrast the functions of photosynthesis and respiration.*
- *Describe the structure of an ATP molecule.*
- *Summarize the ATP-ADP cycle.*

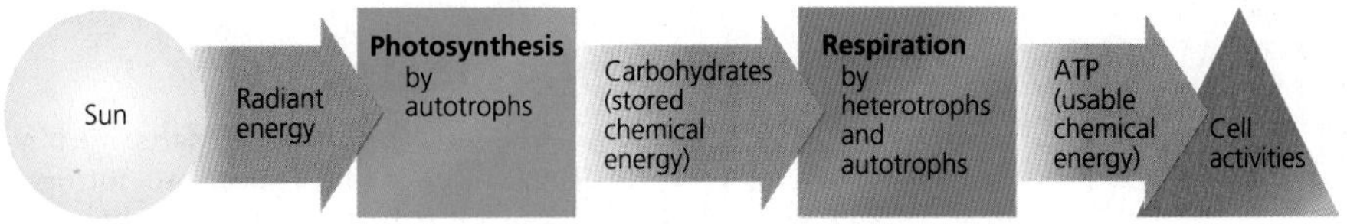

Figure 7-1 Energy for most living organisms comes from the sun and is converted to usable form through photosynthesis and respiration.

Lesson Plan

Section Focus

This section introduces key concepts in Chapter 7: the importance of energy to living organisms; energy use in autotrophs and heterotrophs—photosynthesis and respiration; biochemical pathways; and ATP.

Section Themes

The theme of **Energy** is evident in this section, which explains how energy flows through all living things. Solar energy is converted to chemical energy in photosynthesis. In heterotrophs and autotrophs, the process of respiration converts the energy in glucose to ATP.

Motivating Activity

Have students suggest materials they would need to build a self-contained space station or underwater lab. *(Students may suggest food, water, common household items. They may discuss Biosphere II, a sealed habitat in the Sonoran desert.)* Give students graph paper and have them design a space station or underwater lab. Remind them that the habitat is to be self-contained; no food or oxygen—only energy—can be brought in once the structure is finished. *(Hydroponic systems provide food and O_2 and remove CO_2. Wastes are chemically trapped and sometimes recycled through plants. Solar energy panels trap energy.)* Ask students to explain the relationship of autotrophs and heterotrophs in their structure. *(Autotrophs get energy for life activities from food they make using light energy. Heterotrophs get their energy by eating autotrophs or other heterotrophs.)*

Videodiscs

- *2532, Glucose Molecule (s)*
- *2528, Water Molecule (s)*

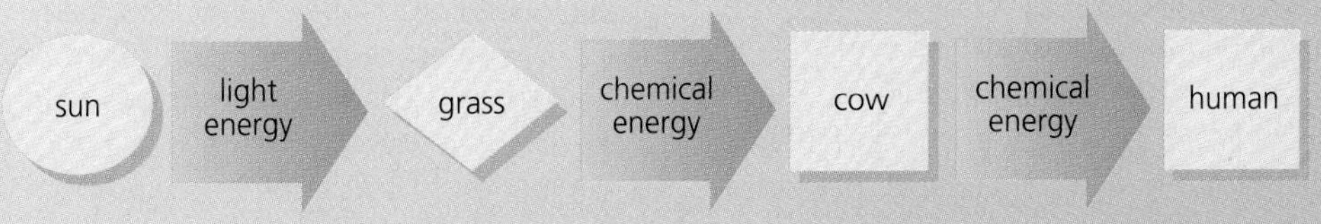

Graphic Organizer Use this sequential diagram in Reteaching on p. 95.

Teaching Strategies

Applying Prior Knowledge Ask students to relate information from Section 4.2 to energy use in living things. *(Glucose, a carbohydrate and the main source of energy for both plants and animals, is metabolized during respiration. Lipids are a form of stored energy. Proteins such as enzymes are essential in intermediary metabolism.)* Point out that respiration is the main part of intermediary metabolism, introduced in Section 3.3.

Interpreting the Visuals Ask students to recall the formula of glucose from Chapter 4, p. 50. Refer students to Figures 7-1, 7-2, and 7-3 on pp. 93–94. Ask students what elements appear in photosynthesis and respiration. What molecules do they form? *(Carbon, oxygen, hydrogen, nitrogen, and phosphorus; as molecules of CO_2, H_2O, O_2, glucose, and ATP)* Point out that just a few of the many compounds involved are illustrated.

Have students identify the different forms of energy. *(Solar, or light, and chemical)* Point out that heat energy is also given off by the sun, as body heat, and through decomposition.

■ *See* **Overhead Transparency** *T7 and* **Blackline Masters** *13 and 14.*

Guided Practice

Ask students to summarize the graphics in this section. *(Figure 7-1, p. 93, shows a linear flow of energy from the sun to its use in cells. Figure 7-2, p. 94, models the cyclic relationships of organisms and processes; the photograph shows the dependence of a heterotroph on autotrophs. Figure 7-4, p. 95, models how energy in the form of ATP is generated for cell use in the ATP-ADP cycle.)* Have students define vocabulary terms used in the illustrations.

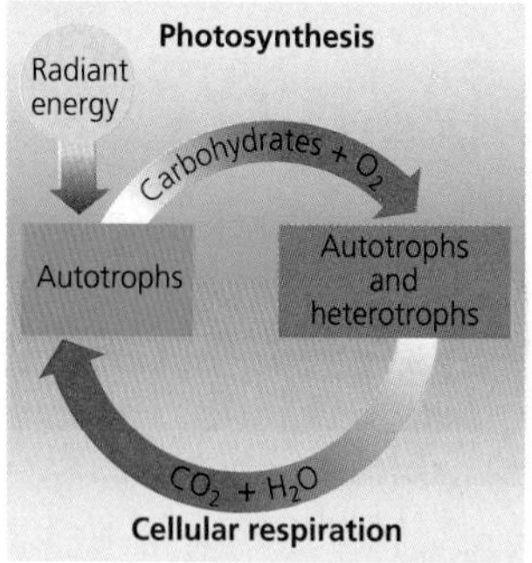

Figure 7-2 Autotrophs produce carbohydrates and oxygen by photosynthesis. Both autotrophs and heterotrophs produce carbon dioxide and water by cellular respiration.

Most autotrophs produce chemical energy by photosynthesis. Figure 7-2 shows that products of photosynthesis—carbohydrates and oxygen—are reactants used in respiration. Products of respiration—carbon dioxide and water—are used in photosynthesis. Both processes can be summarized in equations. Notice the products and reactants in this general equation for photosynthesis:

$$CO_2 + H_2O + \text{light energy} \longrightarrow (CH_2O)_n + O_2$$

Compare this equation for photosynthesis with the following general equation for the breakdown of glucose in respiration:

$$C_6H_{12}O_6 + 6\ O_2 \longrightarrow 6\ CO_2 + 6\ H_2O + \text{energy}$$

It seems that the carbon dioxide, water, and energy made by respiration are the same reactants used in photosynthesis. Yet respiration is not the reverse of photosynthesis. Both processes are very complex; they each involve a specific series of reactions, perform a specific function, and occur at different sites. Such a complex series of reactions is called a **biochemical pathway**. Both photosynthesis and respiration are biochemical pathways.

Biochemical pathways can produce chemical products that are reused. In some cases the product is used within the pathway and keeps the reactions moving in a cycle. In other cases the products produced by one pathway are used in a separate pathway.

In Chapter 7, you will look at the biochemical pathways of photosynthesis and respiration. You will see that energy is often transferred from reaction to reaction, often in the form of **ATP**, or adenosine triphosphate *(uh-DEN-uh-SEEN trie-FAHS-FATE)*. ATP is the storage molecule for energy used by most organisms with the energy needed for life processes.

Figure 7-3 Adenine (yellow), ribose (green), and phosphate groups (blue) bond to form ATP. The energy is stored in the bonds linking the phosphate groups.

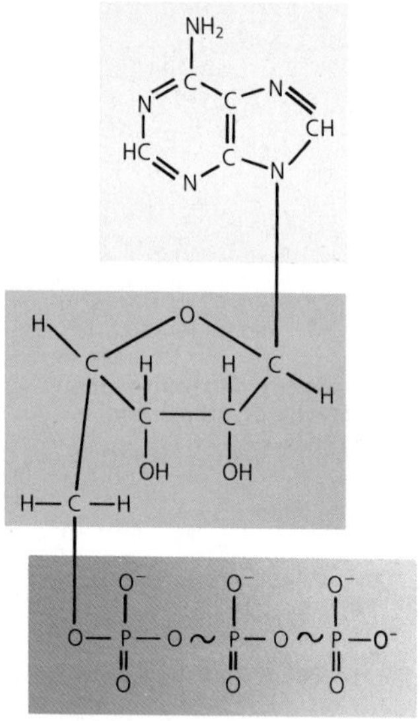

Adenosine Triphosphate

Figure 7-3 shows that an ATP molecule has three parts: adenine, ribose, and phosphate groups. Notice that adenine is a nitrogen-containing molecule. Ribose is a sugar with a five-carbon ring.

Cooperative Learning

Terrarium Divide the class into groups of 4–6 students. Have each group plan an enclosed, self-supporting terrarium. (Students should consider water, soil, light, and specific plants and animals.) If possible, have each group set up a terrarium using a 2-L glass or plastic container, soil, water, plant specimens such as moss, ferns, and liverworts, and small invertebrates such as one or two insects or land snails. Have the class discuss whether each terrarium models a real ecosystem. *(Contains both autotrophs and heterotrophs; nutrients and wastes are recycled within the system; and energy, usually light, is the only addition from outside the system.)*

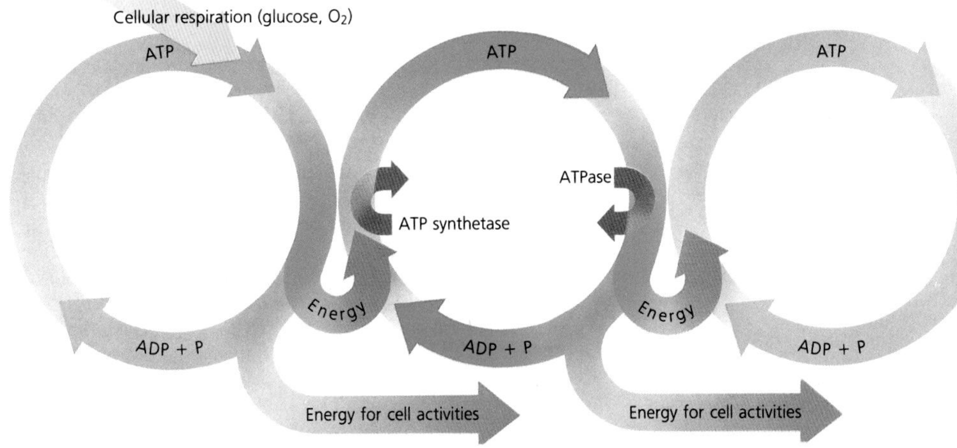

Figure 7-4 When phosphate bonds break, ATP becomes ADP and energy is released. ATP is re-formed when ADP and P bond.

Adenine bonded to ribose is called adenosine. Adenosine bonded to three phosphate groups is called ATP, as its name implies. Adenosine bonded to one phosphate group is called adenosine monophosphate, or AMP. Adenosine bonded to two phosphate groups is called adenosine diphosphate, or **ADP.**

Energy is released when ATP reacts to form ADP or AMP. A wavy line in Figure 7-3 represents a bond that is broken in the reaction. You know that energy must be added to reactants for most chemical reactions to occur. Although energy is used to break ATP's phosphate bonds, more energy is released than is used up. Therefore, the formation of ADP or AMP from ATP is an energy-producing reaction.

ATP-ADP Cycle

In the mitochondria, the ATP-ADP cycle shown in Figure 7-4 provides energy for cell activities. When this energy is needed, an enzyme called ATPase breaks off ATP's third phosphate group, forming ADP and releasing energy.

Usually the freed phosphate group moves to another molecule in a process called **phosphorylation** *(FAHS-FOR-uh-LAY-shun)*. The phosphorylated molecule gains both the phosphate group and the energy. ATP is formed when the enzyme ATP synthetase catalyzes ADP phosphorylation.

Photosynthesis, respiration, and the ATP-ADP cycle form a sequence. Photosynthesis stores energy in chemical compounds; respiration releases this energy. The freed energy forms ATP, and the energy from the breakdown of ATP fuels cell activity.

Section Review

1. What is *ATP?* Describe its structure and function.
2. Contrast how autotrophs and heterotrophs get their energy.
3. What organisms are called producers? Consumers? Why?
4. What two enzymes affect ATP?

Answers to Section Review

1. ATP stores energy needed for life processes. An ATP molecule consists of adenine, ribose, and three phosphate groups.
2. Autotrophs make their own food by using light energy to build organic molecules from inorganic substances. Heterotrophs can't make their own food; they must eat autotrophs or other heterotrophs to obtain energy.
3. Autotrophs such as plants *produce* their own food by photosynthesis. Heterotrophs include animals that get their energy by *consuming* other organisms.
4. ATPase and ATP synthetase.

Independent Practice

- Have students write answers to the Section Review.
- Ask students to write single sentences describing relationships between this section's important concepts—for example, photosynthesis/respiration. *(Photosynthesis converts light energy into chemical energy used in respiration to provide energy for life activities.)*

Check Your Understanding

1. Which are autotrophs: clam, pine tree, fern, green algae? *(All but clam)*
2. When do autotrophs respire? *(All the time, since they need energy for life activities. Respiration doesn't require sunlight.)*

Reteaching

Have students diagram the types of energy transferred to a specific autotroph and at least two heterotrophs, beginning at the sun. An example of a completed diagram appears on p. 93.

- *See* Section Reviews *worksheet, Section 7.1.*

Enrichment

Have students use the library to research autotrophs other than green plants, such as benthic, chemotrophic organisms. Have students explain how these communities survive without sunlight. *(Chemotrophic bacteria metabolize hydrogen sulfide, H_2S, rather than H_2O. See also the Biology in Process feature on pp. 302–303.)*

Closure

Ask students to identify the ultimate energy source for most life forms. *(Solar energy)* Ask them how solar energy becomes available for use by heterotrophs. *(Autotrophs change light to chemical energy through photosynthesis.)*

Videodiscs

- ***2534, Adenosine Triphosphate (s)***

Lesson Plan

Section Focus

Section 7.2 explains photosynthesis in detail: reaction sites in the chloroplast; light-dependent reactions that trap solar energy in chemical bonds, releasing oxygen; light-independent reactions that "fix" carbon from CO_2 to hydrogen and oxygen ions from H_2O, forming intermediate compounds; alternate C_4 and CAM pathways.

Section Themes

Photosynthesis can be described both as a single process and as a series of biochemical reactions that convert a variety of intermediates into specific products, thereby expressing the theme of **Patterns of Change.** For example, the ATP and NADPH products of the light-dependent reactions are reactants of the light-independent reactions.

The theme of **Scale and Structure** is evident in the examination of the structure of chloroplasts and thylakoid membranes. At the cellular and molecular scale, both are adaptations that capture and move around the light and chemical energy needed for life.

Motivating Activity

Obtain a motor and a 1.5–3 V photoelectric cell at a hobby store. Have students use the leads provided to connect the cell to the motor. Have them test the cell's function under light and dark conditions. Ask them to put filters of colored cellophane in front of a light source and observe any differences in function. Point out the similarities between the mechanical setup and a chloroplast. The photoelectric cell is comparable to the thylakoid membranes in a chloroplast. The electrical current generated is comparable to the electrochemical gradient in the thylakoid. In living systems, energy is stored as bond energy.

Section Objectives

- *Explain how the structure of the chloroplast relates to its function.*
- *Distinguish between the light-dependent reactions and the light-independent reactions.*
- *Summarize the main events of electron transport.*
- *Summarize Calvin's investigations of the light-independent reactions.*

7.2 Photosynthesis

In photosynthesis, plants convert solar energy into the chemical energy of carbohydrates, such as sucrose and starch. Plants use this light energy to convert carbon dioxide and water into carbohydrates—food—and the oxygen you need to breathe.

As shown in Figure 7-5, photosynthesis can be divided into three sets of reactions: (1) light absorption by chlorophyll, (2) light-dependent reactions, and (3) light-independent reactions. The absorption of light can be called the energy-capturing stage. Photosynthetic organisms must capture light before the second and third sets of reactions can convert this light energy into stored chemical energy.

Figure 7-5 Photosynthesis has three parts: light absorption; light-dependent reactions; and light-independent reactions.

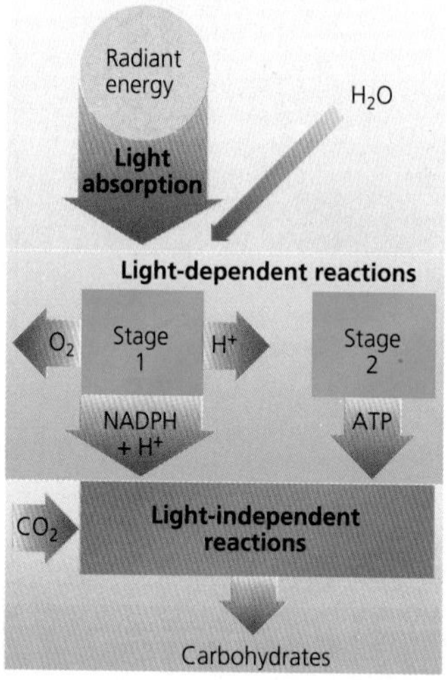

Light Absorption by Chlorophyll

Light-absorbing compounds—pigments—called chlorophylls are found inside chloroplasts. Study the chloroplast shown in the upper right of Figure 7-6. Chloroplasts have three membrane systems—outer, middle, and inner. The inner membrane resembles a cell membrane, consisting of a double-lipid layer embedded with proteins such as the enzyme ATP synthetase. An electron microscope reveals that the chloroplast's inner membrane is arranged in thick stacks called **grana.** Grana are connected to one another by thinner membranes. Each granum is made of many flattened, membranous sacs called **thylakoids** *(THIE-luh-KOIDZ).* Thylakoids are the sites of light absorption.

Chlorophyll molecules are located on the thylakoids. Each type of chlorophyll absorbs varying amounts of red and blue light. Use Figure 7-7 on page 98 to compare the absorption peaks of two types of chlorophylls. Chlorophyll a absorbs more blue light and less red light than chlorophyll b does. All chlorophylls, however, reflect green light. Therefore, organisms containing chlorophylls look green. Accessory pigments trap green and yellow light that cannot be absorbed by chlorophyll and transfer the energy to chlorophyll molecules. Accessory pigments, including yellow, orange, and brown carotenoid pigments, enable plants to use more of the sun's energy.

The structure and arrangement of the grana expose most of the chlorophyll molecules to light at the same time. The grana's shape also provides a large surface area for photosynthesis and for the diffusion of the photosynthetic products across the thylakoid membrane. These products move back and forth between the thylakoid space—the hollow inside a thylakoid—and the stroma. The **stroma** is the protein-rich solution that surrounds the grana. The second set of reactions, the light-dependent reactions, occurs inside the thylakoid. The third set, the light-independent reactions, takes place in the stroma.

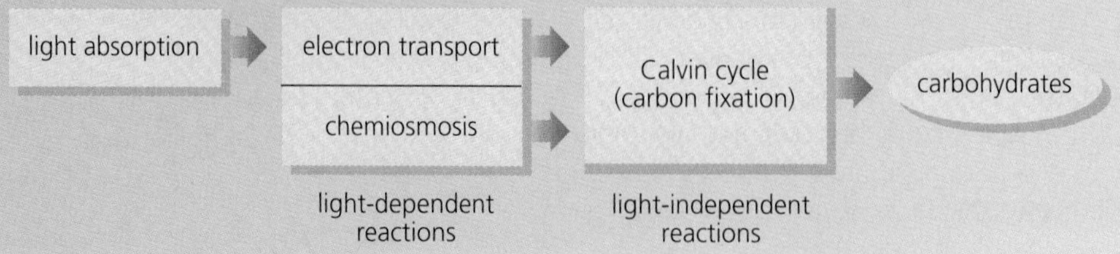

Graphic Organizer Use this sequential diagram in Reteaching on p. 102.

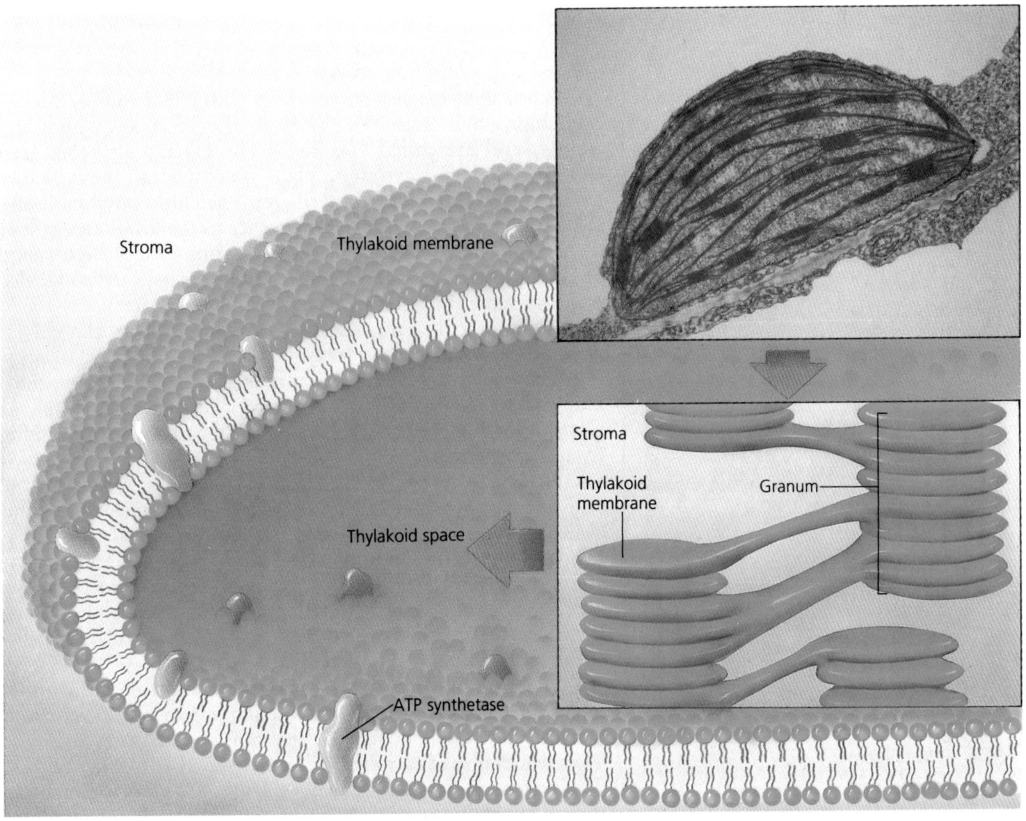

Figure 7-6 A chloroplast (top, right) is the site of light-dependent and light-independent reactions. Light-dependent reactions occur in the thylakoid membrane (green); light-independent reactions, in the stroma (beige).

Light-Dependent Reactions

The set of reactions that convert light energy to chemical energy are called the **light-dependent reactions.** There are two main stages of the light-dependent reactions. The first stage converts sunlight to electrical energy, which is a flow of electrons. This first stage is called electron transport. In the second stage, the electrical energy is changed to chemical energy stored in chemical bonds.

Electron Transport

When light strikes a chlorophyll molecule, the transport of electrons begins. The process takes place in a **photosystem,** a unit of several hundred chlorophyll molecules and carrier molecules. Most plant cells have two types of photosystems: photosystem I and photosystem II, shown in Figure 7-8 on page 99. Both systems are located in the thylakoid. Photosystem I can function on its own to complete the first stage of the light dependent reactions, but both photosystems usually work together. The process begins in photosystem II.

Teaching Strategies

Interpreting the Visuals Ask students to draw Figure 7-5, p. 96, on a full notebook page, and fill in details as they study this section. This activity aids students whose learning style is visual and kinesthetic.

Have students use Figure 7-6, p. 97, to locate the sites of the light-dependent reactions and light-independent reactions. *(Both occur in the chloroplast; the light-dependent reactions in the thylakoid, the light-independent in the stroma.)* Ask students to recall where a similar membrane was first shown in the text and have them describe that structure. *(Chapter 5, p. 67, a cell membrane; a lipid bilayer embedded with proteins such as enzymes)*

Relating Structure to Function Ask students how they would position themselves in relation to the sun on a cold day in order to gain maximum warmth. *(Expose the largest surface area to the sun's rays—front or back perpendicular to the solar energy.)* Ask students to infer what part of a green plant has a structure best adapted for gathering maximum light energy. *(Leaves)* Point out that leaves—having up to half a million chloroplasts per square millimeter of leaf surface—are efficient light-gathering structures.

Testing a Hypothesis Have students speculate on how they might test the hypothesis that oxygen produced through photosynthesis comes from water, not carbon dioxide molecules. Ask students how scientists could tag the oxygen atoms. *(Use radioisotopes)*

Videodiscs

- ***2576, Carbon Dioxide and Water Movement in Leaves (s)***
- ***1935–1937, Chloroplasts (s)***

LEP Activity

This section presupposes knowledge of the basic chemistry discussed in Chapters 3 and 4. Have students review this information in pairs. Have students test each other by defining and giving examples of the following terms: atom, electron, ionic and covalent bond, chemical reaction, chemical equation, organic and inorganic compound, carbohydrate, enzyme, catalyst, and activation energy. *(See definitions in Chapters 3 and 4, pp. 33–54.)* Ask students what CO_2, H_2O, O_2, and $C_6H_{12}O_6$ represent, and what the symbols mean. *(Carbon dioxide, water, oxygen gas, and glucose; C = carbon, O = oxygen, and H = hydrogen atoms; the subscript numbers indicate the number of atoms present in a molecule.)*

Interpreting the Visuals Have students analyze Figure 7-7, p. 98, to determine that each pigment has its own absorption pattern. *(Chlorophyll a primarily absorbs wavelengths of about 430 and 700 nm; chlorophyll b, about 460 and 720 nm; beta-carotene, about 400–520 nm.)* Tell students that chlorophyll a is found in all plants and algae. Chlorophyll b occurs in plants, green algae, and euglenoids. Have the class brainstorm ideas on how this is evidence of adaptations and evolution. *(Within a general pattern, there are diverse solutions to the problem of trapping solar energy. The autotrophs mentioned above all use chlorophyll to trap light, but the type of chlorophyll varies depending on the species and the environment in which it evolved.)*
■ *See* Laboratories, *Investigation 7.1.*

Comparing Concepts Have students speculate as to the nature of an electrical current. Tell them that it is movement of electric charges, either positive or negative, or both. Free electrons in a wire flow from a negative to a positive pole, producing electric current. Point out that hydrogen ions (H^+) consist of atoms with a positive net charge and that their movement can therefore create an electrochemical current. Ask students to describe the movement of hydrogen ions and what results. *(Hydrogen ions move down an electrochemical concentration gradient; as they move, some of their energy is packaged as ATP, made from ADP and a free phosphate group.)* Ask students to recall another example of ion concentrations resulting in motion. *(The sodium–potassium pump on p. 85, Section 6.2)*

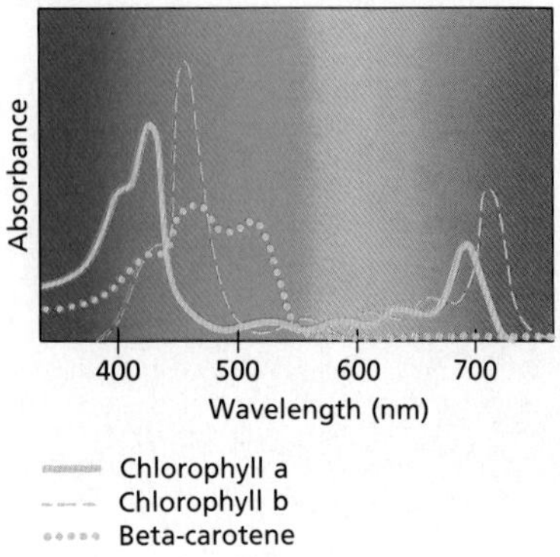

Figure 7-7 Chlorophylls a and b are two of the five types of chlorophylls. Beta-carotene is an accessory pigment. How do these pigments differ in their capacity for light absorption?

When light reaches photosystem II, the electrons of specialized chlorophyll molecules absorb energy. Electrons with a high energy level are called "excited." The excited electrons have enough energy to leave chlorophyll molecules and move to electron carriers. Electrons removed from the chlorophyll molecules move along a chain of carrier molecules to the lower energy level of photosystem I. The passage of electrons from a high energy level to a lower energy level by electron carriers is called an **electron transport chain,** or a hydrogen transport system.

As light strikes photosystem II, it also strikes the chlorophyll molecules in photosystem I. As in photosystem II, electrons in photosystem I move to carrier molecules. The electrons move along an electron transport chain to a lower energy level. An electron leaving photosystem I is replaced by an electron arriving from photosystem II.

Figure 7-8 shows that an electron from photosystem I is carried to a key reactant called $NADP^+$, or nicotine adenine dinucleotide phosphate. $NADP^+$ is a carrier compound that carries hydrogen ions. The addition of an electron from photosystem I and a hydrogen ion to $NADP^+$ forms NADPH, or nicotine adenine dinucleotide phosphate reduced. What is the source of the hydrogen ions? Some are formed from water molecules when electrons leave photosystem II.

The loss of an electron creates an unstable chlorophyll molecule. The chlorophyll molecule in photosystem II returns to a stable state by removing an electron from a water molecule. This reaction breaks water molecules into hydrogen ions (H^+) and oxygen gas (O_2), as shown in Figure 7-8. Hydrogen ions are then available to form NADPH, one of the chemical compounds into which light energy is converted; the other is ATP. The bonds of NADPH and ATP hold energy for later use. ATP is formed by the second stage of the light-dependent reactions, chemiosmosis.

Chemiosmosis

The diffusion of chemicals through a membrane, resulting in ATP formation, is called **chemiosmosis** *(KEM-ee-oz-MOE-suss)*. Electron transport within the thylakoid triggers chemiosmosis. The process is shown in Figure 7-9 on page 99.

As electrons move along the electron transport chain, a concentration gradient of hydrogen ions is formed across the thylakoid membrane. Because the concentration of hydrogen ions is higher inside the thylakoid space than in the stroma, the ions move across the thylakoid. The electrochemical energy of the moving ions triggers the phosphorylation of ADP to ATP by ATP synthetase, a process you read about in Section 7.1. The ATP formed in the stroma is used immediately in **carbon fixation,** the process which forms organic compounds from inorganic compounds through carbon-carbon bonding. Carbon fixation occurs in the light-independent reactions, the third set of photosynthetic reactions.

Interdisciplinary Activity

Physics Light consists of particles of energy, called photons, which travel freely in space in electromagnetic waves. Different types of light and types of radiant energy other than light can be identified by their wavelengths—the distance between a point on one wave and the comparable point on the next wave. Visible light is a small, central part of the electromagnetic spectrum and includes the light required to initiate photosynthesis. Much shorter electromagnetic wavelengths, such as gamma rays, ultraviolet rays, and X-rays, can destroy plant cells. Longer wavelengths, such as infrared rays, microwaves, and radio waves cannot power photosynthetic reactions.

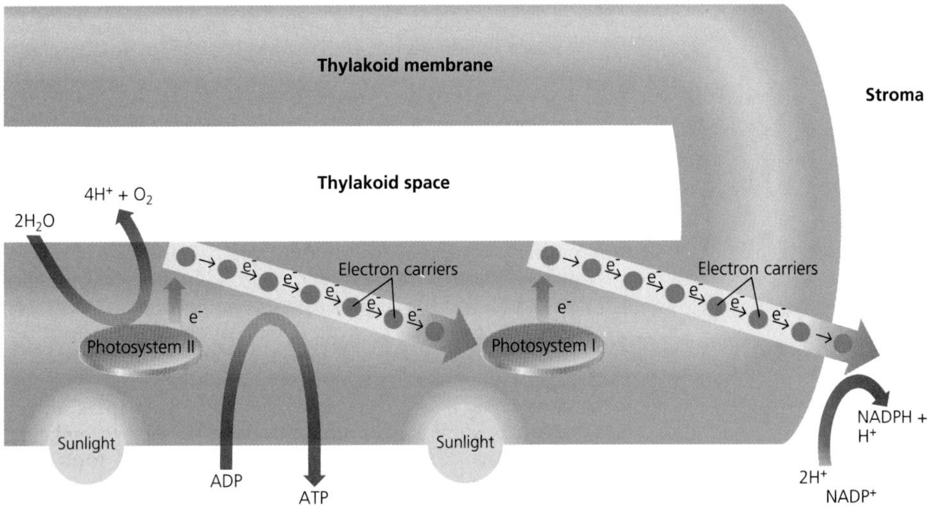

Figure 7-8 Electrons lost by photosystem I are replaced by electrons from photosystem II, which in turn are replaced by electrons released from the breakdown of H_2O.

Light-Independent Reactions

The reactions that form organic compounds by using energy stored during the light-dependent reactions in the bonds of NADPH and ATP are called the **light-independent reactions.** During the light-independent reactions, carbon fixation produces organic compounds through carbon–carbon bonding. Inorganic one-carbon molecules are bonded or "fixed" into organic three-carbon and five-carbon intermediate molecules and eventually form six-carbon molecules. Most plant species in moderate climates fix carbon through the light–independent reactions. These reactions are often called the Calvin cycle and also the C_3 cycle.

Carbon Fixation by the Calvin Cycle

The name "Calvin cycle" honors Melvin Calvin (1911–), the American scientist who worked out the pathway of the light-independent reactions. A photosynthetic cell synthesizes hundreds of molecules in less time than it takes to describe the pathway.

The "Calvin cycle" has four major steps. Each reaction in the cycle is catalyzed by a specific enzyme, and each step produces intermediate molecules. The three-carbon intermediate, phosphoglyceric acid, or PGA, is the product of the first step of the Calvin cycle. Figure 7-10 on page 101 summarizes six complete turns of the Calvin cycle; refer to it as you read the following four-step summary:

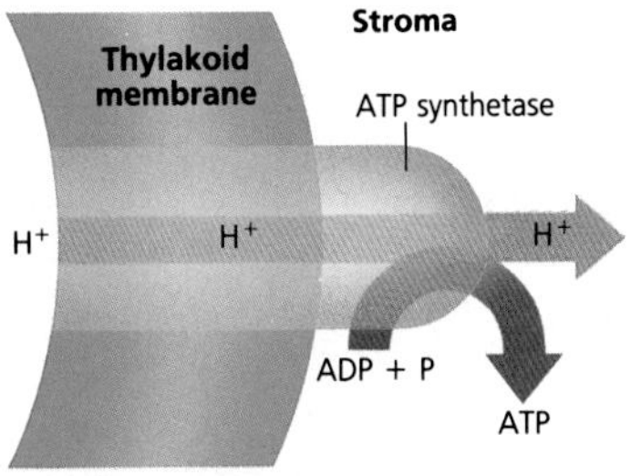

Figure 7-9 Energy for the manufacture of ATP is generated during chemiosmosis as hydrogen ions move through the thylakoid membrane.

1. CO_2 diffuses into the stroma from the organism's environment. An enzyme on the thylakoid binds a CO_2 molecule to a five-carbon ribulose biphosphate molecule (RuBP), forming

Applying Prior Knowledge Have students write definitions of carbohydrates, monosaccharides, disaccharides, and polysaccharides. Ask them to give examples of those found in plants. *(See Chapter 4, pp. 49–50. Carbohydrates are organic compounds composed of carbon, hydrogen, and oxygen in a ratio of two hydrogen atoms to one oxygen atom. A monosaccharide is a simple sugar; examples are glucose, a form of stored energy, and fructose, found in fruits. A disaccharide is a double sugar; an example is sucrose, in sugarcane and sugar beets. A polysaccharide is a molecule composed of three or more monosaccharides; examples are starch, a stored plant food, and cellulose, a rigid structural material.)*

Applying Concepts Ask students to name the two basic types of transport discussed in Chapter 6. *(Passive and active transport)* Ask the class which one best describes chemiosmosis and why. *(Passive; because the hydrogen ions move down an electrochemical gradient without the use of chemical energy)* Point out that the phosphorylation of ADP to form ATP during chemiosmosis occurs by action of ATP synthetase, an enzyme (protein) embedded in the thylakoid membrane, much as carrier molecules are embedded in cell membranes.

Videodiscs

- ***1938, Chlorophyll Solution Fluorescing (s)***
- ***2519–2520, Light: Electromagnetic Spectrum (s)***

Interdisciplinary Activity

Social Studies Ask students what plants people eat. *(Grains, root crops, fruits, vegetables, sugar crops, nuts)* Point out that hunger is widespread even though enough crops are grown to feed everyone and about 160 billion metric tons of carbohydrates are photosynthesized yearly, worldwide. Have students use library resources (encyclopedias, publications of Oxfam or Worldwatch Institute) to research why famines occur. *(Adverse climatic, political, or economic conditions)* Have students list groups working on issues of hunger. *(Farmers, governments, political and religious organizations)* Ask students where most photosynthesis occurs in the world *(Marine phytoplankton)* and have them investigate efforts to use this source of carbohydrates as food for humans.

Guided Practice

Refer students to the general equation for photosynthesis in Section 7.1, p. 94. Emphasize to students that the product $(CH_2O)_n$ represents any one of several carbohydrates—the specific type depends on the number (n) of carbon, hydrogen, and oxygen atoms present. Ask students what carbohydrate (sugar) would be formed if the product listed was $C_6H_{12}O_6$. *(It could be glucose, galactose, or fructose, depending on the structure of the molecule.)* If necessary, have students examine these molecules in Figure 4-4 on p. 50.

Point out to students that tracking numbers of carbon atoms in products and reactants is an aid to understanding the Calvin cycle. Ask students how many CO_2 molecules are used, and how many six-carbon sugar molecules can be produced in six turns of the Calvin cycle. *(In six revolutions of the cycle, six CO_2 molecules are introduced, producing two three-carbon intermediates—six carbons, total—which can react to produce one six-carbon sugar.)*

Independent Practice

- Have students write answers to the Section Review.
- Have students explain the involvement of ATP in photosynthesis. Have them discuss the stage where ATP appears and whether it is being formed or used. *(Light-dependent reactions: ATP is synthesized; light-independent reactions: ATP is used.)*

a six-carbon molecule. In six turns, six CO_2 molecules bind to six RuBP molecules.

2. The new six-carbon molecule immediately splits and forms two molecules of PGA. In six turns of the cycle, 12 molecules of PGA are formed.
3. PGA is changed to phosphoglyceraldehyde, or PGAL. First, each PGA molecule receives a phosphate group from an ATP molecule formed in the light-dependent reactions. Second, the molecule accepts hydrogen ions from NADPH, also a product of the light-dependent reactions. In addition to PGAL, these reactions produce ADP, low energy phosphates (P), and $NADP^+$. In six turns of the cycle, 12 molecules each of ATP and NADPH are used to form 12 phosphates and 12 molecules each of PGAL, $NADP^+$, and ADP.
4. Most of the PGAL regenerates more RuBP. After six turns of the cycle, some PGAL molecules may be used to make glucose. If two PGAL molecules (C_3) combine and form a glucose molecule (C_6), then ten PGAL molecules (C_3) are left to make six RuBP molecules (C_5), using energy supplied by ATP. The energy needs of the cell determine whether the PGAL forms glucose or RuBP.

Biology in Process

Calvin: The Light-Independent Reactions

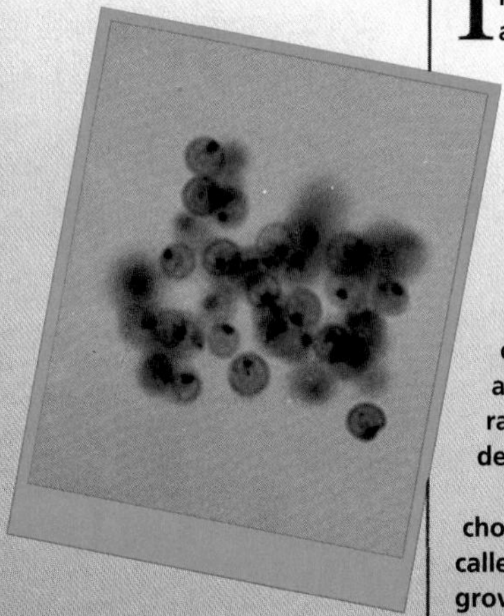

In 1945 a group of botanists at the University of California at Berkeley began investigating the photosynthetic pathways. Melvin Calvin and his coworkers designed an experiment to trace the path of CO_2 during the light-independent reactions. This experimental design utilized a new and important tool—a radioactive isotope of carbon designated carbon-14 (^{14}C).

For this experiment Calvin chose a unicellular green alga called *Chlorella* (left, ×400). By growing *Chlorella* under controlled conditions Calvin established a steady rate of photosynthesis. Calvin then exposed algal cells to light in the presence of radioactive CO_2 ($^{14}CO_2$). The photosynthesizing cells absorbed the $^{14}CO_2$. As the $^{14}CO_2$ was used in the light-independent reactions, it became incorporated into the molecules of the reactants. Such radioactive compounds are said to be labeled.

In order to determine the sequence of the chemical steps occurring in the light-independent reactions, Calvin had to isolate the products at different points in the photosynthetic pathway. To do this, he built a device that enabled him to expose *Chlorella* to $^{14}CO_2$

More Information

Rubisco The enzyme ribulose biphosphate (RuBP) carboxylase is sometimes abbreviated as *rubisco*. Since many molecules of the enzyme are present in every chloroplast, rubisco is one of the most abundant proteins on earth. Little has been discovered about the genes that direct its synthesis, but it is a topic of great interest to biotechnology researchers and development companies working on improving food crops and on increasing plant productivity.

In summary, one full turn of the Calvin cycle fixes one CO_2 molecule and regenerates an RuBP molecule. Three turns of the cycle produce one PGAL molecule. Six turns of the cycle produce a six-carbon sugar, such as glucose. The overall equation for the reactions that produce glucose is:

$$6\ CO_2 + 18\ ATP + 12\ NADPH + 12\ H^+ + 12\ H_2O \longrightarrow \text{glucose} + 18\ P + 18\ ADP + 12\ NADP^+$$

Although the compound glucose is very important to both autotrophs and heterotrophs, photosynthetic autotrophs use intermediate compounds such as PGAL to form a variety of organic compounds. These compounds include amino acids, lipids, and carbohydrates other than glucose. Recall what you read about carbohydrates in Chapter 4, pages 49–50. The carbohydrates formed include other monosaccharides such as fructose and the disaccharide sucrose. Such polysaccharides as glycogen, starch, and cellulose are also formed. Most plants store energy as starch. Cellulose, another polysaccharide, is the primary component of the cell wall in plants. The world probably contains more cellulose than any other kind of organic molecule.

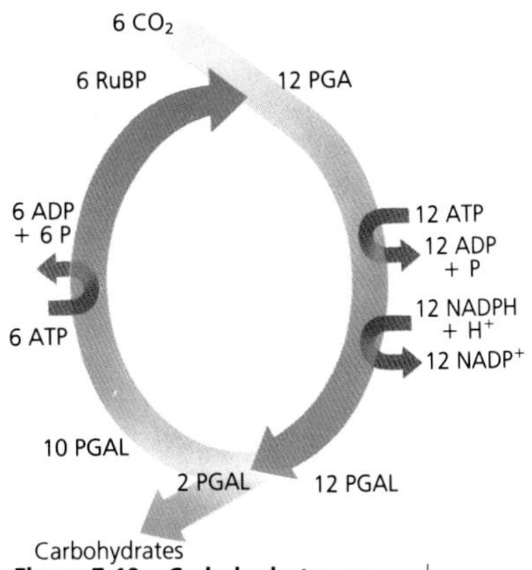

Figure 7-10 Carbohydrates are formed in most autotrophs through a process called the Calvin cycle.

for a set period of time and then kill the cells by dropping them into boiling methanol. The alcohol also inactivated the enzymes that catalyze parts of the photosynthetic reactions.

By varying the time between exposure and killing of the cells Calvin obtained photosynthetic products from different points in the sequence. After a short time only a few compounds were labeled. After a longer time many compounds were labeled.

Calvin then isolated the photosynthetic compounds by using paper chromatography. Once the products were isolated, the sequence in which they occurred could be determined. Calvin reasoned that the compounds that were labeled in the shortest time period were the first compounds in the cycle to have incorporated $^{14}CO_2$. Compounds that appeared after a longer time were formed later in the sequence. In this way Calvin recreated the steps of the light-independent reactions.

The cycle discovered by this technique was renamed the Calvin cycle. In 1961 Calvin was awarded a Nobel Prize for his research.

■ Why did Calvin plunge the algal cells into methanol immediately after exposing the cells to radioactive CO_2?

Biology in Process

Using the Feature

This feature discusses how Melvin Calvin worked out the order of intermediates in the cycle of light-independent reactions. The main process skills featured are experimenting and interpreting data. Remind students that experimenting, in turn, includes such process skills as hypothesizing, observing, measuring, and inferring.

Ask students to explain how the photosynthetic products were "labeled." *(The carbon atoms in the product molecules were C^{14}s, whose radioactivity indicated the presence of the molecules.)*

Answer to the Feature

The hot methanol inactivated enzymes (such as those in lysosomes, ATP synthetase, and ATPase), immediately stopping all cell processes, including photosynthesis.

■ *See* Process Skills, *Chapter 7.*

More Information

Crassulacean Acid Metabolism Desert CAM plants open their stomata (pores) at night and close them in the day, the opposite of plants adapted to temperate climates. This conserves water but also reduces the availability of CO_2 for use in the Calvin cycle. At night CAM plants convert CO_2 to a variety of organic acids, which they store in the vacuoles of mesophyll cells. When the stomata close in the morning, the organic acids are converted, freeing CO_2 for use in the Calvin cycle. ATP and NADPH come from the light-dependent reactions in CAM plants as in other plants.

Check Your Understanding

1. Why does the term *intermediate* describe the role of the CO_2-RuBP molecule formed in the Calvin cycle? *(The CO_2-RuBP molecule is unstable and immediately forms another molecule; it is not a final product.)*
2. What is the role of the thylakoids in the light-dependent reactions? *(The site of electron transport; hydrogen ions transported across the thylakoid produce ATP during chemiosmosis.)*
3. Would you expect a plant to grow best under green or red light? Why? *(Red; most plants can't absorb green light. Without light absorption, photosynthesis could not proceed to the light-dependent and the light-independent reactions.)*

Reteaching

Have students generate a sequential diagram of the reactions that make up photosynthesis. An example of a completed diagram appears on p. 96.
▪ *See* Section Reviews *worksheet, Section 7.2.*

Enrichment

Have students use biochemistry texts to research the structure of chlorophyll. They should note the complexity of chlorophyll and key elements. *(For example, a central magnesium atom)*

Closure

Ask students to review the overall equation for photosynthesis on p. 101. Ask them to name which compounds are required in the light-dependent and which in the light-independent reactions. *(Light-dependent reactions: H_2O; light-independent reactions: CO_2)* Ask students when the products—carbohydrates and oxygen—are formed. *(During light-independent reactions)*

Videodiscs

▪ ***1957–1959, Leaf with Stoma Open/Closed (s)***

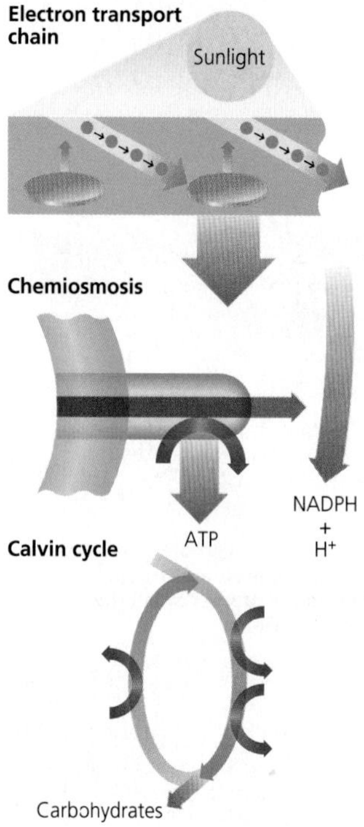

Figure 7-11 This illustration summarizes the process of photosynthesis: from light energy to carbohydrate formation.

Use Figure 7-11 to review the three sets of reactions that make up photosynthesis. Remember that most organisms depend upon the ability of photosynthetic organisms to store solar energy in chemical bonds.

Other Carbon-Fixing Pathways

Scientists have found that the Calvin cycle is the most common method of carbon fixation. However, some plant species living in hot, dry climates have evolved different biochemical pathways for carbon fixation. Two such pathways are the C_4 and the CAM pathways. In the C_4 pathway, a series of reactions occurs before carbon dioxide enters the Calvin cycle.

The **C_4 pathway** is a carbon-fixing process in which carbon dioxide is bound to a compound to form a four-carbon intermediate that enters the C_3 cycle. The C_4 pathway is an adaptation of plants to environments having high temperatures, dry conditions, and abundant light. C_4 plants, including corn, sugarcane, and crabgrass, are very efficient at using available carbon dioxide and can fix carbon about four times as fast as can plants using only the C_3 cycle. This allows C_4 plants to grow quickly in hot, dry climates. The C_4 pathway requires more energy than the C_3 cycle, but most C_4 plants grow in abundant light, where energy is readily available. In the C_4 pathway, carbon dioxide is first fixed to a three-carbon compound instead of the five-carbon RuBP used in the Calvin cycle. The four-carbon intermediate next undergoes a series of reactions until the carbon dioxide is transferred to RuBP, entering the Calvin cycle.

Cactuses, pineapples, and stonecrops have a different adaptation to very hot, dry climates. Such plants use a process called CAM, or crassulacean acid metabolism, instead of the C_4 pathway. The process is named for the plant family in which it was first discovered—Crassulaceae. **CAM** is a process by which a plant takes in carbon dioxide during the night, stores it as organic acids, and then releases carbon dioxide during the day for use in the Calvin cycle. In plants that use only the Calvin cycle, carbon dioxide enters through pores during the day. As carbon dioxide enters, water leaves the plant through the pores. The hotter and drier the air, the faster water is lost. Since CAM works in cool night temperatures, CAM plants lose less water, giving them a survival advantage over C_3 plants in hot, dry environments.

Section Review

1. Define *CAM*.
2. Name the reactants and products of photosynthesis.
3. Which reactants are used in the light-dependent reactions, and which in the light-independent reactions?
4. Which set of reactions requires light? Explain.
5. Explain how the structure of the thylakoid membrane relates to its function.

Answers to Section Review

1. Crassulacean acid metabolism; used by certain plants in dry climates as an alternate path to fix carbon in photosynthesis
2. Reactants: carbon dioxide and water; products: carbohydrates and oxygen
3. Light-dependent reactions: H_2O, $NADP^+$, H^+ (in electron transport chain); H^+, ADP, and P (in chemiosmosis); light-independent reactions: CO_2, ATP, NADPH, H^+, RuBP
4. Light-independent reactions do not require light but can and do occur in light. Thus the reactions can take place in light and dark.
5. The flattened, stacked structure is ideal for exposing a large number of chlorophyll molecules to light and for providing a large surface area for photosynthesis.

7.3 Respiration

Take a deep breath and then slowly exhale. You have just experienced external respiration, during which you brought oxygen-rich air into your lungs, and you exhaled air carrying waste carbon dioxide. Cellular respiration, the subject of this section, differs from external respiration; it is a set of chemical reactions that occur inside every organism's cells, including yours. During cellular respiration, food molecules are broken down to release the energy in their bonds.

The organic compounds made by plants during photosynthesis are the food that supplies the energy used by autotrophs and heterotrophs for life processes. This section examines the biochemical pathway of cellular respiration, by which carbohydrates, specifically glucose, are broken apart to release energy. There are actually two types of cellular respiration—anaerobic and aerobic—as shown in Figure 7-12. Use that figure to trace the anaerobic and aerobic pathways. Both pathways begin with the first phase, **glycolysis** *(glie-KAHL-uh-suss),* the process by which glucose is converted to pyruvic acid.

Section Objectives

- *List the major events of glycolysis.*
- *Distinguish between anaerobic and aerobic respiration.*
- *Compare and contrast lactic acid fermentation and alcohol fermentation.*
- *Summarize the events of the Krebs cycle.*
- *Identify the amounts and sources of ATP formed by aerobic respiration.*

Glycolysis

Glycolysis occurs in the cytoplasm and can occur without oxygen. Its reactions are not inhibited by oxygen. The overall result of glycolysis is that one six-carbon glucose molecule is split into two three-carbon pyruvic acid molecules. Each of the four main steps of glycolysis is catalyzed by a specific enzyme. Refer to Figure 7-13 as you read the steps on the following page:

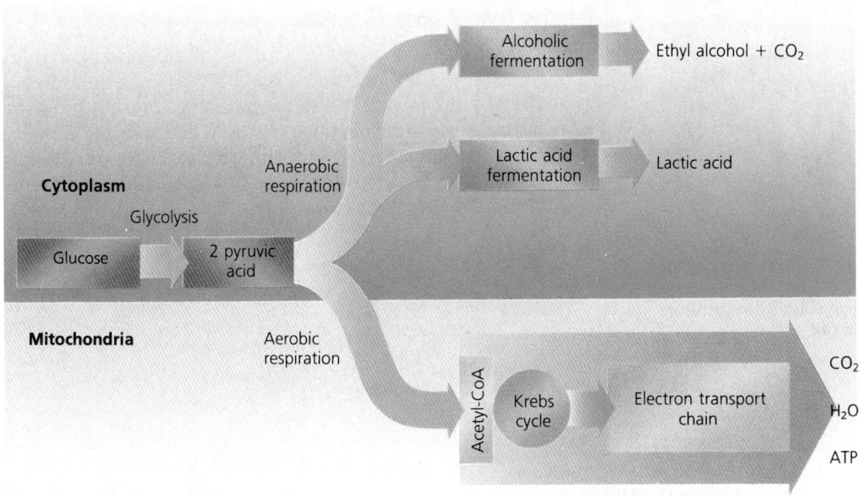

Figure 7-12 Carbohydrates formed during photosynthesis are broken down within heterotrophs and autotrophs through one of the biochemical pathways of respiration.

Respiration Process	Occurs In
▪ glycolysis	▪ cytoplasm
▪ lactic acid fermentation	▪ cytoplasm
▪ alcohol fermentation	▪ cytoplasm
▪ Krebs cycle	▪ mitochondria; matrix
▪ electron transport	▪ mitochondria; inner membrane
▪ chemiosmosis	▪ mitochondria; inner membrane, matrix

Graphic Organizer Use this table in Guided Practice on p. 107.

Lesson Plan

Section Focus

Section 7.3 discusses respiration, the process that supplies energy for both plant and animal cells. Aerobic respiration, including glycolysis, the Krebs cycle, and electron transport, produces as many as 38 ATP molecules per glucose molecule. Anaerobic respiration, consisting of glycolysis and fermentation, produces far fewer—only two ATP molecules.

Section Themes

The breakdown of glucose for use in cell activities continues the emphasis on the theme of **Energy**. Chemical energy in glucose moves to storage compounds and to ATP in the processes of aerobic and anaerobic respiration in both heterotrophs and autotrophs.

A mitochondrion's structure is similar to that of a chloroplast, supporting the theme of **Scale and Structure.** Both are sites of electron transport and chemiosmosis. The cristae of the mitochondria contain the enzymes of the Krebs cycle and the carriers of the electron transport system.

Motivating Activity

Have the class watch as you ignite a sugar cube in a crucible. Have students describe the results. *(Blue and yellow flame, smoke, burnt odor, black residue)* Remind students that sugar, a product of photosynthesis, is often eaten in foods. Ask how they know it is unlikely that their bodies "burn" sugar. *(Students surmise that the body could not withstand such rapid, large releases of energy in the forms of heat and light. They may also recall from Chapter 3, p. 42, that living cells have intermediary metabolism to release energy from food.)*

Teaching Strategies

Applying Concepts Ask students in what way respiration is similar to photosynthesis. *(Like photosynthesis, respiration is a complex biochemical pathway; the reactions in the process make a series of small changes in molecules.)* Ask students how the two processes differ. *(Photosynthesis results in energy being stored for use as carbohydrates. Respiration releases the energy in carbohydrates for use by living cells.)*

Interpreting the Visuals Have the class review Figure 7-1, p. 93, and ask them what it illustrates. *(Energy relationships between the sun, photosynthesis, and respiration)* Ask students how Figure 7-12, p. 103, relates to Figure 7-1. *(Figure 7-12 shows the details of the process represented only as a blue box in Figure 7-1.)*

Ask students how Figure 7-13, p. 104, relates to Figure 7-12. *(It is a detailed model of glycolysis, represented in Figure 7-12 by the first pink box, rotated clockwise 90 degrees on the page.)* Also have students describe the relationships of Figures 7-14, 7-16, and 7-17, pp. 104, 106, and 107, to Figure 7-12. *(Figure 7-14 shows the details of two processes, alcohol and lactic acid fermentation, represented in Figure 7-12 by orange boxes. Figure 7-16 is an expanded, detailed model of the Krebs cycle, represented in Figure 7-12 as a blue circle. Figure 7-17 is an expanded, detailed model of electron transport and chemiosmosis, represented in Figure 7-12 as a blue box. In comparison with Figure 7-12, the processes in Figures 7-16 and 7-17 have been rotated on the page.)*

■ *See* **Blackline Masters** *15 and 16.*

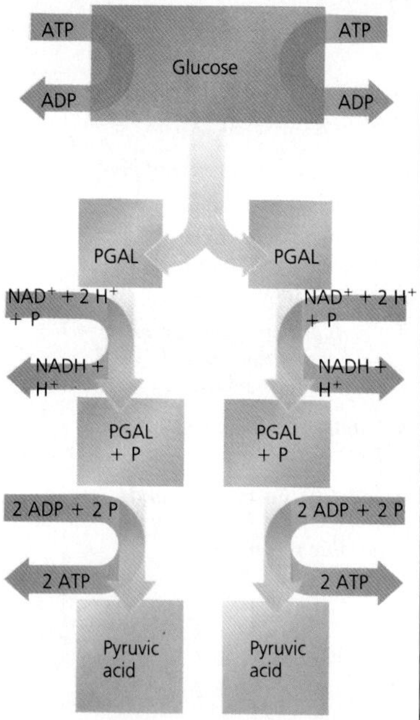

Figure 7-13 Glycolysis, the first stage in anaerobic and aerobic respiration, produces four ATP molecules from one glucose molecule—for a net gain of 2 ATP molecules.

1. Energy of two ATP molecules is used to phosphorylate glucose, forming a new six-carbon molecule.
2. Two three-carbon PGAL molecules form from the six-carbon molecule. (You read in Section 7.2 that PGAL is phosphoglyceraldehyde, an intermediate compound.)
3. A phosphate group is added to each PGAL molecule. At the same time, hydrogen atoms are removed by NAD$^+$, forming two molecules of NADH + H$^+$. NAD$^+$ is a carrier compound similar to the NADP$^+$ discussed in Section 7.2.
4. The phosphate bonds formed in step 3 are broken, generating two ATP molecules from each PGAL molecule and converting PGAL to pyruvic acid.

Glycolysis produces four ATP molecules. Since two ATP molecules were used during step 1, the net gain is only two ATP molecules. However, pyruvic acid molecules formed by glycolysis are also an energy source. Much of this energy will be recovered in the next phase of respiration. As shown in Figure 7-12, pyruvic acid can now enter either of two possible pathways, depending on the type of respiration. **Anaerobic** *(AN-uh-ROE-bick)* **respiration** is the type of respiration that occurs in the absence of oxygen and consists of glycolysis followed by fermentation.

Fermentation

The process of breaking down pyruvic acid without the use of oxygen, **fermentation,** occurs in the cytoplasm. Unlike glycolysis, fermentation does not produce ATP. However, fermentation does regenerate NAD$^+$, which is used for ATP production during glycolysis. Figure 7-14 models two types of fermentation, each named for its product: lactic acid or alcohol.

Lactic Acid Fermentation

The conversion of pyruvic acid to lactic acid, **lactic acid fermentation,** occurs in some unicellular organisms, and in animal cells—your muscle cells, for example. During hard work your muscles can run out of oxygen. When oxygen is not present, NADH carries a hydrogen ion to each pyruvic acid molecule, changing it to lactic acid. The NAD$^+$ that forms is used during glycolysis to form ATP.

Figure 7-14 Both types of fermentation free NAD$^+$ molecules so that glycolysis can continue within a cell.

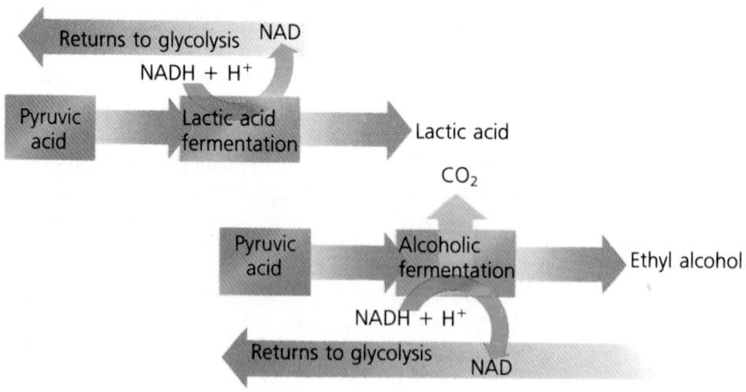

LEP Activity

The term *respiration* can be confusing; most often students think it refers to the mechanical act of breathing. Point out to students that the Latin verb *respire* means "to breathe out." Encourage students to develop memory aids to help them differentiate between external and cellular respiration. For example, **ex**ternal respiration is related to **ex**halation and inhalation. Emphasize to students that inhaled oxygen is transported to the lungs, and then by the blood to **cells.** There, aerobic **cell**ular respiration occurs. Stress to students that in the cell, oxygen is used to break down glucose to release energy, producing water and carbon dioxide. That waste carbon dioxide is transported back to the lungs by the blood, and exhaled.

This lactic acid causes your muscle soreness. Lactic acid is transported in the blood from muscles to liver cells. When oxygen becomes available, lactic acid is converted back to pyruvic acid, which is carried back to muscles by the blood.

Alcoholic Fermentation

Some plant cells and unicellular organisms use the process called **alcoholic fermentation** to convert pyruvic acid to ethyl alcohol. In the absence of oxygen, NADH donates a hydrogen ion to a pyruvic acid molecule, creating ethyl alcohol, carbon dioxide, and NAD^+.

The wine and beer industries depend on unicellular yeasts that produce ethyl alcohol through alcoholic fermentation. Alcoholic beverages are high in Calories because much energy remains in the ethyl alcohol and is not used to form ATP.

Aerobic Respiration

The second type of cellular respiration requires oxygen. **Aerobic** *(AR-OE-bick)* **respiration** is glycolysis followed by the breakdown of pyruvic acid using oxygen as a reactant. Glycolysis does not require oxygen, but oxygen must be available for aerobic respiration to be completed. Reread the summary equation of respiration given in Section 7.1.

The three steps of aerobic respiration occur inside a mitochondrion, the organelle shown in Figure 7-15. Before aerobic respiration begins, pyruvic acid formed in the cytoplasm during glycolysis must diffuse across a mitochondrion's double membrane to the matrix. The matrix, a solution containing enzymes, water, and phosphates, is the reaction site of the first and second steps. The third step occurs in the inner membrane itself. How does a mitochondrion's structure resemble that of a chloroplast?

In the first step of aerobic respiration, shown in Figure 7-16 on the following page, pyruvic acid is converted into an intermediate molecule called acetyl-CoA. First, a three-carbon pyruvic acid molecule loses CO_2 and a hydrogen ion, becoming a two-carbon acetyl group. Next, the acetyl group combines with a

Think

Bread rises as a result of yeast fermentation. How might fermentation cause the bread to rise? Why is sugar often added to the bread dough?

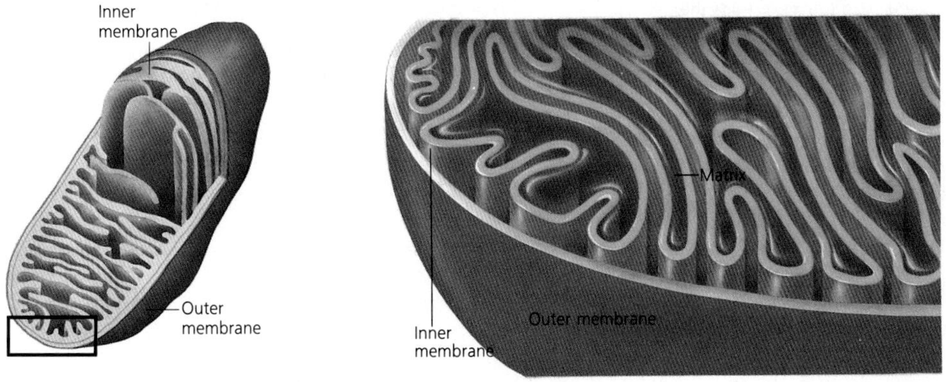

Figure 7-15 Mitochondria, such as the one shown at the left, are the site of aerobic respiration. The Krebs cycle occurs in the inner membrane.

Answer to Think

Yeast fermentation produces bubbles of CO_2 that become trapped in bread dough, causing it to expand, or rise. Sugar is added to the dough to provide the glucose for fermentation.

Relating Concepts Have students compare endothermic and exothermic reactions. *(Endothermic: involves a net absorption of energy; many reactions in a cell are endothermic. Exothermic: involves a net release of energy. See Chapter 3, p. 42.)* Ask students to explain why respiration, which involves the release of energy, does not injure or damage cells. *(Rather than release this energy in quick bursts, cells use intermediary metabolism, a long series of reactions. Each step of the reaction series makes one small change in a molecule and absorbs or gives up only a small amount of chemical energy. This slow process protects the cell from sudden change and helps to maintain homeostasis.)*

Interpreting the Visuals Remind students that Figure 7-13, p. 104, relates to Figure 7-16, p. 106, and also Figure 7-18, p. 108. Ask students how many molecules of pyruvic acid will enter the Krebs cycle. *(Two)* Ask them how many turns of the cycle will follow Figure 7-13. *(Two)*

- *See* **Blackline Master** ***17.***

Videodiscs

- ***Side 1 33499, Cell Functions and Organelles (m)***

Cooperative Learning

Fermentation Have groups of 3–6 students test the effect of substrate on rate of fermentation. Have each group share the preparation of the six 25-mL test tubes. With the tubes in a rack, have students add to each, 10 mL of a 10% solution of one of the following: sucrose (table sugar), fructose, galactose, milk, starch, and protein gelatin. Next, have students add 1/8 teaspoon of baker's yeast to each tube. Then have them seal each tube with flexible wrap. Have each group plan a schedule of observation times to record the amount of bubbling. *(Suggest 0.5-, 1-, 4-, and 24-hour intervals.)* Ask students what causes the bubbles. *(Fermentation; CO_2)* Which substrate ferments most? *(Sucrose)* Not at all? *(Gelatin)*

Observing Applications Arrange a field trip to a sports clinic or hospital physical therapy unit. Ask your guide to demonstrate to students the energy requirements of various forms of strenuous exercise and to explain oxygen debt and when it occurs.

Testing a Hypothesis Point out to students that the CO_2 exhaled in external respiration is a product of cellular respiration. Have them hypothesize what would happen to the amount of CO_2 exhaled per breath after exercise and explain their reasoning. *(Students may hypothesize that the amount of CO_2 increases because more ATP (energy) is produced and used and thus more CO_2.)* Divide the class into groups of 3–4 students and provide each group with a straw, a clock with a second hand, and two beakers, each holding 100 mL of bromthymol blue solution. Point out that bromthymol blue is an indicator that changes color in the presence of CO_2.

Have one student in each group exhale through the straw into the solution in the first beaker for at least 15 seconds, breathing out at a steady rate throughout the test. Caution students not to inhale. Have one student in the group record the amount of time it takes for the color to change. Ask students what color change occurs. *(Blue to yellow)* Direct the student who exhaled to jog in place for about three minutes. Next, direct the jogger to exhale into the solution in the second beaker while another student times the color change. Ask the class what they observed and whether their hypothesis was supported by the evidence. *(The solution takes less time to change color after exercise, supporting the hypothesis that the amount of CO_2 increases.)*

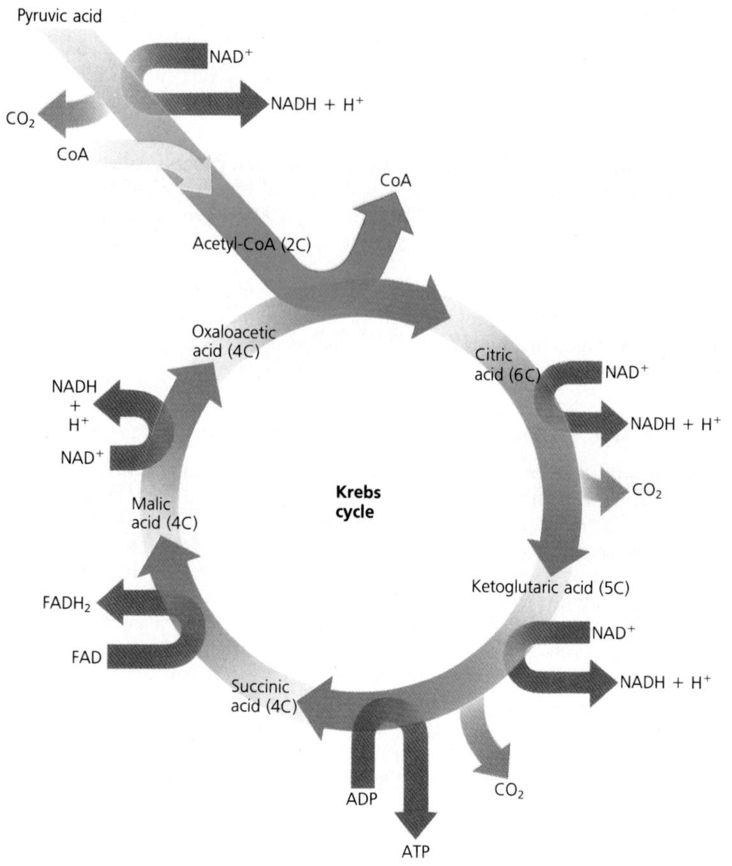

Figure 7-16 This illustration of the Krebs cycle shows how the same acid starts and ends the cycle. Note where hydrogen ions and carbon dioxide are removed.

molecule called coenzyme A, or CoA. The result is acetyl-CoA. In the course of this reaction, NAD^+ accepts the hydrogen ion from pyruvic acid, forming NADH.

Remember that each molecule of glucose undergoing glycolysis produces two molecules of pyruvic acid. Therefore, each glucose molecule yields two molecules of acetyl-CoA. The acetyl-CoA molecules now enter the second step of aerobic respiration, the Krebs cycle. Locate the Krebs cycle in Figure 7-12 on page 103.

The Krebs Cycle

The **Krebs cycle**, shown in Figure 7-16, is a biochemical pathway that releases carbon dioxide and hydrogen ions and results in the formation of ATP. The reactions that make up the cycle

More Information

Muscle Mitochondria Athletes who require quick bursts of energy for their particular type of sport, such as sprinters, have an above-average percentage of "white" in their muscle tissue. These fibers are fueled through anaerobic respiration. Such fibers contrast with red fibers, which have many mitochondria and which provide slow, sustained contractions. The same situation occurs in poultry; dark meat is muscle tissue that has large numbers of mitochondria.

were discovered by Hans Krebs (1900–1981), a German-British biochemist. The Krebs cycle is also known as the citric acid cycle because citric acid is the first intermediate formed.

A six-carbon citric acid molecule is formed when the two-carbon acetyl group from acetyl-CoA combines with a four-carbon oxaloacetic acid molecule, releasing CoA. As the cycle proceeds, new intermediates are formed, CO_2 molecules are released, hydrogen carriers pick up hydrogen ions, and molecules of ATP are formed. Refer to Figure 7-16 as you read.

In the next step, NAD^+ accepts a hydrogen ion from the citric acid molecule. A CO_2 molecule is released, and the five-carbon intermediate, ketoglutaric acid, forms. A CO_2 molecule and a hydrogen ion are again released in the next step, but an ATP molecule and a four-carbon intermediate, succinic acid, form. Next, a hydrogen ion is removed by still another carrier, FAD, and malic acid forms. Immediately afterward, another hydrogen ion is removed, this time by NAD^+. The removal of the hydrogen ion causes the regeneration of oxaloacetic acid, and the cycle is complete. The Krebs cycle begins and ends with molecules of oxaloacetic acid.

Because one glucose molecule sends 2 pyruvic acid molecules into the Krebs cycle, 6 NADH, 4 CO_2, 2 ATP, and 2 $FADH_2$ molecules are formed. Up to this point, a total of 4 ATP and 12 carrier molecules—10 NADH and 2 $FADH_2$—have been formed as a result of glycolysis and the Krebs cycle. The carrier molecules now carry electrons from the Krebs cycle to the electron transport chain, where water and more ATP are formed.

Electron Transport Chain

Compare Figure 7-17 with the photosynthetic electron transport chain shown in Figure 7-8 on page 99. As on the thylakoid membrane, enzymes and carriers line the inner membrane of the mitochondrion. The electrons travel from carrier to carrier, moving toward the lower energy level of the final acceptor, oxygen. At the same time, NADH delivers hydrogen ions to the matrix. In the matrix oxygen combines with hydrogen to form water. Without oxygen, electron transport would not occur, leaving the process of aerobic respiration incomplete.

As in the light-dependent reactions of photosynthesis, ATP is generated by chemiosmosis. Notice that Figure 7-17 shows ATP synthetase on the inner mitochondrial membrane. As electrons move down the energy gradient in the inner membrane, hydrogen ions are pumped across the membrane into the matrix. An electrochemical gradient forms, and hydrogen ions diffuse through ATP synthetase channels. The ATP synthetase uses the energy generated by the movement of hydrogen ions to make ATP.

Scientists have determined exactly how many molecules of ATP are formed in this step. Aerobic respiration yields 10 NADH and 2 $FADH_2$ molecules. Research shows that each NADH molecule yields 3 ATP molecules. One $FADH_2$ molecule

Figure 7-17 The electron transport chain operates along the inner membrane of mitochondria during aerobic respiration.

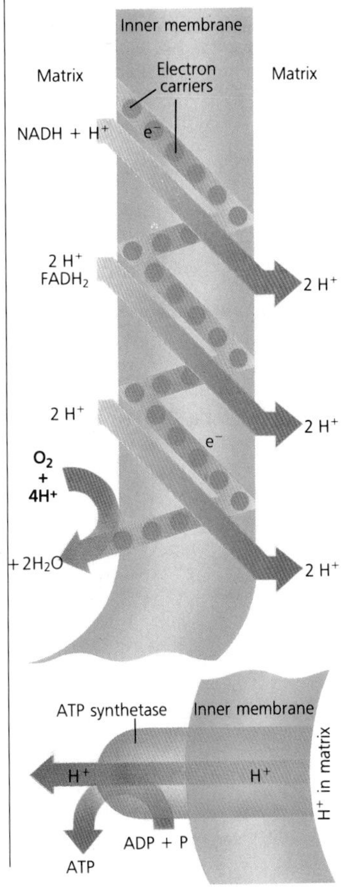

Exploring Careers Ask a baker, brewer, or winery worker to speak to the class about the importance of fermentation in their fields. Be sure to discuss the problems associated with drinking alcoholic beverages.
■ *See* **Laboratories, *Investigation 7.2.***

Guided Practice

Begin a table of the processes that make up cellular respiration. Use the completed table shown on p. 103 as a model. Have students complete the table, filling in either the name of the stage of respiration or the location where it occurs.

Independent Practice

■ Have students write answers to the Section Review.
■ Ask students to create illustrated memory guides for the processes discussed in this section. Each illustration should cue the student to recall a fact about the process. *(For example, a student might sketch a six-carbon ring [glucose] for glycolysis, during which glucose is broken down. For lactic acid fermentation—an exhausted runner [sore muscles]; for alcohol fermentation—a loaf of bread; for electron transport and chemiosmosis—an H^+ skiing downhill [moving down an electrochemical gradient]; for the Krebs cycle—a mitochondrion, site of occurrence.)*

More Information

Electron Transport Chain An analogy can be made between the electron transport system and a line of people moving down an escalator to get in line for a cab. The escalator represents the electron transport chain. Should no cab be available, a line of people backs up. Similarly, if oxygen were not present to pick up electrons and hydrogen ions, the electron transport system would back up. So long as an oxygen "cab" is present, water forms, and the product "keeps moving down the street."

Check Your Understanding

1. What is an advantage of aerobic over anaerobic respiration? *(Aerobic respiration provides more energy—ATP molecules—per glucose molecule.)*

2. How is respiration like and unlike photosynthesis? *(Similarities: both processes occur in specific organelles, require electron transport and chemiosmosis. Differences: Photosynthesis uses CO_2 to generate carbohydrates and oxygen; respiration uses O_2 to degrade glucose and produce water and CO_2.)*

Reteaching

Have students generate a concept map of cellular respiration. An example of a completed concept map is shown on p. 91B.

■ *See* Section Reviews *worksheet, Section 7.3.*

Enrichment

Have students research wine making and the work of Louis Pasteur. Ask students why Pasteur's name is associated with the French wine industry. *(He is credited with having saved the wine industry. He showed that undesired yeasts and bacteria were producing products other than alcohol, and he developed a method—pasteurization—to prevent wine spoilage.)*

Closure

Have students look back at Figure 7-2, p. 94, and use its labels to make a two- to three-sentence summary of this chapter. *(In most autotrophs solar energy is converted to chemical bond energy in glucose through photosynthesis. Oxygen is a by-product. Autotrophs and heterotrophs break down glucose by cellular respiration, releasing energy and forming CO_2 and water.)*

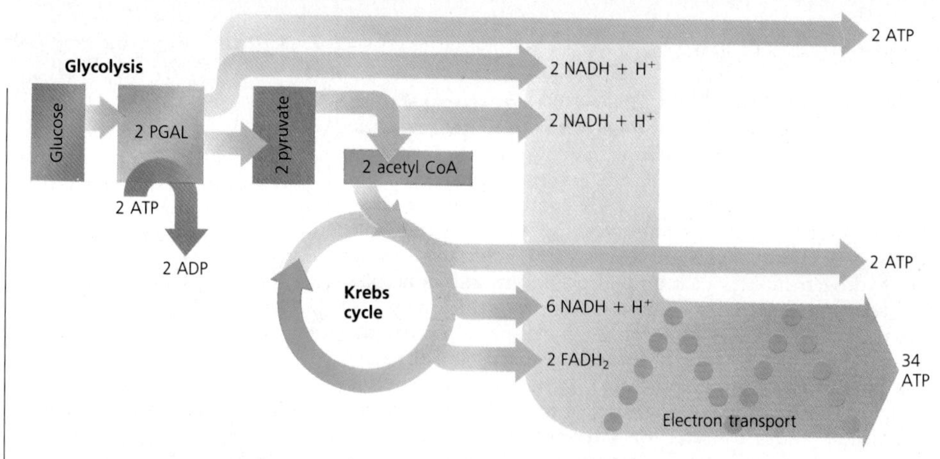

Figure 7-18 How many ATP molecules are produced by respiration? One glucose molecule can yield 38 ATP molecules—34 by the electron transport chain and 2 each by glycolysis and the Krebs cycle.

Table 7-1 Summary of ATP Yield from Aerobic Respiration

Glycolysis	2 ATP
Krebs cycle	2 ATP
Electron transport	34 ATP
	38 ATP

yields 2 ATP molecules. Therefore, the electron transport chain yields a total of 34 ATP molecules.

Energy Yield

What is the maximum number of ATP molecules produced in the aerobic breakdown of glucose? Use Figure 7-18 and Table 7-1 to help you answer this question. Figure 7-18 is a summary of respiration's energy-producing processes, and Table 7-1 is a summary of the ATP yield from aerobic respiration. Glycolysis and the Krebs cycle produce 2 ATP molecules each, and the electron transport chain produces 34 ATP molecules. Therefore, each glucose molecule can produce 38 ATP molecules.

The actual number of ATP molecules produced can vary for several reasons. For example, the electron transport system in brain tissue functions less efficiently than in other tissues and yields only 32 ATP molecules per molecule of glucose. Also, hydrogen ions sometimes leak out of the cell or are used for other cell functions. The ATP produced represents only about half the total energy stored in a glucose molecule. The rest of the energy is still held within the product molecules themselves.

Recall that anaerobic respiration produces no ATP molecules. Only the ATP generated during glycolysis is available to a cell carrying out anaerobic respiration. Thus, aerobic respiration is about 19 times more effective than anaerobic respiration in providing a cell with energy for cellular activities.

Section Review

1. Define *anaerobic respiration* and *aerobic respiration.*
2. Explain how NAD^+ is a hydrogen acceptor.
3. What is the relation between fermentation and sore muscles?
4. With what compound does the Krebs cycle begin and end?
5. Earth's earliest atmosphere had no oxygen, yet some organisms thrived. What do you infer was their method of respiration? Explain.

Answers to Section Review

1. Anaerobic respiration: the breakdown of glucose without the use of O_2, forming lactic acid or alcohol. Aerobic respiration: the breakdown of glucose using oxygen, forming CO_2, H_2O, and as many as 38 ATP molecules.

2. NAD^+ can bond to a hydrogen ion, usually accompanied by an electron. NADH is reduced by accepting a hydrogen ion.

3. Strenuous exercise rapidly depletes available oxygen in muscle cells. Muscle cells then use lactic acid fermentation; the lactic acid product causes muscle soreness.

4. Oxaloacetic acid, a four-carbon compound, combines with acetyl-CoA to begin the cycle. It is regenerated during the cycle. The acetyl group came from pyruvic acid.

5. Early organisms may have used anaerobic respiration, which doesn't require oxygen.

Laboratory

Light Intensity and Photosynthesis

Objective
To determine the effect of light intensity on the rate of photosynthesis in *Elodea*

Process Skills
Hypothesizing, experimenting

Materials
Glass marking pencil, 2 20 × 200-mm test tubes, 2 1000-mL Erlenmeyer flasks, 1 250-mL beaker, distilled water, sodium bicarbonate ($NaHCO_3$), 3 glass stirring rods, 2 15-cm long sprigs of *Elodea,* lamp with 200-watt bulb, balance, strong thread, stopwatch, scalpel, timer, meter stick

Background
1 Name the reactants and products in the general equation for photosynthesis.
2 What role does light play in photosynthesis?

Technique
1 Prepare a solution of water and sodium bicarbonate ($NaHCO_3$) by adding 500 milligrams of $NaHCO_3$ to 200 mL of distilled water in the 250-mL beaker and mixing thoroughly.
2 Remove some of the leaves from the cut end of a piece of *Elodea* and make a fresh cut at a 45° angle. Use two pieces of thread to secure the entire sprig of *Elodea* to a glass stirring rod and place it, cut end up, in a test tube. Immediately add enough $NaHCO_3$ solution to the test tube to cover the sprig entirely.
3 Place the test tube with the sprig in an Erlenmeyer flask containing enough cool tapwater to cover most of the tube. Place the flask 0.5 m from the lamp. After about 5 minutes, observe the cut end of the sprig.
4 Count the number of bubbles formed at the end of the sprig each minute, for a five minute period, and record your results. Replace the tapwater in the flask with fresh cool tapwater.
5 Explain why these bubbles are forming. What are the bubbles made of?
6 Give an operational definition of photosynthesis in *Elodea.*
7 What is the purpose of placing the *Elodea* in an $NaHCO_3$ solution?
8 What is the relationship between the rate of photosynthesis in the *Elodea* sprig and the rate of bubble formation?

Inquiry
1 Discuss the objective of this laboratory with your partners and develop a hypothesis.
2 Design an experiment to test your hypothesis that uses the setup described above in Technique.
3 What are the independent and dependent variables in your experiment? How will you vary the independent variables? How will you measure changes in the dependent variable?
4 What controls will you include?
5 State the purpose of placing the test tube with *Elodea* in an Erlenmeyer flask containing cool tapwater.
6 Make a table to record your data and design a graph to show your results.
7 Using fresh $NaHCO_3$ solution, proceed with your experiment once your design is approved by your teacher.

Conclusions
1 What effect, if any, did changes in the independent variable have on the dependent variable in your experiment?
2 Do your data support your hypothesis? Explain.
3 Can you assume that all plants would behave in the same manner as *Elodea?*
4 Can you think of any sources of error in your experiment?

Further Inquiry
Decreased levels of ozone in the upper atmosphere may increase the amount of ultraviolet radiation reaching the Earth. Design an experiment to test the effect of ultraviolet radiation intensity on the rate of photosynthesis.

(For an overview of photosynthesis and preparatory information related to the laboratory, see p. 91B.)

Background
1. Reactants: CO_2 and H_2O; products: carbohydrates and O_2
2. Provides the initial energy to be stored in chemical bonds

Technique
5. Student may infer that photosynthesis is producing oxygen.
6. Photosynthesis is the formation of bubbles at the cut end of a sprig of *Elodea* immersed in bicarbonate ($NaHCO_3$) solution.
7. $NaHCO_3$ releases CO_2 when mixed with water, speeding up the rate of photosynthesis.
8. A higher rate of photosynthesis increases bubble formation.

Inquiry
1. Each laboratory group should agree on a testable hypothesis.
2. Discuss experimental designs, making sure students understand that light intensity relates to the distance from the source.
3. Independent variable: light intensity, varied by moving the lamp closer to or farther from the flask; dependent variable: oxygen production, measured as the rate of bubble formation.
4. Controls include: excluding light by wrapping the test tube in black paper; checking the surface for bubbles; maintaining constant temperature; control for time's effect on the photosynthetic rate—have some groups begin collecting data with their sample closest to the lamp, other groups with their sample farthest from the lamp.
5. To limit effects of lamp's heat on rate of photosynthesis
6. Data table should include: number of bubbles formed, distance from light, the timed interval. Plot bubble formation rate on the *y* axis, distance from light on the *x* axis.

Conclusions
1. Student data should support answers.
2. Students should recognize whether their data support the hypotheses. Increased bubble rate resulting from intense light supports the hypothesis that increased light intensity increases the photosynthetic rate.
3. No. *Elodea* is a single plant genus. Generalizations based on this laboratory must be similarly tested on plants of other genera.
4. Variation between *Elodea* sprigs; variability in light sources; amount and type of ambient light.

Further Inquiry
Students should recall controls listed in Conclusions, step 4; list possible hazards. *(UV light causes sunburn.)*

Chapter 7 Review

Vocabulary

1. C_4 pathway; the rest are involved in cellular respiration.
2. Anaerobic respiration; the rest relate to the light-dependent reactions in photosynthesis.
3. Heterotrophs are not biochemical pathways.
4. Light-independent reactions; the rest relate to photosynthesis.
5. Autotroph; the rest are parts of chloroplasts.

Review

1. b	**6.** c
2. a	**7.** b
3. d	**8.** d
4. a	**9.** c
5. b	**10.** a

11. Autotrophs can build organic food molecules directly from inorganic compounds. Heterotrophs eat autotrophs or other heterotrophs.
12. Like currency or money, ATP is valuable. It can be stored until needed, then "cashed in." Also, it can be accumulated in large amounts of small units.
13. A series of related reactions, such as the Calvin cycle
14. Chemiosmosis occurs when hydrogen ion concentration is higher on one side of a membrane, creating an electrochemical gradient. The ion movement provides energy needed to synthesize ATP.
15. Desert plants such as cactuses fix carbon at night. Their pores are closed in the daytime, so less water vapor is lost.
16. Yeasts ferment the sugars in grapes by alcoholic fermentation, producing the alcohol in wines.
17. Glycolysis yields pyruvic acid, which diffuses across the mitochondrial membrane to the matrix and is converted to acetyl-CoA, releasing CO_2 and a hydrogen ion. Simultaneously, NAD^+ accepts the H^+, forming NADH. Acetyl-CoA enters the Krebs cycle and combines with oxaloacetic acid to form citric acid.

Chapter 7 Review

Vocabulary

ADP (adenosine diphosphate) (95)
ATP (adenosine triphosphate) (94)
aerobic respiration (105)
alcoholic fermentation (105)
anaerobic respiration (104)
autotroph (93)
biochemical pathway (94)
C_4 pathway (102)
CAM (102)
chemiosmosis (98)
carbon fixation (98)
electron transport chain (98)
fermentation (104)
glycolysis (103)
grana (96)
heterotroph (93)
Krebs cycle (106)
lactic acid fermentation (104)
light-dependent reactions (97)
light-independent reactions (99)
phosphorylation (95)
photosynthesis (93)
photosystem (97)
respiration (93)
stroma (96)
thylakoids (96)

From each set of terms below, choose the term that does not belong and explain why it does not belong.

1. ATP, C_4 pathway, Krebs cycle, glycolysis
2. electron transport chain, chemiosmosis, anaerobic respiration, photosystem
3. photosynthesis, fermentation, respiration, heterotroph
4. chemiosmosis, light-independent reactions, C_4 pathway, CAM
5. grana, stroma, autotroph, thylakoid

Review

1. When cells break down glucose, they release (a) pigments (b) CO_2 (c) O_2 (d) light.
2. Phosphorylation occurs when (a) a phosphate group is added to a molecule (b) a phosphate group is removed from a molecule (c) H_2O is split (d) O_2 is formed.
3. ATP synthetase is an important factor in photosynthesis and respiration because it (a) accepts hydrogen (b) replaces oxygen (c) adds phosphorus (d) catalyzes ATP formation.
4. The products that result from photosynthesis are (a) carbohydrates and O_2 (b) CO_2 and H_2O (c) ATP and H_2O (d) RuBP and H^+.
5. Accessory pigments (a) add color to plants but do not trap light energy (b) trap light energy that chlorophyll cannot absorb (c) occur only in animals (d) transfer energy from chlorophyll to other pigments.
6. A reactant used in the Calvin cycle is (a) H_2O (b) glucose (c) CO_2 (d) citric acid.
7. C_4 photosynthesis enables plants in hot, dry climates to fix carbon (a) only at night (b) at a faster rate (c) with less energy (d) with minimum H_2O.
8. Glycolysis occurs in the (a) stroma (b) mitochondrion (c) thylakoid (d) cytoplasm.
9. Before aerobic respiration can proceed, pyruvic acid must be converted to (a) citric acid (b) glucose (c) acetyl-CoA (d) alcohol.
10. The maximum number of ATP molecules produced by aerobic respiration is (a) 38 (b) 36 (c) 34 (d) 4.
11. Why is it said that all life depends on autotrophs?
12. Explain the sentence "ATP is the currency of energy."
13. What is meant by the term *biochemical pathway?* Give an example of one that occurs during photosynthesis.
14. What role does chemiosmosis play in the formation of ATP?
15. Explain how CAM photosynthesis is advantageous for cactuses.

18. Both occur in a membrane and require an electrochemical gradient to function. The movement of ions through the membrane powers the formation of ATP in both processes.
19. The total net yield depends upon the type of cell as well as the cell's energy requirements.
20. Through his use of radioactive carbon dioxide, Calvin learned the sequence in which intermediate compounds are formed during photosynthesis. The changes take only a few seconds.

16. Why are yeasts used in wine and beer production?
17. Summarize the events that occur from the end of glycolysis through the first reaction of the Krebs cycle.
18. Compare the electron transport chain in photosynthesis and in respiration.
19. What factors determine the total net yield in aerobic respiration?
20. What did Calvin learn by labeling photosynthetic cells with radioactive CO_2?

Critical Thinking

1. The enzyme complex that removes CO_2 from pyruvic acid and transfers it to CoA requires vitamin B_1, also called thiamine. Vitamins generally are not made in the body. What can you infer about the importance of the foods in a human's diet?
2. The generation of ATP by the electron transport system is not 100 percent efficient. Some energy is left in the molecules, and some is released as heat. In animals such as the musk ox shown at the right, the electron transport chain becomes even less efficient in cold winter months. Predict the effect of this decreased efficiency.
3. The wine industry uses alchohol fermentation to produce wine. Considering the conditions needed for this process to occur, as well as the two major products, what type of container do you think the industry would use to ferment grapes?
4. Evidence indicates that the earth's early atmosphere contained no O_2. What types of metabolism would have been possible?

What could be the source of the O_2 present in the earth's atmosphere today?

Extension

1. Read the article by George Hendry entitled "Making, Breaking, and Remaking Chlorophyll," in *Natural History*, May 1990, pp. 37–40. Write a report in which you describe: (1) three major reasons why chlorophyll breaks down regularly in organisms, and (2) how chlorophyll might be recycled in plants.
2. When the sun's rays are blocked by dust or clouds from a volcanic eruption, or large forest or oil fire, what short- and long-term effects might there be on the energy cycle? Assume that some scientists want to list probable effects. What factors do you suggest they study?
3. Collect an algae culture from a local pond or aquarium store. Divide it into two covered bowls, placing one in the dark and the other in light. Keep both at the same temperature. Every other day for ten days, observe both with a dissecting microscope. Draw and record the organisms and debris that you see. What do your observations tell you about the role of light in pond life?

Critical Thinking

1. The diet must include foods that provide an adequate supply of vitamins. Without thiamine, for example, there would be no enzyme catalyzing the removal of CO_2 from pyruvic acid, and the Krebs cycle would be halted.
2. Because the electron transport chain becomes less efficient, more heat is released.
3. The container should prevent oxygen from entering yet allow carbon dioxide to escape.
4. Anaerobic respiration, either lactic acid or alcoholic fermentation, would have been possible and also photosynthesis, which could have produced the oxygen present in the earth's atmosphere today.

Extension

1. The fall color change results from the natural breakdown of chlorophyll, triggered by shorter days and cooler temperatures. There are adaptive advantages—the breakdown insures that only fully functional chlorophyll molecules are present and that components resulting from the breakdown are recycled.
2. In the short term, the atmospheric carbon dioxide level might increase, increasing productivity (and populations) of plant autotrophs. Over the long term, the photosynthetic rate and therefore oxygen production might decrease. Scientists might study the effect of high atmospheric CO_2 levels, and reduced light intensity on rate of photosynthesis.
3. Students will observe more organisms, both free-swimming heterotrophs and green autotrophs, in the bowl exposed to light. They will note a decrease in the number of living organisms, especially autotrophs, in the dark bowl over time—light is necessary to sustain pond life.

Chapter 8 Nucleic Acids and Protein Synthesis

Chapter Overview

This chapter describes the structures and functions of DNA and RNA. Section 8.1 examines the structure of DNA and its replication. Section 8.2 discusses the structure and transcription of RNA. Section 8.3 focuses on the functions of DNA and RNA as they relate to protein synthesis.

Chapter Planning Chart

B	S	A	Sections and Subsections	Page	Features	Page	Resources
•	•	•	**8.1 DNA**				
			Structure of DNA	113	Biology in Process	116	Videodiscs
			Replication of DNA	115	Writing About Biology	124	Blackline Master 18
					Section Review	117	Overhead Transparency T8
							Section Reviews Worksheet
•	•	•	**8.2 RNA**				
			Structure of RNA	118	Laboratory	125	Videodiscs
			Transcription	118	Section Review	119	Blackline Master 19
							Section Reviews Worksheet
•	•	•	**8.3 Protein Synthesis**				
			Protein Structure	120	Think	120	Videodiscs
			Codons	120	Section Review	123	Blackline Master 20
			Translation	121			Process Skills: Nucleic Acid Sequences
							Laboratories: Modeling Nucleic Acids
							Section Reviews Worksheet
			End of Chapter Activities				
					Chapter Review	126	Vocabulary Skills
							Chapter Test
							Computer Test Generator

B *The Basic Level curriculum presents the most fundamental knowledge offered in the course.*
S *The Standard Level curriculum is designed for the average student who is able to master most topics.*
A *The Advanced Level curriculum includes suggestions for teaching the most academically able students.*

Cooperative Learning

Group Activity: Practicing Codes

- **Group Size:** *4 Students*
- **Outcome:** *Students will construct and solve genetic codes.*
- **Individual Accountability:** *Each student will create codes using the English alphabet and the genetic code.*
- **Positive Interdependence:** *The group members will decode each other's coded messages.*

Ask students to define *code.* *(Students may say it is a secret language, a means of saying something briefly.)* Demonstrate a simple code by writing two single-column lists of the alphabet on two separate sheets of paper. Place the lists side-by-side, matching the letters in the two lists. Next, move one list so it is displaced by one or two letters. For example, A = C, B = D, C = E, and so on. Have each student use the code to write a short message and give it to another group member for decoding.

After students solve Critical Thinking questions 2 and 3 in the Chapter Review, have each student write a 30-nucleotide-long mRNA code. Have the group decode both the complementary DNA strand and the translated amino acid chain. Have each group evaluate the areas in which they experienced the most difficulty and compare those problem areas with those of the other groups.

Concept Map

The following is one possible solution to the concept mapping activity in Guided Practice on p. 122.

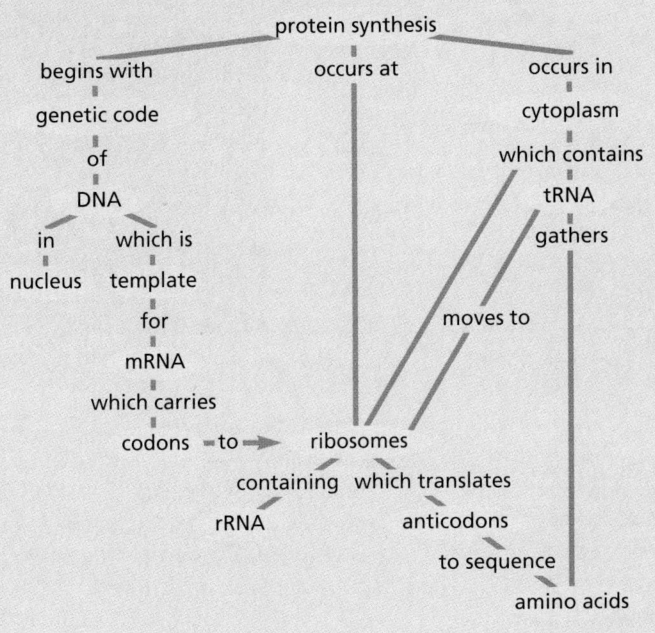

Laboratory Preparation

Overview *(See p. 125.)*

In this lab students learn a qualitative test for DNA and RNA. They are then presented with hypothetical test samples of specific cellular organelles that have been separated by differential centrifugation. They cannot actually perform this separation since the equipment required for differential centrifugation is too expensive for high schools. Therefore, they are asked to infer the results of this test.

Preparation

To prepare diphenylamine, add 15 g diphenylamine to 1 L glacial acetic acid. Add 15 mL concentrated sulfuric acid. Store in a dark bottle. On the day of lab, add 1 mL acetaldehyde solution. To prepare acetaldehyde solution, add 1 mL acetaldehyde to 500 mL distilled water. DNA and RNA can be purchased from a biological supply house. To prepare DNA solution, add 0.1 g DNA for every 200 mL distilled water. Add one drop glacial acetic acid to every 200 mL DNA solution. If necessary, use heat to dissolve DNA. Store in freezer. Prepare RNA solution in the same manner.

Teaching Tips

This is a good time to review the structure and function of some of the cell organelles. Structurally, ribosomes are about half RNA and half protein. The nucleolus is nearly all RNA. Obviously, the chromosomes in the nucleus are DNA. Lysosomes contain digestive enzymes and are therefore mainly protein, with some lipid in the membrane.

Explain the technique of differential centrifugation to students. In this process cells are broken open and then spun at very high speeds. Under certain conditions the different organelles form bands in the centrifuge tube. This important technique makes it possible for scientists to study different kinds of organelles outside of the cell.

Safety

Students should not handle diphenylamine solution. The teacher should dispense diphenylamine during the laboratory. Have students wash their hands after finishing the experiment.

Chapter Themes

Stability Emphasize to students that the DNA code is remarkably stable and consistent. The same triplets of DNA bases specify the same amino acid in most organisms. Point out that eukaryotes have structures that protect their DNA, such as the nuclear membranes.

Scale and Structure Point out to students that the double helix structure of DNA and the structures of the three types of RNA (strand, cloverleaf, and globular) are essential and stable forms. Stress that they can barely be seen with the electron microscope.

Evolution The DNA code is universal and consistent. Stress that at the same time, DNA provides the mechanism for change through mutation. Selective pressures determine whether or not a DNA mutation results in a beneficial adaptation. Such mutations can lead to the evolution of new species.

Chapter Motivating Activity

Show students a floppy diskette, an audiocassette, a photograph, and a written page. Ask them how each item carries information, using what sort of code. *(Magnetic imprints, photochemical spots, letters in words)* What could change the information? *(Magnets, aging and fading of the film or paper)* Ask what could keep the information from changing and whether these measures would be permanent. *(Shields against magnets, acid-free paper; no, eventually the plastic or paper will wear out, decay, and crumble.)* Point out that DNA is used and copied thousands of times with very little change occurring.

Chapter 8 Nucleic Acids and Protein Synthesis

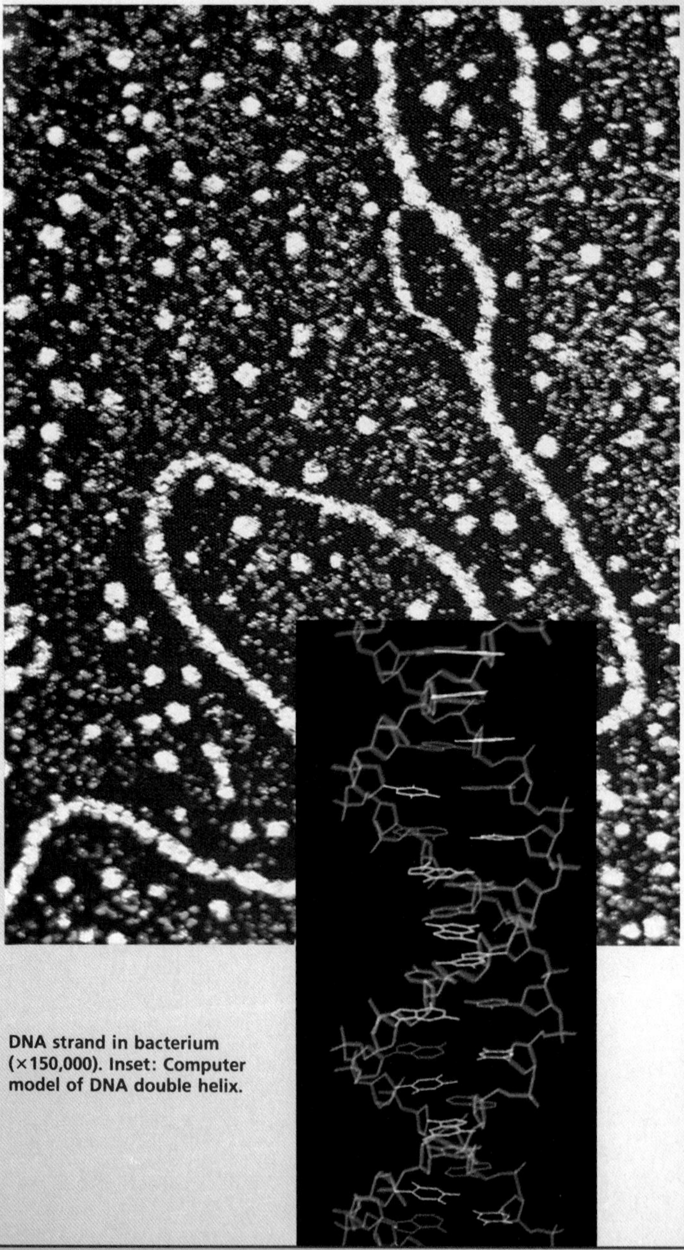

DNA strand in bacterium (×150,000). Inset: Computer model of DNA double helix.

Introduction

Every cell, no matter how simple or complex, must store and transmit the information needed to manufacture proteins. DNA stores the information for protein synthesis. RNA transmits this information for use in building proteins. In this chapter you will learn how the functions of DNA and RNA are related to their molecular structures.

Chapter Outline

8.1 DNA
- *Structure of DNA*
- *Replication of DNA*

8.2 RNA
- *Structure of RNA*
- *Transcription*

8.3 Protein Synthesis
- *Protein Structure*
- *Codons*
- *Translation*

Chapter Concept

As you read, pay attention to the way that DNA and RNA store and transmit information and synthesize proteins. Keep in mind that DNA makes RNA, which in turn makes proteins.

Understanding the Visuals

Identify the long, ropelike strand in the large photograph as DNA. Ask students to speculate as to the cause of the loop. *(Some students may identify this as a copying spot; others may identify it as damage.)*

Have students describe the shape of the double helix in the inset. *(Two intertwined, cylindrical, spiral forms; a twisted ladder)* Emphasize that this structure does not narrow to a point. Have students describe the parts of the model. *(The blue-purple outer structure consists of connected five-sided rings; double red and green, and single yellow and lavender central rings are attached to the outer blue-purple structures.)*

8.1 DNA

What enables cells to have so many different forms and perform so many different functions? Ultimately the source of this amazing diversity is DNA, or deoxyribonucleic acid. In simple terms, DNA controls the production of proteins within the cell. These proteins in turn form the structural units of cells and control all chemical processes within the cell.

Every new cell that develops in your body needs an exact copy of the DNA from its parent cell. Likewise, humans and all other organisms must be able to pass copies of their DNA on to their offspring in order to continue the species. As you will see in this chapter, the structure of the DNA molecule is related to its two primary functions—to store and use information to direct the activities of the cell and to copy itself exactly for new cells that are created.

Section Objectives

- *Explain the principal function of DNA in cells.*
- *Describe the basic structure of a DNA molecule.*
- *Summarize the process of replication.*
- *List some major scientific discoveries that led to the description of DNA structure by Watson and Crick.*

Structure of DNA

As you recall from Chapter 4, the nucleic acids DNA and RNA are complex organic molecules. DNA and RNA are polymers—that is, they are composed of repeating subunits, or monomers. The repeating subunits in both DNA and RNA are **nucleotides.**

Nucleotides

The DNA molecule consists of two long strands, each of which is a chain of nucleotide monomers. Each nucleotide has three parts: (1) a five-carbon sugar molecule called **deoxyribose** *(dee-AHK-sih-RIE-BOSE)*, (2) a phosphate group, and (3) a nitrogen base.

While the sugar molecule and phosphate group are the same in every nucleotide, the nitrogen base may be any one of four different kinds. These bases are **adenine** *(AD-'n-EEN)*, **guanine** *(GWAHN-EEN)*, **thymine** *(THIE-MEEN)*, and **cytosine** *(SITE-uh-SEEN)*. Study the structure of each in Figure 8-1. The first two bases—adenine and guanine—belong to a class of organic molecules known as **purines** *(PYOOHR-EENZ)*, which have a double ring of carbon and nitrogen atoms. The second two bases—thymine and cytosine—are **pyrimidines** *(pie-RIM-uh-DEENZ)*. These molecules have a single ring of carbon and nitrogen atoms.

Figure 8-1 The nitrogen base in a nucleotide is either a purine or a pyrimidine.

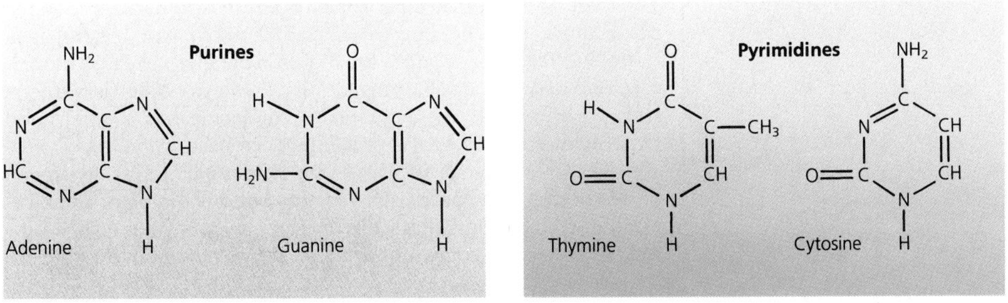

Lesson Plan

Section Focus

Section 8.1 examines in detail the structure of DNA: pairs of nitrogen bases bonded to sugar-phosphate backbones. This molecular arrangement allows for the formation of exact copies as well as for the repair of breaks.

Section Themes

This section emphasizes the theme of **Scale and Structure.** The structure of DNA is determined by its component atoms and their bonds. The double helical structure allows for self-replication, necessary for DNA's function of providing information that directs cell activities in each new cell.

The theme of **Stability** is evident in the accuracy of DNA replication. In addition, there is a cellular mechanism for "proofreading" and repair that reduces errors and maintains the integrity of the DNA molecule.

Motivating Activity

Ask students to list things that can self-replicate without error. Encourage speculation. When the suggestions do not meet the criteria, ask questions to help students see how they fall short. *(For example, an automated car factory produces thousands of identical cars, yet they did not arise from replication of one car. Quality control, an outside force, notes and corrects errors.)* Point out that in most cases the object has not replicated itself; instead, copies of an original "blueprint" have been made. DNA, present in every cell, copies itself and corrects errors.

Videodiscs

- ***Side 1 27255, DNA and Ethidium—Computer Model of DNA (m)***
- ***2672–2685, Molecular Graphics—DNA Sequences/ Views (s)***

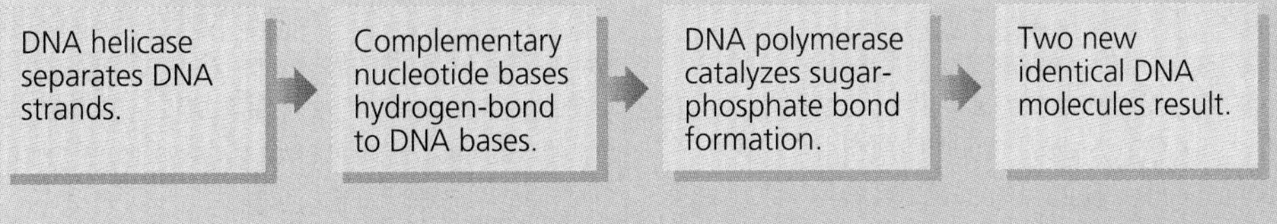

Graphic Organizer Use this sequential diagram in Guided Practice on p. 115.

Teaching Strategies

Interpreting the Visuals Have students examine Figures 8-1, 8-2, and 8-3, pp. 113–115. Ask students which one most closely resembles the photomicrograph of DNA on p. 112. *(None are identical, but Figure 8-3 closely resembles it, having a stringlike structure and open loop.)* Have students describe the ways the nitrogen bases are modeled. *(The computer model on p. 112 represents the purines as two differently colored double rings. The pyrimidines are represented as two differently colored single rings; Figure 8-1 gives the structural formulas of the bases, showing their component atoms and bond patterns; Figure 8-2 represents the purines schematically as double rings—blue for adenine, purple for guanine. The pyrimidines are schematically represented as single rings—red for thymine, green for cytosine. In Figure 8-3 purines and pyrimidines are differentiated by shape. Old bases are blue, new bases orange.)* Ask students to identify what is consistent in the way the bases are modeled. *(The purines are always shown as double rings, five-sided and six-sided. The pyrimidines are always single, six-sided rings.)*
■ *See* **Overhead Transparency** *T8 and* **Blackline Master** *18.*

Building Models Have students construct their own models of a DNA molecule, clearly showing its structural components. Encourage students to use their imagination when choosing materials. *(Students may create two-dimensional posters or three-dimensional models. Materials may include foods, Velcro, cloth, pipe cleaners, plastic foam balls, paper, cardboard, or papier-mâché.)*

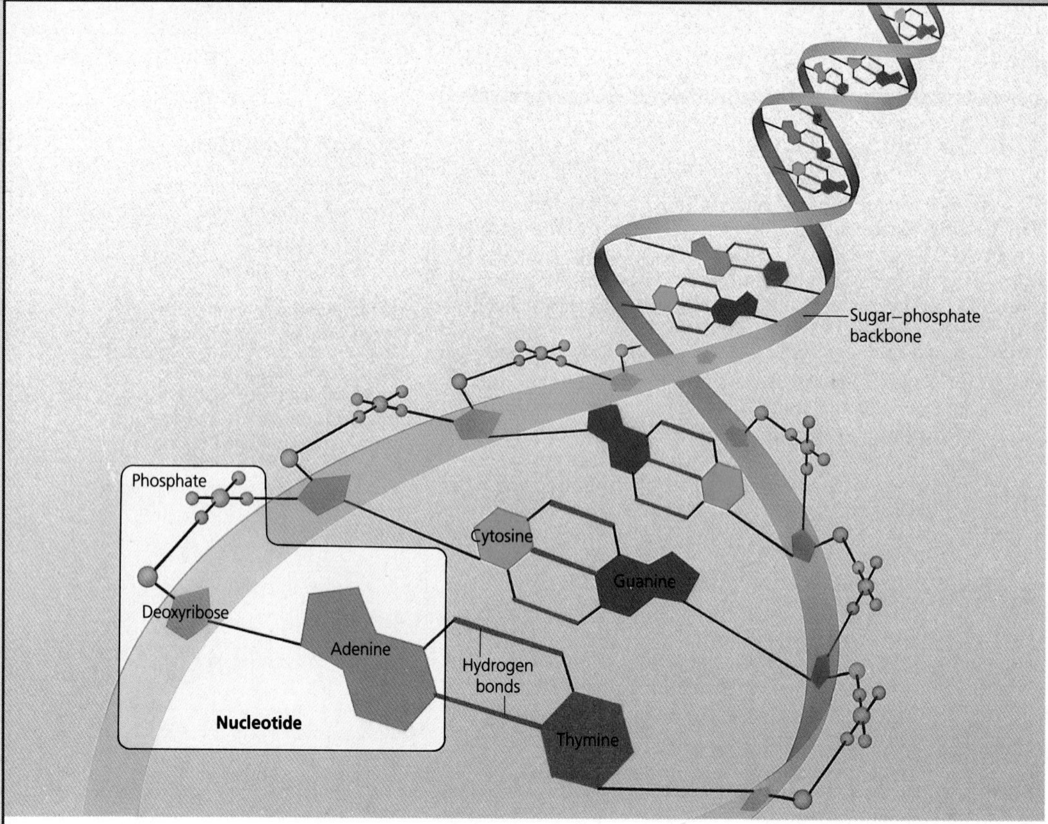

Figure 8-2 The DNA structure resembles a twisted ladder and is described as a double helix.

The Double Helix

Each nucleotide—deoxyribose, phosphate, and nitrogen base—bonds to other nucleotides to form a long strand. Two of these strands bonded together form a molecule of DNA. The two strands twist around a central axis to form a spiral structure called a **double helix.** The double helix structure was first described in 1953 by James Watson (1928–) and Francis Crick (1916–). Their discovery is one of the most significant of the twentieth century.

Figure 8-2 shows the details of the structure of DNA. As you can see, the DNA molecule looks something like a twisted ladder. The sides of the ladder are formed by alternating sugar and phosphate units, and the rungs consist of bonded pairs of nitrogen bases. Notice that the rungs are of uniform length because in each case one base is a double-ringed purine and the other is a single-ringed pyrimidine. An actual DNA molecule has a right-hand twist, with each full turn consisting of ten base pairs.

The two strands of DNA are held together by hydrogen bonds between the bases. A **hydrogen bond** is a type of chemical bond in which atoms share a hydrogen nucleus—that is, one proton. In DNA, hydrogen bonds form between purines and pyrim-

LEP Activity

Students are sometimes overwhelmed by the layers of terms in DNA structure. Constructing models can help to link shapes and names. Have students use the Blackline Master 18 (Figure 8-2) as a template to draw and cut out shapes of the four nitrogen bases, deoxyriboses, and phosphate groups. (If possible, use six different colored papers.) Have students copy the names onto each shape, then use tape to assemble four kinds of nucleotides.

The pairing of a purine and a pyrimidine (A with T, G with C) makes visible and explains the constant width, like a ladder, of the DNA molecule. Have students pair complementary nitrogen bases, using tape to represent hydrogen bonds between the nucleotides of the two strands.

idines. More specifically, adenine always bonds with thymine, and cytosine always bonds with guanine. This occurs because the structure of adenine complements that of thymine in such a way that hydrogen bonds are established. The same kind of complementarity exists between cytosine and guanine. However, adenine and thymine form only two hydrogen bonds, while cytosine and guanine form three.

The fact that adenine always bonds to thymine and cytosine always bonds to guanine has structural and functional consequences. The sequential arrangement of nitrogen bases along one strand is the exact complement of the sequential arrangement of bases on the adjacent strand. Because of this characteristic, the two strands are said to be complementary strands.

Replication of DNA

The scientific world was stunned by Watson and Crick's proposed structure for DNA because it immediately suggested how DNA might be copied—and copied exactly. If the two complementary strands of DNA were to unwind, then each strand could serve as the template, or mold, on which a new complementary strand could be built. This process would produce two new DNA molecules that are exact replicas of the original DNA. Subsequent research has shown that this is exactly what happens.

Process of Replication

The process of the duplication of a DNA molecule is called **replication.** Refer to Figure 8-3 as you read about the process of replication. Replication begins when an enzyme called DNA helicase attaches to a DNA molecule, moves along the molecule, and "unzips" the two strands of DNA. DNA helicase acts by breaking the hydrogen bonds between the nitrogen bases.

After the DNA strands are separated, the now unpaired bases in each strand react with the complementary bases of nucleotides that are floating freely in the nucleus. These complementary bases bond with the bases in the DNA strands by forming hydrogen bonds. As each new set of hydrogen bonds links a pair of bases, an enzyme called DNA polymerase catalyzes the formation of the sugar-to-phosphate bonds that connect one nucleotide to the next one. This process results in two new DNA molecules, each of which consists of one "old" strand of DNA and one "new" strand of DNA.

The process of replication maintains the complementary nature of the DNA molecule. Since adenine (A) can pair only with thymine (T) and cytosine (C) can pair only with guanine (G), the sequence of nucleotides in each new strand exactly matches that in the original molecule. Suppose, for instance, that the sequence of nucleotides in one strand of the original molecule was A-T-T-C-C-G. The complementary strand in the original molecule must have had the sequence T-A-A-G-G-C. Any new strand formed

Figure 8-3 Replication results in two new DNA molecules, each with one old and one new strand.

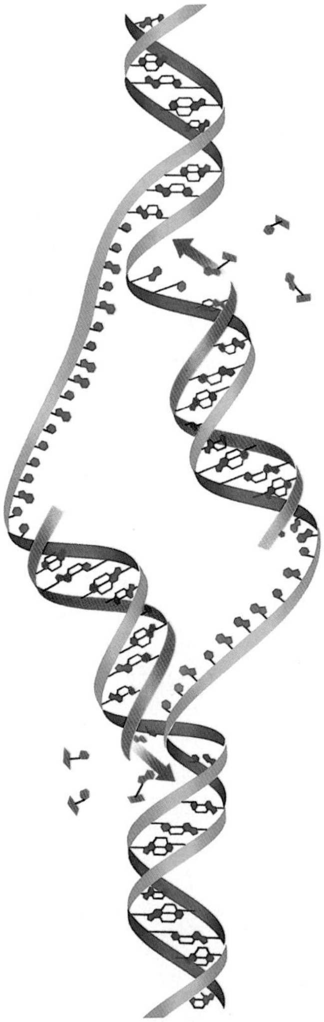

Using Mnemonics Have students create a mnemonic device to help them identify the four bases. *(For example, "**Th**ousands **c**ount **pyr**amids" is a reminder that **th**ymine and **c**ytosine are **pyr**imidines. "**A**ds **g**uarantee **pur**ity" may remind students that **a**denine and **g**uanine are **pur**ines.)*

Identifying Structures Have students draw and label the component parts of several linked nucleotides. Remind students to pair correctly the bases shown. *(A-T, C-G)* Ask students to identify the structural subunit of DNA. *(A nucleotide)* Ask students to name the component parts of a nucleotide. *(A nitrogen base and a deoxyribose sugar–phosphate group. The nitrogen base may be a purine [A or G] or a pyrimidine [T or C].)* Ask students how many types of nucleotides can occur in a DNA molecule. *(Four)*

Using Analogies Have students explain why a ladder is used as an analogy for the structure of DNA. Have students list the similarities and differences. *(Similarities: ladder supports are similar to the sugar–phosphate backbone; the rungs represent the paired nitrogen bases. Differences: DNA is twisted, not flat as is a ladder; a ladder rung is a complete unit—a DNA's "rung" consists of two separate nitrogen bases loosely connected by hydrogen bonds.)*

Guided Practice

On the board, begin a sequential diagram of DNA replication using the Graphic Organizer on p. 113 as a model. Provide only enough information to get students started; have them complete the diagram.

Videodiscs

- ***Side 1 25971, DNA Replication Animation (m)***

More Information

Pauling's Model Other models for the structure of DNA were proposed before Watson and Crick's double helix model was accepted. One notable example was that of Linus Pauling. In 1950, Pauling had determined that a fibrous protein's component chains of amino acids are often arranged in the shape of a helix, called the alpha helix, and are held in that form by hydrogen bonds. Examples of fibrous proteins include collagen, keratin, silk, and elastin. Pauling suggested that DNA structure might be similar, if not identical, to the alpha helix. Although Pauling's model was inaccurate, his findings about protein structure provided additional evidence that led Watson and Crick to the double helix.

Independent Practice

- Have students write answers to the Section Review.
- Have students use the letters that represent DNA bases—A, T, G, C—to form three-letter words such as CAT, TAT, TAG. Then have them write the complementary strands—GTA, ATA, ATC.

Check Your Understanding

1. What is the relationship of nitrogen to DNA? *(The four bases, A, T, G, and C, contain nitrogen as part of their carbon-nitrogen ring structure.)*
2. What is the function of phosphates in DNA? *(Phosphates form bonds between sugars; their role is linkage.)*
3. Why is it necessary for DNA to have a repair mechanism? What is that mechanism? *(DNA is constantly being damaged in human cells by body heat, radiation, and chemicals. Enzymes recognize and replace damaged nucleotides, ensuring accurate replication of DNA.)*

Reteaching

Provide students with partially complete sets of paired bases; for example, G-C G-C C-G A-T T-A A-_ T-_ T-_ A-_ C-_. Have students fill in the missing complementary bases *(A-T T-A T-A A-T C-G)*. Reteach DNA repair by including a miscopy such as T-T. Ask what will happen to the error during replication. *(Enzymes detect the error, cut it out, and replace it with T-A.)*
- *See* Section Reviews *worksheet, Section 8.1.*

Enrichment

Have students use the library to write a biography of Rosalind Franklin. Have them focus on her role in the development of the Watson–Crick DNA model.

using the first strand as a template will also follow the sequence T-A-A-G-G-C. Similarly, any new strand formed using the original T-A-A-G-G-C strand as a template must follow the sequence A-T-T-C-C-G.

Replication of DNA doesn't begin at one end of the molecule and proceed to the other. Rather, copying of DNA occurs simultaneously at many points on the molecule. Enzymes join the individual segments of DNA to each other as they are copied. Because of the size of the DNA molecule, if replication didn't occur in this way, it would take 16 days to copy just one DNA molecule of a fruit fly. Actually, the replication of this fruit fly DNA takes only about three minutes, because about 6,000 sites are being copied simultaneously.

Accuracy and Repair

The entire process of DNA replication occurs with great accuracy. The cell has a built-in "proofreading" function, performed by enzymes or proteins depending on the organism. The degree of accuracy is on the order of one error per billion nucleotides.

DNA also has a mechanism for repair. In human cells, body heat, radiation, chemicals, and other factors can damage DNA.

Biology in Process

Discovering the Structure of DNA

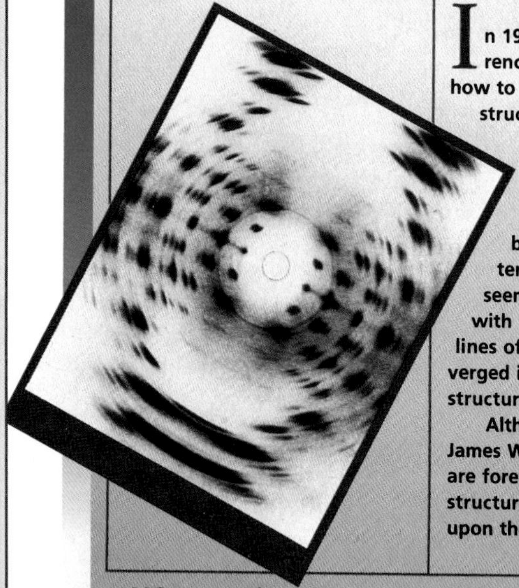

In 1912 British physicist Lawrence Bragg figured out how to use X rays to reveal the structure of crystals. In 1928 British bacteriologist Frederick Griffith determined that traits could be transmitted between strains of bacteria. These discoveries seem to have little to do with DNA, but they launched lines of research that converged in the discovery of DNA structure in the early 1950s.

Although the names of James Watson and Francis Crick are forever associated with the structure of DNA, they drew upon the work of many other researchers in developing their model. Truly in the words of Isaac Newton, they "stood upon the shoulders of giants."

When Watson and Crick began their work together, they already knew a great deal about DNA. Researchers following up on the work of Griffith had demonstrated that DNA is the genetic material. Others had revealed many details of the chemical composition of DNA. Of special note was a discovery by American biochemist Erwin Chargaff. He had shown that in DNA the amount of cytosine equals that of guanine, and the amount of thymine equals that of adenine.

More Information

Molecular Biology Advances in technology such as X-ray diffraction and electron microscopy have led to the development of molecular biology, the study of the structure and function of molecules within the cell. Of growing importance since the 1940s, this branch of biology relates to the disciplines of biochemistry, biophysics, cell physiology, and genetics.

The field of molecular biology expanded rapidly after the structure of DNA and its method of replication were discovered in the 1950s. The industrial field of biotechnology has also grown. It depends on a large-scale ability to synthesize genes and proteins. A useful resource is a recent edition of James D. Watson's *Molecular Biology of the Gene,* a college textbook published by Benjamin/Cummings.

Body heat alone continuously breaks up bonds between deoxyribose and purines. A group of 20 or more repair enzymes recognizes and removes damaged nucleotides and replaces them with new ones, thus ensuring the accurate replication of new DNA.

In studying the structure and replication of DNA, make a note of one thing. The sequence of bases along a strand is, as you will learn, not random. Inherent in the sequence of nitrogen bases is all the information determining the structure and function of an organism.

Section Review

1. What is the difference between a *purine* and a *pyrimidine?*
2. How are the two strands of a DNA molecule bonded together to form a double helix?
3. Why is the process of DNA replication necessary?
4. What important roles do enzymes play during the replication process?
5. Prokaryotic cells lack a nucleus; eukaryotic cells have a nucleus. Suggest an adaptive advantage for confining DNA in a nucleus.

The most direct information about DNA structure available to Watson and Crick came from Bragg's technique of X-ray crystallography. Maurice Wilkins and Rosalind Franklin, researchers at King's College in London, had used X-ray crystallography to produce images of DNA like the one shown at left. By 1952 Franklin's interpretation of these images indicated that DNA is a helix with the sugar–phosphate backbone on the outside. Franklin's images also showed that the diameter of the helix was so large that it must consist of more than one strand of nucleotides.

The main questions left for Watson and Crick (above) to answer were how many strands of nucleotides make up DNA and how those strands are bonded together. Watson and Crick succeeded in answering those questions by combining available information with a technique of model building, which they knew that American chemist Linus Pauling had used to determine aspects of protein structure.

The chain of events that led to the discovery of DNA structure exemplifies the way in which a scientific discovery often draws upon the work done by many scientists over many years. In this particular case, Lawrence Bragg was no doubt pleased that the technique he had developed 40 years earlier played a major role in this landmark discovery, which Watson and Crick made in the laboratory he directed at Cambridge University.

- **In what ways was the process of communicating vital to the success of Watson and Crick?**

Answers to Section Review

1. A purine has a double ring of carbon and nitrogen atoms; a pyrimidine has a single ring of carbon and nitrogen atoms.
2. Hydrogen bonds between complementary bases hold the two strands together.
3. Replication provides exact copies of DNA for new cells produced by cell division.
4. Enzymes separate the DNA strands and catalyze the sugar-to-phosphate bond formation that connects nucleotides to form a new DNA strand.
5. It is probably advantageous for a cell to have DNA and the enzymes involved in replication confined to a small, readily accessible area rather than widely dispersed throughout the cell. Also, the nuclear envelope may protect DNA.

Closure

Emphasize that DNA provides a set of instructions for the construction and maintenance of living things. Have students give examples of similar instructions in everyday life. *(Blueprints for a house, cookbook recipe, diagram for a sports play, TV script)*

Biology in Process

Using the Feature

The two main process skills described in this feature are organizing data and communicating. Open communication between scientists and use of previous research were essential to the discovery of DNA structure.

Ask students how James Watson and Francis Crick used information provided by others in the scientific community to build their model of DNA. *(Wilkins and Franklin's X-ray diffraction work was evidence of the helical structure of DNA. Watson and Crick borrowed Linus Pauling's model-building technique to test their hypotheses. Chargaff's discovery of the relative amounts of purines and pyrimidines provided Watson and Crick with an important clue as to DNA structure.)* Point out that, in addition, Watson and Crick worked very closely with each other, sharing ideas and applying them to the problem. By organizing their own data as well as the data of other scientists, Watson and Crick were able to unravel a complex scientific problem—the structure of DNA.

Answer to the Feature

Because the results of earlier research were published in scientific journals or available in talks, Watson and Crick were able to use information and concepts from many sources to build their DNA model.

Lesson Plan

Section Focus

Section 8.2 focuses on the formation of RNA through DNA transcription. It discusses the structures and functions of RNA.

Section Themes

The theme of **Scale and Structure** is emphasized in this section. The external structures of RNA—single strand, folded strand, or globular—reflect their functions in protein synthesis.

Motivating Activity

Have students write down what they hear as you play a brief portion of an important audiotaped speech. Ask them why the original tape would be kept by the recording company. *(To preserve original, important, historical information; so that high-quality copies can be made)* Ask students to list ways in which the tape and their transcript differ. *(The transcript uses a "code" of written words and letters; the tape uses a magnetic "code." Their transcript could differ if they misheard or miswrote what was on the tape.)* Point out to students that DNA and RNA molecules exhibit similarities and differences as do the tape and the transcript—the same information is carried, but in different forms. Relate the term *transcription* to the word *transcript*, a "writing down"; stress that RNA is transcribed from DNA.

Teaching Strategies

Interpreting the Visuals Have students use Figure 8-5, p. 119, Figure 8-2, p. 114, and the text to identify structural differences between DNA and RNA. *(RNA: ribose, uracil, single strand; DNA: deoxyribose, thymine, double strand)* Stress that only one DNA strand is transcribed.

■ *See* **Blackline Master** ***19.***

Section Objectives

- *Compare and contrast the structure of RNA with that of DNA.*
- *Name the three types of RNA, and describe the structure of each.*
- *Summarize the process of transcription.*

8.2 RNA

DNA stores and transmits the information needed to make proteins but it does not actually use that information to synthesize proteins. That is the primary function of RNA, or ribonucleic acid. In this section we will examine the basic structure of RNA and the process by which it is produced from DNA. In Section 8.3 we will study the role of RNA in the synthesis of proteins.

Structure of RNA

Like DNA, RNA is a polymer consisting of nucleotide monomers or subunits. However, RNA differs from DNA in three important ways. First, an RNA molecule consists of only one strand of nucleotides instead of the two strands of the DNA molecule. Second, RNA has **ribose** as its five-carbon sugar rather than deoxyribose. Finally, RNA has the nitrogen base **uracil** instead of thymine.

In addition, RNA exists in the following three structural forms. Each plays a different role in protein synthesis.

- **Messenger RNA (mRNA)** is a single, uncoiled strand that transmits information from DNA for use during protein synthesis. It serves as a template, or pattern, for the assembly of amino acids during protein synthesis.
- **Transfer RNA (tRNA)** is a single strand of RNA folded back on itself in hairpin fashion, allowing some complementary bases to pair. tRNA exists in 20 or more varieties, each with the ability to bond to only one specific type of amino acid.
- **Ribosomal RNA (rRNA)**, which is RNA in globular form, is the major constituent of the ribosomes. The precise function of rRNA in protein synthesis is not yet fully understood.

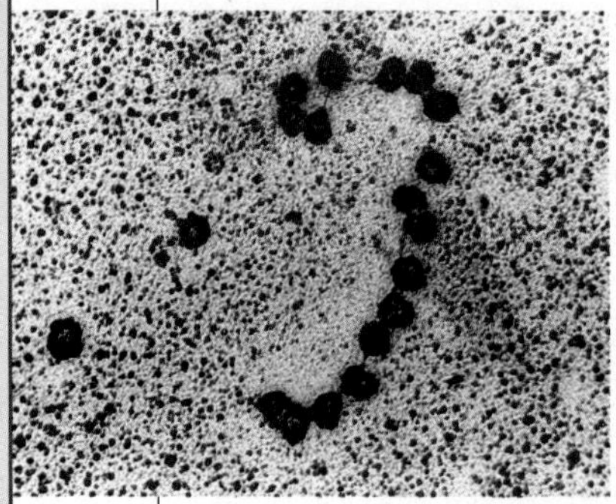

Figure 8-4 Ribosomes, shown in this SEM, are composed of rRNA and proteins.

Transcription

RNA is produced from DNA through a process called **transcription.** RNA molecules are transcribed according to the information encoded in the base sequence of DNA. As you read about transcription, follow the process in Figure 8-5.

An enzyme called RNA polymerase first binds to a DNA molecule and then causes the separation of the complementary strands of DNA. The enzyme next directs the formation of hydrogen bonds between the bases of a DNA strand and complementary bases of RNA nucleotides that are floating in the nucleus. RNA polymerase then moves along the section of DNA, establishing the sugar-to-phosphate bonds between the RNA nucleotides in much the same way as in DNA replication. When RNA polymerase reaches the sequence of bases on the DNA that acts as a termination signal, the enzyme triggers the release of the newly made RNA.

	DNA	RNA		
functional unit	genes	messenger	transfer	ribosomal
strands	two	one		
sugar	deoxyribose	ribose		
bases	A, T, G, C	A, U, G, C		
produced by	replication	transcription		

Graphic Organizer Use this table in Guided Practice on p. 119.

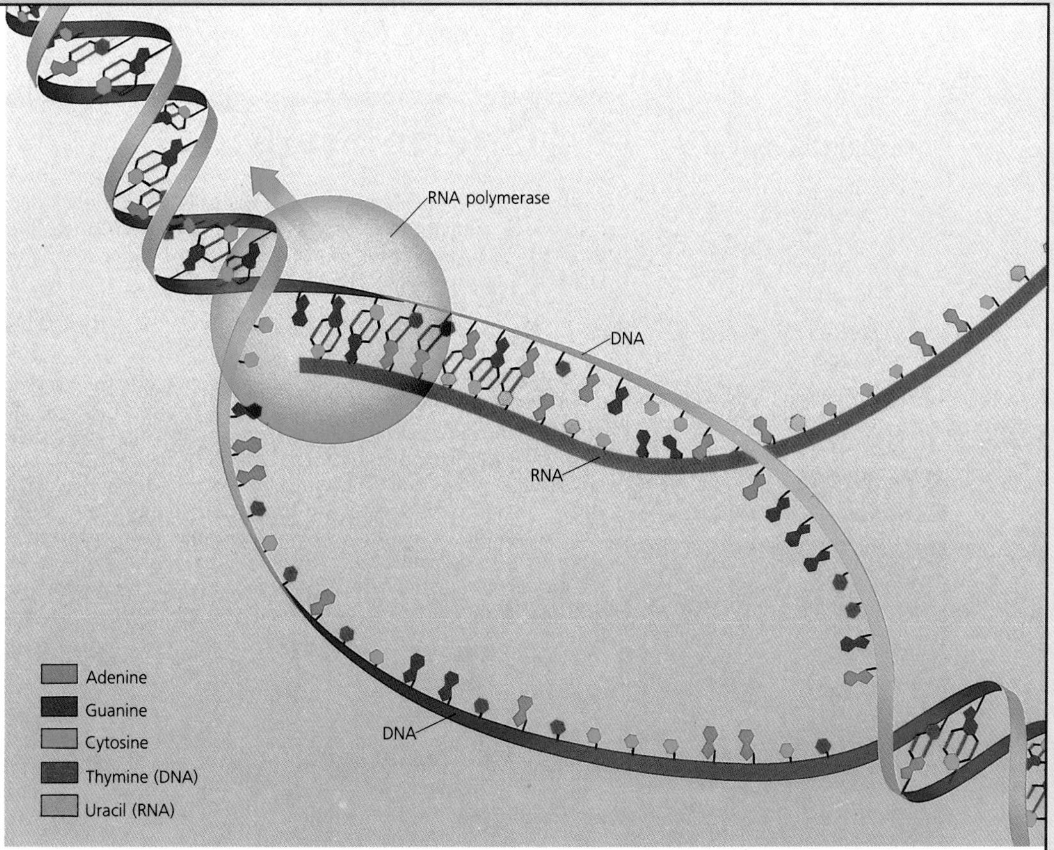

Figure 8-5 During transcription a DNA strand is linked to complementary bases of RNA nucleotides by hydrogen bonds.

All three types of RNA are transcribed in this manner. Each type of RNA then moves from the nucleus into the cytoplasm, where it is involved in the synthesis of proteins.

Notice that the transcription process creates RNA with a base sequence complementary to DNA. As you learned in Section 8.1, genetic information resides in the sequence of bases on a DNA molecule. During transcription this genetic code of DNA becomes inherent in the sequence of bases in RNA.

Section Review

1. What is *transcription?*
2. In what three ways does the structure of RNA differ from that of DNA?
3. What are the three types of RNA?
4. How is the sequence of bases in DNA reflected in the sequence of bases in the RNA made through the transcription process?
5. Why is the presence of nuclear pores advantageous for the movement of RNA?

Answers to Section Review

1. Transcription is the process of producing RNA from DNA.
2. RNA is single stranded; it has ribose instead of deoxyribose; and one of its bases is uracil rather than thymine.
3. RNA can be messenger, transfer, or ribosomal RNA.
4. The bases in RNA are complementary to the DNA from which the RNA was transcribed.
5. Messenger RNA leaves the nucleus through nuclear pores and travels to the cytoplasmic sites of protein synthesis.

Guided Practice

On the board, begin a table similar to the one on p. 118, comparing DNA and RNA. Have students complete the table.

Independent Practice

■ Have students write answers to the Section Review.
■ Have students list a series of three DNA bases, then write the complementary RNA strand. *(DNA: ACA TAT GAG; RNA: UGU AUA CUC)*

Check Your Understanding

1. What is the relationship of RNA to DNA? *(RNA is produced from DNA through transcription; RNA synthesizes proteins as directed by DNA.)*
2. If the process of using sheet music to create a tape is analogous to RNA transcription, what represents DNA? *(Sheet music, the master code)*

Reteaching

Have students list the "ingredients" required for RNA synthesis. *(DNA, RNA polymerase, free-floating RNA nucleotides)* What is RNA polymerase? *(The enzyme that catalyzes transcription)* Point out that ATP provides energy for the process.
■ *See* Section Reviews *worksheet, Section 8.2.*

Enrichment

An organism's cells all contain the same DNA yet can differ in structure and function. Have students research *cell differentiation.* For examples of tissue types, see Chapter 42, p. 638.

Closure

Have students explain the importance of accurate transcription. *(Inaccurate RNA messages affect synthesis of proteins required in the life activities of a cell.)*

Videodiscs

■ *2535–2537, Molecular Structures: Alanine/Valine/Glycine (s)*
■ *1596, Staining for RNA (s)*

Lesson Plan

Section Focus

Section 8.3 draws on student knowledge of the structures and functions of DNA and RNA to discuss protein synthesis. The roles of codons and anticodons in translation are explored.

Section Themes

The universality of the genetic code is evidence of the theme of **Stability**. In most living organisms, the same triplets of DNA bases specify the same amino acid. In addition, tRNA and ribosomes from many eukaryotic cells are often interchangeable.

Motivating Activity

Point out that a biochemical pathway such as respiration consists of a complex series of reactions and that specific enzymes catalyze specific reactions. Ask students what enzymes are made of and where they come from. *(Enzymes are protein; a gene in the DNA codes for synthesis of each polypeptide that a cell can make.)* Remind students that proteins consist of one or more polypeptide chains.

Show students an unfastened, bilaterally symmetrical necklace made of multicolored beads of graduated sizes. Intertwine the two halves. Ask students how it is similar to a protein. *(Each bead represents an amino acid. The necklace consists of two symmetrical halves, representing a two-polypeptide protein.)* Ask what determines the type of protein formed. *(The sequence of amino acids)* What determines that sequence? *(DNA)*

Answer to Think

Since algae, coral, and marine worms use the same genetic code, they (and all life) could have evolved from a common ancestor.

Section Objectives

- *List two characteristics of the genetic code.*
- *Distinguish between a codon and an anticodon, and state where each is found.*
- *Summarize the process of translation.*

Think

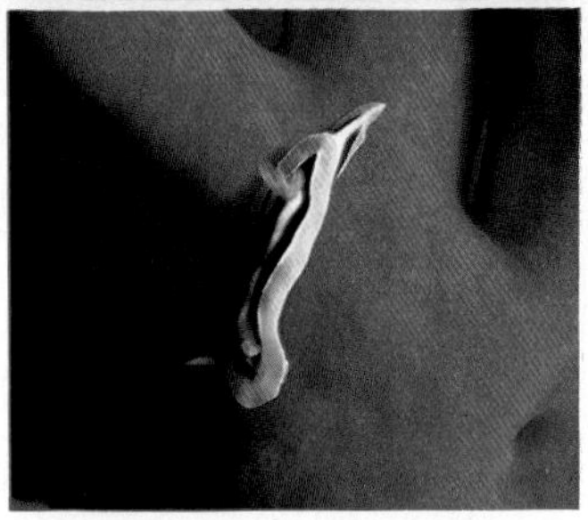

These organisms use the same genetic code. What does this suggest about evolution of life on earth?

8.3 Protein Synthesis

Now that you know about the structures of DNA and RNA, let's take a look at the process of protein synthesis itself. **Protein synthesis** is the formation of proteins using information coded on DNA and carried out by RNA.

Protein Structure

Depending on its complexity, an organism may have from several hundred to several thousand different proteins as part of its makeup. Each protein molecule is made up of one or more polymers called polypeptides, each of which consists of a specific sequence of amino acids linked together by peptide bonds. As you know from Chapter 4, there are 20 different amino acids. A protein may consist of hundreds or thousands of amino acids, and all these amino acids must be arranged in a particular sequence for the protein to function properly. In fact, all structural and functional characteristics of a protein are determined by its amino acid sequence.

Codons

The assembly of amino acids into a specific protein is the task accomplished during protein synthesis. Before you study the sequence of events that occurs in protein synthesis, you must understand how the information necessary for creating proteins is encoded in nucleic acids.

The **genetic code** is the system that contains information needed by cells for proper functioning. This information is built into the arrangement of the nitrogen bases in a particular sequence of DNA. Since DNA makes RNA, which makes proteins, the DNA ultimately contains the information needed to put the amino acids together in the proper sequence.

As you learned in Section 8.2, mRNA is transcribed using DNA as a template. The genetic code inherent in the DNA is thus reflected in the sequence of bases in mRNA. A specific group of three sequential bases of mRNA is called a **codon.** In effect, each codon codes for, or recognizes, a specific amino acid using tRNA as an intermediary. As you will see, each codon attracts a group of bases on tRNA, and each tRNA has a specific amino acid attached to it.

Table 8-1 lists all of the 64 possible codons. You will note that each amino acid listed in the table has several codons. These codons often differ from each other only by the base in the third position. A few codons do not encode amino acids at all. Instead, they are "start" signals that engage a ribosome to start reading an mRNA molecule or "stop" signals that cause the ribosomes to stop reading mRNA.

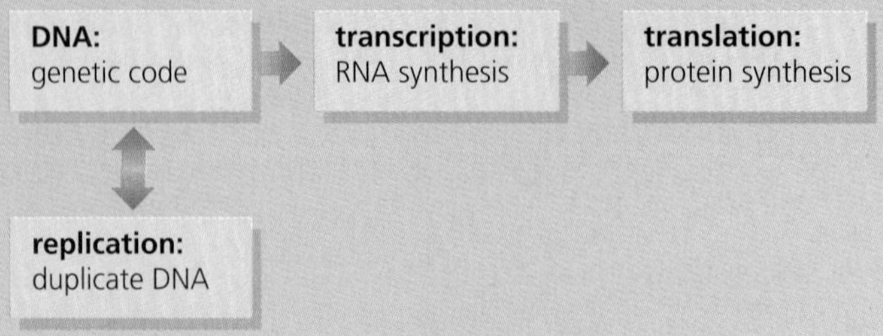

Graphic Organizer Use this sequential diagram in Independent Practice on p. 122.

Table 8-1 Codons in mRNA

First Base	Second Base: U	Second Base: C	Second Base: A	Second Base: G	Third Base
U	UUU } Phenyl-	UCU	UAU } Tyrosine	UGU } Cysteine	U
	UUC } alanine	UCC Serine	UAC	UGC	C
	UUA } Leucine	UCA	UAA } Stop	UGA Stop	A
	UUG	UCG	UAG	UGG Tryptophan	G
C	CUU	CCU	CAU } Histidine	CGU	U
	CUC Leucine	CCC Proline	CAC	CGC Arginine	C
	CUA	CCA	CAA } Glutamine	CGA	A
	CUG	CCG	CAG	CGG	G
A	AUU } Isoleucine	ACU	AAU } Asparagine	AGU } Serine	U
	AUC	ACC Threonine	AAC	AGC	C
	AUA	ACA	AAA } Lysine	AGA } Arginine	A
	AUG Methionine	ACG	AAG	AGG	G
G	GUU	GCU	GAU } Aspartic	GGU	U
	GUC Valine	GCC Alanine	GAC } acid	GGC Glycine	C
	GUA	GCA	GAA } Glutamic	GGA	A
	GUG	GCG	GAG } acid	GGG	G

The coding for amino acids shown in Table 8-1 is universal. For example, UUU is the codon for the amino acid phenylalanine in bacteria, mice, and humans. AUG is the universal "start" code. Every organism uses essentially the same genetic code.

Translation

The process of assembling protein molecules from information encoded in mRNA is called **translation.** The process of translation begins when mRNA moves out of the nucleus by passing through the nuclear pores. The mRNA then migrates to a group of ribosomes, where the actual synthesis of proteins takes place.

Amino acids floating freely in the cytoplasm are transported to the ribosomes by tRNA. Notice in Figure 8-6 that each kind of tRNA has a region that bonds to a specific amino acid. Notice also that the opposite loop of the cloverlike structure of tRNA bears a sequence of three bases called an **anticodon.** The tRNA anticodon bases are complementary to—and thus pair with—the codon of mRNA.

The assembly of a polypeptide begins when a ribosome attaches at an AUG codon on the mRNA. The AUG codon pairs with an anticodon UAC on a specific tRNA. Since the tRNA with this anticodon carries methionine, the first amino acid in the chain is always methionine. However, this does not mean that all polypeptides begin with methionine, because this first methionine is later removed from the chain.

Figure 8-6 Each kind of tRNA transports a specific amino acid to the ribosomes.

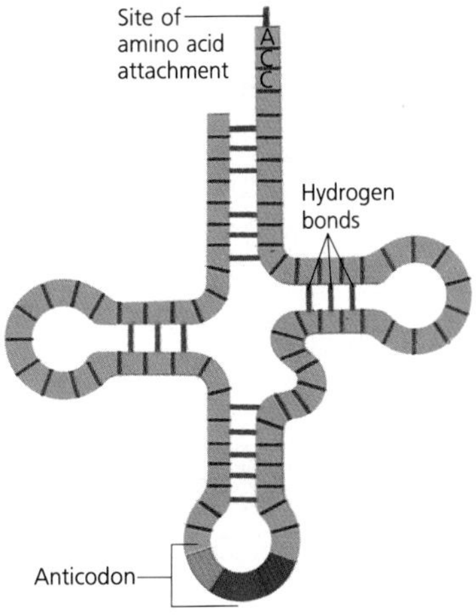

Teaching Strategies

Defining Terms Tell students that *translation* means explaining something in a different manner—in code, for example. Have students identify the codes and the product of protein synthesis. *(mRNA is the code of DNA; an amino acid chain, a protein, is the product.)*

Interpreting the Visuals Point out that Table 8-1 illustrates codons in mRNA. Have students explain what the table shows and how to determine what specific amino acid a specific codon codes for. *(A codon consists of three bases. The table gives the possible triplets formed from the four bases and the amino acid each codes for. For example, given the codon UUC, a student locates the first base, U, in the first column; the second base, U, in the middle section under* Second Base; *the* Third Base, C, *in the first row. UUC codes for phenylalanine.)* Point out that more than one code can translate to the same amino acid.

■ *See* **Blackline Master** *20.*

Locating Structures Ask students to locate codons and anticodons. *(Codons, on mRNA; anticodon, on tRNA loop, opposite the site of amino acid attachment)*

Interpreting Data Ask students to name the universal start code. *(AUG)* According to Table 8-1, what amino acid does it code for? *(Methionine)* Ask what this implies about all proteins. *(The first amino acid is always methionine.)* Now ask students to locate the stop code in Table 8–1. *(UGA; fourth column)*

■ *See* **Process Skills,** *Chapter 8.*

Videodiscs

■ ***Side 1 22695, Protein Synthesis: Transcription of DNA to RNA (m)***

Cooperative Learning

DNA Sequencing Give each group of 3–4 students lists of several DNA sequences and amino acid sequences. Ask each group to transcribe and translate a DNA sequence. Have them use Table 8-1 to "work backwards" from their amino acid sequence to find possible DNA base orders. *(DNA: AAA TGA ATA yields the mRNA sequence UUU ACU UAU and codes for phenylalanine-threonine-tyrosine. This amino acid order also can have mRNA codons of UUC; ACC or ACA or ACG; UAC.)* Point out that the same amino acid sequence can be coded by different DNA sequences, but a specific DNA sequence can code for only one specific amino acid sequence. Have each student find all the mRNA codes for each listed amino acid. Have each group compare their findings with those of other groups.

Interpreting the Visuals Ask students what is shown exiting through the nuclear pore in Figure 8-7, p. 122. *(mRNA)* Have students describe the shape of a ribosome. *(Two tightly connected spheres)* Have them refer to Figure 8-2, p. 114, and the color key in Figure 8-5, p. 119, and infer the base represented by each color in Figure 8-7. *(Blue = adenine; red = thymine; green = cytosine; purple = guanine; yellow = uracil)* Then have students use Table 8-1 to name each amino acid on each of the six tRNAs in Figure 8-7. *(Left to right: green-blue-blue = CAA = glutamine; purple-blue-green = GAC = aspartic acid; purple-blue-green = GAC = aspartic acid; yellow-yellow-blue = UUA = leucine; blue-green-green = ACC = threonine; blue-blue-green = AAC = asparagine)*

- ***See* Blackline Master *20.***
- ***See* Laboratories, *Investigation 8.***

Reviewing Concepts Ask students to recall from Chapter 4, pp. 52–53, that a polypeptide is a long chain of amino acids. Ask students what determines the external shape of the protein. *(The amino acid sequence)* Emphasize that a protein may be made of several intertwined polypeptides. Show students a model of hemoglobin, which consists of four chains.

Guided Practice

Have students create a concept map showing the relationships of DNA, RNA, and protein synthesis. An example of a completed concept map is shown on page 111B.

Independent Practice

- Have students write answers to the Section Review.
- Have students make a sequential diagram of protein synthesis. An example of a completed diagram is shown on p. 120.

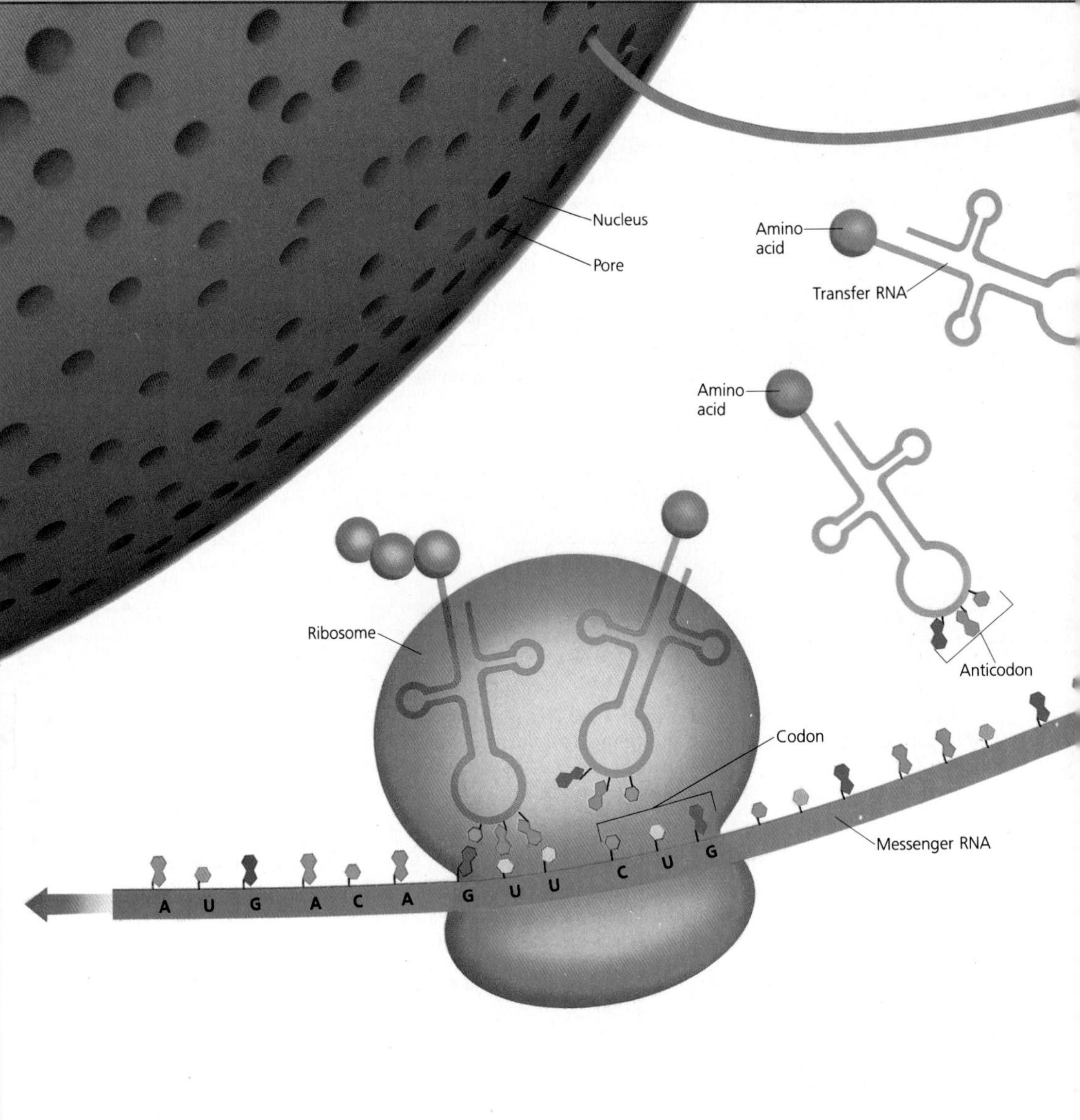

As you can see in Figure 8-7, usually several ribosomes are simultaneously translating the same mRNA. As a ribosome moves along the strand of mRNA, each codon is sequentially paired with its anticodon and the specified amino acid is added to the chain. An enzyme in the ribosome catalyzes a reaction that binds each new amino acid to the chain. In this reaction a peptide bond is formed with the last amino acid in the chain. The process continues, with each amino acid being linked to the chain in turn. Eventually the ribosome reaches a "stop" codon. This codon brings the

Interdisciplinary Activity

Mathematics Have students calculate the largest number of three-letter sequences—codons—that can be made using the four letters of the four different bases. *(4 cubed, or 4^3, = 4 x 4 x 4 = 64.)* Molecular biologists used this answer as a clue to the size of the codons. With four bases, a sequence of only two letters would give information for 4^2 or 16 amino acids. However, 20 amino acids are known. With a sequence of three letters, 64 different arrangements are possible—more than enough to code for all 20. This led to the hypothesis that each amino acid could have more than one codon.

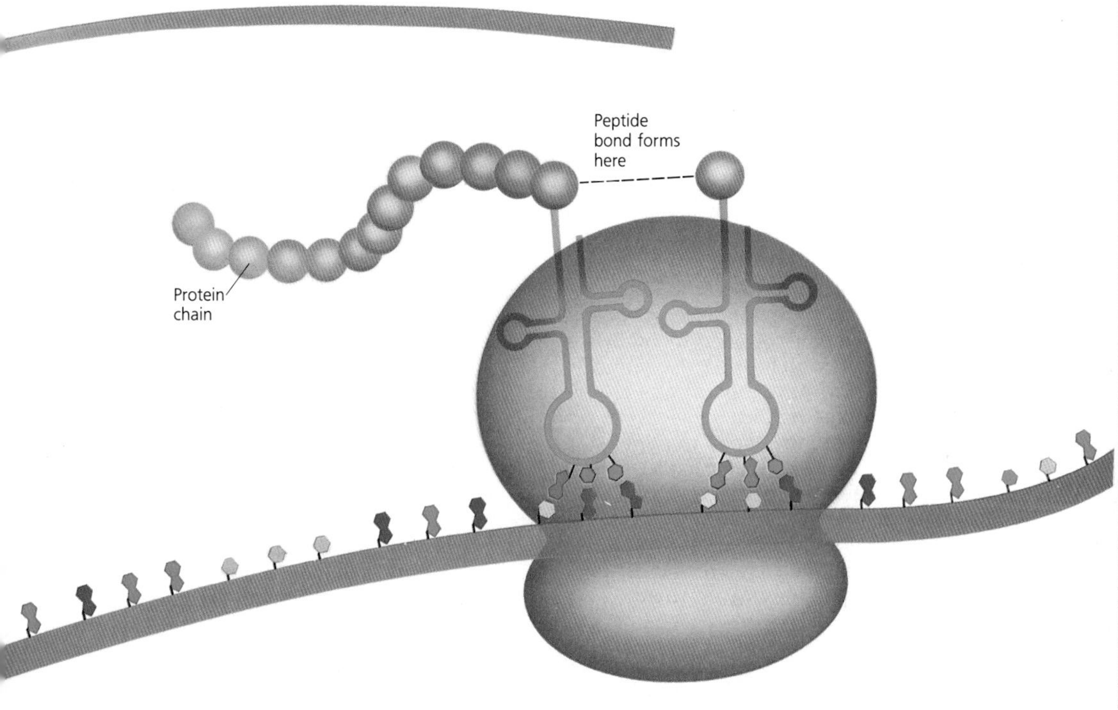

process to an end. At this point the mRNA is released, and the polypeptide is complete.

As you have seen, the manufacture of specific proteins is a function of the order of bases in mRNA. In turn, the base sequence of mRNA is complementary to that of a specific region of DNA. The region of DNA that directs the formation of a polypeptide is called a **gene.** Since most proteins consist of more than one polypeptide, information from several genes may be required to produce a particular protein.

Figure 8-7 When a codon is sequentially paired with its anticodon, tRNA adds a specific amino acid to the chain.

Section Review

1. What is *translation?*
2. Distinguish a codon from an anticodon, and explain the significance of each.
3. How does the physical structure of transfer RNA relate to its function?
4. Explain how the genetic code is formed and why the genetic code is said to be universal.
5. Do you think that all of an organism's genes are always involved in the continuing process of making proteins? Defend your answer.

Answers to Section Review

1. Translation is the process by which protein molecules are assembled from the information encoded in mRNA.
2. A codon is a series of three bases in mRNA that codes for a specific amino acid; the anticodon on tRNA is the set of three bases complementary to the codon.
3. The structure of tRNA allows an amino acid at one end to be positioned in a polypeptide when the anticodon at the other end pairs with its codon.
4. The genetic code is formed by the order of nitrogen bases in DNA. It is universal because the same codons code for the same amino acids in all life forms.
5. Not all proteins are needed at all times; genes are active only when a protein is needed. Specialization is possible because different genes are active in different cells.

Check Your Understanding

1. How are transcription and translation related? *(Transcription produces copies of mRNA that code for the synthesis of a polypeptide chain through translation.)*
2. Explain why a strand of DNA and one of mRNA can't be identical. *(RNA contains uracil and ribose; DNA has thymine and deoxyribose.)*

Reteaching

Have students use common objects to construct a model of a polypeptide. *(Students may string different types of pasta or beans on a thread, or glue coins or other small objects on paper.)* Have them label the amino acids and indicate their mRNA codons. Ask students what directs polypeptide formation. *(The region on DNA called a gene)*

■ *See* Section Reviews *worksheet, Section 8.3.*

Enrichment

Explain to students that mRNA is rapidly broken down in cytoplasm. Have students speculate on the possible advantages of having temporary RNA. *(Degradation of mRNA reduces wasteful synthesis of excess proteins. Also, its component parts can be reused.)*

Closure

Have students create an analogy comparing protein synthesis to factory production. *(Sample answer: Information in the product blueprints [DNA] is carried to the work sites [ribosomes] by messengers [mRNA]. Carts [tRNA] deliver materials [amino acids] needed by the assembly line workers to produce the final product [protein] according to the messengers' directions.)*

Videodiscs

■ ***Side 1 28381, Enzyme Structure (m)***

Background

In his 1967 preface, Watson says he relates his personal version of how DNA structure was discovered. Before reading *The Double Helix*, many nonscientists imagined science as an impersonal, restricted process. The book revealed that personalities and events could affect progress and results.

Watson's writing conveys the adventurous spirit that permeated the team's work, a "youthful spirit of arrogance" and a belief that "the truth, once found, would be simple as well as pretty." Watson points out the importance of relaxation and varying one's work load, allowing time to process information subconsciously.

Encourage students to read *The Double Helix*; few memoirs are so readable or have been quoted so extensively 25 years after first publication. The subject matter—DNA, the hereditary directions for all life forms—directly relates to all of us.

Discussion

1. Recall the figures in Chapters 3 and 4; what types of models do you infer Watson used? *(Ball-and-stick construction sets)*

2. What was the "messy backbone"? *(Paired identical bases would cause an irregular backbone, varying the diameter of the molecule.)*

3. What does Watson say about talking with colleagues? *(Scientists check ideas with each other frequently.)*

Extension

Show students a videotape about the discovery of the molecular structure of DNA and its method of replication—for example, the BBC's "Race for the Double Helix." Have each student write a report on the video.

Writing About Biology

The Double Helix

The following excerpts are from The Double Helix, James Watson's account of the discovery of the structure of DNA.

The α-helix had not been found by staring at X-ray pictures; the essential trick, instead, was to ask which atoms like to sit next to each other. In place of pencil and paper, the main working tools were a set of molecular models superficially resembling the toys of preschool children. . . .

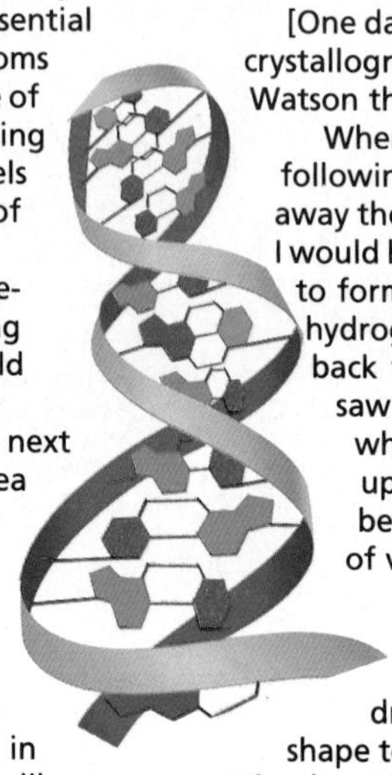

I went ahead spending most evenings at the films, vaguely dreaming that at any moment the answer would suddenly hit me. . . .

Not until the middle of the next week, however, did a nontrivial idea emerge. It came while I was drawing the fused rings of adenine on paper. Suddenly I realized the potentially profound implications of a DNA structure in which the adenine residue formed hydrogen bonds similar to those found in crystals of pure adenine. If DNA was like this, each adenine residue would form two hydrogen bonds to an adenine residue related to it by a 180-degree rotation. Most important, two symmetrical hydrogen bonds could also hold together pairs of guanine, cytosine, or thymine.

I thus started wondering whether each DNA molecule consisted of two chains with identical base sequences held together by hydrogen bonds between pairs of identical bases. There was the complication, however, that such a structure could not have a regular backbone since the purines (adenine and guanine) and the pyrimidines (thymine and cytosine) have different shapes.

Despite the messy backbone, my pulse began to race. . . . The existence of two intertwined chains with identical base sequences could not be a chance matter. Instead it would strongly suggest that one chain in each molecule had at some earlier stage served as the template for the synthesis of the other chain. . . .

[One day elapsed during which American crystallographer Jerry Donahue convinced Watson that his model was incorrect.]

When I got to our still empty office the following morning, I quickly cleared away the papers from my desk top so that I would have a large, flat surface on which to form pairs of bases held together by hydrogen bonds. Though I initially went back to my like-with-like prejudices, I saw all too well that they led nowhere. When Jerry came in I looked up, saw that it was not Francis, and began shifting the bases in and out of various other pairing possibilities. Suddenly I became aware that an adenine-thymine pair held together by two hydrogen bonds was identical in shape to a guanine-cytosine pair held together by at least two hydrogen bonds. All the hydrogen bonds seemed to form naturally; no fudging was required to make the two types of base pairs identical in shape. Quickly I called Jerry over to ask him whether this time he had any objection to my new base pairs. When he said no, my morale skyrocketed. . . .

Upon his arrival Francis did not get more than halfway through the door before I let loose that the answer to everything was in our hands. . . .

Write

- **James Watson used time away from his laboratory and a set of models similar to preschool toys to help him solve the puzzle of DNA. In an essay discuss how play and relaxation help promote clear thinking and problem solving.**

 James D. Watson, excerpted from The Double Helix. *Copyright © 1968 James D. Watson. Reprinted with permission of Atheneum Publishers, an imprint of Macmillan Publishing Company.*

About the Author

After earning a Ph.D. at age 21, Chicago-born biologist James Dewey Watson went to the Cavendish Laboratory at Cambridge University, England, where he teamed up with Francis Crick. Their work in determining the structure of DNA won them a Nobel Prize in 1962.

Currently Watson is the director of the Cold Spring Harbor Laboratory in New York, a position he assumed in 1968. Watson is the leading force in the National Institute of Health's Human Genome Initiative, a controversial project that plans to map all the genes on every human chromosome.

Laboratory

Testing for Nucleic Acids

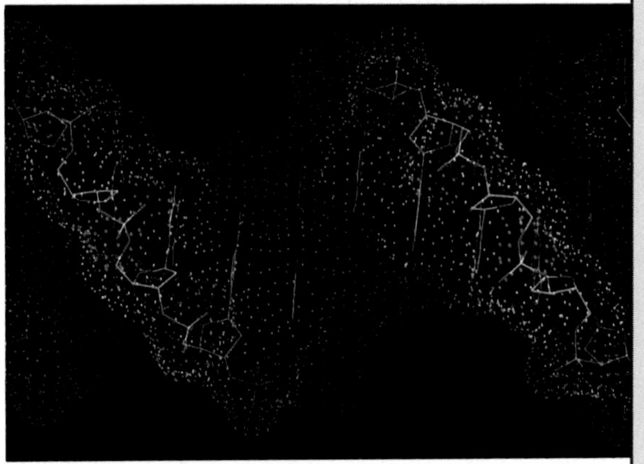

Objective
To learn how to test for nucleic acids

Process Skills
Experimenting, hypothesizing, inferring

Materials
400-mL beaker, hot plate, glass marking pencil, 3 test tubes, test tube holder, medicine droppers, DNA solution, RNA solution, water, tongs, diphenylamine (dispensed by your teacher)

Background
1 Review the structure of the cell in Chapter 5. What is the structure and function of the following organelles: ribosomes, rough endoplasmic reticulum, lysosomes, nucleus?
2 Where in the cell are DNA and RNA found? What is the function of each?

Inquiry
1 Prepare a hot water bath by pouring 200 mL of water into a 400-mL beaker and boiling the water on a hot plate.
2 While the water is heating, label three test tubes *A*, *B* and *C*. Place them in a test tube holder. Your teacher will put 40 drops of diphenylamine in each test tube. Diphenylamine is a reagent that tests for the presence of nucleic acids.
3 Using a clean dropper, add 20 drops of DNA solution to test tube A.
4 Using a clean dropper, add 20 drops of RNA solution to test tube B. Why is it important to use a clean dropper?
5 Using a clean dropper, add 20 water drops to test tube C. What is the purpose of this test tube? Why should it be boiled?
6 Use tongs to place the test tubes in the boiling water. Heat for 25 minutes. Remove the test tubes from the water bath with the tongs and allow them to cool for 10 minutes. Notice the color of each test tube. If you had tested an unknown solution, how would you know whether it contained DNA, RNA, or neither DNA nor RNA?
7 A complex technique, differential centrifugation, separates different cell organelles. While it is not possible to use this technique in high schools, you can infer the results obtained if you performed the diphenylamine test on organelles separated by differential centrifugation.
8 What result would you expect if you tested the following for the presence of nucleic acid: ribosomes, rough endoplasmic reticulum, and lysosomes? Explain your answers.
9 If you tested the nucleus with diphenylamine, would you get a clear-cut result? Explain your answer.

Conclusions
1 How does diphenylamine differentiate between DNA and RNA?
2 What would you have to do to get a clear result when testing a nucleus with diphenylamine?

Further Inquiry
What results would you expect if you tested salmon sperm for nucleic acid? Explain.

(For an overview of nucleic acids and preparatory information related to the laboratory, see p. 111B.)

Background
1. Ribosomes consist of protein and RNA and are found where the cell produces protein; rough endoplasmic reticulum is membrane (lipid and protein) lined with ribosomes (RNA and protein); lysosomes contain digestive enzymes (protein); the nucleus contains RNA (nucleolus) and DNA (chromosomes).
2. DNA is found in the nucleus and mitochondria; RNA is found in ribosomes on the endoplasmic reticulum, and in the cytoplasm. Some RNA is found in the nucleus where it is made from DNA. DNA provides the information needed for protein production within the cell; RNA uses that information to carry out protein production.

Inquiry
4. To avoid contaminating the B sample with DNA from the previous step
5. Test tube C is the control to see what happens if neither DNA nor RNA is present. It needs to be treated exactly like the experimental test tubes and must also be boiled.
6. If it contained DNA, it would turn purple. If it contained RNA, it would turn green. If it contained neither, it would not change color.
8. Ribosomes contain RNA, so the solution would turn green. Rough endoplasmic reticulum is lined with ribosomes—ribosomal RNA—so the solution would turn green. Lysosomes contain neither DNA nor RNA, so the solution would not change color.
9. Because the nucleus contains both DNA and RNA, the color would probably be a muddy mixture of purple and green.

Conclusions
1. Diphenylamine stains DNA purple and RNA green.
2. Before using diphenylamine, you would have to separate different nucleic acids from each other (one way to accomplish this is by differential centrifugation). Alternatively, you would have to use two other tests that were specific for either DNA or RNA to make sure they were both present in the nucleus.

Further Inquiry
You would expect the solution to turn purple since animal sperm contains DNA in the chromosomes.

Vocabulary

1. In the process of translation, one "language" (sequence of bases in mRNA) is converted to another (sequence of amino acids in a protein).
2. Messenger RNA carries the "message" from the code of DNA to the sites of protein synthesis, ribosomes in the cytoplasm.
3. In the process of transcription, a sequence of DNA bases is "transcribed" or written into a complementary sequence of bases in RNA.
4. The prefix *deoxy-* indicates that this sugar molecule has one less oxygen atom than a ribose molecule.
5. A hydrogen bond is a chemical bond in which atoms share a hydrogen nucleus.

Review

1. a	**6.** d
2. b	**7.** c
3. d	**8.** d
4. c	**9.** c
5. c	**10.** b

11. The double-stranded structure of DNA allows it to replicate itself, passing identical information to new cells. The sequences of four bases allow it to form a code.
12. Enzymes separate part of the two DNA strands. With the aid of other enzymes, nucleotides are assembled into two strands complementary to the original DNA strands.
13. Franklin's images indicated that DNA was a double-stranded helix with the sugar–phosphate backbone on the outside.

Chapter 8 Review

Vocabulary

adenine (113)
anticodon (121)
codon (120)
cytosine (113)
deoxyribose (113)
double helix (114)
gene (123)
genetic code (120)
guanine (113)
hydrogen bond (114)
messenger RNA (mRNA) (118)
nucleotide (113)
protein synthesis (120)
purine (113)
pyrimidine (113)
replication (115)
ribose (118)
ribosomal RNA (rRNA) (118)
thymine (113)
transcription (118)
transfer RNA (tRNA) (118)
translation (121)
uracil (118)

Explain why each of the terms below is an appropriate name for the process or thing to which it refers.

1. translation
2. messenger RNA
3. transcription
4. deoxyribose
5. hydrogen bond

Review

1. DNA (a) encodes the information needed for making proteins within the cell (b) directs RNA to make lipids (c) directs RNA to produce glucose (d) produces carbohydrates.
2. The physical structure of the genetic code is DNA's sequence of (a) sugars (b) nitrogen bases (c) phosphates (d) hydrogen bonds.
3. Proteins are composed of (a) nucleotides (b) nitrogen bases (c) deoxyribose (d) amino acids.
4. The general shape of a DNA molecule is a (a) sphere (b) folded chain (c) helix (d) branched chain.
5. RNA (a) is double-stranded like DNA (b) has the same four nitrogen bases as DNA (c) contains ribose (d) contains thymine.
6. The pattern of base pairing in DNA can be summarized by the rule that (a) purines always pair with purines (b) any purine can pair with any pyrimidine (c) pyrimidines only pair with pyrimidines (d) adenine pairs with thymine, and cytosine pairs with guanine.
7. DNA replication (a) involves RNA polymerase (b) occurs at one site (c) requires a DNA molecule to start the process (d) needs several days' time to occur.
8. Transporting amino acids to ribosomes for assembly into needed proteins is the function of (a) DNA (b) mRNA (c) rRNA (d) tRNA.
9. Transcription occurs (a) at ribosomes (b) in the cytoplasm of the cell (c) in the nucleus of the cell (d) as the last step in protein synthesis.
10. The number of bases in a codon is (a) 2 (b) 3 (c) 4 (d) 5.
11. What are some ways in which the structure of a DNA molecule is related to its function?
12. How is a DNA molecule duplicated in the process of replication?
13. What information did Rosalind Franklin's work with X-ray crystallography provide to Watson and Crick?
14. Name the three types of RNA present in cells, and describe the function of each.
15. Name at least three major structural differences between RNA and DNA.
16. What roles do enzymes play in the transcription process?
17. What is the relationship between codons and anticodons?

14. Messenger RNA transmits information from DNA for use as a template, or code, for building proteins. Transfer RNA carries amino acids to the ribosomes. Ribosomal RNA is the major constituent of the ribosomes, the sites of protein synthesis.
15. RNA: single strand, contains ribose and uracil; DNA: double strand, contains deoxyribose and thymine.
16. Enzymes separate the two strands of DNA and catalyze bond formation between sugars and phosphates of the nucleotides to form a new strand of nucleotides.
17. The sequence of bases in an anticodon is complementary to that in the corresponding codon.
18. They signal "start" and "stop."

18. What functions are carried out by those few codons that do not code for amino acids?
19. Why may the production of a particular protein require information from more than one gene?
20. What is the role of the ribosome in protein synthesis?

Critical Thinking

1. Use Table 8-1 to find the codons that compose the amino acid alanine. How many codons code for alanine? How do they differ from one another? What significance might this pattern of differences have?
2. Refer again to Table 8-1. Using the table, determine the sequence of amino acids that is specified by the following list of codons: AUG UCU AAC AAA CAG GCU UAA.
3. Using the list of codons in question number 2, figure out the base sequence of DNA that codes for them. List the order of DNA bases that must have been transcribed to establish this sequence of codons.
4. Suggest a reason why a system composed of three bases per codon is required to code for amino acids. Would a system with two bases per codon work to code amino acids?

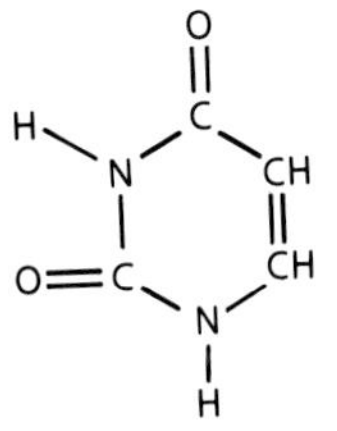

Uracil

5. The diagram above shows the chemical structure of uracil. Compare this diagram with Figure 8-1. How does the chemical structure of uracil differ from the chemical structure of thymine? How is it possible that both thymine and uracil can bond with adenine despite this difference in structure? (You may wish to look again at the patterns of hydrogen bonding in Figure 8-2 to help you answer this last question.)

Extension

1. Prepare a report on the contributions of one of the following scientists to the discovery of the structure of DNA: Erwin Chargaff, Francis Crick, Rosalind Franklin, Linus Pauling, James Watson, or Maurice Wilkins. James Watson's book *The Double Helix* is a good source of information on Crick and Watson. *The Eighth Day of Creation* by Horace Freeland Judson covers all of these scientists.
2. Read the article by Peter Radetsky entitled "Genetic Heretic," in *Discover,* November 1990, pp. 79–84. Explain how Thomas Cech has upset some widely held ideas about some basic processes of life.
3. On a piece of cardboard or construction paper, draw the DNA bases. Cut them out and label each one. Demonstrate to your classmates how hydrogen bonds are established, and why only complementary bases pair.
4. Read the article by Harold Vaimus entitled "Reverse Transcription" in *Scientific American,* September 1987, pp. 56–64. Explain the process of reverse transcription, telling in what organisms reverse transcription takes place and what purpose reverse transcription serves in those organisms.

19. Each gene codes for one polypeptide, and many proteins consist of several polypeptides.
20. The ribosome holds mRNA and is the site of matching up the anticodons of tRNA with codons of mRNA so that an enzyme can form the peptide bonds.

Critical Thinking

1. The four codons for alanine differ only at the third position. This redundant pattern provides several ways to bring in an amino acid and thus minimizes errors of translation.
2. Methionine–serine–asparagine–lysine–glutamine–alanine-stop
3. DNA must be TAC AGA TTG TTT GTC CGA ATT.
4. Three bases per codon provides more than enough units for the 20 amino acids. Two bases would provide only 4^2 or 16 units.
5. Thymine has a CH_3, or methyl group, attached to one of the carbons in the ring. Uracil has only a hydrogen atom attached at the equivalent site. This difference does not affect bonding; the hydrogen bonds formed with adenine occur on the other side of the molecule.

Extension

1. Student reports should focus on the scientist's research as it relates to the discovery of the structure of DNA but may include biographical information.
2. Student reports should include a description of Thomas Cech's research methods leading to the discovery of RNA's enzyme-like ability to catalyze the release of introns. Encourage students to discuss possible practical applications of ribozyme—combating the AIDS virus and cancer-causing oncogenes.
3. Students draw and label adenine, guanine, thymine, and cytosine. Students should point out that adenine and thymine form only two hydrogen bonds, whereas cytosine and guanine form three.
4. Student reports should focus on the function of reverse transcription in the organisms in which it occurs.

Chapter 9 Chromosomes, Mitosis, and Meiosis

Chapter Overview

Chapter 9 explains the processes of cell reproduction. Section 9.1 focuses on chromosome structure and numbers of chromosomes in various species. Section 9.2 discusses mitosis as part of the cell cycle and the role of mitosis in growth and tissue repair. In Section 9.3 the focus is meiosis and its role in providing gametes—egg and sperm—essential in sexual reproduction.

Chapter Planning Chart

B	S	A	Sections and Subsections	Page	Features	Page	Resources
•	•	•	**9.1 Chromosomes**				
			Chromosome Structure	129	Think	130	Videodiscs
			Chromosome Numbers	130	Section Review	130	Section Reviews Worksheet
•	•	•	**9.2 Mitosis**				
			The Cell Cycle	131	Biology in Process	134	Videodiscs
			Interphase	132	Laboratory	139	Blackline Master 21
			Phases of Mitosis	132	Section Review	135	Overhead Transparency T9
			Cytokinesis	134			Process Skills: A Model of Mitosis
							Laboratories: Cell Size
							Laboratories: Mitosis
							Section Reviews Worksheet
•	•	•	**9.3 Meiosis**				
			Phases of Meiosis	136	Section Review	138	Videodiscs
			Formation of Egg and Sperm	138			Science in Action Videotape: Cell Structure and Function/ Cell Division
			Asexual and Sexual Reproduction	138			Blackline Master 22
							Section Reviews Worksheet
			End of Chapter Activities				
					Chapter Review	140	Vocabulary Skills
							Chapter Test
							Computer Test Generator

B *The Basic Level curriculum presents the most fundamental knowledge offered in the course.*
S *The Standard Level curriculum is designed for the average student who is able to master most topics.*
A *The Advanced Level curriculum includes suggestions for teaching the most academically able students.*

Cooperative Learning

Group Activity: The Cell Cycle

- **Group Size:** *3 students*
- **Outcome:** *Students will differentiate among the cell cycle, interphase, and mitosis.*
- **Individual Accountability:** *Each group member will develop one area of a concept map.*
- **Positive Interdependence:** *The group will develop a joint concept map.*

Have one student in each group develop a concept map showing the sequence of major events of mitosis. Ask a second student to map the sequence of major events of interphase and show its relationship to mitosis. Have a third student map significant characteristics of the cell cycle. Then tell each group member to explain the map to the other members of the group.

Have the group compile their individual maps to produce one map illustrating relationships among cell cycle, interphase, and mitosis. Encourage students to consider and discuss how processes are related as they develop their map. Stress that all phases of mitosis need not be shown. An example of a completed concept map appears below.

Concept Map

The following is one possible solution to the concept mapping activity in Cooperative Learning above.

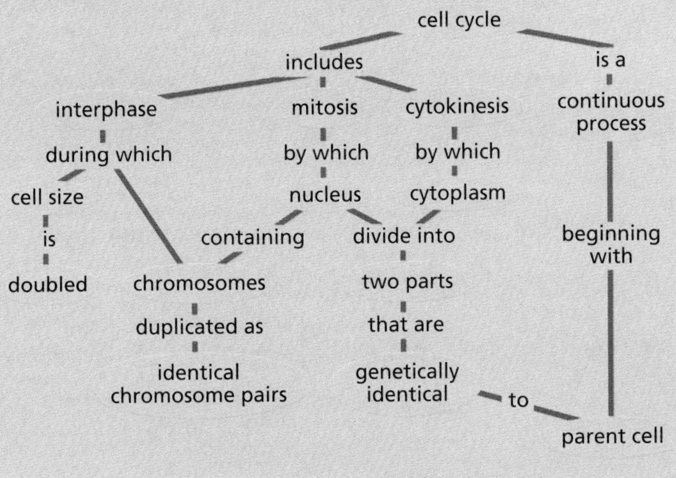

Laboratory Preparation

Overview *(See p. 139.)*

By examining many onion root-tip cells and by identifying their phase of mitosis, students discover that it is a continuous process. Students collect data to estimate the relative length of the four phases.

Preparation

Purchase slides of onion root tips from a biological supply house or have students prepare their own slides after first observing prepared ones. Several days before the lab, place the root tips of onions in water to initiate root tip lengthening through mitosis. Just before the lab, use a sharp scalpel to cut 3-mm-long root tips and place them in 6M HCl for ten minutes. Have students use forceps to transfer the tips to slides. Next, have them add a drop of aceto-orcein stain. Have students use the scalpel to mince the tips, then cover the specimens with a coverslip. Next, have students put paper towel and then a cork over the coverslip and press gently but firmly until the tips are flattened. Explain that the acid weakened the cell walls, making flattening easier. If glass instead of plastic coverslips are used, caution students that flattening an improperly prepared root tip may break the coverslip. If the tip can't be flattened, have students return it to the acid for ten minutes and try again.

Teaching Tips

Students should be able to identify the phases of mitosis before they begin the investigation.

Emphasize that cells in a root tip begin to divide at different times so that a variety of phases will be observed. Have students first use low power to observe the cells. Warn students to avoid splintered slides and damaged microscope objective lenses. Remind them to watch as they move the microscope objective lens and to focus upward only.

Misidentification of the phase of mitosis is a common student error. For instance, the polar view of a cell in anaphase can be confused with metaphase. Point out to students that such errors are one reason that scientists make many observations over long periods of time, take averages, and repeat experiments before drawing conclusions.

Safety

If students prepare their own slides, caution them to use care when working with HCl and stain. Caution them to avoid getting acid or stain on skin or clothing; wash contaminated areas and wipe up spills immediately. Have students handle scalpels and glass slides with care.

Chapter Themes

Patterns of Change Emphasize that metabolism occurs throughout the cell cycle. However, periods of growth and periods of specific activity alternate to form a pattern seen throughout the life of most cells.

Stability Point out to students that the same phases of mitosis and meiosis can be observed in cells of many organisms. Mitosis in plants, animals, and other eukaryotes results in increased cell numbers without a change in the cell's genetic information. Meiosis is necessary for sexual reproduction.

Evolution During meiosis, segregation of homologues, independent assortment, and crossing-over between chromatids provide variation. Emphasize that variations, which become apparent as the diploid organism lives in its environment, provide raw material for evolution.

Chapter Motivating Activity

Ask each student to bring to class a picture of a plant, an animal, or a unicellular organism. Have on hand at least one photograph of each as well as pictures of humans of different ages. Also include pictures of humans or other animals recovering from injuries such as broken bones. Ask students which pictures show an organism with cells dividing. *(All pictures)* Encourage students to speculate about where and when in each organism cell division is occurring. *(Cell division occurs more often in young, growing individuals than in older individuals and where damaged or destroyed cells are being replaced.)* Emphasize that cells such as skin cells and cells lining the intestines divide throughout life.

Chapter 9 *Chromosomes, Mitosis, and Meiosis*

Introduction

In the previous chapters in this unit you have learned about the inner workings of the cell and about the structure of DNA. In this chapter you will learn about the ways in which cells divide. Cell division perpetuates life and allows for the growth and reproduction of organisms.

Chapter Outline

9.1 Chromosomes
- *Chromosome Structure*
- *Chromosome Numbers*

9.2 Mitosis
- *The Cell Cycle*
- *Interphase*
- *Phases of Mitosis*
- *Cytokinesis*

9.3 Meiosis
- *Phases of Meiosis*
- *Formation of Egg and Sperm*
- *Asexual and Sexual Reproduction*

Chapter Concept

As you read about cell processes, pay attention to the way that intercellular structures change during these processes.

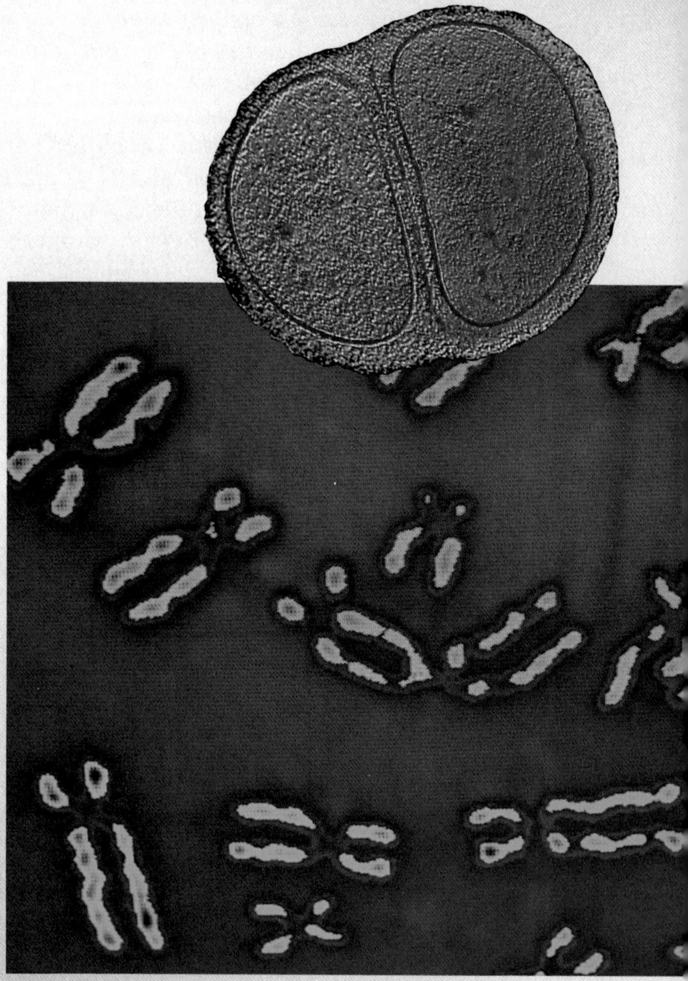

Human chromosomes (×55,000). Inset: Cell division occurring in the bacterium *Staphylococcus epidermidis* TEM (×17,500).

Understanding the Visuals

Ask students to identify the large oval *(A dividing bacterium)* and the irregular X-shaped forms *(Some chromosomes found within a human cell)*. Encourage students to speculate about the relationship illustrated by these two photographs. *(Students may recall from Chapter 5 that cells, including human cells and bacteria, contain genetic information in the form of DNA. Students may also recall that DNA and proteins exist as fine strands of chromatin that, during cell division, coil and condense to become visible as chromosomes.)* Point out that the bacterium's single, circular chromosome is very different from eukaryotic chromosomes and that bacterial cells do not divide by the process that students will study in Chapter 9.

9.1 Chromosomes

Cell division is the process by which cells reproduce. A unicellular organism divides and forms two new individuals. Multicellular organisms result from divisions of the zygote, a single cell. Even the zygote is produced by the union of two other cells, usually a sperm cell and an egg cell, and each of these cells arose from other cells. Insightful nineteenth-century biologists recognized a pattern: all cells come from preexisting cells. How cells divide is the subject of this chapter.

Information in the cell is contained in genes. Genes code for the proteins that carry out cellular functions. When a cell divides, genes are separated into daughter cells in an orderly, predictable process. This process involves the formation of chromosomes.

Section Objectives

- *Identify the structures of a chromosome.*
- *Summarize how DNA becomes a chromosome.*
- *Explain the difference between a diploid cell and a haploid cell.*

Chromosome Structure

Recall from Chapter 5 that densely stained areas exist inside the nuclear membrane of a nondividing cell. The substance that takes up stain in these areas is chromatin *(KROE-muh-tin)*. Experimental evidence has shown that chromatin is composed of DNA and proteins. The DNA in chromatin exists as thin, uncoiled strands.

When cell division begins, DNA replicates. Then the replicated strands of DNA begin to coil, as shown in Figure 9-1. As coiling proceeds, DNA becomes tightly wrapped around globules of **histones,** a group of special protein molecules. DNA and histones in this coiled form can be seen as a rod-shaped structure called a chromosome. Note that only the physical arrangement of the DNA strand is changed in its transition from chromatin to chromosome. The chemical makeup of the DNA remains unchanged.

Each chromosome consists of two identical parts, each called a **chromatid** *(KROE-muh-tid)*. The two chromatids are often called sister chromatids. The point at which each pair of chromatids is attached is called the **centromere** *(SEN-truh-mir)*.

Figure 9-1 During the initial phases of cell division the DNA within cells coils and becomes organized into chromosomes, each of which is composed of two chromatids.

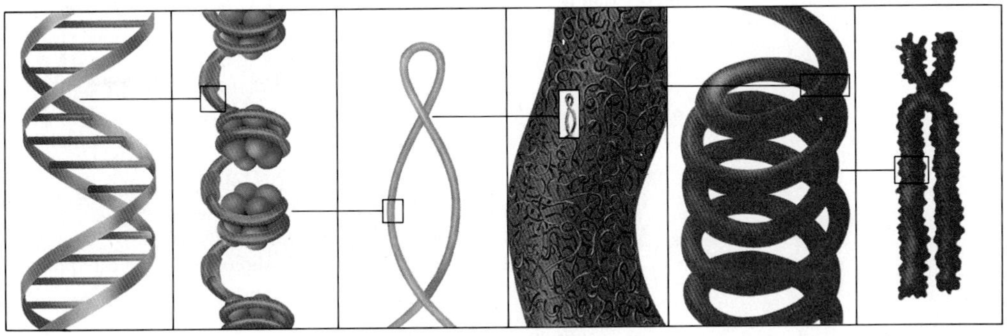

chromatin: DNA in thin, uncoiled strands → cell division: DNA replicates → DNA coils around histones → chromosome: DNA in two identical chromatids

Graphic Organizer Use this sequential diagram in Closure on p. 130.

Lesson Plan

Section Focus

This section focuses on eukaryotic chromosomes. Features of a chromosome's structure are identified. The variation in chromosome numbers for different species is discussed.

Section Themes

The chromosome number is specific and essentially constant for each species, illustrating the theme of **Stability.** For example, all normal cats have 32 chromosomes. Stability is also apparent in chromosome structure. Genes generally stay at the same place on a particular chromosome.

Motivating Activity

Obtain a copy of a normal, female, human karyotype from a college textbook or genetics counselor. Give each student a copy. Ask students what they see. *(There are 46 chromosomes that are X-shaped, with two identical parts [chromatids] attached at one point [centromere].)* Ask what characteristics could be used to match chromosome pairs. *(Chromosome size, length of chromatids, position of centromere.)*

Teaching Strategies

Interpreting the Visuals Use the text and Figure 9-1, p. 129, to trace the relationships of DNA to chromatin and to chromosomes. Have students identify structural components of chromatin and chromosomes. *(Chromatin is DNA and proteins. Chromosomes consist of replicated DNA strands coiled around histones. A chromosome occurs as two chromatids attached at a centromere.)* Stress that after replication, one DNA copy goes to each chromatid.

Videodiscs

- *1640–1650, Chromosomes (s)*
- *2626–2627, Chromatin (s)*

Answer to Think

Each chromosome has different kinds and amounts of DNA.

Guided Practice

Have students copy Table 9-1, change the head *Number* to *Diploid Number* and add a *Haploid Number* column. Ask students to distinguish *diploid* from *haploid*. (Diploid: *total chromosome number in a body cell, with both chromosomes of a homologous pair*. Haploid: *egg or sperm cell with only one chromosome of a homologous pair.)*

Independent Practice

- Have students write answers to the Section Review.
- Have students draw and label parts of two homologues.

Check Your Understanding

1. What differentiates an egg cell from a body cell? *(An egg cell is haploid; it has half the chromosomes found in a body cell.)*
2. What is the relationship of chromatin to chromosome? *(Both are made of DNA; a chromosome is supercoiled, replicated chromatin.)*

Reteaching

Have students infer the likely result if gametes in sexually reproducing organisms were 2N instead of 1N. *(Increasing numbers of chromosomes in successive generations.)*
- *See* Section Reviews *worksheet, Section 9.1.*

Enrichment

Have students do research to determine if the chromosome numbers of species that can interbreed are close in number. *(Yes; for example: horse–64; donkey–62)*

Closure

Have students create a sequential diagram relating chromatin to chromosome. An example of a completed diagram is shown on p. 129 (Graphic Organizer).

Think

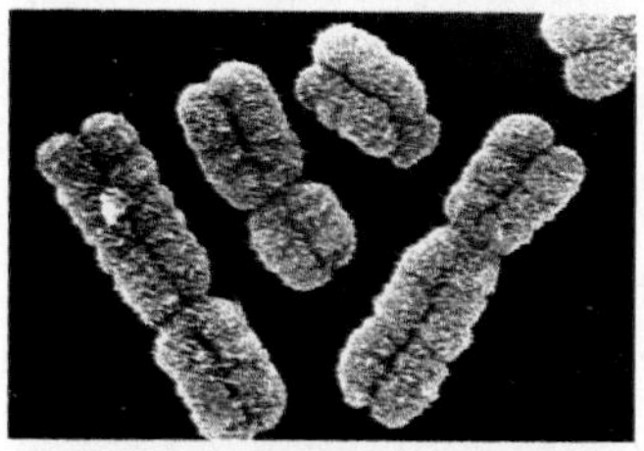

These are human chromosomes as seen under a scanning electron microscope. Why do chromosomes differ in size and shape?

Table 9-1 Chromosome Numbers of Various Species

Species	Number	Species	Number
Alligator	32	Fruit fly	8
Ameba	50	Garden pea	14
Brown bat	44	Goldfish	94
Bullfrog	26	Grasshopper	24
Carrot	18	Horse	64
Cat	32	Human	46
Chicken	78	Lettuce	18
Chimpanzee	48	Onion	16
Corn	20	Redwood	22
Earthworm	36	Sand dollar	52

Chromosome Numbers

Every species has a characteristic number of chromosomes in each cell. The number varies considerably among species. A certain nematode worm species, for example, has only 2 chromosomes in each cell, while certain protozoa have over 300 chromosomes in each cell. A potato, a plum, and a chimpanzee each have 48 chromosomes in each cell. As you might guess from this information and from the chromosome counts given in Table 9-1, chromosome number does not indicate the complexity of the species.

In all sexually reproducing organisms chromosomes occur in pairs. The two members of each pair are called **homologous chromosomes** or homologues. Each chromosome of a pair has the same size and shape as its homologue. Viewed with a microscope, the two homologous chromosomes are indistinguishable. However, the pair is structurally different from all other homologous pairs in the cell.

A cell that contains both chromosomes of a homologous pair is termed **diploid.** The notation 2N refers to diploid cells. For example, the diploid, or 2N, number of a human body cell is 46, and the cell contains 23 homologous pairs of chromosomes. A cell that has only one chromosome of each homologous pair is termed **haploid.** The notation 1N refers to haploid cells. For example, the haploid, or 1N, number of a human egg or sperm cell is 23, and there are no homologous chromosomes in either cell.

Section Review

1. Explain how a chromatid differs from a chromosome.
2. What is the structure of the DNA in chromatin?
3. When do we refer to DNA as a chromosome?
4. What is the difference between a diploid cell and a haploid cell?
5. Why might two organisms that contain the same number of chromosomes not possess similar traits and appearance?

Answers to Section Review

1. Each chromosome consists of two chromatids, joined at the centromere.
2. In the chromatin state, DNA is uncoiled and so is seen as thin strands.
3. DNA is called a chromosome when rod-shaped structures become visible at the beginning of cell division.
4. A diploid cell contains both chromosomes of a homologous pair. A haploid cell contains only one homologue.
5. Traits and appearances are determined by hereditary material carried on chromosomes, not by the quantity of chromosomes.

9.2 Mitosis

Mitosis *(mie-TOE-suss)* is the division of the cell nucleus in which the chromosomes in the parent cell divide into two identical sets. In body cells, also called somatic cells, mitosis is the process by which the number of cells is increased without changing the information contained in the DNA or the amount of DNA in those cells. In unicellular organisms, such as a yeast cell, mitosis is a means of reproduction. All offspring have the same DNA and hence contain the same genetic information.

What triggers a cell to divide? Cell biologists have observed that the size of a cell seems to be a factor that stimulates its division. You may recall from Chapter 5 that when a cell grows, its surface area expands more slowly than its volume does. Thus its volume eventually becomes disproportionately large in comparison with its surface area. The surface area is not large enough to allow the necessary amounts of nutrients to enter the cell and to allow wastes to pass out. Therefore as the surface-to-volume ratio becomes relatively small, the cell may divide. Many other mechanisms probably play a role in initiating cell division.

Section Objectives

- *Define* cell cycle, *and tell what occurs in a cell during each phase of this cycle.*
- *Describe the changes that take place during each of the three phases of interphase.*
- *Name the structures that appear in a cell during mitosis, state when they appear, and explain their functions.*
- *Describe the process by which Walther Flemming developed a model of cell division.*

The Cell Cycle

The process of mitosis is part of the cell cycle. The **cell cycle** is the sequence of events that occurs in a cell from mitosis to mitosis. Figure 9-2 represents five events of the cell cycle and the amount of time usually required for each. The five events of the cell cycle consist of the three phases of interphase, mitosis, and cytokinesis. Although biologists give these events names, the cell cycle is a continuous process. **Interphase** is a period of cell growth and development that precedes mitosis and follows cytokinesis. Mitosis is the division of the cell nucleus. The process of **cytokinesis** is the division of the cytoplasm of a parent cell and its contents into two daughter cells.

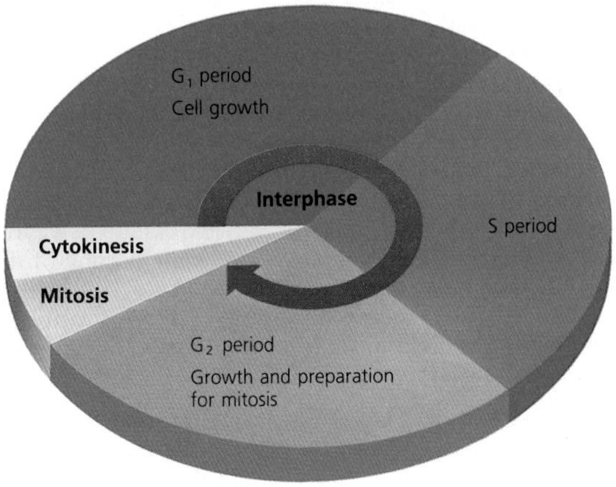

Figure 9-2 From mitosis to mitosis a cell typically passes through a five-event cycle. Note that there are three phases in interphase.

Mitotic Phase	Chromosomes	Spindle
prophase	condense from chromatin	appears
metaphase	line up at equator	attaches to chromosomes
anaphase	move to poles	shortens
telophase	unwind into chromatin	disappears

Graphic Organizer Use this table in Guided Practice on p. 134.

Lesson Plan

Section Focus

This section describes the cell cycle and mitosis, dynamic processes that were revealed through photographs and biochemical studies. Encourage an understanding of the processes rather than memorization of the names of phases.

Section Themes

This section emphasizes two themes: **Patterns of Change** and **Stability.** The cell cycle—including metabolic activity, growth, and mitosis—repeats throughout the life of many cells. Mitotic stages and processes are the same for diverse cells in most eukaryotes.

Motivating Activity

Use four decks of playing cards to have students model the distribution of genetic material during the cell cycle and mitosis. Give each group of two to three students their cell's genetic material—four pairs of cards, each matching pair being a different suit and number or face from the other pairs. Ask what the paired cards represent. *(Homologous chromosomes)* Ask what must happen before two new cells can be formed that have the same genetic information—the same cards—as the original cell. *(The playing cards—the genetic material—must first replicate.)* Have students choose cards from the undistributed decks that match their first set and place each card on its twin. Ask what this represents. *(Each doubled card is a chromosome made of two chromatids.)* Direct division of the doubled cards to model mitosis without using terminology. ■ *See* Process Skills, *Chapter 9.*

Videodiscs

■ ***1651–1656, Animal Cell Division (s)***

Teaching Strategies

Interpreting the Visuals Use Figure 9-2, p. 131, to clarify the relationship of cell division and interphase to the cell cycle. Ask students which sections represent interphase *(Blue)* and which sections represent active cell division *(Yellow)*. Stress that cells spend most of their lives in interphase.

Relating Concepts Have students create a list of events that occur in each phase of interphase. *(G_1—cell size doubles, enzymes and organelles roughly double in number; S—DNA in chromatin replicates; G_2—rapid cell growth, synthesis of enzymes and structures)* Next, have students identify the processes discussed in earlier chapters that may be occurring during each of the phases. *(G_1—cellular respiration, protein synthesis [transcription and translation]—Chapters 7 and 8; S—DNA replication—Chapter 8; G_2—cellular respiration, protein synthesis—Chapters 7 and 8)*

■ *See* **Laboratories,** ***Investigation 9.1.***

Identifying Structures Have students identify and count the number of chromosomes shown in Figures 9-3 and 9-4, pp. 132–133. *(Drawings show 12 chromosomes, best counted at anaphase. Photographs may show only 6.)* Then have students find the centrioles in Figures 9-3 and 9-4. *(Short, dark rods)* Ask students what structures are associated with them. *(Spindle fibers)*

■ *See* **Overhead Transparency** ***T9 and*** **Blackline Master 21.**

Interphase

Interphase, like cell division, is a continuous process. Biologists have differentiated three distinct phases in interphase. Look back at Figure 9-2 to see the three phases of interphase, G_1, S, and G_2. The **G_1 phase** is the first period of interphase. In G_1 the cell doubles in size, and enzymes and organelles, such as mitochondria and ribosomes, roughly double in number. In the **S phase** the DNA that makes up the chromatin replicates. In the **G_2 phase** the cell undergoes rapid growth that prepares it for mitosis, synthesizing necessary enzymes and structures.

As you can see from Figure 9-2, the three phases of interphase constitute the largest part of the cell life cycle. In other words, cells spend most of their lifetime in interphase. However, the actual life spans of eukaryote cells vary. In ideal conditions a yeast cell lives for about two hours before it divides and forms two new cells. An ameba in a laboratory culture may live for a few days before it divides. In animals some cells of the early embryo may divide every 15 to 20 minutes.

In multicellular organisms many cells remain in interphase permanently. Cells that stop growing and dividing remain in the G_1 phase. The muscle and nerve cells of animals are incapable of dividing and so remain in the G_1 phase throughout their existence. In dividing cells interphase immediately precedes mitosis.

Phases of Mitosis

The fourth event in the cell cycle is mitosis, a continuous process that scientists divide into four phases: prophase, metaphase, anaphase, and telophase. As you read, keep in mind that mitosis produces two identical nuclei with the same number of chromosomes as the parent cell.

Prophase is the first phase of mitosis. Prophase can be subdivided into three steps. During early prophase, as shown in Figure 9-3, the chromatin coils and forms chromosomes. Simultaneously both the nucleolus and the nuclear membrane break down and disappear. In organisms other than plants two dark spots appear next to the disappearing nucleus. These small, dark cylindrical bodies, called **centrioles** *(SEN-tree-OLEZ)*, move away from each other, going toward opposite ends, or poles, of the cell.

The middle step of prophase is marked by the initial development of spindle fibers—microtubules of protein. There are two types of spindle fibers—polar and kinetochore fibers. **Polar fibers** extend across the cell from centriole to centriole. **Kinetochore** *(kuh-NET-uh-kor)* **fibers** extend from the centromeres of a chromosome to the centrioles. The kinetochore is the portion of the centromere that controls chromosome movement.

The last step of prophase is marked by the formation of **asters,** protein fibers that radiate from each centriole. Asters are not found in plant cells.

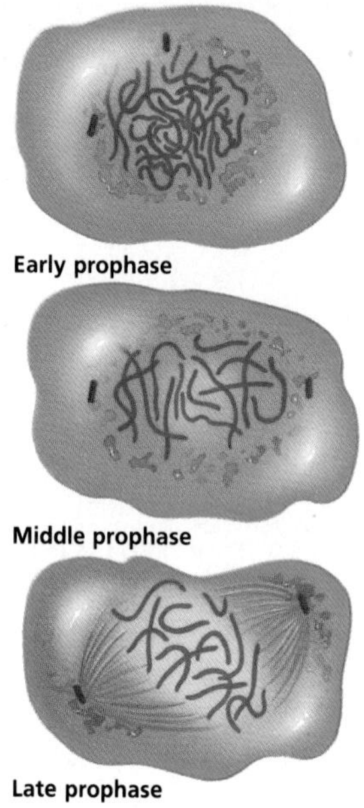

Figure 9-3 Prophase, the first phase of mitosis, is characterized by the formation of chromosomes and the development of spindle fibers and asters.

More Information

Human Chromosomes For many years biology and genetics textbooks said that 48 was the normal diploid number of human chromosomes. In 1956, scientists J. H. Tjio and A. Levan published a historic paper that proved that the correct number is 46. Due to advances in mammalian tissue culture techniques, they were able to use cultures of white blood cells that could easily be obtained from a routine blood sample. Addition of a plant derivative greatly increased the number of cells undergoing mitosis, and placement of the cell cultures in a hypotonic solution produced better spreading and separation of the chromosomes. These methods made clear, accurate counts possible.

Metaphase is the second phase of mitosis, as seen in Figure 9-4. During metaphase kinetochore fibers move the chromosome to the center, or equator, of the cell. Once in place at the equator of the cell, the chromosome is held in the center by the kinetochore fibers. As you can see from Figure 9-4, metaphase is characterized by the arrangement of all chromosomes along the equator of the cell.

Anaphase is the third phase of mitosis. First, the centromere of each pair of chromatids divides. Then the chromatids separate and move toward opposite poles of the cell. The movement of chromosomes is rapid and dramatic.

How do chromosomes move? Spindle fibers—both polar fibers and kinetochore fibers—play important roles in the movement of chromosomes. A polar fiber that arises from one centriole has a molecular structure that is oriented in an opposite manner from the fiber that arises from the other centriole. These polar fibers are connected to each other by bridges of protein. With the aid of ATP these polar fibers push against each other and force each other toward opposite sides of the cell. In addition, the kinetochore fibers are broken down and shortened at their place of attachment to the centriole. The overall effect is that the chromatids move to opposite sides of the cell.

Telophase is the final phase of mitosis. At the beginning of telophase the two identical sets of chromatids are clustered at opposite sides of the cell. During telophase the centrioles and spin-

Figure 9-4 Scientists divide mitosis into four phases: prophase, metaphase, anaphase, and telophase. Plant cells (top) and animal cells (bottom) are shown below.

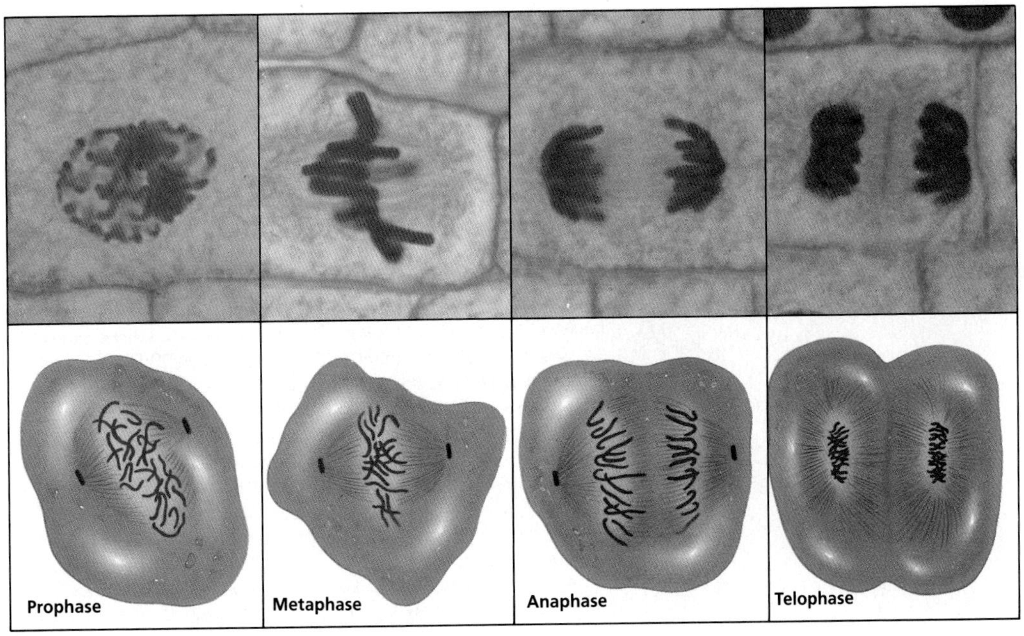

Relating Prior Knowledge Explain that scientists discovered that when a nucleus bursts, chromosomes are dispersed over a wider area, making them easier to count. Ask students what process would give these results. *(Osmosis; nuclei treated with distilled water will swell and burst.)*

Comparing Structures Provide students with prepared slides of animal (*Ascaris,* whitefish) and plant (onion, lily) cell mitosis, available from biological supply companies. (See the Laboratory on p. 139.) Have students compare the two cell types. *(Typically, animal cells are rounded; plant cells are rectangular.)* Have students locate and compare animal and plant cells in each stage of mitosis. *(Prophase, metaphase, and anaphase are similar, although plant cells do not have centrioles. Animal cell telophase is different in shape; no cell plate forms—cells constrict at the center and pinch off.)* Point out that rounded animal cells make chromosomes difficult to see.

- *See* Laboratories, *Investigation 9.2.*

Making Inferences Using their knowledge of the text, have students infer why even slight injuries to the brain and spinal cord can be serious and permanent. *(They may recall that muscle and nerve cells remain in interphase permanently. Since nerve tissue cells do not undergo mitosis, damaged or injured cells are not replaced, although some repair occurs.)*

Videodiscs

- *Side 2 8398, Cell Division: Mitosis in the African Blood Lily (m)*
- *2561–2568, Mitosis (s)*
- *1657–1662, Plant Cell Division (s)*
- *1668–1692, Mitosis in Broad Bean (s)*

Cooperative Learning

Making Models Tell students that they will model mitosis in a four-chromosome cell. Give each group of four students four differently colored pipe cleaners representing the four chromosomes. Have each group "replicate" their cell's DNA by giving each group member a second pipe cleaner identical to the first. Ask what each pipe cleaner represents. *(A chromatid)* Have each group member create a chromosome by joining the two pipe cleaners at the center or threading them through a "centromere" bead. Give each group a large sheet of paper and have them draw the outline of a cell large enough to accommodate the pipe cleaners. Have each group model alignment and separation of their chromosomes as mitosis occurs.

Interpreting the Visuals Ask students to identify the relationship between Figures 9-2 and 9-3, pp. 131–132. *(Figure 9-3, prophase, is the first phase of mitosis, shown as the first, darker yellow portion in Figure 9-2.)* Ask students to identify the relationships of Figures 9-4 and 9-5, pp. 133–134, to Figure 9-2. *(Figure 9-4 shows all four phases of mitosis and relates to Figure 9-2 as does Figure 9-3. Figure 9-5 shows cytokinesis, the lighter yellow portion in Figure 9-2—the second part of cell division.)*

Guided Practice
Have students make a table listing changes in spindles and chromosomes during mitosis. An example of a completed table is shown on p. 131.

Independent Practice
- Have students write answers to the Section Review.
- Give students two terms and ask them to write a sentence that expresses the relationship between the terms. *(For example, given* G_2 phase *and* mitosis, *student answers may include: The G_2 phase is the period of interphase when the cell grows and prepares for mitosis—division of the cell nucleus.)*

Check Your Understanding
1. Name the stages of mitosis, in order. *(Prophase, metaphase, anaphase, telophase. Interphase is not part of mitosis.)*
2. When does the DNA of a dividing cell begin to replicate? *(DNA is replicated during the S phase of interphase.)*
3. What mitotic characteristics differentiate a plant cell from an animal cell? *(Plant cells lack centrioles and aster fibers. Animal cells do not form a cell plate.)*

Figure 9-5 In animal cells the cell membrane narrows at the center and eventually divides in two. This process is called cytokinesis.

dle fibers disappear. The chromatids unwind and elongate into the threadlike structures of DNA that are now called chromatin. A nuclear membrane then forms again around each mass of chromatin, and finally a nucleolus appears. Cytokinesis then occurs.

Cytokinesis

The process of cytokinesis usually takes place immediately after mitosis. Cytokinesis occurs when cytoplasm from the original cell splits and forms two new cells. Each newly formed cell houses one of the two nuclei formed during mitosis. In dividing the cytoplasm cytokinesis also separates the other structures distributed throughout the cytoplasm, such as ribosomes, Golgi bodies, and mitochondria. The two new cells that have formed during cytokinesis are generally equal in size.

Figure 9-5 demonstrates the way in which cytokinesis occurs in animal cells. Notice how it differs from the same process in plants, which is shown in Figure 9-6. In animal cells cytokinesis begins during early anaphase. The cell membrane pinches in and, after telophase, divides the cell at its center, forming two daughter

Biology in Process

A Model of Cell Division

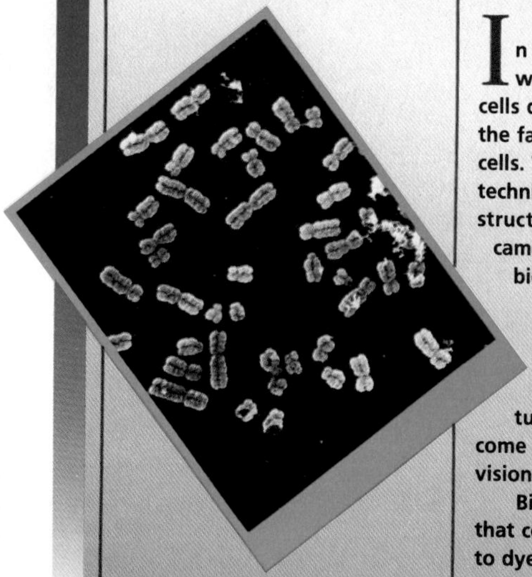

In the mid-1800s, biologists who wanted to learn how cells divide were hindered by the fairly transparent nature of cells. Therefore, developing a technique to make the substructures of cells visible became a priority among these biologists. Only if scientists could distinguish the inner parts of a cell could they then identify and observe the structures of cell division and so come to understand the cell division process.

Biologists hypothesized that cell structures would react to dye as other materials do—each structure, according to its individual properties, absorbing a certain amount or kind of dye. They predicted that the application of dye to a cell would thus make transparent cell parts visible.

Biologists began testing their hypothesis by applying various dyes to various types of cells and observing the visual effects of each dye. The first biologists who applied dyes to cells achieved mixed results. For example, one biologist found that a dye obtained from logwood stained a nucleus black. This dying procedure distinguished the nucleus from the cytoplasm but masked the inner structures of the nucleus.

Interdisciplinary Activity
Technology Ask students what tools are used to study mitosis. *(Students may suggest microscopes, slides, cameras.)* Have students use the library to research techniques used to observe mitosis. Ask students to explain the use of cameras and the roles of tissue cultures, time-lapse photography, micromanipulation, and electron microscopy (EM) in mitosis research. *(Still photographs provide a permanent record of a temporary event. Films or videotapes can also reduce observation times through time-lapse photography and provide a record of the sequence of events. Tissue cultures of different cell types allow comparisons. Fine, glass needles are used to reach inside cells and extract a chromosome to fix and prepare for EM, providing specific data about a specific chromosome.)*

cells. In plant cells vesicles formed by the Golgi bodies fuse at the equator and form the **cell plate,** a membrane across the middle of the cell. A new cell wall then forms on both sides of the cell plate. One cell is thus separated into two.

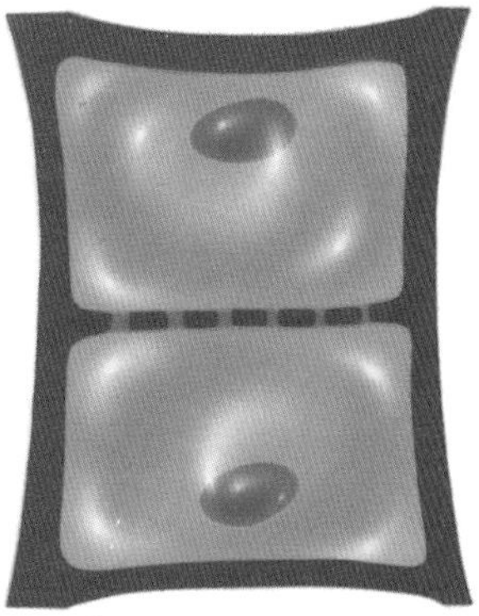

Figure 9-6 In plants a cell plate forms and eventually divides the cell during cytokinesis into two daughter cells.

Section Review

1. Define the term *cytokinesis,* and explain how cytokinesis differs from mitosis.
2. During which of the three phases of interphase—G_1, S, or G_2—does DNA replicate?
3. What is the distinction between polar fibers and kinetochore fibers?
4. What is the role of spindle fibers in each phase of mitosis? At what points do the spindle fibers appear and disappear? What changes do the fibers undergo? What functions do they perform in each phase?
5. Why might a cell require so much less time to complete the process of cytokinesis than it does to complete the process of mitosis?

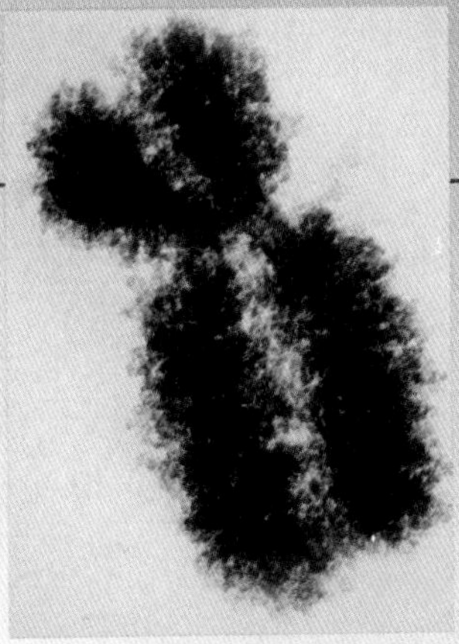

Finally, in 1879 a German anatomist named Walther Flemming noted that by applying synthetic red dyes to cells he could observe their substructures. In fact, certain threadlike substructures absorbed so much dye that Flemming called these darkly stained structures *chromatin,* from the Greek word for "color."

This was the result scientists had predicted could be achieved with the application of dye. However, the stain killed the cell to which it was applied. Therefore, Flemming could not simply stain cells to observe them dividing as scientists had hoped. Nevertheless, using the technique of cell staining, Flemming attempted to infer how cells divide.

He devised a method of creating a kind of moving picture. He based this method on the assumption that he would be viewing cells in various phases of division. Flemming inferred that he would capture the equivalent of still photos of cells in these various phases if he drew a picture of each cell as he saw it. Therefore Flemming drew each cell after he stained it. Then he sorted these drawings until he created a model of the cell division process. Flemming published this model in 1882. He called this process *mitosis,* which means "thread," because he observed that the threadlike chromatin plays a central role in the process.

■ What assumption did Flemming make that could have rendered his model inaccurate had he been incorrect?

Answers to Section Review

1. Cytokinesis is the division of a parent cell's cytoplasm and its contents into two daughter cells. Mitosis is strictly the division of the cell nucleus and its contents.
2. DNA replicates in the S phase.
3. Polar fibers extend from centriole to centriole. Kinetochore fibers extend from a centromere to a centriole; these fibers control chromosome movement.
4. Prophase—spindle fibers appear, polar fibers begin to attach; metaphase—kinetochore fibers extend from centriole to centromere, moving chromosomes to equator; anaphase—polar fibers force each other toward the cell poles, and the kinetochore fibers disappear, moving the chromatids to the poles; telophase—spindle fibers disappear.
5. Cytokinesis is less complex; it separates material into equivalent portions.

Reteaching

Have students identify the meanings of the prefixes in each phase of mitosis. *(*Pro-, *"early";* meta-, *"with," "between";* ana-, *"upward," "on";* tel-, *"over a long distance")*

■ *See* Section Reviews *worksheet, Section 9.2.*

Enrichment

Have students research polyploidy in plants. Many food crops—wheat, plums—have this condition. Alternatively, have them investigate haploidy in animals such as aphids or bees.

Closure

Ask students to relate the roles of the cell cycle and mitosis to a cell's life. *(The cell cycle is like normal, daily living; mitosis produces two identical offspring cells.)*

Biology in Process

Using the Feature

This feature focuses on the process skills of hypothesizing and inferring. Emphasize that scientists used their knowledge of the effect of dyes on common materials to hypothesize that dyes would similarly affect cells. Ask students to summarize how the best dyes for staining cells were discovered. *(Biologists tested many dyes, eliminating those that did not work, until an effective one was discovered.)* Ask students how Flemming used inference to create a model of cell division. *(Flemming inferred that staining dividing cells provided "snapshots" of each phase of the process. He drew each cell and then sorted the drawings into what he inferred was the order of occurrence.)*

Answer to the Feature

Flemming assumed that the dye did not alter the cells and their chromosomes.

Lesson Plan

Section Focus

This section discusses the formation of gametes—egg and sperm—through meiosis, a process that reduces the number of chromosomes by half.

Section Themes

The same phases and processes of meiosis occur in diverse cells of most eukaryotes, illustrating the theme of **Stability**. During meiosis, segregation of homologues, independent assortment, and crossing-over illustrate the theme of **Patterns of Change.** Fertilization of two gametes provides a unique diploid offspring.

The theme of **Evolution** is also apparent. Meiosis and fertilization produce varied organisms having adaptations that may be of survival value in their environment. This provides a mechanism for evolution.

Motivating Activity

Tell students they will use playing cards to model the first half of meiosis. Each card will represent an entire chromosome. Have them select cards of two suits of the same color and shuffle them. What do two cards of the same number or face—for example, a queen of spades and a queen of clubs—represent? *(Homologous chromosomes)* Next, have students match the cards, making two piles; each pile holds one of a pair. Ask what this division represents. *(The separation of homologous chromosomes into two daughter cells)* Emphasize that this activity models just the first half of meiosis. Stress that after the second half of meiosis, each newly formed cell will have half the number of chromosomes of the parent cell.

Section Objectives

- *Define* meiosis, *and state its outcome.*
- *Summarize the events that occur during meiosis I and meiosis II.*
- *Describe the formation of egg and sperm in animals.*
- *Explain why sexually reproducing organisms have a survival advantage over organisms that reproduce only by mitosis.*

9.3 Meiosis

Remember that mitosis produces daughter cells having the same number of chromosomes as the parent cell. **Meiosis** *(mie-OE-suss)* is the process of nuclear division that reduces the number of chromosomes by half. This process of cell division is involved in sexual reproduction. In animals meiosis often results in haploid egg cells and haploid sperm cells. In plants meiosis results in haploid spores that later lead to the production of egg and sperm cells. In both plants and animals the two 1N cells fuse during fertilization to form a 2N zygote that develops into a new organism.

Phases of Meiosis

In meiosis two nuclear divisions take place instead of one as in mitosis. In **meiosis I,** the first division, the homologous chromosomes are separated into separate cells. In **meiosis II,** the second division, the chromatids of each chromosome are segregated into separate cells. The result is that all daughter cells have one-half the number of chromosomes of the parent cell.

Meiosis I

Meiosis I, like mitosis, follows a period of interphase. As you read the following description of the four phases of meiosis I, refer to Figure 9-7.

- Prophase I: DNA strands coil, shorten, and thicken, and are referred to as chromosomes. As in the prophase of mitosis, spindle fibers appear. Then the nuclear membrane and the nucleolus disappear. A second step, which does not take place during mitosis, occurs: Every chromosome lines up next to its homologue. This pairing of homologous chromosomes is called **synapsis.** These homologous chromosomes twist around each other to form a **tetrad,** which is a group of two chromosomes. The word *tetrad* means "four" and refers to the four chromatids that compose the two chromosomes. As tetrads form, portions of chromatids may be exchanged, either between the two

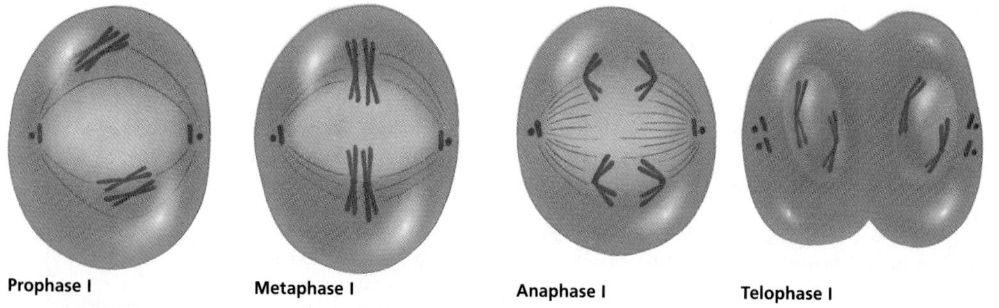

Figure 9-7 Notice that during prophase of meiosis I homologues line up next to each other, forming tetrads. Two daughter cells are formed by the end of telophase I.

Meiotic Phase	Meiosis I	Meiosis II
prophase	spindle appears; tetrads of homologous chromosomes form	new spindle forms; chromosomes coil again
metaphase	tetrads move to cell equator	chromosomes move to cell equator
anaphase	homologous pairs of chromosomes separate	sister chromatids separate and move to opposite poles
telophase	cytoplasm divides	cells divide; 4 daughter cells result

Graphic Organizer Use this table in Closure on p. 138.

homologues or between sister chromatids. This phenomenon, called **crossing-over,** results in the exchange of genes.

- Metaphase I: The tetrads are moved by spindle fibers to the equator of the cell. The homologous pairs of chromosomes remain together.
- Anaphase I: The homologous pairs of chromosomes separate, as shown in Figure 9-7. As in the anaphase phase in mitosis, one chromosome of each pair is pulled by action of the spindle fibers to one pole of the cell, and the other is pulled to the opposite pole. Each chromosome is still composed of two chromatids joined by a centromere.
- Telophase I: The cytoplasm divides, forming two daughter cells. This is the final stage of meiosis I.

During meiosis I the parent cell produces two daughter cells, each with one member of each pair of homologous chromosomes. Chromosome number has been halved, but each chromosome, having been replicated earlier, has twice the original amount of DNA.

Meiosis II

Meiosis II occurs in each cell formed during meiosis I and is not preceded by DNA replication. Refer to the diagrams in Figure 9-9 as you read about the phases of meiosis II.

- Prophase II: The chromosomes of some organisms—particularly plants—coil again, having uncoiled between telophase I and prophase II. New spindle fibers form. In animals chromosomes generally do not uncoil after meiosis I.
- Metaphase II: The chromosomes are moved to the cell equator. Each chromosome is made of two sister chromatids that are joined by a centromere that is attached to a spindle fiber.
- Anaphase II: The centromeres joining the chromatids divide, freeing each sister chromatid from the other. Then each sister chromatid is moved toward an opposite pole.
- Telophase II: As the spindle dissolves, a nuclear membrane forms around the chromosomes in each daughter cell. Meiosis II is complete, and cytokinesis occurs. The two nuclear divisions of meiosis result in four daughter cells from a single parent cell, each with half the number of chromosomes of the parent.

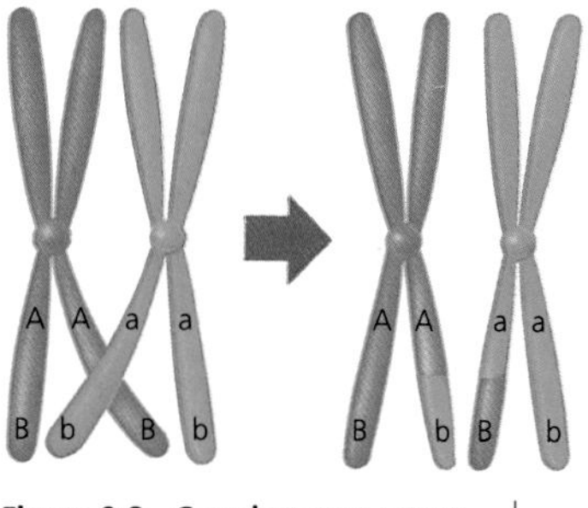

Figure 9-8 Crossing-over occurs when chromosomes that make up a tetrad exchange portions of their chromatids. This results in an exchange of genes.

Figure 9-9 By the end of meiosis II each 2N parent cell has divided into four haploid daughter cells.

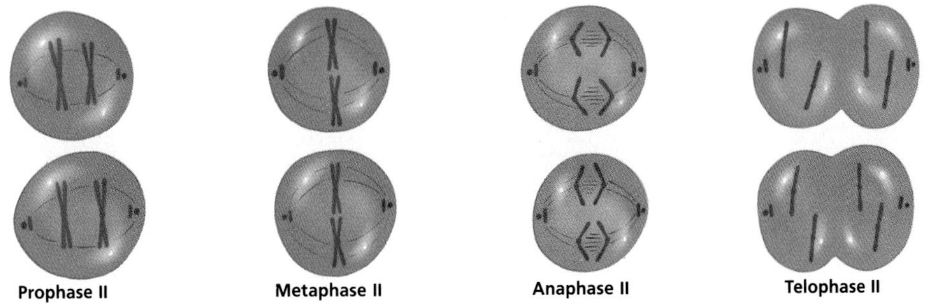

Teaching Strategies

Interpreting the Visuals Ask students to relate Figure 9-7 to Figure 9-9. *(The figures show the two phases of meiosis.)* Point out that the two phases sometimes follow each other rapidly; however, in egg development, meiosis II occurs only at the time of ovulation.

Comparing Processes Have students compare each meiotic phase with each mitotic phase. *(For example, in prophase I of meiosis every chromosome lines up next to its homologue. No such pairing occurs in prophase of mitosis.)*

Guided Practice

Help students analyze crossing-over during synapsis of homologues in meiosis I (Figure 9-8, p. 137). Ask how crossing-over relates to evolution. *(It is a source of genetic variation.)* Give students other cellular genotypes than the one shown in Figure 9-8; help them write the results of meiosis and of a subsequent fertilization. *(For example, suppose that an ovary cell has RSt and rST genes on one chromosome pair. Meiotic products are RSt and rST; with crossing-over, the following are also possible: RST, RSt, rSt, rST.)* Tell students to assume that a sperm is rst. Ask what offspring can result without crossing-over. *(RrSstt or rrSsTt)* Point out that with crossing-over, the following can result: RsSsTt, RrSstt, rrSstt, and rrSsTt. However, only those offspring with two recessive genes (ss, rr, or tt) would express them.
■ ***See* Blackline Master 22.**

Videodiscs

■ ***2552–2560, Meiosis (s)***
■ ***Side 2 33467, Animation: Spermatogenesis (m)***
■ ***1693–1712, Spermatogenesis in Grasshopper Testis (s)***
■ ***Side 2 38275, Cleavage in Mouse Egg (m)***

LEP Activity

The terms used to describe chromosomes and spindle fibers can be confusing. Use plastic fishing line to help students distinguish between similar terms. The line will represent spindle fibers (to the kinetochore, between the poles, and as aster rays). Use identically colored pipe cleaners to represent chromosomes—one pipe cleaner is one chromatid. Ask students to identify the centromere. *(The point at which two chromatids are attached)* Have students arrange the "chromosomes" as tetrads to show the synapsis of homologues. Have students model meiosis I on a large sheet of paper representing a cell. Ask what happens first. *(Homologues go to the equator of the cell in pairs.)* Ask what happens next. *(Homologues move to the poles of the cell.)* Have students then model meiosis II.

Independent Practice

■ Have students write answers to the Section Review.

■ Ask students to compare asexual with sexual reproduction. *(Asexual reproduction by fission or mitosis uses one parent and produces identical offspring. Sexual reproduction uses meiosis and fertilization, so considerable variation can be introduced.)*

Check Your Understanding

1. What is a major difference between prophase I and prophase II? *(Synapsis of homologues in prophase I is not repeated in prophase II.)*

2. What is a major difference between anaphase I and anaphase II? *(Homologous pairs go to one or the other pole at anaphase I; at anaphase II one or the other chromatid goes to each pole.)*

Reteaching

Have students refer to Figures 9-7 and 9-9, pp. 136–137, and draw each phase of meiosis. Ask students to label each drawing and describe each with one or two sentences.

■ *See* **Section Reviews** *worksheet, Section 9.3.*

Enrichment

Ask students what might be the advantage of having only one egg, but four sperm, complete meiosis. *(More male gametes increase the probability of fertilization. One egg retains all the nutrients needed for the first cell divisions after fertilization.)*

Closure

Have students work in small groups or pairs to create a table summarizing the events of meiosis I and meiosis II. An example of a completed table is shown on p. 136.

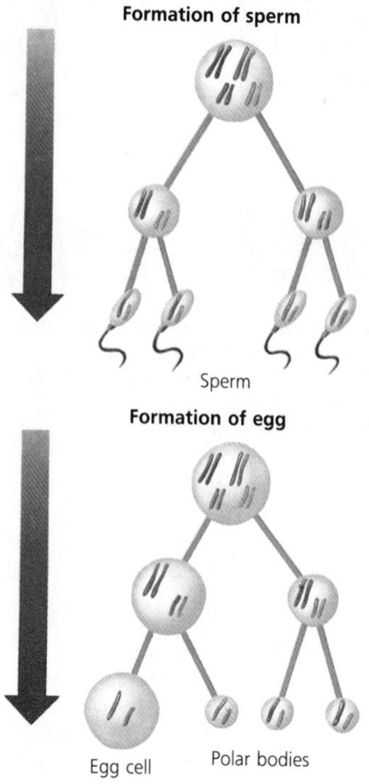

Figure 9-10 In the formation of male gametes a parent cell divides by meiosis. This leads to the development of four sperm. In the formation of female gametes a parent cell divides by meiosis. This leads to the development of an egg and three polar bodies.

Formation of Egg and Sperm

In animals 1N daughter cells produced by meiosis often differentiate to form **gametes** *(GAM-eets)*, sexual reproductive cells. In many animals male gametes, called sperm, are produced in the male reproductive organs. Each new cell becomes a sperm cell. Female gametes, or eggs, are formed in the female reproductive organs. The cytoplasm of the parent cell that undergoes meiosis often divides unequally, with the **ootid**—the egg cell—receiving almost all of the cytoplasm. The other three cells formed during meiosis I and meiosis II—called **polar bodies**—receive little or no cytoplasm and eventually disintegrate. Thus the result of each meiotic division is one haploid egg cell.

Asexual and Sexual Reproduction

Asexual reproduction is the production of offspring from one parent, without the union of gametes. In unicellular organisms new cells are created by binary fission, or mitotic division: a normal cell cycle. In multicellular organisms new cells are formed by various means, such as cloning or budding. Since asexual reproduction occurs only by mitosis, it results in offspring that are genetically identical with the parent.

Sexual reproduction is the production of offspring through meiosis and subsequent fusion of gametes. Such offspring are genetically different from both parents. This is because in meiosis genes are combined in new ways through **genetic recombination.** During meiosis I, genetic recombination results when (1) crossing-over occurs between chromatids of homologues and portions of the chromatids are exchanged, and (2) homologous pairs of chromosomes separate independently.

Genetic recombination introduces variation between parents and their offspring and hence among the different offspring. This variation gives some offspring a better chance of surviving in a changing environment. For example, if disease strikes a crop of grain, a few plants may have variations that make them resistant to the disease. While many individuals will die, these few plants will survive and reproduce, keeping the species alive. Thus organisms that reproduce sexually have a survival advantage over organisms that reproduce asexually.

Section Review

1. Define *meiosis I* and *meiosis II*.
2. What is the function of crossing-over?
3. What is the difference between an ootid and polar bodies?
4. How does genetic recombination help a species survive?
5. During which phase of meiosis I do you think genetic recombination occurs besides during crossing-over in prophase? How might genetic recombination occur in this stage?

Answers to Section Review

1. In meiosis I, homologous chromosomes are separated into separate cells. In meiosis II, chromatids of each chromosome are segregated into separate cells.

2. Crossing-over results in gene exchange.

3. An ootid, or egg cell, receives almost all the cytoplasm, whereas polar bodies receive little or none. The polar bodies disintegrate, and the ootid may be fertilized.

4. Genetic recombination provides variation between parents and offspring, possibly giving some offspring a better chance of survival in a changing environment.

5. Homologous chromosomes are sorted independently at anaphase I, a process which increases the likelihood of variation and genetic recombination.

Laboratory

Observing Mitosis

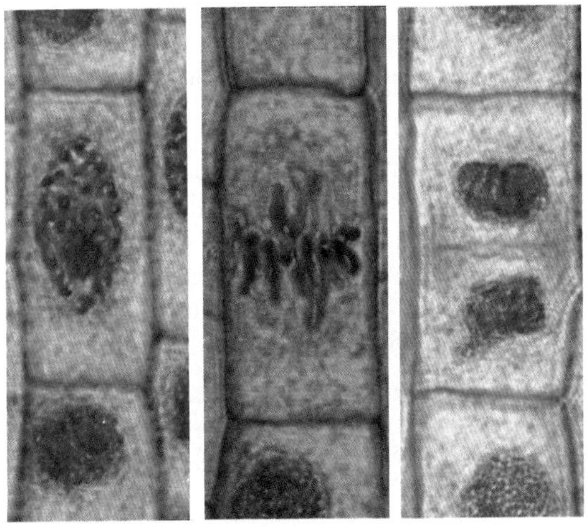

Objective
To examine dividing cells in order to determine the relative length of each stage of mitosis

Process Skills
Classifying; collecting, organizing, and analyzing data

Materials
Microscope, prepared slide of a longitudinal section of *Allium* (onion) root tip

Inquiry

1 Review with your teacher the visible characteristics of each stage of mitosis. Make a list of these characteristics to aid you in your observations. Remember: Interphase is not a phase of mitosis.
2 Using low power on your microscope, focus on the apical meristem of the onion root tip. This is the area just behind the root cap. Why is this a good place to look for cells undergoing mitosis?
3 Examine the apical meristem carefully and choose a sample of about 50 cells to classify. Look for a group of cells that seems to have been actively dividing. The cells will appear to be in rows, so it should be easy to keep track of them.
4 Prepare a chart for entering your data. Head five columns *Stage, Tally Marks, Count, Percent,* and *Time*. Under the column labeled *Stage* list *Prophase, Metaphase, Anaphase,* and *Telophase*.
5 For each of the cells in your sample identify the stage of mitosis, and place a mark in the *Tally Marks* column next to the appropriate stage. Count the tallies for each stage, and fill in the *Count* column.
6 Calculate the percentage of cells found in each stage, and enter the figures under *Percent*. The percentage of cells found in each stage is a measure of how long each stage lasts. Why is this so?
7 In *Allium* interphase is about 15 hours long, while mitosis normally takes 83 minutes at room temperature. With this information as your basis, how would you fill in the column labeled *Time?* Make the necessary calculations, and record your results in the column.
8 Make another, similar chart, but leave out the *Tally Marks* column. Collect and record the count for each stage of mitosis for the entire class. Fill in the percent and time information using the data collected by the entire class.

Conclusions

1 How can you determine that mitosis is continuous by examining fixed cells?
2 What are the relative lengths, in percentages, of the stages of mitosis in onion root tip?

Further Inquiry
In addition to the fact that it is a larger sample, why might the class data be more representative of what is happening in the onion root tip than individual data?

Laboratory

(For an overview of mitosis and preparatory information related to the laboratory, see p. 127B.)

Inquiry

2. The root tip is the growing area, where cell division occurs.
6. Students calculate the percentage of cells found in each phase by dividing the number under *Count* by the total number of cells counted. It is logical to assume that if more cells of a particular phase were seen at the moment the root tip slide was fixed, more cells would have been in that stage longer.
7. Assume that *Time* must total 83 minutes, and calculate percentages expressed as a decimal multiplied by 83 for each phase of mitosis.
8. Student charts should reflect class data.

Conclusions

1. The stage of some cells is easy to classify, but most are hard to classify because stages blend into one another. This leads students to infer that the process is continuous.
2. Answers should reflect the data.

Further Inquiry

Several longitudinal sections can be made from a single root tip—the class data may give a more accurate idea of what is occurring in the whole volume of dividing tissue.

Vocabulary

1. Mitosis results in two diploid cells, each identical to the parent cell; meiosis results in four unique haploid cells.
2. In meiosis I, homologous chromosomes are separated into the two daughter cells; in meiosis II, the chromatids of each chromosome are segregated into separate cells.
3. Synapsis is the pairing of homologous chromosomes prior to forming a tetrad.
4. Asexual reproduction produces offspring from one parent without the union of gametes. Sexual reproduction produces offspring with the union of gametes, usually from two parents.
5. Crossing-over is the exchange of chromatid portions, resulting in gene exchange. Genetic recombination includes crossing-over and independent separation of homologous chromosome pairs.

Review

1. d	**6.** a
2. b	**7.** c
3. b	**8.** b
4. a	**9.** d
5. c	**10.** a

11. Each daughter cell must receive the same genetic information as the parent cell.
12. Chromosomes always occur in pairs in sexually reproducing organisms.
13. As a cell grows, its surface area increases at a slower rate than its volume. Nutrients cannot diffuse in, nor wastes diffuse out, quickly enough for the cell to survive. Cell division provides a smaller surface-area-to-volume ratio again.
14. Cell biologists found that differentiating among five stages communicates their observations most clearly.

Chapter 9 Review

Vocabulary

anaphase (133)
asexual reproduction (138)
aster (132)
cell cycle (131)
cell plate (135)
centriole (132)
centromere (129)
chromatid (129)
crossing-over (137)
cytokinesis (131)
diploid (130)
G_1 phase (132)
G_2 phase (132)
gamete (138)
genetic recombination (138)
haploid (130)
histone (129)
homologous chromosome (130)
interphase (131)
kinetochore fiber (132)
meiosis (136)
meiosis I (136)
meiosis II (136)
metaphase (133)
mitosis (131)
ootid (138)
polar body (138)
polar fiber (132)
prophase (132)
S phase (132)
sexual reproduction (138)
synapsis (136)
telophase (133)
tetrad (136)

Explain the difference between the terms in each of the following sets.

1. mitosis, meiosis
2. meiosis I, meiosis II
3. synapsis, tetrad
4. asexual reproduction, sexual reproduction
5. crossing-over, genetic recombination

Review

1. All cells come from (a) sperm cells (b) zygotes (c) egg cells (d) preexisting cells.
2. Chromatin is (a) a dark stain (b) a dense substance within the nuclear membrane of a nondividing cell (c) one of the two identical parts that make up a chromosome (d) the point at which each pair of chromatids is joined.
3. Every species has (a) diploid and haploid cells (b) a distinctive number of chromosomes per cell (c) at least eight chromosomes per cell (d) a number of chromosomes that varies with the complexity of the organism.
4. Mitosis (a) can increase the number of body cells without changing the information contained in the DNA of those cells (b) is a means of reproducing sexually (c) is never triggered by cell size (d) results in daughter cells that are genetically different from each other.
5. Interphase is (a) a time when cells rest between divisions (b) the phase when the cytoplasm divides (c) a time of cell growth and development (d) a small part of the life cycle of the cell.
6. Cytokinesis (a) differs in animals and plants (b) does not occur in plants (c) immediately precedes mitosis (d) is a process of nuclear division.
7. Polar fibers are (a) the final product of meiosis (b) the final product of cytokinesis (c) the microtubules of protein that extend across a cell from centriole to centriole (d) the dark, cylindrical bodies that move toward opposite ends, or poles, of a cell.
8. When all chromosomes are arranged along the equator of a cell, the cell is in (a) prophase (b) metaphase (c) anaphase (d) telophase.
9. Meiosis I produces (a) a parent and two daughter cells (b) four daughter cells (c) two diploid cells (d) two haploid cells.
10. The ootid receives (a) almost all the cytoplasm from the original parent cell (b) little cytoplasm (c) the same amount of cytoplasm as other gametes (d) no cytoplasm.
11. Why do cells divide equally and in an orderly process in mitosis?

15. No. A cell either remains in interphase or divides into two new cells. Each new cell may then go through a cell cycle.
16. Cells in the G_1 phase don't grow or divide but do still metabolize—for example, nerve and muscle cells.
17. The cell plate divides the cytoplasm during plant cell mitosis. A cell wall then forms on each side of the plate.
18. Flemming discovered a dye that made cell structures visible, and he developed a model of cell division.
19. The process that forms two new unicellular organisms by asexual reproduction is binary fission.
20. Some multicellular organisms reproduce asexually by cloning or budding.

12. In what type of organisms do chromosomes always occur in pairs?
13. Explain why size might trigger cell division.
14. The cell cycle is a continuous process. Why have biologists differentiated five distinct events in this cycle?
15. Does the same cell go through the cell cycle more than once? Why?
16. Some cells remain in the G_1 phase of interphase. Describe the character of these cells, and give an example.
17. What function does a cell plate perform? How?
18. What are the two most significant contributions Walther Flemming made to the study of cell biology?
19. What does the term *binary fission* refer to? In what type of organisms does this process occur?
20. What are two of the ways by which multicellular organisms may reproduce asexually?

Critical Thinking

1. The photograph at the right shows cell division in a lily anther. The daughter cells will form pollen grains. Do you think that the photograph shows mitosis or meiosis? Support your answer.
2. Some human liver cells have 92 chromosomes. Explain how such cells probably arose.
3. In the female meiosis results in an ootid and three polar bodies. The ootid receives almost all the cytoplasm from the meiotic cell. In sperm formation the cytoplasm is divided equally among four sperm. Which parent contributes more mitochondria to the new embryo?
4. Suppose that in a certain plant with a haploid number of 12, DNA replication took place and the chromatids in anaphase of meiosis II separated but that cytokinesis did not occur. How many chromosomes would the zygote have if the resulting egg was fertilized by a normal sperm?

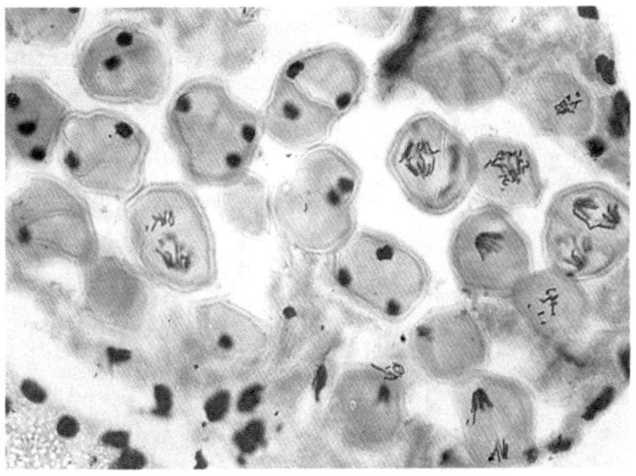

Extension

1. Read Rick Weiss's article "Uneven Inheritance," in *Science News,* July 7, 1990, pp. 8–11. Give an oral report: describe how Arthur Beaudet discovered a case of a patient with a double dose of some genes from one parent and no equivalent genes from the other parent.
2. Make a bar graph showing the stages in meiosis, including interphase, on the *x*-axis and the N number of human chromosomes on the *y*-axis.
3. A chemical called colchicine blocks the process of cytokinesis. Use your school library or public library to research colchicine. Present a report to your class explaining how colchicine prevents cytokinesis and describing how colchicine is used in horticulture.

Critical Thinking

1. Since pollen grains are haploid gametes, the picture must show meiosis.
2. Liver cells, with 92 chromosomes, probably arose when duplicated chromatids separated during anaphase of mitosis without cytokinesis then occurring.
3. Mitochondria are in the cytoplasm. Since the egg contains more cytoplasm than the sperm, the female contributes more mitochondria.
4. 36 chromosomes—24 maternal and 12 paternal

Extension

1. Student reports should define uniparental disomy and discuss how research on the gene causing cystic fibrosis led to its discovery. Students should include information on the disorders it may cause. Encourage the use of graphics to illustrate how the error in chromosomal segregation occurs.
2. Interphase—2N; Prophase I, Metaphase I, and Anaphase I—4N; Telophase I, Prophase II, Metaphase II, and Anaphase II—2N; Telophase II—1N
3. Colchinine, an extract from crocuses, blocks formation of the mitotic spindle. It also causes the number of chromosomes in a plant cell to double, resulting in offspring that are much larger than the parent plants.

Discussion
Guide the discussion by posing the following questions.

1. How has drug therapy been improved by the development of new methods of medication? *(Treatment is much more specific; dosage can be regulated with precision; the risk of toxicity or ineffectiveness is reduced.)*

2. Why are liposomes good vehicles for carrying medication? *(Their similarities to biological membranes and lipid layers make them effective drug carriers. Other advantages include being nontoxic and biodegradable, and not producing an immune response.)*

3. What developments have fueled recent improvements in drug treatment? *(Advances in materials science and biotechnology have made possible new physical and chemical means of administering drugs. Answers should include the development of polymer materials, pumps, and monoclonal antibodies.)*

4. How might advances in methods of medication affect your life? *(Answers will vary. Students should consider the benefits of better treatment methods on common conditions, such as diabetes, heart and kidney disease, and high blood pressure.)*

5. What are some problems you have experienced with traditional drug therapy? *(Answers will vary but may include negative attitudes toward injections and other invasive methods, difficulties with taking pills or capsules, individual sensitivities to drugs, and reactions to overmedication and large dosages.)*

Intra-Science

How the SciencesWork Together

The Question in Biology: *Must Medicines Be Pills?*

When physicians prescribe drug treatment, it is often in the form of pills, injections, ointments, or eye drops. However, recent developments may change all that. How a drug enters the body is becoming as important as what drug to take—maybe more.

Some new methods of medicating patients are making existing drugs safer and more effective to use. Tight spaces between cells in membranes prevent many drugs from entering certain parts of the body. One new technique of medication involves chemically altering drugs so that they can pass through these narrow spaces between cells in membranes. Therefore, by linking a drug to a carrier molecule, it can pass through some membranes.

Much drug research today involves studying microscopic vesicles that carry drugs through biological membranes. One type of vesicle, or tiny sac, is called a liposome. Liposomes are a layer of lipid surrounding a small portion of liquid. Water–soluble drugs can fill liposomes and be injected into the body. Liposomes tend to be nontoxic and usually do not stimulate an immune response. In use, liposomes can pass through a membrane and decompose, releasing their dose of drug. For example, liposomes have been used to deliver arsenic to diseased liver cells, carry vaccines, and treat cancers.

In addition to using liposomes, medications can be made more effective with the aid of surgically applied syringe pumps and implants, or medicated patches. These medicinal devices supply medicines to a specific part of the body for a certain period of time, from a few days to several years. Specially coated tablets are an older form of controlled release devices. These tablets usually take less than a day to supply their full amount of medication, and their usefulness often varies from patient to patient.

Another improved method of medication directs medicines to target tissues. A tiny syringe pump can guide drugs to cancers in specific tissues while sparing the healthy tissues of the body. The pump can also control the release of insulin, morphine, and other drugs.

Using another medicinal device, doctors can now prescribe contraceptives in implants. During a minor

Connections to Other Disciplines

Agriculture Controlled-release devices are being used to fertilize crops and residential landscapes. These devices can supply pesticides to plants from the ground up over a period of time. Have students investigate these examples and others and then report their advantages and disadvantages.

Sociology Fifteen countries around the world have approved use of the first contraceptive implant, making long-term family planning available to poor women who may not be able to follow or afford complex pill regimes. Encourage students to discuss some advantages and disadvantages of this use of contraceptive implants.

surgical procedure, a doctor inserts the implant, a slim nondegradable polymer packet, which releases contraceptives to the user for up to five years.

Thousands of travelers already benefit from a device called the skin patch, which works well for drugs that easily permeate skin. On airplanes, trains, boats, or even buses you may have seen passengers wearing these devices (reservoirs of medicine) behind an ear to prevent motion sickness. Since the skin behind the ear is highly permeable, the device has a better chance of regulating the release of medicine.

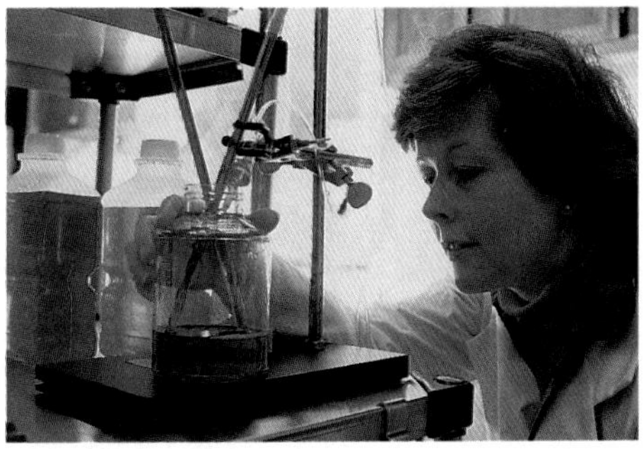

The Connection to Engineering

Liposomes can be obtained from many different sources. However, if liposomes are to gain widespread applications, the mass production of lipids must be designed. Chemical engineers will also need to improve and extend the storage of liposomes without diminishing their ability to decompose in the body. In addition researchers are investigating methods of making liposomes that are sensitive to specific stimuli. Such liposomes might release drugs in response to an enzyme, heat, light, or the acidity of a body fluid.

■ *Why might mass production be advantageous to the use of liposomes?*

The Connection to Materials Science

Scientists are constantly designing and adapting various materials to biomedical needs. For example, the plastic tubing used today in some heart and lung machines and in kidney dialysis equipment was originally developed for sausage casings and women's girdles. A particular challenge of designing polymers for implants is to make a polymer that degrades in a specific way, such as by eroding only from the surface. Synthesizing ideal polymers (large carbon-based compounds), however, will require experimentation with a variety of new materials.

■ *Why might surface erosion be desirable in a polymer implant?*

The Connection to Other Sciences

Scientists are also perfecting ways to target specific cells for drug treatment by joining drugs to a monoclonal antibody. Monoclonals result when natural antibodies are cloned or mass-produced in a laboratory by genetic engineering. Monoclonals, like antibodies produced in your body by white blood cells, can detect disease-causing organisms or abnormal cells in the body and eliminate them. Coupled with a drug, a radioisotope, or a toxin, monoclonals are being tested in treatment for cancer, septic shock, and AIDS. Because harmful reactions to mouse antibodies can occur in humans, biotechnologists are looking for ways to mass–produce human monoclonal antibodies.

■ *Describe a possible advantage of using monoclonals with radioisotopes.*

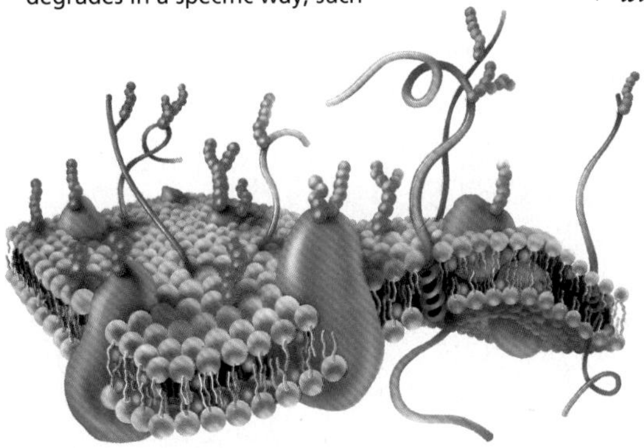

The Connection to Careers

Understanding the properties of drugs and how they react in new medication methods will involve a wide range of specialists, including pharmacologists, medical practitioners, biochemists, lab technicians, radiologists, and genetic engineers. Attorneys will be needed to advise biotechnology labs on patents for new designs and products. For more information about related careers in the biological sciences, turn to page 842.

Intra-Science

6. Should more money be spent on biotechnological research or for better national health care? Explain your choice. *(Encourage students to consider the benefits and disadvantages of their choice as they offer rationales.)*

Answers to

Chemical Engineering Mass production would reduce the cost of liposomes and promote their use in many new applications.

Materials Science The rest of the polymer could stay intact, regulating release of the drug.

Other Sciences Monoclonals mimic natural antibodies in their ability to detect diseased cells. During chemotherapy or testing they can be used to transport a dose of radioisotope specifically to diseased cells.

Enrichment

Creating a new drug in today's market costs at least $150 million. Improving a delivery system is a better investment and can allow companies to continue reaping benefits even after the drug patent itself expires, usually after only 17 years. Encourage students to find out why prescription drugs are so expensive in our society.

Unit 3 Genetics

Chapters

Unit Overview

This unit builds on the study of cells in Unit 2. Chapters 10, 11, and 12 teach students the role of chromosomes and genes in the inheritance of traits and the development of organisms. Chapter 10 describes the work of Gregor Mendel, the basic principles that he formulated, and Sutton's chromosome hypothesis that explains the mechanism behind Mendel's principles. Students are thus introduced to genes, alleles, and genetic crosses. Chapter 11 introduces mutations and highlights various aspects of human genetics. Chapter 12 describes gene expression in prokaryotes and eukaryotes and also explains how genes direct development. In Chapter 13, students will learn how genetic principles are applied to improve sources of food, medicine, and other products using both traditional and new forms of applied genetics.

Issues in Biology

Use your discretion in introducing the following topic for class discussion, and be sensitive to family and community values.

In pregnancies that appear to be at risk, techniques such as amniocentesis and chorion villi sampling can spot chromosomal abnormalities as well as certain mutations in a fetus. When prenatal screening shows that the fetus carries a severe genetic disorder, the parents have the option of terminating the pregnancy. Ask students to list arguments for and against terminating a pregnancy on the basis of a severe genetic disorder.

Prenatal screening also reveals the sex of the fetus. Some parents may want to terminate a pregnancy if the fetus is not the desired sex. Ask students to consider whether prenatal screening should be controlled to avoid its potential misuse.

Research in Progress

Because cancer results from defective genes in somatic cells and because some cancers are inherited, much cancer research focuses on genes. Researchers interested in the interaction of heredity and the environment are currently studying how people with a genetic predisposition to cancer are affected by carcinogens.

Many other laboratories are studying oncogenes (see Section 12.2). Researchers are applying DNA technology (see Section 13.2) in order to understand how point mutations, translocations, or deletions can transform certain normal genes—called proto-oncogenes—into oncogenes, which are then responsible for unregulated cell growth. Changes in the DNA in oncogenes will be used more and more by physicians to diagnose cancer and to follow tumor development.

Interdisciplinary Activity

Government Environmental factors affect human genes through the action of mutagens and carcinogens on DNA. Several agencies of the U.S. government regulate the levels of mutagens and carcinogens in the environment, the food supply, and the workplace. Have students research the regulations enforced by the Environmental Protection Agency (EPA), Food and Drug Administration (FDA), and the Occupational Safety and Health Administration (OSHA), or equivalent state agencies. Ask students to focus on how these agencies decide that a particular chemical is mutagenic and/or carcinogenic. Students can find information on governmental agencies in libraries or in printed media at home. There are many appropriate articles in news magazines.

Resources

Chapter	Print: For the Teacher	Print: For the Student	Audiovisual/Software
10	■ Gordon Edlin, *Genetic Principles: Human and Social Consequences,* Jones and Bartlett, 1984. ■ Eldon J. Gardner and D. Peter Snustad, *Principles of Genetics,* 8th ed., Wiley, 1991.	■ C. Decker, "Extra DNA Causes Mendel's Peas to Pucker," *Science News,* February 10, 1990, 87. ■ Julie Ann Miller, "Building a Better Mouse," *Bio-Science,* February 1987, 103–106.	■ *The Fascinating Story of Cell Growth.* Apple 128K. IBM PC 128K. 2 disks. Scholastic, 1986. ■ *The Gene.* Video or 2 filmstrips with cassettes, 16–19 min. each. Teacher's guide. Hawkhill, 1984. ■ *Heredity.* Film, 15 min. Britannica. ■ *Heredity I: Traits, Genes, and Alleles.* Filmstrip or transparencies with cassette. Teacher's guide. Biology Media.
11	■ Isaac Asimov, *How Did We Find Out About DNA?,* Walker, 1985. ■ Karl H. Muench, *Genetic Medicine,* Elsevier, 1988. ■ Neil A. Holtzman, *Proceed with Caution: Predicting Genetic Risks in the Recombinant DNA Era,* Johns Hopkins University Press, 1989.	■ Stephen S. Hall, "James Watson and the Search for Biology's 'Holy Grail,'" *Smithsonian,* February 1990, 41–49. ■ Larry Thompson, "Mom and Pop Genes," *Discover,* February 1991, 20. ■ Rick Weiss, "Uneven Inheritance," *Science News,* July 7, 1990, 138.	■ *Chemistry of Heredity I: Identification of Genetic Material and DNA Structure.* Film, 15 min. Britannica. ■ *The Gene.* Two filmstrips with cassettes, 16–19 min. each. Hawkhill. ■ *Heredity.* Film, 15 min. Britannica.
12	■ David T. Suzuki et al., *An Introduction to Genetic Analysis,* 4th ed., W.H. Freeman and Company, 1989.	■ M. D. Lemonick, "Of Fireflies and Tobacco Plants," *Time,* November 17, 1986, 87. ■ John Rennie, "Homeobox Harvest," *Scientific American,* June 1991, 24.	■ *The Fascinating Story of Cell Growth.* Apple 128K. IBM PC 128K. 2 disks. Scholastic, 1986. ■ *Origin of Cellular Life.* Still-frame video, 46 min. Biology Media. ■ *Regulation of Gene Expression in Eucaryotes.* Still-frame video, 32 min. Carolina Biological.
13	■ Jerry E. Bishop and Michael Waldhoz, *Genome: The Story of Our Astonishing Attempt to Map All the Genes in the Human Body,* Touchstone, 1990. ■ Margery L. Oldfield, *The Value of Conserving Genetic Resources,* U.S. Department of the Interior, National Park Service, 1984.	■ Deborah Erickson, "Down on the Pharm," *Scientific American,* August 1990, 102–103. ■ Doug Stewart, "These Germs Work Wonders," *Reader's Digest,* January 1991, 83–86.	■ *Children of the Future.* Film, 55 min. Britannica, 1987. ■ *Genetic Engineering.* Apple II, 48K. Operating instruction, glossary, and software on disk with backup. Helix. Dist. by Carolina Biological. ■ *Significant Hazards? The Somerville DNA Debate.* Film or video, 24 min. Fanlight, 1984.

Science in Action Video Series

In teaching Unit 3, you may wish to use the second topic of videotape *The Atoms and Molecules of Life/DNA and Protein Synthesis,* from the Science in Action Video Series. Models and graphic animation are used in this videotape to help students understand the structure and function of the DNA molecule.

Introducing the Unit

The material in Unit 2, from cell structure to sexual reproduction, begins the discussion of reproduction and inheritance. To lead students from Unit 2 into the study of genetics, ask them the following questions.

1. Given what you know about meiosis, how do you think that a child inherits traits from both parents? *(In the formation of gametes, homologous chromosome pairs separate. After two gametes fuse to form the zygote, each chromosome pair is made up of a chromosome from each parent, each transmitting traits from one parent.)*

2. How do you think that chromosomes transmit a genetic disorder? *(The chromosomes carry genes, which code for proteins with cellular functions. A defective gene coding for a defective protein could be the cause of a disorder.)*

3. What do you think might happen if a mistake in replication occurs in the DNA of a cell that produces gametes? *(There would be a change in the sequence of bases in the DNA, possibly resulting eventually in a change in a protein assembled in cells of the offspring inheriting the mistake. The offspring would differ from its parents.)*

4. As you begin Unit 3, what questions can you ask about the functions of cells during sexual reproduction? *(Sample questions: How can cells that have similar cellular structures grow into mosquitoes and humans, or into grass plants and orange trees? Are reproductive cells related to human diseases? Why can one person in a family be color blind while others in the same family are not? How have researchers investigated inheritance? How can knowledge of what happens in reproductive and other cells help people?)*

Unit 3 Genetics

Chapters

"The multiplicity of shape, color, and behavior in individuals and in species is produced by the coupling of genes, as Mendel guessed. . . . But the question is not how the genes are arranged; the modern question is, How do they act? The genes are made of nucleic acid. That *is where the action is."*

Jacob Bronowski

The striking coloration of Indian corn is inherited just like your eye color or the shape of a bird's beak. Scientists working in the field of genetics study the patterns of inheritance of such traits as well as the biochemical mechanisms that underlie those patterns. In this unit you will learn about these patterns and mechanisms as well as about technologies that alter these mechanisms to produce desired traits.

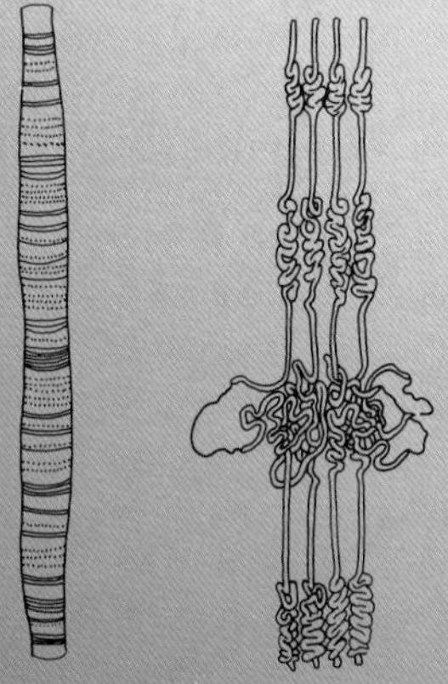

Salivary chromosomes of fruit fly, *Drosophila melanogaster*

Indian corn, *Zea mays*

Using the Opening Quotation

Ask volunteers to restate the quotation in their own words. If versions differ, have the class seek a single interpretation. *(Bronowski pointed out that Mendel guessed an answer to the more obvious question of how genes are arranged, but had no way of answering the modern question of how genes act.)* Tell the students that Mendel worked in the mid-1800s. Ask them why Mendel could not have asked the "modern question." *(People in Mendel's time did not know about chromosomes, genes, and DNA. Technology was not yet available to investigate the structural details of cells.)*

SEM of human chromosomes (×6,900)

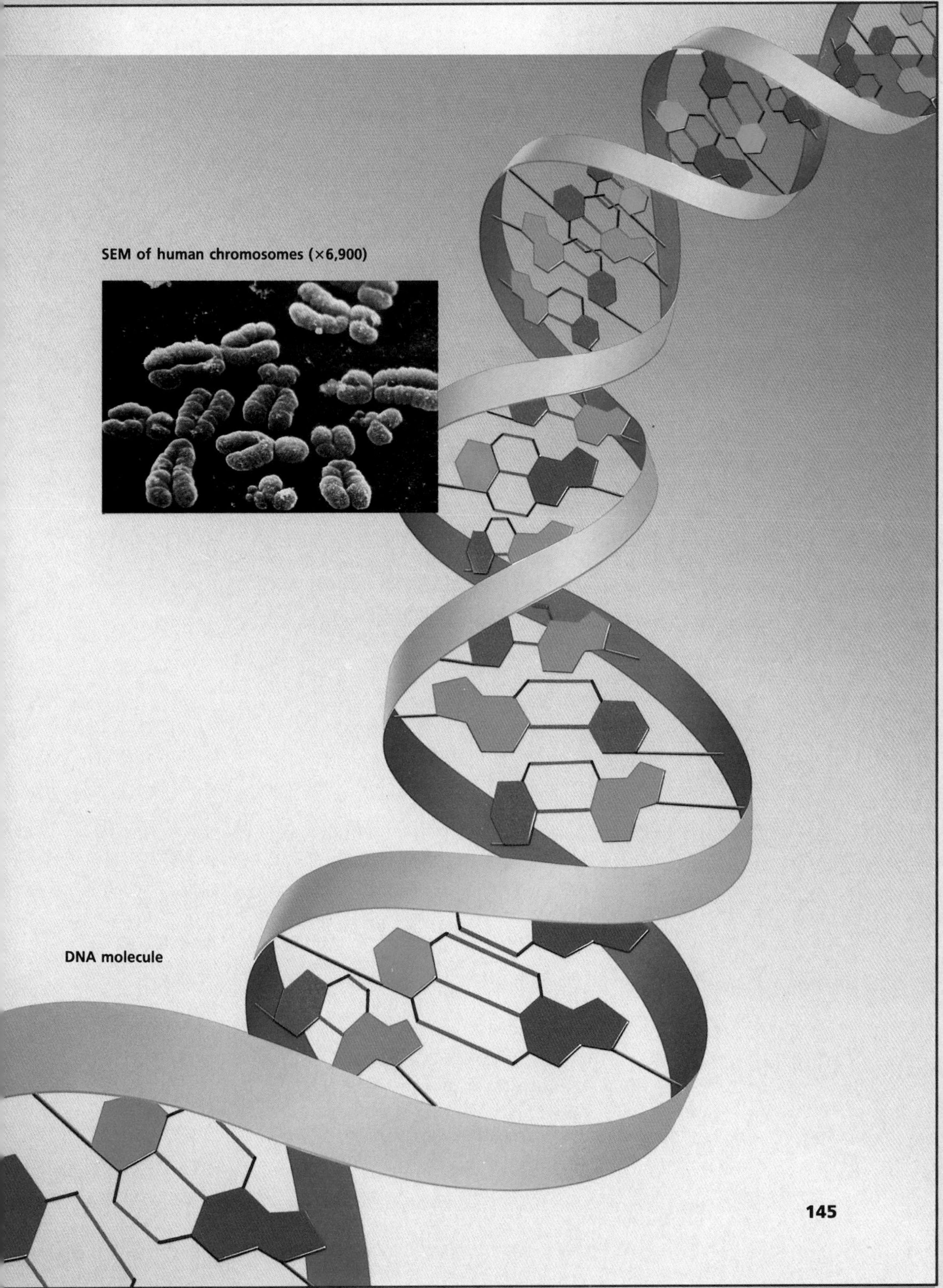

DNA molecule

UNIT 3

Unit Themes

Evolution The study of genetics shows how individuals inherit different characteristics from their parents (Chapter 10), a mechanism fundamental to evolutionary change. Mutations (Chapter 11), the raw material of natural selection, occur by chance, but the constraints of the genetic process also make organisms surprisingly stable. Humans also manipulate and select hereditary traits in plants and animals (Chapter 13).

Patterns of Change Development is implicit in all genetic studies, beginning in Chapter 10. Gene expression (Chapter 12) biochemically controls the developmental changes from zygote to adult in all multicellular organisms. In the long run, evolutionary trends depend on the expression of mutant genes.

Scale and Structure The structure of chromosomes is related to their function—the transmission of inherited traits. The genes on chromosomes are responsible for coding traits, making each species unique. On a smaller scale, the molecular structure of the DNA in genes is responsible for their biochemical functions (Chapters 11, 12).

Systems and Interactions The work of geneticists in the understanding of human disorders (Chapter 11) and in studies of cancer (Chapter 12) has contributed to the general understanding of how human organ systems function and how they can malfunction.

Understanding the Visuals

Ask students to consider how the illustrations relate to the quotation. Point out that the photograph of corn represents "the multiplicity of shape, color, and behavior." Ask students to describe one inherited trait of the corn shown. *(Kernel color—nonyellow in two shades)* Encourage students to think of other possible traits inherited in corn. *(Examples: kernel texture—wrinkled or smooth; flavor—sweet or sour; height of stalks—tall or short)*

Explain that the scanning electron micrograph of human chromosomes shows the "coupling of genes, as Mendel guessed." Ask students which illustration shows "where the action is." *(The action is in the DNA, the drawing on the right.)*

145

Chapter 10 Fundamentals of Genetics

Chapter Overview

Chapter 10 lays the foundation for students' study of genetics. Section 10.1 discusses the work of Mendel and Sutton as an introduction to basic genetic principles of dominance and recessiveness, segregation, and independent assortment. Section 10.2 presents examples of genetic crosses, using various gamete and zygote combinations. It also emphasizes the role of probability in predicting genetic makeup of offspring.

Chapter Planning Chart

B	S	A	Sections and Subsections	Page	Features	Page	Resources
•	•	•	**10.1 The Legacy of Gregor Mendel**				
			Mendel's Experiments	147	Biology in Process	150	Videodiscs
			Mendel's Results and Conclusions	148	Section Review	152	Section Reviews Worksheet
			Chromosomes and Genes	152			
•	•	•	**10.2 Genetic Crosses**				
			Genotype and Phenotype	153	Think	154	Videodiscs
			Probability	154	Laboratory	159	Blackline Master 23
			Predicting Results of Monohybrid Crosses	154	Section Review	158	Overhead Transparency T10
							Blackline Master 24
			Predicting Results of Dihybrid Crosses	157			Process Skills: Genetics Prediction
							Laboratories: Genetic Probability
							Section Reviews Worksheet
			End of Chapter Activities				
					Chapter Review	160	Vocabulary Skills
							Chapter Test
							Computer Test Generator

B *The Basic Level curriculum presents the most fundamental knowledge offered in the course.*
S *The Standard Level curriculum is designed for the average student who is able to master most topics.*
A *The Advanced Level curriculum includes suggestions for teaching the most academically able students.*

Cooperative Learning

Group Activity: Control of Inherited Traits

- **Group Size:** *6 students*
- **Outcome:** *Students will hypothesize about control of inherited traits.*
- **Individual Accountability:** *Each group member will evaluate the group's hypotheses about control of inherited traits.*
- **Positive Interdependence:** *The group will compare observations, brainstorm, and share in the reasoning process.*

Have each group select a familiar animal. Then ask each group member to list one distinctive characteristic of this animal that can vary from one organism to another—for example, size, shape, color, age, or behavior.

Divide the group in half, and challenge each subgroup of three to try to decide whether or not each trait on the list is inherited. Tell students that they must support each decision with good reasoning.

Then have the original group of six recombine and share their conclusions about which traits are inherited. Last, have them brainstorm one or more hypotheses about structures and processes that control inherited traits. Have each group member state whether or not he or she supports each hypothesis, giving reasons. Keep a list of hypotheses so that students can evaluate their merits as they study this unit.

Concept Map

The following is one possible solution to the concept mapping activity in Reteaching on p. 152.

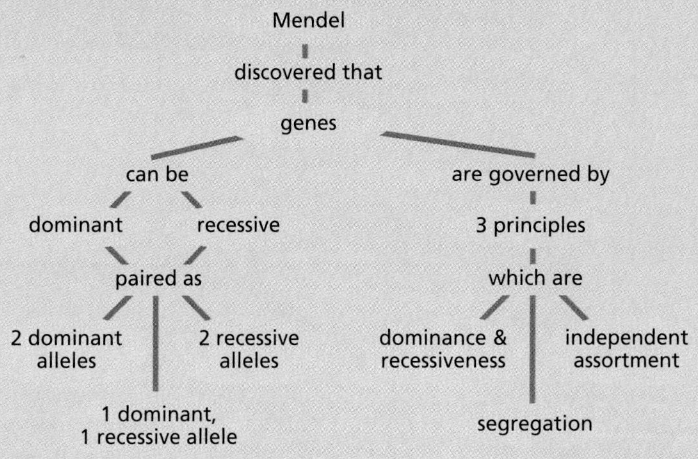

Laboratory Preparation

Overview *(See p. 159.)*

In this lab, students collect and analyze data from corn ears that display results of simple monohybrid and dihybrid crosses. They compare observed data with expectations predicted through the use of Punnett squares to draw conclusions regarding parental genotypes and phenotypes. Students also relate their conclusions to Mendelian principles of segregation and independent assortment.

Preparation

Order the two types of corn ears from a biological supply house. Ear A should have a ratio of 3 purple kernels : 1 yellow kernel. Ear B should have a ratio of 9 purple, smooth : 3 purple, wrinkled : 3 yellow, smooth : 1 yellow, wrinkled. Smooth kernels may be described in supply catalogs as "starchy," and wrinkled as "sweet." Label the ears A and B; provide one ear of each per team.

Teaching Tips

In Inquiry step 2, students should not count kernels. You may have to refer them to Section 10.2, Genetic Crosses. Some students may need help with Punnett squares; tell them to follow examples given in the student text, substituting alleles for corn color. Note that codominance is not a factor in this laboratory.

In Inquiry step 4, students should choose the monohybrid cross that best fits their estimated ratio from step 2.

As students make their predictions, remind them that each combination of alleles is random and independent; it is not influenced by, and does not have influence on, other combinations.

Teams are asked to pool their data for steps 6 and 11. Have the combined teams do all calculations based on these pooled data. A larger database is likely to give an appropriate ratio. Refer students to Section 2.2, Biological Tools and Techniques.

Chapter Themes

Scale and Structure Although Mendel's use of samples containing large numbers to investigate breeding relationships was unusual in his time, the consistent appearance of common patterns in his data indicated specific, predictable events on the cellular level. Stress that Sutton later verified Mendel's results in his studies of chromosomes. Highlight the use of large samples to find principles of biology that relate to individual interactions.

Patterns of Change Emphasize that although variations within a population are governed by genetic principles, probability plays a central role in determining genetic makeup of any organism produced by sexual reproduction. Chance events govern both division of chromosomes during meiosis (gamete formation) and pairing of alleles during zygote formation.

Chapter Motivating Activity

Have students observe pictures of different dog breeds, then make a list of inherited traits for each breed. (For example, body shape, size, and type of fur.) If students do not mention behavioral traits, help them list characteristic breed behaviors such as hunting or guarding.

Ask students how a breeder might predict whether a specific behavior was likely to be passed on to offspring. *(Inherited behaviors possessed by parents are more likely to be passed on.)* Ask how matings between dogs of a pure breed differ from matings between mongrel dogs. *(Purebred offspring have fewer variations and more predictable traits.)* Ask how dog owners keep a breed pure. *(Their dogs mate only with dogs of the same breed.)*

Chapter 10 *Fundamentals of Genetics*

Introduction

Parents pass their traits on to their offspring. However, not all of the parents' traits will actually appear in the offspring. The white tiger shown here had yellow parents. In this chapter you will learn how to predict which traits are likely to appear in the offspring. Such predictions are based on the work of Gregor Mendel, an Austrian monk and a pioneer in the field of genetics.

Chapter Outline

10.1 The Legacy of Gregor Mendel
- *Mendel's Experiments*
- *Mendel's Results and Conclusions*
- *Chromosomes and Genes*

10.2 Genetic Crosses
- *Genotype and Phenotype*
- *Probability*
- *Predicting Results of Monohybrid Crosses*
- *Predicting Results of Dihybrid Crosses*

Chapter Concept

As you read, notice how Mendel's experimental design helped him develop his principles. Then apply these principles to help predict the outcome of genetic crosses.

	R	R′
R	RR	RR′
R′	RR′	R′R′

White tiger, *Panthera tigris*, India. Inset: Japanese four o'clock, *Mirabilis japonica*, Punnett square.

Understanding the Visuals

Ask students how the tiger in the photograph differs from most other tigers. *(The base color of the coat is white, not yellow.)* What makes it different from other tigers? *(The factors controlling coat color must be different.)* Ask students why the condition is so rare. *(The factors producing white fur in tigers must be rare, or very few tigers have the factors.)*

Have students make observations about the four flowers. *(They have the same shape, but one is dark red, two are pink, and one is white.)* Ask them to examine the Punnett square beside the flowers. Explain that they will later learn how to use such squares to predict inherited traits that new offspring, including humans, will probably have.

10.1 The Legacy of Gregor Mendel

In 1843 at the age of 21 Gregor Mendel entered a monastery in Brünn, Austria, where he was given the task of tending the garden. In 1851 he was sent to the University of Vienna to study science and mathematics. His studies of mathematics included training in the new field of statistics, which would later prove invaluable to his research.

When Mendel returned to the monastery, he used his knowledge of statistics to analyze biological phenomena. He observed that some tall pea plants produced tall offspring, while other tall pea plants produced short offspring. Likewise some pea plants with yellow seeds yielded offspring with yellow seeds, but others yielded offspring with green seeds. The phenomenon Mendel was observing is called **inheritance,** the passing of traits by heredity. **Heredity** is the transmission of traits from parents to their offspring.

To see whether there was any predictable pattern to inheritance, Mendel decided to study the hereditary patterns of pea plants. Mendel studied seven characteristics of pea plants, each of which occurred in two contrasting traits: seed texture (round or wrinkled), seed color (yellow or green), seed coat color (colored or white), pod appearance (inflated or constricted), pod color (green or yellow), position of flowers along the stem (axial or terminal), and stem length (tall or short). Mendel hoped to discover if there were predictable patterns in the inheritance of traits—and, if so, what these patterns were. Mendel used statistical methods to analyze the results of thousands of crosses between individual plants. In nine years he bred thousands of pea plants. The patterns he found form the basis of our knowledge of genetics.

Mendel's Experiments

An important aspect of Mendel's experimental design was his decision to study each characteristic and its two contrasting traits individually. He began by growing plants that were pure for each trait. Plants that are **pure** for a trait always produce offspring with that trait. Pea plants pure for the trait of yellow pods always produce offspring with yellow pods. A **strain** is the term used to denote all plants pure for a specific trait. Mendel produced strains by allowing the plants to go through a natural process called self-pollination.

Self-pollination is a reproductive process in which fertilization occurs within a single plant. The reproductive structures of seed plants are located inside the flowers. In pea plants each flower has both sperm-producing and egg-producing structures. The anthers produce pollen grains that contain sperm. Eggs are

Section Objectives

- *Describe Mendel's experiments, results, and conclusions.*
- *State and explain Mendel's three principles.*
- *Give examples of how scientific knowledge of genes and chromosomes supports Mendel's principles.*
- *Summarize the observations that led Sutton to propose the chromosome theory.*

Figure 10-1 Mendel transferred pollen from an anther to a stigma of the same pea plant in order to produce purebred strains by self-pollination.

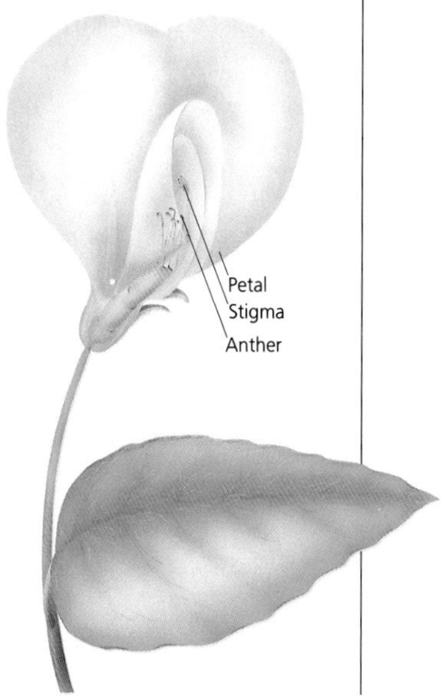

Mendel (1865)
A pair of factors controls the expression of each inherited trait.

Sutton (1900)
Factors are carried on chromosomes.

Biologists Today
Factors are now called genes, which are segments of DNA.

Graphic Organizer Use this sequential diagram in Guided Practice on p. 150.

Lesson Plan

Section Focus

This section describes Mendel's classic experiments that uncovered three principles governing the separation of genes during meiosis and their recombination during zygote formation. As students study various genetic crosses, they will notice how statistical methods were first used in experiments on inheritance.

Section Themes

This section emphasizes the theme of **Stability**. Genetic change occurs in similar ways throughout different populations of organisms. In most cases populations do not change significantly from one generation to the next. Mendel and Sutton used different experimental methods to illustrate the same basic patterns.

Motivating Activity

Put two or more flowering plants, such as a geranium and coleus, on a table. Ask students to brainstorm a list of traits they think might be inherited. *(For example: flower shape, flower color, structure of stamens and pistils, position of blossoms on stems, shape of sepals, leaf shape, leaf color pattern, pattern of veins, pattern of stem growth, presence or absence of hairs on stems)* Tell students that they will discover how such inherited traits are controlled. They will also study how such knowledge will enable them to make predictions about traits of future offspring.

Videodiscs

- ***Side 3 18190, Flowering Plant Life Cycle (m)***
- ***1640–1650, Chromosomes (s)***

Teaching Strategies

Describing Scientific Processes Ask students to state Mendel's basic scientific question about inheritance. *(Is there any predictable pattern to inheritance?)* Summarize Mendel's experimental strategy. *(His strategy was to develop pure strains of plants for pairs of traits and study these paired traits individually through a series of breeding experiments.)* What was new about Mendel's method? *(He used statistical analysis to study large samples.)*

Drawing Conclusions Ask students to infer why study of large samples might be advantageous to a geneticist looking for inheritance patterns. *(Patterns obtained from large samples are less likely to be distorted by rare events that can occur by chance.)*

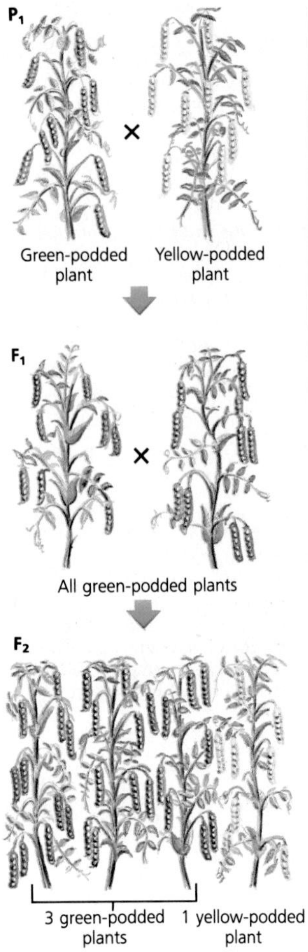

Figure 10-2 Pure green-podded plants crossed with pure yellow-podded plants produce only green-podded plants. Yet when this second generation is permitted to self-pollinate, some yellow-podded plants appear.

produced in structures called ovules. The ovule is contained in an ovary, the tip of which is called the stigma. **Pollination** is the transfer of pollen from anthers to stigma. In self-pollination pollen is transferred from anthers to stigma in the same flower or in flowers of the same plant. By allowing the plants to self-pollinate, Mendel obtained 14 strains, one for each of the 14 traits. He called each strain a **parental generation,** or **P_1 generation** for short.

Mendel then applied **cross-pollination** to these strains by transferring pollen from the anthers of a plant pure for one trait to the stigma of another plant pure for the contrasting trait. For example, if he wanted to cross a plant pure for the trait of yellow pods with one pure for the trait of green pods, he dusted the pollen from a yellow-podded plant onto the stigma of a green-podded plant. Then he allowed the seeds to grow.

Next he recorded how many of each type of offspring each P_1 plant produced. Mendel called the offspring of the P_1 generation the **first filial generation,** or **F_1 generation.** He then self-pollinated flowers from the F_1 generation and collected the seeds. Mendel called the plants in this generation the **second filial generation,** or **F_2 generation.** Following this process, Mendel performed thousands of crosses and documented the results of each.

Mendel's Results and Conclusions

In one of his experiments Mendel crossed two plants, one pure for green pods and one pure for yellow pods. The resulting seeds produced an F_1 generation with only green-podded plants. No yellow pods developed even though one parent had been pure for yellow pods. Only one of the two traits found in the P_1 generation appeared in the F_1 generation. If Mendel had concluded his research at this point, he might have interpreted the results to mean that crosses between green-podded plants and yellow-podded plants always produced offspring with green pods. However, Mendel self-pollinated the F_1 plants and then planted seeds from the resulting F_2 generation. When they grew, he observed that about three-fourths of the F_2 plants had green pods and one-fourth had yellow pods. The apparently lost trait had reappeared.

Study Table 10-1 to see the results of Mendel's crosses. Whenever Mendel crossed strains, one of the P_1 traits vanished from all of the F_1 plants. In every case that trait reappeared in a ratio of about 3 : 1 in the F_2 generation. This pattern emerged in thousands of pollinations. Mendel called the trait that appeared in the F_1 generation the dominant trait. The trait that appeared to be lost in the F_1 generation but that reappeared in the F_2 generation he called the recessive trait.

After studying the results of these crosses, Mendel concluded that patterns of inheritance were governed by three principles: (1) the principle of dominance and recessiveness, (2) the principle of segregation, and (3) the principle of independent assortment.

LEP Activity
To emphasize the scientific approach that Mendel used, guide students in reviewing the scientific processes presented in Chapter 2. Have students match experimental procedures that Mendel used to specific scientific processes.

Help students identify the process of observing *(Observing which traits were inherited)*, collecting data *(Performing breeding experiments)*, measuring and counting *(Recording the results of experiments)*, analyzing data *(Finding patterns in results)*, forming a hypothesis *(Proposing the existence of "factors" and developing his three principles)*, and communicating *(Writing his paper in 1865)*.

Table 10-1 Mendel's Crosses and Results

Trait	P_1 cross	F_1 generation	F_2 generation	Actual ratio	Probability ratio
Position of flowers along stem	 Axial × terminal	 Axial	651 axial 207 terminal	3.14 : 1	3 : 1
Height of plant	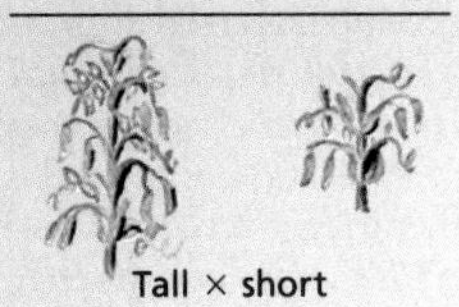 Tall × short	 Tall	787 tall 277 short	2.84 : 1	3 : 1
Pod appearance	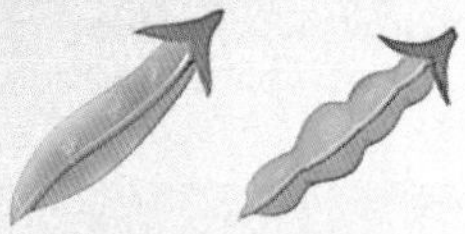 Inflated × constricted	 Inflated	882 inflated 299 constricted	2.95 : 1	3 : 1
Pod color	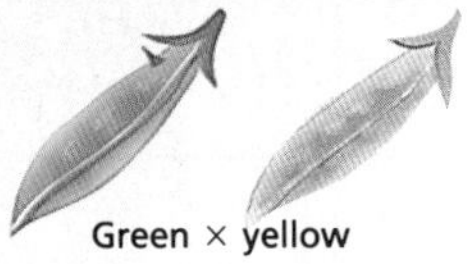 Green × yellow	 Green	428 green 152 yellow	2.82 : 1	3 : 1
Seed texture	 Round × wrinkled	 Round	5,474 round 1,850 wrinkled	2.96 : 1	3 : 1
Seed color	 Yellow × green	 Yellow	6,022 yellow 2,001 green	3.01 : 1	3 : 1
Seed coat color	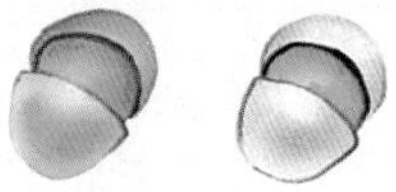 Colored × white	 Colored	705 colored 224 white	3.15 : 1	3 : 1

Interpreting the Visuals Have students use the horizontal and vertical headings to analyze the information presented in Table 10-1, p. 149. Have them describe in their own words what is presented. Make sure that they understand that each experiment began with a cross between two parent plants having different traits but that the F_2 generation was produced from the self-pollination of a single plant. For example, pure axial-flowering plants were crossed with pure terminal-flowering plants producing only axial-flowering offspring. When these offspring were permitted to self-pollinate, 3/4 of their offspring had axial flowers, while 1/4 had terminal flowers.

Ask students to relate this evidence to Mendel's conclusion about factors. Have them contrast the actual ratios with the probability ratios and infer why probability ratios are more useful to a scientist looking for inheritance patterns. (*Scientists often find that natural events can be explained by simple numerical relationships.*) Also, remind students that a ratio of 3 : 1 means 3/4 : 1/4 of a population or 75% : 25%; it does not mean that 1/3 are homozygous recessive.

Interdisciplinary Activity

Social Studies Historical events from the mid-1800s and early 1900s contributed to development of scientific thought. Machines were growing in importance, and many people began to consider biological processes mechanistic. An increase in trade and wealth resulted in a better-educated public, and more information about natural history became available.

Have students research the effects of nineteenth century industrialization and expansion of trade on science. For example, students might research the exploration of part of sub-Saharan Africa or one of the Pacific islands. Moreover, public interest in animals in zoos, especially unusual animals, was on the rise. The public joined scientists in speculating on processes that produced unusual hereditary traits.

Applying Concepts Review with students the material in Chapter 9 that outlines the steps in meiosis.

Guided Practice

Help students create a sequential diagram that summarizes how human understanding of genetics has progressed since Mendel's time. An example of a completed diagram appears on p. 147.

Independent Practice

- Have students write answers to the Section Review.
- Ask students to write sentences expressing relationships between the following pairs of terms: inheritance and heredity *(Heredity is transmission of traits from parents to offspring; inheritance is passing of traits by heredity.)*; a pure plant and a plant strain *(A pure plant for a given trait produces only offspring with this trait; a strain is composed of all plants pure for a given trait.)*; F_1 generation and F_2 generation *(The F_1 generation is the first generation produced in a breeding experiment; the F_2 generation is composed of the offspring produced by interbreeding the F_1 organisms.)*; experiment and conclusion. *(An experiment is an operation designed to gain information; a conclusion is the idea that comes from the information gained in an experiment.)*

Principle of Dominance and Recessiveness

Mendel suggested that something within a plant controlled the expression of a characteristic. He named this "something" a factor. Each characteristic he was studying had two traits; for example, the characteristic of pod color could be expressed as either green or yellow. Thus he inferred that each characteristic was the result of the interaction of a pair of factors.

Mendel looked next at how factors interacted by studying the F_1 generation of plants. He observed that only one trait of each characteristic appeared in the F_1 generation. In attempting to explain this phenomenon, Mendel arrived at the **principle of dominance and recessiveness:** one factor in a pair may mask the other factor, preventing it from having an effect. Mendel called the one factor **dominant** since it masked or dominated the other factor for this trait. He called the other factor **recessive** since it was masked in the presence of a dominant factor for that characteristic. Interpreting the data in light of this principle, Mendel then concluded that the factors that produced traits visible in the F_1 generation were dominant over the factors that produced traits that didn't appear in that generation.

Biology in Process

Sutton and the Chromosome Theory

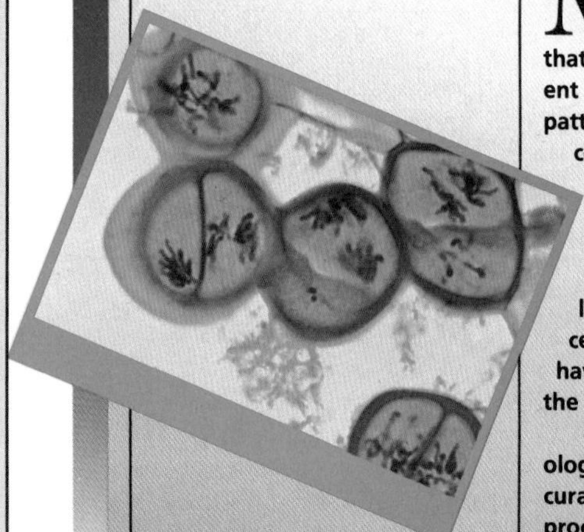

Mendel's work elegantly illustrated that traits are passed from parent to offspring in predictable patterns. However, Mendel could not identify the cellular mechanism by which the information was communicated from generation to generation. He lacked information about cell structure that might have enabled him to discover the mechanics of inheritance.

In the 1870s and 1880s, biologists provided the first accurate descriptions of the processes by which genetic information is communicated from generation to generation: mitosis and meiosis. The discovery of these processes led to the realization that a connection exists between Mendel's work and the modern science of genetics. In 1902, a young biologist named Walter S. Sutton bridged the two bodies of work by proposing that Mendel's "factors" are carried on chromosomes.

Two processes that Sutton used in his studies were observing and inferring. Through microscopic observations of grasshopper sperm, Sutton discovered that before meiosis occurs, the chromosomes lined up in pairs that were alike in size and shape. From these observa-

Cooperative Learning

A Model of Meiosis Have students work in pairs to model what happens to two pairs of genes during meiosis. Ask each student to model one gene pair using 4 pipe cleaners and paint, dye, or adhesive colored papers. The first student will use slightly different colors to represent a gene pair made of a dominant allele, R, and a recessive allele, r. The second will use a different single color to represent a gene pair made of two recessive alleles, bb.

Have students follow Figure 9-7 on pp.136–137, and use their supplies to show what allele pairs are possible in the gametes at the completion of meiosis. *(Rb and rb)* Have each student pair prepare a single explanation relating their model to one or more of Mendel's laws. *(Students should refer to the principle of segregation.)*

Principle of Segregation

Mendel then asked why the traits that disappeared in the F_1 generation reappeared in the F_2 generation. Mendel reasoned that if each parent had two factors, each offspring must have two factors. Each parent could not be passing two factors or the offspring would have four. Mendel concluded that each reproductive cell received only one factor for each characteristic. He then stated the **principle of segregation:** the two factors for a characteristic segregate, or separate, during the formation of eggs and sperm.

Principle of Independent Assortment

Mendel also crossed plants that differed in two characteristics, such as in height and seed color. The data from these more complex crosses showed that traits produced by dominant factors did not necessarily appear together. A green seed pod produced by a dominant factor could appear in a short pea plant, produced by recessive factors. Mendel concluded that the factors for different characteristics were not connected. He stated the **principle of independent assortment:** factors for different characteristics are distributed to reproductive cells independently.

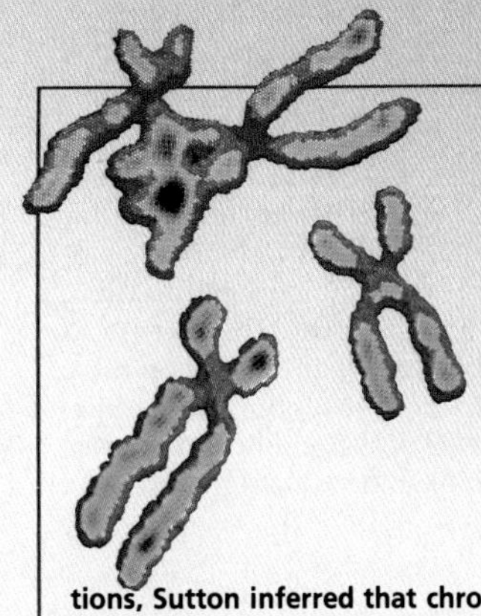

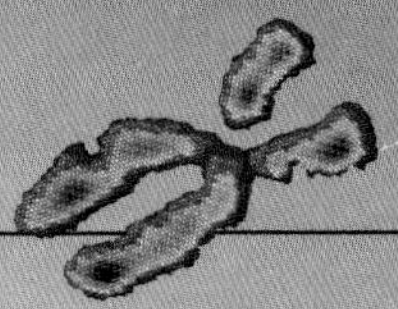

tions, Sutton inferred that chromosomes, like Mendel's factors, occurred in pairs.

Sutton next observed that pairs of chromosomes separated during meiosis, one member of each pair going to each gamete. He also noted that pairs generally separated independently. This is what Mendel proposed in his laws of segregation and independent assortment. Finally, Sutton saw that a sperm cell and an egg each carry half the number of chromosomes found in body cells. Through fertilization they produced a new organism with a full set of chromosomes.

Sutton drew upon his knowledge of reproductive biology to interpret these observations. He knew that the egg and sperm provided the only physical link between generations. Since these cells were the sole link, Sutton inferred that they were the only possible carriers of hereditary factors.

Therefore, Sutton concluded that Mendel's hereditary "factors" were carried on chromosomes. Sutton hypothesized that hereditary information was transmitted from one generation to the next generation via chromosomes. This hypothesis corresponds well with Mendel's principles and is supported by both Mendel's and Sutton's observations. It explains how offspring receive one set of traits from each parent, and it accounts for the independent transmission of the separate traits.

- **What were the inferences Sutton made on which he based his chromosome theory?**

Biology in Process

Using the Feature

This feature provides a clear illustration of one way science progresses—by building on the work of past researchers. Mendel's experiments were an extraordinary breakthrough in understanding the process of inheritance; yet when he reported his results in 1865, no one comprehended the significance of his work.

More than 30 years passed before researchers investigating cell behavior during mitosis and meiosis began to relate their discoveries to Mendel's work. The credit for this recognition is usually given to Sutton because he published his results first.

While Sutton was carrying out his investigations, however, a German biologist, Theodore Boveri, was performing similar experiments and drawing conclusions similar to Sutton's. Such simultaneous discoveries are not uncommon in science. In fact, repetition is crucial in verifying new information.

Answer to the Feature

Sutton combined his observations of chromosome behavior with his previous knowledge of inheritance, and inferred that chromosomes carried the "factors" that Mendel had referred to years earlier.

Sutton based his chromosome theory on the following inferences: (1) chromosomes, like Mendel's factors, occur in pairs, and (2) sperm and egg are the only possible carriers of hereditary factors.

Videodiscs

- ***2636, Independent Assortment (s)***
- ***Side 3 23751, Pea Life Cycle (m)***

Section 10.1

Check Your Understanding

1. Contrast the functions of mitosis and meiosis *(Mitosis increases the number of cells in an organism. Meiosis produces sex cells that function in reproducing new organisms.)*

2. How is Mendel's idea that factors segregate independently different from today's ideas about chromosomes? *(Today, we know that the "factors" are on homologous chromosomes that separate independently and that the chromosomes contain many factors that are linked together.)*

Reteaching

Have students work in small groups to create a concept map that describes some of Mendel's major discoveries. An example of a completed concept map is shown on p. 145B.

■ *See* Section Reviews *worksheet, Section 10.1.*

Enrichment

Have students research the origin and development of corn from the original type to modern varieties. (The wild teocinte plant may share a common ancestor with maize, or corn.) Ask students to report on breeding activities that have utilized differing alleles.

Closure

There is some evidence that Mendel purposely failed to report data that conflicted with his conclusions. Encourage students to debate the responsibility of a scientist to report all experimental data, even data that conflict with conclusions that he or she is convinced are correct.

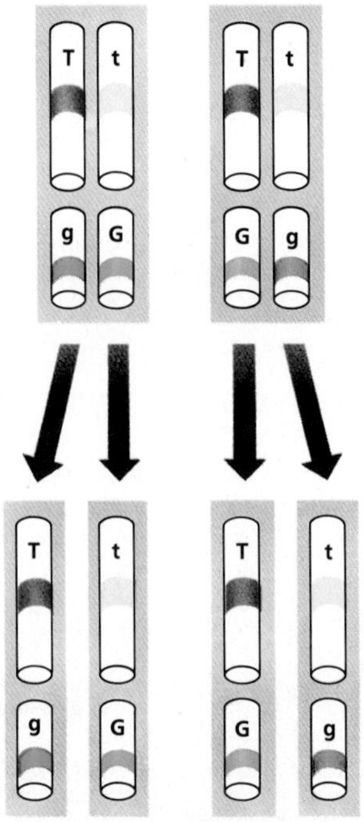

Figure 10-3 The arrangement of chromosomes (left or right) during the first division of meiosis determines the type of gametes produced. DNA replication and the second meiotic division are omitted for simplicity.

Chromosomes and Genes

Most of Mendel's findings agree with what biologists now know of the structure and function of genes and chromosomes. However, when Mendel presented his findings in a paper he wrote in 1865, scientists had not yet discovered chromosomes, nor did they possess any knowledge of meiosis. Lacking a way to explain Mendel's findings, the scientific community did not understand or care about them. Also, scientists of that time had not yet used statistics to understand biological phenomena. Mendel's pairing of statistics and natural science seemed odd to them.

Not until the year 1900 did biologists realize the connection between Mendel's obscure paper and ongoing work on inheritance. During that year Mendel's paper was rediscovered three times by biologists working independently. Shortly thereafter biologist Walter Sutton proposed the chromosome theory, which linked observations of meiosis with Mendel's principles. Now not only are Mendel's principles accepted, but his quantitative methods are also used extensively by biologists.

Instead of just studying factors, biologists today also study genes. A **gene** is the segment of DNA on a chromosome that controls a particular hereditary trait. Because chromosomes occur in pairs, genes occur in pairs. Each of several alternative forms of a gene, called an **allele**, is the equivalent of Mendel's "factor." Scientists use letters to represent alleles, capital letters to refer to dominant alleles and lowercase letters to refer to recessive alleles. For example, the allele for the dominant trait of tallness in pea plants is represented by T, and the allele for the recessive trait of shortness by t. The allele for the dominant trait of green pod color is represented by G; the allele for yellow pod color by g.

Current knowledge of chromosomes and meiosis also supports the principle of segregation. When gametes are formed, they receive one chromosome from each homologous pair of chromosomes. This means that when the gametes combine in fertilization, the offspring receives one allele from each parent. This fact—that when chromosomes segregate independently, any alleles on these chromosomes also segregate independently—supports the principle of independent assortment. However, though these principles are correct in general, some variations in hereditary patterns are not explained by Mendel's principles.

Section Review

1. Define *self-pollination.*
2. Name an important aspect of Mendel's experimental design.
3. Name and briefly explain Mendel's three principles.
4. What is the relationship between genes and alleles?
5. How might Mendel's conclusions have differed if he had studied two traits determined by alleles carried on the same chromosome?

Answers to Section Review

1. A reproductive process in which gametes from the same plant join to form zygotes
2. Mendel studied each trait individually and also used large samples.
3. The principle of dominance and recessiveness states that one factor in a pair may block the expression of the other. The principle of segregation states that a pair of factors separate during the formation of sex cells. The principle of independent assortment states that each pair of factors is distributed to the gametes independently of other pairs.
4. Each of several alternative forms of a gene is an allele.
5. Mendel would not have observed independent assortment occurring for all traits, so he probably would not have formulated his principle of independent assortment.

10.2 Genetic Crosses

Geneticists still rely on Mendel's principles to predict the likely outcome of genetic crosses. In this section you will learn how to use Mendel's principles to determine the likely outcome of several examples of two kinds of genetic crosses. You will acquire the knowledge to predict the probable genetic makeup of offspring resulting from specified crosses. You will also learn how to interpret this genetic information to determine the probable appearance of these offspring.

Genotype and Phenotype

The genetic makeup of an organism is its **genotype.** The external appearance of an organism is its **phenotype.** For example, the genotype of a pure tall plant is TT. It consists of two dominant alleles for height—T and T. The plant's phenotype, or appearance, is tall. The genotype of an F_1 pea plant is Tt if one parent has contributed one allele for tallness and the other parent has contributed one allele for shortness. The phenotype of that plant is tall, since the dominant gene is expressed and the recessive gene is not expressed. Thus a phenotype of tallness may be produced by either of two genotypes—TT or Tt.

When both alleles of a pair are the same, an organism is said to be **homozygous** for that characteristic. An organism may be homozygous dominant or homozygous recessive. A pea plant homozygous dominant for height has the genotype TT. A pea plant homozygous recessive for height has the genotype tt. When the two alleles in the pair are not the same, for example, in the genotype Tt, the organism is **heterozygous** for that characteristic.

Mendel studied traits that had only two alleles. Biologists now know that some traits are determined by many alleles. When three or more alleles control a trait, it is said to have **multiple alleles.** The trait of blood type in humans is determined by multiple alleles. The alleles called I^A, I^B, and i^O all affect the characteristic of blood type. Among the possible genotypes for blood type are I^Ai^O, I^Bi^O, and i^Oi^O. However, no matter how many alleles determine a trait, an individual can only have two alleles for a given characteristic, one inherited from each parent.

Section Objectives

- *Define* probability, *and explain how it is used to predict the results of genetic crosses.*
- *Use a Punnett square to predict the results of monohybrid and dihybrid genetic crosses.*
- *Explain how a testcross reveals the genotype of an individual whose phenotype is dominant.*
- *Distinguish monohybrid crosses from dihybrid crosses.*

Figure 10-4 The difference in coloration in these cottontail rabbits (*Sylvilagus* sp.) is a phenotypic difference. A difference in phenotype usually indicates a difference in genotype.

Type of Cross	Pair(s) of Alleles Studied	Boxes in Square	Maximum No. of Genotypes	Maximum No. of Phenotypes
Monohybrid	1	4	3	2
Dihybrid	2	16	9	4

Graphic Organizer Use this table in Independent Practice on p. 156.

Lesson Plan

Section Focus
This section emphasizes application of Mendel's principles in predicting the effect of specific genetic crosses. These predictions can be used with confidence only when studying large samples because probability determines outcomes.

Section Themes
The theme of this section is **Patterns of Change.** The patterns are illustrated by Punnett squares that chart various types of monohybrid and dihybrid crosses involving both homozygous and heterozygous parents and offspring.

Motivating Activity
Ask students what methods they might use to predict the outcome of a sports event such as a football game. *(Answers might include considering the abilities and experience of participants, looking at a previous related event, analyzing similar types of events, and using a model such as a coin toss.)* What are some patterns that might help predict an outcome? *(A team might have won two-thirds of their past games. A win might have occurred every time a team played a certain opponent or nearly all the times they played at home.)* Do such patterns enable students to be certain of the outcome of future sports events? *(No. The prediction of such future outcomes can be based only on probability, not certainty.)* Stress that some events such as sports are partly affected by chance. Others such as coin tosses are totally chance events.

Videodiscs
- *2637–2639, Genetics: Possible Gametes (s)*
- *2631–2632, Life Cycles (s)*

Answer to Think

The red square is one of 16 possible target squares. Thus, the probability of hitting the red square is 1 in 16, or 1/16. The probability that a blindfolded player would hit the red square with two successive dart throws is 1/16 × 1/16, or 1/256.

Teaching Strategies

Inferring Relationships Imagine an animal species whose members are mostly brown, but which has black individuals appearing regularly in its wild populations. Suppose that both parents of a black animal were brown. Ask students to explain how they could produce black offspring. *(If the allele for brown hair C were dominant over the allele for black hair c, heterozygous brown parents Cc could produce black offspring cc.)* Ask students to determine possible genotypes of the black animal's siblings. *(Some siblings might also have been black, but they might have had brown fur from either CC or Cc genotypes.)*

Think

If you were blindfolded and threw a dart and hit the board above, what is the probability that you would hit the red square? If you threw two darts, what is the probability that you would hit the red square with both darts? Express your answers in fractions.

Probability

Probability is the likelihood that a specific event will occur. It is expressed as a decimal, a percentage, or a fraction. It is determined by the following formula:

$$\text{Probability} = \frac{\text{number of one kind of event}}{\text{number of all events}}$$

For example, in Mendel's experiments the dominant trait of yellow seed color appeared in the F_2 generation 6,022 times. The recessive trait of green seed color appeared 2,001 times. The total number of individuals was thus 8,023. Using the probability formula above, the probability that the dominant trait will appear in a similar cross is 6,022/8,023, or 0.75. Expressed as a percentage, the probability is 75 percent. Expressed as a fraction, the probability is 3/4. The probability that the recessive trait will appear in an F_2 generation 2,001/8,023, or 0.25. Expressed as a percentage, the probability is 25 percent. Expressed as a fraction, the probability is 1/4. Probability tells us that there are three chances in four that an offspring of two heterozygous individuals will have the dominant trait and one chance in four that it will have the recessive trait.

In genetics, as in other systems based on probability, the expected ratios occur only when there are many trials. For example, many coin tosses should yield a result of heads 50 percent of the time and tails 50 percent of the time. However, if you tossed a coin only a few times, you probably wouldn't get this result. Only after many, many tries would you be likely to get the ratio of heads predicted on the basis of probability—0.5, or 50 percent, heads and 0.5, or 50 percent, tails.

Predicting Results of Monohybrid Crosses

A cross between individuals that involves one pair of contrasting traits is called a **monohybrid cross.** A cross between a pea plant that is pure for tallness and one that is pure for shortness is an example of a monohybrid cross. There is a simple way to establish the probabilities of the results of a monohybrid cross. Biologists use a diagram called a **Punnett square,** named for its inventor, R. C. Punnett, to aid them in predicting probabilities.

Example 1: Homozygous × Homozygous

Let's use a Punnett square to predict the results of a monohybrid cross between a homozygous tall pea plant (TT) and a homozygous short pea plant (tt). Draw a square and divide it into four parts. Represent the alleles contributed by the homozygous dominant parent by writing two *T*'s, one next to each of the boxes on the left side of the square. Represent the alleles contributed by the homozygous recessive parent by writing two *t*'s, one above each

Cooperative Learning

Probability with Coins Divide the class into pairs. One person in each pair tosses the coin, while the other records whether the toss turns up heads or tails. The first person should toss the coin 100 times. The recorded data should include total number of tries, number of heads, and number of tails. After 100 tosses, students switch tasks and carry out another 100 tosses.

Collect the whole class's data by recording on the board the number of heads and number of tails obtained by each student. Determine how many students obtained exactly 50/100, or the 1/2 ratio predicted by probability analysis.

Tally group results and obtain a class average. Determine whether the class ratio is closer to the expected 1/2 results than were the ratios obtained by students.

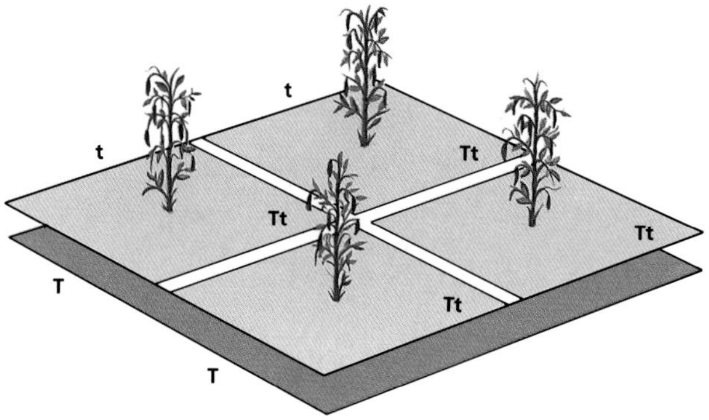

	t	t
T	Tt	Tt
T	Tt	Tt

Homozygous × homozygous

box across the top of the square. Fill in each box with the letters that are above it and beside it outside the square. The Punnett square should contain the same results as the square in Figure 10-5. These results indicate the probable genotypes of such a cross. One hundred percent of the offspring would be Tt.

What phenotypes will result from such a cross? According to Mendel's principle of dominance and recessiveness, a dominant allele masks the expression of a recessive allele. Since all offspring are Tt, each has a dominant and a recessive allele for height. Therefore in all offspring the dominant allele for height will be expressed, and 100 percent of the offspring will be tall.

Figure 10-5 A tall homozygous and a short homozygous pea plant will produce only tall heterozygous offspring.

Example 2: Homozygous × Heterozygous

Now let's predict the outcome of a cross between a guinea pig that is homozygous for the dominant trait of rough coat (RR) and a guinea pig that is heterozygous for this trait (Rr). The lower case r stands for the recessive allele. Genotype rr results in a smooth coat. Set up and complete the square. Compare your results with those shown in Figure 10-6. The probable genotypic ratio is 2RR : 2Rr. In other words, you could expect that 50 percent of the offspring of this pair would be homozygous dominant for rough coat and the other 50 percent would be heterozygous for this trait. The probable phenotypic ratio is four out of four rough coated, or 100 percent rough coated.

Figure 10-6 A guinea pig homozygous for rough coat and one heterozygous for rough coat produce all rough-coated individuals, half of which are homozygous.

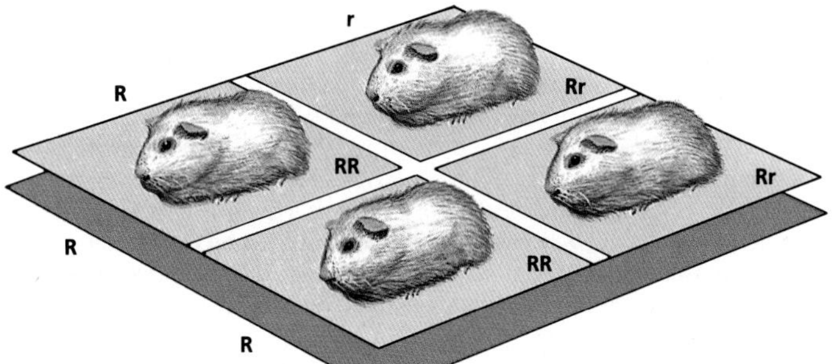

	R	r
R	RR	Rr
R	RR	Rr

Homozygous × heterozygous

Interpreting the Visuals Guide students in working through the Punnett squares (Figures 10-5 through 10-11) on pp. 155–158. Remind them that letters outside the square represent alleles that each parent can pass on. During meiosis, allele pairs separate, and the parent is able to pass on only one allele of the pair to each offspring. Work out a way to designate that letters outside the squares represent alleles in eggs and sperm from parents.

Group students in pairs, and assign each pair a monohybrid cross and a dihybrid cross from Section 10.2. Direct students in each pair to draw their monohybrid Punnett square on a sheet of paper, then add labels or symbols that will further clarify what the Punnett square represents. Have one student in each pair explain the monohybrid square to the other. Then let them reverse roles.

When students think that they understand the monohybrid square, let them repeat the process with the dihybrid squares.

Notice that in Figure 10-11, long hair is indicated by fuzziness around the edges of the animal drawings. Emphasize that the animals drawn in squares represent proportions of a sample larger than just one litter of guinea pigs.

■ *See* Overhead Transparency *T10 and* Blackline Masters *23 and 24.*
■ *See* Process Skills, *Chapter 10.*

Videodiscs

■ *1713–1719, Genetics: Monohybrid Cross (s)*
■ *1730–1738, Genetics:* Sordaria brevicollis

More Information

Creating Hybrid Crops Since the early years of this century, Mendelian genetics has been used as a basis for creating hybrid crops. For example, varieties of corn have been cross-bred for sweetness, early ripening, large size of kernels, and enhanced protein content. Currently, researchers are trying to develop a perennial corn plant in order to reduce costs of plowing and planting corn fields every year. Also, since present corn farming methods involve heavy use of herbicides and fertilizer afterward spread by runoff, a perennial corn plant would considerably reduce farm-generated pollution.

Guided Practice

Review the way a testcross is done for a monohybrid. *(Mate the unknown genotype with a homozygous recessive.)* Ask students to plan a testcross for a dihybrid for color and seed texture and tell you how to set up a Punnett square on the board. *(Students should tell you to represent the gametes for the second parent by four homozygous recessives for color and smoothness—ry.)* Ask students how they would show whether or not a plant with round, yellow seeds was homozygous dominant for both traits. *(In a testcross, all the offspring will have round, yellow seeds.)* Then ask how students could tell if a plant with round, yellow seeds was heterozygous for both traits. *(Such a plant would produce four types of offspring: round, yellow; round, green; wrinkled, yellow; and wrinkled, green.)*

■ *See* **Laboratories, *Investigation 10.***

Independent Practice

■ Have students write answers to the Section Review.

■ Have students create a table that contrasts Punnett squares of monohybrid and dihybrid crosses for dominant/recessive allele pairs. An example of a completed table appears on p. 153.

	B	b
B	BB	Bb
b	Bb	bb

Heterozygous × heterozygous

Figure 10-7 Crossing two rabbits both heterozygous for black coat tends to produce two heterozygous black offspring, plus one purebred black and one purebred brown individual.

Example 3: Heterozygous × Heterozygous

In rabbits the allele for black coat (B) is dominant over the allele for brown coat (b). To predict the results of crossing two parents that are both heterozygous (Bb) for coat color, set up and complete a Punnett square. Your completed square should match the square shown in Figure 10-7. As you can see, one-fourth of the offspring would have genotype BB, one half would have the genotype Bb, and one-fourth would have the genotype bb. Since B is dominant over b, three-fourths of all offspring from this cross would have the black phenotype, and one-fourth would have the brown phenotype. The probable genotypic ratio of a monohybrid cross of two heterozygous individuals is 1BB : 2Bb : 1bb. The probable phenotypic ratio is 3 black : 1 brown.

Example 4: Testcross

In rabbits both BB and Bb result in a black coat. How might you determine whether a black rabbit was homozygous (BB) or heterozygous (Bb)? You could perform a **testcross**, the procedure in which an individual of unknown genotype is crossed with a homozygous recessive individual. A testcross can determine the genotype of any individual whose phenotype is dominant.

If the rabbit in question were homozygous, what type of offspring would a testcross produce? To predict this, set up a Punnett square. Write the alleles for one parent, B and B, next to the boxes along the left side of the square and the alleles for the other parent, b and b, above the boxes of the square. Now complete the square, and compare your results with those in Figure 10-8. Notice that all genotypes produce dominant phenotypes. Therefore, if all the offspring of the testcross have the dominant phenotype, then the individual in question must be homozygous dominant.

Now suppose the rabbit in question were heterozygous. Set up another Punnett square, writing the alleles for one parent, B and b, next to the boxes along the left side of the square and the alleles of the other parent, b and b, above the boxes. Complete the square. Figure 10-8 illustrates the results. The probable genotypic ratio is 2Bb : 2bb. The probable phenotypic ratio is 2 black coated : 2 brown coated. Thus, if about half of the offspring are brown, the individual in question must be heterozygous.

	b	b
B	Bb	Bb
B	Bb	Bb

	b	b
B	Bb	Bb
b	bb	bb

Figure 10-8 A testcross is used to determine the genotype of an unknown individual.

LEP Activity

Help students comprehend the related terms *genotype* and *phenotype.* Stress that a genotype summarizes an organism's genes, which are usually expressed as letters such as TT or Tt for plant height. Capital letters represent the dominant form of the gene, while lowercase letters represent the recessive form. Suggest that students always add a simple code beside their Punnett squares such as "T = tallness" and "t = shortness."

Remind students that when they want to learn two closely related terms or ideas, it is often helpful to learn one term so well that they can recall its meaning immediately. They can then build the second idea from the first. For example, an organism's phenotype—the way it appears—is caused by its genotype. Phenotypes can be described in

Example 5: Codominance

Mendel restricted his studies to traits for which one allele dominated completely over the other. However, this is not true for all traits. **Codominance,** or incomplete dominance, is the phenomenon that occurs when two or more alleles influence the phenotype. This results in an trait intermediate between the dominant and recessive traits. In Japanese four o'clocks, for example, both the allele for red flowers (R) and the allele for white flowers (R′) influence the phenotype. Neither allele is dominant. When these plants self-pollinate, red-flowered plants produce only red-flowered offspring, and white-flowered plants produce only white-flowered offspring. However, when red and white four o'clocks are crossed, the F_1 offspring all have pink flowers. One hundred percent of the offspring of this cross possess the (RR′) genotype which results in a pink phenotype.

What would be the result of crossing two pink-flowered (RR′) Japanese four o'clocks? You can solve the problem by filling in a Punnett square, as shown in Figure 10-9. The Punnett square method yields the following probable genotypic ratio: 1RR : 2RR′ : 1R′R′. Given that neither the allele for red flowers (R) nor the allele for white flowers (R′) is completely dominant, the probable phenotypic ratio must be 1 red, 2 pink, and 1 white.

	R	R′
R	RR	RR′
R′	RR′	R′R′

Codominance

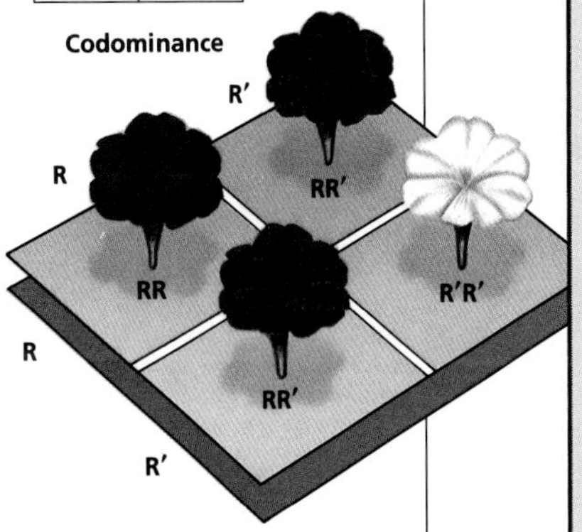

Figure 10-9 Crossing pink four o'clocks produces red, white, and pink offspring.

Predicting Results of Dihybrid Crosses

A **dihybrid cross** is a cross between individuals that involves two pairs of contrasting traits. Predicting the results of a dihybrid cross is more complicated than predicting the results of monohybrid cross. There are more possible combinations of alleles to work out. For example, to predict the results of a cross involving both seed texture and seed color, you have to consider how the four alleles from each parent can combine.

Example 6: Homozygous × Homozygous

Suppose that you want to predict the results of a cross between a pea plant that is homozygous for round, yellow seeds and one that is homozygous for wrinkled, green seeds. In pea plants the allele for round seeds (R) is dominant over the allele for wrinkled seeds (r), and the allele for yellow seeds (Y) is dominant over the allele for green seeds (y). Therefore you will predict the results of a cross between a parent of the genotype RRYY and a parent of the genotype rryy. Use a Punnett square to do this. This Punnett square will need to contain 16 boxes. Now list the independently sorted alleles from one parent—RY, RY, RY, and RY—along the left side of the Punnett square and the independently sorted alleles from the other parent—ry, ry, ry, and ry—along the top of the square. Then fill in each box with the letters that are above it outside the square and those that are to the left of it outside the square. Compare your results with those shown in Figure 10-10.

	ry	ry	ry	ry
RY	RrYy	RrYy	RrYy	RrYy
RY	RrYy	RrYy	RrYy	RrYy
RY	RrYy	RrYy	RrYy	RrYy
RY	RrYy	RrYy	RrYy	RrYy

Homozygous × homozygous

Figure 10-10 This particular dihybrid cross produces only one type of offspring.

Check Your Understanding

1. Why are calculated ratios in a Punnett square probable rather than certain? *(It is not possible to predict which gametes will join during actual fertilization.)*

2. What would be the phenotypic ratio of the cross BbRR × bbRr, with B = black, b = white, and Bb = gray in a codominant relationship; and R = rough, and r = smooth, where R is dominant to r? *(1 : 1 gray rough to white rough)*

3. Why doesn't the phenotype of an organism always reveal its genotype? *(In allele pairs in which the recessive allele is masked by the dominant allele, homozygous and heterozygous organisms look alike for this trait.)*

Reteaching

Ask students to complete a Punnett square for a heterozygous cross for two of the offspring in Figure 10-10. *(RrYy, in which R is round, r is wrinkled, Y is yellow, and y is green)* What would be the phenotypes and their proportions in the sample? *(9 round, yellow : 3 round, green : 3 wrinkled, yellow : 1 wrinkled, green)*

- *See* Section Reviews *worksheet, Section 10.2.*

Videodiscs

- *1716, Dihybrid Cross (s)*

everyday language such as tall or short, white or black. It is not necessary to use symbols for phenotypes.

Because each genotype produces a specific phenotype, it is always possible to determine an organism's appearance if you know its genotype. Suggest that students add a simple code to their Punnett squares, for example that "TT and Tt = tall" while "tt = short." After they have used these simple codes for a while, they will remember genotypes and phenotypes more easily.

Section 10.2

Enrichment

Some recessive traits can cause disorders when an individual is homozygous for the trait. For example, deleterious recessive genes can become prevalent in populations of endangered animals that begin inbreeding because they are limited in numbers.

Have students research the work being done with inbred endangered species such as African cheetahs and Florida panthers. International wildlife protection organizations are good resources for information about this problem.

Closure

Ask students to make up examples of the following crosses: homozygous × homozygous, homozygous × heterozygous, heterozygous × heterozygous, and codominant. For fun, encourage attributes of made-up life forms; for example, cross a normal heterozygous guinea pig (Ee) with one homozygous with recessive genes for rabbit ears (ee). *(Half the offspring would be normal and the other half would have rabbit ears.)*

	SB	Sb	sB	sb
SB	SSBB	SSBb	SsBB	SsBb
Sb	SSBb	SSbb	SsBb	Ssbb
sB	SsBB	SsBb	ssBB	ssBb
sb	SsBb	Ssbb	ssBb	ssbb

Heterozygous × heterozygous

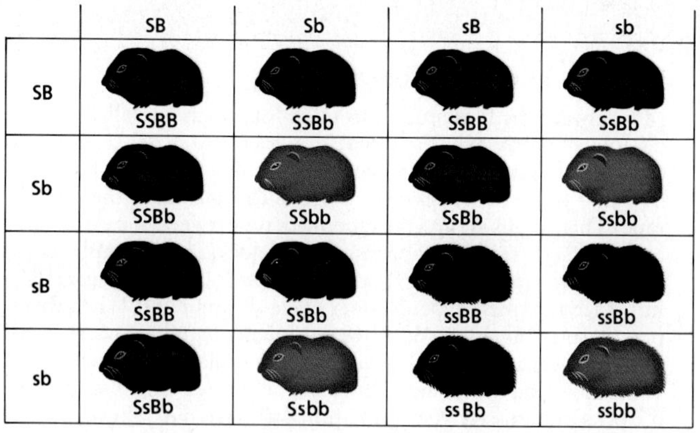

Figure 10-11 A dihybrid cross of two heterozygous individuals produces nine genotypes and four phenotypes.

As illustrated in figure 10.10, the genotype of all of the offspring of this cross will be heterozygous dihybrids, RrYy. Therefore the phenotype of all the offspring will have round, yellow seeds.

Example 7: Heterozygous × Heterozygous

In guinea pigs the allele for short hair (S) is dominant over the allele for long hair (s). The allele for black hair (B) is dominant over the allele for brown hair (b). Use a Punnett square to predict the probable offspring of a cross between two individuals heterozygous for both characteristics (SsBb). As shown in Figure 10-11 the offspring are likely to possess nine different genotypes that will result in the following four phenotypes:

- 9/16 of the guinea pigs will have short, black hair.
- 3/16 of the guinea pigs will have short, brown hair.
- 3/16 of the guinea pigs will have long, black hair.
- 1/16 of the guinea pigs will have long, brown hair.

The results from this dihybrid cross support the principle of independent assortment. In the next chapter you will learn about variations to this principle.

Section Review

1. Explain the terms *genotype* and *phenotype*.
2. What is the formula used to determine probablility? In what ways can probability be expressed?
3. Would a testcross be needed to determine the genotype of a Japanese four o'clock with pink flowers? Why or why not?
4. Explain how you would use a Punnett square to predict the probable outcome of a monohybrid cross.
5. The offspring of two short-tailed cats have a 25 percent chance of having no tail, a 25 percent chance of having a long tail, and a 50 percent chance of having a short tail. What can you hypothesize based on this information about the genotypes of the parents?

Answers to Section Review

1. An organism's genetic makeup is its genotype. An organism's external appearance is its phenotype.
2. Probability = the number of one kind of event ÷ the number of all events; expressed as a decimal, percentage, ratio, or fraction
3. No. The pink flowers result from two incompletely dominant alleles, one for red and one for white flowers.
4. Divide a square into four boxes. Place symbols representing one parent's alleles on the left side and the other parent's alleles across the top. Fill in each box with the appropriate two symbols. The boxes reveal all possible genotypes.
5. Each short-tailed parent has two codominant alleles, one for a long tail and one for no tail.

Laboratory

Genetic Inheritance in Corn

Objective
To analyze monohybrid and dihybrid crosses

Process Skills
Predicting, collecting data, inferring

Materials
Corn ears A and B

Background
1 Explain how a Punnett square is used as a model. What does each of its parts represent?
2 In your own words, explain the principle of independent assortment.

Inquiry
1 The kernels on corn ear A are offspring of a monohybrid cross for color. What are the phenotypes?
2 Purple results from the dominant allele (P) and yellow from the recessive (p). Without counting the kernels, estimate the phenotypic ratio, the ratio of purple to yellow kernels.
3 Use your knowledge of the different types of monohybrid crosses to determine all the color ratios possible in a corn ear. Use Punnett squares to support your answers.
4 Compare your answer from step 2 with your answer from step 3 to predict the type of monohybrid cross that produced ear A.
5 Test your prediction. Count the number of purple and yellow kernels, calling off the colors while your partner records them.
6 Combine your data with those of two other teams. Why is combining data a good idea? Use the combined data to find and record the observed phenotypic ratio.
7 Use your results from step 6. Divide the larger number in your ratio by the smaller. Round the answer to the nearest whole number to find the ratio of P of p. What is the monohybrid cross that produced ear A?
8 Draw the Punnett square for the monohybrid cross in step 7. What are the phenotypes and genotypes of the parents and offspring? What are the phenotypic and genotypic ratios in the offspring?
9 Compare your estimated ratio from step 2 and predicted ratio from step 4 with the observed ratio from step 7. Which was the most accurate prediction?
10 A dihybrid cross for color and texture produced the kernels on corn ear B. The allele for purple (P) is dominant over yellow (p). The allele for smooth texture (S) is dominant over wrinkled (s). What are the phenotypes? Use a Punnett square to predict the phenotypic ratio.
11 As in step 5, count the kernels on ear B for each of the four phenotypes. Repeat step 6. Find the phenotypic ratio and compare it with the predicted ratio.

Conclusions
1 What is your evidence for the genotypes and phenotypes of the parents of ear A?
2 How do your observations for ear B support the principle of independent assortment?

Further Inquiry
Predict the expected phenotypic ratio of corn ear B if yellow and wrinkled were dominant.

Laboratory

(For an overview of genetic inheritance and preparatory information related to the laboratory, see p. 145B.)

Background

1. A Punnett square models a genetic cross. The top row and left column represent the parents' gametes. Each of their two alleles is represented by a letter. The insides of the square show possible genotypes of the offspring.
2. Students should explain that factors for different traits are distributed to reproductive cells independently.

Inquiry

1. Yellow and purple color.
3. Cross PP × PP yields all purple kernels, PP. Cross pp × pp yields all yellow kernels, pp. Cross PP × pp yields all purple kernels, Pp. Cross PP × Pp yields all purple, 2PP : 2Pp. Cross pp × Pp yields 2 purple : 2 yellow, 2Pp : 2pp. Cross Pp × Pp yields 3 purple : 1 yellow, 1PP : 2Pp : 1pp.
4. Students should choose the closest match between the step 3 ratios and their step 2 estimate.
6. Combining data provides a larger database, which reduces sampling errors and provides more accurate results.
7. The ratio should be 3 : 1. Ear A was produced by the cross Pp × Pp.
8. Parental phenotypes are all purple (Pp). Offspring phenotypes are purple (PP or Pp) and yellow (pp).
9. Step 4, using the Punnett square, probably gave a more accurate prediction.
10. Phenotypes: purple smooth, purple wrinkled, yellow smooth, yellow wrinkled. The ratio for cross PpSs × PpSs is 9 : 3 : 3 : 1.
11. The Punnett square done in step 10 should give a close prediction of the observed ratio.

Conclusions

1. A comparison of the actual ratio with predicted ratios is the evidence that the parental ears were both heterozygous purple (Pp).
2. The observed ratios should be similar to the predicted ratio for a dihybrid cross as shown in Example 7, p. 158.

Further Inquiry

The phenotypic ratio will be the same as when purple and smooth are dominant, except the opposite alleles will be expressed. Students should refer to the Punnett square they constructed in step 10.

Chapter 10 Review

Vocabulary

1. Cross-pollination: pollen is transferred from one plant to another of the same species. Self-pollination: pollen is transferred from anthers to stigma of the same plant.
2. The allele for the trait that is expressed is dominant, while the allele for the trait that is masked is recessive.
3. Each of several alternative forms of a gene is an allele.
4. Homozygous: both alleles of a pair the same for a trait. Heterozygous: the two alleles in the pair not the same for a trait.
5. A monohybrid cross tests for only a single trait. A dihybrid cross tests for two traits.

Review

1. Cross each tall plant with a short plant. A homozygous tall plant will have all tall offspring. If a tall plant is heterozygous, about half its offspring will be tall and half, short. A testcross.

	t	t
T	Tt	Tt
T	Tt	Tt

	t	t
T	Tt	Tt
t	tt	tt

2. Gametes: B and b; phenotypic ratio: 100% black; genotypic ratio: 100% Bb

	b	b
B	Bb	Bb
B	Bb	Bb

3. Both phenotypes: smooth coat; genotype: rr

	r	r
r	rr	rr
r	rr	rr

4. Phenotypic ratio is 1 red : 1 pink. Genotypic ratio is 1 RR : 1 RR′.

	R	R′
R	RR	RR′
R	RR	RR′

Chapter 10 Review

Vocabulary

allele (152)
codominance (157)
cross-pollination (148)
dihybrid cross (157)
dominant (150)
first filial, or F_1, generation (148)
gene (152)
genotype (153)
heredity (147)
heterozygous (153)
homozygous (153)
inheritance (147)
monohybrid cross (154)
multiple alleles (153)
parental, or P_1, generation, (148)
phenotype (153)
pollination (148)
principle of dominance and recessiveness (150)
principle of independent assortment (151)
principle of segregation (151)
probability (154)
Punnett square (154)
pure (147)
recessive (150)
second filial, or F_2, generation (148)
self-pollination (147)
strain (147)
testcross (156)

Explain the difference between the terms in each of the following sets.

1. cross-pollination, self-pollination
2. dominant, recessive
3. allele, gene
4. heterozygous, homozygous
5. monohybrid cross, dihybrid cross

Review

1. A gardener has two tall pea plants. How can the gardener determine whether the two plants are homozygous or heterozygous for the gene determining tallness? Show the two Punnett squares as evidence for your conclusion. What is this type of cross called?
2. In rabbits the allele for black coat color (B) is dominant over the allele for brown coat color (b). What would be the results of a cross between an animal homozygous for black coat color (BB) and one homozygous for brown coat color (bb)? Show the gametes, Punnett square, and phenotypic and genotypic ratios.
3. In guinea pigs the allele for rough coat (R) is dominant over the allele for smooth coat (r). In order for all the offspring to be smooth coated, what should the phenotype and genotype of the male and female parents be? Show the Punnett square to support your answer.
4. In Japanese four o'clocks the alleles for red flower color (R) and for white flower color (R′) are codominant. Thus a plant with the phenotype RR′ will have pink flowers. Show the Punnett square and genotypic and phenotypic ratios for a cross between a plant with red flowers and one with pink flowers.
5. In peas the allele for axial flowers (A) is dominant over the allele for terminal flowers (a). The allele for inflated seed pods (I) is dominant over that for constricted pods (i). A cross between two peas with axial flowers and inflated pods gives the following offspring: 20 with axial flowers and inflated pods, 7 with axial flowers and constricted pods, and 5 with terminal flowers and inflated pods. What is the most probable genotype for the two parents? Explain the results and show the Punnett square. How can the explanation be checked?
6. For question 5 give all the possible crosses between two peas with axial flowers and inflated pods.
7. What would be the results of a cross between two pea plants that were heterozygous for both tall plants and round seeds? Show the Punnett square, and state the genotypic and phenotypic ratios.

5. AaIi; abnormal ratio probably due to the small sample; do testcrosses using aaii.

	AI	Ai	aI	ai
AI	AAII	AAIi	AaII	AaIi
Ai	AAIi	AAii	AaIi	Aaii
aI	AaII	AaIi	aaII	aaIi
ai	AaIi	Aaii	aaIi	aaii

6. AAII × AAII, AAIi × AAII, AaII × AAII, AaIi × AAII, AAII × AaII, AAIi × AaII, AaII × AaII, AaIi × AaII, AAII × AAIi, AAIi × AAIi, AaII × AAIi, AaIi × AAIi, AAII × AaIi, AAIi × AaIi, AaII × AaIi, AaIi × AaIi

8. In Japanese four o'clocks the alleles for red flower color (R) and the allele for white flower color (R′) are codominant. Show the Punnett square and the genotypic and pheontypic ratios of the cross of the genotype: RRTt × RR′Tt. Assume tall (T) is dominant over short (t).
9. Suppose that you are an explorer who has found a new species of plant. Some of the plants have red flowers and some have yellow flowers. You cross a red-flowered plant with a yellow-flowered plant and all the offspring have orange flowers. What is the most probable explanation? How would you prove it? Support your answer with a Punnett square.
10. In rabbits the allele for black coat color (B) is dominant over the allele for brown coat color (b). The allele for straight hair (S) is dominant over that for curly hair (s). Someone gives you a male rabbit with black straight hair and a female with brown curly hair. If you bred these two, would you expect to get any with brown curly hair in the first generation? Explain your answer with four Punnett squares.

Critical Thinking

1. The law of independent assortment applies not only to genetics but also to games of pure chance. Suppose that you have 10 Ping-Pong balls in a jar, each marked with a number from 1 to 10. If you mix them thoroughly and take out one, the chances are 1 in 10 that you will get a particular number, for example 5. If you have two such jars, the chances of drawing a 5 from each jar is 1 in 100 (1 in 10 for each jar, or a total of 1 in 100 for drawing 5, 5):

$$\frac{1}{10} \times \frac{1}{10} = \frac{1}{100}$$

Suppose that you have 5 such jars. What is the chance of drawing the number 31456?
2. Cystic fibrosis is a genetically transmitted condition in which the body produces excess mucus that clogs the lungs and intestines. Persons who are heterozygous (Ff) for cystic fibrosis are carriers. Persons who are homozygous recessive (ff) have the disease. The Punnett square above shows the cross between a normal adult and a carrier. Show the Punnett squares for the crosses between each of these four F_1 individuals and another who is a carrier. How many individuals in the F_2 generation will be carriers? How many will be affected by the disease?

	F	F
F	FF	FF
f	Ff	Ff

Extension

1. Read the article by C. Decker entitled "Extra DNA Causes Mendel's Peas to Pucker" in *Science News*, February 10, 1990, p. 87. Give an oral report in which you explain the genetic cause of the wrinkling trait in peas.
2. Toss a penny and a nickel together 32 times, and record the results as they fall: number of heads, nickel; number of tails, nickel; number of heads, penny; and number of tails, penny. How does this illustrate independent assortment?

7. Phenotypes: 9 tall, round : 3 tall, wrinkled : 3 short, round : 1 short, wrinkled

	TR	Tr	tR	tr
TR	TTRR	TTRr	TtRR	TtRr
Tr	TTRr	TTrr	TtRr	Ttrr
tR	TtRR	TtRr	ttRR	ttRr
tr	TtRr	Ttrr	ttRr	ttrr

8. Phenotypes: 6 red, tall : 6 pink, tall : 2 red, short : 2 pink, short

	RT	Rt	R′T	R′t
RT	RRTT	RRTt	RR′TT	RR′Tt
Rt	RRTt	RRtt	RR′Tt	RR′tt
RT	RRTT	RRTt	RR′TT	RR′Tt
Rt	RRTt	RRtt	RR′Tt	RR′tt

9. The most probable explanation is that alleles for red flower color and yellow flower color are codominant. If you self-pollinate the orange plants, you should get a phenotypic ratio of 1 red : 2 orange : 1 yellow.

	R	R′
R	RR	RR′
R′	RR′	R′R′

10. Yes, but only if the male rabbit were heterozygous for both curly and brown hair. The four possible crosses are:

	bs	bs	bs	bs
BS	BbSs	BbSs	BbSs	BbSs
Bs	Bbss	Bbss	Bbss	Bbss
bS	bbSs	bbSs	bbSs	bbSs
bs	bbss	bbss	bbss	bbss

	bs
BS	BbSs

	bs
BS	BbSs
BS	BbSs
bS	bbSs
bS	bbSs

	bs
BS	BbSs
BS	BbSs
Bs	Bbss
Bs	Bbss

Critical Thinking

1. One in 100,000

2. Probability ratios: carriers are 8 of 16, or 50%, while 2 of 16, or 12.5%, have the disease.

	F	F
F	FF	FF
f	Ff	Ff

	F	F
F	FF	FF
f	Ff	Ff

	F	f
F	FF	Ff
f	Ff	ff

	F	f
F	FF	Ff
f	Ff	ff

Extension

1. Students can use the library for further research on Mendel.

2. The nickel and penny, like chromosomes, are independent of each other.

Chapter 11 Inheritance Patterns and Human Genetics

Chapter Overview

Chapter 11 continues the discussion of the principles of inheritance begun in the previous chapter. Section 11.1 examines genetic change—mutations in chromosomes and genes. Section 11.2 discusses patterns of inheritance, such as sex-linked traits and crossing-over within linkage groups. Section 11.3 explores human genetics, including the genetic control of certain disorders in humans.

Chapter Planning Chart

B	S	A	Sections and Subsections	Page	Features	Page	Resources
	•	•	**11.1 Mutation**				
			Chromosome Mutations	163	Section Review	164	Videodiscs
			Gene Mutations	164			Science in Action Videotape: DNA and Protein Synthesis
			Mutagens	164			Section Reviews Worksheet
		•	**11.2 Genetic Patterns**				
			Sex Determination	165	Think	168	Videodiscs
			Sex Linkage	165	Section Review	168	Blackline Master 25
			Linkage Groups	166			Overhead Transparency T11
			Crossing-Over	167			Blackline Master 26
			Chromosome Mapping	167			Section Reviews Worksheet
•	•	•	**11.3 Human Genetics**				
			Studying Human Genetics	170	Writing About Biology	169	Videodiscs
			Human Genetic Traits	171	Biology in Process	172	Process Skills: Pedigrees
			Detecting Genetic Disorders	175	Laboratory	177	Laboratories: Human Genetic Traits
					Section Review	176	Section Reviews Worksheet
			End of Chapter Activities				
					Chapter Review	178	Vocabulary Skills
							Chapter Test
							Computer Test Generator

B *The Basic Level curriculum presents the most fundamental knowledge offered in the course.*
S *The Standard Level curriculum is designed for the average student who is able to master most topics.*
A *The Advanced Level curriculum includes suggestions for teaching the most academically able students.*

Cooperative Learning

Group Activity: Human Inheritance Patterns

- **Group Size:** *3 students*
- **Outcome:** *Students will be able to compare and contrast crosses involving autosomal recessive, autosomal dominant, and sex-linked recessive traits.*
- **Individual Accountability:** *Each student will construct three Punnett squares for a human trait.*
- **Positive Interdependence:** *The group will verify the conclusions of group members and compare results.*

Have one student in each group choose a disorder from the "Single Allele, Dominant" section of Table 11-1. Have a second student choose a disorder from the "Single Allele, Recessive" section. Have the third student choose from the "Sex-linked" section. Then ask each student to make a Punnett square to illustrate the mother transmitting the defect, a second square to illustrate the father transmitting the defect, and a third square in which both parents have the defective allele. Have students record predicted phenotype ratios for their own squares.

After completing the Punnett squares, each group member should report his or her findings to the other group members. Encourage the others to verify the conclusions by diagramming the crosses themselves. Finally, have the group as a whole discuss how the three kinds of inheritance differ.

Concept Map

The following is one possible solution to the concept mapping activity in Reteaching on p. 164.

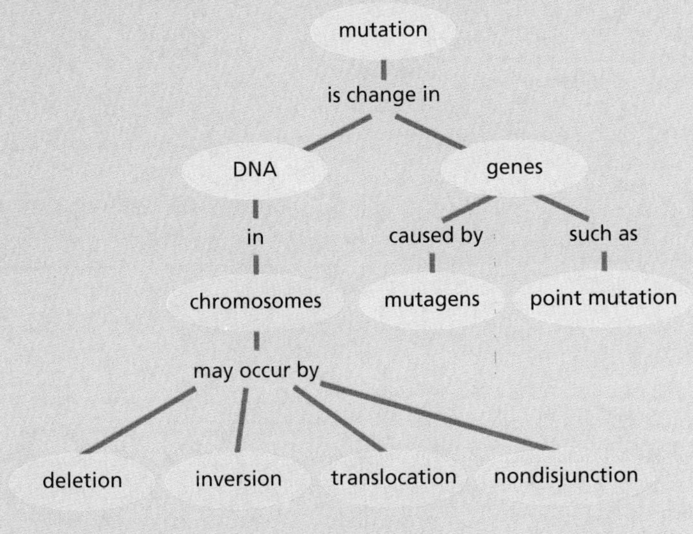

Laboratory Preparation

Overview *(See p. 177.)*

In this lab students survey a variety of hereditary human traits to produce a personalized phenotypic profile. Students then combine information regarding the genetic nature of each trait with each profile, allowing them to speculate about their genotype for each trait. Finally, students collect data reflecting the frequency of each trait within the class and comment on the relationships, if any, between the frequency of a trait, its evolutionary advantage, and its genetic nature.

Preparation

If possible, collect photographs or drawings of both the dominant and recessive forms of each of the traits being studied.

Teaching Tips

Some students may need to be reminded of the principle of dominance and recessiveness, the principle of segregation, and the principle of independent assortment. A common misconception is that a dominant allele is expressed with greater frequency than is a recessive allele.

Students should be shown examples of the traits being studied. Show photographs or draw examples on the board of the phenotypes resulting from both the dominant and the recessive alleles.

Chapter Themes

Evolution Inheritance of mutations is what makes evolution possible. Emphasize that mutations are the raw material of adaptation and evolution. Point out the element of randomness involved in when and where mutations occur.

Human offspring inherit parental traits by genetic mechanisms similar to those of pea plants and fruit flies. Help students appreciate the universality among diverse species of many genetic patterns—for example, sex determination.

Scale and Structure Highlight the relationship of the structures of genes and chromosomes to their functions through class discussions of mutations, linkage, and mapping. Make explicit the connection between molecular structure—that is, DNA sequences—and more easily observable structures, such as eyes and fingers.

Chapter Motivating Activity

Direct a brainstorming session on biological differences and similarities among humans. Have students recall differences in human physical traits that they have seen. Make a list on the board. Also elicit suggestions of internal differences, such as a predisposition to diabetes.

Then ask students what biological features all humans have in common. Together make a list of similarities, both external and internal. Stress the fact that there are more similarities than differences. Point out that although many of the features students suggest are genetic, some are not.

Chapter 11 *Inheritance Patterns and Human Genetics*

Introduction

The DNA of chromosomes contains information that regulates inheritance patterns. What exactly are these patterns? Why do some traits run in families, while others seem to appear out of nowhere? In this chapter you will learn how biologists use their knowledge of chromosome behavior to study how inheritance patterns operate.

Chapter Outline

Chapter Concept

As you read, pay attention to the scientific processes that were used to discover inheritance patterns and to the way these processes are applied to issues of human genetics.

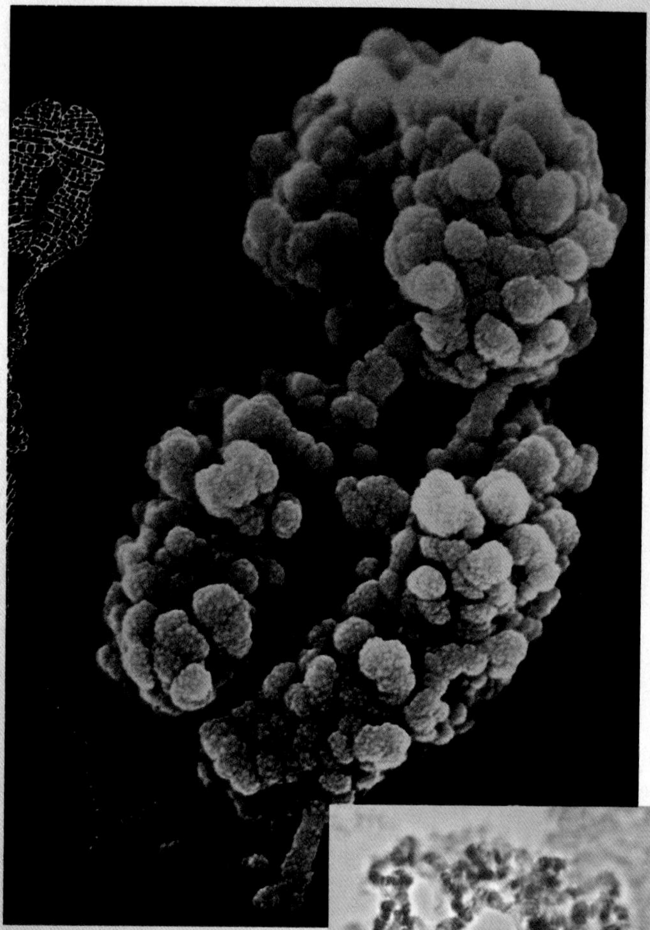

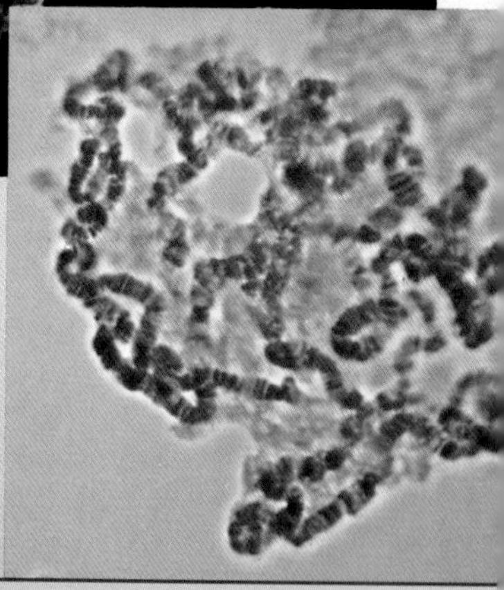

Color-enhanced SEM of a human chromosome (×125,000). Inset: Chromosomes in *Drosophila* salivary gland (×2,048).

Understanding the Visuals

Ask students how the two photographs differ and why the *Drosophila* chromosomes show less detail. *(Different magnification explains the difference in detail. The shapes also differ.)* Point out that the *Drosophila* chromosomes were dyed purple.

Have students examine the photographs closely. They should see that chromosomes appear to be made up of smaller units. Ask them to compare the textures of the chromosomes. *(In the human chromosome, small lumps are gathered into larger lumps;* Drosophila *chromosomes have light and dark bands.)* Make sure that students understand that the lumps and bands are not genes, although genes are located at specific positions on chromosomes.

11.1 Mutation

As you learned in Chapter 8, DNA ultimately directs the production of the proteins that affect an organism's metabolism and development. Therefore changes in DNA may affect the production of proteins and in turn result in a new phenotype. A change in DNA is called a **mutation.** Mutations can involve entire chromosomes or specific genes. They may take place in any cell. **Germ cell mutations** occur in sex cells, such as eggs and sperm. They do not affect the organism itself but are passed on to offspring. **Somatic mutations** take place in body cells. They are passed on to daughter cells through mitosis.

The majority of mutations are harmful. Most of these are called lethal mutations because they prevent the individual from developing much beyond the zygote stage. However, some mutations result in phenotypes that have an evolutionary advantage and are therefore beneficial. These mutations ultimately provide the variation upon which natural selection acts.

Chromosome Mutations

Chromosome mutations often occur during cell division. These mutations are either changes in the structure of a chromosome or loss of an entire chromosome. **Deletion** occurs when a piece of a chromosome breaks off. All of the information on that piece is lost. **Inversion** occurs when a piece breaks from a chromosome and reattaches itself to the chromosome in the reverse orientation. If a broken piece attaches to a nonhomologous chromosome, the result is a **translocation.** Figure 11-1 shows these mutations.

Section Objectives

- *Distinguish between a point mutation and a frame shift mutation.*
- *Name three types of chromosome mutation.*
- *Identify two external causes of mutation.*

Figure 11-1 In chromosome mutations a piece of chromosome breaks off. In some cases the piece may reattach in a reversed position, and in others it may attach to a nonhomologous chromosome.

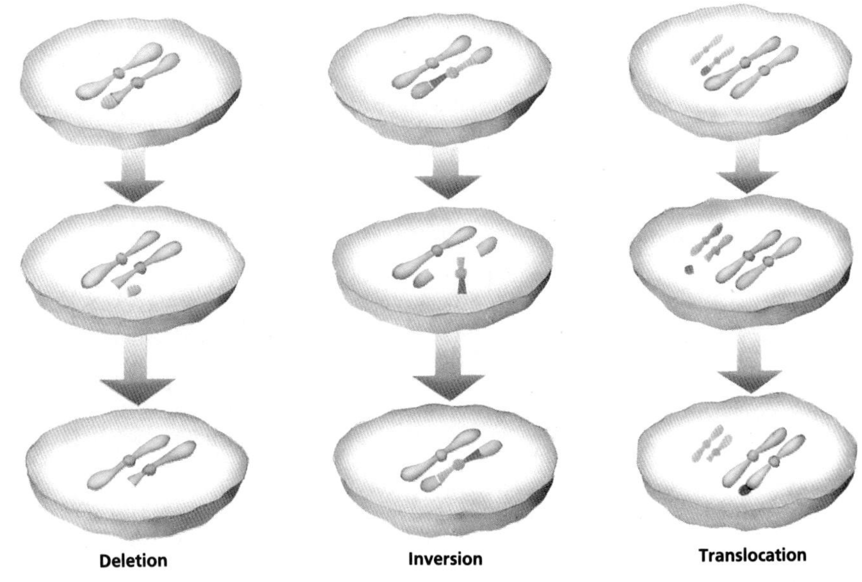

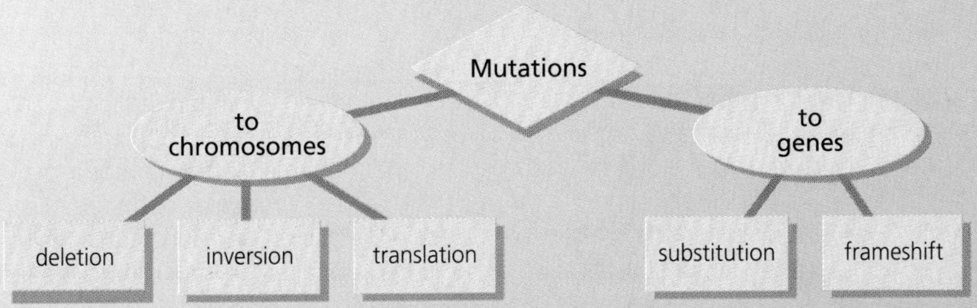

Graphic Organizer Use this organizational chart to summarize key concepts in Section 11.1.

Section 11.1

Lesson Plan

Section Focus

This section describes changes that can occur in chromosomes and genes and explains what is known about the causes of such mutations.

Section Themes

This section emphasizes two themes: **Scale and Structure** and **Patterns of Change.** Mutations—changes in the structures of genes and chromosomes—lead to offspring with traits different from those of their parents.

Motivating Activity

To tap students' prior knowledge of mutations, ask them to brainstorm reasons why many people are concerned about releases of nuclear radiation into the environment. *(Some students may be able to tell the class about the 1986 Chernobyl incident.)* Then ask students if they know why the destruction of atmospheric ozone by fluorocarbon compounds may cause harm to organisms. *(The ozone layer is a barrier to mutagenic solar ultraviolet radiation.)* Point out that most mutations are not the result of human activities but occur naturally. Mutations can be harmful, beneficial, or neutral.

Teaching Strategies

Applying Concepts Give students a sequence of 24 DNA bases. Have them use Table 8-1 on p. 121 to determine the amino acid sequence coded by these bases. Ask different students to change a base in the middle, delete a base, or add a base. Have students determine how their mutations affect the sequence of amino acids.

Videodiscs

- ***Side 1 25971, DNA Replication (m)***
- ***1640–1650, Chromosomes (s)***
- ***2552–2560, Meiosis (s)***

Guided Practice
Have students make paper-strip chromosomes. Tell them to write the letters A through H evenly along the length of each strip. Then guide students in cutting the strips and retaping them in the appropriate configurations to illustrate deletion, inversion, and translocation.

Independent Practice
■ Have students write answers to the Section Review.
■ Have students diagram a DNA sequence to show how an inversion results in a changed amino acid sequence.

Check Your Understanding
1. When are chromosome mutations most likely to occur? *(During cell division)*
2. How can somatic cell mutations be minimized? *(By avoiding exposure to mutagens as much as possible)*
3. When are harmful mutations most likely to affect organisms? *(When they occur in gametes or in growing children)*

Reteaching
Ask students to make a concept map showing what a mutation is and what can cause one. An example of a completed concept map is shown on p. 161B.
■ *See* Section Reviews *worksheet, Section 11.1.*

Enrichment
Have students research the relationship between cancer and one of the following: smoking, toxic waste dumping, nuclear waste storage, and sunlight. Have students report their findings to the class.

Closure
Point out that the less common allele of an allele pair often arises as a mutation of the more common allele. Have students suggest ways in which mutations can be helpful, harmful, and neutral.

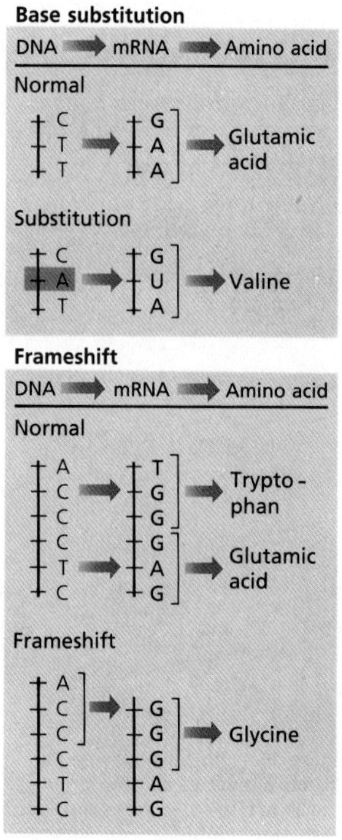

Figure 11-2 In a point mutation one nitrogen base changes to produce a different amino acid. A frameshift mutation also disturbs this process of protein synthesis.

Another kind of chromosomal mutation, called **nondisjunction,** occurs when a replicated chromosome pair fails to separate during cell division. When nondisjunction occurs, one daughter cell receives an extra copy of a chromosome, and the other daughter cell lacks that chromosome entirely. Some human disorders resulting from nondisjunction are discussed in Section 11.3.

Gene Mutations

Gene mutations may involve a single nitrogen base within a codon or larger segments of DNA. A codon, as you recall from Chapter 8, consists of three nitrogen bases that cause a specific amino acid to be inserted into a polypeptide during protein synthesis. The substitution, addition, or removal of a single nitrogen base is called a **point mutation.** As Figure 11-2 shows, if one nitrogen base is substituted for another, the altered code may signal the insertion of a different amino acid into the protein chain. The protein will thus have a different chemical structure. The addition or deletion of a nitrogen base is a point mutation called a **frameshift mutation.** An addition or deletion causes the genetic message to be read out of sequence. The result is usually the inability of the gene to code for the proper amino acids. The bottom of Figure 11-2 illustrates the effects of a frameshift mutation.

Mutagens

What causes mutations? Some mutations are chemical mishaps with no apparent external cause. As in all complex systems, sometimes by chance things go wrong. Often, however, mutations are caused by **mutagens**—environmental factors that damage DNA. For example, overexposure to sunlight can cause skin cancer, for ultraviolet light has a mutagenic effect on the DNA in skin cells. Other mutagens, some of which cause cancer, include cigarette tars, asbestos, and certain viruses. Researchers often use a procedure called the **Ames test** to identify mutagenic substances.

Radiation causes mutations in both germ cells and somatic cells. The children of many survivors of the atomic bomb attacks on Hiroshima and Nagasaki in 1945 were stillborn or suffered birth defects. Radiation increased somatic mutations in the bone marrow cells of many survivors, resulting in a higher incidence of leukemia, a form of cancer.

Section Review

1. What is a *mutation?*
2. Which type of mutation affects the organism but not its offspring? Which type affects offspring?
3. List and describe three types of chromosome mutation.
4. List three examples of mutagenic substances.
5. Why might base substitutions frequently go unnoticed?

Answers to Section Review
1. A change in DNA
2. Somatic mutation; germ cell mutation
3. Deletion is the loss of part of a chromosome. Inversion occurs when a broken chromosome piece reattaches itself in the reverse order. In translocation the broken piece reattaches itself to a nonhomologous chromosome.
4. Mutagenic substances: cigarette tars, asbestos, some viruses; ultraviolet light and atomic radiation are also mutagenic.
5. One answer is that more than one codon may code for an amino acid. Thus a change in one nitrogen base may not affect the code. Alternatively, the substituted amino acid may not alter the structure or chemical properties of the protein.

11.2 Genetic Patterns

In the early 1900s geneticist Thomas Hunt Morgan of Columbia University began a series of breeding experiments with *Drosophila melanogaster,* the common fruit fly. Many characteristics of *Drosophila* make them ideal subjects. They are easy to maintain in the laboratory, have a generation time of only 10 to 15 days, produce hundreds of individuals from each mating, and have easily distinguishable physical characteristics. Also, *Drosophila* has only eight chromosomes, making it easier to determine the relationship between chromosomes and inheritance patterns.

Sex Determination

Morgan observed that of *Drosophila*'s four pairs of homologous chromosomes, one pair was different in males and females. In females the chromosomes of this pair were identical. In males the chromosomes were different. One chromosome looked like those of the pair of females, but the other was shorter and hook-shaped. Morgan called the large chromosomes X chromosomes. He called the short, hook-shaped chromosome the Y chromosome. Morgan correctly hypothesized that X and Y chromosomes are **sex chromosomes,** chromosomes that determine an individual's sex. All the other chromosomes, those not included in sex determination, are called **autosomes.**

Recall from Chapter 9 that homologous chromosomes segregate during meiosis I. The sex chromosomes pair and segregate in the same manner as other chromosomes. Female gametes each receive one X chromosome. Male gametes receive either an X or a Y chromosome. If an egg is fertilized by a sperm containing an X chromosome, the resulting zygote will be XX, and the new individual will be female. If an egg is fertilized by a sperm containing a Y chromosome, the resulting zygote will be XY, and the new individual will be male.

As shown in Figure 11-3, these combinations of chromosomes make it probable that 50 percent of the offspring of any mating will be male and 50 percent female. In most organisms the males are XY, and the females are XX. In birds, however, the males are XX, and the females are XY. In grasshoppers, the males, with only an X chromosome, are XO, and the females are XX.

Sex Linkage

The discovery of sex chromosomes led Morgan to hypothesize that some traits were always associated with one sex or the other. His experiments confirmed this hypothesis. Although most fruit flies have red eyes, Morgan once observed a male fruit fly with white eyes. When he crossed a female with this male, the results followed Mendel's prediction: the F_1 generation all had red eyes.

Section Objectives

- *Explain how sex chromosomes determine sex inheritance in* Drosophila.
- *Explain why sex-linked traits appear more often in males than in females.*
- *Describe the evidence that indicates that all chromosomes have linkage groups.*
- *Define* crossing-over, *and tell how it creates genetic variation.*
- *Summarize the procedure involved in constructing a chromosome map.*

Figure 11-3 A female fruit fly has XX sex chromosomes, and a male, XY sex chromosomes. As this Punnett square shows, half of the offspring will probably be female, and half will be male.

	X	Y
X	XX	XY
X	XX	XY

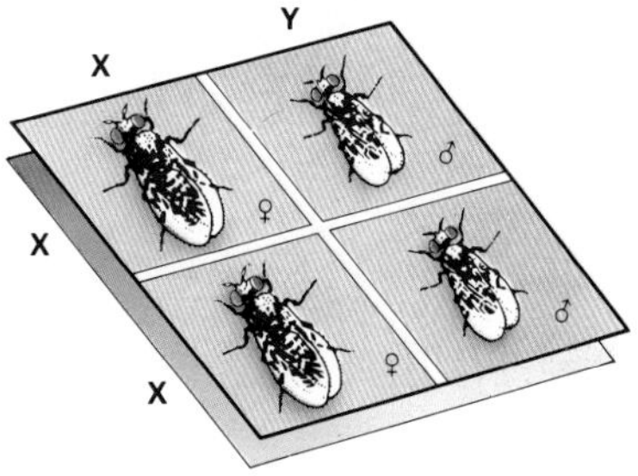

observation of sex chromosomes → discovery of sex-linked traits → demonstration of autosomal linkage groups → inference of crossing-over → chromosome mapping

Graphic Organizer Use this sequential diagram in Describing Scientific Processes on p. 166.

Lesson Plan

Section Focus

This section teaches how certain chromosomes determine sex, how all the genes on one chromosome form a linkage group, and how chromosomes sometimes "trade" portions—that is, cross over. Students will learn how the discovery of crossing-over led to mapping alleles on chromosomes.

Section Themes

The theme of **Scale and Structure** is evident throughout this section. The different shapes of X and Y chromosomes and the location of genes in linkage groups illustrate chromosomal structure on a microscopic and submicroscopic scale. The relationship of the structure of X and Y chromosomes to their function is reflected in sex determination of *Drosophila* and other organisms and in patterns of inheritance of genes carried on the X chromosome.

Motivating Activity

Use an overhead projector to show students a large illustration of a fruit fly. Ask students why they think that geneticists use *Drosophila* in their research. *(Fruit flies show a variety of traits, are easy to obtain and breed, and have short generation times and large numbers of offspring.)* Then have students consider the relative difficulty of using humans as genetic subjects. For instance, how long would it take to study three generations of humans? *(About 60 years)* Can you get large numbers of offspring in a generation, so you can make a proper statistical analysis? Explain. *(No. Most families have only a few children.)*

Videodiscs

- ***1720–1729, Fruit Fly*** **(Drosophila)** ***Types (s)***

Teaching Strategies

Describing Scientific Processes Focus on how T. H. Morgan's *Drosophila* research, as surveyed in the section, led to an understanding of inheritance patterns. On the board copy the sequential diagram on p. 165. Ask students what process skills Morgan used to arrive at his conclusions. *(See Section 2.1, p. 17.)*

Making Models Have each student create two pipe cleaner "chromosomes." Tell half the students to make two X chromosomes and half to make an X and a Y, with the X longer than the Y. Have three-fourths of the students put a green spot in the same location on their X chromosomes and one-fourth put a blue spot. Ask students to assume that green is a dominant allele for a normal trait and that blue is a recessive allele for an abnormal trait. Record data on the board on the numbers of males and females that show the abnormal trait. Then have pairs of students use their pipe cleaners to arrange matings and to determine the ratio of male and female offspring likely to show the abnormal trait.

Interpreting Data Give students the following problem: Linked genes on homologous chromosomes are known to be ABC and abc, respectively, with genes a, b, and c in the sequence a-b-c; in crosses of heterozygous parents, some of the offspring receive chromosomes with ABc or abC and other offspring receive Abc or aBC, with ABc/abC occurring twice as often as Abc/aBC. Ask students to use this crossing-over data to compare how far apart the genes are. *(Because crossing-over occurs twice as frequently between b and c as between a and b, genes b and c are twice as far apart as genes a and b.)*

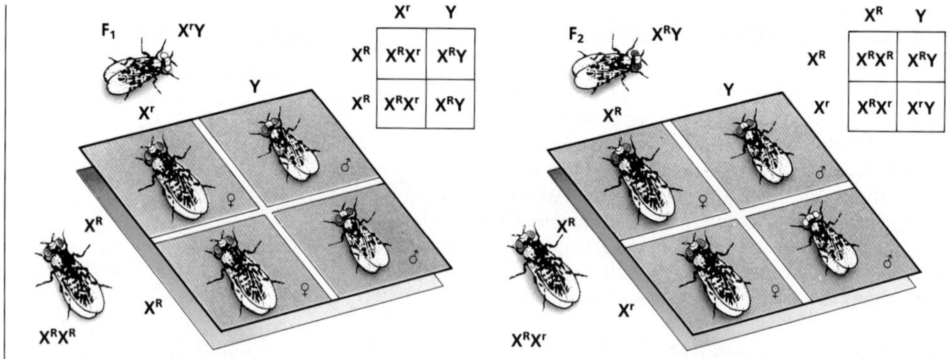

	X^r	Y
X^R	X^RX^r	X^RY
X^R	X^RX^r	X^RY

	X^R	Y
X^R	X^RX^R	X^RY
X^r	X^RX^r	X^rY

Figure 11-4 Eye color is a sex-linked trait in fruit flies carried on the X chromosome—R for dominant red and r for white. Determine the sex and eye color of the F_1 and F_2 generations.

Figure 11-5 When traits are linked, their probable distribution is the same as that for body color and wing length in the fruit fly, as shown here.

	GL	gl
GL	GGLL	GgLl
gl	GgLl	ggll

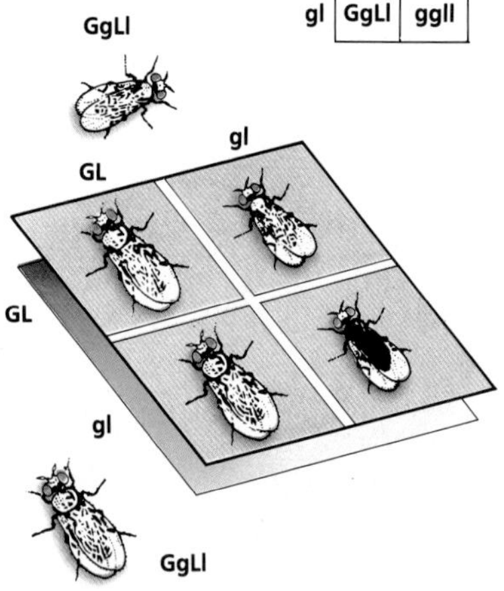

Morgan next crossed members of the F_1 generation and produced the expected ratio of three red-eyed flies to one white-eyed. However, all the white-eyed flies were male. Why weren't any females white-eyed? Morgan hypothesized that the allele for red eyes was carried on the X chromosome. Figure 11-4 shows his reasoning. Assume the X chromosome carries the gene for eye color, either X^R or X^r. If an X^RX^R female is crossed with an X^rY male, all of the F_1 females will be X^RX^r, and all of the F_1 males X^RY. In the F_2 generation half the females will have the X^RX^R genotype, and half the X^RX^r genotype. All will have red eyes. Half the F_2 males will be X^RY, or red-eyed; half will be X^rY, or white-eyed. Morgan concluded that eye color in *Drosophila* was a **sex-linked trait**—one determined by alleles on the sex chromosomes.

Linkage Groups

Genes are found on chromosomes. Since there are thousands more traits than chromosomes, each chromosome must carry many genes. The group of genes located on one chromosome is a **linkage group.** These genes are usually inherited together.

Morgan demonstrated the existence of linkage groups by studying *Drosophila.* In *Drosophila* the allele for gray body (G) is dominant to that for black body (g), and the allele for long wings (L) is dominant to that for short wings (l). Mendelian genetics predicts that when strains are crossed, the F_2 generation will have a phenotypic ratio of 9:3:3:1. When Morgan performed the cross GGLL × ggll, the F_2 generation showed the 3:1 phenotypic ratio seen in Figure 11-5, not the Mendelian ratio.

Morgan correctly hypothesized that the genes for body color and wing size are in the same linkage group and are inherited together. By doing many genetic crosses within a species it is possible to determine the number of linkage groups for that species. The number always equals the number of chromosomes. *Drosophila,* with 4 pairs of chromosomes, has 4 linkage groups. A human, with 23 pairs of chromosomes, has 23 linkage groups.

LEP Activity
Help students visually contrast Morgan's F_2 results in his sex-linkage experiments with the results he would have gotten if there had been no sex linkage. First, draw Punnett square A (see right) on the board to show what Morgan initially expected from the cross of two F_1 fruit flies, assuming that the eye-color trait was not sex-linked (Rr × Rr). Then show by copying Figure 11-4 (p. 166) the F_2 ratio Morgan actually found; in fact, eye color is sex-linked ($X^RX^r \times X^RY$). Point out the differences between the two Punnett squares on the board.

You can also use two contrasting Punnett squares on the board to clarify how Morgan showed linkage between body color and wing size. With Punnett square B (see right), first show what would have been the results of a cross with GgLl × GgLl assuming independent

Crossing-Over

Morgan noticed that sometimes not all the alleles in a linkage group were inherited together. For example, in *Drosophila,* the allele G for gray bodies is dominant to g for black bodies, and R for red eyes is dominant to r for purple eyes. Morgan crossed a ggrr fly with a GgRr fly. In the F_2 generation 151 offspring had a gray body and red eyes, and 131 had a black body and purple eyes, almost a 1 : 1 ratio. Morgan expected this result from his studies of linkage groups. However, 8 offspring had gray bodies and purple eyes, and 10 had black bodies and red eyes.

Morgan realized that these results could have occurred only if the alleles somehow had changed or become rearranged. Mutations could have caused the changes, but mutations usually occur in only one individual out of tens of thousands. The alleles must therefore have become rearranged. Morgan inferred that this rearrangement had taken place through crossing-over, the exchange of alleles between homologous chromosomes. Figure 11-6 shows how crossing-over accounts for the individuals in this cross that are not predicted by Mendelian inheritance laws.

Chromosome Mapping

Crossing-over occurs more often between some alleles than between others. Since most alleles occupy a fixed place on a chromosome, it follows that the smaller the distance between two alleles, the greater the likelihood that these alleles will not be separated by crossing-over. Alfred H. Sturtevant, Morgan's student, used crossing-over data to construct a **chromosome map**—a diagram of allele positions on a particular chromosome.

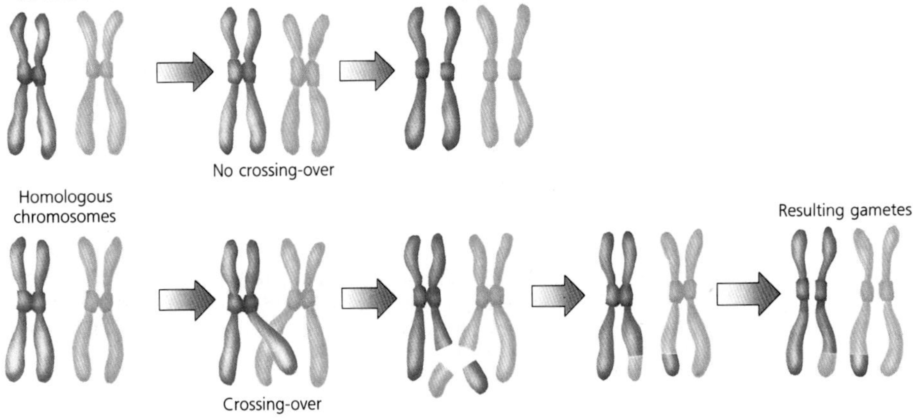

Figure 11-6 When traits are not distributed according to the expected ratio in offspring, crossing-over of alleles may have occurred.

Interpreting the Visuals Take students step-by-step through the sex linkage of eye color in *Drosophila* (Figure 11-4, p. 166) and the crossing-over of homologous chromosomes (Figure 11-6, p. 167). Ask students to compare the role of X and Y chromosomes in transmitting sex-linked traits.

- *See* **Overhead Transparency** ***T11 and*** **Blackline Masters** ***25 and 26.***

Guided Practice

Simulate the process of chromosome mapping by making homologous chromosomes out of strips of paper and marking them with symbols for allelic genes. Show students how crossing-over can result in different genetic combinations in offspring receiving the altered chromosome. For example, if crossing-over occurs between AB/ab homologues, the resulting chromosomes will be Ab and aB. Therefore, in a cross of AaBb with aabb, some offspring will show both the A and b phenotypes or both the a and B phenotypes.

Independent Practice

- Have students write answers to the Section Review.
- Provide students with genetics problems involving sex-linked characteristics or other linkage groups. For example, in a cross of X^RY and X^RX^r, what are the chances of a female offspring showing the recessive trait? *(The female will always get the R allele from her father, so she cannot exhibit the recessive trait.)*

Videodiscs

- ***2633, Crossing-Over (s)***

assortment. Then show with Figure 11-5 (p. 166) on the board what happened in Morgan's experiment because GL and gl are in fact linked. Again, point out differences between the two Punnett squares.

Punnett Square A

	R	r
R	RR	Rr
r	Rr	rr

Punnett Square B

	GL	Gl	gL	gl
GL	GGLL	GGLl	GgLL	GgLl
Gl	GGLl	GGll	GgLl	Ggll
gL	GgLL	GgLl	ggLL	ggLl
gl	GgLl	Ggll	ggLl	ggll

Section 11.2

Check Your Understanding

1. How do the X and Y chromosomes of the fruit fly differ? *(X looks like the autosomes; Y is shorter and hooked.)*

2. When Morgan noticed alleles in a linkage group that were not inherited together, why did he not conclude that mutations had occurred? *(Mutations usually occur in one individual out of tens of thousands.)*

3. If two alleles in a linkage group show crossing-over 12 percent of the time, how far apart are they on the chromosome? *(12 map units)*

Answer to Think

Since there was a 3 percent crossover (15 out of 500 offspring), the two alleles are 3 map units apart.

Reteaching

Have students work in small groups to compare the following crosses involving eye color of *Drosophila*: $X^RX^r \times X^rY$, $X^rX^r \times X^RY$, and $X^RX^R \times X^rY$. Ask students to specify the genotypes and phenotypes expected for female and male offspring in each cross. *(For example, the offspring expected in the first cross are X^RX^r, X^rX^r, X^RY, and X^rY—both females and males can be red-eyed and white-eyed.)*

■ *See* Section Reviews *worksheet, Section 11.2.*

Enrichment

Obtain from a biological supply house *Drosophila* that are the F_1 product of crosses in which linkage is expected. Have students examine the flies, determine the ratios, and then make further crosses.

Closure

Have students summarize the following terms: sex linkage, linkage groups, and crossing-over. Students can illustrate their summaries with diagrams.

Figure 11-7 Geneticists study the rate of crossover between alleles to construct a chromosome map, which shows the relative position of an allele on a chromosome.

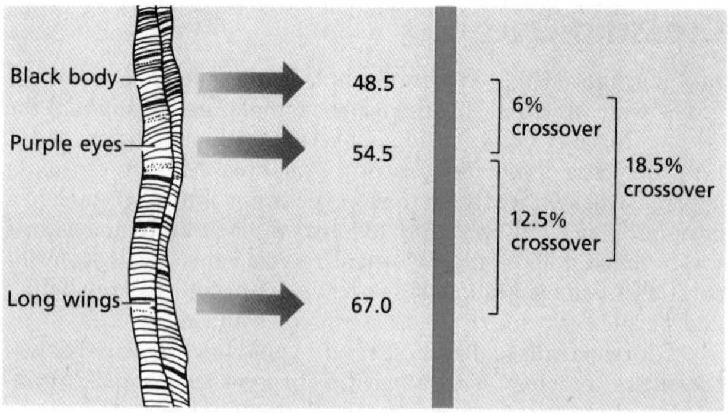

Think

In *Drosophila* the alleles for red eyes (R) and brown body (B) are dominant to the alleles for white eyes (r) and yellow body (b). Suppose Morgan crossed a heterozygous red-eyed, brown-bodied female (RrBb) with a white-eyed, yellow-bodied male (rrbb). Of 500 offspring, 7 have red eyes and yellow bodies, and 8 have white eyes and brown bodies. How many map units apart are the two alleles?

To construct a chromosome map, researchers compare the frequency of crossover for three characteristics, such as eye color, body color, and wing shape. Suppose, for example, that in crosses of *Drosophila,* wing shape and eye color were linked 90 percent of the time. Then the alleles for the two characteristics would be separated during crossing-over 10 percent of the time. If wing shape and body color were linked 93 percent of the time, they would be separated through crossing-over 7 percent of the time. If eye color and body color were linked 83 percent of the time, they would be separated through crossing-over 17 percent of the time.

Geneticists use such data when constructing a chromosome map. Two alleles that are separated by crossing-over 1 percent of the time are considered to be 1 **map unit** apart. In our example the alleles for wing shape and eye color are 10 map units apart, the alleles for wing shape and body color are 7 map units apart, and the alleles for eye color and body color are 17 map units apart. With this data it is possible to establish the relative position of these three alleles on a chromosome. By doing many such comparisons it is possible to determine the actual position of the alleles on a chromosome. Figure 11-7 shows the position of three alleles on *Drosophila* chromosome number 2. It also shows how data on crossover rates are used to determine the position of the three chromosomes relative to each other. Scientists have used this procedure to map the chromosomes of numerous species.

Section Review

1. Distinguish between *sex chromosomes* and *autosomes.*
2. How does sex chromosome inheritance result in an approximate 50:50 ratio of males to females?
3. How does crossing-over increase genetic variability?
4. How do geneticists determine the position of an allele on a chromosome?
5. Construct a Punnett square to show how a white-eyed female *Drosophila* could be produced.

Answers to Section Review

1. Sex chromosomes determine the sex of an organism; all other chromosomes are autosomes.

2. An individual has a 50 percent chance of inheriting either an X or a Y chromosome from the father. This chromosome determines the sex of the individual.

3. Crossing-over increases genetic variability by redistributing genetic material between homologous chromosome pairs so that traits occur in different combinations.

4. By determining the frequency of crossing-over and constructing a chromosome map

5. The square would show a cross between a white-eyed male (X^rY) and a heterozygous red-eyed female (X^RX^r).

Writing About Biology

Knowledge as Power

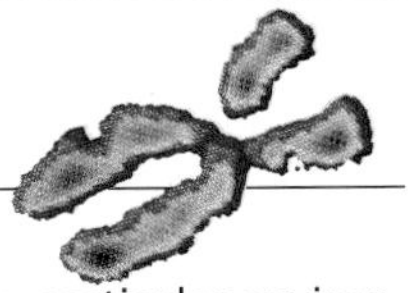

This excerpt is from Genethics: The Ethics of Engineering Life *by David Suzuki and Peter Knudtson.*

Still, there is nothing inherently sinister about geneticists scrutinizing DNA molecules for evidence of genetic predispositions to diseases associated with the workplace—or, for that matter, with the home, the hospital, urban neighborhoods or any other human habitat. All human disease—from cholera and dysentery to cancer and heart disease—are the manifestations of a complex interaction of hereditary and environmental forces. In a just world, an assortment of cheap, reliable genetic tests might be used to alert all human beings at an early age to the statistical risk of contracting many common diseases in certain settings.

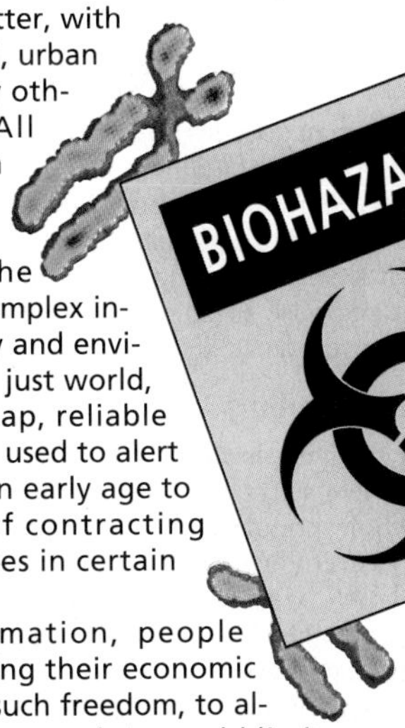

With that information, people might be free, assuming their economic conditions permitted such freedom, to alter their behavior in ways that would limit their long-term exposure to those pathogens, water pollutants, dietary practices and other identified environmental factors to which they were diagnosed most vulnerable. . . .

Similarly, the predictive power of genetic tests might also be used altruistically to benefit workers exposed to hazardous job conditions. In American industries alone, for example, nearly 400,000 workers contract disabling occupational illnesses each year—from blood disorders and skin inflammations to respiratory ailments and cancers—and an estimated 100,000 die from such diseases. Tests that encouraged those workers who might be genetically susceptible to particular environmental hazards to avoid those hazards could thus prevent injuries and prolong lives.

But the same tests could also be used to hire or fire workers because of their inherited capacity to tolerate high levels of toxic chemicals, radioactivity or other job hazards. Used in this fashion, new genetic knowledge could result in individuals having less, rather than more, control of their health and lives. And unscrupulous companies could save money by relying exclusively on genetically resistant workers instead of committing funds to cleaning up polluted workplaces.

In genetics, the truth of Francis Bacon's aphorism "Knowledge is power" seems vastly magnified simply because of the nature of the search. Genetics, perhaps more than any other branch of science except brain biology, probes deeply into the identity of individual human beings. By venturing into the privacy of human genomes, geneticists are not simply satisfying, as some would insist, their own insatiable scientific curiosities. Whether they recognize it or not, they are also creating new opportunities for others to harness this scientific knowledge—for good or for ill—in ways that will influence the lives of fellow human beings.

Write

- **In a short essay, discuss how citizens can evaluate the potential uses of new scientific knowledge. Suggest who in our society should be making choices about how science is applied.**

From Genethics: The Ethics of Engineering Life *by David Suzuki and Peter Knudtson. Copyright © 1989, 1990 by New Data Enterprises Ltd. and Peter Knudtson. Reprinted by permission of Harvard University Press.*

Background

The ability of molecular biologists to detect minute differences in DNA sequences has made new techniques available for medical genetics. Genetic screening examines a person's genetic constitution for clues to the probability that this person might develop or transmit a hereditary defect or disease. As statistical risk is introduced into people's lives, it may influence the making of life choices in ways that we have not yet anticipated.

Discussion

After students have read "Knowledge as Power," ask them to discuss the following questions.

1. The authors made up the word *genethics.* What does *ethics* mean? How might the word be related to genetics? *(Ethics is a set of moral principles that deal with what is "good" and "bad." Students may suggest that the use of biological knowledge should take ethical values into account.)*

2. Do you agree with Bacon that "knowledge is power"? Explain your answer in the context of genetics. *(Allow for personal opinion. Genetic knowledge can be powerful for whoever can understand and use it.)*

Extension

Point out the collaborative authorship of *Genethics.* Have pairs of students form writing partnerships in which one student acts as content expert and the other as wordsmith. Tell them to select jointly a topic in modern genetics to be the focus of a written report. Have the content expert provide the research notes for the wordsmith to create a first draft, and then have both students collaborate on editing and revising.

About the Authors

David Suzuki is a geneticist and science broadcaster. He is Professor of Biology at the University of British Columbia. Peter Knudtson is a freelance science writer living in Vancouver.

Suzuki and Knudtson coined the term *genethics.* Their book explores what are the appropriate moral guidelines, or genethic principles, for citizens to follow in making decisions about a variety of controversial issues such as genetic screening, gene therapy, biological weapons, environmental damage to DNA, genetic diversity, and genetic maps.

Section 11.3

Lesson Plan

Section Focus

This section allows students to compare human genetics with the inheritance of traits in plants and fruit flies. Human traits are coded for by alleles, which are inherited, as are the alleles of other organisms. Scientists are developing methods for detecting and diagnosing human genetic disorders.

Section Themes

The theme of **Evolution** encompasses the study of inheritance in humans. Traits are transferred from parents to offspring in one of several inheritance patterns. Nondisjunction is an example of one of the unexpected changes that can occur in inheritance. The section shows students that human genetics is basically the same as the genetics of the other eukaryotic organisms in this unit.

The theme of **Patterns of Change** is directly illustrated by human pedigree charts. By studying pedigrees, students can see different trends for the inheritance of autosomal and sex-linked traits.

Motivating Activity

Have students survey the class for those students who have dimples (small indentations in the cheeks when a person smiles) and those who are color-blind (see Figure 11-10, p. 174). Ask students if they know other people with dimples, and find out what students have observed about the inheritance of this trait. Do the parents of those with the trait have it? Do their brothers and sisters?

Have students complete the Laboratory on p. 177 before beginning Section 11.3.

▪ *See* **Laboratories, *Investigation 11.***

Section Objectives

- *Name three methods of studying human genetics.*
- *Name two disorders that are controlled by a single allele.*
- *Distinguish between polygenic traits and traits controlled by multiple alleles.*
- *Identify the methods of detecting genetic disorders during pregnancy.*
- *Describe the procedure scientists used to identify the location of a gene responsible for cystic fibrosis.*

11.3 Human Genetics

The 23 pairs of human chromosomes contain at least 40,000 genes, about 7 times more than are found in *Drosophila.* Consequently human inheritance patterns are significantly more complicated. Nevertheless, the principles you read about in Chapter 10 and in this chapter apply to human beings. In this section we will study some human genetic patterns. Most of the examples are diseases or disorders, but keep in mind that the vast majority of alleles control beneficial traits. Geneticists concentrate on disease-carrying genes because they are easily traced through generations and because they are of great concern to people. Table 11-1 lists some well-known human traits and their pattern of inheritance.

Table 11-1 Inheritance Patterns of Human Traits

Single Allele, Dominant
▪ Huntington disease
▪ Achondroplasia (dwarfism)
▪ Cataracts
▪ Polydactyly (extra fingers or toes)
Single Allele, Recessive
▪ Albinism
▪ Cystic fibrosis
▪ Phenylketonuria
▪ Hereditary deafness
Sex-linked
▪ Color blindness
▪ Hemophilia
▪ Muscular dystrophy
▪ Icthyosis simplex (scaly skin)
Polygenic
▪ Skin, hair, and eye color
▪ Foot size
▪ Nose length
▪ Height
Multiple Alleles
▪ ABO blood groups
▪ Rh blood factor

Studying Human Genetics

The study of human genetics poses difficulties that Morgan didn't face in studying *Drosophila.* For example, it may take 75 years to produce three generations of humans, and each pair of humans will produce only a few individuals. In addition, ethical concerns prevent scientists from using the same procedures to study humans that they use to study other organisms. How then do scientists gather evidence about human inheritance?

Population Sampling

One tool for studying human genetics is **population sampling,** in which researchers select a small number of individuals that represent the whole population. Selecting members of the sample according to carefully formulated statistical rules helps ensure that the study will yield accurate results.

For instance, geneticists used population sampling to estimate the percentage of people in the United States who could taste the chemical phenylthiocarbamide (PTC). "Tasters" detect a bitter taste to PTC, while "nontasters" do not detect any taste. By testing a few thousand randomly selected individuals the geneticists have estimated with a high degree of certainty that in the entire United States 65 percent of the people are tasters and 35 percent are nontasters.

Twin Studies

Geneticists also study identical twins to distinguish between genetic and environmental influences on specific traits. Identical twins are those that develop from the union of a single egg and sperm. Because identical twins have the same genetic inheritance, their differences may result from environmental influences such as home life or education. Genetic and environmental effects are even more easily seen if the twins are raised by different families. Twin studies are controversial among scientists, however, and their results must be analyzed with care.

Name of Trait	Inheritance Pattern	Caused by	Phenotype
sickle cell anemia	single allele	codominant alleles	deformed erythrocytes
hemophilia	sex-linked	recessive allele	inadequate blood clotting
Down syndrome	chromosomal	nondisjunction	mental retardation

Graphic Organizer Use this table in Organizing Information on p. 171.

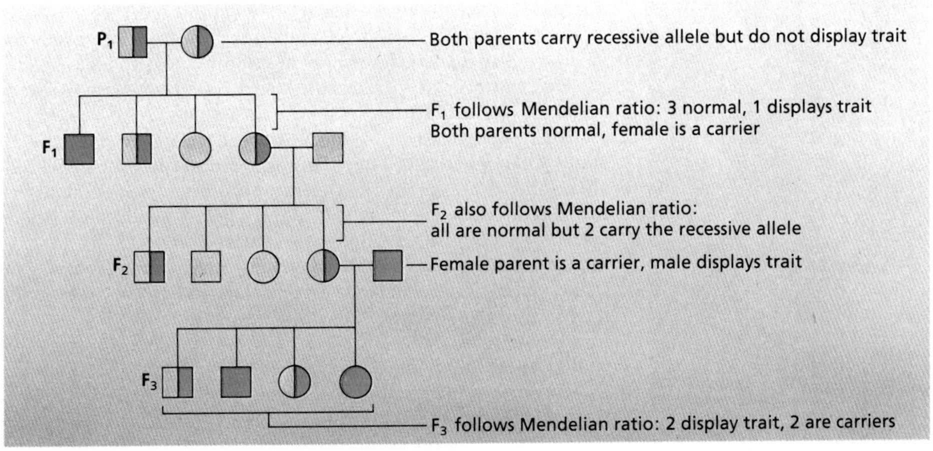

Figure 11-8 By studying inheritance patterns of a certain trait over several generations of a family, geneticists sometimes can determine who is a carrier of the trait.

Pedigree Studies

Geneticists may also trace a **pedigree,** a family record that shows how a trait is inherited over several generations. Analysis of inheritance patterns produces a pedigree like the one shown in Figure 11-8. A pedigree often reveals a **carrier,** someone who is heterozygous for a trait. Carriers do not have the trait themselves but may pass it on to their offspring.

Human Genetic Traits

Studies of human genetics, including population sampling, twin studies, and pedigree analysis, have identified a number of patterns of inheritance. More modern genetic techniques, which are discussed in Chapter 12, have added to our knowledge of human genetics.

Single-Allele Traits

Traits controlled by a single allele of a gene are called single-allele traits. Geneticists have identified about 200 human traits that are coded by single, dominant alleles. About 250 other single-allele traits are coded by homozygous recessive alleles. Some single-allele traits are controlled by a codominant allele.

Sickle-cell disease, often called sickle-cell anemia, is a single-allele disorder that operates in a codominant system. The dominant allele A produces normal hemoglobin that results in round erythrocytes. The codominant allele A′ codes for abnormal hemoglobin and results in sickle-shaped erythrocytes. AA individuals have normal hemoglobin and normal erythrocytes. Heterozygous individuals (AA′) have both normal and abnormal hemoglobin and intermediate shaped cells. A′A′ individuals only have sickle cells.

Teaching Strategies

Interpreting the Visuals Refer students to the pedigree charts in Figures 11-8 (an autosomal trait) and 11-11 (a sex-linked trait), and have them compare how the traits are passed on from generation to generation. ■ *See* Process Skills, *Chapter 11.*

Drawing Conclusions Explain that sickling of erythrocytes results when bonding patterns in hemoglobin are changed as the result of a point mutation that replaces a single amino acid (glutamic acid) in the hemoglobin chain with another amino acid (valine). Then review with students Table 8-1 on p. 121, and have them find glutamic acid and valine. Finally, ask students if a large genetic change is required to make a large change in an organism. *(No; the mutation for sickle-cell anemia shows how a small change in the hemoglobin gene can make a large change in the properties of the protein, which causes a serious disease in people.)*

Organizing Information Have students make a table of the human genetic traits covered in this section. Include columns for the name of the trait, its inheritance pattern, its genetic cause, and a description of its phenotype. Use the table on p. 170 as a model.

Videodiscs

- *2635, Normal Human Diploid Chromosomes (s)*
- *2640, How the Sperm Cell Determines Sex (s)*
- *Side 2 16113, Sickling Red Blood Cells (m)*
- *2636–2639, Independent Assortment and Possible Gametes (s)*
- *Side 2 16313, Platelets and Clotting (m)*

Inferring Relationships This section is a good place to introduce the "nature versus nurture" controversy, which is the argument between those who view the environment as the major force in human development and those who consider genetic heritage to be more important.

Ask questions to help students sort out the concepts. For instance: Some short people who were born in foreign countries and emigrated to the United States have had children who are taller than they are. Was the height of the children caused by their heredity or their environment? Encourage students to give rationales for their opinions on this issue. *(Allow for personal opinion.)* Explain that scientists consider differences between the typical diet in the United States and diets in other countries to be responsible for whether genetic potential was fully expressed. Point out that the nutrition of the parents was not necessarily worse, just different. Remind students that short people in the United States generally are *not* less healthy than tall people.

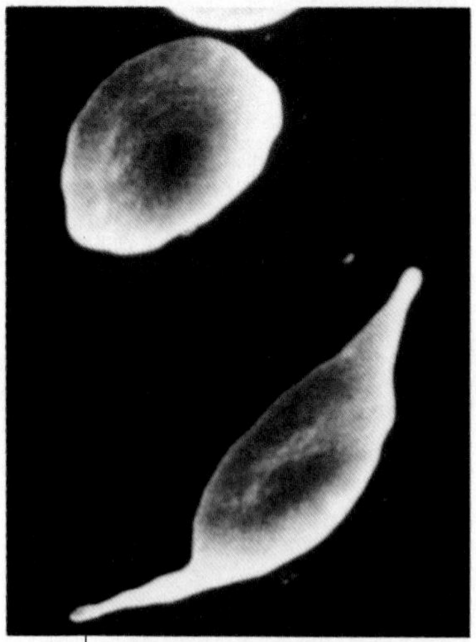

Figure 11-9 Sickle-cell disease is a genetically transmitted disorder that causes erythrocytes to become deformed and to clump together.

Sickle cells, shown in Figure 11-9, clump together, clog the capillaries, causing great pain, and impair the flow of oxygen to the body. The inadequate supply of erythrocytes produces severe anemia, which in turn leads to fatigue, headaches, cramps, and eventually to the failure of vital organs.

Sickle-cell disease primarily affects Blacks. In the United States about 9 percent of the Black population carry the sickle-cell allele. In Africa as many as 40 percent of some Black populations carry it. In these areas the sickle-cell allele actually gives some carriers an adaptive advantage. The parasite responsible for malaria, a leading cause of death in western Africa, cannot survive in sickle cells. Consequently, heterozygous individuals are more likely to survive malaria than normal individuals are.

Huntington disease, or HD, is a single-allele trait that is caused by a dominant allele. The first symptoms of HD—mild forgetfulness and irritability—appear when the victims are in their thirties or forties. In time Huntington disease causes loss of muscle control, uncontrollable physical spasms, severe mental illness, and eventually death.

Because the HD allele is dominant, any person who inherits the allele will develop the disease. Unfortunately, most carriers do

Biology in Process

Genetic Markers and Cystic Fibrosis

In 1989 two research groups working collaboratively in Michigan and Ontario announced the discovery of a gene responsible for cystic fibrosis (CF), the most common severe autosomal recessive disease among white North Americans. Children born with the disease experience difficulty in breathing. Mucus clogging their lungs becomes a growth medium for a variety of bacteria that cause respiratory infections. CF is eventually fatal—a child with the disease can expect to live for 20 to 30 years at most.

"Looking for a cystic fibrosis gene was like looking for a house in a city between New York and Los Angeles without a street address," said Dr. Lap-Chee Tsui of the research team. If you know that the house is in Tulsa, Oklahoma the task becomes a little easier. If you know that the house is close to a fire station and a church, the task becomes easier still. Genetic markers—short recognizable sections of DNA—are the biological equivalents of the fire station and the church. By looking for linkages between the inheritance of cystic fibrosis and the inheritance of known markers, the team was finally able to locate the gene

172 *Chapter 11*

More Information

Huntington Disease The search for a genetic marker for the Huntington disease (HD) allele took North American investigators to Lake Maracaibo in Venezuela. Among the villagers there are an unusual number of HD victims. The HD victims and their families, a relatively isolated population, may have descended from a European sailor from the 1800s or a Venezuelan ancestor who experienced a spontaneous mutation. The villagers call the devastating sickness in Spanish *El Mal,* literally meaning "the bad."

The investigators obtained blood samples from HD victims, then looked for small variations in the DNA associated with the inheritance of *El Mal*—eventually finding a genetic marker for the HD allele.

not know they have the disease until after they have had children. Thus the disease is unknowingly passed on from one generation to the next. Recently, however, geneticists discovered a **genetic marker**—a short section of DNA that indicates the presence of an allele that codes for a trait—for the HD allele. People who possess this genetic marker have a 96 percent chance of developing HD. By conducting a simple test on sample cells, geneticists are now able to inform a person of the presence of the marker before he or she has children.

Polygenic Traits

In humans, characteristics are sometimes controlled by a single gene, but frequently a characteristic may be controlled by several genes. A trait that is controlled by two or more genes is called a **polygenic trait.** Skin color, for example, is determined by the additive effect of from four to seven genes. Each contributes a certain amount of the protein melanin, a color pigment. The more melanin produced, the darker the skin; the less melanin produced, the lighter the skin. A similar mechanism determines eye color. Light blue eyes have little melanin. Very dark brown eyes have a great deal of melanin.

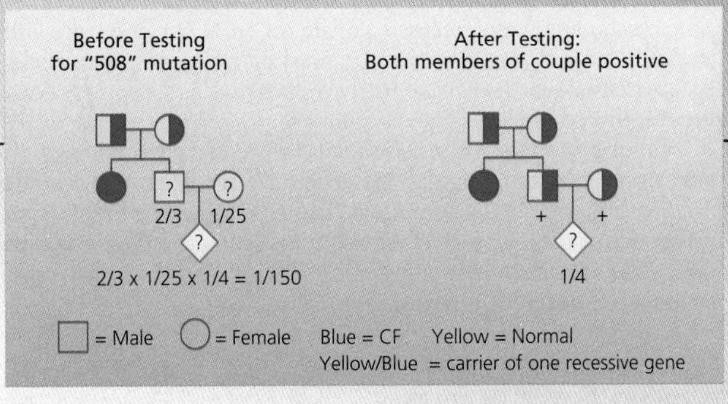

responsible for CF—it is on chromosome 7.

Next, the researchers identified the nucleotide sequence of the CF gene, which enabled them to look for a mutation that never occurred in normal genes. Each biological parent of a CF child has one mutant gene and one normal gene. By comparing chromosomes from the parents with chromosomes from their child, researchers found that the most common CF mutation is the deletion of a codon. This deletion means that a phenylalanine will be missing at position 508 in the CF protein, which is composed of 1,480 amino acids.

Now that scientists have identified the CF protein, which regulates the transport of chloride ions out of cells, they can begin to understand how defective CF protein harms the body. They hope soon to be able to experiment with a number of possible treatments.

Medical geneticists have begun to use a test for the presence of the mutation in position 508 in genetic screening for CF. In the general public, one person in 25 is a carrier, and a person whose sibling had CF has a 2/3 chance of being a carrier. But if that person and his or her spouse both test positive for the position-508 mutation, any of their children have a probability of 1/4 of inheriting two recessive genes.

■ How are scientists able to predict the chances of passing on cystic fibrosis to a child?

Biology in Process

Using the Feature

The feature focuses on the process skills of collecting and analyzing data and on predicting. Emphasize to students that initially researchers used linkage data to find the general location of the suspected CF gene on chromosome 7, but eventually they compared the DNA of mutant and normal genes to identify the mutant base pairs. Point out that scientists used the normal genes as a control group.

The screening of possible carriers involves the process of predicting, and prospective parents tested for the position-508 mutation may need genetic counseling to understand the predictions. Refer students to the pedigree, and ask them what might be the impact upon a couple hearing that any future children have a 1/4 chance of inheriting cystic fibrosis as opposed to a 1/150 chance.

Point out that in 25 to 30 percent of the cases, the disease is caused by one of 50 mutations other than the position-508 mutation. Ask students to discuss the situation that results from the absence of a test to screen for these other mutations. *(If a person tests negative for the position-508 mutation, he or she still has a chance of carrying one of the less common CF mutations.)*

Answer to the Feature

Scientists can test prospective parents who have a family history of CF for a common CF mutation, and predict their chances of passing on the disease.

Exploring Careers Ask a genetics counselor or a physician to speak to students about the process and advisability of genetic counseling.

Comparing Concepts Make sure that your students are careful to distinguish between sex-linked traits and sex-influenced traits and between a polygenic trait and one caused by multiple alleles. Point out that sex-linked traits are determined by alleles located only on the X chromosome. Stress that alleles on autosomes code for sex-influenced traits, and that male or female hormones "influence" the expression of these traits. Point out that in the case of multiple-allele traits, three or more alleles of the same gene are inherited two at a time. On the other hand, a polygenic trait is coded by several individual genes.

Guided Practice

Construct pedigrees with three or four generations for either single allele, multiple allele, sex-linked, or sex-influenced traits. The pedigree shown below is one example. Provide only enough information to get students started, and let them determine what kind of trait is being inherited, as well as what possible genotypes.

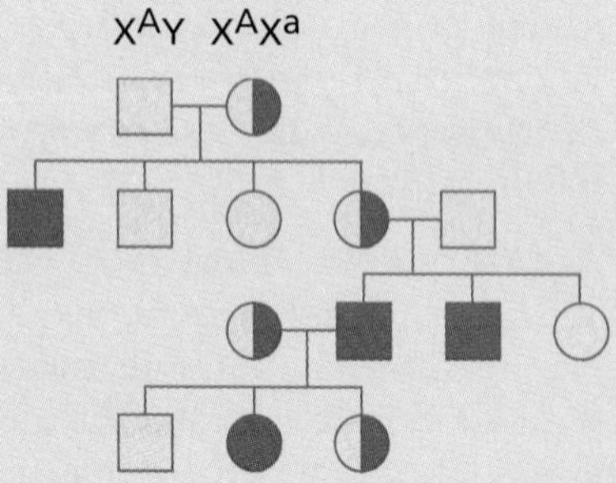

Table 11-2 Possible Genotypes and Phenotypes

Genotype	Blood Type
I^A I^A	A
I^A i^O	A
I^B I^B	B
I^B i^O	B
I^A I^B	AB
i^O i^O	O

Multiple-Allele Traits

Some human traits are controlled by multiple alleles, three or more alleles of the same gene that code for a single trait. For example, in humans there are three alleles that code for blood type: I^A, I^B, and i^O. Any individual has two of these alleles, which together make up the gene for blood type. The alleles I^A and I^B are codominant, and both are dominant to the i^O allele. Study Table 11-2 to see which combination of alleles determines each blood type.

The kind of antigen or antigens produced by a specific combination of alleles determines blood type. An **antigen** is a substance that causes the body to produce an antibody. The presence of antigen A or B determines the type of blood a person can receive in a transfusion. Mixing incompatible types of blood causes the cells to clump together, or agglutinate. For example, type O blood has no antigens and contains A and B antibodies. Therefore people with type O blood can receive blood only from donors with type O blood.

Sex-Linked Traits

Certain human traits are sex linked; that is, the alleles for these traits appear only on the X chromosome. Males have only one X chromosome. Since no complementary portion of the Y chromosome exists, any single recessive allele on an X chromosome will be expressed because it cannot be masked by a dominant allele. Males are therefore far more likely than females to express recessive sex-linked alleles.

Color blindness is a recessive sex-linked disorder in which an individual cannot distinguish between certain colors. Many kinds of color blindness exist, the most common being the inability to distinguish red from green. About 8 percent of males are color blind. The condition is rare in females. Figure 11-10 presents test patterns for different types of color blindness.

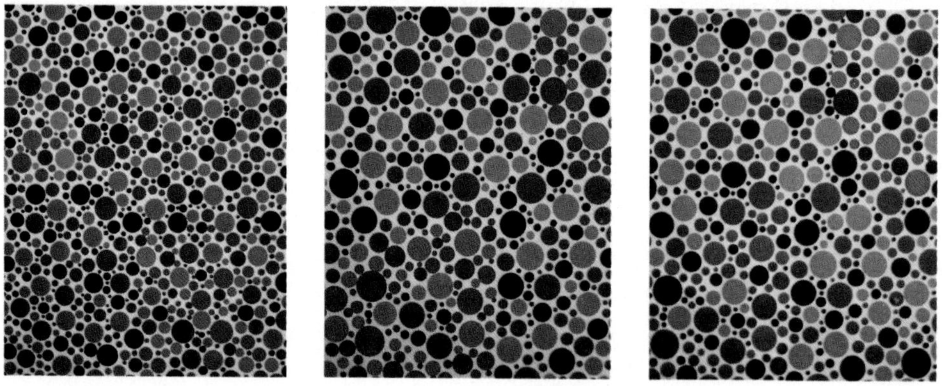

Figure 11-10 Color blindness, a recessive sex-linked trait, affects about 8 percent of males. The patterns test for different types of color blindness: red–green (left and center) and blue–yellow (right). An individual who cannot see the characters in the pattern may have that type of color blindness.

Cooperative Learning

The Human Karyotype Have students work in groups of three to produce a karyotype from a photograph of human chromosomes that were stained in a squashed cell. Have one group member cut out the chromosomes. Have the second group member arrange them into pairs. Have the third group member then paste the chromosomes down onto a sheet of paper. Tell the sorting student to follow the advice of the other two, and ask all three students to decide on the criteria for sorting—the differences and similarities.

You can find photographs of unpaired human chromosomes in college biology or genetics textbooks. Make an enlarged photocopy for each group.

Another recessive sex-linked trait that is found primarily in males is **hemophilia.** The blood of hemophiliacs lacks a protein that is essential for clotting. Though very different in their manifestations, both color blindness and hemophilia are inherited through the same pattern. Study Figure 11-11 to see how a recessive, sex-linked allele is inherited.

Sex-Influenced Traits

The presence of male or female sex hormones influences the expression of certain human traits, called **sex-influenced traits.** The alleles that code for most of these traits are on the autosomes. Males and females have the same alleles, but the trait is expressed in only one sex. Pattern baldness is a familiar sex-influenced trait. The allele for baldness, B, is dominant in males but recessive in females. Both men and women with BB alleles will eventually lose their hair. A heterozygous woman (BB′) will not lose her hair, but a heterozygous man (BB′) will. These differences result from the presence of particular sex hormones.

Nondisjunction

Some genetic disorders result from nondisjunction. Remember from Section 11.1 that nondisjunction is the failure of chromatids to separate during cell division. When this occurs during meiosis II, the result may be a sperm or an egg cell with either an extra or a missing chromosome. In humans, for example, if nondisjunction occurs during sperm formation, one sperm cell may have 22 chromosomes, and another may have 24. If one of these gametes combines with a normal egg, the zygote will have either 45 or 47 chromosomes. A zygote with 45 chromosomes has only one of a particular chromosome, a condition called **monosomy.** A zygote with 47 chromosomes has three of a particular chromosome, a condition called **trisomy.**

An extra chromosome 21, for example, results in **Down syndrome,** a disorder characterized by mental retardation, a fold of skin above the eyes, and weak muscles. Nondisjunction also affects sex chromosomes. Klinefelter syndrome results from the trisomic genotype XXY. Klinefelter individuals may be mentally retarded and have low fertility. Turner syndrome is a monosomic condition with the genotype XO. An XO female is characterized by immature physical development, sterility, and a webbed neck.

Detecting Genetic Disorders

A person with a family history of genetic disorders may wish to undergo genetic screening before having children. **Genetic screening** is an examination of a person's genetic makeup. It may involve making a **karyotype,** which is a picture of an individual's chromosomes. The individual's blood may also be tested for the presence or absence of certain enzymes. These procedures can reveal potential genetic disorders that might be passed on to children.

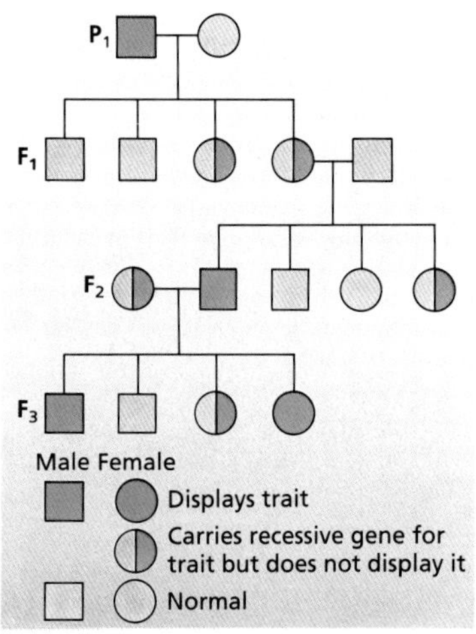

Figure 11-11 Hemophilia, a sex-linked trait, is expressed primarily in males. Most females with the allele are heterozygous and therefore are carriers.

Independent Practice

- Have students write answers to the Section Review.
- Give students crosses of various types on which to practice, or give them the products of such crosses and ask them to work back to determine the type of inheritance that is being shown. For example, if a child is born with type O blood, what possible genotypes can be inferred for the parents? *(Both parents of a type O child must have an i^O allele. They can be I^Ai^O, I^Bi^O, or i^Oi^O.)*

Check Your Understanding

1. How does a pedigree identify a carrier of an autosomal recessive trait? *(Both parents must be carriers if any of their offspring show the trait.)*
2. Why is a blood type called a multiple-allele trait? *(It is controlled by three alleles, although only two alleles are present in one individual.)*
3. From which parent does a boy inherit color blindness? Why? *(The son inherits color blindness from his mother, because the Y chromosome from his father does not carry an allele for color blindness.)*
4. Explain how nondisjunction causes Down syndrome. *(During meiosis, the chromatids of chromosome 21 do not separate. Therefore, the zygote receives an extra chromosome 21 during fertilization.)*

Interdisciplinary Activity

History Genetics and history came together in the story of Queen Victoria of England and her descendants. The queen was a heterozygous carrier of hemophilia, the disorder in which a person lacks a blood protein essential for clotting. Have students research the genetic pattern of Victoria's descendants. Visually oriented students can prepare a poster-sized pedigree to show the rest of the class how the trait spread through several European families. Other students can research the history of Queen Victoria's offspring, including the last royal family of Russia.

Reteaching

Compare the inheritance in humans of recessive single-allele, dominant single-allele, multiple-allele, and sex-linked traits. Use examples from the pupil text—sickle-cell disease, Huntington disease, blood type, and color blindness—and show on the board some Punnett squares for each trait. Ask students to identify similarities and differences in patterns of inheritance.

■ *See* Section Reviews *worksheet, Section 11.3.*

Enrichment

Have students use library resources to research human genetic disorders other than those covered in the section. Possible topics include fragile X syndrome, thalassemia, and Tay-Sachs disease. Ask them to identify the inheritance pattern of each disorder and report their findings to the class.

Closure

Divide the class into small groups. Have students discuss why people who are in groups at high risk for certain disorders (such as sickle-cell anemia) or whose families have a history of genetic disease (such as Huntington disease) might need genetic counseling. *(Students might mention, for example, the concerns of a couple who are unsure about the chances of their passing a genetic disorder on to their offspring.)*

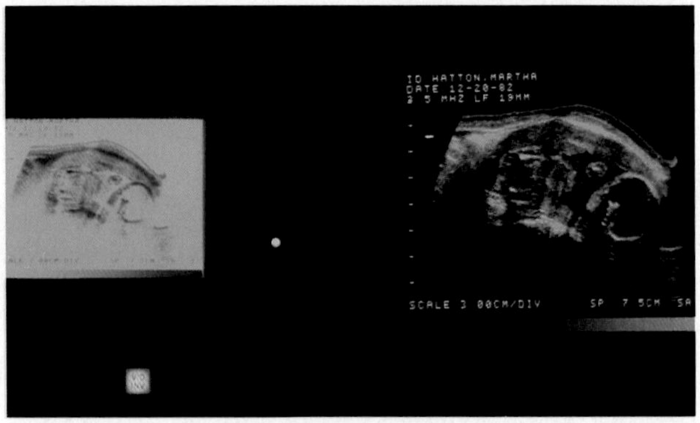

Figure 11-12 By using ultrasound physicians can create an image of the fetus in the uterus. Can you see the image of the fetus?

To prepare a karyotype, a scientist removes chromosomes from a cell, then stains and photographs them. Each chromosome is cut from the enlarged photo and matched with a photograph of its homologue. Scientists can then spot chromosomal abnormalities. Couples at genetic risk may wish to undergo **genetic counseling,** a type of counseling that informs them about problems that could affect their offspring.

Physicians can also diagnose more than 200 genetic disorders in the fetus through procedures such as amniocentesis, fetoscopy, ultrasound, and chorion villi sampling. In **amniocentesis** the physician uses a needle and syringe to remove a small amount of amniotic fluid from the amnion, the sac that surrounds the fetus. The physician makes a karyotype and analyzes cells that have sloughed off from the fetus and float in the amniotic fluid. In **fetoscopy** the physician inserts a tiny camera through a small incision in the uterus. The physician can observe the fetus's development and take skin and blood samples for analysis. Physicians may also analyze fetal development by using **ultrasound,** a technique in which high-frequency sound waves bounce off the fetus, forming an image. Figure 11-12 shows such an image, called a sonogram. In **chorion villi sampling** the physician analyzes a sample of the chorion villi, which grow between the mother's uterus and the placenta. Since the villi have the same genetic makeup as the fetus, the physician is able to detect genetic disorders.

Section Review

1. Distinguish between *sex-linked* and *sex-influenced traits.*
2. What methods do geneticists use to study human genetics?
3. How does an individual who is heterozygous for the sickle-cell gene benefit in equatorial regions?
4. List three genetic tests that can be done on the fetus during pregnancy.
5. If a couple has four children with different blood types, what are the genotypes of the parents' blood types?

Answers to Section Review

1. Sex-linked traits are carried on the X chromosome. Sex-influenced traits are carried on autosomes, and their expression is controlled by sex hormones.
2. Population sampling, twin studies, and pedigree studies
3. Being heterozygous improves the chances of surviving malaria, a leading cause of death in equatorial areas.
4. Amniocentesis, fetoscopy, ultrasound, chorion villi sampling
5. One parent is I^Ai^O and the other is I^Bi^O.

Laboratory

Exploring Hereditary Traits

Objective
To determine your possible genotypes for some inherited traits

Process Skills
Observing, communicating, inferring

Materials
Pencil, paper

Inquiry

1 Make a table with three columns and nine rows. Head the columns Trait, Phenotype, and Possible Genotypes. In the first column list the nine traits shown below.

2 In the second column of the table, write yes or no depending on whether or not you possess each trait. Work with a partner. For traits that you cannot observe directly, ask your partner for help. Each of the traits listed is controlled by a dominant allele.

- *Tongue-rolling* (R): Stick out your tongue and try to roll up the sides so that the tongue forms a U-shape.
- *Free earlobe* (F): The lobe of the ear hangs freely below the point of attachment to the head.
- *Widow's peak* (W): The midpoint of the hairline along the front of the forehead points downward.
- *Straight thumb* (N): When extended from the palm of the hand, the top segment of the thumb forms a straight line with the bottom segment. (See figure.)
- *Bent little finger* (B): The last segment of the little finger bends in toward the ring finger.
- *Left-over-right thumb crossing* (L): When the hands are folded in a natural fashion, the left thumb crosses over the right.
- *Chin cleft* (C): The center of the chin has an indentation resembling a deep dimple.

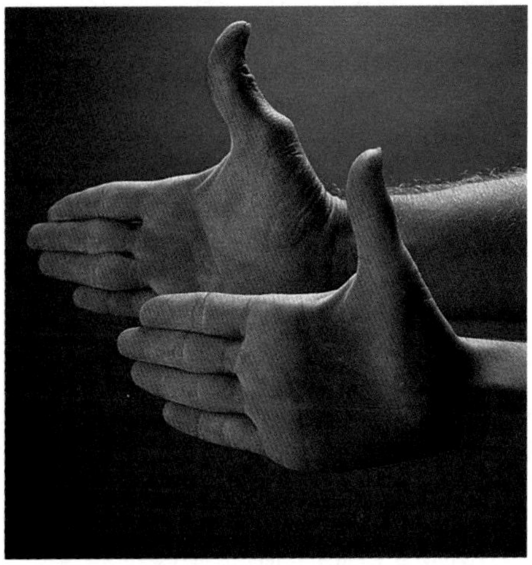

- *Mid-digital hair* (H): Hair is present on the middle section of any of the fingers.
- *Short big toe* (T): The big toe is shorter than the second toe.

3 In the third column of the table, record your possible genotypes for each trait, using the appropriate symbols.

4 Compare your traits with those of your classmates. Which trait or traits are most common among your classmates?

Conclusions

1 Which observations are evidence that the most common trait may not be determined by the dominant allele? Which dominant alleles studied today were most common?

2 What factors should be considered before comparing the frequency of traits in the classroom with their frequency in the U.S. population?

Further Inquiry
Review all the traits studied and discuss in class possible adaptive advantage of each trait.

(For an overview of hereditary traits and preparatory information related to the laboratory, see p. 161B.)

Inquiry

3. Answers for the possible genotypes include: RR, Rr, rr; FF, Ff, ff; WW, Ww, ww; NN, Nn, nn; BB, Bb, bb; LL,Ll, ll; CC, Cc, cc; HH, Hh, hh; TT, Tt, tt.

4. Answer will depend on the characteristics of your local population.

Conclusions

1. Several of the dominant forms of the traits studied in the lab are not common in most populations. In these cases, the homozygous recessive phenotype occurs more frequently. The alleles most commonly expressed will vary from one local population to another.

2. The class is a very small sample size and is not likely to reflect accurately the actual frequency of traits in the larger U.S. population. Refer students to Section 2.2, p. 28.

Further Inquiry
Encourage students to be imaginative and speculative. Remind them that some traits may not have an obvious adaptive or survival advantage.

Vocabulary

1. One map unit is the distance that equals one percentage point of crossing-over.
2. The addition or deletion of a nitrogen base is called a frameshift mutation.
3. A genetic marker is a short DNA segment that can be used to locate the alleles for a trait.
4. Monosomy involves having only one chromosome of a particular pair; trisomy involves having three of a particular chromosome.
5. In genetic screening, karyotypes of the prospective parents are prepared, and their blood is tested for enzymes that could suggest genetic abnormalities. In genetic counseling people are informed about genetic problems that could affect potential offspring.

Review

1. c	**6.** b
2. d	**7.** c
3. d	**8.** b
4. c	**9.** d
5. a	**10.** a

11. Mutations may simply occur by chance, without external cause. They may also be caused by environmental factors called mutagens.
12. When a replicated chromosome pair fails to separate during cell division, the chromosomal mutation is called nondisjunction.
13. Male fruit flies have the genotype XY; females are XX. In birds, males are XX; females are XY. In grasshoppers, males are XO; females are XX.
14. In a cross between a heterozygous red-eyed female (X^RX^r) and a red-eyed male (X^RY), all white-eyed offspring were male (X^rY).
15. They have the same genetic makeup; differences between them may be the result of environmental factors.

Chapter 11 Review

Vocabulary

Ames test (164)
amniocentesis (176)
antigen (174)
autosome (165)
carrier (171)
chorion villi sampling (176)
chromosome map (167)
deletion (163)
Down syndrome (175)
fetoscopy (176)
frameshift mutation (164)
genetic counseling (176)
genetic marker (173)
genetic screening (175)
germ cell mutation (163)
hemophilia (175)
Huntington disease (172)
inversion (163)
karyotype (175)
linkage group (166)
map unit (168)
monosomy (175)
mutagen (164)
mutation (163)
nondisjunction (164)
pedigree (171)
point mutation (164)
polygenic trait (173)
population sampling (170)
sex chromosome (165)
sex-influenced trait (175)
sex-linked trait (166)
sickle-cell disease (171)
somatic mutation (163)
translocation (163)
trisomy (175)
ultrasound (176)

1. What is a map unit?
2. What is a frameshift mutation?
3. Define a genetic marker.
4. Distinguish monosomy from trisomy.
5. Distinguish between genetic screening and genetic counseling.

Review

1. The addition or removal of a single nitrogen base results in (a) nondisjunction (b) trisomy or monosomy (c) a frameshift mutation (d) a translocation.
2. A point mutation involves substitution, addition, or deletion of a (a) codon (b) gene (c) DNA strand (d) nitrogen base.
3. The advantages of using *Drosophila* in genetic studies do not include individuals having (a) a short life cycle (b) many individuals produced in a mating (c) easily distinguishable characteristics (d) many chromosomes.
4. If a heterozygous red-eyed female *Drosophila* is crossed with a red-eyed male, the eyes of male offspring will be (a) all red (b) three-fourths red, one-fourth white (c) half red, half white (d) one-fourth red, three-fourths white.
5. The first chromosome map was constructed by (a) Alfred H. Sturtevant (b) Thomas Hunt Morgan (c) Gregor Mendel (d) Walter Sutton.
6. Geneticists may use pedigrees to determine (a) genetic and environmental effects on a trait (b) whether someone is a carrier for a disorder (c) the frequency of a gene in a population at large (d) the position of a gene on a chromosome.
7. Baldness is a (a) sex-linked trait (b) polygenic trait (c) sex-influenced trait (d) multiple-allele trait.
8. Klinefelter syndrome is an example of (a) monosomy (b) trisomy (c) a point mutation (d) a translocation.
9. The test that can yield information on the fetus is (a) fetoscopy (b) chorion villi sampling (c) ultrasound (d) all of the above.
10. Karyotypes enable scientists to identify (a) chromosomal abnormalities (b) blood type (c) point mutations (d) carriers for recessive traits.
11. What causes mutations?
12. What is nondisjunction?
13. Identify the genotypes of male and female fruit flies, birds, and grasshoppers.

16. Geneticists have identified a genetic marker; 96 percent of people with this marker develop HD.
17. The sickle-cell allele results from a point mutation that causes a base substitution, thus altering the structure of the hemoglobin molecule.
18. Genotypes I^AI^A and I^AI^O
19. Hair, skin, or eye color
20. Researchers looked for and found linkages between the inheritance of cystic fibrosis and known genetic markers, then found the nucleotide that produces CF.

14. What evidence led Morgan to hypothesize that the gene for eye color in *Drosophila* was carried on the X chromosome?
15. Why are identical twins useful in studies in human genetics?
16. How do geneticists detect the allele for Huntington disease?
17. How is the sickle-cell allele produced?
18. Identify the possible genotypes that could produce blood type A.
19. Give an example of a polygenic trait.
20. How did Dr. Tsui and the research team finally identify the gene responsible for cystic fibrosis?

Critical Thinking

1. The diagram at the right shows the banding pattern of human chromosomes 8 and 14. These chromosomes sometimes break at the dotted lines, and translocation occurs. Draw the mutant chromosomes that would result from such a translocation. Note: This translocation has been found in Burkitt lymphoma, a cancer of the immune system.
2. The mutagens known as substituted acridines are planar molecules with three-ring structures. They are about the same size as a DNA base pair and can slip between DNA base pairs, causing a frameshift mutation. Suppose one strand of DNA read TAC, GAA, TCG, GGT, ATT before mutation. If acridine caused a *G* to be inserted between two *A*s, what would the new sequence be? The commas are only to help identify groups of three.
3. In *Drosophila* body color and wing length are on the same chromosome. Gray body (G) is dominant to black body (g) and long wings (L) are dominant to short wings (l). Draw a Punnett square for the cross GgLl × GgLl, and show the phenotypic and genotypic ratios. Assume both dominants are on the same chromosome.
4. Sickle-cell disease is caused by a point

Chromosome 8 Chromosome 14

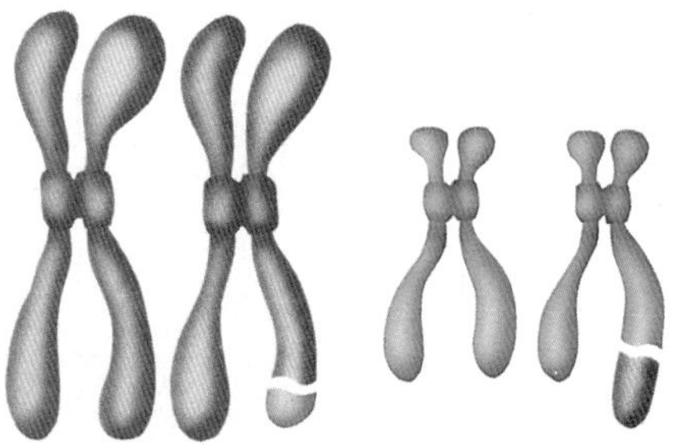

mutation in the hemoglobin gene, resulting in a valine being substituted for a glutamic acid. Show the sequence of the codon before and after the point mutation. Refer to Chapter 8 for the code.
5. The levels of enzymes in normal humans vary. Suppose you are a geneticist who wants to determine the normal level of a certain enzyme in human white blood cells. What types of people should you include in your sample?
6. Generally individuals who are heterozygous for sickle-cell disease have no symptoms of the disease. However, they should avoid extreme oxygen stress such as vigorous sports at high altitudes. Explain why this would be necessary.

Extension

1. Read the article by Larry Thompson entitled "Mom and Pop Genes" in *Discover*, February 1991, p. 20. Discuss the significance of the surprising discovery about chromosome number 15.
2. Using the notation given in this chapter, make a pedigree of your own family. If there is a history of disease, such as cancer or diabetes, be sure to note that.

Critical Thinking

1.

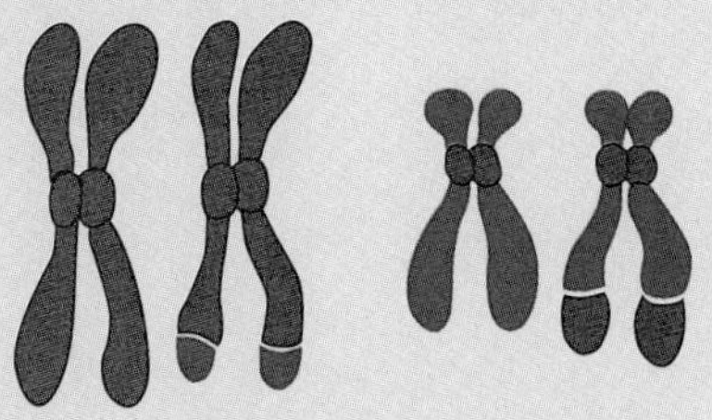

2. The sequence should be: TAC, GAG, ATC, GGG, TAT, T.
3. The phenotypic ratio is 3 gray-bodied, long-winged : 1 black-bodied, short-winged. The genotypic ratio is 1 GGLL : 2 GgLl : 1 ggll.

	GL	gl
Gl	GGLL	GgLl
gl	GgLl	ggll

4. The normal sequence of the codon is GAG (mRNA codon). The mutant codon is GUG.
5. A sample should include people of both sexes, all races, different ages, and as many ethnic groups as possible.
6. Exercise at high altitudes requires a great deal of oxygen, yet oxygen levels are low at high altitudes. This shortage of oxygen could cause symptoms in heterozygous individuals since they do have some sickle cells.

Extension

1. Students should stress that "Mom and Pop genes" function differently from genes that follow Mendelian principles.
2. Be sensitive to the feelings of students not living with their biological parents. Although many students enjoy exploring family genetic history, this activity can be problematic for students who were adopted or are living with foster families or a stepparent.

Chapter 12 Gene Expression

Chapter Overview

In Chapter 12 students will learn how genes control cellular events under normal conditions and how the process of normal cell division can be disrupted. Section 12.1 describes the chemistry of gene activation and the genetic control of protein formation. Section 12.2 introduces the process of tissue development in multicellular, sexually reproducing organisms and also relates ungoverned tissue development to cancer.

Chapter Planning Chart

B	S	A	Sections and Subsections	Page	Features	Page	Resources
		•	**12.1 Control of Gene Expression**				
			Gene Expression in Prokaryotes	181	Section Review	183	Videodiscs
			Gene Expression in Eukaryotes	182			Blackline Master 27
							Overhead Transparency T12
							Laboratories: Gene Regulation
							Section Reviews Worksheet
		•	**12.2 Morphogenesis**				
			Homeotic Genes	184	Biology in Process	184	Videodiscs
			Cancer	186	Think	186	Process Skills: Causes of Cancer
					Laboratory	187	Section Reviews Worksheet
					Section Review	186	
			End of Chapter Activities				
					Chapter Review	188	Vocabulary Skills
							Chapter Test
							Computer Test Generator

B *The Basic Level curriculum presents the most fundamental knowledge offered in the course.*
S *The Standard Level curriculum is designed for the average student who is able to master most topics.*
A *The Advanced Level curriculum includes suggestions for teaching the most academically able students.*

Cooperative Learning

Group Activity: Eukaryotic Gene Expression

- **Group Size:** *3 students*
- **Outcome:** *Students will compare the three basic processes in gene expression.*
- **Individual Accountability:** *Each student will diagram or outline one of the three processes.*
- **Positive Interdependence:** *The group will discuss the processes and verify that each member understands all three.*

Refer the students to "Gene Expression in Eukaryotes" on pp. 182–183. Have one student of each group review the first two paragraphs. *(The student should note the anatomy of nucleosomes, their uncoiling, and the subsequent availability of DNA for chemical reactions.)* Have a second group member review "Enhancer Control." *(This subsection can be represented by a diagram, for example, one with arrows indicating that estrogen plus a receptor activates an enhancer that permits RNA polymerase to form a protein that breaks down estrogen.)* The third group member will review "mRNA Cleavage." *(This student should note the gene anatomy and the action in the cytoplasm, with the exon mRNA plus cap and tail ready to synthesize proteins.)*

Suggest that each student prepare a simplified version of his or her portion, condensing the text into an outline, diagram, or other summary. Then have each student explain the process he or she has summarized to the other members of the group.

Concept Map

The following is one possible solution to the concept mapping activity in Guided Practice on p. 182.

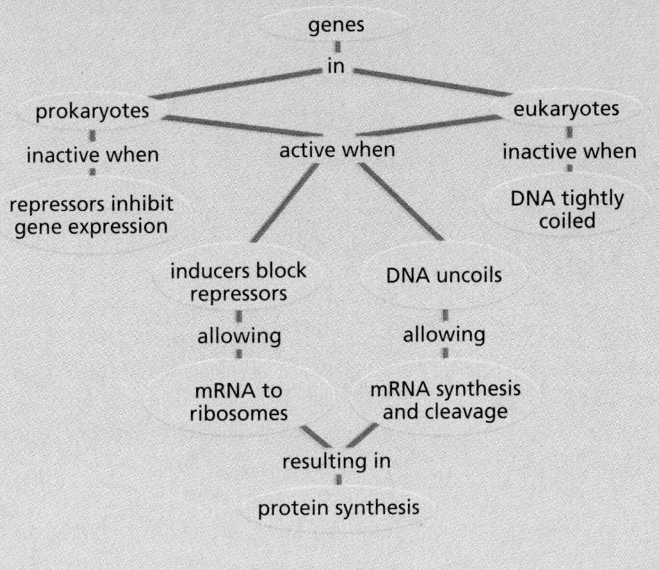

Laboratory Preparation

Overview *(See p. 187.)*

During development and in adult metabolism, multigene groups often direct the formation of complex body parts. Each gene has its characteristic protein synthesized at a specific time under specific conditions.

The hatching and larval leg development of brine shrimp is an example of such complex development. This crustacean, *Artemia salina,* lives in salt or brackish water. Out of water, its fertilized eggs withstand desiccation for years, but a salt solution stimulates the embryo to hatch into a larva called a nauplius, which has 12 larval stages. Early larvae have three pairs of legs, then grow additional pairs. *Artemia* eat flagellates and bottom detritus; yeast is a good laboratory food.

Preparation

If possible, use two aquariums per group of 3–10 students or, if necessary, per class. In place of aquariums, you can also use clean, wide-mouthed, 4-liter clear glass or plastic containers. Use noniodized salt to make the NaCl solution of 0.35% to 1.5%.

Swimming larvae hatch and develop in 24–48 hours, depending on local conditions. Have volunteers feed yeast to the larvae each week.

Teaching Tips

Help students identify the role of environment in gene expression; brine shrimp eggs hatch only in water.

Before removing the larvae and aerator to the clean solution in aquarium 2, be sure that most eggs have hatched. Emphasize to students that transferring the shrimp weekly to a clean aquarium of freshly made salt solution (alternating aquariums 1 and 2) keeps the shrimp healthy and comfortable. To concentrate shrimp for easy capture and transfer, place a bright light at one end of the aquarium.

Depending on the size of the developing larvae, direct students to use either a compound or dissecting microscope. Have them describe specific examples of the increasing complexity they observe.

Ask students to observe other structures and behaviors: What is the mouth shape? *(Round)* Which legs bring food to the mouth? *(Those just behind the antennae)* Count the body segments. *(3, then 12, then 20)*

Dispose of the brine shrimp usefully. They are an excellent food for aquarium fish (rinse first).

Safety

Remind students to wash their hands after each laboratory session.

Chapter Themes

Scale and Structure This chapter will introduce students to the innermost workings of cells. Emphasize the fact that even at the tiniest scale, the life of an organism is dependent on a myriad of "moving parts." Help students understand that a change in one small part of a molecule can cause a large change in an organism.

Systems and Interactions Stress that gene expression is due to a series of chemical reactions. Note how genes are involved in regulating the formation of various molecules, turning their production on and off. There are systems within the nucleus of a cell, which interact with systems in the cytoplasm of the cell.

Chapter Motivating Activity

Discuss illustrations of different kinds of developing embryos (Figure 15-5 on p. 224 is an example). Ask students to consider how a multicellular organism can grow from a single cell to a whole fish or rabbit or gorilla.

Remind students that all developmental changes are the result of chemical reactions. Ask them to name the group of organic compounds that control all the chemical reactions that take place in cells. *(Enzymes, a type of protein)* What controls the production of proteins? *(DNA, or genes)* What, then, causes a single cell to develop into a specific type of multicellular organism? *(DNA, or genes, through protein synthesis)*

Chapter 12 Gene Expression

Introduction

As you learned in Chapter 8, the information for protein synthesis is encoded in the DNA of a cell. Yet not all the cells of a single organism require identical amounts or types of proteins at all times. In this chapter you will learn how genes control the production of proteins in prokaryotes and eukaryotes and how this production affects the development of the organism. The study of gene expression is one of the most active areas of modern biological research.

Chapter Outline

Chapter Concept

As you read, notice how gene control results in changes in the organism's morphology and physiology.

Adult form of green darner, *Anax junius*. Below: Larval form of green darner.

Understanding the Visuals

Have students describe the differences between the larval and adult darner. *(They have significantly different body proportions: the adult is slimmer and more elongate, and its wings are fully developed.)* Remind students that new cells are produced as an organism grows and matures. Ask what cellular process causes the development of an insect from egg to larva to pupa to adult. *(Mitosis)* How do the chromosomes and genes compare in all cells of an insect? *(They are the same.)* The larva looks like a complete animal. Why did it not stay in the larval stage? *(Directions encoded in its genes caused the developmental changes.)* Stress that many detailed scientific questions about these processes remain unanswered.

12.1 Control of Gene Expression

Genes control the synthesis of proteins, which are the basis of the structure and physiology of a cell. **Gene expression** is the activation of a gene that results in the formation of a protein. By controlling gene expression cells regulate which proteins are active at any given time.

Gene Expression in Prokaryotes

Scientists first studied gene expression in prokaryotes. Much of our initial knowledge of gene expression comes from the work of French scientists François Jacob (1920–) and Jacques Monod (1910–1976). Jacob and Monod determined how genes control the metabolism of the disaccharide lactose in *Escherichia coli.*

Lactose provides energy for the intestinal bacterium *E. coli.* However, enzymes must both alter the cell's permeability to lactose and split lactose into two monosaccharides—glucose and galactose. These enzymes are proteins made up of a number of polypeptides. The DNA segment on the *E. coli* chromosome that codes for these polypeptides is called the ***lac* operon,** shown in Figure 12-1. An **operon** consists of three segments: a **promoter,** an **operator,** and **structural genes.** The activation of these segments on the operon controls gene expression.

Section Objectives

- *Define the* lac *operon, and explain how it is turned on and off.*
- *Describe control of a eukaryotic enhancer sequence.*
- *Explain how mRNA cleavage controls gene expression in eukaryotes.*

Figure 12-1 During the metabolism of lactose, the *lac* operon turns on. Lactose removes the repressor, allowing RNA polymerase to begin transcription of mRNA.

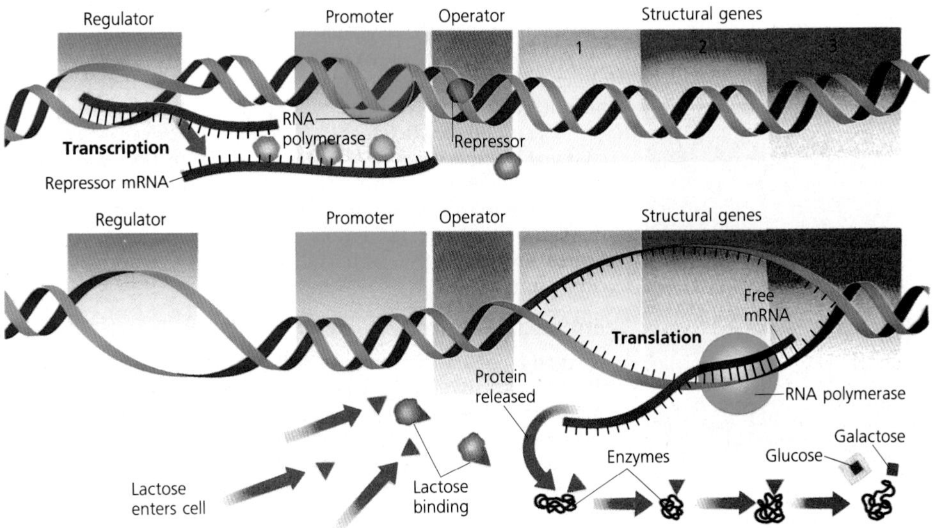

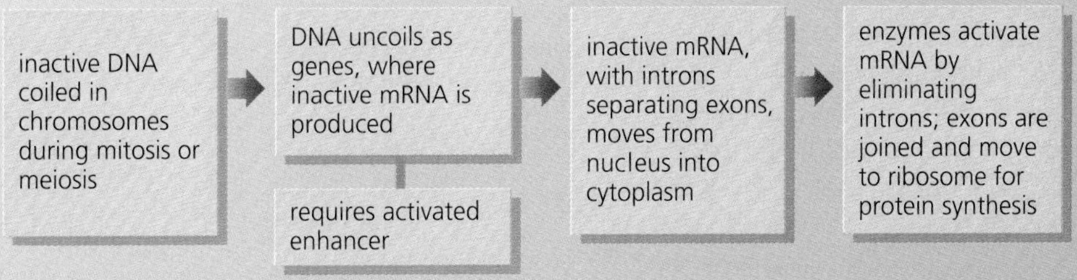

Graphic Organizer Use this sequential diagram in Reteaching on p. 183.

Lesson Plan

Section Focus

This section describes the complex chemical processes of gene expression in prokaryotes and eukaryotes.

Section Themes

This section emphasizes **Systems and Interactions.** In every living cell, the production of enzymes is constantly being turned on and off, enhancers are activated and deactivated, and introns are excised from mRNA before it interacts with cytoplasmic materials to form proteins.

Motivating Activity

Divide students into groups of about five or six, and direct them to keep their texts closed. Tell them each group will be in competition with other groups to remember material they learned back in Chapter 5. Tell them that after you name the topics to be recalled, each group should produce a numbered list giving as much information as they can recall about the topic. Tell them all correct information will be considered, including how to spell the terms. After all necessary general directions are understood, announce the two topics: "prokaryotes" and "eukaryotes." *(See the text on p. 65 for answers.)* After collecting results, explain to students that they will be studying prokaryotes and eukaryotes again in this lesson.

Teaching Strategies

Reviewing Concepts Review the meaning of the terms *monosaccharide* (p. 49), *disaccharide* (p. 50), *polypeptides* (p. 53), and *enzymes* (p. 53) used in the lesson.

Videodiscs

- ***Side 1 22695, Protein Synthesis (m)***

Using Analogies To help students understand the turning on and off of genes, demonstrate the components of the *lac* operon by plugging in a lamp and turning it on and off. Ask students to identify what corresponds to the inducer *(the switch in "on" position)*, promoter *(the electricity)*, operator site *(the lamp socket)*, and repressor *(the switch in "off" position)*.

Interpreting the Visuals Help students analyze Figure 12-1, p. 181. Tell them to follow the color coding. The blue repressor comes from the blue regulator gene. Stress that the top section represents the "off" condition of the gene, when no lactose is present. The bottom section represents the "on" condition, in which lactose has bound the repressors, the gene has begun its work, and lactose is being split into two monosaccharides.

- *See* **Overhead Transparency** *T12 and* **Blackline Master** *27.*
- *See* **Laboratories,** *Investigation 12.*

Guided Practice

Help small groups of students work together to create concept maps that show the major points in gene expression. An example of a completed concept map appears on p. 179B.

Independent Practice

- Have students write answers to the Section Review.
- Have students create a drawing that depicts gene expression in eukaryotes (pp. 182–183). Urge them to use different shapes and colors to clarify the events, and to add labels so that other students can follow the drawing.

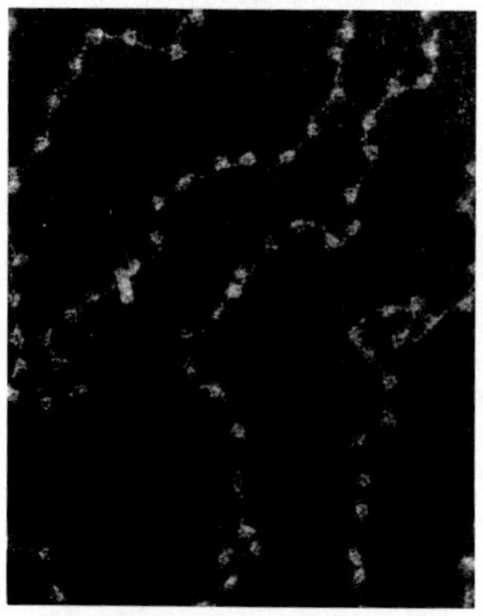

Figure 12-2 The knoblike areas along these DNA strands are nucleosomes.

When lactose is not present in the cell, one repressor attaches to the operator region of the *lac* operon while other repressor molecules float freely in the cell. A **repressor** is a molecule that inhibits a gene from being expressed. A **regulator gene,** which lies close to the *lac* operon, codes for the repressor. The presence of a repressor molecule prevents the action of the enzyme RNA polymerase. Since RNA polymerase is needed to make the mRNA that will produce the enzymes that break down lactose, no enzymes will be produced while a repressor is attached to the operon.

An **inducer** is a molecule that initiates gene expression. In this example lactose is the inducer. It temporarily binds to the repressor on the operator portion and removes it. Lactose also binds to all other repressor molecules in the cell, so that none can interfere with the promoter. RNA polymerase can then begin to act. It moves from the promoter section of the operon, past the now-free operator region, and into the structural genes of the operon. Here RNA polymerase transcribes the DNA code into mRNA, which then migrates to the ribosomes and forms three enzymes: beta-galactosidase, permease, and transacetylase. These enzymes cleave lactose into glucose and galactose and regulate cell permeability to lactose. These actions decrease the amount of lactose in the cellular environment. When the level of lactose in the cellular environment is low, the repressor temporarily rebinds to the operator, and the *lac* operon is shut off.

Gene Expression in Eukaryotes

Gene expression in eukaryotes is different from that in prokaryotes. In eukaryotes gene expression is partly related to the coiling and uncoiling of DNA. Eukaryotic DNA coils into chromosomes only during mitosis or meiosis. At other times uncoiled DNA, along with histones, exists as chromatin. DNA wraps around the histone complex to form beadlike structures called **nucleosomes.**

The tightly coiled form of DNA, called **heterochromatin,** contains inactive genes, those that are not being expressed. When chemical bonds are broken in the nucleosomes, the DNA begins to uncoil. It is the uncoiled form of DNA, called **euchromatin,** that is the site of active transcription of DNA into mRNA. Thus the degree to which DNA is uncoiled indicates the degree of gene expression.

Enhancer Control

Next to a eukaryotic gene is a region called an **enhancer,** which must be activated for the gene in the euchromatin to be expressed. Activation of enhancers has been studied in the expression of the gene controlling production of estrogen, a female sex hormone.

When estrogen is present in the cell, it binds to a receptor protein in the cytoplasm. This complex then travels through the pores of the nuclear membrane. Once inside the nucleus the receptor–estrogen complex attaches to the enhancer portion of the

Interdisciplinary Activity

Language Arts Have students use dictionaries to determine the meaning of the following terms in everyday language: *repressor, regulator, inducer, enhancer.* Then have them compare these definitions with those given on p. 182 and summarize how the scientific meaning compares with the meaning in everyday language.

Figure 12-3 How does gene expression control the change from juvenile to adult?

gene. RNA polymerase can then synthesize the RNA that makes the protein that breaks down estrogen. The presence of the protein reduces the amount of estrogen, and the lack of estrogen blocks the action of RNA polymerase.

mRNA Cleavage

The cleavage of mRNA after it has been formed on a DNA segment also controls gene expression. In eukaryotes a gene consists of two interspersed regions—introns and exons. **Introns** are the inert segments of DNA, which do not code for proteins. **Exons** are the segments that function as the codons during protein synthesis.

Both introns and exons are transcribed into mRNA. When mRNA migrates from the nucleus to the cytoplasm, it is cleaved by enzymes, and all of the introns drop out of the nucleotide sequence. The exons remaining are then spliced together. A cap and a tail, each made up of a nitrogen base, attach to each end. The shortened mRNA strand then migrates to the ribosomes, where protein synthesis occurs. The expression of genes is thus regulated through chromosome uncoiling, control of the enhancer region, and cleavage of mRNA that has been formed by the gene.

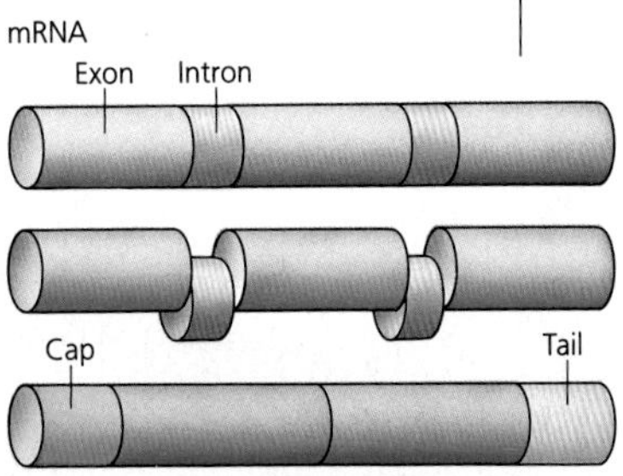

Figure 12-4 When mRNA migrates to the cytoplasm, introns (red) are excised, and exons (blue) are spliced together. A nitrogen base attaches to each end of the gene, forming a cap and a tail.

Section Review

1. What is a *lac* operon?
2. How does lactose affect the functioning of the *lac* operon?
3. What dictates the degree of DNA transcription in eukaryotes?
4. How does mRNA cleavage control gene expression in eukaryotes?
5. What region of a prokaryotic gene would you say is analogous to the enhancer region of a eukaryotic gene?

Check Your Understanding

1. How is the control of gene expression related to the specialization of tissue in complex organisms? *(Each body cell of an organism contains all of its genes, but only some genes are active, depending on the cell's function. The control of gene expression produces cells specialized for different functions.)*
2. How is estrogen related to the enhancer in the eukaryotic cell system? *(Estrogen must be present as part of the estrogen-receptor complex before the enhancer turns on the gene that breaks down estrogen.)*

Reteaching

Have students create a sequential diagram that summarizes the steps in gene expression in eukaryotes, beginning with DNA in an inactive state. An example of a completed diagram (Graphic Organizer) appears on p. 181.
■ *See* Section Reviews *worksheet, Section 12.1.*

Enrichment

Have students investigate in science magazines recent research in decoding mRNA. Ask them to find out what is known about the "start" and "stop" signals for protein synthesis and about the ways point mutations can interfere with normal starting and stopping of protein synthesis.

Closure

Have students formulate a summary of the effects of controlled gene expression on the cells and tissues of organisms.

Videodiscs

■ *2532, Glucose (s)*
■ *Side 2 33467, Spermatogenesis (m)*
■ *1693–1712, Spermatogenesis (s)*
■ *Side 4 22818, Crab, Brittlestar, and Scallop (m)*

Answers to Section Review

1. The segment of DNA on the *E. coli* chromosome that controls the production of enzymes that break down lactose
2. Lactose binds with the repressor molecules, thus freeing the operator region so that transcription can take place.
3. The extent to which DNA is uncoiled
4. In eukaryotes, a gene can be expressed only after the inert segments of mRNA, or introns, have dropped out and the mRNA exons have been spliced together.
5. The operator region

Lesson Plan

Section Focus

This section outlines the way in which genes control the development of *Drosophila* from fertilized egg to adulthood. It also examines cancer, the uncontrolled growth of cells.

Section Themes

This section emphasizes **Scale and Structure** in discussing the development of new structures in a maturing organism as its growth is guided by its genetic code. The section also exemplifies **Systems and Interactions** within the cells, since cancer is an example of abnormal interactions in the biochemical systems of cells.

Motivating Activity

Obtain tadpoles or pictures of tadpoles in different stages of development. Remind students that tadpoles begin as fertilized eggs and mature to adult frogs. Ask students to observe the different stages and place them in a logical order of development. Ask why frog development regularly happens in the same pattern. *(Genes control the chemical reactions in the cells of the maturing organism.)*

Teaching Strategies

Clarifying Concepts Stress that the lesson describes morphogenesis in fruit flies. Morphogenesis does not proceed in the same way in humans.

Discussing the Issues Obtain from the American Cancer Society and other organizations photos and literature concerning the cause, effect, and treatment of cancers. Discuss several kinds of cancer and have students point out their similarities and differences, explaining why one cure will not work for every kind of cancer.

■ *See* **Process Skills, *Chapter 12.***

Section Objectives

- *Describe* Drosophila *development and the influence of homeotic genes.*
- *Explain why scientists think that cancer represents out-of-control cell division.*
- *Describe the ways in which viruses and other carcinogens can cause cancer.*
- *Summarize the experimental investigation used to identify anti-oncogenes.*

12.2 Morphogenesis

The development of form in an organism is called **morphogenesis.** In Section 12.1 you learned how genes are turned on and off in prokaryotes and eukaryotes. How is the expression of genes manifested in the morphogenesis of these organisms? Let's study some cases of gene expression to better understand the normal and abnormal development of organisms.

Homeotic Genes

All multicellular, sexually reproducing organisms begin life as zygotes. A zygote undergoes repeated cycles of cell growth and division and in many organisms eventually forms into a hollow ball of cells called a **blastula. Cell differentiation,** the change in the morphology or physiology of a cell in relation to its neighboring cells, begins in the blastula. One surface of the blastula eventually forms a pocket, and the ball of cells is then called a **gastrula.** Cells in the gastrula differentiate further and form the tissues of the embryo and the adult organism.

Biology in Process

Oncogenes and Anti-oncogenes

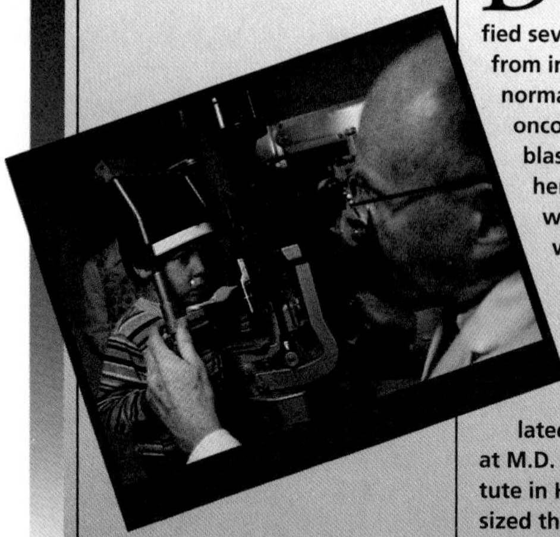

During the past 30 years, scientists have identified several cancers that arise from inherited mutations of normal genes they called oncogenes. Recently, retinoblastoma became the first hereditary cancer for which an anti-oncogene was isolated (p. 185).

In 1971 Alfred G. Knudson, Jr., published his analysis of data from 48 retinoblastoma cases accumulated over a 25-year period at M.D. Anderson Tumor Institute in Houston. He hypothesized that there were two distinct patterns of this rare childhood cancer. In one, children with no family history of retinoblastoma showed tumor formation in only one eye. Other children, with tumors in both eyes, had a clear family history of retinoblastoma.

Knudson wondered if the gene responsible for this inherited disease was also involved in the noninherited cases. In cases where tumors appeared in both eyes, Knudson hypothesized that one recessive mutation was inherited and present in all the cells of these children. But tumor growth might only be initiated when a second mutation, a somatic mutation, occurred on the homologous

Types of Cancer	▪ carcinomas (skin and nerves) ▪ sarcomas (bone and muscle) ▪ lymphomas (blood-forming tissues) ▪ leukemia (immature white blood cells)
Causes of Cancer	▪ carcinogens (tobacco, asbestos, ultraviolet light) ▪ viruses ▪ oncogenes

Graphic Organizer Use this table in Guided Practice on p. 185.

One of the most thoroughly studied examples of morphogenesis is that of the fruit fly, *Drosophila*. In *Drosophila* the gastrula changes into an elongated larva. Genes control the morphogenesis of a specific region in the larva into a specific part in the adult *Drosophila*. Genes that control the development of specific adult structures are called **homeotic** *(HOE-mee-AHT-ick)* **genes.** In the fruit fly these homeotic genes are located on the third chromosome of the genome.

Homeotic genes instruct cells of the larva to form tissues called **imaginal** *(im-AJ-un-'l)* **disks,** which become prominent in the pupa stage. A *Drosophila* larva has nine pairs of imaginal disks and a single genital disk. Hormones cause each disk to develop into a specific structure characteristic of the winged adult, also called an imago. Figure 12-5 illustrates the correspondence between the structural characteristics of the adult and the imaginal disks that will develop into those characteristics.

Under normal conditions an imaginal disk always develops into the same specific adult structure. For instance, a leg disk will always produce a leg. In fact, if a developmental biologist transplants a leg imaginal disk to the wing disk area, a leg will form on the adult where a wing should be.

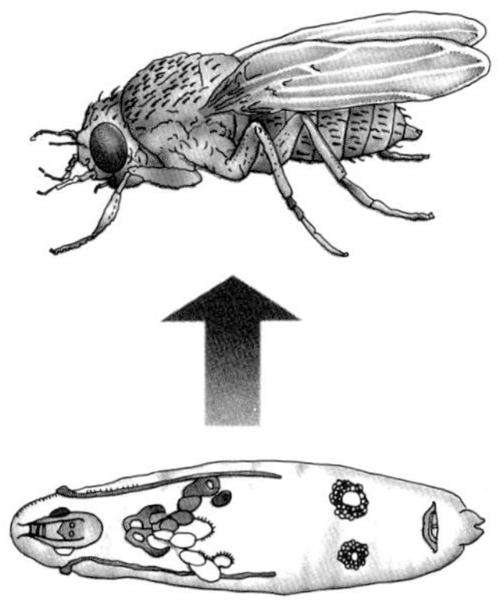

Figure 12-5 Each imaginal disk in the fruit fly larva develops into a specific structure in the adult.

chromosome. In noninherited retinoblastoma Knudson suggested that two somatic mutations must occur within a single immature retinal cell. This two-mutation model could account for both patterns of the disease.

One clue to the physical location of the Rb gene came from microscopy studies by Jorge J. Yunis of the University of Minnesota Medical School. He was studying retinoblastoma tumor cells and observed that chromosome number 13 often had a deletion near a specific location (p.185).

By 1983, several researchers had found evidence to support Knudson's "two-hit" hypothesis.

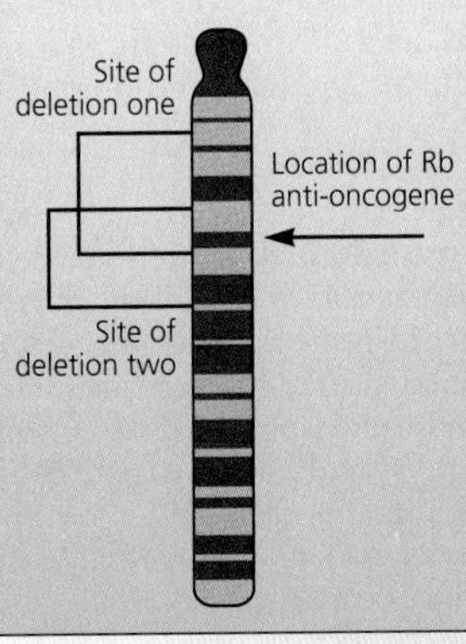

The deletion on chromosome number 13 observed by Yunis removed a gene called Rb that apparently held an oncogene in check. The loss of Rb's control initiated tumor growth.

Today, anti-oncogenes are known as tumor-growth suppressor genes. When they mutate or are damaged, the proteins they code for are either not expressed, or expressed defectively—leading to a predisposition to cancer. Testing can identify this predisposition.

Molecular biology research continues to identify the specific proteins coded for by supressor genes. Such research will help scientists determine exactly how carcinogens are implicated in somatic mutations and may eventually offer a means of developing tumor-specific treatments for many different types of cancers.

- **What discoveries in retinoblastoma helped establish the existence of anti-oncogenes?**

Cooperative Learning

Genetic Control of Development Have students work in groups of three, and have each recall an example of a gene-controlled process or event that was described in the chapter. Then have them try to identify gene-controlled structures and processes that occur in humans as they mature. Suggest that they concentrate on inherited characteristics, not learned characteristics. *(Sample answers: changes in size and body proportion during early childhood, body changes during puberty, body changes during aging.)* Help students realize that maturation and aging are genetically controlled, with each species having its characteristic age span.

Guided Practice

Have students make a table that lists the types of cancer and some causes of cancer. An example of a completed table appears on p. 184.

Independent Practice

- Have students write answers to the Section Review.
- Have students write a description of a science fiction monster from a movie or book. Have them state whether they think such a monster could really exist in nature, then explain their reasoning based on what they know about morphogenesis.

Biology in Process

Using the Feature

This feature shows how the process skills of observing, hypothesizing, and collecting data led researchers to the discovery of an anti-oncogene. Knudson hypothesized that two mutations caused retinoblastoma, then showed that about two-thirds of the cases with no family history of retinoblastoma were due to double somatic mutations within a single cell.

The possibility of missing genetic material was suggested by Yunis's observation of a deletion on chromosome number 13. Experiments demonstrating that a normal gene product suppressed cell growth added more support for the anti-oncogene hypothesis.

Answer to the Feature

Mutations could be acquired through inheritance or by somatic mutation; chromosomal deletions could be responsible for tumor initiation; and proteins were identified that could inhibit the growth of cancer cells.

Videodiscs

- ***Side 4 19464, Butterfly Development (m)***

Answer to Think

Both observations strongly suggest that the onset of cancer is linked with some type of error in gene expression that results from mutation. However, scientists do not yet know the exact cause-effect relationship between gene expression and cancer.

Check Your Understanding

1. What is the relationship between homeotic genes and imaginal disks in the fruit fly? *(Homeotic genes instruct cells to form imaginal disks.)*
2. Normally when fruit fly larvae develop, they are protected from sunlight. How might their development into adults be affected if the larvae were restricted to sunny places? *(The ultraviolet light might cause mutations as it does to some other organisms.)*

Reteaching

Have students write a short paragraph explaining why cancer is discussed after morphogenesis. *(Morphogenesis is controlled development according to a definite pattern. The uncontrolled growth of cancer shows the opposite situation.)*

■ *See* Section Reviews *worksheet, Section 12.2.*

Enrichment

Have students report on the most recent statistics about various kinds of cancer.

Closure

Ask students how human behavior and society's habits contribute to the incidence of cancer. Ask them what life-styles and environments can reduce the risk of cancer. *(For example, certain diets or use of energy)*

Videodiscs

■ ***Side 2 38275, Cleavage in a Mouse Egg (m)***

■ ***Side 2 41291, Cleavage in a Frog Egg (m)***

Think

Many carcinogens, such as X rays, ultraviolet light, asbestos, and tobacco, are also known mutagens. In addition, chromosomal mutations such as nondisjunction and translocation have frequently been observed in cancerous cells. What does this suggest about the relationship between cancer and gene expression?

Cancer

Sarcomas grow in bone and muscle. **Lymphomas** are solid tumors that grow in the tissues that form blood cells. Tumors in blood-forming tissues may cause **leukemia,** the uncontrolled production of immature white blood cells.

Tumors

A **tumor** is an abnormal mass of cells that results from ungoverned cell division. A tumor may be either benign or malignant. The cells of a **benign tumor** remain within the mass. Generally, benign tumors pose no threat to life. The cells of a **malignant tumor** undergo **metastasis** *(muh-TASS-tuh-suss),* or break away and cause new tumors to form in other locations. The diseases caused by malignant tumors are collectively referred to as cancer.

Malignant tumors can be categorized according to the types of tissue they affect. **Carcinomas** grow in the skin and nerves. **Sarcomas** grow in bone and muscle. **Lymphomas** are solid tumors that grow in the tissues that form blood cells. **Leukemia** is an abnormal growth of immature white blood cells.

Causes of Cancer

The term **carcinogen** *(kahr-SIN-uh-jun)* refers to any substance that causes cancer. Whether a person actually develops cancer seems to depend on many factors, including genetic predisposition, the number of exposures, and the amount of carcinogen in each exposure. Well-known carcinogens include tobacco, asbestos, and ultraviolet light. Viruses also cause cancer in plants and animals and have been implicated in various kinds of leukemia.

Oncogenes

Scientists have determined that some genes, when expressed, can cause a normal cell to become cancerous. **Oncogene** is the term for such genes, which are the most recently identified sources of cancer. In some cases oncogenes may be genes that have a normal function in cell metabolism. However, as you have read, the control of gene expression is a complex process. If the control of gene expression of an oncogene goes awry, the gene may be expressed continually, resulting in the uncontrolled division of a cell. Carcinogens may in some way interfere with oncogene control and thus cause cancer.

Section Review

1. List the three types of malignant tumors.
2. What is the role of homeotic genes in *Drosophila?*
3. How is cancer related to gene expression?
4. Name three factors that determine whether cancer will develop after exposure to a carcinogen.
5. What do you infer would happen if an imaginal disk were transplanted into an adult fruit fly?

Answers to Section Review

1. Carcinoma, sarcoma, lymphoma, leukemia
2. Homeotic genes instruct cells to form imaginal disks. Hormones then cause disks to develop into specific adult structures.
3. Cancer is caused by a disorder in gene expression that results in uncontrolled cell division.
4. Genetic predisposition, amount of carcinogen in exposure, and number of exposures
5. Probably nothing would happen. In an adult, the genetic codes for the hormones involved in metamorphosis would not be expressed, so the disk would probably not develop in its normal fashion.

Laboratory

Gene Expression and the Development of Brine Shrimp

Objective
To infer the role of gene expression by observing brine shrimp development

Process Skills
Observing, inferring, hypothesizing

Materials
2 4-liter aquariums filled with 1.5% salt solution, aerator, measuring spoon, brine shrimp eggs, medicine dropper, depression slides, compound microscope, unlined paper, dry baker's yeast, dip net, dissecting microscope

Background

1 What part of a cell controls cell activities and tissue type? Describe and explain.
2 What turns genes on and off?
3 Brine shrimp are jointed-legged, marine animals. After the eggs hatch, each stage of larva develops more pairs of legs. What is the development of form called? What is the importance of cell differentiation to this process?

Inquiry

1 Your teacher has filled two aquariums for each lab group. Label one aquarium 1 and the other 2. Put the aerator in aquarium 1. What might be its function?
2 Add 1/2 teaspoon of brine shrimp eggs to aquarium 1. Wait at least 24 hours.
3 After 24 to 48 hours, use the dropper to move some eggs to a depression slide. Use a compound microscope to examine hatching eggs under low power. Why start on low power?
4 Make a drawing of several larvae. How many pairs of legs do you see? Record a detailed description of the larvae.
5 Add 1/2 teaspoon of yeast to the fresh salt solution in aquarium 2. Move the aerator from aquarium 1 to aquarium 2.

6 Use a dip net to move all the brine shrimp from aquarium 1 to aquarium 2. What might be the reason for adding yeast and for moving the aerator to this aquarium?
7 Once a week for three weeks, repeat steps 5 and 6, alternating aquariums.
8 Every other day, observe larvae under a microscope and draw them. Note any changes in body shape that you observe. What structures are visible? Be sure to compare body shapes among the several larval stages. What happens to the number of legs over time? What other changes do you observe?

Conclusions

1 Arrange your drawings in order of age and size of larvae. What can you conclude about body part complexity?
2 Leg muscles are made of proteins. You know that a different gene directs the synthesis of each protein. What can you infer about the sequence of body changes and protein synthesis as brine shrimp larvae develop?

Further Inquiry
The activity of brine shrimp slows in cool temperatures. If you repeated this experiment with water cooler than room temperature, what might happen to the rate of larval development?

Laboratory

(For an overview of genes and development in brine shrimp, and preparatory information related to the laboratory, see p. 179B.)

Background

1. Genes on the chromosomes control cell activities and tissue types. Genes are short DNA segments that code for proteins, which control all the specific structural and functional characteristics of an organism.
2. Both internal and environmental factors are involved in turning genes on and off.
3. The development of form in an organism is called morphogenesis. Cell differentiation, the change in the morphology and physiology of a cell in relation to its neighboring cells, leads to formation of tissues and organs and the overall form of the organism.

Inquiry

1. The aerator ensures that the shrimp have enough oxygen.
3. Beginning at low power prevents damage to the objectives, facilitates location of the subject, allows for ease in focusing, and provides an overall view of the subject.
4. Young larvae have three pairs of legs.
6. The brine shrimp feed on the yeast cells and take in the oxygen provided by the aerator.
8. As they mature, larvae have four, seven, then ten pairs of legs, which beat in a wavelike motion. With time, a head, tail, body segments, stalked eyes, antennae, and gut develop.

Conclusions

1. Drawings in order of age and size show increasing complexity of body parts.
2. Each body part is controlled by many genes, each having one product. Different genes become active later in the sequence of development. Since brine shrimp undergo several changes in body form as they develop, many different genes must control each stage. These genes are turned on and off.

Further Inquiry

Since brine shrimp activity slows with cooler temperatures, cell activity is probably slowing as well. And, since larval development is directed by genes and cell activity, the rate of larval development also probably slows.

Vocabulary

1. In the *lac* operon, the operator is attached to the repressor, causing transcription to be prevented until lactose enters the cell. The promoter produces RNA polymerase when the operon is turned on.
2. Heterochromatin is the tightly coiled form of DNA that contains inactive genes. Euchromatin is the uncoiled form of DNA with sites of active transcription of DNA into mRNA.
3. An exon is a segment of DNA that actively codes for a protein. An intron is an inactive segment of DNA. After being transcribed into mRNA, the introns must drop out for protein synthesis to occur.
4. A benign tumor remains self-contained and usually is not life-threatening. A malignant tumor, or cancer, metastasizes and forms new tumors in other parts of the body.
5. A sarcoma is a malignant tumor that grows in bone or muscle tissue. A carcinoma is a malignant tumor that grows in skin or nerve tissue.

Review

1. c	**6.** c
2. b	**7.** b
3. d	**8.** b
4. a	**9.** d
5. b	**10.** a

11. Jacob and Monod studied the *lac* operon in *Escherichia coli.*
12. The *lac* operon shuts off when lactose is no longer present in the cell and the repressor molecule attaches to the operator.
13. After it binds to a receptor protein, estrogen enters the nucleus of a cell, where it is broken down by enzymes.
14. Introns drop out of an mRNA strand after the mRNA migrates to the cytoplasm.

Chapter 12 Review

Vocabulary

benign tumor (186)
blastula (184)
cancer (186)
carcinogen (186)
carcinoma (186)
cell differentiation (184)
enhancer (182)
euchromatin (182)
exon (183)
gastrula (184)
gene expression (181)
heterochromatin (182)
homeotic gene (185)
imaginal disk (185)
inducer (182)
intron (183)
lac operon (181)
leukemia (186)
lymphoma (186)
malignant tumor (186)
metastasis (186)
morphogenesis (184)
nucleosome (182)
oncogene (186)
operator (181)
operon (181)
promoter (181)
regulator gene (182)
repressor (182)
sarcoma (186)
structural gene (181)
tumor (186)

Explain the difference between the terms in each of the following sets.

1. operator, promotor
2. heterochromatin, euchromatin
3. exon, intron
4. benign, malignant
5. sarcoma, carcinoma

Review

1. Gene expression occurs through the process of DNA (a) replication (b) translation (c) transcription (d) synthesis.
2. The repressor molecule is coded for by the (a) structural gene (b) regulator gene (c) imaginal disk (d) nucleosome.
3. The site of active DNA transcription in eukaryotes is called (a) an operon (b) an enhancer (c) heterochromatin (d) euchromatin.
4. When present in a cell, lactose acts as (a) an inducer (b) a repressor (c) a promoter (d) a regulator.
5. In eukaryotes introns and exons are interspersed regions of (a) chromatin (b) DNA (c) tRNA (d) histones.
6. Lactose is to estrogen as inducer is to (a) repressor (b) operon (c) enhancer (d) regulator.
7. The process of cell differentiation begins in the (a) zygote (b) blastula (c) gastrula (d) larva.
8. Prokaryotes differ from eukaryotes in that prokaryotes have (a) introns and exons (b) no nucleus (c) no chromosomes (d) an enhancer region.
9. Imaginal disks become prominent during the (a) zygote stage (b) gastrula stage (c) larva stage (d) pupa stage.
10. A malignant tumor that grows only in bone or muscle tissue is a (a) sarcoma (b) lymphoma (c) carcinoma (d) leukemia.
11. In which organism did Jacob and Monod study the *lac* operon?
12. What causes the *lac* operon to shut off?
13. What happens to estrogen after it binds to a receptor protein?
14. At what stage are introns removed from an mRNA strand?
15. Distinguish between cell differentiation and morphogenesis.
16. Describe evidence that the morphological destiny of an imaginal disk is unrelated to its location.
17. Describe the characteristics of a blastula and a gastrula.
18. What happens when a malignant tumor undergoes metastasis?
19. Name three commonly known carcinogenic substances.
20. What key observation made by Jorge J. Yunis of chromosomes in retinoblastoma cells led scientists to conclude that there were genes that controlled oncogenes?

15. Cell differentiation is the change in structure or morphology of a cell in relation to neighboring cells. Morphogenesis is the change in form in an organism that results from cell differentiation.
16. If an imaginal disk, such as a leg disk, is transplanted to a wing disk area, a leg will grow where a wing should be.
17. A blastula is a hollow ball of cells formed in many organisms from a zygote after it undergoes repeated cycles of cell growth. A gastrula is formed when one surface of a blastula forms a pocket. The cells in the gastrula differentiate further, forming the tissues of the embryo and adult organism.
18. When a tumor metastasizes, some cells break away from the original cell mass and form new tumors in other parts of the body.

Critical Thinking

1. Of what advantage is it to the bacterial cell to make digestive enzymes for lactose only when lactose is present in the cellular environment?
2. A molecular biologist isolates mRNA from the brain and liver of a mouse and finds that the types of mRNA are different. Can these results be correct, or has the biologist made an error? Explain your answer.
3. Kwashiorkor is a disease in children caused by a diet high in carbohydrates but low in protein. When children with kwashiorkor suddenly are put on a diet rich in protein, they may become very ill with ammonia poisoning, even dying from it. The high level of ammonia in their blood is due to the inadequate metabolism of protein. What does this tell you about the enzymes that metabolize protein?
4. Examine the heads of *Drosophila* in the photographs above. Compare the abnormal *Drosophila* (right) with the normal one (left). The mutation *Antennapedia* codes the development of a leg from an antennae site. What type of mutation, do you think,

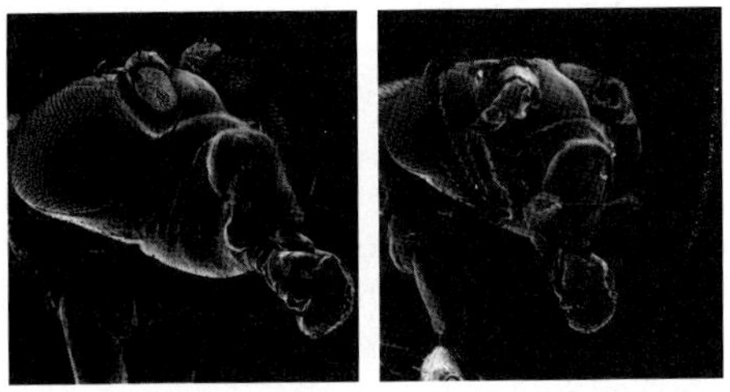

is the *Antennapedia* mutation? Explain your answer.
5. In one person cancer may be cured through the use of a certain drug or by means of radiation treatment, whereas in another person cancer may be unaffected by these treatment methods. Suggest the most likely explanation for this difference in response.
6. *Drosophila* feed on fermenting fruit, which often contains a large amount of alcohol. If *Drosophila* are fed a diet that has a high alcohol content, there is an increase in the amount of dehydrogenase, an enzyme that metabolizes alcohol, in the digestive tract. What does this increase tell you about the enzyme?

Extension

1. Read the article by John Rennie entitled "Homeobox Harvest" in *Scientific American*, June 1991, page 24. Prepare an oral report in which you include answers to the following questions: (1) What are homeobox genes? and (2) What evidence suggests that homeobox genes are a universal set of gene regulators in both the plant and animal kingdoms?
2. Construct models showing gene expression in prokaryotes and eukaryotes. Your model of the prokaryote should include promoter, operator, structural genes; repressor; regulator gene; RNA polymerase; inducer; mRNA; and ribosomes. Your model of the eukaryote should show DNA, heterochromatin, euchromatin, enhancer, receptor protein for the gene you choose, RNA polymerase, mRNA with introns and exons, and ribosomes. The gene for estrogen is a good example of a eukaryote to use for your model.
3. Construct a chart in which you compare the qualities in bacteria and fruit flies that make them ideal experimental tools for the scientist. Make sure to include similarities as well as differences between the two species.
4. Use the library to research the latest information on oncogenes and their protein products. Make an oral report to the class in which you show how your findings support the theory that cancer arises from out-of-control cell division or from differentiation.

19. Tobacco, asbestos, and ultraviolet light are carcinogens.
20. The deletion on chromosome number 13, which removed a gene called Rb that held an oncogene in check

Critical Thinking
1. Protein synthesis requires amino acids and energy. Thus, it is more efficient to make digestive enzymes only when they can be used on lactose.
2. The results are probably correct because different genes, and therefore different mRNA, are expressed in the two tissues.
3. The genes that control the enzymes are switched off or have very low activity when the diet lacks adequate protein. The genes are switched on by a high-protein diet, but the earlier lack of protein temporarily results in inadequate protein metabolism.
4. This is a mutation of homeotic genes forming the imaginal disks. This mutation produced a normal adult structure in an abnormal location.
5. There are different kinds of cancer, with different causes, so the same treatment will not work in all cases. Also, people with the same kind of cancer may respond differently because of differing body chemistry.
6. The expression of the gene that codes for production of dehydrogenase is controlled by the amount of alcohol present.

Extension
1. Tell students to save their research until they study Chapter 15, when they can relate it to the study of evolution.
2. Students might choose to work in two dimensions, with cut paper of different colors, or in three dimensions with materials such as clay, pipe cleaners, yarn, cotton balls, and so forth.
3. Student answers should include a discussion of bacteria as typical prokaryotes versus fruit flies as typical eukaryotes.
4. Students should look for information on oncogenes and anti-oncogenes and the mutations that affect them.

Chapter 13 Applied Genetics

Chapter Overview

Chapter 13 concludes the study of inheritance by showing how people can use the knowledge of genetics to improve organisms and develop cures for diseases. Section 13.1 examines controlled breeding for specific phenotypes. Section 13.2 describes techniques of inducing mutations, chemically modifying plant growth, and altering chromosomes.

Chapter Planning Chart

B	S	A	Sections and Subsections	Page	Features	Page	Resources
	•	•	**13.1 Controlled Breeding**				
			Mass Selection	191	Think	192	Videodiscs
			Inbreeding	192	Section Review	192	Section Reviews Worksheet
			Hybridization	192			
		•	**13.2 Manipulating Genes**				
			Inducing Mutations	193	Biotechnology	194	Videodiscs
			Inducing Polyploidy	193	Laboratory	197	Blackline Master 28
			Genetic Engineering	194	Section Review	196	Overhead Transparency T13
			Gene Sequencing	196			Process Skills: The Products of Biotechnology
							Laboratories: Manipulating DNA
							Section Reviews Worksheet
			End of Chapter Activities				
					Chapter Review	198	Vocabulary Skills
							Chapter Test
							Computer Test Generator

B *The Basic Level curriculum presents the most fundamental knowledge offered in the course.*
S *The Standard Level curriculum is designed for the average student who is able to master most topics.*
A *The Advanced Level curriculum includes suggestions for teaching the most academically able students.*

Cooperative Learning

Group Activity: Breeding Pet Fish

- **Group Size:** *4 students*
- **Outcome:** *Students will design a plan for controlled breeding.*
- **Individual Accountability:** *Each student will propose a trait to be controlled through selective breeding.*
- **Positive Interdependence:** *The group will explore the essential elements of controlled breeding.*

Have each group of students imagine that they have just inherited twenty tanks of pet fish from an eccentric relative. The tanks include a variety of familiar types, such as guppies and goldfish, which have been allowed to breed freely. The four heirs have decided to breed the fish and sell them to a pet store. What should they do to increase their chances of selling the fish successfully?

Suggest that the group first plan to examine the fish, determining in advance what information they will need. Second, have each student select at least one inherited fish trait considered desirable for a pet fish. Then, have the group formulate a plan to breed the fish so the offspring will have the desirable traits students have identified. Afterward, have the entire class brainstorm the essential ideas involved in controlled breeding.

Concept Map

The following is one possible solution to the concept mapping activity in Reteaching on p. 196.

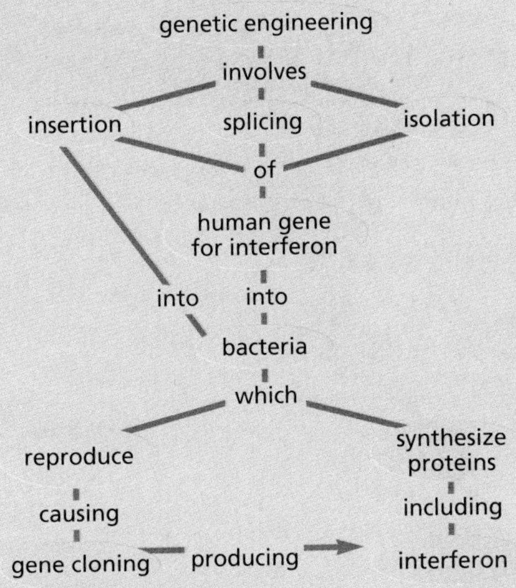

Laboratory Preparation

Overview *(See p. 197.)*

This laboratory investigates how the crossing-over of alleles can be used to investigate a genetic disease. Pairs of alleles, or different forms of a gene, are found in corresponding locations on homologous chromosomes. Each member of an allele pair is linked with the other genes on the same chromosome. Usually, linked genes are inherited as a group from the parent. However, as meiosis takes place in the parent, linkage sequences can be separated by crossing-over. During crossing-over, sections of paired chromosomes are exchanged, causing one or more genes to be separated from the original linkage group and linked to a new group.

The subjects of this laboratory are two human gene pairs whose alleles are linked. The first pair affects the functioning of the kidney, with the dominant allele causing a disease called adult polycystic kidney disease, or APKD. The second pair, called markers, are located near the first pair. The several forms of marker alleles can be used to trace the inheritance patterns of the APKD allele.

Preparation

No advance preparation is required for this lab.

Teaching Tips

Explain that during gel electrophoresis, longer, heavier marker alleles travel slower than smaller ones, so the different alleles become fixed in different positions. (Gel electrophoresis is described in more detail on p. 28.)

Remind students that for any two linked genes, the frequency of separation due to crossing-over is equal to the number of map units separating those two genes. For example, if separation occurs 1% of the time, the genes are said to be 1 map unit apart.

Emphasize that each individual's marker genes are known from the gel electrophoresis data. In addition, the presence or absence of the disease is known for generations I and II. Point out that students must make inferences about which markers are paired with the APKD allele and what events were, or might be, the result of crossing-over.

As students begin to analyze the grandmother's genotype, tell them to assume that she is heterozygous for the disease. In diseases caused by a dominant gene, heterozygosity is the more common pattern.

Urge students to add helpful information, such as drawings like that on p. 197, to their copy of the pedigree. It may help students to read the pedigree if they use faces instead of symbols for males and females. It may also help to use names instead of numbers.

Chapter Themes

Evolution Ask students to explain the meaning of "applied" in the chapter title. Point out that throughout most of human history, people have been causing changes that modified a species or variety of organisms for particular purposes—for example, breeding animals for specific purposes and modifying food crops for desirable traits.

Scale and Structure Explain that this chapter continues to describe ways that minuscule genetic structures within cells control the larger structures of organisms.

Systems and Interactions Explain that this theme is related to the theme of **Scale and Structure** because the chemical interactions that take place within cellular systems occur at the microscopic and submicroscopic levels. Also stress the amazing techniques that biologists have developed to make genes carry out specific desired functions.

Chapter Motivating Activity

Display photographs of various breeds of horses. Have students identify the characteristics that breeders purposely encouraged in these breeds. (*Examples: the quarter horse, bred for fast starting, turning, and stopping, to cut cattle from herds; the Percheron, bred for mild disposition and for moving heavy loads; the Morgan, bred for appearance and strength; the thoroughbred, bred for speed and stamina in racing and jumping; and the pinto, palomino, and Appaloosa, bred for colors or color patterns.)*

Chapter 13 Applied Genetics

Introduction

Scientists have used a knowledge of genetics to develop new sources, and improve existing sources, of food, medicines and vaccines, and other products essential to life. In this chapter you will learn how scientists apply genetic principles to benefit human society. You will learn about traditional practices and about new technologies, the potential of which have yet to be realized.

Chapter Outline

Chapter Concept

As you read, note the ways in which scientists have applied their knowledge of both the chemical aspects of genetics and inheritance patterns.

Color-enhanced TEM of *Escherichia coli* plasmids (×104,285). Inset: Hereford cow and crossbred calf, Iowa.

Understanding the Visuals

Have students observe the yellow rings in the chapter opening photo. Explain that plasmids are rings of DNA found in bacteria. Have them note the magnification obtained by the TEM (transmission electron microscope). Ask how such a powerful magnification was achieved. *(By the use of electrons instead of light)* Then ask them to observe the differences in color pattern between cow and calf and infer why there is a difference and what it has to do with DNA. (Point out the word *crossbred* in the caption, as a hint.) *(Students can infer that the cow has been bred to a bull of another variety to produce a better calf. DNA controls all inherited characteristics.)*

13.1 Controlled Breeding

Archeological evidence shows that humans began cultivating plants and animals for food about 10,000 years ago. Their selection of specific organisms for breeding was a simple form of applied genetics. **Applied genetics** is the manipulation of the hereditary characteristics of an organism to improve or create specific traits in offspring.

Controlled breeding involves manipulating the hereditary characteristics of offspring by selecting parents with specific phenotypic traits. This process enables a breeder to develop new strains of a species or to maintain existing strains. For example, the controlled breeding and cultivation of corn plants have produced varieties that yield more than ten times as much grain as varieties used early in this century. Applying controlled breeding to plants and animals has traditionally been based upon three techniques: mass selection, inbreeding, and hybridization.

Mass Selection

Mass selection is the process of choosing a few individuals to act as parents from a large pool of individuals. For example, a farmer may breed only the two or three cows in a herd that produce the most milk. Because these individuals produce the most milk, they are the most likely to produce offspring that will also produce large amounts of milk.

Luther Burbank (1849–1926), an American plant breeder, achieved great success with mass selection around the turn of the century. Burbank grew large numbers of fruits, flowers, vegetables, and grains, and selected only those with desirable traits for further breeding. He developed over 800 new plant varieties, including the seedless grape and the spineless cactus.

Section Objectives

- *Describe the process of mass selection.*
- *Compare the advantages and disadvantages of inbreeding.*
- *Explain how hybridization can produce new varieties of organisms.*

Figure 13-1 Luther Burbank developed daisies and potatoes by the process of mass selection.

Lesson Plan

Section Focus

This section describes three methods of controlling the breeding of animals and plants to produce offspring with specific desirable phenotypes.

Section Themes

This section emphasizes the theme of **Evolution** as it describes how people, rather than forces of nature, change animals and plants.

Motivating Activity

To help students understand the effects of controlled breeding, ask them to consider the following example: A mutation produces a male lamb having a wool color that is new to its species. What might happen to that trait in a wild population of sheep? What might happen to that trait in a domestic herd if the sheep breeder considered the new color desirable? *(In nature, the trait would probably remain rare and might even disappear completely. By contrast, a breeder would mate the distinctively colored animal to as many ewes as possible. The chances are that some or many of its offspring would carry the new trait.)*

Teaching Strategies

Reviewing Concepts Explain to students how each controlled breeding technique is based on the principles of segregation, independent assortment, and dominance and recessiveness.

Videodiscs

- *1714, Monohybrid Cross: Green/Albino Tobacco Seedlings (s)*
- *1716, Dihybrid Cross: Purple/Yellow/Starchy/Sweet Corn (s)*

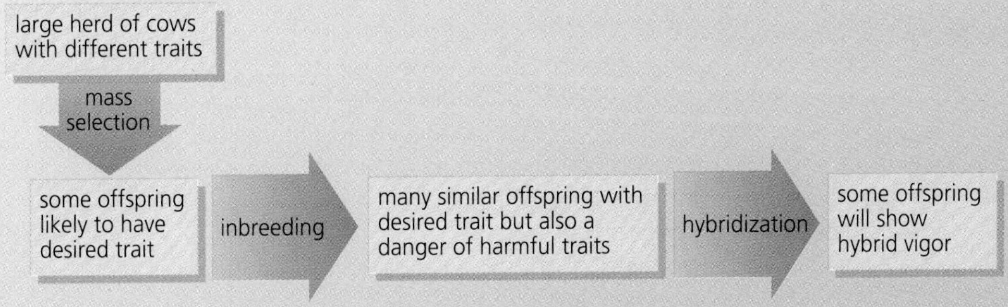

Graphic Organizer Use this sequential diagram in Guided Practice on p. 192.

Section 13.1

Answer to Think

Recessive alleles controlling deafness are probably found close to the alleles for white fur and blue eyes on the chromosome.

Guided Practice

Ask students to create a sequential diagram showing how mass selection, inbreeding, and hybridization might be used to breed cows having desired traits. An example of a completed diagram appears on p. 191.

Independent Practice

■ Have students write answers to the Section Review.

■ Some hybrids produced from different but closely related species are sterile. Ask students to develop a hypothesis to explain this. *(The zygote may have received some chromosomes that did not match. Later these may not pair during meiotic synapsis.)*

Check Your Understanding

1. What kind of traits cannot be transmitted through controlled breeding? *(Traits acquired exclusively from the environment)*

2. Why can inbreeding be harmful? *(Harmful homozygous recessive traits increase.)*

Reteaching

Ask students to write a definition for each type of controlled breeding.

■ *See* Section Reviews *worksheet, Section 13.1.*

Enrichment

Have students choose a domesticated animal, research its history, and relate that history to Section 13.1.

Closure

In the 1970s, much of the U.S. corn crop was destroyed by a fungus because most farmers used the same hybrid, which was susceptible to the fungus. Ask students for suggestions on preventing such problems.

Think

Many white cats with blue eyes are deaf. Suggest a mechanism by which the selection for this phenotype also results in deafness.

Inbreeding

A breeder who wants to maintain or to intensify desirable traits in a plant or animal species may practice a type of controlled breeding referred to as **inbreeding.** Inbreeding is based on the assumption that individuals that possess similar phenotypes also will possess similar genotypes. When phenotypically similar individuals are bred, offspring are more likely to be similar to their parents. In addition, offspring are likely to possess the same desired phenotype.

Most modern domestic breeds of dogs and cats were developed through inbreeding. Unfortunately, inbreeding can eventually produce weaker organisms because it increases the incidence of harmful homozygous recessive traits. For example, dachshunds were initially bred to dig badgers and rodents out of long narrow holes. However, while their long spinal column is adapted for this task, the spinal column is also prone to slipped or stressed vertebral disks.

Hybridization

Hybridization is another type of controlled breeding. In **hybridization** two different but related species or varieties of plants or animals are crossed. The products of this type of crossbreeding are called **hybrids.** Hybrids possess a different genotype and usually a phenotype different from that of either parent. When two different but closely linked species are crossed, the chromosome incompatibility during meiosis causes most of their hybrid offspring to be sterile.

Some hybrid individuals grow faster and larger and are healthier than either parent. Such an individual is said to display **hybrid vigor.** For example, hybridization has produced large tomatoes that resist wilting in hot weather. In addition, hybrid cattle may be resistant to some diseases that attacked their parents. Hybridization can reverse the damaging effects of inbreeding and results in hybrid vigor in the offspring. This occurs because hybridization increases the number of heterozygous genes in an organism, thus reducing the likelihood that a harmful, recessive allele will be expressed.

Section Review

1. What is *controlled breeding?*
2. Why does inbreeding of a plant or animal species often produce weaker offspring?
3. What method does a plant or animal breeder use to produce hybrid organisms?
4. Why do hybrid organisms often display hybrid vigor?
5. Do you think mass selection is practiced less frequently today than it was in Burbank's time? Why?

Answers to Section Review

1. Selection of parents with specific phenotypes in order to manipulate the hereditary characteristics of offspring

2. Inbreeding increases the occurrence of harmful homozygous recessive traits.

3. Two different but related species or varieties of plants or animals are crossed.

4. Hybridization reverses the negative effects of inbreeding (occurrence of harmful recessive traits) by increasing the number of heterozygous genes.

5. Yes. Today people have a greater understanding of inheritance patterns and can breed organisms more selectively.

13.2 Manipulating Genes

Controlled breeding is used to create the characteristics of progeny by selecting parents according to phenotype. Other techniques in applied genetics manipulate the genes themselves. Among these techniques are induction of mutations, induction of polyploidy, and use of genetic engineering and gene splicing.

Inducing Mutations

As you know, mutations are changes in the DNA of an organism. Mutations introduce new alleles to the genetic makeup of an organism. Mutations occur at a very low rate in nature. However, in 1927 the American geneticist H. J. Muller (1890–1967) found that he could induce a much greater rate of mutation in *Drosophila* by treating the flies with X rays. He then selected the resulting mutants for controlled breeding. Breeders have since used mutagens to create new traits in many organisms. People can then use those organisms whose mutations are beneficial to humans. For example, X rays induce mutations in bacteria. These mutations are then selected and propagated if they are useful.

Inducing Polyploidy

Breeders can also introduce desirable traits into a species by inducing **polyploidy,** a condition in which cells contain multiple, complete sets of chromosomes. Although polyploidy is rare and usually lethal in animals, it often occurs naturally in plants. As you can see in Figure 13-2, polyploid individuals are often larger or hardier than their parents.

Plant breeders artificially induce polyploidy by administering **colchicine,** a chemical that prohibits the formation of the cell plate during cell division. Colchicine is usually applied by placing the roots of the plant in a colchicine solution. Chromosomes in the cells of the plant go through the phases of cell division, but the cell plate does not form. Therefore, two complete sets of chromosomes exist. When the plant is removed from the colchicine solution the cells will again form cell plates during mitosis. Thus all resulting cells will contain an extra set of chromosomes.

Figure 13-2 Note the significant size difference between the polyploid strawberries in the top row and the normal strawberries in the bottom row.

Section Objectives

- *Explain how scientists can alter an organism's genetic makeup by inducing mutations and polyploidy.*
- *List the steps involved in engineering bacteria able to manufacture human interferon.*
- *Describe the process of gene sequencing and name some of its uses.*
- *Summarize the process of a polymerase chain reaction.*

Technique	inducing mutations	inducing polyploidy	genetic engineering	gene sequencing
Procedure	X-rays, followed by controlled breeding	colchicine	genes cut by enzymes, put into bacteria	use of DNA sequencer
Results	new alleles in a population	plant cells with multiple sets of chromosomes	desired protein produced	knowledge of position and order of specific genes

Graphic Organizer Use this table in Comparing Processes on p.194.

Lesson Plan

Section Focus

This section introduces ways in which people manipulate genes directly—instead of controlling breeding—to improve species or produce useful molecules.

Section Themes

This section emphasizes the theme of **Systems and Interactions,** showing how genes and chromosomes direct biochemical activities within cells.

Motivating Activity

Conduct a discussion on the pros and cons of genetic engineering. After introducing the concept, ask students to list possible advantages and disadvantages associated with genetic engineering, including engineering affecting humans. *(Possible advantages: better crops and domestic animals; plants that grow well on eroded land or quickly restore destroyed forests; eradication of some diseases. Possible disadvantages: unplanned dangers to health; damaging environmental side effects; threats to human rights and dignity.)* Make sure students understand the ethical issue here, that a society might try to impose genetic controls on its citizens. Have students read the Intra-Science feature on mapping the human genome on pp. 200–201.

■ ***See* Process Skills, *Chapter 13.***

Teaching Strategies

Describing Scientific Processes

Have students identify the different techniques scientists are using to manipulate genetic material. *(They are causing mutations with X-rays, recombining genes, inducing polyploidy with colchicine, isolating genes with restriction enzymes, and sequencing genes with the DNA sequencer instrument.)*

■ ***See* Laboratories, *Investigation 13.***

Comparing Processes Tell students to organize a table that names and describes four ways scientists manipulate genes, and summarizes the results of each method. A sample table appears on p. 193.

Interpreting the Visuals In discussing Figure 13-4, p. 196, explain that scientists use the plasmid because it is replicated independently of the bacterial chromosome and is easily manipulated. Also, have them answer these questions: What has been done before the events shown in the illustration? *(A restriction enzyme has cut the interferon gene from a human chromosome.)* What are the next three steps in the process? *(The plasmid is cut open, the gene is inserted, and the plasmid is put into a bacterium.)* How does gene cloning happen? *(Through the reproduction of bacteria)*
■ *See* **Overhead Transparency** ***T13 and*** **Blackline Master** ***28.***

Guided Practice

Have students write on index cards the following terms: *recombinant DNA, interferon, restriction enzyme, DNA plasmid, clone.* Have pairs of students use the cards to test their partner's understanding.

Independent Practice

■ Have students write answers to the Section Review.
■ Have students summarize the material on p. 193, making sure that their summary answers these questions: What natural circumstance is each technique based on? *(Mutations; multiple complete sets of chromosomes in some plants)* What is the process? *(Increasing the mutation rate by X-rays; placing roots in colchicine solution)* What is the result? *(Mutated organisms that can be selected for controlled breeding; plants that are larger or hardier)*

Genetic Engineering

The understanding of the molecular basis of inheritance has led to a new form of applied genetics called **genetic engineering,** in which scientists directly manipulate genes. Genetic engineering frequently involves the use of **recombinant DNA,** which is composed of DNA segments from at least two different organisms.

Genetic engineering has many commercial applications. An example is the use of recombinant DNA technology to make **interferon,** a protein produced naturally by the human body to inhibit the reproduction of viruses. The production of synthetic interferon involves (1) isolating the human gene that codes for interferon production, (2) splicing this gene into a strand of bacterial DNA, (3) inserting recombinant DNA into a bacterium, and (4) cloning the bacterium and collecting the product.

Isolation of a Gene

The first step in this process is isolating the human interferon gene. Genetic engineers use **restriction enzymes,** proteins that cut a DNA molecule into pieces. The restriction enzyme *Eco*RI cuts DNA wherever the sequence C-T-T-A-A-G occurs, as shown in

Biotechnology

The Polymerase Chain Reaction

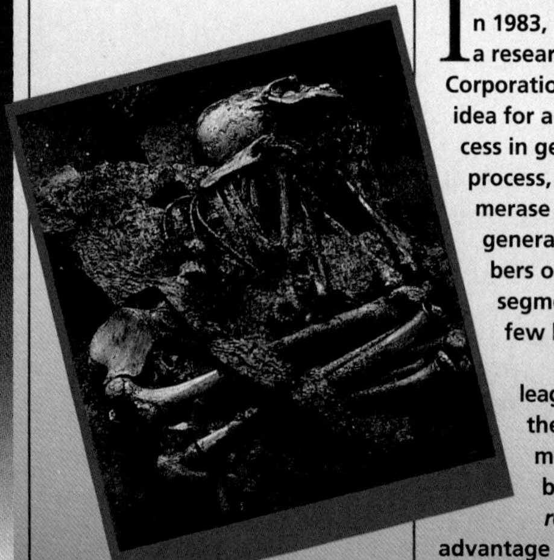

In 1983, Dr. Kary Mullis—then a researcher at the Cetus Corporation—came up with an idea for an exciting new process in genetic research. The process, now known as polymerase chain reaction (PCR), generates unlimited numbers of copies of a targeted segment of DNA in just a few hours.

Mullis and his colleagues at Cetus called the new process "polymerase chain reaction" because it is a chemical *reaction,* which takes advantage of the capability of the enzyme DNA *polymerase* to make copies of DNA under certain conditions. Because PCR repeats the same three steps over and over (p. 195), the process is called a *chain* reaction.

Step 1 in the process involves heating the targeted double-stranded DNA to break its hydrogen bonds and thus produce single strands of DNA. In Step 2, at cooler temperatures, two short chains of specifically ordered nucleotides called "primers" are allowed to bond to complementary segments in each of the single strands of DNA. Step 3 uses DNA polymerase to extend the two primers by synthesizing new strands of DNA. Then, in a repeat of Step 1, the new DNA

LEP Activity

Have students construct models of the production of interferon by gene recombination. They can use paper, yarn, clay, or other materials, and base their models on Figure 13-4, p. 196. Suggest that they show the cell membranes of a human cell and a cell of *E. coli*. Have them put a chromosome in the human cell and a plasmid of another color into the bacterium. Direct them to use scissors to cut out a segment of the human DNA. They can then remove the plasmid from its cell, cut one segment from it, insert the segment of human DNA, then replace the spliced plasmid in its cell. Ask them what the result will be when the bacterial cell divides. *(Two new cells with the human gene)* Ask what the bacterial cells can now do that they could not do before. *(Make interferon)*

Figure 13-3. Other restriction enzymes cut DNA at different nucleotide sequences. By using the proper restriction enzyme scientists can cut the human interferon gene out of its chromosome. Once the gene for interferon is removed, it is separated from the rest of the DNA and then inserted into a strand of bacterial DNA.

Gene Splicing

Gene splicing is the process by which a gene from one organism is placed into the DNA of another organism. In our example, the human interferon gene is placed into the DNA of *E. coli,* the common bacterium of the human intestine. In addition to a single, circular chromosome, *E. coli* contains a single, small ring of DNA called a **plasmid.** Human DNA is inserted into this plasmid.

The plasmid ring is removed from the bacterium and then opened with a restriction enzyme. The human interferon gene and the bacterial plasmid have "sticky ends"—unpaired bases at each end of the DNA segment, where they were cleaved by restriction enzymes. As the human DNA is spliced into the plasmid DNA, the unpaired bases of each bond readily. As shown in Figure 13-4 on the following page, a newly formed plasmid contains both human and bacterial DNA.

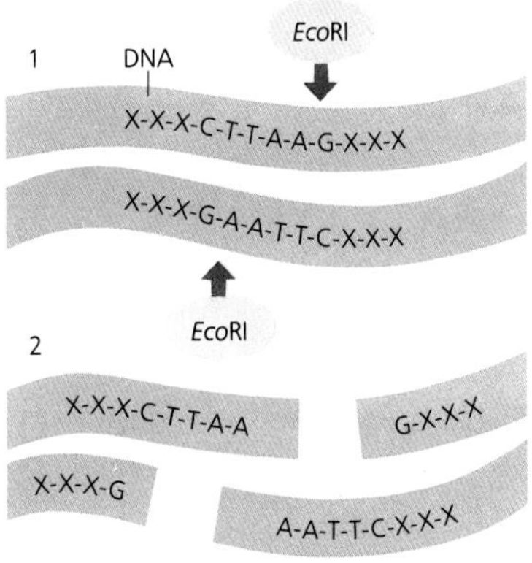

Figure 13-3 Restriction enzyme *EcoRI* cleaves double-stranded DNA at the sequence C-T-T-A-A-G, freeing two single-stranded complementary ends.

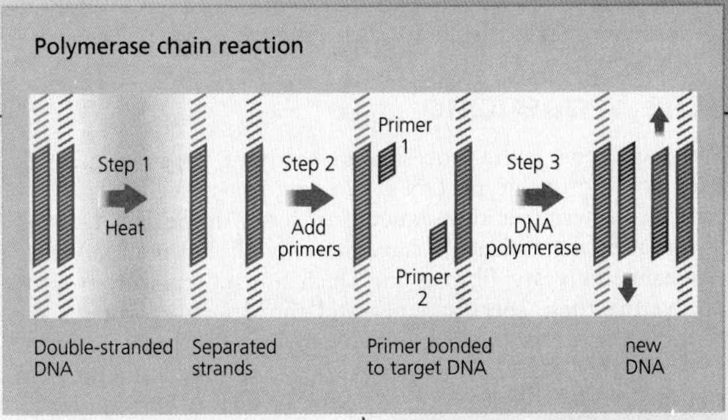

is heated, beginning a cyclic process or chain reaction. Within a few hours, PCR will produce more than a billion copies of the targeted DNA.

Geneticists carried out the first trials of PCR technology cautiously in a single test tube. Since 1988 the PCR technique has been done by machine, aided by DNA polymerase extracted from a bacterium that normally lives in hot springs. Because this heat-stable enzyme is not destroyed by the heat needed in Step 1 to separate strands of DNA, the polymerase can be reused in repeated PCR cycles.

By the late 1980s, investigators recognized the exceptional potential and great versatility of PCR, and the technology is now being applied to many fields of biology. Forensic investigators can make DNA fingerprints from a single hair left at the scene of a crime. Archaeologists can study DNA samples from the brains of mummies that have been preserved in bogs for thousands of years (p. 194). Doctors can detect at early stages cancer, AIDS, sickle-cell anemia, and many other diseases and also make prenatal diagnoses of genetic diseases. All these accomplishments are now possible with quantities of DNA once considered too minute for gene cloning in bacterial cultures.

Biotechnology

Using the Feature

In the polymerase chain reaction, the two strands of targeted DNA are first separated and then reconstructed. Because each cycle of PCR doubles the number of fragments, one tiny snippet of DNA can yield billions of copies in a few hours. The process can even amplify a specific sequence of DNA present in one cell, allowing investigators to successfully analyze the genetic material.

To help students understand the consequences of a chain reaction, ask a volunteer to sketch on the board a second cycle of PCR that would follow the three steps shown in the diagram in the feature (p. 195). Then have other volunteers sketch subsequent PCR cycles.

The Human Genome Project is an attempt to map all of the genes in the human body (see Intra-Science on pp. 200–201). Ask students how PCR technology can help scientists accomplish this goal. *(PCR can generate many copies of a small quantity of DNA quickly and automatically.)*

Videodiscs

- ***Side 1 22695, Protein Synthesis (m)***
- ***Side 1 25971, DNA Replication (m)***

Interdisciplinary Activity

Social Studies In the Soviet Union about 1938, basic applied genetics came to a virtual standstill and remained inactive until 1964. This development occurred because of Trofim Lysenko, who for political reasons adopted a Lamarckian approach to plant breeding. The Communist Party, then under Joseph Stalin, gave official sanction to Lysenko and his ideas. An eminent true geneticist, Nikolay Vavlov, was sent to a labor camp. This story describes a classic attempt to control science for political reasons. Have students research and write reports on the political situation and the results of Lysenko's influence on Soviet science and agriculture.

Check Your Understanding

1. The protein insulin, necessary for the treatment of diabetes mellitus, can now be manufactured instead of being extracted from organs of cattle and pigs. Suggest what production process might be involved. *(Genetic engineering using bacteria)*

2. How can the knowledge gained from gene sequencing help in developing cures for diseases? *(Scientists can find genes in organisms that will produce proteins that might help cure some diseases.)*

Reteaching

Ask students to create a concept map showing how interferon is produced by genetic engineering. An example of a completed concept map is shown on p. 189B.

■ *See* Section Reviews *worksheet, Section 13.2.*

Enrichment

Show students the movie *The Andromeda Strain*. Although the organism in the movie was not genetically engineered, the film portrays fear of a released dangerous microorganism. Have students research measures genetics researchers use to prevent such occurrences.

Two other films that use cloning as a premise are *The Boys from Brazil* and Woody Allen's *Sleeper.*

Closure

Ask students these questions: What precautions should be taken before releasing genetically altered life forms into the environment? Should genetic engineering be limited only to less developed life forms? Should human genes be genetically altered? Ask students to support their answers with reasoning.

Videodiscs

■ *Side 1 13433, Cloning (m)*

■ *Side 1 3301, Diabetes—History of Diabetes Research (m)*

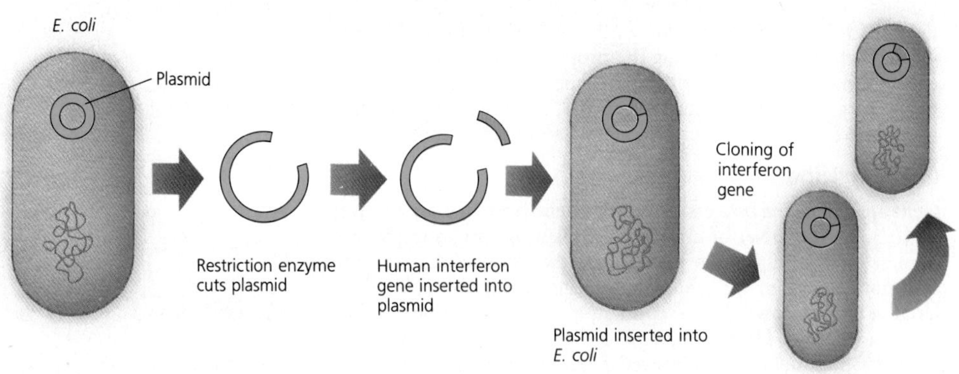

Figure 13-4 A plasmid with both human and bacterial DNA results when a human interferon gene is spliced into an *E. coli* plasmid.

Insertion, Cloning, and Collecting

Once a DNA fragment is incorporated into a plasmid, the plasmid is inserted into another bacterium, which is then placed in a culture medium, where it divides. Each time a bacterium divides a new copy of the plasmid DNA, which includes the human interferon gene, is created. This process by which the human gene is replicated is called **gene cloning.** Because *E. coli* can divide every 20 minutes, gene cloning is an efficient way to produce many copies of a specific genetic sequence. The gene for human interferon is thus expressed in bacterial cultures and the resulting interferon protein is collected and eventually used by physicians.

Gene Sequencing

Gene sequencing is the process of determining the exact order of bases in a fragment of DNA. An instrument called a DNA sequencer determines the sequence of bases in the DNA. Using gene sequencing, scientists have recently discovered the genes responsible for cystic fibrosis and Duchenne muscular dystrophy. Discovering these specific genes and the defective proteins for which they code may make it possible to design therapies aimed at the actual gene defect. Scientists are working to identify the base sequence of every gene on the 23 pairs of human chromosomes. Geneticists have established an international organization called the Human Genome Organization (HUGO) to complete this project.

Section Review

1. What is *recombinant DNA?*
2. Why do scientists induce polyploidy in plants?
3. How is recombinant DNA expressed?
4. Summarize the process of gene sequencing.
5. What characteristics of the *E. coli* plasmid do you think make it a useful organism for use in recombinant DNA technology?

Answers to Section Review

1. A DNA segment composed of segments from at least two different organisms
2. Because polyploid plants are often hardier and larger than normal organisms
3. Usually through bacterial cultures in which the cloned gene manufactures the desired protein
4. Scientists obtain a sample of DNA, then run it through a DNA sequencer, which determines the sequence of base pairs in the original DNA fragment.
5. The small size of *E. coli* and the fact that it can divide every 20 minutes make the growing of large numbers of organisms easy, and the circular shape of the plasmid facilitates gene splicing.

Laboratory

Molecular Genetic Diagnosis

Objective
To understand how diseases can be diagnosed by using genetic markers

Process Skills
Inferring, predicting, analyzing data

Materials
Pencil and paper

Inquiry

1. Adult polycystic kidney disease (APKD) is controlled by a dominant gene. The gene that causes APKD is a mutation of one of the genes for kidney function. Persons with APKD usually do not show symptoms until middle age. Recently it has become possible to genetically diagnose the disease by sampling a small segment of DNA, called a marker, from a site near this gene.
2. This DNA segment comes in various lengths. Markers of different lengths can be thought of as different alleles. The markers can be identified by a technique called gel electrophoresis, which separates markers by determining how far each type of DNA can travel in an electric field.
3. The gene and the marker are 5 map units apart. Although the gene and the marker are linked, crossing-over can separate them. What is the probability that the two will become separated by crossing-over?
4. The figure (top shows the pedigree of an APKD family. Generations are indicated by Roman numerals; individuals by Arabic numerals. Circles indicate females; squares males. Blue symbols indicate persons with APKD. The third generation is all children.
5. The markers shown in the figure (bottom) are labeled according to length—ranging from A, the longest, to H, the shortest. Why does each person have two markers?

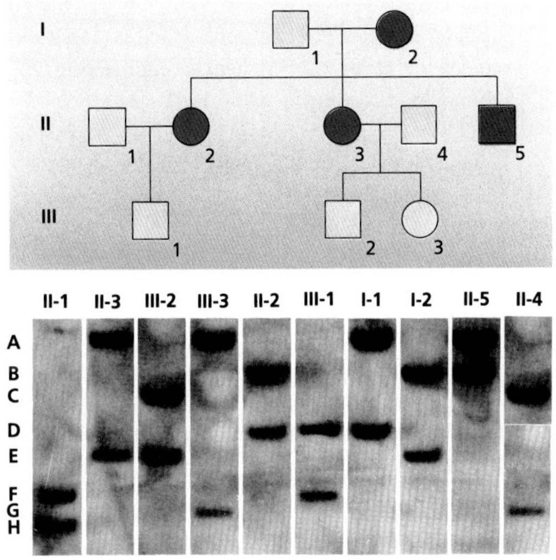

6. Make a copy of the pedigree.
7. Under the symbol for each individual, write the markers identified for that person. Why are no third-generation individuals shown as having the disease?

Conclusions

1. The grandmother (I-2) has APKD. Based on the expression of the disease in generation II, which marker is probably linked with the APKD gene? Explain your answer.
2. If APKD is linked with the B marker, how would II-3 have acquired the APKD gene? What is the probability of this event?
3. What is the probability that III-2 has APKD?
4. What is the probability that III-1 or III-3 has the disease?

Further Inquiry
Suppose that in generation I the grandfather was the individual with APKD. Would disease in the second generation be possible as shown? How would the change affect members of the third generation?

(For an overview of molecular genetic diagnosis and preparatory information related to the laboratory, see p. 189B.)

Inquiry

3. By definition, if two linked genes are 5 map points apart, they separate 5% of the time; that is, the probability of separation is 0.05.
5. Individuals inherit one marker from each parent.
6. Suggest that students also represent each individual's pair of chromosomes with the kidney (K) and marker (M) alleles drawn like this:

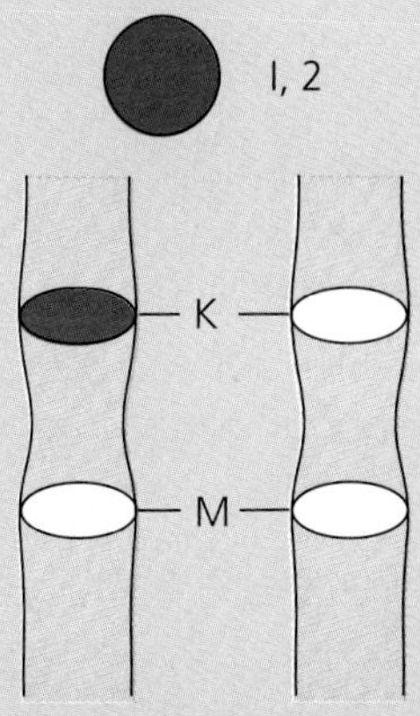

Also suggest that students use a shadow or color to identify each diseased individual in the pedigree and each APKD allele. Stress that at this point students have not yet determined the presence or absence of the disease in the third generation.
7. When students determine the markers for each individual, they should add those two letters to their pedigree. Point out that they do not yet know which marker allele is linked to each APKD allele. When they make inferences about marker linkages in Conclusions, they should add that information to the drawing made in step 6.

Also students should see that no diseased individuals are shown in the third generation because they are still children and the disease does not appear until middle age.

Conclusions

1. Marker allele B; it appears in 2 of the 3 diseased individuals in generation II, whereas E appears in only 1 of 3.
2. II-3 must have acquired the APKD gene linked to allele E when crossing-over occurred during meiosis. The probability is 5%.
3. Probability is 95%, since E is linked to the APKD gene in the mother, II-3.
4. Each has a 5% chance because the APKD gene could be linked to the A and D markers only by crossing-over.

Further Inquiry

Generation II as shown would still be possible. However, the probability of III-1 or III-3 acquiring the disease would be 95%. The probability of III-2 acquiring the disease would be 5%.

Vocabulary

1. Mass selection
2. Inbreeding is the mating of two similar, closely related organisms. Hybridization is the mating of two different but related organisms.
3. *Poly-* means "many"; *-ploid* means "multiplication of chromosome number." When cells contain multiple sets of chromosomes, the condition is appropriately called polyploidy.
4. Gene splicing
5. A plasmid is a small ring of DNA found in bacteria such as *E. coli.*

Review

1. b
2. c
3. a
4. c
5. b
6. d
7. a
8. b
9. b
10. a
11. The selection and cultivation of specific plants and animals for food
12. The seedless grape and the spineless cactus
13. Weak spines
14. Because hybrids receive different chromosomes from each parent, the chromosomes are unable to pair together properly during meiosis.
15. He induced mutations in *Drosophila* by exposing them to X-rays.
16. Polyploid organisms have multiple, complete sets of chromosomes. They are usually larger and hardier than normal organisms.
17. By analyzing the segment with a DNA sequencer
18. They cut apart DNA molecules at specific points, making it possible to isolate a particular gene. They also break open plasmids so that new genetic material can be spliced into them.

Chapter 13 Review

Vocabulary

applied genetics (191)
colchicine (193)
controlled breeding (191)
gene cloning (196)
gene sequencing (196)
gene splicing (195)
genetic engineering (194)
hybrid (192)
hybridization (192)
hybrid vigor (192)
inbreeding (192)
interferon (194)
mass selection (191)
plasmid (195)
polyploidy (193)
recombinant DNA (194)
restriction enzyme (194)

1. Name the type of controlled breeding practiced by Luther Burbank.
2. Distinguish between inbreeding and hybridization.
3. Look up the meanings of the word roots *poly-* and *-ploid* and tell why polyploidy is appropriately named.
4. Which type of genetic engineering involves the use of restriction enzymes?
5. What is a plasmid?

Review

1. Controlled breeding involves control of (a) the genetic makeup of an organism (b) parent selection (c) the breeding environment (d) the number of offspring that will be produced.
2. Humans began cultivating plants and animals for food about (a) 2,000 years ago (b) 1,000 years ago (c) 10,000 years ago (d) 5,000 years ago.
3. Luther Burbank developed the seedless grape through the use of the controlled breeding process of (a) mass selection (b) inbreeding (c) hybridization (d) inducing mutation.
4. The purpose of using the inbreeding technique is to (a) develop new species (b) develop new traits within a species (c) maintain or intensify desirable traits (d) eliminate undesirable traits.
5. Compared to its parents, a hybrid individual usually has the (a) same phenotype and same genotype (b) different phenotype and different genotype (c) same phenotype and different genotype (d) different phenotype and same genotype.
6. H. J. Muller induced mutations in *Drosophila,* common fruitflies, by exposing them to (a) ultraviolet radiation (b) colchicine (c) *Eco*RI (d) X rays.
7. Polyploid individuals contain multiple sets of (a) all chromosomes (b) sex chromosomes only (c) nuclei (d) cell plates.
8. Interferon is a protein that (a) cleaves DNA molecules together (b) destroys viruses (c) induces polyploidy (d) inhibits blood clotting.
9. Recombinant DNA technology is used to produce the substance (a) insulin (b) interferon (c) human growth hormone (d) human sex hormones.
10. *E. coli* containing recombinant DNA can reproduce as often as (a) every 20 minutes (b) every 30 minutes (c) every hour (d) every 2 hours.
11. What was the earliest form of applied genetics practiced by humans?
12. Name two plant varieties developed by Luther Burbank.
13. What weakness developed when dachshunds were inbred?
14. Why are hybrid organisms often unable to reproduce?
15. What was H. J. Muller's contribution to the field of applied genetics?
16. How do polyploid organisms differ from normal organisms?
17. How do scientists determine the exact

19. Because the bacterium that carries the gene for interferon reproduces rapidly and thus can produce large amounts of interferon in a short time
20. Because it is a chemical reaction catalyzed by the enzyme DNA polymerase, and it repeats the same three steps over and over

base sequence of a DNA segment?

18. What role do restriction enzymes play in the creation of recombinant DNA?
19. Why is gene cloning an efficient method of producing a substance such as interferon artificially?
20. Why did Dr. Kary Mullis and his colleagues call their process of DNA synthesis a "polymerase chain reaction?"

Critical Thinking

1. List an advantage and a disadvantage of developing new plant and animal varieties using mass selection instead of genetic engineering techniques.
2. Male championship horses are often bred with their female offspring. This usually produces horses that possess many of the same exceptional traits as the paternal parent. What method of controlled breeding is being used here? Why might the resulting offspring inherit positive traits?
3. The United States government has stringent regulations requiring researchers to confine genetically engineered organisms to the laboratory. What concerns do you think might have led to the enactment of these regulations?
4. Bananas sold commercially are of the triploid variety—that is, they possess three sets of chromosomes. However, these bananas are infertile and must be produced through hybridization. Why are they unable to reproduce?
5. Examine the restriction map of the *E. coli* plasmid pBR 322, shown at the right. This is a commonly used plasmid composed of 4,363 base pairs. The map shows sites at which certain restriction enzymes cut the DNA of the plasmid. For example, *Sph*I cuts the plasmid at base pair 566. Suppose you want to isolate from the plasmid the gene that codes for resistance to the antibiotic tetracycline, which is indicated as Tc^r. What restriction enzymes would you use? How many base pairs long is the Tc^r gene? How might you check to be certain that your procedure was successful?

Restriction Map of pBR 322 DNA

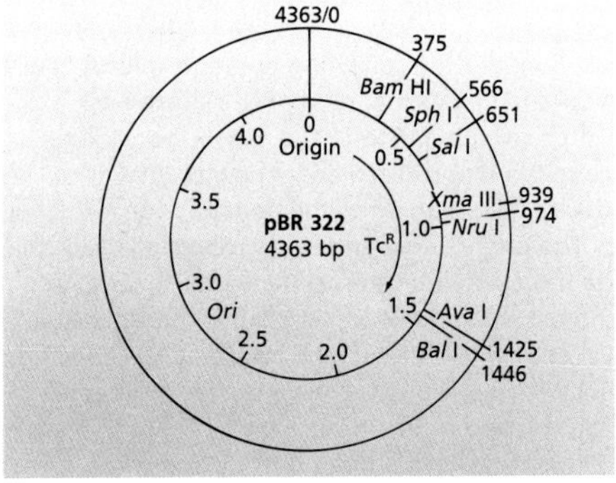

Extension

1. Read the article by Deborah Erickson entitled "Down on the Pharm" in *Scientific American*, August 1990, pp. 102–103. Present an oral report in which you include answers to the following questions. (1) What is a transgenic animal? (2) What are the potential uses of transgenic animals? (3) What impact have transgenic animals had on medical research? (4) How are government institutions involved? (5) What problems and controversy surround the use of transgenic animals?
2. Recent practical applications of genetic engineering are often in the news. Look in issues of *Time* and *Newsweek* from the last several months for recent medical products produced with the help of genetic engineering, and present an oral report on these developments.

Critical Thinking

1. An advantage is that mass selection selects for a total phenotype instead of merely considering one gene. Thus, the plant will be better adapted overall. A disadvantage is that mass selection takes longer than genetic engineering to develop a new variety.
2. Inbreeding; the resulting offspring would receive from both parents genes that result in the expression of favorable traits.
3. Concerns that genetically engineered organisms might cause disease or have other harmful effects on the environment
4. Because they possess an uneven number of chromosome pairs
5. You would use the restriction enzymes *Bam* HI, and *Bal* I. The gene would be 1,071 base pairs long. To determine whether the procedure was successful, you would reinsert the plasmid into the bacterial cell, clone the bacterium, and expose the new bacterial colony to tetracycline. If the bacteria are not resistant to tetracycline, the procedure has been successful.

Extension

1. Encourage students to create visual aids to use during their oral reports. Have them draw schematic diagrams on the board or on poster paper showing the process whereby transgenic organisms are produced.
2. Newspapers, too, often report on genetic engineering as regular news, in science sections, and as business news. Have students clip such articles and post them on the class bulletin board.

Discussion

Guide the discussion by posing the following questions.

1. What advantages do you think result from having the work of many scientists consolidated through the Human Genome Project? *(Answers will vary. Students should consider the size of the project, the huge quantity of data to be collected, and the potential for coordination of data.)*

2. How do you think that family pedigrees might continue to be useful in mapping human genes? *(A pedigree will identify family members with a genetic disorder. The DNA from several family members with a similar genetic disorder can be compared for similarities and differences.)*

1. What factors make the Human Genome Project feasible now in a way that it would not have been even in 1980? *(Answers should include the increase in the capability of computers to process information; the improved technology for mapping and sequencing bases and genes; the decrease in time and cost involved.)*

4. Why will analysis continue long after the data are collected? *(The collection of data is only one step in the experimental process. The amount of data to be collected is tremendous and analysis may be more difficult than collection.)*

5. How might the data collected by the Human Genome Project affect your life? *(Answers will vary. Students should think in terms of possible prediction of disease, new cures, impact on decisions about having children, and potential job and insurance discrimination.)*

Intra-Science

How the Sciences Work Together

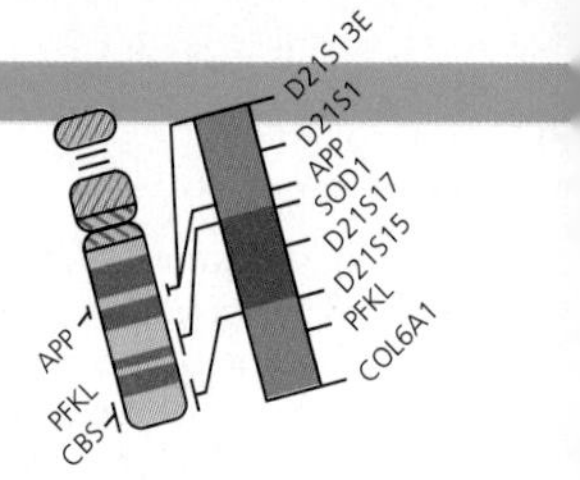

The Question in Biology: *Can the Human Genome Be Mapped?*

Consider the following human exploits: Lewis and Clark's mapping of the Northwest Territory. The building of the atomic bomb. The race to the moon. Then add a new endeavor to that list: the mapping of the genetic code.

The project now underway to explore and catalog the makeup of the human genetic code, or genome, will require an almost incomprehensible level of scientific effort. The information collected will fill the equivalent of 13 sets of *Encyclopaedia Britannica*, and maybe more.

Scientists have argued bitterly about the value of the $3 billion Human Genome Project. David Baltimore of Rockefeller University has warned that "It would be a distortion of research priorities if the initiative took significant resources away from other areas of biological science." To many other scientists, the potential benefits are irresistible. "We will see a new dawn of understanding about evolution and human origins, and totally new approaches to old scientific questions," said Allan Wilson of the University of California at Berkeley. Consequently, the federally funded Human Genome Project was launched in 1987 to coordinate the work of numerous research projects throughout the country. The effort, which will continue through the year 2000, is two-fold. Some laboratories are working to "map" the location of the 100,000 genes on the human chromosome. Other researchers are identifying and recording the sequence of the more than 3 billion DNA nucleotides.

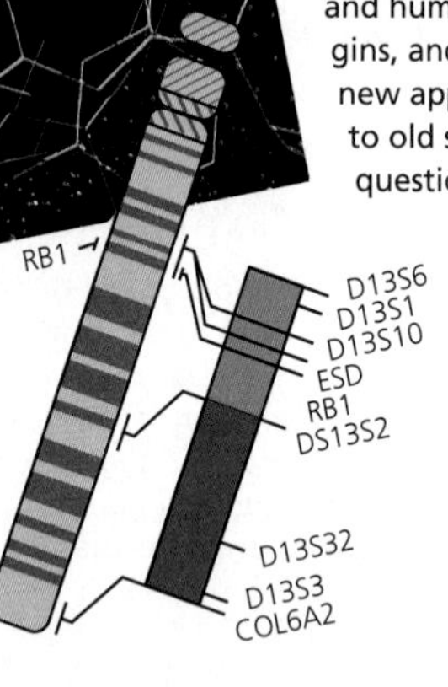

The task is a little like trying to measure the Grand Canyon with a yardstick. So the project has focused first on mapping only 2 percent of the human genome—the genes that code for proteins. An understanding of these genes could yield critical information about fatal and crippling diseases and replace scientific speculation with solid facts.

The Connection to Computer Science

Geneticists began unraveling the mystery of the human genome in 1911, when studies of family pedigrees revealed that the gene for red-green

200

Connections to Other Disciplines

History The Human Genome Project is not the first instance of a massive, concerted research effort. Encourage students to find out about other megaprojects—such as the Manhattan Project during World War II and efforts in the 1960s by the National Aeronautics and Space Administration (NASA) to send astronauts to the moon.

Language Arts Walter Gilbert, a scientist at Harvard University, has stated at several national meetings, "Sequencing the human genome is like pursuing the holy grail." Suggest that students research the term "holy grail" in the Arthurian legends of Galahad and Percival, and ask why they think that Gilbert chose this simile.

color blindness was located on the X chromosome. Since then the ability to locate genes has advanced rapidly. The completion of this century-long investigation, however, depends on the use of computers.

Besides organizing and storing the volumes of data generated in the Human Genome Project, computers also perform a crucial analytical function. Because biologists work with relatively small portions of DNA at any one time, they may not see larger patterns in the sequence of nucleotides. Yet such large patterns may exist and could prove important. By analyzing the "big picture," computers and computer scientists can help make sense of the information that is being collected in laboratories across the country.

■ *Why is the role of computers so important in the Human Genome Project?*

The Connection to Chemistry

Scientists want to work only with expressed DNA, the 2 percent of the genome that actually codes for protein. Finding this small portion amid the unexpressed DNA is a needle-in-a-haystack job performed by biochemists.

Since they know that messenger RNA is produced only when a gene is functioning to produce a protein, biochemists find the DNA they want to work with by identifying which DNA is complementary to mRNA. They then use several methods to analyze small bits of DNA, base by base, until the strands are completely sequenced.

A skilled technician can sequence only about 300 bases a day. So biochemists are working to develop new techniques to locate and sequence genes faster and less expensively.

■ *Why might automation of sequencing help biochemists?*

The Connection to Other Sciences

The mapping of the human genome will bring extensive changes to the field of medicine. Eventually, the project may generate tests for most of the nearly 4,000 known hereditary diseases. Scientists predict that genetic screening will enable doctors not only to diagnose inheritance of diseases, but also to detect susceptibilities to problems that develop later in life. In the latter case, doctors may then be able to recommend a diet and lifestyle that can help prevent the problem.

But researchers in fields from molecular genetics to occupational safety worry that the benefits of gene mapping may be overshadowed by its misuses. What if insurance companies refuse to insure people who have genes for hereditary diseases? What if employers refuse to hire people who have "bad" genomes? Scientists heading the genome project have spearheaded discussions about its ethical implications. Some have even suggested passing laws to protect individual privacy in regard to DNA.

■ *What benefits may come from mapping the locations of disease-causing genes?*

The Connection to Careers

Decades after the last nucleotide base of the human genome has been located and placed in sequence, scientists will still be working to understand the significance of the data. The knowledge of biologists, geneticists, computer scientists, and physicians will be required to meet the challenge. Laboratory technicians, computer programmers, and other support staff will be needed. Physicians, genetic counselors, and lawyers will be increasingly involved in the numerous issues that arise as people know more about their genomes. For more information about related careers in the biological sciences, turn to page 842.

6. If you are likely to develop an incurable disease later in your life, how would you feel about knowing this information ahead of time? *(Allow for personal opinion.)*

7. Do you think that a law should be passed to try to prevent the misuse of genetic information? If so, what kind of law do you think would be most useful? *(Students should explain their answers.)*

Answers to

Computer Science Without computers, scientists would be swamped with organizing and storing vast quantities of data. They would also be less able to recognize patterns in nucleotide sequences. Some students may suggest that computers speed up data processing.

Chemistry Automation should increase the amount of work one technician can accomplish in a day. Students may suggest that automated analysis can free biochemists to do work that is mentally more challenging.

Other Sciences Potential benefits include finding cures for diseases, predicting the occurrence of diseases, and preventing diseases.

Enrichment

One study in the Human Genome Project involves mapping and sequencing the complete genome of the white laboratory mouse *Mus musculus.* Ask students to investigate the importance of mice in genetic research. Ask them how knowing the genetic make-up of the mouse may help scientists who do research with these animals.

Unit 4 Evolution

Chapters

Unit Overview

Unit 4 continues the study of inheritance and mutations begun in Unit 3 by describing the effect these processes produce over time—the evolution of species. Chapter 14 describes early theories and experiments, and presents Oparin's modern theory of how life developed from nonliving matter. Chapter 15 discusses Darwin's theory of organic evolution by natural selection. Chapter 16 describes what a species is and explains how natural selection forms new species. Chapter 17 provides a detailed exposition of evolution in action, focusing on humans and their presumed closest ancestors. Chapter 18 presents the modern system of classifying organisms.

Issues in Biology

Use your discretion in introducing the following topic for class discussion, and be sensitive to family and community values.

The concept of evolution is controversial in some communities so it must be treated with delicacy. Some students and parents may be creationists, who believe in a literal interpretation of the Bible.

Therefore, it is important to emphasize the theoretical framework presented in Unit 4. Scientists have gathered data of various kinds. From these data they have made certain inferences. In the classroom, students examine the evidence and inferences that are essential parts of the present culture and modern scientific literacy. However, nobody can prove positively how modern organisms developed. What students believe is up to them. Ask students to discuss how comprehending the concept of evolution can enrich their appreciation of nature.

Research in Progress

The ancestral origin of humans has been a longstanding mystery to evolutionary biologists. Scientists are now attempting to solve this mystery. Recently, biochemists at the University of California at Berkeley analyzed genetic sequences from 189 people of diverse races. To simplify the study, researchers analyzed only mitochondrial DNA, which is passed almost exclusively through the maternal line. Using computer programs, scientists constructed a genealogical tree of modern humans, concluding that the common maternal ancestor lived in Africa about 200,000 years ago.

French scientists are conducting a similar study to determine the common paternal ancestor of modern humans. In this case, they are analyzing the Y chromosome, passed almost exclusively through the paternal line. So far researchers are concluding that the common paternal ancestor also lived in Africa about 200,000 years ago. While these studies have faced much criticism and controversy, they have opened up great new possibilities for molecular biological research.

Interdisciplinary Activity

Health A clear example of natural selection in action is now having significant effects on humans. Have students research the resistance of bacteria to antibiotics; evolution occurring within bacteria only since the 1940s is directly affecting human health. One related subject for student research is the evolution of viruses: new influenza strains are constantly appearing and other viral diseases are becoming more virulent. Another related subject is the growing resistance of insects to DDT and other insecticides and what farmers can do about it.

Resources

Chapter	Print: For the Teacher	Print: For the Student	Audiovisual/Software
14	■ John Horgan, "In the Beginning..." *Scientific American,* February 1991, 116–125. ■ Lynn Margulis and Dorion Sagan, *Microcosmos: Four Billion Years of Microbial Evolution,* Simon & Schuster, 1986.	■ Bennett Daviss, "Yikes! It's Al-i-i-i-ve!" *Discover,* December 1990, 28. ■ Edwin Kiester Jr., "A Bug in the System," *Discover,* February 1991, 70–76.	■ *Blue Planet Earth.* Video, 28 min. Landmark Films, 1987. ■ *From Protistans to First Multicellular Animals.* Film, 18 min. Benchmark, 1986.
15	■ Stephen Jay Gould, *Bully for Brontosaurus,* W.W. Norton and Company, 1991. ■ Andrew Scott, *The Creation of Life: Past, Future, Alien,* Basil Blackwell, 1988.	■ Stephen Jay Gould, "Darwin and Paley Meet the Invisible Hand," *Natural History,* November 1990, 8–16. ■ Carl Zimmer, "Family Affairs," *Discover,* January 1991, 64–65.	■ *Biovideo: The Evidence for Evolution.* Video, 30 min. Cabisco Video/BBC. Distributed by Carolina Biological. ■ *Stephen Jay Gould: His View of Life.* Film and video, 57 min. Time-Life, 1984.
16	■ Peter R. Grant, "Natural Selection and Darwin's Finches," *Scientific American,* October 1991, 82–87. ■ V. C. Wynne-Edwards, *Evolution through Group Selection,* Blackwell Scientific Publications, 1986.	■ Darcy B. Kelley and Dennis L. Gorlick, "Sexual Selection and the Nervous System," *BioScience,* April 1990, 275–283. ■ Julie Ann Miller, "Interactions Drive Species Diversity," *BioScience,* November 1990, 715.	■ *Natural Selection.* Video, 20 min. Teacher's guide. Films for the Humanities & Sciences, 1985.
17	■ Glynn Isaac, *The Archaeology of Human Origins,* Cambridge University Press, 1989. ■ Roger Lewin, *Human Evolution: An Illustrated Introduction,* 2nd ed., Blackwell Scientific Publications, 1989.	■ Philip E. Ross, "Crossed Lines," *Scientific American,* October 1991, 30–32. ■ James Shreeve, "Argument Over a Woman," *Discover,* August 1990, 52–59. ■ James Shreeve, "Madam, I'm Adam," *Discover,* June 1991, 24.	■ *Evolution and Human Equality.* Narrated by Stephen Jay Gould. Video, 42 min. Insight Video, 1987. ■ *Evolution of Man.* Video, 20 min. Films for the Humanities & Sciences, 1987.
18	■ Lynn Margulis and Karen V. Schwartz, *Five Kingdoms: An Illustrated Guide to the Phyla of Life on Earth,* 2nd ed., W. H. Freeman, 1988. ■ R. J. G. Savage, *Mammal Evolution: An Illustrated Guide,* Facts on File, 1986.	■ Jared Diamond, "The Search for Life on Earth," *Natural History,* April 1990, 28–32.	■ *Classifying Living Things.* Film or video, 21 min. Encyclopædia Britannica, 1986. ■ *The Five-Kingdom Classification.* Film or video, 23 min. Benchmark Films, 1987. ■ *Life Science.* Apple. Curriculum Data Base. 2 disks. User's handbook. Activity units. Scholastic.

Introducing the Unit

The material in Unit 3, reproduction and inheritance, is a logical prerequisite for the study of evolution in this unit. To promote the transition to Unit 4, ask students the following questions.

1. Why do similar organisms have similar traits? *(Because of their genetic makeup. If chromosomes and genes are similar, the organisms are similar.)*

2. What happens to offspring when there is a genetic mutation in a cell that produces gametes? *(The offspring will be different in some ways from the parents.)*

3. Can a change in one organism affect a population? *(If conditions are right, the change can spread over several generations through a population and result in the development of a new kind [species] of organism.)*

4. What questions can you ask about the history of life? *(Sample questions: How and where did life begin? How do changes in genes spread through a population? Is evolution happening now? What is some evidence for present and past changes? Did humans evolve from apes? Were Neanderthals really human? What is a species? How do scientists keep track of all the organisms living today?)*

Unit 4 Evolution

Chapters

"Each organism instructs; its form and behavior embody general messages if only we can learn to read them. The language of this instruction is evolutionary theory."

Stephen Jay Gould

On the facing page you see a flower that looks like an insect and an insect that looks like a leaf. What biological processes have produced these oddities? What advantages do these organisms derive from their misleading appearances? You will learn answers to questions such as these as you study this unit on evolution, the process of change over time that modifies species in ways that enhance their survival.

Labyrinthodont, *Ichthyostega*, ancestral amphibian

Fossil of fish and palm leaf

Using the Opening Quotation

Ask students what the structure and behavior of an organism reveals. Some students will answer that structure and behavior reveal what kind of organism it is and what its life-style is. For example, structures may indicate whether an organism is terrestrial or aquatic. Point out that the Gould quotation implies that each organism can contribute to our understanding of evolution. Help students recognize that most organisms are the latest generation in a long, evolutionary line, according to modern theory.

Ask how we can learn to read messages from organisms. *(We can study evolution in general and then study an organism with this in mind, using evidence to hypothesize about what the organism's ancestors might have been like.)*

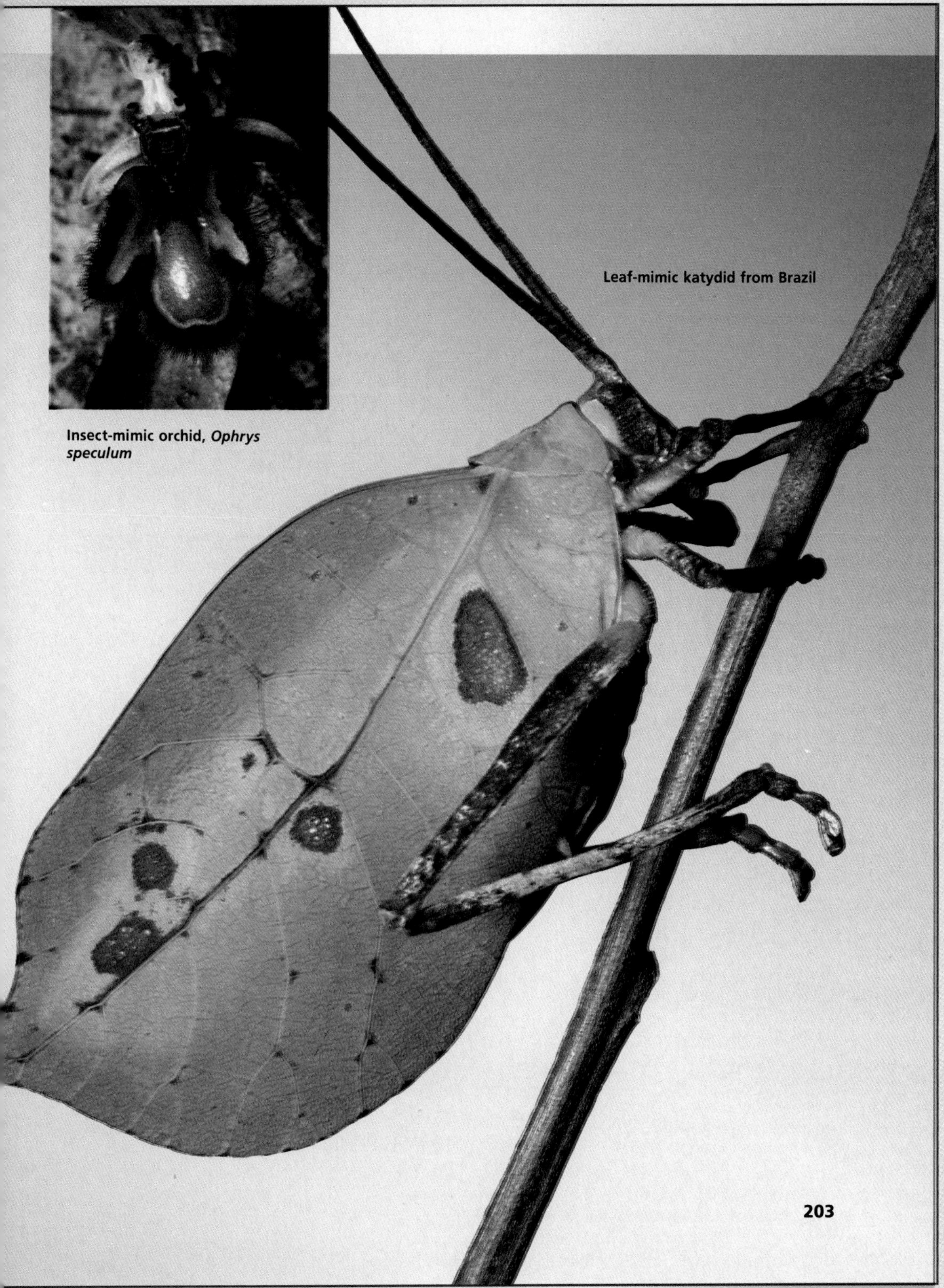

Insect-mimic orchid, *Ophrys speculum*

Leaf-mimic katydid from Brazil

Unit Themes

Evolution This unit focuses on the study of evolution starting with the origin of life on earth (Chapter 14) through mechanisms of speciation (Chapters 15, 16) to development of modern humans (Chapter 17) and the great variety of living organisms (Chapter 18).

Scale and Structure Species are defined largely on the basis of structures (Chapters 16, 17). Evolutionary changes in populations are traced by structural changes ranging in scale from gene rearrangements to the development of elephant tusks. Modern classification of organisms (Chapter 18) relies on structures such as odd-toed and even-toed hooves of mammals.

Patterns of Change Evolutionary changes occur randomly, but over time they result in directional trends under the pressure of natural selection. Other patterns are involved within general trends such as those of divergence, convergence, and coevolution (Chapter 15). The modern taxonomic system organizes the results of all the trends through time (Chapter 18).

Systems and Interactions This theme is stressed in Chapter 15 and is implicit in the other chapters. Evolution through natural selection occurs as organisms interact with their environments, which may be stable or changing.

Understanding the Visuals

Have students closely observe and describe the katydid and orchid. *(The katydid is an insect that looks like a plant part. The orchid is a flower that looks like an insect.)* Ask students to infer how the leaflike appearance has affected katydid evolution. *(Its appearance enhances the katydid's chance to survive and reproduce—to pass on its genetic composition and traits to a new generation.)* Ask students to infer how the insect-like appearance is an advantage for the orchid. *(It has helped attract pollinators to the plant.)*

Chapter 14 The Origin of Life

Chapter Overview

Chapter 14 describes methods that scientists have used in attempting to explain the origin of life. Section 14.1 shows how the work of three scientists over three centuries helped disprove the early belief that organisms can arise spontaneously from nonliving matter. Section 14.2 presents the most widely accepted modern theory of how life began on earth. In Section 14.3, students learn about earth's earliest organisms.

Chapter Planning Chart

B	S	A	Sections and Subsections	Page	Features	Page	Resources
•	•	•	**14.1 Spontaneous Generation**				
			Redi's Experiment Spallanzani's Experiment Pasteur's Experiment	205 206 206	Section Review	207	Videodiscs Blackline Master 29 Overhead Transparency T14 Process Skills: Spontaneous Generation Section Reviews Worksheet
•	•	•	**14.2 Origin of Life on Earth**				
			Formation of the Earth The Appearance of Life on Earth	208 209	Laboratory Section Review	215 211	Videodiscs Blackline Master 30 Laboratories: Coacervates Section Reviews Worksheet
	•	•	**14.3 The First Forms of Life**				
			The First Prokaryotes The Changing Earth The First Eukaryotes	212 213 214	Biology in Process Think Section Review	212 214 214	Videodiscs Section Reviews Worksheet
			End of Chapter Activities				
					Chapter Review	216	Vocabulary Skills Chapter Test Computer Test Generator

B *The Basic Level curriculum presents the most fundamental knowledge offered in the course.*
S *The Standard Level curriculum is designed for the average student who is able to master most topics.*
A *The Advanced Level curriculum includes suggestions for teaching the most academically able students.*

Cooperative Learning

Group Activity: Spontaneous Generation

- **Group Size:** *4 students*
- **Outcome:** *Students will recognize the historical context of the theory of spontaneous generation.*
- **Individual Accountability:** *Each student will express a 1600s viewpoint about spontaneous generation.*
- **Positive Interdependence:** *The group will propose a method to disprove spontaneous generation.*

Before students read Chapter 14, ask them to imagine they are living in the early 1600s and have observed fish apparently coming from dried mud, flies from meat, and spoilage in boiled broth. To explain their observations, have one student pair recount the common viewpoint of the 1600s and defend the theory of spontaneous generation—that life could arise from nonlife. Have the second student pair oppose the theory, using only evidence available in the early 1600s. *(Sample arguments: The mating of domestic animals produces young; flowers form seeds that become plants; the housefly has an observable life cycle.)*

Ask students to suggest experiments to disprove spontaneous generation. What technology did scientists of the 1600s invent to gather necessary evidence? *(Lens and microscope)*

Concept Map

The following is one possible solution to the concept mapping activity in Relating Concepts on p. 209.

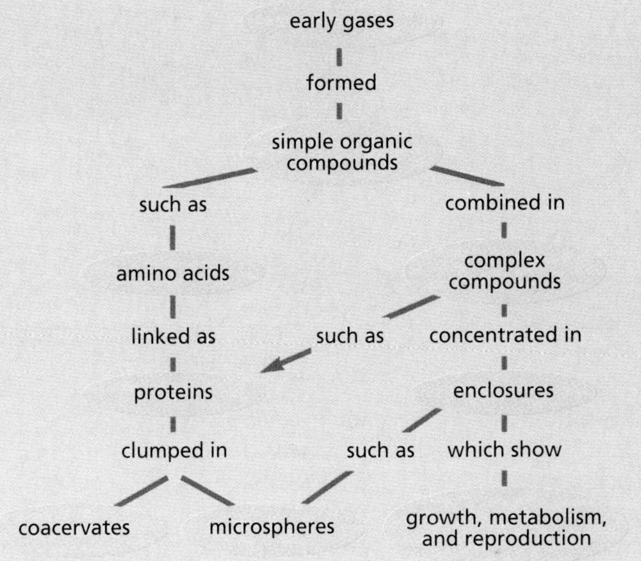

Laboratory Preparation

Overview *(See p. 215.)*

In this lab, students will produce microspheres by heating certain amino acids. They will observe the microspheres and then compare them with living cells. Students' comparisons will focus on the presence or absence of a membranelike boundary and internal organelles.

Microspheres and living cells share several characteristics that are not discernible in this lab. For example, the contents of both microspheres and living cells differ from the surrounding liquid. Both will shrink if placed in a hypertonic solution or swell if placed in a hypotonic solution. Like bacterial cells, microspheres can be either Gram-positive or Gram-negative, depending on their amino acid makeup. Fission occurs in acidic microspheres when the pH is raised.

Current hypotheses about the prebiotic earth consider all these shared characteristics to be indications that the evolution of life could have begun with something similar to simple microspheres.

Preparation

Order enough amino acids ahead of time to supply all lab stations with 1 g each of aspartic acid, glutamic acid, and glycine. Prepare 1% NaCl solution by adding 5 g of sodium chloride to 500 mL of distilled water.

Teaching Tips

For Inquiry step 2, demonstrate the careful and safe handling of the ring stand apparatus while setting the Erlenmeyer flask in the hot-water bath. Also, for step 5, demonstrate the proper handling of the hot Erlenmeyer flask with the tongs.

To assist students in answering the question in Inquiry step 6, point out that coacervates and microspheres might form at room temperature but too slowly to observe.

To expand Further Inquiry, you may wish to suggest that students design a control for their microsphere experiment and test it. *(To incorporate a control, repeat the experiment with the same ingredients but omit the amino acids.)* Ask what would be the purpose of the control. *(To show that microspheres do not form in boiled 1% NaCl solution alone, indicating that the microspheres in the experiment formed from the heated amino acids)*

Safety

Caution students not to ingest the amino acid powders, and to wash their hands after handling them.

Chapter Themes

Evolution The development of simple unicellular organisms was the first step in the evolution of life. Point out that the progression from anaerobic, heterotrophic prokaryotes to eukaryotes occurred through a series of random changes.

Scale and Structure Basic cell structures originated in coacervates and microspheres and in eukaryotes that were formed through the invasion of some prokaryotes by others. Explain that further evolution entailed modifications of and additions to the basic structures.

Energy Emphasize that life could have begun when coacervates and microspheres developed the capability of releasing energy from substances in the environment.

Chapter Motivating Activity

Have students examine rock samples such as granite and sandstone. Tell them to imagine what the earth was like when it consisted only of nonliving materials—rock, sand and silt, water, and atmosphere. Ask students to suggest the "raw materials" for the first cell and to describe the structure of its parts. List these suggestions on the board and diagram the first cell on the board, based on students' descriptions.

Ask students what nonliving substances life might have evolved from. *(Student responses might include the gases in the atmosphere and water.)* Some scientists also propose that life may have evolved from clay. Encourage students to offer hypotheses for how life evolved from the nonliving substances they suggest.

Chapter 14 The Origin of Life

Introduction

How did life on earth begin? Over the centuries scientists have sought the answer to this question by engaging in the various processes of science. In this chapter you will learn how scientists have used observing, hypothesizing, experimenting, and other processes in studying the origin of life.

Chapter Outline

Chapter Concept

As you read, look for examples of the many processes of science involved in answering questions about how life began on earth.

Lake of Kilauea Volcano, Hawaii. Inset: The Andromeda Galaxy.

Understanding the Visuals

Ask students how photographs of a volcanic eruption and a galaxy can represent the origin of life on earth. Point out that volcanic eruptions were very common on the young earth. *(The mixture of hot gases and other matter from them may have helped provide the raw materials and conditions capable of forming organic compounds—precursors of life on earth. The Lake of Kilauea represents such early conditions on earth.)* Then remind students that life on earth would not be possible without the sun, one star in billions throughout the many galaxies in the universe. Ask students to give rationales for why they think life could or could not exist elsewhere in the universe.

14.1 Spontaneous Generation

Can mud produce live fish? Will rotting meat give rise to flies? Does the air generate microorganisms? In the past, people asked such questions in pondering a deep mystery of science: How did life arise on earth? Then, as today, people attempted to unravel this mystery by relying primarily on their observations. Fish appeared in ponds that had gone completely dry during the previous season. That mud might have given rise to such fish seemed a reasonable explanation for what people observed. Flies swarming from rotten meat and clear broth clouding up with bacteria were other phenomena people attempted to explain. Their observations led them to the conclusion that living organisms could arise from nonliving matter. This process, known as **spontaneous generation,** was one way people explained how new life formed.

In attempting to learn more about the process of spontaneous generation, scientists performed controlled experiments. As you read about each of the experiments described below, refer to the figures that show the experimental setup.

Section Objectives

- *Define* spontaneous generation *and list some observations people used as evidence for this theory about how life began.*
- *Summarize the results of experiments by Francesco Redi and by Lazzaro Spallanzani to test the theory of spontaneous generation.*
- *Describe how Louis Pasteur's experiment disproved the spontaneous generation of microorganisms under existing conditions.*

Redi's Experiment

In times past, as now, flies were such pesky creatures that most people were too busy brushing them off to bother studying them. In fact, not until the 1600s did anyone notice that flies had different developmental forms. In the middle of that century, the Italian scientist Francesco Redi (1626–1697) observed that tiny white wormlike maggots turned into sturdy oval cases from which flies eventually emerged. He also observed that maggots seemed to appear where adult flies had previously landed. These observations led him to question the commonly held hyphothesis that flies were generated spontaneously from rotten meat.

Figure 14-1 shows an experiment Redi set up in 1668 to test the spontaneous generation of flies. The control group consisted

Figure 14-1 In Redi's experiment maggots were found only in the control jars because only there could flies reach the meat.

Redi's Experiment

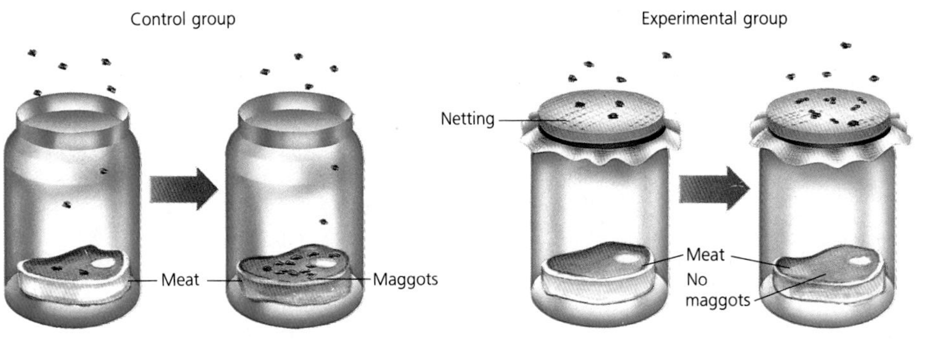

Scientist	Disputed Theory	Conclusions from Experiment
Redi	Maggots come from meat.	Maggots come from eggs laid by flies.
Spallanzani	Microorganisms come from "vital force" in air.	Microorganisms travel in air.
Pasteur	Boiling destroys air's "vital force."	Solid particles in air transport microorganisms.

Graphic Organizer Use this chart to summarize the experiments described in Section 14.1.

Lesson Plan

Section Focus

This section presents the theory of spontaneous generation and explains why it once seemed reasonable. It shows how Redi, Spallanzani, and Pasteur helped disprove the theory through controlled experiments.

Section Themes

The theme of **Systems and Interactions** is evident in the interactions of meat with flies and of sterile broth with airborne microorganisms. When scientists altered the systems, the interactions changed. Pasteur's experiment underscores the theme of **Evolution,** since it confirmed the theory of biogenesis.

Motivating Activity

Display some rotten fruit and ask students why it is rotten. *(Bacteria are living on it.)* Ask students to suggest why before the mid-1600s a person might have explained that the fruit rotted because of foul juices from within. Then ask them how a scientist in the 1600s might have tested the hypothesis that tiny organisms in the air caused the rotting. *(Student responses should describe controlled experiments.)*

Teaching Strategies

Interpreting the Visuals Ask students to think of possible sources of experimental error in Figures 14-1 and 14-2 . *(Sample answers: Redi—not covering the jar before flies entered it; Spallanzani—not sealing the flask before microorganisms entered it, or not heating the system enough to kill all the microorganisms)* Note that Figure 14-2 shows the experimental flask sealed properly with a stopper.

Videodiscs

- ***1186–1192, Insecta: Diptera—Various Flies and Stages (s)***

Interpreting the Visuals Have students identify the microorganisms in three places in Figure 14-3 on p. 207. *(Stages 2 and 3—in the curve of the neck; stage 4—entering the broken neck)* Ask them to explain how Pasteur's experiment had a control group and an experimental group. *(Although there was only one flask, it was the control while its curved neck was intact, and it became the experiment when its curved neck was removed.)* How did Pasteur show that there was no "vital force"? *(The broth was continuously exposed to the air.)*

■ *See* **Overhead Transparency** ***T14 and*** **Blackline Master** ***29.***

Guided Practice

Remind students that an experiment is preceded by a hypothesis. Ask them to suggest the hypotheses that led to the three experiments described in this section. *(Sample answers: Redi—Flies come from eggs laid by other flies; Spallanzani and Pasteur—Microorganisms come from other microorganisms in the air.)*

■ *See* **Process Skills,** ***Chapter 14.***

Independent Practice

■ Have students write answers to the Section Review.

■ Ask students to identify the independent and dependent variables in Figures 14-1, 14-2, and 14-3, pp. 205–207. *(14-1: Independent variable—presence or absence of cover on jar; dependent variable—presence or absence of maggots on meat. 14-2: Independent variable—presence or absence of seal on flask; dependent variable—presence or absence of microorganisms in broth. 14-3: Independent variable—presence or absence of curved neck on flask; dependent variable—presence or absence of microorganisms in broth)*

Figure 14-2 Spallanzani's flask was tightly sealed after boiling. The contents remained uncontaminated.

of uncovered jars that contained meat. The experimental group consisted of similar jars covered with netting. The netting allowed air to enter, while preventing flies from landing on the meat. After a period of time, maggots swarmed on the meat in the open jars. The net-covered jars remained free of maggots despite the flies buzzing all around. The results of Redi's experiment convinced most people that flies come from eggs laid by other flies; flies do not arise spontaneously from rotting meat.

Spallanzani's Experiment

At about the same time that Redi carried out his experiment, other scientists began using a new tool—the microscope. Their observations with the microscope revealed that the world was teeming with tiny creatures. These microorganisms seemed so simple in structure, so numerous, and so widespread that many people concluded that microorganisms must arise spontaneously from a "vital force" in the air.

In the 1700s another Italian scientist, Lazzaro Spallanzani, (1729–1799), designed an experiment, shown in Figure 14-2, to test spontaneous generation of microorganisms. Spallanzani hypothesized that microorganisms formed not from air, but from other microorganisms. He assumed that boiling broth in a flask would kill all the microorganisms in the flask—those in the broth, those on the inside of the glass, and those in the air in the flask. Spallanzani knew that boiled broth was clear. He also knew that a flask of boiled broth left unsealed would soon become cloudy, contaminated with microorganisms. Spallanzani sealed his experimental flask of boiled broth by melting the glass top shut. He found that the broth in the sealed flask remained clear.

Spallanzani concluded that boiled broth became contaminated only when microorganisms from the air entered the flask. However, Spallanzani's opponents objected to his method and disagreed with his conclusions. They claimed Spallanzani boiled his flasks so long that he destroyed the "vital force" in the air inside the flask. Air lacking this "vital force" could not generate life, they claimed. Scientists continued to debate the spontaneous generation of microorganisms into the 1800s.

Pasteur's Experiment

By the mid-1800s the spontaneous generation controversy had grown so fierce that the Paris Academy of Science offered a prize to anyone who could clear up the issue once and for all. The winner of the prize turned out to be the French scientist Louis Pasteur (1822–1895).

Refer to Figure 14-3 to see how Pasteur set up his prize-winning experiment. To answer objections to Spallanzani's experiment, Pasteur made a curve-necked flask that allowed air to enter. Broth boiled in this flask remained clear and uncontami-

Interdisciplinary Activity

History Have students research the career of Louis Pasteur to discover his role in history. Investigating his career will show them how biology blends with other disciplines, such as medicine and economics, throughout history.

Tell students to list Pasteur's findings, the significance of each, and their effect on medicine, economics, and other disciplines. Have students also describe people's knowledge about bacteria at the time, and the relationship between the experiment presented in the text and the pasteurization process.

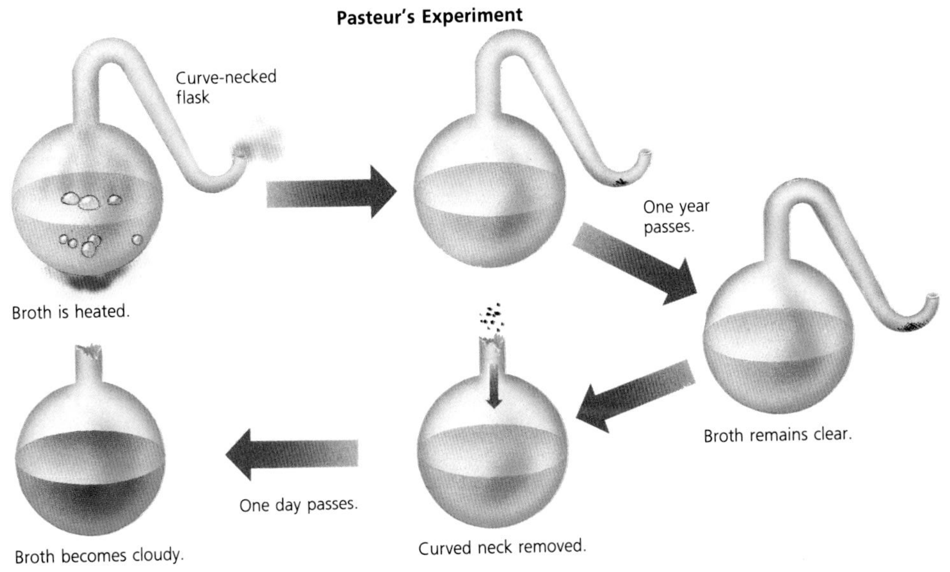

Figure 14-3 In Pasteur's experiment broth became contaminated only when the curved neck was removed from a flask.

nated for more than a year, even though it was exposed to air. The curve in the neck of the flask trapped particles in the air, preventing them from reaching the broth. When Pasteur removed the curved neck, the broth clouded with microorganisms within a day. From such experiments, Pasteur concluded that "productions of infusions [liquids contaminated with microorganisms], previously heated, have no other origin than the solid particles which the air always transports."

With this experiment Pasteur claimed to have "driven partisans of the doctrine of spontaneous generation into the corner." The theory died a sudden death. **Biogenesis** (*BIE-oe-JEN-uh-suss*), the theory that living organisms come only from other living organisms, became a cornerstone of biology.

Section Review

1. What is the theory of spontaneous generation, and how did people use the theory to explain what they observed?
2. How did Redi's experiment help disprove spontaneous generation of flies?
3. Why did proponents of the theory of spontaneous generation object to Spallanzani's experiment?
4. Describe Pasteur's experiment and his results.
5. What would have happened if Pasteur had tipped one of his flasks so that the broth in the flask came into contact with the inside of the curved neck? Would these results have supported his conclusion? Why or why not?

Answers to Section Review

1. Living organisms can arise from nonliving matter. Accept examples from p. 205.
2. Maggots did not appear on meat when flies were kept away.
3. They claimed he had destroyed the "vital force" in the air in the flask.
4. Pasteur used a curve-necked flask that allowed air but not dust or other particles to reach the sterile broth inside. The broth remained uncontaminated until Pasteur removed the curved neck of the flask.
5. The broth would have become contaminated. That would have supported Pasteur's conclusion because the contamination would have resulted only from contact between the broth and particles trapped in the curved neck.

Check Your Understanding

1. What scientific processes did Redi, Spallanzani, and Pasteur use? (*Observing, hypothesizing, predicting, experimenting, inferring, and communicating*)
2. Why did some people in the 1700s believe that a "vital force" in the air could generate life? (*They lacked data for understanding what happened.*)
3. How is Pasteur's experiment similar to the canning of fruit? (*Both show that heated food kept free from microorganisms will not spoil.*)

Reteaching

Tell students that because mosquito larvae appeared in a tub of water on the back porch, a scientist hypothesized that mosquitoes come from water. Have students draw and label an experimental design to test the hypothesis. *(Student drawings should resemble Figure 14-1 on p. 205, with water instead of meat, tubs instead of jars, and an outdoor location.)*

■ *See* Section Reviews *worksheet, Section 14.1.*

Enrichment

Give students culture tubes, tube racks, nutrient broth, and heat-resistant tube caps or cotton plugs. Tell them to design and set up their own spontaneous generation experiments. Assist students in sterilizing the tubes and nutrient broth. Have them prepare complete lab reports.

Closure

To convey the implications of the theory of biogenesis, ask students how life began if living things come only from other living things. *(Answers should indicate that although life does not come from nonlife today, it must have long ago.)* Ask students to speculate on how the earth was different in the past. Use their ideas as a lead-in to the next section.

Lesson Plan

Section Focus

This section describes the four developments that must have occurred before life first appeared on earth: formation of simple organic compounds; formation of complex organic compounds; concentration and enclosure of organic compounds; and evolution of growth, metabolism, and reproduction.

Section Themes

This section emphasizes two themes: **Energy** and **Scale and Structure.** Scientists hypothesize that energy from heat and/or lightning caused simple organic compounds to form from gases in the earth's early atmosphere. The structure of organic molecules became more complex, and they eventually became enclosed in membranes and developed the ability to obtain energy from substances in the environment.

Motivating Activity

Display posters or photographs of the other planets. Ask students why life as we know it does not exist on any of them. *(Atmospheres, if present, do not contain the right combination of gases; planets between earth and the sun are too hot; those beyond earth are too cold.)* Point out that, among the nearest planets, Venus's surface temperature is about 475°C, and its atmosphere is mostly sulfuric acid droplets. Mars's mean surface temperature is –20°C, and its atmosphere has no liquid water. Stress that the conditions on earth, including an abundance of liquid water, are unique in our solar system.

Section Objectives

- *Outline the modern scientific understanding of the formation of the earth.*
- *List four developments scientists hypothesize were necessary before life could have originated on earth.*
- *Summarize Oparin's theory of the origin of life and describe an experiment performed to test the theory.*
- *Compare and contrast coacervates and microspheres with living cells.*

14.2 Origin of Life on Earth

Pasteur's experiment left scientists with a dilemma. If living organisms in the existing environment can arise only from other living organisms, how could life on earth have begun? To answer this question, we first need to take a look at the early history of the earth.

Formation of the Earth

Use Figure 14-4 to trace the steps in the early history of earth. Using evidence from computer models of the sun, scientists hypothesize that about 5 billion years ago the solar system was a swirling mass of gas and dust. Within a few million years, most of this material had collapsed inward and formed the sun. The remaining dust and gas ringed the young sun as an enormous disk. This material is thought to have collected in clumps that formed the planets, including the earth.

According to evidence from meteors assumed to be the same age as earth, our planet is dated at about 4.6 billion years of age. Beginning as a ball of very hot rock, the young planet was quite different from today's earth. Meteorites bombarded its surface. Volcanic eruptions constantly shook the planet. Lava released hot gases that formed the early atmosphere. In time the temperature at

Figure 14-4 It took more than a billion years for the modern earth to form from a swirling mass of gases.

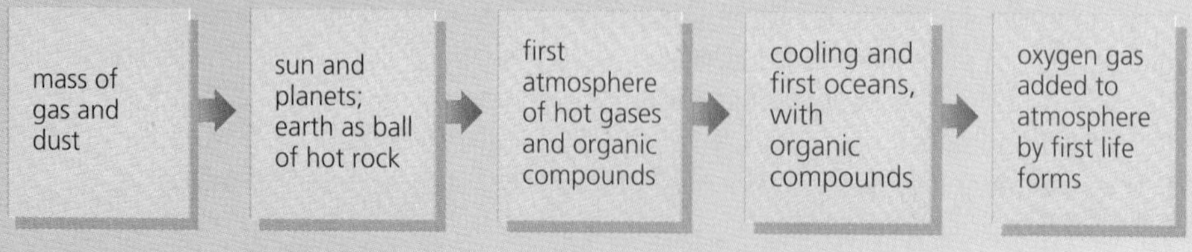

Graphic Organizer Use this sequential diagram in Sequencing Events on p. 209.

the earth's surface dropped below the boiling point of water. The water vapor in the air condensed and fell to earth as rain. In this way the oceans formed about 3.8 billion to 3.9 billion years ago.

The Appearance of Life on Earth

The above account of the earth's formation and early history is the theory that best fits the available scientific evidence. However, no rocks have survived to provide direct evidence about the earth's earliest eras. The oldest rocks on earth are only about 3.9 billion years old.

Though we know little about the earth's infancy, we do have records of early forms of life on earth. Some rocks up to 3.5 billion years old contain **fossils**—remains or traces of once-living organisms. These first fossils are of ancient prokaryotic cells. (Remember that prokaryotes lack a membrane-bound nucleus and membrane-bound organelles.) These microscopic fossils, or **microfossils**, are probably not the remains of the first cells that lived on earth. Instead these fossilized cells probably descended from a long line of unpreserved prokaryotes.

For life to come into being, scientists agree that four developments must have occurred. These include the following: the formation of simple organic compounds important to life; the formation of complex organic compounds, such as proteins; the concentration and enclosure of these organic compounds; and the linking of chemical reactions involved in growth, metabolism, and reproduction. Let's look at each of these developments.

Formation of Simple Organic Compounds

As you know, organic compounds—those containing carbon—are essential to life. Carbon and all the other elements found in organic compounds existed on earth when the planet came into being. In time the main elements of life—carbon, hydrogen, nitrogen, and oxygen—came to form gases in the atmosphere.

How these elements present in the atmosphere could have formed simple organic compounds important to life is a challenging scientific puzzle. One of the most popular hypotheses put forth to solve this puzzle was developed by the Soviet scientist Alexander I. Oparin in 1923. Oparin (1894–1980) suggested that the atmosphere of the primitive earth contained ammonia (NH_3), hydrogen gas (H_2), water vapor (H_2O), and compounds made of hydrogen and carbon, such as methane (CH_4). At temperatures well above the boiling point of water, the gases in the atmosphere might have formed simple organic compounds, such as amino acids. According to Oparin, when the earth cooled and water vapor condensed to form lakes and seas, these simple organic compounds would have collected in the water. Over time the compounds entered complex chemical reactions. Oparin hypothesized that proteins and other organic compounds important to life would have resulted from these reactions.

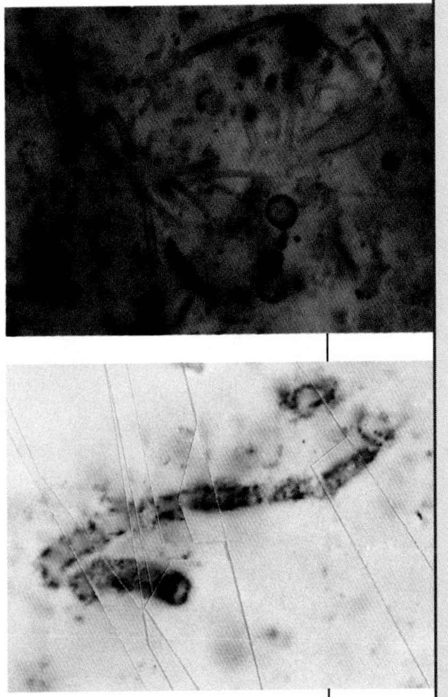

Figure 14-5 These microfossils show spheroid cells and filaments (top) and a closeup of a filament (bottom).

Teaching Strategies

Applying Concepts Have students review compounds and chemical reactions (Chapter 3), organic compounds and the importance of water (Chapter 4), and cell processes (Chapter 7). Ask students how peptide bonds (p. 53) relate to Section 14.2. *(One type of complex organic compound—proteins—could form initially only as a result of the linking of amino acids by peptide bonds.)*

Sequencing Events Have students draw a sequential diagram showing the changes in the earth and its atmosphere that are described in this section, beginning with the mass of gas and dust that was the original solar system. Use the sequential diagram on p. 208 as a model.

Making Inferences Explain that the earth is still hot at only 50 km below its surface and that a small portion of it is still molten. This molten material sometimes comes to the surface as lava during volcanic eruptions. Point out that modern volcanoes emit components of the primitive atmosphere hypothesized by Oparin. Ask students how this information supports his hypothesis. *(The early earth had constant volcanic eruptions.)*

Relating Concepts Have students draw a concept map showing the important developments in the origin of life. An example of a completed concept map is shown on p. 203B.

Videodiscs

- ***2026, Fossil: Brachiopoda (s)***

Cooperative Learning

Organic Compounds Divide the class into groups of four and tell them to review Section 4.2 (pp. 49–54). Have one member of each group draw the structure of a carbohydrate (Figure 4-4), another draw a fatty acid (Figure 4-5), a third an amino acid (Figure 4-6), and the fourth a nucleotide (Figure 4-9). Then have each group prepare and present drawings that indicate which of these molecules formed from methane (CH_4) and which formed from ammonia (NH_3). *(The carbon in all four types of organic molecules must have come from methane. The nitrogen in amino acids and nucleotides must have come from ammonia.)*

Interpreting the Visuals Ask students how the device shown in Figure 14-6 worked. *(Electric sparks energized chemical reactions among gases, forming organic compounds.)* Ask how the device simulated primitive earth. *(The gases represented earth's early atmosphere; the sparks, lightning; and the U-shaped part of the tube, early lakes and seas.)* Ask why oxygen was not included. *(Earth's early atmosphere lacked oxygen.)* Ask whether the device produced life. *(No)*

■ *See* **Blackline Master** ***30.***

Applying Concepts Tell students to imagine they are observing a microscopic cell-like structure apparently budding. Ask how they would determine whether this is true reproduction. *(The transfer of genetic material)*

■ *See* **Laboratories,** ***Investigation 14.***

Guided Practice

List in random order on the board the four developments leading to the origin of life. Then have students number the stages in correct sequence and give an example of each. *(1. Formation of simple organic compounds: alanine; 2. formation of complex organic compounds: proteins; 3. concentration and enclosure of organic compounds: microspheres; 4. evolution of growth, metabolism, and reproduction: respiration)*

Independent Practice

■ Have students write answers to the Section Review.

■ Ask students to write an explanation of the difficulties in investigating the origin of life. *(Hypotheses about the origin of life cannot be tested because no one can observe what happened eons ago. Indirect evidence can come from laboratory simulations and analysis of ancient rocks.)*

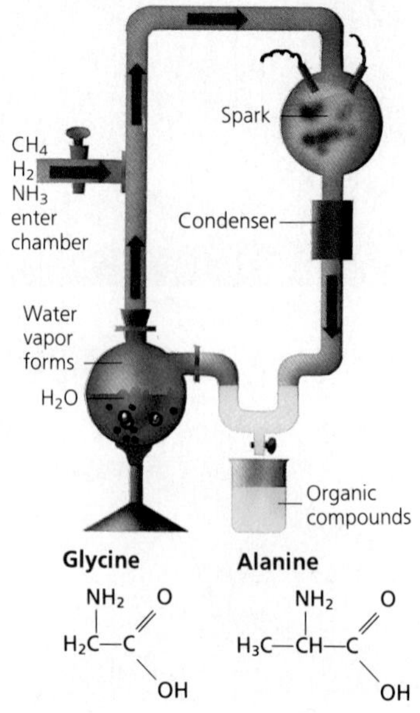

Figure 14-6 Miller and Urey's device testing Oparin's hypothesis produced organic compounds, including the amino acids shown.

Oparin developed his hypothesis by reading the writings of hundreds of scientists working on a wide range of problems. His hypothesis rests on the results of experiments done by these scientists. However, Oparin did not run experiments to test his hypothesis. That work was left for later scientists.

In 1953 the American scientists Stanley L. Miller (1930–) and Harold C. Urey (1893–1981) set up an experiment using Oparin's hypothesis as a starting point. Their setup is illustrated in Figure 14-6. They made a chamber containing the gases Oparin assumed were present in the young earth's atmosphere. As the gases circulated in the chamber, sparks, representing lightning, supplied energy to drive chemical reactions. The experiment generated organic compounds including the amino acids—the building blocks of proteins—listed in the figure.

Since the 1950s, scientists have continued to explore the origin of simple organic compounds. Their experiments have produced a variety of compounds, including various amino acids, ATP, and the nucleotides in DNA. Such results suggest many ways that vital organic molecules might have formed on the young earth.

Formation of Complex Organic Compounds

How could simple organic compounds have formed complex organic compounds essential to life? This question has been partially answered for one group of organic compounds—proteins. Remember that proteins are chains of amino acids. Some scientists have performed experiments that suggest that amino acids might have formed chains spontaneously in the early atmosphere. Other scientists have shown that amino acids will link up when heated in the absence of oxygen gas. In either or both of these ways, amino acids could have combined and formed complex proteins. Similar mechanisms might have led to the formation of carbohydrates, lipids, and nucleic acids.

Concentration and Enclosure of Organic Compounds

The next step in the origin of life, according to most scientists, was the concentration and enclosure of complex organic compounds. Experiments have shown that proteins clump together to form microscopic droplets. Coacervates and microspheres are two types of these droplets. **Coacervates** *(koe-AS-ur-VATES)* are actually collections of droplets, made of molecules of different types, that have irregular shapes. **Microspheres,** on the other hand, are round and usually form from only one type of molecule.

Coacervates and microspheres bear a resemblance to living cells. Coacervates, microspheres, and cells are all set off from the environment by a membranelike boundary. All three can selectively take up certain substances from their surroundings. Internally, different types of molecules cluster in different areas of these structures. Also, certain chemical reactions can take place more easily inside these structures than they can in water. Coacer-

More Information

The First Nucleic Acid The idea that life began with RNA has been gaining widespread acceptance in the scientific community. Given that RNA is single-stranded and more extensively involved in protein synthesis than DNA, it seems plausible that RNA could have evolved in organisms before DNA. Later, DNA arose as a variant of RNA, specialized for preserving the genetic integrity of an organism. The idea was reinforced when scientists discovered that certain RNA segments, called ribozymes, can catalyze reactions as protein enzymes can, thus demonstrating that RNA could possibly encode and drive the functions necessary for a living cell to exist.

vates can grow; microspheres can bud, forming smaller microspheres. Under the microscope both of these structures sometimes look so much like living cells that scientists have sometimes mistaken them for new species of bacteria.

One process that must have occurred on the young earth was the enclosure of nucleic acids in membranes. Once DNA was separated from the environment by some kind of boundary, it would be protected and might be able to carry out the precise reactions of replication. Such a process has been recreated in the laboratory. Figure 14-7 shows a mixture of lipids and DNA exposed to conditions of wetting and drying that may simulate those in ancient tidepools. When the mixture was hydrated, the DNA and lipids intertwined with one another. When it was dried, the lipids sandwiched the DNA molecules. When rehydrated, the lipid membranes dispersed again, but now the DNA was enclosed in lipid vessels. In this way nucleic acids might have been concentrated and enclosed in membranes on the young earth.

Evolution of Growth, Metabolism, and Reproduction

As lifelike as coacervates and microspheres appear, they lack the complexity of living cells. Coacervates and microspheres can neither maintain stable growth nor reproduce. They also cannot metabolize—that is, they are unable to obtain energy from substances in the environment. But over time coacervates and microspheres might have developed these capabilities, which are necessary for life. So endowed, these nonliving structures might have eventually crossed over the border into the living world.

In summary, evidence suggests that, sometime between 4.6 billion and 3.5 billion years ago, life arose on earth, generated from nonliving matter. However, such spontaneous generation could not occur on earth today. The atmosphere of the young earth lacked oxygen gas. Though this substance is essential to most forms of life today, it would have destroyed organic compounds in the hot atmosphere of the young earth by the chemical process called oxidation. In fact, the oxygen gas in our atmosphere was almost certainly generated by living organisms. These living organisms helped change conditions on earth. Thus, the unique circumstances under which life spontaneously arose are no longer present on earth.

Section Review

1. What is a *fossil?*
2. How do scientists think the earth formed, and what do they think the earth was like during its first billion years?
3. According to scientists what four developments must have occurred before life came into being?
4. What was Oparin's hypothesis, and how was it tested?
5. Make a chart comparing and contrasting coacervates and microspheres with living cells.

Figure 14-7 Membrane vessels and twisted multilayer membranes have been formed in the laboratory under conditions that may have existed on the young earth. The membranes in this photograph have formed boundary layers that have encapsulated DNA.

Answers to Section Review

1. Fossils are remains or traces of once-living organisms.
2. Scientists think that the earth formed from a clump of dust and gas that surrounded the sun. It began as a ball of very hot rock that slowly cooled.
3. Formation of simple organic compounds; formation of complex organic compounds; concentration and enclosure of organic compounds; evolution of growth, metabolism, and reproduction
4. Hot gases in the atmosphere formed simple organic compounds, which collected in water and formed complex organic compounds. Miller and Urey sent electric current through gases, producing simple organic compounds.
5. Accept charts that reflect features discussed on pp. 210–211.

Check Your Understanding

1. What was the significance of heat in the development of life? *(The chemical reactions that resulted in the formation of simple and complex organic compounds may have occurred at above-normal temperatures.)*
2. If oxygen gas had been present in earth's early atmosphere, what effect would it have had on the development of life? *(It would have prevented the development of life by destroying the organic compounds essential to life.)*
3. A sample of coffee contains microscopic lumpy droplets made of proteins and lipids. The droplets do not reproduce. What are they? *(Coacervates)*

Reteaching

Have students list laboratory simulations performed by scientists to model ancient events that led to the origin of life. *(Formation of amino acids by Miller and Urey; formation of proteins from amino acids; clumping of proteins to form coacervates and microspheres; enclosure of DNA in lipid vessels)*

■ *See* Section Reviews *worksheet, Section 14.2.*

Enrichment

Have students research the nature and occurrence of Precambrian fossils (those over 600 million years old).

Closure

Tell students to imagine that they have discovered microscopic spheres in soil from Mars. Ask what they would look for to help them decide whether the spheres are coacervates or living cells. *(Evidence of stable growth, reproduction, and metabolism)*

Videodiscs

- ***2535, Alanine (s)***
- ***2537, Glycine (s)***
- ***2528, Water Molecule (s)***
- ***2529, Methane (s)***

Lesson Plan

Section Focus

This section describes the first organisms on earth—anaerobic, heterotrophic prokaryotes—and the evolution of photosynthetic prokaryotes, which added oxygen to the atmosphere. This led to development of aerobic organisms. The first eukaryotes may have evolved through endosymbiosis, or invasion of prokaryotes by other prokaryotes.

Section Themes

The theme of **Evolution** encompasses the evolution of prokaryotes and eukaryotes as well as the transition from anaerobic respiration to photosynthesis to aerobic respiration. The theme of **Scale and Structure** is exemplified by endosymbiosis, which attempts to explain the evolution of eukaryotes.

Motivating Activity

Display photographs or posters of various protists. Point out adaptations such as cilia, flagella, eyespots, and siliceous "skeletons." Ask students to speculate on the following: Were the first living cells aerobic or anaerobic? Simple or complex? How might they have obtained energy to live? Encourage a variety of answers and ask for supporting reasons.

Teaching Strategies

Applying Concepts Ask students what the eventual outcome of the development of life might have been if autotrophs had not evolved. (*Competition for food might have ended all life if the nutrients were consumed faster than they could form naturally.*)

Guided Practice

Have students explain how the first prokaryotes, which lacked cilia and flagella, obtained food. *(They absorbed nutrients from the surrounding water without swimming.)*

Section Objectives

- *List three characteristics that describe the organisms scientists think were the first forms of life on earth.*
- *Describe how prokaryotes and eukaryotes might have evolved.*
- *Name two ways that oxygen in the atmosphere influenced the evolution of life.*
- *Summarize the endosymbiont hypothesis, and describe some of the evidence that supports the hypothesis.*

14.3 The First Forms of Life

A remote and desolate corner of Australia was nicknamed "the North Pole" by prospectors of the 1800s. However, this region was a gold mine for twentieth-century scientists. There they found the 3.5-billion-year-old microfossils mentioned in Section 14.2. As you know, these fossils were probably not the earth's first organisms. Scientists hypothesize that the first cells were anaerobic, heterotrophic prokaryotes.

The First Prokaryotes

Prokaryotes were probably the first organisms on earth. As you have read, the atmosphere of the young earth lacked oxygen gas. This suggests that the first prokaryotes must have been anaerobic. They probably derived their energy from the metabolic pathway of glycolysis. Remember that glycolysis does not require oxygen.

Bathed in the earth's warm seas, the first prokaryotes probably just floated into the organic molecules they used for food. Because they gathered food from their surroundings rather than

Biology in Process

The Evolution of Eukaryotes

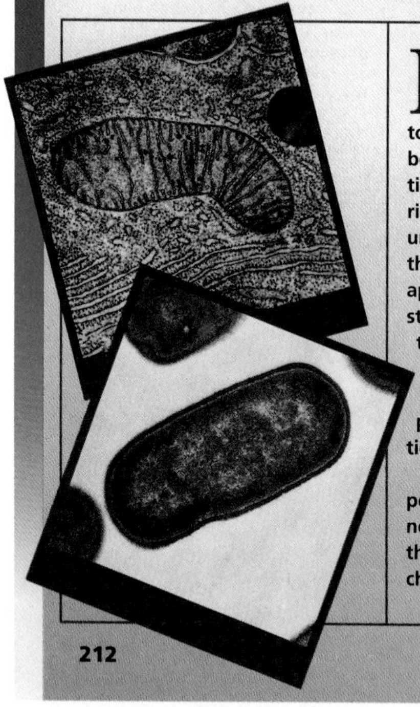

Look at the photographs of a mitochondrion (p. 212, top) and a bacterium (p. 212, bottom). Then compare the sections of a chloroplast (p. 213, right) and a blue-green bacterium (p. 213, left). Do you notice the similarities in the size and appearance of these pairs of structures? If so, you have made the same observation that led scientists in the late 1800s to propose an endosymbiont hypothesis to explain the evolution of eukaryotes.

In the early 1900s this hypothesis fell out of favor as genetic studies began to suggest that all cell traits are carried on chromosomes in the nucleus.

In the late 1950s, Lynn Margulis, then a graduate student in genetics, observed patterns of genetic transmission that could not be explained by nuclear chromosomes alone. She suspected that these unusual patterns of heredity indicated the presence of DNA somewhere outside the nucleus.

Her suspicions were confirmed in 1962 when scientists discovered DNA in the chloroplasts of algae. How did DNA get into these chloroplasts? During the next 25 years, Margulis challenged the scientific establishment, collecting data that suggested eukaryotic cells could have evolved from a

212

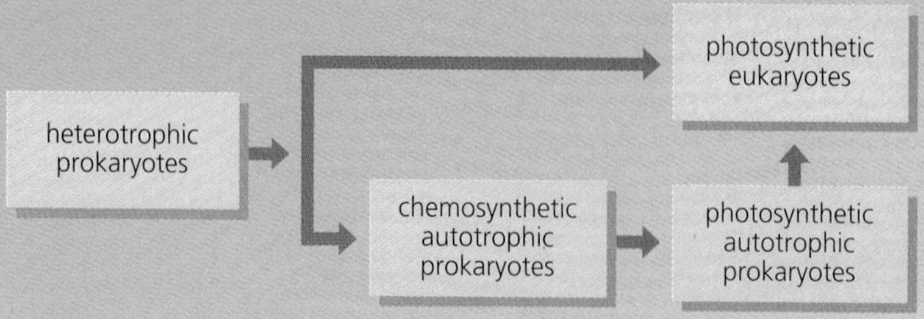

Graphic Organizer Use this sequential diagram in Reteaching on p. 214.

making it, they were heterotrophic. In time, however, the heterotrophic prokaryotes would have multiplied, increasing competition for nutrients. Organisms that could make their own food would have had a distinct advantage. These conditions may have led to the development of the earth's first autotrophs. These autotrophs probably made food by using chemical energy from other molecules rather than by using energy from sunlight. Next, photosynthesizing prokaryotes probably evolved. The cell structure and organization of the 3.5-billion-year-old microfossils indicates that these organisms were among the first photosynthesizing prokaryotes.

The Changing Earth

Changes in types and numbers of fossils indicate that major changes in earth's environment occurred about 2.8 billion years ago. At that time photosynthesizing organisms that gave off oxygen gas as a waste product first arose. The generation of oxygen by prokaryotes changed the world. Oxygen could destroy some essential coenzymes, but organisms that bonded oxygen gas to other compounds prevented it from doing damage. This bonding is one of the first steps in aerobic respiration. So it seems that

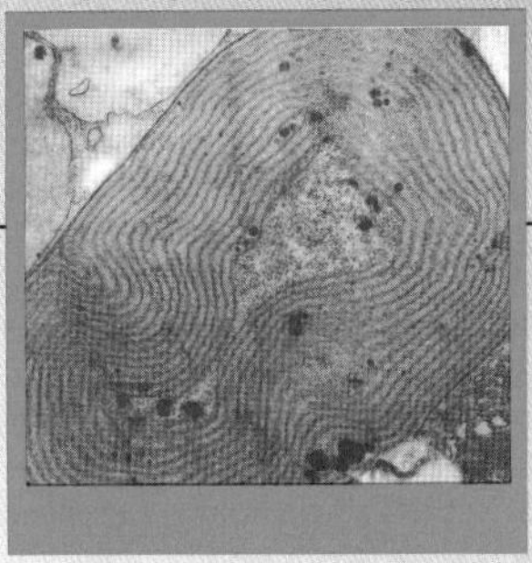

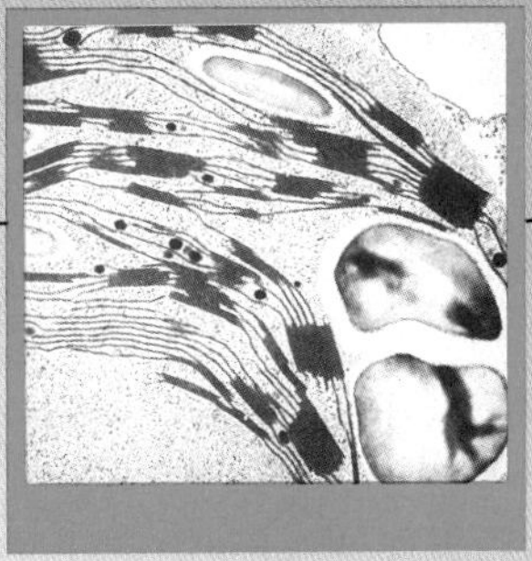

merger of two or more different kinds of cells early in their evolution.

Margulis's work raised new questions about the origin and evolution of cellular organelles. What happened to these genomes after they were acquired by eukaryotic cells? Did they arise from single or multiple endosymbiotic events?

Comparisons of RNA sequences in ribosomes support the view that both land plants and algae were formed through multiple endosymbioses and that some eukaryotes acquired their chloroplasts from other eukaryotes.

Margulis's next challenge is to find the symbiotic origins of the flagellum, to support her hypothesis that spirochetes are the ancestors of the whole intracellular transportation network. Although the ancestry of the nuclear genome remains a mystery, the RNA of organelles seems to have a bacterial ancestry. Chloroplasts are related to cyanobacteria, and mitochondria are related to photosynthetic bacteria. The studies of Margulis and others have shown that the single-celled eukaryotes, more diverse than previously thought, remain an untapped well of information for the molecular biologist with an interest in evolution.

- **Some protists that can live in low-oxygen environments, such as the giant ameba, lack mitochondria. However, mitochondria occur in almost all other eukaryotes. Could we use this fact to conclude that the ameba developed before it acquired mitochondria?**

Biology in Process

Using the Feature

The process skills used in this feature are observing, hypothesizing, and collecting data. Dr. Lynn Margulis has worked to substantiate the endosymbiont hypothesis as a preferred explanation for eukaryote evolution. Others have gone on to show that endosymbiosis may have occurred many times in the evolutionary process and that the RNA from the nuclei and the RNA from the organelles have differing lineages. Dr. Margulis is currently investigating how centrioles may have evolved from swimming bacteria. Recently, molecular biologists found DNA in kinetosomes, the structures at the base of flagella from which these cell "tails" grow. Ask students how this might be used as supporting evidence for the endosymbiont hypothesis. *(Kinetosomes, like mitochondria and chloroplasts, may originally have been, or have been part of, a separate organism. Certainly the presence of extranuclear DNA indicates that they may be carrying DNA from separate cell lineages and supports the supposition that flagella may have been separate organisms at some time in the past.)*

Answer to the Feature

The ameba might have developed before acquiring mitochondria, but it is also possible that the ameba acquired mitochondria and later lost them because they were not useful in that particular environment.

Videodiscs

- ***2540–2541, Photosynthetic Prokaryote/Eukaryote (s)***
- ***2543, Eukaryote Cells (s)***

LEP Activity

Help students build on what they learned in earlier chapters. Review with students the definitions of *prokaryotes* and *eukaryotes* (p. 65 and Figure 5-5), *mitochondria* (p. 69 and Figure 5-12), and *chloroplasts* (pp. 74 and 96–98 and Figure 7-6). Then have students list the characteristics of prokaryotes and eukaryotes on the board, using Table 5-1 on p. 74 to self-check their lists. As a lead-in to the inference that prokaryotes evolved before eukaryotes did, ask students which type of cell is simpler in structure. *(Prokaryotes)*

Independent Practice

- Have students write answers to the Section Review.
- Have students write an explanation of how photosynthesis changed the world. *(It added oxygen gas to the atmosphere and led to aerobic respiration and the earth's ozone layer.)*

Check Your Understanding

1. In what kind of environment today might you find organisms resembling the first prokaryotes? *(One with little or no oxygen)*

2. How might food-getting among the first autotrophs have differed from that of photosynthesizing prokaryotes? *(They probably made food by using chemical energy from other molecules rather than sunlight.)*

Answer to Think

Tell students that the top photo shows a "bloom," or rapid population increase, of algae and blue-green bacteria in a pond. Blooms cause oxygen depletion in the water. Thus, students should infer that the environment in the top photo would support anaerobic, heterotrophic prokaryotes.

Reteaching

Have students diagram the possible evolution of the first eukaryotes from the first prokaryotes. Use the sequential diagram on p. 212 as a model.

- *See* **Section Reviews** *worksheet, Section 14.3.*

Enrichment

Have students do library research to report on the life and habitat of *Nitrosomnas,* an autotroph that gets its energy from inorganic molecules.

Closure

Ask students what major evolutionary changes occurred after eukaryotes evolved. *(Sample answers: multicellularity, sexual reproduction, and hard parts)*

Think

Some environments still support anaerobic, heterotrophic prokaryotes. Which of these two environments do you think would be able to support such organisms? Why?

aerobic respiration may have first been an adaptation to prevent the destruction of essential organic compounds by oxygen.

As you read in Chapter 7, aerobic respiration can liberate much more energy from a glucose molecule than anaerobic respiration can. Therefore aerobic respiration probably gave some organisms an advantage and in time they became dominant.

The release of oxygen through photosynthesis had another effect. Ultraviolet light from the sun is hazardous. It can damage DNA. Before oxygen built up in the atmosphere, the only way organisms could shield themselves from these deadly rays was by living in water. Water absorbs energy from ultraviolet light.

When oxygen was released into the atmosphere, it provided a second protective shield from ultraviolet radiation. Some oxygen gas (O_2) absorbs energy from ultraviolet light and splits into single oxygen atoms (O). Then oxygen gas reacts with the single atoms of oxygen and forms a layer of ozone (O_3) that encircles the globe. This process, which continually occurs in the atmosphere, prevents most harmful radiation from reaching the earth.

The First Eukaryotes

Prokaryotes are so much simpler than eukaryotes that most scientists infer that prokaryotes evolved first. The fossil record supports this inference. Scientists do not know exactly how eukaryotes evolved. Certain prokaryotes, specifically bacteria and blue-green bacteria, may have come to live inside other prokaryotes, thus gaining protection. The bacteria in turn may have provided extra energy for the host prokaryotes. The blue-green bacteria may have provided extra food. Such a relationship, in which different organisms live in close association, is called symbiosis.

Eventually the bacteria and cyanobacteria might have evolved into mitochondria and chloroplasts. In addition, a nucleus could have formed when membranes enclosed DNA. Remember that a nucleus and organelles are distinguishing features of eukaryotes. The idea that a eukaryote's mitochondria evolved from bacteria and its chloroplasts evolved from cyanobacteria is the basis of **endosymbiosis,** also called the endosymbiont hypothesis. Fossil evidence indicates that eukaryotes had evolved by 1 billion years ago.

Section Review

1. Explain the endosymbiont hypothesis of eukaryote evolution.
2. Why do scientists think the first forms of life on earth were anaerobic, heterotrophic prokaryotes?
3. How might autotrophic prokaryotes have evolved?
4. What do scientists speculate was the initial function of aerobic respiration?
5. Some forms of air pollution damage the earth's ozone layer. How might such damage affect life?

Answers to Section Review

1. Blue-green and other bacteria may have lived within other prokaryotes in symbiosis and evolved into the chloroplasts and mitochondria of eukaryotes.

2. Scientists infer that the first organisms were prokaryotic because they were simple, anaerobic because no oxygen was available, and heterotrophic because organic molecules (food) surrounded them.

3. They had an advantage over heterotrophs when competition made food scarce.

4. It prevented the destruction of essential organic compounds by oxygen.

5. Such damage might destroy some life forms by allowing harmful ultraviolet radiation to reach the earth's surface.

Laboratory

Making Microspheres

Objective
To make microspheres from amino acids and to compare their structure to living cells

Process Skills
Observing, hypothesizing

Materials
500-mL beaker, hot plate, 2 125-mL Erlenmeyer flasks, ring stand with clamp, balance, aspartic acid, glutamic acid, glycine, glass stirring rod, tongs, clock or timer, 1% NaCl solution, 50-mL graduated cylinder, dropper, microscope slide, coverslip, microscope

Inquiry

1. Fill a 500-mL beaker one-half full with water and heat it on a hot plate. Leave space on the hot plate for a 125-mL Erlenmeyer flask to be added later.
2. While waiting for the water to boil, clamp a 125-mL Erlenmeyer flask to a ring stand. Add 1 g each of aspartic acid, glutamic acid, and glycine to the flask and combine these dry powders with a stirring rod.
3. When the water in the beaker begins to boil, move the ring stand carefully so the flask of amino acids sits in the hot-water bath.
4. When the amino acids have heated for 20 minutes, measure 10 mL of NaCl solution in a graduated cylinder and pour the solution into a second Erlenmeyer flask. Place the second flask on the hot plate beside the hot-water bath.
5. When the NaCl solution begins to boil, use tongs to remove the flask containing the solution from the hot plate. Then, still holding the flask with tongs, slowly add the NaCl solution to the hot amino acids while stirring.
6. Let this solution boil for 30 seconds. Why do you think you heated the solutions?
7. Remove the solution from the water bath, and allow it to cool for 10 minutes.
8. Use a dropper to place a drop of the solution on a microscope slide and cover the drop with a coverslip.
9. Place the slide on the microscope stage. Examine the slide under low power for tiny spherical structures. Then examine the structures under high power. These tiny sphere-shaped objects are microspheres. How do you think the microspheres were formed?

Conclusions

1. In what ways do microspheres visually resemble living cells?
2. In what ways do microspheres differ visually from living cells?

Further Inquiry

1. What do you think would happen if you added too much or too little heat? How can you test for the right amount of heat to use?
2. Do you think your microsphere experiment would have worked if you had substituted other amino acids? How can you test your hypothesis?

Laboratory

(For an overview of microspheres and preparatory information related to the laboratory, see p. 203B.)

Inquiry

6. Students may suggest that heating the solutions speeds the processes of protein formation and protein clumping, so that microspheres can be produced within a reasonable time.

9. Encourage speculation. Students may suggest that proteins clumped together.

Conclusions

1. They have a membranelike boundary.

2. They have no nucleus or organelles.

Further Inquiry

1. Students may infer that overheating would alter or destroy the amino acids and that underheating would not permit quick formation of proteins or microspheres. They may suggest experiments similar to the one they conducted in this lab but using different amounts of heat.

2. Students may infer that other amino acids would behave in a manner similar to those used in this lab. They may suggest similar experiments using different amino acids.

Vocabulary

1. *Bio*- means "life"; *-genesis* means "the origin or coming into being of something" and often means the beginning of life. These word parts combined mean that the origin of life is life.
2. Fossils are remains or traces of once-living organisms; fossils in 3.5-billion-year-old rocks provide a record of early forms of life on earth.
3. Coacervates and microspheres are microscopic droplets of molecules that have clumped together. They are similar to living cells in that they have a membranelike boundary; they can selectively take up substances from their surroundings; different types of molecules cluster in different areas within them; certain chemical reactions can take place more easily within them than in water; and they grow or bud. They differ from living cells in that they cannot maintain stable growth, metabolize, or reproduce.
4. *Spontaneous* can mean "developing without apparent cause"; *generation* means "bringing into existence." This theory assumed that living organisms arose suddenly from nonliving matter without apparent cause.
5. *Endo*- means "within"; *sym*- means "together." Since *bio*- means "life," *endosymbiosis* is a good name because it reflects the idea that bacteria and cyanobacteria living together within a prokaryotic cell evolved into the mitochondria and chloroplasts of eukaryotic cells.

Review

1. a
2. c
3. b
4. b
5. d
6. b
7. a
8. c
9. a
10. a

Chapter 14 Review

Vocabulary

biogenesis (207)
coacervate (210)
endosymbiosis (214)
fossil (209)
microfossil (209)
microsphere (210)
spontaneous generation (205)

1. Using a dictionary, find the meaning of the word parts *bio*- and *-genesis* and relate them to the theory of biogenesis.
2. How do fossils give evidence about the origin of life?
3. Define coacervates and microspheres; compare them with living cells.
4. Why is "spontaneous generation" a good name for the theory it describes?
5. Use a dictionary to find the meaning of the prefixes *endo*- and *sym*-. Why is "endosymbiosis" a good name for the theory it describes?

Review

1. In the 1600s and 1700s people used the theory of spontaneous generation to explain (a) how new life started (b) how simple organic compounds formed (c) how coacervates and microspheres originated (d) how eukaryotes evolved.
2. Redi's experiment was important because it showed that (a) maggots give rise to microorganisms (b) flies swarm on rotting meat (c) flies do not form from rotting meat (d) air contains a "vital force."
3. People objected to Spallanzani's experiment because (a) he used an open jar of meat as a control (b) he heated his flasks of broth for a long time (c) he drew the necks of his flasks into a curved shape (d) his flasks contained microorganisms.
4. The neck of Pasteur's flasks (a) allowed both air and particles to enter the flask (b) allowed air to enter but kept particles out (c) allowed particles to enter but kept air out (d) kept both air and particles out.
5. Scientists think the earth formed (a) from the sun (b) from water vapor (c) from volcanoes (d) from gas and dust.
6. The oldest fossil is about (a) 4.6 billion years old (b) 3.5 billion years old (c) 3.5 million years old (d) 2 million years old.
7. The elements that formed simple organic molecules essential to life probably originally came from (a) the atmosphere (b) the moon (c) the sun (d) the oceans.
8. Miller and Urey's experiment (a) proved Oparin's hypothesis about the origin of life (b) disproved the hypothesis (c) provided evidence for the hypothesis (d) did not apply to the hypothesis.
9. Coacervates and microspheres are (a) collections of organic molecules, concentrated and enclosed within a boundary (b) the first forms of life (c) the oldest microfossils (d) new forms of bacteria.
10. The generation of organisms from nonliving material does not occur today mainly because (a) the presence of oxygen in the atmosphere prevents organic compounds from spontaneously forming (b) coacervates and microspheres take up all the extra nutrients on earth (c) heterotrophs take up all the extra nutrients on earth (d) there is not enough energy to drive the chemical reactions to form complex organic compounds necessary for life.
11. What kinds of organisms are thought to have been the first life-forms on earth?
12. Which environmental factors probably favored the evolution of autotrophs?
13. By what process did the first autotrophs probably make glucose?
14. How might the bonding of oxygen gas have served evolving organisms?
15. How did the formation of the ozone layer permit organisms to colonize land?
16. What were some observations that might

11. Anaerobic, heterotrophic prokaryotes
12. The scarcity of nutrients resulting from competition, and the advantage to organisms of making their own food
13. Using chemical energy from other molecules
14. It prevented oxygen gas from destroying essential organic compounds.
15. The ozone layer protected them from harmful ultraviolet radiation.
16. Fish appeared in ponds that had gone completely dry during the previous season; flies swarmed from rotten meat; clear broth became cloudy with bacteria.
17. If living organisms can arise only from other living organisms, how could life on earth have begun?
18. To supply energy to drive the chemical reactions in the chamber; lightning

have supported the theory of spontaneous generation?
17. Why did the theory of biogenesis pose a dilemma regarding the origin of life?
18. In the Miller–Urey experiment, what was the function of the electrical sparks and what did they represent?
19. Why do scientists assume that the 3.5-billion-year-old microfossils found in Australia were probably not representatives of the first organisms on earth?
20. What genetic phenomena originally led Lynn Margulis to become interested in the endosymbiont hypothesis?

Critical Thinking

1. People once believed fish could form from the mud of a temporarily dry pond. How could you demonstrate that this conclusion is false?
2. Do you think life could have originated on other planets? Justify your answer.
3. According to a recent hypothesis lightning may not have existed on the young earth. How could you modify the Miller–Urey experiment to reflect this new idea? What sources of energy could you use to replace the "lightning"?
4. Some scientists hypothesize that life changed the conditions on earth and in the earth's atmosphere just as conditions on the earth and in its atmosphere change life. What examples from this chapter might back up this hypothesis?
5. The diagram on the right compresses the history of the earth into a 12-hour clock to help you understand the relative time of different events. Note that the formation of the earth occurred at midnight on the clock. The oceans formed at about 2:00 A.M., while the oldest human fossils date from just before noon. Based on fossil evidence, about what time on the clock did the first prokaryotes appear? About what time did the first eukaryotes appear?

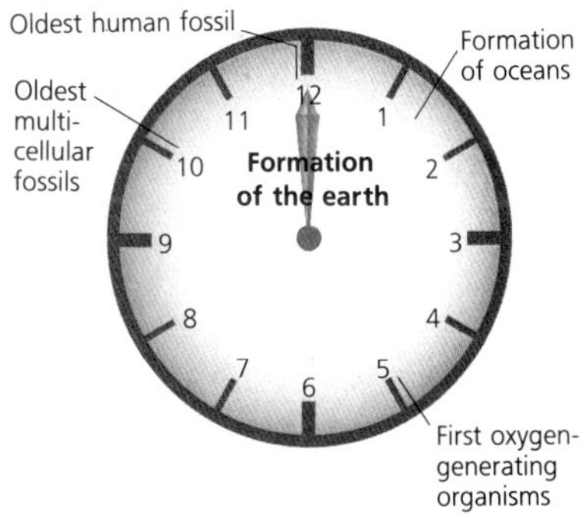

Extension

1. Scientists studying the atmosphere have observed a large hole in the ozone layer above the continent of Antarctica. Use current science magazines to find out about this phenomenon. Present a report to your class summarizing different hypotheses about the causes of this hole.
2. Read the article by Edwin Kiester, Jr., entitled "A Bug in the System" in *Discover,* February 1991, pp. 71–76. How do the discoveries about mitochondrial DNA relate to the information included in the Biology in Process feature, *The Evolution of Eukaryotes?*
3. Make a time line to show the important events in the history of earth described in this chapter. Start your time line with the formation of the earth. Be sure to indicate dates for the formation of the oceans, the age of the oldest microfossils, the first photosynthetic organisms to generate oxygen gas, and the origin of eukaryotic cells. You may wish to continue this time line as you study the rest of the unit.

19. The cell structure and organization of the microfossils indicate that they were photosynthetic, whereas the first organisms were probably heterotrophic.
20. Patterns of transmission of genetic material not explainable by nuclear chromosomes alone

Critical Thinking

1. Answers should describe an experiment to test the hypothesis that fish eggs in dried mud give rise to the fish appearing in a pond after a dry period. One such experiment could compare two artificial mud-bottomed "ponds"—one bottom made from sterile soil, the other from dried mud originally from a pond that contained fish.
2. Answers should consider conditions that would probably have had to exist on other planets for life to begin, including an atmosphere containing carbon, temperatures between the boiling and freezing points of water, and a form of energy to drive chemical reactions that would form organic compounds.
3. Other sources of energy could include heat, light, ultraviolet radiation, and mechanical energy (simulating earthquake or volcanic tremors).
4. Answers may include: Photosynthetic organisms added oxygen gas to the atmosphere of the earth and led to the development of the earth's protective ozone layer; organisms performing aerobic respiration bonded oxygen gas to other compounds.
5. The first prokaryotes appeared at about 3:00 A.M., the first eukaryotes at about 9:00 A.M.

Extension

1. Suggest that students' reports include evidence on differences in the size of the ozone hole during different seasons.
2. Help students recognize that both articles discuss the evolution of and interactions between the eukaryotic cell and its organelles.
3. Have students compare their time lines with the "clock" of the earth's history shown in Critical Thinking question 5.

Chapter 15 Evolution: Evidence and Theory

Chapter Overview

Chapter 15 highlights the theory of organic evolution by natural selection. Section 15.1 introduces evidence from the fossil record and studies of modern animals. Section 15.2 develops Charles Darwin's theory of evolution by natural selection and the context in which he did his research. Section 15.3 presents three kinds of evolutionary trends.

Chapter Planning Chart

B	S	A	Sections and Subsections	Page	Features	Page	Resources
•	•	•	**15.1 Evidence of Evolution**				
			Evidence from Fossils	219	Think	223	Videodiscs
			Evidence from Living Organisms	222	Section Review	224	Blackline Master 31
							Overhead Transparency T15
							Blackline Master 32
							Section Reviews Worksheet
•	•	•	**15.2 Darwin's Theory of Evolution**				
			Evolutionary Theory Before Darwin	225	Writing About Biology	227	Videodiscs
			Darwin's Background	225	Biology in Process	228	Process Skills: Evolution
			The Voyage of the *Beagle*	226	Laboratory	233	Laboratories: Patterns of Variation
			Darwin in England	226	Section Review	230	Section Reviews Worksheet
			Evolution by Natural Selection	229			
			The Origin of Species	230			
•	•	•	**15.3 Patterns of Evolution**				
			Divergent and Convergent Evolution	231	Section Review	232	Videodiscs
			Coevolution	232			Section Reviews Worksheet
			End of Chapter Activities				
					Chapter Review	234	Vocabulary Skills
							Chapter Test
							Computer Test Generator

B *The Basic Level curriculum presents the most fundamental knowledge offered in the course.*
S *The Standard Level curriculum is designed for the average student who is able to master most topics.*
A *The Advanced Level curriculum includes suggestions for teaching the most academically able students.*

Cooperative Learning

Group Activity: Comparing Fossils

- **Group size:** *4 students*
- **Outcome:** *Students will compare the formation of different kinds of fossils.*
- **Individual Accountability:** *Each student will illustrate the origin of one type of fossil.*
- **Positive Interdependence:** *The group will compare the relative scientific value of each kind of fossil.*

Have each student in a group do research in the library on one of the following fossil types: petrifactions (hard parts replaced by minerals), molds and casts, imprints, and footprints and trackways. Then ask each student to make an outline or a diagram illustrating the formation of that type of fossil. Have each student present his or her outline or illustration to the other group members, and then have the group discuss what kinds of information can be obtained from the fossil type and what important kinds of information have been lost.

Suggest that students think of sand and mud becoming sandstone and shale. Sand can fill impressions in dry or wet mud, and vice versa. Water filtering through the ground carries minerals. As a discussion question, ask them to consider why soft parts are not preserved. *(Animals and bacteria feed off the soft parts.)*

Concept Map

The following is one possible solution to the concept mapping activity in Relating Concepts on p. 226.

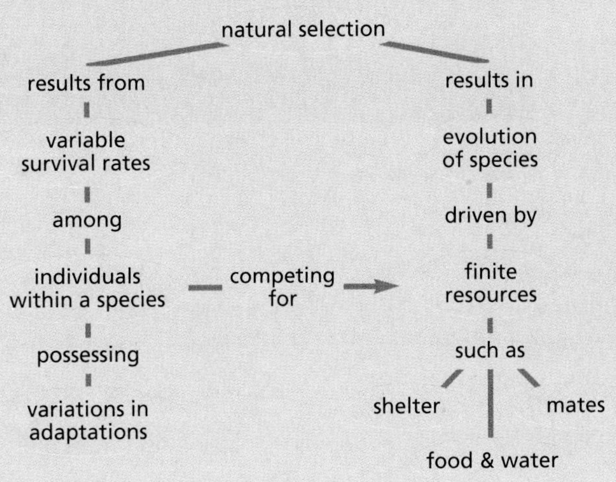

Laboratory Preparation

Overview *(See p. 233.)*

In this lab students observe and graph variations in peanut size. Other traits, either human or nonhuman, can be substituted. Some of these have been suggested in Further Inquiry.

It is important to stress that variation is common in all species and is the raw material of natural selection. If all individuals in a species were genetically identical, all would respond identically to a change in the environment. Thus, if an environmental change proved lethal to any one individual, it would be lethal to all, and the species would become extinct.

Preparation

Peanuts in the shell can be purchased in the supermarket. Be sure to purchase a single brand to ensure that the peanuts are the same species (there are more than 100 different kinds of peanuts).

Teaching Tips

Make sure all students measure the peanuts the same way. A good idea is to have them break each peanut open and measure the longest length of the cotyledon in millimeters.

Discuss with students why very large and very small peanuts appear infrequently. Encourage them to imagine environmental changes that would change the survival distribution. Remind students of the differential reproduction that would follow an environmental change. That is, a mutant, which might not have reproduced in the old environment, will reproduce more rapidly in the new.

Refer students to the Unit 6 Intra-Science on p. 432 and the discussion of negative effects of inbreeding food crops to ensure desired traits.

Discuss with students how rapidly the environment is changing today, often as a direct result of human action. Point out that although variation makes it more likely that a species will survive environmental changes, many species do not have any individuals that can survive extreme or rapid environmental changes.

Safety

Remind students not to eat in the laboratory. Students should wash their hands after the lab, especially if they have been handling specimens.

Chapter Themes

Evolution This chapter continues the thread of Chapter 14, explaining the changing of organisms through time. Emphasize to students that fossils provide evidence that organisms have changed through time. Tell them that the question "Why?" is answered by the theory of natural selection.

The chapter presents evidence for students to consider. Students may know of or believe in alternative interpretations of the evidence; stress that the one given here is the one most scientists consider to be the best explanation of the evidence. Section 15.3 outlines three clear patterns of evolutionary change in organisms.

Many examples in the text involve modern organisms; make sure students understand that the same processes have been at work throughout the past.

Scale and Structure Patterns of evolution are traced through the changing structures of organisms. Remind students that the structures are closely related to the life processes of organisms. When a change occurs in an environment, organisms that have acquired changed structures will adapt successfully.

Chapter Motivating Activity

Using an overhead projector or reference books, display for the class illustrations of several kinds of dinosaurs as they appeared in life. Have students identify specialized adaptations of various kinds. (*Carnivorous, herbivorous, locomotive, protective, and so forth*) Have the class consider why there were so many different kinds of dinosaurs. Where did they come from? *(From earlier, more basic reptiles)* What happened to them? *(They became extinct. Their environments changed, but they did not adapt fast enough.)*

Chapter 15 *Evolution: Evidence and Theory*

Introduction

Life on earth began billions of years ago with simple unicellular organisms. Today organisms exhibit an enormous range of differences as well as some surprising similarities. In this chapter you will learn about the theory of evolution. Evolution can help explain similarities and differences between species and also how lifeforms change.

Chapter Outline

15.1 Evidence of Evolution
- *Evidence from Fossils*
- *Evidence from Living Organisms*

15.2 Darwin's Theory of Evolution
- *Evolutionary Theory Before Darwin*
- *Darwin's Background*
- *The Voyage of the* Beagle
- *Darwin in England*
- *Evolution by Natural Selection*
- The Origin of Species

15.3 Patterns of Evolution
- *Divergent and Convergent Evolution*
- *Coevolution*

Chapter Concept

As you read, evaluate whether the evidence presented in the chapter supports the theory of evolution.

Giant tortoises, *Geochelone elephantopus*, on the Galápagos Islands. Inset: Charles Darwin.

Understanding the Visuals

Display, or sketch on the board, a map of Darwin's route, to show the isolation of the Galápagos Islands. A good resource for this information is *The Voyage of the Beagle,* by Darwin himself. Emphasize the geographical isolation of the Galápagos as a primary factor in the evolution of the animals Darwin found there. Point out that Darwin was surprised to learn that the Galápagos tortoises were not only different from those on the South American continent, but also that tortoises from one island were different from tortoises on other islands. Ask students to speculate on the cause for these differences. *(Isolated breeding groups might develop different characteristics over time.)*

15.1 Evidence of Evolution

The Australian microfossils you read about in Chapter 14 are the oldest evidence of life on earth. As you remember, these were the remains of 3.5-billion-year-old prokaryotes. The first life-forms were probably older, perhaps by millions of years. Biologists theorize that all organisms that exist today descended from those first cells. **Evolution** is the theory that species change over time. According to this theory, today's species descended from more ancient forms of life by structural and physiological modifications. If the theory is true, then the world we observe should contain evidence supporting the idea that species change. Let us examine the natural world to see if such evidence exists.

Section Objectives

- *State what is meant by evolution.*
- *Describe different types of fossils, and explain how the age of a fossil can be determined.*
- *Outline how the fossil record suggests that species have changed over time.*
- *Summarize the evidence of evolution provided by living organisms.*

Evidence from Fossils

If today's species have come from more ancient forms, then we should be able to find remains of those species that no longer exist. Scientists have found such evidence in the form of fossils. Fossils—traces of once-living organisms—are found most commonly in layers of sedimentary rock. This type of rock begins to form when water and wind form layers of sand and silt. These actions can bury remains of an organism so quickly that bacteria and other decomposers are sealed off, preventing decomposition. After time the sedimentary layers become rock.

The most common fossils found in sedimentary rocks are from the hard parts of organisms, including shells, bones, teeth, and woody stems. Sometimes minerals replace the original remains, often molecule by molecule. Such replacement preserves the microscopic structure of the organism.

Fossils can form in other ways. For instance, insect fossils have been found trapped in hardened resin. Such fossils show details as small as the insect's tiny leg hairs. In another instance, woolly mammoths that were frozen in Arctic ice have been dug up with their skin, bones, and muscles perfectly preserved.

Fossils are not always the body parts of an organism. An **imprint** is a type of fossil in which a film of carbon remains after the other elements of an organism have decayed. A **mold** is a type of fossil in which an impression of the shape or track of an organism has survived. Figure 15-1 shows how a fossil **cast** forms when sediments fill in the cavity left by a fossil mold.

Figure 15-1 A fossil mold is formed when a trilobite buried by sediments dissolves. The mold is then filled with sediments, forming a cast.

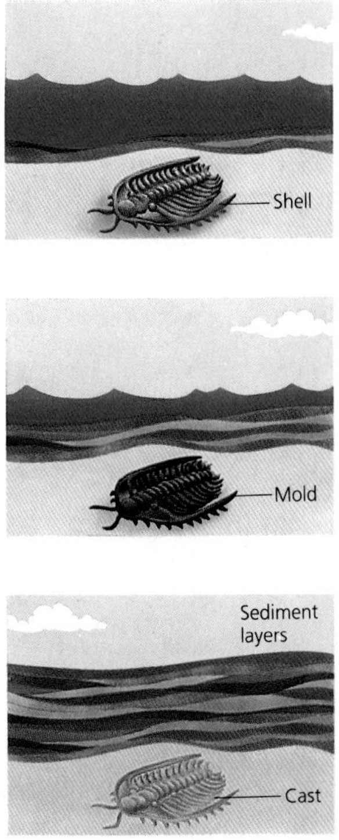

Dating Fossils

If scientists suggest that fossils are the remains of organisms that lived long ago, they should be able to prove it. Scientists have therefore developed ways to date, or determine the age of, fossils.

The relative age of fossils is determined from their position in sedimentary rock. In undisturbed sedimentary rock the bottom layers are the oldest and the top layers are the youngest. Fossils

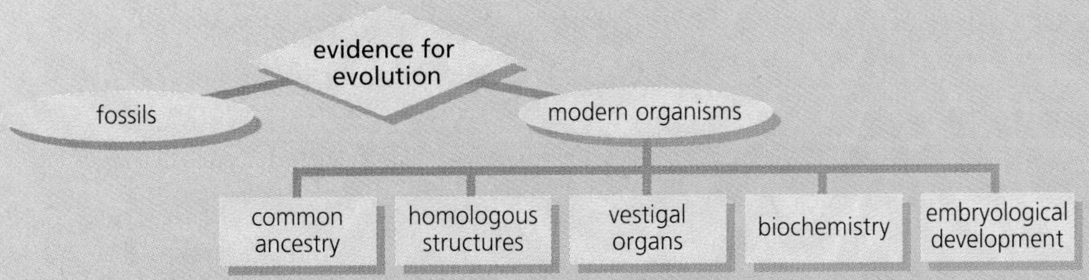

Graphic Organizer Use this chart to summarize key concepts in Section 15.1.

Lesson Plan

Section Focus

This section first describes the significance of fossils as one type of evidence for evolution and then illustrates the evidence for changes in species over time that researchers have found by studying modern organisms.

Section Themes

In examining the fossil record, this section emphasizes the theme of **Evolution**. Throughout geologic time, changes have occurred in organisms from the earliest bacteria to modern plants and animals. The theme of **Scale and Structure** also appears in the anatomical evidence from living organisms.

Motivating Activity

Have students cover leaves or shells with petroleum jelly and set them in plaster of Paris (mixed like a thick milk shake). After the plaster sets, they can remove the objects and reveal molds. Ask students how they can make casts of the "fossils."

Teaching Strategies

Applying Concepts Ask students for examples of situations in which they need to evaluate indirect evidence and make inferences. For instance, the fact that it is raining 500 miles west of here today indicates that it will rain here tomorrow. *(Because the car in front of the one I am in has the left turn signal on, I infer that the car will turn left.)* Encourage students to note the use of indirect evidence and inferences as they read this section. For example, ask students if there is direct evidence in Figure 15-2 on p. 220, that all the horses illustrated are in the same line of descent. *(No; nobody was there to record it. We infer, however, that all the horses illustrated belong in the same evolutionary line.)*

Examining Evidence If you have a fossil collection, have students study samples; otherwise, project photographs or drawings. Discuss what kinds of organisms they represent, and ask students how similar they are to modern organisms. Many ancient organisms, especially early vertebrates, do not have close living relatives; in such cases, have students identify how they differ from their modern counterparts.

If you have brachiopods, ask students to distinguish them from clams. *(Their shells are bilaterally symmetrical; the only bivalves with such shells are scallops. Also, brachiopod valves are not mirror images of each other; those of clams are.)* Other common fossils are of clams, snails, and corals. All such fossils are generally similar to their living descendants. If you have trilobite fossils, ask students how they are different from modern animals, such as sow bugs. *(Trilobites have three sections from front to back and three from side to side.)* Diatomaceous earth used in aquarium filters provides excellent examples of microfossil diatoms for microscopic examination.

Interpreting Data Ask students to suggest how the adaptations of horse evolution might have been advantageous, based on the information in Figure 15-2. How might the changes in the legs and feet have increased the odds of survival. *(They could run faster over hard ground with the longer legs and single hooves. Feet with more toes are better on soft ground.)*

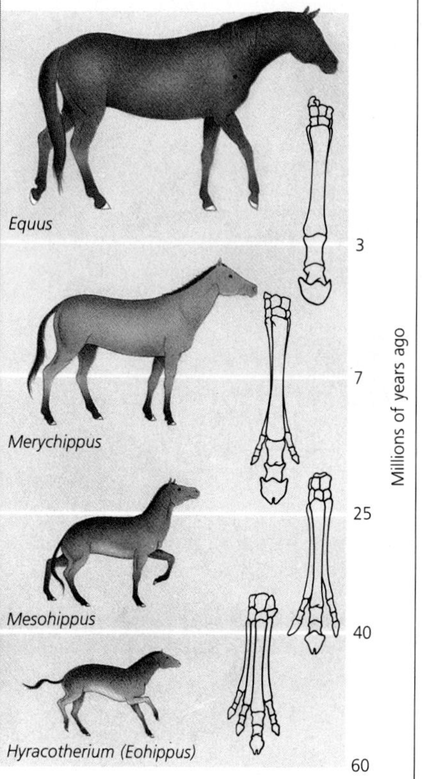

Figure 15-2 Fossil records of horse foot structure show structural differences over time.

found in the lower layers are older. Those found in the upper layers are younger. Thus a fossil's position in sedimentary rock beds gives its age relative to other fossils.

The absolute age of a fossil is determined by dating the fossil with radioactive isotopes. Radioactive isotopes have unstable nuclei that break down, or decay, and form other elements. These isotopes decay at a constant, known rate. The period of time it takes for one-half of the radioactive material to decay is called the **half-life** of the isotope. Remember that isotopes of an element differ in number of neutrons. Carbon-12, the most common and stable isotope of carbon, has 6 protons and 6 neutrons and therefore has an atomic mass of 12. Carbon-14, an unstable, radioactive isotope of carbon has 6 protons and 8 neutrons and an atomic mass of 14. Carbon-14 decays to nitrogen-14. The half-life of carbon-14 is about 5,700 years.

The ratio of carbon-14 to carbon-12 in the atmosphere is assumed to be constant over time. Organisms take up the two isotopes of carbon in about the same ratio that the isotopes are found in the atmosphere. Thus, when an organism dies, the ratio of carbon-14 to carbon-12 in its remains will be the same as that in the atmosphere. As time goes by, the amount of carbon-14 will decrease as it changes into nitrogen-14. However, carbon-12 does not decay. By comparing the ratio of carbon-14 to carbon-12 in a fossil with the ratio of these isotopes in the atmosphere, scientists can date fossils that are up to 50,000 years old.

Scientists use other radioactive isotopes, such as potassium-40, to date older fossils. Potassium-40 has a half-life of 1.28 billion years. Uranium-238 is another radioactive isotope with a long half-life that can be used to date older fossils. Uranium-238 is used to determine the age of cores of silt taken from seabeds.

The Fossil Record

By dating fossils and examining geologic strata, scientists have been able to put together a time scale for the history of life on earth. Table 15-1, the geologic time scale, outlines this history. Study the time scale carefully to learn when various kinds of organisms first appeared.

Fossil evidence indicates that over time organisms of increasing complexity appeared on the earth. Bacteria and blue-green bacteria are the first fossils that were preserved from the Precambrian era. During the beginning of the Paleozoic era, complex multicellular invertebrates dominated life in the oceans. By the end of the Paleozoic era, plants and animals had colonized the land surface of the earth.

The fossil record contains many examples that could be interpreted to mean that species evolved from more ancient organisms. Examine the fossil evidence shown in Figure 15-2. Compare the foot structure of the different species of fossil horses. The similarities and differences between the feet of horses from different epochs strongly suggest that horses changed over time.

LEP Activity

The half-life of carbon-14 is about 5,700 years. Have students imagine a fossil that originally had 100 g of carbon-14 and now has 0.781 g. Have them show how to determine the age of the fossil. They can begin by dividing in half the 100 g in 5,700 years. That gives 50 g at 5,700 years. They can continue with a two-column chart, showing the number of grams on the left and the number of years on the right. At each step, they divide the grams by 2 and add 5,700 years. *(The fossil is 39,900 years old.)*

Table 15-1 Geologic Time Scale

End Date (millions of years ago)	Era	Period	Epoch	Organisms
0.1	Cenozoic	Quaternary	Recent	Modern humans appear
			Pleistocene	Woolly mammoth
2.5		Tertiary	Pliocene	Large carnivores; apes
7			Miocene	Land mammals diversify
26			Oligocene	Primitive apes; horses
38			Eocene	Small horses
53			Paleocene	First carnivores; primates
65	Mesozoic	Cretaceous		Dinosaurs die out; flowering plants appear
135		Jurassic		Age of the dinosaurs; birds arise
195		Triassic		First dinosaurs; mammals; forests of conifers
225	Paleozoic	Permian		First seed plants
280		Carboniferous		First reptiles appear
345		Devonian		First insects and amphibians appear
395		Silurian		Fishes dominant; first modern vascular plants invade land
430		Ordovician		Modern groups of algae and fungi appear
500		Cambrian		First fish; many invertebrates and marine plants
600	Precambrian			First eukaryotes; blue-green bacteria and bacteria abound

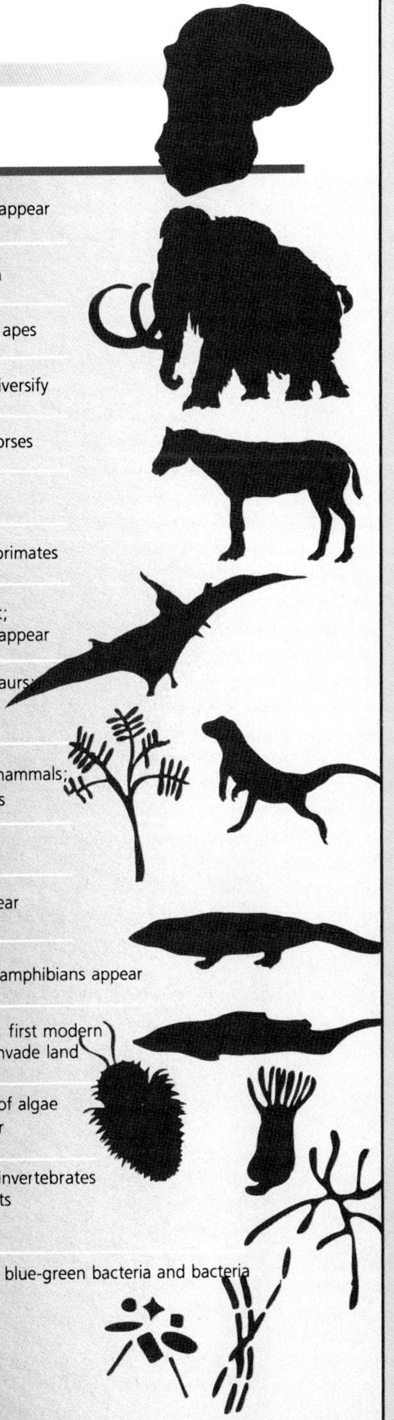

Applying Concepts Plants take in carbon-14 in the form of carbon dioxide in the atmosphere. Ask students how animals take in carbon-14. *(They eat plants or animals that eat plants.)*

Radioactive isotopes provide absolute dates of fossils. Using geologic principles—older rock layers tend to lie beneath younger layers—one can determine relative ages of fossils. Ask students if a fossil found 5 cm beneath an undisturbed rock layer containing fossils dated by radioactive isotopes at three million years would be more or less than three million years old. *(It would be more than three million years old. In order to be buried beneath the three-million-year-old fossils, it would have to have lived earlier.)*

Interpreting the Visuals Have students study Table 15-1, p. 221. Ask students questions based on the chart: In what era did the first dinosaurs appear? *(Mesozoic)* How many years ago did the first insects appear? *(345 million)* In what period are we living now? *(Quaternary)* Which appeared earlier, the primates or the flowering plants? *(The plants—the flowering plants appeared in the Cretaceous period and the primates at the beginning of the Tertiary period.)*

■ *See* **Overhead Transparency** ***T15 and*** **Blackline Master** ***31.***

More Information

Extinction's Heavy Toll Scientists estimate that 99 percent of all animal and plant species that ever existed are now extinct. Most people do not realize how many species have been found by paleontologists. Museum exhibits can show only small samples.

For example, many dinosaur books popular with younger students have suggested that there were a large number of dinosaur species. In the last few years, many new species of organisms have been discovered. In one small area of Wyoming, rocks of earliest Eocene age have given up fossils of 55 species of animals, and that is only part of the fauna that lived in the area at that time.

Interpreting the Visuals Refer students to Figure 15-4, p. 223. Ask students what each forefoot (or hand) is adapted for. *(The penguin has flippers to help in swimming; separate fingers would be a disadvantage. The alligator front foot is adapted to walking on soft ground. The bat fingers are long to make the wing large for flying. The human hand is adapted for grasping.)* Ask students whether the human hand is relatively nonspecialized or highly specialized. *(It is more like that of the alligator; the other two are more specialized.)*

- *See* Blackline Master *32.*

Comparing Structures Display any skeletons you have in your collection and project photographs of others. Show particularly the variation among legs, feet, and heads. Have students identify the differences between the human skeleton and the others. *(For instance, the legs and feet of cows, horses, sheep, and deer are greatly modified. The bird wings and feet are different. Deer, elk, and moose have antlers; cows and bison have horns. Cats have cutting and slashing teeth and sharp claws.)*

Evidence from Living Organisms

By examining fossils and by determining their relative and absolute ages, scientists have collected evidence that supports the theory that species changed over time. Further evidence is derived from living organisms. In order to determine if species change, scientists compare common ancestry, structure, biochemistry, and development of organisms alive today. As you read this section, study this evidence and critically evaluate whether it indicates that species may have arisen by descent and modification from ancestral species.

Evidence of Common Ancestry

If species change over time, then scientists should be able to cite examples showing that a group of living species may have come from a common ancestor. Let us examine one of many cases for which this seems to be true. Gracing the islands of Hawaii is a family of birds commonly called the Hawaiian honeycreepers. Figure 15-3 shows 7 of the 23 Hawaiian honeycreeper species, all of which are found only in Hawaii. All Hawaiian honeycreepers have similarities in skeletal and muscle structure that indicate they are closely related. However, each of the Hawaiian honeycreeper species has a bill specialized for eating certain foods. Scientists suggest that all 23 honeycreeper species apparently arose from a single species that migrated to Hawaii.

Homologous Structures

If a bat, a human, an alligator, and a penguin all evolved from a common ancestor, then they should share common anatomical traits. In fact, they do. Compare the forelimbs of the human, the

Figure 15-3 Like all species of Hawaiian honeycreepers, the seven shown below can be identified by their beaks.

222

Cooperative Learning

Geology Divide the class into groups of three to four students and assign each group a different section of the Geologic Time Scale (Table 15-1, p. 221) to research. Tell them to focus on finding out about the geological changes that were taking place, as well as the species that appeared or existed. Suggest that students look for information about glaciers and land formations, plate motions, and climate changes. Have each group present an oral report on their section of the Geologic Time Scale. Ask each group to divide among group members the tasks of research, recording, drawing, and presentation.

bat, the penguin, and the alligator, shown in Figure 15-4. Find the humerus, radius, ulna, and carpals in each forelimb. Though the limbs look strikingly different on the outside and though they vary greatly in function, they are very similar in skeletal structure. More significantly, they are derived from the same structures in the embryo. Structures that are embryologically similar, but have different functions, are called **homologous structures.** Though these animals look different, a comparison of homologous structures indicates that they are quite similar. This suggests that these animals evolved from a common ancestor.

Vestigial Organs

Some organisms have structures or organs that seem to serve no useful function. For example, humans have a tailbone at the end of the spine that is of no apparent use. Some snakes have tiny pelvic bones and limb bones, and some cave-dwelling salamanders have eyes even though members of the species are completely blind. Such seemingly functionless parts are called **vestigial** *(veh-STIJ-ul)* **organs** or structures. Vestigial organs are often homologous to organs that are useful in other species. The vestigial tailbone in humans is homologous to the functional tail of other primates. Thus vestigial structures can be viewed as evidence for evolution: organisms having vestigial structures probably share a common ancestry with organisms in which the homologous structure is functional.

Biochemistry

Biochemistry also reveals similarities between organisms of different species. For example, the metabolism of vastly different organisms is based on the same complex biochemical compounds. The protein cytochrome c, essential for aerobic respiration, is one such universal compound. The universality of cytochrome c is evidence that all aerobic organisms probably descended from a common ancestor that used this compound for respiration. Certain blood proteins found in almost all organisms give additional evidence

Think

The wings of moths and the wings of birds serve similar functions but differ in structure. Thus they are called *analogous* structures. Do you think analogous structures provide evidence of evolution?

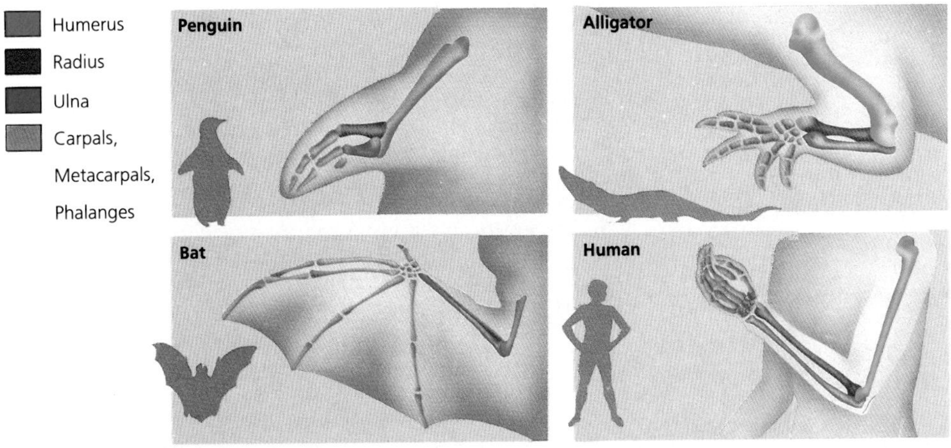

Figure 15-4 The forelimbs of the penguin, the alligator, the bat, and the human are all derived from the same embryological structure.

Answer to Think

Similar functions do not always reflect similar anatomical structures or a shared evolutionary background. For example, bird wings, unlike moth wings, are supported by bone.

Guided Practice

Provide the class with a series of examples of evidence supporting evolution and have students identify each type of evidence. For example: Some snakes have pelvic bones. *(Vestigial structure)* Early mammal embryos have the beginnings of gill slits. *(Embryological development)* Human blood proteins are very similar to those of chimpanzees and less similar to those of horses. *(Biochemistry)* Evidence indicates that the varieties of domestic chickens are derived from the jungle fowl of southeast Asia. *(Common ancestry)* All bivalves have two shells, on the right and left sides of their bodies. *(Homologous structures)*

Independent Practice

- Have students write answers to the Section Review.
- Have students examine Figure 15-5, p. 224, and answer the following questions: What are some major differences in the second stage between the fish and the mammals? *(The appearance of fins and the disappearance of the external ear hole in the fish)* In the third stage, in what way is the rabbit more like the fish than the gorilla is? *(It has a tail.)*

Videodiscs

- *2588–2589 Homologous Forelimbs (s)*

Section 15.1

Check Your Understanding

1. Why is inferring emphasized in this section? *(When we study past events that we cannot observe, we can only examine the available evidence and draw conclusions.)*

2. What are some reasons for the incompleteness in the fossil record? *(The circumstances favoring fossilization—rapid burial or freezing—are exceptional.)*

Reteaching

With help from students, list on the board specific evidence that would have to be collected in order to support an evolutionary relationship between different species. For example, tell students that butterflies and geese both fly, but geese are more closely related to penguins, which swim. Ask students how geese can be shown to be closely related to penguins but not to butterflies.
■ *See* Section Reviews *worksheet, Section 15.1.*

Enrichment

Have each student research a type of fossil and give a report on how it was preserved, its estimated age, where the organism lived, and whether any descendants live today.

Closure

Have students imagine that the photos in a family album have accidently been dumped out on the floor and must be reorganized. Have them devise methods to determine who is related to whom and how to place the photos in chronological order. *(Relationships can be inferred by physical resemblance and family portraits; age can be inferred by appearance of photos, dates printed on back of photos, and obvious clues in style of dress, furnishings, and so on.)* Relate students' methods to those that scientists use to decide how species are related.

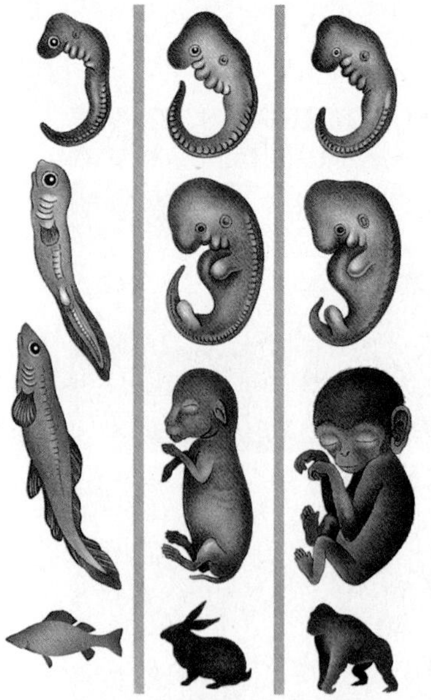

Figure 15-5 Although all three adult organisms look quite different, the developing embryos of the rabbit and gorilla look similar.

that these organisms descended from a common ancestor. Such biochemical compounds, including cytochrome c and blood proteins, are so complex it is unlikely that almost identical compounds would have evolved independently in widely different organisms.

Further studies of cytochrome c in different species reveal variations in the amino acid sequence of this molecule. For example, the cytochrome c of monkeys and cows is more similar than the cytochrome c of monkeys and fish. Such similarities and differences suggest that monkeys and cows are more closely related than are monkeys and fish. Scientists have similarly compared the biochemistry of universal blood proteins. Their studies reveal evidence of degrees of relatedness between different species. This evidence implies that some species share a more recent common ancestor than other species do. From such evidence scientists have inferred the evolutionary relationships between different species of organisms.

Embryological Development

The similarities described above are not the only ones scientists have noticed among organisms of different species. Figure 15-5 shows that embryos of certain species develop almost identically, especially in the early stages. Based on your knowledge of gene expression from Chapter 11 you can infer that such similarities indicate the species have genetic similarities. Again, these similarities can be considered evidence that the organisms shown probably descended from a common ancestor.

The similarities between living species—in ancestry, in homologous and vestigial structures, in embryological development, and in biochemical compounds—all could be explained as extremely remarkable coincidences. However, a far more probable explanation of these similarities is that species have arisen by descent and modification from more ancient forms. Additionally, the fossil record contributes compelling evidence that species have changed over time. The fossil evidence and evidence from living organisms strongly suggest that species evolve.

Section Review

1. What are homologous and vestigial structures, and how do they provide evidence of evolution?
2. How do scientists date fossils, and what fossil evidence indicates that species may have changed over time?
3. How does embryology suggest common ancestry?
4. What evidence of common ancestry is provided by biochemical studies?
5. The American scientist Stephen Jay Gould calls the study of evolution "a historical inquiry." How is the study of evolution similar to and different from the study of history? What role does the gathering of evidence play in both?

Answers to Section Review

1. Homologous structures are embryologically similar in different species. Vestigial structures are functionless. Both represent similarities between organisms that can be explained by descent from a common ancestor.

2. By noting the relative positions of layers of rock that have fossils, and by using radioactive elements to measure fossil age; recent fossils differ from older fossils.

3. Embryos of different species go through similar stages, indicating common genes and, therefore, common ancestors.

4. The universality of certain blood proteins and of compounds essential to metabolism

5. Both require that evidence be collected to make a theory of past events, but the study of evolution is centered on observations and experiments about the natural world.

15.2 Darwin's Theory of Evolution

Scientists at the beginning of the 1800s knew of some kinds of fossils, and they were very aware of homologous and vestigial structures. Many scientists suspected that some kind of evolution had given rise to the living things around them. However, they had no unifying theory to explain how evolution might have occurred. Two scientists led the way in the search for a mechanism of evolution. The first was Jean Lamarck. The second was one of the greatest figures in biology, Charles Darwin.

Evolutionary Theory Before Darwin

The first systematic presentation of evolution was put forth by the French scientist Jean Baptiste de Lamarck (1774–1829) in 1809. Lamarck described a mechanism by which he believed evolution could occur. This mechanism, known as "the inheritance of acquired characteristics," is illustrated in Figure 15-6.

Assume that there were salamanders living in some grasslands. Suppose, Lamarck argued, that these salamanders had a hard time walking because their short legs couldn't trample the tall grasses or reach the ground. Suppose that these salamanders began to slither on their bellies to move from place to place. Because they didn't use their legs, the leg muscles wasted away from disuse and the legs thus became small. Lamarck's theory said that the salamanders passed this acquired trait to their offspring. In time the salamander's legs were used so rarely that they disappeared. Thus, Lamarck argued, legless salamanders evolved from salamanders by inheriting the acquired characteristic of having no legs.

Lamarck presented no experimental evidence or observation and his theory fell out of scientific favor. The next significant idea came from the British scientist Charles Darwin.

Darwin's Background

Charles Darwin (1809–1882), like many people of genius, did not at first appear to have extraordinary talents. From a young age

Section Objectives

- *Compare Lamarck's theory of evolution with Darwin's theory of evolution.*
- *List some of the evidence that led Darwin to the idea of how species might change over time.*
- *Define* natural selection, *and outline the reasoning that led Darwin to conclude evolution could occur by means of natural selection.*
- *Describe Kettlewell's experiment with the two varieties of moths, summarize his results, and explain how he interpreted these results.*

Figure 15-6 According to Lamarck's theory the legs of salamanders could disappear because of disuse. Thus legless salamanders would have evolved from salamanders with legs.

Lesson Plan

Section Focus

This section explains the Lamarckian theory of the inheritance of acquired characteristics. It then outlines the origin and development of Charles Darwin's theory of evolution by natural selection; it describes the theory and the significance of the book Darwin wrote.

Section Themes

This section is the heart of the theme of **Evolution.** The theory of evolution by natural selection explains how interactions between organisms, and between living things and the environment, led to changes in existing species and the extinction and creation of species. In short, Darwin's theory of natural selection is the "unifying one for all biology," as the text states.

Motivating Activity

Show the class pictures of a wolf and a variety of dogs. Scientists infer that domestic dogs have a common wolflike ancestor. Ask students why there are so many different kinds of dogs today and what genetic process that they studied in Chapter 11 could be involved. *(Mutations)* How did the changes become so pro-nounced? *(Breeders selected for certain characteristics, in order to use dogs for various purposes or because they liked the shape or the coat of a new variety. A breeder who wants short-legged dogs will pick from each litter to be bred the puppies with the shortest legs.)* Stress the word *selected.* Just as a breeder selects, so there is selection in nature, though not with a conscious purpose.

■ *See* Laboratories, *Investigation 15.*

Videodiscs

■ *2590–2593, Evolutionary Relationships: Classification (s)*

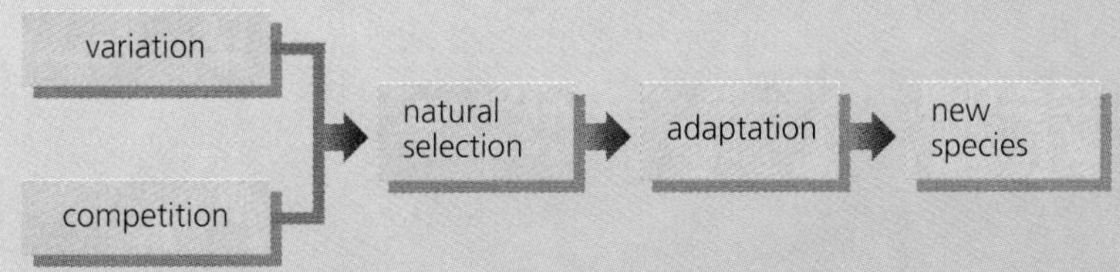

Graphic Organizer Use this sequential diagram in Independent Practice on p. 228.

Teaching Strategies

Summarizing Contributions Many students' familiarity with Charles Darwin is limited to the popular idea that his theory links human evolution to primates. To introduce the full breadth of Darwin's work, ask students to list his accomplishments based on their reading. Point out that Darwin's book *The Origin of Species* is still widely read today. *(Sample list: Studies of natural history at Cambridge; voyage on the* Beagle, *collecting and observing; study of the fossil record; studies of homologous structures, vestigial organs, and embryological development; consultations with breeders; breeding and seed dispersal experiments; formulation of natural selection theory; publication of the book)*

Relating Concepts After they have read Section 15.2, have students draw a concept map relating key concepts of the theory of natural selection. An example of a completed concept map is shown on p. 217B.

Inferring Relationships A good reference for this section is Ruth Moore's *Evolution*, from Time-Life Books. If possible, show students illustrations of all the varieties of bills of Darwin's finches. Point out the distinctive bill features. Have students speculate on which one was probably the common ancestor and give reasons for their choices. *(No one knows the answer.)* Ask students on what evidence they might make a hypothesis. *(Sample hypothesis: The ancestor came from South America. Therefore, a researcher might find out what the bills are like in related South American finches.)*

Darwin disliked school and preferred observing birds and collecting insects to studying. He was sent to medical school in Scotland when he was 16. Young Darwin found medicine "intolerably dull." He was much more interested in attending natural history lectures.

Seeing that Darwin lacked enthusiasm for becoming a doctor, his father suggested he study for the clergy. Darwin was agreeable to the idea and enrolled in the university at Cambridge, England, in 1827. Here again, Darwin admitted, "My time was wasted, as far as the academical studies were concerned."

However, Darwin found that his friendship with John S. Henslow, professor of botany, made life in Cambridge extremely worthwhile. Through long talks with Henslow, Darwin's knowledge of the natural world increased. Henslow encouraged Darwin in his studies of natural history. In 1831 Henslow recommended that Darwin be chosen for the position of naturalist on the ship the HMS *Beagle*.

The Voyage of the *Beagle*

The *Beagle* was chartered for a five-year mapping and collecting expedition to South America and the South Pacific. Darwin's job as ship naturalist was to collect specimens, make observations, and keep careful records of anything he observed that he thought significant.

Figure 15-7 Darwin spent five years on the *Beagle* as ship naturalist, collecting new species and recording his observations.

At the beginning of the voyage Darwin read a geology book given to him by Henslow. This book, *Principles of Geology* by Charles Lyell, spurred his interest in the study of landforms. In Chile Darwin observed the results of an earthquake: the land had been lifted by several feet. In the Andes he observed fossil shells of marine organisms in rock beds at about 4,300 m. He came to agree with Lyell that over millions of years earthquakes and other geologic processes could change the geology of the land. Because the land changed, new habitats would form. Darwin realized that animals would have to adapt to these changes.

During the *Beagle*'s five-year trip the captain often dropped Darwin off at one port and picked him up months later at another. One reason that Darwin was so eager to study life on land was that he suffered from terrible seasickness and couldn't wait to get off the *Beagle*. During his time on land Darwin trekked hundreds of miles through unmapped regions. He observed thousands of species of organisms and collected many different types of fossils. On the long sea voyages he used his time to catalog his specimens and write his notes.

Darwin in England

When Darwin returned to England in October 1836, his collections from the voyage were praised by the scientific community. Darwin sent many specimens to experts for study. A bird special-

Writing About Biology

Wyoming Reverie

This excerpt is from The Dinosaur Heresies *by Robert Bakker.*

From my Field Book, 1981 . . . July 3, 6:35 A.M. Como Bluff, Wyoming. 7,020 feet above sea level. No human being or human structure visible. Air clear, dry, cool. . . .

I'm still excited by the first dinosaur of the summer. I sit here on the crest of a little sandstone hogback, remnant of a stream that flowed a hundred million years ago, and look down on my crew's work of the last four days. It's becoming a sizeable hole, a proper dinosaur dig, twenty-five feet across, dug by pickax, army-surplus trenching shovel, ice-pick, and fingernails.

I saw my first dinosaur in . . . the American Museum of Natural History in New York, at the age of nine. But those skeletons seemed tamed by civilization, mounted as they were on steel and plaster. . . . A dinosaur in the rock is different. This one before me is huge, and its six-foot long thigh bone, which would dwarf any elephant's, lies half exposed to the Wyoming sunrise. Its coal black form is clearly etched against the surrounding pale rock by thousands of careful chisel marks. . . .

From where I sit on the quarry's rim I can see the dinosaur's great trochanters, the attachment site of the immense hip muscles, and the bone surface pitted and rough where tendons and ligaments were anchored to the femur. A hundred thousand millenia ago, those tendons and muscles were full of dinosaur blood coursing through capillary beds, bringing oxygen to the cells that powered the stride of this ten-ton giant. Muscles pulsed in cycles of contraction and release, and the hind limb, fully twelve feet long from hip to toenails, swung through its stroke covering six feet with every pace.

Broken chips of bone lie under my boots, wretched fragments from now unidentifiable bones which had eroded long before we found the site. . . . Some of the broken bits are incredibly delicate bubbles of bone, a frothy texture of holes and vesicles that housed the living substance of the animal's cells. These bits crumble into shards if I rub them too hard, but in life the brittle bone crystals were embedded in a fabric of tough connective tissue, collagen fibers whose great tensile strength combined with the hardness of the bone crystals to produce a living bony architecture capable of resisting enormous loads of both compression and tension. Collagen has long since rotted away, along with all the muscle fibers and blood vessels. But the fossilized bone faithfully preserves the canals left by every capillary that made its passage through it to serve the dinosaur in life. . . .

Reverie is normal in Wyoming at sunrise. I suppose a no-nonsense laboratory scientist might think I was wasting my time communing with the spirit of the fossil beast. But scientists need reverie. We need long walks and quiet times at the quarry to let the whole pattern of fossil history sink into our consciousness.

Write

- **Write a short essay explaining why you think scientists may need reverie. In what way might it help them find answers to their questions? Does Bakker's line of reasoning here have anything to do with the concern that Lewis Thomas expressed in the beginning of his essay on p. 28?**

From The Dinosaur Heresies *by Robert Bakker. Copyright © 1986 by Robert Bakker. Reprinted by permission of William Morrow & Co.*

Background

Bakker is reminding us of what many scientists believe; to get the most out of scientific activity, you have to use your imagination. He thinks of a petrified bone not just as a stony object, but as part of a living organism. From such thoughts stem inferences, hypotheses, new questions, and plans for new research. That is how science progresses. Scientific research is not mechanical; it is very personal and human.

Discussion

After students have read "Wyoming Reverie," ask them to discuss the following questions.

1. Would Robert Bakker be a successful scientist if he dug up the bones, cleaned and repaired them, described them in a notebook, and then put them in storage and forgot them? Explain. *(No, because he would not be advancing our knowledge of dinosaurs)*

2. What is he more likely to do with the bones? *(If there is a reason for it, he will describe his findings in print. In any case, he will use the bones to help understand the appearance of the animal, its physiology, its way of life, and maybe even its habitat. He will strive to learn from the bones as much as he can about the past. Eventually, he will publish his conclusions, as he did in* The Dinosaur Heresies.*)*

Extension

Encourage students to write an essay discussing how they use their own imagination. How is reverie important to them?

About the Author

Robert Bakker is Adjunct Curator of the University of Colorado Museum, an author, and an experienced paleontologist. His enthusiasm for dinosaurs is catching, and he often involves amateurs in his quarrying operations and in cleaning and repairing the bones in the laboratory.

His years of research on dinosaurs have led him to some controversial but fascinating new images of them. He sees them as agile, warm-blooded reptiles. Among other things, he shows why he believes the duckbill types did not swim, as previously thought, and suggests that *Apatosaurus* could rear up on its hind legs.

Guided Practice

Have students study Figure 15-8, p. 228. Tell students that bird beaks are generally adapted for a particular food source; some finches eat plant material, others eat insects. Some eat mostly plants along with some insects. Some eat mostly insects along with some plants. Ask the class to speculate about which finch ate what type of food. *(The large ground finch eats hard cactus seeds; the warbler finch can pick insects out of small cracks and holes; the woodpecker finch will find insects in tree trunks and branches.)* Ask which finch would have an increased chance of survival in a heavily wooded environment. *(Woodpecker finch)*

Independent Practice

- Have students write answers to the Section Review.
- Have students make a sequential diagram of Darwin's theory, using key terms from the text. An example of a completed diagram is shown on p. 225.

Check Your Understanding

1. How would Lamarck explain the evolution of a species of blind fish living in a cave? *(According to his theory of the inheritance of acquired characteristics, the fish in the cave didn't use their eyes, and so their vision was lost.)*

2. What understanding from modern genetics would you add to Darwin's theory of natural selection to bring its explanation of evolution up to date? *(Genetic mutations cause variations.)*

Figure 15-8 The large ground finch, *Geospiza magnirostris* (top), warbler finch, *Certhidea olivacea* (middle), and woodpecker finch, *Camarynchus pallidus* (bottom), have beaks specialized for their food source.

ist, or ornithologist, studied Darwin's bird collections from the Galápagos Islands, located about 1,000 km west of South America. He reported that Darwin had collected 13 similar but separate species of finches. Each finch species had a distinctive bill specialized for a particular food source. Other experts studied Darwin's fossils and classified them as remains of extinct mammals. The fossils included rodents the size of hippopotamuses.

The similarities of the Galápagos finches led Darwin to infer that the finches shared a common ancestor. The similarities between the fossil mammals Darwin collected and modern mammals led him to believe that species change over time.

In 1837 Darwin began his first notebook on evolution. For several years Darwin filled his notebooks with facts that could be used to support the theory of evolution. He found evidence from his study of the fossil record: he observed that fossils of similar relative ages are more closely related than those of widely different relative ages. Comparing homologous structures, vestigial organs, and embryological development of living species gave him additional evidence of evolution. He consulted animal and plant breeders about changes in domestic species. He ran his own breeding experiments and also did experiments on seed dispersal.

Biology in Process

Observing Natural Selection

Direct evidence of natural selection began to come to light before Darwin published *The Origin of Species*. This evidence involved two varieties of a moth species called the peppered moths—one light and one dark. Find the light and dark peppered moths on the lichen-covered tree trunk in the picture. In Darwin's day the light variety was found throughout the countryside, where such lichen-covered trees were common.

The dark variety of peppered moth was first observed near English cities in 1848. This variety was hardly noticeable on the dark, soot-covered tree trunks near industrial areas. Over the next hundred years scientists observed a greater number of dark moths relative to light moths near the cities.

In the 1950s H. B. Kettlewell, an English scientist, tested the hypothesis that the difference in numbers of the light and dark peppered moths was due to natural selection. Kettlewell marked, released, and recaptured the peppered moths in the country and near a city. Kettlewell assumed that the relative numbers of moths of the two varieties he recaptured indicated their relative survival

Interdisciplinary Activity

Geography A description of Darwin's career brings science, history, and social studies together. Tell students that some of the places he visited on his voyage were Brazil, Patagonia, Tierra del Fuego, Chile, Peru, the Galápagos Islands, Tahiti, New Zealand, and South Africa (Cape Town). Have students research the different cultures he observed and compare them with Victorian England. Have students seek information on religion in Victorian England and discover why many people objected to Darwin's theory. Finally, ask students to research the opposition that some religious groups maintain toward Darwin's theory today.

Evolution by Natural Selection

The central question still remained: if evolution occurred, by what means did it occur? In 1838 Darwin read a book called *Essay on the Principle of Population* by a British economist, Thomas Malthus (1776–1834). Malthus stated that a human population growing unchecked would double every 25 years. Resources such as food, air, and water cannot increase at the same rate, Malthus argued. Thus human beings are involved in an intense "struggle for existence," competing for the limited resources. This idea helped Darwin uncover the mechanism he needed.

Combining the idea of competition with his other observations, Darwin explained how evolution could occur. First, he stated that variation exists among individuals of a species. Second, he stated that scarcity of resources in a burgeoning population would lead to competition between individuals of the same species because all use the same limited resources. Such competition would lead to the death of some individuals, while others would survive. From this reasoning Darwin concluded that individuals having advantageous variations are more likely to survive and reproduce than those without the advantageous variations.

Kettlewell's data for 1953

Location		Color of peppered moth: Light	Dark
Unpolluted countryside (Dorset)	Number released	469	473
	Number recaptured	62	30
Polluted city (Birmingham)	Number released	437	447
	Number recaptured	64	154

rates. His results are shown in the chart. Kettlewell interpreted the data to mean that dark moths survived better near cities and light moths survived better in the country. Thus the experiment demonstrated natural selection had occurred in these species of peppered moths.

Kettlewell inferred that the adaptation of color conferred a selective advantage to the moths. He hypothesized that birds could see light moths more easily on sooty trunks near cities and dark moths more easily on lichen-covered trunks in the countryside. Therefore, near cities more light moths would serve as prey, and more dark moths would survive and reproduce. In the countryside the opposite result would occur.

Recent experiments, however, have raised questions about this explanation. They indicate that the peppered moths probably rest not on tree trunks, but in shadows on the underside of tree branches. In this position dark moths are less visible than light moths whether the trees are soot-covered or lichen-covered. Scientists now question whether color is the main adaptation conferring a selective advantage to the light moths. Further experiments may help scientists better understand the selective mechanism in this case.

- **What are some possible sources of experimental error in Kettlewell's experiment? How could you change the experiment in order to reduce the chance of introducing experimental errors?**

Biology in Process

Using the Feature

Observing, experimenting, and interpreting data are the main science processes discussed in this feature. Help students identify possible weaknesses in the design of Kettlewell's experiment. *(He could not control various environmental factors such as pollutants and food supply.)* Point out to students that differences in observation methods appear to have led to conflicting conclusions. Ask students to state the different methods. *(Tagging, releasing, and recapturing moths as opposed to simply observing them)* Ask students how scientists might resolve unanswered questions about peppered moths. (*Design and perform more experiments*)

Answer to the Feature

Error sources include the different proportions of the two varieties released in the two environments and the relatively small number of moths recaptured. To reduce the error, release the same number of moths of each type in both environments, find ways to recover more moths, and subject the data to rigorous statistical analysis.

Reteaching

Have students list as many reasons as they can why only a few of the thousands of eggs laid by frogs survive to become adult frogs. Have them relate their reasons to selective pressures that favor certain eggs or tadpoles with certain genes. *(Sample answer: ponds that dry up quickly favor tadpoles that go through metamorphosis in the shortest time.)*

- *See* Process Skills, *Chapter 15.*
- *See* Section Reviews *worksheet, Section 15-2.*

Enrichment

Have students research more of the pre-Darwinian thinking about evolution—Anaximander, Buffon, and Cuvier—and write a brief outline. Another good research topic is the Scopes trial of 1925. Have students write reports, or suggest that interested students perform a scene from the play "Inherit the Wind," written by Jerome Lawrence and Robert E. Lee.

Closure

Remind students of the Motivating Activity (p. 225) with which you started this section. Ask them to compare and contrast natural selection and artificial selection. *(In natural selection, the environment favors the survival of certain organisms, such as those that are well camouflaged. In artificial selection, humans favor the survival of certain organisms, such as a cow that produces the most milk.*

Videodiscs

- *Side 4 45808, Ptarmigan: Camouflage (m)*

Figure 15-9 The willow ptarmigan, *Lagopus lagopus*, is brown (top) through most of the year but turns white (bottom), in winter as a means of camouflage.

Darwin coined the term **natural selection** to describe the process by which organisms with favorable variations survive and reproduce at a higher rate. An inherited variation that increases an organism's chance of survival in a particular environment is called an **adaptation.** Over many generations, an adaptation could spread throughout the entire species. In this way, according to Darwin, evolution by natural selection would occur.

As an example Darwin noted that the ptarmigan turns white in winter. This color change, he inferred, helped protect it from predators, which would have a hard time spotting the bird in snow. Ptarmigans that didn't change color in winter would be spotted easily and eaten. In this way, Darwin implied, ptarmigans that turned white in winter would be more likely to survive, reproduce, and pass this adaptation to future generations.

The Origin of Species

Darwin compiled evidence for evolution by natural selection for about 20 years. Between 1842 and 1844 he wrote a 230-page essay summarizing his theory and the evidence for it. In the 1850s he began working on a detailed, multivolume book to present his theory to the scientific community.

Darwin might never have completed the book if another British scientist, Alfred Russel Wallace (1823–1913), had not come up with the same idea in 1858. While living in the Malay Archipelago in the Pacific Ocean, Wallace formulated his theory and wrote it in an essay, which he sent to Darwin. Darwin's fellow scientists persuaded him to let them present his theory and Wallace's essay jointly at a scientific meeting. The presentation "excited very little attention," according to the modest Darwin.

However, the publication of Darwin's book *The Origin of Species* in 1859 changed biology forever. The first printing of the book sold out in one day. Darwin clearly and logically presented the idea that natural selection is the mechanism of evolution. In Darwin's own lifetime many scientists became convinced that evolution occurs by means of natural selection. Today this theory is the unifying one for all biology.

Section Review

1. What is *natural selection?*
2. How might reading Lyell's book on geology have influenced Darwin's thinking about evolution?
3. What evidence from Darwin's voyage on the *Beagle* originally led him to the idea that species undergo change?
4. What types of evidence did Darwin present to back up the theory of evolution by natural selection?
5. Use the example of the evolution of the legless salamander to compare and contrast Darwin's theory of evolution to Lamarck's theory of evolution.

Answers to Section Review

1. Individuals with variations that give them advantages over others are most likely to survive and reproduce.
2. Darwin recognized that if the land had changed, as Lyell reasoned, animals would have had to adapt to their new habitats.
3. The limited distribution of the closely related Galápagos finches and the comparison of the fossil mammals with modern mammals
4. Evidence of common ancestry; homologous structures; vestigial organs; and embryological evidence; changes in species due to domestic breeding; fossil evidence
5. Lamarck could have inferred that the ancestral salamander's legs became smaller through disuse and that this acquired trait was passed on. Darwin would have inferred that shorter legs had a selective advantage.

15.3 Patterns of Evolution

As you will read in Chapter 16, natural selection can ultimately lead to the formation of new species. Sometimes many species evolve from a single ancestral species. As you know, similarities in skeletal and muscular structure of Hawaiian honeycreepers led scientists to conclude that the 23 species of honeycreepers evolved from one ancestral species. Such an evolutionary pattern, in which many related species evolved from a single ancestral species, is called **adaptive radiation.** Adaptive radiation most commonly occurs when a species of organisms successfully invades an isolated region where few competing species exist. If new habitats are available, new species will evolve.

Divergent and Convergent Evolution

Adaptive radiation is one example of divergent evolution. **Divergent evolution** is the process of two or more related species becoming more and more dissimilar. The red fox and the kit fox provide an example of two species that have undergone divergent evolution. The red fox lives in mixed farmlands and forests, where its red color helps it blend in with surrounding trees. Compare the color of the red fox to that of the kit fox, shown in Figure 15-10. The kit fox lives on the plains and in the deserts, where its sandy color helps conceal it from prey and predators. Notice also that the ears of the kit fox are larger than those of the red fox. The kit fox's large ears are an adaptation to its desert environment. The enlarged surface area of its ears helps the fox get rid of excess body heat. Similarities in structure indicate that the red fox and the kit fox had a common ancestor. As they adapted to different environments, the appearance of the two species diverged.

In **convergent evolution,** on the other hand, unrelated species become more and more similar in appearance as they adapt to the same kind of environment. The two unrelated types of plants

Section Objectives

- *Explain why adaptive radiation is a form of divergent evolution.*
- *Compare and contrast divergent evolution with convergent evolution.*
- *Define and give an example of coevolution.*

Figure 15-10 The color of the red fox, *Vulpes vulpes* (left), helps it blend in with the trees in its habitat, while the sandy color of the kit fox, *Vulpes macrotis* (right), conceals it from predators in the desert.

	Type of Environment	Two or More Species	Examples
Convergent Evolution	similar	similar but unrelated	cactus and euphorbia
Divergent Evolution	different	related but different	red fox and kit fox

Graphic Organizer Use this table in Reteaching on p. 232.

Lesson Plan

Section Focus

This section describes divergent, convergent, and interspecific patterns of species evolution.

Section Themes

This section further develops the theme of **Evolution.** Patterns in evolution—divergent, convergent, and coevolutionary trends—are explained. Evolution is not unidirectional. Some species grow less alike, others grow more alike, and some change in response to changes in others.

Motivating Activity

Use illustrations of a shark, a porpoise, and a fossil ichthyosaur. Ask students to speculate on why the animals look so similar even though one is a fish, one a mammal, and one a reptile. *(Students may conclude that for any fast-swimming predator, the most maneuverability and least resistance to water flow are adaptive advantages.)*

Teaching Strategies

Organizing Information To help students understand the crucial role adaptation plays in the theory of evolution by natural selection, have them write down lists of adaptations mentioned in the text or captions, and why these adaptations are useful, as they read this section. *(Adaptations in foxes are color, ear size, slender muzzle, and long tongue. Adaptations in plants are fleshy stems, thorns, flower color, and odor.)*

Videodiscs

- *Side 4 26120, Cephalopod: Nautilus (m)*
- *Side 4 20892, Cephalopod: Octopus (m)*
- *Side 4 25744, Cephalopod: Cuttlefish (m)*

Independent Practice

- Have students write answers to the Section Review.
- Show illustrations of polar bears, *Ursus maritimus,* and brown bears, *Ursus arctos.* Explain to students that they belong to different species. Have students write a brief essay describing what evolutionary trend the species exhibit. *(Divergent evolution)*

Check Your Understanding

1. Lions and tigers have a common ancestor. Is their dissimilar appearance an example of convergent or divergent evolution? *(Divergent)*
2. Birds eat berries, then the seeds pass through their digestive tracts and are dispersed. What pattern of evolution is shown here? *(Coevolution)*

Reteaching

Have students make a table comparing convergent and divergent evolution. They should compare the species' environments and their genetic relationship. Use the table on p. 231 as a model.

- *See* Section Reviews *worksheet, Section 15.3.*

Enrichment

Have students research other examples of coevolution. *(The sphinx moth and the tobacco blossom; ants and acacia trees)* Have them present their findings orally to the class.

Closure

Ask students to describe specific circumstances in which adaptive radiation would be likely *(Geographic isolation of a species due to changes in landforms, changes in climate)* List their ideas on the board.

Videodiscs

- *1419–1420,* **Struthis camelus:** *Ostrich (s)*
- *1421,* **Dromaius novaehollandiae:** *Emu (s)*

Figure 15-11 The cactus, *Cereus gigantea* (left), and the spurge, *Euphorbia* sp. (right), both have fleshy stems that store water and protect them from predators.

shown in Figure 15-11 have adapted to desert environments. Notice the resemblance of the cactus, which grows in the American desert, to the euphorbia, which grows in the African deserts. Both have fleshy stems armed with spines. These adaptations help the plants store water and ward off predators.

Coevolution

Coevolution is the joint change of two or more species in close interaction. Predators and their prey sometimes coevolve; parasites and their hosts often coevolve; plant-eating animals and the plants upon which they feed also coevolve. One example of coevolution is between plants and the animals that pollinate them.

In tropical regions bats visit flowers to eat nectar. The fur on the bat's face and neck picks up pollen, which the bat transfers to the next flower it visits. Bats that feed at flowers have a slender muzzle and a long tongue with a brushed tip. These adaptations aid the bat in feeding. Flowers that have coevolved with bats are light in color. Therefore, bats, which are active at night, can easily locate them. The flowers also have a fruity odor attractive to bats.

Divergent and convergent evolution and coevolution are different ways organisms adapt to the environment. These are examples of how the diversity of life on earth is due to the ever-changing interaction between a species and its environment.

Section Review

1. Define and give an example of *adaptive radiation.*
2. How do the red and the kit fox show divergent evolution?
3. What is convergent evolution, and how are cactuses and euphorbs an example of this evolutionary pattern?
4. How do bats and bat-pollinated flowers provide an example of coevolution?
5. Adaptive radiation most commonly occurs on newly formed remote islands. Why do you think this is true?

Answers to Section Review

1. The evolutionary pattern in which many related species evolve from a single ancestral species; Hawaiian honeycreepers
2. Similarities in structure indicate a common ancestor; differences in color and ear size show that they have diverged somewhat in adapting to different environments.
3. A process in which unrelated species become more similar as they adapt to the same environment. Cactus and euphorb stems store water in a dry environment.
4. Some bats feed on flower nectar. Their hairy faces and necks pick up pollen. Bat-pollinated flowers attract bats.
5. They are isolated environments where little competition exists. In such an environment, many different species can evolve from a single ancestral species.

Laboratory

Variation and Natural Selection

Objective
To study how variation within a species is the basis for natural selection

Process Skills
Measuring, collecting and analyzing data, inferring

Materials
Metric ruler, graph paper, peanuts in the shell

Background
1 Variation has been described as "the raw material of natural selection." What is variation?
2 What determines an individual's phenotype? How might a mutation of a genotype prove beneficial to a species?
3 Explain why it is advantageous for a species to show variation among individuals.

Inquiry
1 Crack open the peanut shells and measure the length of 100 peanuts in millimeters. Record your results in a table, giving the lengths and the number of peanuts for each length. Why is the fact of different lengths evidence of variation within the species?
2 Make a bar graph using your data from step 1. What should you label the vertical axis? The horizontal axis? Which is the independent variable? the dependent variable?
3 Combine the class data and graph them in a separate bar graph. Describe any differences between your data and the class data. How can you account for these differences?
4 Describe the overall shape of your bar graph from step 3. What may have caused the peanut-size variation you observed?
5 Use the class data to calculate average peanut length. How do the numbers of average-length peanuts compare with the numbers of very large and very small peanuts?
6 According to the class data, what size is the largest peanut measured? the smallest? The peanut supplies the seed with energy. What is the relationship of peanut size to the amount of energy available to the seed?

Conclusions
1 What might have caused the large and small sizes of the peanuts measured? If the environment changed so that a very large peanut was an advantageous variation, what would happen over time to the peanut population in response to such a change?
2 Describe an environmental change that would favor the much larger peanut. Can you think of a change that would favor the much smaller peanut?
3 Why do you think most peanuts are not the size of the smallest peanut measured?
4 How might you determine whether a trait (such as very large peanut-size) is a result of genetic or environmental factors?

Further Inquiry
Measure and graph variations found in other species. For example, measure human finger length, adult human height, pine needle length, acorn weight, or the length of the hind legs of grasshoppers. For each object measured, hypothesize environmental changes that could lead to the selection of an extremely small or large size.

Conclusions
1. Mutations. Over time, the majority of peanuts would be the larger size.
2. Large peanuts might be favored in an environment having more daylight hours—longer periods of photosynthesis. Fewer daylight hours—shorter periods of photosynthesis—might favor a smaller peanut.
3. Insufficient food would be available.
4. Collect seeds and raise plants from the large peanuts. If most of the peanuts grown from those seeds were also large, that would indicate the trait was genetic.

Further Inquiry
With a large enough sampling size, a typical bell-shaped curve should be visible when the data are graphed.

(For an overview of variation and preparatory information related to the laboratory, see p. 217B.)

Background
1. The differences between members of a species
2. Genes, units of DNA, determine phenotype. A mutation might result in a phenotype that has an evolutionary advantage. Recombination and crossing-over can also produce a change in DNA.
3. Having variations means that, as the environment changes, individuals with favorable traits will survive and reproduce at a higher rate than those without the advantageous variation.

Inquiry
1. Variation means differences. Since the peanuts belong to the same species, the differences in their length show that there is variation within the species.
2. Number of Peanuts. Length of Peanut. The independent variable is the length of a peanut in millimeters. The dependent variable is the number of peanuts of each length.
3. Student's data may differ significantly from class data. Differences are probably due to the change in sampling size.
4. Student may describe the graph as hill-like or bell-shaped. Variation is caused by differences in DNA, possibly a result of mutation.
5. The average peanut length is calculated by adding all the lengths and dividing by the total number of peanuts measured. Typically, there will be many more peanuts of or near average length than there are very small or very large peanuts.
6. Student answers will vary. The larger the peanut, the more energy available to the seed. The smaller the peanut, the less energy available to the seed.

Vocabulary

1. Casts, imprints, and molds are all fossils. An imprint is a thin film of carbon left after all other elements have evaporated or rotted. A mold is an impression left after remains of an organism have disintegrated. A cast forms when sediments fill a fossil mold.
2. An adaptation is an inherited trait that increases an organism's chance of survival in a particular environment. Natural selection is the process by which individuals with advantageous adaptations are more likely to survive and reproduce than those without the adaptations.
3. Homologous structures are body parts of different species that are similar in structure and develop from the same part of the embryo. Vestigial organs serve no apparent function in one species but are homologous to useful structures in other species.
4. Evolution is the theory that species change over time. Coevolution is the joint evolution of two or more species in close interaction.
5. In convergent evolution unrelated species become more similar as they adapt to the same environment. In divergent evolution related species become increasingly dissimilar as they adapt to different environments.

Review

1. c	**6.** c
2. b	**7.** b
3. a	**8.** a
4. b	**9.** d
5. d	**10.** d

11. The concepts are that species change over time and that today's species have arisen by descent and modification from ancestral forms.
12. Students should list the following: fossil evidence, evidence of common ancestry, homologous structures, vestigial organs, embryological evidence, biochemical evidence.
13. The skeletal and muscle structure of the 23 species of Hawaiian honeycreepers indicate that the birds are closely related.
14. Salamanders would pass the trait of short legs, acquired through disuse during their lifetime, to their offspring. Thus the legless salamander would eventually evolve through the inheritance of acquired characteristics.
15. Members of a species with favorable variations would be more likely to survive and reproduce than others.
16. Wallace sent Darwin an essay in which he put forth a theory identical to Darwin's. This spurred Darwin to present his and Wallace's ideas and to publish *The Origin of Species*.
17. He cited fossil evidence, homologous structures, vestigial organs,

Chapter 15 Review

Vocabulary

adaptation (230)
adaptive radiation (231)
cast (219)
coevolution (232)
convergent evolution (231)
divergent evolution (231)
evolution (219)
half-life (220)
homologous structures (223)
imprint (219)
mold (219)
natural selection (230)
vestigial organ (223)

Explain the difference between the terms in each of the following sets.

1. cast, imprint, mold
2. adaptation and natural selection
3. homologous structures and vestigial organs
4. evolution and coevolution
5. convergent and divergent evolution

Review

1. Most fossils are found in (a) ice (b) resin (c) sedimentary rocks (d) sand.
2. Radioactive isotopes such as carbon-14 can be used to date fossils because (a) the isotopes vary in number of protons (b) the isotopes decay at a relatively constant rate (c) the position of the fossil in undisturbed sedimentary rock indicates its age (d) the geologic time scale outlines the history of life on earth.
3. Changes in the foot of different species of fossil horses indicate that (a) horses have changed over time (b) horses have homologous structures (c) horses have vestigial organs (d) horses have a long half-life.
4. The fact that the metabolism of different species of organisms is based on the same biochemical compounds is evidence that (a) species change over time (b) organisms descended from a common ancestor (c) species have different genes (d) cytochrome c is essential for anaerobic respiration.
5. The first systematic presentation of evolution was proposed by (a) Erasmus Darwin (b) Charles Darwin (c) Alfred Russel Wallace (d) Jean Baptiste de Lamarck.
6. In his essay on population Malthus argued that a human population would double every 25 years if (a) species inherited acquired characteristics (b) the earth did not change over millions of years (c) resources were unlimited (d) species did not undergo adaptive radiation.
7. According to the process of natural selection, individuals having variations that give them an advantage in obtaining limited resources will likely (a) be preserved as fossils (b) survive and reproduce (c) diverge markedly (d) evolve.
8. Adaptive radiation is most likely to occur (a) in isolated regions (b) in mixed farmlands and forests (c) on the plains and in deserts (d) in tropical regions.
9. When related species become dissimilar as they evolve, they undergo (a) convergent evolution (b) coevolution (c) adaptive radiation (d) divergent evolution.
10. As environments change, organisms must (a) diverge evolutionarily (b) converge evolutionarily (c) coëvolve (d) adapt or move to new habitats.
11. What two concepts formed Darwin's basis for the theory of evolution by natural selection?
12. Name five types of evidence of evolution.
13. How do Hawaiian honeycreepers provide evidence of evolution?
14. How did Lamarck think legless salamanders evolved?
15. How could natural selection result in evolution of new species, according to Darwin?
16. What role did Wallace play in Darwin's presentation of the theory of evolution?

17. What evidence did Darwin use to prove that evolution had occurred, and why was his theory accepted by scientists?
18. Kettlewell assumed that color was the adaptation that conferred a selective advantage to peppered moths in their respective environments. What evidence causes scientists to question this assumption?
19. Why is adaptive radiation considered a form of divergent evolution?
20. Define *coevolution,* and give four examples of types of coevolution.

Critical Thinking

1. Scientists have recently found that organisms can exchange DNA without sexual reproduction. What role do you think this ability may have played in evolution?
2. Biologists have discovered that many genes are the same in different species. How does this fact provide evidence for evolution?
3. In addition to formulating the theory of evolution by natural selection, Charles Darwin also did detailed scientific investigations of many different types of organisms. For example, Darwin published studies of coral reefs, barnacles, orchids, insectivorous plants, and fungi. How might the information Darwin gathered by doing this type of research have contributed to the formulation of the theory of evolution?
4. The ancestor of the modern panda was a meat-eating hunter. Its paws were therefore adapted for running after prey, not for making fine movements. Yet the modern panda appears to have a "thumb." The panda, a vegetarian, uses this "thumb" to help it strip leaves off bamboo stalks. The panda then eats the shoots. As the diagram above shows, the panda's "thumb" is actually a small bone in its wrist, not a separate digit. Explain how natural selection could have led to this unique "thumb".

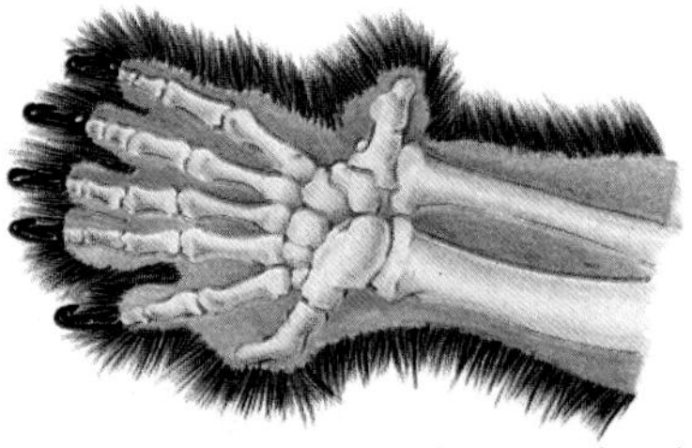

5. In the desert rodents are more active in the cool of night. The kit fox mentioned in the text preys on such animals. What role other than cooling does this suggest for the enlarged ears of the kit fox?

Extension

1. Read the article by Stephen Jay Gould entitled "Darwin and Paley Meet the Invisible Hand" in *Natural History,* November 1990, pp. 8–16. Prepare an oral report in which you discuss Paley's theory about the "good" design of organisms and how Darwinism dismantles that theory. How does Darwin's work reflect the influence of Thomas Malthus and Adam Smith?
2. Though he never became as famous as Charles Darwin, Alfred Russel Wallace made many important contributions to the field of biology in the late 1800s and early 1900s. Use biographies, autobiographies, and an encyclopedia to find information on the life of Alfred Russel Wallace. Write a report highlighting Wallace's contributions to biology.
3. Make an instant fossil. Take 2 or 3 leaves, a coin, or even an apple and drop dampened plaster of Paris around the object. Let the plaster of Paris dry and then break it open with a hammer. Point out the mold.

embryological evidence, and evidence from breeding. The theory was accepted because of the strength of Darwin's evidence and logic.

18. Recent experiments indicate that moths rest in shadows on the undersides of branches rather than on trunks. In this position, dark moths are less visible than light moths.

19. In adaptive radiation many species diverge from a single ancestral form.

20. Coevolution is the joint change of two or more species in close interaction. It occurs with predators and prey, with parasites and hosts, with plant-eating animals and plants, and with flowers and animals that feed on nectar or pollen.

Critical Thinking

1. This could increase the variation in populations and might speed up evolution, especially if the environment changes; there would be a better chance of some organisms surviving.

2. The same DNA in different species could be explained by descent from a common ancestor.

3. With this varied background, Darwin made generalizations that provided the basis for his theory and made observations that provided evidence to support his theory.

4. The panda's "thumb" is an adaptation that would have decreased competition for food; pandas with the "thumb" could eat bamboo instead of competing for prey.

5. While hunting at night, the fox would rely more on hearing and less on sight to find its prey.

Extension

1. Students should be able to explain how Paley dismisses alternative arguments to his central assertion—that organisms are well designed (implying a designer).

2. Reports should include notice of the close similarity between Wallace's and Darwin's research methods and conclusions. Students might be interested to learn about other instances in science when exciting leaps in understanding have been made simultaneously by more than one individual.

3. If plaster of Paris is not available you might provide moist sand, or you could ask students to brainstorm other ways of modeling fossils using materials at hand.

Chapter 16 Evolution: Speciation

Chapter Overview

Chapter 16 outlines how and why new species appear and existing species disappear. This is the most profound result of the process of evolution. Section 16.1 formalizes the modern definition of *species* and the description of a stable population. Section 16.2 describes how natural selection acts and other processes disrupt genetic equilibrium. Section 16.3 begins by describing natural situations in which speciation is known to occur, and ends with a discussion of punctuated equilibrium and causes of extinction.

Chapter Planning Chart

B	S	A	Sections and Subsections	Page	Features	Page	Resources
	•	•	**16.1 Genetic Equilibrium**				
			The Concept of Species	237	Biology in Process	238	Videodiscs
			Variation of Traits in a Population	239	Think	240	Blackline Master 33
			Allele Frequencies and Genetic Equilibrium	240	Section Review	241	Section Reviews Worksheet
			The Hardy–Weinberg Principle	241			
		•	**16.2 Disruption of Genetic Equilibrium**				
			Mutation	242	Think	244	Blackline Master 34
			Migration	242	Laboratory	251	Overhead Transparency T16
			Genetic Drift	243	Section Review	246	Laboratories: Resistance in Bacteria
			Natural Selection	244			Section Reviews Worksheet
		•	**16.3 Formation of Species**				
			Isolated Populations	247	Section Review	250	Videodiscs
			Rates of Speciation	249			Process Skills: Speciation
			Extinction	249			Section Reviews Worksheet
			End of Chapter Activities				
					Chapter Review	252	Vocabulary Skills
							Chapter Test
							Computer Test Generator

B *The Basic Level curriculum presents the most fundamental knowledge offered in the course.*
S *The Standard Level curriculum is designed for the average student who is able to master most topics.*
A *The Advanced Level curriculum includes suggestions for teaching the most academically able students.*

Cooperative Learning

Group Activity: Modeling Disruptive Selection

- **Group Size:** *One-third of the class*
- **Outcome:** *Students will model disruptive selection of moths by acting as predators.*
- **Individual Accountability:** *Each student will make model moths, collect moths, and record moths collected.*
- **Positive Interdependence:** *The class will analyze the results of the model.*

Have students make templates of a moth by taping together two triangles with 3-cm sides. Have each group use the templates to make at least 16 moths. Have one group use black paper, the second group use newspaper, and the third group make moths with one black paper wing and one newspaper wing. Tape to the classroom floor two five-meter squares, one of black paper and one of newspaper. Scatter equal numbers of each type of moth over the two squares. Divide the class into two groups, each to collect moths on one of the two paper squares. Give each student 30 seconds to collect moths. Have students record the numbers of each kind of moth collected. Have them then determine which moth was easier to find on which paper, and relate these results to the peppered moth experiment described in Chapter 15, p. 228.

Concept Map

The following is one possible solution to the concept mapping activity in Independent Practice on p. 240.

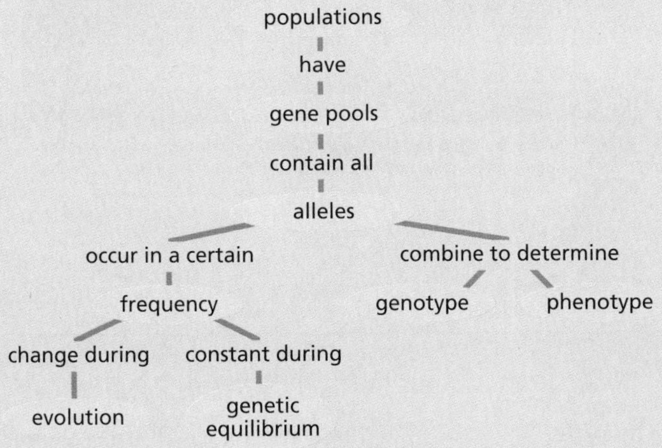

Laboratory Preparation

Overview *(See p. 251.)*

In this lab, students investigate what happens to gene frequencies in populations with and without selection pressure. Students observe that without selection, gene frequencies in a large, randomly mating population stay the same. Such a population is said to be in Hardy–Weinberg equilibrium. With selection (in this case, strong selection) in a large, randomly mating population, students observe that allele frequencies will change. They also learn that it is difficult to completely eliminate an allele from a population.

Preparation

If time does not permit students to complete the entire laboratory, divide the class into two groups. One group can do steps 1 through 4, and the second group can do steps 5 through 10.

The three containers should be opaque and capable of being opened so that a student can put in a hand. Brown paper bags, cigar boxes, and shoe boxes with lids work well.

Teaching Tips

Remind students that for the matings to be truly random, the alleles must be drawn blind.

As students make their predictions, remind them that each pick of the alleles is random and independent; it is not influenced by, nor can it influence, the preceding or succeeding pick(s).

Some students or lab groups may get skewed results. If this is the case, you may want to pool class data for each step and work with these pooled data. Such a large database is likely to be closer to a random distribution.

Chapter Themes

Evolution Emphasize the fact that the species is the focus of evolution; the most dramatic result of evolution is the changing of one species into another. This chapter outlines how such a change takes place.

Scale and Structure As you did in Chapter 15, stress that structures are at the base of the first (morphological) definition of *species.* One of the ways that scientists recognize the development of a new species is by changes in one or more structures. An example of such structures in finches appeared in Chapter 15, p. 228.

Systems and Interactions Point out the importance of the ecosystem here. Members of a species become adapted to their environments over generations through natural selection. If the environment changes more rapidly than the species can adapt, it becomes extinct.

Chapter Motivating Activity

To initiate a discussion on what can happen to various species if the ecosystem changes, use an overhead projector to show a world map with the extent of glaciation today compared with the last peak of glaciation 20,000 years ago. Ask students to speculate on what the effects of the extended ice sheets on particular species might have been. *(The cold may have killed some species, caused others to migrate.)* Tell students that events such as ice ages, which substantially affect ecosystems, are the rule in nature rather than the exception. Have students brainstorm a list of changes taking place in the environment today, as a result of human activities or natural causes, that could affect the evolution of species. *(The ozone hole, global warming, destruction of habitats, appearance of new viruses such as HIV)*

Chapter 16 Evolution: Speciation

Introduction

No one knows exactly how many species of organisms exist on earth today. In a tropical rain forest alone there are many thousands of species of plants, insects, birds, and mammals, each with its own adaptations. How did all of these species evolve? In this chapter you will trace the process of speciation and gain a better understanding of evolution.

Chapter Outline

16.1 Genetic Equilibrium
- *The Concept of Species*
- *Variation of Traits in a Population*
- *Allele Frequencies and Genetic Equilibrium*
- *The Hardy–Weinberg Principle*

16.2 Disruption of Genetic Equilibrium
- *Mutation*
- *Migration*
- *Genetic Drift*
- *Natural Selection*

16.3 Formation of Species
- *Isolated Populations*
- *Rates of Speciation*
- *Extinction*

Chapter Concept

As you read, follow the steps that lead to the evolution of a new species.

Poppies in bloom, Antelope Valley, California. Inset: Variation among red-tailed monkeys, *Cercopithecus ascanius*.

Understanding the Visuals
The photograph shows two intermingled populations of poppies of the genera *Papaver*, or field poppy, and *Eschscholzia*, the yellow California poppy. Ask students what they might expect to see if they observed plants from the two genera up close. *(One might expect to find differences in traits such as flower shape, leaf shape, and so forth.)*

Have students identify the differences among the three monkey faces. *(Differences include brow shape, nose color, hair color, and so forth.)* Tell students that in this chapter they will learn how such obvious differences could arise and how they both are produced by and contribute to the process of evolution.

16.1 Genetic Equilibrium

A **species** is a group of individuals that look similar and whose members are capable of producing fertile offspring in the natural environment. In this section you will learn about this modern definition of species. You will also learn how to view populations of species as genetic entities and how changes in genes in a population can result in evolution.

Section Objectives

- *Compare the morphological concept of species with the biological concept of species.*
- *Describe how scientists study variation of a given trait in a population.*
- *Define* genetic equilibrium.
- *Explain the conditions of the Hardy–Weinberg principle.*
- *Contrast Gould's method of classifying* Cerion *with that of nineteenth-century scientists.*

The Concept of Species

The word *species* is derived from a Latin word meaning "kind" or "appearance." You are probably already familiar with this definition. For instance, you might realize that all gorillas are of the same species. You would base your belief on the fact that individuals in this group look alike. We use the concept of species because we naturally tend to group together things that look alike.

The Morphological Concept of Species

Long ago scientists used to classify organisms solely on the basis of similarities and differences in internal and external structures—that is, on their **morphology.** When differences in appearance are used as the major criterion for classifying an organism, the organism is said to have been classified by the **morphological species concept.** Because morphological characteristics are easy to observe, the morphological species concept is extremely useful. Using this concept, scientists can readily communicate about the characteristics, behavior, and relationships of organisms.

However, using the morphological species concept has limitations. For example, it sometimes happens that organisms that appear different enough to be called different species will interbreed and produce fertile offspring. Figure 16-1 shows two vari-

Figure 16-1 Interbreeding of the red-shafted flicker and the yellow-shafted flicker produces a fertile hybrid with the coloration shown.

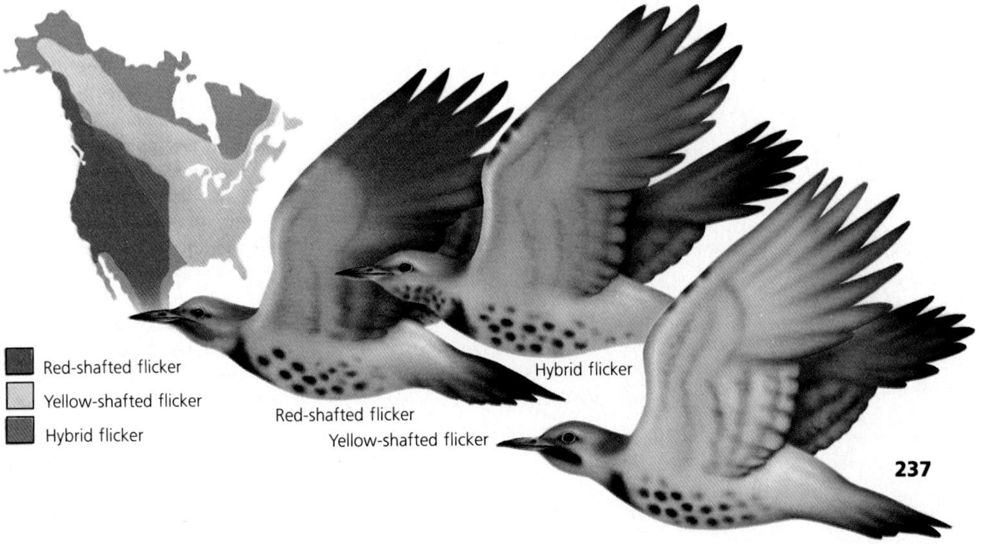

Lesson Plan

Section Focus

This section gives the modern definition of *species* and introduces the concept of population. It describes what constitutes a stable population.

Section Themes

This section emphasizes the theme of **Scale and Structure** in the discussion of the structures that are the physical traits of species, and the minute, intracellular structures of the chromosomes and genes. For example, structural differences are the basis of the morphological concept of species.

Motivating Activity

Tell students that a population is made up of all the members of the same species living in a particular location at the same time. Then ask students to name populations that live in a nearby area, such as a park, vacant lot, farm, or even a crack in the sidewalk. (*Answers will vary according to geographic locale but should include a number of plants and animals, for example, dandelions and pigeons. Some students may incorrectly suggest an ethnic community within the area as a population. This answer is based on a misunderstanding about the concept of species, which is addressed in this section.*) Tell students that in this section they will explore ways that these nearby populations might evolve in the future.

Videodiscs

- **644–645, Selaginella lepidophylla; Selaginella pilifera—*Two Species of Resurrection Plants (s)***

Species Concept	Based on
morphological	physical similarities
biological	reproductive compatibility

Graphic Organizer Use this table to clarify definitions in Section 16.1.

Teaching Strategies

Making Connections Ask students why Darwin might have named his famous book *The Origin of Species*. *(Because the species is the biological unit by which evolution is measured.)* Ask students to suggest a definition for the term *species*. Tell them that the most current definition, which they are about to learn, is central to the study of biology.

Drawing Conclusions Point out to students that other types of animals, such as frogs, present the same classification problem as the flicker. Further difficulties are also associated with the morphological definition of *species*. For example the shape of a salmon's head changes during its lifetime. Can a buck with antlers be called a different species from a doe with none? *(No, many animals such as deer and elk have significant differences between the sexes.)* Ask students for a familiar example of a single animal species that includes several varieties with obvious differences and similarities. *(Humans)*

Inferring Relationships Ask students on what basis scientists designate the species of a fossil organism. *(Morphology, because scientists cannot study the reproductive capability of nonliving organisms; see* More Information, *p. 239.)* Classifying fossil organisms is a common use of inferring. Ask students how scientists determine that a particular species evolved from another species. *(On the basis of details of the fossil's morphology and relative positions in the geologic time scale)* Stress that the biological concept of species helps only those studying evolution in living organisms.

eties of birds, a yellow-shafted flicker and a red-shafted flicker. The yellow-shafted flicker lives in the eastern part of North America, and the red-shafted flicker lives in the western part. However, where their ranges overlap, the birds interbreed and produce fertile offspring. The offspring of two morphologically dissimilar organisms is called a **hybrid.** The hybrid flickers have a different coloration from that of either the yellow-shafted or the red-shafted flickers.

Using just the morphological concept of species, scientists might have classified the yellow-shafted, red-shafted, and hybrid flickers each as separate species. The morphological concept of species is limited because it does not account for the reproductive compatibility of morphologically different organisms.

The Biological Concept of Species

Because of limitations of the morphological concept of species, scientists expanded their definition of species to include reproductive compatibility. When organisms are classified solely by whether or not they naturally breed with one another and produce fertile offspring, they are said to have been classified by the **biological species concept.**

Biology in Process

Classifying Cerion

The snails shown are members of a group of Bahamian land snails of the genus *Cerion (SIR-EE-on)*. Scientists have observed variation in the snails' shell size, structure, and color. Nineteenth-century scientists, using the morphological species concept, classified up to 600 species.

This long list of snail species discouraged scientific study of *Cerion*. Under the morphological species concept members of different species could be distinguished only by minute differences in their shells. The American scientist Stephen Jay Gould studied *Cerion* by using both the biological and the morphological concepts of species.

Gould observed *Cerion* in the northern Bahamas, a group of islands formed from two submerged landmasses, or banks. Little Bahama Bank and Great Bahama Bank, shown on the map, are separated by a deep channel.

Each island of the northern Bahamas has one coast facing the open ocean and one coast facing the interior of its bank. Gould observed that *Cerion* on the ocean coasts of both banks had thick, ribbed shells and a uniform color. Those on the interior coasts of both banks had

Cooperative Learning

Classifying Species Divide the class into groups of four students. Have the groups imagine that they are scientists on an island that is inhabited by plants, insects, birds, and mammals. The group's goal is to classify the organisms by species. Each group member can take responsibility for one type of organism. Tell each group to develop classification procedures that take into account the main criteria necessary for classification. Have each student list the characteristics and behaviors he or she would need to observe in order to determine species. Then have the other group members review each list and develop a group-approved list. *(The students should list morphological characteristics as well as determine whether or not morphologically different animals can have fertile offspring—mating.)*

Using both the biological and morphological concepts of species, modern scientists have arrived at the definition of species stated at the beginning of this chapter, that is, a group of individuals that look similar and whose members are capable of producing fertile offspring in the natural environment. In reality scientists today classify organisms by using both morphology and reproductive compatibility, as well as many other characteristics that you will learn about in Chapter 18.

The modern concept of species is important to the study of evolution because it acknowledges the fact that individuals pass on genes to the next generation. Scientists use this concept of species not only to classify organisms but also to study how species change over time.

Variation of Traits in a Population

To study how species change, scientists must first understand populations. A **population** is made up of all the members of the same species that live in a particular location at the same time. For example, all the fish of a single species that live in a pond make up a population.

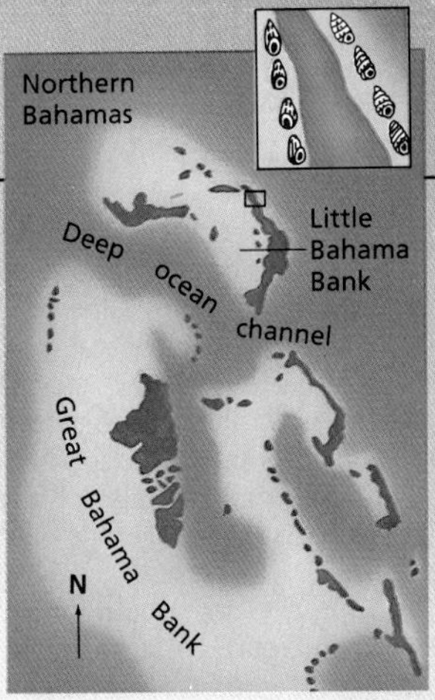

thin shells, few ribbings, and a mottled color.

On each island where the ranges of the ocean and interior varieties of *Cerion* overlapped, Gould observed *Cerion* with various combinations of ribbing and mottling. This indicated that the two varieties on each island interbred and produced fertile hybrids. Thus Gould concluded that all varieties on a single island were members of the same species.

Detailed study of the snail's reproductive anatomy revealed that all varieties of *Cerion* on each island of Little Bahama Bank had the capacity to interbreed with one another. Likewise the *Cerion* on all the islands of the Great Bahama Bank had the capacity to interbreed. Thus Gould hypothesized that *Cerion* on Little Bahama Bank were members of the same species, as were those on Great Bahama Bank. However, as a result of differences in reproductive anatomy *Cerion* of Little Bahama Bank were probably unable to interbreed with those of Great Bahama Bank. Thus *Cerion* from the two banks were members of two separate species.

By using both the biological and the morphological concepts of species, Gould was able to untangle the web of detail left by previous researchers of *Cerion*. Further study may help scientists learn how the species evolved.

- **How did Gould use observation in determining the classification of *Cerion*?**

Interpreting the Visuals Ask students to use Figure 16-3, p. 241, to explain how the genotype frequency is determined. *(The first step is to count the alleles of each type. In the first generation, 4 out of 16 are R′, or 25 percent, and 12 out of 16 are R, or 75 percent. In the second generation, there are still only 4 R′ alleles; they are merely situated differently.)* Ask students how a white flower could appear in the second generation when there were no white flowers in the first generation. *(The white flower is the offspring of two pink flowers, each of which contributed an R′ allele.)*

- *See* Blackline Master *33.*

Biology in Process

Using the Feature

The feature shows Gould first using the process skills of observing and collecting data. He then hypothesized that all individuals on an island were of the same species. Finally, he experimented by studying the reproductive anatomy and confirmed his hypothesis. Ask students whether Gould's revising of the number of species of *Cerion* would cause a revision of the number of populations. *(Yes. One species in a place equals one population.)*

Answer to the Feature

Gould observed the geographical distribution of varieties of *Cerion* on each island and found that the two coastal varieties could interbreed and produce fertile hybrids. He also observed reproductive anatomy in order to determine whether *Cerion* from different islands could interbreed.

Videodiscs

- *1525–1526, Animalia; Mammalia; Artiodactyla; Giraffidae—Giraffes (s)*
- *Side 4 29906, Giraffe (m)*

More Information

Fossil Species In determining fossil species, paleontologists are limited to using morphological characteristics that are shown by often incomplete fossils. They can only hypothesize whether certain organisms of the past could interbreed or not.

Most fossil mammals are identified by the shapes of their teeth, amphibians and reptiles by details of their skull bones and vertebrae. Shellfish species are based only on shell shape, since the animals inside are unknown. Many fossil plants are known only from leaves; the species are determined by leaf shapes and vein patterns. Other plants are known only from petrified stems and are characterized by wood anatomy.

Applying Concepts Refer students to their notes from the Cooperative Learning activity on the newly discovered island, p. 238. Have students identify the conditions that must be met for there to be genetic equilibrium on the island. *(No mutations, no migration, large population, random mating, no natural selection)*

Answer to Think

Accept any example students back up with facts. For example, variation in skin wrinkling among humans of the same age might be due to differences in exposure to sun and wind.

Guided Practice

On the board, make a chart of Japanese four o'clock populations with different numbers of white, pink, and red flowers from those in Figure 16-3, p. 241. You can use red, white, and pink chalk or simply write the words *red, white,* and *pink*. Be sure also to write the genotype. Have students figure out the phenotype and genotype ratios for the populations. Ask students if the next generation will have different ratios, and why or why not. *(No, because genetic equilibrium has not been disturbed)* Ask under what conditions the frequencies could be expected to change. *(One Hardy–Weinberg condition has to change.)*

Independent Practice

- Have students write answers to the Section Review.
- Once students have read the section, have them summarize the concepts of genetic equilibrium with a concept map. Have them include constant and changing allele frequencies. Supply students with other key terms if necessary. An example of a completed concept map appears on p. 235B.

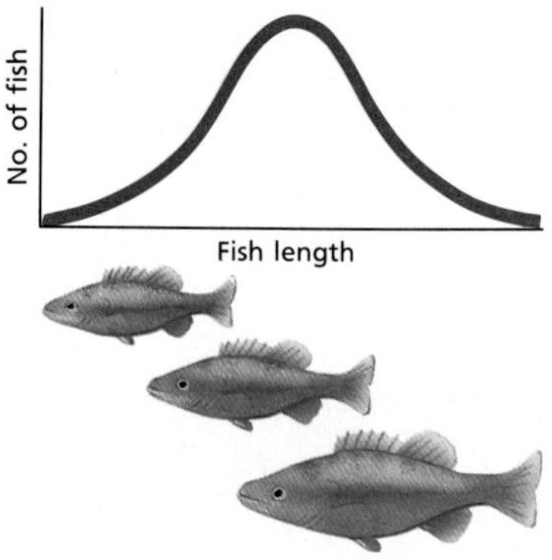

Figure 16-2 A bell curve illustrates how most members of a population are grouped in an average range for a given trait while only a few are at the extreme ends of the range.

Think

Organisms often show variation caused by environmental factors. For example, most plants grown in nitrogen-poor soil will be smaller than plants of the same species grown in nitrogen-rich soil. What are some other examples of variation in a species due to environmental factors?

Within a population, individuals vary in many observable traits. For example, fish in a pond vary in length, weight, and color. Scientists study variation in a certain trait by measuring that trait in a large sample. Figure 16-2 shows the results of such measurements. It is a graph of the range of lengths in a population of mature fish. The shape of the graph looks like a bell, and the graph is called a **bell curve.** The bell curve shows that a few fish are extremely short and a few are extremely long, but most are of average length. In nature many traits in populations show variation according to the bell curve pattern.

What causes variation in traits? Sometimes variations are due to environmental factors. Often variations are due to heredity, and this is the kind we are going to discuss. Each individual inherits a different combination of genes from its parents. As you remember from Chapter 10, a difference in **genotype**—the genetic makeup of an individual—usually results in a difference in **phenotype**—the outward appearance of the organism.

As you learned in Chapter 11, variations in genotype arise through mutation, recombination, and crossing-over. Mutation changes individual genes. Genetic recombination, the reassortment of genes during meiosis, results in new gene combinations. Crossing-over, the interchange of chromatid portions of homologous chromosomes during meiosis, also leads to new genotypes. All of these mechanisms cause the variations in traits in a population.

Allele Frequencies and Genetic Equilibrium

From the above discussion you can see that the variation of traits in a population is often controlled by genes. It follows, then, that changes in the genes cause changes in the corresponding traits. Often the most meaningful way to understand how species change over time—that is, how they evolve—is to think of a population as simply a collection of genes. The collection of genes for all the traits in a population is called a **gene pool.** The gene pool of a population thus contains all the alleles for all the genes. An **allele frequency** is the percentage of a specific allele of a gene in the gene pool.

Consider the population of Japanese four o'clock flowers shown in Figure 16-3. As you learned in Chapter 10, these flowers show codominance for color. This means that Japanese four o'clock flowers with red flowers are homozygous (RR) for the red trait, the plants with white flowers are homozygous (R′R′) for the white trait, and the plants with pink flowers are heterozygous (RR′).

Because Japanese four o'clocks exhibit codominance for color, you can infer the genotype by observing the phenotype. Then, when you know all the genotypes, you can calculate the allele frequencies. Compare the parent generation and the off-

Generation	Phenotype frequency		Genotype frequency
First generation	White	0	R = 0.75
	Pink	0.5	R′ = 0.25
	Red	0.5	
Second generation	White	0.125	R = 0.75
	Pink	0.25	R′ = 0.25
	Red	0.625	

Figure 16-3 Though these Japanese four o'clocks differ phenotypically from generation to generation, the allele frequencies remain the same.

spring of Japanese four o'clocks in Figure 16-3. Notice that the two generations differ in numbers of individuals of each of the three phenotypes. Nevertheless, the allele frequencies for R and R′ are the same for both generations. This means that the allele frequencies of these Japanese four o'clock plants has not changed from generation to generation. A population in which allele frequencies do not change from generation to generation is said to be in **genetic equilibrium.**

The Hardy–Weinberg Principle

In 1908 a British mathematician, Godfrey Hardy (1877–1947), and a German physician, Wilhelm Weinberg (1862–1937), independently outlined the conditions necessary for genetic equilibrium. The **Hardy–Weinberg principle** states that a population will remain in genetic equilibrium if, and only if, all of the following conditions are met: (1) no mutations occur; (2) individuals neither enter nor leave the population through migration; (3) the population is large; (4) individuals mate randomly; (5) and natural selection does not occur. However, if even one of these conditions does not hold true, allele frequencies of the population may change. When the allele frequency changes, the range of traits in a population will change. In other words, evolution will occur.

Section Review

1. What is the definition of *allele frequency*, and how does it relate to evolution?
2. Compare the morphological concept of species with the biological concept. How are both concepts important?
3. What is genetic equilibrium?
4. What is the Hardy–Weinberg principle, and under what conditions does this principle apply?
5. In what way is the understanding of the biological concept of species important for understanding evolution?

Check Your Understanding

1. What do you think caused the *Cerion* snails on the two Bahama banks to become different species? *(Mutations have probably occurred in at least one of the populations, so they can't interbreed.)*
2. What is the difference between *genotype* and *phenotype?* (Genotype *is the genetic makeup;* phenotype *is outward appearance.)*
3. A population of four o'clocks is 50 percent red with a genotype of RR, and 50 percent pink with a genotype of RR′. What is the frequency of the red allele in this population? *(75 percent)*

Reteaching

Determine the gene pool of the class for the ability to roll the tongue. For the purposes of this exercise assume that 50 percent of the tongue rollers are RR and 50 percent are Rr. Nonrollers are homozygous recessive (rr). Ask students to calculate the allele frequencies within the gene pool of the class.
■ *See* **Section Reviews** *work-sheet,* **Section 16.1.**

Enrichment

Have each student prepare a report on an endangered species. The report should explain the criteria used to determine "endangered" status and what measures, if any, are being used to preserve the species. *(California condors, Bengal tigers, whooping cranes, the black cabbage tree; protective measures include habitat management, breeding programs, and legislation.)*

Closure

Tigers and lions sometimes mate in zoos, producing "ligers" or "tigons." On the basis of morphological and biological data, have the students decide if tigers and lions are of one species or two. *(There are two species, because breeding does not take place in natural settings.)*

Answers to Section Review

1. *Allele frequency* is the percentage of an allele of a gene in a gene pool. Evolution occurs when the allele frequency changes.
2. The morphological concept concerns differences in anatomy. The biological concept concerns the ability of organisms to interbreed. A proper species definition requires the use of both concepts.
3. *Genetic equilibrium* is the state in which the allele frequencies of a population do not change from generation to generation.
4. A population will remain in genetic equilibrium under the following conditions: no mutation, no migration, large population, random mating, and no natural selection.
5. Changes in the breeding patterns of organisms can lead to evolution.

Lesson Plan

Section Focus

This section describes how genetic equilibrium can be disrupted, paving the way for the possible formation of new species.

Section Themes

This section emphasizes the theme of **Systems and Interactions.** Members of a population experience interactions of various kinds. Some interactions maintain genetic equilibrium in a population. Others disrupt genetic equilibrium and change a population.

Motivating Activity

Use the photo of the albino koala, Figure 16-4 on p. 242. Ask students to speculate on how such a color could occur. *(Albinism is a rare recessive trait.)* Ask students why there is a trait for albinism at all in the population. *(Mutation)* To emphasize that natural selection influences the gene pool, ask if they think that an albino koala has the same chance for survival that other koalas have. *(No, its albinism would make it an easier target for predators and may be associated with eye and skin problems.)*

Teaching Strategies

Making Hypotheses Have students describe examples of human interference with animal and plant populations. Ask what condition of the Hardy–Weinberg principle applies in these cases. *(Humans interfere with migration, mating, and population size, and in some cases, natural selection.)* Promote a discussion of what is likely to happen. *(Extinction may occur, or better-adapted varieties will evolve through natural selection.)*

Section Objectives

- *Summarize how mutation and migration each disrupt genetic equilibrium.*
- *Define genetic drift, and give an example of how genetic equilibrium could be disrupted through genetic drift.*
- *Describe how natural selection differs from mutation, migration, and genetic drift in terms of its ability to cause significant changes in a gene pool.*
- *Contrast the effects of stabilizing, directional, and disruptive selection on variation in a trait over time.*

Figure 16-4 Most koalas, *Phascolarctos cinereus,* are gray (top). Why might some be white (bottom)?

16.2 Disruption of Genetic Equilibrium

Evolution occurs when genetic equilibrium is disrupted. Review the Hardy–Weinberg conditions presented in Section 16.1. In Section 16.2 you will learn how changes in the allele frequencies of a population occur when these conditions are not met. You will learn also that natural selection is the most significant factor causing changes in the gene pool.

Mutation

Mutation is a physical change in a gene or chromosome. Remember from Chapter 11 that mutations include point mutations, such as the addition or removal of a single nucleotide in genes, and chromosome mutations, such as the gain or loss of one or more chromosomes.

Mutations affect genetic equilibrium by producing totally new alleles for a trait. In addition mutations can change the frequency of the alleles already present in the gene pool. For example, the mutation that causes the sickle-cell trait occurs spontaneously in about 5 out of 100 million people. This means that an allele for normal hemoglobin will spontaneously undergo mutation into the allele for the abnormal hemoglobin in 5 out of 100 million people. Spontaneous mutations are too infrequent to cause major changes in genetic equilibrium. However, mutations caused by harmful radiation can cause major genetic changes.

Migration

Migration—the movement of individual organisms into or out of a population—can alter allele frequencies in a population. Consider a population of squirrels, for example. This population is characterized by particular allele frequencies for certain traits. Suppose individuals from another population of squirrels move into the area and interbreed with the original population. The second group may introduce alleles that were absent in the gene pool of the first group. Also, the second group will probably have allele frequencies for certain traits that differ from those of the original population. Thus because of immigration—the movement of new individuals into a population—allele frequencies of this population of squirrels will be altered, and genetic equilibrium will be disrupted. Emigration—the departure of individuals from a population—also disrupts genetic equilibrium. The movement of genes into or out of a population through migration is called **gene flow.** Gene flow does not always involve the movement of individuals from place to place. It may involve the movement of sperm, for example, when sperm in plant pollen is transported by wind.

genetic equilibrium → disrupted by:
- mutation
- migration
- genetic drift
- natural selection

→ evolution

Graphic Organizer Use this sequential diagram in Analyzing Concepts on p. 244.

Genetic Drift

Two of the necessary conditions for maintaining genetic equilibrium as stated by the Hardy–Weinberg principle are the presence of a large population and random mating. The Hardy–Weinberg principle is based on the laws of probability, which do not necessarily hold for small and medium-sized populations. In small populations chance can significantly affect allele frequencies from one generation to the next. **Genetic drift** is the phenomenon by which allele frequencies in a population change as a result of random events or chance.

Several species of giant land turtles called Galápagos tortoises live on the Galápagos Islands. Before the 1900s thousands of these tortoises inhabited the Galápagos island of Española. Settlers introduced goats and pigs to the island, and these animals competed with the tortoises for food. As a result tortoise populations dwindled. By 1970 the total population of this species of Galápagos tortoises had shrunk to fewer than 20 members. In such a small population it is possible that one allele of a particular gene will be found in only one tortoise. If that tortoise failed to breed, the allele would be eliminated from the gene pool forever. Elimination of the allele would change allele frequencies for that trait. Thus in the small population of Galápagos tortoises genetic equilibrium could be disrupted by chance. Also, when a population is too small, one individual may not be able to mate as frequently as another individual. This is an example of nonrandom mating, which may also affect allele frequency. All examples of genetic drift occur in small to medium-sized populations. In these populations the effect of nonrandom mating may cause major changes in allele frequencies.

While mutation, migration, and genetic drift can change the gene pool, they usually do not cause significant changes that lead to the formation of new species. Natural selection does cause significant changes leading to the formation of new species.

Figure 16-5 One tortoise subspecies living on the Galápagos Islands is *Geochelone elephantopus* ssp. *vandenburghi.*

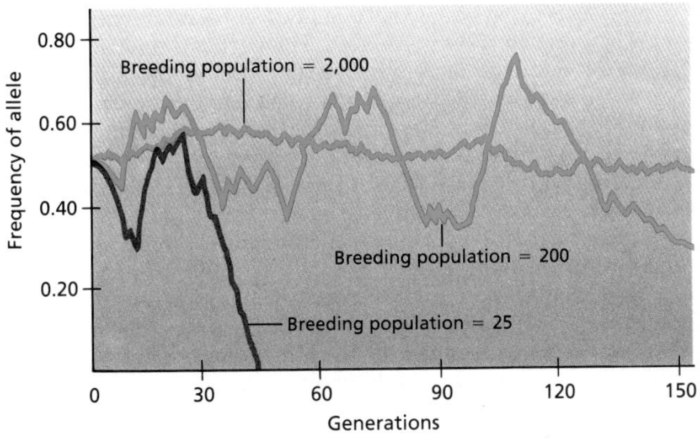

Figure 16-6 Genetic drift is significant only in small and medium-sized populations. In a small population a particular allele may disappear completely over a few generations. In a larger population a particular allele may vary widely in frequency due to chance but still be present in enough individuals to be maintained in the population. In a much larger population the frequency of a particular allele may vary slightly due to chance but will remain relatively stable over generations.

Applying Knowledge Review the examples of mutation, migration, genetic drift, and natural selection provided in this section. Have students come up with their own real or hypothetical examples of disruptions in genetic equilibrium in human populations or in other populations not caused by humans. Summarize all the examples on the board. *(Possible examples: mutation—a larger tail fin on a fish, so it can swim faster; a better way for a plant to disperse seeds; migration–if wider than normal pollen dispersal occurs, allele frequency can be affected; a drought in an area could cause animals to migrate into another area and affect the local gene pool there; genetic drift—if a new, large housing development is built and the food supply of the small mammals who live there is lessened, the population there will become smaller and an allele could disappear; natural selection—if a virus either mutated or newly arrived from another region, to which some people had had natural immunity but others had been fatally vulnerable, succeeding generations would be made up of only immune individuals.)*

Interpreting the Visuals Have students study Figure 16-6, on p. 243, and answer the following questions. What is the graph comparing? *(The frequency of an allele in three different-sized populations over generations)* Which line on the graph represents a population in which the frequency of the allele changes very little over many generations? *(The green line)* What is significant about the red line's intersecting the *x*, or horizontal, axis? *(It means that the allele frequency becomes zero for the smallest breeding population after roughly 45 generations.)*

Cooperative Learning Activity

Studying Genetic Equilibrium Have students work in groups of four. Have each group make two flash cards for one of the conditions that disrupts genetic equilibrium. *(Mutation, migration, nonrandom mating, small population, any form of natural selection)* Direct students to write the term for the condition on one side of each card and sketch a graph or an illustration or write a paragraph depicting the term on the other side of the card. Suggest that each student use one example from the text and another example from a reference book in the library. When the cards have been completed, have one member of the group shuffle them and show the descriptive sides, challenging the others to identify the terms.

Answer to Think

Answers will vary but may include the following: seed eating, shape of bill, large eyes, coloration, perching feet, dark streak from the corner of the eye, specific song.

Comparing Factors Ask students to compare the abilities of the following factors to cause changes in a gene pool: mutation, migration, genetic drift, and natural selection. *(Mutations make some changes such as introducing a new allele, but they do not have a major effect on the gene pool. Migration does not necessarily cause a significant change because migrating groups are usually not very different from the local one. Genetic drift can cause an allele to disappear, which is a major change in the gene pool, but does not necessarily lead to evolution. Natural selection is the force that causes large changes and the formation of new species over time.)* Emphasize to students that a new allele will make a major difference in the gene pool only if it is promoted by natural selection over time. The original mutation does not make a big difference.

■ *See* **Laboratories, *Investigation 16.***

Analyzing Concepts Have students draw a sequential diagram summarizing how genetic equilibrium can be disrupted to cause evolution. They should start by making a list of relevant terms from this section of the text. An example of a completed diagram is shown on p. 242.

Think

Name five adaptations of the song sparrow, *Melospiza melodia,* that you infer are the result of natural selection.

Natural Selection

The Hardy–Weinberg principle states that for a population to remain in genetic equilibrium natural selection must not occur. In fact natural selection does occur. It is an ongoing process in nature, and it is the single most significant factor disrupting genetic equilibrium. As you learned in Chapter 15, natural selection results in higher reproductive rates for individuals with certain phenotypes, and, hence, certain genotypes. As a result of natural selection some members of a population are more likely to contribute their genes to the next generation than others are. Thus by the action of natural selection allele frequencies change from one generation to the next. Each of four types of natural selection—stabilizing, directional, disruptive, and sexual—causes changes in the gene pool of a population.

Stabilizing Selection

Stabilizing selection is a type of natural selection in which individuals with the average form of a trait have an advantage in terms of survival and reproduction. The extreme forms of the trait, on the other hand, confer a disadvantage to the organism. For example, in some species of lizards conditions may exist where average size is an advantage in terms of survival and reproduction. Lizards that are larger than average will be more easily spotted, captured, and eaten by predators than average-sized lizards will. On the other hand, lizards that are smaller than average might not be able to run fast enough to escape predators and therefore will also be at a disadvantage. Thus conditions are such that average-sized lizards would be most likely to survive and therefore to reproduce.

The graph on the upper left in Figure 16-7 illustrates the effects of stabilizing selection on the trait of body size in a population of lizards. The red line shows the initial variation in lizard size as a standard bell curve. Remember that the pattern of variability for many traits may be described as a bell curve. The blue line represents the variation in lizard body size several generations after a new predator was introduced. This particular predator was most easily able to capture both the highly visible large lizards and the slower small lizards. In other words the introduction of the new predator caused the large and small lizards in this population to be selected against. Notice that the blue bell curve is not as wide as the original bell curve. This difference indicates that the two extremes in size have been selected against by the predator. Thus, in this case, stabilizing selection acted to reduce the size range in the lizard population.

Stabilizing selection is most effective in a population that has become well adapted to its environment. Since most populations are reasonably well adapted to their environments most of the time, stabilizing selection is the most common type of natural selection.

LEP Activity

To help students understand the graphs in Figure 16-7, p. 245, have them begin by reproducing a graph of stabilizing selection in their notebooks (preferably on graph paper). Have them label the horizontal axis for lizard length in centimeters from 10 to 20 and the vertical axis for number of lizards from 0 to 20. Write the following data on the board and have students plot the points: 2 lizards at 11 cm, 2 at 19 cm; 6 at 12 cm, and 6 at 18 cm; 10 lizards each at 13 and 17 cm; 14 lizards each at 14 and 16 cm, and 20 at 15 cm. Ask students to draw a curve for this population.

Then have students assume that a new predator has changed the population by selectively catching and eating certain individuals before they reproduce. Write the following data for the new population on

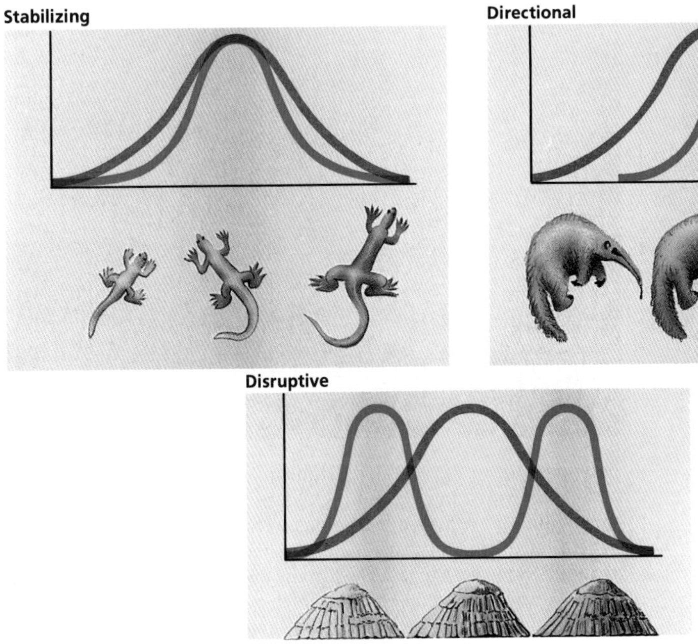

Figure 16-7 Stabilizing, directional, and disruptive selection can all be illustrated as changes (blue) of the standard bell curve (red).

Directional Selection

Directional selection is a type of natural selection in which individuals with one of the extreme forms of a trait have an advantage in terms of survival and reproduction. The graph on the upper right in Figure 16-7 shows the effects of directional selection on the trait of tongue length in anteaters. Anteaters feed by breaking open termite nests, extending a sticky tongue into the nest, and lapping up the termites. Suppose that the area was invaded by a new species of termite that built very deep nests. Anteaters with long tongues could more effectively prey on these termites than could anteaters with short tongues. In other words anteaters with long tongues would likely have a selective advantage. Thus directional selection acts to favor one extreme of a trait.

Disruptive Selection

Disruptive selection is a type of natural selection in which individuals with either of the extreme forms of a trait have an advantage in terms of survival and reproduction. The average form of the trait, on the other hand, confers a selective disadvantage to the organism. The bottom graph in Figure 16-7 also shows the effects of disruptive selection on the trait of shell color in marine animals called the limpets. The shell color of limpets varies from pure white to dark tan. On rocks covered with goose barnacles, which are white, white-shelled limpets are at an advantage. Birds that

the board, and have students plot the points in a second color: 0 at 11 cm and 19 cm: 4 at 12 cm and 18 cm ; 6 at 13 cm and 17 cm; 12 at 14 cm and 16 cm; 20 at 15 cm. Ask students to plot the new curve in the second color.

Ask students how the second graph contrasts with the first. *(There are fewer of the smallest and largest lizards.)* Have them suggest an explanation for this change. *(The smallest lizards might not be as fast in escaping predators. The largest may be the most conspicuous to predators.)* Have them summarize the events represented by the two graphs. *(The individuals of average size were most likely to survive and reproduce.)*

Interpreting the Visuals Have students explain what each graph in Figure 16-7, p. 245, shows and how the title relates to the graph. *(The first graph shows that the population has stabilized at the medium lengths. The second graph shows movement of a trait in a certain direction; specifically, long tongues were selected for over time. The third graph shows that over time the medium-colored limpets have been eliminated in favor of the extreme forms.)*

■ *See* **Overhead Transparency *T16 and* Blackline Master *34.***

Guided Practice

Build students' understanding of the factors that disturb genetic equilibrium by returning to the example of the Japanese four o'clocks in Figure 16-3, p. 241. Have students copy the genotypes of the first generation on paper and then tell them to subject the gene pool to factors that disturb genetic equilibrium. For example, have one R′ change to an R and ask what has happened and how the change will affect the gene pool. *(Mutation, gene pool changes slightly)* Or have all the red plants die and ask what kind of selection is occurring. *(Directional selection, gene pool changes drastically)* Suggest other changes and ask students to name the type of disruption occurring in each one.

Independent Practice

■ Have students write answers to the Section Review.

■ Have students describe a progression from a mutation to a potential new species. Remind students that original mutations are generally subtle. *(Answers should specify the mutation, what the advantage is, what happens during natural selection, and how the gene pool is modified over time.)*

Check Your Understanding

1. Why is genetic drift not significant in large populations? *(Chance cannot significantly alter allele frequency.)*

2. Identify the type of natural selection occurring in the following examples:

a. Lions with large, strong, sharp canine teeth are better able to survive than lions with short, weak, blunt canines. *(Directional)*

b. Female cardinals mate with males with the brightest red feathers. *(Sexual)*

Reteaching

Ask students why the founding of a small community in a new environment is a situation in which genetic drift is likely to occur. *(A small population won't have the genetic diversity of the whole species.)*

■ ***See* Section Reviews *worksheet, Section 16.2.***

Enrichment

Have students research situations in which genetic drift has occurred in a population of humans or other organisms. *(The splitting off of a small number of individuals, as in the founding of a community such as the old order Amish, or cases in which a population is reduced to only a few members and then protected, such as the northern elephant seal)* Have students report their findings to the class.

Closure

Give students the following examples of selection in populations, and ask them to decide what kind of selection is occurring. For instance, in one population of birds, the females mate with males with long tail feathers. *(Sexual)* In another population, predators easily catch birds with long tail feathers. *(Directional)* Finally, in a third population of birds *both* situations occur. *(Stabilizing)*

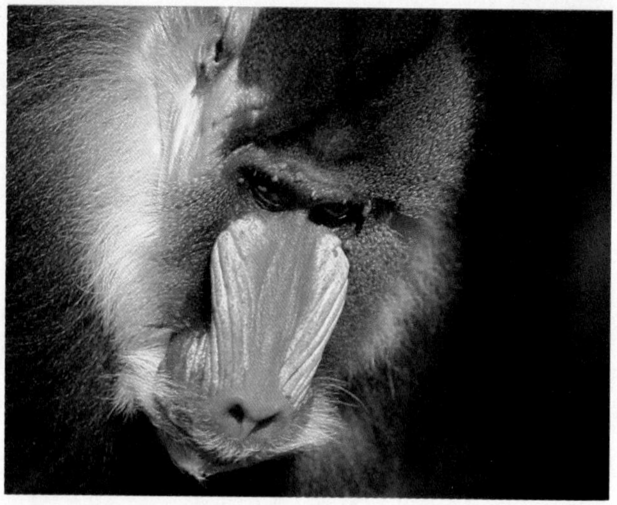

Figure 16-8 Sexual selection causes the vivid coloration that distinguishes the male mandrill baboon, *Papio sphinx,* from the female of the species.

prey on limpets have a hard time identifying the white shells against the white background. On bare, dark-colored rocks dark-shelled limpets are at an advantage. The limpet-eating birds also have a hard time locating the dark shells against the dark background. However, it is easy for the birds to spot limpets with shells of an intermediate color, which are visible against both the white and the dark backgrounds. In summary, disruptive selection eliminates the intermediate form and favors the extreme forms.

Sexual Selection

Sexual selection is the preferential choice of a mate based on the presence of a specific trait. For example, in the tropical beetle, females preferentially mate with males having an elongated snout. Therefore male beetles with a longer snout are more likely to reproduce and pass their genes on to the next generation. Thus the longer snout is sexually selected for in the male of this species. Sexual selection may be stabilizing, directional, or disruptive.

Natural selection is the most significant factor that disrupts genetic equilibrium and causes changes in the gene pool of a population. Such changes, by definition, lead to evolution in a species.

Section Review

1. What is *genetic drift?*
2. Explain how mutation and migration disrupt genetic equilibrium.
3. Compare and contrast stabilizing, directional, and disruptive selection, and give an example of each.
4. What is sexual selection?
5. Scientists infer from observation that the eyespots on the tail of the male peacock evolved through sexual selection. Draw graphs that show possible mechanisms for the sexual selection of the male peacock's tail.

Answers to Section Review

1. A change in the gene frequencies of a population due to chance
2. Mutation changes allele frequencies when new alleles are introduced. Migration changes allele frequencies when individuals enter or leave a population.
3. Stabilizing: organisms with average form of a trait have advantage over those with extreme forms; lizards. Directional: selection favors one extreme form of a trait; anteaters. Disruptive: selection favors both extreme forms of a trait over the average form; limpets.
4. The preferential choice of a mate based on the presence of a specific trait
5. Number of male peacocks on the *y* axis; variation in circles (no circles, colored circles, circles that look like eyes) on the *x* axis. The graph should show a standard bell curve.

16.3 Formation of Species

Disruption of genetic equilibrium, as discussed in Section 16.2, leads to changes in the gene pool of a population. As you have read, it is natural selection that causes the most significant genetic changes in a population. However, such changes do not necessarily lead to **speciation**—the formation of new species. In this section you will learn how speciation occurs.

Section Objectives

- *Define geographic isolation, and explain how it can lead to speciation.*
- *Give two examples of ways reproductive isolation can lead to speciation.*
- *Summarize the theory of punctuated equilibrium.*
- *Outline the role of adaptation in the survival or extinction of a species.*

Isolated Populations

Remember that a species is defined as a group of organisms that look similar and have the ability to interbreed and produce fertile offspring in the natural environment. For a new species to arise, either interbreeding or the production of fertile offspring must somehow cease among members of a formerly successful breeding population. For this to occur, populations or segments of a population must somehow become isolated.

Two forms of isolation prevent interbreeding or cause infertility among members of the same species. These forms of isolation are geographic isolation and reproductive isolation.

Geographic Isolation

Geographic isolation is the physical separation of members of a population. Populations may be physically separated when their original habitat becomes divided, as, for example, when new land or water barriers form. Also, when part of a population colonizes a new, remote area such as an island, the colonizers may become geographically isolated from other populations of the species. For example, when a group of American finches colonized the Hawaiian islands, the group became geographically isolated from the parent population. These finches eventually gave rise to the 23 species of Hawaiian honeycreepers discussed in Chapter 15.

Geographic isolation of a population may occur as a result of physical changes in an environment. When a river changes course or even when a highway is built across a field, populations may become geographically isolated.

Let's study a specific example in which geographic isolation may have led to speciation. The desert of Death Valley, California, has a number of isolated ponds formed by springs. Each pond contains a species of fish that lives only in that pond. Scientists suggest that these species arose through geographic isolation.

How did these fish become isolated in Death Valley? Geologic evidence from a study of wave patterns in sedimentary rocks indicates that most of Death Valley was covered by a huge lake during the last ice age. When the ice age ended, the region became dry. Only small, spring-fed ponds remained. Members of a fish species that previously formed a single population in the lake may have become isolated in different ponds.

Figure 16-9 Two types of pupfish that live in ponds in Death Valley are *Cyprinodon salinus* (top) and *Cyprinodon milleri* (bottom).

Lesson Plan

Section Focus

This section describes the ways in which isolation of populations promotes changes in populations so great that new species form. It also discusses theories of how fast new species form and the general assumption of the cause of extinction.

Section Themes

This section particularly emphasizes the theme of **Evolution**—development of new species and extinction of existing species. Populations are not static aggregations of organisms but plastic systems, always containing the potential for change.

Motivating Activity

In his book *After Man: A Zoology of the Future,* Dougal Dixon speculates about animal species that may exist in the future. Have students discuss what future anatomical and physiological changes they think might take place in existing species. Have students also speculate about possible environmental pressures that might lead to species changes they have described. *(Environmental pressures—aside from humans—might be changes in climate caused by the greenhouse effect, or geographic rearrangement of dry and moist areas due to changing global weather patterns. A more local change might be a forest fire that denudes a large area or the effects of a large volcanic eruption.)* If possible, have a copy of Dixon's book on hand for interested students to read.

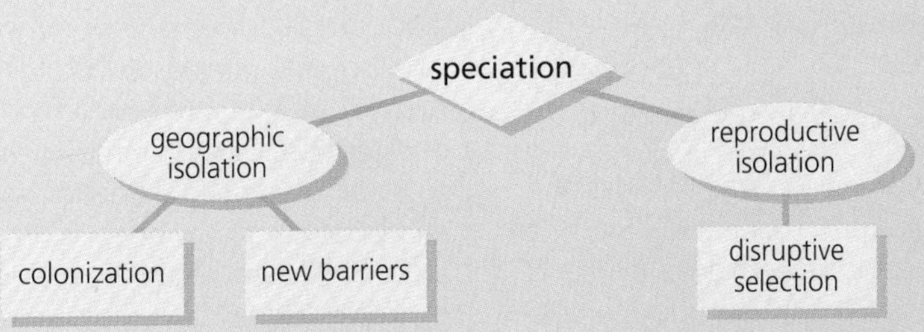

Graphic Organizer Use this organizational chart in Reteaching on p. 250.

Teaching Strategies

Differentiating Change Help students distinguish between evolution as a change in species over time, and speciation—the formation of new species. It is a matter of degree. Most evolution results from population changes brought about by disruption of genetic equilibrium. Only occasionally do such changes become great enough to cause new species to appear. Ask students to identify the key factor in the formation of new species as they read the section. *(Isolation of some members of a species).* Ask students how geographic isolation and reproductive isolation are essential to the formation of new species. *(They both prevent successful breeding between two or more populations of a species, which then evolve differently.)*
■ *See* Process Skills, *Chapter 16.*

Applying Concepts In order to build on knowledge from previous sections, use again the diagram of Japanese four o'clocks in Figure 16-3, p. 241 to teach mechanisms of speciation. Have students predict the effect on a third generation if a series of disasters kills all the plants with white and pink flowers in the second generation. *(The R′ allele would disappear and all flowers would be red.)* Ask students what they think would happen if different colors of flowers bloomed at different times. *(Reproductive isolation: separate populations, each with flowers of a single color, would evolve.)* Make up other situations and have students predict the results. For instance, if a seed from a white-flowered plant were carried to an isolated island, what would the resulting population be like? *(All white blossoms)*

The environments of the isolated ponds differed enough that natural selection and perhaps genetic drift acted on the separate populations. Eventually the fish in the different ponds may have diverged so much genetically that they could no longer interbreed even if brought together. In this way geographic isolation of fishes in Death Valley probably led to the formation of new species. Geographic isolation, plus reproductive isolation, probably is the usual cause of the formation of new species.

Reproductive Isolation

Sometimes groups of organisms within a population become isolated genetically without prior geographic isolation. When barriers to successful breeding arise among population groups in the same area, the result is reproductive isolation. **Reproductive isolation** is the inability of formerly interbreeding organisms to produce offspring.

Reproductive isolation can arise through disruptive selection. Remember that in disruptive selection the two extremes of a specific trait in a given population are selected for. The wood frog and the leopard frog, shown in Figure 16-10, have become reproductively isolated, possibly as a result of disruptive selection. Though the wood frog and the leopard frog sometimes interbreed in captivity, they do not interbreed where their ranges overlap in the wild. The wood frog usually breeds in early April, and the leopard frog usually breeds in mid-April.

This reproductive isolation may have resulted from disruptive selection. In the ancestral frog species frogs that bred earlier and frogs that bred later may have both been selected for, while frogs that bred between these times may have been selected against, perhaps because some predator was especially active during that time. The two groups of frogs may have become reproductively isolated because of differences in breeding times. Probably it was in part through such reproductive isolation that speciation occurred in these frogs. Eventually different selection pressures led to the type of morphological variations seen in Figure 16-10.

Figure 16-10 As the graph shows, peak mating activity in frog species can vary widely. Such variance has led to reproductive isolation in the wood frog, *Rana sylvatica* (top), and the leopard frog, *Rana pipiens* (bottom).

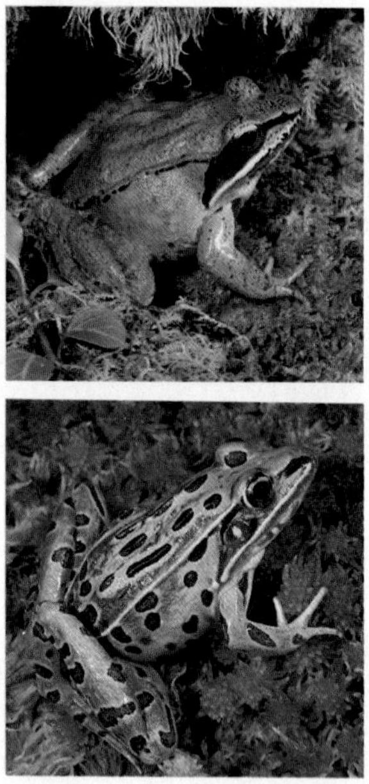

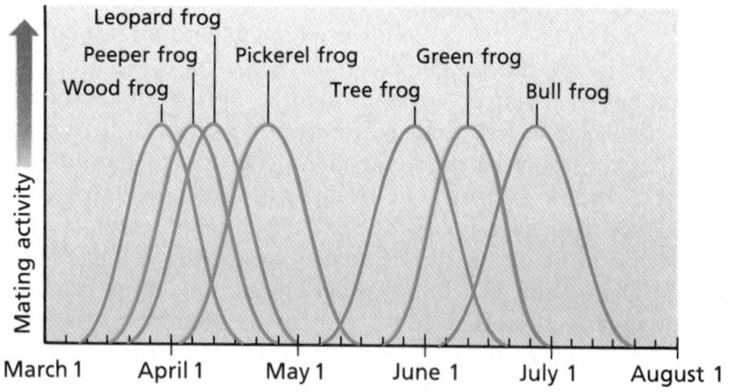

Interdisciplinary Activity

Geology Have students pursue the topic of extinction through paleontology, paleoanthropology, and history. Ask students to compile a list of extinct organisms that includes possible or known causes of extinction. Students can easily research the extinction of dinosaurs and find references to the periodic massive extinctions in geologic history. Have students seek the reason why mammoths and mastodons became extinct. *(There is good evidence that humans killed them off.)* Have students also research some modern cases of extinction. Direct them to make a table comparing extinctions due to natural causes and those caused by humans. In a classroom discussion, relate the mammoth and mastodon extinctions to the present status of the African elephant.

Rates of Speciation

How fast do new species form? Because their generation times are short, new species of unicellular organisms may evolve in years, months, or even days. For plants and animals Darwin theorized that new species formed gradually over millions of years. Yet scientists know of examples in which species arose in only thousands rather than millions of years. For example, archaeological evidence indicates that settlers from Polynesia introduced banana trees to the Hawaiian islands about a thousand years ago. Today several species of moths, unique to the Hawaiian islands, feed on bananas. These moth species are closely related to other plant-eating moths in Hawaii. Thus scientists suggest that the banana-eating moths arose from other plant-eating moths, undergoing adaptive radiation in less than the thousand years that banana trees have existed in Hawaii.

Evidence from the fossil record has led some scientists to propose that speciation need not occur gradually but can occur in spurts. According to the theory of **punctuated equilibrium,** all populations of a species may exist for a relatively long time at or close to genetic equilibrium. Then this equilibrium may be interrupted by a brief period of rapid genetic change in which speciation occurs.

Some scientists argue that if new species evolved gradually, the fossil record should show many examples of transitional forms—species with characteristics intermediate between those of ancestral species and new species. However, for most organisms such transitional forms are absent from the fossil record. Instead the fossil record shows that most species remained the same for hundreds of thousands or for millions of years. Then new, related species suddenly appeared. Whether new species form gradually or rapidly is still a point of debate among scientists. However, scientists agree that natural selection, whether gradual or rapid, is the most important factor in speciation.

Figure 16-11 Moths that feed on Hawaiian banana trees are believed to be an example of a rapidly evolving species.

Extinction

Just as new species form through natural selection, species also die off—or become **extinct.** What causes extinction? For a species to continue to exist, some members must have traits that allow them to survive and pass their genes on to the next generation. If the environment changes, for instance, the species will become extinct unless some members have adaptations that allow them to survive and reproduce successfully under the new environmental conditions. Changes in climate and competition among species are examples of environmental changes to which species must adapt in order to survive.

Environmental changes caused by human beings have led to the extinction of hundreds of organisms in the past few centuries. Most of these changes involve the destruction of habitats. For

Discussing Issues Invite a speaker who can discuss endangered species in your region to visit the class. Ask the speaker to address the impact, if any, of species protection on industry, for example the spotted owl and logging, or marine mammals and fishing. Possible speakers are a local naturalist or representative of a wildlife organization.

Guided Practice

Challenge students to think of as many examples of isolation as they can. List each reasonable suggestion on the board and have students decide if the isolating mechanism is geographic or reproductive. *(Sample answers: the top of a tall mountain; a park in the middle of a large city; a mutation in part of a population that causes a change in the reproductive system so that mutated organisms cannot breed with members of the original population)*

Independent Practice

- Have students write answers to the Section Review.
- Ask students to predict ways in which the Death Valley pupfish (Figure 16.9, p. 247) could (1) become extinct *(The springs might dry up.)*; (2) form more species *(A pond might become much larger and new food sources and/or environments develop so that the original species radiates adaptively; reproductive isolation)*; and (3) go through rapid genetic change. *(The adaptive radiation described for [2] may happen relatively fast.)*

Videodiscs

- *Side 4 29044, Kangaroo (m)*
- *Side 4 8547, Koala (m)*
- *1469–1474, Animalia; Mammalia; Marsupialia–Marsupials (s)*
- *Side 4 9794, Blue Whale (m)*
- *2026, Fossil: Brachiopoda (s)*

Check Your Understanding

1. An irrigation canal has been built through a species' territory. What kind of isolation has occurred? *(Geographic)*

2. Female birds will often respond only to one particular mating dance. A certain species of bird in captivity is genetically compatible with another captive species, but the two species have different mating dances. How are the two species isolated? *(Reproductive isolation)*

Reteaching

Have students organize a chart of key terms from this section relating to speciation. An example of a completed organizational chart appears on p. 247.

▪ *See* Section Reviews *worksheet, Section 16.3.*

Enrichment

Have students write an essay on how people can stop threatening species or causing extinction. Suggest that students research such cases as those of the spotted owl and the California condor, or the situation in the rain forests of Central America and Brazil. Make sure that students take note of instances in which people claim that protection of a species is detrimental to their livelihood. *(Owls and logging)*

Closure

Tell students that extinction is not a freak event of nature but more like the rule. Scientists estimate that 99 percent of all plant and animal species that ever existed are now extinct. Ask students to speculate about how massive extinctions, such as the one at the end of the Cretaceous period, in which roughly 95 percent of all species became extinct, might change rates of speciation. *(Sample answers: More rapid speciation because small groups migrate to new environments, or slower because usual predators extinct)*

Figure 16-12 The black-footed ferret, *Mustela nigripes* (left), may be on the way to extinction because humans have encroached on the habitat of its prey, the prairie dog, *Cynomys ludovicianus* (right).

example, the conversion of the prairies of central North America into farmland and grazing ranges caused a decline in the large population of prairie dogs in the region. In turn the black-footed ferret, which preys solely on the prairie dog, has also greatly declined in numbers. This weasellike animal may soon become extinct, because members of the species do not have variations that result in reproductive success in this changing environment.

The example of the ferret shows how species depend on others for survival. The decline in population of one species has led to the near extinction of another. Extinction is a natural process. However, the rapid rate at which species are becoming extinct as a result of the destruction of habitats by human beings may endanger the survival of many life-forms. Over the billions of years of evolution, species of organisms have evolved with unique adaptations to problems presented by a diverse and changing environment. Once a species has become extinct, the unique solution to life we call a species will be lost forever.

Section Review

1. What is the theory of *punctuated equilibrium?*
2. How can geographic isolation lead to speciation?
3. Explain how disruptive selection can lead to reproductive isolation.
4. What is the relationship between adaptation to change and extinction?
5. Do you think that the potential extinction of the black-footed ferret is mainly a natural process or is strictly the result of human intervention? Support your opinion with facts.

Answers to Section Review

1. A species may exist for a long time at or close to genetic equilibrium followed by the sudden interruption of the equilibrium by a brief period of rapid genetic change.

2. When segments of a population become physically isolated, each segment adapts to its own environment. Eventually, the segments diverge so much genetically that their members cannot interbreed.

3. Organisms that have two extreme forms of a reproductive trait may not be able to interbreed.

4. Inability of a species to adapt to changes in the environment can lead to extinction of the species.

5. Accept either answer, if it is supported by evidence or logic.

Laboratory

Factors That Influence Natural Selection

Objective
To demonstrate the effect of natural selection on genotype frequencies

Process Skills
Modeling, predicting, analyzing data

Materials
200 black and 200 white beads; 3 containers labeled *Parental, Next Generation,* and *Dead*

Background

1. What is natural selection?
2. What is the result of natural selection?

Inquiry

1. Place all the beads in the *Parental* container. Black is the dominant allele for black coat (B), and white is the recessive allele for white coat (b) in a hypothetical animal. Assume that the container holds gametes from a population of 50 BB, 100 Bb, and 50 bb.
2. Remove two beads without looking. What does this simulate? Record the genotype and phenotype of the zygote. Put the alleles into the *Next Generation* container.
3. If you repeated step 2 fifty times, would allelic and phenotypic frequencies of the zygotes be similar to parental frequencies?
4. Actually repeat step 2 fifty times. Record each genotype and phenotype produced. Calculate the frequencies of alleles and phenotypes. Compare your results with your prediction from step 3.
5. Return the beads to the *Parental* container. Again remove two beads as you did in step 2, and record the genotype and phenotype of the zygote.
6. Now assume that animals with white coat phenotype are incapable of reproducing. What is their genotype? If the zygote from step 5 had white coat phenotype, put the zygote's alleles into the *Dead* container. If the zygote had black coat phenotype, put its alleles into the *Next Generation* container. What genotypes would these animals have?
7. If animals with white coat phenotype can't reproduce, predict what would happen to gene frequency if step 5 were repeated until the parental gene pool was empty. Repeat step 5 until the pool is empty. Compare results with your prediction.
8. Transfer the beads from *Next Generation* into the *Parental* container. Repeat step 5 again until the parental pool is empty.
9. Repeat step 8 two more times, and predict whether the allelic frequencies of each generation will change.
10. Calculate the frequencies of the final genotypes produced. Compare the results with your prediction from step 9.

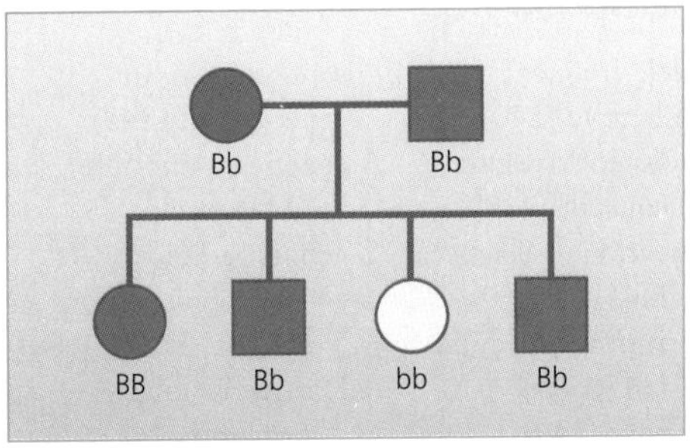

Conclusions

1. Compare the frequency of recessive alleles produced by steps 1–4 with that from steps 5–10. Did you predict the frequencies?
2. Did the frequency of the b allele change uniformly through all generations? If not, what happened?

Further Inquiry
If you continued steps 5–10, would you eventually eliminate the b allele? Form a hypothesis and test it.

Laboratory

(For an overview of natural selection and preparatory information related to the laboratory, see p. 235B.)

Background
1. Natural selection is the process by which organisms with favorable variations survive and reproduce at a higher rate.
2. Natural selection causes allele frequencies to change from one generation to the next, resulting in changes in the gene pool of a population.

Inquiry
2. The procedure simulates random mating.
3. Predictions will vary but the frequencies probably will be similar.
4. If students' results differ from their predictions, have them discuss why.
6. White coat phenotype would have the genotype bb. Black coat phenotype would have the genotypes BB or Bb.
7. Sample answer: The frequency of white coat phenotype will be greatly reduced.
9. Students should consider whether the b allele will continue to appear less and less frequently.
10. Answers depend on students' predictions.

Conclusions
1. The recessive allele decreases in frequency in steps 5 through 10. Students should recognize whether their data correlate with their predictions.
2. No; the decrease in the frequency of the b allele began to slow in later generations.

Further Inquiry
Students may test their hypotheses by continuing to form new generations in which the homozygous recessive individuals cannot reproduce. The b allele should remain in the gene pool.

Vocabulary

1. Members of separate biological species cannot interbreed or produce fertile offspring; members of separate morphological species differ in internal or external anatomy.
2. In directional selection, one extreme is at a selective advantage; in disruptive selection, either of the extreme forms of a trait are at a selective advantage; in stabilizing selection, the average form of a trait is at a selective advantage.
3. Genetic drift is a change in gene frequencies due to chance. Genetic equilibrium is a lack of change in gene frequencies from one generation to the next.
4. A species is a group of organisms whose members are *capable* of breeding with one another in nature and producing fertile offspring. A population is any *actual* interbreeding group of organisms living in a particular location at the same time.
5. Geographic isolation results when segments of a population are physically separated. Reproductive isolation results when biological barriers arise between members of the same population in the same geographic area.

Review

1. a **6.** c
2. c **7.** b
3. d **8.** c
4. b **9.** b
5. d **10.** c

11. This concept does not account for the reproductive compatibility of morphologically different organisms.
12. Stabilizing selection
13. The Hardy–Weinberg principle applies when all the following conditions are met: no mutations; no migrations; large population; individuals mate randomly; no natural selection.

Chapter 16 Review

Vocabulary

allele frequency (240)
bell curve (240)
biological species concept (238)
directional selection (245)
disruptive selection (245)
extinct (249)
gene flow (242)
gene pool (240)
genetic drift (243)
genetic equilibrium (241)
genotype (240)
geographic isolation (247)
Hardy–Weinberg principle (241)
hybrid (238)
migration (242)
morphological species concept (237)
morphology (237)
mutation (242)
phenotype (240)
population (239)
punctuated equilibrium (249)
reproductive isolation (248)
sexual selection (246)
speciation (247)
species (237)
stabilizing selection (244)

Explain the difference between the terms in each of the following sets.

1. biological species, morphological species
2. directional, disruptive, and stabilizing selection
3. genetic drift, genetic equilibrium
4. population, species
5. geographic isolation, reproductive isolation

Review

1. A morphological species is characterized by (a) similarities of appearance in its members (b) gene flow (c) the ability of members of different species to interbreed (d) the inability of members of different species to interbreed.
2. Organisms classified as separate species according to the biological species concept (a) can usually interbreed (b) cannot usually be identified on the basis of morphology (c) cannot usually interbreed (d) are formed through mutation.
3. If a population is in genetic equilibrium, (a) evolution has occurred (b) speciation has occurred (c) allele frequencies change from one generation to the next (d) allele frequencies remain the same from one generation to the next.
4. Mutations affect genetic equilibrium by (a) changing the position of a gene (b) introducing new alleles (c) causing immigration (d) causing emigration.
5. Genetic drift is any change in gene frequencies that is due to (a) migration (b) crossing-over (c) extinction (d) chance.
6. Mutation, migration, and genetic drift (a) tend to lead to the formation of new species (b) tend to lead to disruptive selection (c) do not alone cause speciation (d) cause sexual selection.
7. Directional selection, disruptive selection, and stabilizing selection are all examples of (a) genetic equilibrium (b) natural selection (c) random changes in a gene pool (d) speciation.
8. The most common way for new species to form is through (a) mutation (b) disruptive selection (c) geographic and reproductive isolation (d) genetic equilibrium.
9. According to the theory of punctuated equilibrium (a) speciation occurs gradually (b) speciation occurs rapidly (c) speciation occurs when populations are isolated (d) speciation never occurs.
10. Extinction of a species is most often due to (a) geographic isolation of the species (b) reproductive isolation of the species (c) the lack of successful variations (d) random changes in the gene pool of the species.

14. Populations of a single species became geographically isolated by the formation of the deep channel that now separates the two landmasses.
15. Migration can cause the introduction of new alleles when individuals immigrate into an area, the loss of alleles when individuals emigrate, or a shift in the proportion of alleles when individuals immigrate or emigrate.
16. It causes the most significant changes in allele frequencies in a population.
17. Sexual selection is considered a type of natural selection.
18. During the Ice Age, all fishes in Death Valley lived in one huge lake. The lake evaporated at the end of the Ice Age, leaving geographically isolated ponds. The fishes diverged genetically by becoming adapted to their respective

11. What are the limitations of the morphological concept of species?
12. What type of selection is shown when the bell curve narrows over time?
13. Under what conditions does the Hardy–Weinberg principle apply?
14. How might geographic isolation have led to the evolution of the two *Cerion* species classified by Gould?
15. How can migration alter allele frequencies for certain traits?
16. Why is natural selection considered the most important factor in evolution?
17. What is the relationship between natural selection and sexual selection?
18. How do scientists hypothesize that geographic isolation led to the formation of new species of fishes in California's Death Valley?
19. Describe how the wood frog and the leopard frog are reproductively isolated. How might this isolation have arisen as a result of disruptive selection?
20. What factors have contributed to the potential extinction of the black-footed ferret?

Critical Thinking

1. Give three examples showing that evolution is still occurring today. Refer to magazines such as *National Geographic* and *National Wildlife*.
2. The biological concept of species states that a species is a group of organisms that can interbreed and produce fertile offspring in nature. A mule is the sterile offspring of a horse and a donkey. By the definition above do a horse and a donkey belong to the same species?
3. In the late 1800s hunting reduced the population of a species of giant elephant seals to about 20 individuals. How might such a reduction in population have disrupted genetic equilibrium?
4. Look at the maps on the right showing the earth as it was 550 million years ago and as it is today. Notice the difference in the placement of the continents. How could this change have affected the evolution of organisms in these areas?

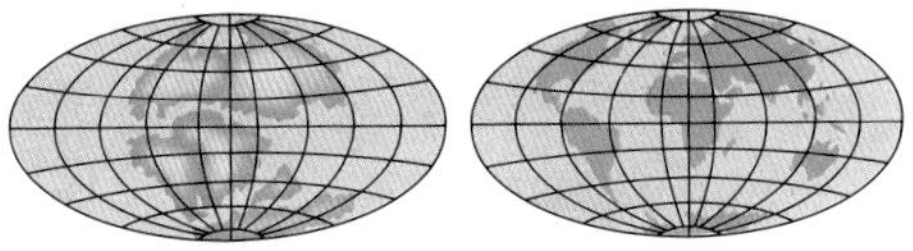

5. A species of flightless bird called the dodo once inhabited Mauritius Island in the Indian Ocean. The animals thrived until humans came and killed them all. How did the dodo's inability to fly affect its extinction?

Extension

1. Read the article by Julie Ann Miller entitled "Interactions Drive Species Diversity" in *BioScience,* November 1990, p. 715. How do the interactions between plant producers and insect consumers promote species diversification in both?
2. Visit an area where plants or animals are bred. Possible places include farms, zoos, plant arboretums, seed companies, and nurseries. Find out how the breeders manipulate the genetic makeup of the plants or animals, and prepare an oral report on how this manipulation speeds up or slows down evolution. If you cannot visit one of the suggested locations, look in the *Readers' Guide to Periodical Literature* for articles on plant and animal breeding.
3. Do research and make a list of five or more examples of sexual selection in animals.

Critical Thinking

1. Accept any answers that students can support with facts.
2. Since the horse and donkey cannot produce fertile offspring, they would not belong to the same species.
3. It might have led to genetic drift and possibly to *nonrandom* mating and natural selection.
4. In the map on the left, some continents are connected. Organisms could have crossed back and forth between continents. In the map on the right, all continents have separated, leading to geographic isolation of former interbreeding populations. This would result in increased speciation.
5. The birds could not fly away and escape, so they were easy prey for human hunters.

Extension

1. Answers will vary but should include the idea that adaptations developed by plants that protect themselves against herbivores promote the plants' own diversification. Herbivores are then forced to diversify to overcome the plant's defenses.
2. Selective breeding generally speeds up the process of change within a species, sometimes leading to speciation.
3. Examples of sexual selection can be found in college-level texts and reference books.

ponds and were no longer able to interbreed, thus forming new species.
19. The wood frog and leopard frog breed at different times and thus are reproductively isolated. In the ancestral frog species, both frogs that bred earlier than average and frogs that bred later than average may have been selected for, while frogs that bred in between these times may have been selected against.
20. The conversion of prairie into farmland and grazing land and hence the decline in population of the prairie dog is one factor in the potential extinction of the black-footed ferret. The ferret's inability to adapt to these changes—for example, by finding another food source—is another factor in its potential extinction.

Chapter 17 Human Evolution

Chapter Overview

Chapter 17 concludes the evolutionary story with the origin and evolution of humans. Section 17.1 introduces primate relatives of humans and distinguishing characteristics of humans and their closest relatives, apes. Section 17.2 outlines the fossil record of human evolution.

Chapter Planning Chart

B	S	A	Sections and Subsections	Page	Features	Page	Resources
•	•	•	**17.1 The Study of Human Origins**				
			Classification of Humans	255	Think	256	Videodiscs
			Primate Characteristics	255	Section Review	257	Laboratories: Human Evolution
							Blackline Master 35
							Process Skills: Human Evolution
							Section Reviews Worksheet
•	•	•	**17.2 Hominid Evolution**				
			Australopithecus	258	Biology in Process	260	Videodiscs
			Homo habilis	259	Laboratory	263	Blackline Master 36
			Homo erectus	260	Section Review	262	Overhead Transparency T17
			Homo sapiens	261			Section Reviews Worksheet
			Theories of Hominid Evolution	262			
			End of Chapter Activities				
					Chapter Review	264	Vocabulary Skills
							Chapter Test
							Computer Test Generator

B *The Basic Level curriculum presents the most fundamental knowledge offered in the course.*
S *The Standard Level curriculum is designed for the average student who is able to master most topics.*
A *The Advanced Level curriculum includes suggestions for teaching the most academically able students.*

Cooperative Learning

Group Activity: Primate Characteristics

- **Group Size:** *4 students*
- **Outcome:** *Students will compare the characteristics of various primates.*
- **Individual Accountability:** *Each group member will research two kinds of primate.*
- **Positive Interdependence:** *The group will cooperatively prepare an outline of primate characteristics.*

Have each group member research two kinds of primate: tree shrew, lemur, tarsier, monkey, gibbon, orangutan, gorilla, and chimpanzee. Tell students to make sure that someone in each group is investigating each type of primate. First, have each student make an outline of the primate's traits and habitat. Then have members of each group compare outlines and discuss what are the major similarities and differences among primates. Finally, have each group prepare a table summarizing common primate traits and listing the major differences. Tell students to note the faces of the various primates and describe the transition in facial characteristics from the tree shrew to humans.

Concept Map

The following is one possible solution to the concept mapping activity in Reteaching on p. 262.

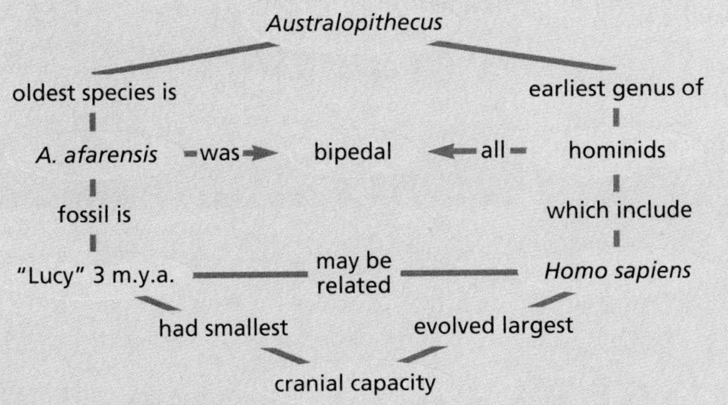

Laboratory Preparation

Overview *(See p. 263.)*

In this lab students gain an understanding of the assumptions derived from the use of comparisons of amino acid sequences as a measure of evolutionary relationships. Students should understand that proteins are three-dimensional and depend on shape to interact properly. They will then comprehend the assumption that some amino acids in the sequence are less important for function than others. If different amino acids make the same contribution to shape, or if a slight change in shape does not interfere with function, different amino acids will appear at the location as a result of random genetic change, that is, mutation and recombination.

Preparation

No outside preparation is required for this lab.

Teaching Tips

Divide the class into four-person teams. Have each team member inspect two strips (organisms) for Inquiry step 3.

Students may be intimidated by the array of colors and symbols in the figure. First, ask them what the colored bands represent. *(Groups of consecutive amino acids)* Then ask them whether it is important to be able to name the amino acids represented by the letters. *(No, it is only necessary to know if they are the same or not.)* Finally, explain to students that the essential task in step 3 is to compare the vertical column of symbols of each nonhuman to the human strand, one by one.

Remind students that although it is easier to compare the amino acid sequences of adjacent organisms than compare each one with the human sequence, they must compare each animal to human cytochrome c.

Chapter Themes

Evolution Remind students that the genetic principles that apply to other animals apply just as well to humans. Remind them also that the story of human evolution outlined in this chapter is a series of inferences based on incomplete fossils. Therefore, each new fossil find has the potential to make a significant contribution to our understanding of human evolution.

Tell students that human evolution seems to have occurred through radiation, a common pattern in which groups of related species evolve from a common ancestor.

Scale and Structure As in previous chapters, living species are defined partly on the basis of structures, but fossil species are defined entirely on the basis of structures. Thus the morphological concept of species is a foundation for interpreting fossil finds.

Chapter Motivating Activity

Display photos of gorillas and humans. Have students state characteristics that humans share with gorillas and those that distinguish gorillas and humans. Tell students to imagine that they have never seen either organism before. Ask students if they think that humans descended from gorillas or vice versa. *(Can't decide on the basis of photos alone)*

Mention that some people in Darwin's time thought incorrectly that he claimed that humans evolved from apes such as the gorilla. Ask students whether it is possible to infer an evolutionary relationship between two species on the basis of structures alone. *(No, in comparing species, other evidence such as fossils or genetic comparisons is necessary.)*

Chapter 17 Human Evolution

Introduction

Twelve years after *The Origin of Species* was published, Charles Darwin wrote another book, on the subject of human evolution. In this book, *The Descent of Man*, Darwin cited evidence that humans are most closely related to the group of animals that includes monkeys and apes. Darwin's work was a landmark in the scientific study of human origins. In this chapter you will read about some of the latest theories of human origins and evolution.

Chapter Outline

Chapter Concept

As you read, look for the many scientific processes involved in studying human evolution.

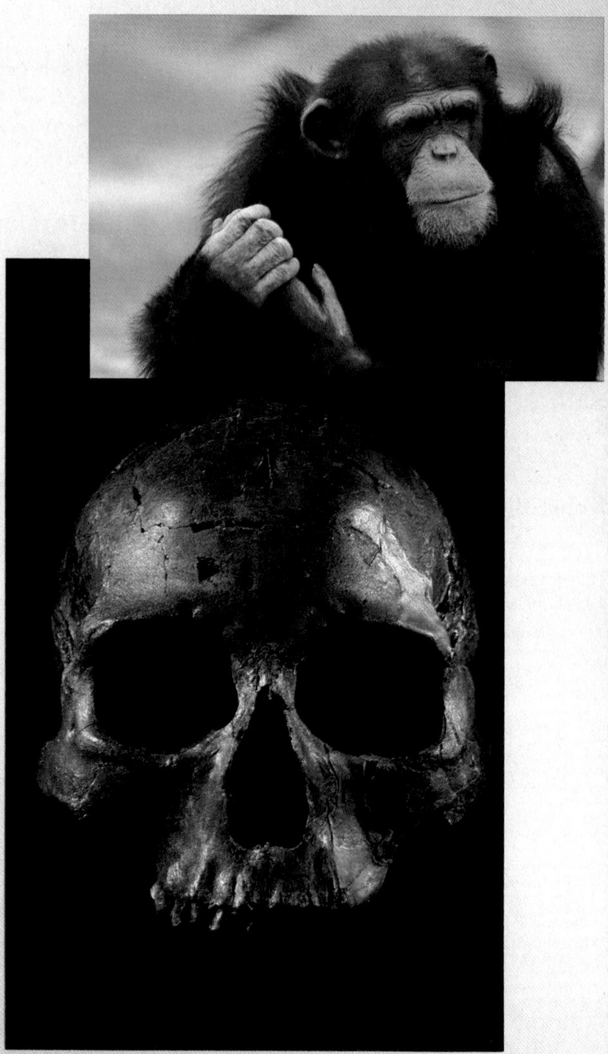

***Homo sapiens* skull, 300,000 years old. Inset: Face of a chimpanzee, *Pan troglodytes*.**

Understanding the Visuals

Ask students to list features of the 300,000-year-old skull that are different from the chimp's features. *(Bulbous brain case, the smooth forehead, and relatively flat, or short, face)* Ask students to identify the distinctly apelike features of the chimpanzee head. *(Sloping forehead, ridged brow, flat nose, jutting chin)*

Ask what expression they detect on the chimp's face. *(Intelligence, puzzlement)* Point out the humanlike position and appearance of the hands. State that chimps are the closest ape relatives to humans; in fact their DNA is over 98 percent identical to human DNA! Recommend the reading of Jane Goodall's *Through a Window.*

17.1 The Study of Human Origins

Scientists who study human evolution are called **paleoanthropologists** *(PAY-lee-oe-AN-thruh-PAHL-uh-jists)*. Paleoanthropologists unearth fossils and observe them carefully. Because most fossil skeletons are far from complete, these scientists must make inferences from subtle clues. For example, a curved piece of skull bone allows them to infer the size of the brain; wear on a fossil tooth may give some indication of diet; markings on fossil limb bones often show where muscles were attached and what mode of locomotion was used.

Based on their observations and inferences, paleoanthropologists construct models that shed light on the morphology and habits of early humans and their ancestors. They use these models to formulate theories about human evolution. Because human fossils are few and fragmentary, each new fossil find is a potential source of significant information. Thus paleoanthropology is a rapidly changing field that is characterized by exciting new theories and vigorous debates.

Classification of Humans

Before paleoanthropologists can decide how to classify fossils, they must understand how humans are related to other animals. Evidence from fossils, comparative morphology, and biochemistry indicates that humans belong to the order of mammals called primates. **Primates** include tree shrews, lemurs, tarsiers, monkeys, and apes, as well as humans.

Primate Characteristics

Fossil evidence and evidence from comparative morphology indicate that the majority of extinct primate species lived in trees. Most modern primate species are also tree dwelling, or arboreal. Scientists infer from this that many of the characteristics that primates share may have evolved as adaptations to arboreal life. For example, most primates have highly movable fingers and toes, which have flattened nails rather than claws. These characteristics allow arboreal primates to grasp branches and cling to tree trunks securely.

Good vision is another adaptive trait of tree dwellers. Cones, color-sensitive cells in the eyes, give primates color vision. This allows primates to locate ripe fruit in trees. Front-facing eyes and a reduced snout enable primates to integrate images from both eyes simultaneously and thus perceive depth accurately. Therefore arboreal primates can gauge distances as they leap or swing from branch to branch.

Section Objectives

- *Describe how scientists gather evidence of human ancestry.*
- *List some traits shared by all primates.*
- *Name two distinguishing characteristics of anthropoids.*
- *Give examples of traits unique to humans.*

Figure 17-1 The movable fingers and toes, front-facing eyes, and small snout of the tarsier, *Tarsius syrichta*, are adaptations for living in trees.

Lesson Plan

Section Focus

This section lists characteristics of the Order Primates, characteristics of the anthropoids within the primates, and finally, characteristics of humans within the anthropoids.

Section Themes

This section emphasizes the theme of **Scale and Structure** as it examines characteristics of the primates and subgroups of primates. Morphology provides evidence of evolutionary relationships among species and evidence of the environment that helped determine evolutionary trends in primates.

Motivating Activity

To help students realize advantages of an opposable thumb, have them restrict the use of their thumbs. Provide masking tape to secure their thumbs against their forefingers. Provide various objects for them to try to hold. Have them think of how they would perform everyday activities, for instance, eating an apple. Have them try to write something and fold a piece of paper. How about getting dressed in the morning? Could they button their shirts?

Teaching Strategies

Organizing Concepts As students read this section, have them keep lists of traits that humans share with other primates as well as comparative lists of traits that are uniquely human.
■ *See* **Laboratories, *Investigation 17.***

Videodiscs

■ ***2590–2593, Classification/ Evolutionary Relationships (s)***

primate ancestors lived in trees

→ primates developed:
- movable toes and fingers
- good vision
- erect carriage

→ anthropoids developed:
- opposable thumb
- larger cranial capacity
- more erect carriage

→ humans developed:
- bipedalism
- largest cranial capacity
- complex language

Graphic Organizer Use this sequential diagram to summarize key concepts in Section 17.1.

Interpreting the Visuals Direct students' attention to Figure 17-3, p. 257, which is a comparison of a human and chimpanzee. In addition to differences labeled in the illustration, have students compare the proportions of arms and legs of the human and chimp. Have students note differences in the pelvis. Help them understand that if they found some fossil bones, they could tell what animal the bones came from.

- *See* Blackline Master *35.*

Guided Practice

Describe a series of traits to the class and have students classify each one as characteristic of all primates, only anthropoids, only apes, only humans, or none of them. Include traits discussed in the section, such as opposable thumbs, color vision, bipedalism, and also a few that have nothing to do with primates, such as hooves, claws, or venom.

- *See* Process Skills, *Chapter 17.*

Independent Practice

- Have students write answers to the Section Review.
- Have students list common traits of humans and chimpanzees, and other characteristics in which they differ. *(Common traits include opposable thumbs, capability of sitting, standing, and walking, and large cranial capacity relative to body size. Differences include foot structure, language use, tool use, jaw shape.)*

Answer to Think

Humans make tools deliberately, using foresight and planning. Chimpanzee behavior does not indicate a plan to use tools. This is a rudimentary form of tool use.

Figure 17-2 The gibbon, *Hylobates* sp. (top), and the gorilla, *Gorilla gorilla* (bottom), are anthropoids.

Think

Chimpanzees sometimes strip blades of grass to use for pulling termites out of their nests. How does this compare with the way humans make and use tools?

The ability to hold the body in a vertical position is another adaptation for life in the trees. As primates evolved, the sense of smell became less acute. Therefore primates probably became more dependent on their eyesight. Being able to hold themselves erect while feeding probably allowed them to easily spot and flee from approaching predators.

Characteristics of Anthropoids

Monkeys, apes, and humans form a subgroup of primates called the **anthropoids** *(AN-thruh-POIDZ)*. The well-developed collarbone, rotating shoulder joints, and partially rotating elbow joints give anthropoids skeletal strength and flexibility. The **opposable thumb**—a thumb that can be positioned opposite the other fingers—gives anthropoids precision grip. Most anthropoids also have an opposable big toe, which gives them increased grasping ability.

Compared with other primates, anthropoids have a large brain for their body size. The fossil record shows that as primates evolved, brain size increased. Scientists estimate brain size by measuring the brain case of fossil skulls. The size of the brain case is called **cranial capacity.** A large cranial capacity relative to body size is a distinguishing characteristic of anthropoids. Large cranial capacity is not necessarily a sign of intelligence, although in some primate lineages a larger brain may correspond to greater mental abilities.

In comparison with other primates, humans and apes—including gibbons, orangutans, gorillas, and chimpanzees—have a large cranial capacity relative to body size. Humans and apes have also become increasingly capable of sitting, standing, or walking erectly. The lower vertebrae that form the tail in monkeys are reduced in apes and humans, leaving them without a tail.

Characteristics of Humans

Bipedalism—upright walking on two legs—is a uniquely human trait. Other primates occasionally walk on two legs, but usually they swing from branches or walk on all fours. Differences in the pelvic bones of apes and humans, shown in Figure 17-3, correlate with differences in modes of locomotion. The broad shape and muscular attachments of the human pelvis are adaptations for bipedalism. The pelvis supports the internal organs during upright walking. Another adaptation for bipedalism is the shape of the human foot. The bones of the big toe are aligned with those of the other toes. This causes body weight to be distributed evenly during upright walking.

Figure 17-3 shows that the human jaw and teeth differ from those of apes. These differences reflect differences in diet. The ape's U-shaped jaw has wide spaces between the teeth that allow it to pull branches through the teeth and strip off the leaves. The human jaw is rounder than the ape jaw. The teeth are smaller and less specialized, an adaptation to the varied diet of humans.

Interdisciplinary Activity

Anthropology Because paleoanthropology relies heavily on inferences, scientists may bring biases to their work of which they are not even aware. Have students read either of two books by Welsh scientist Elaine Morgan: *Descent of Woman* or *The Aquatic Ape.* These books examine the issue of gender bias in the study of human evolution and provide fascinating alternative theories. Direct students to take notes on Morgan's criticisms of traditional theories. Finally, lead a class discussion on the topic of bias in the study of anthropology. Have students suggest different types of bias. *(Cultural, gender, class, race, anthropomorphic)*

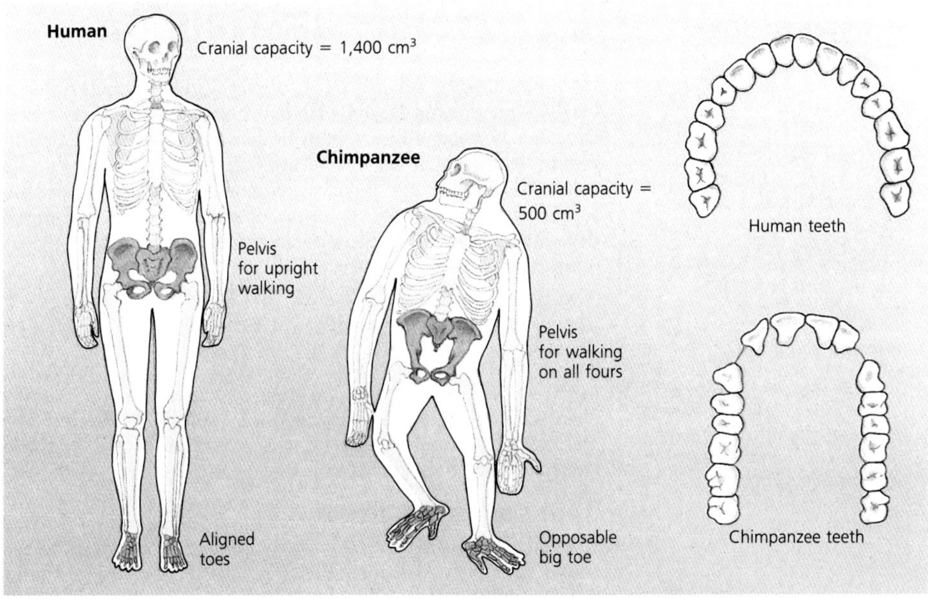

Figure 17-3 **Human physical characteristics, compared with those of the chimpanzee, include a larger cranial capacity, a broader pelvis, and a big toe aligned with the other toes. The human jaw is rounder and the teeth are less specialized. Can you find other comparisons suggested by the drawings?**

Humans have an average cranial capacity of 1,400 cm^3. The human cranial capacity is larger than that of any other primate. The high forehead of humans is indicative of the large size of the frontal part of the brain. This part of the brain is important for a unique human trait—the ability to communicate through verbal language. Apes communicate through sounds and gestures; they can also be taught to use certain forms of sign language. However, apes living in the wild have not developed any complex, flexible set of signals that can compare to those that make up the languages of humans.

Section Review

1. What do paleoanthropologists study, and how do they gather their information?
2. Name several characteristics of primates, and explain how these characteristics are adaptations to life in the trees.
3. What features distinguish anthropoids from the other primates?
4. What are three specifically human traits?
5. Evidence from fossil pollen found with human remains indicates that primates ancestral to humans probably inhabited the edges of the forests, where trees were scattered rather than close together. How might this type of environment have influenced the evolution of bipedalism?

Check Your Understanding

1. How would you know that a resting gibbon was an arboreal primate? (Hint: study Figure 17-2.) *(Forward-facing eyes, arms with great range of movement, relatively long arms)*
2. How would you know that a fossil skull with nose and mouth region missing came from a modern human instead of a gorilla? (Hint: study Figure 17-2.) *(Lack of eyebrow ridges; higher, more rounded forehead)*

Reteaching

Show students teeth, skulls, and other bones from a variety of animals (obtained from biological supply companies or veterinarians.) Ask which teeth belonged to carnivores *(Sharp teeth for piercing and tearing)*, to herbivores (*Flat teeth for grinding*), and to omnivores *(Generally less-specialized teeth)*. Ask them to infer the size and age of the animals. *(Answers should describe the size of teeth and amount of wear.)* Make students aware of how much information can be inferred from such evidence.
■ *See* Section Reviews *worksheet, Section 17.1.*

Enrichment

Show students a video about anthropoid apes from the National Geographic Society, for example, "Search for Mankind." Ask them to turn in an outline.

Closure

Ask students how primate characteristics can be advantageous for living both in trees and on the ground. *(Sample answer: depth perception aids both jumping from limb to limb and killing prey with tools.)*

Videodiscs

■ ***2497–2510, Human Skeleton (s)***
■ ***Side 4 30484, Gorilla Walking (m)***

Answers to Section Review

1. They collect and observe fossils, compare them with living primates, and make inferences about human evolution.
2. Movable digits with flat nails allow them to grasp tree trunks and branches. Good vision allows them to find fruit in trees and swing through them. Being able to adopt erect posture helps them spot predators.
3. Features include a well-developed collarbone, rotating shoulder joints, partially rotating elbow joints, opposable thumb, and relatively large cranial capacity.
4. Bipedalism, a round jaw with relatively unspecialized teeth, and language.
5. Since trees were farther apart, primates couldn't always swing from one tree to another.

Lesson Plan

Section Focus

This section describes ancient humans, their inferred ancestors, and relatives of the ancestors. The section ends with two theories that attempt to explain relationships among fossil species.

Section Themes

This section continues the emphasis on **Scale and Structure** by comparing hominid fossils and adds the theme of **Evolution** with treatment of the hypothetical patterns of human evolution. Sometimes, the current hypotheses are rejected or revised when new fossil structures are discovered.

Motivating Activity

Help students realize that paleoanthropologists must infer an entire body structure and lifestyle from a few bits of bone and tool remains. Have students imagine that during a volcanic blast, a modern apartment building collapsed and was buried under tons of volcanic ash along with its contents and some inhabitants. Then have them imagine that the building is not uncovered for two million years. Finally, have them describe the kinds of fossils and artifacts that might be found, what their condition would be, and what they would tell about people and their life-styles today. *(Human and pet skeletons would be preserved in some cases. Glass, ceramics, plastics, and stainless steel would be unchanged, while other iron and steel would corrode; wood might have rotted but have left natural molds in the ash; paper might be partly preserved, as in modern dumps; cotton cloth would decompose; bones, shells, and possibly seeds from food would be preserved.)*

Section Objectives

- *List three evolutionary trends characteristic of the hominid line.*
- *Contrast the age and physical features of the remains of different australopithecine species.*
- *Compare* Homo habilis, H. erectus, *and* H. sapiens.
- *Outline two theories of hominid evolution.*
- *Explain how the discovery of the black skull has caused paleoanthropologists to reevaluate their theories of hominid evolution.*

17.2 Hominid Evolution

Hominids are a subgroup of primates that includes human beings—the species *Homo sapiens*—and their immediate ancestors. Paleoanthropologists study hominid evolution by examining fossils, from which they have inferred the evolutionary trends toward bipedalism and increased cranial capacity. They have also found evidence of the evolution of culture—behavior that is dependent on learning and on passing knowledge from one generation to the next. Note the evidence of these trends as you read.

Australopithecus

The earliest genus of hominids is called *Australopithecus (aw-STRAY-loe-PITH-uh-kuss),* meaning "southern ape." The first australopithecine fossils were dubbed "southern" because they were found in South Africa. However, remains of *Australopithecus* have since been found in eastern Africa as well.

Australopithecus afarensis

The oldest australopithecine skeleton unearthed to date was found in eastern Africa in 1974. This fossil is between 3 million and 3.5 million years old. The shape of the pelvic bone indicates that the remains are those of a female. Scientists have nicknamed her Lucy. They classify Lucy and morphologically similar skeletons as *Australopithecus afarensis*. This species existed between 3 million and 4 million years ago.

A. afarensis was shorter than modern humans, less than 1.5 m tall. Fossil footprints and the shapes and sizes of pelvic and leg bones indicate that the species was bipedal. From the fossil skulls scientists infer that *A. afarensis*'s cranial capacity was between 380 and 450 cm^3, less than one-third that of modern humans.

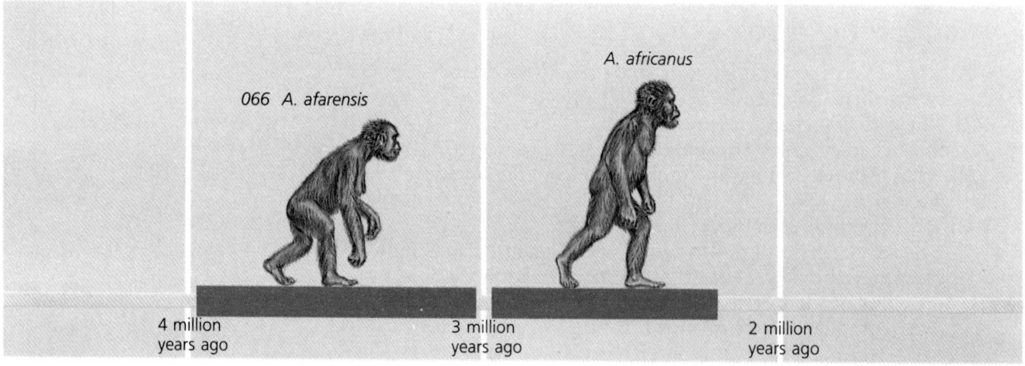

Figure 17-4 Various hominids have existed over the past 4 million years. Today only *Homo sapiens sapiens* remains. Keep in mind that males and females evolved simultaneously.

Hominid Name	*A. afarensis*	*A. africanus*	*A. robustus* and *A. boisei*	*H. habilis*
lived when?	3–3.5 m.y.a.	2.2–3 m.y.a.	1–2 m.y.a.	1.6–2 m.y.a.
height	<1.5 m	>1.5 m	>1.5 m	>1.5 m
cranial capacity	380–450 cm^3	450–550 cm^3	450–600 cm^3	600–800 cm^3
tool use?	no tools	no tools	no tools	tools

Graphic Organizer Use this table in Independent Practice on p. 261.

Australopithecus africanus

The next oldest species of australopithecines, *Australopithecus africanus,* lived 2.2 million to 3 million years ago. The first fossils of this species were found in 1924 in South Africa. *A. africanus* was slightly taller and heavier than *A. afarensis.* Its cranial capacity was slightly larger, between 430 and 550 cm^3.

Australopithecus robustus and *Australopithecus boisei*

Two other australopithecine species probably arose after *A. africanus. A. robustus* fossils have been found in southern Africa; *A. boisei* fossils have been found in eastern Africa. Most of their remains are between 1 million and 2 million years old. Both species had heavier skulls and larger back teeth than *A. africanus.* Their cranial capacity was between 450 and 600 cm^3.

Homo habilis

In the early 1960s paleoanthropologists working in East Africa found a hominid skull with a relatively large brain case. This fossil was the first evidence of such an early hominid species having a cranial capacity as great as 600 to 800 cm^3. These remains were found along with stone tools that were presumably made and used by the hominids. This finding led to the naming of a new species, *Homo habilis,* meaning "handy human." Remains of *H. habilis* were later found in southern as well as eastern Africa. These fossils are between 1.6 million and 2 million years old.

Some studies of the insides of *H. habilis* skulls indicate that one region of the brain essential to speech was developed in this species. Tool marks on animal bones found near the hominid fossils indicate that *H. habilis* ate meat. Yet some fossils indicate that *H. habilis* was no taller than earlier australopithecines.

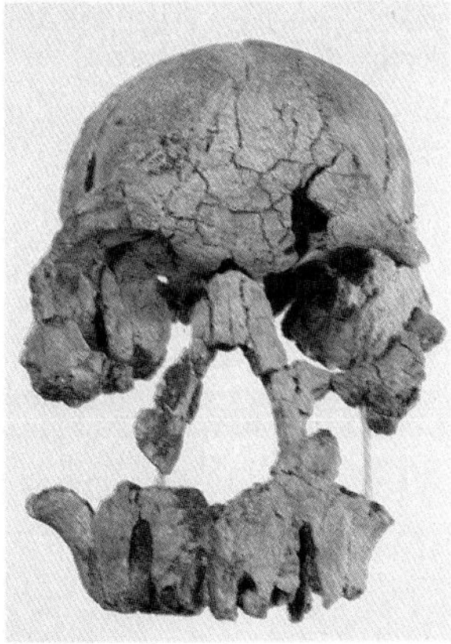

Figure 17-5 The skull of *Australopithecus africanus* (top) is more apelike than that of *Homo habilis* (bottom).

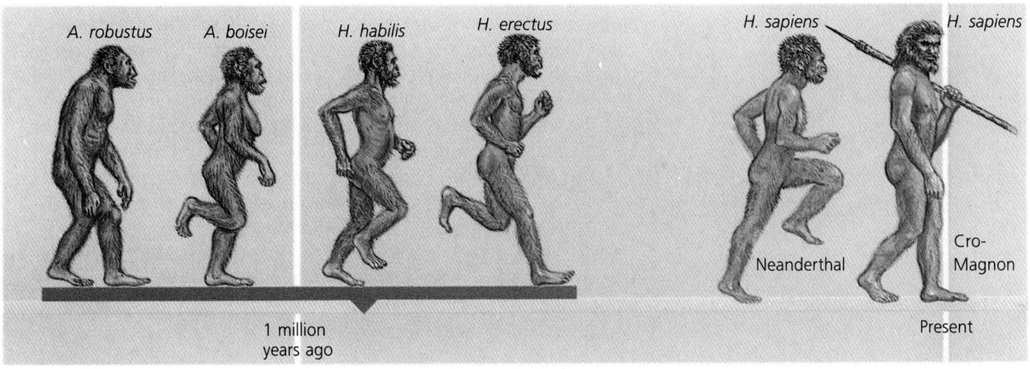

Teaching Strategies

Understanding Terms Some explanation of the system for naming groups of organisms is useful here. As students will read in the next chapter, a group of related genera is classified as a family. Family names end in *-idae.* Therefore, a hominid is a member of the family Hominidae, comprising the genus *Homo* and the genus *Australopithecus.* The family is further divided into subfamilies, whose names end in *-inae.* The genus *Homo* is in the Subfamily Homininae. *Australopithecus* is in the Subfamily Australopithecinae, and members of this subfamily are australopithecines.

Interpreting Data Review with students how radioactive elements are used to estimate the age of fossils (Section 15.1, p. 220). Ask students whether carbon-14 is likely to be used often by paleoanthropologists. *(No, because it can't be used to date objects much older than 50,000 years.)*

Exploring Word Roots Students often find it easier to retain new scientific terminology if they learn the original meaning of roots of terms. Ask students to use a dictionary to find the meaning and original language of the following roots: *paleo- (It means "ancient," Greek); anthropo- (It refers to human beings, Greek);* and *-ology (It means: "the study of," Greek).*

Exploring Careers Invite a paleontologist or paleoanthropologist from a local college or university to visit your class. Encourage the speaker to bring slides or fossils to show students and give a brief lecture about his or her current research. Ask students to prepare questions for the guest scientist.

Cooperative Learning

Interpreting Hominid Fossils Divide the class into seven groups. Assign each group one of the hominid species discussed in this section (combine *A. robustus* and *A. boisei*). Have each group prepare a presentation on the assigned hominid. Have each group member choose a task as follows: (1) sketch a map of where the remains were found, (2) write about who found the remains and when, (3) write a description of the remains, and (4) highlight the status of the hominid in one or more current phylogenies. Refer students to the *General Science Index* for the latest articles on these hominids. Each group can cooperatively prepare the report and vote on the representative who will present the report to the class.

Interpreting the Visuals Using Figure 17-7, p. 262, have students compare the alternative theories of hominid evolution. First, ask students to describe the most basic difference between the two "family trees." *(One shows* A. afarensis *giving rise to three lineages; the other shows* A. afarensis *giving rise to two lineages.)* Next, ask students what could cause scientists to disagree about something so fundamental. *(The fragmentary nature of the hominid fossil record leaves a great deal of room for interpretation by scientists.)* Then ask students to look also at the diagram in Biology in Process, p. 261. Ask students to point out an important difference between Johanson's diagram and the two diagrams shown in Figure 17-7. *(Johanson's diagram shows* A. boisei *on a different branch from* A. africanus *and* A. robustus.*)* Finally, ask students where Cro-Magnon and Neanderthal should be placed on both diagrams in Figure 17-7. *(Since they are both considered* H. sapiens, *they should be placed within this species at the top of each diagram.)*

■ *See* Overhead Transparency *T17 and* Blackline Master *36.*

Guided Practice

Write the following hominid names on the board: Neanderthal, *A. boisei, H. erectus, A. afarensis, H. habilis,* Cro-Magnon, *A. robustus,* and *A. africanus.* Without using their textbooks, have the students write down the order in which these hominids appear in the fossil record. *(*A. afarensis, A. africanus, A. robustus, A. boisei, H. habilis, H. erectus, *Neanderthal, Cro-Magnon; accept reasonable variations as long as they are supported by the text.)*

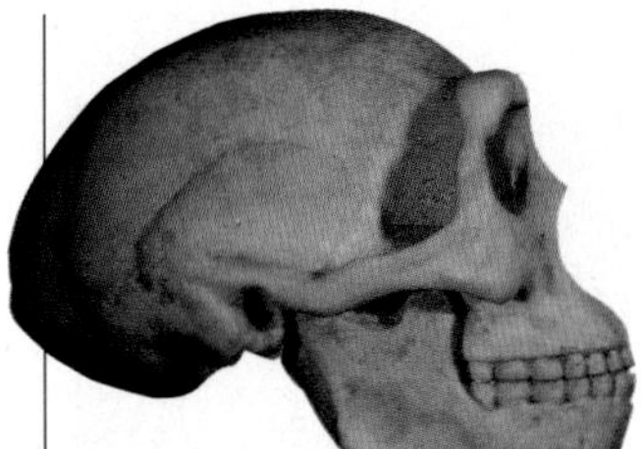

Figure 17-6 This reconstruction of *Homo erectus* indicates a thick skull, a prominent brow, a low forehead, and a small chin.

Homo erectus

In 1891 paleoanthropologists working on the Pacific island of Java discovered remains of a skull and thigh bone that were older and more distinctly human than any fossils found previously. They named this species *Homo erectus,* "upright human." *H. erectus* fossil remains have since been found in many other parts of the world. They range between 0.5 million and 1.6 million years old.

Compared with modern humans, *H. erectus* had a thick skull, large brow ridges, a low forehead, and a very small chin. Cranial capacity ranged between 700 and 1,250 cm^3. An almost complete *H. erectus* skeleton was found in East Africa in 1984. These remains are of a 12-year-old male who stood about 1.7 m tall. This indicates that an adult *H. erectus* might easily have been as tall as a modern human.

Although *H. erectus* ate mainly plant foods, members of this species were also successful hunters. They used stone tools, such as the hand ax, possibly for removing thick animal hides. Traces of charred bones indicate that *H. erectus* built fires for cooking and probably also for warmth.

Biology in Process

The Black Skull

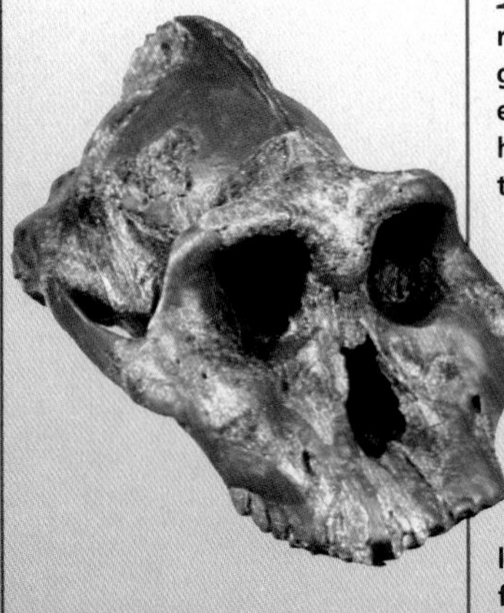

A fossilized skull found in Kenya's West Turkana region in 1985 has created a great deal of controversy as scientists attempt to place it in the hominid family tree. Paleoanthropologists Richard Leakey and Alan Walker named their find the Black Skull for its unusual color (p. 260). Now in the Kenya National Museum, the skull is identified by its museum catalog number as KNM-WT 17000.

The hominid who was the Black Skull lived about 2.6 million years ago and had a small, flat-bottomed brain case; large teeth; and a bony ridge running down the back of the head.

Leakey and Walker asserted that the remains belonged to a member of the robust hominid species *Australopithecus boisei,* which lived about 2 million years ago.

Other paleoanthropologists disagreed. Among them was Donald Johanson, who had discovered Lucy, the most complete australopithecine skeleton found so far. Johanson and his colleagues compared 32 characteristics of the Black Skull with *A. boisei* and its contemporary *A. robustus,* and with *A. afarensis,* who lived about 3.5 million years ago. They found in the Black Skull "a baffling mixture of very primitive and very ad-

LEP Activity

For students who are not proficient in English, this section might prove confusing with its emphasis on unfamiliar names. Have students construct a time line of hominid evolution based on the information in the section, supplemented by reference books or articles in your classroom or the school library. Encourage individual students to work on one section of the time line, for example, the section from *H. erectus* to the present, including Neanderthal and Cro-Magnon. They may use Figure 17-4, pp. 258–259, as a model, but urge them to take a different approach if they wish. When individual sections of the time line have been completed, students can collaborate to piece the sections together.

As part of this exercise encourage students to make sketches or trace figures from the

Homo sapiens

Two skulls between 250,000 and 350,000 years old were found in Germany and Great Britain in the 1930s. These skulls are evidence of hominids transitional between *H. erectus* and *H. sapiens.* They have both the large brow ridges of *H. erectus* and the very large cranial capacity of *H. sapiens.*

Neanderthals

Hominid fossil skeletons from 35,000 to 130,000 years ago have been found in Europe, Asia, and Africa. They belong to a group called Neanderthals *(nee-AN-dur-THAWLZ).* Neanderthals were early *H. sapiens.* According to the fossil evidence, Neanderthals had heavy bones, thick brow ridges, and a small chin. However, skull sizes indicate that Neanderthals had a cranial capacity averaging 1,450 cm^3. This is slightly larger than the cranial capacity of modern humans. Fossils of leg and trunk bones indicate that the Neanderthals were about 1.5 m, or 5 ft, tall and stocky. Neanderthals were adapted to the cold climate of northern Europe. They lived in caves and stone shelters. They carefully shaped stone tools for scraping hides to make clothing.

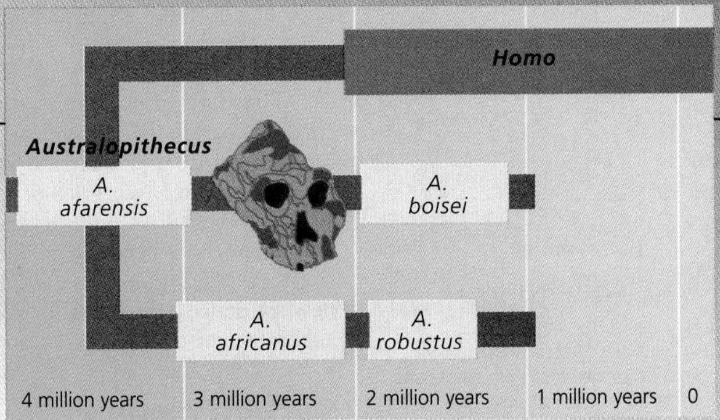

vanced traits," as Johanson noted, only two of which are shared exclusively with *A. boisei.*

Where does the Black Skull fit into the hominid family tree? Is it a missing link between the species *A. africanus* and the more robust hominids, *A. boisei* and *A. robustus*? Does the Black Skull suggest that *A. africanus* was an evolutionary dead end? Or is it, as Leakey and Walker have maintained, an example of *A. boisei,* with unusual features?

Johanson and his colleagues devised four alternative family trees. They placed the Black Skull as a distinct species that was the descendant of *A. afarensis* and was either the ancestor of *A. robustus* or of *A. boisei,* or both. The version shown here (p. 261) is the most popular among scientists. It is certain that the Black Skull is not directly related to *Homo sapiens,* but the discovery has led scientists to reevaluate their thinking about our ancestry.

Johanson writes in *Lucy's Child,* "The very traits that we have assumed to be uniquely human may have evolved in quite separate lineages, giving rise to ancient cousins much more like our own ancestors than we have always believed."

■ How did inferring the relationships between the Black Skull and other australopithecines help Johanson revise the hominid family tree?

text to illustrate their time lines. Suggest that they create images that capture for themselves the meaning of terms such as *H. habilis* ("handy human") and *H. erectus* ("upright human"). They can use a dictionary to look up meanings of additional terms. *(Images could include stick figures, cartoons, or realistic renderings, as long as they convey a distinct impression of the species.)*

Independent Practice

■ Have students write answers to the Section Review.

■ Have students make a table showing each species of *Australopithecus* and *Homo,* how long ago it lived, its cranial capacity, its height, and whether or not it used tools. An example of a completed table is shown on p. 258.

Biology in Process

Using the Feature

The feature focuses on the process skills of organizing data, classifying, and inferring. Point out that all the possible hominid family trees developed by Johanson and his colleagues begin with *A. afarensis.* The Black Skull could be the ancestor of *A. robustus* and *A. africanus,* and the bridge between *A. afarensis* and the genus *Homo,* or *A. africanus* could lead to both *A. robustus* and *Homo,* with the Black Skull leading to *A. boisei. A. africanus* may be an evolutionary dead end, and the Black Skull may lead to both *A. robustus* and *A. boisei.* In the version shown in the feature, the Black Skull is an ancestor of *A. boisei,* and *A. africanus* leads only to *A. robustus.* Ask students how these four family trees differ from those shown on p. 262. *(Although neither family tree on p. 262 shows the position the Black Skull may have occupied, the bottom view essentially agrees with the third of Johanson's family trees.)*

Answer to the Feature

Johanson saw that the Black Skull had both less advanced and more advanced characteristics, suggesting that it might represent a bridge species.

Videodiscs

■ ***2664, Human Brain (s)***

Check Your Understanding

1. Which was the first hominid species to leave fossils indicating the trait of speech? *(H. habilis)*
2. What are indications that Neanderthals were probably as intelligent as modern humans? *(Brain size and ability to live in a cold climate)*

Reteaching

Have students draw a concept map showing theoretical relationships between *H. sapiens* and some of their ancestors. Tell students to base their maps on the content in Section 17.2, which begins with a discussion of *Australopithecus*. Students should not include all hominid species discussed in the text but rather should try to include trends in hominid evolution such as bipedalism, cranial capacity, or language. An example of a completed concept map is shown on p. 253B.

■ *See* **Section Reviews** *work-sheet, Section 17.2.*

Enrichment

Have students research the Piltdown hoax and report it to the class. Have them lead a discussion of why the "Piltdown Man" does not fit onto the present human family diagram.

Closure

Have students look at Figure 17-4, pp. 258–259, and compare the illustration of *A. afarensis* with *H. habilis* and *H. erectus*. Remains of tools and bones indicate that the latter two were successful hunters. Ask students how *H. habilis* and *H. erectus* were better adapted for hunting than was *A. afarensis*. *(They were larger, stronger, had more upright posture, and better-developed brains.)*

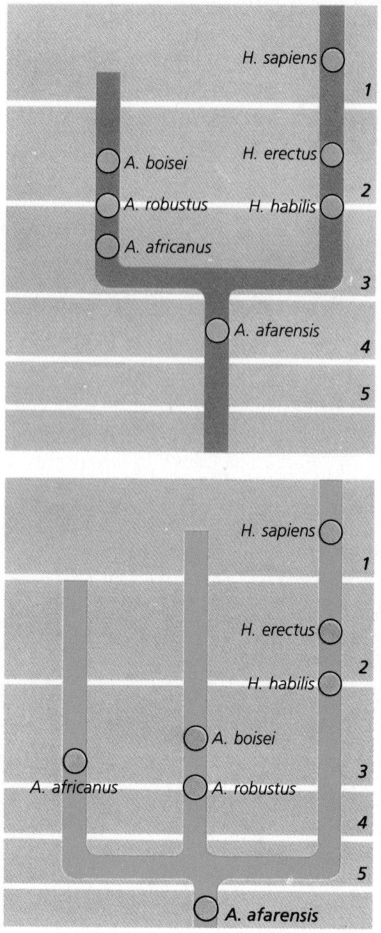

Figure 17-7 Paleoanthropologists offer at least two different views of human evolution.

Cro-Magnons

Hominid fossil skulls from about 35,000 years ago were first found in caves in southwestern France in 1868. Since then the fossil remains of these people, referred to as Cro-Magnons, have been found elsewhere in Europe as well as in Africa, Asia, and even Australia. Cro-Magnons had a cranial capacity of about 1,400 cm^3. They are distinguished from Neanderthals by their high forehead, prominent chin, and lack of brow ridges. Taller than Neanderthals, they stood about 1.8 m, or almost 6 feet, tall. Cro-Magnons were *H. sapiens* and are regarded by scientists as modern humans.

Cro-Magnons had a sophisticated culture. They made many types of tools, including a wide variety of blades, harpoons, scrapers, and even drills, fishhooks, and needles. They decorated the walls of caves with colorful paintings of the animals they hunted.

Theories of Hominid Evolution

Paleoanthropologists differ in their interpretations of how humans evolved. This is because scientific theories are based on the best available evidence and hominid fossil evidence is fragmentary. Compare the two diagrams of hominid evolution in Figure 17-7. The top diagram suggests that *A. afarensis* gave rise to two lines of hominids about 3 million years ago. One line led to the later australopithecines. The other led to hominids who were directly ancestral to modern humans.

The bottom diagram shows an alternate interpretation. According to this theory skeletal remains classified as *A. afarensis* are placed into a preaustralopithecine genus. This theory suggests that *Homo* and two lines of *Australopithecus* diverged between 4.5 million and 6.0 million years ago.

The debate between paleoanthropologists illustrates that this science is an ongoing process. Precise observation and analysis of new evidence and reevaluation of theories will present a more accurate and detailed picture of human evolution.

Section Review

1. Name seven hominid species.
2. How did the australopithecines differ from one another in terms of changes in their physical features over time?
3. Compare *Homo habilis, H. erectus,* and *H. sapiens* with regard to evolutionary trends.
4. Compare two theories of hominid evolution.
5. According to fossil evidence Neanderthals died out about 35,000 years ago. Some scientists hypothesize that the Neanderthals were killed off by the Cro-Magnons. Others hypothesize that the two groups interbred. What evidence would you look for to evaluate these theories?

Answers to Section Review

1. *A. afarensis, A. africanus, A. robustus, A. boisei, H. habilis, H. erectus,* and *H. sapiens*
2. Basically, over time they became increasingly larger in size and cranial capacity increased. Accept answers that include more detail.
3. From *H. habilis* to *H. sapiens,* brain size became larger, height probably increased, and culture became more sophisticated.
4. One theory says that the *Homo* line diverged from the australopithecines 3 million years ago. The other theory says that a split took place from 4.5 to 6 million years ago and gave rise to a third branch.
5. Accept any answer students can justify.

Laboratory

Amino Acid Sequences and Evolutionary Relationships

Objective
To infer evolutionary relationships among species by comparing the amino acid sequences of the same protein in different organisms

Process Skills
Classifying, inferring

Materials
Pencil, paper

Inquiry

1 The greater the time organisms have been diverging from a common ancestor, the greater the difference that can be expected in their amino acid sequences. This statement is based on the assumption that the rate of change of a specific amino acid sequence is the same in different organisms. Think of other methods used to determine evolutionary relationships. How is this biochemical method different?

2 Cytochrome c, a protein found in the mitochondria of many organisms, consists of a chain of about 100 amino acids. The figure shows the corresponding parts of the cytochrome c amino acid sequence of nine vertebrates. The numbers along the side of the figure refer to the position of these sequences in the chain. The letters identify the specific amino acids in the chain.

3 Make a table to record your data. Head columns *Species* and *Number of Differences.* For each vertebrate count the amino acids in the sequence that differ from the human sequence, and list them in your table.

4 List the eight vertebrate sequences in descending order according to their degree of evolutionary closeness to humans. Which organism of all the vertebrates listed is most closely related to humans?

	Horse	Chicken	Tuna	Frog	Human	Shark	Turtle	Monkey	Rabbit
42	Q	Q	Q	Q	Q	Q	Q	Q	Q
43	A	A	A	A	A	A	A	A	A
44	P	E	E	A	P	Q	E	P	Y
46	F	F	Y	F	Y	F	F	Y	P
47	T	S	S	S	S	S	S	S	S
49	T	T	T	T	T	T	T	T	T
50	D	D	D	D	A	D	E	A	D
53	K	K	K	K	K	K	K	K	K
54	N	N	S	N	N	S	N	N	N
55	K	K	K	K	K	K	K	K	K
56	G	G	G	G	G	G	G	G	G
57	I	I	I	I	I	I	I	I	I
58	T	T	U	T	I	T	T	I	T
60	K	G	N	G	G	Q	G	G	G
61	E	E	N	E	E	Q	E	E	E
62	E	D	D	D	D	E	E	D	D
63	T	T	T	T	T	T	T	T	T
64	L	L	L	L	L	L	L	L	L
65	M	M	M	M	M	R	M	M	M
66	E	E	E	E	E	I	E	E	E
100	K	D	S	S	K	K	D	K	K
101	A	A	A	A	A	T	A	A	A
102	T	T	T	G	T	A	T	A	T
103	N	S	S	S	N	A	S	N	N
104	E	K	—	K	E	S	K	E	E

Conclusions

1 Examine the list you prepared in step 4. The values listed for the chicken and the horse differ by only one. Can you infer from this that the chicken and the horse are closely related to each other? Why or why not?

2 Why can it be said that proteins behave like molecular clocks?

Further Inquiry
Other proteins, such as hemoglobin, can be used to establish degrees of evolutionary relatedness among organisms. Would you expect to find the same number of differences in the cytochrome c and hemoglobin amino acid chains when comparing organisms? Why or why not?

Laboratory

(For an overview of amino acid sequences and evolutionary relationships, and preparatory information related to the laboratory, *see p. 235B.)*

Inquiry

1. This biochemical method is different in that it does not depend on fossils and archeological finds.

4. The monkey is the most closely related to humans. (Since reptiles are more advanced than amphibians, the turtle might be ahead of the frog on the list, even though both have eight differences from the human.)

Species	Number of Differences
monkey	1
rabbit	4
horse	6
chicken	7
turtle	8
frog	8
tuna	9
shark	14

Conclusions

1. No. The chart focuses only on comparisons with humans, and it shows only 25 of about 100 amino acids in cytochrome c.

2. Proteins can be said to behave like a clock because they change gradually over time. The number of differences among them might be considered a measure of time.

Further Inquiry

No. Students should understand that differences that occur in amino acid sequences of hemoglobin over time are not necessarily related to differences that occur in cytochrome c over time.

Vocabulary

1. *Bi-* means "two"; *-ped* means "feet"; *-ism* means "the condition of." *Bipedalism* means "the condition of having two feet," which implies walking on two rather than four feet.
2. *Hom-* means "man"; *anthropo-* means "resembling a human being."
3. The thumb can be positioned opposite the four fingers for grasping.
4. *Cranial* refers to *cranium,* which originally came from a Greek root meaning "head." The cranium is made up of bones that surround the brain. Cranial capacity suggests the amount of space that the cranium encloses, which is the limiting factor for the size of the brain.
5. *Paleo-* means "ancient"; *anthropo-* refers to human beings; and *-logy* means "the study of." An anthropologist may or may not study fossil bones, which are the main subject of study for *paleo*anthropologists.

Review

1. d	**6.** c
2. b	**7.** d
3. b	**8.** d
4. a	**9.** a
5. c	**10.** b

11. Anthropoid traits include a well-developed collarbone, rotating elbow and shoulder joints, opposable thumbs and/or big toes, and large cranial capacity.
12. Upright walking allows movement on plains and the locating of predators and prey.
13. Bipedalism and the development of language
14. When viewed from above, a human jaw is rounder than the jaw of an ape. Humans lack spaces between their teeth; human teeth are smaller and less specialized than those of apes.
15. The size of the brain case of a fossil skull indicates cranial capacity.

Chapter 17 Review

Vocabulary

anthropoid (256)
bipedalism (256)
cranial capacity (256)
hominid (258)
opposable thumb (256)
paleoanthropologist (255)
primate (255)

1. Using a dictionary, find the meanings of the word parts that make up the word *bipedalism.* Why is "bipedalism" a good name for the mode of locomotion it describes?
2. What is the meaning of the root *hom-* in *hominid?* What is the meaning of the root *anthropo-* in *anthropoid?*
3. Why is the primate thumb described as *opposable?*
4. Using a dictionary, look up the meaning of *cranial.* Why is "cranial capacity" an accurate way to describe the size of the brain case?
5. Use a dictionary to find the meaning of the word parts that make up *paleoanthropology.* How might the work of a paleoanthropologist differ from that of an anthropologist?

Review

1. Paleoanthropologists reconstruct the bodies of human ancestors on the basis of (a) fingerprint patterns (b) comparisons of living species (c) written descriptions in ancient sources (d) fossil fragments.
2. The earliest primates probably lived in (a) the grasslands (b) the forests (c) the deserts (d) the mountains.
3. Humans are well adapted to upright walking because they have (a) good color vision (b) a broad pelvis (c) a big toe that is opposable to the other toes (d) the ability to use language.
4. One difference between *A. africanus* and the two species *A. robustus* and *A. boisei* is that (a) *A. africanus* had a less massive skull (b) *A. africanus* had a more massive skull (c) *A. africanus* had bigger teeth (d) *A. africanus* made tools.
5. *H. habilis* was so named because evidence indicates this species (a) was bipedal (b) used language (c) made tools (d) ate meat.
6. One feature that distinguishes *H. erectus* from *H. sapiens* is that *H. erectus* (a) had a large chin (b) had thinner bones (c) had a low forehead (d) used fire.
7. Hominid fossils that range in age between 250,000 and 350,000 years of age show some features of *H. erectus* and some features of (a) *A. boisei* (b) *H. habilis* (c) Cro-Magnons (d) *H. sapiens.*
8. Cro-Magnons are regarded as (a) a transitional species between *H. erectus* and *H. sapiens* (b) a transitional species between australopithecines and ancestral humans (c) ancestors to Neanderthals (d) identical to modern humans.
9. Among the hominids, fossil evidence indicates that there was an evolutionary trend toward bipedalism, increased cranial capacity, and (a) the development of culture (b) the development of vegetarianism (c) the development of robustness (d) the development of brow ridges.
10. Because of the black skull's combination of features, some scientists infer it is ancestral to (a) *H. habilis* (b) *A. boisei* (c) *A. afarensis* (d) *A. africanus.*
11. What are some traits of anthropoids?
12. How is upright walking an adaptive trait for humans?
13. What are two behavioral traits that are unique to humans?
14. How do the jaw and teeth of humans differ from those of apes?

16. Most hominid fossil remains have been found on the continent of Africa.
17. Evidence indicates that Neanderthals lived in caves and stone shelters; remains of stone tools for scraping hides for clothing have been found.
18. Scientists have found sophisticated Cro-Magnon tools, including harpoons, scrapers, drills, fishhooks, and needles. Cro-Magnons also decorated walls of caves with paintings of animals they hunted.
19. Accept answers that include information in Figure 17-7.
20. The unusual features of the Black Skull meant that either *A. boisei* skulls varied widely, or a new species had been discovered, so new family trees were needed.

15. How do scientists use fossil evidence to draw conclusions about the cranial capacity of hominids?
16. On which continent have most fossil remains of hominids been found?
17. What evidence do paleoanthropologists have that Neanderthals were well adapted to the cold climate of northern Europe?
18. Why do scientists hypothesize that Cro-Magnons had a sophisticated culture?
19. Diagram two theories of hominid evolution.
20. How did the discovery of the black skull show that previous theories of hominid evolution must have been in error?

Critical Thinking

1. The photo at the right shows the size and arrangement of the teeth of a baboon. What can you infer about the baboon's diet from observing the size and spacing of its teeth?
2. In comparison with humans, apes do not have a well-developed voice box or facial muscles. How might the ape's anatomy affect its ability to use spoken language?
3. According to the fossil evidence *H. habilis* made stone tools deliberately. They traveled long distances to collect specific types of rocks and minerals; then they shaped the rocks by chipping them at the edges. What does this reveal about *H. habilis*'s ability to use foresight? Why might this ability be significant?

4. Cro-Magnon remains have been found with reindeer bones in certain areas of southern Europe. What does this fact suggest about the diet of Cro-Magnons and the environment in which they lived?

Extension

1. Read the article by James Shreeve entitled "Madam, I'm Adam" in *Discover,* June 1991, p. 24. Explain how studies of the male Y chromosome led French geneticists to a molecular "Adam." What aspects of this research invite criticism from other scientists?
2. Visit a local zoo to observe the behavior of monkeys, apes, or other primates. Pay close attention to the facial expressions of the animals. Notice the ways in which the animals interact. Take notes on what you observe. What similarities and differences do you see between the behavior of the primates you observed and that of humans? If it is not possible to visit a zoo, study pictures of primates in books or magazine articles about primates. What inferences can you make about primate behavior from the pictures?
3. Some of the fossils you have read about in this chapter were discovered by Richard Leakey. Leakey comes from a family of famous anthropologists. Both his father, Louis Leakey, and his mother, Mary Leakey, have made important contributions to the study of human evolution. Use an encyclopedia or other reference to find biographical information about the Leakeys. Write a report about the Leakeys and about the discoveries that members of this family have made.

Critical Thinking

1. Accept any inference that students can back up with specific observations. For example, spacing of the baboon's teeth suggests that they clean leaves from branches as apes do. Pointed canine teeth suggest the piercing of prey.
2. Apes would not easily be able to use spoken language because the voice box is not well developed. Lack of development in the facial muscles prevents apes from using spoken language because they cannot move the lips and tongue with precision, as is necessary to produce sounds in spoken language.
3. Accept logical answers. For example, use of foresight in tool making is a sign of increased intelligence and learned behavior, which accompanies cultural development. Cultural development gave hominids more flexible behavior, enhancing their ability to adapt to environmental changes.
4. Remains suggest that people hunted reindeer and that the climate of Europe was colder than it is today.

Extension

1. Students should note that Lucotte based his study on the fact that most of the Y chromosome is passed intact from father to son. Lucotte's critics say that his analysis of the Y chromosomes was not detailed enough.
2. Warn students to avoid anthropomorphism; while an animal's behavior might be similar to a human's, its motivation might be different.
3. Point out that Richard Leakey's role in the field of paleoanthropology has at times been the subject of controversy among his colleagues. Ask students to find out why.

Chapter 18 Classification

Chapter Overview

Chapter 18 outlines the methods by which biologists classify living organisms and infer their evolutionary relationships. Section 18.1 describes the structure of the classification system. Section 18.2 examines types of evidence used in classifying organisms and how the evidence is used. Section 18.3 lists the primary distinguishing characteristics of the five kingdoms.

Chapter Planning Chart

B	S	A	Sections and Subsections	Page	Features	Page	Resources
•	•	•	**18.1 History of Taxonomy**				
			Binomial Nomenclature	267	Section Review	268	Videodiscs
			Levels of Classification	268			Process Skills: Classifying Fingerprints
							Laboratories: Dichotomous Keys
							Blackline Master 37
							Section Reviews Worksheet
•	•	•	**18.2 Modern Taxonomy**				
			Evidence Used in Classification	269	Think	271	Videodiscs
			Inferring Phylogeny	270	Laboratory	275	Section Reviews Worksheet
			Biosystematics	271	Section Review	271	
•	•	•	**18.3 Five-Kingdom System**				
			Monera	272	Biology in Process	272	Videodiscs
			Protista	273	Section Review	274	Blackline Master 38
			Fungi	274			Overhead Transparency T18
			Plantae	274			Section Reviews Worksheet
			Animalia	274			
			End of Chapter Activities				
					Chapter Review	276	Vocabulary Skills
							Chapter Test
							Computer Test Generator

B *The Basic Level curriculum presents the most fundamental knowledge offered in the course.*
S *The Standard Level curriculum is designed for the average student who is able to master most topics.*
A *The Advanced Level curriculum includes suggestions for teaching the most academically able students.*

Cooperative Learning

Group Activity: Classifying Organisms

- **Group Size:** *5 students*
- **Outcome:** *Students will produce a classification system for 10 organisms.*
- **Individual Accountability:** *Each student will contribute ideas to the group classification system.*
- **Positive Interdependence:** *The group will discuss the ideas and agree on a system.*

Ask students to practice their skills of observing and classifying. Display ten specimens or photographs of living and fossil organisms—at least one example from each of the five kingdoms. Have each group of students develop its own classification system for the displayed specimens. Tell students to discuss among themselves on what characteristics of the organisms they will base decisions about classification. One person in each group should be designated to summarize the group's conclusions in writing. Encourage students to classify the specimens in whatever ways they consider to be most appropriate, such as by shape, color, or complexity.

Finally, have each group compare their system with accepted taxonomy. Conclude by asking the class as a whole whether the systems they created would be acceptable to most biologists. *(Probably not; the students' systems are unlikely to provide the precision and universality required by biologists.)* Lead students to the conclusion that an acceptable system must classify every organism, and no two different organisms can be called by the same name.

Concept Map

The following is one possible solution to the concept mapping activity in Independent Practice on p. 270.

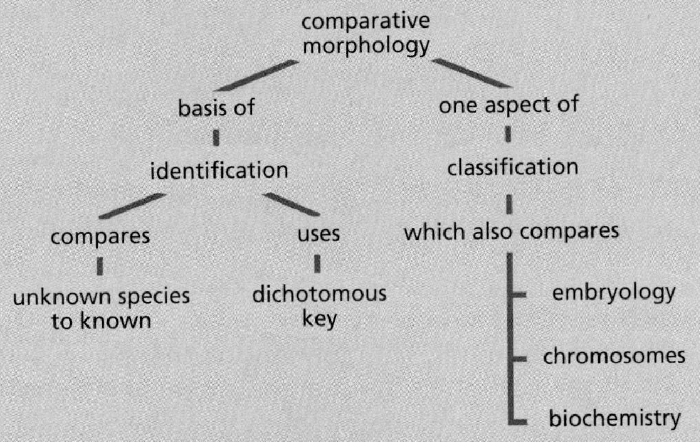

Laboratory Preparation

Overview *(See p. 275.)*

In this lab students learn organized ways to approach the complexity and diversity of the natural world and to retrieve information efficiently through step-by-step progression. Students observe traits of animals and make independent choices to identify the animals. The dichotomous key illustrates levels of classification schemes. Students realize that the key, while useful, does not necessarily reflect phylogeny.

Preparation

All of the organisms are available from biological supply houses and may be obtained living or preserved. Possible specimens include: sea star (Class Asteroidea), sea urchin (Class Echinoidea), sea cucumber (Class Holothuroidea), tapeworm (Class Cestoidea), roundworm (Phylum Nematoda), leech (Class Hirudinea), *Nereis* (Class Polychaeta), *Lumbricus* (Class Oligochaeta), *Limulus* (Subphylum Chelicerata), grasshopper (Subphylum Uniramia), and crayfish (Subphylum Crustacea).

Teaching Tips

Make sure that students understand the meaning of all terms used in the lab—for example, *radial* and *bilateral symmetry*.

Remind students to stop once they have identified the name of a specimen.

Point out that the key makes use solely of characteristics of external anatomy.

Safety

If live specimens are used, remind students to handle them in a humane manner.

Chapter Themes

Evolution The classification system described in this chapter is used by biologists as a tool for inferring evolutionary relationships between species. Point out to students that, in a general way, the classification system reflects the trends of evolution.

Scale and Structure Comparing structures, whether microscopic, macroscopic, or embryological, is fundamental to classification of organisms. Help students appreciate, however, that similar appearance does not always imply a close relationship.

Patterns of Change Now that students are familiar with the concept of evolution, help them see that past random changes have resulted in trends that have led to the groups of the classification scheme.

Chapter Motivating Activity

Start a brainstorming session by asking students to devise a classification system for the objects in the classroom. What would be the major categories? *(They might be furniture, books, lab equipment, and illustrations on the wall.)* Ask what the subdivisions would be in each category.

Urge students to think of other ways to classify the same objects. Ask them which system is best and elicit reasons for their choices. Point out that biologists have been confronted with the task of devising a system that allows them to classify all the diverse forms of life on earth. Ask students what basic criteria such a system must meet, and what is the necessity for it. *(Universality, inclusiveness, fine levels of distinction. A system is needed so that biologists can communicate without confusion about organisms.)*

■ *See* **Process Skills,** ***Chapter 18.***

Chapter 18 *Classification*

Introduction

Scientists discover and name thousands of new species every year. The science of identifying, classifying, and naming organisms is called taxonomy. In their work taxonomists may also make inferences about the evolutionary relationships among species. In this chapter you will learn about the modern taxonomic system by which all living things are classified.

Chapter Outline

18.1 History of Taxonomy
- *Binomial Nomenclature*
- *Levels of Classification*

18.2 Modern Taxonomy
- *Evidence Used in Classification*
- *Inferring Phylogeny*
- *Biosystematics*

18.3 Five-Kingdom System
- *Monera*
- *Protista*
- *Fungi*
- *Plantae*
- *Animalia*

Chapter Concept

As you read, consider how scientists try to develop workable classification systems to organize their knowledge.

Bioluminescent ctenophore.
Inset: Oak, *Quercus* sp., leaves.

Understanding the Visuals

The opener photographs illustrate the problems taxonomists have in classifying organisms. Have students list the obvious biological differences between the ctenophore and the leaves. Tell students that the ctenophore is a marine organism, also called a comb jelly, that floats and swims mostly near shores and consumes large amounts of plankton. Point out that to a scientist the names comb jelly and oak tree are not acceptable classifications since neither specifies one particular species. Tell students that an acceptable classification system distinguishes between closely related species of oak trees. Point out that the oak leaves in the photograph look similar, but actually belong to two species. Ask students to identify the difference. *(The two leftmost leaves have four sets of lobes; the one on the right has fewer.)*

18.1 History of Taxonomy

Taxonomy *(tacks-AHN-uh-mee)* is the science of grouping organisms according to their presumed natural relationships. Organisms were first classified more than 2,000 years ago by the Greek philosopher Aristotle, who classified living things as either plants or animals. He divided animals into land, water, and air dwellers. He divided plants into three subcategories on the basis of stem differences. Aristotle's system was favored by scientists until the eighteenth century. Then, in a period of expanding scientific exploration in which many new organisms were found, biologists began to recognize that Aristotle's categories did not accommodate all the variations among living things. Driven by their need to communicate about these organisms, biologists devised a number of classification systems, most of which proved to be somewhat unworkable.

These early scientists used either common names or long scientific descriptions, both of which caused confusion. **Common names,** such as *robin* and *fir tree,* are the everyday names given to organisms. Common names may not describe organisms accurately. For example, a jellyfish is not a fish. Sometimes the same common name is used for different species. For instance, a maple tree might actually be a sugar maple, a silver maple, or a red maple. Also, some organisms have more than one common name. In the United States the tree shown in Figure 18-1 is called a buttonwood tree, a plane tree, or a sycamore, depending on the region. To avoid this kind of confusion, some early scientists used long Latin descriptions to name organisms.

Binomial Nomenclature

Understandably, scientists tried to devise simpler naming systems. The system used today, called binomial nomenclature, is based on the work of the Swedish naturalist Carolus Linnaeus.

Linnaeus (1707–1778) developed a system of grouping organisms into hierarchical categories. He placed structurally similar organisms into a group he called a species, similar species into a larger group called a **genus,** and similar genera into a **family.** Similar families were placed in an **order;** similar orders, in a **class;** and similar classes, in a **phylum.** Finally, Linnaeus placed phyla into either the plant or animal **kingdom.**

Rather than list all seven categories in naming an organism, Linnaeus chose to use only the species name—that is, the genus name and the epithet denoting the species. For example, Linnaeus classified human beings into the genus *Homo.* The epithet that denotes the human species is *sapiens.* Therefore humans belong to the species *Homo sapiens.* Linnaeus's system is called **binomial nomenclature** *(bie-NOE-mee-ul NOE-mun-CLAY-chur).* Binomial means "two names."

Section Objectives

- *Summarize the importance of taxonomy for biologists.*
- *Describe the system of binomial nomenclature.*
- *List the categories of the classification system used today.*

Figure 18-1 Although called by different names in different parts of the country, this tree is known as *Platanus occidentalis* to scientists throughout the world.

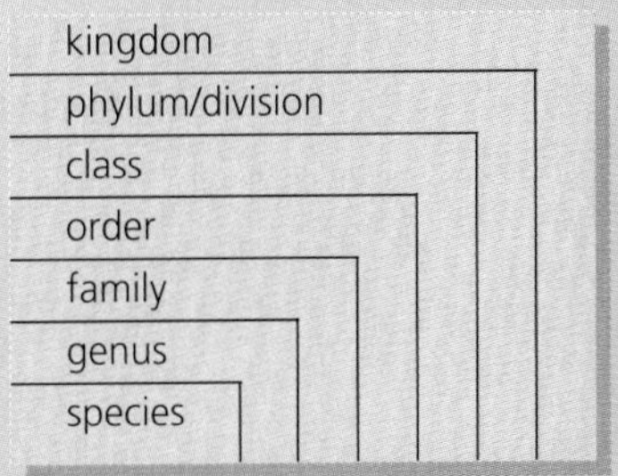

Graphic Organizer Use this diagram to summarize the key concepts in Section 18.1.

Lesson Plan

Section Focus
This section describes early taxonomy and the system that Linnaeus devised.

Section Themes
The primary theme of this section is **Patterns of Change.** The Linnaean system of naming large categories and subdividing them into smaller and smaller subcategories reflects in part what has occurred as evolution has diversified life on earth.

Motivating Activity
Have students work in small groups to devise their own classification schemes for identifying different leaves. Use lobed leaves and leaves with an entire margin; use leaves with parallel, pinnate, and palmate vein patterns. With the entire class, have each group discuss the rationale for the system they devised.

Teaching Strategies
Classifying Species Tell students that dogs, *Canis familiaris*; cats, *Felis domesticus;* wolves, *Canis lupus;* and foxes, *Vulpes vulpes,* belong in Order Carnivora. Ask students to identify which of the the other animals is most closely related to the dog and to state the basis for their answer. *(The wolf,* Canis lupus, *because it has the same genus name)*

Guided Practice
Give the class the complete hierarchy of classification for the domestic cat: Animalia, Chordata, Mammalia, Carnivora, Felidae, *Felis, domesticus.* Then, using an encyclopedia or other reference, ask them to find the complete hierarchy for another common animal.

Videodiscs
- *785–790, Jellyfish (s)*
- *1229–1234, Starfish (s)*

Independent Practice

- Have students write answers to the Section Review.
- Give students the following list of organisms: hamster, chimpanzee, goldfish, mushroom, housefly. Have students list the organisms according to how closely related they are to humans, starting with the most distant relation, and then explain their answer. *(Mushroom, housefly, goldfish, hamster, chimpanzee)*
- *See* Laboratories, *Investigation 18.*

Check Your Understanding

1. Give a common name of an organism and state why it is not acceptable as a scientific name. *(Sample answer:* Jellyfish *does not identify the species; the organism is not a fish.)*
2. Into what category are similar families of organisms placed? *(Order)*

Reteaching

Using the organisms listed in Table 18-1, p. 268, ask students: To what kingdom does the Family Aceraceae belong? *(Plantae)* To what class does the Order Primates belong? *(Mammalia)*

- *See* Blackline Master *37.*
- *See* Section Reviews *worksheet, Section 18.1.*

Enrichment

Broccoli, cauliflower, and brussels sprouts are all varieties of the same species. Have students investigate the development of *Brassica oleracea.*

Closure

Ask students to speculate on the meaning of the Latin *Ursus horribilis. (It is the scientific name of the grizzly bear.)*

Videodiscs

- *644–646,* **Selaginella lepidophylla; Selaginella pilifera—** ***Two Species (s)***

Table 18-1 Classification of Three Organisms

Common Name	Kingdom	Phylum/ Division	Class	Order	Family	Genus	Specific Epithet
Bacterium	Monera	Schizophyta	Scotobacteria	Spirochaetales	Spirochaetaceae	*Cristispira*	*petinis*
Box elder	Plantae	Anthophyta	Dicotyledonae	Sapindales	Aceraceae	*Acer*	*negundo*
Human being	Animalia	Chordata	Mammalia	Primates	Hominidae	*Homo*	*sapiens*

Figure 18-2 The twinflower, *Linnaea borealis,* is a member of the cornflower family.

The binomial name of a species is called its **scientific name.** For example, *Rana pipiens* is the scientific name of the leopard frog. Usually the scientific name that a taxonomist chooses either describes the organism or the range of the organism, or honors another scientist or a friend. For instance, the Latin name *Trifolium agrarium,* meaning "three-leaved" and "found in fields," refers to a clover that is common in meadows. Figure 18-2 shows *Linnaea borealis,* a species that grows in northern regions. The flower was Linnaeus's favorite; *borealis* means "northern."

Levels of Classification

Today taxonomists use Linnaeus's seven levels of classification. Botanists use the term **division** in place of phylum when classifying plants. Study the sample classifications in Table 18-1.

Often taxonomists classify species into subspecies, varieties, or strains, thus denoting variation within a species. The subspecies of a species are morphologically different and are often geographically separated. For example, the northern timber wolf is a subspecies of *Canis lupus* called *Canis lupus* ssp. *occidentalis.* The notation *ssp.* means "subspecies."

The varieties of a species are morphologically different and are often not geographically separated. Some have been produced by humans. For instance, peaches and nectarines are varieties of *Prunus persica.* Botanists refer to the peach tree as *Prunus persica* var. *persica,* and to the nectarine as *Prunus persica* var. *nectarina. Var.* means "variety."

A strain is a biochemically dissimilar group within a species. Strain is usually used in reference to microorganisms. A strain is often represented by letters or numbers. For instance, two strains of the intestinal bacterium *Serrata marcescens* are called *S. marcescens* D1 and *S. marcescens* 933.

Section Review

1. What is *taxonomy,* and why is it important?
2. What criterion did Linnaeus use to classify organisms?
3. What do the two parts of a scientific name denote?
4. List the levels of classification from the largest group down.
5. Give several examples of common names that might cause confusion if scientists were to use them.

Answers to Section Review

1. Taxonomy is the science of grouping organisms according to their presumed natural relationships; it helps scientists study and communicate about a variety of species.
2. The structural similarities and differences among organisms
3. Genus name and specific epithet
4. Kingdom, phylum or division, class, order, family, genus, species
5. Examples might include the sea horse and the prairie dog.

18.2 Modern Taxonomy

In this section we will focus first on the evidence used to identify organisms that have already been classified or to classify new organisms as they are discovered. You will learn how studying morphology, embryology, chromosomes, biochemistry, and physiology enables scientists to identify and classify organisms. You will also learn that many modern taxonomists are not content just to identify and classify species. They are also interested in inferring the **phylogeny** *(fie-LAHJ-uh-nee),* or the evolutionary history, of a species.

Section Objectives

- *List the kinds of evidence used by modern taxonomists in classifying organisms.*
- *Define* phylogeny, *and explain its role in taxonomy.*
- *Explain how family trees illustrate phylogeny.*
- *Define the role of biosystematics in inferring evolutionary relationships.*

Evidence Used in Classification

Most taxonomists base their classifications primarily on comparative morphology. They study an organism's morphological features to determine its taxonomic category. When taxonomists attempt to either identify or classify a plant, for example, they look first at the structure of the plant to determine its similarity to known species. Are its flower petals separate, for example, or are they fused into a tube? Are its flowers purple or white or pink? Does the plant have one leaf per stem or several? By looking at a series of such features taxonomists can usually determine the species of an organism—or can determine the species to which it is most similar. Taxonomists usually rely on special books or manuals to aid them. Identification often involves the use of a **dichotomous key**—a written set of choices that leads to the name of the organism.

However, morphological evidence in itself may not be sufficient for accurately identifying or classifying an organism. Therefore taxonomists also compare the embryology, chromosomes, or biochemistry of organisms.

Embryological evidence is often used in classification, especially at the level of the larger classification categories. For example, the wings of a bird and the wings of an insect are called analogous structures since they develop from different tissues in each embryo. Analogous structures do not provide any evidence of an evolutionary relationship between organisms. However, certain embryological evidence may indicate that seemingly dissimilar species may well be related. For example, the bones of the forelimb in the lizard are embryologically similar to those in the cat. Recall that such structures are known as homologous structures. This suggests that the two organisms may share a similar phylogenetic origin.

Taxonomists find other evidence for identification and classification by comparing the chromosomes of different organisms. For example, taxonomists studying two similar mushrooms can prepare a karyotype for each organism. By counting chromosomes and comparing chromosome shapes these scientists may determine whether two mushroom species are closely related.

Figure 18-3 Through the study of morphological differences taxonomists have classified the brown bear (top) as *Ursus arctos* and the polar bear (bottom) as *Ursus maritimus*.

Lesson Plan

Section Focus

This section describes the kinds of evidence used in classifying organisms and how the evidence is used for inferring phylogeny and studying speciation.

Section Themes

This section emphasizes the themes of **Scale and Structure** and **Evolution.** It describes the types of structural evidence used in the study of relationships between organisms and their phylogeny and speciation.

Motivating Activity

Display pictures or specimens of animals whose common names are misleading, such as a horseshoe crab *(More closely related to spiders than crabs)*; a sow bug *(A crustacean, shown on p. 483)*; a starfish *(An echinoderm, not a fish)*; a cowbird *(Has nothing to do with cows);* and a woolly bear *(An insect larva)*. Ask students to infer how each organism acquired its common name.

Point out that common names vary from language to language. Ask students to give common names of organisms in other languages. Conclude by stating that a common name of an organism is never as useful to a biologist as the scientific name.

Teaching Strategies

Identifying Scientific Processes

Ask students what scientific processes taxonomists use when they study relationships between organisms. (*Collecting evidence, observing and organizing observations, inferring anatomical and physiological relationships, and, in some cases, inferring evolutionary relationships)*

Videodiscs

- ***Side 4 3787, Alligator, Snapping Turtle (m)***

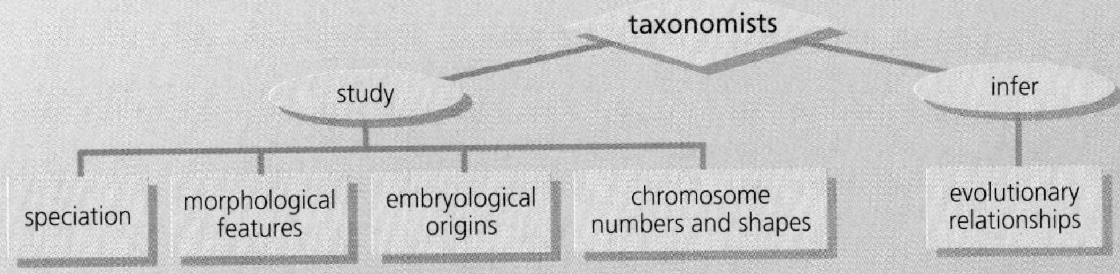

Graphic Organizer Use this chart to summarize the key concepts in Section 18.2.

Classifying Organisms A fish that has no close relationship with any modern fish, *Latimeria chalumnae,* was first discovered in 1938 in the Indian Ocean. Ask students to hypothesize how the scientist who studied the fish determined how to classify it. *(He compared it with fossil fish.)* Tell students that the scientist inferred it belonged to the group of coelacanth crossopterygians, the fossils of which had dated from Cretaceous Period and earlier.

Applying Concepts Have students consider similarities and differences in organisms at different levels of classification. Ask them what plants and animals, which are in different kingdoms, have in common. (Review with students the characteristics of life, Section 1.2.) Then ask what an elephant and a bear have in common. List on the board the common features in all cases.

Guided Practice

In order to help students understand the concept of homologous structures, have them review Figure 15-4, p. 223. After they compare the forelimb structures of the penguin, alligator, bat, and human, have students infer which of the other three organisms is most closely related to humans. *(The bat)* Ask them to identify a structure in the bat that is analogous to a human structure and that the other organisms lack. *(The thumb)*

Independent Practice

- Have students write answers to the Section Review.
- Ask students to make a concept map that relates comparative morphology to the practices of classifying and identifying organisms. Tell them to use terms from Section 18.2. An example of a completed concept map is shown on p. 265B.

Taxonomists can use biochemical comparisons of organisms to further refine their classifications. Recall from Chapter 8 that the sequence of nucleotide bases in genes is reflected in the amino acid sequence of a protein. Comparing the proteins, amino acid sequences, DNA, and RNA in different organisms can help researchers determine the degree of genetic similarity among various organisms.

Physiological studies are especially useful in the classification of bacteria. For example, members of the genera *Enterobacter* and *Escherichia* can both ferment the sugar lactose. However, members of *Enterobacter* can use citric acid as their sole source of carbon, while members of *Escherichia* cannot. Species of these bacterial genera look similar under the microscope, but they are classified into different genera on the basis of their physiological differences.

Figure 18-4 A phylogenetic tree shows the evolutionary relationship of species. The finches closest to the ends of the branches are the most recently evolved species.

Inferring Phylogeny

A major task of some modern taxonomists is inferring the phylogeny of a group of species. Taxonomists are able to infer the

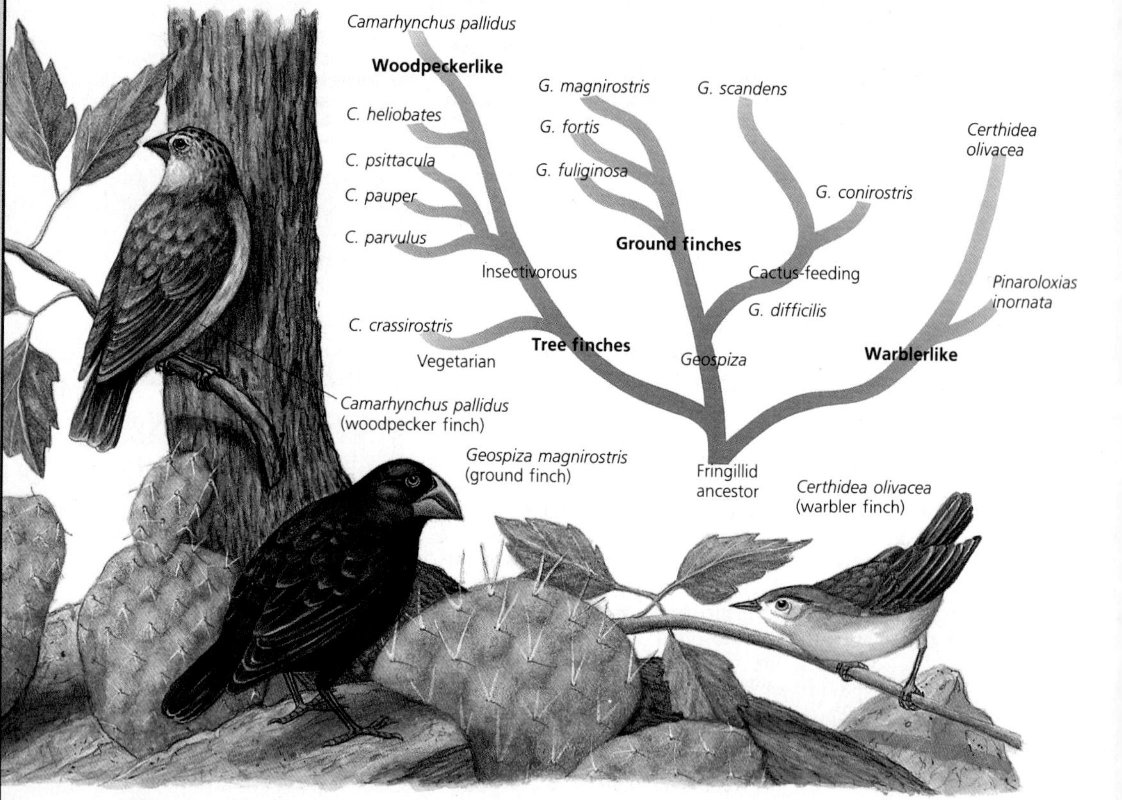

LEP Activity

Students are sometimes confused by the difference between the singular and plural forms of the Latin words used in taxonomy. Have students use a dictionary to make a list of the singular and plural forms of such terms as *phyla* (singular: *phylum*) and *genera* (singular: *genus*) and *species* (singular and plural). In addition, write a helpful mnemonic device on the board to aid students in recalling the categories of classification; for example: King Phillip Came Over For Good Soup. Encourage students to devise other mnemonics if they prefer. Finally, clarify for students which of the categories show the broadest and which show the closest relationships among members. *(Kingdoms are broadest; species are closest.)*

probable evolutionary relationships among species that have been classified on the basis of the kinds of evidence listed on the last two pages. Look at the Galápagos finches in Figure 18-4 as an example. As you read in Chapter 15, the finches that Darwin observed on the Galápagos Islands were classified based on similarities and differences of their bills. Taxonomists infer that the group of species having the most similar bills evolved along the same evolutionary lines.

Taxonomists commonly illustrate the inferred phylogeny of related organisms with a diagram called a phylogenetic tree. A **phylogenetic tree** is a visual model of the inferred evolutionary relationships among organisms. Figure 18-4 shows a phylogenetic tree of Galápagos finches. The species that are illustrated at the tips of the branches represent those organisms that have evolved most recently. The main branches and the trunk of the tree represent the organisms from which the recently evolved organisms arose. Branches in close proximity imply that a close evolutionary relationship exists between the organisms on those branches.

Biosystematics

As you learned in Chapter 16, many taxonomists use reproductive compatibility to infer evolutionary relationships. **Biosystematics** is a form of taxonomy that examines reproductive compatibility and gene flow. Biosystematists assess the genetic variation in populations and among species. Using such information, biosystematists make inferences about the ancestral history of a species.

Essentially, biosystematists study speciation, the evolution of one species into two. They collect data on variations in a population of organisms. The biosystematists then analyze the data to construct a model of the genetics of the population. As an example, in Wisconsin a single population of fly maggots has begun to feed, mature, and then reproduce near either apple trees or cherry trees. Because the two kinds of trees bear fruit at different times of the year, the apple-eating maggots and the cherry-eating maggots may eventually become reproductively isolated from one another through the mechanism discussed in Chapter 16. A biosystematist might infer that in this case speciation is occurring.

Section Review

1. What is *phylogeny?*
2. List some types of evidence used by modern taxonomists to classify organisms.
3. What do branches that are close together on a phylogenetic tree indicate?
4. How does the science of biosystematics aid in the classification of species?
5. Why is it important for taxonomists to continually collect new specimens?

Think

The organism shown above is called a tardigrade. What characteristics do you think might be considered important in classifying this organism?

Answers to Section Review

1. The evolutionary history of a species
2. Possibilities include evidence from the morphology, embryology, biochemistry, physiology, and chromosomes of an organism.
3. That the organisms on those branches are closely related
4. By using information from genetic studies to make inferences about the ancestral history of a species
5. New specimens might be new species. Also, new specimens can be used to study variation within a species.

Answer to Think

Answers will vary but may include limb structure, organ structure, movement, and the general morphology of the body.

Check Your Understanding

1. Is the following evidence chromosomal or physiological? Some bacteria live on iron; others live on sulfur. *(Physiological)*
2. Is the following evidence morphological or embryological? Male deer and male elk have antlers. *(Morphological)*

Reteaching

Have students look at Figure 15-8, p. 228, which shows three species of finch. Ask students to locate these finches on the phylogenetic tree on p. 270. From the relative positions of the three species on the tree, have students infer which two are most closely related. *(*G. magnirostris *and* C. olivacea*)*

■ *See* Section Reviews *worksheet, Section 18.2*

Enrichment

With the accumulation of enough evidence, a sixth kingdom, viruses, may eventually be established. Ask students to describe how technology may change our classification system. *(As our ability to observe smaller organisms improves, their differences become more apparent, necessitating new categories.)*

Closure

Ask students whether a shark or an elephant is more closely related to a dolphin. *(Elephant)* Remind students that dolphins and elephants are both mammals.

Videodiscs

■ ***2593, Evolutionary Relationships (s)***
■ ***2585, Mollusk: Hypothetical Ancestor (s)***
■ ***Side 4 4142, Crocodile (m)***

Lesson Plan

Section Focus

This section describes the basic characteristics of the five kingdoms in the classification system.

Section Themes

The theme of **Scale and Structure** is evident in the way that distinctions between kingdoms are based, in part, on cell and tissue structures. Because biologists can observe structural differences microscopically and molecularly, they now have a five-kingdom system as opposed to the two-kingdom system.

Motivating Activity

Show students a specimen of an organism that is difficult to classify, such as a coral or a sponge. Ask if the specimen is a plant or an animal, and ask students to defend their classification. As they attempt to classify, ask students to consider what observations they would need to make before they could make a firm classification. *(They might use a microscope to examine cell structure, and they might observe the organism alive in a natural setting.)* Point out that technology has allowed us to observe distinctions between organisms that Aristotle and Linnaeus could not have observed.

Teaching Strategies

Applying Concepts Ask students what is the most basic difference between plants and animals. *(Autotrophic vs. heterotrophic)* Engage students in a discussion of how autotrophs and heterotrophs interact with their environments. Ask them which came first in the original development of life. *(Heterotrophs)* Then ask them which is the more important group now, and why. *(Autotrophs, because without autotrophs, most heterotrophs could not live)*

Section Objectives

- *Describe the five-kingdom system of classification.*
- *List the characteristics that distinguish monera from protists.*
- *Describe how RNA-sequencing studies may lead to a revision of the five-kingdom classification system.*

18.3 Five-Kingdom System

Aristotle divided organisms into either the plant or the animal kingdom, but today scientists recognize that some organisms belong to neither. Most modern taxonomists use a five-kingdom system. As you read, keep in mind that this system is only one of many current attempts to organize the diversity of life-forms.

Taxonomists place an organism into one of the following kingdoms: Monera *(moe-NIR-uh)*, Protista *(proe-TISS-tuh)*, Fungi *(FUN-jie)*, Plantae *(PLAN-tee)*, and Animalia *(AN-uh-MAY-lee-uh)*. The criteria used to define kingdoms include cell structure, tissue structure, nutritional requirements, and developmental patterns.

Monera

The Kingdom Monera is made up of prokaryotic organisms, which lack nuclei and other membrane-bound organelles. Many monerans live in aquatic and terrestrial habitats and obtain nutrients primarily through absorption. Other monerans are autotro-

Biology in Process

Classifying Archaebacteria

The ability to examine the chemical foundations of life—DNA and RNA molecules—could soon revolutionize the way organisms are classified. Since the 1960s Carl R. Woese, a microbiologist at the University of Illinois, has studied the ribosomal RNA structures of more than 6,000 organisms. During his study he concluded that a certain group of prokaryotes called archaebacteria (p. 273) were so significantly different from all other organisms that he proposed a new model for classification based on molecular structure. Woese prefers to call these prokaryotes Archaea to distinguish them from bacteria. The archaebacteria are microscopic organisms that thrive in habitats hostile to other forms of life such as the hot waters near undersea and terrestrial volcanic vents (p. 272), high-sulfur areas, and places with no oxygen at all. Woese asserts that archaebacteria are different from the bacteria they have been classified with—as different as they are from eukaryotes—because archaebacteria evolved a radically different set of adaptations in response to their challenging habitats. For example, many archaebacteria are chemosynthesizing rather

	Monera	Protista	Fungi	Plantae	Animalia
prokaryote	X				
eukaryote		X	X	X	X
autotrophic	X	X		X	
heterotrophic	X	X	X		X
tissue systems			X (most)	X	X

Graphic Organizer Use this table in Independent Practice on p. 274.

phic, producing food either by photosynthesis or chemosynthesis. Most monerans reproduce asexually, although members of some species exchange genetic material. Scientists have identified only about 5,000 moneran species—a small number in comparison with other kingdoms. Nevertheless, the Kingdom Monera includes the greatest number of living things on earth, since almost every moneran species has billions of individuals. Familiar monerans include *Escherichia coli,* the bacteria that are normally present in the intestines of humans, and *Clostridium tetani,* the bacteria that cause tetanus.

Protista

The Kingdom Protista is made up of eukaryotic organisms that lack specialized tissue systems. Remember that eukaryotes do have true nuclei and membrane-bound organelles. Protists may be unicellular or multicellular. They live in aquatic or moist habitats and obtain their food by ingestion, absorption, or photosynthesis. They reproduce sexually and asexually. More than 50,000 species have been placed in the Kingdom Protista. Examples of protists include the algae and the protozoa.

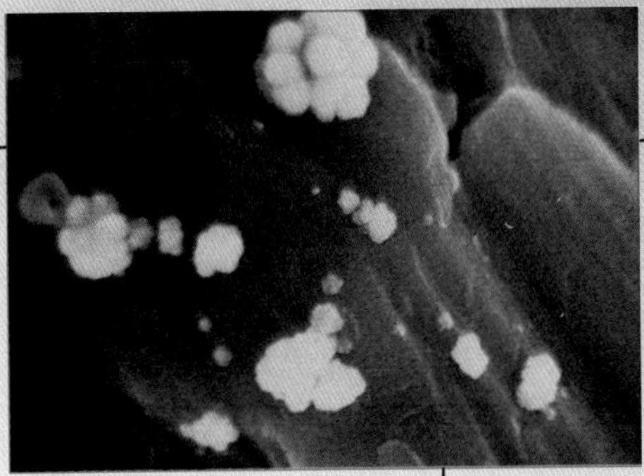

than photosynthesizing organisms. In addition sequence analysis of some of their RNA molecules reveals intervening sequences, called introns, like those of eukaryotes.

Woese and his coworkers suggest creating a taxonomic level above kingdom, which they call domain. In Woese's model there are three domains:

Bacteria—prokaryotes with ribosomes containing a typically bacterial type of rRNA.

Eucarya—cells with distinct nuclei (eukaryotes); this domain would include the kingdoms Animalia, Plantae, and Fungi. The Kingdom Protista would be distributed into new kingdoms within this domain, based on their genotypes.

Archaea—prokaryotes with ribosomes containing a type of rRNA that is uniquely different from either of the other domains.

Woese argues that a new model is needed. First, because the five-kingdom system ignores the vast differences between prokaryotes and eukaryotes by assigning all prokaryotes to the Kingdom Monera. Second, classifying prokaryotes on the basis of what they lack (a nucleus) is not a valid criterion. Third, and most important, molecular criteria are now generally replacing classical phenotypic criteria. Scientists are now able to determine the essential similarities among organisms by actually studying their genetic structure.

- **What part did the process of observing play in Woese's conclusion that Archaea represent a distinct group?**

Guided Practice

Have students suggest examples of organisms in each kingdom in Table 18-2, p. 274, and indicate why they belong in the designated kingdoms. Ask them to list the numbers of species in each kingdom and determine which kingdoms dominate the earth now. *(Numbers of species are: 5,000 in Monera, 50,000 in Protista, 100,000 in Fungi, 350,000 in Plantae, and more than a million in Animalia.)*

- *See* **Overhead Transparency** *T18 and* **Blackline Master** *38.*

Biology in Process

Using the Feature

The feature focuses on the process skills of observing, analyzing data, and modeling. Point out to students that molecular evaluations show that the differences among archaebacteria, the other monerans, and eukaryotes are profound. Woese maintains that the differences he observed evolved early in the history of living cells. Ask students what hurdles remain before Woese's three-domain system of classification could be widely accepted. *(Answers may include the time needed for communicating the model to other scientists; allowing them to examine and replicate Woese's evidence; and resistance to changing the five-kingdom system, which has only recently gained acceptance.)*

Answer to the Feature

By comparing the RNA structures of archaebacteria with those of other organisms, Woese observed that the rRNA of some archaebacteria had more in common with eukaryotes than with prokaryotes.

Videodiscs

- *2590–2592, Classification System (s)*
- *2594,* Euglena (s)

Cooperative Learning Activity

Creating a Mural Ask students to illustrate the five kingdoms of life by making a mural. Provide them with a generous amount of mural paper. Divide the class into five groups and assign each group a kingdom. Within each group ask some students to take responsibility for illustrations and others to do research and write captions. Encourage students to use pictures or articles cut from old newspapers and magazines. When the mural is completed, have one person from each group present an oral report to the class about that group's particular kingdom, using the mural as a visual aid.

Section 18.3

Independent Practice

■ Have students write answers to the Section Review.

■ Ask students to make a table comparing the five kingdoms without consulting their texts. An example of a completed table is shown on p. 272.

Check Your Understanding

1. Why would it be useless to classify organisms into kingdoms on the basis of size, shape, or color? *(Such categories would not show their presumed evolutionary relationships.)*

2. Although animals and most fungi are eukaryotic, multicellular heterotrophs, biologists place them in different kingdoms. Why? *(Fungi absorb nutrients; animals ingest nutrients.)*

Reteaching

Have students identify, by kingdom, organisms with particular characteristics. Examples are: a single-celled organism without a nuclear membrane *(Monera)*; an autotrophic eukaryote with cell walls *(Plantae)*; a unicellular, autotrophic eukaryote *(Protista)*; heterotrophs that absorb nutrients *(Fungi)*; or a motile, multicellular heterotroph *(Animalia)*.

■ *See* Section Reviews *worksheet, Section 18.3.*

Enrichment

Ask students to identify and list the kingdoms to which organisms mentioned or illustrated in Chapters 14, 15, and 16 belong.

Closure

Remind students that a two-kingdom system of classification was used in the past—plant and animal. Ask students which organisms did not fit well in either kingdom and why five kingdoms are now used. *(For example, fungi differ from both animals and plants because they are heterotrophs that absorb nutrients.)*

Table 18-2 The Five-Kingdom System

Kingdom	Monera	Protista	Fungi	Plantae	Animalia
Type of cells	Prokaryotic	Eukaryotic	Eukaryotic	Eukaryotic	Eukaryotic
Unicellular or multicellular	Most are unicellular	Most are unicellular	Most are multicellular	Multicellular	Multicellular
Mode of nutrition	Heterotrophy and autotrophy	Heterotrophy and autotrophy	Heterotrophy	Autotrophy	Heterotrophy
Examples					

Fungi

The Kingdom Fungi is made up of heterotrophic unicellular and multicellular eukaryotic organisms. Fungi absorb nutrients rather than ingesting them. Most species are terrestrial. They reproduce sexually and asexually. The 100,000 fungi species include mushrooms, yeasts, puffballs, rusts, and bread molds.

Plantae

The Kingdom Plantae consists of the plants, all of which are multicellular and autotrophic. Most plants are terrestrial. They reproduce sexually and asexually. The more than 350,000 species of plants include mosses, ferns, conifers, and flowering plants.

Animalia

The Kingdom Animalia is made up of eukaryotic, multicellular, heterotrophic organisms that obtain nutrients by ingesting food. Animals are terrestrial and aquatic. Most reproduce sexually; a few can reproduce asexually. There are more than a million animal species, including organisms as diverse as spiders and elephants. Table 18-2 summarizes the five-kingdom system.

Section Review

1. Name the five kingdoms.
2. What are the main criteria used to define kingdoms?
3. How are monerans different from all other organisms?
4. What is the primary difference between fungi and plants?
5. Suggest some possible techniques that could be used to reclassify the organisms in the Kingdom Protista.

Answers to Section Review

1. Monera, Protista, Fungi, Plantae, and Animalia
2. Cell structure, tissue structure, nutritional requirements, and developmental patterns
3. Monerans are prokaryotic.
4. Fungi are heterotrophic; plants are autotrophic.
5. Possibilities include conducting genetic and biochemical studies that compare members of the kingdoms, searching for fossil evidence of similarities among protists and other organisms, and studying other kingdoms to identify characteristics their members may share with protists.

Laboratory

Using a Dichotomous Key to Identify Organisms

Objective
To correctly identify unknown organisms using a dichotomous key

Process Skills
Observing, classifying

Materials
11 unidentified invertebrate specimens, living or preserved

Inquiry

1. In this investigation you will use a dichotomous key to identify and classify a group of unknown invertebrate organisms. Pick a specimen and study it briefly. Then go to step 1 of the key. Note that only one of each pair of statements applies to the organism you are identifying. Pick either 1a or 1b—whichever describes your specimen. Then follow the directions to the next step.
2. Continue in this manner until you arrive at the name of the specimen.
3. Choose another specimen and repeat the process.
4. Continue working through the key with new specimens until your teacher says to stop.

Key

1a	Body has radial symmetry (Phylum Echinodermata)	Go to 2
1b	Body has bilateral symmetry	Go to 4
2a	Radiating arms present	Class Asteroidea
2b	No arms present	Go to 3
3a	Covered with spines	Class Echinoidea
3b	Elongated body	Class Holothuroidea
4a	Body flat	Class Cestoidea
4b	Body not flat	Go to 5
5a	Body divided into repeating units	Go to 6
5b	Body not divided as above	Phylum Nematoda
6a	Hard external covering (Phylum Arthropoda)	Go to 9
6b	Soft external covering (Phylum Annelida)	Go to 7
7a	Bristles absent	Class Hirudinea
7b	Bristles present	Go to 8
8a	Leglike appendages present	Class Polychaeta
8b	Leglike appendages absent	Class Oligochaeta
9a	Feelerlike antennae on head absent	Subphylum Chelicerata
9b	Feelerlike antennae on head present	Go to 10
10a	Unbranched antennae	Subphylum Uniramia
10b	Branched antennae	Subphylum Crustacea

Conclusions

1. Name the specimens you have identified.
2. When designing a dichotomous key, must the two parts of each step describe opposite characteristics? Can you think of a more important criterion for deciding how to construct the parts of a step? Explain your answer.
3. Are there some species of organisms that cannot be identified with a dichotomous key? Explain your answer.

Further Inquiry
In this investigation you used a dichotomous key to identify some unknown organisms. How might you repeat the investigation using a trichotomous key?

Laboratory

(For an overview of a procedure for identifying organisms and preparatory information related to the laboratory, see p. 265B.)

Inquiry

1. Some students may have difficulty using a dichotomous key for the first time because they may not understand the format. Explain that each step involves making a selection between two mutually exclusive options. For example, in step 4, they must decide whether the organism is flat or not flat. After each decision, they should look over at the direction line directly adjacent to the choice they have made and follow that direction or note the classification. If the student decided, in step 4, that the organism was flat, he or she should then record the classification "Class Cestoidea" and stop. In some cases students will be directed to go to a step that is not in order. Stress the importance of following the direction lines in the right column; students make many of their mistakes with dichotomous keys by trying to read the left column all the way through from the start.

Conclusions

1. Specimen names will vary according to how many specimens the student has time to key.
2. Characteristics need not be opposite ones as shown by key step 3. What is necessary is that the step be constructed so that all organisms to be classified are either *a* or *b*.
3. Answers will vary. Some closely related species may be difficult to key on the basis of physical characteristics.

Further Inquiry

Students should suggest ways to repeat the investigation using a trichotomous key, such as by organizing the information in the form of a branching chart.

Vocabulary

1. A common name may not describe an organism accurately and may vary from place to place. A scientific name identifies a genus and a species and is universal.
2. The word *division* is used in place of the word *phylum* when classifying plants.
3. *Phylo* is from the Greek word meaning "tribe, race or clan"; *geny* is from the Greek word for being born. Phylogeny describes the evolution of a genetically related group of organisms.
4. Biosystematics is the study of reproductive compatibility and gene flow.
5. Most dictionary definitions of biological species mention that organisms within a species are presumed to be related and can interbreed to produce fertile offspring. Linnaeus only used structural similarity as the criterion for species identification.

Review

1. d	**6.** a
2. a	**7.** a
3. c	**8.** c
4. c	**9.** a
5. a	**10.** c

11. Both divided organisms into plants and animals and grouped them on the basis of similar features.
12. They prevent confusion and allow scientists to communicate accurately.
13. The phylum; for plants it is called the division.
14. Plants are autotrophic; fungi are heterotrophic.
15. Morphological evidence
16. Populations of maggots in Wisconsin have separated into two populations living on either apple or cherry trees. As the trees bear fruit at different times, these populations may become reproductively isolated.
17. The Kingdom Monera; almost every moneran species has billions of individuals.
18. One or more characteristics of the organism, its geographic range or location, or the name of the person who discovered it
19. Archaebacteria are so different from other prokaryotes in genetic material and cell chemistry that some taxonomists argue that they cannot be classified in Kingdom Monera.
20. Embryological evidence can show which tissues in the embryo give rise to a particular structure. That information can be used to determine whether or not two organisms may be closely related.

Chapter 18 Review

Vocabulary

binomial nomenclature (267)
biosystematics (271)
class (267)
common name (267)
dichotomous key (269)
division (268)
family (267)
genus (267)
kingdom (267)
order (267)
phylogenetic tree (271)
phylogeny (269)
phylum (267)
scientific name (268)
taxonomy (267)

1. Distinguish between a common name and a scientific name.
2. What is the difference between a phylum and a division?
3. Using a dictionary, find the meaning of the word parts *phylo-* and *-geny* in *phylogeny*. Explain why this term is appropriate for discussing common ancestry of organisms.
4. Define *biosystematics*.
5. Look up the word *species* in a dictionary. How does the dictionary definition compare with Linnaeus's use of the term? Suggest explanations for the differences.

Review

1. A scientific name includes information about (a) species and phylum (b) division and genus (c) genus and order (d) genus and species.
2. Aristotle classified plants on the basis of differences in their (a) stems (b) flowers (c) leaves (d) roots.
3. A group of related classes of organisms make up a (a) genus (b) order (c) phylum (d) kingdom.
4. Linnaeus defined a species as a group of organisms that (a) reproduced asexually (b) reproduced sexually (c) shared many common characteristics (d) shared a common ancestor.
5. Biosystematists study the process of (a) speciation (b) taxonomy (c) genetics (d) development.
6. A unique characteristic of the Kingdom Monera is that all of its members are (a) prokaryotes (b) heterotrophs (c) eubacteria (d) archaebacteria.
7. In a phylogenetic tree, close branches indicate (a) close evolutionary relationships (b) the most recently evolved species (c) common habitats (d) common aspects of behavior.
8. The Kingdom Protista includes (a) bacteria (b) plants (c) algae (d) mushrooms.
9. Some protists are similar to plants in that they (a) carry on photosynthesis (b) have advanced tissues (c) may ingest nutrients (d) are very small.
10. Taxonomists can use data from RNA-sequencing techniques to (a) predict future changes in species (b) determine when a species diverged from a common ancestor (c) identify genetic similarities among species (d) explain the origin of life.
11. How were Aristotle's and Linnaeus's classification systems for organisms similar?
12. Why are scientific names important in scientific work?
13. What is the second largest level in today's classification system?
14. What are the differences between plants and fungi?
15. What is the major type of evidence that scientists use to identify and classify organisms?
16. Give an example that shows how speciation may be occurring within a population.
17. Which of the five kingdoms contains the greatest numbers of living things on earth?
18. Name three things you might learn about an organism by investigating the meaning of its scientific name.

19. Why do some taxonomists propose that the Kingdom Monera be split into two separate kingdoms?

20. How might a taxonomist use embryological evidence in classifying an organism?

Critical Thinking

1. Develop a hierarchical classification system with at least three levels for your books or record albums or for your favorite songs. Explain the criteria you use to group individual items at each of the different levels.
2. Immediately after the microscope was invented, taxonomists began to use it in their work. What reasons might they have had for doing so?
3. Recently scientists found ways to "map" DNA molecules down to specific genes. New technology allows them to create "DNA fingerprints," genetic profiles of individuals. Crime specialists think the DNA fingerprints will make the positive identification of criminals an exact science. How is the creation of genetic profiles similar to one method used by some taxonomists?
4. Biologists think that there are probably millions of undescribed and unclassified species on earth. Why do you think so many species might still be undescribed or unclassified today?

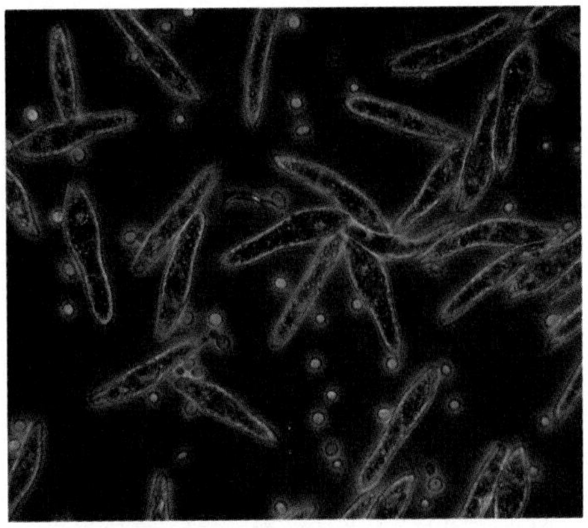

5. If no one had devised a system of binomial nomenclature, what problems would scientists have had today in communicating about organisms?
6. Examine the photograph above of a member of the Division Euglenophyta. What characteristics do you see that might make this organism difficult to classify further?

Extension

1. Collect half a cup of water from a shallow pond. Using a microscope, study several samples from the water. Draw the organisms you find, and classify them as best you can into kingdom and phylum.
2. A number of years ago scientists found a living fish, called the coelacanth, which is one of a class of fishes long thought to be extinct. Write a research report describing how taxonomists decided where to classify this discovery.
3. Read the article by Jared Diamond entitled "The Search for Life on Earth" in *Natural History,* April 1990, pp. 28–32. What discoveries have challenged common conceptions of the limits to biological adaptation on Earth? Why is taxonomic research so crucial to biology today?
4. Visit the zoo and list the scientific names of all the animals you see, or use your library to research ten organisms. Record the scientific and common names of these organisms. For each animal list a trait that led taxonomists to classify the organism in its genus or family.

Critical Thinking

1. Students might take into consideration the age of the book, recording, or song; characteristics or categories such as genre, author or composer, performer, and so on. The same criteria must be applied to each item classified at each level.
2. The microscope revealed the vast diversity of microorganisms and their structures.
3. Some taxonomists compare nucleotide sequences in DNA and RNA to determine relationships between organisms.
4. Scientists have not yet studied every habitat completely and therefore presume that many unknown species exist. One example of a recently discovered habitat is the thermal vents on the ocean floor.
5. They might have had to use an inconsistent system of long descriptive names and short common names that varied from country to country.
6. The organisms are single cells, have chloroplasts for photosynthesis, and have flagella for movement. The presence of chloroplasts indicates that the organisms are algae; because of the flagella, they may be classified as protozoa.

Extension

1. If pond water is not available, students could try mixing soil with water, and then drawing off a sample of the muddy water to check for microbes.
2. The coelacanth belongs to the class of bony fishes, Osteichthyes, and the family Coelacanthidae.
3. Students may offer examples of new findings: a new species of primates and male menopause in brown marsupial mice.
4. If a trip to a zoo cannot be arranged, consider taking students to an aquarium or greenhouse.

Discussion

Guide the discussion by posing the following questions.

1. What do you think drives people to search for life in outer space? *(Accept all reasonable answers. Students are likely to raise the issue of wanting to know if we are alone in the universe.)*

2. What is the likelihood that another planet in the universe is capable of supporting life? *(Trillions of planets in other solar systems may be able to support life.)*

3. Why could an atmosphere different from that of the ancient earth support the evolution of life? *(As long as the molecules contained the necessary elements and had certain properties, lightning could provide the energy needed to bring about the synthesis of amino acids.)*

4. Identify one reason that the apparent motion of suns is significant to planetary scientists. *(Scientists think that the apparent change in the motions of stars will prove the existence of planetary systems. Although most scientists believe that planets exist in other solar systems, none have actually been found.)*

5. In addition to intelligent life forms, what other forms of life might scientists encounter elsewhere in the universe? *(Extraterrestrial life may be as diverse as life on earth, ranging from the simple and microscopic to the highly complex.)*

6. Why is it unlikely that humans will soon travel to other solar systems? *(Because other stars are so far away, even if engineers could design a spaceship fast enough to get there at the speed of light, the amount of energy required to fuel such a ship would be prohibitive.)*

Intra-Science

How the Sciences Work Together

The Question in Biology: *Is There Life on Other Planets?*

As space technology advances, the search for life on other planets continues. Earth is one of nine planets orbiting our sun. From 1 to 10 billion stars like the sun are contained in our galaxy; over 100 billion galaxies are in the universe. With potentially trillions of planets in existence, many of them may very possibly support life.

The desire to find life on other planets is not new. People have wondered for centuries whether or not life exists elsewhere in the universe. "The question of extraterrestrial life . . . has been debated almost from the beginning of recorded history," says Michael J. Crowe in his book *The Extraterrestrial Life Debate*. Despite the advances in space technology in the past 30 years, scientists have not yet found conclusive evidence that life exists beyond Earth. At the same time, however, there is no evidence that it does not. Scientific interest in finding extra-terrestrial life has generated a new branch of biology called exobiology.

Exobiologists study conditions on other planets to determine whether life could exist there. They also explore the conditions that might have existed on ancient Earth. As you learned in Chapter 14, the atmosphere of ancient Earth included gases such as methane, ammonia, nitrogen, carbon dioxide, hydrogen, and water vapor. These gases contained all the elements that eventually combined to form organic compounds. As a result of such studies, some scientists speculate that life could also evolve in atmospheres unlike ancient Earth's. Lightning could provide the energy necessary to synthesize amino acids, the building blocks of protein. However, to find out if life exists on other planets, exobiologists will have to rely on other scientists, particularly astronomers and physicists.

The Connection to Astronomy

Although most scientists believe the universe contains many solar systems, no planets have been observed outside of our own solar system. However, over the past ten years, a team of Canadian scientists has monitored the speed of eighteen nearby stars similar to our sun. The scientists have observed that nine of the suns appear to wiggle. The wiggling motion could be explained by the presence of planetary systems. Further research may confirm that planets are circling these stars and identify places to search for extraterrestrial life.

■ *Describe the scientific significance of discovering planets outside our solar system.*

The Connection to Physics

Humans are unlikely to travel very soon to other solar systems. Light from Earth takes eight years to travel to and return from Proxima Centauri, the star closest to our sun. Even if engineers designed a spaceship that could approach the speed of light (300,000 km per second), the energy required to power it would surpass the amount consumed on Earth in one year.

The best chance for detecting intelligent life in other solar systems lies in electromagnetic communication. Using radio telescopes, messages from outer space can be received on

278

Connections to Other Disciplines

Mathematics The Drake equation attempts to estimate the number of intelligent civilizations in our galaxy that might try to communicate with us. Have students find out the factors in that equation. They will find a discussion of the Drake equation in *Cosmos* by Carl Sagan. Challenge students to explain why different scientists have proposed answers ranging from zero to one million.

Language Arts Science fiction is one of the largest genres of literature. Many science fiction books are a mixture of fact and fantasy. Ask students to write a science fiction short story to describe the events of a first encounter between humans and extraterrestrials. Encourage students to read their stories to the class. During class discussion, ask students to distinguish the facts from the fiction in each story.

Earth. Scientists began the first search for radio signals from extraterrestrial life in 1960. In 1973 the "Big Ear" program at Ohio State University became the first full-time search program. Another major project, Megachannel Extraterrestrial Assay (META), involves an ongoing spot search for radio signals.

Beginning in the fall of 1992, NASA is scheduled to participate in the search. Radio telescopes around the world—including the world's largest, the 1,000-foot dish in Puerto Rico—will be listening for signals from over 1,000 stars within 100 light-years of Earth. Scientists have expected that in its first half hour of operation, this project will generate more information than all previous programs put together.

- *How might a radio message from extraterrestrial life change life on Earth?*

The Connection to Other Sciences

Every second at each NASA observational site, computers process enough data to fill a complete set of encyclopedia. Among all this data, researchers are looking for patterns of signals from an intelligent source. This comprehensive data analysis is possible only because of technological advancements in computer science.

- *How have advancements in computer science affected the search for extraterrestrial life?*

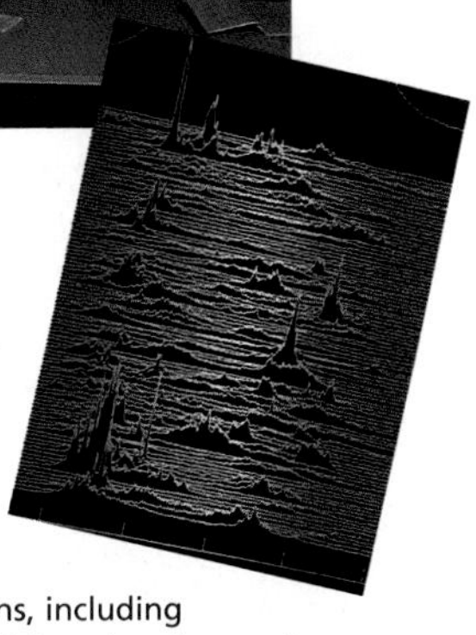

The Connection to Careers

As technological advances have expanded our capabilities for space exploration, scientists have begun to take the search for extraterrestrial life more seriously. The search attracts people from various vocations, including biologists, astronomers, physicists, chemists, and geologists. In addition, other professionals, such as engineers, computer scientists, and even anthropologists, are contributing to the study of life on other planets. For more information on related careers in the biological sciences, turn to page 842.

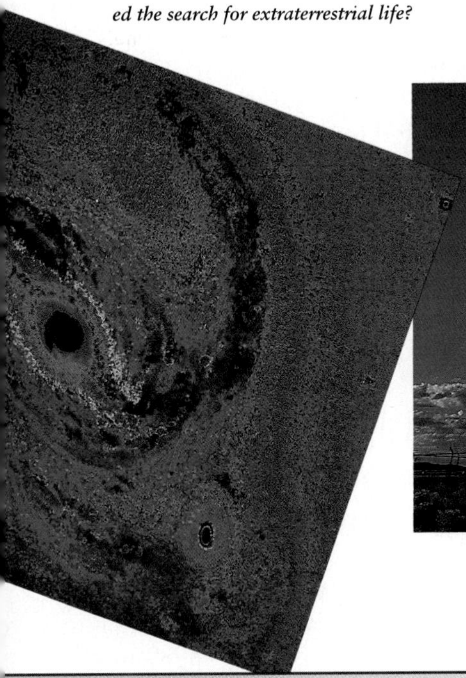

Intra-Science

7. Besides the long travel time, describe some other problems people must consider before traveling to a planet in another solar system. *(Students may mention a variety of problems, especially those related to the biological necessities of human life.)*

8. What reasonable predictions might you make regarding the intellect of a being capable of transmitting radio or other signals throughout space? *(In addition to being highly intelligent, the communicating extraterrestrial is likely to have an excellent understanding of science, math, and technology, like most scientists and technicians on earth.)*

9. Explain why governmental and private funds should or should not support the scientific search for extraterrestrial life. *(Answers will vary. Students should be encouraged to express and explain their opinions. Many may comment that social and economic needs on earth outweigh the need for expensive scientific research in space.)*

Answers to

Astronomy The discovery of planets in another solar system may further explain the natural phenomena of our own planet and solar system.

Physics Some scientists speculate that radio contact from extraterrestrial beings would affect civilization more than the discovery of earth's true shape.

Other Sciences Advancements in computer technology make it possible to analyze huge quantities of data in a short amount of time.

Enrichment

Most scientists involved in the search for extraterrestrial life doubt that our first contact would be a visitor from outer space arriving on earth. Ask students to find out why scientists believe such a scenario is unlikely.

Unit 5 Microorganisms

Chapters

Unit Overview

Unit 5 begins the taxonomic study of living organisms by examining the kingdoms Monera, Protista, and Fungi. Chapter 19 introduces viruses and compares them with living and nonliving things. In Chapter 20 students will learn about the classification, structure, and physiology of monerans. In Chapter 21 students begin the study of protists by examining protozoa and learning the chief characteristics of the four protozoan phyla. Chapter 22 continues the study of protists by focusing on algae. Chapter 23 introduces fungi and compares them with funguslike protists.

Issues in Biology

Use your discretion in introducing the following topic for class discussion, and be sensitive to family and community values.

During the past several years, sexually transmitted diseases have been on a steady rise in the United States. One of the least familiar—though the most widespread—is chlamydia. Each year an estimated 4 million Americans are infected with the bacterium *Chlamydia trachomatis*. This bacterium has been called a "microbial Stealth" (analogous to the missile) because it produces few immediate noticeable symptoms. However, though chlamydia is treatable with antibiotics, it leads to infertility in more than 20,000 women annually and is linked to a dramatic rise in tubal pregnancies.

Have students consider the disadvantages of sexually transmitted diseases against the advantages of abstinence and safe-sex practices. Ask students to speculate on why chlamydia is not well known and suggest how people can be made more aware of this disease.

Research in Progress

As early as the 1860s, scientists recognized that lichens are very sensitive to air pollution as some species died out in urban areas. Today scientists in Los Angeles use a species of lichen as a bioindicator that helps monitor air pollution. In one test, lichens are ground up and heated to form gases, the components of which are separated by a gas chromatograph. Then a mass spectrometer, which identifies elements, isotopes, and organic molecules by their mass and electric charge, is used to identify the components of urban pollutants.

Analysis of lichens has helped scientists recognize that air pollution is more widespread than they suspected. For example, lichens gathered from Isle Royale in Lake Superior have shown high levels of sulfur dioxide, though no factories or autos are nearby. Lichens gathered from northern Europe have shown quantities of radioactive elements from Chernobyl, the site of a nuclear power plant disaster in the Soviet Union.

Interdisciplinary Activity

Health Almost every pathogen that infects humans can be classified as either a virus, moneran, protist, or fungus. Fortunately, many medicines are derived from organisms in these same groups. Divide the class into small groups and have them research the diseases and medicines associated with microorganisms discussed in Unit 5. Create a large table students can fill in with the name of each disease, organism that causes it, symptoms, and treatment. Another table could have spaces for students to list each medicine, organism from which it is derived, and diseases it is used to treat. Help students make connections between the two tables.

Resources

Chapter	Print: For the Teacher	Print: For the Student	Audiovisual/Software
19	■ Arnold J. Levine, *Viruses,* Scientific American Library, 1992. ■ Abner Louis Notkins and Michael B. A. Oldstone, *Concepts in Viral Pathogenesis III,* Springer-Verlag, 1989.	■ John Langone, "Emerging Viruses," *Discover,* December 1990, 63–68. ■ J. R. Sullivan, "Viruses at Sea," *SeaFrontiers,* September-October 1990, 24–28.	■ *Viruses.* Video, 16 min. Lucerne Films, 1987. ■ *Viruses: What They Are and How They Work.* Film or video, 18 min. Encyclopædia Britannica, 1988.
20	■ Vincent A. Fischetti, "Streptococcal M Protein," *Scientific American,* October 1990, 76–92. ■ Frederick C. Neidhardt et al., *Physiology of the Bacterial Cell: A Molecular Approach,* Sinauer Associates, 1990.	■ K. A. Fackelmann, "Pipe-dwelling Bacteria Use Slimy Strategy," *Science News,* January 6, 1990, 6. ■ Carol L. Moberg, "Penicillin's Forgotten Man: Norman Heatley," *Science,* August 16, 1991, 734–735.	■ *Bacteria.* Film, 23 min. National Geographic, 1985. ■ *The Isolation and Growth of Bacteria.* Video, 15 min. Films for the Humanities & Sciences. Distributed by Carolina Biological.
21	■ Graham Bell, *Sex and Death in Protozoa,* Cambridge University Press, 1988. ■ Gerald J. Tortora, Berdell R. Funke, and Christine L. Case, *Microbiology: An Introduction,* 3rd ed., Benjamin/Cummings, 1989.	■ R. Cowen, "Genetic Trickery Probes Tropical Parasites," *Science News,* November 10, 1990, 292. ■ Sandra L. Hersh, "Marine Hitchhikers," *SeaFrontiers,* July-August 1990, 24–26.	■ *Living Things in a Drop of Water,* 2nd ed. Film, 12 min. Encyclopædia Britannica, 1985. ■ *The Microorganism Simulator.* Apple II, 48K. Disk. Focus, 1987. ■ *Protists: Form, Function, and Ecology.* Film or video, 23 min. Encyclopædia Britannica, 1985.
22	■ Harold C. Bold and Michael J. Wynne, *Introduction to Algae: Structure and Reproduction,* 2nd ed., Prentice-Hall, 1985. ■ Robert Edward Lee, *Phycology,* 2nd ed., Cambridge University Press, 1989.	■ J. Emmett Duffy and Mark E. Hay, "Seaweed Adaptations to Herbivory," *BioScience,* May 1990, 368–374. ■ Glen Martin, "Otter Madness," *Discover,* July 1990, 36–39.	■ *Algae.* Film or video, 14 min. Encyclopædia Britannica, 1988. ■ *Making Seaweeds Worth Eating.* Video filmstrip or transparencies with cassette, 22 min. Teacher's guide. Biology Media.
23	■ David Arora, *Mushrooms Demystified: A Comprehensive Guide to the Fleshy Fungi,* 2nd ed., Ten Speed Press, 1986. ■ Elizabeth Moore-Landecker, *Fundamentals of the Fungi,* 3rd ed., Prentice-Hall, 1990.	■ Donald W. Jackson, "Nature's Little Wonders," *The Conservationist,* March-April 1991, 42–47. ■ Raymond Sokolov, "The Universal Mushroom," *Natural History,* December 1990, 78–83.	■ *Fungi,* revised edition. Film, 14 min. Encyclopædia Britannica, 1987. ■ *The Impact of Fungi on Man and His Environment.* Video filmstrip or transparencies with cassette, 21 min. Teacher's guide. Carolina Biological.

Introducing the Unit

The material on cells in Unit 2 and the discussion of prokaryotes and eukaryotes in Unit 4 provide background for the study of microorganisms. The explanation of classification at the end of Unit 4 leads into the taxonomic study of organisms. Ask the following questions to introduce microorganisms.

1. Based on what you have learned about the five-kingdom system of classification, which kingdoms do you think are included under the general heading *Microorganisms? (Monera, Protista, Fungi)*

2. From what you have learned, give examples of organisms in each kingdom. *(Students can mention any bacteria for Monera, examples of protozoa and algae for Protista, and any type of fungus for Fungi.)*

3. Speculate on the types of environments in which you might find microorganisms. What roles do you think that they play? *(Microorganisms are found in every environment, from bottoms of oceans to tops of mountains and everywhere in between. Microorganisms are also found living in every other type of organism. There are autotrophic microorganisms and heterotrophic ones, including predators, saprophytes, and those in symbiotic relationships.)*

4. From what you learned about the structures of living things, what is the simplest form a microorganism can take and still be considered a living thing? *(It could be unicellular with a cell membrane, cytoplasm, and a chromosome made of DNA.)*

Unit 5 Microorganisms

Chapters

"Nature is to be found in her entirety nowhere more than in her smallest creatures."

Pliny the Elder

When you think about living things, you may tend to think only of plants and animals. In this unit, however, you will learn about the great diversity of living things that are neither plants nor animals—bacteria, protozoa, algae, and fungi. You will also learn about viruses, which stand at the boundary between the living and the nonliving worlds.

Mushrooms, *Hygrophorus miniatus*

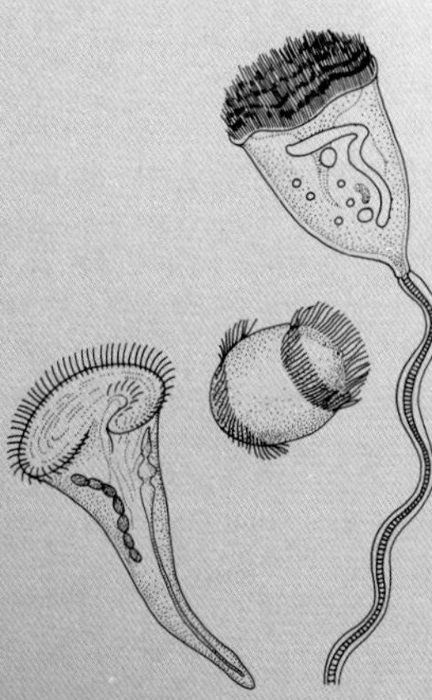

Three protozoa (left to right): *Stentor, Didinium, Vorticella*

Using the Opening Quotation

Read the opening quotation aloud and challenge students to speculate on its meaning. *(In the smallest creatures, one can more easily get a sense of the interactions among organisms and between them and the environment in order to appreciate the complexity of the biosphere.)* Ask students if they agree with the quotation. *(Encourage students to give rationales for their opinions.)*

Point out that Pliny the Elder was a Roman scholar and author of a 37-volume natural history. He lived from A.D. 23 to 79, long before the invention of the microscope. Ask students how the quote could apply to microorganisms. *(The essential components of life can be found even in the smallest organism.)*

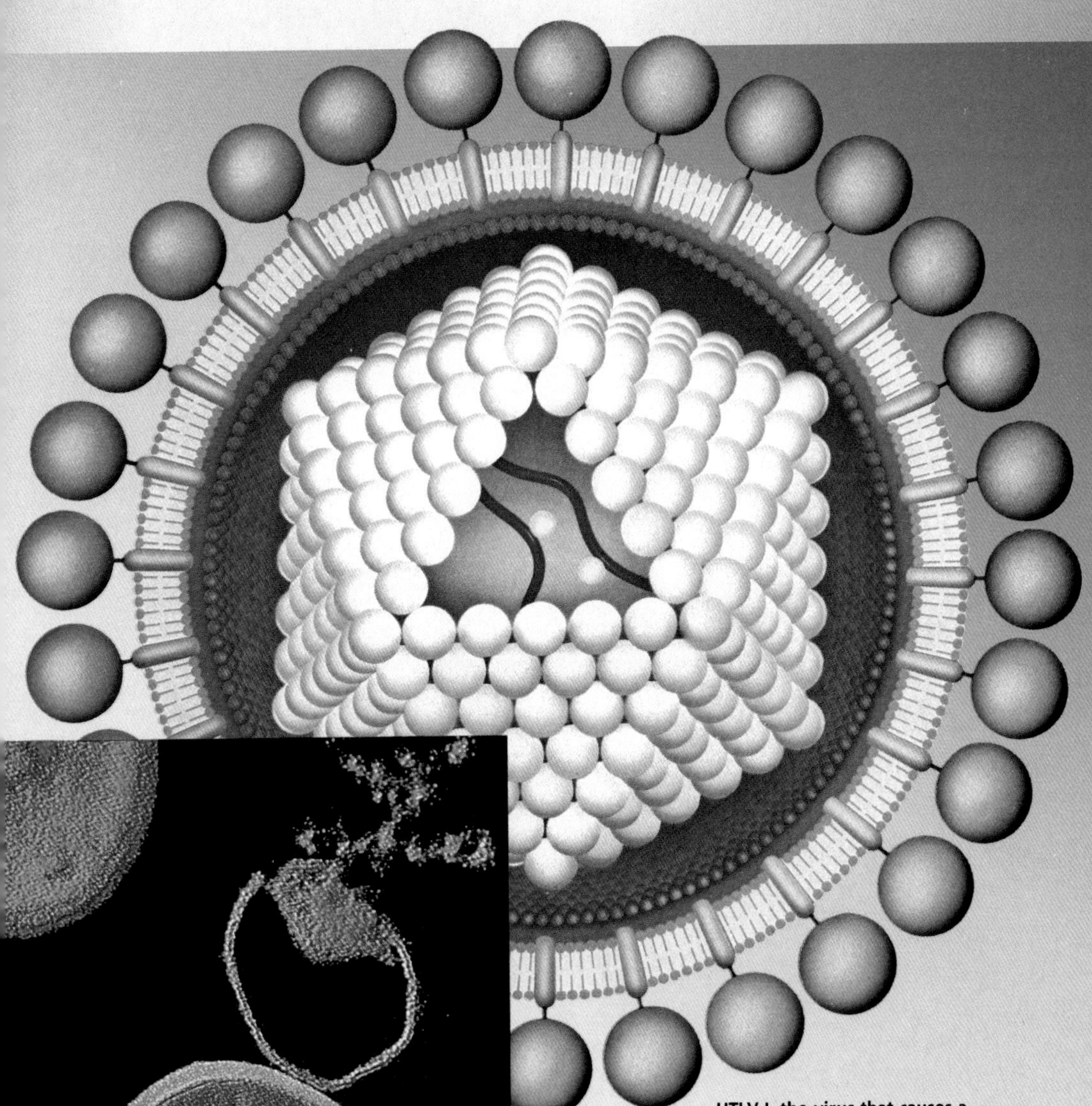

HTLV-I, the virus that causes a form of human leukemia

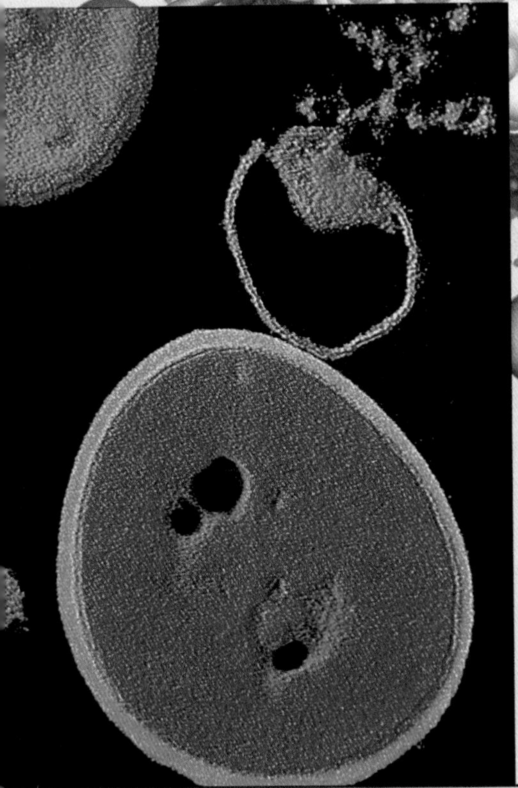

Bacteria, *Staphylococcus aureus* (bacterium at top bursting due to effects of antibiotics, ×41,000)

Unit Themes

Evolution The taxonomic study of microorganisms points out the evolution of organisms from simple to complex. This is evident in the evolution of prokaryotes (Chapter 20) and eukaryotes (Chapter 21). According to endosymbiosis, some organelles arose from parasitic prokaryotes (Chapter 21). Scientists also hypothesize that green algae (Chapter 22) are ancestors of plants. Fungi (Chapter 23) probably arose from prokaryotes, or possibly from red algae.

Patterns of Change The life cycles of various microorganisms are examples of cyclic change. The lytic and lysogenic cycles in viruses (Chapter 19) demonstrate how viruses cause changes in their hosts. Similar patterns can be observed in the reproductive life cycles of unicellular and multicellular algae (Chapter 22) and fungi and funguslike protists (Chapter 23).

Scale and Structure The scale of monerans, protists, and fungi varies from unicellular to colonial to multicellular. Viruses (Chapter 19) and some bacteria (Chapter 20) are so small that they can invade host cells. Structures such as the locomotive structures in protozoa (Chapter 21) are used to classify microorganisms.

Systems and Interactions Microorganisms interact with other organisms and the environment in many ways. Pathogenic microorganisms such as viruses (Chapter 19) and some bacteria (Chapter 20) cause diseases. Autotrophs such as algae (Chapter 22) are the first links in many food chains. Saprophytes such as fungi (Chapter 23) break down organic material and release basic nutrients. Lichens and mycorrhizae (Chapter 23) are examples of mutualism.

Understanding the Visuals

Have students survey the visuals and consider the scale of the organisms they represent. Which image appears the largest? *(The virus)* How do you think that this compares with its actual size? *(Viruses are the smallest objects depicted; they can only be observed with electron microscopes.)* Ask how the actual size of the bacteria compares with the actual size of the protozoa. *(The bacteria are smaller than the protozoa, which can be easily seen with a light microscope.)* How do you think that the photo of the mushrooms compares with their actual size? *(It is slightly larger than life size.)* Lead students to conclude that not all organisms they will study in this unit are microscopic. Point out, however, that microorganisms are included in each of the kingdoms Monera, Protista, and Fungi.

Chapter 19 Viruses

Chapter Overview

Chapter 19 examines the characteristics of viruses that contribute to their success as infectious agents. Section 19.1 explains how viruses are identified and classified by their structures. Section 19.2 makes connections between structure, reproductive processes, and disease as it describes the phases of virus reproduction.

Chapter Planning Chart

B	S	A	Sections and Subsections	Page	Features	Page	Resources
•	•	•	**19.1 Structure and Classification**				
			Studying Viruses	283	Biology in Process	286	Videodiscs
			Structure	284	Section Review	287	Process Skills: Viruses: Living or Nonliving?
			Classification	285			Laboratories: Virus Models
							Section Reviews Worksheet
•	•	•	**19.2 Reproduction and Evolution**				
			The Lytic Cycle	288	Laboratory	291	Videodiscs
			The Lysogenic Cycle	289	Section Review	290	Blackline Master 39
			Evolution	290			Blackline Master 40
							Overhead Transparency T19
							Section Reviews Worksheet
			End of Chapter Activities				
					Chapter Review	292	Vocabulary Skills
							Chapter Test
							Computer Test Generator

B *The Basic Level curriculum presents the most fundamental knowledge offered in the course.*
S *The Standard Level curriculum is designed for the average student who is able to master most topics.*
A *The Advanced Level curriculum includes suggestions for teaching the most academically able students.*

Cooperative Learning

Group Activity: Viral Diseases

- **Group Size:** *4 students*
- **Outcome:** *Students will make connections between viral groups and the diseases they cause.*
- **Individual Accountability:** *Each student will research one aspect of viral structure or disease.*
- **Positive Interdependence:** *Each group will depend on the efforts of its members to present their viral group to the class.*

Have each group of students choose a viral group from Table 19-2, pp. 284–85. Ask one student in each group to research the name of the viral group and devise a visual to show how the prefix of the group name describes the diseases caused by such viruses. Have another student research one disease caused by a virus in the viral group. Have two students prepare a poster or chart displaying information they have compiled about target host cells, transmission, infection mode, symptoms, and vaccines. Then have each group work together to make a model of a typical virus from their viral group. The scale for the model should be one millimeter equals one nanometer.

When their work is complete, have each group give a presentation about their viral group to the class. Encourage students to discuss and explain their results.

Concept Map

The following is one possible solution to the concept mapping activity in Cooperative Learning on p. 285.

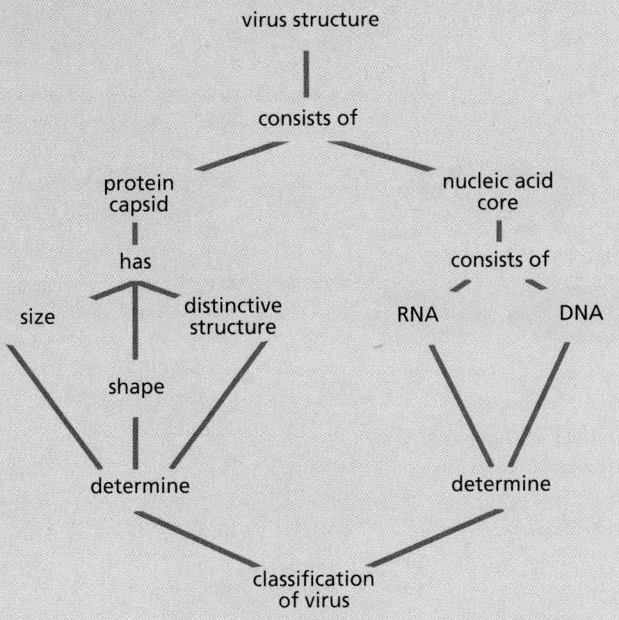

Laboratory Preparation

Overview *(See p. 291.)*

In this lab exercise, students investigate the effects of the tobacco mosaic virus (TMV) on healthy plants. Students obtain TMV from cigarette tobacco and prepare mixtures for applying the virus to plant leaves. They develop a hypothesis about the effect of TMV on tobacco and then design an experiment to test that hypothesis.

When healthy tobacco plants are attacked by TMV, their leaves become bleached or mottled yellow. TMV is just one of many viral diseases in plants. TMV is important in the history of science; almost 100 years ago, researchers realized that a tobacco disease could be transmitted by what they then called a "filterable agent"—something not removed by the finest of filters that would separate bacteria. Later, researchers identified filterable agents as viruses.

Preparation

Start tobacco seedlings about two weeks prior to the lab. Tobacco seeds or preplanted seedlings can be obtained from biological supply houses.

To prepare 0.1 *M* dibasic potassium phosphate solution, add 6.8 g KH_2PO_4 and dilute to 500 mL with distilled water.

Extract tobacco from cigarettes of various brands before the lab. Place each brand in a separate dish.

Teaching Tips

Have students read the Technique section of the lab before they design their inquiry.

Review with students the scientific processes they will use. These include hypothesizing, experimenting, analyzing data, inferring, and communicating. A reference experiment or review of terms may help students recall how to establish independent and dependent variables and controls in their experiments. Advise students to think about potential errors before beginning.

Point out that by using the controls identified in step 4 of Inquiry, students can identify which of the materials transmits the virus.

Safety

Remind students that although they cannot be infected by TMV, they should thoroughly wash their hands and all laboratory equipment that has come into contact with TMV. Students should also conduct this investigation away from gardens and house plants because TMV spreads from plant to plant.

Chapter Themes

Systems and Interactions Although viruses are considered nonliving, they can interact with a variety of organisms, as do many infectious organisms. Help students recognize that although viruses have few characteristics of life, they are highly effective agents of infection.

Evolution The impact of viruses on the evolution of other cells is evident in the manner of viral reproduction. Stress to students that viral reproduction and transduction have real effects on subsequent populations of both viruses and the cells they encounter.

Scale and Structure Point out the unique features of viral structure, including a nucleic acid within a protein coat. Emphasize that the components of a virus contribute to the virus's sole lifelike function—reproduction.

Chapter Motivating Activity

Display illustrations or three-dimensional models of some typical viruses. Several examples can be found in Table 19-2. Ask students to describe the different shapes as you display them. Then monitor small-group discussions in which students brainstorm everything they know about viruses at this time. In addition to viral diseases, students might consider topics such as size, shape, physical structure and composition, function, and so on. Have volunteers in each group make a list of student responses on chart paper. Call on students to present the charts during class discussion.

Chapter 19 *Viruses*

Introduction

Viruses are organisms that straddle the threshold between living and nonliving things. They lack several of the essential features of all life-forms and reproduce by taking over the genetic machinery of host cells. The release of viruses from host cells results in the spread of many infectious diseases in both plants and animals.

Chapter Outline

Chapter Concept

As you read, look for ways in which the structure and reproduction of viruses make them highly effective agents of infection.

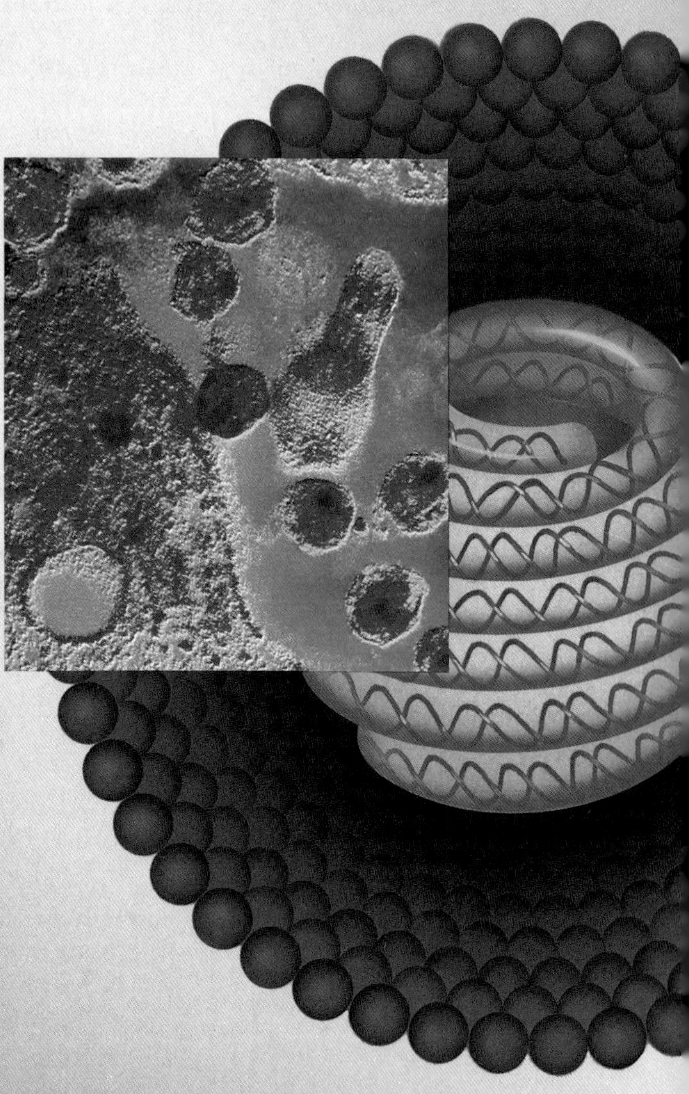

Artist's model of an influenza virus. Inset: Color-enhanced TEM of AIDS (HIV) virus inside a stricken T4 cell (×30,000).

Understanding the Visuals

Have students study the artist's model of the influenza virus. Ask students how many parts they can see. *(Three—the outer layer, the inner double-stranded helix, and the vertical helix)* Ask students to compare the outer layer to something in their everyday life. *(Perhaps a collection of tennis balls or "bubble wrap")* Elicit suggestions on the purpose of the vertical helix. *(It envelopes the double-stranded helix.)*

Ask students to identify the viruses inside the cell in the inset. *(The yellow-orange stained areas are made of viruses.)* Encourage students to offer views about the consequences of HIV within a T4 cell. *(HIV destroys T4 cells.)*

19.1 Structure and Classification

A **virus** is a biological particle composed of genetic material and protein. A typical virus consists of either RNA or DNA encased in a protein coat called a **capsid.** When a virus causes a disease, the virus is said to be **virulent** *(VIR-yuh-lunt).* If the virus does not cause disease immediately, it is said to be **temperate.**

Viruses are constructed of compounds usually associated with cells, but they are not considered living organisms. They have some, but not all, of the characteristics of life listed in Chapter 1. They have no nucleus, cytoplasm, organelles, or cell membrane. They do not reproduce by either mitosis or meiosis, nor are they capable of carrying out cellular functions. Study Table 19-1, in which viruses are compared and contrasted with cells.

Because they are not cells, viruses can only reproduce by invading a host cell and using the enzymes and organelles of the host cell to make more viruses. They are therefore **obligate intracellular parasites,** which means they require a host cell to reproduce. Outside a host cell a virus is a lifeless particle with no control of its movements. It is spread on the wind, in water, in food, or via blood or other bodily secretions.

Studying Viruses

Scientists knew as early as 1800 that some factor existed that was smaller than bacteria and that could transmit disease. However, they were unaware of the nature of the factor until 1935, when Wendell Stanley (1904–1971) first isolated the virus that causes tobacco mosaic disease. The electron microscope was the first tool that permitted scientists actually to look at viruses. Recent advances such as tissue culture, serology, electrophoresis, and nucleic acid sequencing help virologists learn more about viruses.

Tissue culture is the growing of living cells in a controlled medium. This technique is the foundation for viral research. By

Table 19-1 Comparing Viruses and Cells

	Virus	Cell
Structural parts	Protein, nucleic acid core	Nucleus, cytoplasm, organelles, membrane
Nucleic acid	Either DNA or RNA	Both DNA and RNA
Reproduction	Requires a host cell	By mitosis and meiosis
Cellular respiration	No	Yes
Crystallization	Yes	No

Section Objectives

- *Compare and contrast viruses and cells.*
- *Describe the structure of three types of disease-causing viruses.*
- *Distinguish between DNA and RNA viruses.*
- *Name and describe two disease-causing particles that are smaller than viruses.*
- *State how Pasteur developed a rabies vaccine.*

Lesson Plan

Section Focus

This section explains how viruses are studied and classified. It introduces the basic structural components of viruses and gives examples of diseases caused by viruses, viroids, and prions. Students will learn how viral structure is related to function.

Section Themes

This section stresses two themes: **Scale and Structure** and **Systems and Interactions.** Although the structure of a virus limits viral activity to that of an obligate intracellular parasite, the genetic composition of a virus determines its interaction with a host organism. The result of the interaction is often a disease in the host.

Motivating Activity

Explain to students that many common diseases are caused by either bacterial or viral infection. Point out that while antibiotics cure many bacterial diseases, drugs have not been developed to cure many viral illnesses. Ask students how a viral illness is eventually cured. *(The immune system produces antibodies that help to destroy the virus.)* Have students make a list of 10 to 20 diseases. Then challenge them to identify the diseases caused by viruses. Make a composite list of viral diseases on the board. Ask students how people treat common viruses such as colds or chicken pox. *(With rest, fluids, diet, vitamins, medications, and remedies that relieve symptoms or bolster the immune system)*

Videodiscs

- ***Side 1 33499, Cell Structure: General Functional Anatomy (m)***
- ***Side 1 25971, DNA Replication (m)***
- ***Side 1 22695, Protein Synthesis (m)***

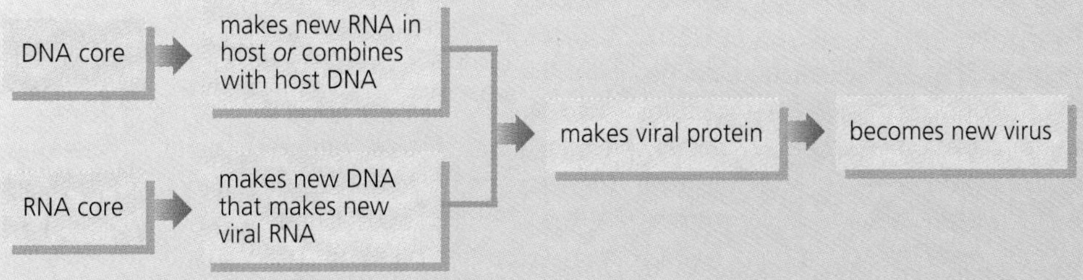

Graphic Organizer Use this sequential diagram in Sequencing Events on p. 285.

Teaching Strategies

Identifying Viruses Provide students with copies from a microbiology textbook of electron micrographs of animal or plant cells, bacteria, and viruses. Clarify which characteristics make viruses distinct from bacteria or other cells by asking students to compare the components of a virus with the components of a typical animal cell like the one shown on p. 66 of their textbooks. Describe some of the components that may not be visible, such as DNA or RNA. Emphasize the tiny size of viruses (many of them could fit inside a cell). Then ask students what advantages viruses derive from their extremely small size and relatively simple composition. *(Because of their size, viruses can invade and infect a variety of host cells. Viruses can spread widely and remain inactive in a lifeless state until they become active within host cells.)*
■ *See* Process Skills, *Chapter 19.*

Inferring Relationships Ask students to describe those pieces of computer code commonly called "computer viruses." *(A sequence of instructions, secretively inserted into a software program, that causes the computer to halt its programmed activity and replicate the virus's instructions)* Ask students to relate the action of a biological virus to that of a computer virus. *(A biological virus directs the genetic code of a cell to replicate the virus; similarly, a computer virus controls programmed code to force the computer to copy the virus.)*

Exploring Careers Invite a representative from an AIDS research laboratory, public health clinic, or hospital to talk about the techniques used to study viruses. Have students formulate several thoughtful questions in advance.

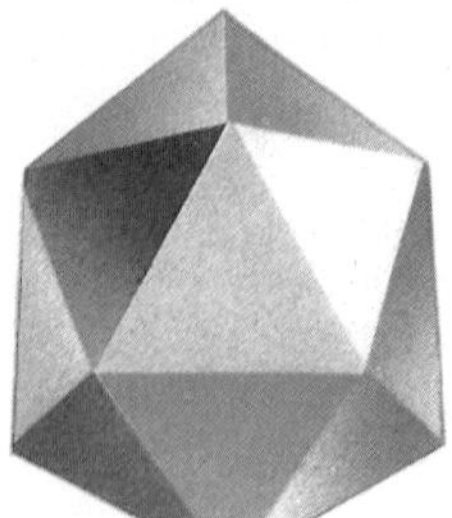

Figure 19-1 Many viruses, including the polio virus, are shaped like polyhedrons and typically are covered by a protein coat called a capsid.

infecting a tissue culture of living cells with a strain of a virus, researchers can grow viruses and examine them.

Researchers grow large quantities of a virus in tissue cultures and then subject the viruses to serological and electrophoretic studies. **Serology** *(suh-RAHL-uh-jee)* is the study of biological fluids. In particular, serologists often determine an organism's antibody responses to viruses. **Electrophoresis** *(ih-LECK-truh-fuh-REE-sus)* is a process that separates fragments of large molecules, such as proteins and DNA, on the basis of their electrical charge and size. Electrophoresis can be used to determine the protein components of viruses. In addition, DNA and RNA sequencing have enabled virologists to determine the sequence of bases in viral nucleic acids. Using these techniques and others, virologists have determined the structures of many viruses.

Structure

The structure of the polio virus shown in Figure 19-1 is typical of many viruses. The virus particle is about 20 to 30 nm in diameter. The capsid is shaped like an **icosahedron** *(ie-KOE-suh-HEE-drun)*—a polyhedron with 20 triangular faces. The capsid is made of protein subunits that fit together like the pieces of leather on a soccer ball. The capsid surrounds a single strand of RNA.

Most icosahedral viruses are between 15 and 200 nm in diameter. The approximately 200 kinds of viruses that cause the common cold are mostly icosahedral viruses about the size and shape of the polio virus. Some viruses, such as the virus that causes tobacco mosaic disease, a disease of tobacco plants, are rod shaped when viewed under the electron microscope. These viruses have a helical strand of nucleic acid that runs the length of the

Table 19-2 Some Common Viruses That Cause Diseases

DNA Viruses

Viral Group	Size (nm)	Structure	Examples of Diseases Caused
Papovaviruses	45–55	Polyhedral	Warts
Adenoviruses	70–80	Polyhedral	Respiratory and intestinal infections, conjunctivitis, sore throat
Herpesviruses	150–200	Enveloped polyhedral	Herpes, chickenpox, shingles, infectious mononucleosis
Poxviruses	100 × 200 × 300	Helical	Smallpox

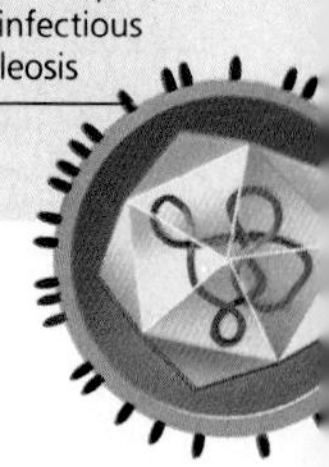

More Information

It is known that viral interaction can be highly specific to certain host organisms. Viral reproduction often occurs only in specific host cells as well. For example, of the influenza viruses, type A causes most flu epidemics, type B is found primarily in children, and type C is rare. Rabies afflicts several mammal species, but the virus infects only nerve cells. The AIDS virus, HIV, specifically attacks human T cells.

Viruses can also cause noninfectious diseases, such as tumors in plants and animals. Sometimes transduction alters a normal cell so that it divides uncontrollably, forming a tumor. The Rous sarcoma virus, for example, causes malignant tumors in chickens and other domestic fowl.

virus and is surrounded by a helically arranged protein coat. The protein coat makes up about 95 percent of the mass of this type of virus. Rabies and mumps are caused by helical viruses.

The virus that causes acquired immune deficiency syndrome, or AIDS, is even more complex. The AIDS virus is shown on the right. This virus, called the HIV, has two single strands of RNA in its core. These strands are surrounded by two layers of protein. A layer of lipids surrounds these inner protein layers. **Glycoprotein** molecules, proteins with sugar chains attached, are embedded in the lipid layer and form the capsid of the virus.

Classification

Because viruses are not considered living things, they are not classified by the system of nomenclature discussed in Chapter 18. Viruses instead are classified as DNA viruses or RNA viruses, depending on the type of nucleic acid in the capsid. As shown in Table 19-2, viruses contain either RNA or DNA, never both.

DNA and RNA Viruses

DNA and RNA viruses differ in the manner in which they alter the machinery of a host cell. Once inside the host cell, a DNA virus may directly produce new RNA that then makes more viral proteins. Alternatively the virus DNA may join to the DNA of the host cell and then direct the synthesis of new viruses.

RNA viruses perform in another way. Some RNA viruses enter the cell and make new proteins directly. They do so by releasing the RNA, which then migrates directly to the cytoplasm, where it uses the host ribosomes to make proteins. The polio virus, which is an RNA virus, acts in this manner.

RNA Viruses

Viral Group	Size (nm)	Structure	Examples of Diseases Caused
Picornaviruses	20–30	Polyhedral	Poliomyelitis, infectious hepatitis, common cold
Myxoviruses	80–120	Enveloped helical	Influenza A, B, C
Rhabdovirus	70 × 180	Enveloped helical	Rabies
Retroviruses	100	Glycoprotein enveloped complex	AIDS (depressed immune system)

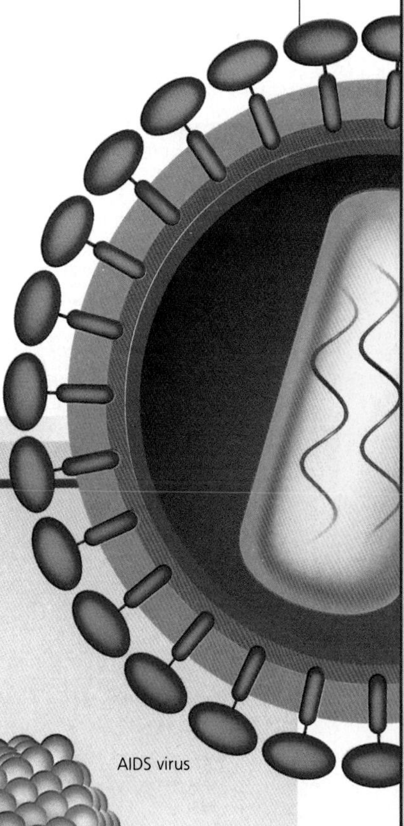

AIDS virus

Polyhedral

Section 19.1

Sequencing Events Direct students to read about virus classification on pp. 285 and 286. Ask students to draw a sequential diagram that shows the action pathways of DNA and RNA viruses. An example of a completed diagram is shown on p. 283.

Interpreting the Visuals Refer students to the viroid in Figure 19-2. Have them compare and contrast this particle with the viruses depicted on pp. 284 and 285. *(A viroid is smaller than a virus and has no surrounding capsid; it consists of a short, single strand of RNA.)*

Guided Practice

Refer students to the illustrations of viruses on pp. 284 and 285 and help them to understand that cutaway views show components that normally are difficult to observe even with very powerful imaging techniques, such as electronmicroscopy. Focus on what makes each virus unique, including size, shape, or special attachment structures. Have students draw their own labeled cutaway views of typical complex viruses. Hang the drawings up and help students identify the structures viruses have in common. *(One or more strands of DNA or RNA surrounded by a capsid)*

■ ***See* Laboratories, *Investigation 19.***

Independent Practice

■ Have students write answers to the Section Review.

■ Give students diagrams of several different viruses copied from a microbiology textbook and ask them to rank the viruses in order of complexity. Have students defend their choices.

Videodiscs

■ ***Side 1 30483, Tomato Virus—Assembly from Subunits (m)***

Cooperative Learning

Grouping Viral Structures Ask students to review Section 19.1 and jot down ideas about how the structural components and the nucleic acid core of viruses help scientists identify an unknown virus and place it in the proper viral group. Then have pairs of students share their ideas and concur on a concept map that integrates their ideas, showing how viral structure and nucleic acid core are related to the scientific description and classification of viruses. One example of such a map appears on p. 281B.

Check Your Understanding

1. Why is *obligate intracellular parasite* an accurate term for a virus? *(The existence and reproduction of a virus is dependent on a host cell.)*

2. What structural characteristics help virologists identify a virus? *(Nucleic acid core, capsid shape, complexity, and size)*

3. On what basis are viruses classified? *(Viruses are classified as DNA viruses or RNA viruses according to shape and the type of nucleic acid they contain.)*

Reteaching

Ask students to compare the components of a virus with the components of a typical plant cell like the one shown on p. 73 of their textbooks. Encourage students to identify some of the structural characteristics of the plant cell and the virus. Review some of the components that may not be visible, such as DNA or RNA.

■ *See* Section Reviews *worksheet, Section 19.1.*

Enrichment

Ask students to write an essay on whether it is possible to speak of "killing" a nonliving thing such as a virus. Students might first research what it means to kill a living thing such as a bacterium.

Figure 19-2 Viroids, which are smaller than viruses, cause diseases in some plants. They consist of a short, single strand of RNA.

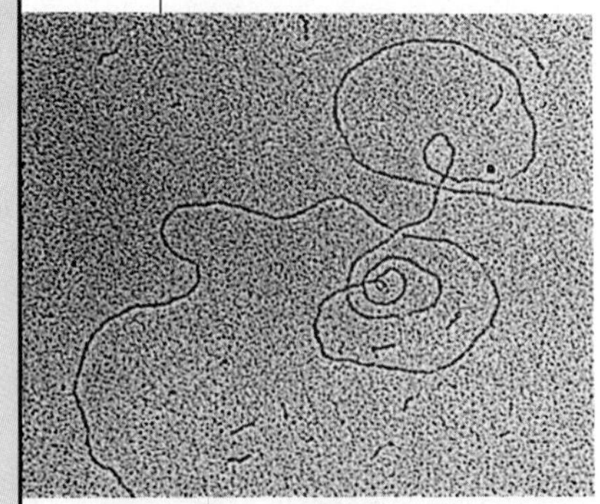

Other RNA viruses, called retroviruses, act differently. In addition to RNA, **retroviruses** contain an enzyme called reverse transcriptase. **Reverse transcriptase** is an enzyme that makes DNA from RNA. In normal cells, you recall, DNA makes RNA. The RNA in turn makes proteins. In retroviruses RNA makes DNA with the aid of reverse transcriptase. The DNA then makes the new RNA. This RNA in turn makes the proteins that become part of the new viruses. The AIDS virus is a retrovirus.

Viroids and Prions

In the last three decades scientists have isolated certain disease-causing particles that are smaller and simpler than viruses. One of these is the viroid. A **viroid** *(VIE-ROID)* is a short, single strand of RNA with no surrounding capsid. Look at the viroid pictured in Figure 19-2. The strand of RNA shown there looks like a tangled piece of string. It does not contain enough RNA to make proteins. Scientists suggest that this RNA strand somehow interferes with normal cell functions and causes the production of new viroid strands by using the host cell's enzymes. Diseases caused by viroids include those that harm potato, coconut, chrysanthemum, and citrus crops, as well as other plants.

Biology in Process

Louis Pasteur and the Rabies Treatment

Louis Pasteur was almost 60 years old and semi-paralyzed when in 1881 he began his search for a treatment to keep people who had contracted rabies from dying. To discover a treatment for this dread disease, Pasteur first had to find a way of growing a weakened strain of the germ. When injected, a weakened strain would help the body's disease-fighting mechanisms combat the rabies virus (right, ×65,400). Then he had to test the treatment before releasing it for widespread use.

Pasteur knew that rabies attacked nerve tissue; the mad behavior exhibited by rabid dogs was proof. Therefore, he reasoned, if he inoculated the brain of a healthy dog with the rabies virus, he could grow the virus in the animal. Pasteur did this and succeeded in culturing the virus.

Pasteur noted that all the dogs he had inoculated contracted the disease and that some managed to recover. Those that did recover became resistant to subsequent injections. This reaction, because it showed that this virus behaved like other microorganisms, suggested to Pasteur that a single infection could provide future immunity.

Interdisciplinary Activity

Geography Since 1981 when HIV, the virus that causes acquired immune deficiency syndrome (AIDS), was first identified, AIDS has become a major health concern worldwide. Have students locate statistics on AIDS cases for several years for as many countries or continents as possible. Suggest that students construct a table, write a report, or encode a world map to show the geographic distribution of AIDS worldwide. Have students search the data for trends in the spread of this disease.

A **prion** *(PREE-AHN)* is a glycoprotein particle containing a polypeptide of about 250 amino acids. Even without nucleic acids prions are capable of reproducing in some mammalian cells. Prions are implicated in diseases with long incubation periods. For instance, prions cause scrapie, a slow degeneration of the nervous system in sheep and goats. Another prion disease is kuru, a degenerative nerve disease that can be contracted by touching the brains of deceased individuals. It occurs among some New Guinea highland tribes whose funeral rites include touching the brains of deceased ancestors.

Section Review

1. What is a *capsid?*
2. What are the similarities between viruses and cells? What are the differences?
3. Compare and contrast the structures of a polio virus and a tobacco mosaic virus.
4. What is reverse transcriptase? What is its function?
5. Why might the study of viroids and prions lag behind the study of viruses?

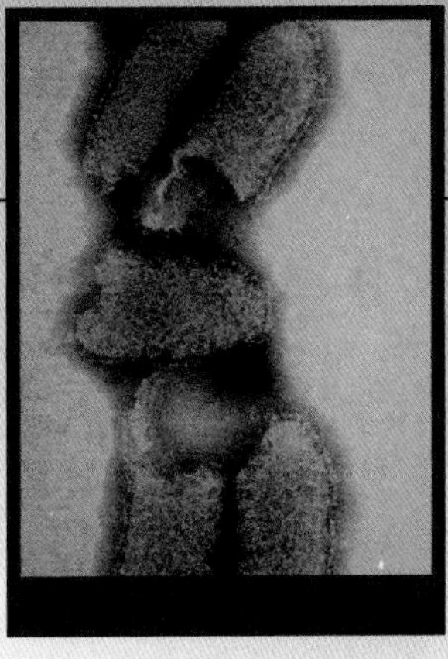

Pasteur next turned his attention to cultivating a weakened strain of the virus to use in his treatment. This time Pasteur injected the virus into a spinal cord removed from a rabbit. The spinal cord was then slowly dried. As the cord dried, the virulence of the virus decreased. By varying the time of drying Pasteur was able to produce virus samples of varying degrees of strength.

By 1884 Pasteur had developed a rabies treatment that consisted of a series of shots of increasingly virulent virus. He inoculated dogs with a series of virus samples. The first preparation contained dead viruses, which are harmless to the animal. Each subsequent shot was more virulent than the last. Finally he was able to prevent the expression of rabies in dogs.

Though this treatment worked well in animals, Pasteur was reluctant to try it on humans. "What is possible on the dog may not be so on man," he worried. In July 1885, however, two physicians pleaded with Pasteur to treat nine-year-old Joseph Meister, who had been bitten by a rabid dog. The physicians convinced Pasteur that without treatment Joseph was "doomed to inevitable death." The treatment was administered, and Joseph survived.

By the time of Pasteur's death in 1895, 20,000 people had been treated with "the Pasteur Treatment." The death rate was less than one-half of one percent.

■ Could Pasteur have tested his treatment in any way other than by using it on a human victim of rabies?

Closure

Ask students why viruses cannot be grown on nutrient agar as bacteria are, but must be cultured in living tissues. *(Viruses cannot carry out the cellular functions necessary for independent growth but can only reproduce within the cells of living tissues.)*

Biology in Process

Using the Feature

The feature focuses on the process skills of observing, hypothesizing, and experimenting. Emphasize that Louis Pasteur repeatedly used this sequence of skills to solve the problem of saving the lives of those who contracted rabies.

Point out that Pasteur's observations of mad behavior in rabid dogs led him to hypothesize that the rabies virus attacks nerve tissue. He tested this hypothesis by inoculating healthy dogs' brains with rabies. Ask students what Pasteur observed in the dogs he inoculated. *(Some died, while others recovered with immunity to the virus.)* What hypothesis did Pasteur form next? *(A single infection may not cause death and may provide future immunity to a virus.)* Ask students to explain how Pasteur tested this hypothesis. *(By inoculating dogs with a series of progressively stronger viral strains)*

Answer to the Feature

No; even though his rabies treatment was successful in dogs, Pasteur did not know whether it was effective in humans without testing it on them.

Answers to Section Review

1. A protein coat that encases the DNA or RNA of a virus

2. Both contain similar compounds; viruses lack cellular structures, do not perform cellular functions, and cannot reproduce independently.

3. Both have a protein coat that surrounds a nucleic acid core. Polio virus is icosahedral (or polyhedral) and TMV is helical.

4. An enzyme present in retroviruses; it makes DNA from RNA.

5. Due to small size and lack of certain viral characteristics, viroids and prions cannot be studied with all viral techniques.

Lesson Plan

Section Focus

This section focuses on the reproductive cycles of virulent and temperate viruses, both of which use the genetic apparatus of host cells. Students will learn how viral reproduction contributes to the disease and to the evolution and survival of new viruses in host cells.

Section Themes

The theme of **Systems and Interactions** is exemplified by the interactions of viruses with host cells during viral reproduction. The theme of **Evolution** is also associated with viral reproduction and transduction. Rapid reproduction of viruses and transduction of genetic material into host cells can influence the subsequent evolution of viruses and phenotypic variation in the host.

Motivating Activity

Direct students' attention to the photograph in Figure 19-5, p. 289, and ask them to identify the viruses and host cell. Ask students how they think so many viruses got into the cell. Emphasize that through reproduction one virus could produce all the others. Challenge students to calculate the number of viral replications needed for one virus to become 2048 viruses. *(11)*

Teaching Strategies

Inferring Relationships Explain that shingles is a disease that may develop years after a person has been infected by the chicken pox virus. Ask students to use their knowledge of viral reproduction to explain the reappearance of these diseases. *(The virus enters a lysogenic stage after the initial infection until it is reactivated to cause symptoms.)*

Section Objectives

- *Describe the structure of a bacteriophage.*
- *Name the five phases of the lytic cycle.*
- *Explain how the process of transduction occurs.*
- *State a possible theory for the evolution of viruses.*

19.2 Reproduction and Evolution

Scientists first learned about virus reproduction by studying **bacteriophages,** viruses that infect bacteria. Phages *(FAY-juz),* as they are called, can be easily studied because their bacterial hosts multiply quickly in cell cultures.

The most commonly studied phages are those of the T group. They are named T1, T2, T3, and so forth. The T phages infect the bacterium *Escherichia coli,* the common bacterium of the human digestive tract. The T-even phages (T2, T4, T6) are virulent. They are capable of destroying *E. coli* cells.

Examine the structure of the T4 phage in Figure 19-3. Notice that its morphology is different from that of the viruses described in Section 19.1. DNA in the viral core is surrounded by a protein coat that forms a polyhedron. Beneath the head is a collar of protein and a sheath that rests on a base plate. Tail fibers emerge from the base plate. As you read about the reproduction of the T4 phage, notice how the structure of the virus suits its function.

The Lytic Cycle

The **lytic cycle** is a fundamental reproductive process in viruses. The term *lyse* means to "break open," a reference to the liberation of the new viral particles from the host cell. The T4 phage reproduces by the lytic cycle and thus can serve as an example of viral reproduction. The lytic cycle has five phases, each of which is continuous with the others. The phases are adsorption, entry, replication, assembly, and release. Study Figure 19-4 as you read.

1. During adsorption the virus attaches itself to a specific host cell. The tail fibers of the virus contain proteins that have a chemical affinity with the bacterial cell wall. In fact, specific areas of the wall, called **receptor sites,** are the places where the virus attaches itself.
2. During entry the T4 phage releases an enzyme that weakens a spot in the cell wall of the host. Then, much like a hypodermic needle, the T4 presses its sheath against the cell and injects its

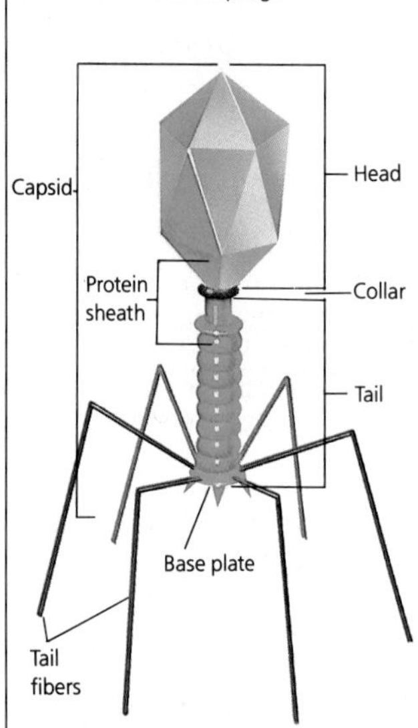

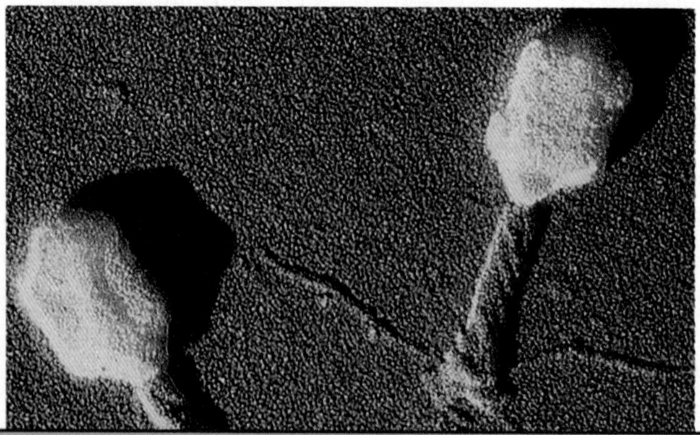

Figure 19-3 Note the polyhedral structure of a T4 bacteriophage (above). The false-color SEM (right) shows phages that infect *E. coli* (× 60,000).

CAUSE		EFFECT
adsorption: tail fibers of phage attach to cell wall	→	cell wall weakens at attachment

Graphic Organizer Use this cause-and-effect diagram in Guided Practice on p. 289.

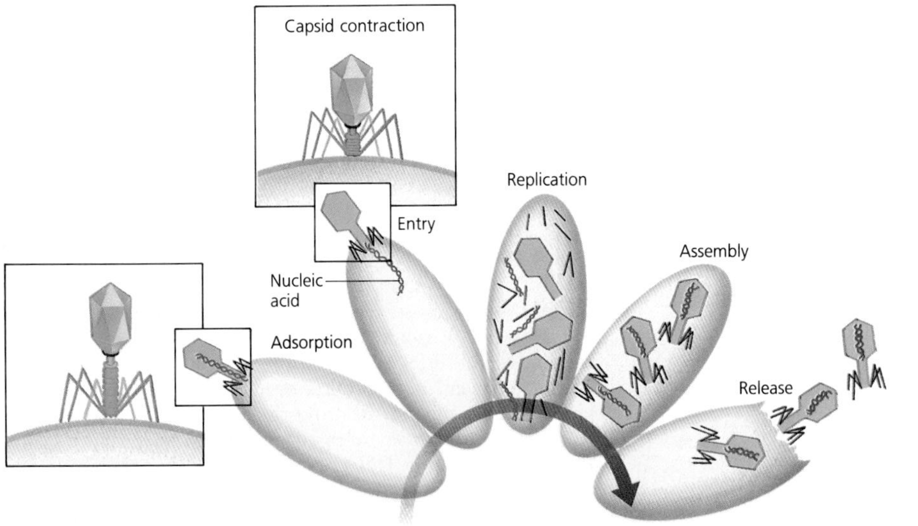

Figure 19-4 During a lytic cycle a phage goes through five phases during which it invades a host cell and eventually destroys the cell.

DNA into the host cell through the weak spot in the wall. The empty capsid remains on the outside of the cell. In contrast, many viruses enter their host cell intact. Once inside, the capsid dissolves and the genetic material is released. This process is called uncoating.

3. During replication the viral DNA takes complete control of cell activity. It inactivates the *E. coli* DNA. The genes contained in the DNA of the viral genome then take over. They direct the cell to make viral DNA and the viral proteins that make up the structural portions of the phage. This happens when viral DNA makes RNA from nucleotides in the host cell by using the enzymes of the host cell.
4. During assembly proteins coded for by phage DNA act as enzymes that put new virus particles together. The entire metabolic activity of the cell is thus directed toward assembling new T4 phages. The result is a cell stuffed with new viruses.
5. During release the T4 phages release an enzyme that digests the bacterial cell wall from within. The disintegration of the infected host cell, called **lysis** *(LIE-SISS)*, allows new viruses to leave the cell. The new virus particles can then infect other cells, and the process can start again.

Figure 19-5 The dark spots are phages that have been inside this *E. coli* cell 30 minutes. Notice that the heads of the phages point toward the center of the cell and the tails toward the membrane (×30,000).

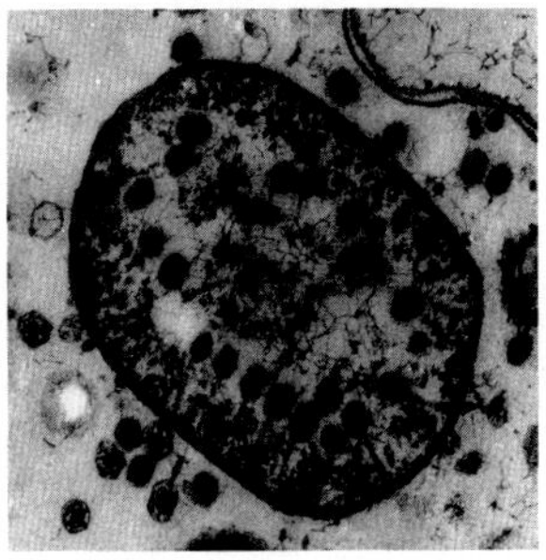

The Lysogenic Cycle

During the lytic cycle viruses enter the cell, use its components to make new viruses, and destroy the cell in one continuous process, which usually takes a day or two. However, some temperate viruses can infect a cell without causing its immediate destruction. Temperate viruses undergo a kind of life cycle called a **lysogenic cycle,** which has been most thoroughly studied in bacteriophages. Study this cycle in Figure 19-6 on the following page as you read.

Interpreting the Visuals Guide students through the structure of a bacteriophage, shown in Figure 19-3, p. 288. Ask them to describe how its structure suits its function. *(The DNA is protected by its capsid; tail fibers attach the phage to a host cell; the tail compresses to inject DNA into host.)* Have students trace the phases of the lytic cycle in Figure 19-4, p. 285. Which phase is most destructive to the host cell? *(Release; it disintegrates the cell.)*

■ ***See* Overhead Transparency *T19 and* Blackline Masters *39 and 40.***

Guided Practice

Have students construct a series of cause-and-effect diagrams like the one shown for the adsorption phase on p. 288 (Graphic Organizer). Tell them to describe the causes and effects for the phases of a bacteriophage lytic cycle, including entry, replication, assembly, and release. *(Entry: phage injects DNA, cell is invaded; replication: phage DNA controls cell activity, cell makes viral DNA and proteins; assembly: viral protein acts as enzyme, host cell metabolism directs assembly of new phages; release: new phages release enzyme that digests cell wall, releasing phages.)*

Independent Practice

■ Have students write answers to the Section Review.

■ Ask students how a medical researcher's understanding of the biological interactions of viruses with host cells will help develop treatments and cures for viral diseases. *(Such knowledge will help researchers understand how to interrupt or prevent viral interaction without killing the host cell or organism.)*

Videodiscs

■ *2539,* E. coli *(s)*

■ *2549, T4 Phage (s)*

LEP Activity

Refer students to the names of the five lytic phases depicted in Figure 19-4: *adsorption, entry, replication, assembly,* and *release*. Have students look up each term in a dictionary. Then have them draw pictures that symbolize each of these words. For example, a student may draw a key in a lock to show *adsorption*, a person passing through a door for *entry*, a pile of mimeographed sheets for *replication*, someone making a model for *assembly*, and fireflies escaping a jar for *release*. Have students share their drawings.

Check Your Understanding

1. How does the lysogenic cycle differ from the lytic cycle? *(Instead of immediately creating new RNA and proteins, the DNA of a temperate phage attaches to the host DNA and is replicated, causing no harm to host cells until external stimuli cause it to become virulent.)*

2. What role does natural selection play in the evolution of viruses? *(Natural selection favors the reproduction of, and thus evolution toward, those viruses best able to resist host immune systems.)*

Reteaching

Have small groups of students construct and label a model of a T phage using a round-headed bolt, one or two nuts, and stiff wire. Have students use Figure 19-3, p. 288, as a guide.

■ *See* Section Reviews *worksheet, Section 19.2.*

Enrichment

Have students research the history of viral diseases, such as yellow fever, smallpox, HIV, or rabies, and report on the effects of a particular virus on humans. Ask students to determine where and when the disease was first recorded, how it is transmitted, and any associated economic or social effects.

Closure

Ask students to classify the common cold, AIDS, rubella, cold sores, and mumps according to whether they are caused by virulent (lytic cycle) viruses or temperate (lysogenic cycle) viruses. *(Virulent: common cold, rubella, and mumps; temperate: AIDS and cold sores)* Ask students how the lysogenic cycle affects the rhythm of a disease. *(It halts both virus reproduction and associated disease manifestations.)*

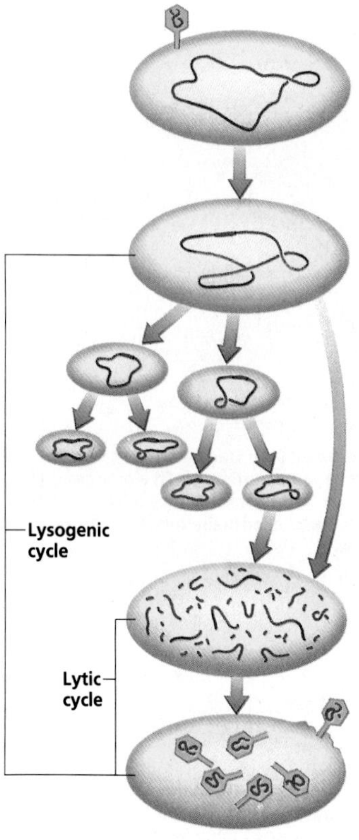

Figure 19-6 In contrast to a lytic cycle in which a phage quickly destroys a cell, in a lysogenic cycle a phage enters a cell and remains inactive until an external stimulus causes the phage to become virulent.

A temperate phage enters a bacterium in much the same way the T4 bacteriophage does, by attachment of tail fibers and injection of the DNA into the host cell. At this point, however, the lysogenic cycle differs from the lytic cycle. Instead of immediately creating new RNA and proteins the DNA of the temperate phage attaches itself to the host DNA. It becomes, in effect, an additional set of genes. The phage, now represented only by a short DNA segment, is called a **prophage.** When host DNA replicates or when the host cell divides, the prophage acts just like an inert segment of the DNA of the host. It causes no harm to the cell.

However, various external stimuli—exposure to radiation or certain chemicals, for instance—can cause the prophage to become virulent. It then takes over the host cell, produces new viruses, and ultimately destroys the cell.

Temperate viruses released during cell lysis may take with them a portion of the DNA of the host cell. When the phage enters a new host, it may introduce genes from the former host into the new host. In this process, called **transduction,** a virus transfers DNA from cell to cell and thus causes a change in the genetic code of bacterial cells. This results in genetic recombination and hence phenotypic variation in the new host bacterium.

Evolution

How and when did viruses evolve? No fossil evidence of viruses has been found. However, scientists form inferences about the evolution of viruses. Because they are obligate intracellular parasites, viruses probably did not arise until cells had evolved, since their existence requires cells. If this is so, then viruses probably either formed spontaneously from existing nonliving organic material or evolved as simplifications of previously existing cells.

Whatever their origin, existing viruses often evolve very rapidly by natural selection. Suppose that cold viruses invade a human body. The human immune system may destroy most of these viruses. The few that remain will have been naturally selected and will be resistant to immediate attack by the immune system. These resistant viruses enter cells and produce hundreds or thousands of viruses in a few days. The immune system will respond to repel the viruses eventually but not until many new ones have been formed. The short generation time of a virus means that natural selection acts quickly to select for viral types that are capable of withstanding destruction in the next host.

Section Review

1. What is a *prophage,* and how does it function?
2. How does a bacteriophage differ from a polyhedral virus?
3. What are the five phases of the lytic cycle?
4. Why do scientists think that viruses evolved after cells?
5. What is the significance of transduction?

Answers to Section Review

1. The DNA of a temperate phage attached to a host DNA; it replicates along with host DNA until an external stimulus causes it to become virulent and produce new viruses.

2. While both have a nucleic acid core surrounded by a polyhedral coat, a bacteriophage has a protein collar, protein sheath, base plate, and tail fibers extending beneath its polyhedral head.

3. Adsorption, entry, replication, assembly, and release

4. Viruses are obligate intracellular parasites. They probably did not arise until cells had evolved, forming from nonliving organic material or from existing cells.

5. It results in genetic recombination and phenotypic variation among bacteria.

Laboratory

Tobacco Mosaic Virus

Objective
To study the effect of the tobacco mosaic virus on leaves of tobacco plants

Process Skills
hypothesizing, experimenting

Materials
4 tobacco plants, glass-marking pencil, tobacco from several brands of cigarettes, mortar and pestle, 10 mL 0.1 *M* dibasic potassium phosphate solution, 100-mL beaker, cotton swabs, 400-grit carborundum powder

Background
The tobacco mosaic virus, TMV, infects tobacco as well as other plants.

1 What is a virus?
2 How do viruses enter a host cell?
3 In what form do viruses exist outside of host cells?
4 Describe how viruses spread among organisms.

Technique

1 Place pinches of tobacco from different brands of cigarettes into a mortar. Add 5 mL of potassium phosphate solution and grind the mixture with a pestle.
2 Pour the mixture into a beaker. This mixture can be used to infect the tobacco plants with TMV. What does this assume about cigarette tobacco? NOTE: Wash your hands and all laboratory equipment used in this step with soap and water. Why?
3 Moisten a swab with the mixture and sprinkle a small amount of carborundum powder onto the moistened swab. Apply the mixture to the tobacco leaf by scraping the swab over the surface several times. What is the purpose of the carborundum powder?

Inquiry

1 Discuss the objective of this laboratory with your partners and develop a hypothesis.
2 Design an experiment to test your hypothesis that uses the setup described above in Technique.
3 What are the independent and dependent variables in your experiment? How will you vary the independent variable? How will you measure changes in the dependent variable?
4 What controls will you include?
5 How will you record your results?
6 Obtain noninfected tobacco plants and proceed with your experiment after receiving approval from your teacher.

Conclusions

1 Do your data support your hypothesis? Explain.
2 What differences, if any, did you detect in the susceptibility of older and younger leaves to the virus?
3 What were some of the possible sources of error in your experiment?
4 Greenhouse operators generally do not allow smoking in their greenhouses. Aside from health and safety issues, how might your results support this rule?
5 What was the purpose of grinding the leaves in Technique, step 1? Why is tobacco from different brands of cigarettes used?

Further Inquiry
Tobacco Mosaic Virus is capable of infecting different species of plants. Design an experiment to determine which of several types of plants are most susceptible to the virus.

Conclusions

1. Students should recognize whether their data support their hypothesis.
2. Answers should be supported by data.
3. Errors could include insufficient grinding of leaves to obtain virus, inappropriate amount of carborundum, uneven amounts or uneven application of virus mixture, insufficient sampling of each leaf type, and contamination due to carelessness.
4. TMV in smoke may infect plants.
5. It releases the virus from infected cells. It increases the chance of obtaining TMV.

Further Inquiry

Students can apply the virus mixture to various plants and use an identical group of plants as controls.

(For an overview of tobacco mosaic virus and preparatory information related to the laboratory, see p. 281B.)

Background

1. A virus is a biological particle composed of genetic material and protein.
2. In the case of the T4 bacteriophage, the virus attaches to the cell wall of a host and releases an enzyme that weakens a spot in the wall. Then the virus injects its DNA into the host cell.
3. Outside of host cells, viruses are lifeless particles with no control of their movements.
4. Viruses are spread via wind, water, food, blood, or other bodily secretions.

Technique

2. Cigarette tobacco is commonly infected with TMV. Washing the equipment and hands decreases the possibility of accidental spread of the virus. To avoid infecting all the plants, stress the importance of using each swab only once.
3. The powder abrades the leaf and facilitates infection.

Inquiry

1. Encourage students to consider that older leaves may have a different susceptibility to TMV than younger leaves.
3. The independent variable is the virus mixture application; the dependent variable is any observed changes in the tobacco leaves at the application sites. Students can vary where they apply the virus mixture. They can draw, photograph, or make notes about the application sites.
4. Controls could be plants treated with potassium phosphate solution only, water and carborundum, potassium phosphate and carborundum, or simply water.
5. Students can present results in tables or graphs of area infected per unit of time.

Vocabulary

1. *Obligate* means "restricted to only one life-style"; *intracellular* means "occurring within a cell"; *parasite* means "an organism that lives in or on another organism." Thus, *obligate intracellular parasite* means that a virus can exist only by living within a cell.
2. Electrophoresis separates fragments of viral DNA and proteins by their electrical charges, providing data about structure. Serology reveals animal antibodies that develop in response to a virus; this is helpful in virus identification and disease diagnosis. Tissue cultures provide standardized media on which to grow and study viruses.
3. A phage is a bacteriophage, or virus that infects bacteria. A prophage is a segment of the DNA of a temperate virus that has attached to the DNA of a host cell.
4. Transduction is the viral transport of DNA from cell to cell.
5. *Lysis* means "a process of disintegration or dissolution (as of cells)." The lytic cycle is the series of phases that begins and ends with the breaking open of a cell wall. *Lysogenic* means "capable of causing or undergoing lysis."

Review

1. b **6.** b
2. c **7.** c
3. b **8.** d
4. d **9.** d
5. a **10.** b

11. Use of the electron microscope, infection of tissue cultures with specific strains of virus, serology, electrophoresis, and nucleic acid sequencing
12. It consists of a lipid layer, embedded with glycoprotein molecules, that surrounds two protein layers.
13. Retroviruses make DNA from RNA with the aid of an enzyme called reverse transcriptase. This DNA makes new RNA that makes new viral components.
14. Kuru is caused by prions and is contracted by handling infected human brains. The effect is a degenerative nerve disease.
15. They enable a bacteriophage to attach to a host cell by means of their chemical affinity with the cell wall.
16. The viral DNA inactivates the host cell DNA. Then the genes of the viral DNA use the genetic machinery of the host cell to make viral DNA and proteins, both components of new bacteriophages.
17. A virulent virus causes disease by destroying its host cell. A temperate virus acts as an inert part of the host cell genome until or if it is stimulated to become virulent.

Chapter 19 Review

Vocabulary

bacteriophage (288)
capsid (283)
electrophoresis (284)
glycoprotein (285)
icosahedron (284)
lysis (289)
lysogenic cycle (289)
lytic cycle (288)
obligate intracellular parasite (283)
prion (287)
prophage (290)
receptor site (288)
retrovirus (286)
reverse transcriptase (286)
serology (284)
temperate (283)
tissue culture (283)
transduction (290)
viroid (286)
virulent (283)
virus (283)

1. In a dictionary look up the words *obligate, intracellular,* and *parasite.* How do these words apply to viruses?
2. How do electrophoresis, serology, and tissue culture each contribute to the study of viruses?
3. Distinguish a phage from a prophage.
4. What is transduction?
5. Use what you know about the meaning of the word *lyses* to explain the meaning of *lysogenic* and of *lytic* cycles. If necessary use your dictionary to help you.

Review

1. Viruses and cells are alike in that both (a) have membranes (b) reproduce (c) respire (d) synthesize proteins.
2. Electrophoresis is used in the study of viruses to (a) diagnose and classify them (b) determine their nucleic acid sequence (c) identify their protein components (d) observe their structure.
3. *Icosahedron* refers to the structure of a virus's (a) nucleic acid (b) capsid (c) phage (d) lipid layer.
4. Viruses are classified primarily according to (a) disease caused (b) structure (c) size (d) nucleic acid.
5. Reverse transcriptase functions to (a) make DNA from RNA (b) unite viral DNA with the host DNA (c) release viral RNA to make proteins (d) transfer host DNA from one cell to another.
6. Viroids differ from viruses in (a) their larger size (b) the absence of a capsid (c) the absence of nucleic acids (d) their longer incubation period.
7. The sheath of a bacteriophage is used to (a) attach the phage to the bacterial wall (b) enclose the nucleic acid (c) transmit the nucleic acid to the bacterium (d) take over the genetic machinery of the cell.
8. *Lyses* refers to the disintegration of (a) the bacteriophage capsid on entering the cell (b) the DNA of the host cell (c) a T4 phage enzyme (d) the host cell.
9. Temperate phages reproduce by (a) immediately taking over the genetic machinery of the host cell (b) producing DNA that in turn produces viral DNA (c) attaching themselves to the ribosomes of the host cell (d) attaching themselves to the DNA of the host cell.
10. Transduction occurs when (a) a T4 phage moves from outside to inside a cell (b) a virus transfers DNA from one cell to another (c) a phage uses protein from one host cell and DNA from another (d) a virus transfers from the lysogenic cycle to the lytic cycle.
11. Name five techniques for studying viruses.
12. Describe the capsid of the AIDS virus.
13. How do retroviruses reproduce?
14. What causes the disease kuru, and how does kuru affect the body?
15. What is the function of the tail fibers of a bacteriophage?
16. Once a bacteriophage is inside a host cell, how are the components of new phages produced?

17. Distinguish between a virulent virus and a temperate virus.
18. What causes a temperate phage to become virulent?
19. How does the short generation time of most viruses work to their advantage?
20. How did Pasteur develop a weakened strain of rabies to use as a treatment?

Critical Thinking

1. Some people suggest that the drug AZT (azidothymidine) can help patients with AIDS. This drug blocks the enzyme reverse transcriptase. Explain how AZT might help patients.
2. People who have had a hepatitis-B viral infection have a greater chance of developing liver cancer later in life, especially if they are exposed to aflatoxin. Aflatoxin is a mold toxin found in some foods, such as contaminated peanut butter. What does this relationship suggest to you about the role of the hepatitis virus in causing cancer to develop?
3. Lambda (λ) is a bacteriophage that attacks *E. coli* and may enter a lysogenic life cycle. Once it enters the lysogenic life cycle, the phage inhibits the entry of more phages. What is the evolutionary advantage of the phage's "immunizing" its host against further lambda infection?

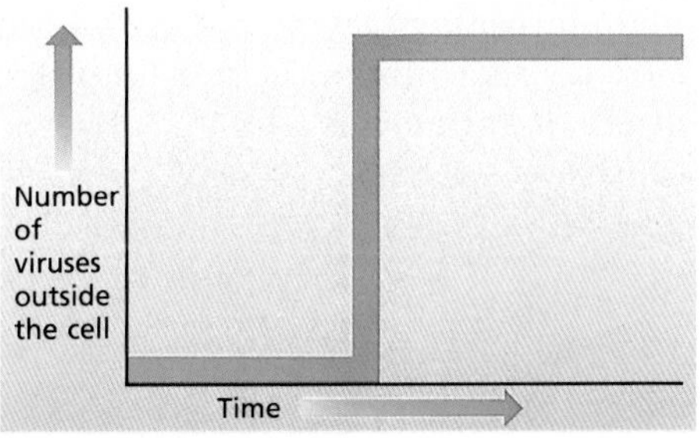

4. Shingles is a disease caused by the same herpes virus that causes chicken pox. How do you account for the fact that shingles often appears years after the initial chicken pox attack?
5. Look at the graph above. Discuss how the sharp jump in the number of viruses outside the cell corresponds to the phases of the lytic cycle.

Extension

1. Read the article by John Langone entitled "Emerging Viruses" in *Discover,* December 1990, pp. 63–68. Give an oral report in which you discuss how both human practices and the viruses themselves promote the continuing emergence of "new" viruses.
2. Look in the *Reader's Guide to Periodical Literature* for three articles on AIDS and its causes. Give a report to the class in which you discuss what you find.
3. Call your local hospital or family doctor and ask how viral diseases are diagnosed. If possible, visit the clinical laboratory of a hospital to see how the tests are done.
4. Research and write a report on some viral disease, such as polio or smallpox, that is now preventable. In your report discuss the process scientists followed in identifying the cause of the disease, isolating the virus, formulating a vaccine, and testing the vaccine.
5. Research and write a report on present-day scientists, such as those at the Center for Disease Control in Atlanta, who are searching for preventions or cures for viral diseases. In your report discuss the processes these scientists use to find preventions and cures and the precautions they take to ensure that they do not become contaminated with the viruses that they work with.

Critical Thinking

1. AIDS is caused by the retrovirus HIV that must use the enzyme reverse transcriptase to reproduce. By blocking this enzyme, AZT can prevent HIV from reproducing.
2. Although the research is not complete, the virus probably stays in the liver cells in a temperate stage and may be activated by certain substances, such as aflatoxin.
3. Infection by a second phage could kill the cell by lysis or cause abnormal DNA replication. Death of the *E. coli* would stop phage reproduction.
4. Shingles is caused by the reactivation of a temperate virus that often lies dormant for years before entering its disease-causing lytic cycle.
5. The jump corresponds to the release phase of the lytic cycle when new viruses break out of the host cell.

Extension

1. Students' reports may cover information from the Langone article as well as from other current articles on the emergence of new viruses.
2. If necessary, review with students how to use the *Readers' Guide to Periodical Literature.* Encourage students to find articles from various sources for balanced coverage.
3. You may wish to visit a clinical laboratory as a class field trip. Have students prepare questions in advance.
4. Invite students to present their reports to the class and have the class compare the processes that scientists followed for the various viral diseases reported on.
5. Encourage students to contact the CDC to request appropriate information.

18. Certain external stimuli, such as exposure to radiation or certain chemicals
19. Because of short generation times, thousands of new virus individuals are created before the immune system manages to destroy most of them. Those viruses that do survive develop resistance and reproduce new resistant individuals.
20. Pasteur cultivated the rabies virus in the spinal cord of a rabbit. As the cord dried, the virulence of the virus decreased. By varying the drying time, Pasteur isolated the desired weakened strains.

Chapter 20 Bacteria

Chapter Overview

Chapter 20 continues the discussion of microorganisms begun in Chapter 19 and focuses on monerans, or bacteria. Section 20.1 examines the four phyla of the Kingdom Monera, with a detailed look at the Phylum Schizophyta. Section 20.2 discusses the structure, movement, nutrition, respiration, and reproduction of monerans. This section also identifies some common diseases caused by bacteria.

Chapter Planning Chart

B	S	A	Sections and Subsections	Page	Features	Page	Resources
•	•	•	**20.1 Evolution and Classification**				
			Evolution	295	Section Review	298	Videodiscs
			Classification	295			Section Reviews Worksheet
•	•	•	**20.2 Biology of Monerans**				
			Structure and Movement	300	Writing About Biology	299	Videodiscs
			Nutrition	301	Think	301	Blackline Master 41
			Respiration	301	Biology in Process	302	Overhead Transparency T20
			Reproduction	302	Laboratory	305	Process Skills: The Growth Rate of Bacteria
			Production of Toxins	303	Section Review	304	Blackline Master 42
			Antibiotics	304			Laboratories: Effectiveness of Bactericides
							Section Reviews Worksheet
			End of Chapter Activities				
					Chapter Review	306	Vocabulary Skills
							Chapter Test
							Computer Test Generator

B *The Basic Level curriculum presents the most fundamental knowledge offered in the course.*
S *The Standard Level curriculum is designed for the average student who is able to master most topics.*
A *The Advanced Level curriculum includes suggestions for teaching the most academically able students.*

Cooperative Learning

Group Activity: Bacterial Diseases

- **Group Size:** *3 students*
- **Outcome:** *Students will identify the cause, symptoms, and treatment of a bacterial disease.*
- **Individual Accountability:** *Each student will be responsible for researching one aspect of a bacterial disease.*
- **Positive Interdependence:** *Group members will prepare a short report to the class.*

Assign to each group a bacterial disease to research, using those listed in Table 20-1 on p. 304. Have groups research three areas: (1) pathogen and infection, (2) symptoms of the disease, and (3) treatment and prevention. Tell each group member to concentrate on one of the three areas of research, but suggest that all group members watch for information that may not readily fall into one of the three areas, such as historical information about epidemics.

After completing their research individually, group members should reassemble to integrate the information gathered. Have each group prepare a short report to the class on the disease. The report will include visual aids such as pictures and drawings.

Concept Map

The following is one possible solution to the concept mapping activity in Reteaching on p. 304.

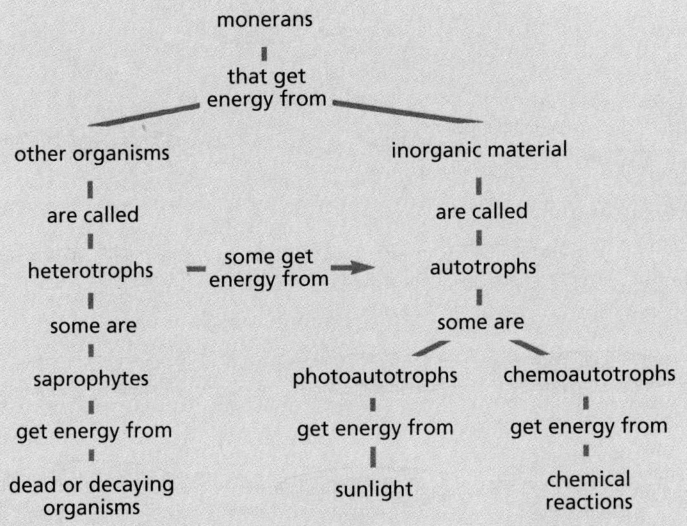

Laboratory Preparation

Overview *(See p. 305.)*

In this lab, students use basic sterile techniques and sampling techniques and observe the basic principles of bacterial growth. The lab gives students an awareness of places where there might be a lot of bacteria. This lab also gives students good practice in organizing a table.

Preparation

Nutrient agar, in premixed or prepoured form, or in the form of a powder that must be mixed with water and sterilized, is available from a biological supply house. Sterilize glass petri dishes, or purchase sterile disposable ones. Wide transparent tape (3/4-inch) is advantageous because it picks up more bacteria from the surface. Allow 10 minutes a day for five subsequent days for students to record their observations.

Teaching Tips

Students will probably need help in organizing the table for their data. Remind them that the day on which they prepare the plates is called "Day 0." That way, "Day 1" represents plates that have been incubating for one day. It may take two or three days for colonies to become clearly visible. Placing the dishes in a 37°C incubator will speed up the process but might lead to the incubation of human pathogens.

You may wish to take one dish of agar and leave it open for the class period. The dish can then be covered and incubated with the student plates. This plate will demonstrate the bacteria present in the air.

Hold the plates up to a window to see the bacteria under the best possible light.

Safety

Remind students to wash their hands after setting up or examining the plates.

When students are finished with the plates, they can be taped together so the tops don't fall off when they are discarded. If you are using glass petri dishes, they should be autoclaved before being washed.

Chapter Themes

Evolution Prokaryotes are the simplest of organisms and are generally thought to represent the most ancient organisms on earth. Emphasize that eukaryotes evolved from bacteria. Point out that plants probably evolved from photosynthetic prokaryotes such as *Prochloron*. Also stress that classification of monera is based on evolutionary development.

Scale and Structure Highlight the relationship of the structures of monera to their functions through discussions of mobility, reproduction, and photosynthesis.

Energy Help students identify the significance of the autotrophic ability of some monerans. Photoautotrophs transform energy of the sun into a form of energy useful to other living organisms. Emphasize that autotrophic bacteria are the first level of the energy pyramid that sustains life on earth.

Chapter Motivating Activity

Show students a sample of blue-green bacteria or photos such as those in Figure 20-4 and ask what kind of organism they think that it is. *(Most will say that it is a plant or algae.)* Then ask what makes it plantlike. *(It is green, which implies that it carries on photosynthesis.)* Explain that in the obsolete two-kingdom classification system this organism was considered a plant. Now, after much study of its structure, it is considered a moneran, or bacterium. Ask students what they think of when someone says *bacteria. (Most students think of disease.)* Point out that blue-green bacteria are not pathogens. Explain to students that in this chapter they will learn about many kinds of bacteria, only some of which cause diseases.

Chapter 20 *Bacteria*

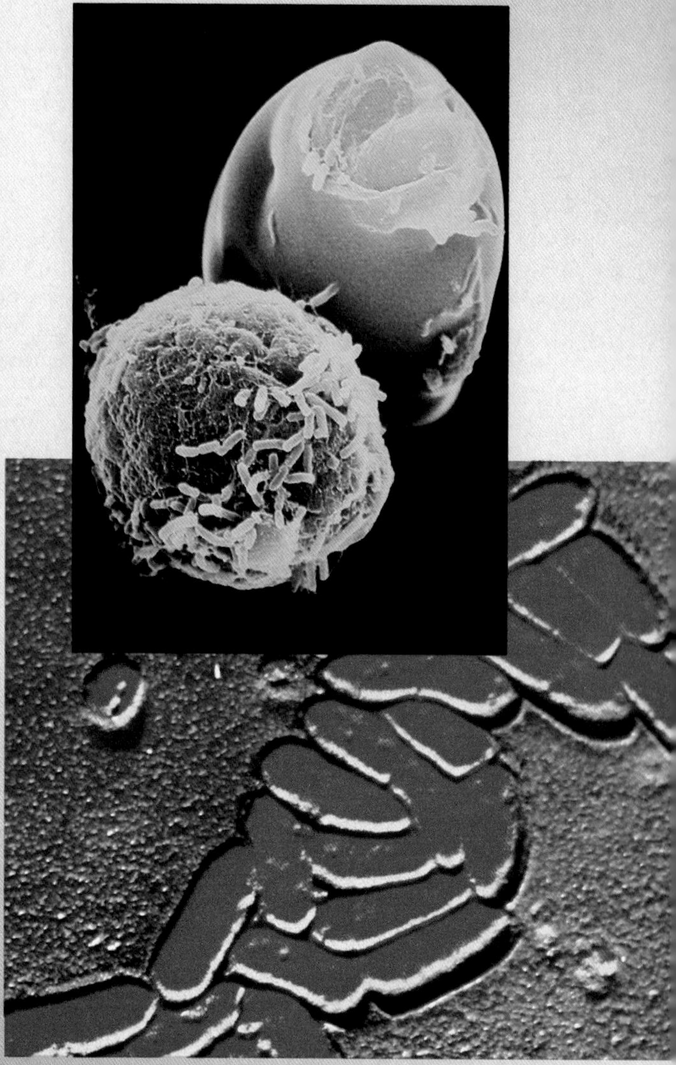

Aggregate of the bacillus *Erysipelothrix rhusiopathiae* (×2,900). Inset: Color-enhanced SEM of the bacillus *Agrobacterium tumifaciens* on tobacco cells (×1,070).

Introduction

Monerans, or bacteria, are the most numerous organisms on earth. You probably think of them first as agents of disease. Some bacteria do cause deadly diseases, such as bubonic plague, typhus, and gangrene. However, many others are essential to all other living things. For example, many monerans are decomposers, that is, they break down organic matter into substances that other organisms can use. In this chapter, we will study the structure and physiology of monerans, as well as ways in which monerans affect humans.

Chapter Outline

Chapter Concept

As you read, look for morphological and physiological variations among monerans.

Understanding the Visuals

Have students look at the two SEM images of bacteria and ask what structural information about bacteria they can infer. *(These bacteria seem to be small, unicellular organisms that clump together.)* Further challenge students for structural details. (Erysipelothrix *shows rod shape, but little else can be seen regarding structural details.)* Point out that this lack of detail is just as significant as if many details could be seen. Then ask students to explain the name of the lower bacteria in terms of where they are found. (Agrobacterium *implies "agriculture bacterium," a name that makes sense for a bacterium found on tobacco cells.)*

20.1 Evolution and Classification

Bacteria is the common name given to most organisms in the Kingdom Monera. All monerans are prokaryotic—they are characterized by the absence of a nucleus and membrane-bound organelles. They are also microscopic. For example, the smallest cells known to exist are monerans called mycoplasmas, which measure 0.20 to 0.25 μm in diameter. The average moneran is about 1 μm long; some, however, may be as long as 500 μm.

Evolution

Fossil monerans have been found in Australian deposits more than 3.5 billion years old. Monerans have evolved into many forms and now live in nearly every environment, many of which cannot support other living things.

The classification of monerans into an evolutionary hierarchy is not easy. Many of them look alike; it can be difficult to separate them into species based solely on structure. However, by relying on physiology in addition to morphology, scientists have determined a probable phylogenetic classification of monerans.

Classification

The Kingdom Monera is subdivided into four phyla: Archaebacteria *(AHR-kee-oe-back-TIR-ee-uh),* Schizophyta *(skuh-ZAHF-uh-tuh),* Cyanophyta *(SIE-uh-NAHF-uh-tuh),* and Prochlorophyta *(PROE-klor-AHF-uh-tuh).* These organisms differ in both morphology and physiology.

As you can see in Figure 20-1, monerans are usually spherical, rod-shaped, or spiral. Spherical monerans are called *cocci;* rod-shaped monerans, *bacilli;* and spiral monerans, *spirilli.*

Section Objectives

- *Explain the differences between the members of the Phylum Archaebacteria and the members of the Phylum Schizophyta.*
- *Describe the four classes in Phylum Schizophyta.*
- *Distinguish between Gram-positive and Gram-negative bacteria.*
- *Describe the Phyla Cyanophyta and Prochlorophyta.*

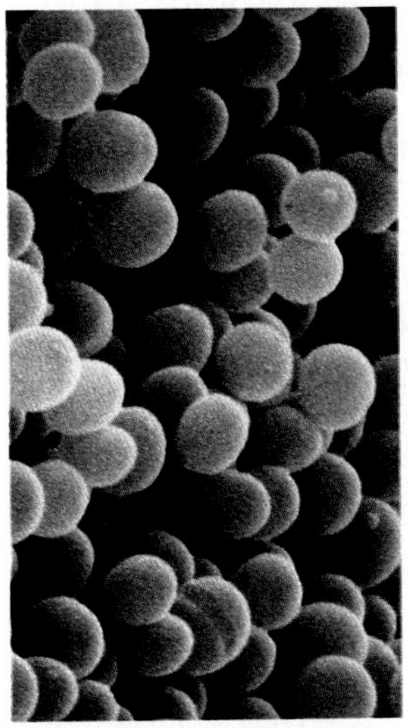
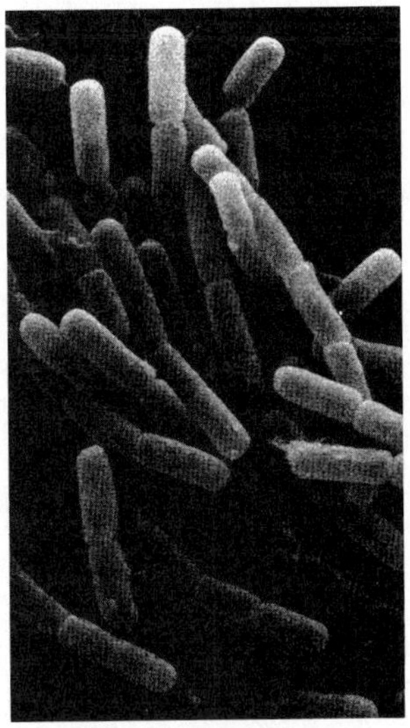
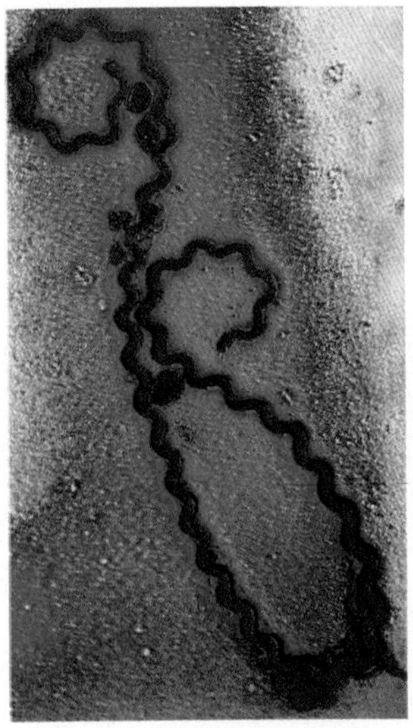

Figure 20-1 The most common shapes among monerans are represented here by *Staphylococcus aureus,* sphere-shaped (×3,945); *Bacillus cereus,* rod-shaped (×8,000); and *Leptospirilla ichterohaemorrhagiae,* spiral-shaped (×4,400).

Class	Characteristics	Example
Eubacteria	free living in soil and water	*Mycoplasmas orale*
Actinomycota	rod-shaped; branching filaments	*Streptomyces*
Rickettsiae	parasitic; reproduces only in specific hosts	*Chlamydia trachomatis*
Spirochaeta	spiral-shaped; flagella	*Treponema pallidum*

Graphic Organizer Use this table in Reteaching on p. 298.

Lesson Plan

Section Focus

This section describes the evolution of monerans and discusses the four phyla of the Kingdom Monera. Students will identify the characteristics that are the basis for moneran classification.

Section Themes

This section emphasizes the theme of **Evolution** in its discussion of moneran classification. Biological classification is an attempt at identifying evolutionary divergence. This section also emphasizes the theme of **Energy** in its discussion of archaebacteria that live near ocean vents, and organisms of the phyla Cyanophyta and Prochlorophyta, which are photosynthetic.

Motivating Activity

Show students a spoonful of soil, and have them speculate on how many individual bacteria are likely to be present in the soil. (Write student responses on the board.) Then ask students to draw a square centimeter on a piece of paper. Ask them to speculate on how many bacteria are present on a square centimeter of the human gum. (Again write their responses on the board.) Finally, hold up a gram mass and ask how many bacteria are likely to be found in this much digested food in a person's large intestine. (Write student answers on the board.) After allowing informal debate on the figures, give these answers: 10 billion bacteria in a spoonful of soil, 1 billion per cm^2 of human gum, 10 billion per gram of digested food in the human large intestine.

Videodiscs

- ***1840, Schizophyta: Bacteria (s)***

Teaching Strategies

Interpreting the Visuals Refer students to Figure 20-1 on p. 295 and have them note the magnification for these images. Then encourage students to relate names of these bacteria to their shapes. Ask what part of the name of each organism provides information about its shape. *(The last part of its genus name,* -coccus, *indicates that the first moneran is spherical;* -bacillus *tells that the second is rod-shaped;* -spirilla *tells that the third is spiral-shaped.)*

Making Hypotheses Ask students to describe the environments in which archaebacteria are found. *(In harsh environments such as those that lack free oxygen or have high salt concentration or extreme temperatures)* Point out that archaebacteria have characteristics that differ from other bacteria. Ask what might account for such differences. *(They evolved in different environments than other bacteria.)* Challenge students to hypothesize about when archaebacteria evolved on earth compared with other organisms. *(Archaebacteria probably evolved very early in earth's history.)* How does the name of these monerans imply that scientists have formed a similar hypothesis? *(The prefix* archae- *means "ancient," like the related word* archaic.*)* See Biology in Process—Classifying Archaebacteria—on pp. 272–273 in the student text.

Figure 20-2 Some archaebacteria thrive in hot springs such as this one in Yellowstone National Park.

Some monerans cluster together; others form chains or filaments. The prefix *staphylo-* is used to describe cells that form clusters. Therefore a cluster of spherical moneran cells is called a *Staphylococcus.* The prefix *strepto-* is used to describe cells that form filaments. Therefore a filament of rod-shaped moneran cells is called a *Streptobacillus.*

Archaebacteria

Members of the Phylum Archaebacteria are adapted to the harsh environments in which they live. Although **archaebacteria** are similar in many ways to other monerans, they also have unique characteristics that have led scientists to place them in their own phylum. For example, the transfer RNAs and cell walls of archaebacteria differ from those of other bacteria. Archaebacteria include methanogens, extreme halophiles, and thermoacidophiles.

The **methanogens** live only in the absence of free oxygen. These anaerobic monerans are called methanogens because they use carbon dioxide and hydrogen to form methane and water. Methanogens live in the digestive tracts of sheep and cattle and at the bottoms of bogs, lakes, and sewage treatment ponds.

The **extreme halophiles** *(HAL-uh-FILEZ)* live only in areas of high salt concentration, such as the Great Salt Lake and the Dead Sea. The **thermoacidophiles** *(ther-moe-uh-SID-uh-FILEZ)* live only in places that are very acidic and where temperatures are very hot, often reaching 90° C. For example, members of the genus *Sulfolobus* live in acidic hot springs where the temperature averages 80° C and the pH is less than 2. Nevertheless, these monerans maintain an internal pH that is nearly neutral. Members of the genus *Thermoplasma* are found in smoldering coal tailings where the temperatures are often higher than 90° C.

Some other kinds of archaebacteria live around volcanic vents that are found miles below the ocean's surface. These monerans use the sulfur gases that bubble from the vents as their energy source. Scientists think that the environments in which present-day archaebacteria live may be similar to those that existed during the formative stages of life on earth.

Schizophyta

The largest moneran phylum is Schizophyta, all the members of which are commonly referred to as bacteria. Schizophyta is divided into four classes:

- Class Eubacteria *(YOO-back-TIR-ee-uh)* contains the largest number of and many of the most familiar bacteria.
- Class Actinomycota *(ACK-tuh-noe-MIE-KOE-tuh)* contains rod-shaped organisms that form branched filaments.
- Class Rickettsiae *(rick-ET-see-ee)* contains mostly nonmotile intracellular parasites
- Class Spirochaeta *(SPIE-ruh-KEE-tuh)* contains large spiral-shaped organisms.

More Information

Monerans Microbiologists have identified and named more than 5,000 species of bacteria. The oldest fossil evidence for bacteria has been found in rocks approximately 3.5 billion years old. These bacteria—probably the first cellular life—resembled archaebacteria. The Phylum Schizophyta contains the monerans that are considered most characteristic, and this phylum encompasses by far the most species. Blue-green bacteria, or cyanobacteria, were until the 1960s considered a form of algae. Prochlorophyta contains only one genus, *Prochloron.* These photosynthetic monerans contain chlorophyll a and b and are thought to be the evolutionary precursors of plants.

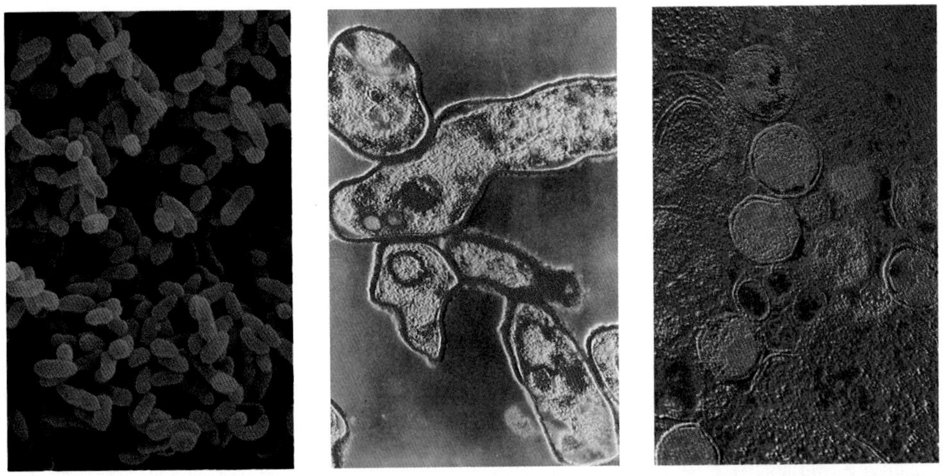

Most members of the Class Eubacteria are free-living soil and water bacteria. **Eubacteria** tend to live in less harsh environments than archaebacteria. Eubacteria are further classified by their reaction to a Gram stain. A **Gram stain** is a test that uses a series of dyes to stain bacterial walls. **Gram-negative bacteria** have an outer covering of lipopolysaccharides and stain pink. **Gram-positive bacteria** lack this covering and stain purple. Gram-positive eubacteria are susceptible to antibiotics. Gram-negative eubacteria are difficult to treat with antibiotics. Mycoplasmas, the smallest monerans, are eubacteria.

Members of the Class Actinomycota, called **actinomycotes,** are Gram-positive bacteria that form colonies of branching, multicellular filaments. Some actinomycotes decompose dead plants and animals; some cause diseases, such as diphtheria and tuberculosis. Others, especially members of the species *Streptomyces,* are the source of many antibiotics.

Members of the Class Rickettsiae, called **rickettsiae,** are parasitic Gram-negative bacteria that can reproduce only in certain cells of a specific host. Insects often carry these bacteria and transmit them to mammals. Typhus, for example, is a rickettsial disease transmitted by lice.

Members of the Class Spirochaeta, called **spirochetes,** are spiral-shaped or curved bacteria. Most spirochetes use flagella to move. One species of spirochete causes the sexually transmitted disease syphilis. Another causes Lyme disease, an ailment with symptoms similar to those of arthritis that is transmitted by ticks.

Cyanophyta and Prochlorophyta

Members of the Phylum Cyanophyta are called **blue-green bacteria.** These bacteria have some traits that are similar to those of plants and plantlike protists. Blue-green bacteria are photosynthetic. They also capture solar energy with chlorophyll a, one of the pigments found in plants, use water during photosynthesis, and produce oxygen.

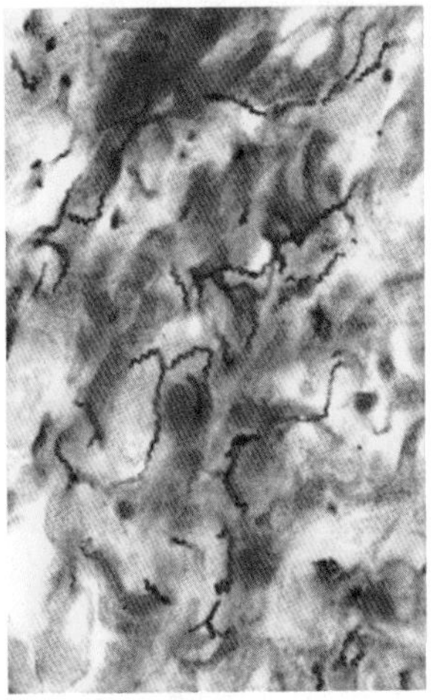

Figure 20-3 The four classes in the Phylum Schizophyta are shown in these color-enhanced photos (left to right): *Klebsiella pneumoniae,* a eubacterium (×1,970); *Corynebacterium diphtheriae,* an actinomycote (×12,000); *Chlamydia* sp., a rickettsia (×17,600); and *Treponema pallidum,* a spirochete (×700).

Identifying Organisms Emphasize the diversity of environments in which monerans live by naming an environment and asking students to answer with a type of moneran. For example, ask what kind of moneran might be found free living in soil. *(Eubacteria)* What kind might be found in an acidic hot spring? *(Archaebacteria)* In a clump on the surface of a lake? *(Blue-green bacteria)*

Exploring Careers Have a hospital laboratory technician visit the class to speak about how bacteria can be identified by various stains and other tests. Ask that the technician concentrate on the Gram stain.

Guided Practice

Ask students which moneran phyla contain photosynthetic bacteria. *(Cyanophyta and Prochlorophyta)* Ask how the photosynthetic pigments differ in cyanophytes and prochlorophytes. *(Blue-green bacteria contain chlorophyll a, whereas* Prochloron *members contain another pigment similar to that in chloroplasts of plants.)* Explain that *Prochloron* contain chlorophyll a and b. Plant chloroplasts contain both of these pigments as well. Ask students to infer the evolutionary relationship between the Phylum Prochlorophyta and members of the Kingdom Plantae. *(The prokaryotic members of* Prochloron *possibly evolved into plants or became the chloroplasts of plants. The latter hypothesis, termed* endosymbiosis, *is discussed in Chapter 21.)*

Interdisciplinary Activity

Economics Bacteria are often thought of in terms of disease or considered as unseen and irrelevant organisms. Students may be surprised to find out how monerans are used in different nations or cultures for practical and economical purposes. Have students investigate the different beneficial uses of monerans worldwide, such as in making cheese and yogurt, in producing antibiotic medicines, for purifying waste water, and for enriching soil. Encourage students to use their findings to contribute to a bulletin board display on the multicultural uses of bacteria. Posters depicting the uses could form the bulletin board display.

Section 20.1

Independent Practice

■ Have students write answers to the Section Review.

■ A doctor believes that a patient's illness is caused by a bacterial infection but is unsure whether antibiotics will be effective. Ask students to discuss how the doctor could resolve this problem. *(Sample answer: Use a Gram stain to determine if the bacteria are susceptible to antibiotics.)*

Check Your Understanding

1. Why do scientists rely on physiology as well as morphology to help them classify monerans? *(The morphology of many monerans is so similar that it is difficult to separate species without studying their physiology.)*

2. How do their environments suggest that archaebacteria evolved early in earth's history? *(The harsh conditions in which present-day archaebacteria live may be similar to those that existed during earth's early history.)*

Reteaching

Have students make a table organizing information about the classes in the Phylum Schizophyta. Use the table on p. 295 as a model.

■ *See* **Section Reviews** *worksheet, Section 20.1.*

Enrichment

Have students compare the role bacteria play in the digestive process of ruminants such as cattle with the role bacteria play in human digestive processes.

Closure

Return to the blue-green bacteria from the Chapter Motivating Activity, p. 294. Have students describe what they know about these organisms. *(They are photosynthetic, usually encased in a jellylike substance, and often clump together in colonies.)*

Videodiscs

■ *2540,* **Anabaena** *(s)*

Figure 20-4 The Phylum Cyanophyta includes such diverse organisms as (left to right) *Chroococcus* sp. (from a peat bog, ×400), *Lyngbia spirillans* (on agar, ×10), and *Anabaena* sp. with *Microcystis* sp. (×60).

Most scientists now classify cyanophytes as monerans because, like other prokaryotes, they lack membrane-bound nuclei. In addition, their cell walls are chemically similar to those of other prokaryotes. Unlike other prokaryotes, however, blue-green bacteria are usually encased in a jellylike substance and often clump together in colonies. For example, *Anabaena* is a single filament, while *Nostoc* is a cluster of cells.

Some blue-green bacteria are also distinguished from other prokaryotes by having specialized cells and therefore a division of labor within the colony. The members of some genera produce cells called heterocysts when their nitrogen supplies are depleted. **Heterocysts** are specialized cells that convert nitrogen from the atmosphere into a form that the organism can use in cellular metabolism.

A rapid increase in the population of a blue-green bacteria, which may discolor a lake, river, or part of the ocean, is called a **bloom.** Since blue-green bacteria thrive on the phosphates and nitrates found in sewage, these population explosions often occur in polluted water.

Members of the Phylum Prochlorophyta are photosynthetic bacteria that live symbiotically with the marine chordates known as tunicates. Members of the genus *Prochloron* contain phytosynthetic pigments unlike those in blue-green bacteria but similar to the chloroplasts of eukaryotes.

Section Review

1. Differentiate between *Streptococcus* and *Staphylococcus.*
2. List the habitats of the three types of archaebacteria.
3. Explain the structural difference between a Gram-positive bacterium and a Gram-negative bacterium. Give an example of each.
4. When do blue-green bacteria form blooms?
5. Why do scientists think archaebacteria were the first form of life on earth?

Answers to Section Review

1. *Streptococcus* is a filament of spherical bacteria; *Staphylococcus* is a cluster of spherical bacteria.

2. Methanogens live in the digestive tracts of sheep and cattle and at the bottom of bogs, lakes, and sewage-treatment ponds; extreme halophiles live in areas where salt is highly concentrated; thermoacidophiles live in hot, highly acidic areas.

3. Gram-negative bacteria such as rickettsiae have a lipopolysaccharide covering; gram-positive bacteria such as actinomycotes lack this covering.

4. When levels of phosphates and nitrates increase

5. They are adapted to harsh environments similar to that of early earth.

Writing About Biology

Bad News Bacteria

This excerpt is from "Bad News Bacteria," an article by Karen Wright.

Muppeteer Jim Henson's sudden death in [1991] shocked millions of children and adults. . . . But to medical researchers Henson's death was unsettling on a different count. The bacterial infection to which he succumbed—a particularly virulent strain of group A streptococcus—causes a newly recognized kind of toxic shock, called toxic shock-like syndrome (TSLS), that can fell otherwise healthy people within hours of the onset of symptoms. . . . No one yet knows why the organism that gives rise to strep throat, impetigo, and scarlet and rheumatic fever in children is suddenly causing an acute, fatal disease in adults.

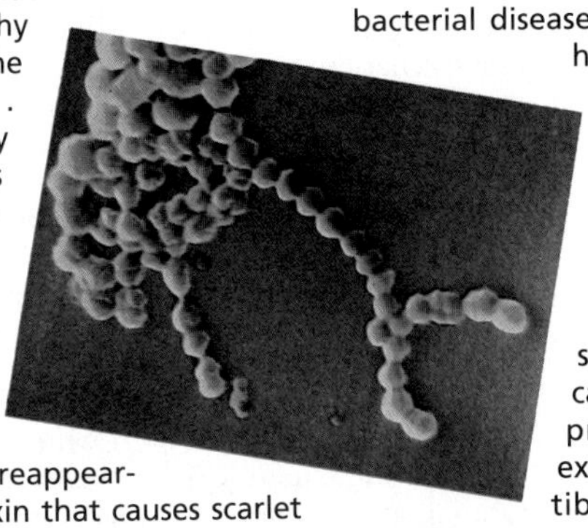

One theory holds that TSLS is due to the reappearance of the bacterial toxin that causes scarlet fever. . . . But that's only one hypothesis, and the appearance of TSLS is confirmation of the fact that bacterial diseases are still far from being understood at the molecular level. The pacemaker for the cyclical variations in virulence, for example, has never been established. In recent years the tools of molecular biology have helped researchers pick apart some aspects of virulence, including some of the genetic "master switches" that control bacterial toxicity. Many of the protein products of those genes, however, are still shrouded in mystery.

In addition, the problem of treating bacterial infections is greatly complicated by another issue: resistance. The widespread use of antibiotics—in humans and in animal feed—has fostered the rise of drug resistance among harmless and harmful bacteria alike. Most strains are resistant to at least one antibiotic—and some of them are resistant to almost all the known antibacterial treatments. What is even more disturbing is that it is now clear that harmless bacteria can serve as a reservoir for resistance genes, which can then be transferred to virulent strains within an individual, spawning a microbial one-two punch: a highly virulent, resistant pathogen. . . .

Stanley Falkow, a microbial geneticist from Stanford . . . thinks that many current bacterial diseases are "essentially diseases of human progress." He cites outbreaks of salmonellosis propagated by mass preparation of food and the menstrual toxic shock syndrome that resulted from more absorbent tampons.

In some respects the spread of bacterial resistance can also be seen as a plague of progress, Falkow argues. For example, the routine use of antibiotics in animal feed began with the aim of preventing disease in farm animals and promoting their growth. Yet the use of antibiotics may have become a kind of "poison pill"—by applying tremendous selective pressure in favor of the resistant strains.

It has been known for some time that the genes for resistance can be carried by commensals (the normal human microbial flora) such as nonpathogenic forms of *Escherichia coli*. In fact, it seems such normal flora have become a reservoir of resistance determinants that pathogenic bacteria can tap.

Write

- **Write a newspaper editorial discussing your stand on the routine use of antibiotics in animal feed. Should governmental regulatory agencies curb the practice?**

From "Bad News Bacteria" from Science, vol. 249, no. 4964, *July 6, 1990. Copyright © 1990 by Karen Wright. Reprinted by permission of Karen Wright.*

About the Author

Karen Wright is a free-lance writer based in New York City. She has contributed to *Science*, *Omni*, and the *New York Times Sunday Magazine*, among other publications.

Wright is also an editor for *Issues in Science and Technology*, published quarterly by the National Academy of Sciences, and she also works as an adjunct professor at New York University in the Science and Environmental Reporting Program. Formerly, Wright was a staff writer for *Nature* and *Scientific American*.

Background

Group A streptococcus, which caused scarlet fever epidemics earlier in this century, stopped making toxin A in the 1940s. While some investigators think that TSLS is simply scarlet fever returning in a more severe form, others disagree. Some epidemiologists think that TSLS is a new disease. They think that the bacteria could be producing an entirely new toxin or mutated version of the old one.

Discussion

After students have read "Bad News Bacteria," ask them to discuss the following questions.

1. Explain how routine use of antibiotics has affected the natural selection of bacteria. *(Routine use of antibiotics in animal feed favors the survival of resistant strains. Less-resistant strains of bacteria perish, while the resistant strains survive to reproduce and spread disease. In a similar way, the routine prescription of antibiotics to fight bacterial infections in hospitals has stimulated the rise of drug-resistant bacteria.)*

2. How does the difficulty of pinpointing why TSLS occurs typify the scientific uncertainty surrounding the mechanisms of bacterial diseases? *(Scientists are still uncertain why a species of bacteria, such as group A streptococcus, can have different effects on various populations at different times.)*

Extension

Ask students to depict a fictional situation in which they demonstrate factual knowledge of the history, symptoms, diagnosis, typical patient, treatment, and prevention of scarlet fever. Have small groups of students do library research on scarlet fever and then write a short story or role-play a medical team fighting an epidemic of the disease in history.

Section 20.2

Lesson Plan

Section Focus

This section describes the structure, movement, nutrition, respiration, and reproduction of monerans. Students will also study about bacterial toxins and the diseases they cause and about antibiotics.

Section Themes

This section emphasizes the theme of **Scale and Structure** in its discussion of the cellular structure of monerans. The use of flagella in movement shows the relationship between structure and function. The discussion on nutrition, the modes by which monerans utilize energy from the sun and other sources, emphasizes the theme of **Energy.** The discussion of toxins, bacterial disease, and antibiotics emphasizes the theme of **Systems and Interactions.** Bacterial toxins interact with a host by disrupting its body systems and causing disease.

Motivating Activity

Bring two samples of milk to class—one of fresh, pasteurized milk and another of the same kind of milk that has soured and curdled. Have students observe the samples and notice the differences. Ask students to infer what kind of organism caused the observed changes. *(Bacteria)* Explain that the taste of soured milk is due to lactic acid produced by bacteria. Challenge students to speculate on where the bacteria came from since the milk was pasteurized. Guide the discussion to include spores, contamination, and heterotrophic versus autotrophic nutrition.

Section Objectives

- *List the distinguishing features of moneran cells.*
- *Describe autotrophy and heterotrophy in monerans.*
- *Describe the way in which organisms can survive in vent communities deep in the ocean.*
- *Distinguish between endotoxins and exotoxins.*
- *Explain the basic effect of antibiotics.*

20.2 Biology of Monerans

The structures and physiology of monerans are diverse. These variations reflect the numerous habitats to which monerans are adapted.

Structure and Movement

Study the electron micrograph of the moneran in Figure 20-5. Monerans are prokaryotic; their DNA is located in the cytoplasm. The DNA is arranged in a single, circular chromosome. In addition, monerans do not have membrane-bound organelles. Some monerans have **plasmids,** smaller circular strands of DNA that are capable of replicating independently. All monerans except the mycoplasmas have walls that differ structurally and chemically from those of eukaryotes. Some monerans have rigid cell walls; others have flexible ones.

Many monerans can produce **capsules,** protective layers of polysaccharides around their cell walls. Under natural conditions many prokaryotes also produce a net of polysaccharides called the **glycocalyx** *(GLIE-koe-KAY-licks)* that helps them stick to the surface of rocks, teeth, and host cells. Some monerans attach themselves to objects with protein strands called **pili.**

Under adverse conditions, many monerans encase their DNA and some of their cytoplasm in a tough envelope. This structure, called an **endospore,** can lie dormant for years. When favorable conditions return, the endospore coating breaks and the cell becomes active. Anthrax, an often fatal disease of sheep and cattle, can survive in endospore form for 60 years.

Monerans have different ways of moving. Many move by rotating stiff flagella that are bent into S-curves. When the flagella are rotated in one direction, the monerans move in a straight line; when rotated in the opposite direction, they tumble. Spirochetes use filaments that wrap around the cell to move.

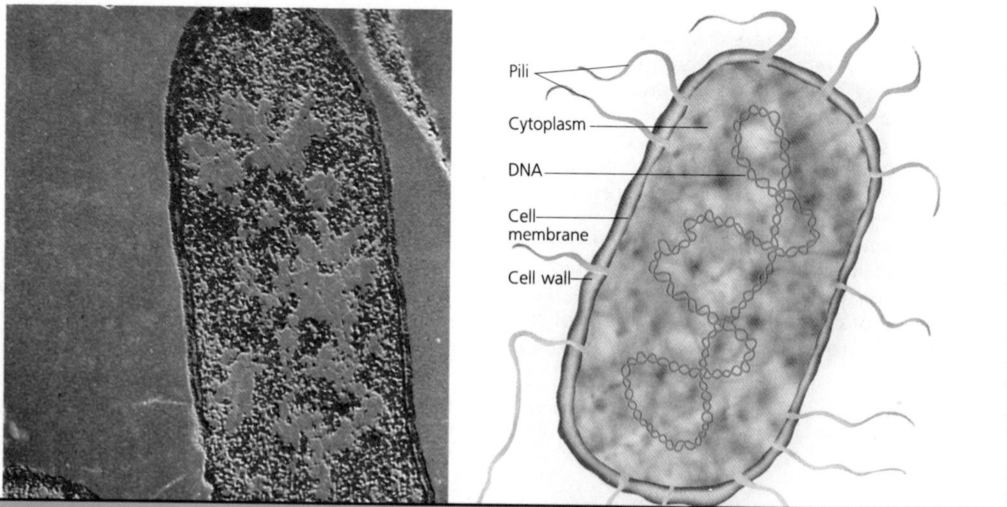

Figure 20-5 *Enterobacter* **is a typical moneran. In the color-enhanced TEM (left, ×23,520), the DNA appears green. The diagram (right) shows structural features.**

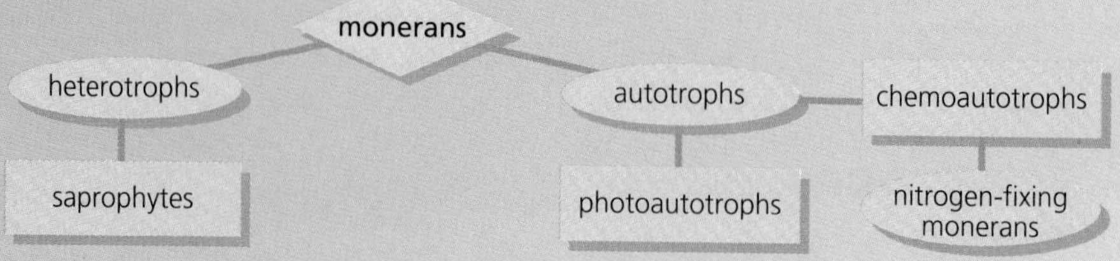

Graphic Organizer Use this organizational chart in Guided Practice on p. 303.

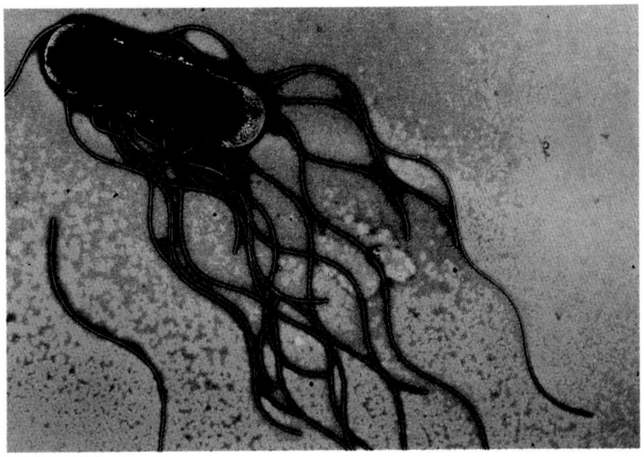

Figure 20-6 Some bacteria, such as this Gram-negative *Salmonella* sp., move by means of long flagella (×39,233).

Nutrition

Monerans may be heterotrophic or autotrophic. Most monerans are **heterotrophs—**that is, they use food produced by other organisms. A heterotroph that feeds on dead or decaying organic matter is called a **saprophyte** *(SAP-ruh-FITE)*. By decomposing matter, saprophytic bacteria release carbon and other elements for use by other organisms. Saprophytes are therefore essential to the recycling of nutrients in every ecosystem.

Monerans that produce their own food from inorganic material are **autotrophs.** Those that use sunlight as a source of energy are called **photoautotrophs.** Photoautotrophs have different chlorophylls that enable them to absorb light of various wavelengths. Some have the same pigments found in plants; others have unique pigments that absorb longer wavelengths.

Some autotrophic monerans, called **chemoautotrophs,** use the energy of chemical reactions instead of sunlight to synthesize food. Some chemoautotrophs can also fix nitrogen. **Nitrogen fixation** is the process by which gaseous nitrogen (N_2) is converted into ammonia compounds. Plants need nitrogen to synthesize proteins, but they cannot use gaseous nitrogen. They can, however, use the nitrogen in ammonia. Because most of the nitrogen on earth is gaseous and because only monerans can convert gaseous nitrogen into forms that plants can use, plants—and therefore most life-forms—depend on these nitrogen-fixing monerans.

Respiration

Many monerans are **obligate anaerobes,** that is, they cannot survive in the presence of oxygen. Among these are the methanogens. **Facultative anaerobes** can live with or without oxygen. *Escherichia coli,* which is common in the human digestive tract, is a facultative anaerobe. Monerans that cannot survive without oxygen are called **obligate aerobes.** The obligate aerobe that causes tuberculosis, *Mycobacterium tuberculosis,* lives in the lungs.

Think

Many organisms find the odor of decaying organic matter repulsive. What adaptive advantage might this ability give living organisms?

Teaching Strategies

Interpreting the Visuals Refer students to Figure 20-5, p. 300, and have them compare the TEM image with the labeled drawing. Ask students which structures they can identify in the TEM image. *(Cell wall, cell membrane, cytoplasm, and DNA)* Which structures labeled in the drawing cannot be seen clearly in the TEM image? *(Pili)* Finally, ask which structures are visible in the photo in Figure 20-6 that are not labeled on the drawing in Figure 20-5. *(Flagella)* See also the Laboratory, Observing Pathogens, on p. 683.

■ *See* **Overhead Transparency** *T20 and* **Blackline Master** *41.*

Answer to Think

Many infectious bacteria can be found in decaying matter. An organism that is repelled by such substances would likely avoid any contact and thus be less likely to become infected.

Comparing Terms Have students review the role of oxygen in respiration, as presented in Chapter 7. Ask students to compare anaerobes with aerobes. *(Anaerobes do not require oxygen while aerobes do.)* Then challenge students to define the terms *obligate* and *facultative. ("Necessary" and "optional," respectively)* Finally, help students construct an oxygen-use continuum on the board. *(Show obligate anaerobes at the far left, facultative anaerobes in the middle, and obligate aerobes at the far right.)*

Videodiscs

■ *Side 1 31819, Bacterial Cells and Membranes (m)*

■ *2550, Endospore Formation in* Bacillus cereus *(s)*

LEP Activity

Give each pair of students construction paper, various colors of yarn, poster board, and glue. Ask each pair to make a model of a typical moneran such as the one shown in Figure 20-5. Students can use different colors of paper and yarn for the various structures, which should be labeled. Then ask each pair to make a second model, showing another type of moneran. For example, students could make one with flagella instead of pili or one in a different shape. Call on each group to describe their models and explain how they differ.

Contrasting Processes Ask students to name the two processes by which monerans reproduce. *(Binary fission and conjugation)* To what cellular process is binary fission similar? Explain. *(Mitosis; cell DNA replicates, separates into two, and ends up in two separate cells.)* Stress that even though the processes are much the same, *mitosis* is usually reserved for describing division in eukaryotic cells.

Next, turn students' attention to the process of conjugation. Point out that not all monerans can perform conjugation, but those that do also divide through binary fission. Ask students why it is advantageous for a species to be able to reproduce by conjugation. *(Binary fission produces clones, while conjugation increases genetic variability, allowing greater opportunity for adaptation.)*

■ *See* Process Skills, *Chapter 20.*

Interpreting the Visuals Refer students to Table 20-1, p. 304, and question them about the information. For example, ask what bacterium causes tuberculosis. *(Mycobacterium tuberculosis)* How could someone become infected with this bacterium? *(Through airborne transmission such as by breathing in the pathogen)* Ask students to infer what phylum and class this bacterium belongs to. *(Phylum Schizophyta, Class Eubacteria; students should conclude that for airborne transmission, the bacterium must be "free living," as described in Section 20.1.)* Continue a similar line of questioning about the other diseases in the table.

■ *See* Blackline Master *42.*

■ *See* Laboratories, *Investigation 20.*

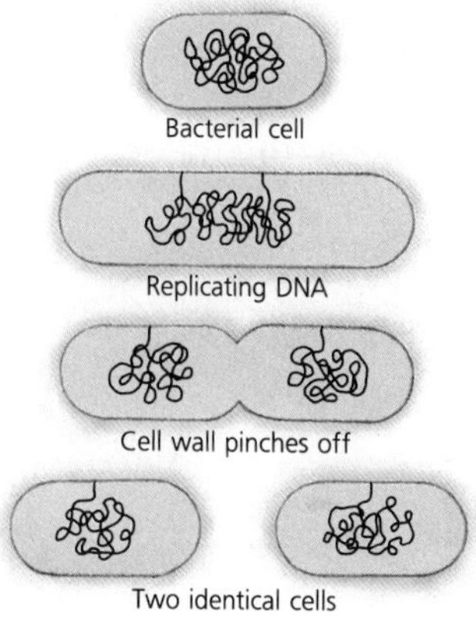

Figure 20-7 Binary fission is the most common means of bacterial reproduction.

Reproduction

Some monerans reproduce rapidly. Under optimal conditions, *E. coli* cells, for example, can divide every 15 minutes. In one week, a moneran can produce millions of cells. Heat, cold, predation, and lack of food inhibit the rate of reproduction.

Binary Fission

Monerans usually reproduce by splitting in two, an asexual process called **binary fission.** First the DNA in the cell replicates. Then the plasma membrane and cell wall grow inward, forming two daughter cells with identical genetic material.

Conjugation

Occasionally the genetic materials of two monerans of the same species are recombined in a process called **conjugation.** A portion of the DNA of one moneran passes across a bridge, formed by the pili, into another moneran. This piece of DNA then lines up with the homologous piece of DNA in the recipient cell. The homologous portion is destroyed and the new DNA is substituted. This exchange of genetic information increases genetic variability.

Biology in Process

Deep-Sea Hot Springs

In 1974 American and French scientists explored the Mid-Atlantic Ridge with the submersibles *Alvin* and *Cyana* searching for deep-sea hot springs, or vents (p. 302). But it wasn't until 1977 that scientists discovered the first active vent in the Galápagos Rift of the Pacific. Since then active vents (shown by dots on the map, p. 303) have been located in deep waters along known lines of volcanic activity. What scientists did not expect to find was a dense population of unexpected and unknown species—a whole ecosystem—living in and around the vents.

Since photosynthesis requires light, it occurs primarily in the upper 100–200 meters of the oceans. How did the organisms found living in darkness approximately 2,500 meters down derive nutrition and energy?

The researchers found several clues. Water samples taken near the vents smelled like rotten eggs, and water chemistry studies showed high concentrations of hydrogen sulfide (H_2S). The vent waters were also highly turbid and had a milky-bluish color indicating the presence of masses of bacteria.

For nearly 100 years, scientists have known that some chemosynthetic bacteria can use

More Information

Conjugation Conjugation in prokaryotes has been found only in Gram-negative bacteria. Plasmids control conjugation, which occurs between a donor cell that has a certain kind of plasmid and a recipient cell that does not. The plasmid replicates and passes through the conjugation tube. In some cases the plasmid integrates with the recipient's genetic material.

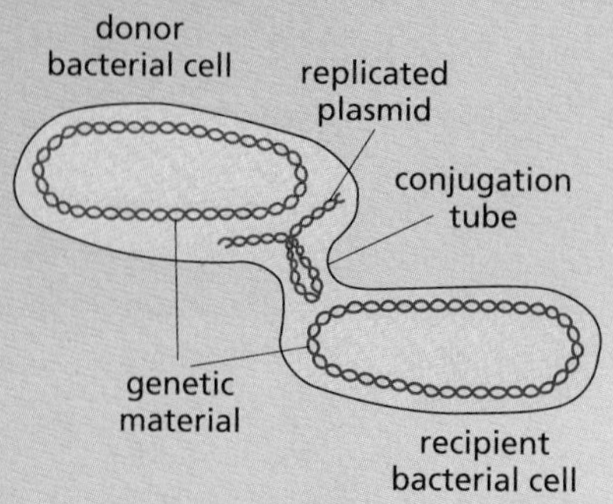

Production of Toxins

Any organism that causes a disease is called a **pathogen.** Diseases that are caused by pathogenic bacteria include bubonic plague, leprosy, tuberculosis, and typhus. Most pathogenic bacteria enter the human body through the respiratory or gastrointestinal tract. You will learn more about these diseases in Chapter 44.

In most cases bacterial diseases are caused by the toxins that are produced by bacteria. A **toxin** is a poisonous substance that disrupts the metabolism of the infected organism. Bacteria produce two types of toxins, endotoxins and exotoxins. **Endotoxins** are found in the cell walls of most Gram-negative bacteria. Endotoxins all cause the same symptoms: fever, weakness, and damage to the circulatory system. Typhoid fever is one example of a disease that is caused by endotoxins. **Exotoxins,** which are products of the metabolism of some bacteria, are secreted into the area surrounding the bacteria. Exotoxins are the most potent poisons known. One nanogram of the tetanus exotoxin, for example, is sufficient to kill a guinea pig. Exotoxins cause diseases such as diphtheria and botulism.

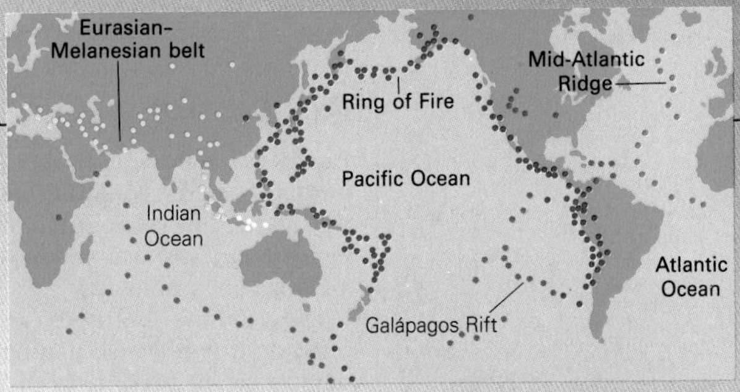

H_2S in the same way that photosynthetic organisms use sunlight. The researchers isolated and studied the vent bacteria and found them capable of metabolizing H_2S. The mystery was solved—the bacteria could produce the carbohydrates needed by vent organisms. All that remained was to show that vent organisms somehow consumed the bacteria.

Zooplankton and polychaete worms were observed feeding on bacteria in several instances, but giant clams (*Calyptogena magnifica*) also thrived nearby in clear, bacteria-free waters. Giant tube worms (*Riftia pachyptila*) from these sites seemed incapable of feeding at all. They lacked a mouth, stomach, and intestinal tract.

Microscopy of the clam gills and the blood-rich tissues of the worms demonstrated that both housed numerous kinds of symbiotic bacteria. These bacteria received the oxygen and H_2S necessary for chemosynthesis from their hosts' gills or blood system, and the hosts received carbohydrates from the bacteria. Furthermore, the host organisms avoided being poisoned by sulfides with sulfide-binding proteins that protected their respiratory enzymes.

- **What observations led researchers to believe that the vent bacteria were the basic source of energy in the vent communities?**

Guided Practice

Help students identify the types of monerans by constructing an organizational chart on this topic. An example of a completed chart is shown on p. 300.

Biology in Process

Using the Feature

The feature focuses on the two process skills of observing and inferring. Scientists observed characteristics of vent communities that led them to infer that bacteria at the vent sites metabolized hydrogen sulfide to provide nutrients for other vent organisms.

Ask students how studying the vent communities might help us understand other communities based on chemosynthesizing bacteria. *(Since the food chain in either instance will be based on chemosynthesizing bacteria, there may be other similarities in these ecosystems as well.)*

Answer to the Feature

Researchers observed that phytoplankton could not exist in the vent community. However, the vents were rich in hydrogen sulfide, which researchers knew could be metabolized by some bacteria. Researchers hypothesized that bacteria might be the foundation of the food chain in the vent communities.

Videodiscs

- ***2622, Bacterial Conjugation (s)***

Cooperative Learning

Disease Prevention Divide students into groups of three and challenge each group to make a list of items that are used in school and at home to help prevent the spread of bacterial infection. Items might include disposable cups, tissues, disinfectants, antibacterial soaps, mouthwashes, and so on. To begin the list, each group member could focus on one area such as the kitchen or bathroom. Then group members can compile individual lists into a master list. Instruct group members to rate the effectiveness of each item in blocking the transmission of pathogens. Have each group present its list in a class discussion.

Independent Practice

- Have students write answers to the Section Review.
- Have students use their student book and other books to list some benefits and disadvantages of bacteria.

Check Your Understanding

1. How is an endospore an adaptation for monerans? *(During harsh conditions monerans can form an endospore to preserve their genetic material and some cytoplasm.)*
2. Why are saprophytes essential to the recycling of nutrients? *(Saprophytes release carbon and other elements in the process of decomposing matter.)*
3. How may exposing bacteria to antibiotics lead to the rise of resistant bacteria? *(Sometimes when bacteria are exposed to antibiotics, most bacteria die, but some resistant bacteria survive to reproduce, giving rise to a resistant population of bacteria.)*

Reteaching

Help students review how the monerans get energy by having them construct a concept map on this topic. An example of a completed map is shown on p. 293B.

- *See* Section Reviews *worksheet, Section 20.2.*

Enrichment

Have students do library research on nitrogen-fixing bacteria to learn how the nitrogen-fixing process works. Have students prepare labeled drawings and make a presentation to the class.

Closure

Encourage students to discuss any experiences they may have had with using antibiotics. Ask students to infer how the course of their illnesses would have been different without antibiotics.

Videodiscs

- *2686, Molecular Graphics—Lysozyme (s)*

Table 20-1 Some Bacterial Diseases

Bacterium	Disease	Transmission	Symptoms
Clostridium tetani	Tetanus	Endospores enter wound	Neurotoxins are produced that cause muscle spasms; death results from spasms of respiratory muscles
Clostridium perfringens	Gas gangrene	Endospores enter wound	Gases are produced that cause soft tissues to swell and die
Rickettsia rickettsii	Rocky Mountain Spotted Fever	Carried by ticks	Chills, fever, pain in legs and joints
Rickettsia typhi	Endemic murine typhus	Carried by rodents and fleas	Rashes, prolonged high fever
Salmonella sp.	Food poisoning	Contaminated or inadequately cooked food	Nausea, abdominal cramps, diarrhea
Yersinia pestis	Bubonic plague	Carried by fleas on rodents	Enlarged lymph nodes, hemorrhaging, fever, possibly death
Streptococcus sp.	Strep throat	Airborne	Fever, exhaustion, sore throat, enlarged lymph nodes
Mycobacterium tuberculosis	Tuberculosis	Airborne	In active disease, coughing, weight loss, possibly death
Corynebacterium diphtheriae	Diphtheria	Airborne	Fever, sore throat, swelling of neck, possibly death

Antibiotics

Antibiotics are chemicals that are capable of inhibiting the growth of some bacteria. Many of these antibiotics are produced by living organisms. The first antibiotic, penicillin, a product of the fungus *Penicillium,* was discovered by Alexander Fleming (1881–1955), a British bacteriologist.

Antibiotics are useful and necessary. However, antibiotics often destroy not only pathogens but also useful bacteria. Many pathogenic bacteria have also become resistant to antibiotics. When a population of bacteria is first exposed to antibiotics, most members of the population die. However, some may have mutations that allow them to survive the antibiotic. These individuals then reproduce, passing their resistance on to their offspring.

Section Review

1. Look up the word *glycocalyx* in the dictionary. Why is this term appropriate for the structure it describes?
2. How does a chemoautotroph differ from a saprophyte?
3. Describe nitrogen fixation and its importance.
4. How does the pilus function in conjugation?
5. What is the role of penicillin in a natural environment?

Answers to Section Review

1. *Glyco-* is from the Greek word for "sweet"; *-calyx* is from the Greek word for "cup." The structure is a sticky sugar covering.
2. A saprophyte is a heterotroph that feeds on dead organic matter; a chemoautotroph synthesizes food using the energy of chemical reactions.
3. In nitrogen fixation, bacteria convert gaseous nitrogen to ammonia, which plants can use. Thus, the process makes an essential nutrient available to plants.
4. Pili form a bridge through which a portion of DNA from one bacterium can pass to another bacterium.
5. The penicillin produced by the fungus in the natural environment probably serves to reduce competition from bacteria.

Laboratory

Culturing Bacteria

Objective
To study where bacteria can be found

Process Skills
Observing, hypothesizing, experimenting

Materials
One petri dish with nutrient agar, transparent tape 3/4 inch wide, marking pens

Background

1 What are favorable conditions for the growth of most bacteria?
2 If bacteria reproduce once an hour, and you start with one bacterium, how many bacteria do you have after 24 hours?

Inquiry

1 Divide your petri dish into four equal quadrants by writing on the outside of the bottom of the dish with the marking pen. Label the quadrants *1* to *4*. Why is it important to write on the bottom of the dish rather than on the top?
2 Take a piece of transparent tape and touch the sticky side to a surface that you think contains a good bacteria sample. Then open the petri dish and touch the nutrient agar on quadrant 2 with the tape. This process transfers bacteria from the surface you selected to the nutrient agar in the petri dish. Remove the tape and throw it away. Close the petri dish immediately. Why is it important to keep the petri dish closed? Why is it all right to open it briefly to touch the tape to the agar? Why is it important not to touch the sticky side of the tape with your fingers?
3 Discuss with your laboratory partner places in school that would be likely to contain bacteria or that have conditions under which bacteria grow best. Repeat step 2 for quadrants 3 and 4.

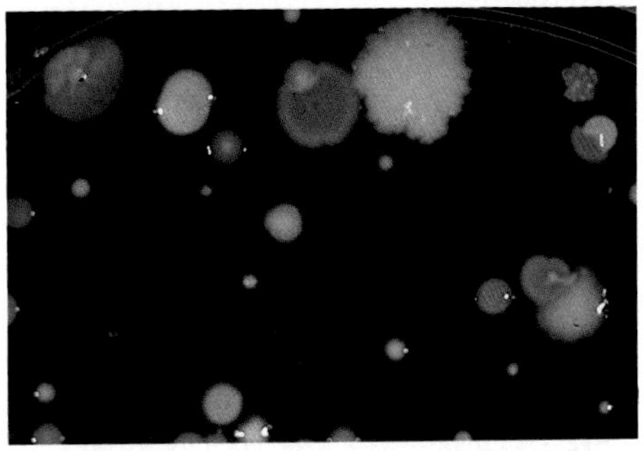

4 Use quadrant 1 as a control. Touch a fresh piece of transparent tape directly to quadrant 1. Why is this a necessary control?
5 Cover your plate and leave it upside down overnight at room temperature. Check daily for bacterial growth as long as you find new colonies. Do not open the petri dish. What is happening that enables you to see bacteria? What does each colony represent?
6 Design and set up a table to record your results. Record how many colonies of bacteria you find in each quadrant.
7 Discard your petri dish as directed by your teacher. Why is it important not to handle the bacteria?

Conclusions

1 On which surfaces did you find the most bacteria? The fewest bacteria? Did your results conform to your expectations? Explain.
2 What are some possible sources of error?
3 Combine the data obtained by the entire class. Which surfaces yielded the most bacteria?
4 Did all the colonies you observed look the same? What is the significance of your finding?

Further Inquiry
You can use this technique to study the occurrence of bacteria outside the school. Think of places either at home or outside that might yield interesting cultures.

Laboratory

(For an overview of bacteria and preparatory information related to the laboratory, see p. 293B.)

Background
1. Most bacteria grow best in warm, moist conditions when nutrients are available.
2. 16,777,216. Students should multiply by 2 for every hour:
at hour 0 1
at hour 1 2
at hour 2 4
at hour 3 8
at hour 4 16 . . .
Bacteria reproduce rapidly. The total assumes that ideal growth conditions continue for 24 hours and that *all* bacteria live.

Inquiry
1. Because the top rotates with respect to the agar
2. Keep the petri dish closed so that bacteria in the air do not fall onto the agar. It is all right to open it briefly. Bacteria are unlikely to contaminate the culture in such a short time. If you touched the sticky side of the tape to your fingers, you would pick up bacteria from your fingers.
3. Likely places would be warm, moist, and contain nutrients. Examples would include shower room floors, drinking fountains, waste barrels, insides of shoes.
4. To see how many bacteria, if any, are on the tape itself
5. The bacteria grow by using the nutrients in the agar. Each colony represents the place where a single bacterium came in contact with the agar.
6. The table should have columns for quadrant number, surface sampled, and number of colonies on days 1 through about 5, as well as descriptions of the sizes, colors, and textures of the colonies. Unless the plates are in an incubator, colonies will probably not appear until day 2.
7. Since the bacteria were isolated from the environment, they may be pathogenic.

Conclusions
1. Answers will vary but should refer to movement using flagella.
2. Not pressing firmly enough on the tape when sampling or transferring the bacteria, failure to take a sample from the dirtiest part of the surface, and leaving the petri dish open too long
3. Student answers will vary. Encourage the class to discuss their results together.
4. All the colonies will probably not look the same because there may be different kinds of bacteria. Some students may observe mold spores as well.

Further Inquiry
Students might try kitchen garbage, coins, or decomposing leaves in the woods.

Vocabulary

1. Chemoautotroph; the other terms describe monera that use food produced by other organisms.
2. Methanogen; the other terms are classes of Schizophyta.
3. Archaebacterium; the other terms are related to disease.
4. Endospore; the other terms relate to the exchange of genetic material.
5. Obligate anaerobe; the other terms are associated with Cyanophyta.

Review

1. b
2. b
3. c
4. d
5. d
6. a
7. b
8. c
9. a
10. a

11. The phylum consists of the classes Eubacteria, Actinomycota, Rickettsiae, and Spirochaeta.
12. Gram-negative cells have a lipopolysaccharide covering and stain pink; Gram-positive cells have no such covering and stain purple. Gram-positive bacteria are more susceptible to antibiotics.
13. Actinomycotes are Gram-positive bacteria that form colonies of filaments. Rickettsiae are Gram-negative, parasitic bacteria. Spirochetes are spiral-shaped bacteria that usually move with flagella.
14. Blue-green bacteria are photosynthetic, contain chlorophyll a, use water during photosynthesis, and produce oxygen. Colonies of blue-green bacteria also show specialization of cells.
15. The capsule is a protective layer of polysaccharides that surrounds the cell wall.
16. By decomposing dead organic matter, saprophytic bacteria release carbon and other elements for use by other organisms.
17. Photoautotrophs use light energy to synthesize food; chemoautotrophs use the energy of chemical reactions to synthesize food.
18. In conjugation, a portion of DNA from one bacterium passes across a bridge formed by pili into another bacterium. The DNA of the first bacterium lines up with the homologous portion of the DNA of the second bacterium, which is destroyed and the new DNA is substituted.
19. Exotoxins are generally found to be more deadly.
20. Hydrogen sulfide

Chapter 20 Review

Vocabulary

actinomycotes (297)
antibiotic (304)
archaebacterium (296)
autotroph (301)
binary fission (302)
bloom (298)
blue-green bacterium (297)
capsule (300)
chemoautotroph (301)
conjugation (302)
endospore (300)
endotoxin (303)
eubacterium (297)
exotoxin (303)
extreme halophile (296)
facultative anaerobe (301)
glycocalyx (300)
Gram-negative bacterium (297)
Gram-positive bacterium (297)
Gram stain (297)
heterocyst (298)
heterotroph (301)
methanogen (296)
nitrogen fixation (301)
obligate aerobe (301)
obligate anaerobe (301)
pathogen (303)
photoautotroph (301)
pilus (300)
plasmid (300)
rickettsiae (297)
saprophyte (301)
spirochete (297)
thermoacidophile (296)
toxin (303)

In each of the following sets, choose the term that does not belong and explain why.

1. heterotroph, saprophyte, chemoautotroph
2. methanogen, spirochete, rickettsiae
3. archaebacterium, exotoxin, pathogen
4. pilus, conjugation, endospore
5. blue-green bacterium, obligate anaerobe, bloom

Review

1. The smallest cell known to exist is a (a) spirochete (b) mycoplasma (c) archaebacterium (d) eubacterium.
2. Rod-shaped monerans are called (a) cocci (b) bacilli (c) halophile (d) spirilli.
3. A thermoacidophile is a(n) (a) spirochete (b) cyanophyte (c) archaebacterium (d) actinomycete.
4. Gram-positive bacteria stain (a) blue (b) pink (c) red (d) purple.
5. Blooms that occur in lakes are the result of (a) antibiotics (b) pathogens (c) rickettsiae (d) population explosions.
6. Bacterial DNA is (a) circular (b) encased in a capsule (c) linear (d) found in the nucleus.
7. The glycocalyx helps monerans to (a) survive unfavorable environmental conditions (b) stick to surfaces (c) metabolize gaseous nitrogen (d) ingest food.
8. In nitrogen fixation, gaseous nitrogen is converted to (a) carbon (b) glucose (c) ammonia (d) methane.
9. An organism that must have oxygen to survive is (a) an obligate aerobe (b) a facultative anaerobe (c) a facultative aerobe (d) an obligate anaerobe.
10. Genetic recombination in monerans can occur during the process of (a) conjugation (b) heterocyst formation (c) binary fission (d) endospore production.
11. What are the four classes in Phylum Schizophyta?
12. Explain the major difference between Gram-positive and Gram-negative bacteria. Which of these two groups is more susceptible to antibiotics?
13. Describe the main characteristics of actinomycotes, rickettsiae, and spirochetes.
14. List three ways in which blue-green bacteria resemble plants.
15. Describe the capsule of a moneran, and state its function.
16. Explain how saprophytic monerans contribute to the recycling of nutrients in the environment.

17. How do photoautotrophs differ from chemoautotrophs?
18. Describe one way in which some monerans can exchange genetic information.
19. Which is generally more deadly, an endotoxin or an exotoxin?
20. What compound is metabolized by bacteria in deep-sea vents?

Critical Thinking

1. Scientists have only recently discovered fossil bacteria. Explain why this discovery may have taken so long.
2. *Clostridium tetani,* the bacteria that cause tetanus, are obligate anaerobes. From this information would you infer that a deep puncture wound or a surface cut would be more likely to become infected by tetanus bacteria? Explain the reason for your inference.
3. Penicillin works by interfering with the ability of bacteria to build a cell wall. Given this fact, explain why Gram-positive bacteria are more susceptible to the effects of penicillin than Gram-negative bacteria are.
4. Some of the bacteria that are normally found in the human intestinal tract are beneficial. For example, *E. coli* produces Vitamin K. However, *E. coli* can also cause diarrhea under exceptional circumstances and can cause serious infections if it invades other parts of the body. Other bacteria found in the digestive tract do not produce substances the body can use, nor do they produce substances that are harmful. What role might they play?

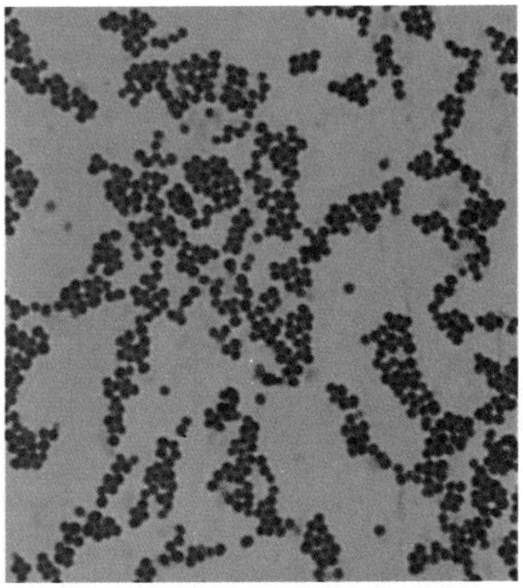

5. Examine the photograph above of bacteria that have been treated with a Gram stain. Would you hypothesize that these bacteria produce endotoxins?
6. Vent communities have some of the densest and most productive populations known to exist. What might explain this?

Extension

1. Read the article by K.A. Fackelmann entitled "Pipe-dwelling Bacteria Use Slimy Strategy" in *Science News,* January 6, 1990, p. 6. Prepare an oral report in which you include answers to the following questions: (1) How do *Pseudomonas* elude germicide attack? (2) What sort of health threat do these bacteria pose? (3) What are possible solutions to the problem of pipe-dwelling *Pseudomonas?* and (4) In general how much evidence do you believe is necessary to warrant a public health emergency?
2. Research and write a report on the use of bacteria in either the processing of several foods or in the treatment of sewage.
3. Visit or telephone your local public health department, and ask for information on bacterial diseases that have been reported in your area in recent weeks.

Critical Thinking

1. Fossil bacteria are very small, and their cells do not contain bones or other hard materials that would be easily preserved.
2. A deep puncture wound is more likely to develop tetanus because oxygen is less likely to be present deep under the skin.
3. Gram-positive bacteria lack the outer covering of lipopolysaccharides that Gram-negative bacteria have. In Gram-positive bacteria, then, the penicillin can more easily interfere with cell wall building.
4. They consume the excess food in the intestinal tract and by doing so possibly prevent the establishment of more harmful bacteria.
5. The bacteria are stained pink and must be Gram-negative. Since most Gram-negative bacteria produce endotoxins, it is likely that these do also.
6. In vent communities, predators that might limit bacterial growth are practically nonexistent. Thus, the bacterial communities can grow to the optimum that the food supply will allow.

Extension

1. (1) *Pseudomonas* secretes a slime that sticks to pipe walls. The germicide kills free-floating microbes but does not kill the microbes embedded in the slime. (2) Some can cause fatal infection in people with weakened immune systems, open wounds, or medical implants. (3) Replacing plastic pipes with stainless steel ones and regular flushing with scalding water may be possible solutions. (4) Encourage students to give a rationale for their opinions.
2. Have students make presentations to the class about these beneficial bacteria.
3. To follow up, invite a public health specialist to address the class on epidemic bacterial diseases.

Chapter 21 Protozoa

Chapter Overview

Chapter 21 introduces the Kingdom Protista, focusing on protozoa. Section 21.1 presents an overview of protozoa by discussing their evolution, classification, ecology, and physiology. In Section 21.2, students will learn about the characteristics common to the members of each of the four protozoan phyla. Some of the major diseases caused by protozoan parasites are also discussed.

Chapter Planning Chart

B	S	A	Sections and Subsections	Page	Features	Page	Resources
•	•	•	**21 Overview of Protozoa**				
			Evolution	309	Section Review	310	Videodiscs
			Classification	309			Section Reviews Worksheet
			Ecology and Physiology	310			
•	•	•	**21 Protozoan Phyla**				
			Sarcodina	311	Think	313	Videodiscs
			Ciliophora	312	Biotechnology	314	Blackline Master 43
			Zoomastigina	313	Laboratory	317	Overhead Transparency T21
			Sporozoa	315	Section Review	316	Blackline Master 44
							Process Skills: Malaria and Sickle-Cell Anemia
							Laboratories: Protista
							Section Reviews Worksheet
			End of Chapter Activities				
					Chapter Review	318	Vocabulary Skills
							Chapter Test
							Computer Test Generator

B *The Basic Level curriculum presents the most fundamental knowledge offered in the course.*
S *The Standard Level curriculum is designed for the average student who is able to master most topics.*
A *The Advanced Level curriculum includes suggestions for teaching the most academically able students.*

Cooperative Learning

Group Activity: Protozoan Diseases

- **Group size:** *3 students*
- **Outcome:** *Students will describe various aspects of protozoan diseases, including the parasites that cause them, symptoms, and treatments.*
- **Individual Accountability:** *Each student will be responsible for researching one aspect of a protozoan disease.*
- **Positive Interdependence:** *The group members will integrate their individual research and make a presentation to the class.*

Have each group research one protozoan disease, such as amebic dysentery, trypanosomiasis, trichomoniasis, giardiasis, leishmaniasis, malaria, and congenital toxoplasmosis. Instruct groups to divide the research among their three members so that one member is responsible for information about the size, shape, or special features of the parasite. Another student should be responsible for information about the symptoms and progress of the disease, and the third should research treatment and prevention methods. When the individual research is completed, have the groups assess the information and integrate it into a short oral presentation for the class.

To ensure individual accountability, also inform students that you may call on any group member to contribute to the group's oral report during class presentation. Require groups to include sketches, tables, or other illustrations in their presentations.

Concept Map

The following is one possible solution for the concept mapping activity in the Guided Practice on p. 314.

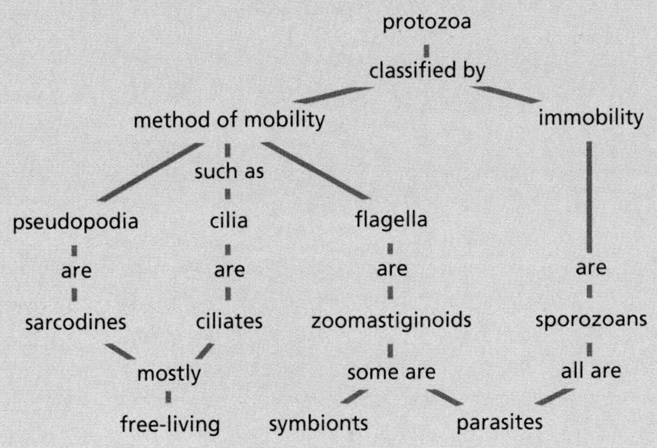

Laboratory Preparation

Overview *(See p. 317.)*

This lab enables students to observe the *Paramecium* and study a few of its simple functions. It offers a good opportunity for students to observe cilia, which are structurally the same as the cilia found in the respiratory passages, Fallopian tubes, and inner ear of humans. It also gives them good practice in lab technique.

Preparation

Live cultures of *Paramecium* and *Euglena* may be obtained from biological supply houses. Aerate the cultures as soon as they arrive by squirting air into the water with a medicine dropper. Keep the cultures capped loosely. If a rice grain has been added to it, the culture should keep for several weeks.

Feed *Euglena* to the *Paramecium* culture at least 20 to 30 minutes before the start of class to ensure that students will observe full food vacuoles.

Teaching Tips

Make sure students understand how food is digested in a food vacuole. The food vacuole, once formed, fuses with a lysosome, which contains digested enzymes. The digested food can then pass through the membrane around the food vacuole and be used by the *Paramecium.* On rare occasions a student may see a small, waste-containing food vacuole being extruded through the anal pore.

It is also important for students to understand how a contractile vacuole functions. Since the concentration of solute molecules is lower in the water than in *Paramecium*'s cytoplasm, water always diffuses into the *Paramecium* until equilibrium of concentration is attained. If the *Paramecium* did not get rid of this water, it would explode.

Stentor and *Blepharisma* have very striking cilia around their mouths and are well worth observing as Further Inquiry. In addition, an *Ameba,* with its pseudopodia, is an excellent protozoan to study. Because all of these organisms eat *Euglena,* students can observe green food vacuoles in any of them. *Stentor* (green) eats *Blepharisma* (pink), so if you mix the two, you can observe stentors with pink food vacuoles.

Safety

Remind students to handle slides and coverslips carefully.

Chapter Themes

Evolution Modern biological classification is based on evolutionary relationships, though on the surface classification seems to be based on morphology or mode of locomotion or some other characteristic. Emphasize that the classification of protists reflects what scientists know about the evolutionary divergence among these organisms.

Scale and Structure As students learn about the various structures and cell plans of protists, stress that each structure evolved as an adaptive response by the species to the environment. Relate structure to function, such as the function of the various organelles of protozoa.

Systems and Interactions Protozoa interact with their environment and other organisms. For humans, diseases caused by protozoa are examples of negative interaction.

Chapter Motivating Activity

In this chapter students will recognize the differences between prokaryotic and eukaryotic organisms. To emphasize the distinction, review with students what they have already learned. Begin by writing *prokaryotic organisms* and *eukaryotic organisms* on the board. Display photographs or drawings of both kinds of organisms. Then ask students to brainstorm characteristics of each. *(The primary difference is the presence of a membrane-bound nucleus in eukaryotic cells, which prokaryotes lack. Students should mention that eukaryotic cells contain specialized organelles, such as mitochondria and chloroplasts. Students should note that prokaryotic organisms are unicellular, whereas eukaryotic organisms can be either uni- or multicellular.)* Point out that most protists are unicellular.

Chapter 21 Protozoa

Introduction

The Kingdom Protista is made up of widely diverse organisms. In this chapter you will learn about the four phyla of protozoa, the so-called animallike protists. They are all heterotrophic and live in both aquatic and terrestrial environments. In Chapter 22 the autotrophic plantlike protists will be covered. Funguslike protists, which are also heterotrophic, are discussed in Chapter 23.

Chapter Outline

21.1 Overview of Protozoa
- *Evolution*
- *Classification*
- *Ecology and Physiology*

21.2 Protozoan Phyla
- *Sarcodina*
- *Ciliophora*
- *Zoomastigina*
- *Sporozoa*

Chapter Concept

As you read, examine how different protozoa are structurally adapted for either free-living or parasitism.

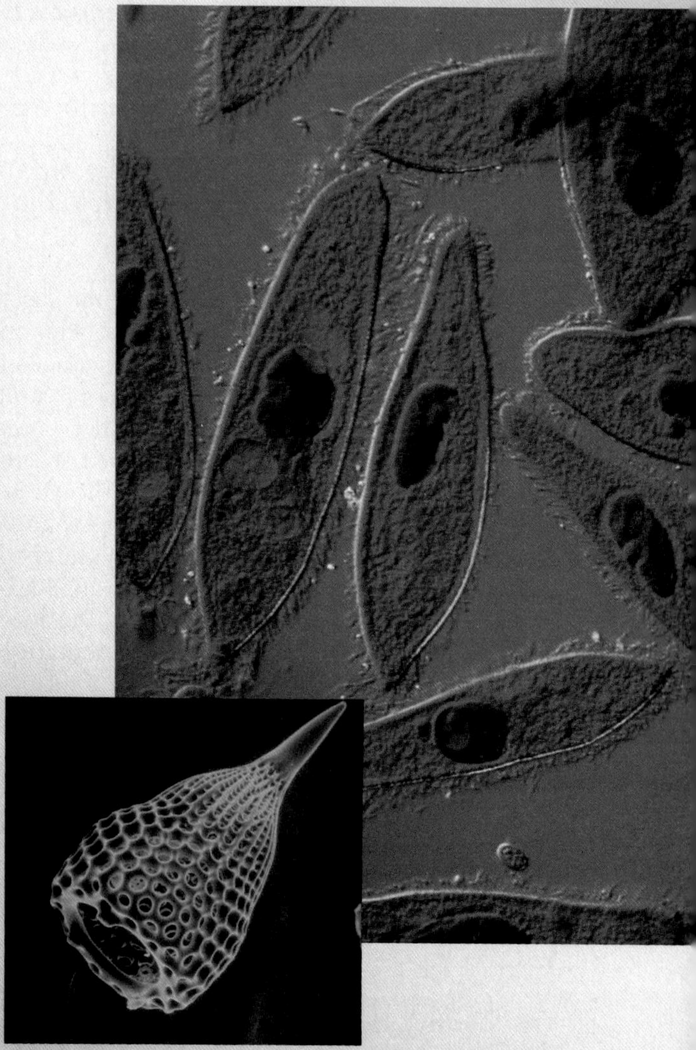

Stained paramecia, *Paramecium caudatum,* (×100). Inset: Color-enhanced shell of a Radiolaria (×700).

Understanding the Visuals

As students look at the chapter-opening photos, ask if these organisms appear this way in nature. *(The paramecia have been stained, and the radiolarian has been color enhanced.)* Focus students' attention on the paramecia, and ask what value staining has for a scientist. *(The membrane around the organisms stains a different color than the cytoplasm and thus must be of a different chemical makeup.)* Explain that this outer covering is rigid and made of a protein. Then have students compare the shapes of the two types of protozoa. Point out that radiolarians are marine protozoa that have a glasslike, silica shell.

21.1 Overview of Protozoa

All members of Kingdom Protista are eukaryotic. Some animal-like protists are commonly called protozoa. Nearly 65,000 species of protozoa are known. All are heterotrophic, living freely or as parasites. Most are microscopic and unicellular, though some form colonies in which cell specialization occurs.

Other protists are plantlike organisms commonly called algae. Unlike protozoa, algae are autotrophic. Funguslike organisms form the third group of protists. Protozoa and funguslike protists differ in their methods of reproduction.

Section Objectives

- *Explain how protozoa may have evolved from prokaryotes.*
- *List the four phyla of protozoa and their characteristics of movement.*
- *Discuss the ecology of protozoa and its relation to their physiology.*
- *Describe why euglenoids are not classified with protozoa.*

Evolution

The first cells were prokaryotic and originated over 3.5 billion years ago. The first eukaryotes found in the fossil record are 1.45 billion years old. Eukaryotes may have arisen much earlier, but because their cells are generally soft, it is not likely that many were preserved in rocks. However, evidence from comparative anatomy and cell physiology strongly suggests that eukaryotes evolved from prokaryotes. According to **endosymbiosis,** prokaryotic parasites once lived inside other prokaryotic cells. Then the parasitic prokaryotes lost the ability to live independently of their hosts and evolved into various cell organelles. Structural and biochemical evidence suggests that mitochondria arose from parasitic bacteria and that chloroplasts arose from parasitic blue-green bacteria. The nucleus, however, probably did not arise from an endosymbiont. It probably came to exist as an organelle when DNA was enclosed within a double membrane.

Classification

Biologists classify protozoa into four phyla: Sarcodina *(SAHR-kuh-DINE-uh),* Ciliophora *(SILL-ee-AHF-ur-uh),* Zoomastigina *(ZOE-uh-MASS-tuh-JINE-uh),* and Sporozoa *(SPOR-uh-ZOE-uh).* These are shown in Figure 21-2 on the following page. The main criterion for classification is mechanism of locomotion.

- Members of the Phylum Sarcodina move by using cytoplasmic projections called pseudopodia.
- Members of the Phylum Ciliophora move by the use of cilia.
- Members of the Phylum Zoomastigina move by use of flagella.
- Members of the Phylum Sporozoa are immobile and parasitic.

Some biologists suggest that organisms called euglenoids should also be considered protozoa. Although *Euglena* and related organisms look and behave much like protozoa, they photosynthesize under certain circumstances. In other words, they can be autotrophic as well as heterotrophic. For this reason scientists often consider them more like algae than like protozoa.

Figure 21-1 These Foraminiferal fossils are similar to marine Foraminifera living today.

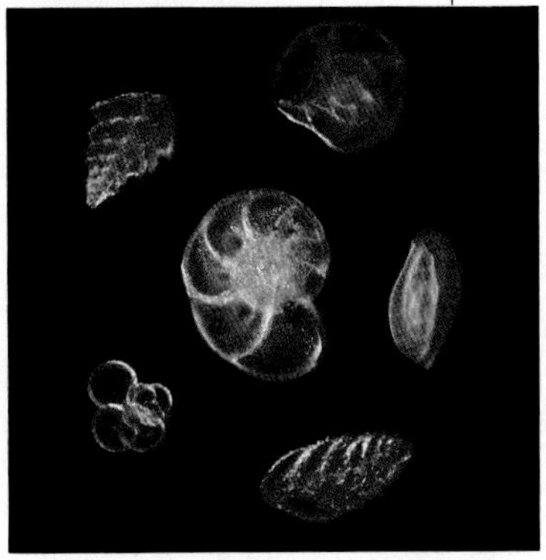

Lesson Plan

Section Focus

This section discusses the evolution of eukaryotes and describes the four protozoan phyla. Students will learn about the ecology and physiology of protozoa.

Section Themes

The section emphasizes the theme of **Evolution.** Some scientists hypothesize that eukaryotes evolved from the interactions of prokaryotes. The interaction of parasitic protozoa with their host illustrates the theme of **Systems and Interactions.**

Motivating Activity

Most students think protozoa live in an environment such as a pond. To show that protozoa live in many environments, add a handful each of soil and dead grass to a wide-mouthed jar. Then fill the jar with distilled water, cover it, and place it in indirect light. A day or two later, have students examine under a microscope samples of water from the jar. Students should see protozoa in the water. Ask where these protists came from.

Teaching Strategies

Drawing Conclusions Point out that protozoa are described as being animallike. Ask students how protozoa are similar to animals. *(Both are heterotrophic and mobile.)* Challenge students to explain how protozoa are different from animals. *(Protozoa are unicellular or colonial, not multicellular, and do not undergo embryonic development.)*

Videodiscs

- ***Side 3 3302, A Drop of Fresh Water: Paramecium, Stentor, Volvox (m)***

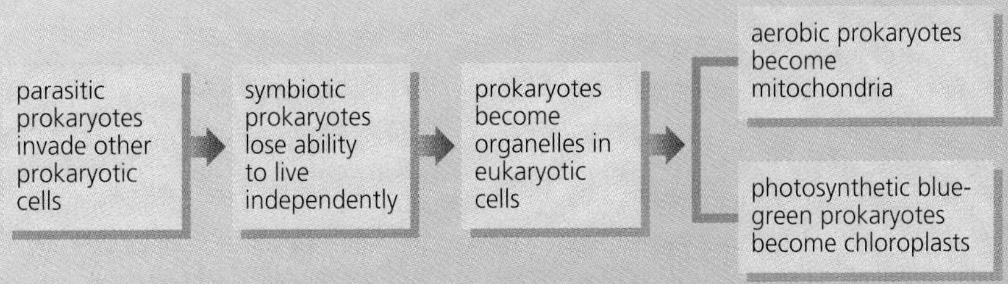

Graphic Organizer Use this sequential diagram in Reteaching on p. 310.

Guided Practice

Help students make generalizations about protozoa by asking the following questions: Are protozoa prokaryotes or eukaryotes? *(Eukaryotes)* Free-living or parasitic? *(Either)* Unicellular or multicellular? *(Unicellular mostly, though some form colonies)* Have or lack a protective covering? *(Most lack protective covering.)*

Independent Practice

■ Have students write answers to the Section Review.
■ Have students speculate in writing about whether protozoa that sense light move toward or away from light and why. *(Away from, for protection)*

Check Your Understanding

1. Why have many scientists inferred that chloroplasts evolved from blue-green bacteria? *(Chloroplasts and blue-green bacteria contain chlorophyll.)*
2. Name some characteristics that identify protozoa as organisms. *(They are cellular and organized at the cellular level; they respond to stimuli, use energy, and reproduce.)*

Reteaching

Have students make a sequential diagram to explain endosymbiosis. A model appears on p. 309.
■ *See* Section Reviews *worksheet, Section 21.1.*

Enrichment

Have students investigate in books on oceanography the makeup of plankton, including zooplankton, phytoplankton, and bacterioplankton. Ask students to assess the importance of plankton in ocean food webs.

Closure

Name different cellular structures used for movement and then ask, for example, which protozoa use cilia. *(Members of the Phylum Ciliophora)*

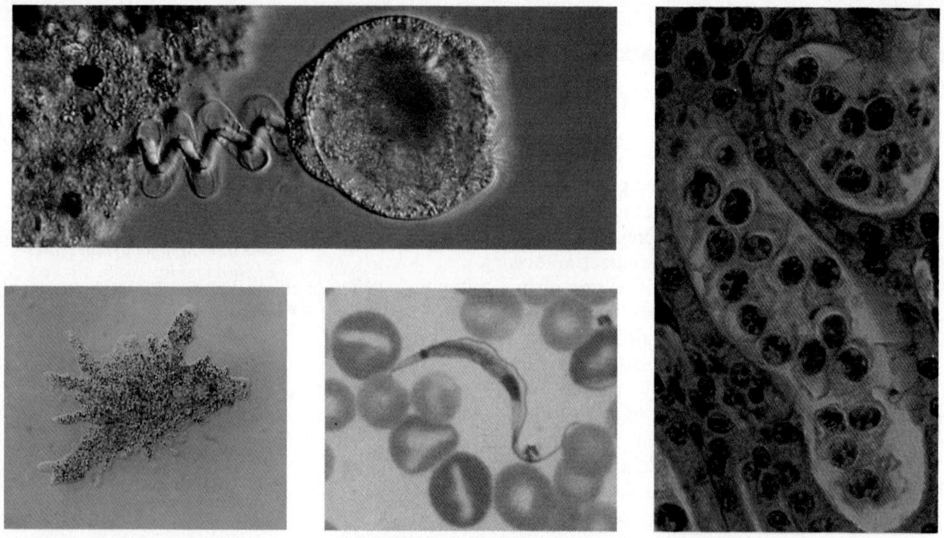

Figure 21-2 The four protozoan phyla are represented by the following organisms, clockwise from upper left: Ciliophora, *Vorticella;* Sporozoa, *Laptotheca;* Zoomastigina, *Trypanosoma lewisi;* Sarcodina, *Ameba.*

Ecology and Physiology

Some species of modern-day protozoa are free-living; others are parasitic. Free-living protozoa live in all habitats in which water is available at some time of the year. Many free-living protozoa make up **zooplankton,** unicellular heterotrophic organisms that drift in water. Other free-living protozoa live in the soil. Parasitic protozoa live in the tissues and bloodstream of their hosts. Many parasitic protozoa cause diseases, which are among the most severe in humans and other animals.

Whether free-living or parasitic, most protozoa lack a protective outer covering. Therefore a semipermeable cell membrane serves as the regulatory boundary between the cytoplasm and the environment. Potassium, calcium, oxygen gas, and carbon dioxide diffuse across the cell membrane.

Most protozoa have physiological mechanisms for monitoring and responding to the environment. For example, many free-living forms have **eyespots,** localized regions of pigments that detect changes in the quantity and quality of light. Protozoa also sense touch and chemical changes in their environments. For instance, when they encounter a noxious chemical, some protozoa back up and try to bypass the chemical.

Section Review

1. What is an *eyespot?*
2. Briefly summarize the theory of endosymbiosis.
3. List the four phyla of protozoa, and describe how members of each move.
4. How do O_2 and CO_2 enter and leave protozoa?
5. What might be some possible ecological roles of protozoa?

Answers to Section Review

1. A region of pigments that detects changes in the quantity and quality of light
2. Scientists hypothesize that when parasitic prokaryotes lost the ability to live independently of their prokaryotic hosts, they evolved into the cell organelles of eukaryotes.
3. Sarcodina, by pseudopodia; Ciliophora, by cilia; Zoomastigina, by flagella; Sporozoa, immobile
4. O_2 and CO_2 diffuse across the semipermeable cell membrane.
5. Protozoa recycle nutrients because they are heterotrophic; they are a major component of zooplankton, an important food source for marine animals; protozoa in the soil are eaten by certain soil animals; protozoa are parasites in many organisms.

21.2 Protozoan Phyla

As you read about the diversity of protozoa in the four phyla, keep in mind that each species is adapted to either a free-living or a parasitic life-style. All are heterotrophic; most are unicellular. All have cellular mechanisms that monitor the environment.

Section Objectives

- *Compare and contrast methods of movement in the four phyla of protozoa.*
- *Describe binary fission in amebas and ciliates.*
- *Describe the process of conjugation in ciliates.*
- *List and explain two diseases that are caused by zoomastiginoids.*
- *List and explain two diseases caused by sporozoans.*

Sarcodina

Biologists have identified about 40,000 species of the Phylum Sarcodina. The most familiar sarcodines are members of the freshwater genus *Ameba.* Amebas are bottom-dwelling scavengers; they feed on decaying organic matter in rivers, streams, and lakes.

Most sarcodines have flexible cell membranes. Many do not have any added protective covering. However, some, such as the marine sarcodines of the genus *Foraminifera,* have calcium carbonate shells with spikelike protrusions. Others, such as the marine sarcodines of the genus *Radiolaria,* have supportive silicon dioxide inside their shells. Freshwater sarcodines called heliozoans have a shell with thin, extended projections.

Movement, Structure, and Nutrition

Sarcodines move by means of pseudopodia. **Pseudopodia** *(SOO-duh-POE-dee-uh)* are cytoplasmic extensions that function in movement. The cytoplasm of a sarcodine is made up of two regions—the ectoplasm and the endoplasm. The **ectoplasm** is the thin, slippery colloidal sol directly inside the cell membrane. The **endoplasm** is the colloidal sol and gel found in the interior of the cell. When movement begins, the endoplasm pushes outward, facilitated by the slippery ectoplasm, and becomes distinguishable as a pseudopodium. At the same time, previously formed pseudopodia are retracted. Hence the sarcodine moves forward by **ameboid movement,** as shown in Figure 21-3. Ameboid movement is a form of **cytoplasmic streaming,** the internal flowing of the contents of a cell.

Figure 21-3 When sarcodines move, the endoplasm and ectoplasm push out to form pseudopodia. Meanwhile, previously formed pseudopodia retract.

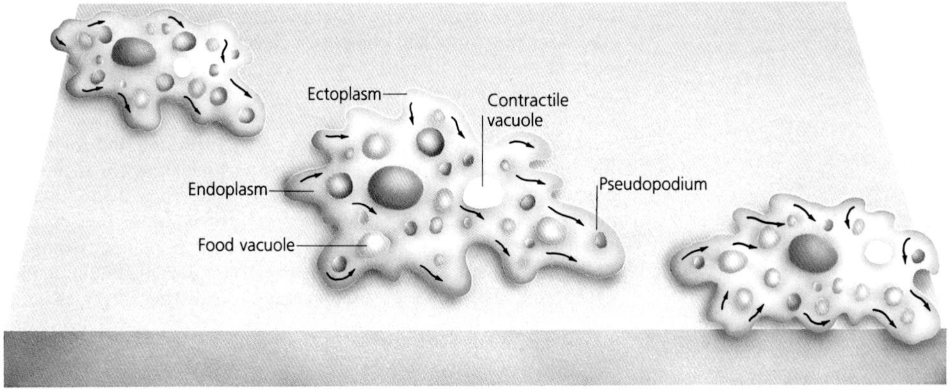

Phylum	Locomotion	Reproduction	Other Features
Sarcodina	pseudopodia	binary fission	silicon shells
Ciliophora	cilia	binary fission; conjugation	two kinds of nuclei
Zoomastigina	flagella	binary fission; sexual reproduction	parasites or symbionts
Sporozoa	immobile	spores	all are parasitic

Graphic Organizer Use this table in Organizing Information on p. 312.

Lesson Plan

Section Focus

This section describes the characteristics common to the members of each of the four protozoan phyla and examines in detail *Ameba, Paramecium,* and *Plasmodium.* It also discusses some typical diseases caused by protozoa.

Section Themes

This section emphasizes the theme of **Scale and Structure** in its discussion of protozoan structures. The analysis of various methods of locomotion shows the relation between structure and function. The discussion of how protozoa interact with other organisms, including material on parasitic relationships, develops the theme of **Systems and Interactions.** The life cycle of *Plasmodium,* for example, depends on interaction with other species.

Motivating Activity

Tell students that one championship college basketball team employed what they called the "ameba defense." Ask if anyone can explain this defense. *(The ameba defense is a zone defense. Rather than staying in rigid positions, team members move widely within certain regions to match up with opposing players.)* Use a microprojector and live amebas to show students how these protists project portions of the cell during movement. Then ask five volunteers to demonstrate how they might copy ameba behavior when playing defense in basketball.

Videodiscs

- ***532, Paramecium Engulfed by Ameba (s)***
- ***1599, Living Cells: Ameba (s)***

Teaching Strategies

Organizing Information To help students organize the material in Section 21.2, have them each construct a table that they can fill in as they read the section. Use the table shown on p. 311 as a model. Encourage students to add as much information as they can to their tables so that they will have an easy reference when they finish the chapter.

Interpreting the Visuals Refer students to Figure 21-3, p. 311, and ask them to explain the labels on the drawing. For example, ask what the difference is between ectoplasm and endoplasm. *(Ectoplasm is the colloidal sol directly inside the cell membrane, whereas endoplasm is the colloidal material in the interior.)* Review with students the colloidal nature of the cytoplasm, as explained on p. 39 in Chapter 3. Then focus their attention on ameboid movement. Ask a volunteer to describe what the figure shows. *(Pseudopodium extension and then cytoplasmic streaming)*

■ *See* Overhead Transparency *T21 and* Blackline Master *43.*

Observing Organisms Set up microscope stations around the classroom and have students observe prepared slides of protozoa from each of the four phyla. Ask students to draw what they see and label any parts they can distinguish. In class discussion, have students compare what they saw on the slides with the labeled figures in the text.

■ *See* Laboratories, *Investigation 21.*

Figure 21-4 A paramecium moves by means of cilia that beat in waves. Water currents created by cilia that line the oral groove move food down the groove to the mouth pore.

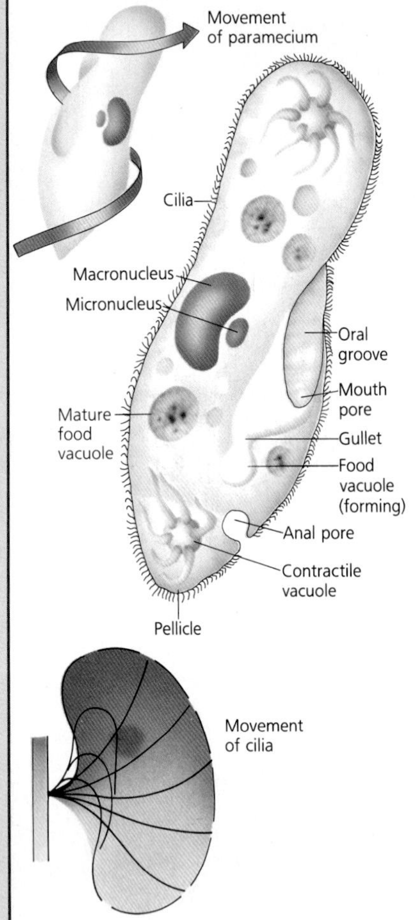

Most freshwater sarcodines are internally similar to the ameba in Figure 21-3. Notice the **contractile vacuole,** an organelle that excretes water. Freshwater organisms are usually hypertonic relative to their environment, and water diffuses into them. To maintain homeostasis, many freshwater unicellular organisms have contractile vacuoles that excrete excess water.

Sarcodines absorb many nutrients by diffusion from the surrounding water and ingest nutrients by **phagocytosis,** the engulfing of food. When a sarcodine contacts food, it surrounds the food with pseudopodia. A portion of the cell membrane then pinches together and surrounds the food in a **food vacuole.** Enzymes from the cytoplasm enter the vacuole and digest the food. Any undigested food leaves the cell in a reverse process that is known as exocytosis.

Reproduction

Sarcodines reproduce by binary fission, an asexual, mitotic division that produces identical offspring. Under ideal conditions it takes less than an hour for an ameba to undergo binary fission. When conditions are poor, sarcodines can form **cysts,** dormant cells each surrounded by a hard layer. When conditions improve, the cell breaks out of the cyst and resumes normal activities.

Ciliophora

The 8,000 species of Phylum Ciliophora move by means of **cilia,** short, hairlike projections that line the cell membrane and beat in synchronized strokes. Ciliates live in marine and freshwater habitats. Members of the freshwater genus *Paramecium,* shown in Figure 21-4, are the most thoroughly studied of the ciliates.

Structure, Nutrition, and Responses

A paramecium never changes shape like an ameba because it is surrounded by a rigid protein covering, the **pellicle.** The pellicle is covered with thousands of cilia arranged in rows. The cilia beat in waves. Each wave passes slantwise across the long axis of the body of the paramecium, causing it to rotate as it moves forward.

Internally a distinctive trait of the ciliates is the presence of two kinds of nuclei—the macronucleus and the micronucleus. The large **macronucleus** controls such cell activities as respiration, protein synthesis, digestion, and asexual reproduction. The much smaller **micronucleus** is involved in sexual reproduction and heredity.

Ciliates have numerous cellular structures adapted for feeding on bacteria and other protists. A paramecium, for instance, has a funnellike **oral groove** lined with cilia. These beating cilia create water currents that sweep food down the groove to the **mouth pore** of the paramecium. The mouth pore opens onto a **gullet,** which forms food vacuoles that circulate throughout the cytoplasm. The contents of the vacuoles are then digested and

More Information

Protozoa The name *protozoa* is derived from a Greek word meaning "first animal," and until fairly recently protozoa were usually considered animals. The Dutch microscopist Anton van Leeuwenhoek was the first to discover protozoa, which he called "animalcules." Over 20,000 species have since been identified.

Perhaps the best-known protozoa are *Ameba* and *Paramecium,* but the best-known protozoan product is chalk. Foraminiferans have calcium carbonate shells that form chalk deposits when the organisms die. The White Cliffs of Dover in England are actually the chalky deposits of ancient foraminiferan shells.

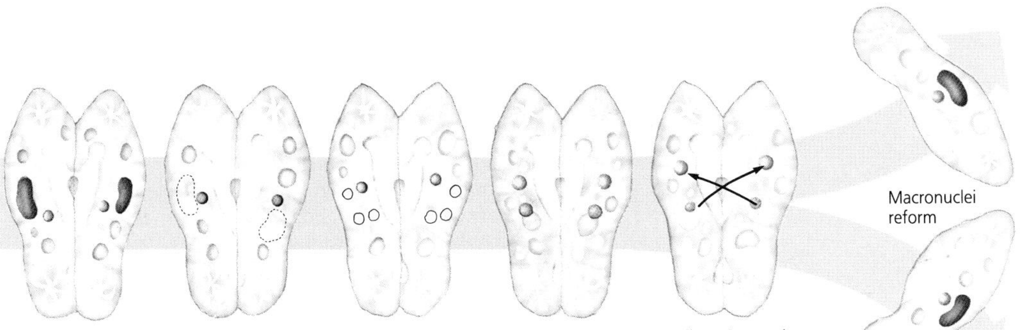

Figure 21-5 Paramecia reproduce by conjugation, a form of sexual reproduction in which genetic material is exchanged by two mating organisms.

absorbed. The indigestible matter remaining in the vacuole moves to the **anal pore,** an opening where waste is eliminated.

Most ciliates exhibit **avoidance behavior,** a reaction away from a potentially harmful situation. A paramecium will back up and move away when it encounters an obstacle in its environment.

Reproduction

Asexual reproduction in ciliates occurs primarily by binary fission. In this process only the micronucleus divides by mitosis. The macronucleus, which contains up to 500 times more DNA than the micronucleus, simply elongates and splits into two parts, each part going to a daughter cell.

Sexual reproduction occurs in many ciliates by a process known as **conjugation.** Conjugation involves individuals from two mating strains, such as the two paramecia in Figure 21-5. The two paramecia lie next to each other. Then the macronucleus of each individual disintegrates. Each diploid micronucleus then undergoes meiosis, producing four haploid micronuclei. In each cell three of these disappear; the fourth moves to the oral groove. Here it undergoes mitosis, producing two haploid micronuclei of unequal size. The smaller micronucleus from one paramecium then exchanges places with the smaller micronucleus from the other paramecium. Each small micronucleus then fuses with each larger micronucleus, forming diploid micronuclei. The two paramecia separate, and macronuclei form again.

Zoomastigina

The 2,500 species of Phylum Zoomastigina, also called Mastigophora, are characterized by the presence of one or more long **flagella.** The undulations of whiplike flagella push or pull the protozoan through the water. Many zoomastiginoids are free-living, moving through lakes or ponds and feeding on small organisms. Some zoomastiginoids are parasites. Among these are members of the genera *Trypanosoma, Leishmania,* and *Giardia.*

Think

Based on what you learned in Chapter 10, what is the adaptive significance of conjugation?

Interpreting the Visuals As students study Figure 21-4, p. 312, ask what primary structures distinguish a paramecium from an ameba. *(The pellicle and cilia)* What two functions do cilia serve? *(Cilia provide movement for the organism and they move food into the oral groove.)* After students have explained the function of each of the labeled parts, have them turn back to Figure 20-5 on p. 300 and note the difference in complexity between a protozoan and a bacterium.

- *See* Blackline Master *44.*

Answer to Think

Conjugation results in recombination of genes, which creates phenotypic variation in the offspring that can be acted on by natural selection.

Contrasting Processes Have students review conjugation in prokaryotes, as explained on p. 302 in Chapter 20. Then have them study the sequence of paramecium conjugation shown in Figure 21-5. Ask students to contrast the two processes. *(In prokaryotic conjugation, only a portion of the DNA from one cell moves into the receiving cell, and the movement is by a temporary bridge between the two organisms. In contrast, in paramecia the DNA of each individual undergoes meiosis, producing haploid micronuclei, and the exchange of genetic material is through the permanent oral groove. Thus, conjugation in paramecia is much more complex than in bacteria.)*

Videodiscs

- *537–542, Protista: Ciliophora (s)*
- *2595, Paramecium (s)*
- *2546, Cilia and Flagella (s)*

LEP Activity

Provide students with index cards and a photocopy of a typical protozoan from each of the four phyla. Have students cut out and paste a picture of a protozoan on one side of a card. On the other side, have them write the names and phonetic pronunciations of the phylum, genus, and locomotive structure of the protozoan. Students can use the completed cards to quiz each other or as individual study aids. Check that students are pronouncing names and structures correctly.

Observing Organisms Ask each student to collect a sample of stream, pond, or lake water and bring it to class. Then have students make wet-mount slides from their samples and use microscopes to look for protozoa. Have some protozoa-rich water on hand, in case student samples lack protozoa. Provide visual guides to help students identify the protozoa.

Exploring Careers Invite a protozoologist or health professional from a nearby university or hospital to speak to the class about parasitic protozoa that cause diseases in humans. Prepare students to ask appropriate questions, such as ones about the diseases discussed in the text.

Interpreting the Visuals Help students relate Figure 21-6, p. 316, to the text by asking what is the carrier of *Plasmodium*. *(Female* Anopheles *mosquitoes)* What happens when a spore-carrying mosquito bites a human? *(The spores of* Plasmodium *reproduce asexually in the human liver and then infect erythrocytes.)* Point out that erythrocytes are red blood cells. Ask what happens when an *Anopheles* mosquito bites an infected person. *(It ingests* Plasmodium *cells, which develop into gametes that combine to form a zygote. The zygote divides and forms new spores.)* How does *Plasmodium* affect humans? (*It destroys erythrocytes and releases toxins, causing anemia, fever, and other malaria symptoms.)*

■ *See* Process Skills, *Chapter 21.*

Guided Practice

Guide students in making a concept map showing the classification relationships among the protozoa discussed in the section. An example of a completed concept map is shown on p. 307B.

Trypanosoma

Several members of the genus *Trypanosoma* are powerful agents of disease. Trypanosomes are slender, elongate, flattened protozoa with one posterior flagellum. They live in the blood of their hosts, which include humans and other animals, and are carried from host to host by bloodsucking invertebrates such as flies.

African **trypanosomiasis,** or sleeping sickness, is a trypanosome disease that occurs in two forms—Gambian, caused by *T. gambiense,* and Rhodesian, caused by *T. rhodesiense.* Both are transmitted by the tsetse fly, which lives only in Africa. Trypanosomiasis is characterized by fever and swollen lymph nodes. In later stages the parasites invade the brain, causing uncontrolled sleepiness. *T. gambiense* may take several years to invade the brain. *T. rhodesiense* affects the host more quickly, and Rhodesian trypanosomiasis is usually fatal.

Leishmania and *Giardia*

Zoomastiginoids of the genera *Leishmania* and *Giardia* cause serious diseases in humans. *Leishmania,* carried by sand flies, cause leishmaniasis, which afflicts millions of people in Africa,

Biotechnology

Controlling Malaria

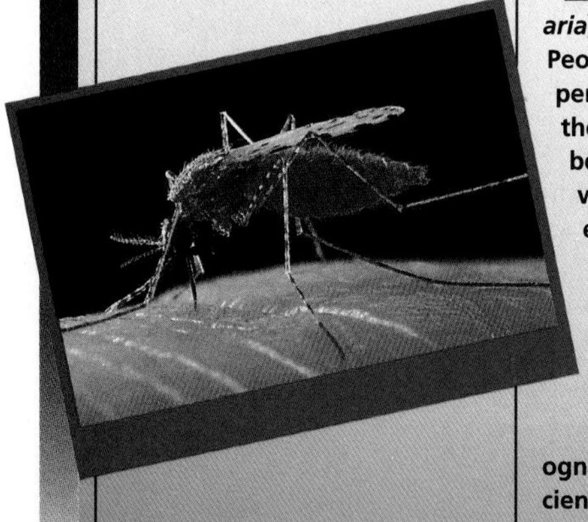

The word *malaria* (from the Italian words *mala aria*) literally means "bad air." People once believed that a person could get malaria from the night air. Because of this belief, many people slept with their windows closed, even in hot weather. This preventive measure worked but not for the supposed reason. Keeping the windows closed kept out the mosquitoes.

Although malaria was recognized in the time of the ancient Greeks, the organism that caused the disease was not identified until the 1880s, and the *Anopheles* mosquito (p. 314) was not identified as the carrier until the 1890s.

In the equatorial regions from South America to Southeast Asia, malaria—transmitted by the night-feeding *Anopheles* mosquito—kills about one in four children under 5 years of age. About 90 percent of malaria cases occur in Africa. Stopping the spread of malaria is an important goal of many health organizations.

One preventive approach is to kill the organism within its human host, but the complex life cycle of *Plasmodium* makes this approach difficult. Some *Plasmodium* strains are resistant to the drugs that are commonly

Interdisciplinary Activity

Geography Unfortunately, under conditions favorable to their growth, several species of protozoa cause disease in many places throughout the world. Have each student choose countries from several different continents and find out which methods of prevention are commonly used in each country to fight protozoan diseases. Students should use library resources, such as World Health Organization publications. Provide a world map on which students can compile their findings.

Asia, and Latin America. The disease is characterized by disfiguring skin sores and may be fatal.

Giardia, carried by muskrats and beavers, cause giardiasis, a disease characterized by fatigue, diarrhea, cramps, and weight loss. Drinking water that is contaminated with *Giardia* will not affect muskrats and beavers, but it can harm humans.

Sporozoa

All 6,000 species in the Phylum Sporozoa have adults with no means of locomotion. All are parasitic. They are carried in the blood and other bodily fluids of their hosts, absorbing nutrients from the fluid in which they float. Several sporozoans, including *Toxoplasma* and *Plasmodium,* cause diseases in humans.

Toxoplasma

The sporozoan *Toxoplasma* is a parasite found in animals. In humans it causes toxoplasmosis, a disease that has few or no symptoms in adults with healthy immune systems but that is often fatal to newborns. One species of *Toxoplasma* causes coccidiosis, a deadly disease affecting birds and young cattle.

used to treat malaria, and the resistant strains are spreading steadily, particularly through the mosquito population in West Africa.

Since the 1970s scientists have been trying to develop a vaccine, but still there is none. Another approach to preventing the spread of malaria is to keep the mosquitoes away from the human hosts of *Plasmodium*. Individuals can keep a barrier between themselves and the mosquitoes.

Recently the World Health Organization conducted a study of mosquito netting treated with the insecticide permethrin. In Gambia in Africa, there were 70 percent fewer cases of malaria when children slept under treated netting.

Mosquitoes breed in swamps, standing water, and wetlands. Pesticides and oil sprays have been used in attempts at mosquito control (p. 315), but they have serious ecological consequences in rain forest and wetland habitats.

One new approach, called biological control, is already being used to help control the spread of the medfly, an agricultural pest spreading through orchards and farms in California. Because biological control interferes only with the breeding cycle of insects, this approach may offer effective mosquito control. For example, male mosquitoes can be irradiated with gamma rays which make them sterile, and then be released into the environment. Females who breed with these males would lay eggs that could never develop. In a few breeding cycles the Anopheles mosquito population could be dramatically reduced.

Cooperative Learning

Protozoa Ask pairs of students to choose and research a protozoan genus, such as *Ameba, Foraminifera, Radiolaria, Paramecium, Trypanosoma, Leishmania, Giardia, Toxoplasma,* and *Plasmodium*. Partners should divide the research responsibilities so that one focuses on structure and movement, the other on nutrition and environment. Have partners share their findings and then work together to prepare a visual presentation of the protozoan genus to be displayed in the classroom.

Biotechnology

Using the Feature

Review with students the life cycle of *Plasmodium* (p. 316). Point out that antimalarial drugs kill the parasite only when it is in the blood. Ask students why a drug that kills the parasite in the liver is not used. *(The symptoms appear during the spore eruption stage in the blood. When the parasite is still in the liver, the need for antimalarial drugs is not yet apparent.)*

Tell students that chloroquine, the drug most often used as both treatment and preventive, is losing its effectiveness because resistant parasites have developed. The drug that is being used instead is mefloquine hydrochloride. However, mefloquine should not be given to pregnant women or to children who weigh less than 30 pounds.

Focus the discussion on the newest approach in dealing with insect pests such as mosquitoes—biological control. Mention that there is also a strain of *Anopheles* in which *Plasmodium* cannot survive. Direct a brainstorming session with students, and have them speculate about how such a *Plasmodium*-resistant mosquito might be used to develop another form of biological control. *(If genetically altered mosquitoes with the trait for resistance could be released into the environment, they might breed with the wild type and pass on the genes for* Plasmodium *resistance.)*

Have students discuss the pros and cons of this approach. *(Pro: environmentally safe, could be a long-term solution. Con: the altered mosquitoes may not compete effectively with the wild type; people may be unwilling to accept the release of additional mosquitoes as a solution.)*

Independent Practice

■ Have students write answers to the Section Review.

■ Have students use Figure 21-6 on p. 316 to write a narrative in their own words describing the life cycle of *Plasmodium.*

Check Your Understanding

1. What is the function of cytoplasmic streaming? *(Sarcodines move by a form of cytoplasmic streaming—ameboid movement.)*

2. How is conjugation in ciliates a form of sexual reproduction? *(Conjugation involves the exchange of genetic material by two organisms.)*

3. What is the function of the pellicle? *(The pellicle gives paramecia shape.)*

Reteaching

Have students compare the mechanisms of locomotion of the four protozoan phyla. Have them first identify the structures used for movement by the members of each phylum and then describe how movement is accomplished. *(Sarcodina—pseudopodia, ameboid movement; Ciliophora—cilia, beat in waves; Zoomastigina—flagella, whiplike undulations; Sporozoa—immobile, carried in body fluids of hosts)*

■ ***See* Section Reviews *worksheet, Section 20.2.***

Enrichment

Have students research the work of Sir Ronald Ross, who discovered the malarial parasite in the digestive system of the *Anopheles* mosquito.

Closure

Ask students why they think the most successful parasites harm their hosts the least. *(There is an adaptive advantage for the parasite whose host does not die; killing the host eliminates the environment favorable to survival.)*

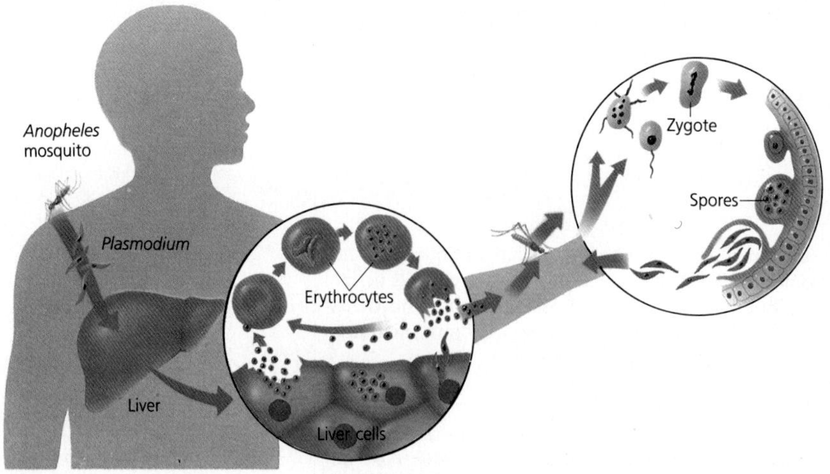

Figure 21-6 The life cycle of *Plasmodium*, which causes malaria, involves more than one host and asexual and sexual reproduction stages.

Plasmodium

Members of the genus *Plasmodium* cause malaria, a disease that kills about 2 million people a year and that is most prevalent in the tropics. Like most sporozoans *Plasmodium* has a complex life cycle with more than one host. As Figure 21-6 shows, when a female *Anopheles* mosquito that is carrying *Plasmodium* spores bites a person, the spores enter the person's bloodstream. They travel to the liver, where they reproduce asexually. The new spores infect erythrocytes and continue asexual reproduction. Every two to three days spores burst out of the erythrocytes and release toxins into the blood. Some of the spores develop into specialized cells.

When a female *Anopheles* bites the infected person, it ingests these cells. In the digestive system of the mosquito the cells develop into gametes that combine to form a zygote. The nucleus of the zygote divides internally many times and forms internal spores. When the zygote membrane bursts, the spores migrate to the salivary glands of the mosquito. If the mosquito then bites another person, the cycle begins again.

The destruction of red corpuscles and the release of toxins into the blood cause the fever, anemia, and other symptoms of malaria. The disease causes the liver and spleen to become enlarged, and in the most acute cases the kidneys fail.

Section Review

1. What is the difference between ectoplasm and endoplasm?
2. How do sarcodines move?
3. How does the micronucleus behave in ciliate conjugation?
4. What is the result of binary fission?
5. How might health workers attempt to control malaria?

Answers to Section Review

1. Ectoplasm is colloidal sol found inside the cell membrane; endoplasm is colloidal sol and gel found in the interior of the cell.
2. By means of pseudopodia
3. The micronucleus undergoes meiosis, producing haploid micronuclei, one of which produces more micronuclei mitotically. Eventually the micronuclei of different organisms are exchanged and fused.
4. Two genetically identical offspring
5. By interrupting the life cycle of *Plasmodium* through control of the mosquito *Anopheles*

Laboratory

Observing *Paramecium*

Objective
To study life functions of the *Paramecium*

Process Skills
Observing, hypothesizing, experimenting

Materials
Medicine droppers, *Euglena* and *Paramecium* cultures, slides, methyl cellulose, coverslips, microscope, distilled water, paper towel, salt water, vinegar

Background
1 What foods do ciliates eat? How do they take in and digest the food?
2 What function does the contractile vacuole serve in the *Paramecium?*
3 What are the functions of the trichocysts?

Inquiry
1 Place one drop of a *Paramecium* culture on a microscope slide. Place the paramecia in a ring of methyl cellulose to slow them down. Cover with a coverslip, and examine one paramecium under low power. How does it move? What structures do you see?
2 Remove the coverslip. Add one drop of *Euglena* culture to the slide. Cover and examine under high power. *Euglena* is a protozoan-like alga you will study in Chapter 22. Its green color is due to chloroplasts. Which organism is bigger, *Euglena* or *Paramecium?* Does the paramecium contain chloroplasts? Why or why not? Which organism might be an autotroph? a heterotroph?
3 Observe the coordinated motion of the paramecium's cilia. What might be the functions of the cilia?
4 Find a paramecium with green vacuoles. Why are they green? Are all vacuoles the same size? Are they moving? What might be happening in them?

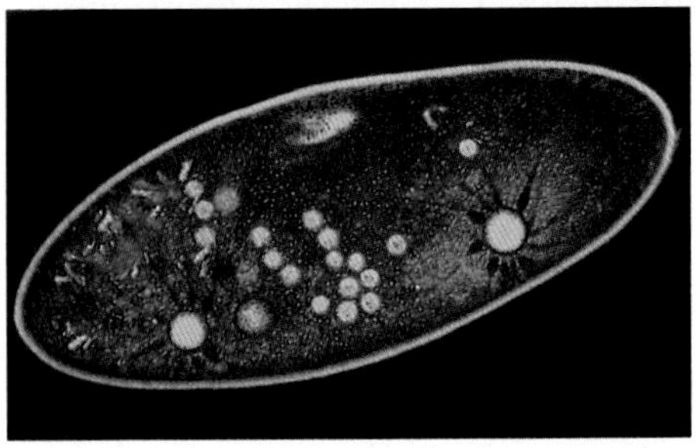

5 Find a quiet paramecium and identify the contractile vacuoles, the two clear, roundish forms at each end. Count how many times they fill and empty in one minute.
6 Use a medicine dropper to put some distilled water at one edge of the coverslip. Draw it to the other side of the coverslip by placing a paper towel at the opposite edge.
7 Count how many times the contractile vacuoles fill and empty in one minute. Did this count differ from that in step 5? Explain.
8 Design an experiment to test the effect of salt water on the emptying and filling of the contractile vacuole. Predict the results.
9 Paramecia have trichocysts, threadlike darts located under their cell membrane. These can be released for self-defense, for capturing prey, or for use as anchors. Repeat step 6, substituting vinegar for the water. Are trichocysts released? Why?

Conclusions
1 How do the structures that you studied today represent adaptations to the life functions of the *Paramecium?*
2 In a pond, would you expect to find more euglena or more paramecia? Explain.

Further Inquiry
Examine other protists such as *Stentor, Blepharisma,* or *Ameba.* Design an experiment to measure the effect of water temperature on the rate of contractile vacuole filling and emptying.

Laboratory

(For an overview of ciliates and preparatory information related to the laboratory, see p. 307B.)

Background
1. Ciliates eat other one-celled organisms. Cilia are used to sweep the food into the gullet. The ciliate engulfs the food and digests it in a food vacuole.
2. The contractile vacuole collects and empties water that enters the ciliate by osmosis.
3. Trichocysts can be used for capturing prey, for defense, or for anchoring the organism.

Inquiry
1. The paramecium's cilia propel it along. Students may list the oral groove, anal pore, vacuoles, macronucleus, or micronucleus.
2. The paramecium is much larger. *Paramecium* has no chloroplasts because it is a heterotroph and does not produce its own food. The chloroplasts in *Euglena* contain chlorophyll that enable it to produce its own food by photosynthesis. *Euglena* is an autotroph.
3. *Paramecium* uses cilia to move and sweep food into its gullet.
4. They are food vacuoles formed when the paramecium ate a euglena, which is the source of the green color. The vacuoles may not be the same size since they get smaller as the paramecium digests the euglena; older food vacuoles are smaller than freshly created ones. They may be moving in the cytoplasm.
5. Contractile vacuoles usually empty about 7 times a minute.
7. They should fill and empty faster in distilled water since osmosis will be more rapid.
8. Students should predict that the contractile vacuoles would fill and empty more slowly since osmosis will be slower.
9. Vinegar is an irritant and might stimulate the release of the trichocysts.

Conclusions
1. Food vacuoles are formed on an ongoing basis to digest food while the organism searches out more food. Contractile vacuoles allow *Paramecium* to get rid of extra water so that cytolysis does not occur. Trichocysts are a defensive adaptation.
2. More euglenas, because autotrophs are at the bottom of the food chain. Heterotrophs, such as *Paramecium*, generally must consume 10 grams of autotrophs for each gram of body weight.

Further Inquiry
The students can follow the same procedure as in steps 5 through 7, varying the temperature of the water.

Vocabulary

1. *Pseudopodium* means "false foot," which is appropriate for the footlike projections used in sarcodine movement.
2. Ectoplasm is the colloidal sol just inside the cell membrane; endoplasm is the colloidal material found in the interior of the cell.
3. A food vacuole encloses food particles and carries them through the cytoplasm, where they are digested and absorbed; a contractile vacuole regulates the amount of water in the organism.
4. *Zoo-* means "animal," and as a prefix tends to be used for "animallike"; *plankton* is from a Greek word for "drifting." Thus, *zooplankton* means "drifting animallike."
5. The response is avoidance behavior.

Review

1. c	**6.** d
2. b	**7.** a
3. b	**8.** a
4. b	**9.** b
5. c	**10.** b

11. *Foraminiferans* have calcium carbonate shells with spikelike protrusions; *radiolarians* have supportive silicon dioxide inside their shells; heliozoans have thin, extended projections on their shells.
12. In ameboid movement, the endoplasm begins to push outward to form a pseudopodium; as the pseudopodium moves outward, old pseudopodia retract into the cytoplasm, causing the organism to move.
13. The contractile vacuole removes excess water so a sarcodine can maintain homeostasis in an aquatic environment.
14. The sarcodine surrounds the food particle with pseudopodia, then part of the cell membrane forms a food vacuole around the food particle.

Chapter 21 Review

Vocabulary

ameboid movement (311)
anal pore (313)
avoidance behavior (313)
cilia (312)
conjugation (313)
contractile vacuole (312)
cyst (312)
cytoplasmic streaming (311)
ectoplasm (311)
endoplasm (311)
endosymbiosis (309)
eyespot (310)
flagellum (313)
food vacuole (312)
gullet (312)
macronucleus (312)
micronucleus (312)
mouth pore (312)
oral groove (312)
pellicle (312)
phagocytosis (312)
pseudopodium (311)
trypanosomiasis (314)
zooplankton (310)

1. Look up the meaning of the word *pseudopodium* in a dictionary, and explain why it is an appropriate name for the structure it represents.
2. Distinguish between the two regions of cytoplasm that are known as ectoplasm and endoplasm.
3. Compare and contrast the functions of a food vacuole and a contractile vacuole in a sarcodine.
4. Look up the word *zooplankton* in a dictionary, and explain the relationships between its word roots.
5. What is the name for the response that protozoa exhibit when trying to escape predators?

Review

1. The theory of endosymbiosis suggests that cell organelles of eukaryotic organisms evolved from (a) free-living protozoa (b) trypanosomas (c) parasitic prokaryotes (d) euglenoids.
2. A key characteristic of protozoan habitats is that at some point during the life cycle they must include (a) algae (b) water (c) blood (d) soil.
3. Many protozoa monitor light intensity with (a) pseudopodia (b) eyespots (c) cilia (d) contractile vacuoles.
4. Pseudopodia consist primarily of (a) pellicles (b) endoplasm (c) ectoplasm (d) cyst cells.
5. The pellicle is a characteristic of the (a) zoomastiginoids (b) sarcodines (c) ciliates (d) sporozoans.
6. Ciliates form food vacuoles in a (a) mouth pore (b) contractile vacuole (c) oral groove (d) gullet.
7. Flagella are characteristic of the Phylum (a) Zoomastigina (b) Sarcodina (c) Sporozoa (d) Ciliophora.
8. African trypanosomiasis or sleeping sickness is transmitted by (a) tsetse flies (b) *Anopheles* mosquitoes (c) kissing bugs (d) muskrats.
9. Members of the genus *Plasmodium* cause (a) toxoplasmosis (b) malaria (c) giardiasis (d) coccidiosis.
10. Malaria is transmitted by (a) tsetse flies (b) *Anopheles* mosquitoes (c) kissing bugs (c) *Trypanosoma cruzi* (d) *Toxoplasma*.
11. Describe the range of variation in types of protective covering among members of the Phylum Sarcodina.
12. Describe the process called ameboid movement.
13. What adaptive significance does the contractile vacuole have in the freshwater sarcodine?
14. Describe the process of phagocytosis in a sarcodine.
15. What is the behavior of the macronucleus and the micronucleus of the two individuals in ciliate conjugation?

15. The macronucleus of each individual disintegrates; the micronucleus in each divides both meiotically and mitotically, eventually producing a micronucleus that fuses with one from the other individual.
16. The ciliate digests food by means of food vacuoles that form in the gullet and circulate throughout the cytoplasm.
17. Humans contract giardiasis by drinking water contaminated with *Giardia*.
18. Sporozoans have no means of locomotion.
19. The diagram should show *Anopheles* spreading *Plasmodium* spores into a human, where the spores reproduce in the liver. The spores then infect and destroy erythrocytes and release toxins, thus causing malaria symptoms. The

16. How does a ciliate digest food?
17. How is the disease known as giardiasis spread to humans?
18. What is the characteristic of the Phylum Sporozoa that distinguishes it from the three other protozoan phyla?
19. Draw a simplified life cycle of a malaria-causing *Plasmodium,* showing the protozoan activity in both the mosquito and the human hosts.
20. What are the symptoms of malaria?

Critical Thinking

1. *Euglena* are often used in experiments in high school laboratories. In view of the fact that *Euglena* can be autotrophic, why is this organism a good choice for use in the laboratory?
2. Many scientists suggest that paramecia are more complex than amebas. What adaptations in paramecia would justify such a classification?
3. Look at the photograph at the right, which shows the shells of several radiolarians, protozoa found in the ocean. What is the function of such shells?
4. Many protozoa feed by means of pseudopodia. What stimulus might cause these cytoplasmic extensions to form in the unicellular animals?

5. Why is movement by means of cilia more efficient than movement by means of pseudopodia?

Extension

1. Read the article by R. Cowen entitled "Genetic Trickery Probes Tropical Parasites" in *Science News,* November 10, 1990, p. 292. How could gene replacement lead to controlling diseases caused by trypanosomatids?
2. Write a brief research paper on the protozoa found as zooplankton in the ocean. Include in your report information about the types of protozoa found in zooplankton and about the species of fish that depend on these protozoa as a food source.
3. Collect water from at least three sources—ponds, lakes, tap, or ditches—and look at the samples under a microscope. Count the different kinds of protozoa in each sample, and draw a picture of all the types you see.
4. Obtain a culture of paramecia or *Euglena* from a biological supply house. Place the protozoa in a depression slide, and test their reactions to different chemicals. Dip a thread into a salt solution, a sugar solution, and ammonia and then hold the thread in the culture. See what reaction takes place. Next cover part of the culture with a piece of cardboard, and observe the reaction. Write a report describing these experiments. Include a title, description of the procedure used, and the results obtained.
5. In chart form compare conjugation and binary fission as forms of reproduction. Include headings such as: protozoa with these forms of reproduction, sexual or asexual, genetic variation, and so forth.

diagram should also show an *Anopheles* biting an infected person and ingesting *Plasmodium* cells. These cells develop into gametes in the mosquito's digestive system. Gametes combine and form a zygote that forms the spores, which start the cycle again.
20. They include fever, anemia, enlarged liver and spleen, and kidney failure.

Critical Thinking

1. Since *Euglena* can be autotrophic, they do not need to be fed.
2. Paramecia have many more organelles than amebas, including specialized ones such as the oral groove, gullet, anal pore, and cilia. Paramecia can also reproduce sexually through conjugation.
3. The shells have spines that provide protection against predators.
4. The proximity of food would be a stimulus that might cause a pseudopodium to form.
5. Cilia are more efficient than pseudopodia because they beat in synchronized strokes.

Extension

1. Gene replacement can trick two types of trypanosomatids into substituting the replacement material for the coding sequence of a naturally occurring gene.
2. Have students identify the other organisms in addition to protozoa that make up zooplankton. Challenge students to create a food web that includes zooplankton.
3. Make sure the students label the drawings according to where the protozoa were found. Provide guides to help them identify the protozoa.
4. Advise students to repeat the steps in the experiment a number of times to ensure validity of results.
5. Encourage students to draw conclusions from their comparison as to which form of reproduction is most advantageous to populations of protozoa.

Chapter 22 Algae

Chapter Overview

Chapter 22 continues the discussion of the Kingdom Protista by examining different types of algae. Section 22.1 describes major features shared by all algae as well as characteristics that scientists use to separate algae into six groups. Section 22.2 compares methods of asexual and sexual reproduction in unicellular and multicellular algae.

Chapter Planning Chart

B	S	A	Sections and Subsections	Page	Features	Page	Resources
•	•	•	**22.1 Structure and Classification**				
			Structure	321	Think	322	Videodiscs
			Classification	322	Biotechnology	324	Blackline Master 45
					Laboratory	331	Overhead Transparency T22
					Section Review	327	Process Skills: The Red Tide
							Laboratories: Algal Blooms
							Section Reviews Worksheet
	•	•	**22.2 Comparative Reproduction**				
			Unicellular Reproduction	328	Section Review	330	Videodiscs
			Multicellular Reproduction	329			Blackline Master 46
							Section Reviews Worksheet
			End of Chapter Activities				
					Chapter Review	332	Vocabulary Skills
							Chapter Test
							Computer Test Generator

B *The Basic Level curriculum presents the most fundamental knowledge offered in the course.*
S *The Standard Level curriculum is designed for the average student who is able to master most topics.*
A *The Advanced Level curriculum includes suggestions for teaching the most academically able students.*

Cooperative Learning

Group Activity: Classifying Algae

- **Group Size:** *2 students*
- **Outcome:** *Students will classify various algae using a dichotomous key.*
- **Individual Accountability:** *Each student will list major characteristics of each division of algae.*
- **Positive Interdependence:** *The group will design a dichotomous key and then use a key designed by another group.*

Have students in each group list characteristics of the six divisions of algae. Encourage them to use visual characteristics that could be easily used to identify one type of algae from another based on observations. Then instruct students to use characteristics on their lists to construct a dichotomous key that can be used to classify algae into one of the six divisions. Remind students that a dichotomous key is a set of paired questions that can be answered only yes or no.

After groups have completed their dichotomous keys, have them exchange keys with another group. Display pictures or specimens of various algae, at least one from each division, and ask groups to classify the algae by using the keys. Encourage students to make constructive criticism for making improvements in another group's key.

Concept Map

The following is one possible solution to the concept mapping activity in Reteaching on p. 330.

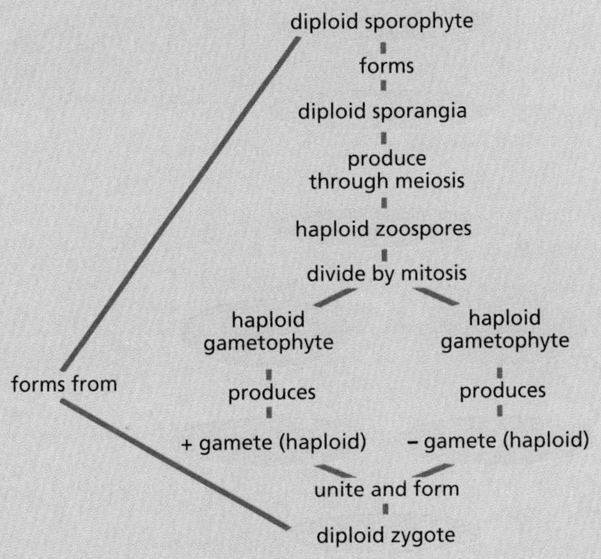

Laboratory Preparation

Overview *(See p. 331.)*

This lab introduces students to a group of algae belonging to the "volvocine series," a series of genera of the Order Volvocales. Members of this order show increasing multicellularity and increasing complexity. Although green plants did not descend from this particular order of green algae, they undoubtedly descended from an ancestor of it. Many differences that students observe in this lab are probably similar to changes that occurred in the actual evolution of green plants.

Preparation

Algae can be ordered from biological supply houses. Aerate the cultures thoroughly with a dropper when they arrive and keep the lids on loosely.

Teaching Tips

Expand on the evidence that green plants evolved from green algae. The biochemical evidence, especially the fact that both green plants and green algae contain chlorophyll a as well as b, is very convincing.

Discuss how one might determine which green algae are the more direct ancestors of plants by comparing their DNAs. Some students may wish to read about the work of Sibley and Ahlquist, who made a tree of bird families based on similarities in DNA. Discuss possible reasons why this work has not yet been done in plants.

Safety

Students should wash their hands when they finish the lab.

Chapter Themes

Evolution Emphasize diversity of algae and that this diversity is due to genetic variability. Also make explicit how the process of sexual reproduction, which is often triggered by changing environment, creates this genetic variability and contributes to the evolution of a new species.

Patterns of Change Various reproductive life cycles of unicellular and multicellular algae can be confusing to students. Simplify these life cycles as much as possible so students understand the major points. Be sure to emphasize the alternation of generations, as this life cycle will become very important in the discussion of plant and fungi reproduction.

Scale and Structure Emphasize features of algae that divide them into six different groups. Point out anomalies of the Division Euglenophyta and challenge students to debate its classification as algae instead of protozoa.

Chapter Motivating Activity

Display pictures of a moneran, a protozoan, and an alga. Ask students to compare and contrast the alga with the moneran and protozoan. *(Both alga and protozoan have a nucleus and organelles; the moneran does not.)* Then ask students to contrast the protozoan and alga. *(The alga has chloroplasts; the protozoan does not.)* Point out that, like protozoa, algae are classified as protists.

Chapter 22 *Algae*

Introduction

Algae are diverse organisms ranging from microscopic, flagellated single cells to giant kelps anchored to rocks by huge rootlike structures. Algae belong to the Kingdom Protista, along with the protozoa. Unlike protozoa, however, algae can make their own food by photosynthesis. In this chapter you will explore the different types of algae. You will also see that algae are characterized by widely diverse structures and methods of reproduction.

Chapter Outline

Chapter Concept

As you read, notice that algae are actually a widely diverse group of organisms that vary in structure, biochemistry, and reproduction.

Kelp *(Macrocystis porifera),* California. Inset: SEM of a dinoflagellate (×100).

Understanding the Visuals

Ask students to describe how the organisms in the two photographs differ. *(The dinoflagellate is unicellular and much smaller than the multicellular kelp.)* Point out that although both organisms seem to be very different, both are classified as algae.

Have students observe the photograph of the kelp more closely. Ask them to infer the function of the balls on the stemlike part of the kelp. *(They help keep the leaflike portions afloat and exposed to sunlight.)* Tell students that multicellular kelp, although it appears outwardly complex, is not organized into specialized tissues.

22.1 Structure and Classification

Algae are a diverse group of eukaryotic, plantlike organisms. They are classified into six divisions of the Kingdom Protista. Algae are autotrophic protists—that is, they have chloroplasts and produce their own food by photosynthesis. In the past some biologists classified algae as plants. Today they do not. One reason is that algae and plants have different methods of reproduction. Algae have gametes that are formed in and protected by **unicellular gametangia** *(GAM-uh-TAN-jee-uh)*, or single-celled gamete holders. Plants have gametes formed in multicellular gametangia.

Although algae form a very diverse group of protists, all algae have several features in common. For example, algal cells often have **pyrenoids** *(PIE-ruh-NOIDZ)*, organelles that synthesize and store starch. In addition, almost all algae are aquatic, and even terrestrial forms require H_2O for reproduction. Many aquatic algae also possess flagella.

Structure

The body of an alga is called a **thallus** *(THAL-us)*. The thallus can be unicellular, colonial, filamentous, or thalloid. Colonial algae are groups of independent cells that move and function as a unit. Filamentous algae consist of cells in a linear arrangement. Thalloid algae are organisms in which cells divide in many directions to create a body that is multicellular and often modified into rootlike, stemlike, or leaflike parts.

Unicellular algae are mostly aquatic. Organisms thus adapted are called plankton. Photosynthetic microorganisms are called **phytoplankton** *(FIE-toe-PLANK-tun)*. Phytoplankton provide food for numerous aquatic organisms. They also generate a great amount of the oxygen we breathe.

Colonial algae are groups of individual algal cells. In colonies the algal cells act in a coordinated manner. Certain cells may become specialized for certain functions. This division of labor allows colonial algae to move, feed, and reproduce efficiently.

A filamentous alga is composed of a row of cells. Some filamentous algae have structures that anchor them to the ocean bottom, where they can exploit an environment inhospitable to many other organisms. Some have branching filaments.

Multicellular thalloid algae are not organized into specialized tissues but can often be very large and outwardly complex. Some algae grow as a complex thallus and are referred to as seaweeds. For example *Ulva,* commonly known as sea lettuce, has a leaflike thallus that may be several centimeters wide but only two cells thick. *Macrocystis,* called the giant kelp, has a rubbery leaflike portion, stemlike areas, and enlarged air bladders.

Section Objectives

- *Explain why algae are classified in the Kingdom Protista.*
- *Describe the three parts of a thallus.*
- *Distinguish unicellular, colonial, and filamentous algae.*
- *List the six divisions of algae and the characteristics of each.*
- *Describe the uses of aquaculture.*

Figure 22-1 ***Volvox*** **is a colonial green alga that exhibits division of labor between cells.**

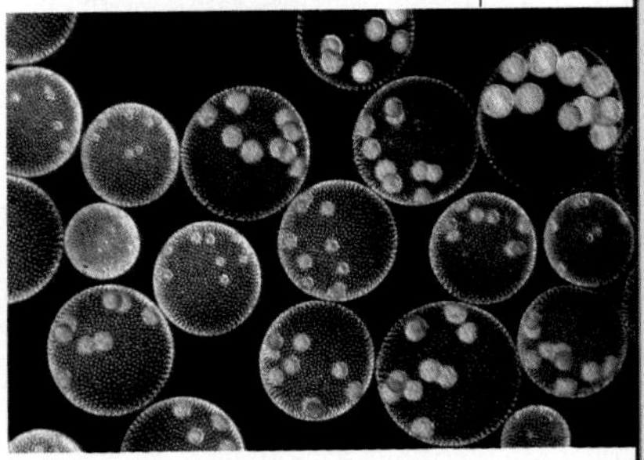

Lesson Plan

Section Focus

This section describes the general structure and common features of algae, as well as major characteristics of the six divisions of algae.

Section Themes

The underlying theme of this section is **Evolution.** Algae are classified as protists based on their evolutionary relationships with other organisms. The process of evolution creates diversity among similar organisms; algae are classified into six different divisions. The description of general and specific body structures of algae in different divisions emphasizes the theme of **Scale and Structure.**

Motivating Activity

If possible, obtain live or preserved specimens of various algae from biological supply houses, or display pictures of algae from scientific reference books. Have students examine the algae and compare their characteristics. Instruct students to make a list of features they think that scientists use to classify algae into different groups. Challenge students to divide algae into groups based on their list of features. After completing the section, encourage students to review their classifications.

Videodiscs

- *581–582, Seashore Algae (s)*
- *579–580, Kelp (s)*
- *2541, Photosynthetic Eukaryote;* Chlamydomonas *(s)*

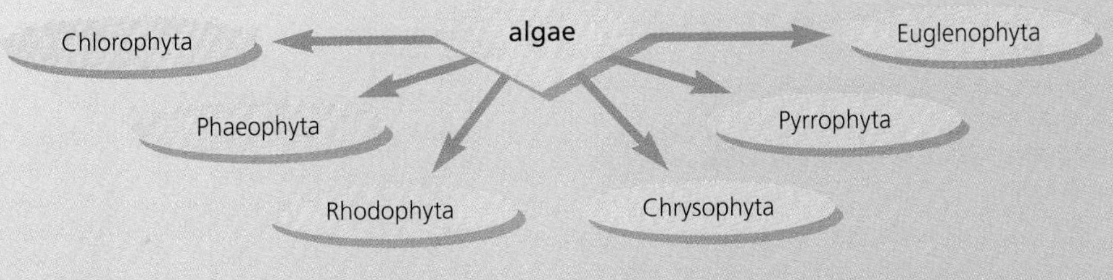

Graphic Organizer Use this organizational chart in Independent Practice on p. 326.

Answer to Think

The gas-filled bladders are adaptations for flotation. They keep the leaflike portions of the thallus near the top of the water where sunlight is available for photosynthesis.

Teaching Strategies

Distinguishing Organisms If necessary, review cell structure (Chapter 5) and metabolism (Chapter 7). Then have students define *autotroph. (An organism that can make its own food)* Ask them to name the organelle that enables algae to make their own food. *(Chloroplast)* Then ask students to describe how algae differ from protozoa. *(Protozoa do not have chloroplasts and are heterotrophic—depend on other organisms for food.)*

Observing Organisms Set up microscope stations where students can observe the four types of thallus structure of algae: unicellular, colonial, filamentous, and thalloid. Have students make drawings of their observations and label the cell parts.

Interpreting the Visuals Use Table 22-1, p. 322, to reinforce major characteristics of the six divisions of algae. For example, ask students to name divisions of algae that have multicellular forms. *(Chlorophyta, Phaeophyta, and Rhodophyta)* Which divisions have chlorophylls a and b? *(Chlorophyta and Euglenophyta)* Which division of algae does not have cell walls? *(Euglenophyta)* Point out that the name of each division (except Euglenophyta) describes the color of its members.

■ *See* **Overhead Transparency T22** *and* **Blackline Master 45.**

Think

Many multicellular algae have gas-filled structures called bladders in or beneath their leaflike regions. What sort of adaptation might this be?

Classification

Biologists classify algae into six divisions, based on color, food-storage substances, and the composition of cell walls. Members of each division have distinctive colors, depending on the photosynthetic pigments in their cells. These pigments absorb light. All algae contain the pigment chlorophyll a. However, different divisions of algae also contain other forms of chlorophyll, such as b, c, or d, each of which absorbs a different wavelength of light. Members of different algal divisions have different accessory pigments as well. Algae also vary in methods of reproduction, as you will learn in Section 22.2. As you read the descriptions of the divisions, refer to Table 22-1.

Chlorophyta

Members of the Division Chlorophyta *(kloe-RAHF-uh-tuh),* the green algae, are a diverse group of organisms of over 7,000 species. They can be unicellular, colonial, filamentous, or thalloid. Most green algae are aquatic, although many inhabit moist terrestrial environments such as soil, rock surfaces, and tree trunks.

Three observations have led biologists to conclude that green algae are the ancestors of plants. First, both green algae and plants have chloroplasts that contain chlorophylls a and b. Second, both green algae and plants store food as starch. Finally, both green algae and plants have cell walls made of cellulose.

Table 22-1 Six Divisions of Algae

Division	Cell Types	Photosynthetic Pigments	Form of Food Storage	Cell Wall Composition
Chlorophyta (*Chloro* = "green"): 7,000 species	Both unicellular and multicellular	Chlorophylls a and b, xanthophylls, carotenes	Starch	Polysaccharides, sometimes cellulose
Phaeophyta (*Phaeos* = "brown"): 1,500 species	Mostly multicellular	Chlorophylls a and c, fucoxanthin (a carotene)	Laminarin (oil)	Cellulose with alginic acids
Rhodophyta (*Rhodo* = "red"): 4,000 species	Mostly multicellular	Chlorophyll a and d, phycobilins	Starch	Cellulose or pectin, many with calcium carbonate
Chrysophyta (*Chryso* = "gold"): 10,000 species	Mostly unicellular	Chlorophylls a and c, carotenes, including fucoxanthin	Chrysolaminarin (oily carbohydrate)	Cellulose, some with silica; possibly no cell wall
Pyrrophyta (*Pyrro* = "fire"): 1,100 species	All unicellular	Chlorophylls a and c, carotenes	Starch	Cellulose
Euglenophyta (*Euglena* = "true eye"): 800 species	Mostly unicellular	Chlorophylls a and b, carotenes in genera with chloroplasts	Paramylon (a starch)	No cell wall; protein-rich pellicle

Interdisciplinary Activity

Social Studies In many cultures throughout the world, seaweed and other algae are important components of the diet. Ask students to do library research to find out what cultures of the world include seaweed in their diets. Have students choose one of these cultures and find out how people use seaweed, how they cultivate it, and what nutrition it provides in their diet. Encourage interested students to find appropriate recipes and prepare seaweed dishes for the class to sample. (Seaweeds are sold in Asian food markets.) Ask students to consider why seaweed is not a major part of most Americans' diets.

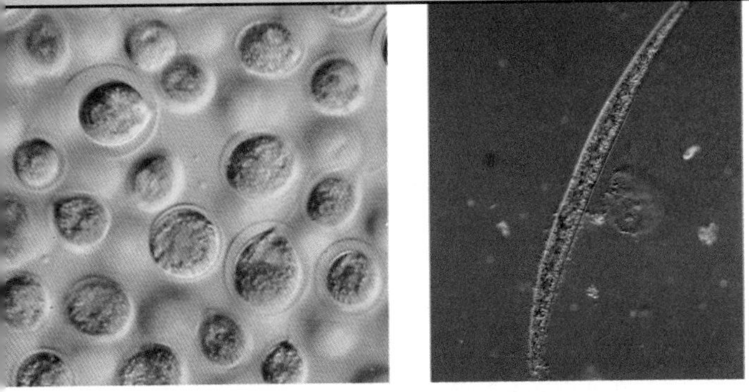

Figure 22-2 ***Chlamydomonas*** **(left) and desmid (right) illustrate the diversity of shape in green algae.**

To understand some of the diversity in unicellular green algae, examine Figure 22-2. *Chlamydomonas* is common in soils and in freshwater ponds and streams. It has a single cup-shaped chloroplast. Each chloroplast contains a pyrenoid, where starch is made. Two anterior flagella enable the organism to swim. An eyespot, which is an area sensitive to light, enables the alga to move either toward or away from light. Desmids are unusual unicellular algae that live primarily in fresh water. In fact, the presence of desmids can be used to indicate the degree of water pollution.

Unlike unicellular algae, colonial algae have some characteristics of multicellular organisms. *Gonium* is perhaps the simplest colonial green alga, consisting of a colony that is one cell thick and shaped in a rectangle. A *Volvox* colony, on the other hand, is round and much larger, containing up to 60,000 cells and exhibiting a remarkable division of labor. Intercellular communication allows the coordination of the many cells in the colony. *Volvox* cells are connected by fine cytoplasmic strands that enable adjacent cells to chemically communicate with each other.

Spirogyra is a filamentous green alga with unusual spiral chloroplasts that stretch from one end of the cell to the other. Examine the *Spirogyra* in Figure 22-3. Can you locate the dotlike pyrenoids associated with the chloroplasts? *Oedogonium* is another common freshwater filamentous green alga. Members of this genus have netlike chloroplasts.

Ulva has a leaflike, photosynthetic body and commonly grows on rocks and pilings. Its thallus collapses during low tide to prevent water loss in the intertidal zone, the area between high and low tides.

Figure 22-3 Notice how the chloroplasts in ***Spirogyra*** **form spirals (×50).**

Classifying Organisms Show students slides or photographs of different types of algae and ask them to classify the different species into one of the six algal divisions. Point out the diversity of algae, emphasizing cell structure, photosynthetic pigments, form of food storage, and cell wall composition.

Drawing Conclusions Emphasize that large numbers of photosynthesizing algae, especially diatoms and dinoflagellates, affect the entire earth. Remind students that during photosynthesis, algae take in carbon dioxide and give off oxygen. Ask students to infer how algae affect air pollution and the greenhouse effect. *(Algae can reduce the amount of carbon dioxide in the air.)* Ask students to predict the fate of animals throughout the world if all algae suddenly died. *(All other animals would probably die because of their reliance on oxygen and food provided by algae.)*

■ ***See*** **Process Skills,** ***Chapter 22, and*** **Laboratories,** ***Investigation 22.***

Comparing Organisms Ask students to name different types of green algae listed in the text. *(Chlamydomonas,* desmids, *Gonium, Volvox, Spirogyra, Oedogonium, Ulva)* Ask what characteristics they share. *(All have chlorophylls a and b, store food as starch, and have cell walls composed of polysaccharides.)* Then encourage students to contrast these green algae. How do they differ in structure? (Chlamydomonas *and desmids are unicellular*; Gonium *and* Volvox *are colonial;* Spirogyra *and* Oedogonium *are filamentous;* Ulva *is thalloid.)*

Videodiscs

■ ***Side 3 4131, A Drop of Water:*** **Volvox** ***(m)***

LEP Activity

Have students make a set of flash cards to help them review this section. On one side of a card, they write the name of the division *(for example, Chlorophyta)*, the common name of the division *(for example, green algae)*, and draw a diagram of a representative member from this division. On the back of the flash card, they write the cell types, photosynthetic pigments, form of food storage, habitats, and importance to humans. Have students practice reviewing by looking at division names and recalling distinguishing information, then looking at information and recalling division. Finally, have students work in pairs to quiz each other.

Inferring Relationships Scientists have hypothesized that members of the Division Chlorophyta are the ancestors of plants. Ask students to explain why other divisions of algae could not be the ancestors of plants. *(Phaeophyta, Rhodophyta, Chrysophyta, and Pyrrophyta do not contain chlorophylls a and b—the chlorophylls found in plants. Euglenophyta, which does have chlorophylls a and b, does not have cell walls.)* Ask students to infer what major evolutionary step separates plants from algae. *(Point out that plants do not require water for reproduction; they have vascular tissue and are adapted to living on land.)*

Observing Organisms Provide students with a live culture of *Euglena* and microscope slides, coverslips, eye droppers, and methyl cellulose. Instruct students to make wet mounts, placing a drop of culture within a ring of methyl cellulose. The methyl cellulose will help slow the movement of *Euglena* and allow students to examine features of the organisms easily with their microscopes. Encourage students to compare their specimens with the euglenoid illustrated in Figure 22-8, p. 327. Ask them to compare *Euglena* with protozoa. (Euglena *do not have cell walls and can become heterotrophic in darkness. However, they have chloroplasts and are able to photosynthesize.)*

Designing Experiments Challenge pairs of students to design an experiment in which they test the response of *Euglena* to light. Ask them to predict in what direction euglenoids will move, and why. Then allow students to do their experiments. *(*Euglena *will move toward a source of light. They use light to make food.)*

Figure 22-4 The structure of these brown algae allows them to exist in the intertidal zone.

Phaeophyta

Members of the Division Phaeophyta *(fee-AHF-uh-tuh),* the brown algae, are multicellular and usually large. Most of the approximately 1,500 species are marine organisms. Their brown color results from the accessory pigment fucoxanthin. The food they produce is stored as **laminarin** *(lam-uh-NAR-in),* a carbohydrate with glucose units linked differently from those in starch.

The large brown alga shown in Figure 22-4 is *Macrocystis.* Members of the genus live in the intertidal zone. Individuals may be more than 100 m long. The thallus is composed of a holdfast, a stipe, and blades. The **holdfast** anchors the thallus to a rock. The **stipe** is the stemlike region. Each leaflike **blade** is a region modified for photosynthesis. The cell walls of these brown algae contain alginic acid, a source of commercially important alginates. Alginates are polysaccharides used to make gels for ice cream and other foods.

Rhodophyta

Members of the Division Rhodophyta *(roe-DAHF-uh-tuh)* are called red algae. Most of the approximately 4,000 species are

Biotechnology

Harvest from the Sea

Do you enjoy chocolate milk, salad dressing, soup, sausage, or canned meat? Do you use toothpaste, hand lotion, or shampoo? If you do, then you have used products with seaweed as an ingredient.

Seaweeds (p. 324) are mentioned in the writings of the early Chinese. The ancient Romans and other Europeans used them as animal feeds, fertilizers, medications, and in cosmetics. But people also consume seaweeds directly. Europeans were eating seaweeds before the 1700s, and the Japanese have been enjoying them for even longer. In Japan brown seaweeds, such as *Laminaria*, are eaten raw, jellied, or baked into breads. Red seaweeds, including dulse, laver or nori, and Irish moss are eaten fresh, dried, or toasted. Green seaweeds, such as sea lettuce are used in soups and salads and as garnishes for meat and fish.

Seaweeds are an excellent source of trace minerals and vitamins, but they also provide important extracts. Alginic acid (stabilizer in food products), agar (culture medium and a food thickener), and carrageenan (gelling and clarifying agent) are all extracted from seaweed.

The Japanese not only have harvested wild seaweeds but

Cooperative Learning

Modeling Brown Algae Instruct groups of three students to work together to devise from common household or classroom items a model for brown algae such as kelp that has a thallus composed of a holdfast, stipe, blade, and air bladders. *(For example, students might use twist ties or pipe cleaners for the holdfast, balloons for air bladders, rubber or plastic tubing for the stipe, and plastic strips for blades.)* Challenge students also to model the adaptive advantage of holdfasts and air bladders for kelp living in intertidal zones. Have each group present its model to the class. Ask students to explain what would happen if the kelp did not have a holdfast. *(The kelp would float away as the tide moved in and out.)*

marine and multicellular. The multicellular forms are generally less than 1 m long. A few unicellular species inhabit land and freshwater environments. Red algae can survive at greater depths than any other algae can; they commonly grow at depths of 150 m and have been discovered at depths of 268 m. How can they photosynthesize at such depths? Examine Figure 22-5. Red algae contain chlorophylls a and d as well as accessory pigments called phycobilins. Phycobilins absorb the violet, blue, and green light that penetrates the depths at which these algae grow.

The cell walls of red algae contain cellulose and are sometimes coated with a sticky substance called **carageenan** *(KAR-uh-GEE-nun)*. Carageenan, which is a polysaccharide, is used to produce cosmetics, gelatin capsules, and some cheeses. Coralline algae, a group of red algae that deposits calcium carbonate in their cell walls, are important components of coral reefs.

Figure 22-5 **Red algae, such as *Spermothamnion turneri*, are able to synthesize food at a water depth of more than 250 m.**

Chrysophyta

Members of the Division Chrysophyta *(kruh-SAHF-uh-tuh)* are called golden-brown algae. There are over 10,000 species of golden-brown algae, the majority of which are commonly called diatoms. Chrysophytes contain chlorophylls a and c and the

they also have farmed algae for over 300 years. Farmers plant bundles of bamboo or oak brushwood in mudflats that flood with seawater. In the spring spores of *Porphyra* algae attach to these bundles and germinate. In the winter the plants yield a large and tender harvest. In the 1940s Dr. Kathleen Drew, a British botanist, discovered that *Porphyra* releases minute spores before dying each spring.

Drew's discovery was so important to *Porphyra* aquaculture that the Japanese erected a monument to her near Tokyo. *Porphyra* is now cultured using clean oyster shells to collect the spores. The colonized shells can be set in nets on wooden frames and the algae will seed spores onto the netting (p. 325).

In the Western Hemisphere the United States and Canada are cooperating in an effort to restore depleted kelp beds. Marine scientists are growing giant kelp to reintroduce into the natural environment. They are also studying the life cycle of kelp to learn how to grow it in seawater greenhouses.

Today seaweeds can be farmed in coastal wetlands or salt marshes—areas unsuitable for other crops. Commercially grown seaweed may well become an important new crop that provides both a source of commercial extracts and a food source for the world's ever-increasing population.

Biotechnology

Using the Feature

The technology used in the feature is aquaculture. Dr. Drew's investigations of the full life cycle of *Porphyra* led to an understanding that allowed direct seeding and increased production of edible seaweeds.

Since then, the life cycles of other seaweeds have been studied and used to develop better aquaculture methods for these plants. Researchers have identified and genetically selected strains that mature faster, yield more extracts, and offer increased nutritive value. Point out that researchers are also interested in studying seaweeds able to synthesize fuels (methane and ethanol) during anaerobic respiration.

Tell students that commercially important animal species are raised in hatcheries. These species include salmon, shellfish (clams, oysters, scallops, crabs, and lobsters), and more recently, sea urchins. Point out that the newest trend in aquaculture is *polyculture*—raising several species together in one large tank. A polyculture typically includes algae, zooplankton, and a larger species such as a fish or shellfish. Ask students why large-scale aquaculture (now considered expensive) may prove practical in the long run. *(Compared with harvesting wild plants and animals, innovative projects may offer benefits in a changing global environment.)*

Videodiscs

- *553–557, Phaeophyta—Examples (s)*
- *558–561, Rhodophyta—Examples (s)*
- *562–567, Protista: Chrysophyta (Diatoms and Yellow-Green Algae) (s)*

More Information

Diatoms Diatoms make up the major portion of sediments on the ocean floor. The deposit off the coast of Lompoc, California, is the thickest discovered so far—about 1 km deep. Diatom deposit is also mined in Nevada, Washington, Kansas, and Oregon and often is used as an abrasive in household cleaners.

Guided Practice
Obtain slides or pictures of *Ulva* (Division Chlorophyta), *Macrocystis* (Division Phaeophyta), and *Porphyra* (Division Rhodophyta) from science textbooks, catalogs, or magazines. Have students observe pictures of these algae and list similarities and differences of their thalluses. (Ulva *and* Macrocystis *have leaflike blades;* Porphyra *does not.* Macrocystis *and* Porphyra *have a stipe;* Ulva *does not. All three have holdfasts.* Macrocystis *has air bladders;* Porphyra *and* Ulva *do not.)*

Independent Practice
- Have students write answers to the Section Review.
- Give students the top level of a chart that shows the classification of algae. Use the organizational chart on p. 321 as a model. Have students extend the chart by adding characteristics for each division.

Check Your Understanding
1. What plantlike and animallike characteristics do different species of algae have? *(Plantlike: cell walls, autotrophic with chloroplasts; animallike: flagella, eye spots, euglenoids can be heterotrophic.)*
2. What major characteristics differentiate the divisions of algae? *(Photosynthetic pigments, form of food storage, and composition of cell walls)*
3. What important role do accessory photosynthetic pigments play? *(Allow absorption of more light at different wavelengths. For example, accessory pigments called phycobilins allow red algae to photosynthesize at greater depths.)*

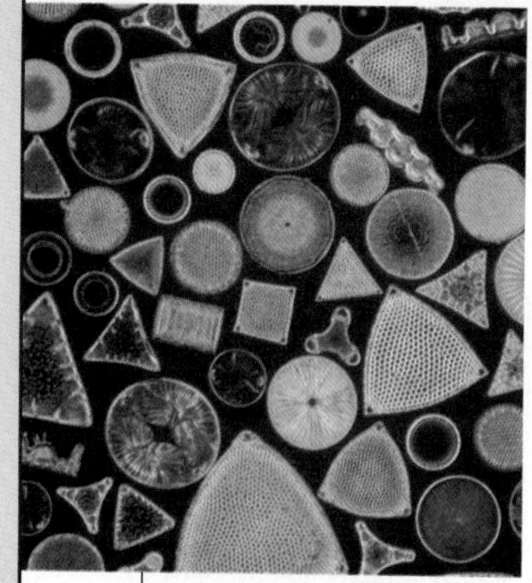

Figure 22-6 The walls of these various diatoms contain silicon dioxide, which makes the shells rigid.

accessory pigment fucoxanthin. Because of the pigment similarities between golden-brown algae and brown algae, scientists suggest that the two divisions have a close evolutionary relationship. Chrysophytes store food in the form of oil, not starch.

Diatoms are unicellular or colonial, nonflagellated, photosynthetic algae with silica-impregnated shells. They inhabit both freshwater and marine environments and are an essential component of phytoplankton. Diatoms are so abundant in some marine environments that they are responsible for the bulk of worldwide photosynthesis.

Diatoms have highly ornamented double walls containing silicon dioxide. The two halves of the wall fit together like the two parts of a box. Each half is called a **valve.** Figure 22-6 shows two types of diatoms. **Centric** *(SEN-trick)* **diatoms** have circular or triangular valves and are most abundant in marine waters. **Pennate** *(PEN-ate)* **diatoms** have rectangular valves and are most abundant in freshwater ponds and lakes. Some pennate diatoms move by secreting threads that attach to the surface of the water. When these threads contract, they pull the diatom forward.

Because their cell walls contain silicon dioxide, diatom shells do not decompose. Rather, the rigid shells of dead diatoms sink and eventually form a layer of material called **diatomaceous** *(DIE-uh-tuh-MAY-shuss)* **earth.** Diatomaceous earth is slightly abrasive; it is an ingredient of many commercial products, such as detergents, paint removers, fertilizers, and insulators.

Pyrrophyta
The approximately 1,100 species of the Division Pyrrophyta *(puh-RAHF-uh-tuh)* are called fire algae, or dinoflagellates. Most dinoflagellates are marine and photosynthetic. Dinoflagellates are an important component of oceanic phytoplankton.

The cell walls of dinoflagellates are made of cellulose. The cellulose forms plates that look like armor when seen under a microscope. The majority of cells are shaped like tops, but many have spinelike projections. Most dinoflagellates have two flagella that each fit into a groove in the cell wall. One groove runs vertically and is called a sulcus. The other groove runs horizontally and is called the girdle. Look at this arrangement in Figure 22-7. Movement of the flagella causes the dinoflagellate to spin like a top as it propels itself through the water.

Figure 22-7 The surface of dinoflagellates is characterized by ornamented cellulose walls.

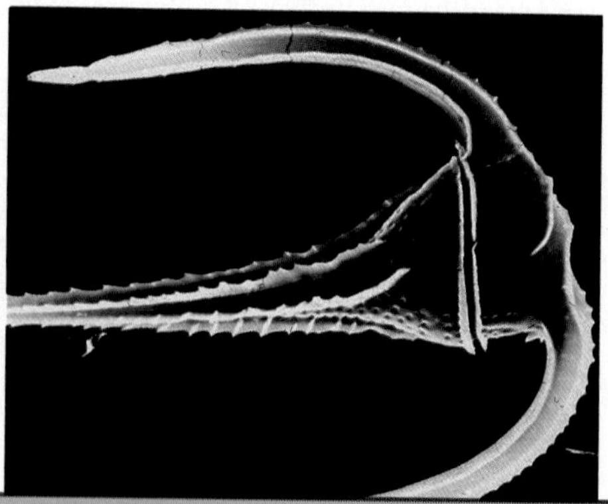

More Information
Algal Blooms Population explosions of algae are an indication of water pollution in freshwater habitats. When water is polluted by phosphates or nitrates from detergents or fertilizers, the indigenous algae grow and reproduce rapidly because of the extra nutrients. After the nutrients have been used up, the algae die and are decomposed by bacteria. During the process of decomposition, the bacteria use much of the dissolved oxygen in the water, leaving none available for other water organisms, causing them to die.

Noctiluca exemplifies another characteristic of many dinoflagellates—the ability to produce light. Organisms that produce light are said to display **bioluminescence** *(BIE-uh-LOO-muh-NESS-ens)*. If you have ever seen a sparkling light display in the sea, dinoflagellates were probably responsible.

Dinoflagellates are also responsible for a phenomenon known as red tide. **Red tides** are discolorations of sections of the ocean caused by population explosions of dinoflagellates such as *Gonyaulax*. During these population explosions, called **algal blooms,** the water appears red because of the pigments in the algae. *Gonyaulax* produces toxins that can cause respiratory paralysis in vertebrates. For example, if people eat mussels that feed on these toxic dinoflagellates, they may suffer a severe neurotoxic reaction called mussel poisoning, which has the potential to be fatal.

Euglenophyta

The approximately 1,000 species of the Division Euglenophyta *(YOO-gluh-NAHF-uh-tuh)* are unicellular algae that have many features in common with green algae. However, they also have many characteristics similar to those of protozoa. Euglenoids contain chlorophylls a and b and store food as starch, but they do not have cell walls. Unlike other algae, euglenoids are not completely autotrophic. If a euglenoid is placed in the dark, it will become heterotrophic. For these reasons some scientists classify euglenoids as protozoa.

The most familiar genus of euglenoids is *Euglena,* members of which are abundant in freshwater ponds and lakes. Examine the *Euglena* shown in Figure 22-8. *Euglena gracilis* is generally elongate and fairly flexible. Like all species of *Euglena,* it is able to change shape because of the presence of a pellicle, a flexible proteinaceous covering. *Euglena gracilis* contains a structure called a reservoir with small openings that lead to the outside. A contractile vacuole is located in the reservoir. The contractile vacuole functions to rid the organism of excess water. Growing out of the reservoir and extending far beyond the cell is the long flagellum. A second flagellum is contained within the reservoir. Only the emergent flagellum moves the euglenoid about. A red-orange eyespot functions as a light detector and guides the photosynthetic alga toward bright areas.

Figure 22-8 ***Euglena gracilis,*** **the most familiar type of euglenoid, is propelled by a long flagellum. An eyespot guides the alga toward light.**

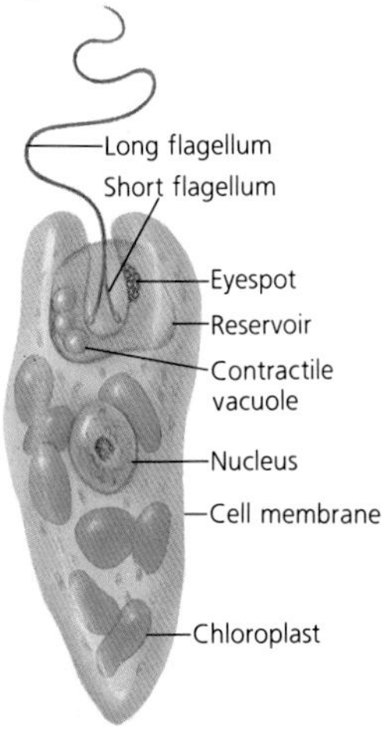

Section Review

1. What is a *unicellular gametangium?*
2. Give an example of a unicellular, a colonial, and a filamentous green alga.
3. Name the three parts of a kelp thallus.
4. Which divisions of algae store food as starch?
5. In what way do unicellular algae differ from members of the Kingdom Monera?

Section 22.1

Reteaching

Create a review game such as Division Diversity with questions that challenge students to give characteristics of algae from the six different divisions. Ask questions similar to the following. Which division can live deepest in the ocean? *(Rhodophyta)* Which division has the largest individual members? *(Phaeophyta)* Which division may be found in your ice cream? *(Phaeophyta)* Which division is considered the ancestor of plants? *(Chlorophyta)* Allow students to work in teams or use their textbooks to answer the questions.

■ *See* **Section Reviews** ***worksheet, Section 22.1.***

Enrichment

Have students use library references and resources to learn about different food chains that include both algae and humans.

Closure

Have students name at least one way in which members of each of the six divisions of algae affect humans. *(Chlorophyta can indicate water pollution; Phaeophyta are used in ice cream and other foods; Rhodophyta are used in cosmetics, gelatin capsules, and cheese; Chrysophyta are used as abrasives; Pyrrophyta can cause respiratory paralysis if eaten; Euglenophyta form the first link of many freshwater food chains.)*

Videodiscs

■ ***568–574, Pyrrophyta: Dinoflagellates (s)***
■ ***Side 1 40704, Bioluminescence (m)***
■ ***2594,* Euglena *(s)***

Answers to Section Review

1. A single-celled gamete holder in which algal gametes are formed and protected
2. *Chlamydomonas* and desmids are unicellular; *Volvox* and *Gonium* are colonial; filamentous green algae include *Spirogyra* and *Oedogonium.*
3. Holdfast, stipe, blade
4. Chlorophyta, Rhodophyta, Pyrrophyta, Euglenophyta
5. Algae are eukaryotic, whereas monerans are prokaryotic. This means that unicellular algae have nuclei and membrane-bound organelles.

Lesson Plan

Section Focus

This section describes asexual and sexual reproduction of unicellular and multicellular algae.

Section Themes

The underlying theme of this section is **Patterns of Change.** Algae have reproductive life cycles that include both asexual and sexual reproduction. Discussion of the parts of algae involved in reproduction emphasizes the theme of **Scale and Structure.**

Motivating Activity

Review with students the processes of mitosis and meiosis (Chapter 9). Remind students that algae can be either unicellular or multicellular. Ask them to speculate on whether multicellular algae could reproduce mitotically. *(No, though some stages may be produced through mitosis.)* Then ask them why it would be advantageous for unicellular algae to reproduce sexually. *(Sexual reproduction allows for genetic variability.)* Have students record their answers and review them after completing this section.

Teaching Strategies

Making Hypotheses Ask students to hypothesize about the adaptive advantage to algae of sexual reproduction during times of environmental stress. *(Students might mention that spores produced during sexual reproduction can wait until conditions are favorable to grow.)*

Section Objectives

- *Describe asexual and sexual reproduction in unicellular algae.*
- *Explain conjugation in filamentous algae.*
- *Distinguish between antheridia and oogonia.*
- *Describe the two main stages in alternation of generations.*

22.2 Comparative Reproduction

Some species of algae reproduce only asexually, thereby generating new organisms that are genetically identical with parent organisms. Other algae can reproduce either asexually or sexually. In these algae sexual reproduction is often triggered during periods of environmental stress.

Unicellular Reproduction

Earlier in this chapter we examined *Chlamydomonas,* a typical unicellular green alga. Members of this genus have both asexual and sexual reproduction. During asexual reproduction *Chlamydomonas* first absorbs its flagella. The haploid cell then divides mitotically one to three times, and two to eight haploid, flagellated daughter cells called **zoospores** *(ZOE-oe-SPORZ)* develop within the parent cell. These motile, asexual reproductive cells break out of the parent cell, disperse, land, and eventually grow to full size.

Sexual reproduction also begins when haploid cells divide mitotically to produce either plus or minus gametes. The plus and minus terminology is used when gametes look similar but differ in their chemical composition. A plus gamete and a minus gamete come into contact with one another and shed their cell walls. They fuse and form a diploid zygote, which develops a thick protective wall. A zygote in such a resting state is called a **zygospore** *(ZIE-goe-SPOR).* The zygospore can withstand unfavorable environmental conditions. When conditions are favorable, the zygospore breaks out of the thick wall. It then divides by meiosis and forms typical haploid *Chlamydomonas* cells.

Figure 22-9 ***Chlamydomonas*** **reproduces both asexually (blue arrows) and sexually (red arrows).**

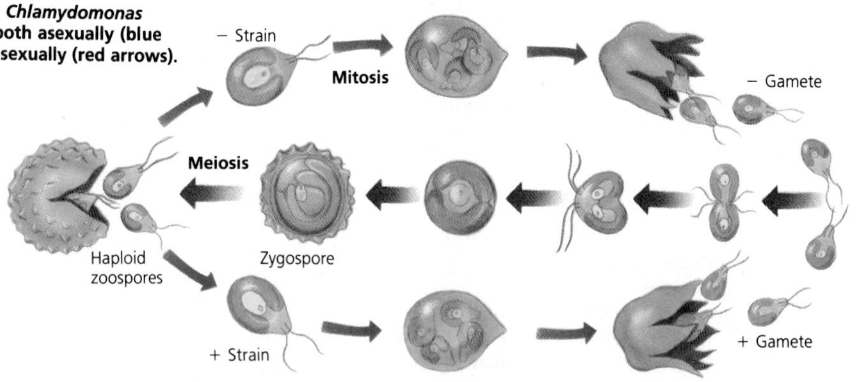

328

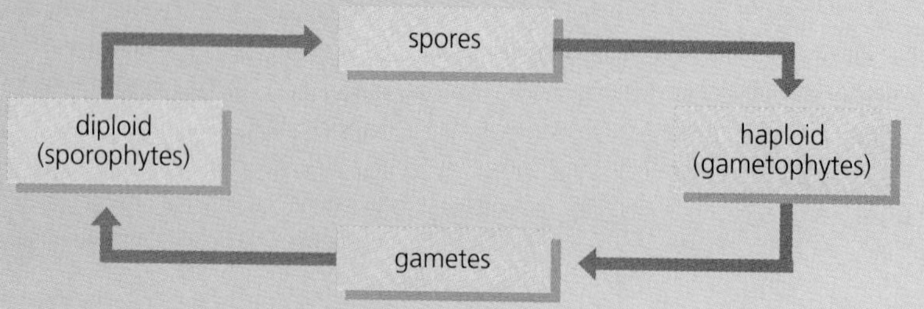

Graphic Organizer Use this cyclic diagram in Interpreting the Visuals on p. 329.

Diatoms also can reproduce sexually or asexually. During asexual reproduction the two valves of the diatom shell split apart. Each valve then grows another valve within itself. This form of reproduction creates increasingly smaller diatoms. However, when it reaches a certain size, a diatom sheds its shell, grows to full size, regenerates its shell, and begins the cycle again.

In sexual reproduction a diploid diatom undergoes meiosis to produce a gamete. Plus and minus gametes unite to form a zygote that will grow into a mature diatom.

Multicellular Reproduction

Reproduction of multicellular algae varies widely among the divisions. Reproduction in red and brown algae is very complex, with that of the red algae often involving three states in a sexual life cycle. Examination of three less complex algal life cycles will enable you to understand something of the reproductive variation in algae.

Conjugation: *Spirogyra*

Spirogyra, a filamentous green alga, reproduces sexually by a process called conjugation, in which one gamete moves to the other through a conjugation tube between adjacent filaments. Study the process in Figure 22-10. First two filaments align side by side. The walls between adjacent cells then dissolve and a conjugation tube forms between the cells. One cell is considered to be a plus gamete. Its contents move through the conjugation tube, enter the adjacent cell, and fuse with the minus gamete. After fertilization the resulting zygote develops a thick wall, falls from the parent filament, and becomes a resting spore. It later produces a new filament.

Egg and Sperm: *Oedogonium*

Oedogonium is another filamentous green alga. As shown in Figure 22-11, *Oedogonium* has cells specialized for producing gametes. Recall that the modified cells that produce and hold the

Figure 22-10 ***Spirogyra*** **reproduces sexually by a process called conjugation. Fusion occurs when a plus gamete moves through a conjugation tube to join a minus gamete.**

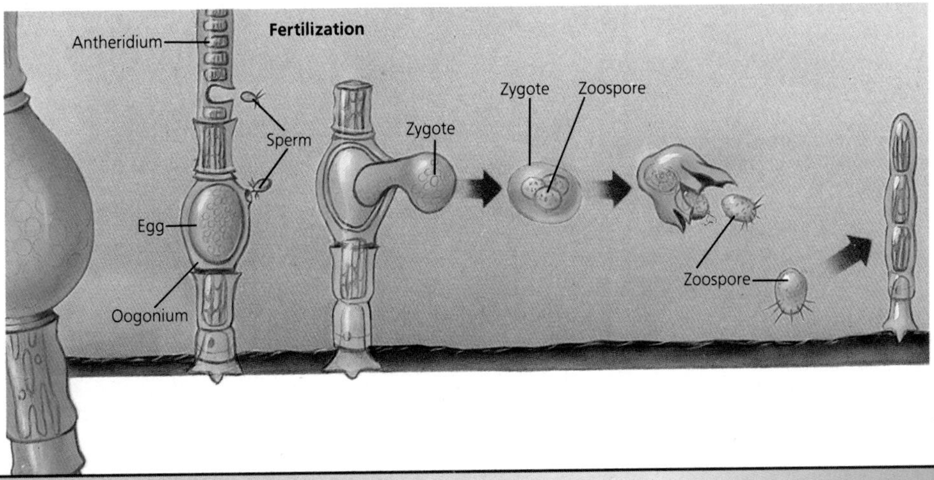

Figure 22-11 ***Oedogonium*** **reproduces sexually by producing male and female gametes. The sperm, released into surrounding water, swim to the egg.**

Observing Structures Set up microscope stations where students can examine prepared slides of *Chlamydomonas* sexual and asexual reproduction, conjugation in algae, and unicellular gametangia in algae. Encourage students to draw pictures of their observations and label them using the figures in this section as guides.

Interpreting the Visuals On the board, copy the cyclic diagram (Graphic Organizer) on p. 328. Then take students through the stages of reproduction in *Ulva* shown in Figure 22-12, p. 330. Point out how *Ulva* follows the pattern of alternation of generations. Ask which *Ulva* stages are haploid. *(Zoospore, gametophyte, and plus and minus gametes)* Which are diploid? *(Zygote, sporophyte, and sporangium)* Emphasize that plants and fungi also have alternation of generations in their life cycles. Remind students that scientists consider ancient green algae, such as *Ulva,* ancestors of green plants.

- *See* Blackline Master *46.*

Guided Practice

Review various types of algal reproduction. Then give students terms such as *zoospore, zygospore, egg, sperm,* and *zygote,* and ask whether each is haploid or diploid. *(Zoospore, egg, and sperm are haploid; zygospore and zygote are diploid.)*

Independent Practice

- Have students write answers to the Section Review.
- Have students determine which algal reproductive cells are motile. *(Gametes and zoospores are flagellated.)*

Videodiscs

- ***2631,*** **Chlamydomonas** ***Life Cycle (s)***

Cooperative Learning

Sexual Reproduction in Algae Divide the class into small groups and assign each group a type of sexual reproduction in algae—unicellular sexual reproduction, conjugation, multicellular algae with unicellular gametangia, and alternation of generations. Have each group design a poster with diagrams and labels of the type of sexual reproduction it was assigned. Require groups to divide the tasks for assembling the information and constructing the poster. Have groups present their posters to the class.

Check Your Understanding

1. How do zoospores differ from zygospores? *(Zoospores are haploid and zygospores are diploid.)*
2. By what process does a diploid cell form haploid cells? *(Meiosis)*
3. What are the two phases of the alternation of generations cycle? *(Gametophyte and sporophyte)*

Reteaching

Ask students to make a concept map showing the alternation of generations in *Ulva*. For each stage, students should indicate whether it is haploid or diploid. An example of a completed concept map is shown on p. 319B.
■ *See* Section Reviews *worksheet, Section 22.2.*

Enrichment

Have students use botany textbooks to research the alternation of generations reproductive life cycle. Ask them to find out how it might have evolved and its adaptive significance. Have students report their findings to the class.

Closure

Propose a hypothetical alga that can resist dry periods and another of the same species that is resistant to cold weather. Ask students what happens to each alga if there is a dry year with a cold winter. *(Both would die.)* What would happen if algae could transfer their resistance to each other? *(Both would live.)* Finally, ask how this transfer could be accomplished. *(By sexual reproduction)*

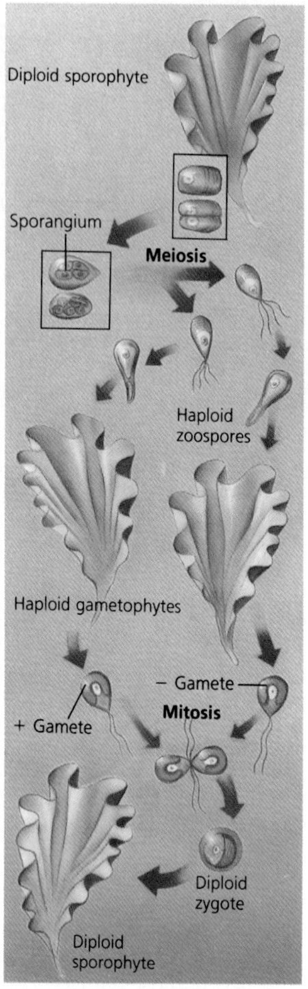

Figure 22-12 Reproduction in *Ulva* occurs through alternation of gametophyte and sporophyte generations.

gametes are called unicellular gametangia. The male unicellular gametangium is called an **antheridium** *(AN-thuh-RID-ee-um)*. It produces sperm. The female unicellular gametangium, the **oogonium** *(OE-uh-GOE-nee-um)*, produces an egg. Flagellated sperm are released from the antheridium into the surrounding water, swim to an oogonium, and enter through small pores. After fertilization the resulting zygote is released from the oogonium and forms a thick-walled, resting spore. The diploid spore then undergoes meiosis, forming four haploid zoospores that are released into the water. Each zoospore settles and divides. One of the new cells will become an anchoring holdfast; the other will divide and form a new filament.

Alternation of Generations: *Ulva*

The last form of multicellular algal reproduction that we'll consider is the complex cycle known as alternation of generations. This cycle is characterized by two distinct multicellular phases: a haploid, gamete-producing phase called the **gametophyte** *(guh-MEET-uh-FITE)*, and a diploid, spore-producing phase called the **sporophyte** *(SPOR-uh-FITE)*.

Examine Figure 22-12, which shows alternation of generations in *Ulva*. The *Ulva* illustrated at the top of the diagram is a diploid sporophyte. The sporophyte forms reproductive cells called **sporangia** *(spo-RAN-jee-uh)* that produce haploid zoospores by meiosis. These zoospores divide mitotically, forming more motile spores. The spores settle through the water, land on rocks, and grow into multicellular, haploid gametophytes. Note that the gametophyte looks exactly like the sporophyte. The gametophyte produces gametangia and then produces plus and minus gametes that unite and form zygotes. As Figure 22-12 shows, the diploid zygote completes the cycle by dividing mitotically into a new diploid sporophyte.

It is of exceptional significance that this life cycle occurs in a green alga. Plants, which presumably evolved from green algae, also have an alternation of generations as their sexual life cycle. As you will learn in Chapter 25, the plant life cycle differs from that of *Ulva* in two respects. The sporophyte and gametophyte do not look alike, and gametes are formed in multicellular rather than unicellular gametangia.

Section Review

1. Explain the difference between an *oogonium* and an *antheridium*.
2. What is the role of a zoospore in algal reproduction?
3. Since diatoms grow smaller whenever they reproduce asexually, why don't they gradually disappear?
4. How does *Spirogyra* reproduce sexually?
5. What is a possible adaptive advantage of sexual reproduction in the diatom?

Answers to Section Review

1. Oogonium is the female gametangium and produces eggs. The antheridium is the male gametangium and produces sperm.
2. Zoospores grow into new, asexual, haploid individuals that are capable of producing haploid gametes.
3. At certain points, asexually reproducing diatoms shed their small shells and grow to a larger size, then generate another shell.
4. *Spirogyra* reproduces sexually through conjugation, in which a plus gamete in one filament moves to another filament through a conjugation tube and joins with a minus gamete.
5. Sexual reproduction increases genetic variability, giving the diatom an adaptive advantage in changing environments.

Laboratory

Colonial Green Algae

Objective
To compare modern green algae with plants

Process Skills
Classifying, hypothesizing, inferring

Materials
Culture of *Chlamydomonas,* depression slides, cover slips, medicine dropper, compound microscope, green plants, mixed culture of the algae *Chlamydomonas, Eudorina, Gonium, Pandorina, Hydrodictyon,* and *Volvox*

Background
1 List reasons why scientists theorize that green plants evolved from green algae.
2 List characteristics of green algae. Include ways in which algae differ from plants.

Inquiry
1 Observe a wet mount of *Chlamydomonas* under low power. Record the number of cells and its colors.
2 Observe a green plant under the microscope. How many cells do you think it has? How might the cells in different parts of the plant differ? Compare your observations with those from step 1.
3 Modern green plants probably evolved from algae similar to those you are observing today. List adaptations necessary for modern green plants to evolve.
4 Examine a wet mount of the mixed algae culture under low power. Draw each type of alga you observe and label it.
5 Use the following key to identify the algae. Choose an alga and start at 1. Decide which choice describes it. If the alga is not identified, go to the next number and make the next decision. Continue until you identify the alga. Repeat these steps with the remaining algae.

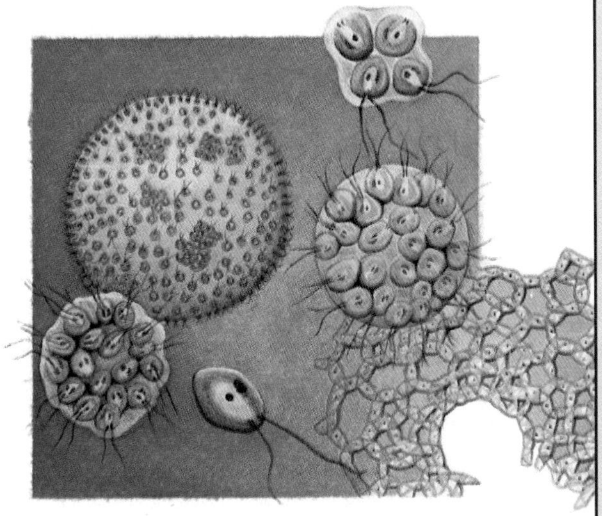

1a Single cells	*Chlamydomonas*
1b Colony of cells	Go to 2
2a Colony flattened or netlike	Go to 3
2b Colony round	Go to 4
3a Netlike colony	*Hydrodictyon*
3b Flattened colony	*Gonium*
4a More than 100 cells in colony	*Volvox*
4b Less than 100 cells in colony	Go to 5
5a Cells close together	*Pandorina*
5b Cells apart from each other	*Eudorina*

6 Describe examples of specialization in these algae. How do some cells depend on others?

Conclusions
1 What differences did you observe between small and large colonies?
2 Which specializations in algae are characteristic of green plants? What can you infer from these similarities?

Further Inquiry
How might you search for evidence of evolutionary relationships among algae and between algae and green plants?

Laboratory

(For an overview of colonial green algae and preparatory information related to the laboratory, see p. 319B.)

Background
1. Both plants and green algae contain chlorophyll a and b in their chloroplasts; both store food as starch; and both have cell walls made of cellulose.
2. Green algae can be unicellular, filamentous, or colonial. As is the case with other algae, green algae reproduce by means of unicellular gamete holders. Many algae have flagella.

Inquiry
1. *Chlamydomonas* has one cell and is green.
2. Most plants have many cells. In many plants only the leaves have the same green color as *Chlamydomonas.* Both the structure and functions of cells in roots, stems, and leaves differ, but all the cells are the same in *Chlamydomonas.*
3. Possible student answers: cell specialization, cells staying together (multicellularity), true roots that enable most plants to live on land.
6. Students may mention multicellularity, coordinated flagella, cytoplasmic connections between cells. *Gonium* has between 4 and 32 cells embedded in a mucilaginous matrix; *Pandorina* shows distinct anterior and posterior halves; *Eudorina* shows more distinct anterior and posterior halves; *Volvox* has many cells (500–50,000) and shows cell specialization.

Conclusions
1. In large colonies, cells are more coordinated; cell specialization is greater; there are some cytoplasmic connections between cells.
2. Multicellularity; cytoplasmic connections between cells that allow communication between cells; cell specialization. Students may infer that modern green plants could indeed have evolved from ancient green algae.

Further Inquiry
Students could suggest comparing either DNA or proteins of different species.

Vocabulary

1. Carageenan; the laminarin is a carbohydrate synthesized and stored by pyrenoids.
2. Sporangium; the oogonium and antheridium produce gametes.
3. Valve; the blade is part of the thallus in multicellular algae.
4. Blade; red tide and bioluminescence are features related to dinoflagellates.
5. Valve; the holdfast and stipe are parts of a multicellular thallus.

Review

1. c	**6.** b
2. a	**7.** c
3. d	**8.** d
4. a	**9.** b
5. d	**10.** a

11. Division Pyrrophyta
12. Color or photosynthetic pigments, food storage, and cell wall composition
13. Division Euglenophyta
14. The blade is specialized for photosynthesis.
15. Laminarin is an oily, not starchy, carbohydrate.
16. Colonial algae are groups of individual algal cells that act in a coordinated manner. Filamentous algae are composed of rows of cells.
17. Chlorophylls a, b, c, and d
18. Environmental stress usually triggers sexual reproduction in algae.
19. Like protozoa, *Euglena* have a contractile vacuole and no cell wall. They can also be heterotrôphic in the absence of light.
20. The similar reproductive patterns in green algae and plants suggest that they have a close evolutionary relationship.

Chapter 22 Review

Vocabulary

algal bloom (327)	diatomaceous earth (326)	phytoplankton (321)	thallus (321)
antheridium (330)	gametophyte (330)	pyrenoid (321)	unicellular gametangia (321)
bioluminescence (327)	holdfast (324)	red tide (327)	valve (326)
blade (324)	laminarin (324)	sporangium (330)	zoospore (328)
carageenan (325)	oogonium (330)	sporophyte (330)	zygospore (328)
centric diatom (326)	pennate diatom (326)	stipe (324)	

In the following groups of terms, choose the term that does not belong and explain why it does not.

1. laminarin, carageenan, pyrenoid
2. oogonium, antheridium, sporangium
3. blade, thallus, valve
4. red tide, blade, bioluminescence
5. valve, holdfast, stipe

Review

1. *Chlamydomonas* and *Euglena* both have (a) a stipe (b) a valve (c) an eyespot (d) an antheridium.
2. In *Ulva* the sporophyte produces (a) sporangia (b) antheridia (c) gametangia (d) carageenan.
3. Diatoms are in the Division (a) Rhodophyta (b) Euglenophyta (c) Chlorophyta (d) Chrysophyta.
4. Red algae contain an accessory pigment known as (a) phycobilin (b) fucoxanthin (c) carotene (d) xanthophyll.
5. An algal bloom that produces red tides in the sea is a population explosion among (a) diatoms (b) red algae (c) desmids (d) dinoflagellates.
6. Motile reproductive cells in algae are called (a) sporangia (b) zoospores (c) zygospores (d) sporophytes.
7. A pyrenoid is (a) a molecule in the cell wall (b) an adaptation for anchorage (c) a food-storage structure (d) a unicellular green alga.
8. Biologists think that the probable ancestors of plants were from the (a) Division Chrysophyta (b) Division Euglenophyta (c) Division Phaeophyta (d) Division Chlorophyta.
9. Conjugation occurs in (a) some unicellular algae (b) some filamentous algae (c) some colonial algae (d) some multicellular algae.
10. Farming the ocean is called (a) aquaculture (b) domestication (c) collecting (d) agriculture.
11. Which algal division has members that are bioluminescent?
12. Name the characteristics considered in the classification of algae.
13. Which division of algae does not have a cell wall?
14. What is the adaptive advantage of a blade?
15. How is laminarin different from other storage molecules?
16. Explain the difference between colonial and filamentous algae.
17. List the types of chlorophyll found in the algae.
18. Under what conditions do most algae undergo sexual, as opposed to asexual, reproduction?
19. In what ways are *Euglena* species like protozoa?
20. What is the evolutionary significance of the alternation of generations found in green algae?

Critical Thinking

1. A few years ago many botanists classified algae, including the blue-green bacteria, as plants. *Euglena* was classified as a photosynthetic protozoan because it was free-swimming. What does this tell you about how scientists go about classifying living things?
2. Along the Pacific Coast of North America there is a saying that it is unsafe to collect and eat shellfish during the months that lack an *r* in their spellings. Name these months, and give a possible scientific explanation for the belief. Keep in mind that shellfish are filter feeders.
3. The horsetail, or *Equisetum,* has silicon dioxide (SiO_2) in its outer cells. Diatoms also contain SiO_2. Explain whether the presence of SiO_2 in both genera indicates a close relationship. (Hint: Consider the types of evolution described in Chapter 15.)
4. How does the absence of a cell wall in *Euglena* make the function of the contractile vacuole critically important?
5. Suppose that you discover a new species of unicellular algae that has chlorophyll and an eyespot but no flagella or cilia. Why would you be surprised at the lack of locomotion?
6. What conditions might trigger sexual reproduction in *Spirogyra?* (Hint: Recall from Chapter 5 what can trigger the division of cells.)

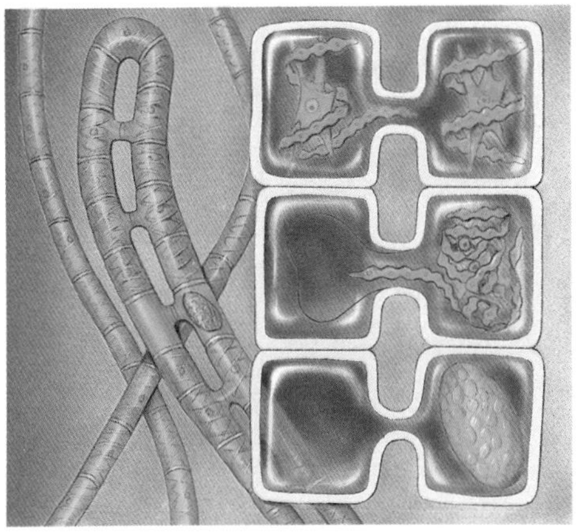

7. How does a diatom "know" it's gotten small enough and must divide sexually?
8. Examine the drawing of lateral conjugation in *Spirogyra,* in which adjacent cells of the same filament have conjugated. Explain whether this type of conjugation offers more or less genetic recombination than does sclariform conjugation, in which conjugation is between the cells of two filaments.

Extension

1. Read the article by Robert Kunzig entitled "Invisible Garden" in *Discover,* April 1990, pp. 67–74. Prepare an oral report in which you discuss the incredible diversity and abundance of phytoplankton. How do phytoplankton influence both land and marine ecology?
2. Go to your local grocery store or supermarket, and find at least three items that contain carageenan, a polysaccharide derived from red algae.
3. Leave a jar of pure clean water near a window or light source. Do not cover the jar. Examine it once a week for signs of green algae. Examine the algae under a microscope. How can algae grow in clean water?
4. Gather samples of soil, dead leaves, old grass, and fresh leaves if possible. Place each sample in a jar or tube of clean water, and leave in light. Examine the samples under a microscope once a week, and make drawings of the types of organisms you find. What does this tell you about the different habitats of algae?

Critical Thinking

1. The classification of living things changes as scientists learn more about different species.
2. May, June, July, August; during these warmer months the number of *Gonyaulax* increase. Shellfish feed on these algae and thus may accumulate the toxins they produce.
3. This is an example of convergent evolution. The two genera are not closely related.
4. Because it lacks a cell wall, *Euglena* has no mechanical support to help prevent the cell membrane from bursting when excess water enters the cell. The contractile vacuole removes excess water by pumping it out.
5. Because the function of the eyespot is to help direct the organism toward light
6. In many species of *Spirogyra,* sexual reproduction is directly related to the ratio between the cell's surface area and volume.
7. By the ratio of its surface area to its volume or by the ratio of the size of its nucleus to the size of its cytoplasm
8. Less. The cells of one filament have the same genetic makeup. The cells of two different filaments may have come from different zygospores and thus have different genetic compositions.

Extension

1. All life in the sea depends on phytoplankton. Each year phytoplankton draw out of the atmosphere about half the CO_2 put into it by people—CO_2 that could otherwise contribute to global warming.
2. Possible items: chocolate, jams, jellies, instant coffee, wine, and ice cream
3. Airborne algal spores that land in water will begin to grow.
4. Algae grow in all of these samples, indicating that algae grows in a variety of terrestrial habitats.

Chapter 23 Fungi

Chapter Overview

Chapter 23 introduces some of the varied organisms in the Kingdom Fungi. Section 23.1 examines fungi and the characteristics of some specific organisms classified in each of the four divisions. Section 23.2 describes four phyla of funguslike protists and helps students compare these organisms to those in the Kingdom Fungi.

Chapter Planning Chart

B	S	A	Sections and Subsections	Page	Features	Page	Resources
•	•	•	**23.1 Biology of Fungi**				
			Evolution	335	Think	340	Videodiscs
			Characteristics and Classification	336	Biotechnology	340	Blackline Master 47
			Zygomycota	337	Laboratory	345	Blackline Master 48
			Basidiomycota	338	Section Review	342	Overhead Transparency T23
			Ascomycota	339			Process Skills: Lichens
			Deuteromycota	341			Laboratories: Fungi on Food
			Mycorrhizae and Lichens	342			Section Reviews Worksheet
		•	**23.2 Funguslike Protists**				
			Acrasiomycota	343	Section Review	344	Section Reviews Worksheet
			Myxomycota	344			
			Chytridiomycota	344			
			Oomycota	344			
			End of Chapter Activities				
					Chapter Review	346	Vocabulary Skills
							Chapter Test
							Computer Test Generator

B *The Basic Level curriculum presents the most fundamental knowledge offered in the course.*
S *The Standard Level curriculum is designed for the average student who is able to master most topics.*
A *The Advanced Level curriculum includes suggestions for teaching the most academically able students.*

Cooperative Learning

Group Activity: Characteristics of Fungi

- **Group Size:** *3 students*
- **Outcome:** *Students will describe the characteristics and ecological effects of fungi or funguslike protists.*
- **Individual Accountability:** *Each student will research one particular aspect of a chosen fungus.*
- **Positive Interdependence:** *Group members will share information and illustrate their findings.*

Assign each group of students a type of fungus or funguslike protist. One group might research rusts, smuts, or mushrooms; another group might research yeasts, molds, mildews, or morels; another might research funguslike protists such as cellular slime molds, plasmodial slime molds, chytrids, water molds, or white rusts. Then have students do library research in mycology texts and other books to collect details on their organism. Within each group, have one student be responsible for researching the general characteristics of the organism, such as its size, color, parts, and structure. Have the second student find out how the organism reproduces. Have the third student research the organism's positive and negative effects on the ecosystem.

After students complete their research, have the groups reassemble so the members can share their findings. Instruct each group to develop a chart or poster illustrating the information its members have gathered. Have each group present its project to the class and answer any questions other students may have.

Concept Map

The following is one possible solution to the concept mapping activity in Relating Concepts on p. 340.

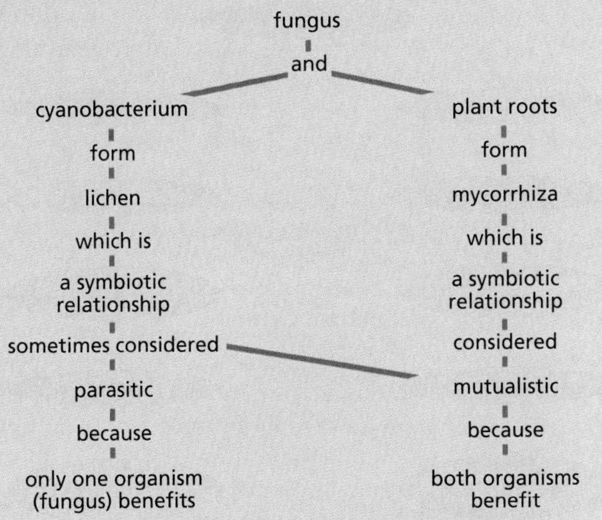

Laboratory Preparation

Overview *(See p. 345.)*

In this lab exercise, students will observe the basic fungal morphology. Fungi are made up of hyphae, a mass of which forms a mycelium. Students will distinguish among the three types of hyphae that are part of *Rhizopus stolonifer.* They will also recognize how this fungus reproduces sexually and asexually. Sexual reproduction involves two different mating strains of hyphae. When two different strains join, each makes a bulge called a progametangium at the point of contact. When the nuclear and cytoplasmic contents of each progametangium are walled off from the rest of the hyphae, the structures become gametangia. The gametangia fuse and a zygospore forms. The zygospore will remain dormant until certain environmental conditions, such as warmth and moisture, are met.

Preparation

Rhizopus cultures are available from biological supply companies. If you choose to grow your own cultures, begin five to seven days before the lab session is scheduled. To do this, expose several pieces of stale bread to the air, or inoculate the bread with dust. Moisten the bread and seal it in a jar. When mold appears, use a sterile wire loop to transfer the samples to petri dishes containing Sabouraud dextrose agar plates.

Teaching Tips

Encourage students to draw the structures of *Rhizopus* as they observe them.

Demonstrate how to tease apart the hyphae so that students can observe the rhizoids.

Some students may have difficulty finding evidence of the stages leading to the formation of zygospores. Encourage students who have exceptional samples to allow other students to observe them.

Safety

Make sure students wash their hands after handling the *Rhizopus* cultures. Also be aware that some students may be allergic to the mold.

Chapter Themes

Patterns of Change The life cycles of fungi and funguslike protists are examples of cyclical change. Emphasize how the forms of organisms change throughout their life cycles.

Scale and Structure Highlight the structures of fungi that allow both asexual and sexual reproduction. Emphasize that the ability of fungi to reproduce both ways allows them to survive in almost any environment.

Point out the structures that fungi and funguslike protists have in common. Encourage students to conclude that the two groups have superficial similarities but are different enough to be classified separately.

Systems and Interactions Discuss the role of fungi in the ecosystem. Emphasize the importance of decomposition in providing the basic components that other living things need for survival. Use the example of mycorrhizae to illustrate one of the mutualistic ways in which fungi interact with other living things.

Chapter Motivating Activity

Display several different samples of fungi, such as bread mold, *Penicillium* mold, baker's yeast, a mushroom, and a bracket fungus. Have students examine the samples with hand lenses or dissecting microscopes. Encourage them to explain what the samples have in common and how they differ. *(Common traits: lack chlorophyll, do not move; different traits: structures, colors)* Ask students why fungi are classified in their own kingdom rather than in the plant kingdom. *(Because fungi, unlike plants, cannot make their own food)*

Chapter 23 Fungi

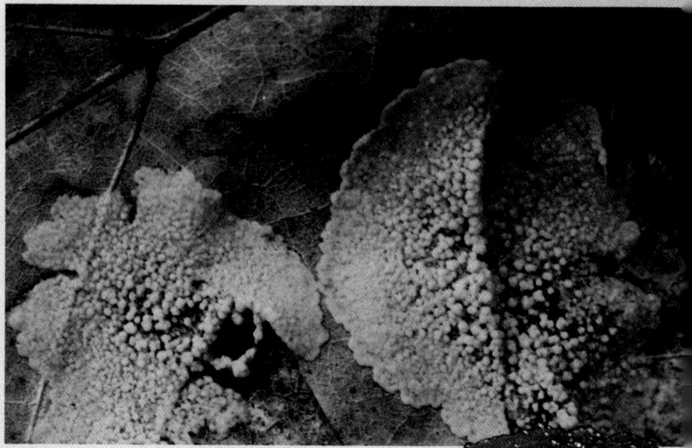

Slime mold in the plasmodial stage. Inset: Mushrooms, *Marasmius* sp., in a Costa Rican rain forest.

Introduction

The Kingdom Fungi is made up of diverse organisms adapted to absorb food from living or dead organisms. Members of this kingdom range from unicellular yeasts to giant bracket fungi. This chapter also discusses four phyla of protists that have funguslike traits but are distinct enough from fungi to be classified in the Kingdom Protista. These phyla are discussed in this chapter because their life cycles are unlike those of other protists.

Chapter Outline

23.1 Biology of Fungi
- *Evolution*
- *Characteristics and Classification*
- *Zygomycota*
- *Basidiomycota*
- *Ascomycota*
- *Deuteromycota*
- *Mycorrhizae and Lichens*

23.2 Funguslike Protists
- *Acrasiomycota*
- *Myxomycota*
- *Chytridiomycota*
- *Oomycota*

Chapter Concept

As you read, identify the importance of fungi and funguslike protists to humans.

Understanding the Visuals

Have students compare the two photographs and decide what these organisms have in common. Point out that they both obtain food from other organisms or dead organic material. Explain that the slime mold is a funguslike protist and the mushroom is a fungus. Ask students to infer why these two organisms are classified differently. *(Encourage students to give a rationale for their inferences.)* Point out that although the two have a few traits in common, they differ in more ways than they are alike. Have students speculate on how both funguslike protists and fungi are important to the environment. *(They act as decomposers, breaking down organic material into inorganic compounds needed by other living things.)*

23.1 Biology of Fungi

Members of the Kingdom Fungi are a diverse group of over 65,000 species living in many different environments. Molds, mildews, rusts, smuts, mushrooms, and yeasts are all fungi. Most fungi are microscopic. Some microscopic fungi, such as the pathogens responsible for athlete's foot, ringworm, and chestnut blight, are harmful. Many microscopic fungi, such as yeasts, are beneficial. Yeasts cause bread to rise and are among the most widely used research organisms. Not all fungi are entirely microscopic. Some fungi produce fruiting bodies that are visible to the unaided eye, such as puffballs, mushrooms, and morels.

Most fungi are saprophytic or parasitic, and a few species are predatory. A saprophyte is an organism that feeds on dead organic material. As fungi digest this material, they recycle the nutrient molecules in it. Organisms that break down organic materials are decomposers. For example, fungi release carbon, nitrogen, and phosphorus molecules when they digest dead plants and animals. These molecules are used by the fungus or by other organisms. Without decomposers, nutrients would not be reused and life could not continue on earth.

A parasite derives its nutrients from a living host organism at the host's expense. Parasitic fungi harm host organisms and cause many plant and animal diseases. For example, the fatal Dutch elm disease is caused by the fungus *Ceratocystis ulmi.* Other fungi, such as wheat rusts, attack crops and cause serious economic loss. Fungi that attack animals cause a variety of diseases, such as histoplasmosis, a serious lung disease.

A predatory fungus is one that captures prey for food. *Pleurotus ostreatus* is an example of a predatory fungus. Also called the oyster fungus, *P. ostreatus* obtains nitrogen by capturing roundworms. After secreting a substance that makes the roundworm sluggish the fungal cells engulf the worm, penetrate its body, and absorb its contents.

Evolution

The oldest fossils that resemble modern fungi are found in Precambrian rocks that are about 900 million years old. The earliest fossils that are distinctly fungi are about 500 million years old, from the Ordovician period. By about 300 million years ago, in the late Carboniferous period, all modern divisions of fungi had evolved. Since most present-day fungi are terrestrial, scientists speculate that fungi underwent adaptive radiation shortly after plants and animals colonized the land. Scientists reason that fungi, like all other eukaryotes, arose from prokaryotes. Fungi are heterotrophic—they cannot make their own food—and therefore probably arose from other heterotrophs. Some scientists, however, theorize that some fungi evolved from red algae.

Section Objectives

- *Describe the origin and evolution of fungi.*
- *Distinguish between a hypha and a mycelium.*
- *List the four divisions of fungi and their key reproductive characteristics.*
- *Explain how geneticists use yeasts in laboratory research.*
- *Define* mycorrhiza *and* lichen *and distinguish between them.*

Figure 23-1 This bracket fungus is a saprophyte that aids in the breakdown of organic material.

Division	Reproductive Body	Reproductive Cells	Spores
Basidiomycota	basidiocarp	basidia	basidiospores
Ascomycota	ascocarp	asci	ascospores

Graphic Organizer Use this table in Organizing Information on p. 339.

Lesson Plan

Section Focus

This section introduces the Kingdom Fungi and discusses the four major groups. It presents the basic pattern of evolution and the characteristics and classification of fungi. It discusses symbiotic relationships in mycorrhizae and in lichens.

Section Themes

In this section, the discussion of fungal reproductive structures and function emphasizes the themes of **Scale and Structure** and **Patterns of Change.** The reproductive structures of fungi continue the cyclical changes of various fungal life cycles. For example, the reproductive body of a mushroom develops basidia on its gills and other reproductive structures that eventually form new mushrooms.

Motivating Activity

Write *saprophyte, parasite,* and *predator* on the board. Ask students to define these words. *(A saprophyte secretes powerful digestive enzymes to break down dead organic matter into simple molecules; a parasite feeds on a living host; a predator captures prey for food.)* Ask students to decide which of these roles fungi take. Help students conclude that some fungi fill each of these roles.

Teaching Strategies

Drawing Diagrams Have students create a food web in which fungi function in two of the three roles: saprophyte, parasite, or predator. Refer students to Chapter 50 if they are unfamiliar with food webs. Encourage them to use examples from the text. (*For example,* Ceratocystis ulmi *is a parasitic fungus on a living elm tree; when the tree dies, a saprophytic bracket fungus gets nutrients from the tree.)*

Section 23.1

Observing Structures Give pairs of students a mushroom, a scalpel, and a hand lens. Have them cut the mushroom in half longitudinally and examine its structures with a hand lens. Provide slides, coverslips, and microscopes and have students make wet mounts of a gill and thin sections of the cap. Have them observe the cell structure of the hyphae and compare it with Figure 23-2.

- *See* Blackline Master *47.*

Distinguishing Terms Write the prefix *karyo-* on the board. Ask students to recall two words in which this prefix is used and tell what the words mean. (Prokaryote, *which is a cell without a nucleus;* eukaryote, *which is a cell that contains a nucleus*) Ask students to infer what *karyo-* means. *(It means "the nucleus of a cell.")* Then challenge students to infer the meanings of the prefixes *homo-* and *hetero-*. *("Alike" and "different," respectively)*

Drawing Conclusions Point out that fungi were once classified in the plant kingdom. Ask students why they think scientists had grouped fungi with plants. *(The structures and immobility of some fungi make them seem more similar to plants than to animals.)* Have students infer why fungi were eventually classified in their own kingdom. *(Although fungi were once considered nongreen plants, scientific research has pointed out how fungi are unique. Scientists created the Kingdom Fungi to make the classification more logical.)*

It seems possible that the first true fungi were unicellular and gave rise to coenocytic fungi. **Coenocytic** *(SEE-nuh-SIT-ick)* refers to filaments without internal cross walls. A coenocytic filament contains many nuclei that move through the cytoplasm. Coenocytes may have given rise to club fungi. Club fungi, in turn, may have given rise to sac fungi. Club fungi and sac fungi have bodies that are divided into distinct cells by perforated cross walls.

Characteristics and Classification

The vegetative filament of a fungus is called a **hypha** *(HIE-fuh)*. Hyphae may or may not be divided into cells by perforated cross walls, each of which is called a **septum.** A hypha grows at its tip, where new membrane material is added by the action of Golgi bodies. A mat of interwoven hyphae is known as a **mycelium** *(mie-SEE-lee-um)*. Branches form in areas away from the tip.

Hyphae cell walls are made of **chitin,** a complex polysaccharide also found in the external skeleton of insects and other invertebrates. Fungi differ from plants, which have cellulose in their cell walls. Fungi, like animals, store food as glycogen, while plants store food as starch.

Fungi reproduce both sexually and asexually. Sexual reproduction in many fungi begins when cells or gametes from two mating strains undergo cytoplasmic fusion. The nuclei, however, may not immediately fuse, but will divide independently. When genetically different nuclei coexist within a hypha, the hypha is said to be **heterokaryotic.** A hypha with genetically similar nuclei is called **homokaryotic.**

Fungi reproduce asexually by producing spores, usually on special branches or modified cells of the hyphae. The small, lightweight spores are often released into the air. They may be carried long distances before they land and germinate into new hyphae. Fungi also reproduce asexually by the fragmentation, or breaking apart, of the hyphae.

Figure 23-2 A mushroom, such as *Amanita parcivolvata* shown at the top, has the main parts illustrated below. Note in the illustration the presence of two nuclei in a single cell.

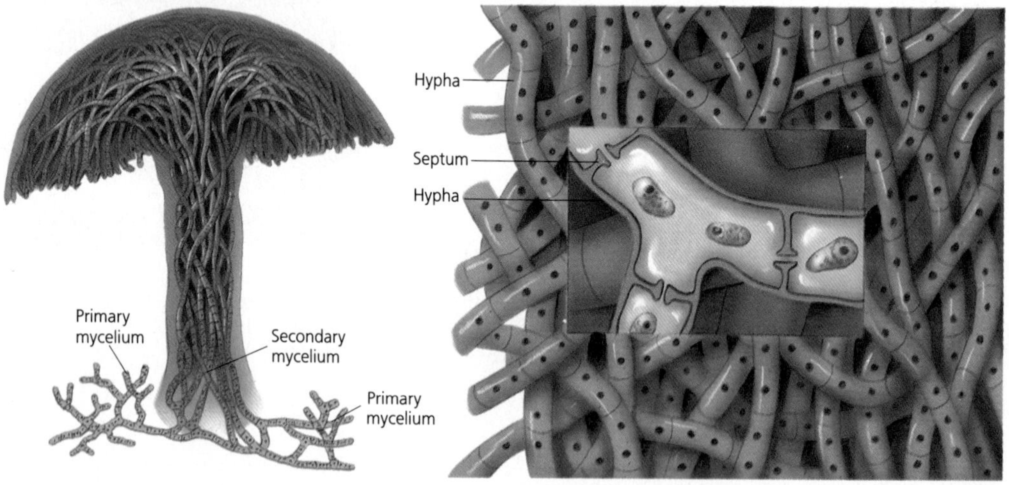

Cooperative Learning

Fungi Classification Divide the class into groups of four. Instruct each student within a group to choose a different one of the four divisions of fungi. Have students do library research on the division they chose, focusing on the harmful and beneficial types of fungi in their division. Then have group members share the information they discovered and work together to develop a chart that illustrates their findings. Have students refer to their charts during a class discussion on the harmful and beneficial types of fungi.

Table 23-1 Classification of Fungi

Division	Body	Asexual Reproduction	Sexual Reproduction	Habitat	Examples
Zygomycota (600 species)	Coenocytic hyphae	Spores from sporangia	Conjugation; zygospores	Mostly terrestrial	*Pilobus* spp., *Rhizopus* spp.
Basidiomycota (25,000 species)	Septate hyphae	Fragmentation	Basidia produce basidiospores	Mostly terrestrial	Rusts, smuts, mushrooms
Ascomycota (30,000 species)	Septate or unicellular hyphae	Conidia; budding	Asci produce ascospores	Terrestrial and aquatic	Yeasts, molds, mildews, morels
Deuteromycota (10,000 species)	Septate hyphae	Conidia	Unknown	Terrestrial	*Cladosporium* spp., *Sporothrix* spp.

Members of the Kingdom Fungi are classified into four divisions based primarily on the structure of hyphae or on the type of reproduction. As you read about the four divisions of the fungi kingdom, refer to Table 23-1.

Zygomycota

The approximately 600 species of the Division Zygomycota *(ZIE-goe-mie-KOE-tuh)* are mostly terrestrial organisms. They are commonly found in soil and dung. Zygomycetes are coenocytic—that is, their hyphae lack septa. However, their reproductive structures are blocked off from the rest of the hyphae by unperforated cross walls.

The Division Zygomycota includes *Rhizopus stolonifer,* the common black bread mold. *Rhizopus* appears as a fuzzy growth on bread and consists of three different types of hyphae. **Rhizoids** are anchoring hyphae that penetrate the bread, produce digestive enzymes, and absorb nutrients. The hyphae that grow across the surface of the bread are called **stolons.** Specialized upright hyphae called **sporangiophores** *(spuh-RAN-ji-oe-forz)* produce sporangia at their tips.

Asexual reproduction in zygomycetes occurs when hormonal action causes upright sporangiophores to form. Sporangia form at the tips of the sporangiophores. The sporangia produce spores that are dispersed by wind.

Sexual reproduction in *Rhizopus* is called conjugation. Conjugation in fungi is a sexual process that occurs when two filaments line up next to each other. A similar kind of conjugation occurs in filamentous algae such as *Spirogyra.* In *Rhizopus* hyphae of two mating strains come close together. Each hypha encloses haploid (1N) nuclei. Hormones cause short branches to form on each hypha and grow outward until they touch. Then septa form near the tip of each branch. Each resulting cell is a gametangium that contains several nuclei. The gametangia fuse;

LEP Activity

Help students make sense of the terminology in the chapter by having them find the meanings of prefixes and root words. For example, direct students' attention to Table 23-1. Explain that the root word in the division names, *mycota,* refers to fungi. Ask students to relate the prefix of each division name to a word in the sexual reproduction column. For example, Zygomycota produce zygospores, Basidiomycota produce basidia, Ascomycota produce asci, and Deuteromycota lack a sexual phase. Have students look up the prefixes *zygo-, basidio-, asco-,* and *deutero-,* and relate these meanings to the fungi's means of sexual reproduction.

Observing Structures Set up several microscopes with slides of *Rhizopus stolonifer.* Have students examine the hyphae in the slides and then draw what they observe. Encourage students to compare their drawings with the hyphae shown in Figure 23-2, p. 336, and to describe how the hyphae differ. *(The hyphae in the mushroom are made up of cells divided by septa; the hyphae in the bread mold do not have septa.)*

■ *See* **Laboratories,** ***Investigation 23.***

Interpreting the Visuals Display a series of scanning electron micrographs showing zygospore formation in *Rhizopus.* Such photographs often can be found in microbiology texts. Have students compare the SEMs with Figure 23-3, p. 338. Based on the text description of reproduction, ask students to relate the process occurring in the SEMs.

Classifying Organisms Using a field guide to fungi, provide students with pictures and general descriptions of some different types of fungi. Have them decide which division (see Table 23-1) each fungus belongs to. For example, have students classify *Mucor racemosus* (Zygomycota), *Amanita virosa* (Basidiomycota), *Tuber californicum* (Ascomycota), and *Candida albicans* (Deuteromycota). For extra credit, some students may wish to collect fungi and identify them.

■ *See* **Overhead Transparency** ***T23 and*** **Blackline Master** ***48.***

Videodiscs

- ***Side 3 5289, Bread Mold Growth (m)***
- ***Side 3 5641, Zygospore Formation (m)***
- ***Side 3 6371, Zoospore Release in*** **Saprolegnia** ***(m)***
- ***Side 3 6291, Puffball Spore Dispersal (m)***

Interpreting the Visuals Have students trace the life cycle of the mushroom shown in Figure 23-4, p. 339. For each stage illustrated, ask students to describe what occurs. *(For example, in the basidium stage, the formation of the septum isolates the two nuclei, which then fuse to form the zygote.)*

Distinguishing Terms Ask students to describe the difference between primary and secondary mycelium. *(Primary mycelium are hyphae with cells containing single nuclei. Secondary mycelium are hyphae with cells containing two nuclei.)* Have students look at the primary and secondary mycelium illustrated in Figures 23-2, p. 336, and 23-4, p. 339. Ask them to explain why one kind of mycelium is called primary and the other secondary. *(The primary mycelium form first from basidiospores. The secondary mycelium form from two mating strains of primary mycelium.)*

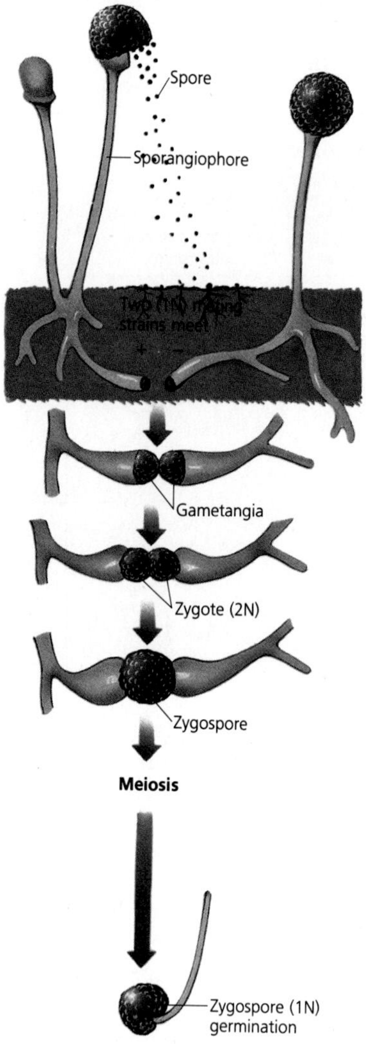

Figure 23-3 ***Rhizopus*** **goes through a sexual reproduction process called conjugation in which two mating strains join. Meiosis occurs when the zygospore germinates.**

then the nuclei fuse in pairs. Each pair contains one nucleus from each mating strain. Thus the zygote contains many diploid (2N) nuclei. Figure 23-3 shows the life cycle of *Rhizopus*.

The wall surrounding the zygote then thickens. The resulting protective, temporarily dormant structure is called a zygospore. Meiosis occurs when the zygospore germinates. Germination usually takes place after one to three months, depending on environmental conditions.

Reproducing sexually and asexually provides an adaptive advantage. During periods when the environment is favorable, the rapid, asexual formation of spores ensures the quick spread of the species. In periods of environmental stress, sexual reproduction ensures genetic recombination before the hyphae die.

Basidiomycota

Scientists place about 25,000 species in the Division Basidiomycota *(buh-SID-ee-oe-mie-KOE-tuh),* or club fungi. Mushrooms, toadstools, and puffballs are classified as basidiomycetes, as are rusts and smuts.

Under proper conditions, such as after a warm rain in the spring, underground hyphae grow upward, intertwine, and produce a **basidiocarp,** the reproductive body of a basidiomycete. A mushroom is a basidiocarp with a flattened **cap** attached to a stem that is called a **stalk.**

On the underside of the cap are radiating rows of **gills.** A specialized club-shaped reproductive cell called a **basidium** *(buh-SID-ee-um)* forms on the gills. Each gill contains thousands of basidia. In each basidium two nuclei become isolated by a complete septum. The nuclei fuse and form a diploid zygote. Meiosis then results in four nuclei that are pushed into cytoplasmic extensions to form **basidiospores.** At maturity basidiospores are released and germinate into new homokaryotic hyphae.

As the homokaryotic hyphae grow, septa form so that each cell contains one nucleus. These homokaryotic, septate hyphae are called the **primary mycelium.** These hyphae grow and fuse with hyphae from another mating strain. When separate mating strains fuse, a **secondary mycelium** results. Hyphae of these mycelia are heterokaryotic, containing one nucleus from each mating strain in each cell. Secondary mycelium intertwines and forms a basidiocarp. A mushroom, for example, is a basidiocarp.

Rusts are a group of parasitic basidiomycetes that cause diseases in plants. Rusts attack many plants but are of particular concern to us when they infect cereal crops such as wheat and oats. Infected plants look rusty because they are covered with reddish brown fungal spores. Rusts do not form basidiocarps. Instead basidia develop on the surface of infected plants.

Smuts, like rusts, are plant pathogens that do not form basidiocarps. The approximately 1,000 species of smuts cover infected organisms with dark masses of spores.

Interdisciplinary Activity

Economics Have students find out what the economic impact of fungi is in the United States. They should discover how the use and sale of fungi contributes to our economy, such as the use of fungi for weed control, for food, or for production of industrial chemicals and medicines. Students can also research mushroom farming and find out how many jobs are created by this use of fungi. Have them contribute their findings to a bulletin board focusing on the economic importance of fungi.

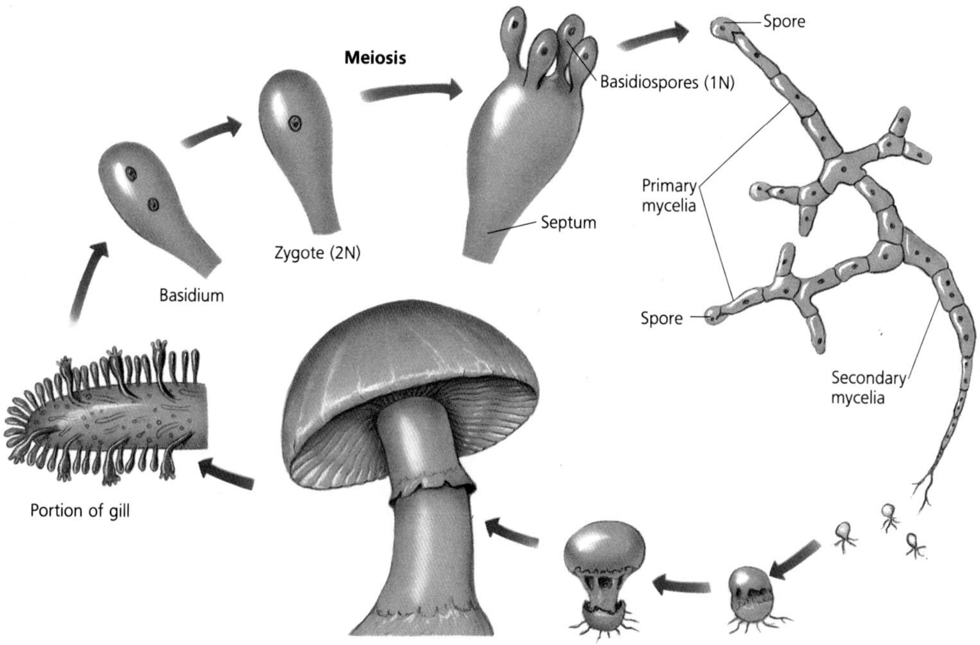

Figure 23-4 The reproductive body of a basidiomycete, a mushroom, develops basidia on the gills lining the underside of its cap. New mushrooms form from a secondary mycelium.

Ascomycota

The Division Ascomycota *(AS-koe-mie-KOE-tuh),* or sac fungi, contains over 30,000 species. This is the largest division of fungi, and some biologists suspect it may have been the most recent group to evolve. Sac fungi live in a variety of habitats, including salt and fresh water. In terrestrial environments ascomycetes live in soil, dung, and rotting logs. Common ascomycetes are morels, powdery mildews, yeasts, and cup fungi.

Sexual reproduction begins when the hyphae of two mating strains form either male or female gametangia. The female gametangium is called an **ascogonium** *(AS-kuh-GOE-nee-um),* and the male gametangium is called an antheridium. The gametangia fuse, and male nuclei move into the ascogonium. Male and female nuclei pair but do not fuse. These cells divide, and the resulting heterokaryotic hyphae grow and intertwine, forming an ascocarp. The **ascocarp** is the reproductive body of an ascomycete. It has various forms, depending on the species.

Sacs called **asci** *(AS-ie)* form on the surface of the ascocarp near the tips of some hyphae. Each ascus *(AS-kuss)* encloses two nuclei. The nuclei fuse in the ascus, and the resulting diploid nucleus immediately undergoes meiosis, producing four haploid nuclei. Each nucleus usually then divides once by mitosis, so each ascus finally contains eight haploid **ascospores.** When an ascus ruptures, it releases ascospores, usually into the air. These land on the ground and germinate, forming new hyphae.

Figure 23-5 The morel, *Morchella deliciosa,* shown here is an edible ascomycete, or sac fungus.

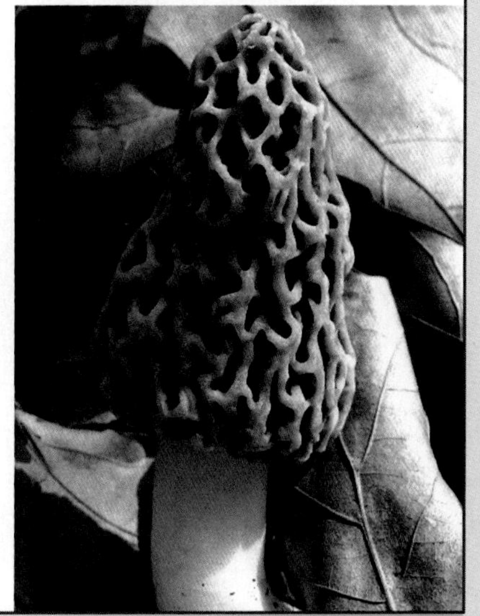

Organizing Information Have students make a table comparing the reproductive structures of organisms in the divisions Basidiomycota and Ascomycota. Have them use the categories of *Reproductive Body, Reproductive Cells,* and *Spores* as column heads. An example of a completed table is shown on p. 335.

Drawing Diagrams Have students carefully read the description of the sexual reproduction stages of sac fungi. Then have them diagram the significant stages. Emphasize that the appearance of the structures students draw is not important; instead, encourage them to focus on visually portraying the steps described. If possible, provide them with resources showing the reproductive structures of ascomycetes.

Comparing Structures Provide students with pictures of several different types of ascomycetes, such as the morel, cup fungus, and yeast. For each picture, help students identify the ascocarp. *(For example, the edible part of a morel is an ascocarp.)* Have them compare the different forms, emphasizing that despite their different appearances, they perform similar functions. Ask them to speculate on the adaptive functions of the different forms. *(Each form is adapted to its environment and means of spore dispersal.)*

Videodiscs

- *Side 3 5641, Zygote Formation in Fungi (m)*

Answer to Think

Each conidium can become a new organism; therefore, producing a large number of spores increases the chances that some will land in favorable conditions and germinate. Even if many spores die, the species number will still increase.

Observing Organisms Set up microscope stations with slides of budding yeast cells, and encourage students to draw what they observe. Ask them to explain what is occurring in the budding yeast cells. *(The cells are reproducing asexually. The parent cell undergoes mitosis, producing a new cell.)*

Describing Organisms Provide students with pictures or live specimens of the three common forms of lichen: crustose, foliose, and fruticose (twofold). Ask students to describe the appearance of each thallus. *(Crustose—crusty; foliose—thin, leafy; two-fold—upright)* Then have students infer the types of environments in which lichens live. *(Lichens can survive in harsh environments that are cold, hot, and/or dry.)*

■ *See* Process Skills, *Chapter 23.*

Relating Concepts Have students draw a concept map that describes the symbiotic relationships between fungi and autotrophic organisms. An example of a completed concept map is shown on p. 333B.

Guided Practice

Scan the text for examples of fungi and ask students to classify each. For example, have students name the division to which black bread mold belongs *(Zygomycota)*; mushrooms and puff-balls *(Basidiomycota)*; morels and yeasts *(Ascomycota)*; and *Penicillium* and athlete's foot fungus *(Deuteromycota)*.

Think

Conidiophores often produce thousands of conidia (SEM, ×500). What is the adaptive advantage of producing large numbers of asexual spores?

Asexual reproduction in ascomycetes involves the production of spores, each of which is called a **conidium** *(koe-NID-ee-um)*. Many conidia are formed on the ends of specialized branches called **conidiophores.**

In unicellular ascomycetes called yeasts asexual reproduction occurs by bud formation. Sexual reproduction involves the formation of a diploid zygote. The zygote results from the fusion of two ascospores. The zygote either may function as an ascus, producing eight ascospores, or may produce diploid cells by budding. If the zygote undergoes meiosis and produces ascospores, the haploid ascospores can reproduce in one of two ways. They can either produce new haploid cells by budding, or they can fuse in sexual reproduction.

Humans are interested in the approximately 600 species of yeasts because of their ability to break down carbohydrates. This ability makes yeast important to the food industry. When carbohydrates are thus broken down, they form alcohol and carbon dioxide. This process causes bread dough to rise and grapes to ferment. Domesticated yeast, usually a strain of *Saccharomyces cerevisiae*, is used in most modern brewing processes. Yeasts are also important tools in genetic research.

Biotechnology

Yeast Research

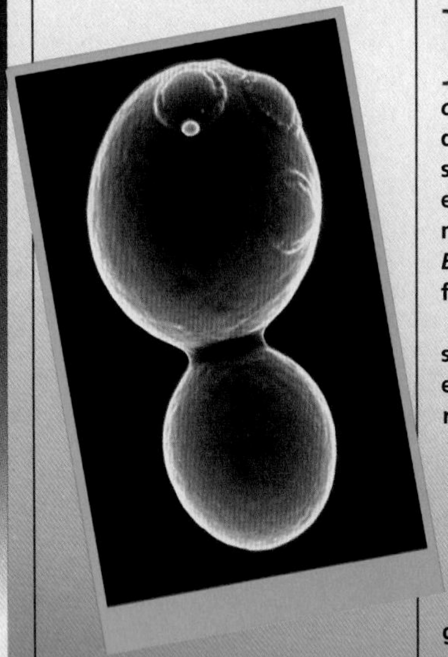

For many years scientists have accepted *Escherichia coli*, a bacterium, as the standard for exploration of gene structure and function. However, today the unicellular ascomycetes known as yeasts rival *E. coli* as the favored organisms for genetic research.

Like bacteria, yeasts are small, simple organisms that are easy to maintain in a laboratory. However, unlike bacteria, yeasts are eukaryotes. Both prokaryotes and eukaryotes have genes that are related to metabolism, replication, and protein synthesis. But prokaryotes lack many of the genes found in eukaryotes—for example, the genes related to the regulation of mitosis and to the structure of chromosomes and mitochondria.

Yeasts can live as both diploid or haploid organisms. Yeasts in their haploid form were first used by geneticists to research recessive mutations. In diploid organisms, these recessive mutations are seen only in homozygous individuals. In haploid organisms, individuals who inherit a single gene show the mutation.

Molecular biologists have already determined the base-pair sequence for about 100 of the genes that code for proteins in yeasts. Scientists have also

More Information

Yeast Two of the earliest processes of civilization are bread making and wine making. Both depend on yeast. Yeast cells produce enzymes that break down sugar into alcohol and CO_2 during fermentation. In bread, bubbles of CO_2 trapped in the dough cause it to rise. The alcohol produced evaporates during baking. In wine, yeast acts on the sugar in grapes and produces alcohol. CO_2 is allowed to escape, except in the case of sparkling wines such as champagne.

Today, yeasts are used to produce a variety of substances, such as protein dietary supplements, vitamins, beverage and industrial alcohol, and various enzymes. Yeast is sold commercially in dried and cake form. Dried yeast is made of ascospores that become active in a moist environment, whereas cake yeast consists of active yeast cells.

Deuteromycota

Deuteromycetes, sometimes called the imperfect fungi, or **Fungi Imperfecti,** are a group of about 10,000 species of fungi in which a sexual reproductive phase has not been discovered. In effect, the Division Deuteromycota *(DOO-tuh-roe-mie-KOE-tuh)* is a taxonomic "holding tank." Biologists can classify these organisms on the basis of their type of asexual reproduction. However, they will not assign deuteromycetes to another division unless they can identify a sexual reproductive phase. The group contains forms that probably have evolved from several different strains. Today it appears that most imperfect fungi have characteristics similar to those of ascomycetes. Deuteromycetes are the organisms that cause ringworm and athlete's foot.

Aspergillus and *Penicillium* are two deuteromycetes that are valuable to humans. Humans use *Aspergillus* to ferment soy beans and make soy sauce. *Penicillium* produces the antibiotic penicillin and gives flavor to Roquefort and Camembert cheeses. Some members of these genera have been reclassified into the Division Ascomycota because their life cycles have been found to contain a sexual reproductive phase.

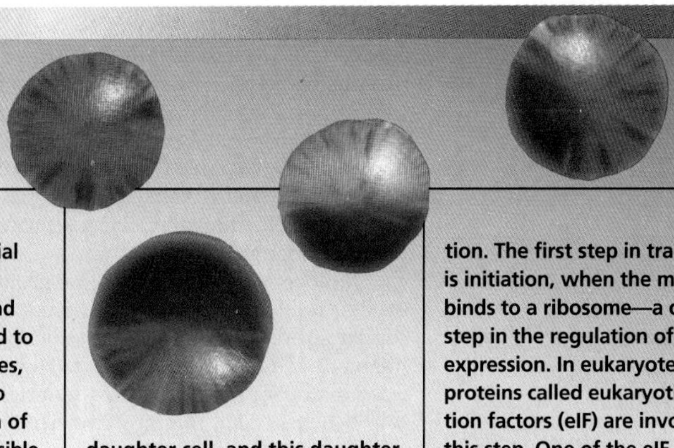

found a way to build artificial chromosomes with specific genes. Bacterial plasmids and restriction enzymes are used to assemble these chromosomes, which are then inserted into yeast cells. If the expression of one of the genes is clearly visible, it can be used as a visual marker to follow the inheritance of the artificial chromosome during sexual reproduction. One ideal marker gene inhibits the production of a red pigment. Diploid yeast cells with one artificial chromosome are pink; normal cells are red. If the artificial chromosomes fail to segregate during meiosis, two marker genes will be in the same daughter cell, and this daughter cell will produce no pigment and appear white. Such abnormalities will show up in the yeast colony as uneven coloring (p. 341). Researchers are already using artificial chromosomes to study abnormal chromosome segregation, such as what occurs in the human disorder, Down syndrome.

The newest genetic research with yeast focuses on translation. The first step in translation is initiation, when the mRNA binds to a ribosome—a critical step in the regulation of gene expression. In eukaryotes several proteins called eukaryotic initiation factors (eIF) are involved in this step. One of the eIF proteins known to function in mouse cells has also been observed at work in yeast cells. This similarity suggests that the mechanisms that control initiation may be the same in both mice and yeasts, and scientists hope to use yeasts to develop a model for eukaryotic initiation. If the model applies to higher eukaryotes, it should also be able to help scientists study genetic defects in humans.

Biotechnology

Using the Feature

Point out to students that many of the enzymes involved in basic cell metabolism are the same or very similar in prokaryotes and eukaryotes. The variation in amino acid base-pair sequences in these proteins increases as organisms more distantly related are compared. To review an important difference between prokaryotes and eukaryotes, ask students why prokaryotes lack genes related to the structure of chromosomes and mitochondria. *(Prokaryotes lack nuclei and membrane-bound organelles such as mitochondria.)*

To help students understand color markers in yeast, compare the inheritance pattern to incomplete dominance. A heterozygous yeast cell, with only one artificial chromosome and one inhibitor gene, will still make some pigment. A homozygous cell with two artificial chromosomes will have two inhibitor genes and make no pigment. A cell with only natural chromosomes will lack the inhibitor gene and will produce the normal pigment. This cell would also be homozygous.

Use Chapter 8 to review the steps involved in gene expression with students. Explain that the first step, initiation, is described in the feature. In the next stage, called elongation, peptide bonds form between amino acids. The third step, called termination, occurs when the end of the mRNA is recognized and translation stops.

Videodiscs

- *2539,* E. coli *(s)*

Section 23.1

Independent Practice

- Have students write answers to the Section Review.
- Give students unlabeled diagrams of Figures 23-3 and 23-4 (pp. 338–339) and have them label each stage.

Check Your Understanding

1. What role do saprophytes play in the ecosystem? *(They are decomposers that digest organic material into simpler molecules that are vital nutrients for many organisms.)*
2. How do fungi differ from plants? *(Fungi store food as glycogen, have cell walls of chitin, and cannot make food.)*
3. Why is the Division Deuteromycota called a taxonomic "holding tank"? *(Scientists have not yet discovered a sexual reproductive phase in these fungi, so they cannot be assigned to another division.)*

Reteaching

Have students diagram the stages in sexual and asexual reproduction for Zygomycota, Basidiomycota, and Ascomycota.
- *See* Section Reviews *worksheet, Section 23.1.*

Enrichment

Have students make spore prints of several mushroom species, examine the spores with a microscope or hand lens, and observe the differences. Have them use their data and a field guide to identify the mushrooms. Caution them to wash their hands when they finish.

Closure

Describe a variety of fungal traits and ask if each is plantlike, animallike, both, or neither. For instance, name characteristics such as cell wall *(Plantlike)*, glycogen storage *(Animallike)*, parasitism *(Both)*, and hyphae *(Neither)*.

Videodiscs

- ***591-602, Fungi: Lichens (s)***

Mycorrhizae and Lichens

Mycorrhizae and lichens represent two types of symbiotic relationships between fungi and autotrophic organisms. These relationships are of great ecological significance: they are instances of **mutualism,** a type of symbiosis in which both organisms benefit.

A **mycorrhiza** *(MIE-kuh-RIE-zuh)* is a symbiotic association between fungi and plant roots. They occur in more than 80 percent of plants. Mycorrhizae help plants absorb water and nutrients, such as phosphorus and potassium, by forming extensive networks of fungal hyphae in the soil. The fungus increases the surface area in the soil available for absorption. The digestive action of fungal enzymes provides nutrients that can be readily absorbed by the plant. The fungi absorb some of the sugars created by the plant during photosynthesis.

Fungal hyphae penetrate roots. Mycorrhizae that contain fungi that penetrate the root cortex cells are called endomycorrhizae, the most common type. The fungus is usually a zygomycete. Mycorrhizae with fungal hyphae that do not penetrate cortex cells are called ectomycorrhizae. They are less common than endomycorrhizae, and the fungus is usually a basidiomycete. Ectomycorrhizae are most common in coniferous forests, especially those with nutrient-poor soils. Mycorrhizae help plants absorb nutrients in such environments and also offer the plant some protection from harsh conditions such as cold and drought.

About 20,000 species of fungi form lichens. A **lichen** *(LIE-kun)* is a symbiotic association between a fungus, usually an ascomycete, and a green alga or cyanobacterium. Although the relationship is mutualistic, it may also be thought of as controlled parasitism. The fungal hyphae penetrate the cells of the photosynthetic partner and absorb food.

Biologists classify lichens into groups according to the nature of their thallus, or body. Crustose lichens grow as a layer on the surfaces of rocks or trees. Foliose lichens, such as the one you see in Figure 23-6, are loosely attached to the substrate and have thin, leafy thalli. Shrubby lichens with upright growths are called twofold lichens. Long, thin growths hanging from tree branches are foliose lichens.

Figure 23-6 What kind of symbiotic relationships result in this mycorrhiza (top) and this foliose lichen (bottom)?

Section Review

1. Explain how a *secondary mycelium* differs from a *primary mycelium.*
2. What is the main characteristic that distinguishes the deuteromycetes from other fungi?
3. Draw a generalized mushroom showing the three main features of the basidiocarp and the location of basidia.
4. Explain why mycorrhizae are said to be mutualistic.
5. Given the morphological evidence, what evolutionary relationship might exist between zygomycetes and ascomycetes?

Answers to Section Review

1. Primary mycelium is homokaryotic; secondary mycelium is heterokaryotic.
2. A sexual phase of their life cycles has not been observed.
3. The drawings should include the stalk, cap, and gills as well as basidia on the gills.
4. In mycorrhizae, fungi benefit from plant sugars, and plants benefit from nutrients absorbed by the fungi.
5. It is probable that zygomycetes evolved before ascomycetes, since zygomycetes are coenocytic.

23.2 Funguslike Protists

The organisms discussed in this section are all protists, not fungi. For many years scientists classified them as fungi because some phases of their life cycles looked funguslike and because they stored food as glycogen. However, many taxonomists now consider these morphological similarities to be superficial. They place these organisms into the four protist phyla shown and described in Table 23-2.

Section Objectives

- *List the four phyla of funguslike protists and their distinguishing characteristics.*
- *Describe the life cycle of a plasmodial slime mold.*
- *Explain how oomycetes differ from other funguslike protists.*

Acrasiomycota

Approximately 65 species of cellular slime molds are placed in the Phylum Acrasiomycota *(uh-KRAZZ-ee-oe-mie-KOE-tuh).* They live on land or in fresh water. The feeding stage of a cellular slime mold is a **myxameba** *(MICKS-uh-MEE-buh),* a uninucleate cell. Myxamebas live on the forest floor or on decaying plants, moving and feeding like amebas. During periods of environmental stress some myxamebas secrete a compound called acrasin. Other myxamebas in the area move against the concentration of acrasin until they clump together, forming a pseudoplasmodium. A **pseudoplasmodium** *(SOO-duh-plazz-MOE-dee-um)* is a group of cells that act together as a unit to form sporangia that produce spores.

The acrasiomycetes are simple both morphologically and physiologically. Because of this organisms such as *Dictyostelium* have been used to study physiology and morphogenesis. Since they are eukaryotic, the cellular slime molds have much more complex mechanisms of gene expression than prokaryotes do. Organisms such as *Dictyostelium* can be easily grown in the laboratory, where scientists monitor the chemical and morphological responses of the organisms under varying environmental conditions. The simplicity of the organisms is relative, however, because their complex physiology is still very far from being completely understood.

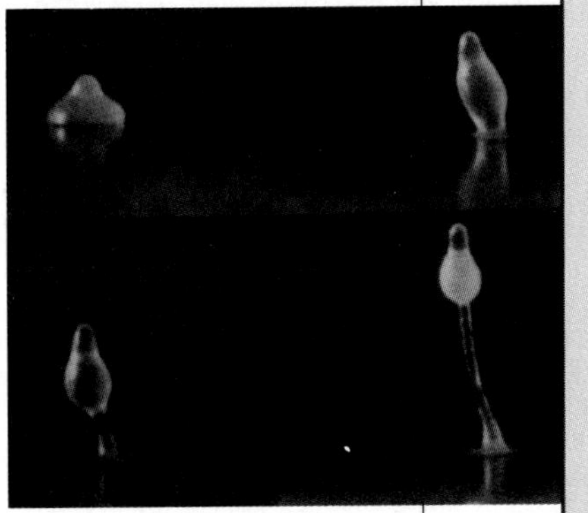

Figure 23-7 ***Dictyostelium*** **is a cellular slime mold widely used in scientific research.**

Table 23-2 Classification of Funguslike Protists

Phylum	Body	Reproduction	Habitat
Acrasiomycota (65 species)	Uninucleate myxameba	Sporangia on stalks	Mostly terrestrial
Myxomycota (450 species)	Multinucleate plasmodium	Sporangia on stalks	Mostly terrestrial
Chytridiomycota (750 species)	Motile cells	Gametes and zoospores	Mostly aquatic
Oomycota (475 species)	Coenocytic hyphae	Gametes and zoospores	Aquatic and terrestrial

Lesson Plan

Section Focus

This section describes four phyla of protists that have superficial similarities to fungi, such as glycogen production and some life-cycle phases. Students will learn some distinguishing characteristics of the protists in each of the phyla.

Section Themes

In its discussion of the structures and classification of funguslike protists, this section emphasizes the theme of **Scale and Structure** by contrasting the uninucleate and multinucleate types.

Motivating Activity

Order a Myxomycota slime mold culture from a biological supply company. Have students use a dissecting microscope or hand lens to observe the plasmodium of the slime mold. Encourage students to compare the slime mold's cytoplasmic streaming with that of an ameba. *(They are similar.)* Ask how the slime mold differs from an ameba. *(The slime mold is multinucleate; an ameba is uninucleate.)*

Teaching Strategies

Drawing Conclusions Have students consider why the four phyla of protists discussed in this section are included in a chapter on fungi. Ask them to name characteristics of these protists that are similar to those of fungi. *(All are heterotrophic and store food as glycogen. Some phases of their life cycles look funguslike.)* Point out that these protists are covered in this chapter since they are similar to fungi and were classified as such for many years.

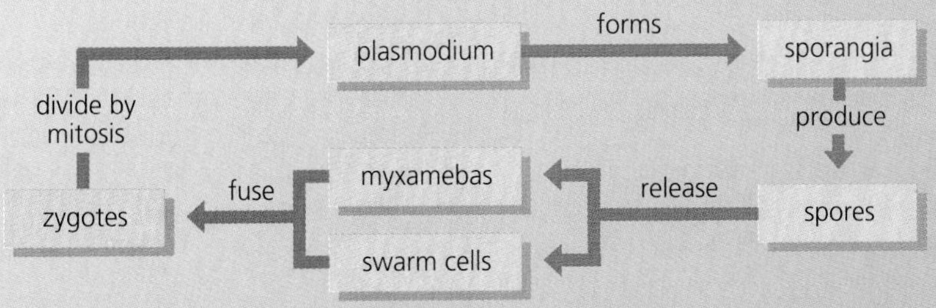

Graphic Organizer Use this cyclic diagram in Guided Practice on p. 344.

Guided Practice
Guide students in diagramming the life cycle of a plasmodial slime mold. Use the diagram found on p. 343 as a model. If possible, provide students with photos as models for illustrating their diagrams.

Independent Practice
- Have students write answers to the Section Review.
- Have each student make a worksheet listing the four protist phyla on the left and listing characteristics of various protists randomly on the right. Have students trade worksheets and match each phylum with the correct characteristics.

Check Your Understanding
1. Why are funguslike protists not true fungi? *(They do not share enough physiological and cellular characteristics with fungi.)*
2. How do the funguslike members of Acrasiomycota and Myxomycota react to environmental stress? *(They produce spores by forming sporangia on stalks.)*
3. What is a myxameba? *(A uninucleate cell that is the feeding stage of a slime mold)*

Reteaching
Give students common names for the organisms discussed in this section and have them name the kingdom, phylum, and habitat of each.
- *See* Section Reviews *worksheet, Section 23.2.*

Enrichment
Have students research the Irish potato famine of the mid-1800s. Ask them why the blight lasted so long and how the funguslike protist was finally isolated.

Closure
Have students compare the funguslike protists in this section with the protozoa described in Chapter 21. Ask them to point out similarities in nutrition and in types of locomotion.

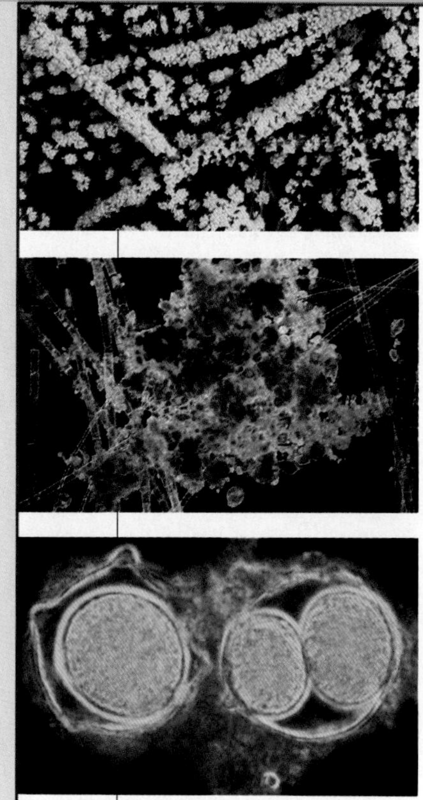

Figure 23-8 A plasmodial slime mold (top), a chytrid (center), and an oomycete (bottom) are examples of funguslike protists.

Myxomycota
Taxonomists place the plasmodial slime molds in the Phylum Myxomycota *(MICKS-uh-mie-KOE-tuh)*, which contains over 450 species. The feeding stage is called a **plasmodium**—multinucleate cytoplasm surrounded by a membrane that moves as a mass, feeding on organic matter.

During periods of stress the plasmodium becomes stationary and produces sporangia on stalks. The sporangia produce spores. Spores may stay dormant for several years; under proper conditions they release either myxamebas or flagellated swarm cells. These fuse, and the nucleus of the resulting zygote divides repeatedly by mitosis; but the cells do not undergo cytokinesis. The result is the multinucleate cytoplasm of the plasmodium.

Chytridiomycota
Biologists place approximately 750 protist species in the Phylum Chytridiomycota *(kih-TRID-ee-oe-mie-KOE-tuh)*. The chytrids are primarily aquatic protists characterized by gametes and zoospores with a single, posterior flagellum. Most chytrids are unicellular. Some chytrids are coenocytic and have hyphae that anchor the organism. Many chytrids are parasites on algae, plants, and insects, while others are saprophytes.

Oomycota
The Phylum Oomycota *(OE-uh-mie-KOE-tuh)* contains over 475 aquatic and terrestrial species, including water molds, white rusts, and downy mildews. Oomycetes are parasitic or saprophytic. One oomycete, *Phytophthora infestans,* the late blight fungus, causes the potato rot that led to the devastating Irish potato famine of 1845–1847.

Oomycetes are coenocytic with branched hyphae. Their cell walls are composed of cellulose, not chitin. Oomycetes form male and female gametangia. The female gametangium, or oogonium, forms eggs; the male gametangium, the antheridium, forms sperm. A zygote resulting from the fusion of egg and sperm develops into a thick-walled, diploid **oospore** *(OE-uh-SPOR)*. Oospores are released into water or moist areas and germinate into coenocytic hyphae. In asexual reproduction oomycetes produce flagellated zoospores, which then produce new hyphae.

Section Review
1. How does a *plasmodium* differ from a *pseudoplasmodium?*
2. Explain the role of sporangia in the myxomycete life cycle.
3. Which phylum contains mostly aquatic organisms?
4. How do oogonia and antheridia function in oomycetes?
5. Why are acrasiomycetes called cellular slime molds?

Answers to Section Review
1. A plasmodium is multinucleate cytoplasm; a pseudoplasmodium is made up of individual uninucleate cells.
2. Sporangia, produced during periods of environmental stress, produce spores that later release either myxamebas or swarm cells.
3. Chytridiomycota
4. Oogonia form eggs and antheridia form sperm, which fuse to form oospores that germinate into hyphae.
5. Because their pseudoplasmodia are made up of coordinated single cells rather than multinucleate cytoplasm

Laboratory

Fungal Morphology

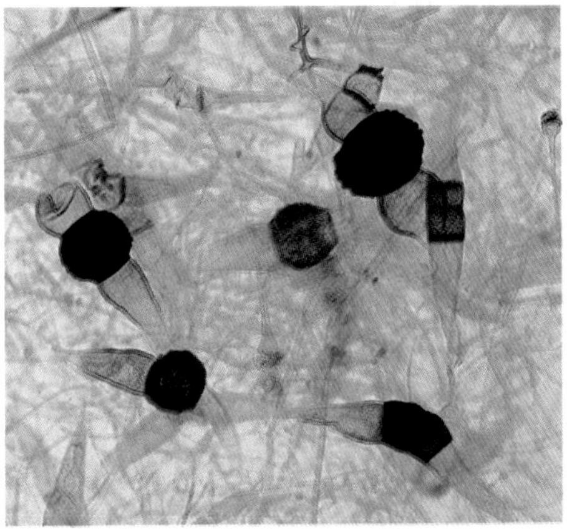

Objective
To study the vegetative and reproductive morphology of *Rhizopus stolonifer,* the common black bread mold

Process Skills
Observing, inferring

Materials
Petri dish containing a single-strain culture of *Rhizopus stolonifer,* petri dish containing plus and minus strains of *Rhizopus stolonifer,* dissecting microscope, probe, unlined paper

Inquiry
1 Remove the cover from a petri dish containing a single-strain culture of *Rhizopus stolonifer*. Do you recognize a familiar odor? What does it smell like?
2 Place the culture dish under a dissecting microscope and observe the mycelium. Note the threadlike stolons that extend horizontally along the surface of the agar.
3 Use a probe to tease apart the hyphae. Note the rhizoids that grow down into the agar. What is the function of the rhizoids?
4 Replace the cover on the petri dish. Carefully turn the petri dish upside down and put the dish back under the dissecting microscope. Focus through the agar to get a better view of the rhizoids.
5 Turn the petri dish right side up. Remove the cover and replace the petri dish under the dissecting microscope. Note the hyphae that extend from the mycelium. These are the sporangiophores. What is their function?
6 Observe the round objects at the ends of the sporangiophores. These are the sporangia. The sporangia produce asexual, haploid spores. Can you think of an adaptive advantage to spores that are produced above the mycelium?
7 Make a drawing of what you see under the dissecting microscope. Label a stolon, rhizoid, sporangiophore, and sporangia.
8 Place a petri dish containing plus and minus strains of *Rhizopus stolonifer* under the dissecting microscope. To what do the plus and minus designations refer?
9 To look for evidence of mating between the two different mating strains, search for zygospores that have formed where the two strains have united. Describe the zygospores. Make a drawing of the zygospores, and show as much detail as you can.
10 Examine your culture carefully. Can you see the stages leading up to the formation of zygospores? Based on your observations, make a drawing that models the mating between the two different strains.

Conclusions
1 Did you observe differences between the plus and minus strains of the mold?
2 Are the zygospores haploid or diploid? Explain your answer.

Further Inquiry
Design an experiment to determine the optimum conditions for growth of *Rhizopus.*

Laboratory

(*For an overview of* Rhizopus stolonifer *and preparatory information related to the laboratory, see p. 333B.*)

Inquiry
1. Most students will recognize the moldy smell. Students may describe it as a sour, spoiled, or rotten smell.
3. Rhizoids anchor the fungus to the agar. They also produce digestive enzymes and absorb nutrients.
5. The sporangiophores produce sporangia at their tips, which produce spores.
6. Spores above the mycelium can be caught and dispersed more easily by the wind.
8. The plus and minus serve to differentiate between the two mating strains of hyphae.
10. Students may see two hyphae joining and an immature zygospore forming between them, such as is shown in the photograph on the page.

Conclusions
1. No; there is no visible difference between the plus and minus strains.
2. The zygospores are diploid because each was formed from two haploid gametes, one from each of the two *Rhizopus* strains.

Further Inquiry
Have students test variables such as moisture, light, and temperature. Make sure they set up controls as a basis for comparison.

Vocabulary

1. *Myco-* means "fungus" and *-rhizo* means "root," so the word *mycorrhizae* appropriately describes the mutualistic relationship between fungi and plant roots.
2. *Spor-* means "seed," *-angio* means "vessel," and *-phore* means "bearer" or "producer." Since a sporangiophore bears sporangia, or "seed vessels," this name is appropriate, although spores, not seeds, are borne.
3. *Coeno-* means "in common" and *-cyte* means "hollow." No septa are present in a coenocytic hypha, so in a sense all the nuclei in the hypha share the hollow space.
4. *Hypha* means "web." Although intertwined hyphae form a weblike mycelium, this word does not seem appropriate for the single hypha.
5. *Conidio-* comes from the Greek roots meaning "dust" or "ashes" *(konis)* and "small one" *(idium)*. The suffix *-phore* means "bearer." Conidiophores bear asexual spores, called conidia, resembling fine dust particles.

Review

1. c **6.** d
2. a **7.** d
3. b **8.** a
4. a **9.** c
5. c **10.** d

11. In yeasts and other kinds of ascomycetes, diploid cells produce four haploid daughter cells by meiosis.
12. They are 500 million years old.
13. In coenocytic hypha the nuclei do not form individual cells and do not act in a coordinated manner as they do in pseudoplasmodia.

Chapter 23 Review

Vocabulary

ascocarp (339)
ascogonium (339)
ascospore (339)
ascus (339)
basidiocarp (338)
basidiospore (338)
basidium (338)
cap (338)
chitin (336)
coenocytic (336)
conidiophore (340)
conidium (340)
Fungi Imperfecti (341)
gill (338)
heterokaryotic (336)
homokaryotic (336)
hypha (336)
lichen (342)
mutualism (342)
mycelium (336)
mycorrhiza (342)
myxameba (343)
oospore (344)
plasmodium (344)
primary mycelium (338)
pseudoplasmodium (343)
rhizoid (337)
secondary mycelium (338)
septum (336)
sporangiophore (337)
stalk (338)
stolon (337)

Look up the meaning of the word roots of the following terms. Tell whether the words are appropriate, and explain why.

1. mycorrhizae *(myco-, -rhizo)*
2. sporangiophore *(spor-, -angio, -phore)*
3. coenocyte *(coeno-, -cyte)*
4. hypha
5. conidiophore *(conidio-, -phore)*

Review

1. Hyphae of secondary mycelium are (a) coenocytic (b) homokaryotic (c) heterokaryotic (d) plasmodial.
2. The common edible mushroom is classified in the Division (a) Basidiomycota (b) Ascomycota (c) Oomycota (d) Zygomycota.
3. The female gametangium in oomycetes is called an (a) ascogonium (b) oogonium (c) antheridium (d) oospore.
4. Fungi that feed on decaying organic matter are referred to as (a) saprophytic (b) parasitic (c) mutualistic (d) symbiotic.
5. *Rhizopus* grows most commonly on (a) soil (b) fruit (c) bread (d) decaying logs.
6. The cross walls that separate cells in hyphae are known as (a) rhizoids (b) gills (c) asci (d) septa.
7. Lichens are symbiotic associations of fungi and (a) roots (b) roundworms (c) water molds (d) algae.
8. The gills of a mushroom contain (a) basidia (b) conidiophores (c) basidiocarps (d) ascocarps.
9. The body of a lichen is referred to as (a) a stipe (b) a hypha (c) a thallus (d) an ascus.
10. Myxameba clump together and form (a) plasmodia (b) mycorrhizae (c) hyphae (d) pseudoplasmodia.
11. How is the yeast life cycle similar to that of other ascomycetes?
12. How old are the first fossils distinctly identified as fungi?
13. How does a coenocytic hypha differ from a pseudoplasmodium?
14. What aspect of the yeast life cycle makes yeasts useful in genetic research?
15. Explain how fungi contribute to nutrient cycling in the environment.
16. Describe mutualism, and give an example of such a relationship involving fungi.
17. What are rust and smuts?
18. Why are deuteromycetes more difficult to classify than other fungi?
19. Where might you look to locate a plasmodial slime mold?
20. Describe the process of conjugation in a zygomycete.

14. Yeasts reproduce rapidly and can survive as either diploid or haploid individuals. This makes them useful in studying dominant and recessive mutations as well as other features of the cell cycle.
15. Saprophytic fungi digest organic materials and return nutrient molecules to the ecosystem to be used by other organisms.
16. Mutualism is a type of symbiotic relationship in which both parties benefit. Mycorrhizae: a mutualistic relationship between a fungus and plant roots; lichen: a mutualistic relationship between a fungus and an alga.
17. Parasitic basidiomycetes that attack plants.

Critical Thinking

1. The cell walls of fungi and the exoskeletons of insects and crustaceans contain chitin. Tell whether this is of phylogenetic significance, and explain why.
2. Many fungi are fatally poisonous to mammals. What is the adaptive advantage of this to the fungi? What is the disadvantage?
3. Long before antibiotics were discovered, it was the practice to place moldy bread on wounds. Explain why this might have helped the wounds to heal.
4. Fungi such as *Penicillium* engage in a kind of "chemical warfare" against other microorganisms by producing chemicals that diffuse outward and kill nearby organisms. Suggest an adaptive advantage of this characteristic of these fungi.
5. Most fungi grow best at a temperature of around 15° to 21° C. *Aspergillus fumagatus,* however, can grow well at 37° C. Knowing this, where would you expect *A. fumagatus* to grow?
6. *Drosophila,* the common fruit fly, eats juices from ripe fruit and yeast. How might the fruit fly help speed the natural decay of fruit?

7. When transplanting a wild plant to garden soil it is very important to include some of the soil from the original habitat. Give a possible explanation, based on the information from this chapter.
8. Examine the photo above of the fruiting bodies of the slime mold *Leocarpus fragilis.* How does the appearance of *Leocarpus fragilis* make it difficult to classify this organism?

Extension

1. Read the article by Raymond Sokolov entitled "The Universal Mushroom" in *Natural History,* December 1990, pp. 78–83. Prepare an oral report in which you discuss how mushrooms are used as food throughout the world. What characteristics of the mushroom add to its accessibility and diversity?
2. Use the library to research ways in which medical science has been influenced by fungi. Investigate the discovery of penicillin and other drugs derived from fungi. Investigate the role played by fungi in various diseases.
3. Obtain basidiospores of edible mushrooms and collaborate with the other members of the class in growing the mushrooms under various conditions of light and temperature. If time permits, experiment with various food sources. Keep records of your results and report your findings to the class.
4. Prepare a yeast culture by adding yeast to a mixture of nine parts of water to one part of molasses. Allow the culture to ferment and examine it under a microscope. Make a drawing of several yeast cells and identify any visible cell parts. Look for instances of budding and add them to your drawing.
5. Research ways in which lichens are valuable to other life forms, including human beings. In what way do lichens help to cultivate new soil? How do they contribute nitrogen to the atmosphere?

18. They cannot be classified according to their sexual forms as other fungi are.
19. It would most likely be found on damp land where organic matter is decaying.
20. Two different strains of hyphae make contact and fuse, producing a gametangium. Nuclei from the two gametangia fuse and form a zygote. The zygote develops a thick outer coating and becomes a zygospore that germinates when conditions are favorable.

Critical Thinking

1. It is an example of convergent evolution.
2. The advantage is that they are not eaten. The disadvantage is that mammals do not carry them and their spores to a new area.
3. Moldy bread sometimes contains *Penicillium,* which produces the antibiotic penicillin.
4. It helps these fungi compete for food, and they can have more space for reproduction and growth.
5. In humans as a pathogen; it is the cause of aspergillosis, a sometimes fatal lung infection.
6. The yeasts stick to its body; as it flies from fruit to fruit, it spreads the yeasts, which ferment the sugars in the fruit.
7. The soil serves as a source of fungi needed to form mycorrhizae.
8. The fruiting bodies resemble fungal fruiting bodies rather than other protist forms.

Extension

1. Encourage students to consider the relationships mushrooms establish with other organisms and the reproductive structures of mushrooms.
2. Some drugs that students might research include streptomycin, Chloromycetin, Terramycin, and Aureomycin. Some fungal diseases that students can find out about include cryptococcosis, thrush, histoplasmosis, and dermatomycosis.
3. Some possible food sources to experiment with include soil, rotting wood, and oats. Encourage students to make generalizations about the growing conditions the fungus needs.
4. Use water at a temperature of 40.5°C to 46°C. Students may observe that many daughter cells begin budding before separating from parent cells.
5. Encourage students to use a variety of library resources in their research.

Discussion

Guide the discussion by posing the following questions.

1. HIV is a retrovirus. How has this fact proved to be significant in the fight against HIV infection? *(Understanding the genetic composition and function of the RNA in HIV is guiding researchers in finding safe, effective drugs and vaccines. The RNA in HIV codes reverse transcriptase, an enzyme that synthesizes DNA from RNA. Some drug therapies inhibit this unique biological pathway.)*

2. Why would the discovery of a safe, effective vaccine against AIDS be more helpful than drug therapy to combat the disease? *(Vaccine would prevent harmful infection rather than treat it.)*

3. Why is the work of health educators and science writers important in the fight against AIDS? *(By disseminating information about AIDS, they help dispel unwarranted fears about the disease and explain how to curb its spread.)*

4. How has public education about AIDS affected your personal behavior and attitude about dating? *(Encourage students to offer examples of how their behaviors and attitudes have changed since AIDS awareness.)*

5. Explain why you think that a person infected with HIV should or should not be permitted to visit the United States from another country. *(Encourage students to offer reasons for their opinions and respect those of their classmates.)*

6. What are some advantages and disadvantages of regular tests for HIV for health workers? *(Early detection of HIV infection may help the person fight the infection. However, many health workers oppose mandatory tests for various reasons, including invasion of privacy and possible career loss.)*

Intra-Science

How the Sciences Work Together

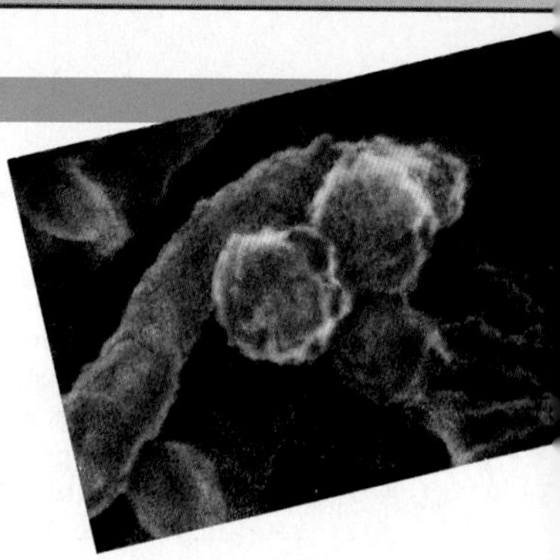

The Question in Biology: *Can We Conquer AIDS?*

Since the first medical account of AIDS in the early 1980s, health officials estimate that the human immunodeficiency virus (HIV) has infected about 8 to 10 million people worldwide. Now, a decade later, health officials, such as Jonathan Mann, founder of the Global Program on AIDS at the World Health Organization, still warn that the AIDS pandemic could get worse before it improves. "Moreover, the decade to come seems inescapably worse. The combination of new HIV infections (estimated at 10 million to 25 million) and the natural history of individuals already infected is expected to result in at least six million new cases of clinical AIDS in adults during the 1990s." Are we doing enough to fight AIDS?

Today, many prospects for ending the spread of AIDS have been explored, including public education about transmission and prevention of HIV infections, screening blood specifically for HIV, early treatment of HIV-infected individuals, and medical research to develop safe and effective drug therapy and vaccines.

Virologists, immunologists, and medical researchers have been studying the life cycle and infection of HIV in humans and other mammals. Safe drug therapy often attacks a pathogen without harming a host. In their search for an effective way to fight HIV, researchers are trying to take advantage of a unique aspect of the HIV life cycle.

As a retrovirus HIV contains RNA that codes an enzyme known as reverse transcriptase. This enzyme catalyzes a process that does not occur in healthy human cells—the transcription of DNA from RNA, producing the transcript DNA. Once the transcript DNA has become a part of the host DNA, a period of dormancy may occur before infected cells produce new HIV, spreading infection to other cells of the body. Since this process occurs only in infected human cells, a drug that specifically inhibits reverse transcription can be an effective drug therapy against HIV infection.

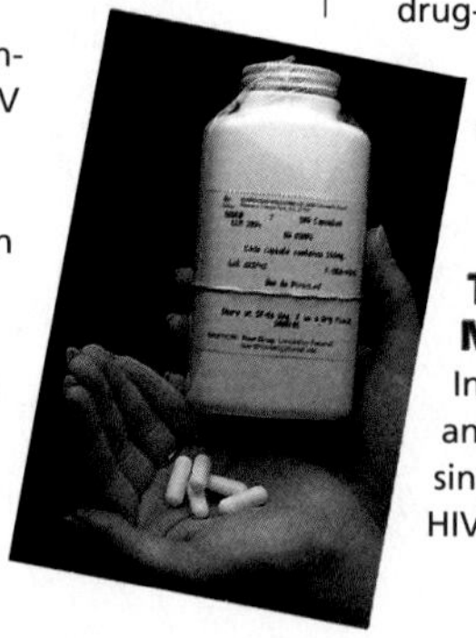

The Connection to Pharmacology

Pharmacologists and biochemists have found a number of drugs that suppress the replication of the HIV virus by inhibiting the action of reverse transcriptase. In 1985 azidothymidine (AZT) became the first such drug approved for clinical testing on AIDS patients. Two years after the first clinical use the Food and Drug Administration approved AZT as a prescription drug to fight HIV infection. AZT has prolonged the survival and has improved the quality of life of patients with advanced HIV infection. Although AZT and several similar drugs can inhibit the spread of HIV within the body, none of the drugs can cure AIDS, and none acts without toxicity or side effects.

As researchers search for new drugs and methods to fight AIDS, scientists worry that today's antiviral drugs may become ineffective, since HIV mutates easily and frequently. The emergence of a drug-resistant strain of HIV seems possible. Vaccine research seems like a better option to combat a mutating virus.

- ***How do AZT and related drugs inhibit the spread of the HIV virus?***

The Connection to Medical Science

In addition to drug therapy, development of an HIV vaccine has received much attention since 1984 when researchers confirmed that HIV causes AIDS. Developing a safe vaccine

Connections to Other Disciplines

History The difficulties facing scientists searching for an HIV vaccine may at times make the task seem impossible. At one time Edward Jenner may have felt the same way, yet he eventually developed a smallpox vaccine. Ask students to find out what problems Jenner encountered and compare them with the ones faced by researchers today.

Social Studies Public education is a vital part of AIDS prevention. Ask students to report on what is being done in their school system and community to educate people about preventing HIV infection.

to prevent AIDS, however, is difficult for several major reasons.

During the period of dormancy in humans, HIV "hides" its genetic material in the genetic material of host T-cells, the very cells that protect the body against HIV infection. An ideal vaccine would prevent HIV from entering and destroying the T-cell. If HIV kills too many T-cells, the body's immune system loses its ability to fight off HIV and other disease-causing agents.

Since HIV mutates easily and frequently, the genetic variation among strains of HIV is extensive. An HIV vaccine for humans will need to stimulate an immune response to any and all genetic variations of HIV.

Efforts to find an effective and safe vaccine are complicated also because testing on humans is risky. In addition, the safety of medical researchers who develop a vaccine must be maintained. Furthermore, since a vaccine may contain an inactivated form of HIV or fragments of the virus, an acceptable vaccine must not induce AIDS or other harm to a recipient. The HIV vaccine must protect absolutely against infection. No vaccine in history has ever reached that degree of protection before. Although there are many manufacturers working to develop an HIV vaccine, the number of vaccine manufacturers continues to decline because vaccine development is extremely difficult, expensive, and risky. Though an HIV vaccine will have tremendous medical and sociological benefits, manufacturers also know that lawsuits could result from vaccine-related illnesses or deaths.

- *How might state or federal laws stimulate manufacture of HIV vaccines?*

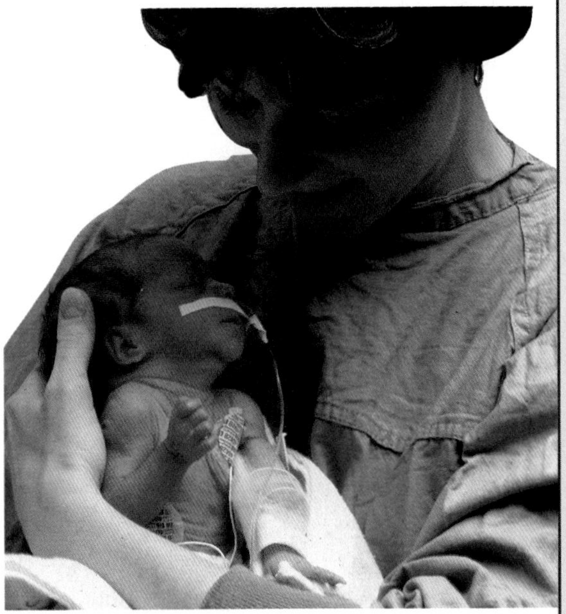

The Connection to Other Sciences

Computer scientists use computers to identify genetic similarities among numerous variations of HIV. Identifying genetic similarities among the different variations of HIV helps identify ways that drugs and vaccines can fight the viruses universally. Computers can also be used to help identify the part of the HIV viral coat that stimulates the strongest immune response: a segment called the V3 loop. Antibodies against the V3 loop have protected chimpanzees against HIV infection.

- *What role do computer scientists play in the fight against AIDS?*

The Connection to Careers

The search for a cure and prevention for AIDS involves people in a variety of careers. Virologists study the structure and life processes of viruses, including viral diseases. Physicians, nurses, and other medical support staff assist in clinical trials of drugs and vaccines. Epidemiologists track the spread of the disease in human populations. For more information on related careers in the biological sciences, turn to page 842.

7. Explain why a classmate might not want you to know that he or she is HIV-infected. *(Many people still harbor irrational fears about AIDS. Encourage students to discuss any lingering fears that they themselves have about AIDS. Ask them to speculate about how their lives would change if they became HIV-infected.)*

8. Explain why you would or would not want to know that a classmate is HIV-infected. *(Student responses may reflect a wide range of emotions or rationales. Encourage students to explain their opinions fully and openly.)*

9. Considerable amounts of state and federal money have gone into AIDS research. Explain why you think that this allocation should be increased or decreased. *(Encourage students to give a rationale for their individual opinions.)*

Answers to

Pharmacology AZT and related drugs suppress the replication of the HIV virus by interfering with the action of the enzyme reverse transcriptase.

Medical Science Student answers will vary. Tell students that the State of California recently passed legislation to encourage development of HIV vaccines. The California law protects the manufacturer of FDA-approved vaccines that are distributed in California from legal damages resulting from use of approved vaccines. The law also creates a compensation fund for recipients harmed by the vaccine.

Other Sciences By analyzing the genetics of HIV, computer scientists help in the search for drugs effective against all strains of HIV.

Enrichment

Because of a potential shortage of volunteers for clinical tests in the United States, some researchers suggest doing these tests in areas of the world where HIV infection is already highly prevalent. Ask students to research the standards of living and rates of HIV infection in the United States, Nigeria, France, and Japan. Have students identify some of the problems medical and health officials may need to consider and overcome as they develop drugs or vaccines to fight the infection.

Unit 6 Plants

Chapters

Unit Overview

Unit 6 gives students an understanding of the structure and function of plants. Chapter 24 describes the importance of plants to humans. People rely on plants for food; medicines; pleasant sights, scents, and tastes; and oxygen to breathe. Chapter 25 explains the classification of plants and their evolutionary adaptations to life on land. Chapter 26 introduces plant tissue systems and how they are organized for specialized functions. In Chapter 27 students will learn about sexual and asexual reproduction in plants. In Chapter 28 students are exposed to the ways in which a plant responds to hormones inside it and environmental conditions outside.

Issues in Biology

Rain forests in Brazil and other tropical countries are being cut down at the rate of about 310 square kilometers every day. In the United States, trees are being cut down in the remaining temperate rain forest in southeast Alaska (the Tongass National Forest). There, as much as 50 percent of the most productive forest land has been logged since 1950, and in the United States as a whole about 25,000 hectares of ancient forests are cut down each year, mostly for lumber exported to Japan. Ask students whether it is right for Americans to urge other countries to slow the destruction of their rain forests while we continue to cut down our own.

Research in Progress

Weeds not only create problems for home gardeners but also account for one-third of all crop losses in the world. Chemical herbicides are effective in weed control, but can be harmful to animal and human populations.

To alleviate these problems, many scientists including researchers at Montana State University are exploring biological alternatives that harness the weed-killing powers of living organisms such as insects and microorganisms. Phytotoxins—plant-killing compounds produced by microbes—are under particular scientific scrutiny because they eliminate the need to release the organisms themselves. Researchers' study of phytotoxins is also uncovering new information about plant physiology and may even lead to new remedies for human diseases.

Interdisciplinary Activity

Government The U.S. Department of Agriculture's National Seed Storage Laboratory (NSSL) is located in Fort Collins, on the campus of Colorado State University. It is the central storage facility for the USDA's National Plant Germplasm System. The billions of seeds stored there are beyond price. The Fort Collins collection is the most diverse in the Western world, containing over 250,000 samples. Have some students write letters to the USDA, requesting information about the seed collection, why seeds need to be saved, and how the agency is funded. Ask other students to focus on how the USDA decides what seeds should be saved and what procedures are used. For example, some seeds are stored in liquid nitrogen tanks. Students can find the address of governmental agencies in a library.

Resources

Chapter	Print: For the Teacher	Print: For the Student	Audiovisual/Software
24	■ Charles B. Heiser, Jr., *Of Plants and People,* University of Oklahoma Press, 1985.	■ Darna L. Dufour, "Use of Tropical Rainforests by Native Amazonians," *BioScience,* October 1990, 652–658. ■ Carolyn Strange, "Cereal Progress via Biotechnology," *BioScience,* January 1990, 5–14.	■ *All Things Plant.* Film, 18 min. Discussion guide. Barr, 1986. ■ *Plants in Peril.* Video, 26 min. Films for the Humanities. Distributed by Carolina Biological.
25	■ V. V. Sivarajan and N. K. B. Robson, *Introduction to the Principles of Plant Taxonomy,* 2nd ed., Cambridge University Press, 1991. ■ Jerome Wexler, *From Spore to Spore: Ferns and How They Grow,* Van Nostrand Reinhold, 1984.	■ Julie Ann Miller, "Plant Phylogeny Aided by Ants and Hummingbirds," *BioScience,* November 1990, 714. ■ Christopher Wills, "Turning Over an Old Leaf," *Discover,* January 1991, 78.	■ *The Frozen World.* Film or video, 55 min. Time-Life, 1984. ■ *The Life of Plants: Survival Against the Odds.* Video, 28 min. Films for the Humanities & Sciences, 1989.
26	■ Millicent E. Selsam, *Tree Flowers,* Morrow, 1984. ■ Malcom B. Wilkens, *Advanced Plant Physiology,* Pitman, 1984.	■ Ricki Rusting, "A Clock in the Trees," *Scientific American,* August 1990, 30.	■ *The Primary Plant Body.* Still-frame video, filmstrip, or transparencies with cassette, 36 min. Teacher's guide. Biology Media, 1987. ■ *The Secondary Plant Body.* Still-frame video, filmstrip, or transparencies with cassette, 20 min. Teacher's guide. Biology Media, 1987.
27	■ Anne Ophelia Dowden, *From Flower to Fruit,* Crowell, 1984. ■ Taylor A. Steeves and Ian M. Sussex, *Patterns in Plant Development,* 2nd ed., Cambridge University Press, 1989.	■ Yvonne Baskin, "A Blue, Blue Rose," *Discover,* November 1990, 28. ■ Ellen Ruppel Shell, "Seeds in the Bank Could Stave Off Disaster on the Farm," *Smithsonian,* January 1990, 94–105.	■ *Plant Life Cycles: Alternation of Generations in Plants.* Video filmstrip or transparencies with cassette, 19 min. Biology Media. ■ *Sexual Encounters of the Floral Kind.* Video, 60 min. Oxford Scientific Films. Distributed by Carolina Biological.
28	■ Peter H. Raven et al., *Biology of Plants,* 4th ed., Worth, 1986.	■ Jeffrey Brune, "A Gardener's Touch," *Discover,* January 1991, 77. ■ R. Cowen, "Plant's Genetic 'Master Switch' Subverted," *Science News,* August 11, 1990, 86.	■ *Growth of Flowers,* 2nd ed. Film or video, 11 min. Teacher's guide. Coronet, 1984. ■ *How Plants Grow: The Inside Story.* Apple, 128K. IBM, 128K. Disk. Scholastic, 1986. ■ *Plant Dynamics.* Video, 57 min. Distributed by Carolina Biological.

Introducing the Unit

In Unit 5 students studied microorganisms in the Kingdom Protista. In Unit 6 students will study macroorganisms in the Kingdom Plantae. To lead students from the study of protists to plants, ask the following questions.

1. Given what you know about algae, how do you think that land plants evolved? *(It is possible that plants evolved from green algae. There is evidence to link green algae with plants—chlorophyll, food stored as starch, cellulose cell walls.)*

2. How do plants support life on earth? *(Plants absorb inorganic substances from the soil and make food, serving as the foundation of many food chains. Plants also provide oxygen to breathe. People use plants to obtain paper and paper products, wood for building homes and other structures, medicines, natural waxes, oils and scent, color, and beauty.)*

3. What patterns of change do you notice in plants? *(The most obvious changes are seasonal and life cycle changes: flowers blooming in spring and summer, growth and formation of fruits, and leaves changing color and falling in autumn.)*

4. What questions can you ask about the structure and function of plants? *(Sample questions: Why do some plants have flowers while others don't? Why do some plants live all year round and others die at the end of a season? Why do trees have so many leaves? What's inside a pine cone?)*

Unit 6 *Plants*

"Plants are the strong scaffoldings on which the original symbiosis of photosynthesis has been raised from ooze and stretched as a canopy across rock bottom."

David Rains Wallace

Eating an insect may strike you as an unusually active thing for a plant to do, but plants actually interact in many dynamic ways with the environment. Consider, for example, the crucial role that plants play in transforming sunlight into usable forms of energy upon which almost all living things depend. What other kinds of interactions are suggested by the illustrations on these pages?

Maple, *Acer* sp., samara

Tuliptree, *Liriodendron tulipifera*

Using the Opening Quotation

Ask volunteers to explain what they think that the quotation means. *(Sample answer: Plants are organisms that brought food and oxygen production out of water onto dry land. Plants are the foundation of life, covering the earth with green leaves like a protective canopy.)* Ask students what the earth would be like today if plants had never adapted to life on land. *(Life as we know it could not exist. Land animals and people would probably not have evolved, since the food chain would exist only in oceans. The atmosphere would contain less oxygen and there would be less soil, since plants help form and maintain soil.)*

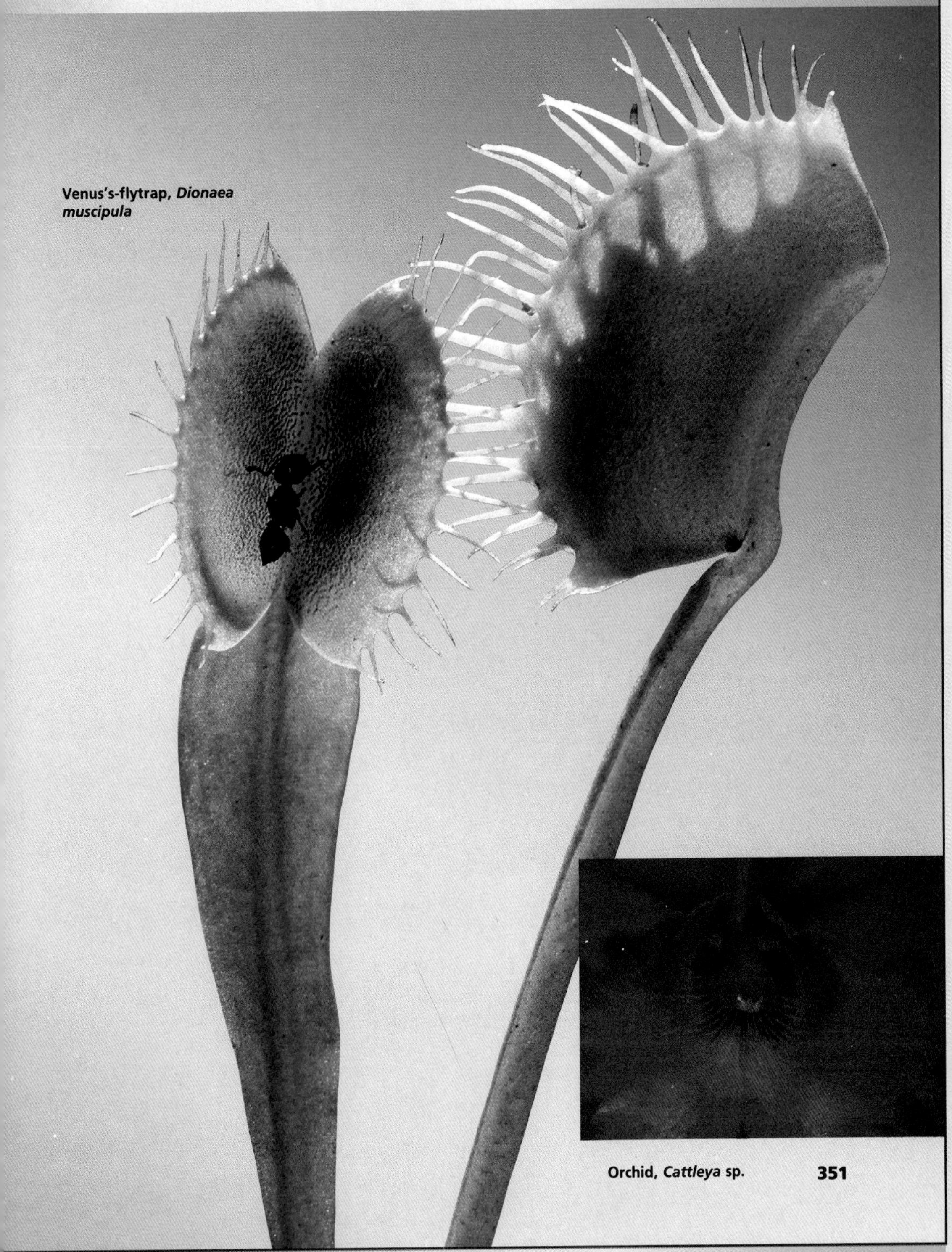

Venus's-flytrap, *Dionaea muscipula*

Orchid, *Cattleya* sp.

351

Unit Themes

Systems and Interactions Plants interact with people and the environment (Chapter 24). Plant tissues work together as a whole (Chapter 26), and interactions with internal and external stimuli produce changes in plants (Chapter 28).

Evolution Plants evolved both by natural selection and through artificial selection by humans (Chapter 24). Plant adaptations to life on land provide a means of classifying them (Chapter 25). Adaptations for survival on land include development of specialized structures such as roots, stems, and leaves (Chapter 27). Plants also evolved adaptations in response to seasonal changes, climates, and varying environmental conditions (Chapter 28).

Scale and Structure The gametophytes and sporophytes of bryophytes are small because they lack vascular systems (Chapter 25). The cellular structure of plant tissues is clearly related to their function (Chapters 26, 27).

Patterns of Change All plant life cycles show alternation of generations (Chapter 25). Plants respond to external and internal stimuli in predictable ways (Chapter 28).

Understanding the Visuals

Ask students to observe each plant structure, then make a hypothesis about its function. *(Sample answers: The "wings" of the maple structure suggest flight, so the structure may move to a new location. The thick tree trunk appears very strong; it probably functions as a support. The booklike structure of the Venus's-flytrap probably traps the insect inside the plant. The bright color of the orchid probably attracts the attention of animals.)*

Ask students whether they think that the green structures of the Venus's-flytrap are really leaves, and have them explain their answer. *(Sample answer: Yes, because they are green and each seems to be attached at the top of a stem.)*

Chapter 24 The Importance of Plants

Chapter Overview

Chapter 24 explains the importance of plants. In Section 24.1 students learn about the uses of plants for agricultural, medicinal, and commercial purposes. Section 24.2 discusses plant ecology and the coevolution of some plants and animals.

Chapter Planning Chart

B	S	A	Sections and Subsections	Page	Features	Page	Resources
•	•	•	**24.1 Plants and People**				
			Plants for Food	353	Biotechnology	356	Videodiscs
			Food Production	355	Laboratory	361	Blackline Master 49
			Other Uses of Plants	356	Section Review	357	Overhead Transparency T24
							Process Skills: Essential Amino Acids
							Laboratories: Plants and Energy
							Section Reviews Worksheet
	•	•	**24.2 Plants and the Environment**				
			Plant Ecology	359	Writing About Biology	358	Laboratories: Plants and Air
			Coevolution of Plants and Animals	360	Think	360	Section Reviews Worksheet
					Section Review	360	
			End of Chapter Activities				
					Chapter Review	362	Vocabulary Skills
							Chapter Test
							Computer Test Generator

B *The Basic Level curriculum presents the most fundamental knowledge offered in the course.*
S *The Standard Level curriculum is designed for the average student who is able to master most topics.*
A *The Advanced Level curriculum includes suggestions for teaching the most academically able students.*

Cooperative Learning

Group Activity: Debating the Green Revolution

- **Group Size:** *4 students*
- **Outcome:** *Students will be able to evaluate the pros and cons of the Green Revolution.*
- **Individual Accountability:** *Each student will prepare a bibliography on techniques implemented as part of the Green Revolution.*
- **Positive Interdependence:** *Pairs of students will debate one another and compare results.*

Point out to students that the Green Revolution (1950–1970) was an attempt to increase food production worldwide that has been both praised and criticized. Ask each group to designate two members to debate the following resolutions. *Resolved that:* Pro: The Green Revolution increased food production worldwide; and Con: The Green Revolution adversely affected food production and the ecology of the earth.

Within each group, all students will research the topic, one pair will debate pro and con, and one pair will offer rebuttals. Allow students time for research, and reserve group time for debating. Encourage students to listen carefully, offer constructive criticism, and allow time for questions to verify the points presented.

When the debates are over, ask each group to report their conclusions to the whole class. Encourage students to suggest ways that food production could be increased without damaging the environment based on the lessons learned from the Green Revolution.

Concept Map

The following is one possible solution to the concept mapping activity in Organizing Information on p. 355.

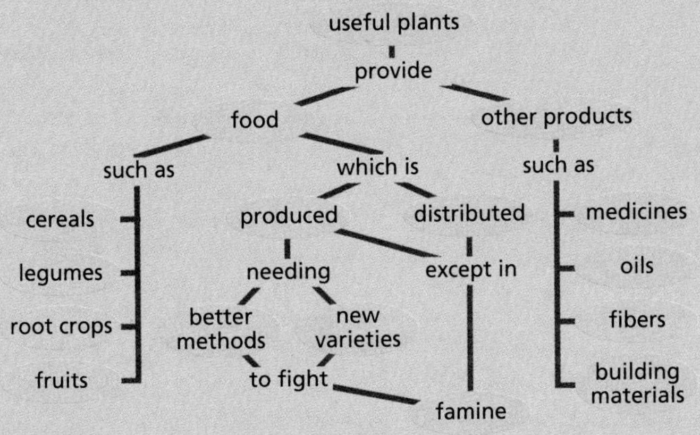

Laboratory Preparation

Overview *(See p. 361.)*

In this lab students study the morphology and anatomy of some food plants that represent the four most common categories of foods—cereals, legumes, root crops, and fruits. Students infer the category to which each food belongs and create a data table.

Preparation

Obtain a variety of plants used as foods, including ethnic foods. Label each plant or its container with a letter. Supermarkets, produce markets, natural food stores, ethnic groceries, and restaurants are good sources for samples. Use whole plants whenever feasible. If only portions are available (corn kernels, as opposed to corn on the cob or the stalk), try to include a picture of the whole plant, for example, from an encyclopedia.

The following are some examples: **cereals:** rice, wheat, corn, oats, rye, millet, barley; **legumes:** most varieties of beans and peas; pinto, fava, or black beans; sweet peas; peanuts in the shell; **root crops:** carrots, potatoes, sweet potato, horseradish, cassava, taro, Jerusalem artichoke; **fruits:** zapote, ugli fruit, banana, tomato, chili pepper, rose hips.

Teaching Tips

Remind students of the four food plant categories presented in Chapter 24. Emphasize that the categories are not taxonomically based. Inform students that Chapters 25–27 will give them more knowledge of plant anatomy and current taxonomy, allowing for a more accurate classification of food plants.

Have students read the Inquiry section carefully before they begin. Discuss other techniques or tests they might use in studying plant parts. Some structures may be more easily located in plants under the dissecting microscope after first being observed on prepared slides with a compound microscope. Most biological supply houses sell prepared slides of some food plants.

Sample answers for Further Inquiry: **stems:** bamboo shoots, asparagus, rhubarb (leaf petiole); **leaves:** lettuce, endive, pokeweed, mustard greens, grape leaves, fiddleheads, celery, brussels sprouts; **flowers:** chamomile, artichoke, broccoli, cauliflower; **seeds and nuts:** many foods listed as cereals and legumes are also seeds; pine nuts, anise, macadamias.

Safety

Remind students to use care when cutting with a sharp scalpel. Remind them not to eat in the laboratory and to wash hands after handling specimens.

Chapter Themes

Systems and Interactions Emphasize for students that a set of crucial interactions takes place between plants and people. Plants provide people with food, medicines, commercial materials, and oxygen. People cultivate plants but also destroy vegetation, which has a critical effect on the biosphere.

Evolution Make sure students understand that people are selecting agents in the evolution of plants. People choose to cultivate plants with characteristics they value. Explain that plants and animals may coevolve beneficial adaptations, as in pollination relationships, or antagonistic adaptations, as in some producer-consumer relationships.

Chapter Motivating Activity

Distribute to each student a small, opaque container that holds a plant part with a distinct odor. (Baby-food jars wrapped in paper, with holes punched in the lids, make good containers. Jars could contain lemon or orange rind, onion slice, vanilla bean, whole peppercorn, garlic clove, crushed pine needles, cinnamon stick, fresh lawn clippings, strawberry, eucalyptus leaves, oregano, mint leaves.) Ask each student in turn to lightly sniff the jar and to recall an interaction with that plant in the past. *(Sample associations: Lemon—I drink lots of lemonade; pine needles—smells like Christmas)* Impress upon students how many daily interactions they have with plants.

Chapter 24 *The Importance of Plants*

Introduction

Plants are the producers of food. They form the base of the ecological food chain on which humans ultimately depend for survival. People also need plants for medicines, clothing, and building materials. In this chapter you will learn why plants are important to humans. You will also learn about the ecological roles of plants and the coevolution of some plants and animals. In the rest of the chapters in this unit you will examine specifics of plant biology.

Outline

24.1 Plants and People
- *Plants for Food*
- *Food Production*
- *Other Uses of Plants*

24.2 Plants and the Environment
- *Plant Ecology*
- *Coevolution of Plants and Animals*

Chapter Concept

As you read, pay attention to the relationship between plants and humans, and consider how an understanding of plant biology will lead to a better understanding of the interaction of science and society.

Potatoes, *Solanum tuberosum,* in test tubes at an agricultural research lab. Inset: Tissue culture of carrots, *Daucus carota,* for cloning.

Understanding the Visuals

Have students examine the photographs and read the caption. Point out that both plants shown are used as food by people. Remind students that they learned about tissue culture in Chapter 19. Ask them what cloning is. *(Students may recall from Chapter 13 that cloning is a way of producing many copies; asexual reproduction will be discussed in more detail in Chapter 27.)* Ask them to compare these two techniques with traditional methods of planting potatoes and carrots. *(Cloning and cell culturing are begun in a laboratory; traditionally, potato eyes and carrot seeds are planted in the ground.)* Explain that all methods of cultivation—including cloning and cell culturing—are methods of artificially selecting and reproducing plants.

24.1 Plants and People

Throughout human history people have used plants. For example, on the evidence of fossilized pollen found at Neanderthal burial sites, scientists believe that flowers have been placed on graves for more than 35,000 years. We still use plants in such ritualistic ways, but the relation between plants and people is primarily that of producer and consumer. Of the 350,000 species of plants people now use about 1,000 for food.

Section Objectives

- *Summarize briefly the history of the cultivation of plants by humans.*
- *Define cereals, legumes, root crops, and fruits, and distinguish between them.*
- *List the lessons learned from the Green Revolution.*
- *Define* famine, *and suggest two cultivation practices that can be used to fight famine.*
- *List several medicinal and commercial uses of plants.*

Plants for Food

The cultivation of plants probably began about 11,000 years ago in a region of the Middle East known as the Fertile Crescent. Wheat, barley, lentils, and peas were the first plants to be domesticated. Olives, dates, and grapes were later cultivated.

In cultivating plants, people propagated those individuals with characteristics that they found most valuable. This form of selection—with people acting as selecting agents—resulted in the evolution of food plants. For example, the wild wheat stalk breaks easily in the wind, an adaptation that increases the dispersal of ripe grains. Early people selected seeds from those plants with stalks that did not break easily. When these seeds were grown, the grains could be harvested before they fell off the plant.

Cereals

Cereals are members of the family Gramineae, the grass family. The grains of cereals are rich in carbohydrates. Cereals are the basis of human nutrition. Over half of the world's cultivated land is devoted to crops such as rice, wheat, corn, oats, sorghum, rye, and millet.

Figure 24-1 The first plants to be cultivated were cereals. Cultivation began about 11,000 years ago in the Fertile Crescent region of the Middle East. The inset map shows the present-day national boundaries in this region.

Lesson Plan

Section Focus

Help students understand that the interactions among plants and people are crucial to human survival. In addition to supplying food and oxygen, plants provide numerous medicines and commercial materials.

Section Themes

This section emphasizes two themes: **Systems and Interactions** and **Evolution.** Humans depend on plants for food, medicines, oxygen, building materials, and many other uses. People have been a part of plant evolution since early humans first began growing crops for food.

Motivating Activity

Bring actual products derived from plants to class and ask students to identify the source of each product. You may wish to include: aspirin *(salicylic acid in bark and leaves of willow, poplar, spirea)*, cotton *(cotton plant)*, paper *(wood pulp)*, rubber *(rubber trees)*, lipstick *(castor oil from castor bean, and carnauba wax from carnauba palm leaves)*, and food items such as cereals, fruits, and spices.

Teaching Strategies

Applying Concepts Ask students to brainstorm about how plants and people are interdependent. *(Answers should include the idea that plants provide food, shelter, medicines, oxygen, and many other useful substances. Humans assist and interfere in plant evolution by selecting, breeding, and propagating plants with desirable characteristics.)*

Videodiscs

- *745 Cornfield (s)*
- *1910–1911 Corn Seed: Seedling (s)*
- *1912–1914, Bean Seed: Seedling (s)*

Green Revolution

Advantages	Disadvantages
▪ great increase in worldwide food production ▪ new varieties of plants were introduced	▪ often new techniques too expensive ▪ tropical soils often not suitable for many of the new crops

Graphic Organizer Use this table in Comparing Costs and Benefits on p. 355.

Interpreting the Visuals Walk students through the maps in Figures 24-1 and 24-2 on pp. 353–354. A wall map can help you place each figure in geographic context. Make sure students know which countries are included in the Fertile Crescent. You may wish to ask students whose heritage is from countries in these regions to describe ethnic foods that include rice, grains, or legumes.

■ *See* **Overhead Transparency** ***T24*** ***and*** **Blackline Master** ***49.***

Observing Organisms Show the class the nodule root system of one or more legumes. (If you live in a rural area, these may be obtained from local farmers. If in an urban area, legumes are easy to grow in the classroom but require nonsterile soil and several weeks to develop adequate root systems with nodules.) Have students cut open the nodules and make wet mounts of the bacteria inside. As an alternative, slides of nitrogen-fixing bacteria are available from biological materials supply houses.

Discussing the Issues Ask students what other foods besides legumes are high in protein content. *(Grains, meats, eggs, milk, cheeses)* Tell students that most people in the world are vegetarians and get their protein primarily from plants. Ask students why. *(Economic reasons—in many countries the cost of eating meat is prohibitive; religious reasons; ethical reasons—not wanting to kill animals to eat; heritage—little if any meat in the cuisine)*

■ *See* **Process Skills,** ***Chapter 24.***

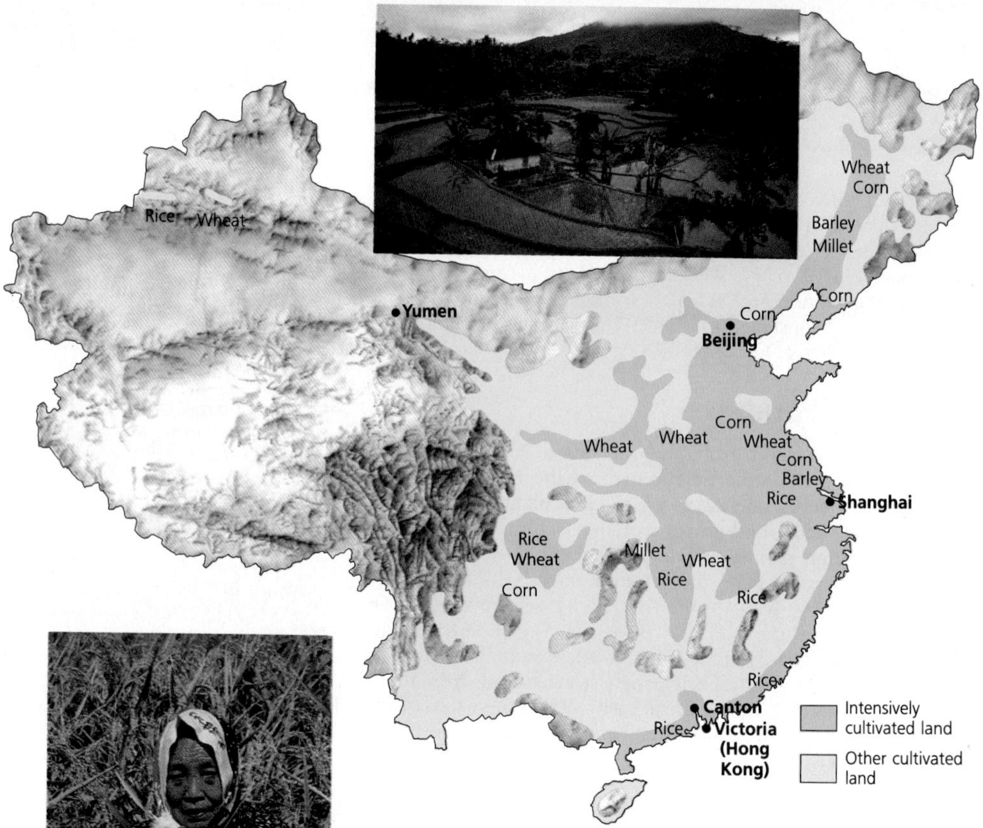

Figure 24-2 Rice is one of the main crops grown in China.

Rice, *Oryza sativa,* is a source of food for more than 60 percent of the world's population. It thrives in regions with abundant rainfall. Figure 24-2 shows the distribution of rice and other cereal crops in China. Wheat, *Triticum officinale,* grows well in moderate to cold climates, including parts of the United States, the Soviet Union, and Canada.

Legumes

Legumes *(LEG-YOOMZ)* are members of the pea family. They bear protein-rich seeds in long pods. Peas, *Pisum sativum;* peanuts, *Arachis hypogaea;* and soybeans, *Glycine max,* are legumes. Legumes often form symbiotic associations with nitrogen-fixing bacteria, which enable them to grow and form protein-rich seeds in nitrogen-poor soil. About 45 percent of a soybean is protein.

Root Crops

Root crops are plants that are grown for the nutrients stored in their roots or modified underground stems. Root crops—such as carrots, *Daucus carota,* and potatoes, *Solanum tuberosum*—are excellent sources of carbohydrates, vitamins, and minerals.

LEP Activity

Many ethnic cuisines include a combination of grains and vegetables or legumes as their primary protein source (rice and beans; corn and beans; wheat, soy, and legumes; rice and soy). Have students make posters illustrating these traditional combinations of grains and legumes. Magazines are good sources for pictures and often include recipes and sometimes a nutritional analysis. Help students list the nutritional benefits of each food source on their posters. Display posters in the classroom.

Fruits

Fruits are mature plant ovaries that enclose a seed or seeds. Grapes, *Vitis* sp., and tomatoes, *Lycopersicon esculentum,* are fleshy fruits called berries. Apples, *Malus* sp., are moist fruits called pomes; walnuts, *Juglans* sp., are dry fruits called nuts. Grains are the fruits of cereals.

Food Production

Scientists estimate that by the year 2000 there will be 6.2 billion people on the earth. To ensure that food will be available to such a large population, there must be more efficient national and international food production and distribution systems. Economists can help improve these systems. Biologists can also play a role by developing new food plants.

The Green Revolution

Between 1950 and 1970 researchers concentrated on improving the productivity of land already under cultivation. Their work led to a great increase in worldwide food production known as the **Green Revolution.** For example, Norman Borlaug, of the International Rice Institute in the Philippines, developed strong-stemmed varieties of rice that produced heavy heads of grain. These varieties were also adapted to tropical and subtropical regions. Borlaug later received the Nobel Peace Prize for his work.

Although the Green Revolution brought about many advances, the resulting distribution of new grains and agricultural techniques brought about some problems. New techniques were often too expensive to use in developing regions. Many farmers could not afford the fertilizers needed to grow the new varieties of plants. Moreover, tropical soils, which are low in essential nutrients, were often not suitable for raising some of the new crops. Researchers today are working on more effective ways to use the grains and techniques developed in the Green Revolution.

Famine

Long, widespread food shortages, called **famines,** occur when food production and distribution cannot meet the need for food. When severe drought struck Ethiopia and several other northern and central African nations in the early 1980s, many people starved.

Some agricultural methods may help reduce the possibility of famine. For example, some root crops, such as cassava, *Manihot* sp., and millet, *Panicum miliaceum,* can be grown in dry areas without expensive fertilizers or irrigation systems. **Agroforestry,** the planting of crops alongside trees in the tropics, maintains the forest, protects the soil from erosion, and shields young crops. In **mixed cropping,** the planting of two or more crops in one field, if one crop fails, the second or third may still produce.

Figure 24-3 Progress in agriculture is represented by research at the Rice Institute of Banos University in the Philippines (top) and mixed cropping, including plants for fodder, a root crop, and a cereal, in Devon, England (bottom).

Collecting Data Have students add a drop of iodine–potassium iodide solution on carrot, potato, and turnip slices to see where starch is stored. Have them observe starch granules through a dissecting microscope. *(Starch granules are stained bluish-black by iodine.)*
■ *See* Laboratories, ***Investigation 24.1.***

Organizing Information Have students make concept maps to show how people use plants. An example of a completed concept map is shown on p. 351B.

Exploring Careers Have a nutritionist or a dietitian speak to the class about planning balanced meals. Ask them to focus on ways to include a variety of plant foods.

Comparing Costs and Benefits Ask students to organize a table showing the advantages and disadvantages of the Green Revolution as presented in the text. An example of a completed table is shown on p. 353.

Guided Practice

Have students write a detailed list, hour by hour, of every item from a plant source they have used or observed so far today. *(Examples: a pencil made of wood; soap made with vegetable oil; cotton clothing and towels from cotton plants; notebook paper.)*

Independent Practice

■ Have students write answers to the Section Review.
■ Have students examine clothing and container labels at home, and list where plants are used. *(Examples: cotton or other plant fibers in clothing; lemon juice in dish detergents and flavored drinks; vegetable oils; flour; popcorn)*

Videodiscs

■ *2535–2537, Amino Acids (s)*

Interdisciplinary Activity

History Ask students to research and identify the causes and effects of famines in the past 25 years. *(Examples: drought in the Sudan and Biafra—not enough water for plant growth; floods in Bangladesh—destroy plants and land; war in Ethiopia and Iraq—takes farmers from their land and destroys crops; chemical farming techniques or slash-and-burn agriculture in West Africa—soils become depleted; insect plagues in North Africa—plants devoured before they can be harvested)* Students should consider the impact of famine on the history, sociology, and politics of each country.

Section 24.1

Check Your Understanding

1. How has the evolution of plants been affected by humans? *(New varieties of plants are produced by hybridization. People also act as selecting agents by planting and preserving varieties with desirable characteristics.)*

2. Is it possible to go through one day without using a product from a plant? Explain. *(No. Although students can wear clothing made of synthetic fibers and can fast for a day, houses and apartments contain wood and plant fibers. The oxygen we breathe and all food that we eat depend on plants.)*

Reteaching

Bring food products to class, including cereal products such as oatmeal, bread, raw rice, and corn; legumes such as lentils, peas, soybeans, or tofu; root crops such as carrots, rutabagas, and sweet potatoes; and fruits such as squash, tomatoes, chili peppers, pineapples, and walnuts. Divide the class into three or four groups, and give each group foods from each major category. Give the groups 10 or 15 minutes to identify their foods as fruits, cereals, legumes, or roots, and to list at least one nutritional benefit derived from each food.

■ *See* Section Reviews *worksheets, Section 24.1.*

Enrichment

Have each student choose a medicine derived from a plant and write a report on its discovery and uses. Suggest that students research traditional herbal remedies as well as modern pharmacology. *(Examples: aspirin, from willow and spirea; digitalis, from foxglove; belladonna, from the nightshade family)*

Figure 24-4 Kozo, a fiber that comes from mulberry trees grown in Japan, is the chief ingredient in a fine, very lightweight paper used in printing.

Other Uses of Plants

Plants play an important role in many areas of our lives. Like the first medicines, many of today's medicines are made from plants. **Digitalis** *(DIJ-uh-TAL-uss)*, which is used in the treatment of heart disease, is obtained from the leaves of the foxglove plant, *Digitalis purpurea*. Periwinkles, *Vinca* sp., are the source of two drugs that are effective against Hodgkin's disease and some leukemias. Two powerful pain relievers, morphine and codeine, are extracted from the opium poppy, *Papaver somniferum*. The chief ingredient of aspirin, **salicylic** *(SAL-uh-SILL-ick)* **acid,** was originally obtained from the bark of the willow tree. The willow is in the genus *Salix*, hence the name salicylic acid. The bark of the cinchona tree, *Cinchona* sp., contains **quinine** *(KWIE-nine)*, a drug used to treat malaria.

People also use many plant fibers. Cotton, *Gossypium hirsutum*, is the most widely used plant fiber in the world. It is most often woven into cloth. Linen is made from the fibers in the stem of the flax plant, *Linum* sp., and the fibers of the hemp plant, *Cannabis sativa*, are made into ropes. The papyrus reed, *Cyperus papyrus*, has been made into paper as well as reed boats.

Biotechnology

Transgenic Crops

Farmers have hybridized plants for thousands of years, but traditional methods of controlled breeding take a long time and thousands of plants to perfect. Hybridization (p. 356) is also limited to closely related species. Genetic engineering techniques provide direct access to genes and make possible experiments using DNA from unrelated plant species, bacteria, or even human genes. Today molecular biologists are using the bacterium *Agrobacterium tumenfaciens* with recombinant DNA technology to transfer genetically engineered DNA into plant cells by plasmid injection. When inoculated by the plasmid, the plant cells become transgenic, incorporating the engineered DNA into their own cells. Transgenic cells are able to pass on the engineered DNA to every daughter cell. This ability to introduce foreign genes into a wide range of plants is creating a revolution in plant biology. Plants can be engineered to resist disease, provide higher yields, or to manufacture proteins for medical and scientific uses. So far, the list of transgenic crops that have been

Cooperative Learning

Textiles from Plants Divide the class into groups of four. Have one student in each group research the techniques used to transform plant fibers into thread. Have a second student research dyeing, weaving, and knitting techniques that are used to create textiles. Have the third student investigate how textiles are made into clothing. Ask the fourth student to act as moderator to help the group members assemble their collective findings and decide what kind of presentation to make to the class. Allow time for each group to report their findings to the class. *(Examples: a poster illustrating yarn and fabric dyeing with plant-based dyes; the history of making linen from flax; the story of how cotton is transformed from a boll to a T-shirt or blue jeans.)*

Linseed oil, which is used in wood finish and paint, is processed from flax seeds. Cellophane and rayon are made from tree cellulose. Building materials can be obtained from conifers, cork trees, and bamboo plants. In some parts of the world, people use palm fronds to cover and insulate their homes.

Other useful products come from plants found in deserts. The oil of the jojoba *(huh-HOE-buh)* shrub, *Simmondsia chinensis,* is used in cosmetics, waxes, and industrial oils. The guayule *(gwie-YOO-lee), Parthenium argentatum,* produces a substitute for the natural rubber found in tropical trees such as the Brazilian rubber tree, *Hevea brasiliensis.*

Section Review

1. Explain *mixed cropping,* and suggest how it might ensure successful crops.
2. Name two problems associated with the Green Revolution.
3. Describe legumes, root crops, and fruits.
4. List three nonnutritional uses of plants.
5. Is the world facing the need for a new Green Revolution? Defend your answer.

developed by plasmid transfer includes alfalfa, carrot, celery, cucumber, Douglas fir, flax, lettuce, oilseed, petunia, poplar, potato, soybean, sugarbeet, sunflower, tobacco, tomato, walnut, and cotton (p. 357).

Two U.S. firms have developed another method of introducing DNA into plants that were previously inaccessible to genetic engineering. This method offers a way to study the gene expression in single cells of cereal grains. Researchers use a machine called a particle gun to shoot tiny, plasmid-coated pellets through the cell wall. Some of these transgenic plants are able to pass on the new genes to

their offspring. These techniques are most often used to improve the ability of a food crop to resist disease, insects, or herbicides, but plants have also been altered to produce large quantities of several useful human proteins.

Scientists are also working on providing cereal crops with nitrogen-fixing nodules that hold symbiotic bacteria. Cereal crops lack such symbionts and require expensive nitrogen-based fertilizers to produce maximum yields. Researchers at the University of Sydney, Australia, estimate that the general use of this technology is still approximately a decade away.

While molecular biologists are hard at work engineering food crops with new traits, ecologists and ethicists ponder the risks involved in dramatically altering the genetic diversity present in nature. Ecological risk analyses will require cooperation among a wide variety of scientific disciplines in the attempt to determine what the global impact—both socially and scientifically—will be before the potential benefits of these new technologies can be fully realized.

Answers to Section Review

1. Mixed cropping is the planting of two or more crops in one area. If one crop fails because of pests or disease, the others may still produce a harvest.

2. The Green Revolution provided many regions with plants that were not suitable for the environments. Many farmers could not afford the necessary fertilizers and the machinery.

3. Legumes are members of the pea family; they bear protein-rich seeds in pods. Root crops are modified underground stems, roots, or tubers that store nutrients. Fruits are mature plant ovaries that enclose a seed or a number of seeds.

4. Plant fibers, in cloth, paper, rope; lumber; medicinal plants; rubber.

5. Yes. An explosive population growth needs matching amounts of food.

Closure

Have students examine the classroom for plant products. If it does not occur to them, ask where the oxygen they are breathing came from.

Biotechnology

Using the Feature

Point out to students that all the methods of introducing new genetic material mentioned in the feature rely on the use of a naturally occurring or genetically engineered plasmid. This is a standard technique in molecular biology research and in recombinant DNA technology.

The particle-gun method of gene transfer uses minuscule pellets of tungsten coated with plasmids to carry the desired gene into the plant cell. Particle guns have already been used to transfer genes into plants successfully. One trial to produce an enzyme in corn resulted in cells that produced 200 times the normal levels of the enzyme.

Encourage students to brainstorm the ecological and ethical issues involved in introducing new genetic material into plant species that may be able to pass on their new characteristics to wild species. *(The engineered genes may affect the wild species in completely unanticipated ways with unforeseen consequences. Ethical issues also arise from ownership of species that offer higher food yields in times of increasing shortages or famine.)*

For more material on the ethical and ecological consequences of genetic engineering of plants, have students look at the IntraScience feature on pp. 432–433.

Videodiscs

■ ***742–743, Sisal Hemp in Field (s)***

Background

Every species requires a certain range of limits (temperature, light, humidity) to survive. These limits define the organism's range of tolerance. If environmental conditions go outside the range of tolerance, the organism will not survive. When conditions begin to approach a tolerance limit, most animals will move to look for a more suitable environment. Plants cannot move if conditions are outside their limits of tolerance. They die.

Discussion

After students have read "Earth's Green Mantle," ask them to discuss the following questions.

1. If the sage were removed, what would happen to the perennial bunchgrass? Explain your answer. *(It would die. It can grow only in the shelter of sage plants.)*

2. Suppose a land management agency wanted to remove antelope from an area such as Carson describes. Would more or fewer people be likely to protest than would protest removal of the sage? Explain your answer. *(Probably more; most people would probably be more aware of the loss of animals than of the interdependence of plants such as the sage and bunchgrass.)*

Extension

Challenge students to find out what the book's title, *Silent Spring*, means. *(Rachel Carson said in her book that pesticides were killing birds so quickly that someday there would be no more birds to sing, and so the spring season would be silent.)* Then have students write essays imagining a walk through the country in a spring without birdsong.

Writing About Biology

Earth's Green Mantle

This excerpt is from the first chapter of Rachel Carson's book, Silent Spring.

The earth's vegetation is part of a web of life in which there are intimate and essential relations between plants and the earth, between plants and other plants, between plants and animals. Sometimes we have no choice but to disturb these relationships, but we should do so thoughtfully, with full awareness that what we do may have consequences remote in time and place. But no such humility marks the booming "weed killer" business of the present day, in which soaring sales and expanding uses mark the production of plant-killing chemicals.

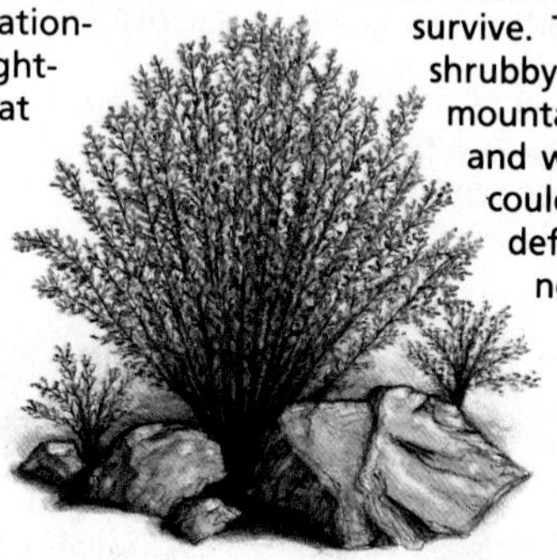

One of the most tragic examples of our unthinking bludgeoning of the landscape is to be seen in the sagebrush lands of the West, where a vast campaign is on to destroy the sage and to substitute grasslands. If ever an enterprise needed to be illuminated with a sense of the history and meaning of the landscape, it is this. For here the natural landscape is eloquent of the interplay of forces that have created it. It is spread before us like the pages of an open book in which we can read why the land is what it is, and why we should preserve its integrity. But the pages lie unread.

The land of the sage is the land of the high western plains and the lower slopes of the mountains that rise above them, a land born of the great uplift of the Rocky Mountain system many millions of years ago. It is a place of harsh extremes of climate: of long winters when blizzards drive down from the mountains and snow lies deep on the plains, of summers whose heat is relieved by only scanty rains, with drought biting deep into the soil, and drying winds stealing moisture from leaf and stem.

As the landscape evolved, there must have been a long period of trial and error in which plants attempted the colonization of this high and windswept land. One after another must have failed. At last one group of plants evolved which combined all the qualities needed to survive. The sage—low-growing and shrubby—could hold its place on the mountain slopes and on the plains, and within its small gray leaves it could hold moisture enough to defy the thieving winds. It was no accident, but rather the result of long ages of experimentation by nature, that the great plains of the West became the land of the sage. . . .

So in a land which nature found suited to grass growing mixed with and under the shelter of sage, it is now proposed to eliminate the sage and create unbroken grassland. Few seem to have asked whether grasslands are a stable desirable goal in this region. Certainly nature's own answer was otherwise. The annual precipitation in this land where the rains seldom fall is not enough to support good sod-forming grass; it favors rather the perennial bunchgrass that grows in the shelter of the sage.

Write

- **Rachel Carson is writing about proposals that land management agencies create more grazing land for cattle interests. Write a short essay describing how Rachel Carson feels about people altering the natural plant life of a region. Discuss the writing techniques Rachel Carson uses to persuade readers to agree with her viewpoint. How much of her argument is based on fact, and how much is opinion?**

 From Silent Spring *by Rachel Carson. Copyright © 1962 by Rachel Carson. Reprinted by permission of Houghton Mifflin Company.*

About the Author

It isn't often that a book intended for the general public makes the world aware of a scientific problem, but it happened in 1962, when *Silent Spring* was first published. American biologist Rachel Louise Carson (1907–1964), in her account of the effect of indiscriminate use of pesticides on the environment, focused attention on the problem. The book became a talked-about best-seller and was largely responsible for a sudden increase in public awareness of environmental dangers resulting from the indiscriminate use of pesticides. It was a quiet beginning that eventually led to public concern about ecology and to action in the form of a ban on the use of DDT in the United States.

24.2 Plants and the Environment

Plants use solar energy in the process of photosynthesis to convert water and carbon dioxide into glucose and oxygen. The biosphere—the portion of the earth's surface on which all life exists—depends on photosynthesis.

Section Objectives

- *Describe what is meant by plant ecology.*
- *Give two examples of how plants recycle nutrients in the environment.*
- *Identify the major threat to the tropical rain forests.*
- *Explain the coevolution of flowers and pollinators.*

Plant Ecology

The study of the interaction of plants and the environment is called **plant ecology.** In addition to creating food, plants cycle chemical elements and nutrients. For example, plants release oxygen through their leaves into the atmosphere. They also absorb elements released from weathering rocks, such as phosphorus, potassium, iron, and magnesium, through their roots. The organisms that eat plants, called consumers, incorporate these elements into their own bodies. Eventually these same nutrients are returned to the earth when the consumers are decomposed by organisms such as bacteria and fungi.

Some plant ecologists apply their knowledge of ecology to solving problems caused in some way by the interaction of plants and people. For example, the demands of a growing human population for food and living space have led to the destruction of vast tracts of the world's tropical rain forests. Erosion soon follows the mass cutting of trees, called **deforestation.** The nutrients in the thin topsoil are easily washed away by rains. Wastelands then develop where lush vegetation and abundant animal life once flourished. Plant ecologists are now studying ways to reduce this destruction and to solve problems caused in other regions by the actions of people.

Figure 24-5 A tropical rain forest supports hundreds of plant and animal species (left). Because the top layer of soil is very thin, trees grow buttresses for added support (right.)

Uses of Plants	Effects on Environment
Medicine	Medicinal plants may be overpicked, resulting in endangered species.
Clothing	Growing cotton, rather than food, may contribute to local food shortages and to excessive use of water.
Food	Overfarming can strip soil of nutrients.
Building Materials	Deforestation, elimination of habitats, global warming

Graphic Organizer Use this table in Closure on p. 360.

Lesson Plan

Section Focus

This section discusses how the demands of a growing human population for food and living space have led to deforestation of vast tracts of tropical rain forest. It discusses some plant and animal species that have coevolved, and it gives examples of relationships that are mutually beneficial or antagonistic.

Section Themes

This section has two basic themes: **Systems and Interactions** and **Evolution.** Plants and animals interact with the environment and with each other. Different species may also coevolve specific kinds of interdependent relationships.

Motivating Activity

Have students observe a classroom terrarium or pictures of the rain forest. Begin a discussion of the role of plants in the biosphere by asking what an animal needs to live, and where the animal gets what it needs. *(Oxygen from the air or water; water from rain or bodies of water; food from plants or other animals)* Emphasize the systems of interaction between plants and animals. Then ask where the plants get the minerals *(From soil or water)* and the CO_2 *(From air)* they need to live.
■ ***See* Laboratories, *Investigation 24.2.***

Teaching Strategies

Inferring Relationships Help students understand that the interactions between plants and people are sometimes mutually beneficial and sometimes antagonistic. For more material on the impact of humans on plants and on global ecology, see the Intra-Science features for Unit 1, pp. 58–59, and Unit 6, pp. 432–433.

Guided Practice

Ask students to name substances that plants recycle. *(Water, carbon dioxide, phosphorus, potassium, iron, magnesium)*

Independent Practice

■ Have students write answers to the Section Review.

■ Have students write sentences to demonstrate an understanding of mutually beneficial and antagonistic relationships between plants and animals.

Check Your Understanding

1. What would happen if there were no decomposer organisms? *(Life would stop. Without decay, nutrients couldn't be recycled.)*

2. Ask students how the carbon now in their bodies got there, when last year it was present in the air as CO_2. *(During photosynthesis plants turned CO_2 into food. The students ate a plant or an animal that had eaten a plant.)*

Answer to Think

The scent attracts carrion flies and beetles that are pollinators.

Reteaching

Have students classify these relationships between plants and animals: a butterfly drinking nectar and pollinating a flower *(Mutually beneficial)*; cutworms eating plant stems *(Antagonistic)*.

■ *See* Section Reviews *worksheet, Section 24.2.*

Enrichment

Have students research and report on the global impact of the destruction of the rain forest. *(Extinction of plant and animal species, impact on indigenous peoples, global warming.)*

Closure

Ask students to prepare a two-column table showing how various uses of plants affect the environment. Use the table on p. 359 as a model.

Figure 24-6 Some orchid species resemble a fly (left). The tobacco hornworm (right) has coevolved as a predator on plants.

Think

The flower of this plant, *Stapelia* sp., smells like rotten meat. Suggest an adaptive significance for this trait.

Coevolution of Plants and Animals

The study of plants and the environment must include an understanding of the interdependence of plants and animals. Some plant and animal species may adapt successively over time in ways that affect their interactions. That is, the organisms may coevolve. These changes may be mutually beneficial adaptations, as in some pollination relationships, or antagonistic interactions, as in producer–consumer relationships.

Many flowering plants have coevolved with their pollinators, organisms that carry pollen from one plant to another while gathering food. In some flowers size, shape, color, or odor make them attractive to their pollinators. For example, in some orchid species the flowers have coevolved with their fly pollinators and now look like the female fly. A male lands on a flower as if he had located a mate. The pollen he touches sticks to his body and is transferred to the next orchid he lands on.

In one example of a producer–consumer relationship, a plant produces toxic chemicals that discourage animals from eating the plant. Jimson weed, a plant in the nightshade family, produces steroid compounds that are distasteful to many animals. However, some animals coevolved with the Jimson weed and developed a tolerance for the steroids. Some insects are actually stimulated by the steroids and continue to eat the plant. In another example, poison ivy leaves are often red, a warning that the plant is toxic. Again, some vertebrates are immune to the toxins. Often families of insects that have coevolved with toxic plants and are immune to their toxins have bright warning coloration that warns predators that they are toxic.

Section Review

1. What is *plant ecology?*
2. How do plants provide essential nutrients in ecosystems?
3. Discuss how the process of coevolution operates in the pollination relationship between orchids and the flies that pollinate them.
4. What phenomenon usually occurs after deforestation?
5. What advantage does an insect that is toxic gain by being brightly colored?

Answers to Section Review

1. Plant ecology is the study of the interaction of plants and their environment.

2. Plants release oxygen during photosynthesis and recycle nutrients from the soil. Nutrients are passed along when plants are eaten.

3. In some orchid species, the flowers have coevolved with their pollinators, which are flies, so that the flowers resemble a female fly. When a male fly lands on a flower, pollen sticks to his body and is transferred to the next orchid he visits.

4. Erosion occurs after deforestation.

5. A brightly colored insect that is toxic is easily remembered and thus avoided by a predator and will have a better chance of survival.

Laboratory

Exploring Food Plants

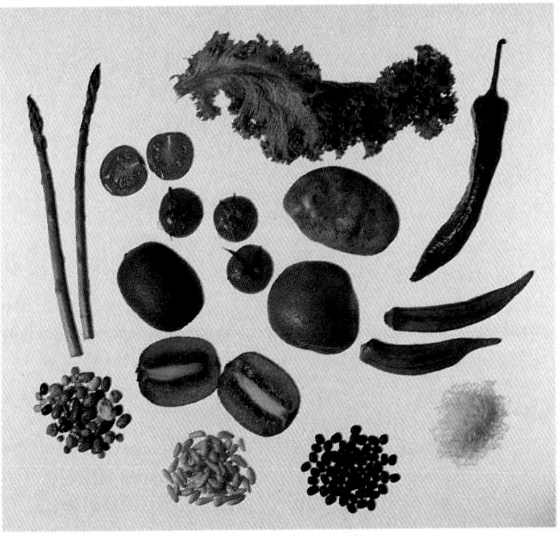

Objective
To observe various foods and infer what plant parts they are

Process Skills
Observing, inferring, classifying

Materials
Scalpel, culture dish, dissecting microscope, variety of food plants

Background
1 What cell structures are unique to plant cells?
2 Most foods eaten by people come from what four categories of food plants or plant parts?

Inquiry
1 Examine all the foods your teacher has provided. Identify by name the food items you know. If you do not recognize the item, use the letter with which it is marked to identify it in the lab.
2 Select one of the food items and carefully observe it. Record all of its distinguishing external characteristics. Be sure to label all your observations either by the name of the food or by its letter.
3 Carefully use the scalpel to cut the food item in half lengthwise. What did you feel or hear as you cut the food? What plant cell characteristic might explain your observations? Put the item in a culture dish and examine it under a dissecting microscope. What do you see? Record your observations.
4 Make several thin cross sections of the food item. Observe them under the dissecting microscope. What do you see? Record your observations.
5 Repeat steps 2–4 for all of the remaining food items. Be sure that you identify your observations by recording each food item's name or letter.
6 The plants and plant parts you have studied are representatives of the four categories of food plants. Infer the category to which each plant or plant part belongs.
7 Create a data table in which you use the names of the four categories from step 6 as the column heads. Enter the name or letter of each food from step 1 under the appropriate column head.

Conclusions
1 What characteristics are the same for all these food items?
2 What evidence is there to support your inference that each of the food items in the lab belongs to the category in which you have placed it?

Further Inquiry
Many other plants and plant parts are used as food. Select a variety of food plants, including unfamiliar items. Determine which ones belong to the four food plant categories studied today and which do not. Which are stems? leaves? flowers?

Laboratory

(For an overview of food plants and preparatory information related to the laboratory, see p. 351B.)

Background
1. All plant cells have a cell wall; vacuoles; and plastids, which include chloroplasts, chromoplasts, and leucoplasts.
2. Cereals, legumes, root crops, and fruits

Inquiry
2. Student observations may include shape, color, size, and odor. Students may note that most cereals are from grasslike plants or from stalks with heads of grain and that legumes are from pods on bushy plants. They may note that the root crops are dirty (dug from the ground) and that most of the fruits are fleshy.
3. Students may report feeling resistance, describe the food as crisp, or report hearing a snapping or crunching sound. The cell walls give a plant its rigidity and support. **Cereals:** students may be able to distinguish the endosperm and plumule, and may identify the latter as a tiny plant. **Legumes:** students may note that the part typically eaten is contained inside a pod. In the seeds, they may observe endosperm and plumule as in the cereals. **Root crops:** students may describe the tissue as dense or fibrous. **Fruits:** may be described as juicy, fleshy, or fibrous and containing seeds or a pit.
4. Cereals: probably as in step 3. **Legumes:** probably as in step 3. **Root crops:** students may note the circular patterns caused by vascular tissues. **Fruits:** probably as in step 3. The seeds of some fruits (apple) form a radial pattern when viewed in cross section.
7. Column heads should be *Cereals, Legumes, Root Crops,* and *Fruits.*

Conclusions
1. All are from plants. Their cells have cell walls, vacuoles, and plastids. Some of the cells have green chlorophyll.
2. Students' observations and knowledge of the four categories should lead them to group food items sharing similar characteristics within a single category.

Further Inquiry
Selected food items will vary. They may include food plants that are root, stem, leaf, flower, fruit, and seed. These foods can be used as an introduction to the plant structures that are described in Chapters 26 and 27. See Preparation on p. 351B for examples.

Vocabulary

1. The study of the interactions of plants and their environment
2. Cereals include rice, wheat, corn, oats, sorghum, rye, and millet.
3. Root crops include carrots, potatoes, and cassava.
4. Agroforestry is the planting of crops alongside trees; mixed cropping is the planting of two or more crops in one field.
5. A famine is a long-term, widespread food shortage that occurs when food production and distribution cannot meet the need for food.

Review

1. b
2. d
3. a
4. b
5. b
6. c
7. a
8. b
9. c
10. a
11. The grains of grasses, or cereals
12. Deforestation can result in soil erosion, wastelands, and the destruction of biological communities.
13. Answers will vary. Wood provides cellulose for paper, cellophane, and rayon; cotton, flax, and hemp fibers are woven into cloth; rubber is used in a variety of products; jojoba oil is used in cosmetics.
14. Agroforestry is the planting of crops alongside trees. Especially in the tropics, the trees help prevent soil erosion and shield the crops from the sun.
15. To find varieties with beneficial adaptations that can be bred into cultivated varieties, and to preserve genetic diversity
16. It produces substances that are distasteful to many animals. Some insects, however, have adapted to these substances and continue to eat the plant.

Chapter 24 Review

Vocabulary

agroforestry (355)
cereal (353)
deforestation (359)
digitalis (356)
famine (355)
fruit (355)
Green Revolution (355)
legume (354)
mixed cropping (355)
plant ecology (359)
quinine (356)
root crop (354)
salicylic acid (356)

1. Define plant ecology.
2. List three cereals.
3. List three root crops.
4. Describe the difference between agroforestry and mixed cropping.
5. Define famine.

Review

1. Some species have evolved so that they produce toxic chemicals as a defense in response to (a) large numbers of pollinators (b) predation (c) nutrients in the soil (d) deforestation.
2. Some plants have coevolved with their pollinators and now produce (a) spines (b) grains (c) toxic chemicals (d) modified flowers.
3. Edible underground structures that store nutrients are called (a) root crops (b) legumes (c) orchards (d) grains.
4. A mutually beneficial or antagonistic adaptive change in two organisms is called (a) predation (b) coevolution (c) pollination (d) famine.
5. Organisms that use plants for food are referred to as (a) predators (b) consumers (c) producers (d) pollinators.
6. The foxglove plant aids in the treatment of heart disease because it is the source of a medication called (a) quinine (b) morphine (c) digitalis (d) salicylic acid.
7. Fruits enclose (a) seeds (b) grains (c) roots (d) berries.
8. Many of the cultivation techniques that were introduced in developing areas to increase productivity during the Green Revolution did not succeed because they were (a) too complicated (b) too expensive (c) too time-consuming (d) too practical.
9. Legumes can produce seeds that are protein-rich even in poor soil because of their symbiotic associations with bacteria that (a) break down carbohydrates (b) absorb oxygen (c) fix nitrogen (d) produce carbon.
10. The cultivation of plants by humans probably began in (a) the Middle East (b) South America (c) North America (d) northern Europe.
11. What group of plants is the major source of food for the world today?
12. List two possible long-term effects that can be caused by the deforestation of a tropical rain forest.
13. Give three examples of plants that are used commercially by humans, and describe how they are used.
14. Describe the technique of agroforestry and list the advantages of its use.
15. Why have scientists begun to study wild varieties of cultivated plants?
16. Describe how the Jimson weed operates as an antagonistic producer in the producer–consumer relationship.
17. Give two examples of ways in which the potential for famine in the world can be decreased.
18. Describe the way in which people act as selecting agents in the evolution of food plants.
19. Name three medicines that were developed from plants.
20. What adaptive advantage might colorful flowers have for plants?

17. Farmers can use plants and cultivation techniques compatible with their region. Examples include planting cassava or millet in dry areas, and using agroforestry and mixed cropping in the tropics.
18. People propagate plants that have characteristics they find valuable, such as robustness or nutritional value.
19. Digitalis, from foxglove; aspirin and quinine, from the bark of trees; morphine and codeine from opium poppies
20. Colorful flowers are more likely to attract pollinators. Plants pollinated more frequently are more likely to reproduce.

Critical Thinking

1. The soybean is the third largest crop grown in the United States. In Asia, soybeans are a staple food. They are eaten fresh, dried, fermented, and processed into tofu. Some soybeans are used for animal feed or for oil. What aspects of the biology of soybeans might explain their importance to various countries of the world?
2. The drawing to the right shows pole beans that have grown up around corn stalks. What is this an example of? What advantage might each plant gain from this arrangement?
3. During the rainy season in the Brazilian rain forest the rivers flood the land. Many fish from these rivers then swim among the land plants and eat their fruit. How might this intermingling of fish and plants help the plants?

4. Many of the new crops that were planted as part of the Green Revolution required heavy applications of pesticides. In many countries the Green Revolution was followed by an increase in such diseases as malaria. Why might this have happened?

Extension

1. Read the article by Darna L. Dufour entitled "Use of Tropical Rainforests by Native Amazonians" in *BioScience,* October 1990, pp. 652–658. Prepare an oral report in which you describe how Amazonians use the tropical rainforest for agriculture, hunting, fishing and collecting. Include information on the history of Amazonians, and discuss ways in which human activities may have changed Amazonian ecosystems over the long term. How do the agricultural systems of Amazonians serve as models of sustainable agroecosystems?
2. Using your library, research the role that plants played in the European discovery and early development of America. Write a report on what you find. Include answers to the following questions in your report: What plant product was Columbus interested in when he sailed to America? What roles did tobacco, cotton, and spruce timber play in the colonial economy?
3. Make a list of all the news items about plants or plant products that appear in your daily newspaper over one week. Don't forget that petroleum, plastics, natural gas, and coal are derived from plants.
4. Choose one food crop—potatoes, sorghum, tea, barley, tomatoes, or sugar cane—and write a report on its history, cultivation, uses, and current production.
5. Using your library, research a famine that has occurred within the last 200 years. Give an oral report in which you describe the causes of the famine, the events that brought about its end, and any changes that were made to prevent future famines in the region.
6. Read the article by Carolyn Strange entitled "Cereal Progress via Biotechnology" in *BioScience,* January 1990, pp. 5–14. Write a report in which you discuss the genetic manipulation of cereals. Why are the breakthroughs being made in this field of research so significant?

Critical Thinking

1. Soybeans have a very high protein content and have root nodules with nitrogen-fixing bacteria. They can grow in poor soils and are an ideal food crop.
2. The drawing shows an example of mixed cropping, or companion planting. Corn needs a lot of nitrogen to grow, some of which is fixed by the roots of the beans. The corn provides the beans with climbing support and partial shade.
3. The fish may help to disperse the seeds of the fruits.
4. Many diseases are carried by insects; for example, malaria is carried by mosquitoes. Pesticides are not species-specific and may kill predators of insects as well as the target insects. Also, mosquitoes that survive pesticides form the foundation of a sturdier, pesticide-resistant mosquito population. New farming techniques may also provide new breeding areas such as irrigation ditches.

Extension

1. They are models of how to preserve soil fertility in the deeply weathered and leached soils common to the rain forest.
2. Columbus was primarily interested in spices. The rise of plantation agriculture, especially for cotton, sugar, and tobacco, shaped the economy of the South, which remained largely unchanged until after the Civil War.
3. You may want to provide space on the bulletin board for posting of the lists.
4. Reports will vary with the food crops chosen.
5. Answers will vary. In that time period, famines have occurred in Africa, India, Bangladesh, China, Ireland, and many other areas.
6. Cereals feed the world. Until now, they have resisted attempts to alter their genes.

Chapter 25 Plant Evolution and Classification

Chapter Overview

Chapter 25 concentrates on features that set plants apart from other living things. Section 25.1 gives students an overview of the Kingdom Plantae. Section 25.2 familiarizes students with the nonvascular plants that compose the Division Bryophyta. Section 25.3 introduces students to the major characteristics of vascular plants, including both seedless and seed plants.

Chapter Planning Chart

B	S	A	Sections and Subsections	Page	Features	Page	Resources
•	•	•	**25.1 Overview of Plants**				
			Adaptations to Land	365	Biology in Process	366	Videodiscs
			Evolution	366	Section Review	368	Section Reviews Worksheet
			Classification	367			
			Reproduction	368			
•	•	•	**25.2 Nonvascular Plants**				
			Musci	369	Section Review	370	Videodiscs
			Hepaticae and Anthocerotae	370			Section Reviews Worksheet
•	•	•	**25.3 Vascular Plants**				
			Seedless Vascular Plants	371	Think	375	Videodiscs
			Seed Plants	373	Laboratory	377	Laboratories: Plant Diversity
					Section Review	376	Blackline Master 50
							Blackline Master 51
							Overhead Transparency T25
							Process Skills: Tree Classification by Leaves
							Section Reviews Worksheet
			End of Chapter Activities				
					Chapter Review	378	Vocabulary Skills
							Chapter Test
							Computer Test Generator

B *The Basic Level curriculum presents the most fundamental knowledge offered in the course.*
S *The Standard Level curriculum is designed for the average student who is able to master most topics.*
A *The Advanced Level curriculum includes suggestions for teaching the most academically able students.*

Cooperative Learning

Group Activity: Designing a Fantasy Plant

- **Group Size:** *3 students*
- **Outcome:** *Students will explain how plant structures are adaptations for obtaining water, carrying on photosynthesis, and reproducing.*
- **Individual Accountability:** *Each group member will design and construct a plant part adapted to a particular survival function.*
- **Positive Interdependence:** *The groups will evaluate and compare their plants after construction.*

Tell groups of students to design and construct a fantasy plant. Explain that each plant must include the following three adaptations: a way of getting water, a structure in which photosynthesis takes place, and a way of reproducing. Plants need not be limited to living on land. Have each group member design and construct one of the three required adaptations. Emphasize that the structures need not be working models.

Provide construction materials such as modeling clay, drinking straws, buttons, toothpicks, sequins, Styrofoam packing material, pipe cleaners, tape, glue, and anything else you can think of. Encourage students to be as wildly creative as they can be in inventing and constructing their adaptations. After groups have had time to assemble their plants, ask each group to present their plant to the class and explain how it is structured to carry out the three required adaptations.

Concept Map

The following is one possible solution to the concept mapping activity in Closure on p. 376.

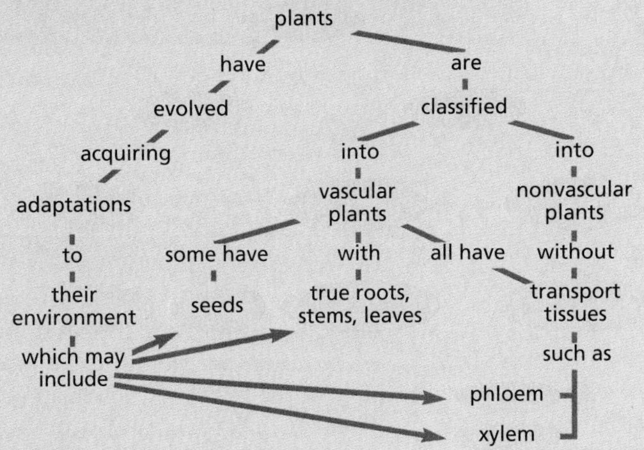

Laboratory Preparation

Overview *(See p. 377.)*

This lab enables students to observe and compare characteristics of vascular seed plants including a representative gymnosperm (conifer) and representative angiosperms (monocot and dicot). Students observe such gross structural differences as presence of flowers or cones, leaf type and arrangement, and venation patterns. Students use their observations to determine distinguishing characteristics of major groups of plants. Students then use their knowledge and observations to classify specimens according to division (Coniferophyta and Anthophyta) and class (Monocotyledoneae and Dicotyledoneae).

Preparation

Specimens should have leaves and flowers or cones in place. Use fresh specimens if possible. This laboratory is best conducted when specimens can be collected outdoors rather than purchased. However, fresh, slightly damaged specimens can often be obtained free from a florist or greenhouse. Preserved specimens are available from biological supply houses. Choose from representative conifers (pine, cedar, juniper, yew, fir, spruce), monocots (lily, sedge, iris, gladiolus, onion, amaryllis), and dicots (magnolia, rose, azalea, morning glory, apple blossom, snapdragon). Label the conifer specimens *A*, the monocots *B*, and the dicots *C*.

Teaching Tips

Remind students of the classification of land plants, especially those classified as gymnosperms and angiosperms. You may want to review the terms *division* and *class* as well as *angiosperm* and *gymnosperm.*

Avoid using highly specialized anthophytes (angiosperms). Petals should be easy to identify and count. Leaf venation should be evident.

This lab can be used as an introduction to plant structures, Chapters 26 and 27. The lab in Chapter 27, Germinating Seeds, can be used for Further Inquiry in this lab.

Safety

Remind students to use scalpels and single-edge razor blades with care. Remind students to wash their hands after handling specimens.

Chapter Themes

Evolution Explain to students reasons why biologists infer that land plants evolved from green algae of the Division Chlorophyta. Both have the same types of chlorophyll, store food as starch, and have cellulose in their cell walls. Highlight plant adaptations to life on land.

Scale and Structure Explain to students that bryophytes are nonvascular plants, most of which are small and lie close to soil or bark of trees in order to absorb water rapidly. Point out to students that leafy forms of bryophytes are gametophytes and that sporophytes have varying shapes ranging from stalk-like to parasol shaped. Help students understand differences between gymnosperms and angiosperms, and between monocots and dicots.

Patterns of Change Emphasize to students that all plants have alternation of generations as a feature of their life cycles. Make sure that students understand that the gametophyte, or haploid stage, looks different from the sporophyte, or diploid stage.

Chapter Motivating Activity

Hold up a coconut and small seed, such as a tomato seed taped to an index card, and ask what the two have in common. *(Both are seeds.)* Hold up a flowering potted plant, such as a geranium, and picture of an oak or a maple tree, and ask what the two have in common. *(Both are flowering plants.)* Impress upon students that organisms may be related even though their external structures may not seem similar.

Chapter 25 Plant Evolution and Classification

Introduction

Kingdom Plantae includes over 350,000 species of multicellular, land-dwelling, photosynthesizing organisms. This chapter will provide you with an overview of plants, from the seemingly most simple to the most complex. It will also concentrate on features that set plants apart from other living things. You will learn more about the details of plant biology as you read the rest of the chapters in this unit.

Chapter Outline

Chapter Concept

As you read, look for characteristics of plant divisions that reflect their relative level of complexity and reveal their possible phylogenetic relationships.

Carboniferous forest. Inset: orchid.

Understanding the Visuals

Point out to students that none of the plants in the illustration of the forest have flowers. Ask students why the two pictures—of the Carboniferous forest and orchid flowers—were chosen to introduce this chapter. *(Some plants evolved flowers; some did not.)* Ask students what they think the brown structures hanging from the plants in the foreground are. *(Students may suggest that these structures look like seeds or fruit. They are probably sporangia.)* Explain that the structure of ferns shown in the drawing is relatively simple compared with the very complex structures of flower-bearing plants.

25.1 Overview of Plants

At the start of the Silurian period, about 430 million years ago, organisms lived only in aquatic environments. Fishes and mollusks were diversifying, and vast colonies of marine algae thrived near turbulent shores. Corals flourished in warm, shallow waters, but the land was almost as barren as the face of the moon.

At the end of the Silurian, about 395 million years ago, evolutionary events occurred that were to have a huge biological impact. Club-shaped plants, no bigger than your little finger, began to grow and survive in the wet mud at the edge of aquatic habitats. Plants had arrived on land.

Adaptations to Land

Biologists infer that land plants evolved from green algae of the Division Chlorophyta that lived in ancient oceans or ponds. The strongest evidence for this inference lies in observed similarities between modern green algae and plants. Both have the same photosynthetic pigments, chlorophyll *a* and *b;* both store food in the form of starch; and both have cellulose cell walls.

Moving from water to land offered organisms some distinct competitive advantages: greater availability of sunlight for photosynthesis, increased levels of carbon dioxide, and decreased vulnerability to predation. However, the land environment also presented challenges. For example, plants on land were exposed to the dangers of drying out, or desiccating, through evaporation. One early adaptation to life on land was the **cuticle** *(KYOOT-ih-kul),* a waxy protective covering. Cuticles prevent desiccation and were naturally selected in early land dwellers.

Gametes also were susceptible to desiccation. Successful land plants developed multicellular structures that helped protect gametes—eggs and sperm—during development. The presence of these **multicellular gametangia** *(GAM-uh-TAN-jee-uh),* or gamete "holders," is the distinguishing feature of plants.

Certain plants evolved with specialized structures that absorbed water from the soil. Some of these plants also evolved complex tissues, called **vascular** *(VASS-kyuh-lur)* **tissues,** that transported water and food from one part of the plant to another. Vascular tissues also helped support the plants, an important function since plants living on land are not supported by the buoyancy of water.

As evolution proceeded, other adaptations occurred. Adaptations that increased the ability of the stems to absorb light were selected for, as were underground stems that anchored plants to the land and absorbed nutrients and water. Many plants evolved with tissues that stored the food made in photosynthesis. Fossil evidence indicates that light-absorbing stems gradually evolved into true leaves. Underground stems gradually evolved into true

Section Objectives

- *Compare and contrast green algae and plants.*
- *Name three adaptations of plants to life on land.*
- *Compare vascular and nonvascular plants.*
- *Define and describe alternation of generations.*
- *Summarize what paleobotanists have inferred regarding plant evolutionary history.*

Figure 25-1 ***Fritschiella,*** **a green alga, has some characteristics that are similar to plants.**

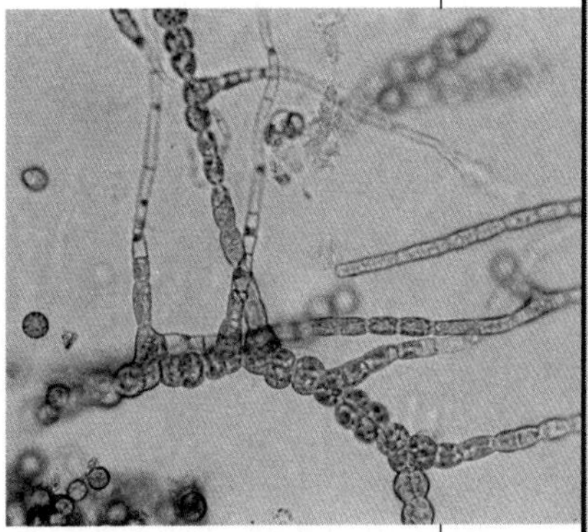

Land Plant Adaptations	Adaptive Advantage
cuticle	prevents desiccation
multicellular gametangia	protect gametes during development
vascular tissues	transport food and water throughout plant
underground stem	anchors plant to land and absorbs nutrients and water
spores	allow widespread dispersal of reproductive cells
seeds	protect and nourish embryos
woody tissues	allow growth to great height, an advantage in gathering light

Graphic Organizer Use this table in Organizing Information on p. 366.

Lesson Plan

Section Focus

This section introduces information on plant adaptations to land and briefly covers plant evolution, classification, and reproduction, including the concept of alternation of generations.

Section Themes

This section is concerned with the theme of **Evolution.** Plants produced such evolutionary adaptations to land as a cuticle, multicellular gametangia, and vascular tissues. The theme of **Patterns of Change** is also clearly illustrated by alternation of generations, the reproductive life cycle common to all plants.

Motivating Activity

To emphasize evolutionary adaptations made by vascular plants to life on land, show the class a beaker with algae, obtained by cleaning an aquarium, and a potted plant. Ask students which has more trouble obtaining water. *(The potted, vascular plant, because it lives on land)* Which is more likely to dry out? *(The potted, vascular plant; it lives on land)* Which needs roots? *(The potted, vascular plant; it lives on land)*

Teaching Strategies

Making Connections As students read the section, have them refer to Table 15-1 on p. 221 to help place the geologic periods in context.

Videodiscs

- ***Side 3 26888, Stomatal Opening (m)***
- ***2542, Plant Cell (s)***

Organizing Information Help students organize information in the subsection Adaptations to Land by having them contribute to a table you write on the board. An example of a completed table is shown on p. 365.

Interpreting the Visuals Once students are familiar with classification of plants, have them interpret the graph in Figure 25-3, p. 367. Ask students which plants were the first to develop. *(Nonvascular plants)* Which division of plants has the most species in existence today? *(Angiosperms)* In what order did land plants appear? *(Nonvascular plants, ferns and fern allies, gymnosperms, and finally angiosperms)* Point out to students that this order is related to the order of development of specific adaptations such as vascular tissue and seeds. *(Example: Ferns and their allies had vascular tissue; gymnosperms had naked seeds; angiosperms had enclosed seeds.)*

Making Inferences Make sure that students understand that nonvascular plants have no tissues having the specific function of transporting water and food from one part of the plant to another. Ask students how then do food and water move in these plants. *(The plants are small, and movement through tissues takes place by diffusion, osmosis, and active transport.)* Ask students where mosses are found. *(In damp places)* Why are mosses limited to growing close to the ground? *(They lack specialized tissue to transport water or support height.)*

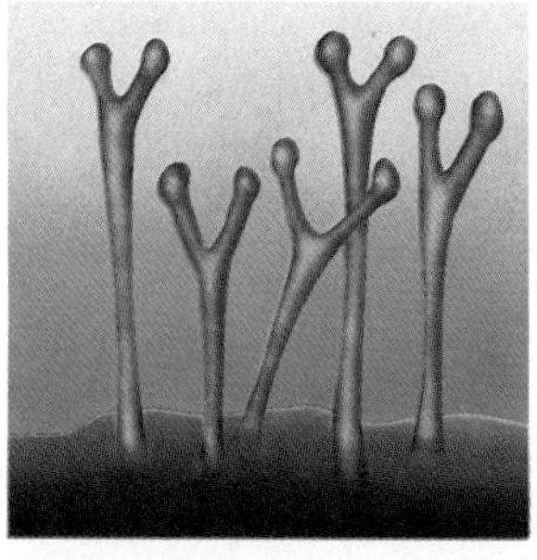

Figure 25-2 ***Cooksonia,*** **the earliest known plant, had reproductive structures at the tips of leafless stems.**

roots. Resistant reproductive cells called **spores** evolved with the first land plants and allowed widespread dispersal of species. Much later some plants developed seeds, which protected and nourished embryos. Some developed woody tissues and grew to great heights, giving them an advantage in gathering light.

Evolution

Much of what we know about plant phylogeny has come from the study of the fossil record.The earliest known plant fossil is of the genus *Cooksonia.* This genus appears in rock dating from the late Silurian period, about 400 million years ago. *Cooksonia* grew to only about 10 cm high and had forked, leafless stems with reproductive structures at the tips. It also had vascular tissue, which suggests that it lived on land. Other leafless plants, such as *Rhynia* and *Zosterophyllum,* appear in fossils from the early Devonian period, about 390 million years ago. Mid-Devonian fossils from about 345 million years ago include plants with true leaves.

Fossils from the late Devonian period indicate that by 340 million years ago trees had evolved. Giant horsetails, giant club mosses, and tree ferns dominated the forests of the late Devonian

Biology in Process

Healing Old Wounds

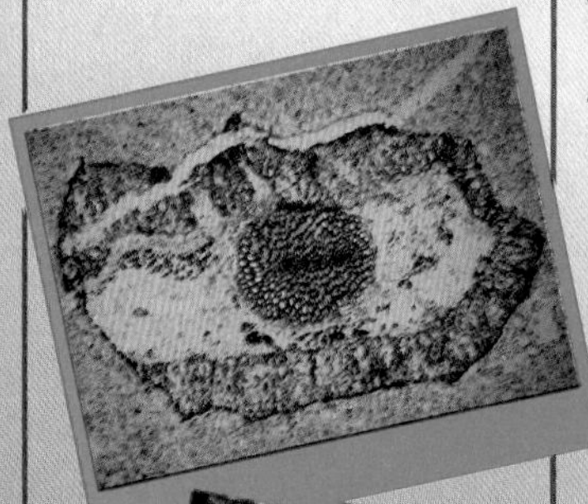

Dr. Harlan Banks, paleobotanist from Cornell University in New York, was tracking down a fossil stem that he could not identify. Banks was examining the internal structure of a microfossil petrified within a stone from the Gaspé Bay area in Quebec, Canada. He had cut the stone into thousands of slices so thin that light could shine through them. As he studied them one by one beneath a microscope, he found something peculiar. An accidental discovery revealed an early adaptation of plants to the upsurge of another life form in their habitat—the arthropods.

Twenty-eight of the stone slices revealed a wound in the plant stem, the legacy of some long-extinct, nibbling arthropod—possibly an early insect-like creature. Dead cells fringed the space where the arthropod had eaten the plant's xylem, inner cortex, and phloem. Although such wounds had been noted before, Banks's specimen was the first to show the growth of periderm, an outer protective tissue found in vascular plants, over the wound site.

No other specimens in the Gaspé Bay rocks or in any of the other specimens Banks had studied showed any evidence of

LEP Activity

Students will be aware of the general characteristics of many common plants. To tap into this prior knowledge, help students list names and characteristics of plants on the board. Students can offer examples from all major plant categories. *(Examples: trees—woody trunks, roots, green leaves; nonvascular plants—contain chlorophyll, multicellular, moist habitat; ferns—lacy, green leaves, strong stems, roots; flowers—green leaves, showy blossom, roots)* Ask students to think about features that all plants share. If possible, take students on a walking tour of the campus or neighborhood to classify plants.

and Carboniferous periods. Ancestors of today's pine trees appeared in the late Carboniferous period, about 280 million years ago. Flowering plants, the dominant group of plants on the earth today, did not evolve until the early Cretaceous period, only 135 million years ago.

Classification

Taxonomists divide land plants into two groups based on whether or not they have vascular tissue. The **nonvascular plants,** members of the Division Bryophyta *(brie-AHF-uh-tuh),* have neither vascular tissue nor true roots, stems, or leaves. Members of the nine divisions of **vascular plants** have water-conducting tissues and most have true roots, stems, and leaves.

Study the classification of plants in Table 25-1 on the following page. You can see that vascular plants are further divided into two groups, the seedless plants and the seed plants. Seedless plants include ferns and the three divisions of plants called fern allies. Seed plants are classified into four divisions of **gymnosperms** *(JIM-nuh-SPERMZ)* and one division of **angiosperms** *(AN-jee-uh-SPERMZ),* or flowering plants.

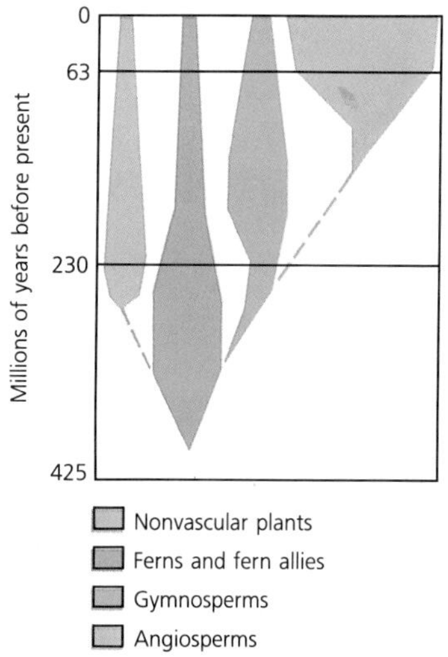

Figure 25-3 The width of each branch is proportionate to the number of species in existence at a given time.

healing. Instead, wounds were usually covered by a hodgepodge of disrupted cells. Here was the first evidence of a group of plant cells organized to heal a wound. Plainly, these fossilized plants were adapting and dealing with injuries in a new way—an important evolutionary development found in all modern vascular plants.

Banks's discovery is leading paleobotany in a host of new directions. Instead of trying to determine only what early plants looked like and how they evolved, botanists are trying to answer other questions, such as: What did the land look like before the first large land animals emerged? How did the plants interact with other creatures? What was the timing of evolutionary innovations? How does the timing of evolutionary developments match changes in the environment? What are the relationships between groups of ancient plants and similar groups of modern plants?

As paleobotanists and other scientists discover answers to questions, we will develop a clearer view and a better understanding of the ancient world. Banks has said, "The record shows that the success of paleobotany in recent decades stems from the ability . . . to learn to overcome the strictures of a morphological background and produce a new generation that has recognized the role of many disciplines of which Earth Sciences is one of the more obvious."

- **How did Harlan Banks infer that the organized cell layer over the wound site represented the formation of periderm?**

Biology in Process

Using the Feature

The feature focuses on the process skills of observing, hypothesizing, and inferring. Point out to students that although Dr. Banks was actually investigating microscopic internal structures of these fossils, he remained open to other observations. He saw peculiar characteristics—dead cells, missing xylem—that indicated a wound in the stem probably caused by an arthropod. He also noticed the evidence of tissue growth that had begun healing the wound before the plant died.

The age of the fossil coupled with Banks's observations led him to hypothesize that early fossilized plants did indeed have the potential for periderm formation. He inferred from the presence of periderm and marks of the injury that plants had been actively evolving in response to their environment as early as 374 million years ago.

Ask students how Dr. Banks's discovery of this tissue-healing activity supports a hypothesis he had made earlier—that the outer cortex of the plant he was studying, *Psilophyton,* was made up of living, growing cells, not dead ones as scientists had previously believed. *(For the tissue to cover the injury site in an organized pattern, it must have been made up of living cells. Dead cells do not grow.)*

Answer to the Feature

Banks had observed organized tissue response to injury by the periderm in modern plants. His previous examinations of fossilized plants had shown only disorganized collections of cells around injury sites. The organization of the cell layer covering the injury site provided evidence of periderm formation.

400 million years ago

Late Silurian
- *Cooksonia*—earliest known plant fossil

390–340 million years ago

Devonian
- leafless plants
- plants with leaves
- trees

340–280 million years ago

Carboniferous
- giant horsetails
- club mosses
- true ferns
- ancestors of conifers

135 million years ago

Cretaceous
- flowering plants

Use this sequential diagram in Reteaching on p. 368.

Section 25.1

Guided Practice
Use Figure 25-4, p. 368, to check students' understanding of alternation of generations. Ask them if a gametophyte is haploid or diploid. *(Haploid)* Are spores formed by mitosis or meiosis? *(Meiosis)* Then ask where in the diagram a seed belongs. *(After fertilization)* Where does a pollen grain belong? *(With gametes)*

Independent Practice
- Have students write answers to the Section Review.
- Ask students to distinguish between sporophyte and sporangium, and between gametophyte and gametangia.

Check Your Understanding
1. Why are nonvascular plants limited to growing small and close to the ground? *(They have no vascular tissue to support them.)*
2. What alternates during alternation of generations? *(Chromosomes, 1N to 2N)*

Reteaching
Have students make a sequential diagram of the evolution of land plants as understood from the fossil record. A sample diagram is shown on p. 367.
- *See* Section Reviews *worksheet, Section 25.1.*

Enrichment
Have students examine prepared slides of both vascular and nonvascular plants under the microscope. Have them compare what they see with Figure 26-9, p. 388, to identify vascular tissues.

Closure
Show students the algae and vascular plant from the Motivating Activity. Ask them what adaptations of the vascular plant help it live on land. *(Examples: cuticle, vascular tissues, roots, stem)*

Table 25-1 Land Plant Classification

Nonvascular plants	Vascular plants: Seedless	Vascular plants: Seed
Division Bryophyta: Mosses, liverworts, hornworts Class Musci Class Hepaticae Class Anthocerotae	Division Psilophyta: Whisk ferns Division Lycophyta: Clubmosses Division Sphenophyta: Horsetails Division Pterophyta: Ferns	*Gymnosperms* Division Cycadophyta: Cycads Division Ginkgophyta: Ginkgos Division Coniferophyta: Conifers Division Gnetophyta: Gnetophytes *Angiosperms* Division Anthophyta: Flowering plants Class Monocotyledonae Class Dicotyledonae

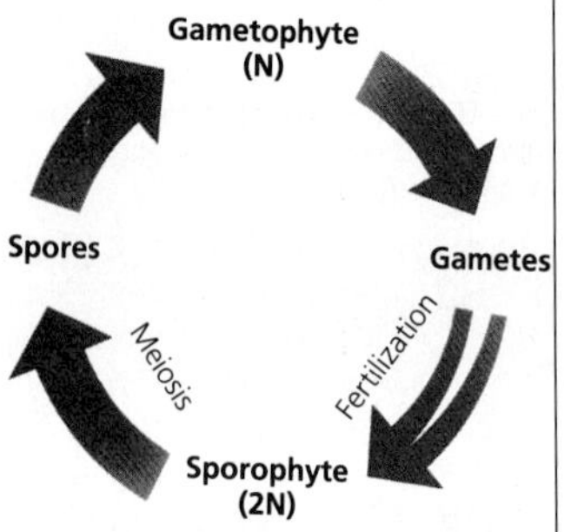

Figure 25-4 In the alternation of generations, plants alternate between a multicellular haploid stage and a multicellular diploid stage.

Reproduction
All plants have a sexual life cycle called **alternation of generations,** in which a haploid (1N) phase alternates with a diploid (2N) phase. As Figure 25-4 shows, a haploid multicellular **gametophyte** *(guh-MEET-uh-FITE)* produces gametes that join in fertilization to form a zygote. The zygote (2N) develops by mitosis into a diploid **sporophyte** *(SPOR-uh-FITE)*. The sporophyte then produces a **sporangium** *(spor-AN-jee-um)*, a spore-bearing sac. Some cells of the sporangium undergo meiosis and produce haploid (1N) spores. These spores are released and then develop into new 1N gametophytes. In all land plants the gametophyte looks different from the sporophyte. This type of life cycle is called a heteromorphic alternation of generations.

In nonvascular plants the gametophyte is the larger and more long-lived phase of the sexual life cycle. For example, the familiar, leafy, highly visible part of the moss plant is the gametophyte. In contrast, vascular plants have dominant sporophytes. In seed-bearing plants the gametophyte is not a separate plant as it usually is in mosses and ferns. An apple tree is an example of a sporophyte. Apple gametophytes are microscopic parts of the apple flower.

Section Review
1. What is the main difference between *vascular plants* and *nonvascular plants?*
2. What are the similarities between today's land plants and the green algae?
3. How has the evolution of spores contributed to the chances of success for land plants?
4. What is the principal difference between a gametophyte and a sporophyte?
5. Why did the cuticle represent an adaptive advantage for early land plants?

368 *Chapter 25*

Answers to Section Review
1. Nonvascular plants do not have specialized tissue systems that move food, water, and minerals from one part of the plant to another, while vascular plants do have these complex conducting systems.
2. Both have the same photosynthetic pigments, both have cellulose walls, and both store food as starch.
3. Spores are resistant to drying out and aid in dispersal.
4. The gametophyte produces gametes, and the sporophyte produces spores.
5. It gave protection from desiccation, allowing plants to survive outside the aquatic environment and begin to colonize dry land.

25.2 Nonvascular Plants

The nonvascular plants include about 23,000 species of mosses, liverworts, and hornworts that form the Division Bryophyta. Structural evidence suggests that bryophytes, though lacking vascular tissue, probably arose from a line of plants that had vascular tissues. For example, some bryophyte capsules have nonfunctioning stomata that resemble the stomata found in vascular plants, which you will learn more about in Chapter 26.

Without complex support and vascular systems, bryophytes seldom grow large. Most are small and lie close to the soil or to the bark of trees, where they can absorb water rapidly.

Bryophytes need water to reproduce because the sperm must swim through water to an egg. These plants live in damp areas but can also live in deserts and other dry environments, reproducing during periods of moisture. They can survive in extreme conditions by occupying small areas that are protected from the surrounding climate. For example, you might find mosses growing in the cool, moist cracks of desert rocks.

Section Objectives

- *Name the three types of plants that make up the Division Bryophyta.*
- *List the distinguishing characteristics shared by nonvascular plants.*
- *Compare sporophytes and gametophytes in bryophytes.*

Musci

Almost every land environment in the world is home to at least one of the more than 14,000 species of mosses of the Class Musci. The thick green carpets you see on shady forest floors actually consist of thousands of tiny moss gametophytes. Each gametophyte is attached to the soil by rootlike structures called **rhizoids** *(RIE-zoidz)*. Unlike roots, rhizoids do not conduct water. However, they do serve as anchors for the plants. Mosses also have leaflike structures only one cell thick that are adapted for photosynthesis and absorb moisture rapidly. Moss gametophytes can be found in sizes ranging from 1 cm to 1 m, but most moss plants are less than 15 cm in length.

Periodically moss gametophytes (1N) produce eggs and sperm. Sperm from one gametophyte fertilizes an egg from another gametophyte. The resulting zygote produces a stalklike sporophyte. The sporophyte forms a sporangium called a **capsule,** which matures and releases spores. The spores develop into tiny, green-branched filaments that grow into mature gametophytes.

Some mosses serve the important environmental function of acting as pioneer species in barren areas. By gradually breaking up the surface of rocks, for example, mosses create a layer of soil in which other plants can begin to grow. In areas devastated by fire, volcanic action, or human activities, pioneer mosses can help trigger the development of new biological communities. Their rhizoids also help prevent erosion by holding soil in place.

Sphagnum is a genus of moss that is a major component of peat bogs in the northern parts of the world. People in northern European and Asian countries mine and dry peat to use as fuel. In

Figure 25-5 Hand-cut sections are removed from peat bogs, dried in the sun, and used for home heating on the Isle of Lewis, Scotland.

Common Names	mosses liverworts hornworts
Structure	nonvascular; no true roots, stems, leaves
Life Cycle	gametophyte dominant; must have moisture to reproduce sexually

Graphic Organizer Use this table for Closure on p. 370.

Lesson Plan

Section Focus

This section classifies nonvascular plants. Division Bryophyta includes mosses (Class Musci), liverworts (Class Hepaticae), and hornworts (Class Anthocerotae)—all low-growing varieties adapted for rapid absorption of moisture.

Section Themes

The theme of **Structure and Function** is evident in descriptions of bryophyte reproductive cycles and structures of gametophytes and sporophytes.

Motivating Activity

Demonstrate the remarkable water-absorbing qualities of bryophytes. Determine the mass of a handful of dry *Sphagnum* moss (available from florists or garden shops) and place it in a beaker of water. After 10–15 minutes, remove the moss and again determine its mass. It can absorb many times its mass in water. Ask students how its ability to absorb water is related to survival of a bryophyte. *(Its leaflike structures are adapted for water absorption.)*

Teaching Strategies

Observing Organisms Many students may not have seen green moss covering a forest floor. If possible, obtain a live moss sample and allow students to look at it with a hand lens or dissecting microscope.

Videodiscs

- ***641, Bryophyta: Sporophyte Capsules of Moss (s)***
- ***Side 3 7798, Plant Reproduction: Moss (m)***
- ***Side 3 6715, Plant Reproduction: Liverwort (m)***
- ***637–639, Bryophyta: Liverworts (s)***

Section 25.2

Guided Practice

Bring moss samples or preserved specimens to class. Ask students to use Figure 27-1, p. 401, to identify gametophyte structures and their function. *(Examples: Antheridium, produces sperm; archegonium, produces egg cell)*

Independent Practice

- Have students write answers to the Section Review.
- Photocopy pictures of mosses, liverworts, and hornworts (gardening magazines and *National Geographic* are good sources). Ask students to identify the varieties and label rhizoids, gametophytes, and sporangia if they are visible.

Check Your Understanding

1. Name two adaptations that allow bryophytes to live on land. *(Cuticle, protects from drying; rhizoids, anchor plant)*
2. Compare rhizoids and roots. *(Both help anchor, but rhizoids contain no vascular tissues.)*

Reteaching

Ask students what adaptive advantage is offered by the circular arrangement of leaflike structures in mosses. *(It permits maximum exposure to light.)* Ask how the ability to absorb water is an advantage to mosses. *(It traps maximum moisture in dry conditions.)*
- *See* **Section Reviews** ***worksheet, Section 25.2.***

Enrichment

Have students research and make miniature terrariums in jars or clear plastic soda bottles. Include mosses and other plants. Have students keep a weekly record, observing changes in plants in the terrariums.

Closure

Have students construct on the board a table describing characteristics of nonvascular plants. A sample is shown on p. 369.

Figure 25-6 The conspicuous, leafy forms of moss plants, *Mnium hornum* (left), and liverworts, *Marchantia* sp. (right), are the gametophyte generation.

Ireland and other countries, this mining is so extensive that it threatens the survival of the bog communities. *Sphagnum* mosses give off an acid that slows down decomposition in the bogs. Archeologists have recovered intact human remains that have been buried in bogs for thousands of years.

Hepaticae and Anthocerotae

Liverworts are bryophytes of the Class Hepaticae. Hornworts are bryophytes placed in the Class Anthocerotae. Combined, both classes have fewer species than does Musci, the class of mosses.

Some liverworts have a thalloid form—that is, a flat body that has distinguishable upper and lower surfaces. Other liverworts have a leafy form, with thin, transparent, leaflike structures arranged along a stemlike axis. Both kinds of liverworts lie close to the ground, an adaptation that allows the plant to absorb soil water readily. In some species the gametophyte is topped by a parasol-shaped structure that holds gametangia.

Hornworts resemble liverworts, but the structural details of their sporangia are different. Like liverworts, hornworts grow in moist, shaded habitats. They share an unusual characteristic with algae: each of their cells has a single large chloroplast rather than numerous small ones.

Section Review

1. What is a *capsule?*
2. How are bryophytes different from all other plant divisions?
3. What role do mosses play in the early development of biological communities?
4. Some liverworts have leaflike structures that absorb water rapidly. In what way is this an important feature for a nonvascular plant?
5. Why are bryophytes classified along with plants instead of with algae?

Answers to Section Review

1. A capsule is a sporangium produced by a moss sporophyte. It grows out of, and is attached to, the archegonium of the moss gametophyte.
2. They do not have vascular tissue.
3. By breaking up rock surfaces, mosses create a layer of soil in which other plants can grow.
4. Because the plant has no vascular transport system, the liverwort must absorb as much water as possible over as much of its surface as possible. The more rapidly and efficiently it can absorb water, the more likely it will be healthy and able to reproduce.
5. Bryophytes have multicellular gametangia.

25.3 Vascular Plants

Why are vascular plants so numerous? Biologists suggest that certain specializations permit vascular plants to live in more kinds of environments than nonvascular plants can. For example, the strong stems of vascular plants enable them to grow tall. The height of vascular plants allows them to rise above other plants, thereby getting an unimpeded source of sunshine. Without the hindrance of shade from other plants, vascular plants are able to make and distribute food efficiently.

Two types of tissue make up the vascular system. **Xylem** *(ZIE-lum)* carries water and dissolved minerals from the roots to the stems and leaves. **Phloem** *(FLOE-um)* transports the sugar made by photosynthesis from the leaves to the rest of the plant. Phloem also carries stored food from the roots to other plant parts. Both types of vascular tissue are composed of cells with thick walls, which also help support the plant stem.

Section Objectives

- *Describe the two main functions of vascular tissues.*
- *Distinguish between gymnosperms and angiosperms.*
- *Summarize the adaptive advantages of seeds.*
- *Distinguish between monocots and dicots.*

Seedless Vascular Plants

Seedless vascular plants were probably much more common during the Devonian period than they are today. The four divisions of modern seedless plants are Psilophyta *(sie-LAHF-uh-tuh)*, Lycophyta *(lie-KAHF-uh-tuh)*, Sphenophyta *(sfee-NAHF-uh-tuh)*, and Pterophyta *(ter-AHF-uh-tuh)*. Members of the first three divisions are fern allies, while members of the last are ferns.

Psilophyta, Lycophyta, and Sphenophyta

The Division Psilophyta is represented by whisk ferns of the genus *Psilotum*. Despite their name, members of this genus are not ferns at all. They have no roots or leaves and produce sporangia on the ends of short branches. These features suggest that *Psilotum* resembles early land plants. Whisk ferns live in tropical and subtropical climates.

The Division Lycophyta includes three related genera: the spikemosses, club mosses, and quillworts. Spikemosses are vascular plants in the genus *Selaginella*. Club mosses, which make up the genus *Lycopodium*, are small evergreen plants that often look like tiny pine trees. Club mosses have numerous leaves with a

Figure 25-7 The whisk fern, *Psilotum* sp. (left), a club moss, *Lycopodium* (center), and the spikemoss, *Selaginella* sp. (right), illustrate the diversity of seedless vascular plants.

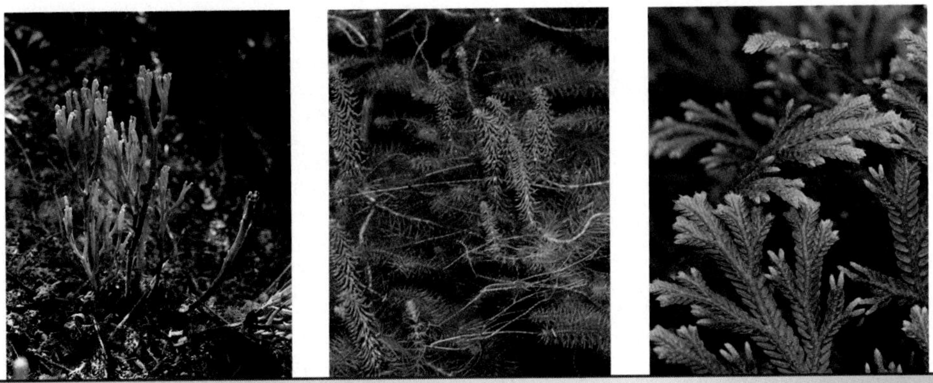

Lesson Plan

Section Focus

This section explains why vascular plants are so numerous, describes four divisions of seedless plants, presents evolutionary advantages of seeds, and compares gymnosperms with angiosperms and monocots with dicots.

Section Themes

The theme of **Evolution** is emphasized in descriptions of divisions of vascular plants in terms of adaptive advantages of their structures. The theme of **Scale and Structure** is also integrated into the section, as characteristic structures of vascular plants are described at the division level.

Motivating Activity

To help students grasp the essential differences among seedless plants, gymnosperms, and angiosperms, bring examples of each variety to class; for example, a potted fern, pine or yew branch with cones, and an apple branch. Ask students which plant grows without seeds. *(The fern)* Which plants bear seeds? *(The yew, pine, and apple)*. Which plant has its seeds protected by a fruit? *(Only the apple)* Point out that only angiosperms have seeds protected by fruits. Ask students to identify the gymnosperm(s) and explain their answers. *(The pine or yew branch, because the seeds are not protected by a fruit)*

Videodiscs

- ***1955–1956, Vascular Cambium and Phloem; Xylem (s)***
- ***644–646,* Selaginella *(s)***

Division	Characteristics	Examples
Psilophyta	not ferns; no roots or leaves; produce sporangia	whisk ferns
Lycophyta	bear spores near bases of leaves	club mosses
Sphenophyta	jointed stems, scalelike leaves; outer cells have silicon dioxide	horsetails
Pterophyta	rhizome; true roots and leaves; produce sporangia on lower surfaces of leaves	ferns

Graphic Organizer Use this table in Organizing Information on p. 372.

Teaching Strategies

Interpreting the Visuals Have students look at Figures 25-7 through 25-9, pp. 371–372. Ask students what generation is represented in each picture. *(Sporophyte)* What reproductive structures does this generation produce? *(Spores)*

Observing Organisms Show students several types of ferns. A florist, greenhouse manager, or fellow teachers probably can lend you examples. Point out the fronds and the underground horizontal stems and roots. Ask students how ferns differ from bryophytes. *(Ferns have phloem and xylem running through their roots, fronds, and stems; bryophytes have no roots, stems, or vascular tissues.)* What enables ferns to surpass bryophytes in height and size? *(Their vascular tissues)*

If any ferns have sori on their undersides, help students cut them open and make wet mounts of their contents. To view the spores, have students observe the slides under a microscope.

Organizing Information It may be easier for students to remember information about seedless vascular plants if it is organized in a table. Have students make tables that list four divisions of seedless vascular plants, their characteristics, and examples. An example of a completed table is shown on p. 371.

Figure 25-8 The quillwort, *Isoetes storkii* (left), bears spores on all leaves, while the horsetail, *Equisetum tamateia* (right), has a spore-bearing, whitish shoot as well as green nonfertile shoots.

Figure 25-9 Tree ferns, *Cyathea smithii,* are the largest living ferns. Which generation is represented here?

tough cuticle that helps retain water. The small quillworts, members of the genus *Isoetes,* live submerged in ponds and lakes. You can see in Figure 25-8 that their tubular leaves resemble small feather quills. Members of all three of these genera bear spores near the bases of their leaves. However, some species of *Lycopodium* have their sporangia-bearing leaves grouped into a conelike structure called a **strobilus.**

The Division Sphenophyta includes plants of the genus *Equisetum,* or horsetails. Horsetails have jointed stems and scalelike leaves. The outer cells of these gritty-feeling plants contain silicon dioxide, the major component of sand. Native Americans and early settlers used horsetails as pot scrubbers. This practice led to another common name for the genus, scouring rushes.

Horsetails thrive near streams and ponds and also grow hardily in the tropics. Some may even grow in dry sand along roadbeds or railroad tracks. As you can see in Figure 25-8, horsetails may have two types of shoots—vegetative and fertile. The vegetative shoots of horsetails have scalelike leaves that are arranged in a whorl and lie flat on the stem. At the top of each fertile shoot is a spore-bearing strobilus. The spores blow away in the wind. They land and develop into small gametophytes.

Pterophyta

Ferns probably originated in the early Carboniferous period, about 335 million years ago. Ancestral ferns, along with giant types of club mosses and horsetails, composed the vast coal-forming forests illustrated at the beginning of this chapter.

The 12,000 species of modern ferns are members of the Division Pterophyta. Ferns are a diverse group. Some are tiny aquatic plants. Others live high in jungle trees or in the cracks of mountaintop rocks. Ferns also grow above the Arctic Circle and in desert regions. The largest living ferns are tree ferns, shown in Figure 25-9. These ferns can reach 25 m in height, and some have leaves 5 m long.

Interdisciplinary Activity

Language Arts Many poems have been written about trees. Suggest that students read one or more of the following poems. Each student might also wish to draw a picture of what one of these poems brings to mind. Robert Frost: "Tree at My Window," "Christmas Trees," "The Sound of Trees," "Stopping by Woods on a Snowy Evening," "In Hardwood Groves," or "Birches." Edna St. Vincent Millay: "City Trees," "Hangman's Oak," "The Oak-Leaves," "The Leaf and the Tree," or "The Hedge of Hemlocks."

Most ferns have an underground stem called a **rhizome**. The rhizome contains vascular tissues and produces roots that absorb water and minerals from the soil. The leaves of ferns arise as tiny coiled leaves called **fiddleheads**. Fiddleheads uncoil and develop into mature leaves called **fronds**. Even the fronds of tropical tree ferns begin as fiddleheads.

Ferns produce sporangia and spores on the lower surface of their leaves. If you turn a fern leaf over, you can see the usually circular sori *(SOE-ree)*. These are clusters of sporangia where spores are formed. When the spores are mature, the sporangium breaks and the spores are scattered.

Seed Plants

Spores of land plants are unicellular reproductive structures formed by meiosis in a sporangium. A **seed**, however, is a multicellular structure that contains an embryo. You will learn more about the nature of a seed in Chapter 27.

Seeds are an evolutionary success story. Seeds increase the chances that a plant will have reproductive success. Inside the tough protective coat of a seed is an embryo and a food supply. When conditions are too hot or too cold, or too wet or too dry, the seed remains inactive. When conditions favor growth, the seed germinates—that is, the embryo begins to grow into a young plant called a seedling.

Seeds helped the seed plants survive while many seedless land plants died out in the dry climate of the late Mesozoic era. Today there are five divisions of seed plants. Seven hundred species of living gymnosperms compose four divisions: Cycadophyta, Ginkgophyta, Coniferophyta, and Gnetophyta. Gymnosperms produce "naked" seeds; they are not enclosed in fruits. The other division is Anthophyta, the angiosperms. Angiosperm seeds are enclosed in fruits.

Cycadophyta and Ginkgophyta

Cycads *(SIE-kadz)* are gymnosperms of the Division Cycadophyta. They flourished during the Mesozoic era, the age of the dinosaurs. Only about 100 species of cycads survive today, most of which are native to the tropics. Like palm trees, most cycads have their leaves at the top of a short, thick trunk. Cycad plants are either male or female and bear large cones like those shown in Figure 25-10.

Like the cycads, ginkgos *(GINK-oze)* flourished in the Mesozoic era. Ginkgos are gymnosperms of the species *Ginkgo biloba*, the only remaining species of the Division Ginkgophyta. Ginkgos are deciduous trees that grow well in cities, since they can tolerate air pollution. Female trees are rarely planted, however, because they produce messy seeds that have a strong, disagreeable odor. Notice the plum-shaped fleshy seeds on the ginkgo shown in Figure 25-10.

Figure 25-10 The cycad, *Encephalartos princeps* (below), and the ginkgo, *Ginkgo biloba* (bottom), are both gymnosperms with male and female individuals.

Observing Structures In some regions of the United States, fiddleheads are sold in produce sections of supermarkets in the spring. If possible, obtain a package and have students examine the fiddleheads under hand lenses or dissecting microscopes. You may even want to cook a batch for students to taste; if so, make arrangements with the home economics department or cook at home.

- *See* Laboratories, *Investigation 25.*

Comparing Terms Explain to students that the word part *-sperm* means "seed." Have students use dictionaries to find out what the words *gymnosperm* and *angiosperm* mean. *("Naked seed"; "vessel seed")* Then point out that plant divisions all end in the word part *-phyta,* and ask students what they think that *-phyta* means. Then have them consult a dictionary to find out. *(It means "plant.")*

Making Hypotheses Make sure students notice that in both cycads and ginkgos individual plants are either male or female. Ask students to form hypotheses about what adaptive advantage this arrangement might have, if any. *(Sample answers: It may not be an advantage; only a few of these species survive today. However, it is an advantage in that if an individual dies, only its eggs or sperm will be removed from the breeding pool, not both.)*

Videodiscs

- *2340, Pterophyta: Fern (s)*
- *647–650, Horsetail Fern (s)*
- *670–674, Coniferophyta (s)*
- *Side 3 9886, Plant Reproduction; Pine Life Cycle (m)*

LEP Activity

To help students understand what is meant by "naked seeds" in gymnosperms, have them cut through an apple, pear, cucumber, or other fruit to reveal the seeds. Make sure they notice that the angiosperm seeds are "clothed" in a fruit. Then present some "naked" pine seeds. Gather mature ovulate cones from pine trees, order from a biological supply house, or buy a small package of pine nuts in a market. Point out how exposed the gymnosperm seeds are when the scales of the cone are open. Tell students that the difference between angiosperm seeds and gymnosperm seeds that makes a gymnosperm seed "naked" depends on a difference at the embryo stage, which is not visible when the seeds are fully developed.

Interpreting the Visuals Review divisions of vascular plants from Table 25-1, p. 368. Make sure that students can list major features of each division: Psilophyta, whisk ferns *(No roots or leaves, sporangia on ends of short branches)*; Lycophyta, club mosses *(Spores near base of leaves)*; Sphenophyta, horsetails *(Jointed stems, scalelike leaves)*; Pterophyta, ferns *(Most have rhizomes, leaves arise as fiddleheads, sporangia on leaf undersurfaces)*; Cycadophyta, cycads *(Most have leaves on short, thick trunk, plants male or female, large cones)*; Ginkgophyta, ginkgos *(Deciduous, male or female, fleshy seeds)*; Coniferophyta, conifers *(Woody, both male and female cones, leaves are needles or scalelike)*; Gnetophyta, gnetophytes *(Vascular systems more like those of angiosperms than of gymnosperms)*; and Anthophyta, flowering plants *(Flowers, either monocots or dicots)*.
■ *See* Blackline Master *50.*

Making Hypotheses Make sure students notice that in conifers individual plants bear both male and female cones. Ask students to form hypotheses about what adaptive advantage this arrangement might have. *(Sample answer: It is an advantage in that if adult trees are widely scattered, they can self-pollinate.)*

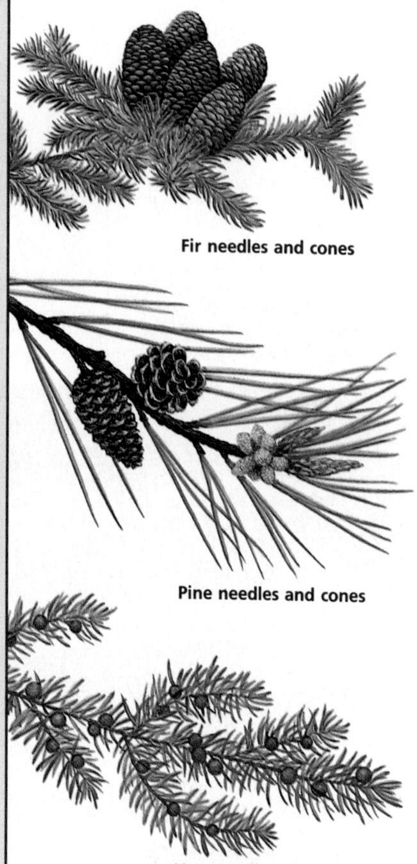

Figure 25-11 The needles and cones of conifers come in many shapes and sizes: fir, *Abies* sp. (top), pine, *Pinus* sp. (middle), and yew, *Taxus* sp. (bottom).

Coniferophyta

The conifers *(KAHN-uh-ferz),* which are gymnosperms of the Division Coniferophyta, include pine trees, cedars, junipers, redwoods, yews, firs, and spruces. Conifers are woody plants with needles or scalelike leaves. Each individual bears both male and female cones. The small male cones, which are strobili, appear in clusters. Most release clouds of dustlike pollen and then fall off their branches. After pollination, the complex, woody female cones close up tightly. This protects the developing seeds, which ripen and then are released.

The oldest living organisms in the world are conifers called bristlecone pines, which are found in the mountains of the Great Basin in California and Nevada. Some of these trees have survived for 4,900 years. Their age has been determined by biologists who specialize in analyzing the rings in the wood of trees and has been supported by radioactive dating techniques. The tallest trees in the world are also conifers. Redwoods growing along the Pacific coast of northern California may grow as high as 110 m, the height of a 30-story skyscraper. The tree most widely used for lumber and papermaking, the Douglas fir, is also a conifer.

Gnetophyta

An odd group of cone-bearing gymnosperms called gnetophytes *(NEE-tuh-FITES)* have vascular systems more like those of angiosperms than of gymnosperms. Botanists classify the 70 species of the Division Gnetophyta into three genera: *Ephedra, Gnetum,* and *Welwitschia.*

Ephedra (ih-FED-ruh) is an American desert genus, with clustered stems that look like horsetails. *Gnetum (NEE-tum)* is a genus of tropical vines or trees, with broad leaves that resemble those of flowering plants.

Welwitschia mirabilis (well-WIH-chee-uh mir-AH-buh-lus) is the only species in the genus. It grows in the Namib desert of southwestern Africa. The Namib lies near the Atlantic Ocean and receives more moisture than most deserts. Some nights a thick fog rolls in over the desert. *W. mirabilis* is modified to take advantage

Figure 25-12 *Welwitschia mirabilis* leaves direct excess water to the root. The underground root is the largest part of the plant.

Cooperative Learning

Plant Posters Divide the class into three groups. Ask students in each group to research and present alternation of generations and the reproductive life cycle of one of the three main groups of plants (nonvascular plants, seedless vascular plants, and vascular plants with seeds). Each group member should cooperate to complete library research and help create a poster to use as a visual aid. Groups should then select one member to present the information to the class using the instructional poster as a visual aid. Allow each group to make their presentation to the class, then display posters in the room.

of the fog. This plant has a single, huge, deeply penetrating root and only two leaves. The leaves extend out from the flat, tablelike stem. The leaves grow at their bases, and would be quite long if not for the wear and tear the tips take in the desert wind. *Welwitschia* leaves absorb the dew that condenses from the surrounding fog.

Anthophyta: Diversity

Today, about 275,000 species of the Division Anthophyta dominate the plant world. Angiosperms are flowering seed plants characterized primarily by the presence of a fruit. You will learn about the fruit in Chapter 27.

Angiosperms grow in many forms. Some are delicate herbs with showy blossoms, such as violets or orchids. In plant biology, the term *herb* refers to a nonwoody plant. Others, such as rosebushes, are woody shrubs. Some, such as the ivy you see growing on buildings, are vines. The oaks, aspens, and birches of the forest are all flowering plants, although you may never have noticed their blossoms. Grasses are also angiosperms, but you must look closely to see their tiny, highly modified flowers.

Angiosperms first appear in the fossil record at the beginning of the Cretaceous period, about 135 million years ago. At that time gymnosperms dominated the plant world. By 100 million years ago, however, flowering plants had probably begun to outnumber gymnosperms.

What led to the relatively sudden success of this new kind of plant? One factor is that angiosperm seeds are themselves enclosed in protective fruits. The fruits of flowering plants protect the seeds and aid in their dispersal. Additionally, angiosperms have highly efficient vascular systems.

Another important factor in the success of angiosperms is that they evolved along with insects. The fossil record indicates that this coevolution, or mutual adaptation, of flowering plants and insects began in the Cretaceous period (135 million to 65 million years ago). Many angiosperms can reproduce only when insects carry pollen from one plant to another. The insects visit the flowers for nourishing nectar and pollen. In doing so they pollinate plants.

Some plants have evolved remarkable means of attracting insects. For example, some flowers produce scent only at night, when the moths that pollinate them are active. Some species produce small amounts of nectar so that insects must visit many plants. You will learn more about pollination in Chapter 27.

Anthophyta: Classification

The Division Anthophyta has two classes—Monocotyledoneae and Dicotyledoneae. One feature that distinguishes these two groups is the number of **cotyledons,** or seed leaves. **Monocots** have a single cotyledon in their embryos, while **dicots** have two. Mature monocot leaves have parallel venation—arrangement of

Think

Through the coevolution of plants and insects, many unique methods of attracting insects to flowers have evolved. What do you think is the value of the bright yellow nectar guides on the purple irises shown here?

Answer to Think

The nectar guides lead insects to the center of the flower, where they will find nectar.

Interpreting the Visuals Take students step-by-step through the monocot and dicot characteristics shown in Figure 25-13, p. 376. Begin with leaves, and point out parallel veins versus net veins. In flowers, point out multiples of three versus multiples of four or five. In seeds, point out one versus two cotyledons.

- *See* **Overhead Transparency** ***T25 and*** **Blackline Master** ***51.***

Guided Practice

Have students turn back to Figure 25-3, the graph on p. 367. Tell them to identify each division in Section 25-3. *(Psilophyta, Lycophyta, Sphenophyta, and Pterophyta belong in "Ferns and Fern Allies"; Cycadophyta, Ginkgophyta, Coniferophyta, and Gnetophyta in "Gymnosperms"; Anthophyta in "Angiosperms.")*

Independent Practice

- Have students write answers to the Section Review.
- Have students use a dichotomous key to classify common leaves.
- *See* **Process Skills,** ***Chapter 25.***

Videodiscs

- ***675–746, Angiosperms: Examples (s)***

More Information

Bodies in the Bog In 1984 peat cutters at Lindow Moss near Manchester, England, discovered the body of a man so well preserved that they called the local police; they thought that they had uncovered remains of a recent murder victim. What they had uncovered were apparently the remains of a Druid prince from about A.D. 60, who had offered himself as a human sacrifice. To learn the full story of the investigation of Lindow Man and the archeologists who used the process skills of science to uncover his story, read *The Life and Death of a Druid Prince* by Anne Ross and Don Robbins (Summit Books, 1989) or *The Bogman and the Archeology of People* by Don Brothwell (Harvard University Press, 1987).

Section 25.3

Check Your Understanding

1. Of what adaptive advantage is having both male and female cones on the same tree? *(A tree growing alone in an area can still reproduce.)*

2. What adaptive advantage do seeds of angiosperms have over seeds of gymnosperms? *(Seeds of angiosperms are enclosed in protective fruits. Fruits may also aid in seed dispersal.)*

3. Of what importance are insects to flowering plants? *(Insects pollinate many types of flowering plants; without pollination, the plants could not reproduce.)*

Reteaching

Provide old magazines and seed or gardening catalogs for students to cut up. Have the class cut out pictures of plants that represent major divisions of vascular plants and sort the pictures into those that produce seeds and those that do not. Then have students sort seed plants into those that flower and those that do not. Finally, have them sort flowering plants into monocots and dicots.

■ *See* Section Reviews *worksheet, Section 25.3.*

Enrichment

Have groups of students research ornamental plants in different regions or countries. *(Examples: bonsai, Japan; ferns, England; cactuses, Southwest United States; African violets, Tanzania; ti plant, Hawaii)*

Closure

To help students organize information presented about evolution and classification of plants, have them make a concept map. An example of a completed concept map is shown on p. 363B.

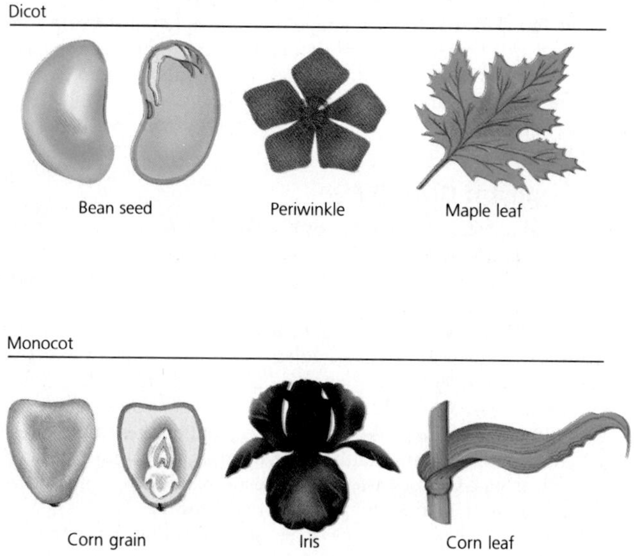

Figure 25-13 Monocots and dicots each have their own characteristic number of cotyledons, flower symmetry, and leaf venation.

veins—while dicot leaves have net venation. You can also recognize monocots by the three-part symmetry of their flowers. In contrast, most dicot flower parts occur in fours or fives, as you can see in Figure 25-13.

The approximately 90,000 monocot species include lilies, sedges, irises, onions, orchids, corn, bamboo, and leeks. A small number of woody trees, including coconuts and other palms, are also monocots. Much of the world's food supply comes from the grains of monocot grasses, such as wheat, oats, corn, rye, and rice.

Dicots include the majority of the flowering plants, such as magnolias, mustards, and maples as well as cactuses and most forest trees. In fact, with about 185,000 species, dicots are the most abundant and diverse group of all the plants that have adapted to life on land.

Section Review

1. What are *xylem* and *phloem,* and what functions do they perform?
2. What is the main difference between gymnosperms and angiosperms?
3. What are the three genera that compose the Division Gnetophyta?
4. What are the three differences that distinguish monocots and dicots?
5. What reproductive advantages do seed plants have over seedless vascular plants and nonvascular plants?

Answers to Section Review

1. They are the two types of tissue that make up the vascular system. Xylem transports water; phloem transports sugars. Xylem lends support to stems.

2. Gymnosperm seeds are not protected by a fruit.

3. *Ephedra, Gnetum,* and *Welwitschia*

4. Monocots have one seed leaf, leaves with parallel veins, and flowers with three-part symmetry. Dicots have two seed leaves, leaf veins in a netlike pattern, and flowers with four- or five-part symmetry.

5. Seeds increase the chances that a plant will reproduce. The embryo and food are protected inside the seed's tough coat; they lie dormant until favorable environmental conditions permit germination.

Laboratory

Observing Vascular Seed Plants

Objective
To compare a representative conifer, monocot, and dicot

Process Skills
Observing, classifying, inferring

Materials
Representative conifers, monocots, and dicots; scalpel

Background
1 What distinguishes a vascular plant from a nonvascular plant?
2 What are the distinguishing characteristics of a conifer? a monocot? a dicot?
3 From what structure did leaves evolve? What might be the main function of a leaf?

Inquiry
1 Get three plant specimens, labeled *A*, *B*, and *C*, from your teacher. Observe and draw each specimen. Label your drawing with each specimen's letter and overall appearance. What other structures or features do you observe?
2 Observe the leaves of specimen A. How are the leaves arranged on the main stalk or twig? Compare leaf placement among the samples. In what way might leaf placement be related to leaf function?
3 Leaf veins are vascular tissue. Which leaves have visible veins? Observe the pattern of venation and record your observations. What are the functions of the veins?
4 Use a scalpel to gently scrape the upper surface of each leaf specimen. What is this waxy material? Compare the amounts.
5 Select and compare the two flowered specimens. What type of symmetry does each type of flower have? Label your drawings with your answer.
6 Which specimen has cones? How does the cone's structure relate to its function?
7 What are the distinguishing characteristics of each specimen? Use your knowledge of vascular seed plants and your observations to infer the division to which each specimen belongs. If possible, identify the plant's class. Record your inferences.

Conclusions
1 What evidence is there that these specimens are vascular plants?
2 Which type of leaf appears to have the smallest surface area? the largest?
3 What evidence did you use to infer each plant's division? class?
4 What structures and functions do each of the specimens have in common?

Further Inquiry
If you were given three seeds, how might you decide which was from a conifer, from a monocot, or from a dicot? Explain your procedure.

Laboratory

(For an overview of vascular seed plants and preparatory information related to the laboratory, see p. 363B.)

Background

1. Nonvascular plants lack vascular tissue, true roots, stems, and leaves.
2. Conifer: "naked" seeds, needles or scalelike leaves usually with a small surface area, and male and female cones. Monocot: single cotyledon, parallel leaf venation, and three-part symmetry of flowers. Dicot: two cotyledons, net venation, and flower parts in fours or fives.
3. From light-absorbing stems; photosynthesis

Inquiry

1. Cones on specimen A and flowers on specimens B and C
2. Specimen A has needles in bundles connected to a twig at the base, or scalelike leaves attached singly opposite each other. Specimens B and C have leaves attached to the stem by a short stalk (petiole). Leaves are arranged for maximum exposure to light.
3. Specimens B and C. Monocots have parallel venation; dicots, net venation. Veins transport water, minerals, stored food, and sugars from photosynthesis in and out of leaves. Specimen A may show some venation.
4. Cuticle. The conifer (A) has the most; amounts on specimens B and C will vary.
5. Specimen B has three-part symmetry. Specimen C is arranged in fours or fives.
6. Specimen A. Cones are reproductive structures that protect pollen (male) or seeds (female).
7. Specimen A is a conifer, Division Coniferophyta. Monocots and dicots are Division Anthophyta. Specimen B is a monocot, Class Monocotyledoneae. Specimen C is a dicot, Class Dicotyledoneae.

Conclusions

1. Veins, stems, and leaves
2. Conifer; angiosperms
3. The presence of flowers or cones, type of flower, leaf surface area, and type of leaf venation
4. A cuticle that slows desiccation and green leaves that indicate the presence of chlorophyll. Specimens B and C had visible vascular tissues (leaf veins).

Further Inquiry

Dissecting or germinating seeds might reveal the presence of one, two, or many cotyledons. Students do not yet know that conifers have multiple cotyledons and may suggest waiting for plants to mature in order to look for leaves, flowers, or cones.

Chapter 25 Review

Vocabulary

1. A rhizoid anchors but does not conduct water; a rhizome is a horizontal, underground stem that conducts both water and nutrients.
2. A gametophyte is a haploid plant that produces gametes; a sporophyte is a diploid plant that produces spores.
3. An angiosperm is a flowering plant with seeds inside a fruit; a gymnosperm lacks flowers and enclosed chambers for its seeds to develop.
4. A monocot has one cotyledon in the seed; a dicot has two.
5. Xylem conducts water and minerals; phloem transports sugars.

Review

1. b	**6.** c
2. b	**7.** d
3. b	**8.** d
4. c	**9.** a
5. b	**10.** c

11. Near the end of the Silurian period, almost 400 million years ago
12. The green algae of the Division Chlorophyta, because they have the same photosynthetic pigments and cellulose cell walls, and store food as starch
13. The gametophyte is haploid, while the sporophyte is diploid.
14. In nonvascular plants the gametophyte is the dominant generation; in vascular plants the sporophyte is dominant.
15. Details of fossils were too tiny to be seen without microtechniques.
16. Lack of vascular tissues, and their need to absorb water through their cell walls
17. They require water to survive and reproduce.
18. They have tissue systems to transport water and nutrients to all parts of the plant.
19. True roots, stems, and leaves
20. Ferns are seedless; flowering plants bear seeds.

Chapter 25 Review

Vocabulary

alternation of generations (368)	fiddlehead (373)	nonvascular plant (367)	spore (366)
angiosperm (367)	frond (373)	phloem (371)	sporophyte (368)
capsule (369)	gametophyte (368)	rhizoid (369)	strobilus (372)
cotyledon (375)	gymnosperm (367)	rhizome (373)	vascular plant (367)
cuticle (365)	monocot (375)	seed (373)	vascular tissue (365)
dicot (375)	multicellular gametangia (365)	sporangium (368)	xylem (371)

Explain the difference between each of the following pairs of terms.
1. rhizoid and rhizome
2. gametophyte and sporophyte
3. angiosperm and gymnosperm
4. monocot and dicot
5. xylem and phloem

Review

1. The Division Bryophyta includes (a) mosses and club mosses (b) hornworts and liverworts (c) liverworts and cycads (d) conifers and ginkgos.
2. Mosses help start new biological communities by (a) detecting air pollution (b) forming new soil (c) producing spores (d) slowing decomposition.
3. Phloem conducts (a) air (b) sugars (c) chlorophyll (d) soil.
4. The presence of silicon dioxide in the outer cells of the plant is a characteristic of (a) ferns (b) mosses (c) horsetails (d) club mosses.
5. Flowering plants are in the Division (a) Psilophyta (b) Anthophyta (c) Gnetophyta (d) Sphenophyta.
6. Seedless vascular plants include all of the following *except* (a) ferns (b) horsetails (c) cycads (d) club mosses.
7. Gymnosperms include all of the following *except* (a) cycads (b) gnetophytes (c) ginkgos (d) quillworts.
8. The great success of angiosperms is due in part to (a) highly efficient vascular systems (b) seeds protected inside fruits (c) coevolution with insects (d) all of the above.
9. A monocot has (a) parallel-veined leaves (b) two seed leaves (c) four-part flowers (d) five-part flowers.
10. The distinguishing feature of all plants is the presence of (a) vascular tissue (b) pollen grains (c) multicellular gametangia (d) rhizoids.
11. When did the first land plants appear?
12. Which division of organisms is believed to represent the ancestors of land plants? Why?
13. What is the genetic difference between the gametophyte and the sporophyte?
14. How is alternation of generations different in nonvascular plants and vascular plants?
15. Why were microtechniques for analyzing fossils necessary before the details of the evolution of land plants could be revealed?
16. What factors limit the size of nonvascular plants?
17. Why must nonvascular plants live in damp environments?
18. What is the principal distinguishing feature of vascular plants?
19. List the structural features of vascular plants that nonvascular plants lack.
20. Why are ferns and flowering plants placed in different divisions?

Critical Thinking

1. The water lily, illustrated at the right, is a vascular plant that lives in aquatic habitats. Do you think its cuticle would be thicker on the upper surface of the leaf or on the lower surface? Explain.
2. Fossils of trees are easier to find than fossils of small plants. Give two possible explanations for this fact.
3. Luminous moss *(Schistostega pennata)* has cells shaped like lenses, with chloroplasts spread out behind the curving cell membrane. In what sort of environment would you expect to find this moss?
4. Cactuses are vascular plants that are adapted to dry environments. What specific adaptations might have been selected for over the course of their evolution?
5. Explain whether or not you would expect to find mosses growing in open fields.

6. While gymnosperm cones are either male or female, angiosperm flowers usually contain both male and female structures. How might this characteristic benefit angiosperms?

Extension

1. Read the article by Julie Ann Miller entitled "Plant Phylogeny Aided by Ants and Hummingbirds" in *BioScience,* November 1990, p. 714. Prepare an oral report in which you discuss how *Centropogon's* interactions with ants and hummingbirds are proving useful for clarifying evolutionary trends. Concentrate on the relationship that appears to exist between pollinator and plant structure. What evidence suggests a lowland origin for *Centropogon*? How do *Centropogon* and sicklebills reveal coevolutionary trends in structure and geographic distribution?
2. Go to your local florist or garden shop and get a handful of *Sphagnum* moss. Let it dry overnight in a warm place. Weigh the moss to the nearest 0.1 g, and record the weight. Then place the moss in water, and weight it down. Let the moss sit overnight. Remove the moss, let the excess water drain off, and weigh the moss again. Calculate the percentage increase in weight as follows:
   (a) Wet weight − dry weight = weight due to water
   (b) Weight due to water/dry weight × 100 = percentage increase due to water
3. Collect leaves from five different types of plants growing in deep shade (such as under a porch, in a forest, or in the shadow of a tall building). Also collect leaves from five different types of plants growing in full sun. Examine the leaves with a hand lens or dissecting microscope, and create a chart using the following columns: (top) sun, shade; (side) leaf hairs on top, leaf hairs on bottom, length of leaf, width of leaf, and thick/thin. Make drawings of the hairs from each leaf. Do the leaf hairs from the different types of plants look different? Do the leaves from the various plants differ in thickness? Are there more hairs on the leaves from the sun or on the leaves from the shade? What else can you conclude?

Critical Thinking

1. The cuticle would be thicker on the upper side of the leaf, because it is exposed to air and sunlight and would dry out. The cuticle on the underside of the leaf is in contact with water and so would not have to be as thick to protect the leaf.
2. First, fossils of trees are larger than those of small plants and are, therefore, easier to find. Second, wood decays less before fossilization than do smaller vascular and nonvascular plants.
3. This moss grows near mouths of caves, in dark holes, in deep woods, and sometimes in basements. Its cells are adapted to focus light on its chloroplasts when light is available.
4. Cactuses have tough, thick, waxy cuticles to reduce moisture loss; leaves reduced to needles; photosynthesis occurs in stems that store large amounts of water.
5. Bryophytes cannot survive in areas that do not have a regular water supply, because they require moist conditions. Some open fields, however, could contain suitable microhabitats.
6. Plants with both male and female parts can often self-pollinate. This increases their opportunity to reproduce, even in the absence of pollinators.

Extension

1. Pollinator relationships seem to indicate evolutionary patterns. Lowland examples can be pollinated by ants; highland examples can be pollinated by hummingbirds.
2. Answers will depend on the amount of moss used.
3. Leaf hairs are similar but vary in diameter and distribution on the leaf. Leaves have various widths and thicknesses. Leaves from sunny areas tend to have more leaf hairs than those from shady areas.

Chapter 26 Plant Structure and Function

Chapter Overview

Chapter 26 introduces plant tissue systems and explains how they are organized for specialized functions. Section 26.1 introduces basic plant tissue systems. Section 26.2 presents the structure and function of roots, Section 26.3 the structure and function of stems, and Section 26.4 the structure and function of leaves.

Chapter Planning Chart

B	S	A	Sections and Subsections	Page	Features	Page	Resources
•	•	•	**26.1 Plant Tissues**				
			Tissue Systems Meristems	381 382	Section Review	382	Videodiscs Section Reviews Worksheet
•	•	•	**26.2 Roots**				
			Root Structure The Function of Roots	384 385	Section Review	386	Videodiscs Blackline Master 52 Section Reviews Worksheet
•	•	•	**26.3 Stems**				
			Stem Structure The Function of Stems	387 389	Think Biology in Process Section Review	388 390 392	Videodiscs Process Skills: Transpiration Section Reviews Worksheet
•	•	•	**26.4 Leaves**				
			Leaf Structure The Function of Leaves	394 395	Laboratory Section Review	397 396	Videodiscs Blackline Master 53 Overhead Transparency T26 Laboratories: Leaf Stomata Section Reviews Worksheet
			End of Chapter Activities				
					Chapter Review	398	Vocabulary Skills Chapter Test Computer Test Generator

B *The Basic Level curriculum presents the most fundamental knowledge offered in the course.*
S *The Standard Level curriculum is designed for the average student who is able to master most topics.*
A *The Advanced Level curriculum includes suggestions for teaching the most academically able students.*

Cooperative Learning

Group Activity: Woody and Herbaceous Plants

- **Group Size:** *6 students*
- **Outcome:** *Students will compare local herbaceous and woody plants.*
- **Individual Accountability:** *Each student will do library research on woody or herbaceous plants.*
- **Positive Interdependence:** *Each group will cooperate to present one report and a poster to the class.*

If appropriate, lead groups on a field trip beforehand to observe local herbaceous and woody plants. Divide the class into groups of six. Assign three students in each group to research specific herbaceous plants common to your area. Have the other three students in each group research specific woody plants common to your area. If appropriate, students may research plants that were once plentiful in your region but have disappeared, or non-native plants introduced to the area (such as kudzu or water hyacinths) that have pushed native plants out of their former habitats. Have each group compile their research, prepare a wall display, and present an oral report to the class.

Concept Map

The following is one possible solution to the concept mapping activity in Reteaching on p. 382.

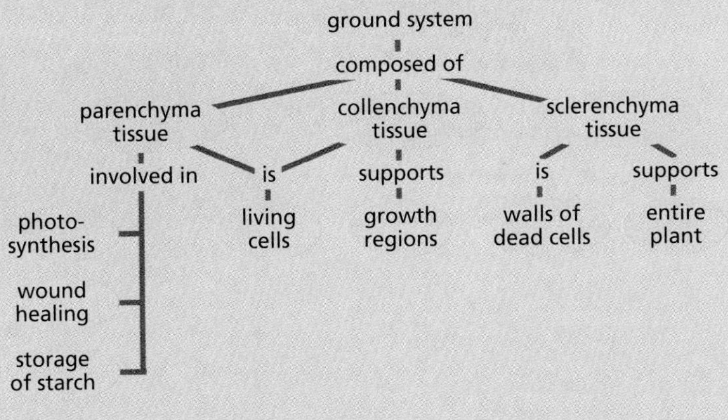

Laboratory Preparation

Overview *(See p. 397.)*

In this lab students investigate the soil-anchoring ability of taproot and fibrous root systems. Corn and bean seeds are planted and grown to 5-cm size. Students measure how many newtons it takes to pull each plant from the soil, the mass of soil that clings to each root system, and the length and diameter of each root system. They then pool data, design data tables, and construct bar graphs.

Preparation

If time is short, you may want to soak the seeds in water for 6–8 hours before students plant them. (Longer soaking may prevent germination.)

This laboratory will be carried out over several nonconsecutive days: (1) Students plant seeds, and the plants are left to grow; (2) they pull up the plants, which are left to dry; (3) they take measurements.

The seeds will take about a week to grow to suitable height; make plans to come back to this laboratory whenever the plants are ready.

Teaching Tips

To enable students to control the water variable, you may want to provide 10-mL graduates, coffee scoops, plant fertilizer spoons, or other small measuring devices that can be used to give the plants equal, but not large, amounts of water. Remind students to water their plants sparingly whenever the soil seems dry—an equal amount of water for each pot.

Have all the groups use the same kind of paper for the placement of the soil. Find the mass of one page of this paper, and provide this measurement to the teams. Make sure the teams subtract the mass of the paper from their mass measurements in step 9 to get an accurate measurement of the soil mass.

Make sure that students are familiar with the construction of bar graphs.

Safety

Remind students to wash their hands thoroughly after handling the soil.

Chapter Themes

Systems and Interactions Emphasize to students that crucial interactions among the tissues of a plant allow the plant to grow and function. Make sure students understand that ground, vascular, and dermal tissues all work together to make the plant function as a whole.

Evolution Help students understand that plant parts are adapted to the habitats in which the plants are found. Roots, stems, and leaves all have specialized adaptations necessary to the plant's survival.

Chapter Motivating Activity

Demonstrate for students the relationship between water absorption and transpiration by placing plastic bags over two identical plants and watering only one. Secure the bags around the stems to avoid water vapor loss. Condensation in the bag over the watered plant due to transpiration should be obvious. (Transpiration is a fairly dramatic response. Cactuses will demonstrate this within 15–20 minutes, leafy plants within a single class period if you add a light over the plants after bagging them.) Ask students how they think the water got into the bag. *(It was absorbed by the root system, it traveled up through the stem, and it evaporated through the leaves.)*

Chapter 26 Plant Structure and Function

Introduction

Plants have adapted to a vast range of environments over the course of their evolution. Most plants begin life by sending down roots and sending up shoots. As plants grow, their cells become specialized for various functions. The tissues made up of these specialized cells are arranged differently in different groups of plants. Such variations directly reflect the forces of natural selection that still operate where the plants live.

Chapter Outline

26.1 Plant Tissues
- *Tissue Systems*
- *Meristems*

26.2 Roots
- *Root Structure*
- *The Function of Roots*

26.3 Stems
- *Stem Structure*
- *The Function of Stems*

26.4 Leaves
- *Leaf Structure*
- *The Function of Leaves*

Chapter Concept

As you read, look for ways in which plant tissue arrangements reflect adaptations to various environmental conditions.

Redwoods, *Sequoia sempervirens*, and Douglas fir trees, *Pseudotsuga menziesii*, Redwood National Park, California. Inset: Cross section of pine stem.

Understanding the Visuals

Have students examine the photographs and read the caption. Ask them to try to name and classify the flowering plant. *(Rhododendron, an angiosperm)* Point out that sequoias, firs, and pines are all conifers. Ask students what kind of plants conifers are. *(Gymnosperms, vascular plants that bear naked seeds)* Remind them that in Chapter 25 they learned that gymnosperms and angiosperms are both vascular plants. Ask them to infer what kind of tissue is shown in the pine stem cross section. *(Vascular tissue)* Ask where else it can be found. *(In the roots and leaves of vascular plants)* Ask students what the functions of vascular tissues are. *(Transport of water, minerals, and sugars)*

26.1 Plant Tissues

Like all organisms plants are composed of cells. Groups of cells that perform a common function make up a **tissue.** Tissues are arranged into tissue systems. Three types of tissue systems are found in plants: ground system, dermal system, and vascular system. These systems are then organized into one of the three plant organs: **roots, stems,** and **leaves.** All of these levels of organization reflect adaptations to the environment.

Section Objectives

- *Describe the three plant tissue systems and the kinds of cells that occur in each.*
- *Describe the two main types of meristem tissue.*
- *Differentiate between primary and secondary growth.*

Tissue Systems

The **ground system** is made up of three kinds of tissue. **Parenchyma** *(puh-REN-kuh-muh)* is living tissue that consists of large, loosely packed, roughly cube-shaped cells with thin cell walls. Parenchyma cells are involved in many functions, including photosynthesis, food storage, and wound healing. In plants that are not woody, they make up over 80 percent of the cells. **Collenchyma** *(koe-LEN-kuh-muh)* is living tissue made up of elongated cells with unevenly thickened, flexible walls. Collenchyma cells are specialized for supporting growing regions of the plant. **Sclerenchyma** *(skluh-REN-kuh-muh)* tissue, which at maturity is made up of the walls of dead cells, supports and strengthens the plant. Sclerenchyma will not stretch and thus is found primarily in regions that have ceased growing. Some sclerenchyma cells are long and thin and are called **fibers.**

Ground tissues are modified for adaptive advantage. Cactuses, for example, have large amounts of parenchyma tissue, which store water in dry environments. Herbs that must be flexible to withstand wind possess a lot of collenchyma tissue. Sclerenchyma tissue is found in plant parts in which hardness is an advantage, such as the shells of nuts or the spines of cactuses.

The **vascular system** includes xylem and phloem tissues. Xylem conducts water and minerals. Phloem conducts food. In angiosperms xylem tissue is made up of the walls of dead cells. In angiosperms xylem has two components—tracheids and vessel elements. Look at Figure 26-1. A **tracheid** *(TRAY-kee-id)* is a long, thick wall with tapering ends. Water moves from tracheid to tracheid through **pits,** which are thin, porous areas of the wall. A **vessel element** is a wall that has slanting ends with holes through which water can pass. Vessel elements are arranged end to end, thus forming long, hollow tubes called vessels. Gymnosperm xylem contains only tracheids.

Unlike xylem, phloem tissue is alive at maturity. The conducting cell of angiosperm phloem is called a **sieve tube member.** Sieve tube members are stacked end to end in a long tube called a sieve tube. Compounds move from cell to cell through regions at the ends of the sieve tube members called **sieve plates.** Each sieve tube member lies next to a specialized neighboring **companion**

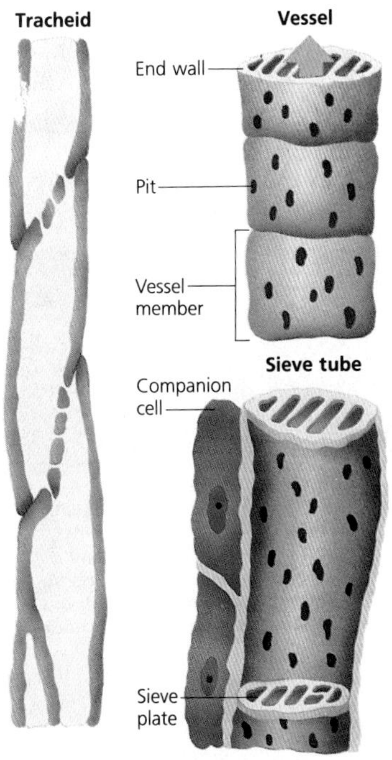

Figure 26-1 Water is conducted in angiosperms through tracheids and vessels. Food is conducted through sieve tubes, which are accompanied by companion cells.

Lesson Plan

Section Focus

This section emphasizes the types of tissue systems found in plants—ground, dermal, and vascular—and discusses primary and secondary growth.

Section Themes

This section encompasses two themes: **Scale and Structure** and **Systems and Interactions.** It examines the structure of plant tissues at the cellular level. It also describes how tissues interact to form systems.

Motivating Activity

Bring to class several weeds or houseplants and ask students which parts of the plant grow. *(Leaves, roots, stems)* Refer to Figure 26-2 on p. 382 as necessary. At least one plant should have roots visible so that students can examine them. Have students also inspect the tips of stems for evidence of growth. If one plant is woody, have students pry apart the stem tissues and observe the colors and textures of the vascular tissues.

Teaching Strategies

Organizing Information Have students organize the information about ground tissue into a table listing structure and function. An example of a completed table is shown below.

Guided Practice

Name a function or describe a tissue, and have students name the appropriate tissue system: ground, dermal, or vascular. Examples are: protects a plant from water loss *(Dermal);* fills the space between dermal and *vascular tissue (Ground); moves* food or water through the plant *(Vascular).*

Videodiscs

- ***1955–1956, Vascular Cambium and Phloem; Xylem (s)***

	Parenchyma	Collenchyma	Sclerenchyma
Living or Dead	living	living	walls of dead cells
Cell Structure	cube-shaped with thin cell walls	elongated with unevenly thickened, flexible walls	some are long and thin
Functions	photosynthesis, food storage, wound healing	support the growing regions of the plant	support and strengthen the plant

Graphic Organizer Use this table in Organizing Information, on the right.

Independent Practice

- Have students write answers to the Section Review.
- Give students pairs of words to distinguish. Examples are: herbaceous plants/woody plants *(Herbaceous do not have vascular cambium; woody have secondary xylem created by vascular cambium)*; xylem/phloem *(Xylem transports water and minerals; phloem transports sugars)*.

Check Your Understanding

1. How is the structure of xylem adapted for its function? *(Xylem consists of hollow tubes that are ideal for conducting water and minerals.)*
2. What happens when the apical meristem is cut off a stem? *(The stem grows fuller and bushier.)*

Reteaching

Have students make a concept map illustrating the composition and functions of the three types of tissue in the ground system. An example of a completed concept map is shown on p. 379B.

- *See* Section Reviews *worksheet, Section 26.1.*

Enrichment

Have each student research a plant that has adapted to an unusual environment—for example, water lily, duckweed, orchid, or bromeliad—and write a report about how its tissues are adapted to its unusual environment.

Closure

Give examples of tissue adaptations such as the hard shell of a walnut, the thick cuticle of a succulent, and the reduced xylem of duckweed. Have students name the tissue system involved in each. *(Shell, ground or sclerenchyma; cuticle, dermal; xylem, vascular)*

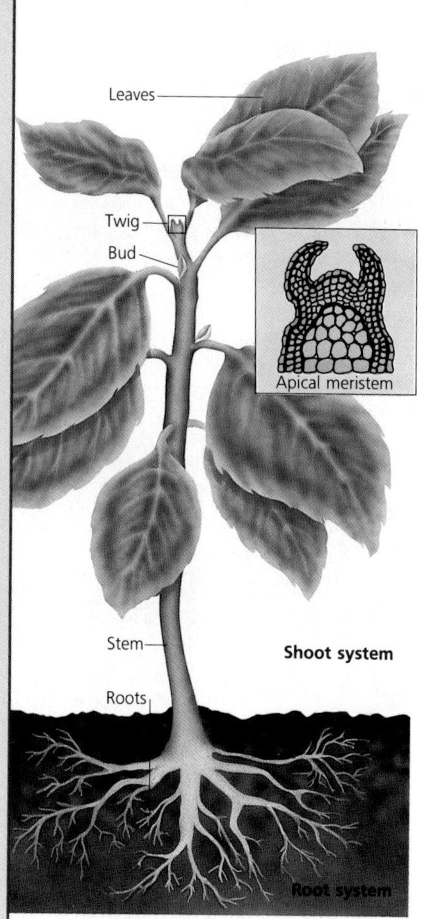

Figure 26-2 Apical meristems, the growing points of plants, occur at the tips of stems and roots. Nodes are the points at which leaves are attached. Internodes are areas between nodes.

cell. Botanists suggest that companion cells help control the movement of sugars through sieve tubes.

Like ground tissue vascular tissue is modified for adaptive advantage. For example, xylem forms the wood of trees, providing strength while conducting water. In aquatic plants such as duckweeds xylem is not used for either support or water conduction and may be nearly absent from the mature plant.

The **dermal tissue system** forms the outside covering of plants. The dermal tissue is composed of the **epidermis** *(EP-uh-DER-muss)*, the outer layer of cells, which is covered with a waxy cuticle. The epidermis functions to protect the plant, reduce water loss, and aid in gas exchange. Openings in the epidermis are called **stomata** *(STOE-muh-tuh)*. Stomata are structures that regulate the passage of gases into and out of the plant. In mature stems and roots the protective epidermis is eventually replaced by **cork,** another dermal tissue. Cork cells are packed closely together and their walls contain a protective fatty substance called suberin.

Dermal tissue is also modified in various plants. For example, plants in dry environments have stomata that are sunk deep in the epidermis, preventing water loss. Stomata, usually found on the lower sides of leaves, are found on the upper side in water lilies, allowing free passages of gases to and from the air.

Meristems

Plants possess **meristems** *(MER-ih-stemz)*, growing regions where cells divide. Plants grow in length by **apical** *(AY-pih-kul)* **meristems** at the tips of stems and roots. Look at Figure 26-2.

Plants also have **lateral meristems,** which grow and increase their circumference. One is the **vascular cambium,** which produces additional vascular tissues. Another is the **cork cambium,** which produces cork. The tissues produced by apical meristems are called **primary growth** tissues. Those produced by the lateral meristems are called **secondary growth** tissues.

Adaptations occur in meristems and their growth patterns. Annual plants are adapted for rapid growth and reproduction. They do not have a vascular cambium, so their tissues remain nonwoody. They are called **herbaceous plants.** Trees are perennial plants, which are adapted for growth year after year. They develop much secondary xylem. They are called **woody plants.**

Section Review

1. Look up the word *dermal* in a dictionary. Why is this an appropriate term for epidermis and cork?
2. Do monocots have cork? Explain your answer.
3. How do tracheids and vessel elements differ?
4. What kind of meristem do monocots and dicots share?
5. Would you expect to find sclerenchyma cells near meristems? Why or why not?

Answers to Section Review

1. *Dermal* means "skin." Epidermis and cork are analogous to the skin.
2. Mostly they do not. Cork is a secondary tissue, and most monocots do not have secondary growth.
3. Tracheids are long cells with tapered ends. Transport between tracheids takes place through pits in the cell walls. Vessel elements are wider than tracheids and have end walls with holes through which substances can pass.
4. Apical
5. No, sclerenchyma occurs only in non-growing regions of the plant.

26.2 Roots

The tissue systems you read about previously are arranged into organs: roots, stems, and leaves. In this section you will study roots. During growth most plants develop a **primary root,** the first root to grow out of a seed. If, as the root system develops, the primary root grows downward and remains the largest root, the organ is called a **taproot.** Many plants, such as carrots, have taproots that are adapted to store food. Taproots of large trees are adapted for growing hundreds of feet down, supporting the plant while reaching water deep in the ground.

In some plants the primary root does not grow large, and numerous small roots develop and remain near the top of the soil. The resulting organ is called a **fibrous root** system. Fibrous roots spread out and anchor the plant. Many monocots, such as grasses and orchids, have fibrous root systems, which are adapted for gathering water close to the surface of the soil.

Other root systems are modified for specialized functions. The prop roots of the corn plant support the stem. Another variation of the root system occurs in mangroves, which are adapted for growing in the shifting soils of tidal areas. When the area is covered with water, no oxygen is available to the roots. Some mangrove root branches are modified for growing up into the air and absorbing oxygen when the tide recedes.

Section Objectives

- *Explain the difference between a taproot system and a fibrous root system.*
- *Distinguish between primary growth and secondary growth in roots.*
- *Describe primary root tissues.*
- *List the three principal functions of roots.*

Figure 26-3 Four plants exhibiting four types of roots are (clockwise from top left) the carrot, *Daucus carota,* (taproot), the orchid (fibrous root), corn, *Zea mays,* (prop root), and the mangrove, *Avicennia* sp., (air root).

Lesson Plan

Section Focus

This section presents the different types of root systems and describes the overall structure and function of roots.

Section Themes

The relationship of root tissues to the function of the whole plant illustrates the theme of **Systems and Interactions.** The theme of **Evolution** is inherent in the adaptations of structures to their functions.

Motivating Activity

Sprout radish seeds until a good primary root with root hairs is visible. (Soak the seeds for an hour or so in water. Then place the wet seeds on moist blotter paper and keep them moist and in a dark area for about 4 days. Check daily, keeping the blotter paper dampened.) Ask students what the function of the root hairs is. *(To absorb water and minerals)* Then ask where the root is growing. *(At the very tip)*

Teaching Strategies

Interpreting the Visuals Refer students to Figure 26.3, p. 383. Ask them to speculate on the differences in root tissue specialized for storage, such as a carrot, as opposed to the specialized tissue of a taproot, or the air roots of mangroves. *(Sample answers: Storage roots have more parenchymal tissue. Taproots have more vascular tissue and many lateral roots. Air roots have large intercellular spaces through which oxygen can diffuse.)*

Videodiscs

- *1931, Root Hair (s)*
- *1941–1945, Root Cross Section (s)*

Structure	Function	Location
root cap	protects root tip	root tip
apical meristem	growth, cell division	behind root cap
epidermis	absorption	"skin" of root
endodermis	regulates transport	part of cortex
vascular cylinder	transport	center of root

Graphic Organizer Use this table in Comparing Structures on p. 385.

Interpreting the Visuals Refer students to Figure 26-4, p. 384. Make sure they can understand why only the root tip is growing. *(That is where cell division is occurring.)*

Applying Concepts Point out to students that root branches and root hairs perform essentially the same functions—increasing the surface-area-to-volume ratio of the root system. Remind students of the surface-area-to-volume ratio of cells, discussed in Section 5.1. If students need help remembering this concept, refer them to Figure 5.3, p. 64.

Observing Structures Have students view onion root tip slides with a microscope. Ask students where the root cells can be seen dividing. *(At the very tip)* Have students observe what happens to the appearance of the cells that are farther up the root. *(The cells appear longer.)* Have students recall the Laboratory "Observing Mitosis" in Chapter 9 on p. 139.

Comparing Concepts *Vascular* means "of or relating to a channel for the conveyance of a body fluid." This term is used to describe xylem and phloem, the conducting tissues of plants; it also describes the conducting tissues of animals. Ask students to describe the similarities. *(Vascular systems conduct materials through the entire body. Plant and animal vascular systems are made of thick-walled, tubular structures.)*

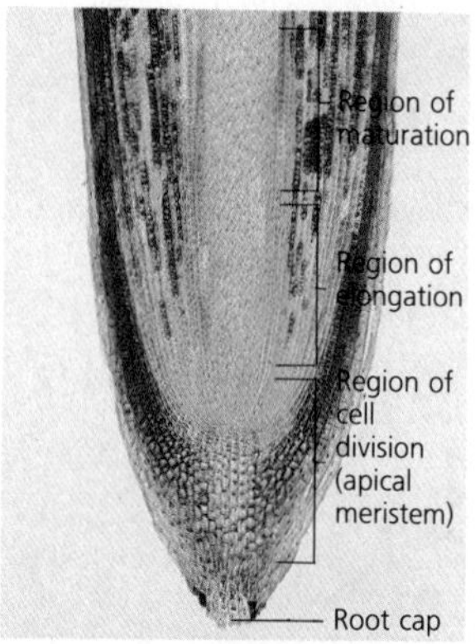

Figure 26-4 The three parts of a root tip, such as the one from a willow tree shown here, are the regions of division, elongation, and maturation (×150).

Figure 26-5 A germinating kernel of field corn, *Zea mays,* has already established primary and secondary roots complete with root hairs.

Root Structure

The root apical meristem produces cells that differentiate into ground tissue, vascular tissue, and dermal tissue. These then differentiate into cells that form the mature root.

The Root Tip

Study Figure 26-4. Notice that the root tip is organized into three parts. The apical meristem is the region of cell division. Cells formed here later grow longer in the region of elongation. Here a root increases in length. Behind this region is the region of maturation, where cells mature and differentiate.

The cells of the meristem also produce parenchyma cells that come to lie in front of the tip. These cells make up the **root cap,** a shield covering the apical meristem. The root cap produces a slimy substance that functions like a lubricating oil, allowing the root tip to move more easily through the soil. Cells lost from the root cap are constantly replaced by the apical meristem.

Primary Growth

Growth, elongation, and maturation in the root tip establish the three tissue systems in the root. Dermal tissue matures to form an epidermis, the outermost cylinder of the root. In young roots epidermal cells often form extensions called **root hairs,** which are specialized for absorbing water and minerals. The root hairs increase the surface area of the root and thus increase its ability to absorb water and nutrients.

Ground tissue matures into the cortex and the endodermis. The **cortex** is located just inside the epidermis, as you can see from Figure 26-6. The largest region of the young root, it is made up of loosely packed parenchyma cells. The innermost cylinder of the cortex is the **endodermis,** a specialized layer of cells that regulates substances entering the center of the root. Each cell of the endodermis is belted by a narrow band of suberin called the **Casparian** *(kass-PAR-ee-un)* **strip.** Substances absorbed by root hairs move freely around the walls of the loosely packed cortex cells and toward the root center. When these substances reach the endodermis, the Casparian strip blocks their passage through the intercellular spaces. Substances must therefore pass through the semipermeable cell membranes of the endodermal cells. The cell membrane of the endodermal cells thus regulates the transport of substances into the interior vascular tissues.

Vascular tissue matures to form the **vascular cylinder,** the innermost part of the root, which contains xylem and phloem. In most plants xylem makes up the central core of the vascular cylinder. Xylem usually has a fluted structure, as shown in Figure 26-6. Phloem lies between the xylem lobes. The outermost rings of cells in the central vascular area are called the **pericycle.** All lateral roots are formed from divisions of these cells. The lateral root forces its way through the cortex and emerges.

More Information

Digesting Old Movies Your students might remember Audrey II from the film *Little Shop of Horrors.* Carnivorous plantlike aliens are also featured in science fiction movies such as *Day of the Triffids* and *Invasion of the Body Snatchers.* There are over 400 known species of carnivorous plants; most of them also carry on photosynthesis. These "weird" plants are adapted to soils so poor in minerals that other plants could not survive. The digesting parts of these plants are usually modified leaf structures, but they are primarily classified by their flower parts. There are also fungi capable of capturing and digesting animal prey, which makes the classic film *The Blob* seem just a bit more plausible.

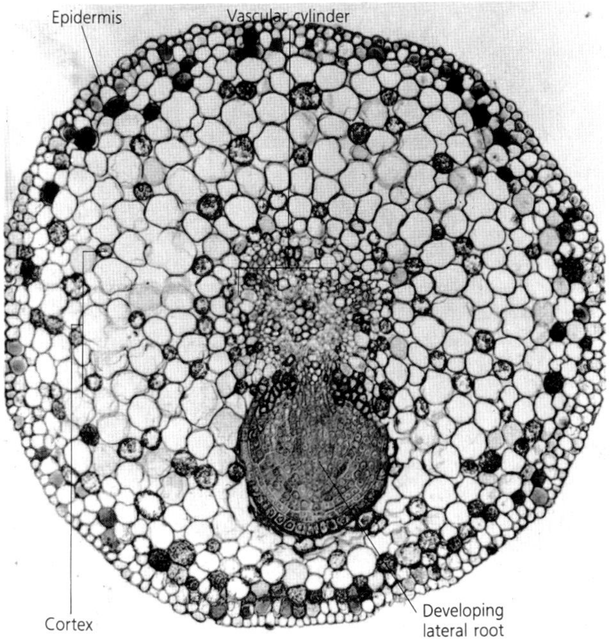

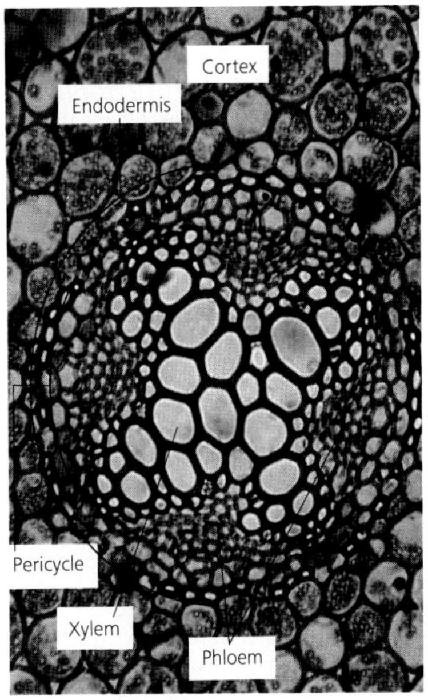

Figure 26-6 Cross section of a buttercup root, *Ranunculus* sp., (above) shows the primary vascular tissue. Lateral roots (left) develop from the pericycle.

The structure of roots is an adaptation for the function of absorbing materials from the soil. The vascular tissues are located in the center of the root, protected by cylinders of both epidermis and cortex. Lateral roots are initiated inside the root and are thus protected during their earliest growth stages. In addition the Casparian strip regulates the flow of material to the interior tissues.

Secondary Growth

Some roots have secondary growth. Secondary growth begins when a vascular cambium forms between primary xylem and primary phloem. As shown in Figure 26-7, vascular cambium produces secondary xylem toward the inside of the root and secondary phloem toward the outside. The secondary root tissues gradually crush the endodermis, cortex, and epidermis, all of which are eventually replaced by cork. Secondary growth in roots is an adaptation for strength and support of the plant stem.

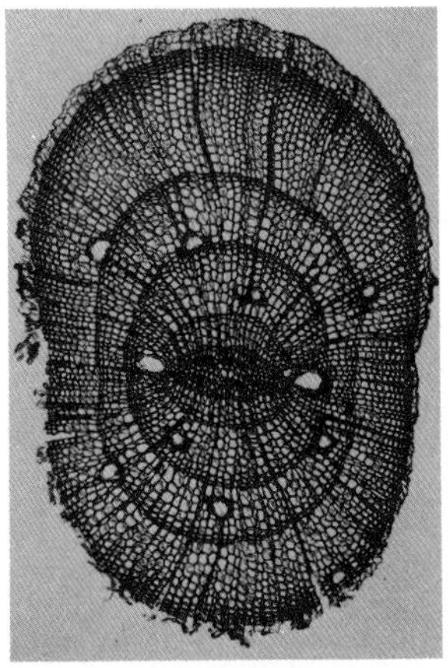

Figure 26-7 Secondary growth in a fir tree root causes the formation of woody tissue (×50).

The Function of Roots

In addition to anchoring a plant in the soil, roots serve two other primary functions. Roots absorb water and minerals, and they store food made during photosynthesis.

Absorption of Water and Inorganic Nutrients

Root hairs contain many dissolved substances such as minerals, sugars, and amino acids. Water in the soil, on the other hand, contains fewer dissolved substances. As a result of the concentra-

Exploring Careers Ask someone employed in the field of forestry, in the lumber business, or in some form of agriculture to speak to the class about the importance of soil quality and content in planting, managing, restoring, and conserving large tracts of land.

Comparing Structures Ask students to list the structure, function, and location of the root tissues mentioned on pp. 384–385. An example of a completed table is shown on p. 383.

Interpreting the Visuals Review the essential plant nutrients and their roles as presented in Table 26-1, p. 386. Make sure students can list the elements and at least one role each plays. *(Nitrogen, synthesis of proteins; potassium, synthesis of amino acids; calcium, maintenance of cell membranes; phosphorus, in nucleic acids; sulfur, in proteins; magnesium, in chlorophyll; iron, manganese, copper, and zinc, in enzymes; chlorine, acts in photosynthesis; boron, role unknown)*

- *See* Blackline Master 52.

Guided Practice

Have students study Figures 26-4 and 26-6, pp. 384–385, while you ask questions about the structure and function of roots. Ask students where a root grows. *(At the apical meristem)* What tissue regulates substances entering the center of the root? *(Endodermis)*

Independent Practice

- Have students write answers to the Section Review.
- Provide photocopies of pictures of root systems from books or seed and plant catalogs. Have students sort the pictures into taproot or fibrous systems.

LEP Activity

An understanding of cross and longitudinal sections is essential to understanding tissue relationships in three dimensions. Bring in a sharp paring knife and several different types of vegetables and fruits, such as squash, cucumber, apple, kiwi, and bean. Cut them in both cross and longitudinal sections so that students will know what is meant by these terms. Have students draw scientific illustrations of both types of specimens. Then ask them to draw cross sections and longitudinal sections of familiar objects.

Section 26.2

Check Your Understanding

1. Do edible roots usually have fibrous or taproot systems? Explain. *(Taproot; they are adapted to store food.)*

2. When transplanting a plant, why is it important to treat the roots with care? *(So that the root hairs are not injured)*

Reteaching

Bring a variety of plants to class and have students classify the root types and root structures that they examine. The plants may be weeds or foods such as carrots or scallions.

■ *See* Section Reviews *worksheet, Section 26.2.*

Enrichment

Encourage students to make their own cross-sectional slides of a carrot root. Provide sharp scalpels, slides, and microscope. Tell students to slice the carrot very thinly. Have students draw and label what they observe under the microscope.

Closure

Bring a variety of "plant food" packages to class. Ask students to compare the ingredients with the nutrients listed in Table 26-1, p. 386, and identify the role each nutrient plays in the life of a plant. *(Nitrogen—synthesis of proteins, chlorophyll, nucleic acids, coenzymes. Phosphorus—found in coenzymes, nucleic acids, ATP. Potassium—synthesis of amino acids, helps stomata open and close)*

Videodiscs

■ *2572, Endodermal Cells (s)*
■ *Side 3 27174, Roots (m)*
■ *1657–1662, Plant Cell Division in Roots (s)*

Table 26-1 Some Essential Plant Nutrients and Their Role in Plant Growth

Element	Role in Plant
Macronutrients	
Nitrogen	Synthesis of proteins, nucleic acids, chlorophyll, coenzymes
Potassium	Synthesis of amino acids; helps open and close stomata in leaves
Calcium	Part of cell walls and membranes; influences cell permeability
Phosphorus	Found in nucleic acids, coenzymes, ATP
Sulfur	Found in proteins, coenzymes
Magnesium	Found in chlorophyll, enzymes
Micronutrients	
Iron	Found in enzymes, chlorophyll
Manganese	Found in enzymes
Zinc	Found in enzymes
Copper	Found in enzymes
Chlorine	Acts in photosynthesis
Boron	Exact role unknown

tion gradient between root hairs and soil water, water moves into the root hairs by osmosis. See Chapter 6 for a review of the process of osmosis. The rate of water absorption is influenced by the amount of water lost through **transpiration,** the evaporation of water from stems and leaves.

Roots absorb a variety of inorganic nutrients, usually by active transport. Plant cells use some nutrients, such as nitrogen and potassium, in large amounts. These elements are called **macronutrients.** They use other nutrients, such as manganese, in smaller amounts. These are called **micronutrients.** Too much or too little of any macronutrient or micronutrient will harm or kill a plant. Nutrient requirements vary among species.

Storage of Food

Roots are also adapted for food storage. Phloem carries the sugars made in leaves to roots and stems for storage. In roots these sugars are converted to starch and stored in areas containing parenchyma cells. You may be familiar with storage roots such as those of beets, carrots, turnips, and sweet potatoes.

Section Review

1. Name the three regions of the root tip.
2. How does a primary root become a taproot?
3. Explain how root hairs increase the ability of a plant to absorb water from the ground.
4. Name two areas of the root where you would probably find parenchyma cells.
5. Compare and contrast endodermal cells and epidermal cells.

Answers to Section Review

1. Division, elongation, and maturation
2. The primary root continues to grow and becomes the largest root in the system.
3. They increase the surface area of the root.
4. Root cap and cortex
5. Endodermal cells are at the center of the cortex, have a line of fatty suberin called the Casparian strip in their cell walls, and regulate the entry of water to the vascular cylinder. Epidermal cells are outside the cortex, covered with a waxy cuticle, and function in the absorption of water.

26.3 Stems

Look at Figure 26-8. Like roots, stems are adapted to different environments. Stems of some plants grow only along the surface of the soil, as you can see by examining the strawberry stolon. Cactuses have green, fleshy stems that both store water and carry on photosynthesis. Stems such as the fleshy underground tuber of a white potato are modified for storing food. Gladiolus and crocus plants have underground stems called corms that are specialized for food storage. All of these differences in stem shape and growth represent adaptations to the environment.

Stem Structure

Did you know that a sign nailed 2 m high on a tree will remain 2 m high, even though the tree may grow much taller? That is because stems grow in length only at their tips, where apical meristem produces new primary tissues. Stems grow in circumference through growth of lateral meristems.

Primary and secondary growth also take place in woody twigs tipped with buds. Buds are lateral branches that include the apical meristem and modified leaves called bud scales. In spring the bud opens and the bud scales fall off the twig. The scales leave scars on the surface of the twig.

Section Objectives

- *Describe differences between monocot and dicot stems.*
- *List the secondary tissues in the dicot stem.*
- *Explain the formation of an annual ring.*
- *Explain the pressure–flow hypothesis, and tell what substances are transported in phloem.*
- *Describe the transpiration–cohesion theory.*

Figure 26-8 Various stem adaptations are illustrated by (clockwise from left) the strawberry, *Fragaria* sp., plant (stolon), the cactus, *Cereus* sp., (green, fleshy stem), a plant with a typical woody stem, and a potato, *Solanum tuberosum*, plant (tuber).

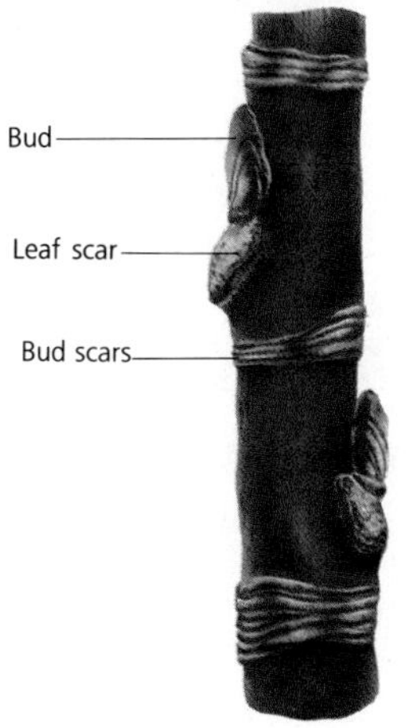

Lesson Plan

Section Focus

This section presents the structure and function of stems, the differences between primary and secondary growth, and the function of the apical meristem.

Section Themes

The theme of **Systems and Interactions** appears in the relationships of stem tissues to the total function of a plant. The theme of **Evolution** underlies the adaptations of structures to their various functions.

Motivating Activity

Present cross sections of a tree to the class. (Obtain cross-sectional slices of a tree from a landowner, tree-cutting service, or the parks department; or else use pictures of a cross section.) Ask students how old the tree was when it was cut down and how the age of a tree can be determined from the cross section. *(Each ring represents one year's growth.)* Point out that tree rings are actually composed of secondary xylem produced by vascular cambium.

Teaching Strategies

Observing Structures Provide students with different types of twigs (preferably winter twigs) and hand lenses or dissecting microscopes. Have students find the buds, leaf scars, and bud scars discussed in the text and shown in Figure 26-8, p. 387. Inform students that they can determine the age of a twig by counting the bud scale scars. You may want to supply field guides for students to use in identifying the trees from which the twigs came.

root absorbs water → **stem** water moves via xylem → **leaf** transpiration and photosynthesis
↓
root sugars are stored as starch ← **stem** sugars move via phloem ← **leaf** sugars are moved to stem

Graphic Organizer Use this sequential diagram in Reteaching on p. 392.

Interpreting the Visuals Focus students' attention on Figure 26-9, p. 388. Emphasize the placement of the vascular bundles in a monocot stem (shown in the figure as scattered red and blue dots) and a dicot stem (shown as yellow and green dots around the perimeter of the stem). Ask them to list monocot and dicot differences, then provide a set of prepared slides of monocot and dicot stems (available from scientific supply houses). Have students identify and compare the placement of the vascular bundles in the different stems with the low power of a compound microscope. *(In monocot stems, vascular bundles are scattered throughout the stem. In dicot stems, vascular bundles form a ring around the perimeter.)*

Comparing Concepts Ask students what their skin does. *(Protects their insides)* Point out that their own skin is a dermal tissue. Ask students how the dermal tissue in plant stems compares with dermal tissue in humans. *(Both are external tissues that serve to protect the individual and prevent fluid loss. Animal dermal tissue also helps regulate body temperature and contains nerves and blood vessels.)* Students will learn more about human dermal tissue in Chapter 42.

Answer to Think

Cactus stems consist mainly of parenchyma, which is specialized for water storage.

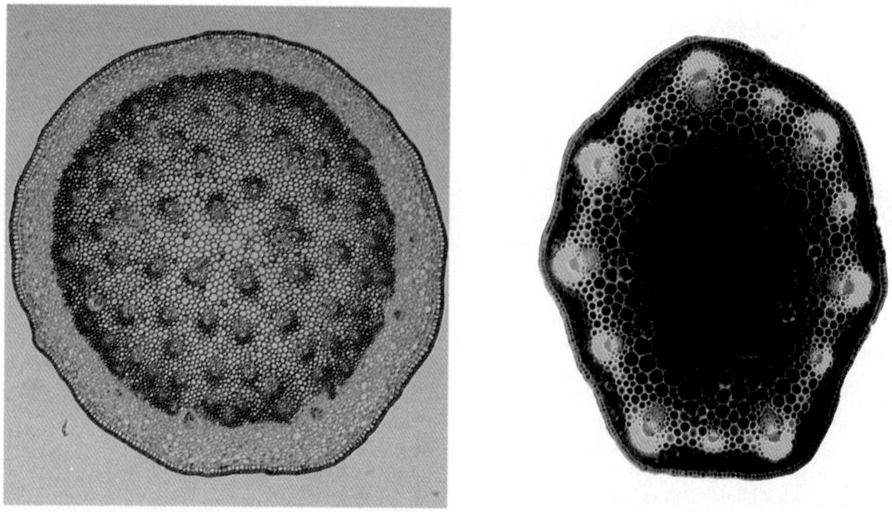

Figure 26-9 Cross-sectional photographs contrast a typical monocot stem (left, ×10) and a typical dicot stem (right, ×10).

Think

Which of the three basic ground tissues would you expect to find the most of in this cactus stem? Why?

Primary Growth

Apical meristems give rise to cells that form the primary dermal, ground, and vascular tissues of a stem. Locate each of these tissues in Figure 26-9. As you can see, the dermal tissue is represented by the epidermis, the outer layer of the stem. Its primary functions are to protect the plant and to reduce the loss of water to the atmosphere.

The ground tissue consists mostly of parenchyma cells. In gymnosperms and dicots, ground tissue forms a cortex and a pith. The cortex lies immediately inside the epidermis, as it does in the root. It frequently contains some flexible collenchyma tissue and may be photosynthetic. The **pith** is located in the center of the stem. Monocot stems are not so precisely divided into pith and cortex as dicot stems are.

Vascular tissue formed near the apical meristem occurs in bundles, long strands that lie embedded in the cortex. Look at the **vascular bundles** shown in Figure 26-9. Each bundle contains primary xylem and primary phloem. Xylem is located nearer the inside of the stem, and phloem is located nearer the outside. This arrangement of xylem and phloem differs from that found in a root, where both types of vascular tissue are located in the center.

Compare the arrangement of vascular bundles in monocots and dicots. In a monocot stem vascular bundles are scattered throughout the ground tissue. In dicot stems the vascular bundles occur in a single ring. Most monocots have no secondary growth and thus retain the scattered arrangement of vascular bundles throughout their lives. However, in many dicots the vascular bundles are eventually replaced by secondary tissues produced by the lateral meristems.

Interdisciplinary Activity

Government Stem anatomy has been used in some unusual ways. Offer the class this background on the Lindbergh kidnapping case: In 1932 the infant son of Charles Lindbergh, first person to fly solo across the Atlantic, was kidnapped and killed. The most damaging piece of evidence that led to the conviction of the suspect, Bruno Hauptmann, was a ladder used in the kidnapping. A botanist established by microscopic examination that one rail on the ladder matched a floorboard from the Hauptmann attic and that the rail and board were originally from a single piece of wood. Have students research the trial and decide whether they think the stem evidence was a good basis for conviction.

Secondary Growth

The vascular cambium in stems arises first between the xylem and phloem in a vascular bundle. Eventually the vascular cambium forms a cylinder. Stems increase in thickness as a result of divisions of cells in the vascular cambium.

Examine Figure 26-10. The vascular cambium produces secondary xylem to the inside and secondary phloem to the outside. It usually produces much more secondary xylem, called wood.

In addition to the vessel elements and tracheids, discussed in Section 26.1, wood contains sheets of parenchyma cells called **rays.** As you can see in Figure 26-10, rays form a flat tissue that radiates from the center of the trunk. Rays store food and also transport food and water laterally across the xylem.

When water is plentiful during spring, the vascular cambium forms new secondary xylem with cells that are wide and thin walled. This wood is called **springwood.** In hot, dry summers the vascular cambium produces **summerwood,** which has smaller cells with thicker walls. The visible difference in density between spring wood and summer wood is called an **annual ring.** Look again at Figure 26-10. The circles that look like bull's-eyes are the annual rings of the tree. Since one such ring is formed each year, you can estimate the age of a plant simply by counting its annual rings. How old is the tree in the figure?

Some vessels of the secondary xylem eventually become clogged and thus useless in transporting water. They also give the xylem a dark color. This dark wood in the center of a tree is called heartwood. The functional, lighter-colored wood nearer the outside of the trunk is sapwood.

The secondary phloem produced toward the outside of the wood is part of the bark. **Bark** is the protective outside covering of woody plants. It consists of cork, cork cambium, cortex, and secondary phloem. The cork cambium produces cork toward the outside and living ground tissues toward the inside. Since cork cells quickly die and cannot expand, the continued production of secondary xylem and phloem causes the outer layers of cork to split. The bark of familiar trees such as oaks and maples thus appears rough and irregular in texture.

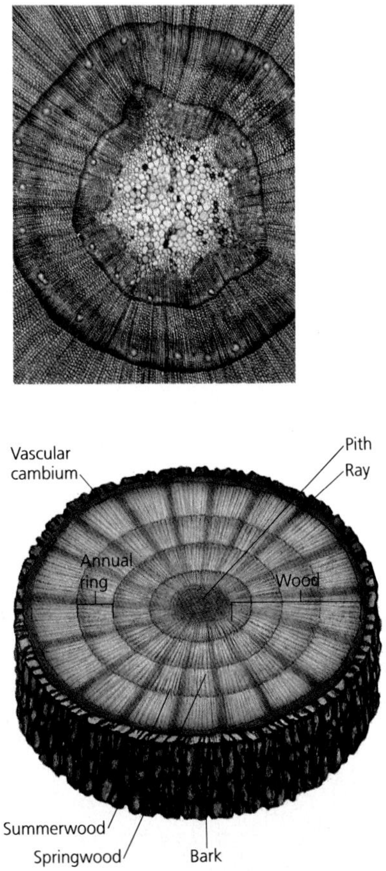

Figure 26-10 A cross section of the stem of a white pine, *Pinus strobus,* shows the rays and annual rings.

The Function of Stems

Whatever their sizes and shapes, most stems have three functions: support, transport, and storage. You have already learned about the support function. Let's examine transport and storage.

Transportation of Food

Sugars are the food that moves in the phloem of plants. Movement of these sugars occurs from **source,** where it is made, to **sink,** where it is stored or used. This movement is explained by the **pressure–flow hypothesis.**

Applying Concepts Ask students whether they know what "girdling" a tree is. *(Girdling is the removal of a ring of bark down to the wood.)* Ask them why removing a ring of vascular tissue around the circumference would kill a tree. (*The area below the girdle soon shows the effects of starvation because the flow of sugar from the leaves has been interrupted. A girdled tree may survive for some time, but it eventually will die even though the movement of water from the roots still occurs. As food in the lower stem and roots is used up, the roots gradually die. Lack of water from the dead roots kills the leaves, photosynthesis stops, and the tree dies.)*

Interpreting the Visuals Ask students how old the tree is in Figure 26-10, p. 389, based on its annual rings. *(Four years)* Have them examine the figure while you read the section on secondary growth aloud. Make sure students are able to identify springwood, summerwood, and the parts of the cross section labeled in the figure.

Videodiscs

- ***1946–1947, Vascular Bundles in Corn Stem (s)***
- ***1932, Celery Showing Dye Uptake (s)***

Interdisciplinary Activity

Mathematics Obtain pieces of various types of lumber. The direction in which the wood is cut determines which internal structures are visible and in which sections they are seen. This, in turn, determines the pattern, or grain, of the wood. Challenge students to find concentric parabolas and ellipses, and to identify which stem structure they are. *(A cut at an angle through the cylinder of the stem reveals growth rings as nested parabolas or ellipses.)* Challenge students to find parallel lines. *(Cuts along a radius of the cylinder produce quarter-sawed wood; it has parallel lines that are growth rings visible from the side.)* Challenge them to find right angles. *(Vascular rays would appear as ribbons across the parallel grain at right angles to the grain.)*

Organizing Information As students read pp. 390–392, have them list the structures of a stem that enable it to carry out its three main functions of support, transport, and storage. *(Support: cortex [if it contains collenchyma], sclerenchyma, xylem [wood]. Transport: xylem, phloem, parenchyma [rays]. Storage: parenchyma)*

Reviewing Concepts Review the major features of active transport in Chapter 6, pp. 84–86, so that students can understand how concentration gradients result in bulk flow of sugars. Also review the basic chemistry of water. Refer students back to Chapter 4, pp. 47–48, to make sure they remember and understand capillarity and cohesion.

Interpreting the Visuals Focus students' attention on Figure 26-12, p. 392. Make sure they understand that water that evaporates from leaves is eventually replaced by water from the xylem. The speed of water movement through a stem changes during the day. Have students study the graph in Figure 26-11, p. 391. Ask them how long it takes for a water molecule to travel from root to leaf. *(About 6 hours)* Ask why water uptake peaks after transpiration. *(Water is taken in to replace water lost through transpiration and evaporation.)*

■ *See* Process Skills, *Chapter 26.*

Sugars are manufactured in photosynthetic cells and pumped by active transport into sieve tubes. This increases the concentration of dissolved substances in the sieve tube, and water enters the sieve tube by osmosis. The sieve tube becomes filled with water. Thus a positive pressure builds up at the source end of the sieve tube. This is the "pressure" part of the hypothesis.

At the sink end of the sieve tube this process is reversed. Sugars are pumped out, and water leaves the sieve tube by osmosis. Therefore pressure is reduced at the sink. The difference in pressure causes sugars to move from source to sink. In other words, the difference causes sugars to "flow."

Transportation of Water and Minerals

Water, which is required by all living cells, is constantly evaporating from stems and leaves. In addition stems and leaves require inorganic nutrients. Water and inorganic nutrients enter a plant through the roots. How do these substances travel from the roots to the top of a tree?

At one time scientists thought that the water absorbed by the roots created a pressure that "pushed" other water up the plant. This sometimes happens. When it does, the pressure of water

Biology in Process

Using Aphids to Study Phloem

What substances move through the phloem? Although this question seems like a rather simple one, its exact answer eluded biologists for many years.

Researchers hypothesized that phloem carried sugars made in photosynthesis. The first experiments designed to test this hypothesis involved cutting into the phloem and collecting the sap that came out. These experiments indicated that sugars were indeed a major component of the phloem sap.

However, the experiments also revealed that the phloem sap contained a slimy substance called P-protein. Furthermore, some of the P-protein remained on the sieve plate and formed a slime plug that blocked the movement of materials out of the sieve tube member. On the basis of this evidence some investigators inferred that slime plugs occurred in undisturbed phloem, and they encouraged a revision of the pressure–flow hypothesis. Other scientists inferred that the formation of slime plugs was a form of wound healing. What researchers needed was a way to ensure that the phloem sap they studied was not contaminated with wound-healing substances that

390 *Chapter 26*

Cooperative Learning

Studying Osmosis Have students work in groups of four to demonstrate how rate of osmosis into sieve tubes is related to concentration of sugar. Assign each group a different concentration of sucrose solution, such as 1%, 2%, 3%, 4%, and 5%. Tell students to: (1) Seal the small (bottom) end of a thistle tube with clay. (2) Pour in 20 mL of the assigned concentration of sucrose in water. (3) Tie wet dialysis tubing to the wide (top) end of the tube. (4) Invert the tube into a beaker of 150 mL distilled water. Have groups compare the rates at which the water levels in the inverted tubes rise. Ask each group to observe what conditions affect the rate of osmosis of water through a membrane. *(Concentration of solute)* causes water to be forced out of the leaves. This process, called guttation, usually occurs at night. Guttation cannot account for most of the movement of water through a plant, however. Scientists now think that water may be "pulled" up a plant. They suggest that water forms a continuous column from roots, through stems, to leaves. This is possible because water is a cohesive fluid; its molecules are strongly attracted to each other.

The movement of this column of water is the basis for the **transpiration–cohesion theory.** Figure 26-12 on the following page shows how water that evaporates from leaves through stomata is eventually replaced by water from the xylem. When a water molecule from the xylem replaces water that has evaporated from the leaf, a low pressure is formed at the top of the water column. Vessel elements and tracheids do not collapse under this low pressure because their walls are thick. Water moves from areas of high pressure to areas of low pressure. This, combined with the strong cohesion of water, pulls the entire water column up from the roots through the plant.

The speed of water movement through a stem changes throughout the day. At midday evaporation is greatest, and water moves rapidly from the roots through the plant. This rapid move-

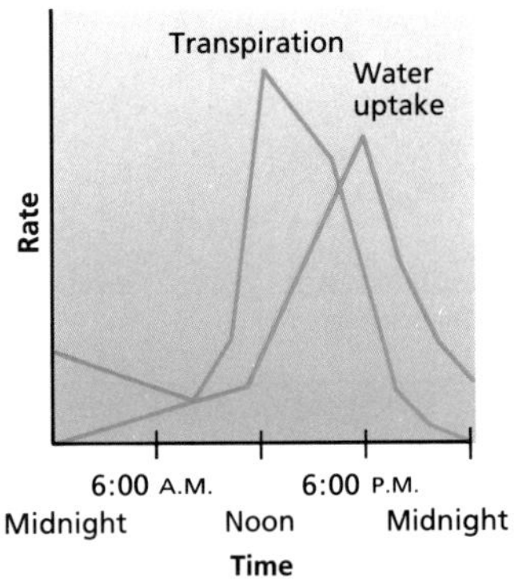

Figure 26-11 The rate of water uptake peaks about six hours after the rate of transpiration peaks.

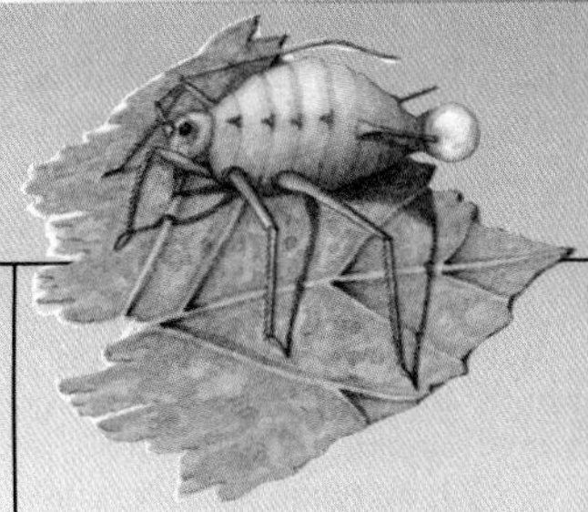

were released when they cut into the phloem.

In the early 1950s two insect physiologists suggested a novel research tool—aphids. They observed that aphids obtained their food from phloem by inserting a "tap" into individual sieve tube members.

The aphid's tap (left) is an extremely small, snoutlike mouthpart called a stylet. Since the contents of the phloem are under positive pressure, sugars in the phloem surge into the aphid. The phloem sap often passes right through the insect and forms a droplet of sugary liquid called honeydew on the aphid's body.

Once an aphid has inserted its stylet into a sieve tube member, researchers anesthetize it with a gentle stream of carbon dioxide. They then sever the aphid from the stylet, leaving the stylet in the sieve tube. About 1 mm³ of sap per hour can be collected from a stylet for up to five days.

Studies using aphids' stylets, in addition to studies involving radioactive isotopes, have provided evidence that slime plugs do not occur in undisturbed plants. P-proteins are not present in the phloem sap collected from aphid stylets. The phloem sap instead contains a fluid that is approximately 20 percent sugar. Amino acids make up approximately 0.1 percent of the sap.

By measuring the rate of flow through stylets placed at various points on the plant, researchers can construct a model of substance movement. They have found that, in some plants, the movement of phloem sap from source to sink occurs at the rate of nearly 100 cm per hour.

- **How have scientists used the process of collecting data in studying phloem?**

LEP Activity

Demonstrate water transport in a stem by splitting the stem of a white flower, such as a carnation, in half lengthwise and placing one half in plain water and the other in water with food coloring. Within a few hours, half the flower will turn the color of the food coloring.

Demonstrate the transpiration-cohesion theory with a string of beads inserted in a clear plastic tube. Explain that the beads represent water molecules, and the tube represents xylem. Slowly pull the beads up and out of the tube. Explain to students that water molecules evaporate from the top of a vessel.

Guided Practice

Project prepared slides of herbaceous monocot and dicot stems onto a screen via microprojector, or use transparencies and an overhead projector. Ask students why no secondary growth occurs in herbaceous monocots. *(No vascular cambium)*

Independent Practice

- Have students write answers to the Section Review.
- Have students write a brief description of the formation of an annual ring. *(Vascular cambium forms more secondary xylem than secondary phloem. This xylem forms a woody deposit each year that becomes an annual ring.)*

Biology in Process

Using the Feature

The feature focuses on the process skill of data collection. Scientists have used various means to collect data to support or refute hypotheses concerning the flow of sap through phloem. The rate of flow and the content of sap may be analyzed by using aphids, which have a stylet that is inserted in the phloem without extensively damaging the vascular tissue. Such data collection not only contributes to the results of single experiments, but provides a base of knowledge from which other inferences may be drawn. Point out to students that data can be collected in a variety of ways from many sources. Remind them that data found relevant or irrelevant in one experiment may later be found to support other hypotheses.

Answer to the Feature

Data indicating rapid movement of sap through the phloem from source to sink provided support for the notion of pressure in the sieve tube.

Section 26.3

Check Your Understanding

1. Of what adaptive advantage are bud scales? *(They protect developing buds so more leaves and lateral branches can grow.)*
2. Why are some tree rings thicker than others? *(In a year with ideal rainfall, sun, and nutrients, a tree would lay down a thick ring. During drought or less than optimal conditions, a tree would produce a narrower annual ring.)*
3. Why does little transpiration occur at night? *(Light is needed for photosynthesis. Lower temperatures slow evaporation.)*

Reteaching

Ask students how water and food circulate around a plant, and make a sequential diagram on the board. An example of a completed diagram is shown on p. 387.

■ *See* Section Reviews *worksheet, Section 26.3.*

Enrichment

Have students research the process of making maple syrup from the sap of sugar maple trees. *(Trees are tapped in the early spring when sap rises. A spout is inserted into the tree, the sap is collected, and then it is boiled down into syrup.)* Ask students why they think the sap drips out of the spout. *(Pressure difference)* Ask what kind of vascular tissue is being tapped. *(Phloem)* Ask why syrup makers are careful not to take too much sap. *(The tree needs food for spring growth.)*

Closure

Have students look at Figure 26-12, p. 392. Review the movement of water through the plant from absorption through the roots to transpiration, while students follow the illustrations.

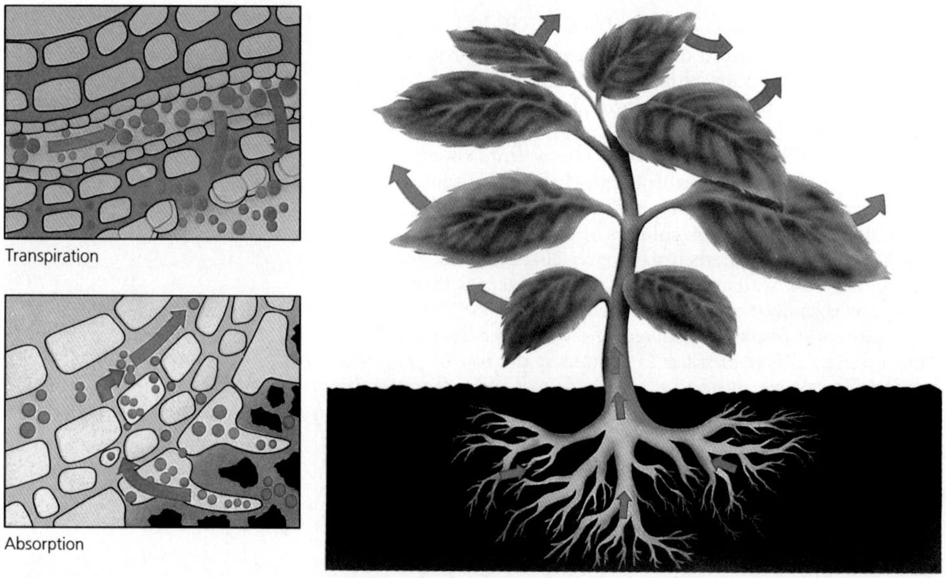

Figure 26-12 The diagrams above show how water moves through xylem from areas of high pressure to areas of low pressure.

ment creates a low pressure in the xylem, so strong that tree trunks actually shrink slightly in diameter during the day. At night there is little transpiration. Water does not move in the xylem, and the trunk enlarges slightly in diameter.

Storage in Stems

Plant stems are adapted for food storage in some species. As you read earlier, white potatoes are tubers, stems that are specialized for storing food. The "eyes" of white potatoes are actually buds that will grow into other stems if placed in the proper environment.

Many plant stems are full of parenchyma cells, which indicates that they store water and food for use by the rest of the plant. Succulents have particularly fleshy stems that retain water and nutrients in areas where water is often unavailable.

Section Review

1. Explain the difference between summerwood and springwood.
2. How does the arrangement of vascular tissues in a stem differ between monocots and dicots?
3. Describe how food moves through stems from source to sink.
4. Describe some adaptations of stems for food storage.
5. How might the rate of transport of water differ between plants in cool, humid environments and those in hot, dry environments?

Answers to Section Review

1. Summerwood has small cells with thick walls. Springwood has large cells with thin walls.
2. In dicots, they are in a single ring; in monocots, they are in scattered bundles.
3. Sugars are pumped into sieve tubes by active transport. Water follows by osmosis, resulting in high pressure at the source end of the tube. At the sink end, sugars are pumped out, and water follows by osmosis. The differences in pressure at the ends causes sugars to flow through the phloem.
4. Tubers are short, thickened stems for food storage. Plants in dry areas have thickened stems for water and nutrient storage.
5. The rate of transport in cool, humid environments would tend to be slower than in hot, dry environments.

26.4 Leaves

Being specialized for capturing sunlight for photosynthesis, most leaves are thin and flat. Although this structure may be typical, it is certainly not universal. Leaves are the most variable organ of plants. This variability represents adaptations to environmental conditions.

Look at the leaves in Figure 26-13. The coiled structure in the figure is a tendril, a kind of modified leaf. The tendrils of plants such as peas and morning glories wrap themselves around objects as the plant grows toward a light source.

Leaves of desert plants are often modified into protective spines. Since spines are relatively small, they reduce the surface area from which water can evaporate. In cactuses, little photosynthesis occurs in the spines; most photosynthesis takes place in the stems.

An uncommon modification of leaves occurs in insectivorous plants such as the pitcher plant. In insectivorous plants leaves often function as animal traps. These plants usually grow in soil that is relatively poor in nitrogen and phosphorus. The insects contain a large amount of these nutrients, and the plant receives essential macronutrients when it digests them.

Section Objectives

- *Identify the main external features of leaves.*
- *Explain the importance of stomata.*
- *Describe the three main regions of leaf tissue.*

Figure 26-13 Plants with diverse leaf adaptations include (left to right) the pea plant, *Pisum sativum* (tendrils), the cactus, *Opuntia* sp. (spines), and the pitcher plant, *Sarracenia* sp. (tubular leaves).

Lesson Plan

Section Focus

This section presents the basic structure and function of leaves and relates their adaptations to their habitats. It also introduces the control mechanisms for gas exchange through stomata.

Section Themes

The theme of **Systems and Interactions** is developed in the explanation of how leaf structures function as a unit. The theme of **Scale and Structure** is explored through descriptions of structure and function at the cellular level.

Motivating Activity

Bring to class a collection of odd and ordinary leaves and have students also collect leaves. (Examples are: pine needles, cactus with spines, Venus's-flytrap, fuzzy African violet leaves, palm fronds, lettuce, rhubarb, curly geranium leaves.) Have students observe and attempt to identify the main external features of each leaf. Point out to students that plants show such variety in their leaves because they have adapted to a wide range of habitats.

Teaching Strategies

Brainstorming Ideas Ask students to list environmental conditions to which plants have adapted. Then have them decide how those adaptations could aid survival. *(Sample answers: Short growing season: many small leaves rather than a few large leaves; less energy and less time need be put into growth of leaves. Dry climate: leaves with small surface area, thick cuticle; slows rate of evaporation)*

Videodiscs

- ***1957–1966, Leaf Sections (s)***

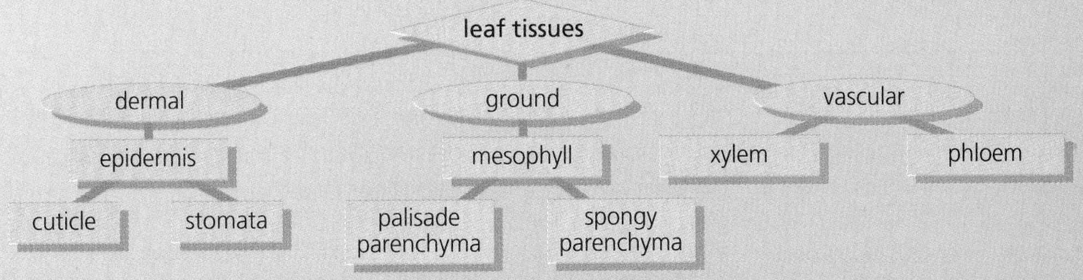

Graphic Organizer Use this chart in Organizing Information on p. 394.

Interpreting the Visuals Walk students through Figure 26-15, p. 394, making sure they can name the three tissue layers represented in the internal structure of a leaf as vascular *(Vascular bundles)*, dermal *(Epidermis)*, and ground *(Mesophyll)* tissue. Ask students what xylem and phloem do in leaves. *(Xylem: transports water and minerals into leaf. Phloem: transports sugars from leaf to rest of plant)* Ask what adaptive advantage is inherent in the shape and arrangement of the palisade parenchyma. *(Increases exposure of chloroplasts to light)*

■ *See* **Overhead Transparency** *T26 and* **Blackline Master** *53.*

Organizing Information Have students generate an organizational chart on the board to show the three types of tissues that make a leaf. An example of a completed chart is shown on p. 393.

Observing Structures To help students see the network of veins in a leaf, have them make leaf rubbings. Tell them to place a piece of paper over a fresh green leaf. Then tell them to hold it firmly in place, and rub a crayon or pastel over the leaf gently until the outline of the leaf and the skeleton of veins are visible. Have students compare the vein networks of monocots and dicots.

Making Inferences In Section 26.2, students learned that root hairs increase the surface-area-to-volume ratio of the root system. Ask students to use this information to infer how trees benefit from having so many leaves. *(With so many leaves, more of the surface area is exposed to light for photosynthesis. For example, an adult maple tree has at least 100,000 leaves, or a total leaf-blade surface area equal to nearly 2,000 m².)*

Figure 26-14 Silhouetted above are the leaves of the sugar maple tree, *Acer saccharum* (top), and the golden-rain tree, *Loelreuteria paniculata* (bottom). The first is a simple leaf; the second is compound.

Figure 26-15 Cells from three tissue systems are represented in the internal structure of a leaf. Can you name the systems?

Leaf Structure

Leaves can be round, straplike, needlelike, or heart shaped, and their edges range from smooth to serrate. Regardless of their external structure, all leaves are made up of ground, dermal, and vascular tissues. Secondary tissues rarely occur in leaves.

The broad, flat portion of a typical leaf is the **blade;** this is the site of most of the photosynthesis in the plant. The blade is attached to the stem by a stalklike **petiole.** The maple leaf shown in Figure 26-14 is a **simple leaf;** it has only one blade and one petiole. In **compound leaves,** such as those of the date palm, the blade is divided into leaflets. In some species the leaflets are divided. The result is a doubly compound leaf.

Venation is the arrangement of veins in a leaf. Leaves of most monocots, such as grasses, have parallel venation, meaning that their main veins are parallel to each other. Leaves of most dicots, such as sycamores, have net venation, meaning that smaller veins branch out from a large central vein.

Figure 26-15 shows the internal structure of a leaf. Leaves consist of cells from three tissue systems. The dermal tissue system is represented by the epidermis. In most leaves the epidermis is a single layer of cells coated with an impermeable cuticle. Water, oxygen, and carbon dioxide enter and exit from the leaf through stomata in the epidermis.

The number of stomata per unit area of leaf varies in different plants. For example, submerged leaves of aquatic plants do not have stomata. However, leaves of corn plants, which grow best in hot weather, have approximately 7,500 stomata per square centimeter of leaf epidermis.

The number of stomata also varies on the upper and lower sides of leaves. Most plant leaves have more stomata on their

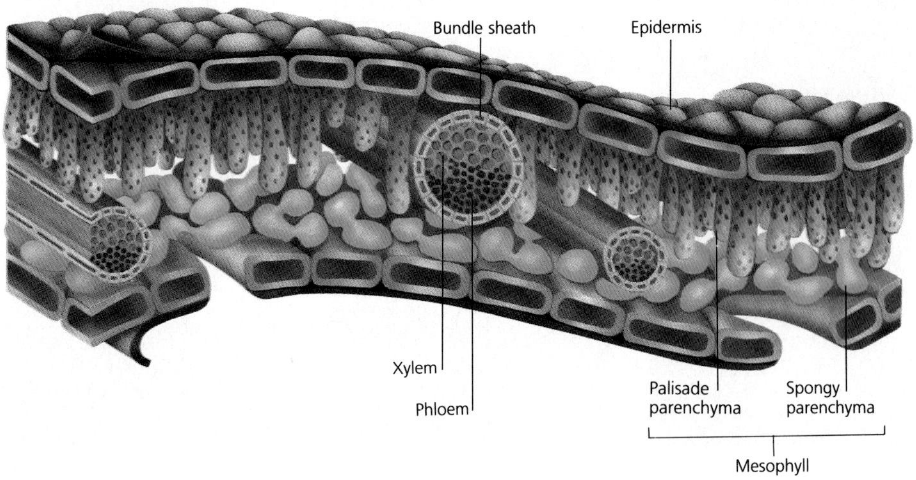

Cooperative Learning

Plant Response Divide the class into groups of six. Give each group one of the following: Venus's-flytrap, pitcher plant, sundew plant (available from supply houses, florists, or nurseries). Have each group experiment to find out how the leaves work to trap insects. *(Venus's-flytrap: one of the trigger hairs must be touched three times in succession. Pitcher plant: insect falls in, and downward-pointing hairs prevent its crawling out. Sundew: insect gets stuck on the sticky tendrils, and sundew curls over it.)* After completing the experiment, each group should report their findings to the class and share their observations.

shaded lower epidermis than on their exposed upper epidermis. For instance, oak leaves have no stomata on their upper surfaces but have thousands of stomata per square centimeter on their lower surfaces. Regardless of their exact distribution, stomata are functional: they regulate gas exchange.

Photosynthesis occurs in the leaf **mesophyll** *(MEZZ-oe-FILL)*, a ground tissue that is made up of chloroplast-rich parenchyma cells. In most plants, the mesophyll is organized into palisade parenchyma and spongy parenchyma. **Palisade parenchyma** occurs directly below the upper epidermis; this is where most of a photosynthesis in the leaf occurs. Palisade cells are shaped like columns and are packed tightly together, increasing the exposure of chloroplasts to sunlight. Between the palisade parenchyma and the lower epidermis is **spongy parenchyma.** It consists of irregularly shaped cells surrounded by numerous air spaces, which allow oxygen and carbon dioxide to diffuse into and out of a leaf.

The vascular tissue system is represented by vascular bundles. In leaves they are called veins. They are continuous with the vascular tissue of the stem and the petiole and lie embedded in the mesophyll. Veins are often surrounded by a tight-fitting **bundle sheath** made up of parenchyma cells.

The Function of Leaves

Leaves are the primary site of photosynthesis in plants. As such, they must absorb light energy and take in carbon dioxide from the environment. Palisade cells in leaves use light energy, carbon dioxide, and water to make sugars. Sugars manufactured in leaves can then be used as an energy source for growth or be transported to roots or fruits and stored until needed.

The temperature of a leaf increases when it absorbs light, just as your skin can get hot on a bright summer day. Transpiration cools leaves while pulling water and dissolved minerals from roots through stems. In corn more than 98 percent of the water that is absorbed by the roots is lost through transpiration.

Modifications for Capturing Light

Leaves absorb light, which provides the energy for photosynthesis. In addition, the chloroplasts in photosynthetic leaf cells are typically arranged in a thin, uniform layer near the lighted side of the leaf. This minimizes the shading of one chloroplast by another.

In many plants leaves are modified for specialized environmental conditions. In deserts, where light is sometimes very intense, leaves often have thick cuticles or hairs. These reflect or block the excess light and reduce water loss. Another adaptation related to light intensity occurs in the so-called window plants. The leaves of these plants actually grow underground. All of the light for photosynthesis comes through a tiny "window" of transparent tissue that protrudes above soil level.

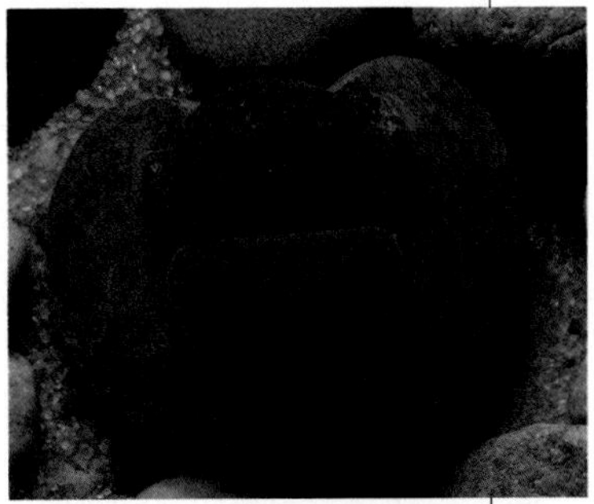

Figure 26-16 The leaves of a stone plant, *Lithops* sp., are modified so that the plant mimics a small stone.

Guided Practice

Write the overall equation for photosynthesis (see Chapter 7, p. 94) on the board, and ask students to name the structures involved in the entrance of CO_2, H_2O, and light; and the exit of O_2 and sugar. *(CO_2 and O_2, stomata; H_2O, xylem and stomata; light, chloroplasts; sugar, phloem)* Use Figure 26-17 on p. 396 to illustrate the opening and closing of stomata.

■ *See* **Laboratories, *Investigation 26.***

Independent Practice

■ Have students write answers to the Section Review.

■ Have students invent visual or other mnemonics to help them remember the structures and functions of leaves. *(Examples: Mesophyll has chlorophyll; both end in* -phyll. *A sponge has lots of holes; so does spongy parenchyma.)*

Check Your Understanding

1. Why are secondary growth tissues absent in many leaves? *(Leaves do not have vascular cambium; many do not survive for more than one season.)*

2. Would leaves of rain forest plants have more or fewer stomata per square centimeter of surface than leaves of temperate or cold climate plants? *(Humidity is the determining factor. Tropical rain forest plants have leaves with many stomata. Leaves of plants in colder, drier regions have fewer stomata.)*

3. How do leaf hairs help reduce water loss? *(They block excess wind and keep surface humidity higher. They also shade the leaf and keep the leaf temperature lower.)*

Videodiscs

■ ***Side 3 26888, Stomatal Opening (m)***

■ ***2612, Leaves and Water Loss (s)***

■ ***2576, Movement in Leaves (s)***

Interdisciplinary Activity

Health Have students do library research to learn about the nutritive value of leaves. *(Dark green leafy vegetables are rich in vitamins A, B_1 [thiamine], B_2 [riboflavin], niacin, C, E, and K, and the minerals phosphorus, magnesium, calcium, and iron.)* Tell students to imagine they are health-conscious restaurant owners. Have them generate breakfast, lunch, and dinner menus for a week that include at least one leafy vegetable at each meal, each day. Tell students to use a leaf variety only two times; lettuce is not the only edible leaf. Ethnic cookbooks can offer a wealth of ideas. Breakfast is difficult, but many greens can be included in omelets or in fresh juice drinks.

Section 26.4

Reteaching

Bring a variety of leaves to class, such as pine needles, maple, corn, oak, ginkgo, ash, spider plant, and iris. Or have students collect a variety of leaves from your local area. Make field guides available so that students can classify the leaves and identify their structures. Huge leaves, tiny leaves, and leaves with interesting colors will help to increase student interest in leaf classification.

■ *See* Section Reviews *worksheet, Section 26.4.*

Enrichment

Take students to a nearby park, and give them a dichotomous key for identifying trees by their leaves. (Have students review the Chapter 18 Laboratory.) Then have the class use the key to identify the trees within a specified area.

Closure

Give several examples of adaptations of leaves to different environments. (Examples are: fleshy leaves of succulents, tendrils of a pea plant.) Ask students how each adaptation aids the plant's success in its environment. *(Fleshy leaves are adapted to store water; tendrils twine to aid in support of the pea plant's stem.)*

Videodiscs

■ *1960, Guard Cell (s)*

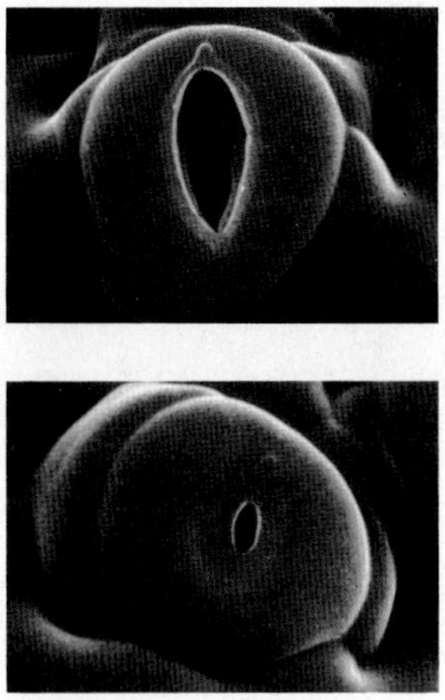

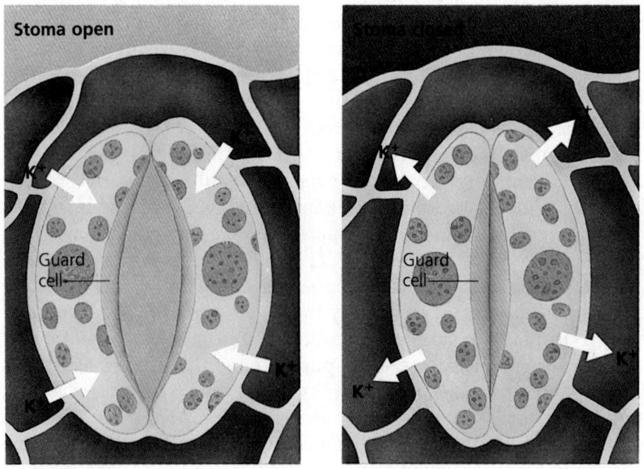

Figure 26-17 SEMs of the leaf of a tobacco plant, *Nicotiana tabacum,* show open (top, ×2,000) and closed (bottom, ×2,000) stomata.

Gas Exchange

Plants obtain carbon dioxide for photosynthesis from the air. Carbon dioxide diffuses into leaves through stomata. A stoma is bordered by two kidney-shaped **guard cells,** each of which has flexible cell walls that allow it to bend.

The opening and closing of a stoma is regulated by turgor pressure in guard cells. Turgor pressure is related to the amount of water in the cells. The stomata of most plants open during the day and close at night. Look at Figure 26-17. During the day light causes nearby epidermal cells to pump potassium ions (K^+) into the guard cells. Water then moves into the cells by osmosis. This influx of water increases the turgor pressure in guard cells and causes them to expand. The cells expand lengthwise, the result being that they bow apart and form a pore. At night the potassium ions are pumped out of the epidermal cells. Water then leaves the guard cells by osmosis; the guard cells shrink, and the pore closes. The opening and closing of stomata reflects one of the major ways in which plants survive diverse environments.

Section Review

1. What is the difference between a simple leaf and a compound leaf?
2. Describe the basic functions of the three leaf tissues.
3. Which leaf would have more stomata, that of a water lily or a sugar maple? Why?
4. Explain the function of the guard cells in regulating stomatal opening and closing.
5. How might the shape of a leaf affect its ability to capture sunlight?

Answers to Section Review

1. Simple leaf: one blade and one petiole; compound leaf: blade is in leaflets.
2. Epidermis has an impermeable cuticle and stomata that regulate gas exchange. Mesophyll carries out photosynthesis. Vascular tissues transport water and food.
3. Maple; it transpires more to keep cool.
4. During the day, light causes the pumping of potassium ions into the guard cells. Water follows by osmosis. The water-filled guard cells bulge apart, creating an opening through which gases can pass. At night, potassium ions are pumped out, causing water to leave by osmosis. The guard cells shrink and the stoma closes.
5. The greater the surface area exposed to the sun, the greater the amount of light that will be captured for photosynthesis.

Laboratory

Root Structure and Function

Objective
To compare the soil-anchoring ability of different root systems

Process Skills
Observing, organizing data, analyzing data

Materials
3 lima bean seeds, 3 corn seeds, 6 7-cm pots, potting soil, water, ruler, adhesive tape, scissors, cord, spring scale, paper, balance

Background
1 Describe the differences between primary roots, taproots, and fibrous roots.
2 What are two main functions of roots?

Inquiry
1 Fill each pot with soil up to 2.5 cm from the rim. Plant a bean seed 1 cm deep in three pots. Plant a corn kernel in the other pots. How much water should you give each plant? What variable(s) are controlled? What variable(s) are not controlled?
2 Where should you place the pots? Why?
3 When the plants are 5 cm high, place a small piece of adhesive tape around each stem at the soil level.
4 Attach one end of a cord to the tape and the other end to a spring scale.
5 To uproot a plant, pull the scale up and away from the plant. Read the scale as you pull. Record your measurement. What does the spring scale measure?
6 Do not shake soil from roots. Place the plant on a sheet of paper.
7 Repeat steps 4–6 for each plant. Use a separate sheet of paper for each plant.
8 Allow the plants to dry overnight.
9 Shake the roots of each plant over the paper. Remove as much soil as possible. Compare the root systems. What type of root system does a bean plant have? A corn plant? Measure and record the mass of the loose soil collected from each plant.
10 Measure and record the length and diameter of each root system.
11 Pool your data with those from other teams. What is the advantage of pooling?
12 Make a table to summarize the data of each team. Find the average for each measurement.
13 Use the averages to make bar graphs that compare the two kinds of plants for each measurement. What variables go across each horizontal axis? What variables go up the vertical axes?

Conclusions
1 Summarize the data in your graphs.
2 Do your data show a relationship between the force required to uproot a plant and any of the other measurements? Explain.
3 What can you infer about the relative anchoring ability of the two root systems?
4 Which root system would be more effective where wind erosion is a problem? Explain.

Further Inquiry
How will reduced water supply affect root growth? Design an experiment to test this.

(For an overview of root systems and preparatory information related to the laboratory, see p. 379B.)

Background
1. A primary root is the first root to grow from the seed; it develops into either a taproot system or a fibrous root system. A taproot is a large, thick root that grows deeply into the soil; a fibrous root forms a wide, branching, shallow system.
2. Roots absorb water and anchor a plant in or on a substrate.

Inquiry
1. The exact amount of water is not critical, but it should be a moderate amount. It is important that the plants receive equal amounts. The controlled variables are pot size, type and volume of soil, depth of seed, and amount of water. The germination and growth potentials of the individual seeds or kernels cannot be controlled.
2. The plants should be placed together in the same area, preferably in moderate light. The exact placement is not critical, but all the plants must receive equal amounts of light/dark/heat.
5. The scale measures the force required to uproot the plant.
9. The beans have taproots; corn has a fibrous root system.
11. The larger the sample, the more the individual differences in germination and growth will average out.
13. Four bar graphs can be made. The name of the plant or root system is across each horizontal axis (independent variables). The vertical axes are labeled with the dependent variables: newtons of force, grams of soil, centimeters or millimeters of root length, and centimeters or millimeters of root system diameter.

Conclusions
1. Answers will vary but should adequately summarize the data.
2. Most students will probably find a relationship between the force required to uproot a plant and the amount of soil retained by the roots. More force is usually required to uproot the bean seedlings.
3. Both systems appear to anchor the plant effectively, but the fibrous root system may bind more soil to the roots.
4. Fibrous roots bind soil more effectively and could resist wind erosion.

Further Inquiry
Hypotheses will vary, but some plants do respond initially to reduced water supply by growing roots faster. Students could redo the experiment using half as much water.

Chapter 26 Review

Vocabulary

1. Epidermis; it is not a secondary growth tissue.
2. Mesophyll; it is not a vascular tissue cell.
3. Vascular cambium; it is not related to primary growth.
4. Sclerenchyma; it is not related to water absorption and transport.
5. Cork; it is not found in leaves.

Review

1. b	**6.** c
2. c	**7.** d
3. c	**8.** b
4. d	**9.** b
5. a	**10.** d

11. Growth produced by the lateral meristems, vascular cambium, and cork cambium causes plants to grow wider.
12. Heartwood is the darker wood in the center of a stem, where xylem is clogged with waste products. Sapwood is nearer the outside of the stem and still transports water and nutrients.
13. Transpiration causes a low pressure to build up in the xylem. Water moves to this area of low pressure; it is a cohesive fluid—its molecules stick together.
14. Sugar is a major component of phloem sap.
15. Modified leaves include spines, tendrils, and the leaves of insectivorous plants.
16. A sweet potato is a root; a white potato is a stem. Both are specialized for food storage.
17. When guard cells fill with water, they pull apart, thus creating an opening through which gases can pass.
18. In a monocot, vascular bundles are scattered throughout the stem; in a dicot, vascular bundles form a ring in the stem.
19. Primary growth originates in apical meristems and occurs in all plants—dicots and monocots; secondary growth originates in lateral meristems and does not occur in monocots.

Chapter 26 Review

Vocabulary

annual ring (389)
apical meristem (382)
bark (389)
blade (394)
bundle sheath (395)
Casparian strip (384)
collenchyma (381)
companion cell (381)
compound leaf (394)
cork (382)
cork cambium (382)
cortex (384)
dermal tissue system (382)
endodermis (384)
epidermis (382)
fiber (381)
fibrous root (383)
ground system (381)
guard cell (396)
herbaceous plant (382)
lateral meristem (382)
leaf (381)
macronutrient (386)
meristem (382)
mesophyll (395)
micronutrient (386)
palisade parenchyma (395)
parenchyma (381)
pericycle (384)
petiole (394)
pit (381)
pith (388)
pressure–flow hypothesis (389)
primary growth (382)
primary root (383)
ray (389)
root (381)
root cap (384)
root hair (384)
sclerenchyma (381)
secondary growth (382)
sieve plate (381)
sieve tube member (381)
simple leaf (394)
sink (389)
source (389)
spongy parenchyma (395)
springwood (389)
stem (381)
stoma (382)
summerwood (389)
taproot (383)
tissue (381)
tracheid (381)
transpiration (386)
transpiration–cohesion theory (391)
vascular bundle (388)
vascular cambium (382)
vascular cyclinder (384)
vascular system (381)
venation (394)
vessel element (381)
woody plant (382)

Choose the term that does not belong in each of the following sets, and explain why.

1. wood, bark, epidermis, ray
2. sieve tube member, mesophyll, tracheid, companion cell
3. apical meristem, primary xylem, vascular cambium, endodermis
4. root hair, transpiration, vessel element, sclerenchyma
5. blade, cork, petiole, vein

Review

1. Bark does *not* contain (a)secondary phloem (b) secondary xylem (c) cork cambium (d) cortex.
2. Dark wood in the center of a tree is (a) springwood (b) sapwood (c) heartwood (d) summerwood.
3. Mesophyll is the site of (a) water absorption (b) food storage (c) photosynthesis (d) secondary growth.
4. Water moves between tracheids through (a) end walls (b) stomata (c) vessel elements (d) pits.
5. Stomata open and close as the result of turgor pressure in the (a) guard cells (b) sieve tube members (c) companion cells (d) bundle sheath.
6. The root apical meristem is protected by the (a) suberin (b) cuticle (c) root cap (d) cortex.
7. Collenchyma and sclerenchyma are (a) vascular tissues (b) meristems (c) dermal tissues (d) ground tissues.
8. Most monocot stems do *not* have (a) primary growth (b) secondary growth (c) xylem (d) phloem.
9. The Casparian strip occurs on (a) epidermal cells (b) endodermal cells (c) pallisade parenchyma cells (d) vessel elements.

20. Herbaceous plants are usually annuals, such as zinnias, and do not develop vascular cambium or secondary xylem and phloem. Woody plants are usually perennials, such as forsythia; they develop vascular cambium and secondary growth.

10. The main site of photosynthesis in cacti is the (a) root (b) spine (c) flower (d) stem.
11. What causes a plant to grow wider?
12. Explain the difference between heartwood and sapwood.
13. Briefly describe the transpiration–cohesion theory of water movement in plants.
14. What substances are transported through phloem?
15. List three modified types of leaves.
16. How is a sweet potato different from a white potato? How are they similar?
17. Explain how guard cells regulate the opening and closing of stomata.
18. Describe the different arrangements of vascular bundles in monocots and dicots.
19. Explain the difference between primary growth and secondary growth.
20. Distinguish between herbaceous and woody plants, and give an example of each.

Critical Thinking

1. A pith cell from a plant can be isolated in tissue culture and, if given the proper plant hormones, will form new plants. What does this tell you about the growth potential of these cells?
2. When transplanting a plant, it is important not to remove any more soil than necessary from around the roots. From your knowledge of the function of roots and root hairs, why is this so important?
3. Suppose you examined a tree stump and noticed that 50 rings in from the surface the annual rings became thinner and closer together than the others. What would you conclude about the climate in that area 50 years ago?

4. Examine the photograph above. Explain how this leaf arrangement is adaptive for plants that grow in the shady areas that receive little sunlight.

Extension

1. Read the article by Ricki Rusting entitled "A Clock in the Trees" in *Scientific American,* August 1990, p. 30. How did Hillam and Baillie use tree rings to determine the precise age of the oldest road yet discovered?
2. Measure transpiration in a common herbaceous plant. Buy two small flower or tomato plants from a local nursery. Make sure the plants are well watered and then cover the pots (including the tops of the pots but not the plants themselves) with a plastic bag or plastic wrap and secure tightly. Weigh the plants to the nearest 0.1 g and record the weight. Turn a fan on one plant, and set another in sunlight for two hours. Weigh the plants again to the nearest 0.1 g and calculate the percentage of water loss resulting from transpiration. Use the following formula:

Original weight − weight after 2 hr = weight change
Weight change ÷ original weight × 100 = percentage weight loss

If no difference is noticed at first, continue the experiment for another two hours or overnight.

Critical Thinking

1. It suggests that each cell has the genetic potential to form a new plant.
2. When the tiny roots and root hairs are destroyed by moving the plant, the plant cannot absorb as much water and minerals.
3. The thin annual rings are a result of poor growth. The most probable cause of this result is a drought. It is also possible that the tree was shaded by another, bigger tree or suffered a severe insect attack that slowed its growth.
4. The petioles are twisted and shortened or lengthened, bringing the leaves into a flat plane in which no leaf shades another.

Extension

1. They matched the tree rings found in samples of lumber taken from the bridge with a reliable master chronology of trees grown in Europe between 5289 B.C. and A.D. 1983.
2. You may want to organize this experiment as a cooperative learning activity.

Chapter 27 Plant Reproduction

Chapter Overview

Chapter 27 presents sexual and asexual reproduction in plants. Section 27.1 details alternation of generations. Section 27.2 explains sexual reproduction and seed formation in flowering plants. In Section 27.3 students will explore the structure of seeds, types of fruits, seed dispersal, and germination of seed plants. Section 27.4 presents asexual reproduction as an adaptation of some types of plants.

Chapter Planning Chart

B	S	A	Sections and Subsections	Page	Features	Page	Resources
	•	•	**27.1 Alternation of Generations**				
			The Life Cycle of Mosses	401	Section Review	404	Videodiscs
			The Life Cycle of Ferns	402			Blackline Master 54
			The Life Cycle of Conifers	403			Overhead Transparency T27
							Section Reviews Worksheet
•	•	•	**27.2 The Life Cycle of Flowering Plants**				
			Parts of a Flower	405	Think	407	Videodiscs
			Pollen Grain Formation	406	Biology in Process	408	Blackline Master 55
			Ovule Formation	407	Section Review	410	Blackline Master 56
			Pollination	408			Laboratories: Flowers and Fruits
			Fertilization	409			Section Reviews Worksheet
•	•	•	**27.3 Fruits and Seeds**				
			Structure of Seeds	411	Laboratory	417	Videodiscs
			Types of Fruits	411	Section Review	414	Process Skills: Plant Reproductive Structures
			Dispersal of Fruits and Seeds	412			Section Reviews Worksheet
			Seed Germination	413			
•	•	•	**27.4 Asexual Reproduction**				
			Vegetative Propagation	415	Section Review	416	Videodiscs
			Artificial Propagation	416			Section Reviews Worksheet
			End of Chapter Activities				
					Chapter Review	418	Vocabulary Skills
							Chapter Test
							Computer Test Generator

B *The Basic Level curriculum presents the most fundamental knowledge offered in the course.*
S *The Standard Level curriculum is designed for the average student who is able to master most topics.*
A *The Advanced Level curriculum includes suggestions for teaching the most academically able students.*

Cooperative Learning

Group Activity: Adaptations for Dispersal

- **Group Size:** *5 students*
- **Outcome:** *Students will determine how seeds and fruits are modified for dispersal.*
- **Individual Accountability:** *Each group member will modify a seed for dispersal by various natural forces.*
- **Positive Interdependence:** *Each group will cooperate to create and present modified seeds or fruits for review by the class.*

Divide the class into groups of five. Distribute about 30 dried bean seeds or pea seeds to each group. Provide a materials box containing construction paper, tissue paper, tape, glue, rubber bands, cotton, craft sticks, feathers, balloons, pipe cleaners, paper clips, string, scissors, and so on. Have the students in each group modify five seeds, one to meet each of the following criteria: (1) float on water for 4 minutes; (2) catch or stick on an animal and be carried 5 m; (3) can be shot at least 1 m from the parent plant; (4) glide at least 1 m away when dropped from the parent plant; and (5) have a feature that can attract a bird or other animal. Give groups adequate time to construct and test their seed adaptations. Then have each group present its seed modifications to the class.

Concept Map

The following is one possible solution to the concept mapping activity in Comparing Adaptations on p. 412.

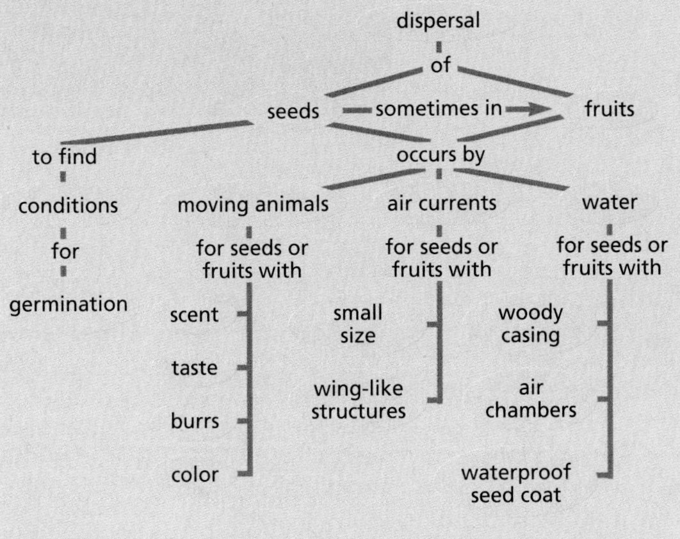

Laboratory Preparation

Overview *(See p. 417.)*

In this lab students investigate the germination of monocot and dicot seeds. First, they examine and compare external and internal structures of soaked bean seeds and corn grains. Then they compare bean seedlings with corn seedlings at 1, 2, 3, and 10 days after germination begins. Students should observe that a dicot seed has two cotyledons that emerge on a stem from the ground, two leaves in the plumule, and a radicle that elongates into a root system with many root hairs. They should also observe that a monocot seed has one cotyledon that stays underground, one leaf in the plumule, and a radicle that forms a branching, but temporary, primary root.

Preparation

Ten days before the lab, germinate at least one corn and one bean seed for each student or team. Soak the seeds for 6–8 hours. (Longer soaking may prevent germination.) To prevent growth of bacteria and mold, soak the seeds for 15 minutes in a solution of 5 mL chlorine bleach and 95 mL water. Plant the seeds in moist sand. Always start more seedlings than you will need so that plants of equal size and vigor may be selected. Sand is the recommended substrate because plants can be gently flooded out of sand; other substrates, such as soil and vermiculite, may be hard to separate from roots. Keep the sand moist.

Each student or team will also need bean seeds and corn kernels, one of each at 1, 2, and 3 days of germination. Start germination of these seeds three, two, and one day before the laboratory, with the procedure described above. Germinate more seeds than you will need.

Also soak one bean seed and one corn seed in water for 24 hours for each student or team.

Teaching Tips

To reduce the number of seedlings required, you may want to assign beans to half the teams and corn to the other half and then have the teams trade plants.

Allow students themselves to flood the seedlings from the sand. They will then see that monocot cotyledons remain below the ground and that dicot cotyledons emerge above the ground.

Tell students about procedures that test for sugars (Benedict's solution) and starches (iodine).

Safety

Tell students to use care with scalpels or razor blades.

Chapter Themes

Systems and Interactions Explain to students that plant reproduction relies on interaction of plant tissue systems. Stress that many plants have both sexual and asexual reproduction. Make sure that students understand that plants produced by asexual reproduction are genetically identical to the parent plant.

Evolution Both sexual and asexual reproduction in plants have adaptive advantages. Stress the reproductive adaptations of flowers and the advantages of various adaptations for dispersal of fruits, seeds, and pollen.

Chapter Motivating Activity

Display a seed of any kind; a runner from a spider plant, ivy, strawberry geranium, or vining philodendron; a leaf from an African violet or wax begonia; a stem from an azalea, ivy, or philodendron; a leaf cut in half from a wax begonia; and a dieffenbachia, dracaena, or split-leaf philodendron plant. Ask students what all of these plants and parts have in common, and write their answers on the board. Point out to students that whole plants may be reproduced from these parts.

Chapter 27 *Plant Reproduction*

Introduction

You know that all plants, from liverworts to apple trees, reproduce by alternation of generations, a form of sexual reproduction. Plants may also reproduce asexually, resulting in offspring that are genetically identical to their parents.

Chapter Outline

27.1 Alternation of Generations
- *The Life Cycle of Mosses*
- *The Life Cycle of Ferns*
- *The Life Cycle of Conifers*

27.2 The Life Cycle of Flowering Plants
- *Parts of a Flower*
- *Pollen Grain Formation*
- *Ovule Formation*
- *Pollination*
- *Fertilization*

27.3 Fruits and Seeds
- *Structure of Seeds*
- *Types of Fruits*
- *Dispersal of Fruits and Seeds*
- *Seed Germination*

27.4 Asexual Reproduction
- *Vegetative Propagation*
- *Artificial Propagation*

Chapter Concept

As you read, note the many plant adaptations that help ensure the protection and dispersal of offspring.

Milkweed, *Asclepias* sp. Inset (top): spore caps of sphagnum moss. Inset (bottom): *Passiflora* sp.

Understanding the Visuals

Have students examine the photographs and read the caption. Ask what the photos show. *(Reproductive structures: seeds, spore caps, and a flower)* Ask what is the function of each structure. *(Seeds: protect and nourish embryo; spore caps: protect spores from the time of development to dispersal; flower: attracts pollinators to produce seeds)* Remind students that alternation of generations was introduced in Chapter 25. Refer them to Figure 25-4, p. 368, to refresh their memories.

27.1 Alternation of Generations

Recall from Chapter 25 that the life cycle of a plant involves alternation of generations. All plants have a diploid (2N) sporophyte generation that alternates with a haploid (1N) gametophye generation. In mosses and other bryophytes the small sporophyte is attached to and nutritionally dependent on the larger gametophyte. However, the evolution of fern allies, ferns, gymnosperms, and angiosperms involved a reversal of this relationship. In these plants the sporophyte is the larger generation.

Seed plants benefit from having a reduced gametophyte. While the sperm of nonseed plants must swim through water to reach eggs in a gametophyte, the gametes of seed plants are protected by being enclosed in structures produced by the much larger sporophyte. As a result seed plants are able to live in a much wider variety of habitats than plants whose reproduction depends on the presence of moisture. In Sections 27.1 and 27.2 we will explore similarities and differences in sexual reproduction in various plants.

Section Objectives

- *Describe the life cycle of mosses.*
- *Summarize the life cycle of ferns.*
- *Describe the life cycle of gymnosperms.*

The Life Cycle of Mosses

Look at the life cycle of a moss, as illustrated in Figure 27-1, and notice that the larger generation is the haploid gametophyte. During certain times of the year most moss gametophytes produce two types of multicellular reproductive structures near their growing tips. The **antheridium** *(AN-thur-ID-ee-um)* is a male reproduc-

Figure 27-1 In the moss life cycle the sporophyte is the physically smaller generation. The gametophyte is the larger, photosynthetic generation. All cells shown in the yellow area are diploid; all cells shown in the tan area are haploid.

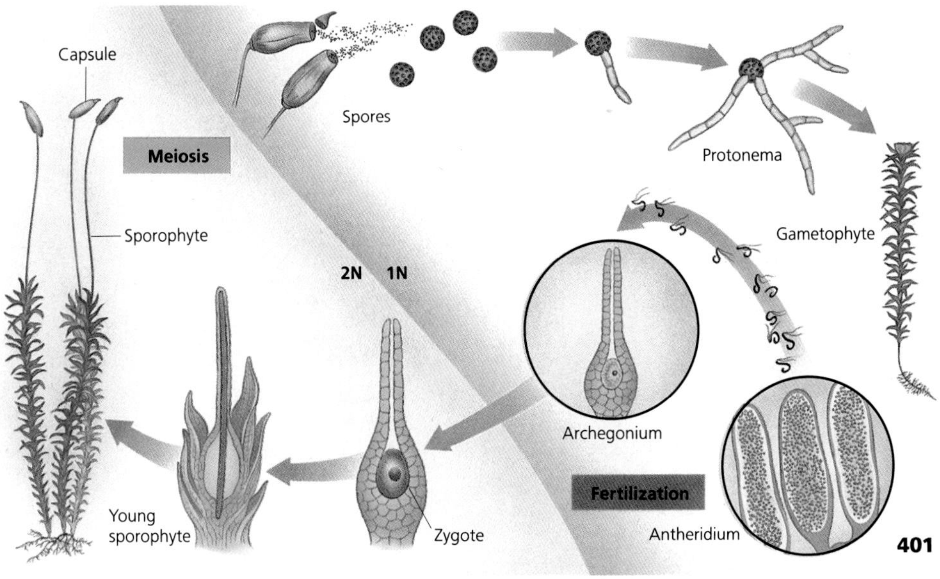

Lesson Plan

Section Focus

This section presents alternation of generations through the life cycles of mosses, ferns, and conifers and emphasizes that all plants have both a diploid sporophyte and a haploid gametophyte generation.

Section Themes

The theme of **Patterns of Change** is examined through alternation of generations in seed plants and nonseed plants. Meiosis and mitosis are also reviewed. The theme of **Evolution** is exemplified by the ability of seed plants, with their reduced gametophytes, to adapt to more varied environments than nonseed plants such as mosses.

Motivating Activity

Display live ferns with sori, or show pictures of them. Students unfamiliar with the fern life cycle may think that sori are some kind of insect or a plant disease. Ask students what the brown structures are. *(Sori, or sporangia)* Bring in live moss, or a picture of moss, with sporophyte capsules visible. Ask students to identify the sporophyte and gametophyte generations of the moss. (*The gametophyte is green. The stalk growing from the gametophyte with capsule is the sporophyte.)*

Videodiscs

- ***Side 3 7798, Plant Reproduction: Moss (m)***

Type	Consists of	Stage	Produces	Produced by
spores	single cell	haploid	gametophyte	bryophytes, whisk ferns, club mosses, horsetails, ferns
seeds	many cells	diploid	sporophyte	gymnosperms and angiosperms

Graphic Organizer Use this table in Independent Practice on p. 404.

Teaching Strategies

Interpreting the Visuals Direct students back to Figure 9-4, p. 133, Figure 9-7, p. 136, and Figure 9-9, p. 137, to review differences between mitosis and meiosis. Take students step-by-step through the life cycles of mosses, Figure 27-1, p. 401, and ferns, Figure 27-2, p. 402. Ask students if the gametophyte is haploid or diploid. *(Haploid)* Ask if the zygote is haploid or diploid. *(Diploid)* Ask what the zygote grows into. *(The sporophyte fern or moss capsule)* Ask what the moss capsule forms. *(Spores)* Ask whether spores are formed by mitosis or meiosis. *(Meiosis; they are haploid.)* Emphasize that the gametophyte is the larger generation in mosses and that the sporophyte is the larger in ferns.

■ *See* **Overhead Transparency** *T27 and* **Blackline Master** *54.*

tive structure that produces hundreds of flagellated sperm by mitosis. The **archegonium** *(AR-kuh-GOE-nee-um)* is a female reproductive structure that produces a single egg by mitosis.

During moist periods sperm break out of an antheridium and swim to an archegonium. They then enter the long neck, travel to the egg, and fertilize it, forming a diploid zygote. The zygote is the first cell of the sporophyte generation. It develops into an embryo. Repeated mitotic divisions of the embryo form a multicellular sporophyte.

The sporophyte at first is a stalk that remains attached to and dependent on the gametophyte for nourishment. Soon, cells at the tip of the stalk divide and form a sporangium called a capsule. Cells within the capsule undergo meiosis to form haploid spores. When the spores are mature the capsule splits open, and the spores are released. They travel on currents of wind. Those that land in favorable environments germinate and produce a slender thread called a **protonema.** The protonema is an early stage of gametophyte development. As the protonema grows, it soon begins to look like a mature moss.

All the moss spores look alike, and all produce similar gametophytes. This phenomenon is known as **homospory.** A life cycle such as that of mosses is thus called a homosporous alternation of generations.

The Life Cycle of Ferns

Compare the life cycle of a moss with that of a typical fern, shown in Figure 27-2. As you can see, the life cycle of a fern is also a homosporous alternation of generations, but the sporophyte, not the gametophyte, is the larger generation.

Figure 27-2 The fern life cycle, like that of a moss, includes a sexually reproducing generation that requires moisture for the sperm to swim to the egg.

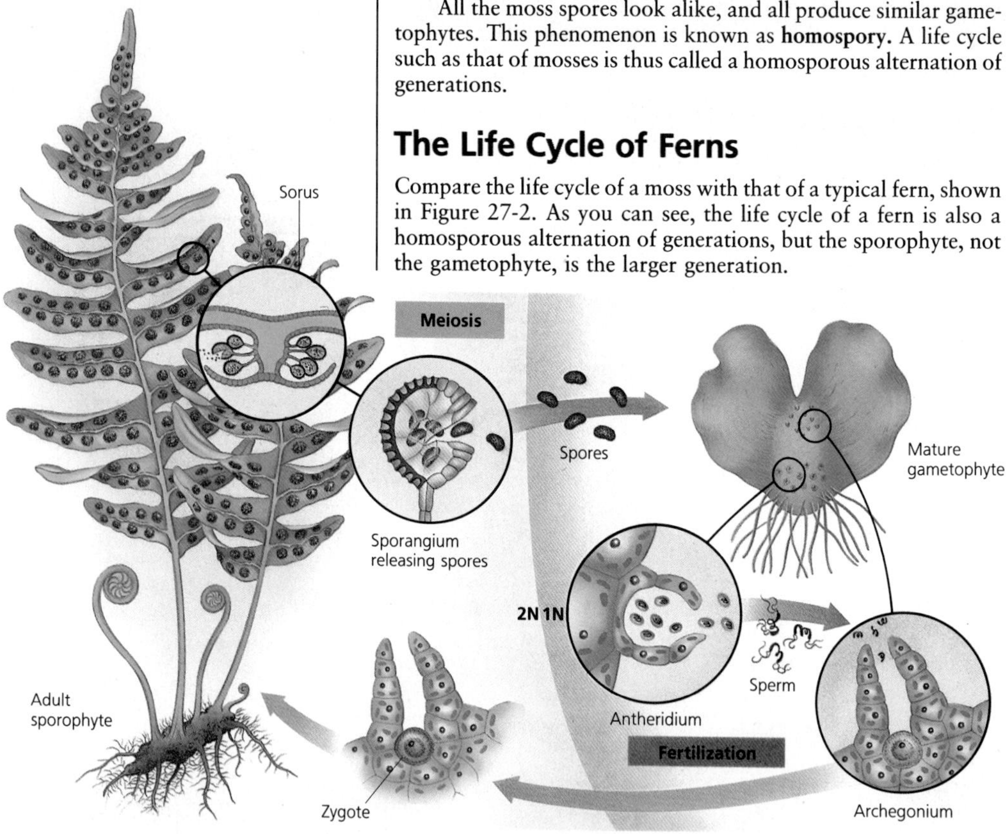

402

Cooperative Learning

Life Cycles Divide the class into groups of three. Assign one student in each group to research a step-by-step description of the life cycle of one of the three main groups of plants: nonvascular plants, vascular seedless plants, and vascular seed plants. After allowing time for research, have students researching each plant group meet to teach one another and share their findings. Then reassemble the original groups and allow students to explain their plant group life cycles to the other group members. Circulate around the room and quiz students on the life cycles of nonvascular plants, vascular seedless plants, and vascular seed plants. Finally, have groups create posters illustrating the life cycle differences among the three plant groups.

Fern gametophytes are heart shaped and about 5 to 15 mm in diameter. They are anchored to the soil by rootlike rhizoids on their lower surfaces. Antheridia and archegonia form on the upper surface of the gametophytes. When water covers the mature gametophyte, the antheridia release spiral-shaped sperm, which swim to the archegonia. Here one sperm fuses with the egg and forms a zygote. The zygote, the first cell of the sporophyte generation, rapidly undergoes mitosis, grows into an embryo, and develops into a young fern. As the sporophyte grows it crushes the gametophyte. The mature fern has an underground rhizome that produces fronds.

In most ferns, cells on the underside of the frond differentiate from surrounding leaf cells and develop into multicellular sporangia. Locate a sporangium in Figure 27-3. In many ferns the sporangia are grouped together in clusters called **sori.** Cells inside a sporangium undergo meiosis and form haploid spores. At maturity the sporangium opens. The spores are released and then carried by air currents to different locations. They land, and if conditions are proper, they germinate and form gametophytes. Notice that all of the spores look alike.

Figure 27-3 Sori are clusters of sporangia found on the underside of fern leaves.

The Life Cycle of Conifers

The conifer life cycle, shown in Figure 27-4, illustrates the major ways in which alternation of generations in seed plants differs from that in mosses and ferns. Conifers and all other seed plants produce two types of spores. This phenomenon is called **heterospory,** and plants with this life cycle have a heterosporous alternation of generations. As you read about the conifer life cycle, refer to Figure 27-4. Notice that even though the life cycle of the

Figure 27-4 Conifers, like all seed plants, have a life cycle that includes the production of two types of spores.

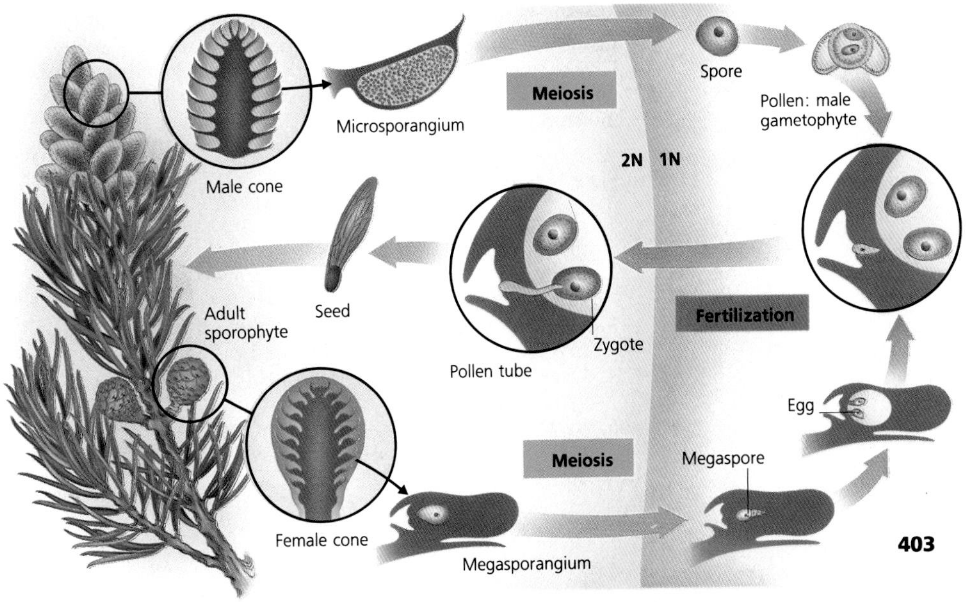

Interpreting the Visuals Focusing on Figure 27-4, p. 403, start with the tree, and guide students through the conifer life cycle. Ask if the sporophyte is haploid or diploid. *(Diploid)* Ask where conifer sporophyte reproductive cells are formed. *(In cones)* Point out to students that female cones have megasporangia and male cones have microsporangia. Ask what the reproductive cells are called. *(Microspores are produced by males; females produce megaspores.)* Ask if they are formed by mitosis or meiosis. *(Meiosis; they are haploid.)* Ask if the zygote is haploid or diploid. *(Diploid)* Ask what the zygote becomes. *(A tree, or sporophyte)* Have students identify how the conifer life cycle differs from the life cycles of mosses and ferns. *(Pollen grains are released instead of sperm that need water to swim.)* Point out that a conifer gametophyte forms within the walls of megaspore and microspore.

Guided Practice

After students have examined Figures 27-1, 27-2, and 27-4, pp. 401–403, name structures one by one, and have students identify each one as haploid or diploid. *(Examples: sporophyte, diploid; spores, haploid; gametophyte, haploid; egg, haploid; zygote, diploid; pollen, haploid; seed, diploid)*

Videodiscs

- ***Side 3 9074, Plant Reproduction: Fern (m)***

LEP Activity

Most students have seen plants grow, and many will have planted seeds. Use their general observations of plants as a starting point for discussing alternation of generations and life cycles. Make sure that students can describe and recognize the physical appearances of common gametophytes and sporophytes. Help students draw a simple linear diagram of the moss life cycle on a strip of paper. Tape the strip into a loop so that students can see that a life cycle is never ending. Repeat the drawing and taping processes for the life cycles of ferns and conifers.

Section 27.1

Independent Practice

■ Have students write answers to the Section Review.

■ Have students construct a table to compare spores with seeds. An example of a completed table is shown on p. 401.

Check Your Understanding

1. What environmental condition is essential for sperm to fertilize eggs in mosses? *(Moisture, so that the sperm can swim to the egg)*

2. Why is it advantageous for ferns to bear spores on the underside of their fronds? *(Sori located there can easily release their spores into the air.)*

Reteaching

Refer students back to the discussion of alternation of generations in Chapter 25, p. 368, for an overview of the concept. Help students recognize that Figure 25-4, p. 368, is a very simplified diagram that summarizes the details illustrated in Figures 27-1, 27-2, and 27-4, pp. 401–403.

■ *See* Section Reviews *worksheet, Section 27.1.*

Enrichment

Give students a map of their area that shows average monthly rainfall and temperature. Ask them to identify areas on the map where mosses, ferns, and conifers might be found, based on their reproductive needs.

Closure

Have students compare alternation of generations in plants with human reproduction. Ask if humans are haploid or diploid. *(Diploid)* What parts of humans are produced by meiosis? *(Gametes. Eggs and sperm are haploid.)*

Videodiscs

■ *Side 3 9886, Pine Life Cycle (m)*

Figure 27-5 The cones of a spruce tree, *Picea* sp., are typical of gymnosperms.

conifer is more complex than that of mosses and ferns, the sequence of phases in the conifer life cycle is the same.

The sporophyte of the pine life cycle is the tree. The entire life cycle of the pine takes two years to complete. During the reproductive season the pine tree produces cones. These cones are of two types, male and female. Cells inside female cones produce sporangia called megasporangia. The megasporangium of seed plants is called an **ovule.** Cells inside the male cones produce sporangia called microsporangia.

As you learned in Chapter 25, the cells in all sporangia divide by meiosis and produce haploid spores. Megasporangia cells produce large spores known as **megaspores.** Megaspores produce megagametophytes. Microsporangia cells produce smaller spores known as **microspores.** Microspores produce microgametophytes.

In seed plants the megagametophyte never breaks out of the megaspore wall. Likewise, microspores produce microgametophytes that form inside the microspore wall. The microgametophyte of seed plants is called a **pollen grain.**

The pollen grain is released from the microsporangium and at the same time from the male cone. It travels on the wind and lands on the female cone. It filters down between the scales until it nears the megagametophyte, which never leaves the cone. By this time the megagametophyte has produced archegonia and eggs. The pollen grain splits open, and a **pollen tube** begins to grow toward the egg. Sperm forms and travels down the pollen tube, fertilizes the egg, and a zygote is formed. A zygote develops into an embryo. A mature ovule that contains an embryo is called a **seed.**

At the beginning of this section you read that seed plants live in a wider range of habitats than plants whose sperms must swim freely through water to reach an egg. One reason for this becomes obvious by examining the life cycle of the pine. Sperm of seed plants are protected in the microgametophyte and thus do not have to swim to the egg. Reproduction in seed plants can therefore take place independently of seasonal rains or other periods of moisture.

Section Review

1. Distinguish between antheridium and archegonium and state the function of each.
2. Draw a generalized diagram of alternation of generations, showing haploid and diploid phases.
3. How are the spores of conifers different from the spores of bryophytes and the spores of most ferns?
4. List three differences between the life cycles of ferns and gymnosperms.
5. In what way did the enclosure of the microgametophyte contribute to the great evolutionary success of gymnosperms and angiosperms?

Answers to Section Review

1. An antheridium is a male gametangium that produces sperm. An archegonium is a female gametangium that produces an egg.

2. Drawings should at least include sporophyte, gametophyte, meiosis, gametes, spores, and fertilization. See Figure 25-4, p. 368.

3. Spores of conifers, which are seed plants, are either of two types—megaspores or microspores—while bryophyte and fern spores are of one type.

4. Gymnosperms have seeds and make two kinds of spores. Ferns have no seeds and have only one kind of spore. Ferns require water for sperm to swim; gymnosperms do not need water for fertilization.

5. By eliminating the need for sperm to swim to the egg, the microgametophyte permits reproduction in a dry environment.

27.2 The Life Cycle of Flowering Plants

Undoubtedly you have admired flowers for their beauty, their bright colors, attractive shapes, and pleasing aromas. Each flower is actually a set of adaptations that helps to ensure successful reproduction. In fact, the very traits that make flowers attractive to people are adaptations that attract animals that carry pollen grains from flower to flower.

Not all flowers are colorful. As you might guess, insects and animals seldom visit flowers that are not colorful. Instead the wind carries the pollen from plant to plant.

Parts of a Flower

Botanists have determined from an examination of plant development that a flower is a highly modified branch. The parts of the flower are modified leaves, usually found in four successive whorls or rings. All these modified leaves are formed on the swollen tip of the branch, which is called the **receptacle.**

Sepals make up the bottom whorl. They surround and protect the developing flower before it blooms. You can see the leaflike sepals in Figure 27-6. All the sepals are collectively called the calyx. **Petals** make up the next whorl and are collectively called the corolla. Most insect-pollinated flowers have brightly colored petals. Petals and sepals of wind-pollinated plants are usually reduced or absent. Because they are not directly involved in reproduction, sepals and petals are called nonessential flower parts.

Section Objectives

- *Name the four main parts of a flower, and state the function of each.*
- *Compare pollen formation and ovule formation.*
- *Relate flower structure to method of pollination.*
- *Describe fertilization in flowering plants.*
- *Summarize the evidence for the adaptive value of nectar guides.*

Figure 27-6 The various parts of a flower can be seen in the harebell, *Campanula rotundifolia* (left), and the rock nettle, *Eucnide* sp. (right). These parts are labeled in the illustration below.

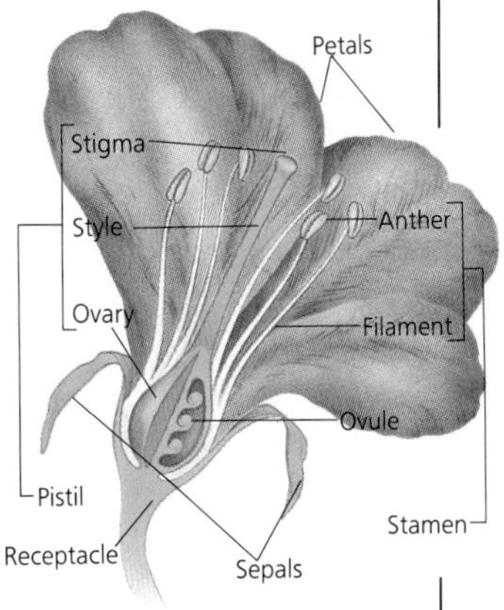

Lesson Plan

Section Focus

This section describes parts of a flower and explains how gametes are formed. Processes of pollination and fertilization are clearly differentiated. Mitosis and meiosis are reviewed again.

Section Themes

The theme of **Evolution** is evident as flowers are described in terms of adaptations that help ensure successful reproduction. The theme of **Systems and Interactions** is emphasized in the descriptions of the reproductive functions of flower parts.

Motivating Activity

Present the class with a variety of flowers or pictures of flowers. Include bright, showy specimens with scent as well as some smaller, less noticeable examples. Make sure that some varieties have stamens and pistils visible. You can often obtain leftover flowers from florists, supermarkets, or gardens for class demonstrations.

Broaden students' ideas about flowers; it is important that they realize that maple trees, for example, have flowers. Ask what is the adaptive advantage of a fragrant, bright bloom. *(Attracts pollinators)* Ask why it is advantageous for wind-pollinated flowers to have small petals. *(Large petals would block air currents and waste energy.)*

Teaching Strategies

Observing Structures Have students look at thin flower petals under a microscope. Petals contain plastids that serve as storage locations for pigments and for oils that give flowers their scent. Examples are: rose, lily, freesia, or narcissus.

Videodiscs

- ***2579–2580, Flower Structures (s)***

Process	Location	Diploid Precursor	Result of Meiosis	Nuclei Produced by Mitosis
pollen formation	stamen (anther)	microspore mother cell	4 haploid microspores	2, generative cell and tube cell, in grain
ovule formation	pistil (ovary)	megaspore mother cell	4 haploid megaspores (3 will die)	8, egg cell, synergids, and antipodals, in embryo sac

Graphic Organizer Use this table in Comparing Functions on p. 408.

Relating Concepts Refer students back to Chapter 10, pp. 147–148. Ask students if Mendel's pea plants were perfect or imperfect. *(Perfect)* Ask how this affected Mendel's procedures. *(For self-pollination Mendel had to do nothing—the pea plants were self-pollinating. In the case of cross-pollination Mendel had to transfer pollen by hand.)*

Making Inferences Ask students to infer an adaptive advantage a monoecious plant might have. *(A single plant could reproduce by itself rather than depend on eggs or pollen from another plant.)* Ask them what adaptive advantage a dioecious plant might have. *(If reproduction depends on two different plants, greater variation is maintained in the gene pool.)*

Interpreting the Visuals Ask students what Figure 27-7, p. 406, shows. *(Evolution of a pistil)* Point out the ovules present on the leaves. Ask how the leaves evolved to become the pistil. *(Over time, plants with more tightly folded leaves reproduced more successfully than plants with unprotected ovules.)*

Interpreting the Visuals Ask students to look at the steps represented in Figure 27-8, p. 406. Ask them what the anther produces and by what process. *(Gametes; by meiosis)* Ask how many microspores each microspore mother cell produces and what they become. *(Four; each becomes a pollen grain.)* How does each microspore become a pollen grain? *(It divides by mitosis to produce two haploid cells, and it produces a thick cell wall.)*

- *See* Blackline Master *55.*

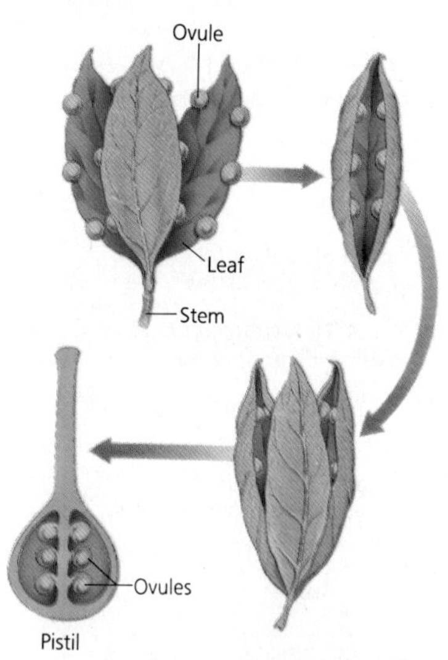

Figure 27-7 A pistil is composed of ovule-bearing leaves that have evolutionarily folded and fused.

The two innermost whorls of flower parts are directly involved in sexual reproduction and are called essential flower parts. The male reproductive structures are **stamens,** and the female reproductive structures are **carpels.** Each stamen has two parts. The **anther** is the microsporangium that produces microspores, then pollen grains. The stalklike **filament** supports the anther. In most flowers the carpels are fused to each other, forming a structure called the **pistil.** Many species have flowers with three, four, or five stamens but only one pistil. Not all species of flowers have both stamens and carpels. Flowers with both are called perfect. Those flowers that lack either one of these structures are called imperfect. Two types of imperfect flowers exist. When male flowers and female flowers are on the same plant, the species is called monoecious. If the flowers are on different plants, the species is called dioecious.

Figure 27-7 shows how carpels are leaves that have folded and fused to form a pistil. This fusion is evident when you make a cross section of the **ovary,** the base of the pistil. The ovary is often composed of chambers, each of which often represents one folded carpel. A stalklike **style** arises from the ovary. The style has a **stigma** at its tip. In most species the stigma is sticky or has hairs, enabling it to trap pollen grains.

Pollen Grain Formation

Figure 27-8 shows the process of pollen formation. Each anther contains four pollen sacs that contain diploid microspore mother cells. Each microspore mother cell undergoes meiosis and produces four haploid microspores. The nucleus of each microspore

Figure 27-8 The process of pollen formation takes place in the anther and results in the formation of a two-celled pollen grain.

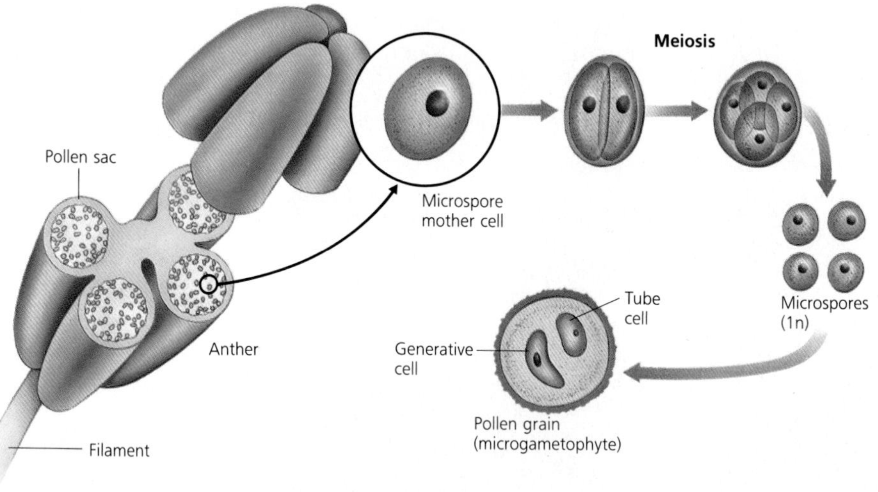

More Information

Pollen Structure and Function The pollen grains of different plant species vary greatly. Wind-dispersed pollen typically is smooth and dry, while pollen carried by insects is often bristly, rough, or sticky. Most pollen grains have conspicuous pores or furrows, which are thin places in the pollen grain through which a pollen tube can grow. Pollen usually is released through longitudinal slits that develop in the microsporangium or sometimes from special pores located on top of the anther.

then divides by mitosis and produces two haploid cells. The two cells remain inside the microspore, which produces a thick wall that surrounds them both. The resulting haploid, two-celled structure is the male gametophyte, the pollen grain. The larger of the two cells is the **tube cell,** which later forms the pollen tube. The smaller cell, called the **generative cell,** will form two sperm.

Ovule Formation

Ovules are megasporangia that are formed in ovaries. Figure 27-9 shows that an ovule contains a large diploid megaspore mother cell. This cell undergoes meiosis to produce four haploid megaspores. Three of these megaspores degenerate and die. The remaining megaspore then enlarges and undergoes three consecutive mitotic divisions to produce eight haploid nuclei. Cytokinesis, however, does not occur. By the time these nuclei have formed, the ovule has formed one or two layers of protective coverings called **integuments** *(in-TEG-yoo-ments)*. The integuments do not completely encase the ovule. At one end of the ovule is a small opening, known as a **micropyle** (MIE-kruh-pile), through which pollen can enter.

What about the eight haploid nuclei? As you can see in the figure, they are initially arranged in two groups of four, with one group at each end of the cell. Here's what happens next:

- One nucleus from each group migrates to the center of the cell. These two nuclei are called **polar nuclei.**
- Cell walls form around each of the remaining six nuclei. The three cells farthest from the micropyle are called antipodals and later may function in nutrition.
- One of the three cells nearest the micropyle enlarges and becomes the egg. The remaining two cells are called helpers or synergids.

This structure, which contains seven cells and eight nuclei, is the mature megagametophyte. It is referred to as the **embryo sac.**

Think

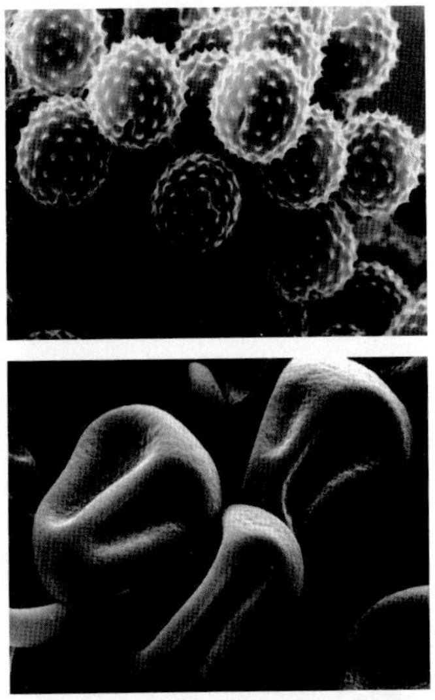

Compare these two pollen grains of two plant species. Do you think that pollen grains might be useful to plant taxonomists? Why do you think so?

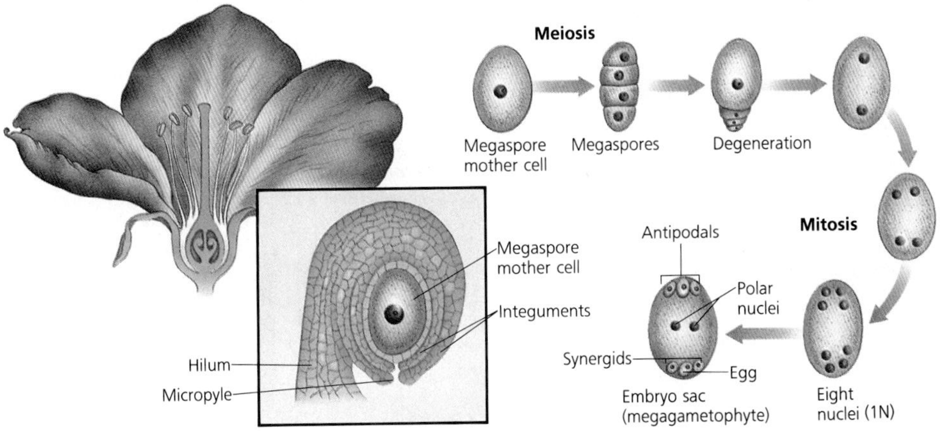

Figure 27-9 In the ovule a mother cell undergoes a series of divisions resulting in the formation of seven cells, one of which is the egg.

Answer to Think

Plant taxonomists use information obtained from pollen grains to help them distinguish among different species. The size, shape, and exterior ornamentation of pollen grains vary from one species to the next. Information obtained from pollen is useful at all taxonomic levels.

Observing Structures Have students observe prepared slides of pollen (available from biological supply houses) through microscopes. Ask students to compare pollen of different species. Use a microprojector to show slides of pollen, and have students speculate on the adaptive advantages of the different shapes. *(Spiky—sticks to animals; smooth or round—easily airborne)*

Interpreting the Visuals Take students step-by-step through ovule formation, as shown in Figure 27-9, p. 407. Stress the roles of meiosis and mitosis in alternation of generations. Ask students if the megaspore mother cell is haploid or diploid. *(Diploid)* Ask how many cells meiosis produces and if they are haploid or diploid. *(Four; haploid)* Ask students what kinds of cells are produced by mitosis. *(Diploid)*

- *See* **Blackline Master 56.**

Observing Structures Obtain prepared slides of cross sections of flower ovaries from a biological supply house. Have students observe them under a microscope at low and high power and look for structures that are illustrated in Figure 27-9, p. 407.

Videodiscs

- ***2277–2278, Pollen Grain (s)***

Interdisciplinary Activity

Visual Arts With help from an art teacher, put together a series of slides of paintings or have students examine art books at the library to find paintings that contain flowers. Have students try to identify kinds of flowers and any structures shown. Examples: Vincent van Gogh, *Sunflowers;* Thomas Hart Benton, *Spring Still Life with Peony;* Charles Demuth, *Kitchen Garden, Flowers,* and *Kiss Me Over the Fence;* Georgia O'Keeffe, *Iris, Yellow Calla–Green Leaves,* and *Oriental Poppies;* John La Farge, *Chinese Pi-tong* and *Flowers in a Persian Porcelain Water Bowl.* O'Keeffe's paintings will be particularly useful. She wanted to capture the essence of flowers so that people would "be surprised into taking time to look at them." Encourage students to paint and display their own pictures of flowers.

Comparing Functions To help students organize information about pollen and ovule formation, have them make a table that compares the two processes. An example of a completed table is shown on p. 405.

Making Models Be willing to make a mess as you demonstrate the transfer of pollen by wind. Tape several empty toothpaste pumps to a table in a circle to represent stamens. In the center put a capped bottle to represent a pistil. Coat the top of the pistil with corn syrup, glue, or petroleum jelly. Pour some cornmeal onto the top of each toothpaste pump to simulate pollen. Use a small fan on low setting to simulate wind. Have students examine the tips of the stamens and the pistil. The cornmeal should be blown off the stamens, and some of it should land on the pistil.

Making Hypotheses Ask students to explain the difference between the two types of pollination. *(Cross-pollination: pollen is transferred from one plant to another of the same species; self-pollination: pollen transferred to the same flower or different flower on the same plant)* Ask students to form hypotheses about what adaptive advantage each type of pollination might have. *(Sample answer: Self-pollination is an advantage where plants of the same species are sparse; cross-pollination maintains wide genetic variety in a population.)*

Guided Practice

Use a flower model, live flowers, or Figure 27-6, p. 405, to point out to students the major structures and functions of a flower. Ask students to identify the female part of the flower. *(Pistil)* Ask where meiosis occurs in flowers. *(In anthers and ovaries)*

Pollination

Before sperm fertilize the eggs contained in embryo sacs, pollen must first be transferred from an anther to a stigma of a flower of the same species. This process is called **pollination.** The transfer of pollen from one plant to another plant of the same species is known as **cross-pollination.** The transfer of pollen from one flower to another flower on the same plant is known as **self-pollination.**

In many plants such as oak trees, pollen is released into the air and carried away in wind currents. Successful wind pollination depends on: (1) the release of large amounts of pollen, (2) ample circulation of air to carry pollen and, (3) individuals being located relatively close to one another.

Most plants with colorful flowers are pollinated by animals. The bright petals and distinctive scents attract animals that feed on pollen and **nectar,** a nourishing solution of sugars and amino acids. When animals gather nectar, the pollen attaches to their bodies. The animals deposit pollen on other flowers as they collect more nectar. Pollinators include bees, hummingbirds, moths, mosquitos, butterflies, beetles, and bats.

Biology in Process

Nectar Guides and Pollination

For many years biologists have wondered if floral nectar guides play a role in insect pollination. Could the lines that appear to lead to the nectar-containing structures in flowers be an adaptation that attracts pollinators? Researchers A. S. Manning and John Free hypothesized that lines or rows of dots guide insect pollinators to the nectar inside the flower. The biologists created a variety of models with which they could test this hypothesis. They began by training bees to land on flat, colored shapes, using honey as bait. Then they experimented with models that did not contain honey in order to learn whether a patterned flower would be more attractive to the bees. Manning and Free used round, blue models with and without yellow lines leading toward the center. They observed that the bees did not land on one model more often than on the other. Thus they inferred that line patterns alone did not make flowers more attractive to insects.

In their next experiment each model had six "petals" and contained honey in the center. One model had no markings; the other had lines

Interdisciplinary Activity

Health Have the class develop a concept for a videotape, rap, or other presentation that could be given to teens and others who have hay fever. The class should brainstorm a list of possible concepts; research information on pollen allergies, allergic response, and treatment from books or allergy specialists; put together a storyboard; and write a script. Work with the media center to reserve and use video or audio equipment. Local hospitals are often willing to provide information for this kind of project. If students get very involved, they may want to make presentations to a health class, assembly, or local hospital health fair.

Fertilization

Fertilization is not the same as pollination. Pollination is the transfer of pollen from an anther to a stigma, while fertilization is the union of gametes. In order for fertilization to occur, the pollen grain must travel to the egg, and sperm must form. The sequence of events leading to fertilization is shown in Figure 27-10 on the following page.

When a pollen grain germinates, the tube cell forms a pollen tube that grows through the stigma and style toward the ovule. The haploid generative cell divides mitotically and forms two sperm. The pollen tube grows through the micropyle and into the embryo sac, forming a passageway through which the sperm enter the embryo sac. One of the sperm fuses with the egg and forms a diploid zygote. This zygote will eventually develop into the embryo.

The second sperm fuses with the two polar nuclei in the embryo sac, producing a triploid (3N) nucleus. This nucleus then divides by mitosis. Repeated nuclear division and, later, cytokinesis, results in a tissue called **endosperm** *(EN-duh-SPERM)*. The endosperm is a nutritive tissue.

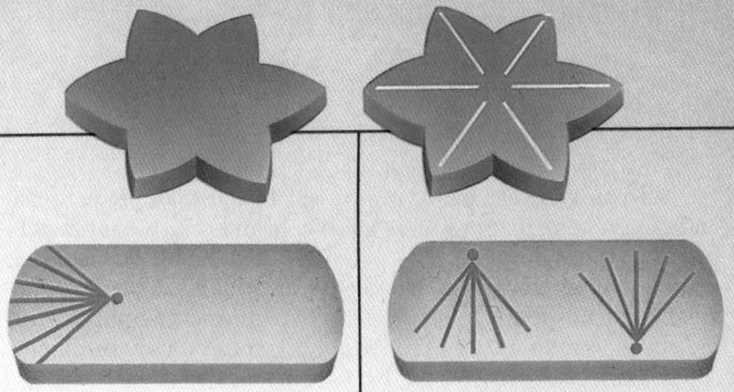

leading toward the center of the "flower." Manning and Free observed the spots where bees landed on each model. They found that bees first landed on the edges of both models. However, when the bees returned to the models, they landed more frequently in the center of the model with lines. From these observations, Manning and Free inferred that bees could learn to follow "guides" to the region of the flower containing nectar.

In a third experiment Manning and Free first observed bees landing on a honeyless model with a "fan" of lines that radiated from a single point. Bees landed on the point only 8.3 percent of the time, and on the lines themselves almost 70 percent of the time.

The bees were then trained with another fan model in which honey was placed at points of intersection. Later, the bees were returned to the model without the honey. The experiment showed that the bees had learned to follow the lines to the point where nectar might be available. Almost 35 percent landed first on the intersection point, and only 57 percent landed first on the lines themselves.

■ Experiments such as these provide evidence that insects follow nectar guides to nectar. What kinds of observations in nature might also support this hypothesis?

Biology in Process

Using the Feature

The process skill emphasized in this feature is experimenting. In order to test the hypothesis that insect pollinators follow markings on a flower that lead to the nectar, Manning and Free designed experiments with models constructed to resemble flowers. Their results supported the hypothesis and revealed that the bees learned to follow the lines rather than followed the lines by instinct. The experiment also suggested that additional observations of pollinators in nature could provide scientists with information relating to the behavior of pollinators.

Students may be curious about how Manning and Free trained their experimental bees. Explain that by using honey as bait, the researchers enticed the insects to land on the models. They then observed landing patterns exhibited by the bees on models with and without honey. Point out to students that in a sense, initial training experiments served as controls in the experimental process.

Answer to the Feature

Observers could watch insects on their first and subsequent visits to nectar-containing flowers. Flowers with and without lines could be tested to find out if the insects can see patterns humans cannot see.

Videodiscs

- *Side 3 24915, Pollen—Electron Microscopy (m)*
- *Side 3 18191, Flowering Plant Life Cycle (m)*
- *2573, Angiosperm Fertilization (s)*

Independent Practice

- Have students write answers to the Section Review.
- Have students list female and male structures in Figure 27-6, p. 405. *(Female: stigma, style, ovary, pistil, receptacle, ovule. Male: anther, filament, stamen)*

Check Your Understanding

1. If the petals of a flower were removed, could it still reproduce? Explain. *(Yes; petals are nonessential, although pollinators might not visit the flower.)*
2. Why must a microspore mother cell undergo meiosis? *(To produce haploid gametes)*
3. Why are insects essential to humans and flowering plants? *(Insects pollinate many flowering plants, including food crops.)*

Reteaching

Have students dissect some flowers and identify the parts using Figure 27-6, p. 405. Have them describe at least one function for each part. *(Examples: anther, produces pollen; sepals, protect flower.)*

- *See* Laboratories, ***Investigation 27, Part I.***
- *See* Section Reviews ***worksheet, Section 27.2.***

Enrichment

Have each student research and report on the coevolution of a pollinator and a flower. Examples are: carrion flies and the European spotted lily; bats and the African sausage tree.

Closure

Propose to students this problem: Imagine that you wish to trace genetic factors through generations of a flowering plant. How would you design an experiment to ensure proper parentage of the generations? *(Sample answers: hand-pollinate flowers; cover pistils to protect them from stray pollen; remove stamens from flowers with unwanted pollen)*

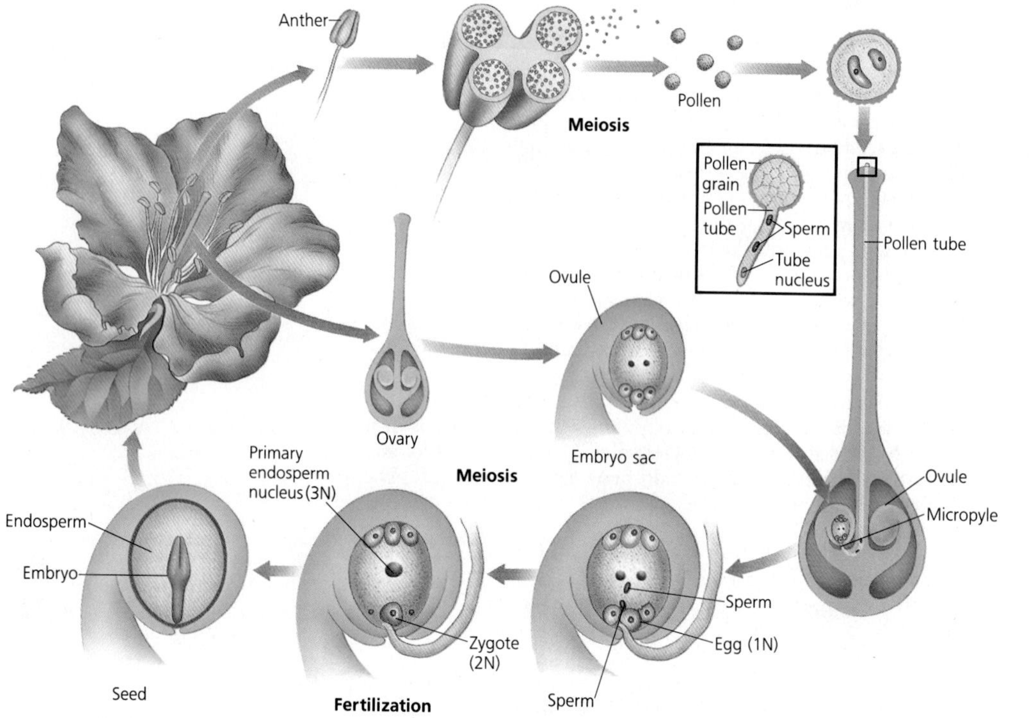

Figure 27-10 Following pollination, a pollen tube and sperm must be produced before fertilization can take place.

As you can see, two types of cell fusion take place in the embryo sac: one that produces the zygote and one that ultimately produces the endosperm. This process, called **double fertilization,** is unique to angiosperms. Double fertilization enhances the survival of angiosperms by providing the angiosperm embryo with the endosperm to use as a food supply. You can review the angiosperm life cycle in Figure 27-10.

Section Review

1. What is the difference between self-pollination and cross-pollination?
2. Draw a generalized flower, showing the sepals, petals, stamens, and a pistil in relation to each other. Be sure to label each structure.
3. Explain the roles of the tube cell and the generative cell in fertilization.
4. Name the seven cells of the embryo sac.
5. What are some possible adaptive advantages associated with cross-pollination?

Answers to Section Review

1. Self-pollination is the transfer of pollen from one flower to another on the same plant. Cross-pollination is the transfer of pollen from the flower of one plant to the flower of another plant of the same species.
2. The labeled drawing should show four whorls, or rings, with sepals forming the outermost ring and, moving inward, petals, stamens, and pistil.
3. The tube cell produces the pollen tube, and the generative cell produces sperm. Sperm travel down the pollen tube, reach the ovary, and fertilize an ovule.
4. Polar nuclei (central cell), egg, two synergids, and three antipodals
5. Cross-pollination increases genetic variation and thereby increases chances that members of a species will survive in a changing environment.

27.3 Fruits and Seeds

Fertilization initiates the development of fruits and seeds. A seed is a fertilized ovule. Ovules are found in an ovary. A mature ovary is called a **fruit.** From these definitions you can easily see that many foods that are commonly called vegetables, such as green peppers, okra, cucumbers, and tomatoes, are actually fruits because they contain seeds.

Structure of Seeds

You learned in Chapter 25 that angiosperms are classified as either monocots or dicots on the basis of the number of cotyledons present in the embryo. However, the number of cotyledons is just one of the differences between monocots and dicots. To understand the other differences, let's examine a bean seed, which is a dicot and a corn grain, which is a monocot.

Look at the bean seed shown in Figure 27-11. Bean seeds are usually kidney shaped. The seed is enclosed by a **seed coat,** which develops from the ovule wall and the integuments of the ovule. Along the concave edge of the seed is the **hilum,** a scar marking the location where the seed was attached to the ovary wall. Near the hilum is the micropyle, the opening through which the pollen tube grew to the embryo sac.

Most of the internal part of the seed is occupied by two large, fleshy cotyledons. Between the two cotyledons is the rest of the embryo having three parts. The **radicle** is the embryonic root. The **hypocotyl** *(HIE-puh-KAHT-'l)* is a stemlike area between the cotyledons and radicle. Finally, the **epicotyl** *(EP-uh-KAHT-'l)* is the region above the cotyledons. The epicotyl plus any embryonic leaves is called a **plumule** *(PLOO-myool).*

Now examine the corn grain shown in the figure. The grain of corn is actually a fruit. The wall of the fruit is, however, very thin. Technically corn is a fruit, but the seed occupies almost the entire grain. In corn the umbrella-shaped cotyledon is pressed close to the starchy endosperm. It does not store food as bean cotyledons do, rather, its function is to absorb nutrients from the starchy endosperm and transfer them to the growing embryo. The embryonic shoot of corn is covered with a cylindrical sheath called a **coleoptile** *(KOE-lee-AHP-t'l),* which protects the shoot during germination. Similarly, the embryonic root is covered with a protective sheath called a **coleorhiza** *(KOE-lee-uh-RIE-zuh).*

Types of Fruits

Fruits protect seeds, aid in their dispersal, and may provide a source of energy for the early growth of the seedling. Scientists distinguish between three major kinds of fruit: simple fruit, aggregate fruit, and multiple fruit. Similarly, there are several variations

Section Objectives

- *Distinguish between simple, aggregate, and multiple fruits.*
- *List the similarities and differences between monocot and dicot embryos.*
- *Describe three adaptations that promote the dispersal of fruits and seeds.*
- *Describe the conditions necessary for seed germination.*

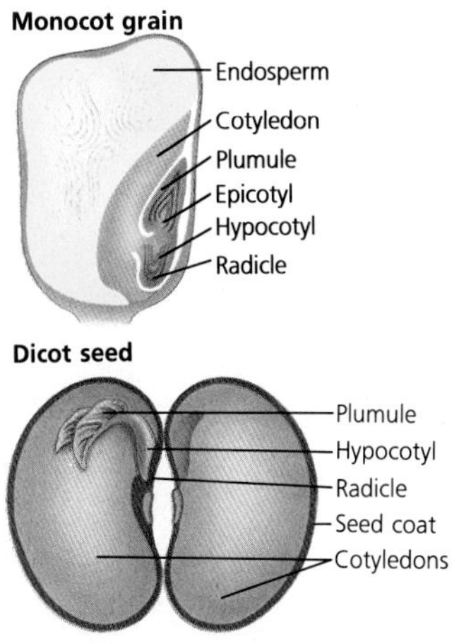

Figure 27-11 In beans the cotyledon is the site of food storage. In corn food is stored in the endosperm and absorbed through the cotyledon.

Lesson Plan

Section Focus

This section emphasizes structure and development of fruits and seeds. Methods of dispersal and the germination process are presented.

Section Themes

The theme of **Evolution** threads through the discussion of how seeds and fruits are adapted for dispersal. The theme of **Systems and Interactions** is developed as the structure of fruits and seeds is described at the tissue level.

Motivating Activity

Bring a variety of seeds or fruits to class. Include tiny seeds such as those of carrots or turnips, large seeds such as beans and coconut, monocot seeds such as grass or corn, dicot seeds such as beans and squash, animal-carried burrs, and wind-borne dandelion or maple seeds. Ask students to speculate on the advantages of the different adaptations. *(Examples: Tiny seeds may be an adaptation that fits more seeds in the fruit. Large seeds may assure enough food for a growing embryo. Burrs aid dispersal.)*

Teaching Strategies

Interpreting the Visuals Direct students' attention to Figure 27-11, p. 411. Ask what structures monocot and dicot seeds have in common. *(Plumule, hypocotyl, radicle, cotyledon)* Ask students to compare the corn kernel with the bean seed with respect to food storage. *(The corn kernel stores food in the endosperm, the bean seed in its cotyledons.)*

■ *See* Process Skills, *Chapter 27.*

Videodiscs

■ *1923–1929,* Capsella: *Cotyledon; Epicotyl (s)*

■ *1910, Corn Seed (s)*

Plant Type	First to Emerge	Location of Cotyledon	Cotyledon Function
dicot (2 cotyledons)	radicle (becomes root)	hypocotyl curves, moves above ground	protects plumule
monocot (1 cotyledon)	radicle (becomes root)	stays underground	transfers sugars to embryo

Graphic Organizer Use this table in Organizing Information on p. 413.

Interpreting the Visuals Walk students through Table 27-1, p. 412, section by section. If possible, use live fruits as props to show structures mentioned. Ask students to name other examples of fruit types listed. *(Examples: grain—rice; nut—acorn; achene—dandelion; berry—orange; drupe—olive; aggregate fruit—blackberry)*
■ ***See*** **Laboratories, *Investigation 27, Part II.***

Comparing Terms Many students are aware that there is a difference between fruits and vegetables, but few will know exactly what this is. Write the headings *Vegetable* and *Fruit* on the board. Have students name examples, and write them under the appropriate headings. Ask students to define the terms *fruit* and *vegetable* according to the lists on the board. *(*Webster's Ninth New Collegiate Dictionary *defines* vegetable *as "a herbaceous plant [cabbage, bean or potato . . .] grown for an edible part that is usually eaten as part of a meal.")* Ask students how this definition differs from the definition of *fruit*. *(A fruit contains one or more seeds.)* Refer again to the two lists on the board, and have students correct any misplaced fruits or vegetables. *(For example, we eat the fruits of zucchini and cucumber plants.)*

Comparing Adaptations Have students draw a concept map that shows adaptations for dispersal of fruits and seeds. An example of a completed concept map is shown on p. 399B.

Table 27-1 Variation in Fruits

Simple fruits

Dry dehiscent fruits have papery or leathery walls and open along seams and usually contain several seeds.
- **Follicles** come from one pistil and split along one seam (columbine, milkweed).
- **Legumes** come from one pistil and split along two seams (peas, honey locust).
- **Capsules** come from more than one pistil and split in a variety of ways (poppy).

Dry indehiscent fruits have paper or leathery walls and do not open along seams and usually contain just one seed.
- **Grains** have a thin ovary wall fused to the seed coat (corn, wheat).
- **Nuts** have a woody ovary wall fastened to a single seed (walnut, butternut).
- **Achenes** have separate seed coats and ovary walls (buttercup, knotweed).
- **Samaras** have ovary walls that form winglike structures (maple, ash).

Fleshy fruits have soft walls; most are indehiscent.
- **Drupes** have woody interior coating forming a stone or pit; they are formed from one to many single-seeded carpels (peach, plum).
- **Berries** lack woody interior coatings; the ovary is fleshy and often juicy; they are formed from one to several many-seeded carpels (tomato, grape).
- **Pomes** have fleshy floral tubes and a leathery interior (apple, pear).

Aggregate fruits

Aggregate fruits develop from flowers having several separate carpels (raspberry, strawberry).

Multiple fruits

Multiple fruits develop from a cluster of flowers (pineapple, fig).

of each type. The kinds of fruits and their variations are described in Table 27-1. Simple fruits derive from one carpel or several united carpels. Aggregate fruits develop from flowers having several separate carpels. Multiple fruits are a grouping of many fruits derived from a cluster of flowers.

Dispersal of Fruits and Seeds

Fruits and seeds are dispersed by animals, wind, and water. You may have walked through a field or park and unwittingly collected stickers or burrs on your shoes or socks. These burrs are actually fruits. The flavor, fragrance, and bright color of many fruits attract animals. When animals eat such fruits, the seeds often pass unharmed through their digestive systems.

Fruits and seeds of some plants are adapted for wind dispersal. For example, fruits of orchids are extremely small and can be carried away by even the smallest gusts of wind. The fruits of

Interdisciplinary Activity

Language Arts Have the class make a list of idioms and expressions that refer to fruits and seeds. Then have each student pick one item from the list and write an explanation of how they think that this expression might have come into the language. *(Examples: Nutty as a fruit cake; like two peas in a pod; a corny joke; the apple of my eye; a tough nut to crack; giving someone the raspberry; strawberry blonde; beaned [hit in the head with a ball]; American as apple pie; a real lemon; the apple does not fall far from the tree; one bad apple; peachy; prune-faced; just sour grapes; juicy gossip)* maple and ash trees, called samaras, have winglike appendages that cause the fruit to flutter through the air.

Fruits and seeds of plants growing near water often contain air chambers that allow them to float. Fruits of coconuts, for example, may float thousands of kilometers on ocean currents. When they finally wash ashore, they can germinate and produce new palm trees.

Seed Germination

Seeds are the dormant stage of a plant's life cycle. **Dormancy** is a state of decreased metabolism that allows an organism to survive conditions unfavorable for growth, such as prolonged drought or intense cold.

Conditions Needed for Germination

What kinds of environmental signals break dormancy and begin germination? Environmental factors such as water, oxygen, temperature, and light can trigger germination. Seeds are very dry and must absorb water to germinate. Water softens the seed coat and activates enzymes that begin turning the endosperm of the seed into simple sugars that provide energy for the growth of the embryo. The germinating embryo needs oxygen for cellular respiration. Also, most seeds will germinate only if the temperature is above 10° C. Light also plays a role in seed germination. You will learn about its role in Chapter 28.

Seeds of some plants germinate only under drastic conditions. For example, some seeds germinate only after being scorched by fire or after passing through the digestive systems of animals. Some seeds, such as those of apples, must be exposed to freezing temperatures before they will germinate.

Seeds of many desert plants contain chemicals that inhibit germination. These chemicals are washed from seeds by heavy rain but not by light showers. This trait ensures that the seeds will germinate only when enough water is available for growth.

Process of Germination

Let's return to the bean and corn seeds we studied earlier. The first visible change associated with seed germination is emergence of the radicle. The shoot begins growing soon after the radicle ruptures the seed coat. The shoots of bean seedlings emerge differently from those of corn seedlings. As you can see in Figure 27-13 on the following page, the bean hypocotyl soon curves and becomes shaped like a hook. Once the curved portion of the hook breaks through the soil, it straightens and pulls the cotyledons and plumule into the air. The embryonic leaves in the plumule emerge, unfold from between the cotyledons, synthesize chlorophyll, and begin to photosynthesize. The seedling then begins to grow rapidly at the apical meristem end of the epicotyl. After food moves into the plant, the shrunken cotyledons fall off.

Figure 27-12 The samara of the red maple, *Acer rubrum*, has winglike parts that enhance its ability to travel from the source.

Making Inferences Ask students to explain the adaptive advantage of having an apple seed germinate only after prolonged exposure to freezing cold. *(This ensures that the seed will not germinate in the late summer or fall, and thus expose the new seedling to killing winter frost.)*

Designing Experiments Have students formulate a hypothesis about the germination of seeds. *(Example: Exposing seeds to equal amounts of rock or classical music will not affect their germination because seeds are not affected by sound.)* Then ask students what variables they will study and how they will study them. *(Examples: germination of bean seeds and type of music, light, heat, water, and humidity)* What will they use for a control group? *(Example: sample of seeds treated identically with the experimental samples—light, heat, water, and humidity—except no exposure to music)* How will they collect and record data? *(Example: seeds will be observed every two days and any change will be noted. Data could be recorded in a table.)* How will the data be presented? *(Example: A histogram could be made to compare the results.)*

Organizing Information To help students organize information about germination, have them create a table comparing germination of monocots with dicots. An example of a completed table is shown on p. 411.

Videodiscs

- *702 Flower Pollinated by Bird (s)*
- *733 Flower Pollinated by Bat (s)*
- *729 Dandelion Seeds (s)*
- *Side 3 23751, Pea Life Cycle (m)*

More Information

Ancient Seeds The duration of seed viability is associated with dormancy. The time that seeds remain viable varies from a brief period to hundreds of years. For example it is reported that seeds of a *Nelumbo* lotus and *Albizzia julibrissen* that had been in the British Museum for 150 years germinated after accidentally getting wet during the Battle of Britain. The record for viability is apparently held by a lotus, *Nelumbo nucifera*, found in a peat deposit in Manchuria by a Japanese botanist. Radiocarbon dating showed the seeds to be about 700 years old, although other evidence suggests an even older age. When the seed coats were filed to permit water to enter, every one germinated.

Guided Practice
Place seeds or fruits around the room at stations. Have students go from station to station, identifying the seeds as monocot or dicot and the type of fruits according to Table 27-1, p. 412. *(Examples: bean—dicot seed; avocado—drupe)*

Independent Practice
- Have students write answers to the Section Review.
- Give students a list of seeds brought into class for the Motivating Activity, and have them classify the seeds as monocots or dicots. *(Answers will vary depending on the variety brought into the classroom.)*

Check Your Understanding
1. What is the adaptive advantage of the radicle's germinating first? *(It absorbs water so the rest of the embryo can grow.)*
2. How might a person walking through a weed-filled lot be helping plant reproduction? *(The movement could release pollen for wind pollination or disperse seeds or burrs.)*

Reteaching
Have students bring in a variety of fruits and classify each fruit using Table 27-1, p. 412.
- *See* **Section Reviews** *worksheet, Section 27.3.*

Enrichment
Have students research the ideal conditions for germination, plant their own seeds in pots in the classroom, raise the plants to seedling size, record their results, and write a report. The plants may then be taken home or given to a nursing home.

Closure
Tell students about the lotus seeds from Manchuria discussed in More Information on p. 413. Ask why they think seeds so old could still sprout. *(Tough seed coats probably protected the embryo.)*

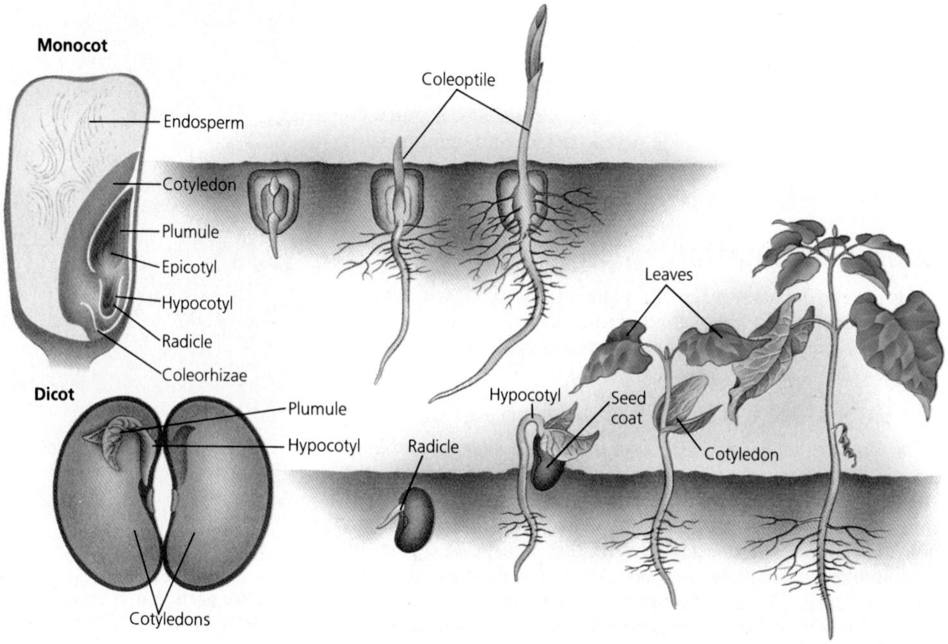

Figure 27-13 During germination, monocot and dicot cotyledons perform different functions.

In contrast the cotyledon of the corn grain remains underground and transfers sugars from the endosperm to the growing parts of the embryo. Unlike the bean shoot, the corn shoot is not hook shaped. It is straight and protected by a coleoptile that pushes through the soil. When the coleoptile breaks through the soil surface, leaves of the plumule quickly unfurl.

In beans the radicle becomes the primary root. It eventually produces lateral roots that help absorb water and help anchor the young plant in the soil. In corn the radical gives rise to the many lateral roots that make up the diffuse root system characteristic of grasses. In both beans and corn, leaves eventually emerge, and the plants begin to carry on photosynthesis. If it is not eaten or cut down, the seedling matures. Eventually the seedling becomes an established plant.

Section Review

1. Explain how carpel arrangement is related to different types of fruits.
2. Describe two main types of simple fruits, and give an example of each.
3. Diagram a dicot seed and a monocot seed, showing endosperm, cotyledons, and the parts of the embryo.
4. What are three main requirements for germination?
5. List three possible evolutionary advantages of dormancy.

Answers to Section Review
1. Simple fruits come from one carpel or several fused carpels, aggregate fruits from flowers with several separate carpels, multiple fruits from a cluster of flowers.
2. Dry fruits such as peanuts and sunflower seeds have papery or leathery walls. Fleshy fruits such as raspberries and avocados have soft walls and juicy, succulent tissue.
3. The diagrams should also include the epicotyls, hypocotyls, radicles, plumules, coleoptile, coleorhizae, and hilum.
4. Answers should include any three: water, oxygen, light, and proper temperature.
5. Through dormancy, plants may survive conditions that are not favorable for germination and growth. Dormant seeds can be carried great distances before they germinate. Dormancy ensures that the seed is mature before growth begins.

27.4 Asexual Reproduction

Sexual reproduction in plants involves the fusion of gametes and produces genetic variation among offspring. Genetic variation is advantageous to plants in several ways. It increases the probability of producing individuals adapted to new environments that may arise through climatic or other changes. Variation makes it less likely that changes in the environment will eliminate an entire species. Variability brought about by sexual reproduction allows some offspring to succeed in new environments. Adaptations to new environments account for much of the diversity in the plant life we see.

Despite the benefits of sexual reproduction, many new individuals do not arise from seeds. Instead some plants arise through asexual reproduction, the production of a new individual without the union of gametes. In asexual reproduction all of the offspring are genetically identical with the one parent. Offspring produced by asexual reproduction are called **clones.**

Asexual reproduction gives a species several adaptive advantages. Clones can be produced rapidly. This feature of asexual reproduction is frequently observed in weeds. A **weed** is a plant specialized for quick growth and reproduction in disturbed areas. In weeds, genetically identical plants rapidly colonize newly created space. Often we think of weeds as just nuisance plants. In fact, they are a highly specialized group of organisms adapted for very specific ecological conditions. The American writer Ralph Waldo Emerson once said, "A weed is a plant whose virtues have not yet been discovered."

Asexual reproduction occurs in plants naturally or artificially. When it occurs naturally, asexual reproduction is called vegetative propagation. When humans manipulate the process of vegetative propagation in plants, asexual reproduction is known as artificial propagation.

Vegetative Propagation

The naturally occurring production of new plants from nonreproductive plant parts is known as **vegetative propagation.** Examine the leaves of *Kalanchoe* shown in Figure 27-14. Buds at the edges of these leaves produce plantlets that when separated from the leaf, become new individuals. Plants such as ferns and crabgrass reproduce asexually with underground rhizomes. Leaves and roots form at each node of the rhizome. The node is a place where leaves attach. Eventually these structures break off and become independent individuals.

Other plants, such as poplars and black locust trees, produce buds on their underground roots that become new individuals. Strawberries produce stolons, aboveground runners that break off from the parent plant and produce new individuals at their nodes.

Section Objectives

- *State the advantages and disadvantages of asexual reproduction.*
- *Compare asexual reproduction with sexual reproduction.*
- *Explain the difference between natural and artificial propogation, and give an example of each.*

Figure 27-14 Vegetative propagation occurs in the leaves of *Kalanchoe*.

Lesson Plan

Section Focus

This section describes asexual reproduction in plants and explains the advantage of producing offspring rapidly.

Section Themes

The theme of **Evolution** is evident in descriptions of adaptive advantages of asexual reproduction, both vegetative propagation and artificial propagation. The theme of **Systems and Interactions** is explored through descriptions of various structures and methods of asexual reproduction.

Motivating Activity

Bring to class a seedless domestic fruit such as a navel orange. Ask the class how they think that a plant with no seeds could be reproduced. *(Students will not yet have read the section and may find the idea puzzling.)* Tell students that they will understand by the time they finish this section.

Teaching Strategies

Making Inferences Most students will be aware that potato "eyes" have something to do with reproduction. Introduce them to the possible cellular mechanisms of vegetative propagation by asking what tissue the eye contains to produce primary growth. *(Apical meristem)* Ask what nutrients in the tuber provide. *(Nourishment for the new plants)*

Videodiscs

- ***Side 1 13433, Cloning (m)***

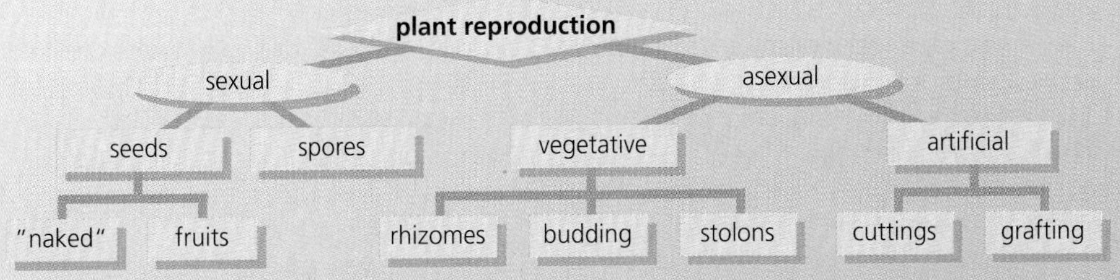

Graphic Organizer Use this organizational chart in Guided Practice on p. 416.

Section 27.4

Guided Practice
Have students make an organizational chart to compare sexual with asexual reproduction of plants. An example of a completed chart is shown on p. 415.

Independent Practice
■ Have students write answers to the Section Review.
■ Have each student write a paragraph, appropriate for a garden or nursery catalog, that describes how a plant is reproduced asexually.

Check Your Understanding
1. Classify the following as sexual or asexual reproduction: potato growing from one eye *(Asexual)*; grafting peach limb to apple tree *(Asexual)*; bee pollinating flower *(Sexual)*.
2. Can asexual reproduction be detrimental to a species? *(Yes; it does not increase genetic diversity, which might help survival in a changing environment.)*

Reteaching
Have students grow new plants from sweet potato eyes suspended by toothpicks over a jar of water. Ask why part of the potato must remain with the eye. *(Nourishment)*
■ *See* **Section Reviews** ***worksheet, Section 27.4.***

Enrichment
Have students make lists, with short descriptions, of instances of vegetative and artificial propagation. *(Examples: vegetative—strawberry runners, crabgrass rhizomes; artificial—grafted fruit trees)*

Closure
Some varieties of *Kalanchoe* (Figure 27-14) are sold with a warning that it is against the law to propagate the plant. Ask students why the originators might not want the plants propagated. *(It might be a patented variety, and the originators would not share in the profits.)*

Figure 27-15 Grafting usually involves the insertion of a branch of one plant into the body of another.

Artificial Propagation

Many economically important plants are propagated artificially in order to rapidly produce large crops. **Artificial propagation** is the human application of vegetative propagation. For example, if you owned a potato farm and found that one of your plants produced large numbers of huge potatoes, you'd like more of these plants since they would increase the size of your crop. You could easily achieve this by planting a piece of a huge potato in which there was at least one eye. The eye will grow into a new individual, genetically identical with its high-yielding parent.

Plants such as bananas and ivy are propagated from cuttings that grow into new individuals. Many trees can also be propagated by grafting, as shown in Figure 27-15. **Grafting** is a technique in which a portion of one individual is inserted into the root or shoot of another individual. This technique allows growers to design their own plants. For example, the drought-resistant roots of one plant can be grafted to shoots that produce large, sweet fruit. Plants such as seedless navel oranges can be propagated only with cuttings or through grafting.

Section Review

1. Distinguish between artificial and natural propagation.
2. Give three examples of vegetative propagation.
3. What are the advantages of sexual reproduction when compared with asexual reproduction?
4. Describe the process of grafting.
5. Explain how fruits such as seedless oranges and seedless green grapes might have come into being.

Answers to Section Review
1. Artificial asexual plant propagation is conducted by humans. Vegetative propagation is naturally occurring asexual reproduction.
2. Plantlets produced from buds at the edges of leaves; new individuals produced by ferns at nodes on their rhizomes; buds produced on the underground roots of poplars; and new individuals produced at the nodes of strawberry stolons.
3. Sexual reproduction results in genetic variation, which increases the likelihood that some individuals will survive if environmental conditions change.
4. A portion of one plant is united with the root or stem of another plant, resulting in a new combination of tissues.
5. Seedless fruits may have begun as mutants that were then artificially propagated by humans.

Laboratory

Germinating Seeds

Objective
To examine structures of monocot and dicot seeds at different stages of germination

Process Skills
Observing, inferring, comparing, classifying

Materials
Hand lens; soaked bean seed; dissecting tray; scalpel or single-edge razor blade; soaked corn kernel; bean seeds and corn kernels germinated 1, 2, 3, and 10 days

Background
1 From what do the plant groups monocots and dicots get their names?
2 What is the primary function of roots?
3 What is the primary function of leaves?

Inquiry
1 Use the hand lens to observe the soaked bean seed. Find a mark on the concave surface. What do you think might be its function?
2 Using the scalpel, remove the seed coat. What is its function?
3 Open the seed. What are the two halves called? What is their function? Find the embryonic plant. Examine the structure of its top part, or plumule. What part(s) of the seedling do you think it will become? How many leaves does the embryonic plant have? Describe their shape. Examine the radicle, the bottom part of the embryonic plant. What is its shape? What part of the seedling do you think it will become?
4 Examine the corn kernel. On one side is a whitish disk, the embryo. Lay the kernel in the dissecting tray, embryo side up. Cut the kernel from top to bottom through the middle of the embryo. Observe the embryonic plant under a hand lens. Compare its structure with that of the bean seed's embryonic plant. What is the shape of its radicle? How many leaves does the plumule have? Describe the shape. Do you think the plumules and radicles of the two embryo plants function in similar ways? Explain.
5 Examine 1-, 2-, and 3-day-old corn and bean seedlings. Compare the development of the root systems of the corn and bean seedlings. Describe similarities and differences.
6 What differences do you observe in the position of the cotyledons as the corn and bean seedlings grow?
7 Compare the 10-day-old seedlings with the 3-day-old seedlings. What has happened to the cotyledons? What explanation can you give? How are the first tiny leaves arranged? How have the root systems changed?

Conclusions
1 Which seed is a monocot? Which is a dicot?
2 Summarize the differences between monocot and dicot seedlings.
3 Which part of the plant emerges first?

Further Inquiry
In what form are nutrients for embryonic plants stored? Put your answer in the form of a hypothesis. Design an experiment to test it.

Laboratory

(For an overview of seed germination and preparatory information related to the laboratory, see p. 399B.)

Background

1. *Mono-* means "alone" or "single." Monocots have a single cotyledon. *Di-* means "twofold" or "double." Dicots have two cotyledons.
2. Roots absorb water.
3. Leaves absorb light energy for photosynthesis.

Inquiry

1. A scar marks the place where the seed was attached to the parent plant.
2. A seed coat protects the seed.
3. The two halves are called cotyledons. They provide nutrients for initial growth. The plumule will become the leaves and stem. There are two triangular leaves. The radicle is shaped like a comma; it will become the primary root.
4. The radicle looks like a bulge. The plumule has one long, thin leaf. The structures are similar in appearance and so probably function in similar ways.
5. In the bean, the radicle emerges first and quickly forms root hairs. The corn radicle also emerges first but forms branch roots, not root hairs.
6. The dicot's cotyledons emerge from the ground. The monocot's cotyledon stays below ground.
7. The bean cotyledons have shriveled; their stored food has been used up by the growing plant. The two leaves are at the stem tip and are opposite each other. The single monocot leaf comes directly out of the soil. The bean's primary root is forming fibrous roots. The monocot's primary root is degenerating and the stem is developing its own set of roots.

Conclusions

1. The corn is a monocot. The bean is a dicot.
2. Students should list the following differences: a monocot seed has one cotyledon, and the radicle forms a primary root that degenerates and is replaced by roots from the stem; a dicot seed has two cotyledons, and the radicle forms a fibrous root system.
3. The root emerges first; it absorbs water for the growth of the seedling.

Further Inquiry

Students may form hypotheses about the presence of fats, proteins, and carbohydrates such as sugars and starches. They may develop procedures to test for these substances.

Chapter 27 Review

Vocabulary

1. The combining form *-cotyl* means "cup-shaped, hollow"; *epi-* means "on," or "above"; and *hypo-* means "under." *Epicotyl* is appropriate because it is the part that lies above the cotyledon, while the hypocotyl lies below.

2. A sporangium encloses spores; a seed encloses an embryo.

3. Both are found in females, are related to reproduction, and are found in flowering plants.

4. In double fertilization one sperm unites with the egg in the ovule, producing the diploid embryo; the other sperm joins with the two polar nuclei, producing the triploid endosperm nucleus.

5. A fruit is a mature ovary. Fruits contain seeds, which are fertilized ovules.

Review

1. b
2. c
3. a
4. d
5. a
6. c
7. b
8. b
9. c
10. d

11. The three factors essential for successful wind pollination are: the plant must release much pollen, air circulation must be good enough to carry pollen to other plants, and other plants must be relatively close.

12. The megaspore mother cell in the ovule undergoes meiosis and produces megaspores.

13. A drupe, such as an olive or a peach, has a seed with a woody coating. A berry, such as a tomato or a grape, does not have a seed with a woody coating. Pomes, such as apples and pears, have a leathery interior seed coating.

14. The diagram should show the following: microspore mother cell, meiosis, four haploid microspores, tube cell, generative cell, and pollen grain.

15. Gymnosperms do not undergo double fertilization as angiosperms do.

16. For example: (1) wind—maple seeds are blown from trees; (2) animals—a bird eats a fruit and the seed passes through the bird's digestive system; or (3) water—a coconut floats to a new site and germinates.

17. In monocot germination the hypocotyl is straight and protected by the coleoptile, and the cotyledon remains underground as the shoot grows. In dicot germination the hypocotyl is often hook shaped and pulls the epicotyl and cotyledons out of the soil as the hypocotyl grows upward. The cotyledons eventually fall off the plant.

18. Seed dormancy is a feature of angiosperm reproduction that increases chances for success by ensuring that

Chapter 27 Review

Vocabulary

anther (406)
antheridium (401)
archegonium (402)
artificial propagation (416)
carpel (406)
clone (415)
coleoptile (411)
coleorhiza (411)
cross-pollination (408)
dormancy (413)
double fertilization (410)
embryo sac (407)
endosperm (409)
epicotyl (411)
filament (406)
fruit (411)
generative cell (407)
grafting (416)
heterospory (403)
hilum (411)
homospory (402)
hypocotyl (411)
integuments (407)
megaspore (404)
micropyle (407)
microspore (404)
nectar (408)
ovary (406)
ovule (404)
petal (405)
pistil (406)
plumule (411)
polar nucleus (407)
pollen grain (404)
pollen tube (404)
pollination (408)
protonema (402)
radicle (411)
receptacle (405)
seed (404)
seed coat (411)
self-pollination (408)
sepal (405)
sorus (403)
stamen (406)
stigma (406)
style (406)
tube cell (407)
vegetative propagation (415)
weed (415)

1. Using a dictionary, find the meaning of the word roots in *epicotyl* and *hypocotyl.* Explain why these terms are appropriate for the structures they describe.
2. Explain the difference between a sporangium and a seed.
3. List three similarities between an ovule and an ovary.
4. What are the stages involved in the process of double fertilization?
5. How is fruit related to a seed?

Review

1. The integuments of the ovule are interrupted by (a) a microspore (b) a micropyle (c) a hilum (d) a stamen.
2. The ovary contains (a) anthers (b) sepals (c) ovules (d) filaments.
3. Bryophyte sperm are produced in (a) antheridia (b) anthers (c) archegonia (d) sori.
4. Pollination occurs when (a) a sperm fuses with an egg (b) insects ingest nectar (c) a spore leaves a sporangium (d) pollen lands on a stigma.
5. Attaching part of one plant to another plant is a process known as (a) grafting (b) cloning (c) cutting (d) natural propagation.
6. The epicotyl in a seed is part of the (a) hilum (b) hypocotyl (c) plumule (d) cotyledon.
7. In pollen, the generative cell forms (a) polar nuclei (b) sperm (c) epicotyl tissue (d) endosperm tissue.
8. Pollen sacs are filled with (a) megaspores (b) microspores (c) megaspore mother cells (d) sperm.
9. The fern rhizome produces (a) gametes (b) rhizoids (c) fronds (d) antheridia.
10. The petals of a flower are collectively called a (a) pistil (b) calyx (b) sepals (d) corolla.
11. What three factors are essential for successful wind pollination?
12. How are megaspores formed?
13. Describe three types of fleshy fruits, and give examples of each.
14. Draw a diagram showing the events and the plant structures involved in the formation of pollen.

15. How do gymnosperm life cycles differ from angiosperm life cycles?
16. Name three methods of seed dispersal, and give an example of each.
17. In what ways does germination differ between monocots, such as corn, and dicots, such as beans?
18. Why is seed dormancy a significant evolutionary development?
19. How do bees use nectar guides to find a nectar source?
20. What is the basic difference between alternation of generations in nonvascular and vascular plants?

Critical Thinking

1. Suppose that a type of moss normally has a 2N chromosome number of 12. If meiosis does not occur in the formation of spores but healthy spores form and grow into new gametophytes, what will the chromosome number of the gametes be?
2. Flowers that are pollinated by wind have smaller petals and sepals than those pollinated by animals do. How might big petals and sepals actually be an adaptive disadvantage to them?
3. Why is it advantageous for a plant to have a starchy endosperm as opposed to a sugary endosperm?
4. Keeping in mind their original function, why are fruits and seeds used as a food source by humans and other animals?
5. The nuts of many trees often germinate on the surface of ground that is hard or covered with grass. The new root may grow an inch or two on the surface before it reaches a soft spot and enters the soil. How does the store of nutrients in the nut make this growth possible?

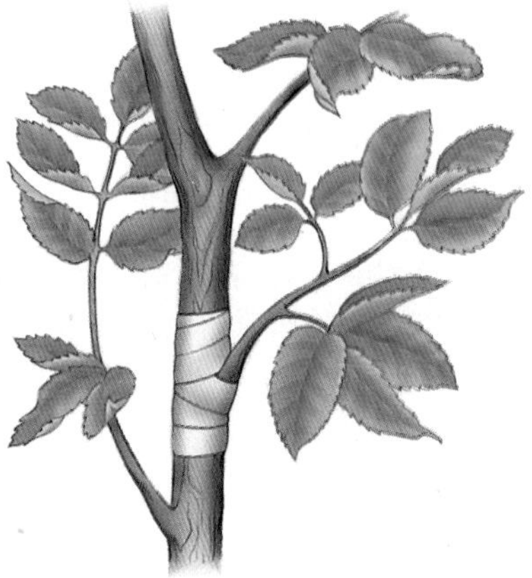

6. Look at the picture above. Most roses are propagated by grafting a new variety onto a stronger wild or an old garden rootstock. When pruning roses in the early spring, it is important to cut off any new shoots that grow on the rootstock. Give a reason for pruning them.

Extension

1. Read "Ant Plantation" in *Natural History,* pp. 10–14. Explain how seed dispersal by ants is beneficial for both plants and ants. How do ant nests provide good environments for seed germination?
2. Examine a head of lettuce, a carrot, a radish, a tomato, a green pepper, a potato, a cucumber, and some green peas or beans. These are all commonly called vegetables, but botanically speaking, some are fruits. Determine which are fruits. Discuss the structure of each in terms of plant anatomy.
3. Read the article by Willem Meijer entitled *Saving the World's Largest Flower,* in *National Geographic,* July 1985, pp. 136–140. Write a report about the unusual reproductive process that the *Rafflesia arnoldii* undergoes.

seeds germinate only when conditions are favorable for growth.
19. Bees follow the fanned lines of the nectar guide to the nectar source. Bees learn to follow these guides once they have learned that nectar is available by following a particular guide.
20. Nonvascular plants have a dominant gametophyte, and vascular plants have a dominant sporophyte.

Critical Thinking

1. The gametes would have 12 chromosomes.
2. Such features would be disadvantageous because large petals and sepals could block wind currents needed to spread pollen.
3. When germination begins, the endosperm can be quickly converted to sugars. If the endosperm were sugary, the seed would be too metabolically active. Starch is a metabolically inactive storage molecule and enables the seed to maintain dormancy.
4. Humans and other animals take advantage of the rich store of starch, fat, and protein stored up for the newly emerging embryo after germination.
5. The new plant has an independent supply of energy and protein that can be used until the plant can take root.
6. The shoots would produce undesirable flowers.

Extension

1. Ant-sowed seeds are protected from many kinds of destruction. Ants appear to be very efficient at the dispersal of many kinds of seeds once thought of as wind dispersed. Ants use parts of the seeds as food for developing larvae.
2. Fruits: tomato, green pepper, cucumber, peas in the pod, bean pods. All contain seeds.
3. Reports should include the facts that the flower is a parasite that germinates from small seeds in the roots of wild grapevines, there are male and female flowers, it has the scent of rotting meat and is pollinated by carrion flies, and seed dispersal is accomplished by ants or other insects.

Chapter 28 Plant Responses

Chapter Overview

Chapter 28 details ways in which plants respond to hormones and external stimuli, including seasonal changes. Section 28.1 describes plant hormones and their functions. Section 28.2 discusses plant tropisms and nastic movements. In Section 28.3, students will learn about plant responses to seasonal environmental changes.

Chapter Planning Chart

B	S	A	Sections and Subsections	Page	Features	Page	Resources
	•	•	**28.1 Plant Hormones**				
			Auxins	421	Biology in Process	422	Blackline Master 57
			Cytokinins	423	Laboratory	429	Overhead Transparency T28
			Gibberellins	423	Section Review	424	Section Reviews Worksheet
			Other Hormones	424			
	•	•	**28.2 Plant Movements**				
			Tropisms	425	Think	426	Videodiscs
			Nastic Movements	426	Section Review	426	Laboratories: Tropisms in Plants
							Section Reviews Worksheet
	•	•	**28.3 Photoperiodism and Vernalization**				
			Flowering	427	Section Review	428	Videodiscs
			Vernalization and Dormancy	428			Process Skills: Florigen
							Section Reviews Worksheet
			End of Chapter Activities				
					Chapter Review	430	Vocabulary Skills
							Chapter Test
							Computer Test Generator

B *The Basic Level curriculum presents the most fundamental knowledge offered in the course.*
S *The Standard Level curriculum is designed for the average student who is able to master most topics.*
A *The Advanced Level curriculum includes suggestions for teaching the most academically able students.*

Cooperative Learning

Group Activity: Seasonal Tourism

- **Group Size:** *6 students*
- **Outcome:** *Students will explain how plants respond to seasonal changes.*
- **Individual Accountability:** *Each student will write a letter to a state agency for information.*
- **Positive Interdependence:** *Each group will present maps of tourist routes to the rest of the class.*

Assign each group three states from regions in which seasonal changes in plants are prominent. (Examples are: autumn foliage in New England or the northern Midwest; seasonal gardens such as Longwood Gardens, Pennsylvania; cherry blossoms in Washington, D.C.; magnolias in Southern states.) Group members should be designated as: (1) outline creator, (2) tour guide or narrator, (3) artist, (4) research coordinator, (5) research assistant, (6) route designer. Students should research information on the plants that grow in each assigned state. Have students in each group also write and mail letters to state tourism offices (addresses in libraries) requesting brochures and information about seasonal tours. When the replies arrive, have each group imagine that they are travel agents planning weekend tours through their assigned states. Tell them to create posters that can be displayed in the classroom, prepare maps with the trip routes indicated, and have each tour guide or narrator describe to the class the seasonal foliage, flowering plantings, or native plants in bloom that would be seen on these trips.

Concept Map

The following is one possible solution to the concept mapping activity in Identifying Relationships on p. 422.

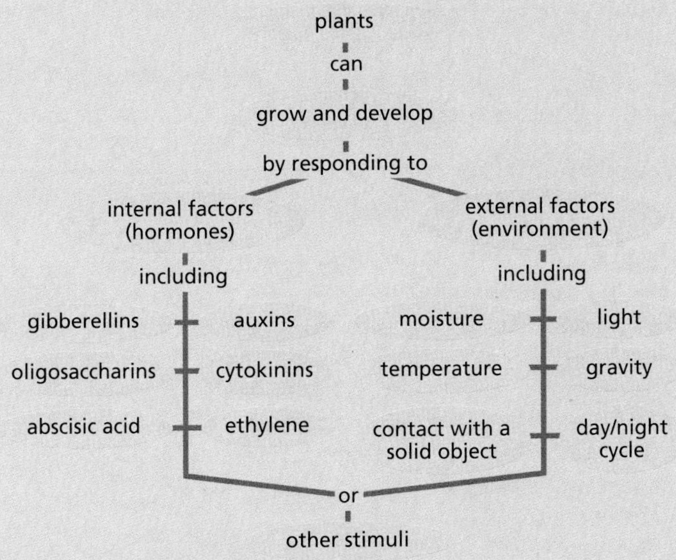

Laboratory Preparation

Overview *(See p. 429.)*

In this lab, students set up a controlled experiment, collect data, and formulate a hypothesis about the effects of the plant growth hormone gibberellin on bean seedlings. Students measure the height of plants treated with the hormone and compare these measurements with the height of untreated control plants. Students should be aware of the function of hypothesis, experimental control, and hormone treatment, as well as of possible sources of error.

Preparation

Soak the bean seeds for 6–8 hours. (Longer soaking may prevent germination.) To prevent growth of bacteria and mold, soak the seeds for 15 minutes in a solution of 5 mL chlorine bleach and 95 mL water. Prepare the potting mixture by mixing equal parts of sand, vermiculite, and potting soil. Always start more seedlings than you need so that plants of equal size and vigor may be selected. Allow 2–3 days for the seedlings to grow at least 3 cm tall before students begin.

To prepare the gibberellic acid solution, add 100 mg gibberellic acid powder to 5 mL ethyl alcohol; mix into 1 L distilled water; add 1 mL wetting agent. *CAUTION:* Extinguish all flames. Ethyl alcohol is extremely flammable. If spilled on skin, flush affected area immediately with water. Wear safety goggles. Pour the solution into dropper bottles for student use. To prepare the control solution, add 1 mL of wetting agent to 1 L distilled water.

This investigation may require one complete lab period for prelab work, one session to set up the experiments, and brief parts of five additional periods to take measurements while the bean seedlings grow.

Teaching Tips

Have students read the Technique section carefully before they design their experiment.

You will have to approve students' experiments before they are actually performed. Make sure students control growing conditions, such as amount of light and water, during the investigation. The plants should be measured the next four times the class meets in lab.

Make sure students understand why they need to plant two pots of seedlings in order to have a controlled experiment.

Safety

Students should wash their hands after using the gibberellic acid solution or handling potting soil mixture.

Chapter Themes

Systems and Interactions Emphasize to students the crucial interactions among a plant's chemical systems and the plant's growth and development. Point out that synthetic auxins have structures similar to naturally occurring plant hormones.

Patterns of Change Stress that changes in the environment create predictable seasonal and cyclic changes in plants. Make sure students understand that plant responses to seasonal change show great variety.

Evolution Plant responses to environmental stimuli have adaptive advantages. Highlight the more common seasonal changes that occur in plants in your area.

Chapter Motivating Activity

Five to 12 days before this lesson, sprout several bean seeds in 2-inch pots, and place half in a box with a rectangular window cut into one side. Place the other half at various locations in the room. Point the window of the box toward the sun so that the seedlings will "bend" toward the light. Show students the seedlings grown in open pots and the seedlings from the box. Most students will have previously seen plants "bending" or "turning" toward the sun but will not know what causes it. Use their observations as a starting point for studying plant responses. Ask them what other plant responses they have observed. *(Sample answers: Flowers opening and closing, leaves unfolding, leaves turning colors in fall)*

Chapter 28 Plant Responses

Introduction

Plants reproduce and grow in response to many environmental factors, such as light, moisture, and temperature. Chemicals inside the plant called hormones are intricately involved in this growth and development. Hormones and other chemicals influence a variety of plant movements and often the timing of flowering and reproduction. These chemical regulators have adaptive significance for plant survival.

Chapter Outline

Chapter Concept

As you read, note the ways in which plants respond to external stimuli and to hormones. Note that these are adaptations to environmental conditions.

Forest in Cornwall, England. Insert: Autumn leaf.

Understanding the Visuals

Point out that the four pictures depict trees in the four seasons. Have students identify which picture depicts which season. *(Fall: colored leaf; winter: bare tree; spring: flowering trees; summer: dense, green forest)* Explain that all four pictures show plants responding to internal and external stimuli. Ask students to name some of the stimuli the plants might be responding to. *(Light, dark, temperature, moisture, internal cues to growth)* Ask how plants other than trees respond to seasonal changes in certain regions of the United States. *(Sample answers: grass turns brown in fall; flowers bloom in spring and summer; leaves on many plants change color and fall in the autumn.)*

28.1 Plant Hormones

Section Objectives

- *List six types of plant hormones and give some functions of each.*
- *Give examples of the adaptive advantages of hormonal responses.*
- *Describe three agricultural applications of plant hormones.*
- *Summarize the experiments that led to the discovery of auxins.*

Plant growth and development are controlled by both external and internal factors. The external factors include light intensity, gravity, temperature, moisture, and length of day. Each species differs in its response to these factors, but in all species external factors trigger changes in internal plant physiology.

The internal factors that control plant growth are chemicals called **hormones.** Because hormones stimulate or inhibit plant growth, many scientists also refer to them as **plant growth regulators.** Hormones affect plants in many ways, from causing them to grow taller to causing leaves to change color in autumn.

Plant hormones are organic compounds that are effective in small concentrations. They are synthesized in one part of the plant and transported to **target tissues** elsewhere in the plant, where they trigger a physiological response such as growth. Botanists have identified six kinds of plant hormones. Though we will discuss these hormones one at a time, keep in mind that plant responses typically result from the interaction of several hormones.

Auxins

Auxins *(AWK-sunz)* are a class of hormones that regulate the growth of plant cells. Chemical structures of three auxins are shown in Figure 28-1. One naturally occurring auxin is **indoleacetic** *(IN-DOLE-uh-SEED-ick)* **acid,** or **IAA.** IAA is produced in actively growing plant regions, such as shoot tips, young leaves, and developing fruits. It is then transported to other parts of the plant where it has many physiological effects.

One of the most important effects of IAA is the altering of plasticity in primary cell walls. In altering plasticity IAA regulates cell elongation. Effects on the target tissue vary with concentration. In a target tissue one concentration of IAA may stimulate cell elongation, while a greater one may inhibit elongation. The effect of an auxin also depends on the target tissue.

Synthetic Auxins

Chemists have synthesized several auxinlike compounds. These are used agriculturally. Naphthaleneacetic *(NAFF-thuh-LEEN-uh-SEED-ick)* acid (NAA) is a synthetic auxin used by farmers to keep fruit from dropping off trees. The use of NAA allows growers to harvest all their fruit in a short period of time. Naphthaleneacetic acid also stimulates the formation of roots.

Farmers use the synthetic auxin 2,4-D to kill weeds. Many broadleaf plants, such as dandelions, are sensitive to synthetic auxins, while many monocots, such as corn, are not. The 2,4-D disturbs the metabolism of the dicot cells, causing the plant to die. As a result applying the proper concentration of 2,4-D to a corn-

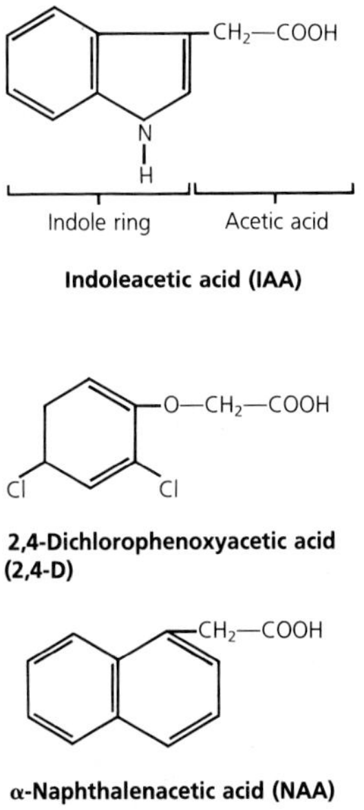

Figure 28-1 The structure of indoleacetic acid, a naturally occurring auxin, differs in detail from two synthetic counterparts.

Lesson Plan

Section Focus

This section focuses on the effects of six kinds of plant hormones: auxins, cytokinins, gibberellins, abscisic acid, ethylene, and oligosaccharins.

Section Themes

This section emphasizes the theme **Systems and Interactions.** It discusses the interactions of the chemical systems of plants with their growth and development. It presents the theme **Patterns of Change** as the responses of the plant to the molecular and cellular action of hormones within plant tissues.

Motivating Activity

To demonstrate the effect of ethylene on the ripening of fruits, place a green banana in a plastic bag by itself and another green banana in a plastic bag with a ripe apple. The banana in the bag with the apple will start to turn yellow within a few hours. The green banana alone will take a day or two. Ask students to form hypotheses about what they observe. *(Example: The green banana with the apple turns yellow faster because the apple gives off some substance that affects ripening.)*

Teaching Strategies

Interpreting the Visuals Tell students the hexagon shapes in Figure 28-1 have a carbon atom at the apex of each angle. Point out that the double lines indicate double bonds. Ask students to identify the differences among these compounds. *(IAA has an indole ring and an acetic acid; 2,4-D has a six-carbon ring, an acetic acid, an oxygen, and two chlorines; NAA has two rings side by side and an acetic acid.)*
■ *See* **Overhead Transparency** *T28 and* **Blackline Master** *57.*

Hormone	Production Sites	Target Tissue
auxins	shoot tips, young leaves, developing fruit	primary cell walls
cytokinins	actively growing regions	roots, stems, phloem, xylem
gibberellins	immature seeds	stem internodes, seeds, fruits
abscisic acid	leaves	stomata
ethylene	fruits, flowers, leaves, roots	buds, seeds, fruits

Graphic Organizer Use this table in Independent Practice on p. 423.

Identifying Relationships Have students draw a concept map showing the external and internal factors that control plant growth and development. An example of a completed concept map is shown on p. 419B.

Identifying Cause and Effect Present various cause-and-effect statements involving plant hormones to students. Have them identify the cause and the effect. Examples: "When the tip of a plant stem is pinched off, the auxin is also removed, and the plant grows bushier." *(Cause: tip with auxin is pinched off. Effect: plant grows bushier.)* "Cells in a root tip elongate after IAA enters the cells." *(Cause: IAA enters cells. Effect: cells elongate.)*

Observing Organisms Have students pinch off the uppermost pair of leaves on a houseplant such as *Coleus* or Swedish ivy. After a week or more, have students observe the plant. The stem behind the pinching should have begun branching into two stems. Ask how this technique would be useful to gardeners. *(Pinching back stem tips makes the plants grow bushier.)*

Identifying Functions Ask students what plant hormone could produce seedless fruit. *(Auxin)* Ask which hormone might cause a plant to grow long and thin quickly. *(Gibberellin)* Ask which hormone would be found in vascular tissue. *(Cytokinin)*

Figure 28-2 Lateral bud growth results when shoot tips are removed (top). Lateral bud growth is inhibited when artificially applied auxin replaces shoot tips (bottom).

field will kill the dicotyledons but will not harm the corn. Synthetic auxins are also used to stimulate fruit development in the absence of pollination and fertilization. Spraying flowers of plants such as watermelons and tomatoes with synthetic auxins can produce seedless fruits.

Apical Dominance

In many plants the branches near the shoot tip are much shorter than those near the base. This pattern of growth results from **apical dominance.** Biologists have determined that in apical dominance the apical meristem produces auxin in a concentration that inhibits the growth of buds near the shoot tip. This limits the length of branches near the shoot apex.

Compare the plants in Figure 28-2. The shoot tips of the plant at the top have been removed, thereby eliminating the source of the auxin. As a result buds near the shoot tip have begun growing. The shoot tips of the plant at the bottom have also been removed. In this case, however, the shoot tip has been replaced with lanolin that contains an auxin. Replacing the shoot tip with auxin inhibited growth of the nearby buds and resulted in apical dominance.

Biology in Process

The Discovery of Auxin

The discovery of auxin involved the work of scientists around the world. Charles Darwin and his son Francis began studying phototropism in oat coleoptiles in the late 1870s. They observed that curvature toward light occurred in the elongating region of the coleoptile and hypothesized that this region sensed light.

The Darwins designed several experiments to test this hypothesis. They first covered the region of elongation with a cylinder of metal foil that prevented light from reaching the tissue. To their surprise this had no effect on curvature. Curvature was stopped only when the foil was placed over the tip of the coleoptile. The Darwins concluded that "when seedlings are freely exposed to lateral light some influence is transmitted from the upper to the lower part, causing the material to bend." They stated that some "influence" had to move from the tip of the coleoptile to the elongating region, causing unequal growth.

In 1926 Dutch plant physiologist Frits Went explained the Darwins' observations. Went asked: (1) Is the nature of the influence electrical or chemical? (2) Can it be isolated?

Interdisciplinary Activity

Technology Tell students that ethylene gas is widely used to initiate fruit ripening. Bananas are normally picked green, stored in ships for transport to North America, and treated with ethylene gas during transit to ripen them for market. Ripening of stored fruit can be suppressed to some degree by ventilating a warehouse to exhaust any ethylene formed by ripening fruits, or by pumping in CO_2 to inhibit the effects of ethylene. Have students research the development of the supermarket tomato. *(Tomatoes were bred to uniform size, shape, and firm texture for durability in transport. They are picked by machine and shipped green for convenience and higher profit by the producers; they are treated with ethylene gas while in transit to ripen them artificially for sale in the market.)*

Cytokinins

Hormones called **cytokinins** *(SIE-tuh-KIE-nunz)* promote cell division. They are produced in rapidly growing regions, including roots, fruits, and seeds. Cytokinins influence many aspects of plant development, including the formation of roots and stems and the differentiation of xylem and phloem. Cytokinins seem to act by binding with RNA and thus affecting the synthesis of proteins, including those necessary for cell division.

Gibberellins

In the 1920s Japanese scientists discovered that a substance caused rice plants that were infected with a fungus of the genus *Gibberella* to grow abnormally tall. Biologists later isolated the substance responsible for this growth. They eventually found that this substance, which they called **gibberellin** *(JIB-uh-RELL-un)*, was a hormone that was also synthesized by plants themselves. Biologists have now isolated over 65 gibberellins.

Gibberellins are found in varying amounts in all parts of a plant. The highest concentration of gibberellins is found in im-

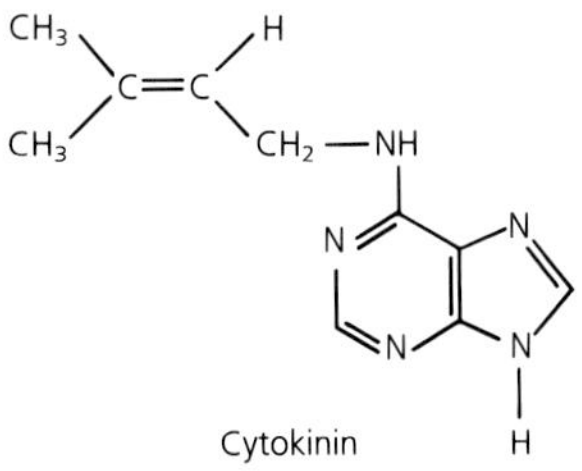

Cytokinin

Figure 28-3 The structure of cytokinin is related to its function.

The Darwins' experiment

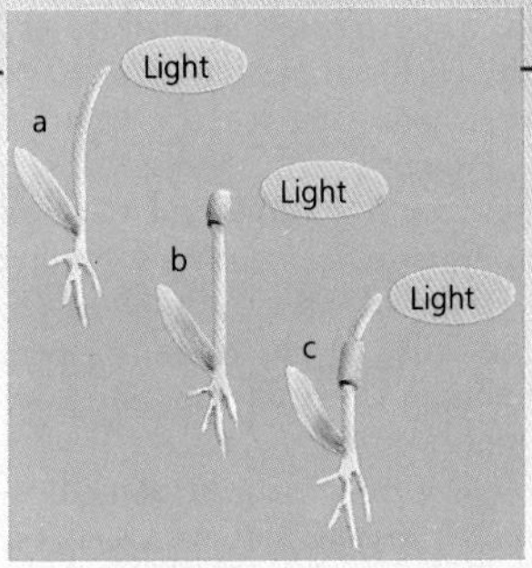

Went's experiment

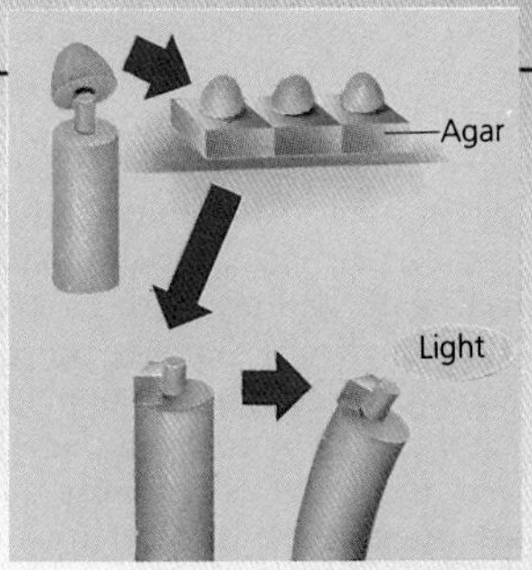

Went designed an elegant experiment. Keeping his seedlings in the dark, he first cut off the tips of several coleoptiles and placed their cut surfaces in contact with agar. After about an hour, he discarded the tips. He then placed small pieces of the agar on one side of the stumps of the plants. The coleoptile grew away from the side on which the agar block was placed. Furthermore, twice as much curvature occurred when two blocks were placed on one side of the coleoptile.

Went performed another experiment to make sure the curvature resulted from a substance that was produced by the coleoptile and transferred to the agar. On one side of a coleoptile he placed a block of agar that had not been in contact with a tip. When no curvature occurred, Went concluded that the influence for phototropism was a diffusable chemical. He also concluded that the influence could be isolated.

Went inferred that the substance in the agar stimulated growth. He named this chemical auxin, from the Greek word *auxein,* meaning "to increase."

- **What evidence allowed Went to conclude that auxin could be isolated from the plant?**

Guided Practice

Ask students where each hormone is produced and what its effect on target tissue is. *(For example, IAA is produced in actively growing regions and alters plasticity in primary cell walls.)*

Independent Practice

- Have students write answers to the Section Review.
- Have students make a table of plant hormones, sites of their production, and target tissues. An example of a completed table is shown on p. 421.

Biology in Process

Using the Feature

Experimentation is the main process skill presented in the feature. Charles and Francis Darwin designed experiments to demonstrate that a certain "influence" caused unequal growth as plants curve toward light. Ask students what a control sample in the Darwins' experiments might have looked like. *(Darwin might have put transparent caps over the tips.)* Plant physiologist Frits Went later identified this "influence" as a chemical now called auxin. The feature shows that careful experimentation can provide data that support a hypothesis or suggest new hypotheses that merit investigation.

Answer to the Feature

Went's ability to reproduce the effect of auxin with agar that had been in contact with coleoptile tips led him to conclude that auxin could be isolated from the plant.

LEP Activity

Tap into students' prior knowledge about plant growth from Chapter 26. Ask them to recall how primary growth occurs. *(Cell division, elongation, and maturation in the apical meristems)* Most students will know that hormones in their own bodies control growth and reproduction. Tell them that plants also have hormones. Then preteach the concept that the processes of growth and reproduction they have already studied in this unit are controlled or even initiated by plant hormones.

Check Your Understanding

1. Why is the concentration of synthetic auxins important? *(A strong concentration will have a different effect from a weaker concentration.)*
2. Why do some plants produce more abscisic acid during drought? *(It causes stomata to close and slows water loss.)*
3. Of what adaptive advantage to a plant are multiple hormones? *(Each may have different target tissues, and plant responses may be the result of interactions among several hormones.)*

Reteaching

Obtain commercial rooting hormone (from a nursery or garden shop). Have students read the label to identify the hormones in the product and their effects. *(Examples: cytokinins, promote cell division; IAA, regulates cell elongation.)* Have students make leaf cuttings of a plant such as a begonia or African violet (laid on damp vermiculite and loosely covered with plastic wrap), with and without using the hormone, and observe the results in five to ten days. *(Cuttings with hormones applied root much faster.)*
■ *See* Section Reviews *worksheet, Section 28.1.*

Enrichment

Have students go to a plant nursery, find all the artificial hormones commercially available, and determine the method of application and use of each. Have them share what they discover in the form of a poster or oral report.

Closure

Gardeners pinch off tips of seedlings to encourage growth of side branches. Ask students to identify the hormone involved and its effect on growth. *(Removing the tip removes a source of auxin. Buds nearby grow lateral branches.)*

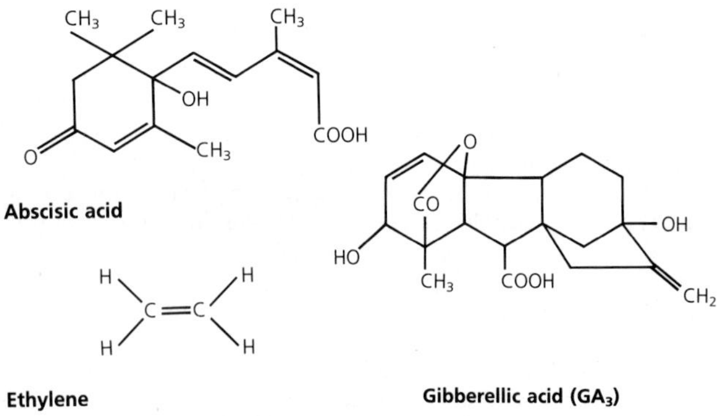

Figure 28-4 Gibberellic acid, abscisic acid, and ethylene, shown in structural form, regulate various aspects of plant growth. Ethylene promotes the ripening of fruit.

mature seeds. Gibberellins have numerous effects on target tissues, the major effect being to promote growth. Before some plants flower, the regions of the stem between the nodes, called internodes, will lengthen. This lengthening, which is called **bolting,** can also be induced by treating a plant with gibberellin. Gibberellins also stimulate seed germination and promote the formation of seedless fruits.

Other Hormones

During the 1960s botanists isolated a hormone called **abscisic** *(ab-SIZE-ick)* **acid** that inhibits the growth of buds and the germination of seeds. Abscisic acid is found in dormant buds, fruits, and roots. During a drought leaves synthesize large amounts of abscisic acid, causing stomata to close and reducing the loss of water.

Unlike other plant hormones, **ethylene** *(ETH-uh-LEEN)* is a gas produced by fruits, flowers, leaves, and roots and released into the air. Ethylene stimulates the ripening of fruit by softening cell walls and promoting the conversion of starches into sugars. Ripening fruits that give off ethylene cause nearby fruits to ripen. Growers often harvest immature tomatoes, store them, and later apply ethylene to ripen them for market.

In the 1980s botanists discovered a new class of plant hormones called **oligosaccharins** *(AHL-ih-goe-SACK-uh-rinz).* These hormones act on primary cell walls. They regulate growth, development, and may contribute to defense against disease.

Section Review

1. How does the origin of the word *hormone* reflect their function?
2. What is the function of auxins?
3. Which hormones can be used to produce seedless fruits?
4. Explain how ethylene differs from other plant hormones.
5. List three possible adaptive advantages of apical dominance.

Answers to Section Review

1. The Greek root of the word *hormone* means "to stir up" or "to set in motion," which is part of what hormones do.
2. Auxins control the growth of plant cells.
3. Synthetic auxin and gibberellin
4. It is a gas and can move through the air.
5. Apical dominance allows plants to grow upward toward light rather than growing wider; it prevents upper branches from shading lower ones, maximizing light-absorbing surfaces; smaller branches at the top of the tree will keep the tree from becoming top-heavy; predators will be unable to reach shoot tips.

28.2 Plant Movements

Plants respond to environmental stimuli such as light, moisture, chemicals, gravity, and mechanical disturbances. These stimuli cause adaptive movements by influencing growth. Plant growth involves the elongation of cells, and most plant movements result from elongation triggered by environmental factors.

Tropisms

A **tropism** *(TROE-PIZZ-'m)* is a plant movement toward or away from an environmental stimulus. Each kind of tropism is named for its stimulus. For example, movements in response to light are called phototropisms. Movement toward an environmental stimulus is called a positive tropism. Thus in Figure 28-5 the shoot tips growing toward light are positively phototropic. Conversely, movement away from a stimulus is a negative tropism.

Phototropism

Phototropism is a plant growth response to light coming from one direction. Scientific analysis has shown that light coming from one direction causes auxin to move to the shaded side of the stem. In most cases the auxin causes cells on the shaded side to elongate more rapidly than cells on the lighted side of the stem. As a result the stem curves toward the light. By orienting the plant toward its light source, phototropism maximizes the amount of light that reaches the photosynthetic cells of the plant.

Thigmotropism

Thigmotropism is a growth response to contact with a solid object. Auxin and ethylene control coiling, which occurs when plants such as morning glories come into contact with an object. Thigmotropism allows a plant to "climb" over and cling to objects, increasing its chances of intercepting light for photosynthesis.

Gravitropism

Gravitropism is a plant growth response to gravity. Usually a root grows down and a stem grows up—that is, roots are positively gravitropic and stems are negatively gravitropic. Gravitropism is also known as geotropism.

Like phototropism, gravitropism appears to be regulated primarily by auxin. If a seedling is placed horizontally, auxin accumulates along the lower sides of both the root and stem. This concentration of auxin stimulates cellular elongation along the lower side of the stem, and the stem grows upward. A similar concentration of auxin inhibits cellular elongation in the lower side of the root, and as a result the root grows downward.

To learn how plant cells sense gravity, scientists have studied the position of inclusions in root cap cells called amyloplasts

Section Objectives

- *Explain the difference between tropisms and nastic movements.*
- *List the environmental stimuli to which plants respond and the tropism named for each.*
- *Describe common nastic movements, and explain their survival values.*

Figure 28-5 As this garden pea seedling demonstrates, roots are positively gravitropic, while shoots are positively phototropic.

Tropism	Stimulus	Positive Example
phototropism	light	plant leans to light source
thigmotropism	solid object	ivy twining up wall
gravitropism	gravity	roots growing down
hydrotropism	water	roots growing into pipes
chemotropism	chemical	pollen tube grows to ovule

Graphic Organizer. Use this table in Guided Practice on the right.

Lesson Plan

Section Focus

This section describes plant responses to external stimuli. It explains the difference between tropism and nastic movement.

Section Themes

This section focuses on the themes of **Systems and Interactions** and **Evolution.** Plants respond to their environment. This ability has adaptive advantages for the plant.

Motivating Activity

Have students plant soaked corn seeds narrow end up, narrow end down, and sideways against the glass of a jar lined with blotter paper or paper toweling kept moist but not too wet. After five days have them record the growth and the direction of roots and stems, and identify stimuli and tropisms involved. *(Roots: down—gravity, gravitropism or geotropism. Stems: up—gravity, negative gravitropism; toward light—light coming from one direction, phototropism)*

Teaching Strategies

Making Inferences Ask students how tropisms and nastic movements are adaptive. *(They help the plant adjust its growth and development to environmental factors.)*

- ***See*** **Laboratories, *Investigation 28.***

Guided Practice

List the five tropisms on the board, and have students give examples. Use the table on the left as a model. Ask students how a nastic response differs from a tropism. *(A nastic response is not in relationship to the* direction *of the stimulus.)*

Videodiscs

- ***Side 3, 25688, Geotropism and Phototropism (m)***
- ***2118–2119, Mimosa (s)***

Section 28.2

Answer to Think

Nastic; the plant is responding to the stimulus independently of the direction that it comes from.

Independent Practice

- Have students write answers to the Section Review.
- Have students write one or two sentences to distinguish between a tropism and a nastic movement. *(Tropisms are movements toward or away from the direction of a stimulus; nastic movements are independent of the direction of the stimulus.)*

Check Your Understanding

1. Of what adaptive advantage is the closing of leaves at night? *(It conserves water and energy.)*
2. What plant response is a pea plant exhibiting when it attaches to and grows up a fence? *(A combination of responses including geotropism and phototropism, but especially thigmotropism)*

Reteaching

Show the class a photograph of a willow tree and explain that willows require large amounts of water. Ask why wise gardeners do not plant willows near water lines. *(Roots could grow into pipes and clog them.)*

- *See* Section Reviews *worksheet, Section 28.2.*

Enrichment

Ask students to think about how scientists on a space shuttle flight might be able to grow seeds so that the roots grow down and the stems grow up in the absence of gravity. *(They would need equipment to orient the seeds during germination in a weightless environment.)*

Closure

Ask students to speculate on why tropisms and nastic movements arose in plant evolution. *(They enhanced the chances of survival for plants.)*

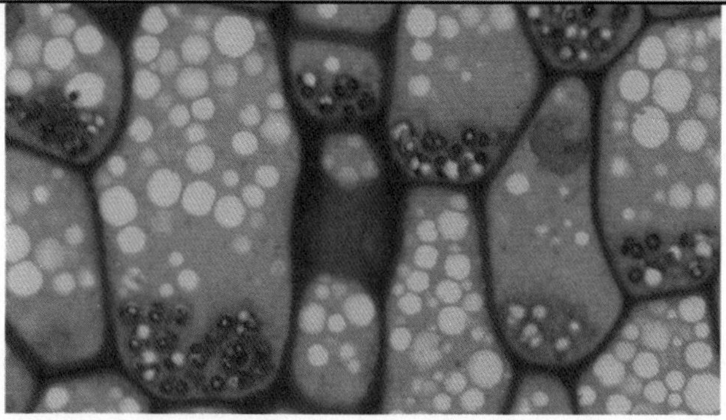

Figure 28-6 The dark bodies at the bottom of the cells are amyloplasts.

(*AM-uh-loe-*PLASTS). Gravity causes amyloplasts, which contain grains of starch, to settle on the lower surface of a cell. When a plant is turned sideways, amyloplasts fall to the lower cell wall. Amyloplasts are thought to cause a movement of calcium ions, which in turn influences the transport of auxins that cause the root to curve in response to gravity.

Think

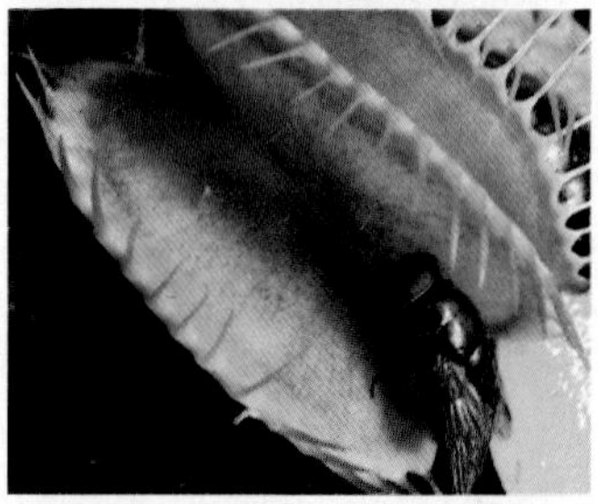

Are the leaf responses of the Venus's-flytrap tropisms or nastic movements?

Chemotropism and Hydrotropism

Plant growth in response to a chemical is called a **chemotropism.** For fertilization to occur, for example, the pollen tube must grow into the ovule through the micropyle. The pollen tube grows in response to chemicals produced by the pistil of a compatible flower. The growth of roots in response to water is called **hydrotropism.** One example occurs when roots encounter water-filled pipes and grow into rather than around them. Negative hydrotropism is an adaptation for avoiding flooded soils.

Nastic Movements

Plant movements that occur in response to environmental stimuli but that are independent of the direction of the stimuli are called **nastic movements.** For instance, when *Mimosa pudica,* the sensitive plant, is touched, its leaflets fold and its petioles lower within a few seconds. This response is triggered by rapid movements of potassium ions between parenchyma cells at the base of the leaflets and petiole. Stimulation causes ions to be pumped out of cells along the lower side of the petiole. Water then rapidly moves out of these cells by osmosis, and the cells shrink. Many nastic movements, such as the closing up of morning glory petals in the evening, have adaptive significance. Nastic movements allow plants to conserve water and food energy when conditions are not favorable for photosynthesis and growth.

Section Review

1. How do a tropism and a nastic movement differ?
2. How might amyloplasts function in gravitropism?
3. Define five tropisms, and give an example of each.
4. Name a kind of negative tropism shown by stems.
5. What role might hormones play in nastic movements?

Answers to Section Review

1. Tropism is movement toward or away from the direction of a stimulus. Nastic movement is independent of the direction of the stimulus.
2. Amyloplasts may influence the transport of hormones that affect geotropic growth.
3. Phototropism—response to light; green shoots growing upward are phototropic. Gravitropism—response to gravity; roots are gravitropic. Chemotropism—response to chemicals within a plant; growth of pollen tube toward an ovule is chemotropic. Hydrotropism—response to water; most roots are hydrotropic. Thigmotropism—response to solid object; a coiling vine is thigmotropic.
4. Negative gravitropism
5. Hormones might influence the biochemical content of cells and thus the tissue changes that result in nastic movements.

28.3 Photoperiodism and Vernalization

Plant responses are strongly influenced by seasonal environmental changes. For example, many trees shed their leaves in autumn and most plants flower only during certain times of the year. How do plants sense seasonal changes? Contrary to what you might suspect, most plants do not mark the seasons by changes in temperature. Instead they respond to changes in day length. This response is called **photoperiodism.**

Biologists don't know exactly how plants monitor changes in day length, but evidence suggests that this response involves a pigment called **phytochrome** *(FITE-uh-KROME)*. Phytochrome exists in two forms: red light–sensitive phytochrome, P_r, and far-red light–sensitive phytochrome, P_{fr}. The P_r absorbs red light of wavelengths of about 660 nm and in doing so is converted to P_{fr}. When P_{fr} absorbs far-red light of wavelengths of about 730 nm, it is converted to P_r. Since sunlight contains proportionally more red light than far-red light, P_r is converted to P_{fr} during the day. At night P_{fr} is slowly converted to P_r. Accordingly, the ratio of P_r to P_{fr} may be a chemical measure of the relative length of day and night. Biologists believe that the changing proportions of the two phytochromes play a role in starting the hormonal changes that cause flowering, though other factors may be involved.

Flowering

Flowering is influenced by several factors, including temperature and the availability of moisture. However, in some plants the most important factor controlling flowering is daylength. Plants vary in their response to duration of light. Many species have a **critical length,** which is the length of daylight above or below which these species of plants will flower. The adaptive value of photoperiodism is that members of a species bloom at the same time each year, when conditions for pollination are most favorable.

Long-day plants flower only when exposed to day lengths longer than the critical length for the plant. For example, wheat plants flower only when days are longer than 10 hours—during the lengthening days of late spring and early summer. Radishes, clover, irises, and beets are other long-day plants.

Short-day plants flower only when exposed to day lengths shorter than the critical length for the plant. For example, ragweed flowers only when days are shorter than 14.5 hours. Most short-day plants flower during the shortening days of the fall, though some bloom in early spring. Chrysanthemums, goldenrods, soybeans, and poinsettias are short-day plants.

Day-neutral plants are not affected by the length of days and nights. Tomatoes, dandelions, and roses are day-neutral.

Section Objectives

- *Define* critical length, *and explain the role it plays in flowering responses.*
- *Describe vernalization, and give examples of human applications of this phenomenon.*
- *Relate abscission zones to dormancy.*
- *Describe the role of phytochrome in plant responses.*

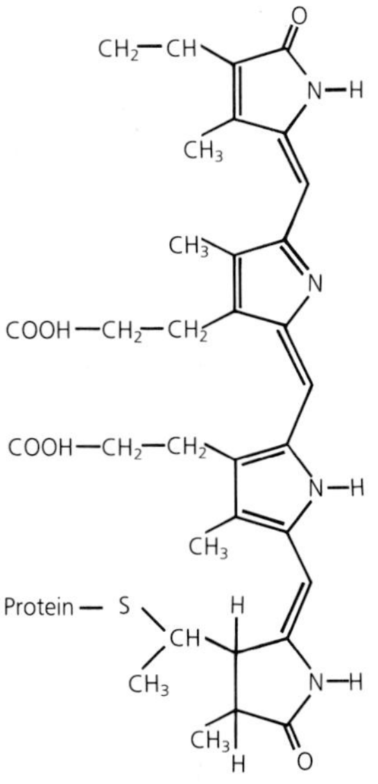

Figure 28-7 The type of phytochrome known as P_r, shown in structural form, converts to P_{fr}, giving plants a means of measuring daylight.

Type	Need to Flower	Flower During
long-day plants	day longer (night shorter) than critical length	late spring, summer
short-day plants	day shorter (night longer) than critical length	early spring, autumn
day-neutral plants	not affected by day-night cycle	spring to autumn is possible

Guided Practice Use this table in Guided Practice on the right.

Lesson Plan

Section Focus
This section describes plant responses to seasonal environmental changes, including photoperiodism and vernalization.

Section Themes
The theme of **Patterns of Change** is evident in the descriptions of photoperiodism and vernalization, which are part of seasonal changes in plants.

Motivating Activity
Show students photographs of seasonal changes in plants. (Examples: autumn foliage; spring magnolias or dogwoods; light-sensitive blooming plants such as Christmas cactus and *Portulaca.*) Ask what factors might cause such plant responses. *(Length of day and night, seasonal changes, and temperature affect such events as leaf growth and flowering.)*

Teaching Strategies
Making Hypotheses A gardener collects carrot seeds in fall, stores them in a warm place, and finds that they do not germinate the next spring. Ask students how the gardener could have obtained better results. *(Cold storage of the seeds would have simulated vernalization, increasing germination rates.)*

■ *See* Process Skills, *Chapter 28.*

Guided Practice
Tell students that despite the terms *short-day* and *long-day,* the critical factor is actually hours of darkness. Have them make a table listing requirements for photoperiodic flowering, and the usual time of year each type occurs. An example of a completed table is shown on the left.

Videodiscs

■ *644–646, Resurrection Plant (s)*
■ *721–724, Cacti (s)*

Section 28.3

Independent Practice

■ Have students write answers to the Section Review.

■ Remind students that the tropics are warm year round and have less variation in hours of daylight and dark than the higher northern or southern latitudes. Have students name plant adaptations they would not expect to find in the tropics. *(Sample answers: short-day flowering, vernalization, dormancy)*

Check Your Understanding

1. Why is a plant pigment an appropriate chemical to respond to changes in hours of day and night? *(Pigments absorb light.)*

2. How might a hot spell during November harm a plant? *(It could break a plant's dormancy period and prevent the plant from developing the next year.)*

Reteaching

Ask students the evolutionary significance of dormancy. *(Allows plants to survive hostile conditions)* Review Chapter 27 on seeds to reinforce students' understanding of the advantages of dormancy.

■ *See* **Section Reviews** ***worksheet, Section 28.3.***

Enrichment

Have students pick an out-of-season flower or bulb and, with information from a gardening book, force the plant to grow or flower out of season. Tulip, crocus, chrysanthemum, and narcissus are all good choices.

Closure

Ask what effect a street lamp would have on a long-day plant *(Might flower earlier than usual)*, a short-day plant *(Might flower later than usual)*, and a day-neutral plant *(No effect)*.

Figure 28-8 An abscission zone forms where the ginkgo petiole attaches to the stem (left). After the leaf falls, a leaf scar remains (right).

Vernalization and Dormancy

Many plants such as turnips, beets, and carrots must be exposed to cold before they will flower. Some seeds require extended periods of cold before they germinate. This requirement, called **vernalization,** is important for crops such as winter wheat, barley, and rye. For example, seeds of winter wheat that are planted in the short days of autumn germinate before winter. Exposure to cold winter temperatures causes the plant to flower early in the spring, and an "early" crop is produced. Farmers in areas with dry summers exploit this phenomenon to grow and harvest crops in the spring before the summer drought.

Most plants do not grow at the same rate year-round. During periods of cold or drought, plant growth ceases or is limited, and plants enter dormancy. Shorter days stimulate the formation of winter-resistant buds and **abscission** *(ab-SIZH-un)* **zones** at the base of leaf petioles. Leaves break off the plant at abscission zones. Before leaves fall, nutrients are transported back into the stem and are used again in the spring. The leaf would die in the cold anyway, so losing leaves allows the plant to retain nutrients.

Section Review

1. Distinguish between *short-day plants* and *long-day plants.*
2. How do farmers use vernalization to their benefit?
3. How does phytochrome enable plants to detect changes in seasons?
4. What is the adaptive advantage of dormancy?
5. What factors might influence flowering times in day-neutral plants?

Answers to Section Review

1. Short-day plants flower when days are shorter than their species' critical length. Long-day plants flower when days are longer than their species' critical length.

2. Farmers can plant wheat that will flower early in the spring, resulting in a crop that can be harvested before it becomes too hot and dry for plants to grow.

3. The ratio of the two forms of phytochrome may serve as a chemical indicator for day length.

4. Dormancy allows a seed or plant to survive conditions unfavorable for growth.

5. Vernalization and hormonal activity. Other answers may be acceptable.

Laboratory

Plant Growth and Response

Objective
To study the effect of a plant hormone on bean seedlings

Process Skills
Hypothesizing, experimenting, collecting and analyzing data

Materials
Flower pots, 20 cm or larger; potting mixture; bean seedlings at least 3 cm tall; glass-marking pencil; ruler; cotton swabs; gibberellic acid solution; water with wetting agent

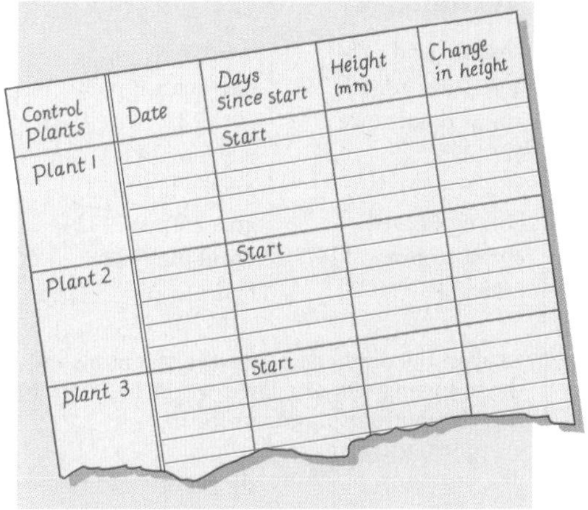

Background

1 Gibberellin is found in all parts of plants but is most concentrated in immature seeds. It is only one group of many hormones that affect plant functions. What is the major effect of gibberellins on plant tissues?

Technique

1 Fill a flower pot with potting mixture. Plant five seedlings, spacing them evenly around the edge. Each seedling's roots should be at least 1 cm below the soil surface.
2 Measure the height of each plant to the nearest millimeter. Measure from the soil surface to the shoot tip.
3 To apply a solution to the seedlings, moisten a cotton swab with the solution and rub it over the leaves and shoot tips. Use a fresh cotton swab for each solution.

Inquiry

1 Discuss the objective of this laboratory with your partners and develop a hypothesis about the effect of gibberellic acid.
2 Design an experiment to test your hypothesis, using the setup described in Technique.
3 What are the independent and dependent variables in your experiment? How will you vary the independent variable? How will you measure any changes in the dependent variable?
4 What controls will you include?
5 How will you record your results?
6 Obtain your materials and proceed with your experiment after receiving approval from your teacher.

Conclusions

1 Use the data you have recorded to calculate the percentage increase, between first measurement and last, in the average height of the two groups of plants.
2 Use your data to make a line graph of height as a function of time.
3 Do your data support your hypothesis? Explain why or why not.
4 What differences, other than height, did you detect in the bean seedlings?
5 What were some of the possible sources of error in your experiment?

Further Inquiry
Design an experiment to determine whether gibberellic acid has any effect in accelerating the actual germination of bean seeds.

Laboratory

(For an overview of plant hormones and preparatory information related to the laboratory, see p. 419B.)

Background

1. Gibberellins promote growth.

Technique

1. Each pot should be labeled with student name and whether it is the experimental or the control.
3. Make sure that students use different swabs for the two solutions.

Inquiry

1. Each laboratory group should agree on a testable hypothesis.
2. Discuss experimental designs with each group of students. The students will need to plant two pots with five seeds each in order to perform the experiment.
3. The independent variable is the application of gibberellic acid solution; the dependent variable is any observed changes in the height of the bean plants. One group of plants will receive the gibberellic acid solution; one group will not. Changes in the dependent variable will be measured in millimeters.
4. Both plant groups will get the same amounts of water, sunlight, darkness, and air circulation. The control plants will be treated with a wetting solution, the experimental plants with gibberellic acid.
5. Suggest that students record their data in a table such as the one shown. They will need to draw two tables, one for their control group of plants, one for their experimental group.

Conclusions

1. Students should compare their two averages.
2. "Start" gives Day 0.
3. Students should recognize whether their data support their hypotheses.
4. Students' data should support their answers.
5. Sources of error include individual genetic differences among seeds; differences in the environment of the two pots; disease or insect predation; accidents or damage to individual plants; error in measuring, labeling, or calculating; incorrect application of the solutions.

Further Inquiry

Students might use the same technique with seeds instead of seedlings and compare the results of the two test runs.

Chapter 28 Review

Vocabulary

abscisic acid (424)
abscission zone (428)
apical dominance (422)
auxin (421)
bolting (424)
chemotropism (426)
critical length (427)
cytokinins (423)
day-neutral plant (427)
ethylene (424)
gibberellin (423)
gravitropism (425)
hormone (421)
hydrotropism (426)
indoleacetic acid (IAA) (421)
long-day plant (427)
nastic movement (426)
oligosaccharins (424)
photoperiodism (427)
phototropism (425)
phytochrome (427)
plant growth regulator (421)
short-day plant (427)
target tissue (421)
thigmotropism (425)
tropism (425)
vernalization (428)

Explain the differences between the terms in the following sets of related words.

1. thigmotropism, gravitropism, chemotropism
2. hormone, plant growth regulator, target tissue
3. vernalization, dormancy, photoperiodism
4. negative tropism, positive tropism, nastic movement
5. critical length, long-day plant, short-day plant

Review

1. Some plants must be explosed to cold before they will flower, a process called (a) photoperiodism (b) vernalization (c) dormancy (d) thermotropism.
2. The growth of roots above the soil surface, where oxygen is absorbed, is a (a) negative gravitropism (b) negative hydrotropism (c) positive phototropism (d) positive chemotropism.
3. Nastic movements occur (a) without a stimulus (c) toward a stimulus (b) away from a stimulus (d) independent of the direction of the stimulus.
4. Cytokinins promote cell elongation and (a) cell aging (b) cell division (c) cell storage (d) cell transport.
5. P_{fr} converts to P_r during (a) long days (b) days (c) short days (d) nights.
6. Plant growth responses specifically involve (a) cell differentiation (b) cell maturation (c) cell elongation (d) cell secretions.
7. Seedless fruits can be produced by the application of auxin or (a) cytokinins (b) gibberellins (c) ethylene (d) oligosaccharin.
8. A ripe avocado will cause other avocados to ripen through the release of (a) auxin (b) ethylene (c) abscisic acid (d) gibberellin.
9. Charles and Francis Darwin observed that phototropism caused stem curvature in (a) the apical meristem (b) the region of cellular elongation (c) the tip of the coleoptile (d) the region of cellular differentiation.
10. Abscission zones are areas where (a) leaves fall off stems (b) plants sense day length (c) abscisic acid is manufactured (d) cuttings are produced.
11. Explain the mechanism for apical dominance.
12. Describe bolting and identify what substance causes it.
13. List three effects of oligosaccharins.
14. Define *critical length,* and explain how it functions in photoperiodism.
15. How might a fruit grower use ethylene on crops?
16. What is an adaptive advantage of the leaf fall, or abscission, process?
17. Explain how a coiling thigmotropism

Vocabulary

1. The words relate to plant responses to touch, gravity, and chemicals, respectively.
2. A hormone is also called a plant growth regulator; a target tissue is the tissue in which a hormone produces its effect.
3. Vernalization is an adaptation in which a seed or a plant must be exposed to cold before germinating or flowering; dormancy is an adaptation in which a seed or a plant undergoes a period of reduced metabolism before germinating or growing; photoperiodism is an adaptation of certain plants that flower in response to specific day lengths.
4. A negative tropism is a response away from the direction of a stimulus; a positive tropism is a response toward the direction of a stimulus; a nastic movement is a response that is independent of the direction of the stimulus.
5. A critical length is a day length above or below which a specific plant will flower. Long-day plants flower when days are longer than their species' critical length, and short-day plants flower when days are shorter than their species' critical length.

Review

1. b
2. a
3. d
4. b
5. d
6. c
7. b
8. b
9. b
10. a

11. Auxin produced by the shoot tip inhibits growth of buds beneath the shoot tip. This results in upward growth at the top of the plant, with little growth in branches directly under the shoot tip.

12. Bolting is a process in which the length of the internodes increases as a result of the presence of gibberellin.

13. Oligosaccharins influence growth, development, and tissue repair. They may also be involved in defense against disease.
14. The critical length is the period of daylight above or below which a photoperiodic plant species will flower. Photoperiodic plants flower in response to days longer or shorter than their critical lengths.

15. Ethylene can be used to ripen fruits that are harvested before they are ripe.
16. The abscission process allows the plant to preserve nutrients by transporting them from the leaves into the stem for storage before the leaves fall.
17. By coiling around nearby objects as it grows, a plant may continue to grow upward and keep a maximum of its surface exposed to the sun.

could result in greater absorption of sunlight for photosynthesis.

18. Name two factors that affect the influence a hormone will have.
19. Why is 2,4-D effective as a weed killer in cornfields?
20. How are hydrotropism and chemotropism similar? How are they different?

Critical Thinking

1. You are walking along a highway that is lined with broadleaf weeds. The tips of these weeds are long, pale, and spindly, with twisted stems and long internodes between leaves. What is the most probable cause of this unusual appearance?
2. How does a gaseous hormone like ethylene give a plant an adaptive advantage?
3. Why is it important that weed killers such as 2,4-D not get into the earth's groundwater supplies, lakes, and rivers?
4. Some plants track the sun to maximize photosynthesis. Look at the picture of the sunflowers. The stems of these plants are not phototropic. What part of the plant is?
5. The seasonal loss of leaves by trees and shrubs serves the adaptive advantage of conserving nutrients. Can you think of another adaptive advantage that loss of leaves would provide?

6. The growth of most deciduous trees in the northern United States and Canada, where winters are severe, is strictly regulated by day length. That is, temperature plays no part in the regulation of their yearly growing cycle. Give a reason why it is important that these plants not have their growing cycle determined by temperature.

Extension

1. Read the article by R. Cowen entitled "Plant's Genetic Master Switch Subverted" in *Science News*, August 11, 1990, p. 86. Give an oral report in which you explain abscisic acid's role in plant protection. How might genetic engineering enhance abscisic acid's influence on plant development?
2. Plant five or six seeds of different species of plants in pots of soil. Allow them to sprout and grow until the plants are about 13 cm tall. Tip the pots on their sides and observe how long it takes the plants to point upward again. Report your findings.
3. Plant five or six beans in each of four pots of soil, and place the pots as follows: one in total darkness, one in natural daylight near a window, one in only the light of a 100-watt incandescent light bulb, and one in the light of a fluorescent lamp, preferably one with a warm light. Make a lab report in which you describe the number and type of plants used, the lights used, and the results. Incandescent bulbs are poor in blue light, whereas the light of a warm fluorescent lamp is more like daylight, since it has both red and blue light. What do your results tell you about the ability of plants to distinguish red from blue light and about the effect of light on their growth?

18. The influence of a hormone is affected by its degree of concentration and by the target tissue it reaches.
19. The weed killer 2,4-D kills dicots but does not harm monocots, such as corn.
20. Hydrotropism and chemotropism are both chemical responses. However, chemotropism occurs between parts of the same plant, whereas hydrotropism is the response of a plant part to environmental water.

Critical Thinking

1. The plants near the road have probably been sprayed with a weed killer such as 2,4-D.
2. The hormone can be transported to nearby plants by air currents and thus acts as a chemical messenger within a population.
3. Because groundwater is used for irrigation, water polluted with 2,4-D could harm dicots.
4. The base of the leaves may be phototropic due to the distribution of auxins.
5. It provides a shade-free environment for new leaves that emerge in spring.
6. If the trees were sensitive to temperature, they might start to grow after a brief warm spell in early spring. If this were followed by a severe cold spell, the trees would die.

Extension

1. The report should mention that abscisic acid (ABA) triggers a series of responses that help plants resist drought and disease. ABA may someday be used as a "master switch" to activate certain genes to produce proteins that are useful to genetic engineers.
2. Tape the tilted pots to the countertop.
3. Make sure that students carefully control all other variables.

Discussion

Guide the discussion by posing the following questions.

1. Explain why transgenic food crops or other genetically engineered organisms should or should not be patented. *(Some students may consider the years of research, work, and money that developers invest in creating new food crops or other organisms. Others may consider that the cost of patented varieties may put poor farmers at a disadvantage.)*

2. What benefits and dangers do you foresee from the use of genetically engineered organisms? *(Students will give varied answers. Encourage them to consider how genetically engineered organisms, such as mice with human immune systems, might help researchers develop new medicines. Ask students to suggest precautions for any dangers they foresee.)*

3. Why do you think that modern farmers have often chosen to give up their traditional crops in favor of genetically uniform varieties? *(Demand is high for food crops that are uniform in certain traits, such as high yield and quality of the crop. Marketing campaigns by seed companies also influence farmers' choices.)*

4. How are gene banks a protection against a shrinking gene pool? *(They act as a genetic reserve, preserving the diversity of genetic possibilities.)*

5. Identify some difficulties of maintaining gene banks. *(Specimens must be rejuvenated every few years, so space and equipment are required to raise seedlings. Special storage is needed to keep seeds cool and dry, so a flood or air-conditioner failure does not ruin an entire store. Some seed companies may refuse to contribute seeds that required a great deal of research and money to develop.)*

Intra-Science

How the Sciences Work Together

The Question in Biology: *Will Plant Breeding Lead to Hunger?*

In 1970 a single fungus wiped out 15 to 20 percent of the total corn crop in the United States. Some states lost 50 percent or more of their corn to *Helminthosporium maydis*, a fungus that causes a corn blight. Why was the crop failure so widespread?

Over thousands of years, humans have bred crops for certain desired traits, such as high yield and size, shape, and color of corn kernels. To ensure uniformity of these traits throughout an entire corn variety, inbreeding has been necessary. At the time of the 1970 crop epidemic, most of the corn grown in the United States was identical in many ways. Market demands for a corn crop with consistent traits had encouraged farmers to plant genetically uniform plants. Genetic uniformity, however, means that a single strain of pathogen, such as *H. maydis*, can destroy an entire crop of a uniform variety of corn.

After the corn epidemic, plant breeders quickly supplied a different variety of seed corn to farmers. Breeders of other crops have since begun efforts to increase genetic diversity among their food crops. However, many U.S. food crops still come from a very limited pool of genetic material. In 1903, for example, U.S. farmers grew 307 varieties of sweet corn. Today they grow only about 12 varieties. Only two varieties of peas occupy 96 percent of the land planted with that crop. Only one variety of yams comprises 69 percent of the entire U.S. yam crop.

If there were worldwide reliance on only one or a few varieties of each food crop, disease or drought could wipe out entire crops around the globe and lead to worldwide famine. As a result of the 1970 corn epidemic, biologists suggest that developing nations would be wise to preserve their indigenous varieties of food crops.

Traditionally, most farmers in developing nations have raised crops that originated in their country or region. These indigenous crops, called landraces, are well adapted to the climate of their region. The genetic diversity of their seeds is a valuable gene pool, which serves as a hedge against genetic uniformity, crop failure, and possible famine. If farmers in developing nations abandon their indigenous crops to grow inbred varieties, the genetic diversity of the gene pool for food crops could be lost forever.

The Connection to Plant Breeding

Whenever uniform crops have been threatened, researchers have often found the disease-resistant varieties they needed among the landraces of developing nations. However, the landraces of some inbred crops have already become extinct. As a

Connections to Other Disciplines

Social Sciences Have students research the history of the U.S. Plant Patent Act of 1930 and the Plant Variety Protection Act of 1970, and describe how other nations are dealing with the question of granting patents for living things.

Government Have students consider the role of government in regulating the environmental releases of transgenic plants. Ask students to role-play a government official, an environmentalist, and a farmer, and have them present each one's point of view on the action the government has taken.

result, genetic engineers hope to find as many other landraces as possible before they also become extinct. Then the genes for drought or disease resistance could be saved.

To preserve landraces, some organizations, such as the Worldwide Fund for Nature, have collected half a million seed samples and stored them in seed banks around the world. In these banks—sometimes just a climate-controlled room—the seeds are kept in bottles, foil packets, or even small paper bags, waiting to be planted.

■ *What are some of the traits of landraces that might be beneficial to inbred varieties of crops?*

The Connection to Agriculture

After transferring the gene for disease or drought resistance from a landrace to an inbred variety, some plant breeders obtain a legal patent for the resulting transgenic, or genetically engineered, plant. Such a patent requires anyone who wishes to raise the patented transgenic plant to pay a fee, or royalty, to the plant breeder. Developing countries, however, object to paying for genetic material originating from their own landraces, and have begun demanding compensation for their contribution to genetically engineered food plants.

■ *Do you think developing nations should receive a share of the profits obtained from crops developed from their landraces? Why or why not?*

The Connection to Other Sciences

Some people are concerned that a transgenic food crop may endanger its environment. They fear that a transgenic organism could pass its genes for herbicide resistance, for example, to a weed. The transgenic weed might become a superweed that could not be killed by current chemical methods, creating the need to spread new, more deadly chemicals on the land.

Some experts claim that the genetic differences between a transgenic food crop and a weed prohibit cross-pollination. However, other experts assert that the genes for herbicide resistance could be passed, for example, through a distant relative to both the food crop and the weed. Experimental data are inconclusive.

Many nations have established safety measures for transgenic experimentation. In the United States, possible dangers to the environment are examined in special field trials, or environmental releases. (However, Margaret Mellon of the National Wildlife Federation has criticized the USDA for failing to provide guidelines for safe field-testing procedures.) The European Economic Community intends to issue controls on transgenic plants. In 1990 India created a regulatory agency for transgenic organisms. Both the Philippines and Mexico have prepared guidelines governing the use and release of transgenic organisms.

While the debate continues, transgenic crops may already be on the shelves of your local supermarket. Transgenic rice, tomatoes, or other foods may be common items in your diet by 1995.

■ *What are the benefits of safety guidelines in the farming of transgenic crops?*

The Connection to Careers

Preserving the genetic diversity and heritage of food crops will require more than the efforts of geneticists and botanists. Diplomats and other negotiators will play an important role in balancing the needs and goals of industrialized nations with the need and goals of developing nations. Attorneys, paralegals, and other legal specialists may be needed to settle patent disputes. Meteorologists and geologists can analyze climate patterns, which may suggest the optimum planting time for drought-resistant varieties of crops. For more information about related careers in the biological sciences, turn to page 842.

6. Wild relatives of crops, such as strawberries, can often be found on government land that is leased for a specific purpose, such as logging. What are some advantages and disadvantages of reserving land for a single purpose? *(Students should consider the economic impact of land use. If the land were solely reserved for wild crops, the jobs and products from the logging industry would be lost. Yet, if the gene pool from the wild variety of a food crop becomes extinct, the survival of the entire food crop could be threatened if the cultivated variety became diseased or destroyed.)*

7. What other uses can you predict for transgenic plants? *(Urge students to consider nonfood applications. Scientists have already altered tobacco plants, potatoes, and rapeseed with human genes to produce antibodies, blood proteins, and painkillers.)*

Answers to

Plant Breeding Some of the beneficial traits that landraces might contribute are faster maturation time and resistance to pests, drought, diseases, and variations in temperature.

Agriculture Urge students to consider the arguments of both sides. While plant breeders may invest much time, work, and money in developing new crops, plant breeders would not have the genetic material they need to engineer the new crops if the landraces were not available.

Other Sciences Safety guidelines could help protect the environment from genetic changes that might destroy existing species, easing the fears some people have about farming transgenic crops.

Enrichment

Many residential areas are built on what was once farmland, and many farmers today are selling their land to home developers. Have students research the agricultural past or present of their community. Ask small groups of students to investigate the pros and cons of dwindling farmland. Have student share their research during class discussion.

Unit 7 Invertebrates

Chapters

Unit Overview

Unit 7 begins the study of the Kingdom Animalia by examining invertebrates. Chapter 29 describes general characteristics of invertebrates and introduces the Phyla Porifera and Cnidaria. In Chapter 30 students compare the Phyla Platyhelminthes, Nematoda, and Rotifera. Chapter 31 describes two related phyla, Mollusca and Annelida. Chapter 32 introduces students to the arthropods, and Chapter 33 studies insects. In Chapter 34 students learn about the echinoderms. Chapter 35 discusses evolutionary trends in invertebrates by comparing morphology and development patterns.

Issues in Biology

Coral reefs form in shallow, nutrient-poor waters of tropical seas. The coral formations provide habitats for hundreds of fish and invertebrate species. They also attract people interested in diving, fishing, and shell collecting. In many places, coral reefs have been made into parks such as the Key Largo National Marine Sanctuary along the Florida keys.

The hard, rocky appearance of a coral reef is deceptive. Coral is actually very fragile, and the tiny coral polyps can survive only under certain narrow conditions. At the Key Largo sanctuary, careless boaters have destroyed large sections of reef, and divers have killed coral polyps by standing on them. Nearly 2 million tourists also add to pollution of the waters each year. Challenge students to debate the issue of protection of coral reefs versus their use for recreation.

Research in Progress

Much media attention has been given the so-called "killer" bees. This aggressive, easily agitated African species was accidentally introduced into southern Brazil in 1956. Since then the African honeybees have made their way some 11,000 km northward to the U.S. border. Their stings have killed several hundred people.

U.S. scientists have been studying the African honeybee to determine its threat to the beekeeping industry and the public in general. Many researchers have examined interbreeding between the African honeybee and more docile local bees. To date, evidence indicates that little interbreeding has actually gone on and that local bees are having trouble competing genetically. Studies of the African honeybee in the temperate climate of North America have led scientists to think their northward spread will be halted by cold temperatures.

Interdisciplinary Activity

Economics Zebra mussels cost the Great Lakes region of North America millions of dollars. Unknown in North America until 1988, these tiny bivalves reproduce at such a rapid rate that their numbers threaten the region's water supply systems and have already caused the temporary shutdown of local manufacturing plants. These mussels also threaten the future of sportfishing in the region. Have students research and write a report on damages and financial losses due to zebra mussels. Encourage students to identify efforts being taken to halt this destruction.

Resources

Chapter	Print: For the Teacher	Print: For the Student	Audiovisual/Software
29	■ Alice Gilbreath, *The Great Barrier Reef: A Treasure in the Sea*, Dillon, 1986.	■ Lucy Bunkley-Williams and Ernest H. Williams, Jr., "Global Assault on Coral Reefs," *Natural History*, April 1990, 46–54.	■ *City of Coral* (Nova). Video, 57 min. Time-Life, 1986. ■ *Simple Multicellular Animals: Sponges, Coelenterates, and Flatworms*. Film, 20 min. Teacher's guide. Benchmark, 1985.
30	■ Christopher Bryant and Carolyn Behm, *Biochemical Adaptation in Parasites*, Chapman and Hall, 1989.	■ Julie Ann Miller, "Long-Lived Worms," *BioScience*, June 1990, 432.	■ *Flatworms (Platyhelminthes)*. Film, 16 min. Encyclopædia Britannica. ■ *Worms: Flat, Round, and Segmented*. Film, 15 min. Coronet.
31	■ Robert A. Hadeen, *The Oyster: The Life and Lore of the Celebrated Bivalve*, Tidewater, 1986.	■ Clarence V. Reynolds, "Invasion of the Zebra Mussels," *Discover*, January 1991, 44.	■ *The Anatomy of the Freshwater Mussel*. Video, 13 min. Teacher's manual and ancillaries. Carolina Biological. ■ *Mollusks: The Mussel Respiration and Digestion*. Film, 7 min. Film guide. Benchmark, 1983.
32	■ Frederick R. Schram, *Crustacea*, Oxford University Press, 1986.	■ Elizabeth Pennisi, "Grasshoppers Change Coats to Beat the Heat," *Science News*, August 24, 1991, 119.	■ *The Anatomy of the Crayfish*. Video, 19 min. Teacher's manual and ancillaries. Carolina Biological. ■ *The Joint-Legged Animal: Arthropods*. Film, 19 min. Encyclopædia Britannica.
33	■ Wolf Engels, ed., *Social Insects*, Springer-Verlag, 1990. ■ John Horgan, "Stinging Criticism," *Scientific American*, November 1990, 29–32.	■ Bernd Heinrich, "The Antifreeze of Bees," *Natural History*, July 1990, 52–59.	■ *Discover Entomology*. Film or video, 15 min. Entomological Society, 1987.
34	■ Robert D. Barnes, *Invertebrate Zoology*, 5th ed., Saunders College/Holt, Rinehart and Winston, 1987.	■ S. Hart, "Crown-of-Thorns No Johnny-Come-Lately," *Science News*, August 26, 1989, 133.	■ *Echinoderms: Sea Stars and Their Relatives*. Film, 17 min. Encyclopædia Britannica.
35	■ Richard C. Brusca and Gary J. Brusca, *Invertebrates*, Sinauer Associates, 1990.	■ William Stolzenburg, "When Life Got Hard," *Science News*, August 25, 1990, 120–123.	■ *Biovideo: Introduction to Invertebrates*. Video, 30 min. Teacher's manual. Cabisco Video/BBC.

Science in Action Video Series

In teaching Unit 7, you may wish to use the videotape *Alternatives to Dissection: The Earthworm and the Frog,* from the Science in Action Video Series. The behavior, internal anatomy and external anatomy of each animal are shown through close-up photography and graphic animation.

Introducing the Unit

The discussion of evolution and classification in Unit 4 provides a background for the taxonomic study of invertebrates. The discussion of heterotrophic organisms in Unit 5 as well as the descriptions of plant adaptation in Unit 6 give students insight into how body structure relates to its function in invertebrates. Ask the following questions to introduce the unit on invertebrates.

1. To which taxonomic kingdom do invertebrates belong? *(Kingdom Animalia)*
2. Based on what you have learned about plants, what do you infer is the major difference between plants and animals? *(Plants are multicellular, autotrophic organisms, while animals are multicellular, heterotrophic organisms.)*
3. How do you think that animals differ from protozoa? *(Animals are multicellular and exhibit specialization, while protozoa are unicellular or colonial and seldom exhibit specialization.)*
4. Considering what you have learned about the evolution of plants, what might be some adaptations of animals to life on land? *(A protective covering similar to a cuticle, a means for absorbing oxygen from air, a method of reproduction that does not require water)*
5. Which do you think adapted to life on land first, plants or animals? Explain. *(Plants probably adapted to life on land first, since they are autotrophic. After plants had become established on land, animals had a source of food.)*

Unit 7 Invertebrates

Chapters

"We should venture on the study of every kind of animal without distaste; for each and all will reveal to us something natural and something beautiful."
Aristotle

If you were asked to list all the animals you could think of in one minute, your list would probably include very few invertebrates, animals without backbones. You may be surprised to learn, then, that about 97 percent of all animal species are invertebrates. Look at the illustrations on these two pages to get a feeling for the great diversity of this group. In this unit you will learn about each of the major phyla of invertebrates and see the myriad ways in which these animals have adapted to almost every environment on earth.

Shrimp on sea anemone

Golden beetle, *Plusiotis resplendens*, from Costa Rica

Using the Opening Quotation

Take a poll to see what animals students think are cute and cuddly and what animals they think are ugly and disgusting. Write students' responses on the board. Then have them identify vertebrates and invertebrates on the list. Have a volunteer read the opening quotation. Then ask students how their feelings or attitudes about invertebrates relate to the quotation. *(Students should conclude that even if they find some organisms unappealing, nevertheless there are things to be learned from them.)* Encourage students to think of examples of useful knowledge that has been obtained through the study of invertebrates. *(For example, much has been learned about genetics through the use of fruit flies.)*

Polychaete

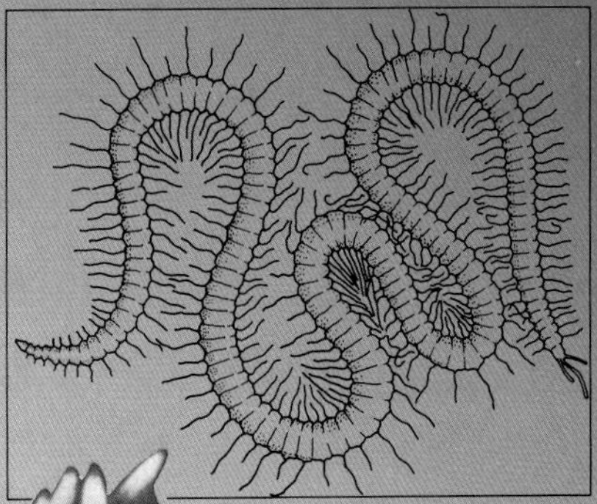

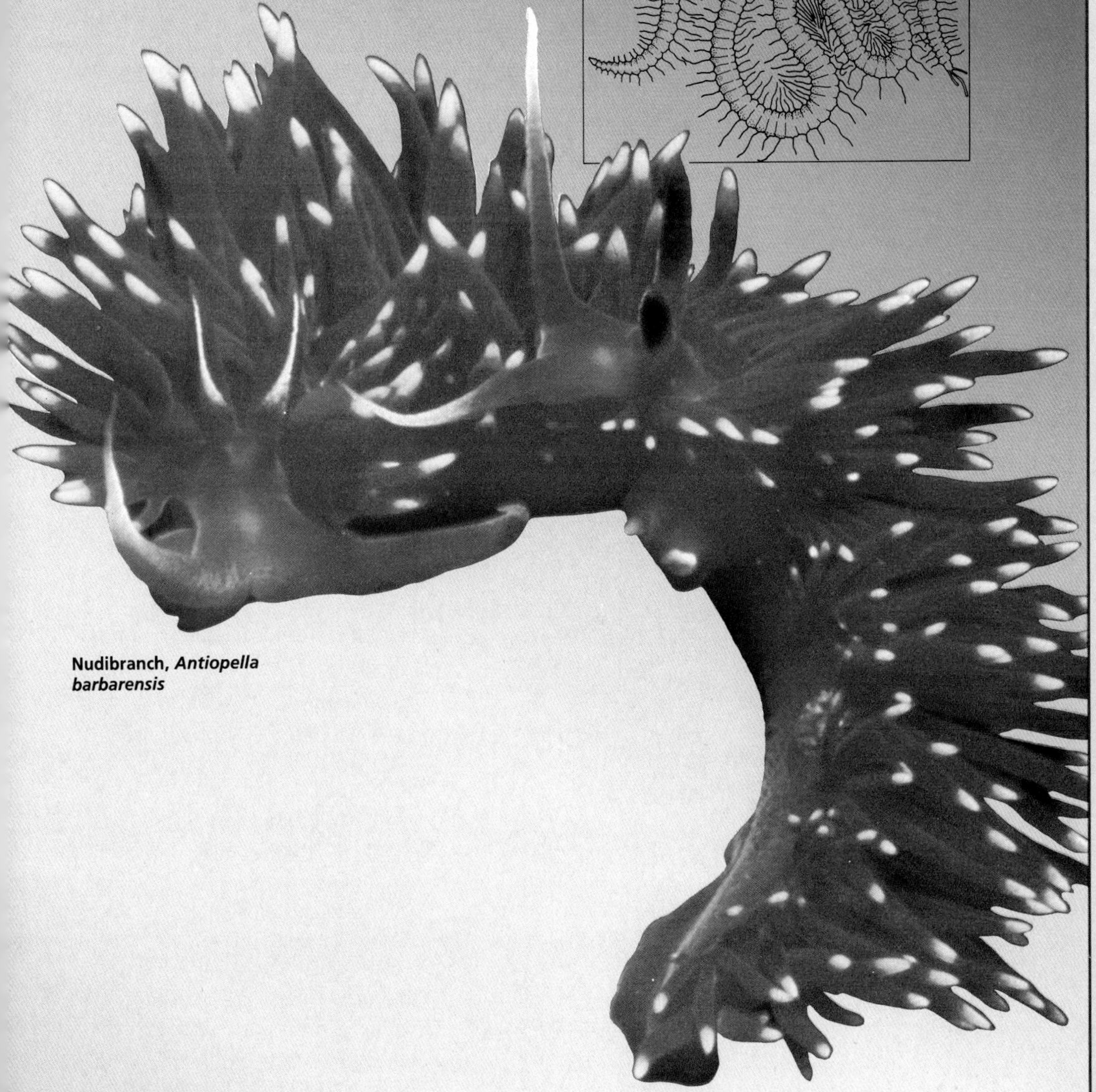

Nudibranch, *Antiopella barbarensis*

Understanding the Visuals

Ask students to study the four organisms shown on pp. 434–435 and note similarities among them. *(Students might note that all four organisms are multicellular and have some means of movement. All are heterotrophs.)* Ask students to infer what characteristic these organisms have in common to be classified as invertebrates. *(They lack a backbone.)* Encourage students to identify significant structures on each organism and to infer from these structures the environment in which the organism lives. *(Shrimp, marine environment; golden beetle, land; nudibranch, ocean floor; polychaete, ocean floor)*

Unit Themes

Evolution Comparative studies of invertebrate development and anatomy indicate evolutionary relationships among invertebrates (Chapter 35). The larval stages of mollusks and annelids (Chapter 31) suggest that they have a common ancestor as do the larvae of echinoderms (Chapter 34) and lower chordates. The morphological diversity among members of the various invertebrate phyla indicates evolution in different environments.

Patterns of Change The life cycles of invertebrates are examples of cyclic change. The life cycles of both jellyfish (Chapter 29) and crinoids (Chapter 34) include a sessile form and free-swimming form. The life cycles of insects (Chapter 33) exhibit either incomplete or complete metamorphosis.

Scale and Structure Invertebrate structures are related to their functions. Structures such as cnidarian tentacles (Chapter 29) and echinoderm tube feet (Chapter 34) are vital to food getting. Hard body parts, such as mollusk shells (Chapter 31) and arthropod exoskeletons (Chapter 32), serve to support and protect.

Systems and Interactions Invertebrate phylogeny (Chapter 35) is characterized by increasingly complex internal organization. More complex invertebrates have organs and organ systems to carry out body processes. Invertebrates interact with their environment and other organisms. Many types of flatworms and roundworms (Chapter 30) live as parasites in other organisms. Insects (Chapter 33) are important as pollinators of flowering plants, but they also destroy many crops.

Chapter 29 Sponges and Cnidarians

Chapter Overview

Chapter 29 examines the basic characteristics of invertebrates and focuses on two phyla, Porifera and Cnidaria. Section 29.1 discusses how patterns of symmetry and development as well as multicellular organization are important in classification. Section 29.2 features the sponges, and Section 29.3 discusses the cnidarians. Both sections emphasize how body structure is related to body function.

Chapter Planning Chart

B	S	A	Sections and Subsections	Page	Features	Page	Resources
•	•	•	**29.1 Invertebrates**				
			Patterns of Symmetry	437	Writing About Biology	440	Videodiscs
			Multicellular Organization	438	Section Review	439	Blackline Master 58
			Patterns of Development	438			Blackline Master 59
			Classification and Evolution	439			Overhead Transparency T29
							Section Reviews Worksheet
•	•	•	**29.2 Porifera**				
			Structure and Function	441	Section Review	443	Videodiscs
			Classification	443			Section Reviews Worksheet
•	•	•	**29.3 Cnidaria**				
			Structure, Function, and Classification	444	Biology in Process	444	Videodiscs
			Hydrozoa	446	Think	448	Blackline Master 60
			Scyphozoa	447	Laboratory	449	Process Skills: Cnidarians
			Anthozoa	448	Section Review	448	Laboratories: Hydra
							Section Reviews Worksheet
			End of Chapter Activities				
					Chapter Review	450	Vocabulary Skills
							Chapter Test
							Computer Test Generator

B *The Basic Level curriculum presents the most fundamental knowledge offered in the course.*
S *The Standard Level curriculum is designed for the average student who is able to master most topics.*
A *The Advanced Level curriculum includes suggestions for teaching the most academically able students.*

Cooperative Learning

Group Activity: Sponges and Cnidarians

- **Group Size:** *2 students*
- **Outcome:** *Students will compare structures and functions of sponges or cnidarians.*
- **Individual Accountability:** *Each group member will develop one area of a concept map.*
- **Positive Interdependence:** *Each group will develop a concept map that illustrates the relationship between structure and functions either in sponges or in cnidarians.*

Divide the class into pairs. Assign Porifera to half the groups and Cnidaria to the other half. Ask one student in each group to develop a concept map showing structural characteristics of the group's phylum. Have a second student map reproduction, digestion, and feeding characteristics of the group's phylum.

After completing their individual concept maps, each student will explain his or her map to the other student in the group. Then have each group compile the individual maps to produce one map that connects the appropriate structural characteristics with the functions to which they are related. Then have a Porifera group and a Cnidaria group pair explain their maps to each other. An example of a completed concept map is shown below.

Concept Map

The following is one possible solution to the concept mapping activity in Cooperative Learning above.

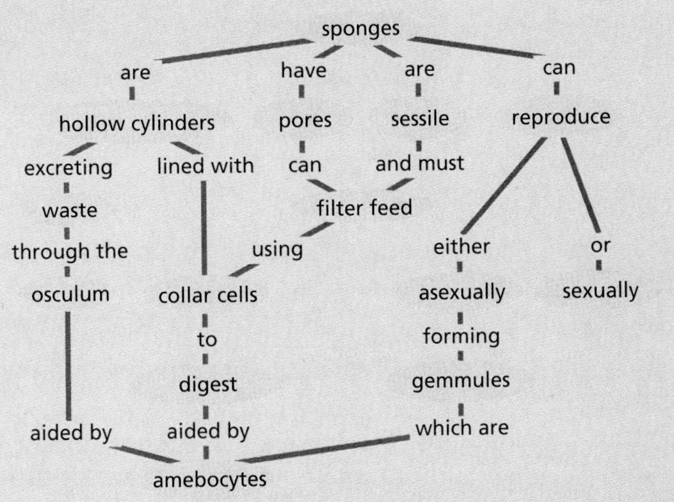

Laboratory Preparation

Overview *(See p. 449.)*

In this lab exercise, students observe a sit-and-wait predator at work. Hydras attach their basal disks to pond weeds or to materials at the bottom of slow-moving bodies of water and use their nematocysts, a cnidarian trademark, to paralyze their prey. A hydra must be prepared for prey that may approach from any direction. Vibrations and chemicals in the water trigger the hydra's feeding behavior. After capturing its prey, the hydra elongates, its mouth expands, and it sways back and forth. If threatened, a hydra protects itself by contracting. A hydra also can move in search of food if necessary.

Preparation

Hydras are easily grown in a culture dish containing a 5-cm sprig of *Elodea* and pasteurized spring water. (To pasteurize spring water, heat 12 to 16 L spring water to 65°C for 15 minutes.) You may also use filtered, sterile pond water. Do not feed hydras for 1 to 2 days before students are to perform this lab.

To develop a brine shrimp culture, sprinkle brine shrimp eggs (available from pet stores) on the surface of a 4% solution of sodium chloride. Larvae will hatch in 18 to 24 hours. Remove larvae with a dropper or a kitchen bulb baster and rinse in a beaker of distilled water to remove any trace of salt just before feeding to the hydras.

Teaching Tips

Suggest that students make sketches as they record their observations.

Demonstrate to students how to pick up organisms with droppers.

If necessary, clarify for students that "feeding behavior" means the observable responses of firing nematocysts and drawing in food. Explain that sensory cells detect specific stimuli, and then a simple nerve net transmits this information to cells that trigger movement.

Some students may have uncooperative hydras that do not demonstrate expected behaviors; encourage students to share information and look at each others' specimens.

Safety

Impress on your students the need for humane treatment of hydras.

Chapter Themes

Evolution Organisms evolve over time in response to environmental pressures and opportunities. Emphasize this theme as you discuss cephalization, symmetry, and the specialized cells, tissues, and organs of invertebrates. Point out that the sponges represent a clear transition from unicellularity to multicellularity.

Scale and Structure Highlight the importance of structure in the behaviors of sponges and cnidarians. Compare feeding and reproductive systems of sponges and cnidarians, and stress the relationship between functions of these systems and structures that carry them out.

Chapter Motivating Activity

Show students a photograph or an illustration of fossils of the Burgess shale formation. (Stephen Jay Gould's book *Wonderful Life* is a good source.) Explain that the Burgess shale formation, a rich fossil deposit in the Canadian Rockies dated at about 570 million years, is a rare and lucky find that includes soft-bodied animals, which rarely fossilize, as well as representatives from all of today's major animal phyla. Guide students in observing and discussing the invertebrates pictured (mollusks, cnidarians, sponges, arthropods, and annelids as well as unfamiliar types that are now extinct). Ask students what the presence in the fossil deposit of the familiar-looking animals suggests. *(That these animals have a long evolutionary history)*

Chapter 29 Sponges and Cnidarians

Introduction

The structure of any organism—from the simplest moneran to the most complex animal—is related to its way of life and its function in its environment. In this chapter, you will first learn about some basic aspects of invertebrates. Then you will study the relationships between structure and function in two of the less complex phyla of animals.

Chapter Outline

29.1 Invertebrates
- *Patterns of Symmetry*
- *Multicellular Organization*
- *Patterns of Development*
- *Classification and Evolution*

29.2 Porifera
- *Structure and Function*
- *Classification*

29.3 Cnidaria
- *Structure, Function, and Classification*
- *Hydrozoa*
- *Scyphozoa*
- *Anthozoa*

Chapter Concept

As you read, look for examples of how body structure is related to feeding, reproduction, and other functions.

Tube coral and encrusting sponge. Inset: Sea nettle jellyfish.

Understanding the Visuals

Tell students to describe traits such as color and shape of the animals pictured. List the traits on the board. *(Sample answers: reddish, bluish-white, translucent; tubular, shapeless, funnel-like.)* Ask students why some animals such as sponges and jellyfish might be confused with plants. *(They look like plants and do not have the overall form commonly associated with animals.)* Encourage students to speculate about traits that are not necessarily obvious, such as texture and hardness. *(Accept reasonable answers; the coral is probably hard, the jellyfish jellylike, the sponges in between.)* Then ask students which animal appears most complex and why, based on the traits they have mentioned. *(Accept all reasonable answers.)*

29.1 Invertebrates

What do earthworms, butterflies, jellyfish, and giant squids have in common? About the only similarity you may note is that they are all animals. Nevertheless, these animals and about 97 percent of all other animal species are **invertebrates,** or animals without a backbone. Rather than sharing common characteristics, species of invertebrates share the common lack of a trait. Thus, it is not surprising that they are an extremely diverse group. They represent more than a dozen phyla and over a million species.

Section Objectives

- *Define* invertebrates, *and explain why they are such a diverse group.*
- *List three kinds of symmetry and give examples of each.*
- *State an advantage and a disadvantage of specialization in cells.*
- *Summarize the process of embryonic development.*

Patterns of Symmetry

Invertebrates exhibit a wide variety of shapes, which can provide clues to each one's particular way of life. One common way to identify animal shapes is by **symmetry,** or the arrangement of body parts around a point or central axis.

Some organisms, including amebas and many sponges, have no definite shape and so are called asymmetrical. Other simple organisms have **spherical symmetry**—that is, they are shaped like globes or spheres. The earliest ancestors of multicellular animals may have been hollow spheres of cells much like a colonial protozoan. This hollow body plan allows the cells to take in food and oxygen and give off wastes much more easily than if the organism were a solid ball of cells. This ability to exchange materials with the environment at any point along the organism's surface is beneficial to species that float in water.

Figure 29-1 illustrates the differences between radial symmetry and bilateral symmetry—the two types of symmetry most common among invertebrates. An organism that shows either of these types of symmetry has distinct ends. An imaginary line drawn from end to end through the center of the organism forms the longitudinal axis. An organism that shows **radial symmetry** can be divided into similar halves by any plane that passes through its longitudinal axis. In contrast, an animal with **bilateral symmetry** can be divided into similar halves by only one specific plane passing through the longitudinal axis. Thus, its left and right sides are mirror images of each other.

A radially symmetrical animal, such as a hydra, is basically cylindrical in shape. Such an animal has two different ends but no left or right side. Radial symmetry is most common in animals that move little if at all. They attach one end of their body to something stationary and feed with the unattached end.

Bilaterally symmetrical animals include worms, insects, spiders, and many other invertebrates. These animals have specialized front and rear ends and upper and lower surfaces. Biologists use the term **anterior** for the front end and the term **posterior** for the hind end. They refer to the top as the **dorsal** surface and the bottom as the **ventral** surface. Most bilaterally symmetrical ani-

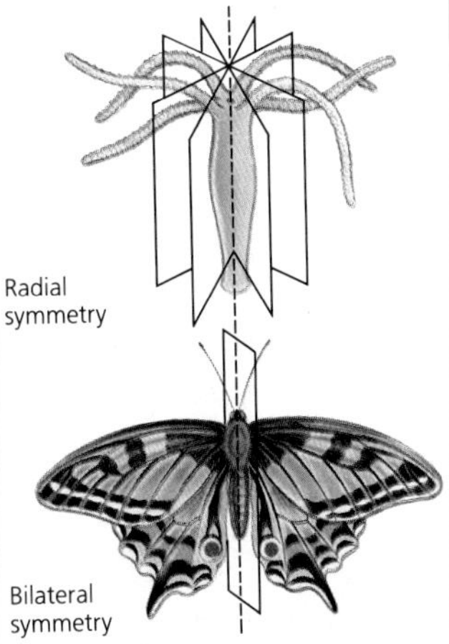

Figure 29-1 Top to bottom: A hydra and a butterfly show radial and bilateral symmetry, respectively.

Type of Invertebrate	Type of Symmetry	Body Plan (Shape)	Level of Organization
sponge	none apparent	hollow	multicellular with no organs
hydra	radial	cylindrical (polyp)	multicellular with organs
jellyfish	radial	cylindrical (medusa)	multicellular with organs

Graphic Organizer Use this table in Independent Practice on p. 439.

Lesson Plan

Section Focus

Invertebrates, animals without backbones, are diverse and have a wide variety of traits. They can exhibit spherical, radial, or bilateral symmetry. Multicellularity in invertebrates has resulted in organ specialization and thus greater complexity. Taxonomists use invertebrate body plans and development patterns to classify them and hypothesize about their evolution and their relationships.

Section Themes

This section underscores two themes: **Evolution** and **Scale and Structure.** Over time multicellular animals with specialized cells (sponges) evolved into animals with tissues (cnidarians). Development of germ layers within cells, formed by gastrulation, gave rise to tissues.

Motivating Activity

Show students specimens or pictures of diverse invertebrates (sea star, earthworm, lobster, spider, snail, cricket, moth, oyster). Ask students to identify different traits of each animal. Then have them identify a common animal trait these animals do not have. *(A backbone)* Use the examples in More Information on p. 438 to emphasize invertebrates' variety.

Teaching Strategies

Interpreting the Visuals Use Figure 29-1 on p. 437 to demonstrate radial and bilateral symmetry. Ask students to find examples of symmetry in geometric figures. *(Radial symmetry in regular polygons; bilateral symmetry by bisecting rectangles, isosceles triangles, and so on)*
■ *See* Blackline Master *58.*

Videodiscs
■ *2355–2414, Invertebrate Examples (s)*

Classifying Organisms Stress that all animals—invertebrates and vertebrates—have the following characteristics in common: they are all heterotrophic, eukaryotic, and multicellular. Ask students to recall from their own experiences or prior knowledge what other characteristics all animals have in common. *(They must digest food, carry on gas exchange, excrete waste, circulate nutrient and waste products to and from cells, coordinate their movements, protect themselves, reproduce, and go through similar embryonic development.)* Then have students group the invertebrates used in the Motivating Activity (p. 437) according to symmetry. *(For example, the sea star is radially symmetrical; the spider, cricket, lobster, and moth are bilaterally symmetrical.)*

Interpreting the Visuals Guide students through the phylogenetic tree pictured in Figure 29-3 on p. 439. Ask students which organisms—according to this tree—are more closely related, cnidaria and nematodes, or nematodes and rotifers. *(Nematodes and rotifers)* Encourage students to answer a similar question about other invertebrate phyla.

■ *See* **Overhead Transparency T29** *and* **Blackline Master 59.**

Guided Practice

Provide different groups of students an invertebrate such as a sponge or a sea star. Have them identify the symmetry of each invertebrate. *(For example, a sponge has no symmetry and a sea star shows pentaradial symmetry.)*

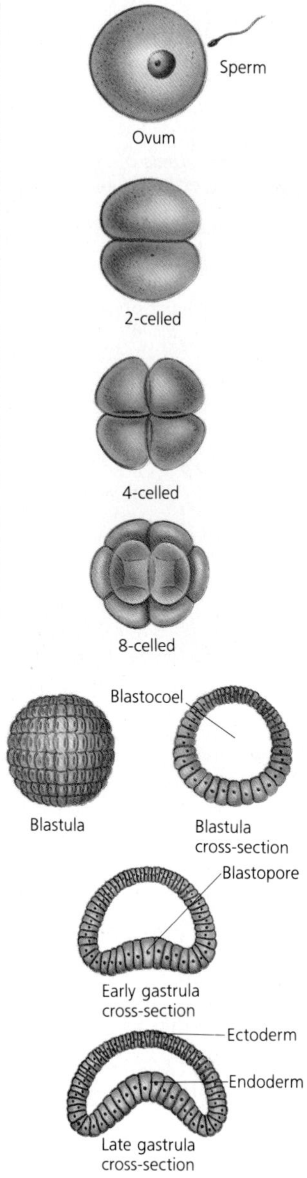

Figure 29-2 This diagram shows early cell division leading to gastrulation.

mals have nerve tissue and sensory organs concentrated in the anterior end. This adaptation, called **cephalization** *(SEFF-uh-luh-ZAY-shun)*, allows their sensory organs to enter a new environment first and provide information about it.

Multicellular Organization

The structural characteristics of invertebrates suggest that they were probably the first multicellular animals, or **metazoans,** to evolve from the single-celled protozoans. Without this essential first step, the enormous variety of shapes and sizes in the animal kingdom may not have evolved as we see them today. Single-celled organisms can grow only so large and so complex. You may recall from Chapter 5 that the size of a cell is limited by the ratio of its surface area to its volume. This ratio must be high enough to allow food and oxygen to enter the cell and wastes to get out. As a cell grows, its volume increases faster than its surface area. Eventually it grows so large that food cannot enter fast enough to support its activities, and wastes begin to accumulate. For this reason, the cell must either divide or die.

One of the advantages of multicellular life is **specialization,** the adaptation of a cell for a particular function. Just as a contractor makes use of carpenters, electricians, and plumbers to build a house, a multicellular organism makes use of specialized cells that perform particular functions, such as digesting food or reproducing. Specialization has enabled metazoans to evolve and adapt to many environments. However, organisms pay a price for the advantages of specialization. Unlike single-celled organisms, specialized cells cannot survive on their own. They are no longer independent but rather interdependent.

Patterns of Development

The body plan and specialized structures of an animal begin to arise early in its development. In sexual reproduction, development begins with a fertilized egg, or **zygote.** The zygote divides and forms an **embryo,** the name given to an organism in its earliest stages of development. In the embryo, successive divisions produce 2 cells, then 4, 8, 16, 32, and so on. Figure 29-2 shows the development of a sea urchin as an example of successive divisions. During early division the embryo does not grow much in size but simply splits into smaller and smaller cells. Soon a hollow sphere of cells called the **blastula** *(BLAST-choo-la)* forms. This process is called blastulation.

As the blastula continues to develop, it changes shape. The cells at one point on the blastula move inward, forming a depression called the **blastopore.** Further infolding forms a cup-shaped embryo called a **gastrula.** You may think of the shape of the gastrula as similar to that of an underinflated basketball that you have pushed in on one side with your fist.

More Information

Diversity By definition, invertebrates are alike in only one way—the absence of a backbone. In other ways, they are extremely diverse. They come in a wide range of shapes and sizes. One of the largest invertebrates is a giant crab that can spread its claws to span 3 meters, while a rotifer's body may be only 0.04 millimeters long. While sponges have no true organs, most organ systems of the giant squid are as sophisticated as those of humans.

Invertebrates flourish in every environment. In every cubic decimeter of the floor of a forest there may live thousands of invertebrates representing more than a hundred different species. In fact, one class of invertebrates, the insects, accounts for more species than the rest of the animal kingdom combined.

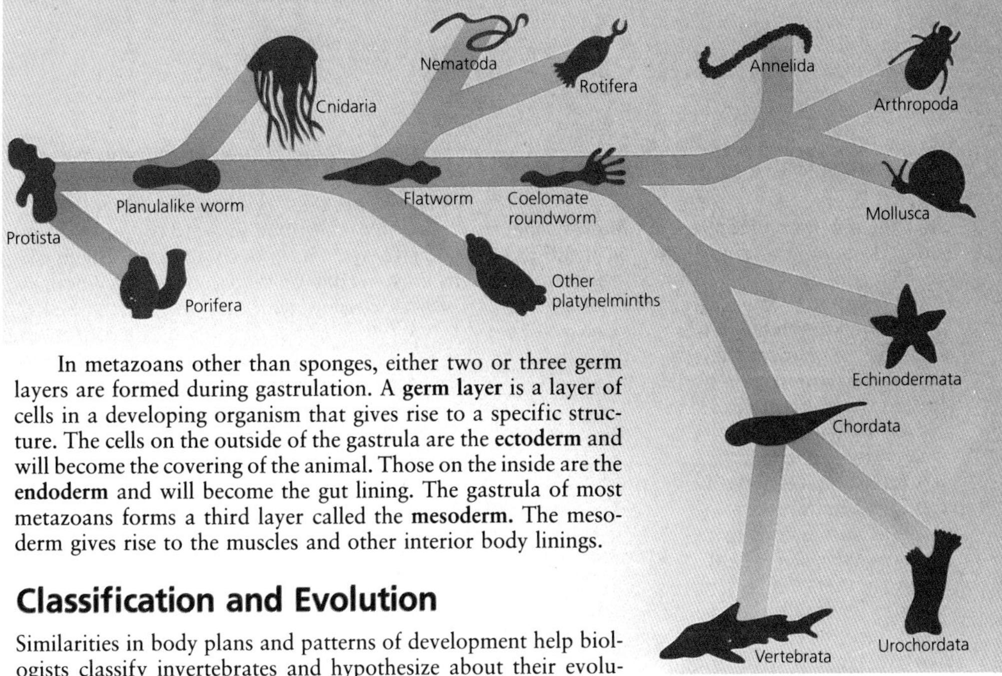

In metazoans other than sponges, either two or three germ layers are formed during gastrulation. A **germ layer** is a layer of cells in a developing organism that gives rise to a specific structure. The cells on the outside of the gastrula are the **ectoderm** and will become the covering of the animal. Those on the inside are the **endoderm** and will become the gut lining. The gastrula of most metazoans forms a third layer called the **mesoderm.** The mesoderm gives rise to the muscles and other interior body linings.

Classification and Evolution

Similarities in body plans and patterns of development help biologists classify invertebrates and hypothesize about their evolutionary history. The early fossil record of invertebrate evolution is fragmentary, and so biologists rely mainly on studies of modern species to develop family tree diagrams like the one in Figure 29-3.

In this chapter you will study two of the less complex invertebrate phyla—Porifera and Cnidaria. Porifera, or sponges, have long fascinated scientists because they so clearly represent the transition from unicellular to multicellular life. They have no gastrula stage, exhibit less specialization of cells than most invertebrates, and have no true organs. Cnidaria, which includes jellyfish, have an endoderm and an ectoderm and have evolved a diversity of body forms and specialized cells. All live in water, mostly in the oceans where their ancestors originated.

Figure 29-3 This diagram shows probable evolutionary relationships among the various invertebrate phyla.

Section Review

1. Define *invertebrate.* Why is it not surprising that a group defined in this way includes a wide diversity of species?
2. Why is cell specialization important for invertebrates?
3. How do radial symmetry and bilateral symmetry differ?
4. What is the main advantage of cephalization?
5. Based on the fact that the development of sponges does not include a gastrula stage, would you expect to find endoderm and ectoderm in a sponge? Explain your answer.

Answers to Section Review

1. An invertebrate is an animal without a backbone. Invertebrates include a wide variety of species because by definition they lack only one trait, a backbone, and therefore may have many other dissimilar traits.
2. Specialized cells and structures permit adaptations to diverse environments.
3. A radially symmetrical organism can be divided into similar halves by any plane that passes through its longitudinal axis. A bilaterally symmetrical organism can be divided into similar halves by only one plane that passes through its longitudinal axis.
4. Cephalization allows an animal's sense organs to enter a new environment first and provide information about it.
5. No. Endoderm and ectoderm only arise through the process of gastrulation.

Independent Practice

■ Have students write answers to the Section Review.
■ Ask students to make a table showing the type of symmetry, body plan (shape), and level of organization of the following invertebrates: sponge, hydra, and jellyfish. This table will be used and expanded in the next section. Use the table on p. 437 as a model.

Check Your Understanding

1. How does specialization allow for evolution of larger animals? *(The size of an organism is limited by volume and surface area. With specialized functions, surface area can increase.)*
2. Why can't a jellyfish have muscles? *(Muscles arise from the mesoderm germ layer, which is not present in jellyfish.)*

Reteaching

Have students brainstorm all the invertebrates they can think of as you write the names on the board. Once the list is complete, eliminate names of vertebrates if necessary, explaining why each animal is not an invertebrate. Emphasize that invertebrates are related solely by the absence of a backbone.
■ *See* Section Reviews *worksheet, Section 29.1.*

Enrichment

Have students select a major problem of animals such as getting food or avoiding predators and prepare a report on how bilateral symmetry helps invertebrates solve this problem.

Closure

Ask students to list three common invertebrates they have seen. *(Spider, mosquito, cockroach, snail, earthworm, and so forth)* Ask students why they are more likely to see invertebrates than vertebrates. *(97 percent of animal species are invertebrates.)*

Background

Pilgrim at Tinker Creek is a Pulitzer-Prize-winning meditation on nature that grew out of notes Dillard made during 1972 while living on Tinker Creek in the Roanoke Valley of Virginia. The book follows the progression of seasons in the valley beginning in January and ending the following December. Each chapter contains the author's observation of some concrete physical event that becomes the point of departure for an informal essay encompassing bits of remembered stories, odd scientific facts, and philosophical questions—told in brilliant, precise prose.

Discussion

After students have read the selection from *Pilgrim at Tinker Creek,* ask them to discuss the following questions.

1. For Dillard, living with nature is something that can be neither ignored nor escaped. What environmental issues does our society currently face? *(For example, pollution, lack of natural resources, destruction of the rain forest)*

2. Why might Dillard feel that she is just "milling around" in a storm but not in a calm situation? *(Allow for personal opinion. When one is surrounded by lots of activity, sorting out the cause of one's own activity can be difficult.)*

Extension

Ask students to write an essay relating Dillard's observations to Aristotle's advice in the quotation on p. 434. *(Dillard is interested in all the creatures she finds in the duck pond, as Aristotle advises. By careful study of them, she makes personal discoveries about their beauty and about her own nature.)*

Writing About Biology

Pilgrim at Tinker Creek

This excerpt is from Annie Dillard's Pulitzer-prize-winning book, Pilgrim at Tinker Creek.

The plankton bloom is what interests me. The plankton animals are all those microscopic drifting animals that so staggeringly outnumber us. In the spring they are said to "bloom," like so many poppies. There may be five times as many of these teeming creatures in spring as in summer. Among them are the protozoans—amoebae and other rhizopods, and millions of various flagellates and ciliates, gelatinous moss animalcules or byrozoans; rotifers—which wheel around either free or in colonies; and all the diverse crustacean minutiae—copepods, ostracods, and cladocerans like the abundant daphnias. All these drifting animals multiply in sundry bizarre fashions, eat tiny plants or each other, die, and drop to the pond's bottom. Many of them have quite refined means of locomotion—they whirl, paddle, swim, slog, whip, and sinuate—but since they are so small, they are no match against even the least current in the water. Even such a sober limnologist as Robert E. Coker characterizes the movement of plankton as "milling around."

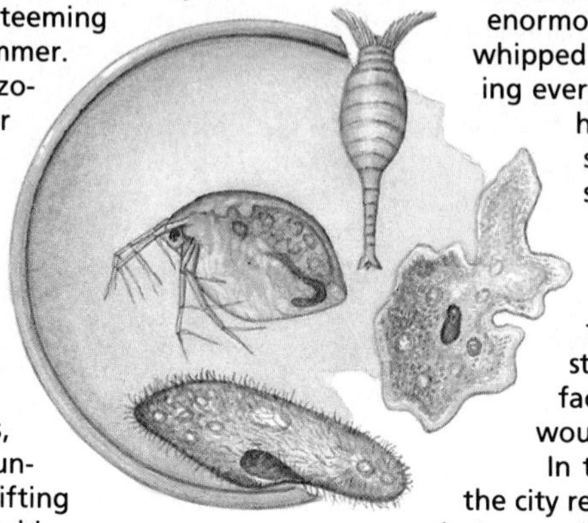

A cup of duck-pond water looks like a seething broth. If I carry the cup home and let the sludge settle, the animalcules sort themselves out, and I can concentrate them further by dividing them into two clear glass bowls. One bowl I paint all black except for a single circle where the light shines through; I leave the other bowl clear except for a single black circle against the light. Given a few hours, the light-loving creatures make their feeble way to the clear circle, and the shade-loving creatures to the black. Then, if I want to, I can harvest them with a pipette and examine them under a microscope. . . .

I don't really look forward to these microscopic forays: I have been almost knocked off my kitchen chair on several occasions when, as I was following with strained eyes the tiny career of a monostyla rotifer, an enormous red roundworm whipped into the scene, blocking everything, and writhing in huge flapping convulsions that seemed to sweep my face and fill the kitchen. I do it as a moral exercise; the microscope at my forehead is . . . a constant reminder of the facts of creation that I would just as soon forget. . . . In the puddle or pond, in the city reservoir, ditch, or Atlantic Ocean, the rotifers . . . spin and munch, the daphnia . . . filter and are filtered, and the copepods . . . swarm hanging with clusters of eggs. These are real creatures with real organs leading real lives one by one. I can't pretend they're not there. If I have life, sense, energy, will, so does a rotifer. The monostyla goes to the dark spot on the bowl: To which circle am I heading? I can move around right smartly in a calm; but in a real wind, in a change of weather, in a riptide, am I really moving, or am I "milling around"?

Write

- **Some people think that all animals have an equal right to life and that humans are not necessarily more important than other animals. What do you think? Write an essay in which you take a stand. Consider the ways that humans use other animals—as pets, as food, and as research subjects.**

Excerpt from Pilgrim at Tinker Creek *by Annie Dillard. Copyright © 1974 by Annie Dillard. Reprinted by permission of Harper & Row, Publishers, Inc.*

About the Author

Annie Dillard is best known for *Pilgrim at Tinker Creek*. Her writings explore philosophy, natural phenomena, the role of the artist in society, and the creative process. Her longtime interest in science and literature informs all her writings. When she was 12 years old, Dillard carried home cups of water from nearby ponds and streams. Using a child's microscope to which she had attached an oversized light bulb that rapidly evaporated her drops of pond water, she "set up and staged hundreds of ends-of-the-worlds and watched, enthralled, as they played themselves out." Her experiences at the Tinker Creek duck pond are rooted in this and other childhood experiences.

29.2 Porifera

The sponges you use today are probably artificial, but in a limited way they imitate one of the important functions of a real sponge. They can soak up and release water because they are extremely porous—much like a real sponge. In fact the phylum name Porifera comes from a Latin word meaning "pore-bearer." Since ancient times, divers have harvested sponges in the Caribbean, Mediterranean, Aegean, and Red seas.

Early biologists thought sponges were plants, and most sponges do indeed resemble plants in some ways. They do not chase and capture food as most animals do. Instead, they are **sessile,** which means that they attach themselves firmly to surfaces and do not move. Sponges grow in many shapes and sizes. They may look like mossy mats, cactuses, or blobs of fungus. They may be only a single centimeter in length or grow to 2 m in diameter. Sponges exist in almost every color of the rainbow.

Structure and Function

The basic body plan of sponges, shown in Figure 29-4, suggests many relationships between structure and function. Simple sponges are hollow cylinders that are closed at the bottom and have an opening at the top called the **osculum** *(AHS-kyoo-lum).* The body wall consists of two layers of cells separated by a jelly-like substance. The covering layer is a pinnacoderm, which some biologists consider true tissue. The cylinder is lined with special **collar cells,** or choanocytes. By beating their flagella, collar cells

Section Objectives

- *Describe the basic body plan of a sponge.*
- *Describe the process of filter feeding in sponges.*
- *Contrast the processes of sexual and asexual reproduction in sponges.*

Figure 29-4 The portion of the sponge at left outlined by a rectangle is shown in internal and external detail at right. An enlarged collar cell is shown in the circle.

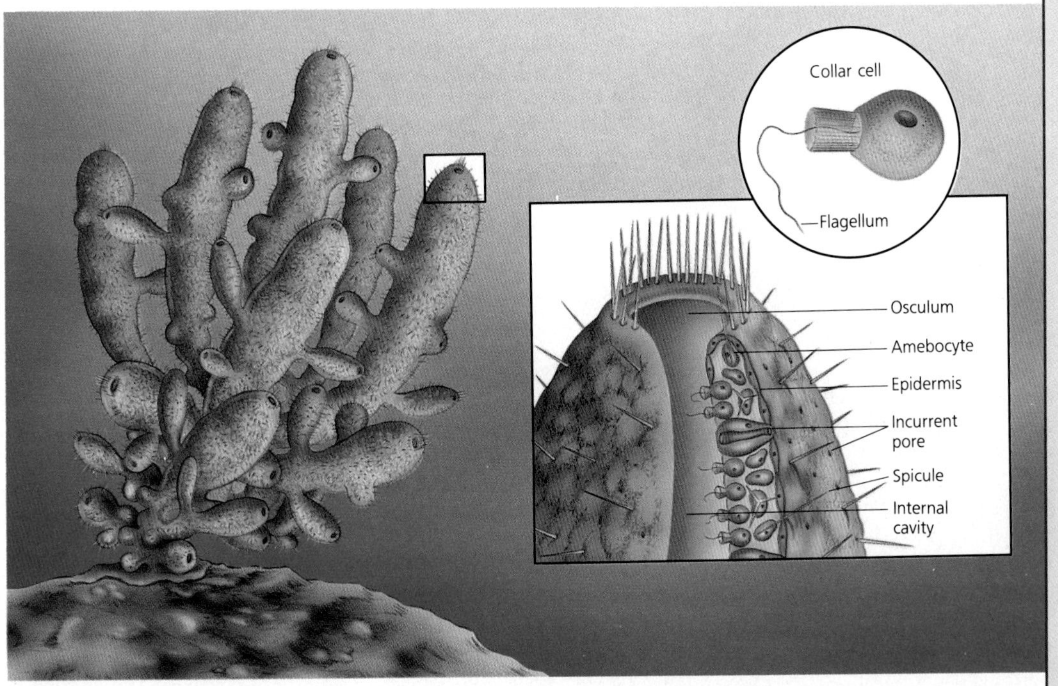

Type of Invertebrate	Phylum	Motility	Feeding	Digestion	Reproduction
sponge	Porifera	sessile	filter	nutrients carried to individual cells	asexual and sexual

Graphic Organizer Use this table in Independent Practice on p. 442.

Lesson Plan

Section Focus

The name Porifera, or "pore-bearer," describes the body of a sponge; a sponge consists of a hollow, porous cylinder that is pierced by canals, adapted as a water-filtering system that distributes food and oxygen and removes wastes. Sponges are aquatic and sessile. Reproduction is both asexual and sexual. The four classes of sponges are divided on the basis of the structure of the skeleton.

Section Themes

Sponges, the earliest examples of the development of animals from unicellular to multicellular organisms, illustrate well the theme of **Evolution.** The theme of **Scale and Structure** is evident in the collar cells that function both in the sponge's feeding and reproductive systems.

Motivating Activity

Show students the skeleton of a natural sponge. Ask them what generalizations they can make from seeing and touching the skeleton of the dead sponge. *(For example, no symmetry, many holes)* Have students compare the natural sponge with a synthetic one; elicit that both sponges are porous and able to hold a large amount of water. How are these features helpful to a living sponge? *(Allow for more food and oxygen to surround the animal's cells)* Point out that a sponge that is 10 cm high must filter more than 100 L of water a day to stay alive.

Videodiscs

- *749–753, Porifera: Calcarea—Examples (s)*
- *754–756, Porifera: Hexactinella (s)*
- *757–759, Porifera: Demospongiae (s)*

Teaching Strategies

Describing Organisms Ask students what they think would happen if a sponge's cells were separated by squeezing the organism through a fine sieve. *(Accept all reasonable answers.)* Tell them that the sponge would reassemble as its cells came in contact. What would happen if the same were done to human muscle tissue? *(It would not reassemble.)* Tell students that this ability of the sponge is cited as evidence that the sponge represents a level of organization between a colony and a true multicellular organism.

Analyzing Relationships Ask students to describe the relationship between the structures of sponges and the functions of feeding and reproduction. *(The cylinder shape of the sessile sponge with its pores and osculum allows water—carrying the sponge's food, waste products, and sperm—to flow in and out; the beating of collar cells draws water into the sponge.)*

Guided Practice

Tell students to write a "performance review" of sponge adaptations. Suggest that they focus on advantages and drawbacks of being sessile as well as on the sponge's ability to reproduce sexually and asexually. *(For example, being sessile lets the sponge receive food carried on currents but does not let it hunt.)*

Independent Practice

- Have students write answers to the Section Review.
- Have students expand the table they began in Section 29.1 by adding the headings *Phylum, Motility, Feeding, Digestion,* and *Reproduction.* Have them fill in new information about sponges and expand previously entered information. Use the table on p. 441 as a model.

draw water into the cavity through numerous pores and canals that penetrate the body. The water is pumped through the interior and leaves through the osculum. As the water passes through the sponge, body cells gather food and oxygen and excrete wastes.

The body of the sponge would collapse without some type of supporting structure. In some sponges, support is provided by a simple skeleton made up of a network of protein fibers called **spongin.** Others have skeletons made up of tiny, hard particles often shaped like spikes and stars called **spicules** *(SPICK-yools).* Spicules are composed of silicon dioxide or calcium carbonate.

Feeding

Because they are sessile, sponges cannot pursue their food. Their structure of pores and canals is thus essential to survival. The same collar cells that pump water through the body also screen food out of that water. This feeding method is called **filter feeding.** The food of sponges includes bacteria, unicellular algae and protozoans, and bits of organic matter. Collar cells engulf food and take it inside the cells to be digested.

The distribution of digested food illustrates how sponges are related to protozoan ancestors. Nutrients travel from collar cells to other specialized cells that roam about and supply the rest of the body with nutrients. Scientists call these cells **amebocytes** *(uh-MEE-buh-SITES)* because they resemble amebas. Amebocytes also carry away carbon dioxide and other wastes and release the wastes into the water passing through the sponge. The current of water carries these wastes away as it leaves through the osculum.

Reproduction

Sponges can reproduce asexually by forming small buds that break off and live separately. During periods of cold or dry weather, some freshwater sponges form specialized buds called **gemmules** *(JEM-yools).* Gemmules are food-filled balls of amebocytes surrounded by protective coats made up of organic material and spicules. The gemmules can survive harsh conditions that may kill the adult sponge that formed them. When conditions improve, the sponge cells emerge and grow into new sponges.

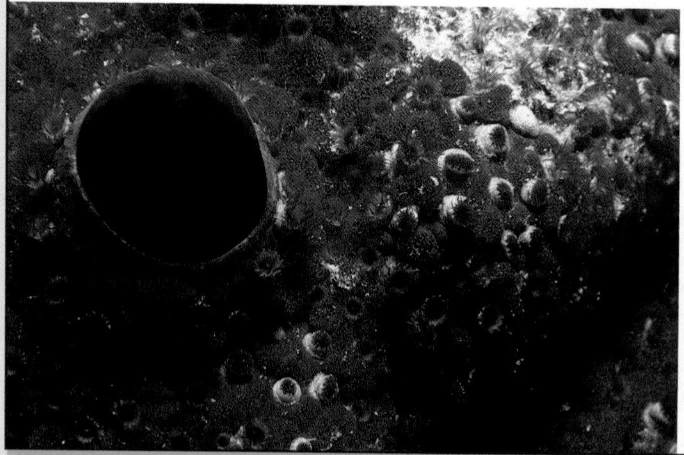

Figure 29-5 The osculum of a sponge is shown at left. At right is a budding trumpet sponge.

LEP Activity

Help students associate the appearances of specimens from the four classes of sponges with their chemical composition. Show students pictures or specimens from each class. (Pictures can be found in invertebrate zoology texts.) Explain that amebocytes, specialized cells that carry nutrients, wastes, and sperm to the sponge, also secrete skeletal material that holds its specialized cells in place. The skeletal material is made of three chemical compounds: spongin, a protein similar to that in hair and fur; calcium carbonate, a stone-hard compound; and silicon dioxide, which is taken out of seawater, concentrated, and laid down in delicate, glassy patterns. Ask students to match these descriptions with the pictures or specimens and name the class to which each sponge belongs.

Sponges also have remarkable powers of **regeneration**, the ability of an organism to regrow missing parts. In fact, a small piece of a sponge can regenerate a complete new organism. In some species even particles small enough to pass through a cloth strainer will regenerate. Sponge divers have long grown new sponges by cutting sponges into pieces, attaching them to weights, and throwing them into the sea to regenerate.

Sponges can also reproduce sexually, as you can see in Figure 29-6. The sperm are shed into the water and enter another sponge through the pores. The sperm are taken in by the collar cells and then carried to an egg by amebocytes. A fertilized egg develops into an immature form called a **larva.** The larva has flagella that enable it to escape from the sponge and swim around. Eventually it settles and attaches to an object. The cells of the larva then undergo a reorganization that forms an adult sponge.

Some species of sponges have separate sexes, but in most species each individual produces both eggs and sperm. Any organism that produces both eggs and sperm is called a **hermaphrodite** *(her-MAFF-roe-DITE).* Self-fertilization rarely if ever occurs in hermaphroditic species, but the sperm of any individual can fertilize the egg of any other individual. Thus the probability of successful fertilization is greater than it would be if only half of the population (the females) produced eggs. Hermaphroditism is common in many invertebrates that are sessile, move slowly, or live in low-density populations.

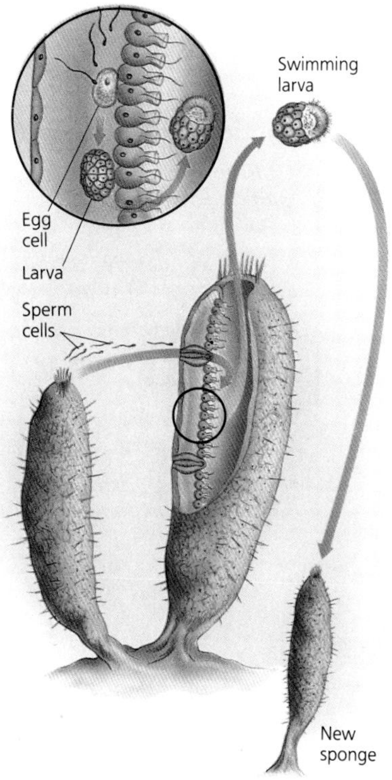

Figure 29-6 The union of sponge egg and sperm results in a zygote that develops into a larva. The larva escapes the parent and grows into a new individual.

Classification

Differences in the composition of the skeleton provide the primary basis for classifying sponges. Biologists have identified four distinct classes of sponges:

- Calcarea have spicules of calcium carbonate.
- Hexactinella have spicules of silicon dioxide.
- Demospongiae have spongin or a combination of spongin and spicules of silicon dioxide.
- Sclerospongiae have spongin plus spicules of silicon dioxide and calcium carbonate.

Section Review

1. What is the difference between *spongin* and *spicules?* What functions do they both perform?
2. Describe the way in which sponges feed.
3. How do gemmules help some freshwater sponges survive unfavorable conditions?
4. What role do amebocytes play in the sexual reproduction of sponges?
5. Since sponges are sessile animals, how is it possible that a population of sponges can spread out into a larger area?

Answers to Section Review

1. Spongin consists of protein fibers; spicules are particles of silicon dioxide or calcium carbonate. Both provide support for sponges.
2. Flagella on collar cells help collect food from water flowing through the sponge.
3. Their protective coats can survive harsh conditions that kill the adult sponge that forms them.
4. They transport sperm to the egg.
5. Larvae have flagella that enable them to move away from the parent before settling; fragments may break off, be moved away by ocean currents, and regenerate.

Check Your Understanding

1. Compare amebas with amebocytes. *(Both look similar and are eukaryotic; amebocytes are specialized cells that are interdependent, while amebas are simple, single-celled organisms.)*
2. How do scientists know that sponges are animals, not plants? *(Cells of sponges do not have cell walls as plants do; sponges cannot carry out photosynthesis.)*
3. Compare collar cells with flagellated protists. *(Collar cells have flagella that move water within the sponge; flagellated protists live and move independently.)*

Reteaching

Have students use the diagram of the structure of a sponge in Figure 29-4 on p. 441 to locate osculum, collar cells, spicules, and amebocytes. Encourage students to relate the structures to the functions of feeding, respiration, excretion, and reproduction.
■ *See* Section Reviews *worksheet, Section 29.2.*

Enrichment

Have students write an essay explaining how sponges fall between typical multicellular organisms and colonies of protozoanlike cells. *(Colonies are groups of cells that show no interdependence. Sponges have specialized cells that show interdependence; however, sponges do not have organs.)*

Closure

Ask students to predict whether or not the Porifera body plan would be successful on land. *(No, because sponges are dependent on the nutrients suspended in water.)*

Videodiscs

■ *760–767, Coelenterata:* Hydra—*Examples (s)*
■ *2600,* Hydra *(s)*

Section 29.3

Lesson Plan

Section Focus

Cnidarians are aquatic and have two basic body forms: the polyp (dominant in hydras, sea anemones, and corals) and medusa (dominant in jellyfish). Some cnidarians display both forms, which alternate during their life cycles. Cnidarians are grouped into three classes based on the stages in their life cycles: Hydrozoa, Scyphozoa, and Anthozoa.

Section Themes

The theme of **Scale and Structure** is illustrated by the traits that characterize this disparate group, cnidarians. While the three classes of cnidarians appear very different, they share such structures as tentacles with nematocysts and a hollow gut. In addition, all cnidarians consist of two cell layers separated by a jellylike material called mesoglea.

Motivating Activity

Show students several vivid pictures of living corals and some specimens of dead corals. Encourage them to apply what they know about sponges to answer the following question: Are corals plants or animals? *(Corals, like sponges, look like plants because they are sessile but are animals because they are heterotrophs.)* Tell students that corals are an example of one class of cnidarians. Ask what traits students notice in corals and what generalizations they can make from these traits. *(For example, corals have hard skeletons that provide a structure for their colonies; they are attached to a surface and must rely on food coming to them.)*

Section Objectives

- *List three characteristics that all cnidarians have in common.*
- *Name and describe the two body forms of cnidarians.*
- *Identify the three classes of cnidarians and give an example of each.*
- *Describe the way a hydra moves and the way it feeds.*
- *Summarize Darwin's theory explaining the formation of coral reefs.*

29.3 Cnidaria

Tiny freshwater hydra, stinging jellyfish, and flowerlike coral all belong to the Phylum Cnidaria. The name of the phylum comes from **cnidocytes** *(NIDE-uh-SITES)*, the stinging cells that characterize these organisms. The members of the phylum are called **cnidarians.** They are also known as **coelenterates** *(sih-LENT-uh-RATES)*, a name that comes from their coelenteron, or "hollow gut." In addition to their stinging cells and hollow guts, cnidarians also have flexible structures called **tentacles.**

Structure, Function, and Classification

As you can see in Figure 29-7, the body of a cnidarian may be either vase shaped or bell shaped. Scientists refer to the vase-shaped form as the **polyp** *(PAHL-ip)*, and to the bell-shaped form as the **medusa** *(muh-DOO-suh)*. The polyp is specialized for a sessile existence, the medusa for swimming. During their life cycles some cnidarians go through both polyp and medusa stages. Jellyfish, for example, go through both stages but spend most of

Biology in Process

Darwin and Coral Reefs

Charles Darwin had had little formal scientific training when he began his scientific voyage on the HMS *Beagle* in 1831. He was, however, a keen observer of natural phenomena and made careful notes on everything that attracted his attention. One source of curiosity for Darwin during the voyage was his observation that coral reefs existed in extremely deep water far out at sea. At the time no one had succeeded in explaining how this phenomenon was possible.

Darwin knew from samplings and depth measurements that corals could not live more than about 55 m below the surface of the water. He also observed that the corals had to attach themselves to something in order to grow. But what sort of foundation existed in waters that were otherwise thousands of meters deep? Darwin reasoned that the foundations were either great banks of sediment or undersea mountains.

Darwin reasoned that accumulations of sediment could not be the answer. The atolls—coral reef islands—were much too far from land; what's more, they were in very clear water. Therefore he inferred that the corals must have attached

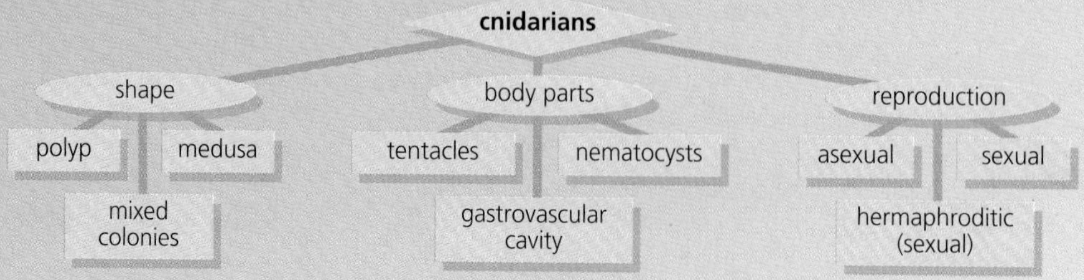

Graphic Organizer Use this organizational chart in Independent Practice on p. 447.

their lives as medusae. Other cnidarians live only as polyps, and still others live as mixed colonies of polyps and medusae.

As either polyp or medusa, the organism consists of two cell layers—the endoderm and the ectoderm. Between these two layers is a jellylike material called **mesoglea** *(MEZZ-uh-GLEE-uh)*.

The relationship between the structure and function of the cnidarians' body parts is clearly seen in the way they feed. The tentacles capture the prey and paralyze it with coiled stingers called **nematocysts** *(nuh-MAT-uh-SISTS)*, located inside the cnidocytes. The tentacles then draw the prey to the mouth. Enzymes inside the **gastrovascular cavity** (the hollow gut) break up the prey, and the specialized cells lining the cavity absorb the food. Undigested food and waste are expelled through the mouth.

Scientists classify cnidarians into three classes:

- Hydrozoa *(HY-druh-ZOE-uh)* include polyps, medusae, and species that alternate between the two.
- Scyphozoa *(SIE-fuh-ZOE-uh)*, the true jellyfishes, spend most of the life cycle as medusae.
- Anthozoa *(AN-thuh-ZOE-uh)* live only as polyps and include anemones and corals.

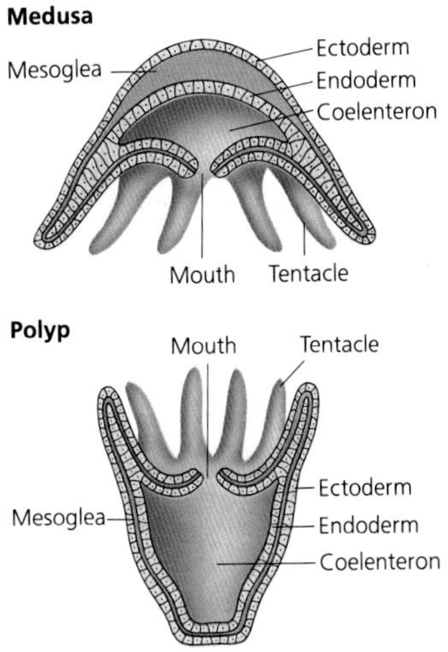

Figure 29-7 The contrasting forms of polyps and medusae result from different arrangements of the same body parts.

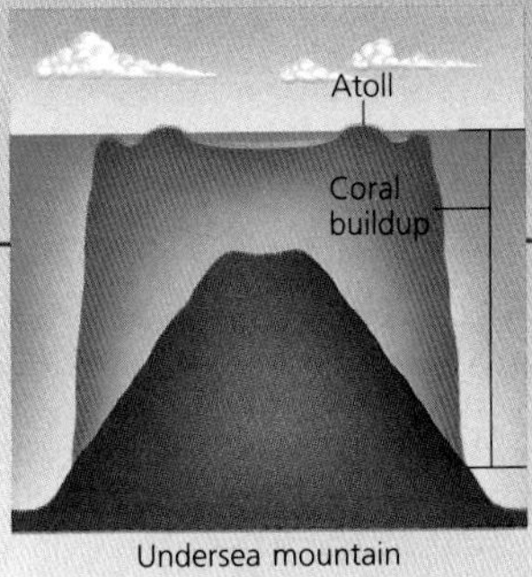

themselves to undersea mountains. But if coral reefs could not grow more than 55 m below the surface, then the tops of the undersea mountains to which the corals were attached must all be at about that level. Was it possible that thousands of mountains scattered over thousands of square kilometers of ocean had all attained such uniform height? Darwin's knowledge of terrestrial mountains told him that this was impossible. Even mountains in the same chain did not exhibit such uniformity.

Through a process of inferring, Darwin arrived at an answer. In his own words:

"If, then, the foundations of the many atolls were not uplifted into the requisite position, they must of necessity have subsided [sunk] into it; and this at once solves every difficulty, for we may safely infer . . . that during a gradual subsidence the corals would be favourably circumstanced for building up their solid frameworks and reaching the surface."

Darwin's inference was challenged at the time and for many years thereafter. Then in 1952, more than 100 years after Darwin's voyage, scientists collected data that supported Darwin's inference. Scientists working on the Pacific atoll of Eniwetok drilled down through nearly a mile of solid coral. At the bottom of the bore, nearly 1,500 m below sea level, they found corals that had lived 65 million years ago. They were attached to the top of an undersea mountain that formerly was at sea level.

- **Why were scientists unable to find data supporting Darwin's inference for so long?**

Biology in Process

Using the Feature

The feature focuses on two process skills: observing and inferring. Darwin observed that coral reefs existed at far greater depths than corals could live. He inferred that the corals when alive existed nearer the surface and that accumulated corals gradually subsided to lower depths. Point out to students that inference always depends on observation along with reasoning and past experience. Tell students to use similar processes to understand the benefit of studying nematocysts. Guide students to consider how nematocysts work and what the stingers' mode of action reveals about the animal that stings and the animal that gets stung. Point out that when a compound poisons a biological system, finding out how the poison works can also tell much about how this system works.

Answer to the Feature

Scientists were unable to find data because they did not have the technology to bore through coral or to date fossils.

Videodiscs

- *Side 3 31821, Coelenterata (m)*

More Information

Soft Corals Corals are divided into two main groups: stony and soft. Unlike stony corals, which are the major builders of reefs, soft corals have more flexible skeletons that are embedded within the flesh of the colony rather than secreted on the outside of their bodies. Colonies of soft corals bend easily and are soft to the touch. Soft corals are among the oldest clearly identifiable animal fossils. The Ediacara fossils from southern Australia, which date back 700 million years to the Precambrian era, are dominated by fossilized remains of thin-bodied cnidarians, including stalked, featherlike corals that are almost identical to the "sea pens" of today.

Teaching Strategies

Interpreting the Visuals Ask students which nematocyst in the diagram in Figure 29-8, p. 446, they think has been "fired." *(The labeled nematocyst; three nematocysts below this is a cross section of an "unfired" nematocyst.)* Explain that an "unfired" nematocyst has a coiled thread inside a capsule that is part of the cnidocyst. A modified flagellum works like a trigger, responding to chemical or mechanical stimuli. Once fired, the nematocyst cannot be reloaded but is eventually reabsorbed.

▪ *See* Laboratories, *Investigation 29.*

Describing Organisms Tap students' knowledge by encouraging individuals to share what they know about cnidarians with the rest of the class. Ask students what body parts all three classes of cnidarians have in common. *(All have stinging cells, hollow guts, and tentacles.)* Students may know something about stingers and tentacles, two characteristics common to all cnidarians. Ask students how the two distinct body forms of cnidarians are related to stages in the life cycles of particular organisms. *(Jellyfish have an early polyp stage but live most of their lives as medusae; hydras live only as polyps.)*

▪ *See* Process Skills, *Chapter 29.*

Interpreting the Visuals Take students step-by-step through the life cycle of the jellyfish shown in Figure 29-9, p. 447. Tell students that jellyfish get their name from the thick layer of mesoglea that forms the major part of the body. Point out that fertilization is external, not internal as in the sponge.

▪ *See* Blackline Master *60.*

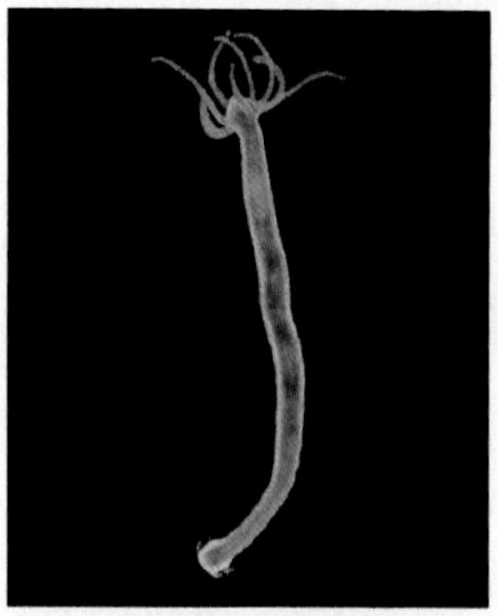

Figure 29-8 The hydra (top) has been diagrammed below to show major external and internal features.

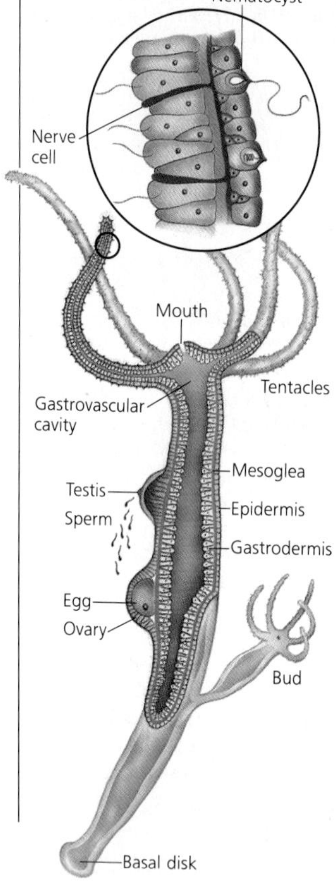

Hydrozoa

The Class Hydrozoa includes about 3,700 species, most of which live in the oceans. However, the freshwater species that make up the genus *Hydra* have been extensively studied. Hydras range in size from only 1 to 4 cm. Most hydras are white or brown, but some appear green because of algae living beneath their outer cells. Hydras live in quiet ponds, lakes, and streams. They attach themselves to rocks or water plants by means of a sticky secretion produced by a group of cells called the basal disk.

Sometimes hydras leave one place of attachment and move to another. The basal disk can secrete bubbles of gas, which cause the hydra to float upside down on the surface. The hydra can also move by somersaulting. This peculiar movement occurs when the tentacles and the mouth end bend over and touch the bottom of the pond while the basal disk pulls free. This and other kinds of movement are made possible by the nerve net, interconnecting nerve cells that are located in the mesoglea.

Feeding in Hydras

Hydras capture prey with nematocysts. They wait for small floating animals to drift past their tentacles. Just a touch triggers a barrage of paralyzing nematocyst barbs, each on a thin thread that entangles the prey. The nerve net signals the tentacles to push the prey through the mouth and into the gut. This space is lined with specialized gastrodermal cells. Some of these cells secrete enzymes that begin the digestion of the food. Others take in the partially digested food and complete digestion.

Reproduction in Hydras

Hydras generally reproduce asexually during warm weather. In asexual reproduction small buds form on the outside of the hydra's body. These buds grow their own tentacles and then separate from the body and begin living independently.

Sexual reproduction usually occurs in the fall, when low temperatures trigger the development of eggs and sperm. The eggs are produced by meiosis along the walls of the body in swellings called **ovaries.** Motile sperm are formed by meiosis in similar swellings called **testes.** In some species eggs and sperm are produced in the same hermaphroditic individual. In others the individuals are either male or female. In either case sperm are released into the water. Some will reach the ovary of a nearby hydra, and one sperm will fertilize an egg cell. The fertilized egg, or zygote, then divides and grows into a ball of cells with a hard cover. The cover is an adaptation that protects the embryo through the winter until it develops into a new hydra in the spring.

Other Hydrozoa

Hydras are definitely not typical of the class. Hydras live independently; most other hydrozoans live in colonies. Although hydras

Interdisciplinary Activity

Literature Ask students to prepare an illustrated report that shows the Greek mythological origin of biological terms such as *hydra, medusa,* and *hermaphrodite.* Tell students to include drawings of the mythological figures or beasts and a synopsis of the myths that involve them.

exist only in polyp form, most other hydrozoans go through a medusa stage. The genus *Obelia* is a colonial hydrozoan that has many polyps attached to branched stalks. Some branches are specialized for feeding, while others are specialized for reproduction.

Perhaps the most remarkable hydrozoan is the Portugese man-of-war, a member of the genus *Physalia (fie-SAY-lee-uh)*, which exists as a colony of specialized polyps and medusae. Tentacles up to several meters long dangle from a large medusa that is specialized as a gas-filled float. The float can measure as much as 30 cm across. The tentacles bear polyps specialized for feeding, digestion, and sexual reproduction. The Portuguese man-of-war preys mostly on small fish, but its nematocysts contain a poison that can be harmful and even fatal to humans.

Scyphozoa

The name Scyphozoa means "cup animals," the dominant form of the life cycle of this class, the medusa. Scyphozoans are known commonly as jellyfish, which are classified into more than 200 species. Some have cups or bells measuring as little as 2 cm across or as much as 4 m. Several species of jellyfish trail tentacles many meters long below them in the water. The nematocysts of some jellyfish carry poisons that can cause severe pain and even death. Jellyfish have killed several dozen people in the seawaters along the northern coast of Australia.

The common jellyfish *Aurelia* is a good example of a scyphozoan whose life cycle includes both medusa and polyp forms. As you can see in Figure 29-9, adult medusae release sperm and eggs into the water, where fertilization occurs. The resulting zygote develops into a blastula. The blastula then develops into a ciliated larva called a **planula,** which settles and attaches to the ocean bottom. The unattached end develops a mouth and tentacles,

Figure 29-9 The life cycle of the common jellyfish *Aurelia* includes both medusa and polyp forms.

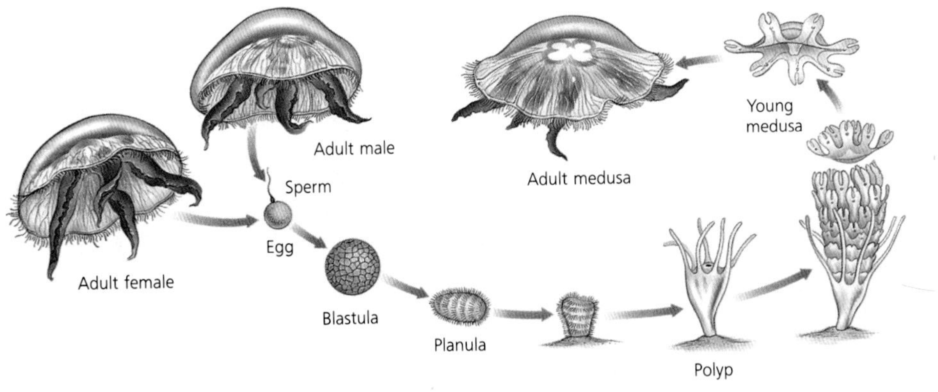

Guided Practice

Help students understand how individual cnidarians can live together in colonies such as coral reefs. Point out that each organism secretes its own skeleton, which becomes part of the coral structure. Ask students why green algae are important to corals. *(They produce oxygen.)* How might the symbiotic relationship between corals and algae benefit other marine life? *(By providing oxygen, food, and shelter)*

Independent Practice

- Have students write answers to the Section Review.
- Have students make an organizational chart of cnidarians that summarizes their shapes, body parts, and modes of reproduction. An example of a completed chart is shown on p. 444.

Check Your Understanding

1. Could corals live on land? Explain your answer. *(Like sponges, corals are sessile; they rely on food coming to them, which would decrease their chances of survival on land.)*
2. Compare cnidarian polyps and sponges. *(Both are sessile, but polyps have a mouth through which food enters and tentacles to snare food; sponges have food directed to them by flagella on their collar cells.)*
3. Compare reproduction in hydras and sponges. *(Both hydras and sponges can have separate sexes or be hermaphroditic; sponges have flagellate larvae, while hydras have hard-covered eggs; sponges do not bud as hydras do.)*

Videodiscs

- *777–779, **Hydrozoa: Portuguese Man-of-War** (s)*
- *780–790 **Scyphozoa: Jellyfish** (s)*

Cooperative Learning

Cnidarian Poster Have students work in groups of three to produce a poster that portrays cnidarians in a fantasy setting. The group should select an activity setting, such as playing baseball or musical instruments, and a title. Have one group member draw sketches and write brief descriptions of different hydrozoans. Assign the second and third group members scyphozoans and anthozoans. Have each group member present the sketches and descriptions to the other group members. Have the group lay out the design of their poster together and individually draw the animals from their cnidarian class to complete the poster. Remind students that, although the settings are fantasy, their drawings should accurately portray cnidarians.

Reteaching

Provide students with several specimens and/or pictures of each of the three classes of cnidarians. Have students list characteristics that all the organisms have in common. Ask them in what ways cnidarians differ from one another. Then have students separate them into three groups, according to the cnidarian classes, and describe how each cnidarian obtains its food. Have students use their texts to determine the life cycle of each group.

■ *See* Section Reviews *worksheet, Section 29.3.*

Answer to Think

Students may answer, for example, that sea anemones had tentacles with which they were observed to capture prey.

Enrichment

Have students collect information and write a report on the ways in which coral reefs are important to humans and the environment, and on the impact of human activities and environmental factors on the reefs. The reports should explain how the structure and function of specific coral reefs such as the Great Barrier Reef are affected by these activities and describe any measures being taken to solve such problems.

Closure

Ask students to imagine cnidarians without stinging cells and tentacles. Have them explain how the lives of these animals would be different. *(Cnidarians use nematocysts to capture prey; without stingers, they would be able to eat only unicellular organisms that floated by them.)*

Videodiscs

■ *Side 4, 14046, Coral (m)*

Think

The word *anthozoa* means "flower animal," a description that fits sea anemones like this one very well. Why then do you think that early biologists did not mistake sea anemones for plants as they did sponges?

becoming a polyp. As the polyp grows, it forms stacks of medusae, each of which buds off and develops into a jellyfish.

Anthozoa

The word *anthozoa* means "flower animals," a fitting description for the approximately 6,100 species of this class. These brightly colored marine cnidarians include sea anemones and corals.

Sea anemones are polyps commonly found in coastal areas. They attach themselves to rocks and other submerged objects by means of a basal disk. Anemones feed on fishes and other kinds of marine life that swim within reach of their tentacles. Some sea anemones have a symbiotic relationship with the clown fish. The fish hides in the anemone's tentacles, protected by a special chemical that prevents the nematocysts from firing. The two animals share food and protect each other from various predators. The movements of the fish also help prevent sediments from harming the anemone.

Corals are small polyps, most of which live in colonies. They build rocklike reefs by cementing their calcium-based skeletons to those of adjoining polyps. When the polyps die, their hardened skeletons remain, serving as the foundation for new coral polyps. Thousands of coral polyps live together in this manner, building up large and colorful reef communities. The reef provides food and shelter for an enormous variety of fishes and invertebrates.

Corals build three kinds of reefs. Fringing reefs form close to a beach, either on the mainland or on an island. Barrier reefs form farther out. One theory holds that barrier reefs were once fringing reefs that became further separated from the mainland or island when coastal lands sank. Atolls, reefs with open lagoons in the middle, form far out at sea. Many are attached to the tops of undersea mountains or extinct volcanoes.

Coral reefs form only in the warm, clear waters at shallow depths. These conditions are required to allow photosynthesis to be carried out by certain algae that live symbiotically inside coral cells. The corals depend upon the algae as a source of oxygen and also as a means of speeding up the accumulation of calcium. The algae in turn depend upon the corals to supply vital nutrients. This symbiotic relationship is yet another example of how invertebrates have adapted to a sessile existence in the oceans.

Section Review

1. What is the origin of the word *cnidarian*?
2. Identify the two stages of life of many cnidarians.
3. Name the three classes of cnidarians, and give an example of each.
4. Describe two examples of symbiosis found among cnidarians.
5. Suggest reasons why coral reefs are most commonly found in tropical waters.

Answers to Section Review

1. The name comes from *cnidocytes,* the stinging cells characteristic of the phylum.
2. Polyp and medusa
3. Hydrozoa (hydra); Scyphozoa (jellyfish); Anthozoa (sea anemone or coral)
4. Sea anemones and clown fish share food and protect each other from various predators. Corals depend on algae inside their cells for oxygen and accumulation of calcium.
5. Tropical areas have the warm temperatures and abundant sunlight needed for algae living inside coral cells to perform photosynthesis.

Laboratory

Feeding Behavior of *Hydra*

Objective
To observe the feeding behavior of *Hydra* and identify their responses to different stimuli

Process Skills
Observing, hypothesizing, experimenting

Materials
Hydra culture, 2 medicine droppers, depression slide, compound microscope, methylene blue, vinegar, 2 culture dishes, pasteurized spring water, dissecting microscope, brine shrimp culture, 50-mL beaker, probe, glass rod, glutathione

Background
1. What structural characteristics do hydras share with all cnidarians?
2. Why will it be important to use hydras that have not been recently fed?

Inquiry
1. Use a medicine dropper to transfer a hydra from its container to a depression slide. The hydra must be transferred quickly or it will attach itself to the dropper. Allow the hydra a few moments to settle down.
2. Using a compound microscope set on low power, identify the hydra's tentacles, mouth, and basal disk. How might these structures contribute to catching prey?
3. Add a drop of methylene blue to the depression containing the hydra to make the tentacles more visible. Then observe at low power the bumps on the tentacles—the nematocysts—as you add a drop of vinegar. Is vinegar a normal part of the hydra's diet? Why do you think it is used in this step?
4. Return the hydra to the culture jar labeled "Used hydras".
5. Place a culture dish that is one-half full with water under a dissecting microscope, and transfer a fresh hydra to the dish. Wait for the hydra to settle down.
6. Fill a 50-mL beaker with water. Use a dropper to pick up several brine shrimp. Rinse them in the water by releasing them from the dropper and immediately picking them up again.
7. Put the brine shrimp in the culture dish with the hydra. Record your observations.
8. Formulate a hypothesis about which kind of stimuli—vibration, touch, and chemicals—initiate a hydra's feeding behavior.
9. Transfer a fresh hydra to a clean culture dish one-half full of water. Lightly tap the dish and observe the hydra's response. How might response to vibration help hydras living in a quiet pond?
10. With a probe gently touch the base of the hydra and then its tentacles. Do you think the hydra's response to touch is feeding or protective behavior?
11. Dip a glass rod into glutathione, and then place it near a hydra. Do not let the glass rod touch the hydra. How does the hydra respond?
12. Compare the hydra's response to the brine shrimp with its responses to vinegar, vibration, touch, and glutathione.
13. Place all hydras back into the container labeled "Used hydras"

Conclusions
1. Do your observations support your hypothesis? Explain.
2. Identify possible sources of error in your technique. How could you improve your inquiry?
3. Consider what you know about sponges and about cnidarians. What advantages does a hydra have over a filter feeder in obtaining food?

Further Inquiry
Design experiments to study the responses of *Hydra* to light, sound, and color.

Laboratory

(For an overview of Hydra *and preparatory information related to the laboratory, see p. 435B.)*

Background
1. Cnidarian characteristics include tentacles, nematocysts, hollow guts, and two cell layers with jelly in between. In the polyp form, hydras are sessile.
2. Recently fed hydras would be less responsive.

Inquiry
2. A hydra must wait for small floating animals to drift by its tentacles and then be able to react quickly.
3. Vinegar is not part of the hydra's usual diet but does cause the nematocysts to fire. A hydra may be sensitive to a prey's chemicals that are mildly acidic.
7. Encourage students to be patient, but if a hydra does not respond with feeding behavior after a few minutes, it may not be hungry. Have them try a fresh hydra.
8. Each lab group should decide on a testable hypothesis. Possible hypotheses: a given stimulus will trigger feeding behavior, cause avoidance, or be ignored.
9. Vibrations in the water of a normally quiet pond—possibly from movement of prey—could alert a hydra to begin feeding behavior.
10. If the hydra fires its nematocysts, it is exhibiting feeding behavior. If the hydra contracts, it may be protecting itself.
11. The hydra should reach for the probe and send out nematocysts in response to the glutathione.
12. When a hydra responds to the brine shrimp, its feeding behavior may be triggered by water vibrations, prey touching its tentacles, or the smell/taste of prey.

Conclusions
1. Student answers should be supported by their observations. Do not let students be discouraged by getting the "wrong" results.
2. Students may mention being gentler in carrying out procedures and waiting longer for hydras to settle down.
3. Hydra feeding behavior is more active than the passive filter feeding of a sponge. Hydras can move if they lack food—by somersaulting and by floating at the water surface.

Further Inquiry
Cover part of the culture dish, make a loud noise near the dish, or place brightly colored objects in the dish (allowing for vibrations to die down).

Chapter 29 Review

Vocabulary
1. Sessile; others are parts of bilateral animals.
2. Spicule; others relate to embryonic development.
3. Nematocyst; others are parts of sponges.
4. Gemmule; others are parts of cnidarians.
5. Mesoglea; others are involved in reproduction.

Review
1. c
2. c
3. a
4. b
5. d
6. c
7. b
8. a
9. c
10. c

11. Specialization is the adaptation of a cell for a particular function; it allows division of labor and adaptation to diverse environments.
12. Concentration of nerve tissue and sensory organs in the anterior end of an organism
13. The zygote divides and forms an embryo, which undergoes repeated divisions that form a blastula; infolding of the blastula forms a gastrula, giving rise to endoderm and ectoderm.
14. They have no gastrula stage, little specialization of cells, and no true tissues or organs.
15. A sponge cannot chase down prey and so requires another method of feeding; filter feeding allows it to trap food from the water that is pumped through its body.
16. Sperm are shed into the water and enter another sponge through incurrent pores; collar cells trap sperm, which are then carried by amebocytes to an egg. A fertilized egg develops into a larva that leaves the sponge, swims about, then settles, attaches to an object, and develops into a sessile adult.
17. The hydra fires nematocysts that paralyze prey and entangle it in threads attached to nematocyst barbs.
18. Hydras live in fresh water, live independently, and exist only as polyps; most other hydrozoans live in the sea, are colonial, and have a medusa stage in their life cycles.
19. Some polyps are specialized for feeding, others for digestion, and still others for reproduction.
20. Corals depend on algae within their cells to perform photosynthesis, so they must live relatively close to the surface to allow sufficient sunlight to reach the algae.

Chapter 29 Review

Vocabulary

amebocyte (442)
anterior (437)
bilateral symmetry (437)
blastopore (438)
blastula (438)
cephalization (438)
cnidocyte (444)
cnidarian (444)
coelenterate (444)
collar cell (441)
dorsal (437)
ectoderm (439)
embryo (438)
endoderm (439)
filter feeding (442)
gastrovascular cavity (445)
gastrula (438)
gemmule (442)
germ layer (439)
hermaphrodite (443)
invertebrate (437)
larva (443)
medusa (444)
mesoderm (439)
mesoglea (445)
metazoan (438)
nematocyst (445)
osculum (441)
ovary (446)
planula (447)
polyp (444)
posterior (437)
radial symmetry (437)
regeneration (443)
sessile (441)
specialization (438)
spherical symmetry (437)
spicule (442)
spongin (442)
symmetry (437)
tentacle (444)
testes (446)
ventral (437)
zygote (438)

For each set of terms below, choose the one that does not belong, and explain why it does not belong.

1. anterior, posterior, dorsal, sessile
2. spicule, blastula, gastrula, embryo
3. amebocyte, collar cell, nematocyst, spicule
4. medusa, gemmule, polyp, cnidocyte
5. ovary, testis, zygote, mesoglea

Review

1. All invertebrates (a) live in water (b) have tentacles (c) have no backbone (d) are hermaphrodites.
2. A hydra shows (a) asymmetry (b) spherical symmetry (c) radial symmetry (d) bilateral symmetry.
3. The dorsal surface of an animal is its (a) top (b) bottom (c) side (d) front.
4. Spongin and spicules are important to a sponge because they (a) trap food (b) provide support (c) remove wastes (d) produce offspring.
5. Both feeding and sexual reproduction in sponges involve (a) gemmules and collar cells (b) spicules and gemmules (c) amebocytes and spongin (d) collar cells and amebocytes.
6. The primary basis for classifying sponges is (a) their shape (b) their color (c) the composition of their skeleton (d) the method by which they reproduce.
7. The characteristics common to all cnidarians include all of the following except (a) stinging cells (b) polyps (c) a hollow gut (d) tentacles.
8. The cnidarian body form specialized for sessile existence is the (a) polyp (b) medusa (c) planula (d) gastrula.
9. The class of cnidarians that exists only as polyps is (a) Hydrozoa (b) Scyphozoa (c) Anthozoa (d) Calcarea.
10. The movements of hydras are coordinated by their (a) mesoglea (b) nematocysts (c) nerve net (d) endoderm.
11. What is cell specialization, and how does it benefit invertebrates?
12. What is cephalization?
13. Summarize the process of embryonic development in invertebrates.
14. In what ways do sponges represent the transition from unicellular to multicellular life?
15. How is a sponge's method of feeding related to the fact that it is sessile?
16. Describe the process of sexual reproduction in sponges.

17. How does a hydra capture its prey?
18. In what ways are hydras not typical of the Class Hydrozoa?
19. What type of specialization is found among the polyps that make up a Portuguese man-of-war?
20. Why do all coral reefs form at about the same depth?

Critical Thinking

1. The pie graph shows the relative numbers of species in each class of Cnidaria. Which segment of the graph represents scyphozoans, A, B, or C? How do you know?

2. Radial symmetry is found only among species that live in water. In what way is radial symmetry not well suited to animals that live on land?
3. A hermaphroditic sponge generally produces eggs and sperm at different times. Based on your knowledge of sexual reproduction, why do you think it is evolutionarily advantageous for the sponge not to produce eggs and sperm simultaneously?
4. Compare and contrast the life cycle of *Aurelia* with alternation of generations in mosses. Be sure to list both similarities and differences.
5. Hydras generally reproduce asexually during warm weather and reproduce sexually in the fall. Based on what you have learned about the hydra embryo, what do you think is the advantage to the hydra of reproducing sexually when the weather turns cool?
6. Sponge larvae have flagella on the outside, whereas adult sponges have flagella in their internal cavity. How is this structural difference related to functional differences of the larval and adult stages in the life cycle of the sponge?

Extension

1. Read the article by Lucy Bunkley-Williams and Ernest H. Williams, Jr., entitled "Global Assault on Coral Reefs" in *Natural History,* April 1990, pp. 46–54. Write a brief report describing how scientists determined a cause for epidemic coral reef bleaching.
2. Create a chart that you can use to summarize information about all the phyla you will study in this unit. Use headings such as Symmetry, Feeding and Digestion, Reproduction, and Habitats. Begin your chart by filling in the information for Porifera and Cnidaria. Continue your chart as you work through the unit.
3. Natural sponges are preferred to synthetic ones in certain professions. In surgery, for example, natural sponges are desirable. Find out what methods are used to gather and prepare sponges to be used by surgeons and others. Write a report and present it to your class.
4. Use the library to research barrier reefs. Present an oral report to the class explaining how these reefs form and describing the communities of living things found on the reefs. If possible, bring along photographs of reef communities to share with the class.

Critical Thinking

1. Segment C; because scyphozoans have the smallest number of different species.
2. Answers should show understanding that radial symmetry is beneficial for sessile animals but that land animals must move about in search of food. A bilateral body plan is much better suited to movement on land.
3. This pattern prevents self-fertilization, which could harm species by increasing the frequency of recessive traits.
4. The life cycles are similar only in that both include two distinct body forms. The major difference is that in moss a diploid form alternates with a haploid form, while in jellyfish medusa and polyp are diploid, and only gametes are haploid.
5. Sexual reproduction produces an embryo in a protective covering, while hydras formed by budding are just as vulnerable to cold as the parent hydra.
6. Sponge larvae use flagella to swim through water and so disperse the population, whereas adult sponges use flagella to pump water through the body and filter food from water.

Extension

1. Stress the difficulty of separating natural events from those caused by humans. Because evidence may be contradictory, politicians hesitate to address such matters as global warming.
2. Have students use the table made in the teacher's edition activities of Sections 29.1 and 29.2 as a model for a master table to be used in this unit.
3. Direct students to include in their reports both farming and harvesting of sponges, financial health of the industry, how sponges are processed for use, and who the consumers are.
4. Also assign students to research and report on fringing reefs and atolls.

Chapter 30 Flatworms, Roundworms, and Rotifers

Chapter Overview

Chapter 30 discusses the classification of body structures in flatworms, roundworms, and rotifers. Section 30.1 deals with the anatomy and other characteristics of the Phylum Platyhelminthes, or flatworms. Section 30.2 discusses the Phyla Nematoda and Rotifera.

Chapter Planning Chart

B	S	A	Sections and Subsections	Page	Features	Page	Resources
•	•	•	**30.1 Platyhelminthes**				
			Turbellaria	454	Think	455	Videodiscs
			Trematoda	455	Laboratory	461	Blackline Master 61
			Cestoda	457	Section Review	457	Overhead Transparency T30
							Blackline Master 62
							Process Skills: Schistosomiasis
							Laboratories: Flatworm Behavior
							Section Reviews Worksheet
•	•	•	**30.2 Nematoda and Rotifera**				
			Nematoda	458	Biology in Process	458	Videodiscs
			Rotifera	460	Section Review	460	Section Reviews Worksheet
			End of Chapter Activities				
					Chapter Review	462	Vocabulary Skills
							Chapter Test
							Computer Test Generator

B *The Basic Level curriculum presents the most fundamental knowledge offered in the course.*
S *The Standard Level curriculum is designed for the average student who is able to master most topics.*
A *The Advanced Level curriculum includes suggestions for teaching the most academically able students.*

Cooperative Learning

Group Activity: Spread of Parasitic Diseases

- **Group Size:** *3 students*
- **Outcome:** *Students will recognize the primary working and living conditions that contribute to the incidence of parasitic diseases.*
- **Individual Accountability:** *Each student will identify conditions that contribute to the spread of a parasitic disease.*
- **Positive Interdependence:** *The group will develop a table that compares living and working conditions in the regions they have studied.*

Have each student in a group identify and choose a different parasitic disease, such as river blindness, schistosomiasis, elephantiasis, clonorchiasis, trichuriasis, or trichinosis. Ask each student to research the living and working conditions of the regions in which incidence of the parasitic disease is common. Have all the students from the different groups who are researching one region do their research together. Then have each student report his or her findings to the other members in his or her original group, and have the group compile a table comparing the diseases researched by group members. Encourage group members to emphasize in their discussion how the parasitic disease is spread and its effects on its victims. Then have all groups pool their information in a class table on the board.

Concept Map

The following is one possible solution to the concept mapping activity in Relating Concepts on p. 454.

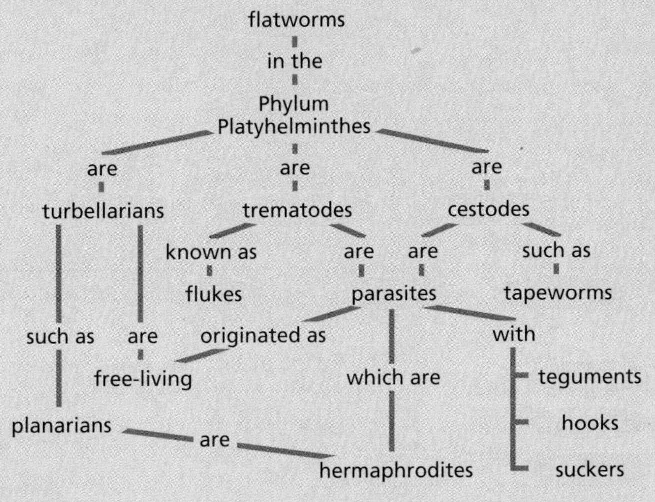

Laboratory Preparation

Overview *(See p. 461.)*

In this lab students examine the structure of a representative free-living flatworm, *Dugesia.* They also observe its feeding behavior and responses to simple stimuli, and they design simple experiments to test its responses to those stimuli.

Preparation

Dugesia are available from biological supply houses. If pond water is not available, set out tap water in open containers the night before the investigation.

An incomplete digestive system, as seen in *Dugesia,* lacks specialized digestive organs such as a stomach or intestines. The same opening is used for both the ingestion of food and the elimination of wastes. The digestive cavity in flatworms is a highly branched sac that allows nutrients to reach all parts of the organism.

Teaching Tips

Review with students the characteristics of flatworms. Emphasize the evolutionary advantages of bilateral symmetry and cephalization, as well as the evolutionary limitations of an incomplete digestive system and the lack of a coelom. Point out that flatworms are the least specialized phylum of those having a mesoderm, bilateral symmetry, and cephalization.

Safety

Remind students to handle flatworms in a humane manner.

Chapter Themes

Evolution Tell students that the advent of bilateral symmetry in animals is a major evolutionary milestone. Explain that the grouping of sensory structures at an animal's anterior end led to the development of a central nervous system. Ultimately, this development led to the evolution of the brain. Stress that the presence of a third germ layer was central in the development of complex tissue and organ systems in higher animals.

Systems and Interactions Many species in the Phyla Platyhelminthes and Nematoda have highly complex life cycles that involve parasitic relationships. Emphasize that these relationships illustrate the intricate interactions among natural systems.

Chapter Motivating Activity

Obtain a preserved heart with heartworms from a veterinarian for students to observe. (A photograph from an invertebrate zoology text may be substituted.) Tell students that dogs are often host to parasitic worms and can be given pills during mosquito season to prevent heartworm infestation. Ask students to speculate on the role mosquitos play in heartworm infestation. *(Mosquitos carry the parasite and transfer it into the bloodstream of another host.)* Dogs are not the only animals vulnerable to worms. Explain that flatworms infest almost all vertebrate species, including humans. Humans are also vulnerable to approximately fifty roundworm species, but only about ten of these species are dangerous to humans.

Chapter 30 Flatworms, Roundworms, and Rotifers

Introduction

As invertebrate species evolved, the complexity of their body structures increased. The sponges and cnidarians discussed in Chapter 29 are among the least complex animals. In this chapter you will learn about invertebrates that show the next level of complexity: flatworms, roundworms, and rotifers.

Chapter Outline

Chapter Concept

As you read, note the increased complexity of body plans as compared with those of sponges and cnidarians. Also notice how organisms are modified for a free-living or a parasitic way of life.

Pelagic worm, *Peobius meseres*. Inset: Male and female *Schistosoma*.

Understanding the Visuals

Have students examine the photographs carefully. Point out that the female *Schistosoma* is long and slender, whereas the male is broader and heavier with a large ventral groove in which the female is held during insemination. Tell students that the colorful *Schistosoma* is a blood fluke, a parasitic flatworm that infects humans and snails at different stages of its life cycle. Explain that schistosomiasis, the severe human disease caused by this flatworm, is common in many tropical areas around lakes and rivers.

30.1 Platyhelminthes

Platyhelminthes, Nematoda, and Rotifera are three phyla of invertebrates whose body plans are more complex than those of sponges and cnidarians. Scientists identify four types of body plans in invertebrates. The relationship among the germ layers differs in each body plan. Germ layers, as you learned in Chapter 29, are layers of cells that originate in the developing embryo and become specific structures in the animal. Most animals have three germ layers: the ectoderm, the endoderm, and the mesoderm. The mesoderm is the embryonic layer that forms between the ectoderm and the endoderm. In animals muscles, bones, and reproductive organs develop from the mesoderm.

The four body types, shown in Figure 30-1, are defined in part by the presence or absence of a **coelom** *(SEE-lum)*, or body cavity. **Acoelomate** *(ay-SEE-luh-MATE)*, for example, means "without a coelom." The four body types, from the least complex to the most complex, are described below:

- The acoelomate body plan with two germ layers is characterized by an ectoderm and an endoderm that are not separated by a cavity. Sponges and cnidarians have this kind of body plan. It is considered the least complex body plan.
- The acoelomate body plan with three germ layers is characterized by an ectoderm, a mesoderm, and an endoderm that are not separated by a cavity. Flatworms are acoelomates with three germ layers.
- The pseudocoelomate body plan is characterized by a **pseudocoelom,** a cavity that forms between the mesoderm and the endoderm. Roundworms and rotifers are pseudocoelomates.
- The coelomate body plan is characterized by a cavity called a coelom, which develops within the mesoderm. Mollusks, annelids, arthropods, echinoderms, and all chordates, including humans, are coelomates. This is the most complex body plan.

The term *worm* does not refer to a specific taxonomic group of animals. Though both are called worms, flatworms and roundworms differ so significantly in their fundamental structure that scientists classify them into separate phyla.

Section Objectives

- *State the distinguishing characteristics of flatworms.*
- *Describe the anatomy of a planarian.*
- *Compare and contrast free-living and parasitic life-forms.*
- *Diagram the life cycle of a fluke.*
- *Describe the life cycle of a tapeworm.*

Figure 30-1 The four basic body plans of animals exhibit a progression from least complex, with only two germ layers, to most complex, with three germ layers and a coelom.

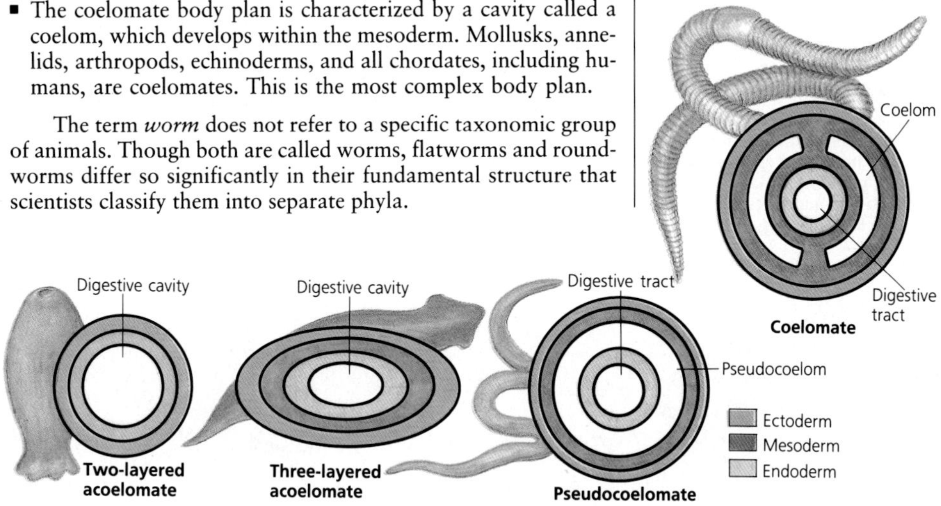

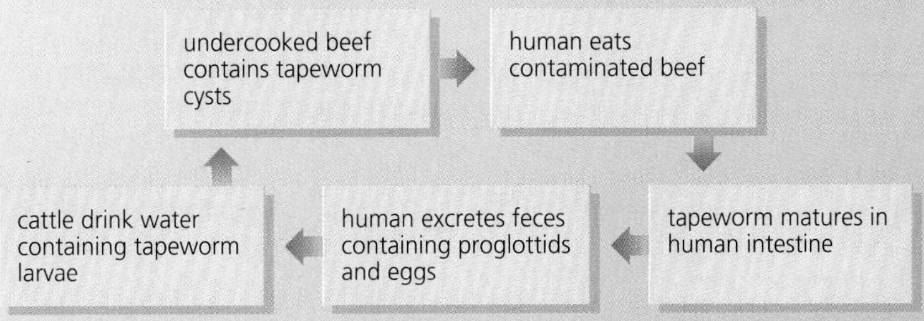

Graphic Organizer Use this cyclic diagram in the LEP Activity on p. 456.

Lesson Plan

Section Focus

The Phylum Platyhelminthes contains three classes: Turbellaria (free-living planaria), Trematoda (parasitic flukes), and Cestoda (parasitic tapeworms). Flatworms are the simplest animals displaying bilateral symmetry, cephalization, and three types of tissue layers organized into organs and organ systems.

Section Themes

The dominant theme in this section is **Evolution.** Bilateral symmetry and cephalization along with a mesoderm germ layer are benchmarks in the evolutionary history of animals.

Motivating Activity

Ask students what comes to mind when they think of worms, and list their responses on the board. *(Long, round, slimy, live in dirt)* Show them photographs of a segmented worm and a variety of planaria, flukes, and tapeworms. Good sources are invertebrate zoology and parasitology textbooks. Point out that worms of the Phylum Platyhelminthes are less complex than earthworms but are among the most numerous animals on earth. Ask students to describe the flatworms pictured. *(Soft-bodied, broad, flat, no segments)* Lead them to identify bilateral symmetry and cephalization.

■ ***See*** **Laboratories, *Investigation 30.***

Teaching Strategies

Interpreting the Visuals Stress to students that the coelom (see Figure 30-1) was one of the most important evolutionary developments among animals. Lead them to see that the coelom permits the gut to move independently of the body wall.

■ ***See*** **Overhead Transparency *T30 and* Blackline Master *61.***

Comparing Terms Remind students of the meaning of the prefix *pseudo* in *pseudocoelom* and where this prefix has been used—for example, *pseudopodia* in ameba.

Interpreting the Visuals Ask students to explain the function of each structure in Figure 30-3. *(Eyespots respond to light, but cannot define images. Excretory canal is a network of ducts for eliminating chemical waste and excess water. Excretory pores are openings through which wastes leave the body. Pharynx is used to suck in food through the mouth. Flame cells move wastes into excretory canals.)* Point out that in parasitic flatworms with hooks and/or suckers, all cells lie close to the outer surface or the intestinal wall, permitting direct absorption of nutrients and oxygen and diffusion of waste products.

Comparing Organisms Show students preserved or living specimens of flatworms (such as flukes and tapeworms) and other organisms (such as roundworms, segmented worms, and insect larvae). Or show photographs from an invertebrate zoology or parasitology textbook. Have students discuss the different characteristics of the flatworms and the other organisms. *(All have the same shape; earthworms and tapeworms appear to be segmented; some clearly have heads.)*

Relating Concepts Have students make a concept map showing the classification and characteristics of flatworms. An example of a completed concept map is shown on p. 451B.

Figure 30-2 A spade-shaped anterior and tapered posterior characterize this type of flatworm. These adaptations allow the organism to move freely and to seek its own food.

Members of the Phylum Platyhelminthes *(PLAT-ee-hel-MINTH-eez)* are called flatworms. Flatworms are bilaterally symmetrical organisms that lack respiratory and circulatory systems. In flatworms, as in most animals, the sense receptors and nerves are concentrated at their anterior end, a characteristic called cephalization. The adaptive advantage of cephalization is that an organism that enters an environment with its sense organs leading the way will have an advantage over those that do not.

The more than 13,000 species of flatworms belong to three classes: Turbellaria, Trematoda, and Cestoda. Only turbellarians are free-living. Trematodes and cestodes live as parasites on or inside other animals. The **parasite** is an organism that lives on or in another organism, called the **host,** for a long period of time. The parasite derives its nutrition and protection from the host. Yet a parasite can harm the host by depriving it of nutrition and by interfering with its internal organ systems. The majority of parasites do not kill their hosts, an adaptation that helps to ensure that the hosts will continue to provide nutrition and protection.

Parasites probably originated as free-living organisms. During evolution some organs that were advantageous to free living became modified for parasitism; some were lost entirely. Because their food is already digested, some parasites lack mouths or well-developed digestive systems. Parasites have hooks or suckers that grip their hosts. Features that prevent parasites from being digested by their hosts are the **tegument,** a thick covering of cells, and the **cuticle,** a nonliving layer secreted by the epidermis.

Turbellaria

The majority of the 3,000 species of the Class Turbellaria live in marine environments. However, the most familiar turbellarian is the freshwater planarian *Dugesia,* which is pictured in Figure 30-3. As you study, notice the adaptations for free living.

The planarian's posterior end is tapered, and its anterior end is shaped like a spade. As an adaptation to its free-living way of life, much of the planarian's body is covered with cilia. A planarian moves by swimming with an undulating motion or by laying down a layer of mucus over which it slides, propelled by the beating of its cilia.

Figure 30-3 A planarian extends its pharynx and sucks food into its mouth and intestine. Wastes are eliminated through the mouth and via ducts lined with flame cells.

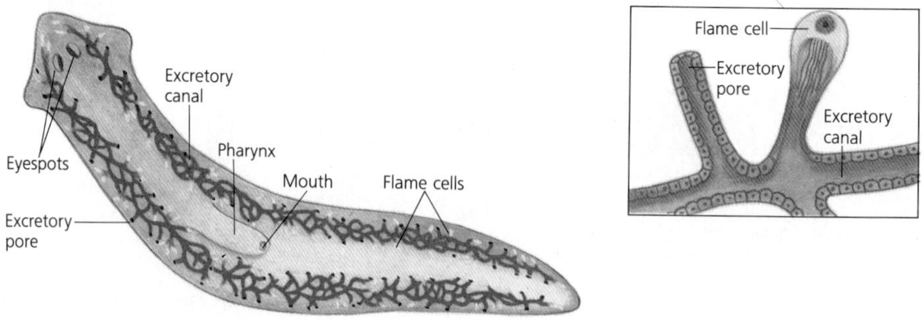

More Information

Schistosomiasis Improvements to a region can present new, unforeseen problems, as was the case with construction of the Aswan High Dam in the Nile River valley in Egypt. The extensive irrigation canals fed by the dam have permitted aquatic snails to flourish, causing an increase in schistosomiasis from a very few cases each year to an estimated incidence of 76% among fishermen living around the lake above the dam, and over 60% in the population in the Nile delta. Before construction, the 500 miles of the Nile River between Aswan and Cairo flooded annually. The alternate flooding and drying killed the snails in which blood flukes live. Damming the river created new habitats for the snails.

Digestion and Excretion

The planarian is a scavenger; it forages for carrion. It also preys on smaller organisms, such as protozoa. Its mouth is located in the middle of its body. A planarian feeds by extending a muscular tube, the **pharynx** *(FER-inks)*, out of its mouth. Food is sucked in through the pharynx and passes into the branched intestine. Nutrients are absorbed through the intestinal wall, and undigested food is excreted through the pharynx and mouth.

Chemical wastes and excess water are eliminated through a network of ducts that run the length of the body. Each duct contains many flame cells. A **flame cell** is a cell that encloses a tuft of cilia that beats, resembling a candle flame. The beating of the cilia moves wastes into the duct to the excretory pores, where the wastes leave the body.

Nervous Control

The planarian nervous system and sense organs are also adapted for free living. It is more organized and cephalized than the nerve net of the *Hydra*. Planarians sense the intensity and direction of light with two anterior eyespots that contain photosensitive cells. Receptors for touch, taste, and smell are concentrated at the anterior end. Two anterior clusters of nerve cells, called **ganglia** *(GAN-glee-uh)*, form a simple brain. The ganglia receive information from sensory cells and then send impulses to the rest of the body through a ladderlike system of two longitudinal nerves connected by tranverse nerves.

Planarians show a surprising ability to learn. Their memory, such as how to find the way through a maze, is stored chemically. One planarian can learn to pass through a maze by eating another planarian that already knows the way.

Reproduction

Planarians reproduce sexually and asexually. They are hermaphrodites—single individuals possessing both male and female sex organs. Because they are free-living, they can encounter mates. In sexual reproduction two planarians simultaneously fertilize each other. Eggs, laid in protective capsules that stick to rocks or debris, hatch in two to three weeks. Freshwater planarians occasionally reproduce asexually in the summer. They attach their posterior ends to a surface and stretch until they tear in two. Each half then regenerates its missing parts.

Trematoda

The Class Trematoda consists of about 6,000 species of parasitic flukes, most of which are shaped like leaves. Some flukes are endoparasites, meaning that they live inside their hosts. Others are ectoparasites, meaning that they live on the external surfaces of their hosts. As you read, notice the adaptations for parasitism.

Think

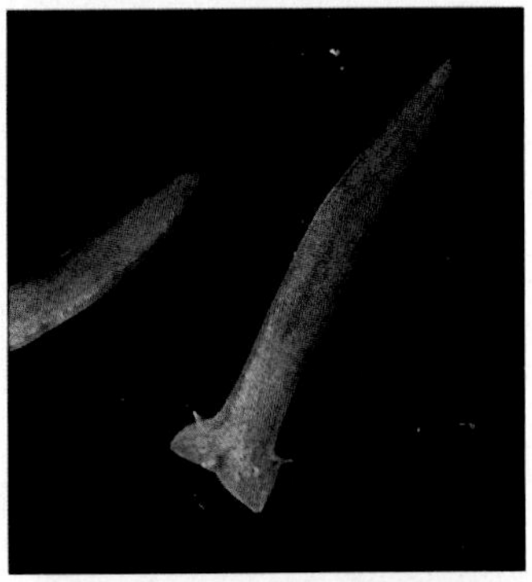

The planarian can reproduce itself by splitting in two and regenerating. What are the advantages and disadvantages of this form of asexual reproduction as compared with sexual reproduction?

Interpreting the Visuals Tell students that the equivalent of a head in the tapeworm is its scolex. Point out that the rest of the body is made up of reproductive units called proglottids that form continually at the scolex. Have students examine the close-up of the proglottid in Figure 30-5 on p. 457. Explain that proglottids are a form of asexual reproduction by budding and are not true segments.
■ *See* Blackline Master *62*.

Guided Practice
Discuss with students the evolutionary significance of bilateral symmetry, mesoderm layer, and cephalization with regard to the later phylogenetic development of animals. Ask students what effect bilateral symmetry had. *(The number and complexity of sense organs increased.)* Now ask why cephalization was important. *(It set the stage for the formation of a brain by locating sense organs in the leading end of a longitudinal body.)* Remind students that the mesoderm, an evolutionary trend first seen in flatworms, made development of many new levels of tissue and organ specializations possible.

Answer to Think
Asexual reproduction can happen quickly and does not require another member of the same species. Sexual reproduction allows for variation in the species through the recombination of genes.

Videodiscs
■ ***Side 4 23455, Marine Flatworm (m)***
■ ***806–818, Turbellaria—Examples (s)***
■ ***2603–2604, Planarian (s)***

Interdisciplinary Activities
Geography Parasitic platyhelminthes inhabit many different areas of the world. Direct students to research parasitic diseases, including river blindness, schistosomiasis, elephantiasis, clonorchiasis, trichuriasis, and trichinosis. Have students prepare a world map showing the geographical distribution of the diseases they have researched. Some of these diseases may be known by local names. For example, in parts of Africa, schistosomiasis is called bilharzia. In addition, have students research the economic consequences of the diseases in the countries in which they are endemic. You may wish to combine this activity with the Cooperative Learning activity on p. 451B.

Independent Practice

- Have students write answers to the Section Review.
- Ask students to write an essay comparing classes of flatworms. Have them pay particular attention to symmetry, body plan, life cycle, motility, feeding, digestion, and reproduction.
- *See* **Process Skills, *Chapter 30.***

Check Your Understanding

1. Compare the digestive systems of planarians and hydras. What is the significance of the differences between the two systems? *(Planarians have a branched intestine; hydras have a single cavity. Hydras have only two tissue layers; planarians have a third, the mesoderm. The planarian digestive system is the first to gain organ level complexity.)*

2. How might the life cycle of the sheep liver fluke hinder human attempts to control the parasite? *(Little opportunity exists to break the cycle; the flukes are hardy survivors in several environments, including two different host animals.)*

3. How does the life cycle of the beef tapeworm illustrate the necessity of sewage treatment? *(Tapeworm eggs are eliminated in the feces of infected humans. Effective treatment of sewage can destroy the eggs before they reach the grass or soil.)*

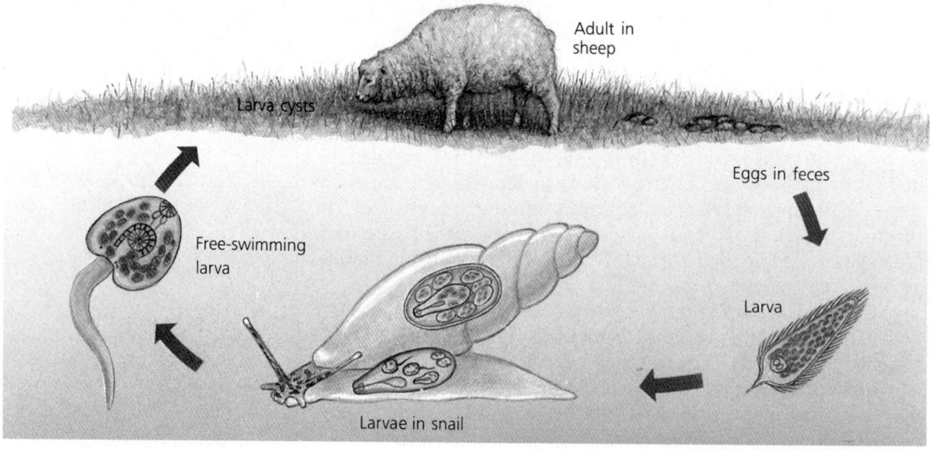

Figure 30-4 During the life cycle of the sheep liver fluke, reproduction occurs both sexually and asexually.

Structure and Reproduction of Flukes

Flukes are adapted to parasitism. They are about 1 cm long, oval shaped, and sheathed in a tough, unciliated tegument. Typically a fluke has two sucker mouths—one on its anterior and one on its ventral surface—that it uses to cling to its host. A powerful pharynx in the anterior sucker sucks in blood, cells, and fluids.

While the nervous and excretory systems of the fluke are similar to those of planarians, its life cycle and reproductive structures are more complex. Typically hermaphroditic, the fluke has a long coiled tube, or **uterus,** that stores eggs until ready for release through a genital pore. A fluke may produce tens of thousands of eggs at a time. A few survive predation and environmental destruction and hatch into larvae, or immature organisms.

The complex life cycle of the economically destructive sheep liver fluke, *Fasciola hepatica,* is illustrated in Figure 30-4. Adult flukes live in the sheep's liver and gallbladder. Flukes mate in these organs and produce eggs. The eggs enter the intestines and are eliminated with the feces of the sheep. The eggs hatch in water, and the larvae then invade snails. Inside snails, the larvae multiply asexually. The larvae leave the snail and form cysts on blades of grass. A **cyst** is a dormant larva surrounded by a hard protective covering. When sheep eat the grass, they ingest the cysts, which hatch in the sheep's digestive tract. The flukes then bore through the intestines into the blood and mature and reproduce in the liver, completing the cycle.

Schistosomiasis

One of the world's most severe public health problems is caused by three species of blood fluke in the genus *Schistosoma.* The blood fluke infests 200 to 300 million people, mostly in Asia, Africa, and South America. The resulting disease, called **schistosomiasis** *(SHISS-tuh-soe-MIE-uh-suss),* affects 20 to 30 times more people than cancer does. The life cycle of a schistosome parallels that of other flukes, with the exception that the adult lives in the

LEP Activity

To underscore visually the complex life cycles of parasites, have students diagram and label the life cycle of the tapeworm. Use the cyclic diagram on p. 453 as a model. Then have students compare their diagrams with the diagram of the life cycle of the sheep liver fluke in Figure 30-4 on p. 456. Ask students what differences they notice between the tapeworm life cycle and the sheep liver fluke life cycle. *(Tapeworms are found outside their hosts only when they are eggs. Sheep liver flukes can be found outside their hosts in egg, cyst, and larval stages.)*

human bloodstream. The spiny eggs of the schistosomes lodge in the human veins, lungs, intestines, bladder, and liver. They block blood vessels and cause internal bleeding and tissue decay that can be fatal.

Cestoda

The Class Cestoda consists of about 1,500 species. Most are parasitic tapeworms. All vertebrates may host tapeworms. Humans, for example, may harbor any of seven different species.

Structure

Like flukes, tapeworms are adapted for the parasitic life. They have tough outer teguments and hooks and suckers to attach themselves to their hosts. Their long, ribbonlike bodies may grow up to 12 m. The nervous system extends the length of the body.

Tapeworms lack sense organs, mouths, and digestive tracts. They absorb nutrients directly through their heavily folded teguments. The folds increase the surface area for absorption. The tapeworm grips its host with hooks and suckers on its knob-shaped head, or **scolex** *(SKOE-leks)*. It grows by producing body sections, called **proglottids** *(proe-GLAHT-udz)*, immediately behind the scolex. Thus the oldest proglottids are at the posterior end. The excretory system drains the proglottid of wastes.

Life Cycle and Reproduction

Each proglottid contains both male and female reproductive organs. Cross-fertilization between two adjacent worms is typical, but self-fertilization between proglottids can also occur. After ferilization the egg-packed proglottid breaks off from the adult and is eliminated with the host's feces.

The life cycle of the beef tapeworm, *Taenia saginatum,* begins when cattle eat grass contaminated with proglottids and eggs. Larvae hatch and bore through the cow's intestine into the bloodstream. The larvae then burrow into muscle tissue and form cysts. Humans become infected when they eat beef that has not been cooked sufficiently to kill the bladder worms inside the cysts. Once the cysts are inside the human intestine, the cyst wall dissolves and releases the bladder worm, which then develops into an adult beef tapeworm.

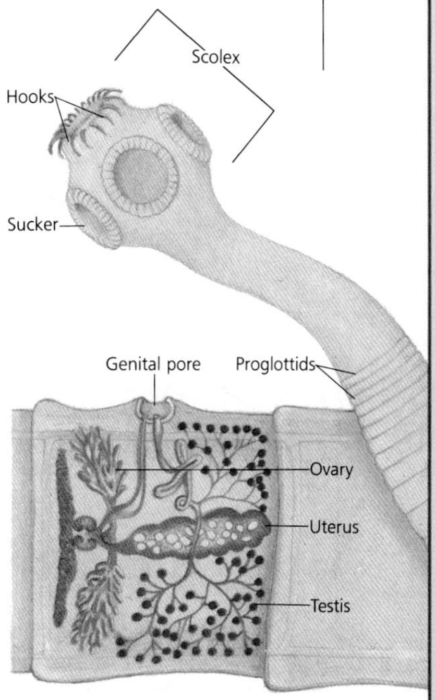

Figure 30-5 A tapeworm grows by adding proglottids behind its head. With male and female reproductive organs in each proglottid, both cross-fertilization and self-fertilization are possible.

Section Review

1. What is a *flame cell?*
2. How are stimuli sensed in flatworms?
3. How does the presence of the blood fluke *Schistosoma* affect the human body?
4. How do tapeworms obtain nutrients without a mouth or a digestive system?
5. Why is it adaptive that a parasite not kill its host?

Answers to Section Review

1. A *flame cell* is a planarian cell containing cilia, which move wastes through canals to excretory pores. The network of flame cells and canals is the excretory system.
2. Through sense receptors and nerves concentrated at the anterior end of the body
3. Adults and eggs lodge in blood vessels, causing internal bleeding. Blocking of the vessels also causes tissue decay.
4. Tapeworms live on nutrients that have already been digested by their hosts. Cells of the tapeworms absorb nutrients directly through their surfaces.
5. If the parasite killed its host, the parasite would also die. It depends on the host for nutrition and protection against adverse conditions and predators.

Reteaching

Have students discuss the evidence of more advanced development in platyhelminthes compared with cnidarians. Tell students to consider feeding, digestion, nervous system, reproduction, and body plan of the animals in these phyla. *(Cnidarians show radial symmetry and a simple digestive system with only one opening, a gastrovascular cavity. Their reproduction can be sexual or asexual. Platyhelminthes show a more complex nervous center, including receptors for touch, taste, and smell, which are concentrated at the anterior end along with ganglia. Their digestion is also more complex, with excretory canals and pores. Reproduction, like that of the cnidarians, can be sexual or asexual.)*

- *See* Section Reviews *worksheet, Section 30.1*

Enrichment

Have students research the hypothesis that parasitic flatworms originated as free-living organisms. Then have them develop a script for a television nature program, illustrated with a sequence of sketches, in which they discuss the pros and cons of the hypothesis.

Closure

Discuss with students the relationship between structure and function in flatworms. Point out that although body structures are adapted to parasitism in some flatworms, all flatworms lack respiratory and circulatory systems.

Videodiscs

- *Side 4 14516 Fluke (m)*
- *819–826, Trematoda: Flukes (s)*

Lesson Plan

Section Focus

Roundworms (Phylum Nematoda) comprise 10,000–80,000 species. They are slender, cylindrical animals that are pseudocoelomates; they also have a complete digestive tract with two openings. The one-way gut is tubelike and is suspended in a fluid-filled body cavity within the body wall. The rotifers (Phylum Rotifera) are microscopic, free-swimming, aquatic animals.

Section Themes

Throughout this section the theme of **Systems and Interactions** is emphasized. The relationship between parasitic roundworms and their hosts illustrates one of the ways in which separate components of a natural system affect each other.

Motivating Activity

Show students a shovelful of good garden soil and ask them to guess how many individual nematodes it might contain. *(As many as a million)* Nematodes are tiny, but they are vitally important in aerating the soil and distributing organic and mineral material in the soil. About fifty species are parasitic, however, and cause damage to crops, livestock, and humans.

Teaching Strategies

Making Inferences Ask students why it might not be a good idea to walk barefoot. *(There is no way of seeing whether an area contains hookworm eggs.)* Tell students that the transmission of human-specific hookworms is the reason human feces should not be used as fertilizer, as is done in many parts of the developing world.

Section Objectives

- *Compare and contrast the body plans of flatworms and roundworms.*
- *Summarize the parasitic relationships of common roundworms and humans.*
- *Describe the anatomy of a rotifer.*
- *Describe a classical study of nematode development.*

30.2 Nematoda and Rotifera

Members of the Phyla Nematoda and Rotifera are characterized by the presence of a pseudocoelom. This body cavity is lined on the inside by endoderm and on the outside by mesoderm. The fluid-filled space contains organs, supports the body, provides the hydrostatic pressure against which muscles can contract, and serves as a storage area for wastes or for eggs and sperm.

Nematoda

Roundworms are classified in the Phylum Nematoda. The number of nematode species is estimated at 10,000 to 80,000. Roundworms have long slender bodies that taper at both ends. Most are covered with a flexible protective cuticle. They range in length from less than 1 mm to as long as the female guinea worm, which can be 120 cm. Roundworms have a digestive tract with two openings, an anterior mouth and a posterior **anus,** the opening through which wastes are eliminated. The sexes are distinct in most species.

Biology in Process

Roundworm Development

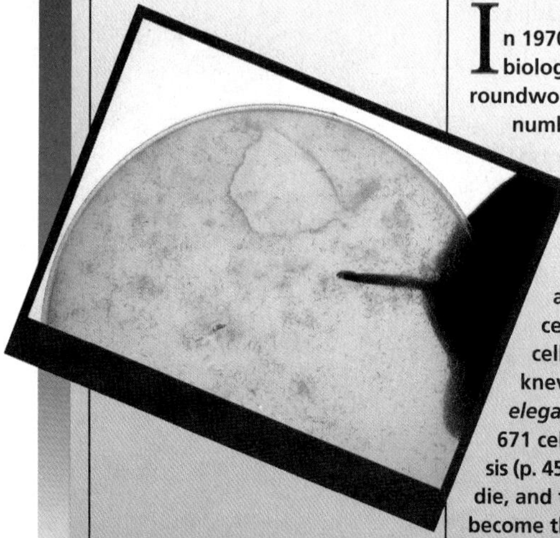

In 1970 most developmental biologists believed that roundworms had a constant number of cells after hatching. The scientists believed that cell growth was being achieved through the formation of vacuoles and extension of the cells rather than through cell division. Biologists knew that *Caenorhabditis elegans* formed a total of 671 cells during embryogenesis (p. 458). Of these, 113 always die, and the remaining 558 cells become the hatchling worm.

John Sulston, a newcomer to developmental biology, observed that adult worms had 57 neurons in the ventral cord while young larvae had only 15 neurons. Sulston set out to discover how 15 cells had become 57. He was completely unaware at the time that such a phenomenon was thought to be impossible. Using a light microscope, which allowed individual nuclei to be observed in living worms, Sulston watched a young *C. elegans* larva to find out which of its 15 cells would divide to generate the 42 new ones. None did. Instead, 10 new cells seemed to appear in the ventral cord as if from out of nowhere. When he observed more larvae, Sulston was able

1 Eggs in food or water enter host
2 Eggs hatch in host's small intestine
3 Larvae go into blood vessels
4 Blood carries larvae to lungs
5 Larvae travel to throat and are swallowed
6 Adult ascarids mate in small intestine
7 Eggs leave body in feces of host

Graphic Organizer Use this list in Guided Practice on p. 459.

The vast majority of roundworm species are free-living on land, in salt water, and in fresh water. About 50 species are plant and animal parasites that cause enormous economic damage and physical suffering throughout the world. Humans are host to about 50 different roundworm species, three of which will be discussed here. In these roundworms notice the adaptations for parasitism.

Ascaris

Ascaris (AS-kuh-russ) is a roundworm parasite found in the intestines of pigs, horses, and humans. *Ascaris* eggs enter the body in contaminated food or water. After hatching in the intestines the larvae bore into the bloodstream and are carried to the lungs and throat. There they are coughed up, swallowed, and returned to the intestines, where they mature and mate. If the host is not treated, knots of worms can block the intestines, causing death. Larvae in the lungs cause a respiratory illness.

The adult female grows up to 30 cm. The much smaller male has a hooked posterior that holds the female during mating. A female produces up to 200,000 eggs a day. The fertilized eggs are shed through a genital pore and exit in the host's feces.

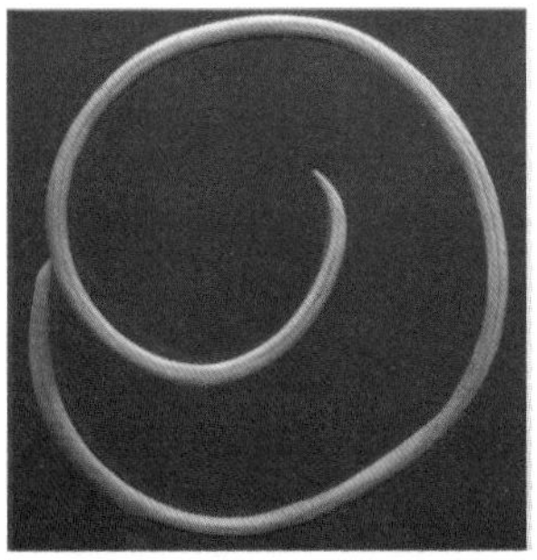

Figure 30-6 **This roundworm, with its long slender body that tapers at both ends, has a shape that is typical of the thousands of species in the Phylum Nematoda.**

to determine that the 10 cells were migrating into the ventral cord from other body areas within the hatchling worms. These 10 cells divided, and each produced six descendants.

Careful observation and coding eventually revealed the developmental history of every cell in *C. elegans*. For example, in Sulston's notation the lineage of one muscle cell is coded *Dapa* (p. 459). Reading the code from right to left shows that the cell originally came from the anterior half (a), of the posterior half (p), of the anterior half (a), of the original parent cell (D).

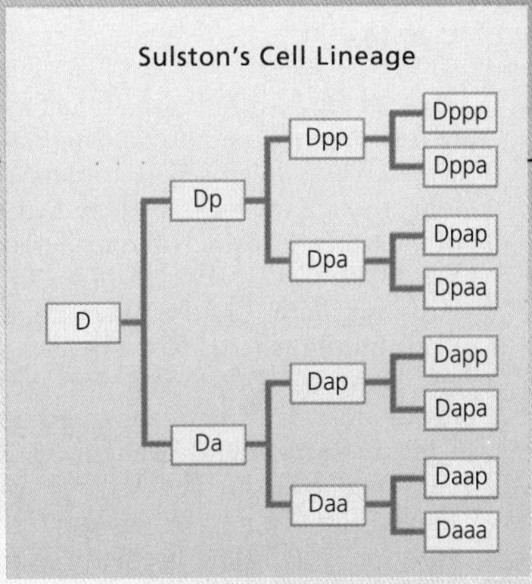

John White, working in the same laboratory as Sulston, determined the function of individual cells in mature and developing worms by selectively destroying certain cells with a laser beam and observing the results. More recently Sulston and H. Robert Horovitz have investigated mutants with defective cell lineages. First, the biologists identify individual genes controlling a specific cell division. Then these genes are further studied to determine how they specify development by encoding proteins that act as receptors or intercellular signals. These data might ultimately aid in understanding how human genes control cell division or how cell division is altered in genetic diseases or cancer.

- **How was unbiased observing important to understanding cell division and development in *C. elegans*?**

Cooperative Learning

Preventing Parasitic Diseases Have students work in groups of three to develop and produce a poster that warns of the dangers of hookworm infestation and tells ways to prevent it. Have the group discuss the dangers and preventive measures that can be taken. Encourage all the group members to agree on the main ideas to be communicated. Then tell one group member to write copy for the poster. Have the second group member develop illustrations for the poster, and have the third group member design the poster using the copy and illustrations. You may wish to display the completed posters in your classroom.

Exploring Careers Ask a veterinarian to visit the class, or arrange a field trip to a local veterinarian's clinic to discuss how parasitic diseases are prevented or treated in pets.

Guided Practice

Have students list the stages of the life cycle of a roundworm. An example of a completed list is on p. 458.

Independent Practice

- Have students write answers to the Section Review.
- A rotifer's mouth uses cilia to sweep food in. Have students review early chapters to find previous mention of cilia. *(Phylum Ciliophora, pp. 312–313)*

Biology in Process

Using the Feature

The process skills used in this feature are observing and experimenting. Important discoveries have been made by researchers uninfluenced by preconceptions. Point out that Sulston began to observe the larvae unaware that biologists held that *no* nematode's cells could divide after hatching. His observations led to the tracing of each cell of the adult worm to a specific division of the original parent cell and an understanding of how some genes act.

To help students understand the concentration needed to observe and record cell lineages, write on the board as many successive divisions *(a* and *p)* of a parent cell *(D)* as possible. Ask students to decode the end cells, using *D*, *a*, and *p*.

Answer to the Feature

Observation allowed researchers to trace individual cells and determine the succession of each cell in the hatchling worm.

Videodiscs

- *834–836, Nematoda (s)*

Check Your Understanding
1. What advantage does the production of large numbers of offspring offer parasite species? *(Increased chances that some will find a host and survive)*
2. What evolutionary trend is shown by the digestive systems of cnidarians, flatworms, and roundworms? *(Increasing complexity, from one opening into a single gastrovascular cavity, to excretory pores and canals, and finally to two openings—a mouth and an anus)*

Reteaching
Have students describe and compare the anatomy of roundworms and rotifers. *(The roundworm has a long, slender body, a pseudocoelom, and a well-defined digestive tract, with a mouth and anus. The rotifer's digestive system is more complex and includes a mastax, a digestive gland, and a bladder.)*
■ *See* Section Reviews *worksheet, Section 30.2.*

Enrichment
Although parasitic roundworms are discussed more often in textbooks, most roundworms are nonparasitic inhabitants of soil where they recycle nutrients. Have students research a free-living roundworm, such as *Turbatrix* (vinegar eel), and write an illustrated report.

Closure
Remind students of the continuing advancement in the complexity of animals. Have students compare Figure 30-3 on p. 454 and Figure 30-7 on p. 460. Ask them how increased complexity is exhibited in rotifers when compared with flatworms. *(By a well-developed digestive system with two openings, a stomach, a mastax, and a bladder)*

Videodiscs
■ ***Side 3 35747, Rotifer (m)***

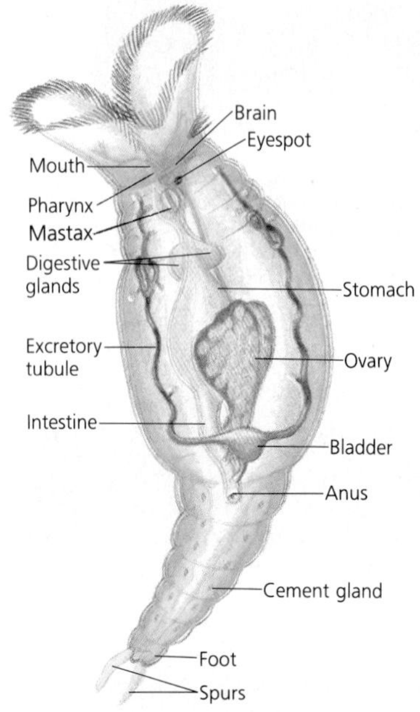

Figure 30-7 Cilia surrounding the mouth of a rotifer sweep food into the mouth. Hydrostatic pressure within the pseudocoelom helps the rotifer maintain its shape.

Ancylostoma and *Necator*

Ancylostoma and *Necator,* two genera of hookworm, seriously harm over 400 million people worldwide. *Necator* causes about 90 percent of the infections in tropical and semitropical regions. The hookworm's mouth has cutting plates that hook onto the intestinal wall. The hookworm feeds on its host's blood, causing anemia. Like *Ascaris,* the hookworm travels through the blood to the lungs and into the throat, where it is swallowed. Hookworms mate in the intestines. Their eggs are shed in the host's feces and hatch on warm moist soil. The larvae then bore through the feet of a new host. Shoes protect against hookworm infestation.

Trichinella

Roundworms of the genus *Trichinella* cause the disease **trichinosis** *(TRICK-uh-NOE-suss)* in humans. Humans become infected when they eat undercooked pork that is contaminated with trichina cysts. The cysts release larvae, which burrow into the wall of the small intestine, where they mature into adults. The adults then produce larvae that pass into the blood and form cysts in the muscles, causing pain and stiffness. Trichinosis is now rare in the United States. Farmers cook meat scraps before feeding them to hogs, and meat-packers freeze pork, which kills the worms.

Rotifera

Most of the 1,750 species of the Phylum Rotifera are transparent, free-swimming, microscopic animals that live in marine or fresh water. These microscopic rotifers are between 100 and 500 µm long, though the male is much smaller than the female. The crown of cilia that surrounds the rotifer's mouth, which can be seen in Figure 30-7, is an adaptation for free living. The cilia sweep food into the mouth. Under a microscope this beating of the cilia looks like rotating wheels. Rotifers feed on unicellular algae, bacteria, and protozoa. This food moves through the pharynx to the **mastax,** a muscular organ that chops up the food. The rotifer has no skeleton. It maintains its shape by the hydrostatic pressure within the pseudocoelom. The nervous system is composed of anterior ganglia and two long nerves that run the length of the body. Cephalization is indicated by the two anterior eyespots.

Section Review

1. Define *trichinosis.*
2. What is the significance of the pseudocoelom in nematodes and rotifers?
3. How can humans prevent hookworm infestation?
4. What is the function of the cilia on the rotifer's head?
5. How is the general body plan of the roundworm adapted to its way of life?

Answers to Section Review
1. Trichinosis is a disease caused by ingestion of the *Trichinella* roundworm.
2. The presence of fluid in the pseudocoelom gives shape to these animals and provides a hydrostatic pressure for muscle contractions to work against. The cavity also contains organs and can store eggs and wastes.
3. By wearing shoes when walking in areas that are likely to be infested with larvae
4. To move food into the rotifer's mouth
5. It is long, flexible, and slender, with pointed tips at either end. Thus, it moves easily through decomposing soil or inside an animal's organ.

Laboratory

Observing Flatworms

Objective
To observe the feeding behavior of flatworms and study their response to different stimuli

Process Skills
Observing, hypothesizing, experimenting

Materials
Dugesia, plastic medicine dropper with the tip cut off, culture dish, pond water, medicine dropper, dissecting microscope, blunt probe, raw liver, small flashlight

Background
1 *Dugesia,* a planarian, is a nonparasitic flatworm belonging to the Class Turbellaria. What are some characteristics of this class? What are some characteristics of the Phylum Platyhelminthes?
2 What is meant by *cephalization,* and why is it an important evolutionary advance?

Inquiry
1 Use a medicine dropper to transfer a flatworm to a small culture dish. Gently cover the flatworm with pond water. Why should you use pond water here and not tap water?
2 Observe the flatworm under the low power of the dissecting microscope. Observe how it moves. Notice the shape of its body. What kind of symmetry does it have? What structural features demonstrate this symmetry? Does the flatworm appear to have a distinct head and tail? How can you tell?
3 Look carefully at the surface of the flatworm under high power. What structures do you see that could account for its movement?
4 Using a blunt probe, gently touch the posterior end of the flatworm. Notice its response. Now gently touch its anterior end. How does the response compare? What can you conclude from your observations?

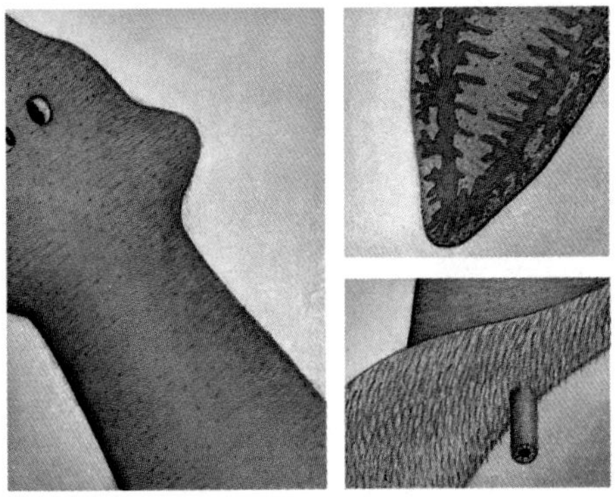

5 Design a simple experiment to test whether a flatworm can sense gravity, and carry it out. What do you conclude?
6 Design an experiment that tests the flatworm's sensitivity to light. Are its anterior and posterior ends equally sensitive?
7 Place a tiny piece of raw liver in the culture dish. Observe the flatworm for several minutes and describe its feeding response. Why is it important to use flatworms that have not been recently fed?
8 After several minutes, use the probe to turn the flatworm over gently. What do you observe? If you have time, watch as the flatworm eats the liver. Where do you think the undigested waste will come out?

Conclusions
1 What evidence does the flatworm show of cephalization?
2 The flatworm has an incomplete digestive system and no circulatory system (blood). How do you think the food gets to the cells after it is digested?
3 Suggest possible sources of error in the experiment that you performed with *Dugesia.*

Further Inquiry
Design experiments to study the responses of planarians to vibrations, sound, or living food.

Laboratory

(For an overview of flatworm structure and preparatory information related to the laboratory, see p. 451B.)

Background

1. Turbellaria are nonparasitic and have bodies covered with cilia. Platyhelminthes have bilateral symmetry, incomplete digestive systems, three layers of tissue (ectoderm, endoderm, and mesoderm), but no body cavity or coelom.
2. Cephalization refers to the concentration of sense organs at the head. This arrangement makes possible more complicated sense organs and brains.

Inquiry

1. Tap water might not be an appropriate temperature and could contain harmful dissolved gases or minerals.
2. *Dugesia* has bilateral symmetry with paired anterior projections and eyespots. Head and tail are distinct in appearance since the head has eyespots and is broader than the tail.
3. Cilia
4. There should be a stronger response at the anterior end where sense receptors are concentrated. However, all students might not observe this.
5. Students could gently turn the flatworm over with their probe. It will right itself in response to gravity.
6. Students might look for increased movement under light and dark conditions. They might look at responses when they shine the light on the anterior and posterior ends. They should expect a greater response to light on the anterior end where the eyespots are located.
7. Hungry flatworms will be more likely to eat.
8. The pharynx extrudes to ingest the liver. Undigested waste will be excreted through the pharynx.

Conclusions

1. Eyespots and anterior projections are at the head. The anterior end is more sensitive to light. The flatworm moves headfirst.
2. The digestive system is so highly branched that it reaches nearly every cell of the body.
3. If the flatworm is sickly, has been roughly handled, or has been fed recently, then it may not respond to stimuli as anticipated.

Further Inquiry

Students might gently shake the dish, make a sudden noise, subject the flatworm to a camera flashbulb, or feed it live protozoa.

Chapter 30 Review

Vocabulary

1. Parasite; the other terms relate to the body plans of organisms.
2. Anus; the other terms are body parts of the planarian.
3. Mastax; the other terms are body parts of the tapeworm.
4. Ganglia; the other terms relate to parasites.
5. Pharynx; the other terms are protective coverings.

Review

1. a	**6.** d
2. b	**7.** c
3. a	**8.** c
4. c	**9.** a
5. a	**10.** d

11. The flatworm is acoelomate, bilaterally symmetrical, shows cephalization, has no respiratory or circulatory systems, and has a digestive system with only one opening.
12. A planarian coordinates its responses to stimuli with its ganglia. Impulses are sent through a ladderlike network of nerves from the ganglia throughout the body.
13. Planarians are hermaphrodites that reproduce sexually through simultaneous cross-fertilization. They also reproduce asexually by splitting in two and regenerating missing parts to form two individuals.
14. Both tegument and cuticle will protect a parasite from being digested by its host.
15. One adaptation of a fluke is tegument, which keeps it from being digested by its host. Another is suckers with which it attaches itself to the host. Flukes also have a powerful pharynx, which is used in feeding on the host's body fluids. Fluke larvae are protected by a hard cyst.
16. Tapeworms have tegument and suckers but have neither mouth nor digestive system. Thus, they must live on nutrients already digested by the host.

Chapter 30 Review

Vocabulary

acoelomate (453)	flame cell (455)	pharynx (455)	scolex (457)
anus (458)	ganglia (455)	proglottid (457)	tegument (454)
coelom (453)	host (454)	pseudocoelom (453)	trichinosis (460)
cuticle (454)	mastax (460)	schistosomiasis (456)	uterus (456)
cyst (456)	parasite (454)		

For each set of terms below, choose the one that does not belong and explain why it does not.

1. pseudocoelom, parasite, acoelomate, coelom
2. pharynx, flame cell, ganglia, anus
3. scolex, mastax, proglottid, tegument
4. schistosomiasis, trichinosis, ganglia, host
5. pharynx, tegument, cuticle, cyst

Review

1. A coelom develops within the (a) mesoderm (b) ectoderm (c) endoderm (d) acoelomate.
2. A planarian uses its pharynx to help it (a) move (b) feed (c) reproduce (d) respond to light.
3. In planarians the flame cell (a) functions to move liquid wastes through the body (b) responds to light and sound (c) is specialized for diffusion (d) controls regeneration.
4. The sheep liver fluke reproduces (a) in water (b) inside a snail (c) inside a sheep's liver (d) inside a sheep's digestive tract.
5. The function of the cyst in flukes is to (a) protect the immature worm (b) fertilize the eggs (c) facilitate movement (d) bore into the host.
6. A tapeworm uses its scolex to (a) locate food (b) communicate with other tapeworms (c) get rid of liquid wastes (d) attach itself to its host.
7. Humans ingest tapeworms by (a) drinking water containing tapeworm larvae (b) walking barefoot on contaminated soil (c) eating contaminated meat (d) wading in contaminated water.
8. A characteristic that differentiates roundworms from flatworms is (a) the presence of a mesoderm (b) a bilaterally symmetrical body plan (c) the presence of an anus (d) cephalization.
9. Trichinosis in human beings results in (a) muscle soreness (b) anemia (c) blockage of blood vessels (d) a respiratory illness.
10. The mastax in rotifers helps them to (a) move (b) sense light (c) reproduce (d) digest food.
11. What are the major characteristics of the flatworm?
12. Describe the structure and function of the nervous system of a planarian.
13. How do planarians reproduce?
14. What is the function of the tegument and cuticle in parasites?
15. What are some adaptations of flukes for a parasitic way of life?
16. How are tapeworms specialized for a parasitic way of life?
17. Compare and contrast roundworms and rotifers.
18. Describe the life cycle of the roundworm *Ascaris*.
19. How can humans protect themselves from the disease trichinosis?
20. Why is the roundworm *Caenorhabditis elegans* frequently selected for laboratory observation?

17. Roundworms and rotifers both have pseudocoeloms, digestive tracts with two openings, bilaterally symmetrical body plans, and some degree of cephalization. Some roundworms are parasitic, whereas all rotifers are free-living. Rotifers have some features that are lacking in roundworms, such as a crown of cilia and a mastax.

18. *Ascaris* eggs are picked up by the host in contaminated food or water. Eggs hatch in the intestine. Larvae travel through the bloodstream, are coughed up into the mouth, and then swallowed. In the intestine they mature and reproduce. Fertilized eggs leave with the feces of the host.

Critical Thinking

1. When would asexual reproduction be advantageous to a free-swimming flatworm?
2. Parasites are specific. This means that they must invade the correct host or they cannot survive. Suggest how members of a species find the correct host.
3. The Aswan High Dam across the Nile River in Egypt was completed in 1970. It was built to increase the supply of irrigation water, to control major flooding, and to provide a source of hydroelectric power. Since the dam was built, there has been an increase of schistosomiasis in the region. Why do you think this happened?
4. Hookworms are extremely common in China, where rice is the main crop. Rice is grown in paddies that are periodically flooded. Considering what you know about how hookworms invade the body, why might hookworm infection be so common in this part of the world?
5. Why do we use the term *eyespot* instead of *eye* to refer to the photosensitive regions at the anterior end of the planarian body?
6. A person infected with a tapeworm may show generalized symptoms, such as tiredness, loss of weight, and low blood count. These symptoms could indicate any number of diseases. How would a doctor make a positive diagnosis?

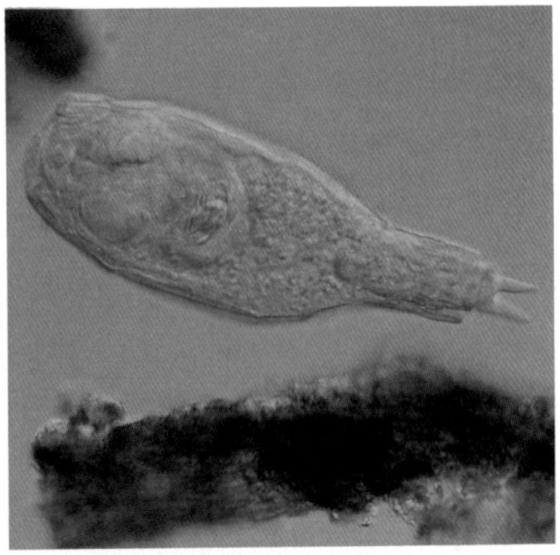

7. Some rotifers can survive being dried out for as long as four years. If their dried bodies are put into water, they revive. For what kind of environment might this characteristic be adaptive?
8. Look at the photograph above of a rotifer. Notice the two extensions, called spurs, at its posterior end. Suggest a possible function for the spurs.

Extension

1. Collect a sample of moist soil or soil and sand from the bottom of a pond. Using a dissecting microscope or a large magnifier, look for nematodes, and observe their behavior.
2. Collect a sample of pond water or make a grass infusion by placing dried grass and other plants in water and letting them stand for a few days. If these are not available, a culture of rotifers can be obtained from a biological supply house. Observe the feeding behavior of rotifers.
3. Research the types of marine species of turbellarians. Draw pictures of them, making sure to color them accurately. List the following information under your drawings: scientific name, common name if known, habitat, area of the world where it is found, food, method of protection.
4. Read the article by Julie Ann Miller and Carolyn Strange entitled "Long-Lived Worms" in *BioScience,* June 1990, p. 432. Write a report in which you explain why *C. elegans* is an ideal model for studying the aging process. What multitrait effects are caused by the age-1 mutation?

19. Humans can protect themselves from trichinosis by eating pork that is free of cysts containing live larvae. This can be guaranteed by cooking pork sufficiently to kill the larvae, by freezing it, or by eating pork from pigs or hogs that have not been fed raw meat.
20. *C. elegans* is easily grown in the laboratory and takes only 12 hours to hatch. Furthermore, the development of the cells of *C. elegans* eggs is predictable, both as to final position and total number.

Critical Thinking

1. When it cannot locate a mate
2. Any answers that suggest chemical or tactile receptors should be accepted.
3. Many new irrigation canals and the lake behind the dam provided favorable habitats for snails, which are host to *Schistosoma* larvae.
4. Hookworm eggs hatch in warm, moist soil, such as rice paddies. Because field workers often go barefoot, they are more likely to become infested.
5. The term *eyespot* better describes the fact that this region merely senses light and does not process images.
6. The doctor could look for proglottids or eggs in the person's feces.
7. This characteristic is adaptive in pools of water that periodically dry up.
8. To anchor the rotifer

Extension

1. Caution students not to handle the soil. Direct them to use tweezers or a probe.
2. Guide students to notice the sweeping action of the double rings of cilia around the heads that has resulted in rotifers being called the wheel animals.
3. Also assign students to research and report on land-dwelling turbellarians.
4. The Human Genome Project, a major study to map human genes, is currently under way. Such a study is possible, in part, because of experience gained in the mapping of genes of species such as *C. elegans*. This project is not without controversy. Encourage students to explore ethical implications, such as the possible use of information about an individual's genes by the health insurance industry.

Chapter 31 Mollusks and Annelids

Chapter Overview

Chapter 31 examines similarities and differences between the Phyla Mollusca and Annelida. Sections 31.1 and 31.2 explain why scientists think that these phyla evolved from a common ancestor and what they consider the adaptive advantages of various body forms.

Chapter Planning Chart

B	S	A	Sections and Subsections	Page	Features	Page	Resources
•	•	•	**31.1 Mollusca**				
			Relationship of Mollusca and Annelida	465	Think	468	Videodiscs
			Characteristics of Mollusks	465	Section Review	470	Blackline Master 63
			Body Plan	466			Blackline Master 64
			Polyplacophora	467			Overhead Transparency T31
			Gastropoda	467			Process Skills: Mollusk Locomotion
			Bivalvia	468			Section Reviews Worksheet
			Cephalopoda	469			
•	•	•	**31.2 Annelida**				
			Oligochaeta	471	Biotechnology	472	Videodiscs
			Polychaeta and Hirudinea	474	Laboratory	475	Science in Action Videotape: Alternatives to Dissection
					Section Review	474	Blackline Master 65
							Laboratories: Live Earthworms
							Section Reviews Worksheet
			End of Chapter Activities				
					Chapter Review	476	Vocabulary Skills
							Chapter Test
							Computer Test Generator

B *The Basic Level curriculum presents the most fundamental knowledge offered in the course.*
S *The Standard Level curriculum is designed for the average student who is able to master most topics.*
A *The Advanced Level curriculum includes suggestions for teaching the most academically able students.*

Cooperative Learning

Group Activity: Anatomy of a Snail

- **Group Size:** *3 students*
- **Outcome:** *Students will be able to describe the anatomical features of a snail.*
- **Individual Accountability:** *Each student will contribute one part of a clay model of a snail's anatomy.*
- **Positive Interdependence:** *Each group will assemble a complete model of a longitudinal section of a snail.*

Give each group at least three different colors of modeling clay. Tell students that each group must make their model in the same scale and must also plan the best use of color. Recommend that they use Figure 31-2 as a reference and, if possible, provide other references such as invertebrate zoology texts. Assign one student in each group to model the snail's shell and mantle. Have a second student model the snail's gill, visceral mass, and digestive tract. Tell the third student to model the snail's head and foot.

After the group models are complete, have each group share their model with the other groups. Require students to verify structural accuracy and provide clarity in presenting the various models.

Concept Map

The following is one possible solution to the concept mapping activity in Analyzing Phylogeny on p. 472.

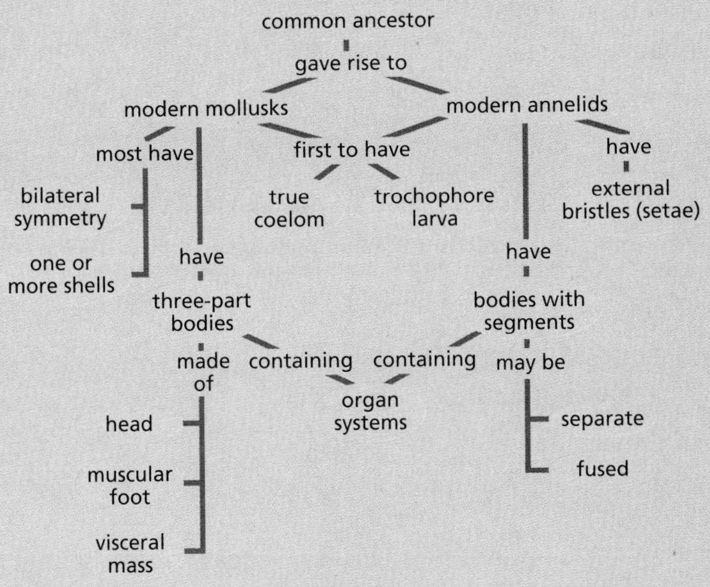

Laboratory Preparation

Overview *(See p. 475.)*

In this lab procedure, students examine the behavior of an earthworm. Students design experiments to test the animal's response to ammonium hydroxide. Students also compare the organism's degree of sensitivity at its anterior and posterior ends. In addition, experiments test the animal's responses to touch and light. Based on their observations, students make inferences about the adaptive advantage of the earthworm's behavior.

Preparation

Prepare a 3% solution of ammonium hydroxide or use undiluted household ammonia instead. Be sure that the pans are clean because traces of preservative can be an irritant to the earthworm. Dim the classroom lights so that excessive light will not interfere with the investigation.

Teaching Tips

Have students read the Technique section carefully before they design their experiment.

Help students identify the head and tail of the earthworm. Point out that the anterior end is more rounded and the posterior end is more pointed.

Explain to students that they can elicit a response from the earthworm by holding the swab near the animal without actually touching it.

Direct students to describe responses of the earthworm in explicit detail. Encourage them to compare results with those of other students in terms of both the earthworm's response and the language used to describe it.

Suggest to students that they set a time limit during which they will observe the earthworm reactions.

Safety

Remind students to handle earthworms in a humane manner.

Chapter Themes

Evolution The development of a coelom in animals is a major evolutionary advance. Emphasize to students that this structure led to the development of a closed circulatory system, provided a fluid environment within which digestive, sexual, and other organs could be suspended, and facilitated muscle-driven body movement.

Scale and Structure Although structures of adult mollusks and annelids differ greatly, their trochophore larvae share a common structure. Stress that such a similarity is not mere coincidence. This shared pattern of development is evidence of their common ancestry.

Chapter Motivating Activity

Show students a set of photographs from nature magazines or invertebrate zoology texts, or a set of specimens, of a squid, oyster, earthworm, leech, and snail. Then display a second set of photographs showing a serving of fried calamari, a string of pearls, an earthworm farm, a leech being used in a medical setting, and a snail in a small aquarium. Ask students to use the second set of photographs to help them infer what the first set of animals have in common. *(These animals as well as other members of their phyla play a significant role in the world's economy. The industries in which these animals have commercial value are diverse—seafood, jewelry, farming, medicine, and hobbies.)* Ask students to name other similar animals that are used commercially. *(Answers may include scallops, clams, and octopuses.)*

Chapter 31 *Mollusks and Annelids*

Introduction

At first glance it's hard to see much resemblance between a feather-duster worm and an octopus. However, these animals share several important characteristics, as do the other organisms in the phyla they represent. Octopuses belong to the Phylum Mollusca, and feather-duster worms to the Phylum Annelida. In this chapter you will learn about the similarities and the differences between these two phyla and about the diversity of species in each phylum.

Chapter Outline

31.1 Mollusca
- *Relationship of Mollusca and Annelida*
- *Characteristics of Mollusks*
- *Body Plan*
- *Polyplacophora*
- *Gastropoda*
- *Bivalvia*
- *Cephalopoda*

31.2 Annelida
- *Oligochaeta*
- *Polychaeta and Hirudinea*

Chapter Concept

As you read, note how the body forms of various species of mollusks and annelids illustrate adaptions for life in particular environments.

Cluster of polychaete worms known as feather dusters, *Sabella crassicornis.* Inset: Octopus, *Haptalochlaena maculosa,* Indonesia.

Understanding the Visuals

Call students' attention to the feathery gills of the polychaete worms. Have students contrast these worms with the ones they studied in Chapter 30. Discuss the differences between the feather duster in the photograph and flatworms and roundworms.

Ask students if the blue-ring octopus in the inset photo matches any impressions they might have about octopuses. Point out that the blue-ring variety is a relatively small octopus that resides on coral reefs but that it makes up for its small size with an extremely toxic venom.

31.1 Mollusca

Despite their very different appearances such familiar invertebrates as chitons, clams, snails, and octopuses are all mollusks, members of the Phylum Mollusca. The word *mollusk* comes from a Latin term meaning "soft" and refers to the bodies of these animals. Although slugs and octopuses have soft bodies, most mollusks have a shell that protects and conceals their soft body.

Relationship of Mollusca and Annelida

Based on comparative studies of both living and fossil species, biologists have concluded that members of the Phylum Mollusca share a common ancestor with the segmented worms of the Phylum Annelida. Mollusks and annelids have similar embryonic development, which you will study in Chapter 35. In addition, mollusks and annelids were probably the first major groups of organisms to have a true coelom—that is, a fluid-filled cavity within the mesoderm. The coelom provides several benefits. By separating the muscles of the gut from those of the body wall, the coelom allows food to move through the body independent of locomotion. The coelom also provides a space in which a circulatory system can function without interference from other organs. In some species the fluid in the coelom also forms a sort of internal hydrostatic skeleton against which the muscles can contract.

The strongest evidence for the common ancestry of mollusks and annelids is the characteristic larval form they share. In both groups the first stage of larval development is a pear-shaped larva called a **trochophore** *(TROCK-uh-for)*. Notice in Figure 31-1 that cilia project from both ends of the trochophore and circle the middle. These cilia propel the trochophore through the water and draw food to the mouth. Free-swimming trochophores aid in the dispersal of many marine mollusks. However, in terrestrial mollusks and in many species of marine annelids, the trochophore develops within the egg and is not free-living. The trochophore will be discussed further in Chapter 35.

Characteristics of Mollusks

Mollusks are a diverse group of more than 100,000 species. Among animal phyla only Arthropoda has more species. Some mollusks are sedentary filter feeders, such as clams and oysters. Others are predatory, such as squids and octopuses—which move about by jet propulsion and have complex nervous systems. Mollusks also have diverse connections with humans. Certain species of snails, for example, are alternate hosts of parasites, such as schistosomes, that are harbored by humans. The feeding habits of snails and slugs cause damage to crops. In contrast, humans prize many mollusks as food or for the beauty of their shells.

Section Objectives

- *List three types of evidence that indicate a close evolutionary relationship between mollusks and annelids.*
- *Summarize the adaptive advantages of a true coelom.*
- *Name the characteristics shared by most mollusks.*
- *Contrast respiration in land snails and sea snails.*
- *Identify the adaptations of clams and squids.*

Figure 31-1 A trochophore is the first stage of development of mollusk and annelid larvae. Cilia at both ends and in the middle propel the organism through water.

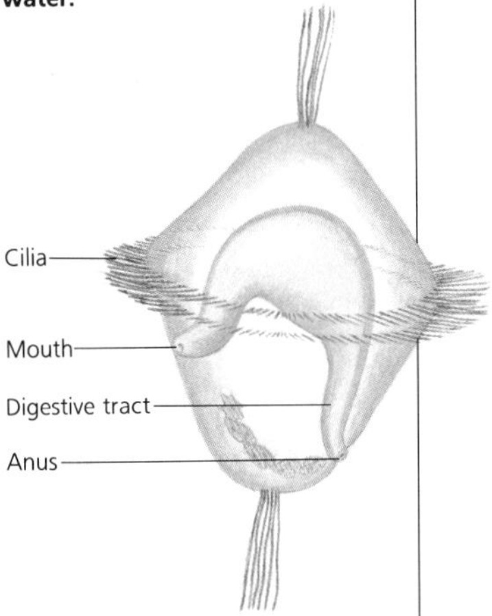

	Gastropods	Bivalves	Cephalopods
Have head, foot, and visceral mass	yes; torsion of visceral mass	yes; head undeveloped	yes; foot divided into tentacles
Have true coelom	yes	yes	yes
Have shells	most, one shell; slugs and nudibranchs, none	two shells	no, except chambered nautilus
Use locomotion	yes	most do not	yes

Graphic Organizer Use this table in Organizing Information on p. 467.

Lesson Plan

Section Focus

The Phylum Mollusca is a diverse group. Mollusks are the first major group to have a true coelom. They have a soft body with a modified head-foot region that is adapted for feeding, sensory reception, and locomotion. Their most distinctive characteristic is the mantle, a modified body wall that forms a cavity and encloses the internal visceral organs.

Section Themes

The is a primary theme in this section is **Evolution.** Development of the internal body cavity, the coelom, in mollusks made a significant advance in animal architecture possible. Evolutionary specialization of the internal organs of coelomates far surpasses that of pseudocoelomates.

Motivating Activity

Create a restaurant menu in which all the food items are mollusks. Project the menu onto a screen with an overhead projector, and ask students what the menu items have in common. *(They are all mollusks.)* Show students a representative selection of mollusks from a fish market or a grocery. *(Abalone, snails, conchs, clams, scallops, oysters, octopuses, limpets, periwinkles, sea hares, squid, and whelks are some possibilities.)* Ask students to name any mollusks they have ever eaten. Have them describe the characteristics of mollusks, based on their experiences and the samples they are looking at. *(Answers may include presence of shells and a rubbery, slippery texture.)*

Videodiscs

- *2585, Mollusks: Hypothetical Ancestor (s)*
- *2590, Classification System (s)*
- *2593, Evolutionary Relation-*

Section 31.1

Teaching Strategies

Drawing Conclusions Discuss with students the evolutionary significance of the coelom. Ask what the limitations of a solid body, that is, a body without a coelom, might be. (*No internal circulatory or digestive system; all organs pressed on by muscles and deformed by muscular activity; cells must be close to sources of oxygen, water, and all other required substances.*) Ask students what are the advantages of a body plan that has an internal body cavity. (*Organs located within a fluid-filled cavity can function without having to resist pressures from surrounding muscles. Fluid that fills the cavity can act as a circulatory system freely transporting food, water, wastes, and gases throughout the body.*)

Interpreting the Visuals Direct students to examine Figure 31-1, p. 465, and observe that in the larval stage of the mollusk, the digestive tract starts out in a simple U-shape. As the larva develops, its visceral mass starts growing upward. Have students contrast the ancient and modern mollusks in Figure 31-2, p. 466, tracing the path of the 180-degree twist made by the snail's digestive tract during its development. Use information in the More Information section below to further clarify the process of torsion.

- *See* **Blackline Master** *63.*

Making Generalizations Stress to students that mollusks show increased complexity compared with other phyla they have studied. Ask what characteristics indicate this increased complexity. (*True coelom; all essential life functions carried out by highly developed organ systems*)

Mollusks have the following characteristics:

- All mollusks have a true coelom.
- The body has three distinct parts: the muscular foot, the head, and the visceral mass.
- Mollusks have organ systems for circulation, respiration, digestion, excretion, nerve impulse conduction, and reproduction.
- Most mollusks are bilaterally symmetrical and have one or more shells.

Body Plan

Mollusk species have numerous variations of the same basic body plan. Figure 31-2 shows one version of the anatomy of a hypothetical ancestral mollusk. Locate in the diagram the three main body parts shared by all mollusks: the muscular foot, the head, and the visceral mass. The muscular **foot** is a large organ used in locomotion. The **head** contains the mouth, sense organs, and cerebral ganglia. The **visceral mass** contains the heart and the organs of digestion, excretion, and reproduction. Covering the visceral mass is the **mantle,** an epidermal layer that in most species secretes a shell.

Organisms with a hard shell of calcium carbonate probably appeared early in the evolution of mollusks. The shell was of an adaptive value to these organisms because it protected the soft body from predators. However, it also conferred a disadvantage since the shell reduced the surface area available for gas exchange. This problem was avoided as a related structural adaptation evolved—the gills. With a large surface area and a rich supply of blood, **gills** are organs specialized for the exchange of gases with water. The delicate gills are protected within the **mantle cavity,** a space between the mantle and the visceral mass.

Biologists use structural differences to classify mollusks into four to seven classes. We will discuss four major classes: Polyplacophora (*PAHL-ee-pluh-KAHF-ur-uh*), Gastropoda (*gass-TRAHP-uh-duh*), Bivalvia (*bie-VALV-ee-uh*), and Cephalopoda (*SEFF-uh-LAHP-uh-duh*).

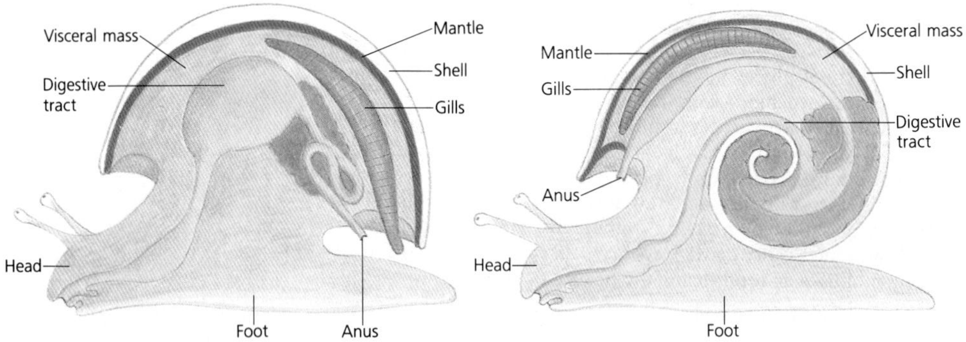

Figure 31-2 A hypothetical ancient mollusk (left) and a modern snail (right) are very similar. The anus on top of the snail's head results from torsion during larval development.

More Information

Torsion The internal realignment process in larval gastropods, called torsion, has consequences beyond allowing the adult animal to withdraw its head when in danger. Because upward growth of the visceral mass is uneven, organs on one side of the body are compressed and fail to develop. Muscle contractions combined with this uneven growth cause the posterior of the mantle cavity to twist toward the right side of the animal. When the larval body makes its 180-degree rotation, the posterior end of the digestive tube becomes positioned just above the animal's head. Spiral development of the shell is a separate and later evolutionary development.

Polyplacophora

Members of the Class Polyplacophora are called chitons. These are primarily animals of the seashore that live on rocks. The word *polyplacophora* means "many plates," a reference to the main characteristic of the class: their shells are divided into eight separate, overlapping plates.

Figure 31-3 Clearly visible here are the eight separate, overlapping plates that make up the shell of this lined chiton, *Tonicella lineata*.

Gastropoda

The largest and most diverse class of mollusks is Gastropoda, which includes about 75,000 species of snails, slugs, abalones, nudibranchs, and conches. The name *gastropoda* means "stomach–foot." Most gastropods have a single shell, or valve, and so are called univalves. Slugs and some other gastropods have no shell.

The body plan of gastropods is based on that of ancestral mollusks. The major difference results from **torsion,** or twisting, which occurs during larval development. In torsion the visceral mass twists 180 degrees in relation to the head. Note the results of torsion by comparing the anatomy of a snail with that of the hypothetical ancestral mollusk in Figure 31-2. The twisting brings the mantle cavity to the front of the animal, thus allowing the animal to draw its head into the mantle cavity when endangered.

Snails

Snails are gastropods that live in a wide range of environments on land as well as in fresh water and oceans. Aquatic snails respire through gills in the mantle cavity. In terrestrial snails the mantle cavity acts as a modified lung that allows the animal to obtain oxygen from the air. The thin membrane that lines the cavity must be kept moist to allow gases to diffuse through it. For this reason snails are most active when the air has a higher moisture content. During dry periods a snail survives by becoming inactive. It retreats into its shell and seals the opening with a mucus plug, which keeps the snail from drying out.

Like all gastropods, snails have an **open circulatory system,** meaning that the blood does not circulate entirely within vessels. Instead blood is collected from the gills or lungs, pumped through the heart, and released directly into spaces in the tissues. From there it returns via the gills or lungs to the heart. The blood-filled space is known as a **hemocoel** *(HEE-muh-SEEL)* or blood cavity.

The main feeding adaptation of snails is the sawlike **radula,** a flexible tonguelike strip covered with chitinous teeth. Aquatic snails use the radula to scrape up algae or other food. Terrestrial snails use the radula to saw off leaves of garden plants.

Land snails are hermaphroditic, but in most aquatic species the sexes are distinct. Eggs are fertilized internally.

Snails move smoothly by the wavelike muscular contractions of the foot. Glands in the foot secrete a layer of mucus on which

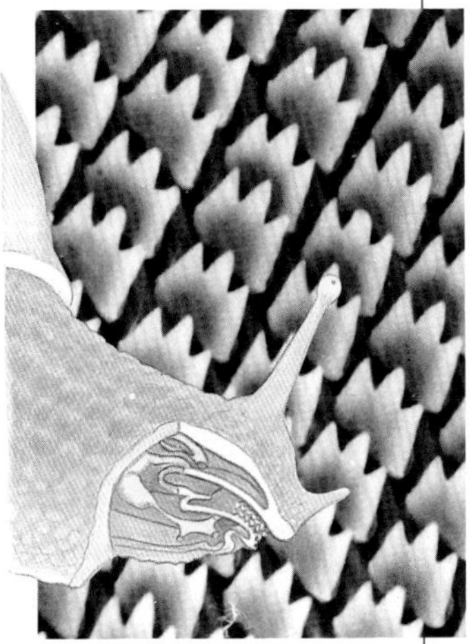

Figure 31-4 Inside a snail's mouth is the radula, a band of tissue covered with chitinous teeth that can scrape food from other surfaces. This SEM shows the sharp edges of these chitinous teeth.

Observing Organisms Obtain live land and aquatic snails and slugs from a pet store or a supply house. Have students observe snails on the side of an aquarium. Have them note the snails' shape and symmetry, and determine how they move, eat, and respond to their environment. Ask students to relate observable structures to their functions. Also ask students to compare snails with other classes of mollusks. *(Answers should include the fact that snails, like most other mollusks, have shells.)* Tell students that an octopus forms a shell in its embryonic stage, then loses it during maturation; a squid has a delicate shell, called a pen shell, under its mantle.

- *See* Process Skills, *Chapter 31.*

Making Hypotheses Discuss with students the potential sanitation problem a snail might have because its anus and kidney openings are above its head. Ask students to form a hypothesis about the way snails keep waste products out of their mouths and gills. As a hint, suggest that students consider how other organisms they have studied move waste products. *(For example, the beating of cilia in the flame cells of planaria moves wastes into the ducts to the excretory pores. Most gastropods use cilia to create currents that sweep clean the areas around the mouth and gills.)*

Organizing Information Ask students to develop a table that displays major characteristics of gastropods, bivalves, and cephalopods. An example of a completed table appears on p. 465.

Videodiscs

- *Side 4 26706, Nudibranch (m)*
- *858–866, Garden Snails (s)*

Interdisciplinary Activity

Visual Arts The chambered nautilus has inspired the work of many painters and other artists. For example, Georgia O'Keeffe is well known for her Santa Fe Music Festival poster series, which features this beautiful cephalopod. Encourage students to find examples of the work of O'Keeffe and other artists who have been inspired by the chambered nautilus.

Answer to Think

The absence of a shell facilitates the diffusion of gases across the surface, and the ruffled surface further increases the area for gas diffusion.

Clarifying Concepts Tell students that visual organs of mollusks can differ greatly. For example, snail's eyes are relatively simple, similar in structure to the eyespots of planaria. However, the eyes of a squid are well developed and are similar in structure to human eyes.

Interpreting the Visuals As students study sessile bivalves, ask them to recall other sessile animals they have studied, such as sponges and sea anemones. Have them consider the differences between these animals and bivalves. Use Figure 31-5, p. 469, to compare the complexity of the clam's anatomy with the simpler anatomy of a sponge, shown in Figure 29-4, p. 441.
■ *See* **Overhead Transparency** ***T31 and*** **Blackline Master 64.**

Guided Practice

Have students describe distinguishing traits of members of the following classes of mollusks: gastropods, bivalves, and cephalopods. *(Most gastropods have a single shell, though slugs have no shell. Bivalves have two shells, and most are sessile. Cephalopods have a well developed head and foot, which is divided into numerous tentacles.)*

Independent Practice

- Have students write answers to the Section Review.
- Have students describe the range of sense organs possessed by mollusks. *(Some mollusks, such as clams, have rudimentary sense organs that respond to light and touch. By contrast, squids have a well-developed eye capable of acute vision and tentacles sensitive to touch.)*

Think

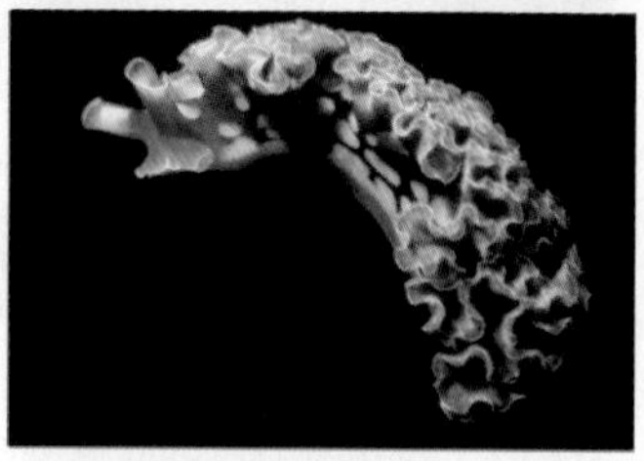

Nudibranchs are gastropods that live in shallow coastal waters. They have no shell, and gas exchange takes place across the body surface. How might the structure of the nudibranch above be related to the function of respiration?

the animal travels at a pace of about 3 m per hour. Two eyes at the end of delicate tentacles on the head help locate food. If danger should arise, the tentacles retract into the head.

Other Gastropods

Slugs look like snails without shells. They survive without shells because they live in moist environments, hiding in shady places by day and feeding at night. Like terrestrial snails, slugs respire through the lining of the mantle cavity.

Some gastropods show unusual modifications of the foot or radula. Instead of having a foot, pteropods, or "sea butterflies," have a winglike flap, which allows them to swim on the surface of the sea. Another adaptation is seen in gastropods with modified radulas. Oyster drills, for example, use their radulas to bore through oysters' shells and feed on the soft tissues inside.

Bivalvia

In contrast with gastropods that move about in search of food, most members of the Class Bivalvia are sessile and filter food from the water. *Bivalvia* means "two valves." Clams, oysters, scallops, and other bivalves have a shell with two valves and a muscular foot. Once this foot is in sand, blood swells the end, causing it to spread and form a hatchet-shaped anchor. The muscles of the foot then contract and pull the animal down in the sand. Bivalves do not have distinct head regions as do gastropods. As an adaptation for sessile existence, ganglia are present in the anterior region.

Each valve consists of three layers secreted by the mantle. A thin outer layer protects the shell against acidic conditions in the water. A thick middle layer of calcium carbonate crystals strengthens the shell. The smooth, irridescent inner layer protects the animal's soft body. If an irritant such as a grain of sand gets inside the shell, the mantle coats it with a secretion known as mother of pearl. Layers of this secretion form a pearl. A hinge connects the two valves of the shell. The animal can close the valves with its powerful adductor muscles. When the adductor muscles relax, the valves open.

Clams

Clams are bivalves that live buried in mud, seashore sand, or sand on the bottom of the sea. Clams have evolved adaptations for filter feeding. The mantle cavity is sealed except for a pair of hollow tubes called siphons. Cilia beating on the gills set up a current that causes water to enter the **incurrent siphon.** Cilia then propel the water over the gills and cause it to exit through the **excurrent siphon.** As the cilia move water over the gills, food—plankton from the water and organic sediments from the sea bottom—becomes trapped in a sticky mucus. Then the cilia move this mucus to the mouth. As water passes over the gills, oxygen diffuses into the blood, and carbon dioxide diffuses out.

More Information

Mother-of-Pearl The brilliant, iridescent interior of abalone and pearl oyster shells is often used decoratively. This striking coloration is produced when the different wavelengths of light are changed as they enter and then are reflected through layers of calcite on the interior of the shell. These thin, leaflike crystal layers are laid nearly parallel to the inner surface of the shell and are separated by a protein called conchiolin, which resembles lacework. Decorative uses of mother-of-pearl include inlays in jewelry, buttons, and other ornaments.

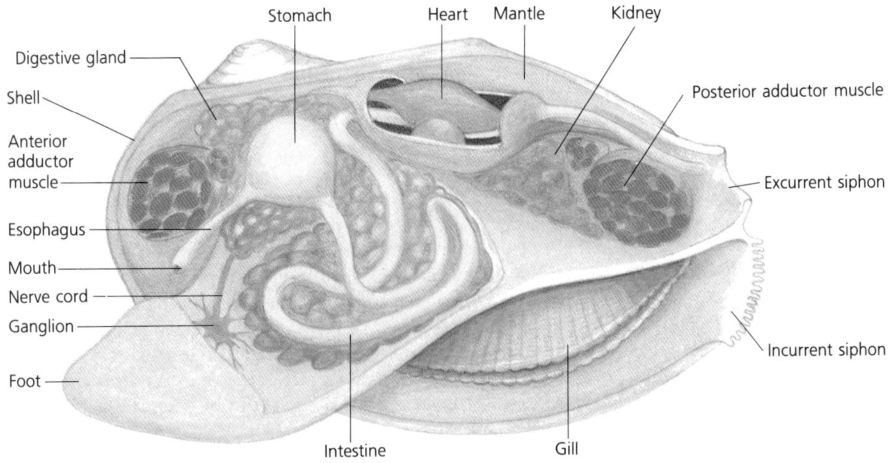

Figure 31-5 One valve has been stripped away here to show the anatomy of a clam. A clam is typically buried in the ocean bottom with its siphons pointing upward.

Clams have rudimentary sense organs. Sensory cells along the edge of the mantle respond to light and touch. Like most mollusks the ganglia that are above the mouth, in the digestive system, and in the foot are connected by two pairs of long nerve cords.

Most species of clams have separate sexes. They reproduce by shedding sperm and eggs into the water, and fertilization occurs externally. The fertilized egg becomes a trochophore larva that eventually settles to the bottom and develops into an adult.

Other Bivalves

Oysters are bivalves that become permanently attached to a hard surface early in their development. Scallops are bivalves that move through the water by opening their valves and then rapidly snapping them shut. This motion expels bursts of water, creating a form of jet propulsion. The teredo, or shipworm, is one of the few bivalves that does not filter feed. Instead, it bores into driftwood or ship timbers. Particles produced by the drilling are ingested by the teredo. The cellulose is broken down by symbiotic protozoa that live in the shipworm's intestine.

Cephalopoda

Cephalopods such as octopuses, squids, cuttlefish, and chambered nautiluses are evolutionarily advanced and complex mollusks. The name *cephalopod,* meaning "head–foot," refers to the large, well-developed head and the prominent foot divided into numerous tentacles. The head and foot are specialized for a free-swimming, predatory existence. Cephalopods capture prey with powerful tentacles equipped with strong suckers. They kill and eat their prey with the help of a sharp, beaklike radula.

Check Your Understanding

1. What is the adaptive advantage of a closed circulatory system for the highly motile cephalopods? *(An active mollusk needs to have oxygen transported quickly to vital organs during vigorous movement; a closed system with blood vessels keeps blood flowing directly to where it is needed.)*

2. What are advantages of the squid's adaptations for reproduction? *(When a male squid transfers packets of sperm to the cavity of the female and when the female guards her fertilized egg mass, their behavior increases the chances that the zygotes will actually hatch.)*

3. Should a snail be described as a radially symmetrical animal? Explain your answer. *(No. A snail does not have similar body parts that radiate from a central axis.)*

Reteaching

Provide students with several specimens or pictures from an invertebrate zoology textbook or other source that show a variety of each of the four mollusk classes. Ask them to observe specimens and group them according to similarity. Have students describe the criteria they used to sort their groups. *(Answers may include presence or absence of a shell, type of shell, method of locomotion, feeding habits, and habitat.)* Have students compare their classifications with the actual mollusk classes.

- *See* Section Reviews *worksheet, Section 31.1.*

Videodiscs

- *868–893, Gastropoda—Examples (s)*
- *933–948, Pelecypoda: Mussels; Clams (s)*
- *948–953, Scallops (s)*

Cooperative Learning

Mollusk Characteristics Divide the class into groups of three. Provide each group with at least three specimens or pictures of organisms from different mollusk classes. Tell students that one member of each group will concentrate on overall size and shape, a second student on the presence or absence of shell(s), and the third on specialized adaptations such as antennae or tentacles. Then have each team try to identify and classify each specimen based on descriptions of the mollusk classes in the student text.

Enrichment
Have students research one class of mollusks. Have them focus on such features as type of shell, configuration of the digestive tract, locomotion, and cephalization or lack thereof. Tell them to develop a hypothetical evolutionary tree showing possible relationships among species and the order in which different species might have developed. Suggest that they use Figure 29-3 on p. 439 as a model.

Closure
Have students imagine that they are part of a scientific team that has discovered a deposit of fossils. Some look like clam shells, so the team infers that some remains are mollusk fossils. Have students say what evidence they would use to decide whether or not each fossil was a mollusk. *(Students should look for the mollusk traits that they have identified during the lesson.)*

Videodiscs
- *Side 4 20892, Octopus (m)*
- *Side 4 26120, Nautilus (m)*

Figure 31-6 The cuttlefish, *Sepia officinalis,* has a pair of narrow fins, which border its body. It uses its eight arms and two tentacles to capture prey. The chambered nautilus, *Nautilus pompilius,* has a shell with roughly 36 chambers.

Cephalopods have a **closed circulatory system,** in which blood circulates entirely within a system of vessels. This efficient circulation rapidly transports the food and oxygen in these highly active animals.

Squids
Like all cephalopods, squids live in oceans. Most grow to about 30 cm in length, but a few species grow much longer. The giant squid may grow to 20 m long and weigh more than 3,360 kg. It is the world's largest known invertebrate.

A squid's head encloses a large, complex brain that controls a highly developed nervous system. The squid's most prominent sense organs are its pair of large eyes, similar in structure to those of humans. Squids have ten tentacles. The longest pair is used for capturing prey; the smaller pairs force the prey into the mouth. The muscular mantle propels the squid by pumping jets of water through an excurrent siphon.

Squids have defensive adaptations. They can squirt an inky substance at enemies. The substance temporarily blinds the enemy and dulls its sense of smell. Pigment cells called **chromatophores,** located on the outer layer of the mantle, enable squids to change color and blend in with their surroundings.

Like all cephalopods, squids have separate sexes. The male uses a specialized tentacle to transfer packets of sperm from its mantle cavity to the cavity of the female, where fertilization occurs. The female lays a mass of fertilized eggs encased in a gelatinous material. She then guards them until they hatch.

Other Cephalopods
Octopuses seldom grow to more than 30 cm in diameter. They have eight tentacles and resemble squids in the ways they move, feed, capture prey, and escape from enemies. Instead of using their jet propulsion to chase prey, they may crawl along the bottom with their tentacles or lie in wait in caves and rock crevices. The jet propulsion may be used to escape danger.

The chambered nautilus is the only existing cephalopod that has retained its exterior shell. The nautilus lives in an outer chamber of its shell and secretes a gas into the other chambers. By regulating the amount of gas in the chambers, the nautilus can adjust its buoyancy and so control its depth in the water.

Section Review
1. What is a *trochophore?*
2. Name three characteristics shared by all mollusks.
3. Why are terrestrial snails more active when the air around them is moist?
4. In what ways is a squid adapted for a predatory way of life?
5. Suggest three ways in which a shell is adaptive.

Answers to Section Review
1. A ciliated pear-shaped larval stage of mollusks and annelids
2. A coelom, all organ systems present, a three-part body (head, foot, visceral mass)
3. The mantle cavity must be moist for respiration to take place.
4. It has a well-developed brain and well-developed senses, a closed circulatory system, tentacles that grasp prey, and jet propulsion that allows rapid movement.
5. Protection, water conservation, and camouflage are among the acceptable choices.

31.2 Annelida

Colorful feather-duster worms, common earthworms, and blood-sucking leeches are all classified in the Phylum Annelida *(uh-NELL-uh-duh)*. The name *annelid* means "little rings," which refers to the many segments that make up the body of an annelid. The diverse species of annelids share certain basic traits:

- All annelids have a true coelom.
- The body is divided into many segments. This phenomenon is called **metamerism.** Some segments fuse during development, while others remain separate segments, or metameric units.
- All organ systems are well developed in most groups.
- Most annelids have external bristles called **setae** *(SEE-tee)*.

The number of setae and the presence or absence of fleshy appendages called **parapodia** provide the basis for classifying annelids into three classes: Polychaeta *(PAHL-ee-KEET-uh)*, Oligochaeta *(AHL-uh-goe-KEET-uh)*, and Hirudinea *(HIR-yuh-DIN-ee-uh)*. Marine worms of Class Polychaeta have many setae; earthworms of Class Oligochaeta have no parapodia and few setae; and leeches of Class Hirudinea have no setae or parapodia.

Section Objectives

- *List the distinguishing characteristics of annelids.*
- *Distinguish between the three classes of annelids.*
- *Identify some traits of earthworms that are adaptations for burrowing in the soil.*
- *Compare earthworms with polychaetes.*
- *Name some characteristics of leeches that are leading to their renewed use by physicians.*

Oligochaeta

We will now look closely at the earthworm's structure, feeding habits, and body systems. As you read, study the adaptations that enable the earthworm to lead a burrowing life.

Structure

The diagram in Figure 31-7 shows the segmentation that is the most distinctive feature of annelids. The more than 100 segments, or metameric units, of the earthworm's body are separated by partitions that divide the coelom. These segments are identical except where fusion has resulted in specialized sections near the

Figure 31-7 Segmentation, as shown in this earthworm, is the most distinctive feature of annelids. The digestive tract is not segmented. Castings and dirt exit through the anus.

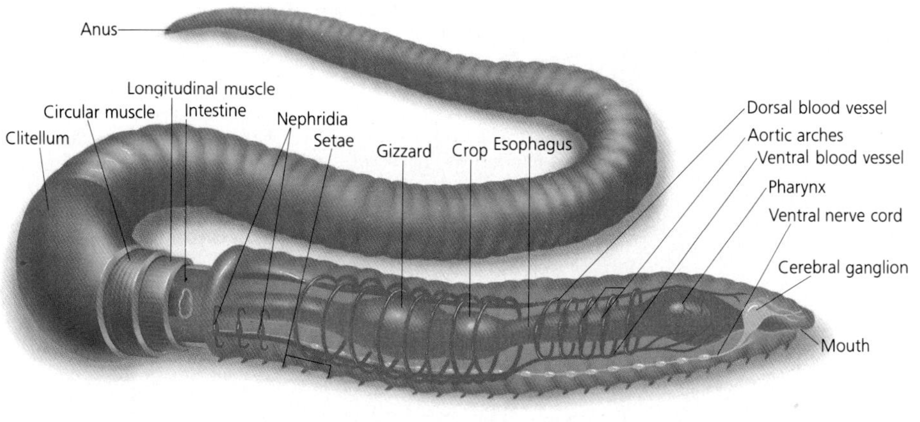

	Oligochaeta	Polychaeta	Hirudinea
Head Structures	mouth, light receptors	strong jaws, antennae, specialized mouthparts	sucker
Locomotion	numerous setae; muscular contraction	numerous setae project from parapodia	no setae; suckers
Habitat	soil	salt water	fresh water

Graphic Organizer Use this table in Guided Practice on p. 473.

Lesson Plan

Section Focus

All annelids have a true coelom. Their bodies are segmented, principally as an adaptation for movement. In most annelid groups, all organ systems are well developed. Earthworms are the most familiar annelids, but polychaetes, or marine annelids, are more abundant and diverse.

Section Themes

The theme of **Scale and Structure** is exemplified by the characteristic structures that enable annelids to play specific ecological roles in their habitats. The presence or absence of certain structures, such as setae, determines how annelids are classified within the phylum.

Motivating Activity

Students may have seen earthworms burrowing in soil or crawling on sidewalks after a hard rain. Build on this experience by asking what other observations students have made about earthworms. *(For example, aspects of their appearance, what they eat)* Tell students that though earthworms appear to be simple animals, their internal anatomy is actually quite complex. Suggest that students note the advanced morphology of earthworms as they read the section.

- ***See* Laboratories, *Investigation 31.***

Videodiscs

- ***Side 3 36231, Sea Mouse Worm (m)***
- ***984–1010, Annelida—Examples (s)***

Teaching Strategies

Interpreting the Visuals Have students use Figure 31-7, p. 471, to help understand how the fluid-filled coelomic chamber provides support and how the circular and longitudinal muscles coordinate to produce an accordionlike movement. Also, discuss the characteristics of each organ and organ system.
■ *See* Blackline Master 65.

Comparing Organisms Show students live or preserved specimens (or photos) of an earthworm and a leech, and ask how they compare with other worms and mollusks. List similarities and differences on the board. Ask students what they know about leeches and earthworms. *(Answers may include that leeches suck blood and that worms are found in soil.)* Point out to students that annelids are more like mollusks than like worms of other phyla.

Evaluating Adaptations Explain to students that of the nearly 9,000 species of annelids, polychaetes are considered the most primitive but that all annelids have well-developed organ systems. Point out that annelids as a group can be considered very successful. Ask students what indicates their success. *(They have adapted to conditions on land and in oceans and fresh water.)*

Analyzing Phylogeny Ask students to draw a concept map showing that modern mollusks and annelids evolved from a common ancestor and thus show similarities and differences. An example of a completed concept map is shown on p. 463B.

anterior and posterior ends. The anterior segments of the worm reflect the cephalization that is an adaptation for burrowing. The head contains the specialized sense organs.

Circular and longitudinal muscles line the interior body wall. To move, the worm anchors some segments by their setae and contracts the circular muscles in front of those segments, producing fluid pressure in the anterior coelom cavities. This pressure elongates the animal and pushes the head forward. With the anterior setae gripping the ground, the longitudinal muscles contract, pulling the posterior along. Divisions in the coelom make simultaneous contraction and expansion of segments possible.

Feeding and Digestion

Earthworms burrow and feed on soil and organic matter at the same time. They digest the organic matter and eliminate waste and undigested matter as dirt and feces called castings. The passing of dirt through the worm's body loosens and aerates the soil.

Soil is sucked into the gut by the muscular pharynx. The soil then passes through a tubelike **esophagus** to a temporary storage area called a **crop,** and from there to the **gizzard.** The thick, muscular gizzard walls contract and grind the soil, releasing and

Biotechnology

Medicinal Uses of Leeches

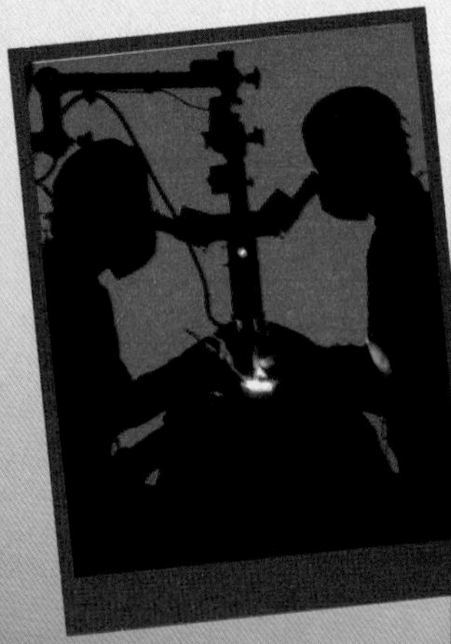

Advanced techniques in microsurgery have often allowed people who have lost a finger or a toe to have the extremity successfully reattached. These operations are so delicate that surgeons must work with tiny surgical instruments and powerful microscopes. To this sophisticated technology some microsurgeons have added an unlikely tool—the leech.

Leeches were used for medical bloodletting throughout the Middle Ages and even as late as the early 1900s. Doctors who used leeches believed that the bloodletting caused by the leeches could improve circulation and remove "bad blood" or "evil humours."

Although medical science has discredited the traditional reasons for using leeches, their use in microsurgery is just one of the new medically sound uses of leeches.

When microsurgery fails, it is often because the soft, tiny veins in the reattached parts become clotted. When that happens, the tissues die, and the part can't rejoin the body and heal. By using leeches the surgeon can sometimes improve the odds of success in difficult cases. After reattaching the part, the surgeon applies the leech. The leech starts

More Information

Earthworm Farming One characteristic of a highly productive farm is often the presence of earthworms in hundreds of thousands per acre. This relationship occurs because aeration of soil by earthworms is extremely beneficial to growing crops. As a result, cultivation of earthworms has grown as a business. Worms are raised in backyards, garages, and cellars. A large worm farm may have five acres of outdoor pits. A small one may be a simple trench or a box in a backyard. The most common earthworm farmed is called a red wiggler, or manure worm, because it is at home in the waste droppings of farm animals. Buyers of worms include farmers, gardeners, and fishers.

breaking up organic matter. The gizzard is adapted for burrowing, as it grinds up soil. Food is digested and absorbed by the blood after it passes through the walls of the tubular intestines.

Circulation

Earthworms transport oxygen, nutrients, and wastes through the body via a closed circulatory system. The blood travels from the anterior to the posterior through a ventral blood vessel and then forward through a dorsal vessel. Five pairs of tubes, the **aortic arches,** link the major vessels near the anterior. Smaller vessels branch into each segment of the body. Contractions of the ventral vessel and aortic arches force blood through the body.

Respiration and Excretion

Earthworms have no gills or other respiratory organs. Oxygen and carbon dioxide diffuse directly across the skin. This exchange can take place only if the skin is moist. Thus earthworms avoid dry ground and extreme heat. Secretions of mucus and the presence of a thin cuticle also help keep the earthworm's skin moist.

Earthworms eliminate nitrogenous wastes through long tubules called **nephridia.** Coelomic fluid enters each nephridium

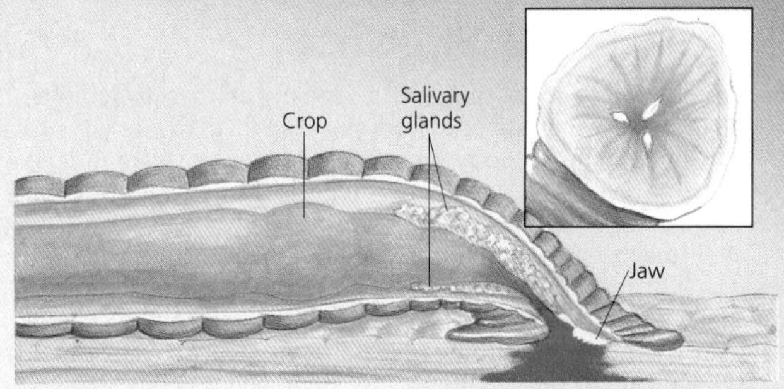

to suck out the congested blood, as shown in the diagram. A period of prolonged, localized bleeding follows. After a few days the blood in the reattached extremity is flowing normally, permitting healing to take place. Then the leech is removed.

Today some researchers are investigating potential medical applications of secretions pro-

duced by leeches. Scientists have known since the 1800s that the saliva of the European leech contains a powerful anticoagulant, a substance that inhibits blood clotting. A similar substance in the saliva of the Amazon leech dissolves clots after they have formed.

Aside from the obvious potential for treating blood clots, some researchers think that leech secretions may prove useful in the treatment of heart attack victims. The leech's anticoagulants could be used to stimulate the flow of blood in cardiac muscles that have been deprived of nourishment by a heart attack.

Comparing Structures Discuss the phylogenetic relationship of nephridia to the kidneys of more highly developed animals. Refer to Chapter 45 for discussion of the role of nephrons in human kidneys.

Guided Practice

Ask students to develop a table comparing heads, forms of locomotion, and habitats of the classes Oligochaeta, Polychaeta, and Hirudinea. An example of a completed table appears on p. 471.

Independent Practice

- Have students write answers to the Section Review.
- Have students briefly describe the overall appearance of the earthworm as well as its individual structures. Tell them to relate each structure to one or more functions.

Biotechnology

Using the Feature

This feature describes the use of leeches in microsurgery, an example of scientists' discovering valid medical uses for organisms whose value was once restricted to superstition or folk medicine. Point out that scientists are also discovering medicinal uses of various species of tropical plants. Guide students to realize that the medicinal potential of various kinds of organisms is a major reason medical researchers urge the preservation of habitats, such as the tropical rain forest, rich in unstudied organisms.

Videodiscs

- *Side 4 23676, Giant Earthworm (m)*
- *1011–1019, Earthworm (s)*
- *1025–1026, Leech (s)*

LEP Activity

Divide students into groups of three. Have them imagine that they own and manage an earthworm farm. One student is the overall manager, one is a science expert, and one is an artist and writer. Direct them to prepare a brochure advertising their earthworms to gardeners. Tell them to illustrate the brochure with pictures and write brief captions that show how to use and care for earthworms. Warn buyers that flooding, drought, pesticide usage, and packed soil are harmful to them. You may wish to use More Information on p. 472 as background for this activity.

Check Your Understanding

1. In what ways are earthworms more complex than flatworms? *(Earthworms have a true coelom and well-developed organ systems. These systems include a cerebral ganglion, blood vessels, nerve cords, intestine, and nephridia. Flatworms have none of these structures.)*

2. Explain why "worm" is not a precise biological term. *(Because it is used for many phyla)*

Reteaching

Ask students how earthworms and leeches differ. Then have students explain why both organisms are considered annelids. *(Leeches have no setae and move by use of a sucker. A leech is classified as an annelid because it exhibits characteristic annelid features, including a true coelom and a segmented body.)*

■ *See* Section Reviews *worksheet, Section 31.2.*

Enrichment

Have students research and report on three annelid species other than earthworms and leeches, such as feather worms, peacock worms, fan worms, or the giant tubeworms found in thermal vents in the Galápagos Rift. The report should illustrate how structural differences among different annelids relate to specific adaptive functions.

Closure

Have students explain why biologists have concluded that the Phyla Mollusca and Annelida evolved from a common ancestor. Urge students to give specific examples of evidence that led to this conclusion, especially stressing specific structures and their functions.

through a ciliated funnel opening. As fluid passes through the nephridia, some water is reabsorbed by blood vessels. The remaining fluid empties through pores on the ventral surface.

Nervous Control

Earthworms are sensitive to light, touch, moisture, chemicals, temperature, and vibrations. Light receptors concentrated in the head and tail sense direction. Most other sense organs and the nerves that control individual muscle contractions are present in each segment. The nerves in each segment form a pair of ganglia that coordinate movements with neighboring segments. A cerebral ganglion or brain in the head controls total body actions. A ventral nerve cord connects the brain with all the ganglia.

Reproduction

Earthworms are hermaphrodites, but an individual worm cannot fertilize its own eggs. Mating occurs when two earthworms join head to tail. Together they form a mucus coat around part of their intertwined bodies. Each injects sperm into the mucus. Sperm from one worm moves to the pouchlike **seminal receptacle** of the other. Simultaneously eggs in the body cavity move through oviducts to the female genital pore. After several days a mucus and chitin sheath is secreted by the **clitellum** *(klie-TELL-um)*, a swelling around the sex organs. As the worm wriggles to slip the sheath off its body, eggs and sperm are joined and fertilization occurs.

Figure 31-8 Numerous setae, which project from parapodia, help polychaetes such as this move through water.

Polychaeta and Hirudinea

Polychaetes are annelids that live in virtually all marine habitats. Some are free-swimming predators that use their strong jaws to feed on small animals. Some burrowing species excavate tunnels by eating the sediment, while others dig and pump water through their bodies or scour the bottom with tentacles.

Polychaetes have numerous setae that help them move. The setae project from the parapodia. Some parapodia function in gas exchange. Polychaetes differ from other annelids by having antennae and specialized mouthparts.

Hirudinea is the smallest class of annelids, consisting of about 300 species of leeches. A leech has no setae. At each end of the body the leech has a sucker, which it uses to effect a crude walking motion. Most leeches live in calm bodies of fresh water.

Section Review

1. Distinguish between *setae* and *parapodia.*
2. In what ways are earthworms adapted for burrowing?
3. How do the annelid and mollusk body plans differ?
4. How do earthworms in the soil benefit plants?
5. Leech saliva contains an anaesthetic. What adaptive advantage do leeches derive from this anaesthetic?

Answers to Section Review

1. Setae are bristles found on the body of most annelids; parapodia are fleshy appendages on some annelids.

2. Adaptations of the earthworm for burrowing include a streamlined shape without appendages, the presence of setae and a segmented coelom, and digestive organs adapted for extracting nutrients from the soil.

3. The annelid body is segmented; the mollusk body is not.

4. Through burrowing, earthworms loosen and aerate soil, making water and nutrients more accessible to plants.

5. The anaesthetic prevents the host from feeling the wound inflicted by the leech. This allows the leech to feed on the host's blood without being noticed.

Laboratory

Behavior of Earthworms

Objective
How does an earthworm respond to light, touch, and to a strong base such as ammonia?

Process Skills
Hypothesizing, experimenting

Materials
Live earthworms, shallow pan, paper towels, cotton swabs, 3% aqueous ammonium hydroxide solution, blunt probe, black paper or piece of cardboard large enough to cover half of the pan, lamp

Background
1. What is cephalization? How does the earthworm benefit from cephalization?
2. Describe how gases enter and exit the earthworm's body.

Technique
1. Place a moist paper towel in a pan and place an earthworm on the paper towel.
2. Observe the behavior of the earthworm for a few minutes.
3. Dip a cotton swab into water and hold it near the anterior end of the earthworm. Observe the response of the earthworm. Next hold the swab near the posterior end of the animal and observe the response.

Inquiry
1. Discuss the objective of this laboratory with your lab partners and develop three separate hypotheses that describe an earthworm's response to light, touch, and to ammonia.
2. Design three different experiments, using the materials provided, that will test your three hypotheses.
3. What are the independent and dependent variables in your experiments? How will you vary the independent variables? How will you measure changes in the dependent variables?
4. What controls will you include?
5. Proceed with your experiment once it is approved by your teacher. Be sure not to touch the worms with ammonia.

Conclusions
1. What effect, if any, did changes in the independent variables have on the dependent variables in each experiment?
2. State whether each hypothesis was supported by the data you collected. Explain.
3. List variables for each experiment that, if not controlled, might affect the results. Was each of your experiments a controlled experiment? Explain.

Further Inquiry
Design a controlled experiment that would determine an earthworm's response to moisture.

Laboratory

(For an overview of earthworms and preparatory information related to the laboratory, see p. 463B.)

Background
1. The presence of an anterior region with specialized sense organs; it allows an earthworm to avoid harmful substances and seek optimum conditions.
2. Gases diffuse directly through the earthworm's skin.

Technique
2. Students should note the earthworm's behavior when it is not receiving a specific stimulus.
3. The earthworm should not have specific responses to the swab dipped in water. This can serve as a control for observing the response to a swab dipped in ammonium hydroxide solution.

Inquiry
1. Each group should agree on testable hypotheses regarding the earthworm's responses to stimuli.
2. Light: Cover half the pan with black paper, then place a light over the exposed portion. Touch: Use a blunt probe to gently touch the anterior end, posterior end, and midpoint of the earthworm. Ammonia: Move a cotton swab dipped in ammonia toward the anterior end, then the posterior end of the earthworm. Accept creative alternatives to these suggestions.
3. Independent variables: amount of light, touch of object, odor of ammonia. Dependent variable: response to each stimulus. Independent variables can be the presence or absence of stimuli; dependent variable can be measured by observing responses of the earthworm.
4. An untouched earthworm in reduced light for the light and touch experiments; a water-dipped swab for the ammonia experiment

Conclusions
1. Student answers should be consistent with their data.
2. Students should state whether their data support their hypotheses.
3. Variables include amount of light, whether the pan is level, proximity of a cotton swab, and amount of moisture. All paper towels, for instance, should be equally moist.

Further Inquiry
Students should devise an experiment in which reactions of earthworms to moist paper towel (the control) and to dry paper towel are compared.

Chapter 31 Review

Vocabulary

1. In an open circulatory system, at least part of the circulation takes place through body cavities; in a closed system, blood circulates entirely within vessels.
2. The gizzard is the digestive organ that grinds up the earthworm's food; the radula is the structure that mollusks use to scrape food.
3. A chromatophore is a cephalopod cell that contains pigment; a trochophore is a ciliated larval form of mollusks and annelids.
4. The mantle is the outer layer of tissue that covers a mollusk body and in most species secretes a shell; the mantle cavity is a space between mantle and visceral mass.
5. The gill is a structure specialized for exchange of gases between blood and a watery environment; nephridia are excretory organs specialized to eliminate nitrogenous wastes.

Review

1. c	**6.** a
2. a	**7.** d
3. d	**8.** c
4. c	**9.** a
5. c	**10.** b

11. Separates muscles of the digestive system from those of the body wall; provides space where a circulatory system can function; contains fluid that may serve as a type of skeleton against which muscles can contract
12. Head, foot, and visceral mass
13. The twisting of a gastropod's body during larval development; because of torsion the mantle cavity is located at the front of the body above the head.
14. A mollusk uses its radula to scrape up food.
15. A gill has a large surface area and rich blood supply, both features that promote gas exchange. Cilia on gills of some bivalves direct food into the mouth.
16. Cilia on a clam's gills direct mucus that has trapped food particles into the mouth.
17. Segmentation enables annelids to move by muscles that alternately expand and contract different segments.
18. To remove congested blood from reattached body parts so that healing can occur; in the future scientists may use leeches to help heart attack victims.
19. Earthworms require a moist environment to maintain a moist body surface across which gases can diffuse.
20. A leech has no setae and moves by alternately attaching its anterior and posterior suckers to effect a crude kind of walking. An earthworm uses its setae to anchor some segments and then moves forward by contracting its circular and longitudinal muscles.

Chapter 31 Review

Vocabulary

aortic arch (473)
chromatophore (470)
clitellum (474)
closed circulatory system (470)
crop (472)
esophagus (472)
excurrent siphon (468)
foot (466)
gill (466)
gizzard (472)
head (466)
hemocoel (467)
incurrent siphon (468)
mantle (466)
mantle cavity (466)
metamerism (471)
nephridium (473)
open circulatory system (467)
parapodia (471)
radula (467)
seminal receptacle (474)
setae (471)
torsion (467)
trochophore (465)
visceral mass (466)

Explain the difference between the terms in each of the following sets.
1. open circulatory system, closed circulatory system
2. gizzard, radula
3. chromatophore, trochophore
4. mantle, mantle cavity
5. gill, nephridia

Review

1. Mollusks and annelids share all of the following characteristics except (a) coelom (b) trochophore larva (c) segmentation (d) bilateral symmetry.
2. Gills are organs specialized for (a) gas exchange (b) movement (c) digestion (d) excretion.
3. Most species in the Class Bivalvia are (a) predators (b) parasites (c) land dwellers (d) filter feeders.
4. The only mollusks with a closed circulatory system are (a) gastropods (b) bivalves (c) cephalopods (d) snails.
5. Terrestrial snails and slugs require an environment with a high moisture content in order to carry out (a) reproduction (b) feeding (c) respiration (d) all of the above.
6. Annelids are placed into one of three classes, based on the number of their (a) setae (b) segments (c) nephridia (d) organ systems.
7. The movement of earthworms requires (a) fluid pressure in the coelom (b) muscle contractions (c) traction provided by setae (d) all of the above.
8. Earthworms respire by means of (a) gills (b) lungs (c) diffusion across the skin (d) all of the above.
9. Parapodia are a distinguishing characteristic of (a) the Class Polychaeta (b) the Class Oligochaeta (c) the Class Hirudinea (d) the Class Bivalvia.
10. Most species of leeches live (a) on land (b) in fresh water (c) in the oceans (d) inside other animals.
11. What are the functions of a true coelom in mollusks and annelids?
12. What are the three main parts of the body plan of mollusks?
13. What is torsion? What effect does it have on the location of the snail's mantle cavity?
14. What is the function of the radula in mollusks?
15. How is the structure of a gill related to its function?
16. Describe the feeding method of the clam.
17. What is the adaptive value of segmentation in annelids?
18. What use do microsurgeons make of leeches? What use might scientists make of leeches in the future?
19. Why do earthworms require a moist environment?
20. How does a leech's method of movement differ from an earthworm's?

Critical Thinking

1. Of what advantage might hermaphroditism be to the land snail?
2. Clams and other mollusks that live in water reproduce by shedding sperm and eggs into the water. How might this process affect the reproductive success of these mollusks? Would you expect the mollusks to shed many sperm and eggs or only a few?
3. In order for an oyster to make a pearl, a piece of sand or rock must get inside its shell. This causes the mantle to secrete a shiny smooth coating on it. Of what advantage might this process be to the oyster?
4. Anglers who use earthworms have observed that when an earthworm is cut in two the segments crawl in different directions. From what you know about the nervous system and muscular system of the earthworm, explain why a cut earthworm would be able to move in different directions.
5. In what way are the feeding habits of the earthworm and the clam similar? In what way do they differ?

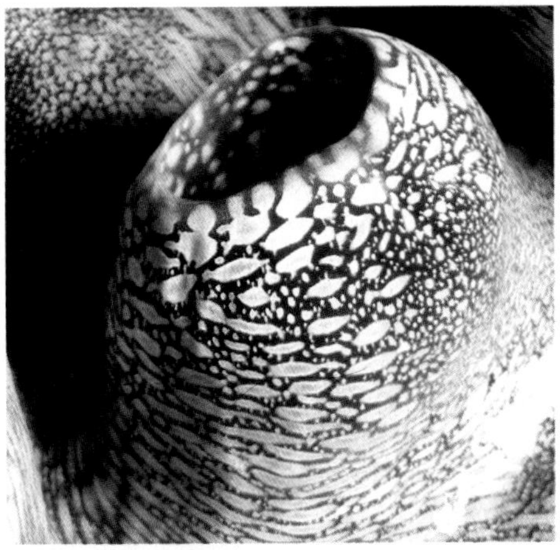

6. Leeches suck and ingest the blood of fish and mammals, taking in two to ten times their own weight in blood. Why aren't leeches considered parasites?
7. Look at the photograph above. What is the adaptive advantage of the clam's long, extended siphons? Keep in mind the habitat of the clam.

Extension

1. As a hobby many people collect the shells of mollusks. You may be able to see some of these shells in your school or in the homes of friends or relatives. Using a book such as *The LaRousse Guide to Shells of the World,* by A. P. H. Oliver, identify five shells or pictures of shells. Draw each one, and under each drawing give the common name, the scientific name, the part of the world where it is found, and the size.
2. Read the article by Thomas A. Lewis entitled "Squid: The Great Communicator?" in *National Wildlife,* August/September 1990, pp. 14–19. Write a report in which you include details of squid anatomy, reproduction, movement, and communication.
3. Research the giant squid. Make a poster in which you compare its size with that of some commonly known object or an average-sized squid. Include some interesting information for the other students such as, for example, proof that the squid is eaten by whales.
4. Annelids and mollusks show an incredible diversity of form. Write a report in which you research the structure and habitat of an annelid or mollusk species that was not covered in this chapter. How does the form of your chosen species illustrate an evolutionary adaptation to the environment in which it lives? Illustrate your report if possible.

Critical Thinking

1. It allows a land snail to mate with any other snail, rather than with just 50 percent of the snail population, increasing the chance of reproduction, since snails move slowly and are often inactive.
2. Tides, currents, and wave action may prevent the meeting of egg and sperm, thus jeopardizing the mollusks' reproductive success. Consequently, students might expect aquatic mollusks to shed numerous sperm and eggs.
3. The secretion covers foreign particles and prevents them from being an irritant.
4. Each section of the nerve net controls muscles of an individual segment, making it possible for the two halves to move in different directions.
5. They both take in part of their environment and filter out food. The earthworm's environment is soil, while the clam's is salt water; each digestive anatomy is adapted for the organism's environment.
6. A leech is not considered a true parasite because it neither derives protection from its host nor lives permanently off its host.
7. They enable the clam to bury itself and still receive oxygen and nutrients.

Extension

1. Have students carry out the same activities for mollusks that have commercial value.
2. Encourage students to research the squid's evolution and focus on its highly developed nervous system.
3. Tell students to consider, as they conduct their research, the similarities and possible relationship between reports of giant sea monsters and the ferocious battles that take place between giant squids and whales.
4. Suggest that students research cockles, limpets, conchs, mussels, watering pots, or piddocks.

Chapter 32 Arthropods

Chapter Overview

Chapter 32 discusses how arthropods have adapted to most of the earth's environments. Section 32.1 examines characteristics and evolution of Phylum Arthropoda. Section 32.2 looks at the body systems of Subphylum Crustacea. Section 32.3 takes a look at other arthropods, including arachnids and myriapods.

Chapter Planning Chart

B	S	A	Sections and Subsections	Page	Features	Page	Resources
•	•	•	**32.1 Phylum Arthropoda**				
			Characteristics	479	Biotechnology	480	Videodiscs
			Movement and Growth	479	Section Review	482	Section Reviews Worksheet
			Evolution and Classification	481			
•	•	•	**32.2 Crustacea**				
			Diversity	483	Laboratory	489	Videodiscs
			The Crayfish	483	Section Review	485	Blackline Master 66
							Overhead Transparency T32
							Blackline Master 67
							Laboratories: Live Crayfish
							Section Reviews Worksheet
•	•	•	**32.3 Other Arthropods**				
			Arachnida	486	Think	487	Videodiscs
			Myriapods	488	Section Review	488	Process Skills: Spider Webs
							Section Reviews Worksheet
			End of Chapter Activities				
					Chapter Review	490	Vocabulary Skills
							Chapter Test
							Computer Test Generator

B *The Basic Level curriculum presents the most fundamental knowledge offered in the course.*
S *The Standard Level curriculum is designed for the average student who is able to master most topics.*
A *The Advanced Level curriculum includes suggestions for teaching the most academically able students.*

Cooperative Learning

Group Activity: Identification of Arthropods

- **Group Size:** *4 students*
- **Outcome:** *Students will identify well-known arthropods by their characteristics.*
- **Individual Accountability:** *Each group member will develop a set of questions and answers about arthropods.*
- **Positive Interdependence:** *Group members will discover the identity of unnamed arthropods presented by members of another group.*

Ask each group to pick a secret arthropod. Caution students against selecting an obscure arthropod that is too difficult to identify. Have each student help prepare the group to answer questions from another group about the following topics for this arthropod: organ systems, external structure, reproduction and development, and behavior and habitat.

Next, pair off the groups and have them play a game of "What's My Lineage?" Have each group select a member of the other group to answer yes or no questions about that group's arthropod. Tell members of the first group to take turns asking questions. When the questioning group has enough information, they may guess the identity of the arthropod. Then have the groups reverse roles. Assign one student to act as moderator of the game and coach students who are unsure of the correct answer.

Concept Map

The following is one possible solution to the concept mapping activity in Classifying Organisms on p. 480.

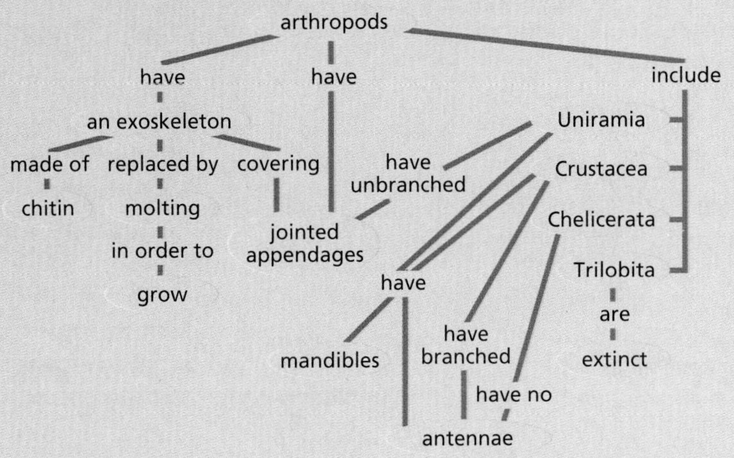

Laboratory Preparation

Overview *(See p. 489.)*

The pill bug is an isopod and a member of the Phylum Arthropoda. In this lab, students observe the behavior of pill bugs under different environmental conditions. Students record their observations of the pill bug's behavior under light, dark, wet, and dry conditions. They relate observations of pill bug behavior to the isopod's natural habitat. They conclude by designing an experiment to test the pill bug's response to temperature.

Preparation

Pill bugs are available from biological supply houses. Sow bugs can be substituted.

Teaching Tips

When conducting the investigation, dim the classroom lights as much as practical to prevent excessive light from affecting pill bug behavior.

This is a good opportunity to discuss characteristics of crustaceans. All crustaceans breathe by gills. Most are aquatic. The few that are terrestrial must live in moist habitats. Students should observe the hard external skeleton and jointed appendages characteristic of arthropods and the two pairs of antennae characteristic of crustaceans.

Safety

Remind students to handle the pill bugs in a humane manner.

Chapter Themes

Evolution Arthropod evolutionary advances in body structures have led to unequaled success in the animal world. Point out to students that adaptations of arthropods have enabled crustaceans, arachnids, and insects to live anywhere in the world and in greater numbers than any other animal phylum.

Scale and Structure Highlight the role that structures unique to each member of an arthropod subphylum play in the survival of the animals in this subphylum. Also stress to students the interdependence of an arthropod's structures and specific ways in which they function together.

Chapter Motivating Activity

Use an overhead projector to show students a series of photographs of arthropods, such as a scorpion, crab, centipede, spider, and grasshopper, over which you have placed a heavy sheet of paper with a cutout window. Reveal only one representative characteristic of the animal, for example, chelipeds, swimmerets, walking legs, antennae, or maxillipeds. Ask students to identify these characteristics. Write students' answers on the board. Then show them the entire photograph of each animal. Ask students to identify the animal. Point out that all of these animals come from the same phylum—Arthropoda. Ask students how the arthropods are distinct from animals in the phyla studied previously. *(Answers may include that these have exoskeletons and appendages, such as legs, claws, and antennae.)*

Chapter 32 *Arthropods*

Spider web. Inset (top): Porcelain crab living in anemone, Philippine Islands. Inset (center): Sea spider, *Pycnogonid colossendeis,* Antarctica. Inset (bottom): Face of a jumping spider, *Phidippus otiosus,* Myakka River State Park, Florida (×6).

Introduction

In previous chapters you have learned about many ways in which groups of invertebrates have adapted to life on land as well as in water. In this chapter you will learn about the characteristics of arthropods that have enabled them to adapt to almost all environments on earth. In the next chapter you will study the insects, the largest group of arthropods.

Chapter Outline

Chapter Concept

As you read, note the ways in which the basic arthropod body plan has become evolutionarily modified for life in specific environments.

Understanding the Visuals

Ask students to describe features of the animals in the chapter opening photographs. Call their attention to walking legs of the sea spider and chelipeds of the crab. Stress to students that these jointed appendages exhibit an evolutionary advance first seen in arthropods. Point out that the jumping spider and the spider in the web also have walking legs as well as other appendages. Ask students what other body characteristic the crab has. Tell students that an exoskeleton is another characteristic of arthropods.

32.1 Phylum Arthropoda

Three-fourths of all animal species belong to the Phylum Arthropoda *(ahr-THRAHP-uh-duh)*. This diverse phylum includes insects and spiders, lobsters and crabs, as well as millipedes and centipedes. Because of the diversity of insects and their importance to people, we will examine them in more detail in Chapter 33. In this chapter we will study primarily the other groups of arthropods.

Section Objectives

- *List three distinguishing characteristics of arthropods.*
- *Relate the structure of the exoskeleton to its function.*
- *Name the four subphyla of Phylum Arthropoda, and explain the characteristics of each subphylum.*
- *Describe three products that researchers have developed from chitin.*

Characteristics

All members of the Phylum Arthropoda share the following characteristics:

- Arthropods have jointed appendages. **Appendages** are extensions of the body and include legs and antennae.
- The arthropod body is segmented. A pair of appendages is attached to each segment. In some species the appendages have been lost or reduced in size during the course of evolution.
- Arthropods have an exoskeleton. An **exoskeleton** is a hard external covering that provides protection and support.
- Arthropods have a ventral nervous system, an open circulatory system, a digestive system, and specialized sensory receptors.

The name *arthropod,* meaning "jointed foot," refers to the jointed appendages. Jointed appendages and an exoskeleton are the most distinctive arthropod traits. The exoskeleton provides much more structural support than the annelid cuticle and gives the internal organs better protection.

The chemical composition and the three-layered structure of the exoskeleton give it versatility and strength. The exoskeleton is composed primarily of protein and a tough carbohydrate called **chitin** *(KITE-'n)*. The waxy outer layer repels water and helps prevent desiccation in terrestrial species. The hard middle layer, which is strengthened by materials such as calcium, provides the primary protection. The inner layer, which is flexible at the joints, allows the animal to move freely. All three layers are secreted by an epidermis that lies just beneath them.

Movement and Growth

Figure 32-1 shows how muscles that are attached to the exoskeleton provide the structural basis for the wide range of movements that occurs in arthropods. Unlike the muscles of annelids, which form continuous sheets in the body wall, the muscles of arthropods occur in bundles that attach to the inside of the exoskeleton on either side of the joints. By alternately contracting and relaxing these muscles, the arthropod in essence operates a system of levers that move the body parts and appendages.

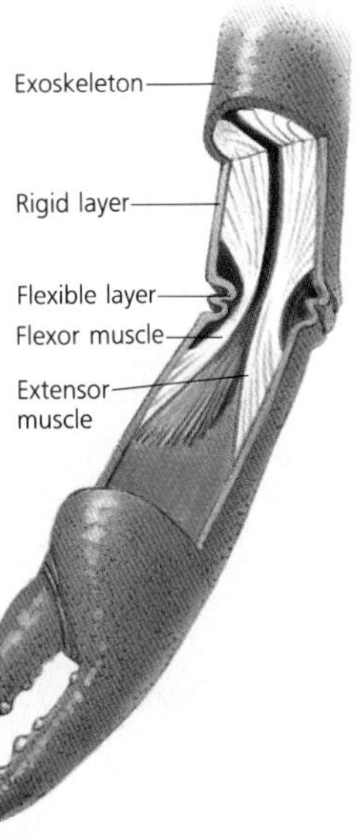

Figure 32-1 Muscles inside the exoskeleton enable arthropods to move their jointed legs.

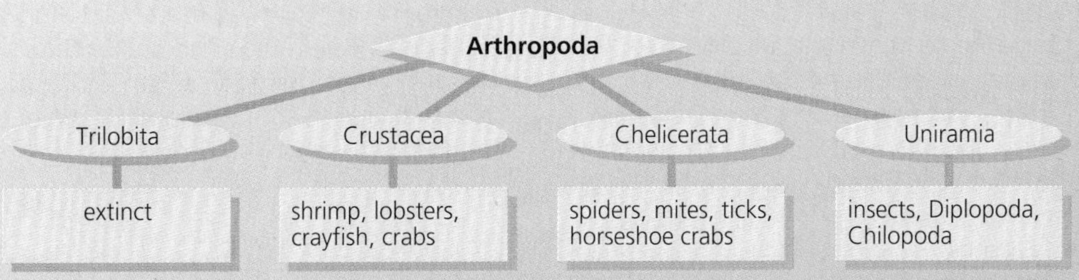

Graphic Organizer Use this organizational chart in Reteaching on p. 482.

Lesson Plan

Section Focus

Arthropods are the most numerous animals, comprising more than three-fourths of all species. Their bodies are segmented and they have an exoskeleton. The jointed appendages of arthropods are often modified for specialized functions, such as food getting, sensory reception, or swimming. Arthropods are subdivided on the basis of structural specializations.

Section Themes

The theme of **Evolution** is seen in the phylogenetically advanced characteristics of arthropods. Compared to annelids, they have evolved body segments that are more specialized, reduced in number, and grouped in various ways. Along with their exoskeletons, they evolved a concentration of muscles in bundles that can bring about movements of adjacent segments and specialized appendages.

Motivating Activity

Show students a specimen or a photograph of a fiddler crab, garden spider, and housefly. Ask students what they know about each animal. *(Answers may include that they have claws, have legs, crawl, or fly.)* Write responses on the board. Then ask students to identify which characteristic the animals have in common. *(Legs)* Point out that all of these animals are arthropods. Then ask students to identify differences among the animals. *(Answers may include movement, size, and color.)* Tell students that there are more than 900,000 species of arthropods, more than all other animal species put together.

Videodiscs

- ***1039–1068, Crustacean—Examples (s)***

Teaching Strategies

Comparing Structures To help students identify characteristics of arthropods, have them look at photographs and specimens of arthropods (insects, crayfish, lobsters, spiders, scorpions, centipedes, isopods, mites, ticks, crabs, and so forth) and other animals (earthworms, mollusks, sponges, flatworms, octopuses, fish, birds, mammals, and so forth). Ask students to identify each animal as arthropod or nonarthropod. After students have identified a few organisms, ask them to list the criteria they are using to make their decisions. Then have students list several essential attributes of arthropods. *(Jointed appendages, segments, exoskeleton)* As an extension, have students make dichotomous keys for these animals. See pp. 269 and 275 for a review of dichotomous keys.

Interpreting the Visuals Have students study Figure 32-3 on p. 482. Ask them which species are extinct. *(Species of sea scorpions and trilobytes)* Ask what animal might be at the end of the Annelida branch. *(Earthworm)* Ask students which class they think would continue branching out most extensively. *(Insects)*

Identifying Structures Bring in a molted exoskeleton of an insect such as a cicada, or ask students who may have collections to bring one in. Ask students to identify where the exoskeleton broke apart. *(Down the back)* Then have students identify as many external parts of the insect as they can to get an idea of how complete a molt is.

Classifying Organisms Have students make a concept map that shows the major features and subphyla of Arthropoda. An example of a completed concept map is shown on p. 477B.

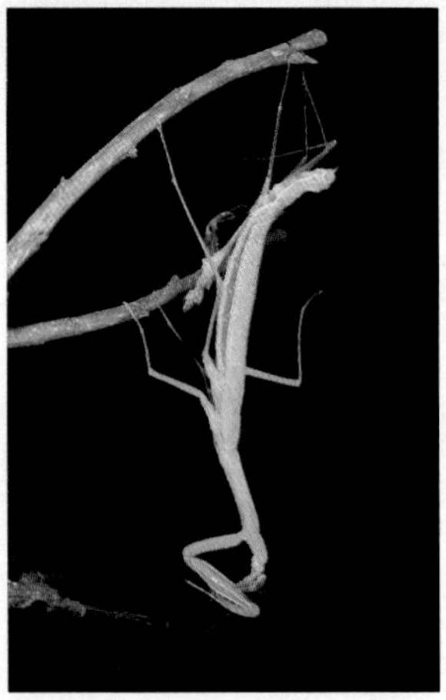

Figure 32-2 A praying mantis sheds its exoskeleton during the molting process.

Because the exoskeleton cannot enlarge as the body enlarges, the exoskeleton must be shed periodically and a new one must be formed. This process is called **molting.** Molting is also called ecdysis. The tissues of the arthropod grow until they put a great deal of pressure on the exoskeleton walls. A hormone is then produced that induces molting.

When an arthropod starts to molt, the cells of the epidermis secrete enzymes that digest the inner, flexible layer of the exoskeleton. Simultaneously the epidermis begins to synthesize a new exoskeleton, using much of the digested material. During this process the outer layer of the old exoskeleton loosens and breaks along specific lines. The old exoskeleton is then shed. The new exoskeleton, which is flexible at first, stretches to fit the now enlarged insect.

An arthropod molts many times during the course of its lifetime. Each time it molts, it becomes larger. However, during molting it is extremely vulnerable to predators because it temporarily lacks a hard shell. Terrestrial arthropods are also susceptible to desiccation during molting. For these reasons, arthropods usually go into hiding when they molt until their new exoskeleton has hardened.

Biotechnology

Protective Properties of Chitin

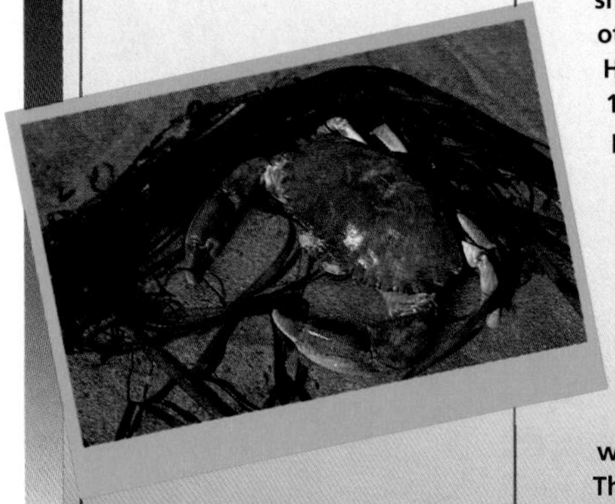

For years seafood packers simply threw away the shells of crabs, shrimp, and other crustaceans. However, by the mid-1970s, this dumping was polluting coastal waters. The U.S. Environmental Protection Agency ordered packers to stop dumping. To help them solve the disposal problem, the federal government agreed to help fund research into new ways to use the shells.

The shells of crustaceans are composed mostly of chitin, a carbohydrate polymer that is able to bind to many proteins. This suggests many possible uses for chitin. Unfortunately, chitin is not soluble in water, which makes it difficult to work with in the lab, so little research has been done with chitin.

Since the ban on dumping crustacean shells, many chitin-based products have been developed. A Japanese company makes surgical sutures and an artificial skin out of a chitin derivative. The chitin-based sutures are used to close an incision after surgery and are absorbed by the body as the wound heals. The artificial skin product is used to protect large, open wounds, such as those caused by severe burns.

LEP Activity

To reinforce visually the appearance of animals in each of the four subphyla of arthropods, have each student create an arthropod ID card. Tell them to include on one side a photograph and a list of the animal's characteristics—such as claws, mandibles, pincers—and identify the organism and its subphylum on the other side. Have students find photographs in old magazines or make photocopies from library magazines and books. Collect the arthropod ID cards and use them as flash cards. Have students try to name each arthropod and identify the subphylum to which it belongs.

Evolution and Classification

Animals with arthropod characteristics evolved more than 600 million years ago. Because all arthropods possess both an exoskeleton and jointed appendages, biologists have long inferred that they all evolved from a common ancestor. However, the most current studies of arthropod structure suggest that there may actually be four separate lines of arthropod evolution. On the basis of these recent studies, arthropods are now classified by scientists into four subphyla:

- Trilobita *(TRIE-luh-BITE-uh)* includes extinct organisms called trilobites.
- Crustacea *(KRUSS-TAY-shuh)* includes shrimp, lobsters, crabs, barnacles, cladocerans, ostracods, crayfish, water fleas, and copepods.
- Chelicerata *(kuh-LISS-uh-RAHT-uh)* includes spiders, scorpions, ticks, mites, sea spiders, and horseshoe crabs.
- Uniramia *(YOO-nuh-RAY-mee-uh)* is the only group that seems to have evolved on land and includes centipedes, millipedes, and all of the insects.

Preliminary testing seems to suggest that the chitin-based artificial skin may actually speed the healing process. In addition chitin is not known to cause an allergic response, so there is little danger of tissue rejection.

In 1988 Ernest Hayes, a chemist from Acadia University in Nova Scotia, Canada, developed a water-soluble compound that is chitin based. The compound, called NOCC, can be dissolved in water and sprayed on fruit. NOCC forms a semipermeable coating that limits the amount of oxygen entering the fruit. As a result treated fruits ripen more slowly than untreated fruits and can be held fresh in cold storage for a longer period of time. Unlike paraffin or wax, the chitin-based spray can be washed off in warm water. So far NOCC spray is approved for use only on fruits that will be washed and peeled before being eaten. If further testing confirms that the compound is harmless, its use will probably be expanded.

The newest use for chitin is in the food industry. A derivative of chitin has already been used to extract protein from waste cooking water. The process could be used to provide a protein source that could feed millions of people. As more new products are developed from discarded shells, the list of human uses for chitin-based products will be greatly expanded.

Guided Practice

Have students examine the crayfish leg shown in Figure 32-1 on p. 479. Tell them to analyze the relationship between the crayfish's structure and how it moves. Guide them to focus on problems related to growth. Ask students what the basic difference is between an arthropod leg and a mammalian leg. *(Muscles attach to the exoskeleton instead of to internal bones as in mammals.)*

Biotechnology

Using the Feature

Research on chitin has yielded a surprising array of products. In addition to the ones mentioned in the feature, there are chitin-based antifungal coatings for seeds, contact lenses, and even a kind of varnish. Tell students that most uses of chitin are similar to its use in nature—as a protective outer covering. Point out that the use of chitin-based compounds as a covering exploits the physical properties of chitin.

Make sure that students understand that chitin in its natural state is not soluble in water. Ask them to suggest advantages of a waterproof covering to a crustacean or an arthropod. *(It slows water loss in marine environments and water absorption in aquatic environments. A strong, rigid body covering made of chitin functions as an exoskeleton, offers some protection against injury and predators, provides a place for attachment of muscles, and helps keep internal organs and tissues from drying out.)* Ask students why NOCC spray would have to be water soluble for use on food. *(People must be able to wash it off before they eat the food.)*

Videodiscs

■ ***2590–2593, Classification; Evolutionary Relationships (s)***

Cooperative Learning

Importance of Arthropods Tell students to imagine a world in which all arthropods have become extinct. Ask them to consider the consequences to humans. Have students do library research in groups of three. Tell one group member to develop a list of ecological consequences of a world without arthropods. Have a second group member develop a list of economic consequences. Tell the third group member to develop a list of consequences to human health. Encourage students to discuss within their groups how items on their lists are interrelated. Then have students prepare a poster that graphically depicts a world without arthropods.

Section 32.1

Independent Practice

■ Have students write answers to the Section Review.

■ Have students explain adaptive advantages and disadvantages of jointed appendages and an exoskeleton.

Check Your Understanding

1. Compare evolutionary development of arthropods and annelids. *(Both have well developed organ systems; arthropods have an exoskeleton and a body that has fewer, more specialized body segments and appendages, including legs and antennae.)*

2. What is molting, and why is it important to arthropods? *(It is the periodic shedding of the exoskeleton; it is essential for arthropod growth because the exoskeleton does not grow.)*

3. What characteristics make arthropods more diverse than annelids? *(Their exoskeletons and appendages have very different shapes.)*

Reteaching

Copy on the board the top levels of the organizational chart on p. 479. Have students extend the chart by contributing appropriate characteristics and representative members of each arthropod subphylum.

■ ***See* Section Reviews *worksheet, Section 32.1.***

Enrichment

Arthropods are among the most rapidly evolving organisms, yet have some of the oldest animal fossils. Have students use library resources to prepare an illustrated magazine article about an extinct arthropod ancestor, such as the trilobite.

Closure

Have students imagine that they have found an invertebrate fossil. Ask them what characteristics would identify whether this is the fossil of an arthropod. *(The exoskeleton, the segmented body)*

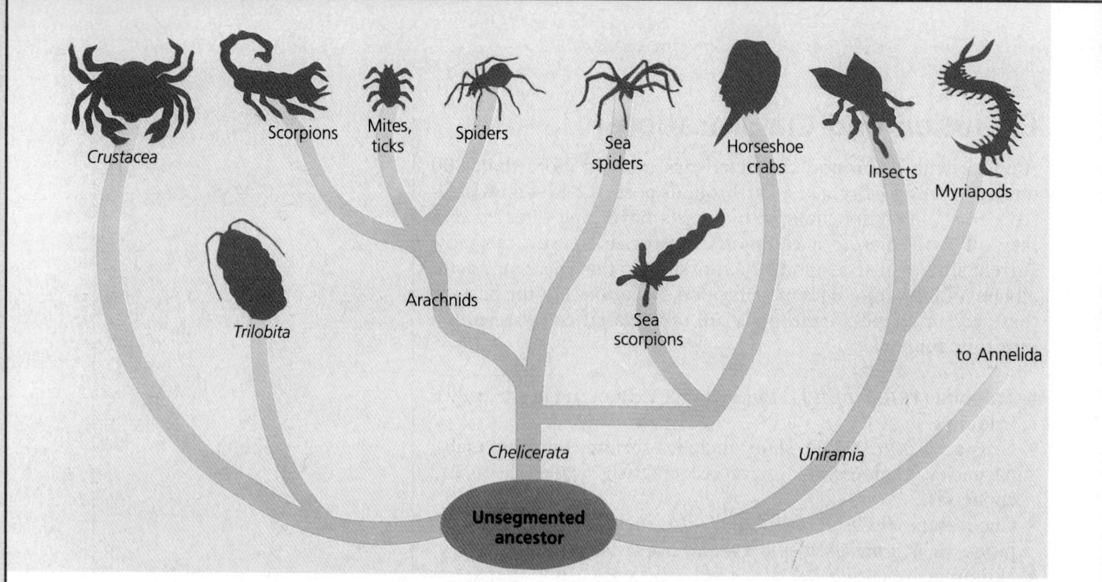

Figure 32-3 The four subphyla of arthropods are shown in this phylogenetic tree. Which species is extinct?

The four separate lines of arthropod evolution are illustrated in Figure 32-3. Members of the four subphyla are distinguished primarily by differences in their embryological development and differences in the morphology of structures such as appendages and mouthparts. Members of Chelicerata are distinguished from other arthropods by the absence of antennae and the presence of pincerlike mouthparts called **chelicerae.** Crustaceans are distinguished by the presence of branched antennae and chewing mouthparts called **mandibles.** The members of Uniramia are also distinguished by having antennae and mandibles, but their appendages are unbranched. *Uniramia* means "one branch."

Despite their differences, the three subphyla of living arthropods have evolved similarly. For example, ancestral arthropods had one pair of appendages per segment, but most living species have fewer appendages than this. In addition, the evolution of these groups shows a general tendency toward less segmentation of the body. For example, ancestral arthropods had many segments, but most modern adults have some segments fused together into larger structures with specialized functions.

Section Review

1. What is an *exoskeleton?*
2. List three characteristics that are shared by all arthropods.
3. How do the exoskeleton and the muscles function in arthropod movement?
4. What are the major structural differences between crustaceans and uniramians?
5. During molting an aquatic arthropod absorbs water and swells. What is the adaptive advantage of this behavior?

Answers to Section Review

1. A hard external covering that protects and supports the organism

2. Answers may include: jointed appendages, an exoskeleton, a segmented body, a ventral nervous system, an open circulatory system, a digestive system, and specialized sensory receptors.

3. Muscles attached to the inside of the exoskeleton on either side of the joints alternately contract and relax, thus operating the appendages like a system of levers.

4. Crustaceans have branched appendages; uniramians have unbranched appendages.

5. Swelling allows a larger exoskeleton to form, with extra room for growth.

32.2 Crustacea

Members of the Subphylum Crustacea have hard exoskeletons that contain calcium carbonate. The approximately 25,000 species of crustaceans include crayfish, lobsters, pill bugs, sow bugs, water fleas, and barnacles. Crustacea is the only subphylum of modern arthropods that contains mostly aquatic members.

Diversity

Most crustaceans are small. Copepods no larger than a comma inhabit the surface waters of oceans, lakes, and streams. Barnacles are sessile crustaceans that attach themselves to rocks and pilings as well as to whales and sea turtles. Barnacles filter plankton from the water with 12 appendages called cirri.

Some crustaceans, such as sow bugs and pill bugs, are terrestrial. Because these animals have seven identical pairs of legs, they are called isopods, which means "same feet." Isopods usually live in damp areas, where their gills can stay moist.

The Crayfish

Crayfish are often studied as representative crustaceans because they are large and abundant. Crayfish are similar to lobsters in their internal and external structures.

External Structure

The body of the crayfish is divided into two sections, the cephalothorax and the abdomen. The **cephalothorax** consists of the fused head and the thorax; it has 13 segments and is covered by a hard carapace. The **abdomen** is divided into seven segments. The seventh segment, called the **telson,** forms a flat triangular section at the tail of the animal. Powerful abdominal muscles can jerk this tail and propel the animal rapidly backward.

Section Objectives

- *Give examples of crustaceans that are adapted to marine, freshwater, and land environments.*
- *Describe the external anatomy of a crayfish, and explain the function of each major part.*
- *Summarize the processes of digestion, circulation, respiration, and excretion in crayfish.*
- *Describe the structure and function of the compound eye in crustaceans.*

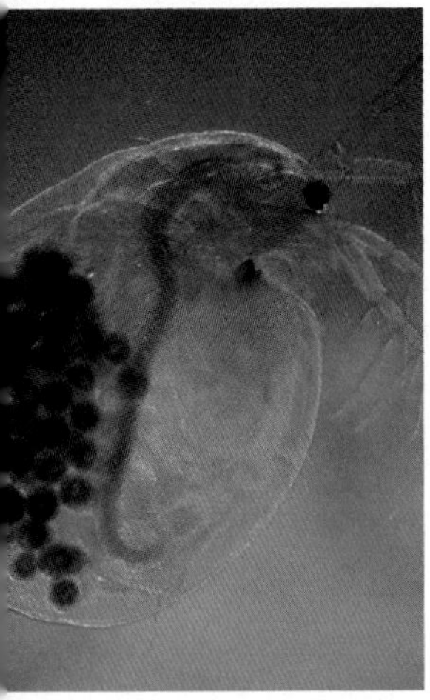
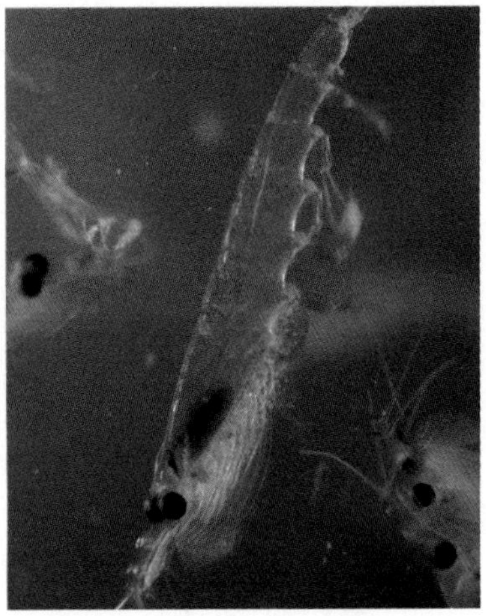

Figure 32-4 The water flea, *Daphnia* sp. (left), the krill (center), and the sow bug (right) are members of the Subphylum Crustacea.

Lesson Plan

Section Focus

Members of the Subphylum Crustacea are primarily aquatic. They have gills, compound eyes, a hard exoskeleton, and mandibles and are distinguished from other arthropods by two pairs of antennae. Their bodies are composed of a cephalothorax and abdomen.

Section Themes

The theme of **Scale and Structure** is illustrated by those characteristics of crustaceans that distinguish them from the other arthropods. An additional pair of antennae and a hard exoskeleton are structures unique to the Subphylum Crustacea.

Motivating Activity

Show students a variety of crustaceans from the grocery store or fish market, such as crayfish, whole and uncleaned shrimp, crabs, and lobsters. Alternatively, photographs of these crustaceans may be displayed. Ask students if they have eaten crustaceans. Ask them what ones and what parts they have eaten. Based on their experiences, list what they know about crustaceans on the board. Tell students that humans come in contact with crustaceans in other ways as well. Point out that the copepods and daphnia that Annie Dillard found in the duck pond at Tinker Creek (Chapter 29, p. 440) are all crustaceans as are barnacles and isopods, such as pill bugs and sow bugs. Ask students to speculate on ways in which these animals might affect humans. *(Some crabs destroy rice fields, isopods bore holes into wood and concrete harbor structures, and copepods carry parasitic worms.)*

Videodiscs

- ***Side 3 36899,* Daphnia *(m)***
- ***2157–2165, Crayfish (s)***

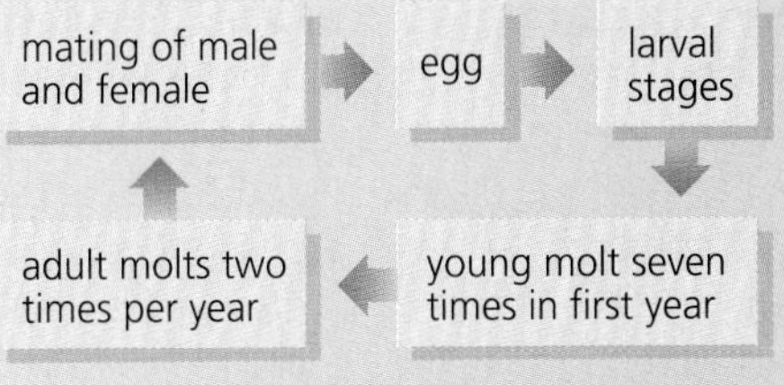

Graphic Organizer Use this cyclic diagram in Reteaching on p. 485.

Teaching Strategies

Interpreting the Visuals Have students examine the external structure of a crayfish and identify its parts and their functions as shown in Figure 32-5 and Table 32-1 on p. 484. Ask students how each structure illustrates adaptation. *(For example, antennae facilitate hunting and movement in low light.)*

■ *See* **Overhead Transparency** *T32 and* **Blackline Master** *66.*

Making Inferences Some crayfish live in caves. Ask students how these animals might differ from other crayfish. *(They are blind and lack pigmentation, their antennae are longer, and they are more sensitive to slight disturbances in water.)*

Interpreting the Visuals Tell students to examine the cross section of a crayfish in Figure 32-6 on p. 485. Ask what other animals have a ventral nerve cord. *(Annelids, such as earthworms)* Tell students that the ventral nerve cords of both annelids and arthropods are actually a fusion of two cords.

■ *See* **Blackline Master** *67.*

Guided Practice

Provide each group of students with a live or preserved crayfish. Have students examine it and use the text to help identify and describe the functions of its external and internal structures. Suggest to students that they refer to Figure 32-5 on p. 484 as they examine the animal.

■ *See* **Laboratories,** *Investigation 32.*

Independent Practice

■ Have students write answers to the Section Review.

■ If a crayfish loses an appendage, it is replaced during the next molt. Have students use sources such as invertebrate zoology textbooks to research this process and represent it with a flow chart and drawings.

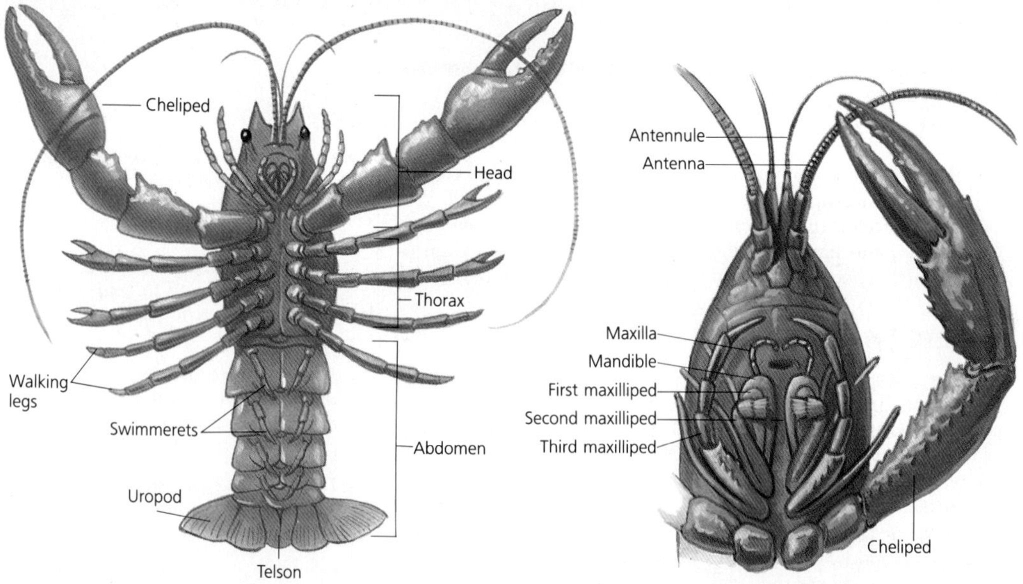

Figure 32-5 A top view (left) shows the major sections of the crayfish. Parts of its head are illustrated at the right.

Table 32-1 Crayfish Appendages

Appendages	Function
Antennules	Appendages with receptors for touch, taste, and equilibrium
Antennae	Specialized for touch and taste
Mandibles	Move up and down to crush food
Maxillae	Move side to side to tear food
Maxillipeds	"Jaws" to hold food
Chelipeds	Claws that capture food and serve as defensive weapons
Walking legs	Enable the crayfish to walk slowly
Swimmerets	Create water currents; function in reproduction
Uropods	Propel crayfish through water

A pair of appendages is attached to each segment of the crayfish. In Figure 32-5 and Table 32-1 note the location and function of the following appendages: **antennules, antennae,** mandibles, **maxillae, maxillipeds, chelipeds,** walking legs, **swimmerets,** and **uropods.** Each appendage develops from the same part of a segment, but is modified to perform a specialized function.

Digestive and Excretory Systems

Crayfish trap food with their chelipeds, tear it with the maxillae and maxillipeds, and chew it with the mandibles. The food then passes through the esophagus to the stomach, where chitinous teeth grind it into a fine paste that is mixed with digestive juices. Digestive glands absorb the mixture, and undigested particles pass through the intestines and out the anus. Excretory organs, called **green glands,** remove wastes from the blood and retain salts, which are scarce in fresh water.

Circulatory and Respiratory Systems

The crayfish has an open circulatory system. Blood flows from a dorsal sinus through small, one-way valves called ostia into the dorsal heart. The heart then pumps the blood into seven large vessels that carry it through the body. Blood leaves the vessels and fills the body cavity, where it bathes the organs and cells. Blood collects in a large ventral sinus. Other vessels then carry the blood through the gills, where it gives off carbon dioxide and takes up oxygen gas. It then returns to the dorsal sinus.

Gills are attached to each walking leg, protected in a chamber under the carapace. As the crayfish walks, water moves across the gills. Also, as the second maxillae move during feeding, the two gill bailers attached to them "bail" water over the gills.

Interdisciplinary Activity

History Armor can be seen as a sort of exoskeleton for soldiers. The types of armor used changed and developed in response to the offensive capability of an enemy. For example, during the First Crusade Europeans in full armor fought Saracens in light mail. In part because the Saracens were so much more mobile, the Europeans were eventually turned back. In subsequent crusades the Europeans made greater use of light mail. Have students research in an encyclopedia or other reference works medieval European, Saracen, or Japanese suits of armor and compare them with the exoskeletons of arthropods. Ask them to make a chart with drawings that point out the advantages and expose the disadvantages of both exoskeletons and suits of armor.

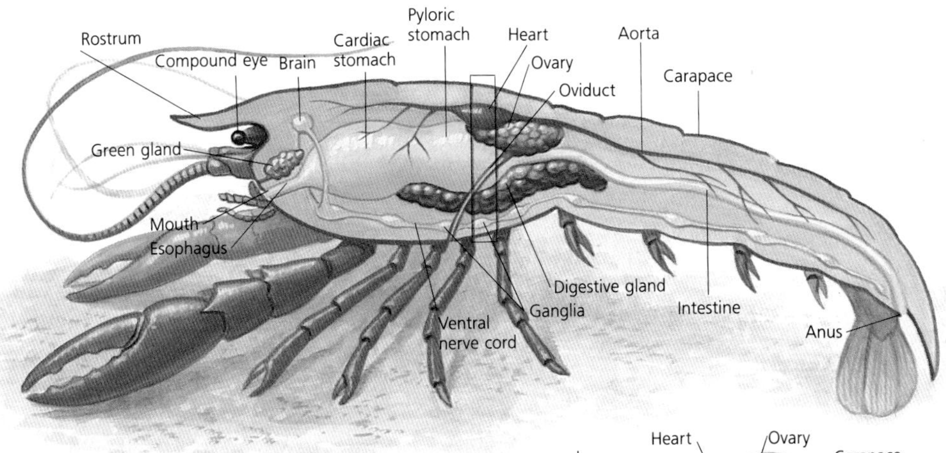

Nervous System

The crayfish nervous system includes a brain and a ventral nerve cord that runs from the brain to the tail. Nerve impulses travel to and from the nerve cord through ganglia. Nerves connect the brain with sense receptors in the antennules, antennae, and eyes.

The eyes are set on two short, movable stalks. Each eye has more than 2,000 light-sensitive lenses. Eyes with many lenses, or **compound eyes,** are highly sensitive to light and detect motion well, even though they can form only very crude images.

A crustacean senses position through the use of statocysts. Statocysts are cells that contain particles of calcium carbonate, which move when the crustacean's position changes. This movement is monitored by the nerves and interpreted by the brain.

Reproduction and Development

Crayfish usually mate in the fall. The male uses its first and second pairs of swimmerets to transfer sperm to the seminal receptacle of the female. The sperm remains there until spring, when it fertilizes the eggs as the female lays them. A sticky secretion attaches the eggs to the last three pairs of the female's swimmerets. The eggs hatch after about six weeks, having gone through several larval stages. The young look like tiny adults. They molt repeatedly—an average of seven times during the first year, then twice a year for the remaining two or three years of their lives.

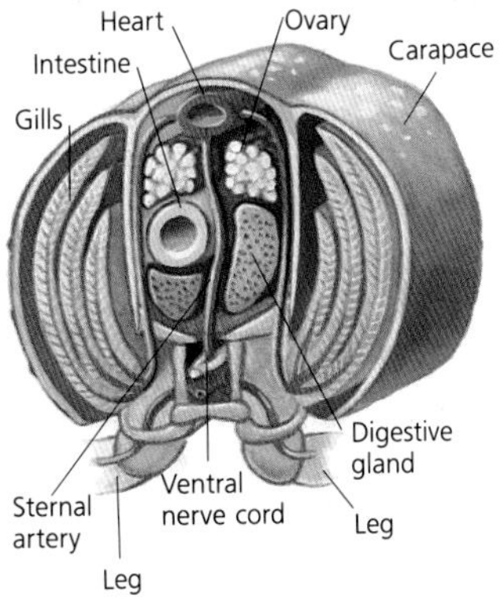

Figure 32-6 The major organs within a crayfish are shown in side view (top) and in cross section (bottom). Note: The cross section corresponds to the rectangle in the illustration above.

Section Review

1. What is a *cephalothorax?*
2. What are the habitats of some crustaceans?
3. What structural adaptations of crayfish promote effective respiration in water?
4. What are the functions of compound eyes?
5. Using what you know about molting, in what year of their lives would you say crayfish grow fastest? Explain why.

Check Your Understanding

1. What is the advantage to a crayfish of having its gills attached to its walking legs? *(Movement of the legs sets up a water flow past the gills.)*
2. What difference in its structure would a crayfish need in order to have a closed circulatory system? *(Veins that lead back to the heart)*
3. Compare the crustacean exoskeleton with the mollusk shell. *(Both provide protection. However, the mollusk shell is made of calcium carbonate and is rigid, while the crustacean exoskeleton, which is made of chitin, has a flexible layer that can be moved by muscles.)*

Reteaching

Have each student select a crustacean and make a diagram of its life cycle, including molting. An example of a completed diagram is shown on p. 483.
■ *See* Section Reviews *worksheet, Section 32.2.*

Enrichment

In 1977 researchers found crabs living at a depth of about 2,000 meters near thermal vents on the Galápagos Rift in the Pacific. Have students research and write a paper about the special adaptations that these animals have developed in this unusual environment.

Closure

Tell students to consider the body structure of the crayfish and its defense mechanisms. Ask them to speculate on the best way to catch a crayfish with a net, and why. *(By scooping up the crayfish tail first, because it jerks its tail to propel itself backward)*

Answers to Section Review

1. The fused head and thorax in a crustacean
2. Answers will vary. Lobsters, crabs, and shrimp live in salt water; *Daphnia* and copepods live in fresh water; isopods live on land.
3. Gills are attached to each walking leg. When the crayfish moves or eats, water is driven over its gills.
4. The functions of compound eyes include detecting motion and sensing light.
5. They grow much faster during the first year of life as indicated by the fact that they molt seven times in the first year.

Section 32.3

Lesson Plan

Section Focus

Unlike the crustaceans, nearly all other arthropods are terrestrial. In the Subphylum Chelicerata, the Class Arachnida are eight-legged land animals with chelicerae and pedipalps, simple eyes, book lungs, and/or tracheae. Mites and ticks have a fused cephalothorax and abdomen; some are parasites. In the Subphylum Uniramia are the classes Chilopoda and Diplopoda, which are many-segmented land dwellers.

Section Themes

The theme of **Evolution** is illustrated by the Subphylum Chelicerata, a distinct evolutionary line in which the anterior end of the body has been modified into chelicerae. These have an evolutionary origin separate from the mandibles seen in crustaceans and uniramians.

Motivating Activity

If possible, show students a scene from the film *Arachnaphobia* and elicit students' reaction. Alternatively, display photographs of a variety of arachnids—for example, deer ticks, daddy long-legs, and centipedes. Ask students if they have encountered arachnids in other films or in literature. How have they been portrayed? *(Answers may include the heroic spider in E. B. White's* Charlotte's Web *as well as vicious, scary, satiric spiders.)* Point out that the first reaction of many people when they see an arachnid is fright, a reaction exploited by horror films. Discuss characteristics of arachnids that frighten people. Explain that many arachnids, though they appear frightening, are beneficial to humans. Ask students how arachnids are helpful. *(They eat insects.)*

■ *See* **Process Skills,** ***Chapter 32.***

Section Objectives

- *Name the three main groups of arachnids, and list their distinguishing structural differences.*
- *Explain the adaptations arachnids have for predatory life on land.*
- *List similarities and differences between millipedes and centipedes.*

32.3 Other Arthropods

Unlike crustaceans, nearly all members of Chelicerata and Uniramia are terrestrial. In this section we will examine the major class of chelicerates, Arachnida, as well as two classes of the Subphylum Uniramia, Diplopoda and Chilopoda.

Arachnida

The Class Arachnida *(uh-RACK-nuh-duh)* is a group of more than 100,000 species, including spiders, scorpions, and mites. Most arachnids are adapted to kill prey with poison glands, stingers, or fangs.

Like crustaceans, arachnids have a body that is divided into a cephalothorax and an abdomen. Attached to the cephalothorax are four pairs of legs, a pair of chelicerae, and a pair of appendages called pedipalps. The **pedipalps** aid in chewing; in some species pedipalps are specialized to perform other functions.

Diversity

Spiders range in length from less than 0.5 mm to 9 cm in some tropical tarantula species. Spiders feed mainly on insects. Various species are adapted to capture prey in different ways. Some chase after prey, some catch prey in "trapdoors" in the ground, and some snare prey in elaborate webs.

Most scorpions live in tropical or semitropical areas; others live in dry temperate or desert regions. Scorpions differ from spiders in two ways. Scorpions have greatly enlarged pedipalps, which they hold in a forward position. They also have a large stinger on the last segment of the abdomen. Most scorpions hide during the day and hunt at night. Scorpions seize their prey with their pincerlike pedipalps. Then the fang injects paralyzing venom, the chelicerae tear the prey, the animal is ingested, and digestion begins. Only a few species have a sting that may be fatal to humans.

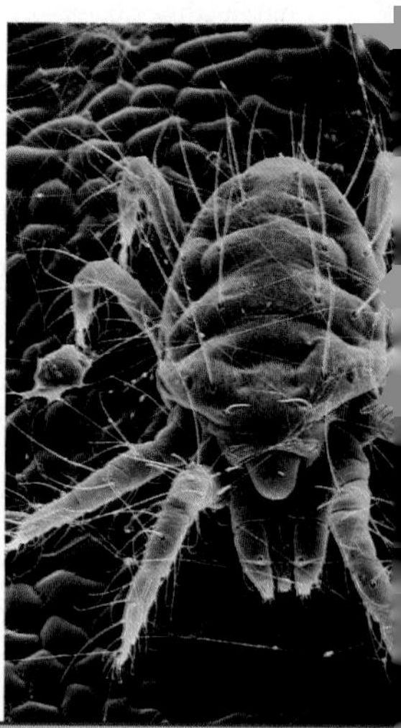

Figure 32-7 The Kenya giant scorpion, *Pandinus* sp. (left, ×0.25), and the Australian black widow spider, *Latrodectus seville* (center, ×4), are deadly arachnids. The red spider mite (right, ×43) is a parasite.

	Arachnida	Diplopoda	Chilopoda
legs	4 pairs	2 pairs each segment except last	1 pair each segment except first and last
body shape	compact, fused and unfused cephalothorax	segmented, round	segmented, flat
habitat	diverse, mostly land	moist soil	moist soil
poisons	inject venoms	spray cyanide	inject venoms

Graphic Organizer Use this table in Reteaching on p. 488.

Unlike other arachnids, mites and ticks have a fused cephalothorax and abdomen. Mites and ticks are the most abundant and most specialized arachnids. Ticks range in size from a few millimeters to 3 cm; most mites are less than a millimeter long.

Some mites and ticks are pests; others transmit diseases. Spider mites damage fruit trees when they suck fluid from the leaves. Many parasitic ticks pierce their host's skin to feed on blood. In the process they can transmit organisms such as those that cause Lyme disease and Rocky Mountain spotted fever.

Structure and Function

Arachnids share many characteristics with crustaceans. For example, the nervous, digestive, and circulatory systems of both groups are structurally similar. However, arachnids are terrestrial and therefore have a unique respiratory system. Spiders respire through openings in the cuticle called **spiracles** *(SPIR-uh-kulz)*. Air passes through the spiracles to the book lungs, the tracheae, or both. **Book lungs,** paired sacs in the abdomen with pagelike components, provide a large surface area for the exchange of gases. **Tracheae** *(TRAY-kee-ee)* carry air directly to the tissues.

The excretory system is also modified for life on land. The main excretory organs, called **Malpighian** *(MAL-PIG-ee-un)* **tubules,** are hollow projections of the digestive tract that collect body fluids, remove wastes, and carry wastes to the intestine. Most of the water is then reabsorbed, and the solid wastes leave the body. Some spiders also have **coxal glands,** organs that remove wastes and discharge them through an opening at the base of the leg.

Spiders have eight simple eyes rather than compound eyes. Many spiders also spin webs. The posterior tip of their abdomen contains three pairs of **spinnerets,** each made up of hundreds of microscopic tubes. Fluid from silk glands passes through the tubes and hardens into a thread that can be spun into webs. Silk is also used to build nests and egg cocoons. The young of some species use a long thread as a balloon to ride the wind to new habitats.

Think

These arachnids, called pseudoscorpions, use their pedipalps to attach themselves to beetles. Why might they do this? What trait seems to distinguish pseudoscorpions from scorpions?

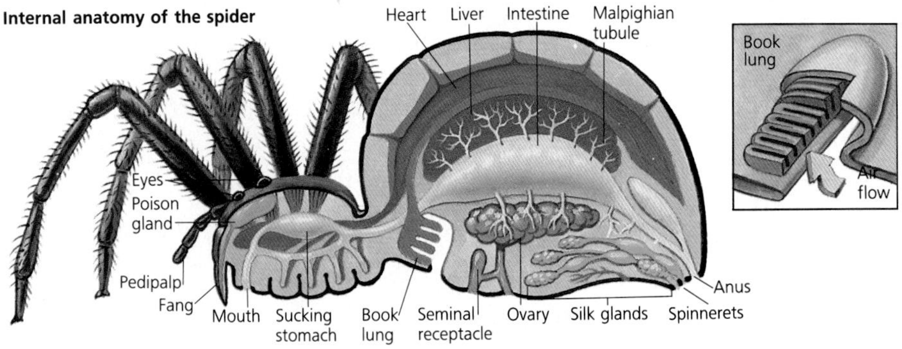

Figure 32-8 Note the structures of the respiratory system that make it possible for a spider to live on land.

Teaching Strategies

Analyzing Structures Direct students to look at the tracheae in Figure 33-6 on p. 498 in the next chapter. Tell them that tracheae are found in some spiders and myriapods as well as in insects, but in no other animals. Point out that the tracheal system is an extensive network of fragile, thin-walled tubes that extend deep into the animal's tissues where gases are exchanged by diffusion. Explain that contraction of the animal's muscles as they move cause tracheae to shrink and expand, which pumps air into and out of the spiracles. Ask students to speculate on why this system of respiration works only in small animals. *(Air could not reach all tissues of a large animal without weakening its structure.)*

Answer to Think

Pseudoscorpions may attach themselves to beetles in order to move to another habitat. Pseudoscorpions are much smaller than scorpions and have no stingers.

Interpreting the Visuals Ask students which of the structures shown in Figure 32-8 on p. 487 are used by the spider to devour prey. *(Fang, poison gland, mouth, sucking stomach)* Have students trace the path of poison and food on the drawing, as you tell them that after a spider has seized its victim, it uses its chelicerae (fangs) to inject a venom from its poison gland. After the victim is paralyzed, enzymes are injected from the spider's mouth into the openings made by the chelicerae. These digestive fluids liquefy the victim's tissues so that the spider can suck them into its stomach.

Videodiscs

- ***Side 3 37755, Net Casting and Bolus Spider (m)***
- ***Side 3 38629, Diving Spider (m)***

More Information

Silk Spinning All spiders are able to spin silk, although not all build webs. Spiders use silk to line nests, form sperm webs or egg sacs, build draglines, or wrap prey securely. The spinnerets can produce both dry and sticky threads of different thicknesses. There are seven different types of silk, although no single species produces all seven. Orb-weaving spiders, which are among the most talented web builders, can make five different kinds. The kind of web varies with the species, and webs are as reliable as anatomical characteristics in identifying spiders. Some webs are sparse and consist of only a few strands. Others consist of beautiful, geometric orbs as shown in the photograph on p. 478. Spiders' silk threads are stronger than steel threads of the same gauge.

Guided Practice
Keep millipedes and centipedes in closed jars with air holes in the lid so students can study them. Have students compare them. *(Millipedes have more legs, round bodies, roll up into a ball; centipedes have flat bodies and claws in the head region.)*

Independent Practice
- Have students write answers to the Section Review.
- Have students identify arachnid adaptations particularly suited for terrestrial life. *(Their respiratory and excretory systems)*

Check Your Understanding
1. What is the advantage of silk's hardening into a thread that can be spun *after* being secreted? *(The body of a spider cannot carry a hardened structure.)*
2. How might the millipede's strong sense of smell but weak vision be adaptive? *(In their dark environment, good vision is unnecessary; a strong sense of smell helps them locate food.)*

Reteaching
Have students draw a table comparing Arachnida, Diplopoda, and Chilopoda, providing structural features of each class. An example of a completed table is shown on p. 486.
- *See* Section Reviews *worksheet, Section 32.3.*

Enrichment
Have students research and report on the differences and similarities between a terrestrial chelicerate and the aquatic horseshoe crab. Tell them to explain why the horseshoe crab is not classified as a crustacean.

Closure
Have students compare the respiratory systems of annelids and arachnids. Remind them that spiders use book lungs and/or tracheae and do not require a moist environment.

Figure 32-9 The millipede (top) of Southern Ontario is from the Class Diplopoda, while the giant centipede, *Scolopendra heros* (bottom), found in Texas, is from the Class Chilopoda.

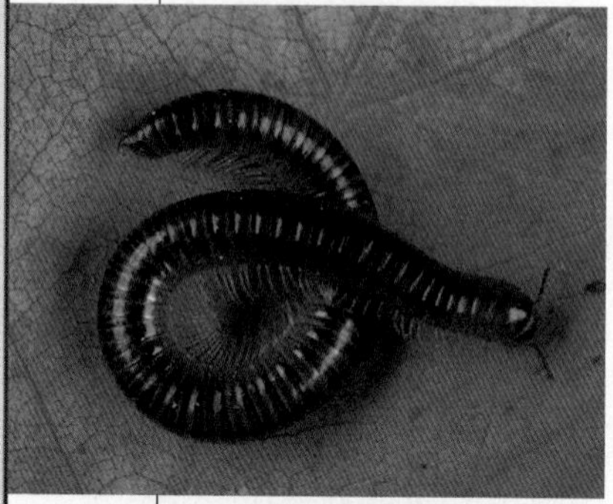

In reproduction, a male spider gathers sperm in special sacs in the tips of his pedipalps. He places the sperm in the seminal receptacle of the female. Later the female lays eggs, which are fertilized by the stored sperm as they pass through the genital pore. The female then seals the eggs in a case of silk. The young spiders go through their first molt inside the case.

Myriapods

Centipedes and millipedes are collectively called **myriapods,** which means "many feet." Myriapods, along with insects, are members of the Subphylum Uniramia. All centipedes and millipedes are terrestrial. Centipedes and millipedes do not have a waxy cuticle. They retain moisture through behavioral adaptations, such as living in damp environments to prevent desiccation.

Millipedes

Millipedes are members of the Class Diplopoda. The term *millipede* means "thousand feet." Millipedes have two pairs of legs on each body segment except the last two. Although millipedes have many legs, they have far fewer than a thousand. The legs of a millipede are strong and well adapted for burrowing through humus and soil. However, these legs are also short, which makes them slow. When threatened, a millipede rolls its body into a coil and may also spray a noxious chemical that contains cyanide.

In cross section the bodies of millipedes are rounded. They live in soil, in logs, and under objects. Many have a strong sense of smell but poor vision. Millipedes are herbivores adapted for chewing plants and decayed matter in the soil.

Centipedes

Centipedes are members of the Class Chilopoda. The term *centipede* means "hundred legs." Centipedes differ from millipedes by having the body flattened in cross section. They also have only one pair of legs per segment, except the first one and the last two. They can also move faster because their legs are longer. Many coil up for defense. Centipedes may have anywhere from 15 to 175 pairs of legs. Voracious predators, centipedes feed on earthworms and on insects such as cockroaches. The first body segment has a pair of clawlike appendages that can inject venom into prey.

Section Review

1. Define *pedipalps,* and explain their function.
2. Name two ways in which scorpions differ from spiders.
3. How is the arachnid excretory system adapted for life on land?
4. How are millipedes and centipedes different?
5. How might the feeding habits of spiders benefit humans?

Answers to Section Review
1. Pedipalps are a pair of appendages that aid in chewing and that can be used to seize prey.
2. Scorpions have much larger pedipalps than spiders and a pointed stinger that curls over the back.
3. It removes wastes in concentrated form and so conserves water.
4. Centipedes are carnivorous, have flattened bodies, and have one pair of legs per segment except for the first and last two segments; millipedes are herbivorous, have round bodies, and have two pairs of legs per segment except for the last two segments.
5. Spiders feed on insects that can damage food crops or carry disease.

Laboratory

Behavior of Isopods

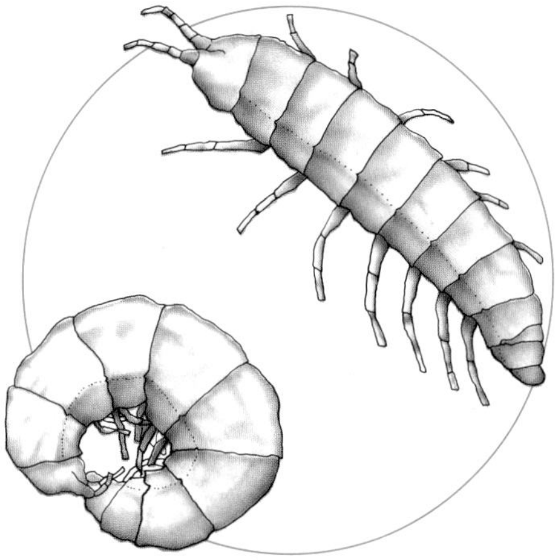

Objective
To study the behavior of isopods

Process Skills
Experimenting, hypothesizing, inferring

Materials
2 sheets of filter paper cut to fit a petri dish, petri dish with cover, aluminum foil, 5 live pill bugs, bright lamp or flashlight, paper towels

Background
1 What are the major characteristics of the Phylum Arthropoda and the Subphylum Crustacea?
2 What is the natural habitat of isopods?

Inquiry
1 Place a piece of filter paper in the bottom half of a petri dish. Wrap aluminum foil around half of the petri dish so that one half is covered, leaving half of the filter paper shaded in darkness.
2 Place five pill bugs, which are isopods, near the light-dark boundary on the filter paper. Be sure to handle the pill bugs gently. Shine a lamp directly over the petri dish so that light and dark areas are accentuated by the light. Based on your knowledge of the natural habitat of pill bugs, can you predict their response?
3 Observe the response of the pill bugs for 3 to 5 minutes. Record your observations. Do they agree with your predictions?
4 Place a second piece of filter paper on a paper towel. Moisten another paper towel thoroughly with water and use the second towel to dampen half of the filter paper. Do not get the filter paper so wet that water is absorbed by the dry half. Remove the first filter paper and foil from the petri dish and replace with the damp filter paper.
5 Place the pill bugs along the boundary between the wet and dry areas. What do you think the response of the pill bugs will be? Explain why.
6 Observe the response of the pill bugs for 3 to 5 minutes. Record your observations. Do they agree with your predictions?
7 With your lab partners, design an experiment to measure the response of the pill bugs to temperature. Think carefully about how you will construct your apparatus. What do you think the response of the pill bugs will be?
8 Carry out your experiment. Did the pill bugs respond the way you predicted?

Conclusions
1 How do the responses of the pill bugs to light reflect an adaptation to their natural surroundings?
2 Considering how pill bugs breathe, why do you think they responded as they did to moisture?

Further Inquiry
Devise experiments that will test the responses of pill bugs to other stimuli such as noise.

Laboratory

(For an overview of isopods and preparatory information related to the laboratory, see p. 477B.)

Background
1. Arthropods have jointed appendages and hard external skeletons made of chitin. Crustaceans breathe with gills and have two pairs of antennae.
2. Isopods are terrestrial. They live in damp areas where their gills can stay moist.

Inquiry
2. Since isopods live in relative darkness, they would probably move away from light.
3. Students should compare their observations with their predictions.
5. Since isopods breathe with gills, they would probably move toward the wet area.
6. Students should compare their observations with their predictions.
7. Students might place half the petri dish on ice or shine a bright light on half the petri dish. If they do the latter, make sure that the petri dish is covered with aluminum foil so that temperature is the only variable—that is, light would be constant if the petri dish were well covered. Recalling the natural habitat of isopods, students should predict that they will move toward moderate temperatures.
8. Students should compare their observations with their predictions.

Conclusions
1. Pill bugs seek dark, moist conditions similar to their natural habitats.
2. Pill bugs need moist conditions to obtain oxygen because they breathe through gills.

Further Inquiry
Students can design simple experiments to test a pill bug's response to a whistle or other shrill sound. It can become increasingly loud until the pill bug responds, or a low tone can be tried first and then higher tones tried to see if there is a difference in response.

Chapter 32 Review

Vocabulary

abdomen (483)
antenna (484)
antennule (484)
appendage (479)
book lung (487)
cephalothorax (483)
chelicera (482)
cheliped (484)
chitin (479)
compound eye (485)
coxal gland (487)
exoskeleton (479)
green gland (484)
Malpighian tubule (487)
mandible (482)
maxilla (484)
maxilliped (484)
molting (480)
myriapod (488)
pedipalp (486)
spinneret (487)
spiracle (487)
swimmeret (484)
telson (483)
trachea (487)
uropod (484)

Explain the difference between each of the following pairs of terms.

1. chelicera, cheliped
2. antenna, antennule
3. spinneret, swimmeret
4. abdomen, cephalothorax
5. telson, uropod

Review

1. All arthropods have (a) a cephalothorax (b) spiracles (c) jointed appendages (d) antennae.
2. The exoskeleton of an arthropod (a) provides protection and support (b) plays a role in movement (c) contains chitin (d) all of the above.
3. The subphylum of modern arthropods that is primarily aquatic is (a) Trilobita (b) Chelicerata (c) Crustacea (d) Uniramia.
4. The major respiratory organs of crayfish are the (a) gills (b) lungs (c) tracheae (d) book lungs.
5. Compound eyes (a) form distinct images (b) detect motion well (c) are found in all arthropods except crayfish (d) are not very light sensitive.
6. Spiders feed mainly on (a) plants (b) decayed matter (c) insects (d) other spiders.
7. Mites and ticks differ from other arachnids by having (a) mandibles (b) a unique respiratory system (c) two pairs of antennae (d) a fused cephalothorax and abdomen.
8. Book lungs help spiders respire on land by (a) carrying oxygen directly to tissues (b) providing a large surface area for the exchange of gases (c) both a and b (d) neither a nor b.
9. Centipedes and millipedes are different in (a) the way their bodies are shaped (b) the number of legs they have on each segment (c) their feeding habits (d) all of the above.
10. Products that have been developed from chitin include all of the following except (a) artificial hair (b) artificial skin (c) varnish and filters (d) contact lenses and surgical sutures.
11. What characteristics do biologists use in order to classify arthropods into four subphyla?
12. Explain the way in which the exoskeleton and muscles produce movement in arthropods.
13. What are the evolutionary trends that are common to all three subphyla of modern arthropods?
14. Which crayfish appendages are specialized for feeding?
15. Contrast the process of respiration in crayfish and spiders.
16. What roles do the swimmerets play in crayfish reproduction?
17. In what ways are spiders adapted for a predatory way of life?

Chapter 32 Review

Vocabulary

1. Chelicerae are fanglike appendages that inject venom; chelipeds are clawlike appendages.
2. Both have sensory receptors, but antennae are much longer and posterior to the antennules.
3. Spinnerets produce silk in spiders; swimmerets are crustacean appendages that create water currents and transfer sperm in reproduction.
4. The abdomen is the posterior section in crustaceans and arachnids; the cephalothorax is the anterior section.
5. The telson forms the tail of a crayfish; uropods are appendages that form fins on either side of the telson.

Review

1. c **6.** c
2. d **7.** d
3. c **8.** b
4. a **9.** d
5. b **10.** a

11. Presence or absence of antennae, chelicerae, and mandibles, as well as whether appendages are branched or unbranched
12. Muscles attached to the inside of the exoskeleton alternately contract and relax to move the joints of the appendages.
13. Reduction in the number of appendages and segments
14. Mandibles, maxillae, maxillipeds, and chelipeds
15. Crayfish respire through gills; spiders respire by means of tracheae or book lungs.
16. Swimmerets carry and protect eggs during their development.
17. Spiders have chelicerae and venom to kill prey; they also use silk to build webs and entrap prey.
18. The tail of the spider's abdomen contains spinnerets, which are made of hundreds of tubes. Fluid from silk glands passes through these tubes, hardening into a silk strand that can be spun.
19. Ticks and mites transmit disease microorganisms when they bite victims.
20. Curling up into a coil and giving off noxious chemicals are defense mechanisms of millipedes.

18. Describe how a spider spins a web.
19. What methods do mites and ticks use to transmit diseases?
20. What defensive behaviors are common in millipedes?

Critical Thinking

1. *Daphnia* eat algae. They also have a prominent eyespot. In what way might the eyespot be connected with the ability of the *Daphnia* to find food?
2. Barnacles are a sessile group of crustaceans. What behavioral adaptations do they have that enable them to compete for food with mobile organisms? What structural adaptations might protect them from predators?
3. The head and thoracic plates of the crayfish are fused into a single carapace. What might be the advantages and disadvantages of this fused arrangement?
4. Examine the photo at right. What type of evolution is exhibited by this spider?
5. The American lobster, *Homarus americanus,* is a nocturnal organism. Like other crustaceans the lobster has compound eyes. Marine biologists have discovered that the lobster's senses of taste and smell are over 1,000 times more powerful than those senses in humans. The lobster uses smell and taste both to search for food and to detect mates. What adaptive advantage would these highly developed senses provide for the lobster?

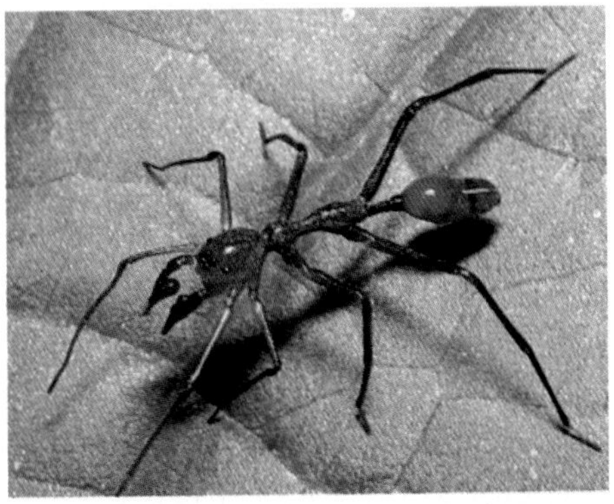

Extension

1. Read the article entitled "Cave Critters" in *Discover,* June 1990, p. 16. Prepare an oral report in which you include answers to the following questions: (1) How did Jill Yeager discover a new class of crustacean? (2) Why did she name the crustacean *Remipedia?* (3) Where have remipedes been found? (4) What is unusual about the habitat of remipedes? (5) How is the anatomy of the remipede similar to that of other crustaceans and how is it different? (6) How could further studies of remipedes provide insight into the adaptive ability of crustaceans?
2. Contact your local public health department and ask for information on arthropod-transmitted diseases that might be found in your area. If possible, find out how many cases of each disease have been reported in the last year.
3. Obtain a sample of pond or stream water, and examine it for *Daphnia* and ostracods. Make drawings of any arthropods you see, and identify them as accurately as you can.
4. Search in a damp, dark area around your school or home for sow bugs or pill bugs. Examine those you find with a hand lens. List characteristics you see that indicate that these organisms are arthropods.
5. Using your library, research and write a report on the life cycle of a horseshoe crab, a scorpion, or a tick.

Critical Thinking

1. The largest populations of algae live in lighted areas. The eyespot of the *Daphnia* senses where the light is strongest in the water and therefore where the most algae are likely to be.
2. Barnacles attach themselves to moving objects, such as ships or whales, or they live where water—and food—is in constant motion, such as on rocks at the tide line. They protect themselves by drawing deep into their hard exoskeleton.
3. Fusion eliminates a vulnerable and weak joint where the head and thoracic plates join. Fusion, however, also eliminates movement at this joint.
4. The similarity of body shapes displayed by ants and this spider is an example of convergent evolution. Students should suggest some adaptive advantage to its looking like an ant.
5. Since the lobster's compound eyes are not able to focus clearly on images, its senses of smell and taste must compensate for its poor vision to allow the lobster to find mates and food.

Extension

1. While it is rare to discover a new class of animals, there are so many arthropods that new discoveries are frequent. This is particularly true of insects, the largest class of arthropods.
2. As an alternative activity, have students research and report on an arthropod-transmitted disease common in the United States.
3. Suggest that students reread the excerpt from *Pilgrim at Tinker Creek* in Chapter 29. As they view the pond water, ask them to compare their reactions with Dillard's reactions.
4. Caution students to handle the animals humanely.
5. Remind students that all of these animals are members of the Class Arachnida.

Chapter 33 Insects

Chapter Overview

Chapter 33 examines structural, behavioral, and developmental characteristics of the Class Insecta. Section 33.1 gives an overview of insect characteristics and diversity. Section 33.2 focuses on internal and external structure as well as reproduction and metamorphosis. Section 33.3 looks at insect social behavior and communication.

Chapter Planning Chart

B	S	A	Sections and Subsections	Page	Features	Page	Resources
•	•	•	**33.1 The Insect World**				
			Characteristics and Classification	493	Section Review	496	Videodiscs
			The Success of Insects	493			Section Reviews Worksheet
			Insects and Human Society	496			
•	•	•	**33.2 Aspects of Insect Biology**				
			External Structure	497	Think	502	Videodiscs
			Internal Structure	498	Laboratory	507	Blackline Master 68
			Development	500	Section Review	502	Overhead Transparency T33
			Defense	502			Blackline Master 69
							Laboratories: Caterpillar Behavior
							Section Reviews Worksheet
•	•	•	**33.3 Insect Behavior**				
			Social Behavior in Honeybees	503	Biology in Process	504	Videodiscs
			Communication	505	Section Review	506	Process Skills: Bee Communication
							Section Reviews Worksheet
			End of Chapter Activities				
					Chapter Review	508	Vocabulary Skills
							Chapter Test
							Computer Test Generator

B *The Basic Level curriculum presents the most fundamental knowledge offered in the course.*
S *The Standard Level curriculum is designed for the average student who is able to master most topics.*
A *The Advanced Level curriculum includes suggestions for teaching the most academically able students.*

Cooperative Learning

Group Activity: Insects and Humans

- **Group Size:** *4 students*
- **Outcome:** *Students will evaluate the impact of an order of insects on humans.*
- **Individual Accountability:** *Each group member will research the help or harm done by an order of insects.*
- **Positive Interdependence:** *The group will make a detailed presentation to a classroom law court.*

Assign each group an insect order that both helps and harms humans, such as Coleoptera, Isoptera, and Hymenoptera. Tell students to imagine a courtroom setting in which their insect order is on trial for "crimes" against humans. Have one pair of students research the insect order's beneficial impact on humans and prepare a defense of its value to society. Have the second pair of students research the insect order's harmful impact on humans and prepare an indictment against it.

Then have each pair present its case to the class. Select one student to maintain an orderly flow of testimony, cross examination, and final argument. Ask other class members to act as jury and weigh the value of the insect order in human society.

Concept Map

The following is one possible solution to the concept mapping activity in Guided Practice on p. 495.

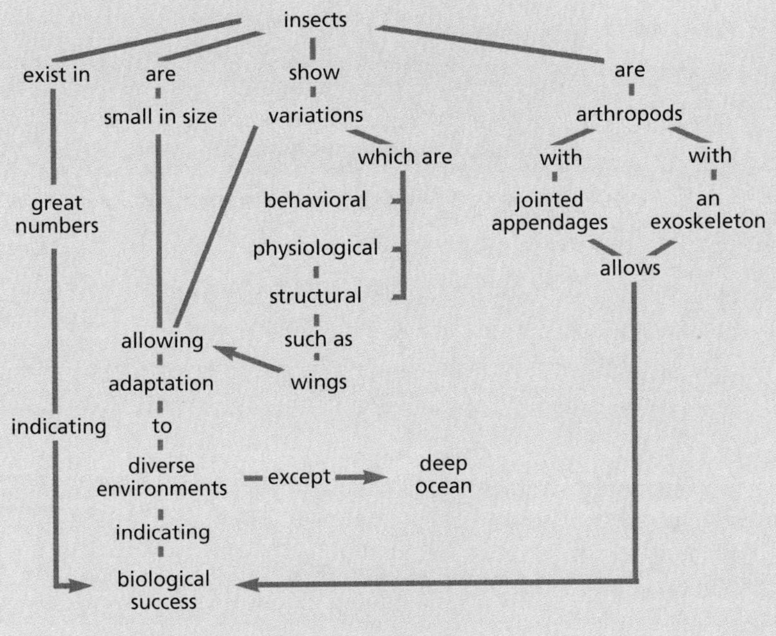

Laboratory Preparation

Overview *(See p. 507.)*

In this laboratory exercise, students examine external features of a wasp, such as the paper wasp, and compare them to diagrams of a grasshopper to verify that all insects share basic characteristics. The genus *Polistes* is a social wasp with a body plan typical of the main characteristics of an insect body.

Preparation

Order the preserved wasp specimens *(Polistes)* ahead of time.

Teaching Tips

Have students include a drawing of the specimen's wing. Tell them to accurately copy the wing pattern and to use at least half of a page for their drawings.

Discuss with students how the small, sterile female wasps become workers. Tell students to notice that the female ovipositor in the worker has been modified into a stinger, which is used in defending the nest from intruders.

Safety

The preservative used on the specimen can be irritating to the skin. Caution students to avoid touching the specimen and especially to avoid rubbing their eyes with contaminated hands. Tell students to wear goggles.

Chapter Themes

Evolution Among invertebrates, insects exhibit key evolutionary advances. Emphasize throughout the chapter that these advances have resulted in enormous physiological, structural, and behavioral diversity as well as the success of the Class Insecta.

Systems and Interactions Point out to students that insects play vital roles in the ecosystems of the world. Therefore, insects have an impact on all other types of organisms. In addition, some species exhibit complex patterns of communication and social behavior.

Chapter Motivating Activity

Bring in newspaper or magazine articles about insects in the news. These may include African honeybees, medflies, beehives that are transported around the United States to pollinate crops, the white fly infestation in California, and mosquitos that carry equine encephalitis. Ask students why damaging insects are so difficult to control. *(Answers will vary, but size, life cycle, and reproductive success are important factors in insect survival.)* Now ask students to imagine a poison that could kill off insect pests, such as African honeybees—the so-called "killer" bees. What other effects would the poison have? *(In this example, it would probably also kill off bees used in pollination, possibly causing crop failure.)*

Chapter 33 Insects

Introduction

Insects account for about three-fourths of all animal species. They are the most successful of all the arthropods, and for this reason an entire chapter is devoted to their study. In this chapter you will learn about some of the factors that have contributed to their success.

Chapter Outline

Chapter Concept

As you read, look for the structural, physiological, and behavioral variations that have made insects such a successful group of animals.

Stink bug, Papua New Guinea. Inset: Virgo tiger moth, *Apantesis virgo*, New York.

Understanding the Visuals

Ask students what characteristics the stink bug and the tiger moth have in common. *(Answers may include bright colors, wings, and antennae.)* Tell students that although the stink bug and tiger moth have only a few obvious similarities, they are both members of the Class Insecta. Explain that these animals are examples of the wide diversity in the external appearance of insects.

33.1 The Insect World

Above all else, the world of insects is a story of great biological success through evolution and adaptation. Insects have thrived on the earth for more than 300 million years, since long before the rise and fall of the dinosaurs. Today insects are the most successful group of animals, in terms of both diversity and numbers.

Section Objectives

- *List the major reasons for the success of insects.*
- *Give examples of three major kinds of variations among insects.*
- *Name at least ten of the major orders of insects, and give an example of each.*
- *Describe the relationship of insects to human society.*

Characteristics and Classification

Many of the adaptations that have made insects successful are characteristics they share with other arthropods. For example, an exoskeleton, jointed appendages, and a segmented body are all common arthropod traits. However, insects are distinguished from other arthropods by the following characteristics:

- The body has three parts: head, thorax, and abdomen.
- The head has one pair of antennae.
- The thorax has three pairs of jointed legs and, in many species, one or two pairs of wings.
- The abdomen is divided into 11 segments. It has neither wings nor legs attached to it.

In spite of the characteristics they share, insect species show an enormous range of variations that have allowed them to succeed in diverse environments. These variations can be grouped into three categories. The first category consists of **structural variations,** such as differences in mouthparts. For example, a wasp has mouthparts adapted for chewing, while an aphid uses its mouthparts to pierce plants and suck fluids. A second group of variations, **physiological variations,** consists of differences in the way internal systems work. For instance, a female mosquito has enzymes that allow it to digest human blood; a grasshopper does not have these enzymes but has others that enable it to digest grass. Finally, **behavioral variations** are differences in the ways insects respond to their surroundings. Honeybees, for example, live in complex societies called hives. Some species of bees, on the other hand, are solitary and usually live part of their lives in holes in the ground.

To make it easier to study such a vast and diverse group of organisms, taxonomists classify insects into more than 30 orders. They base their classification primarily on structural and physiological variations. Study the information about some common orders of insects in Table 33-1 on pages 494–495. How many do you recognize?

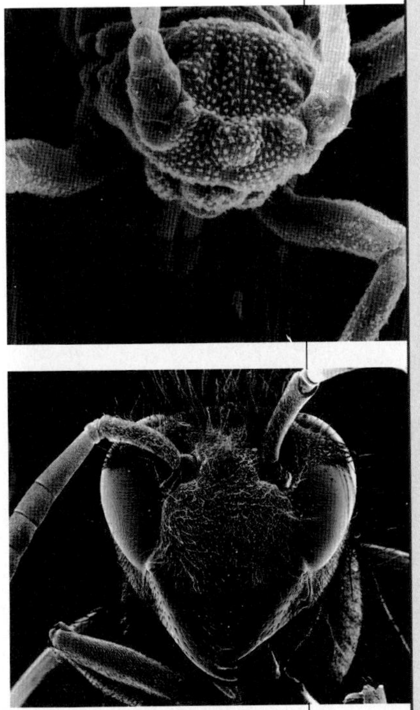

Figure 33-1 SEMs show that aphid mouth-parts (top, ×160) are adapted for piercing and sucking while those of a wasp (bottom, ×100) are adapted for chewing.

The Success of Insects

Insects live almost everywhere in the world except in the deep ocean. Water striders live on the surface of oceans and lakes, and

Lesson Plan

Section Focus

Insects account for about three-fourths of all animal species. This section describes the enormous range of variations that have allowed insects to succeed in diverse environments. These variations are structural, physiological, and behavioral.

Section Themes

The theme of **Systems and Interactions** is evident in the role that insects play in the lives of other types of organisms. Insects are humans' most significant competitors for food. As a group, they play a major role in world ecosystems. Individual species exhibit such strategies as predation, parasitism, commensalism, and mutualism.

Motivating Activity

Show students four or five specimens or pictures of insects from each of the 14 common orders, such as cockroaches, earwigs, ants, dragonflies, and moths. Ask students how these insects are alike and how they are different. *(Answers may include that they all have six legs, that some have one pair of wings, some have two pairs, and some have none.)* List answers on the board. Ask students which insects they would group together and why. Have students compare their groups with the classification in Table 33-1 on pp. 494–495.

	Body Parts	Legs	Wings	Habitat
Myriapods	many segments	1 or 2 pairs per segment	none	moist soil, decaying matter
Insects	head, thorax, and abdomen	3 pairs; none on abdomen	1 or 2 pairs; attached to thorax	extremely diverse

Graphic Organizer Use this table in Independent Practice on p. 495.

Teaching Strategies

Making Connections Many insects are linked to disease. Have students reread the description in Chapter 14 (p. 205) of Francesco Redi's experiment to test the theory of spontaneous generation. Why was Redi's experiment important? *(It undermined the theory of spontaneous generation and opened the way for the eventual development of the germ theory of disease.)* What did it accomplish for our understanding of insects? *(It established for the first time the link between flies and their larvae, maggots.)*

Evaluating Adaptations Show students photographs of insects with unusual behavioral or physical adaptations, such as leafcutter ants, nasute termites, and walkingsticks. Have students speculate about how these adaptations may have originated and how they benefit the insect.

Brainstorming Alternatives Tell students that chemical sprays have been used widely to control insects that damage agricultural crops. Explain that not only have these chemicals proved to be harmful to humans and other animals, but also many strains of insects have developed a resistance to pesticides. Discuss implications of this resistance in terms of the success and adaptability of insects. Ask students to speculate about possible alternatives to the use of pesticides in controlling agricultural pests.

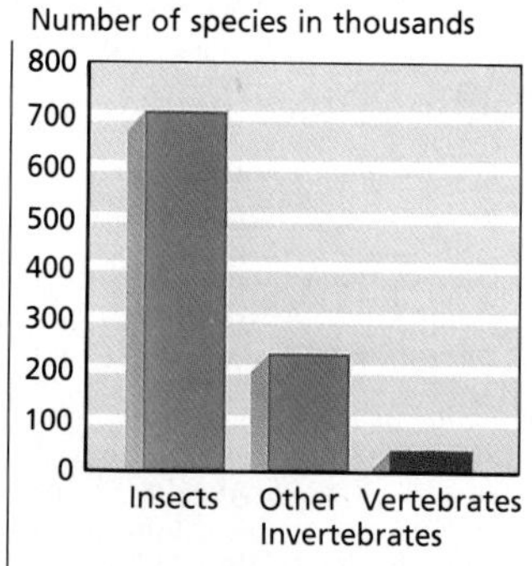

Figure 33-2 Numbers of insect species are compared with those of other groups.

beetles live in the hottest deserts. Snowfleas survive on permanent glaciers on the world's highest mountains. Closer to home, you may find aphids on the leaves of garden plants or beetles under the bark of trees. You may even find a flea or two in the fur of your dog or cat.

As you have read, Arthropoda is the largest animal phylum, and Insecta is by far the largest class within that phylum. **Entomologists,** or scientists who study insects, have classified more than 700,000 insect species. Every year biologists describe thousands of new species. Based on current knowledge, some entomologists estimate that as many as 10 million insect species exist. Figure 33-2 shows the numbers of species in various subgroupings of the animal kingdom. Notice that the number of classified insect species is about three times that of all other classified animal species combined.

Table 33-1 Common Insect Orders

Order	Number of Species	Examples	Characteristics	Significance to Humans
Orthoptera ("straight-wing")	23,000	Grasshoppers, Crickets, Katydids, Cockroaches 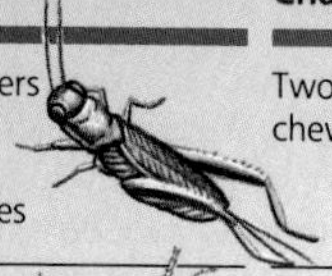	Two pairs of straight wings; chewing mouthparts	Cause damage to crops; pests in houses
Isoptera ("equal-wing")	1,800	Termites 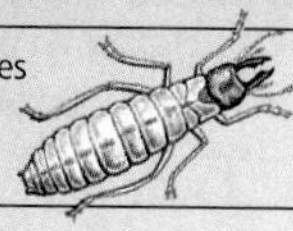	Two pairs of membranous wings; chewing mouthparts	Destroy wood in forests and buildings; recycle resources in forests
Dermaptera ("skin-wing")	1,100	Earwigs 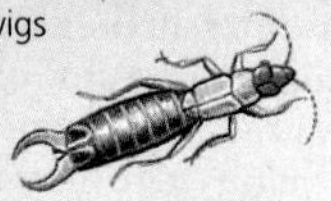	One or two pairs of wings; chewing mouthparts; pincerlike appendages at tip of abdomen	Damage crops and garden plants
Anoplura ("unarmed-tail")	200	Sucking lice 	Wingless; piercing, sucking mouthparts	Parasitize humans and other mammals; carry disease
Hemiptera ("half-wing")	40,000	All true bugs 	Two pairs of membranous wings during part of life; piercing, sucking mouthparts	Damage plants; carry disease
Homoptera ("like-wing")	20,000	Aphids, Mealy bugs, Cicadas 	Membranous wings held like roof over body (some species wingless); piercing, sucking mouthparts	Damage crops and gardens
Ephemeroptera ("for-a-day-wing")	1,500	Mayflies 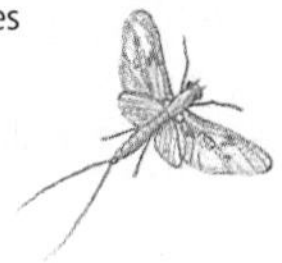	Membranous wings (forewings triangular); nonfunctioning mouthparts in adults	Serve as food for freshwater fish

More Information

Adaptive Radiation Insects have successfully adapted to many environments and have proliferated in number and variety. They have spread out into many habitats and have carved out for themselves widely diverse ecological niches. An animal's niche is the total of all resources that it needs—space, time, food, and mates—and ways in which it acquires and uses these resources. No two species have identical niches. The least successful insect orders have few species and limited niches. Moderately successful insect orders comprise more species, are fairly widespread, and, although limited in habitat, are not uncommon. The most successful insect orders have many species and show a great range of adaptability.

Why have the insects been such a biological success? Like other arthropods, they have benefited from the evolution of an exoskeleton and jointed appendages. Additionally, they can adapt to new environments rapidly because individual insects have extremely short life spans. In many species adults live for only weeks or months. Since generations occur in rapid succession, natural selection can take place more quickly than in organisms that take longer to reproduce.

As they have evolved, insects have had a wide range of environments available to them because of their flying ability and their small size. The power of flight enables insects to disperse readily, to escape from predators, and to move into environments less accessible to other organisms. In addition, the small size of insects allows several species to inhabit different environments within a small area without competing with one another.

Order	Number of Species	Examples	Characteristics	Significance to Humans
Odonata ("toothed")	5,000	Dragonflies Damselflies 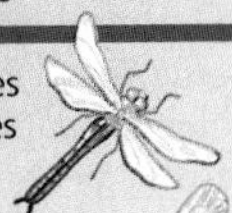	Two pairs of long, narrow, membranous wings; chewing mouthparts	Destroy harmful insects
Neuroptera ("nerve-wing")	4,600	Dobsonflies Lacewings 	Two pairs of membranous wings; mouthparts sucking in larvae, chewing in adults	Destroy harmful insects
Coleoptera ("sheath-wing")	280,000	Weevils Ladybugs Beetles 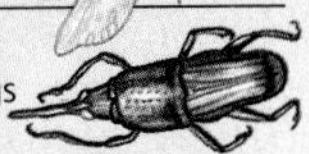	Hard forewings, membranous hindwings; sucking or chewing mouthparts	Destroy crops; prey on other insects
Lepidoptera ("scale-wing")	110,000	Butterflies Moths 	Large, scaled wings; mouthparts chewing in larvae, siphoning in adults	Pollinate flowers; produce silk; damage clothing and crops
Diptera ("two-wing")	85,000	Mosquitoes Flies Gnats 	One pair of wings; sucking, piercing, or lapping mouthparts	Carry disease; destroy crops; pollinate flowers; act as decomposers
Siphonaptera ("tube-wingless")	1,100	Fleas 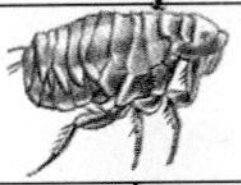	Wingless in adults; mouthparts chewing in larvae, sucking in adults	Parasitize birds and mammals; carry disease
Hymenoptera ("membrane-wing")	100,000	Bees Wasps Ants 	Two pairs of membranous wings (some species wingless); chewing, sucking, or lapping mouthparts; some species social	Pollinate flowers; make honey; destroy harmful insects

Comparing Structures Ask students to name insects with which they are familiar and/or have had some experience. *(Sample answers: houseflies, mosquitos, bees, and cockroaches.)* Tell students that insects have specialized mouthparts for chewing, piercing and sucking, siphoning, and lapping. Point out that mouthparts are used by taxonomists to group insects into orders. Ask students to identify, based on their prior knowledge, which type of mouthparts are shown by the insects they named. *(Houseflies, lapping mouthparts; mosquitos, piercing and sucking mouthparts; bees and cockroaches, chewing mouthparts)*

Guided Practice

Ask students to develop a concept map that shows adaptations that make insects successful. An example of a completed concept map is shown on p. 491B.

Independent Practice

- Have students write answers to the Section Review.
- Remind students that insects and myriapods are members of the Subphylum Uniramia. Have them develop a table that compares myriapods with insects. Tell them to include column headings such as *Body Parts, Legs, Wings,* and *Habitat.* An example of a completed table appears on p. 493.

Videodiscs

- ***1095–1222, Insecta: Variety of Types (s)***

Interdisciplinary Activity

Government Both federal and state involvement in controlling use of pesticides has fluctuated during the last three decades. Have students select one type of pesticide, such as endrin or DDT, and research the history of federal and/or state regulations governing its use. Tell them to include information on the position of government agencies on environmental control and any controversial issues that have arisen from this control.

Section 33.1

Check Your Understanding

1. Explain the role that wings play in the classification of insects and tell why. *(Wing type is an obvious feature, and since there are a limited number of types, insects can be classified accordingly.)*

2. How is the success of insects and flowering plants related? *(Many insects rely on flowers as a food source, and many plants rely on insects for pollination. They could not survive without each other.)*

Reteaching

Have students give examples of diversity in insects. *(Answers may reflect behaviors, mouthparts, physical appearance.)* Ask students what is the evolutionary significance of insect diversity. *(Diversity has allowed insects to move into many environments.)* ■ *See* Section Reviews *worksheet, Section 33.1.*

Enrichment

Assign each student an insect, such as a species of termite, moth, mosquito, or ant, to research and report on. Tell them to focus on the environment that the insect inhabits and the characteristics that make it well adapted to its environment. Remind students to include the ways in which the insect is beneficial and/or harmful to humans.

Closure

Stress the great positive significance of insects in ecosystems. While many insects may seem to be simply pests, such stereotypical images of them often mask a lack of understanding of their role in nature. Have students describe what a world without insects might be like. *(No buzzing of bees, no mosquito bites, no insect pollinators, and so forth.)*

Figure 33-3 The grain weevil, *Sitophilus granarius* (left, × 170), shown emerging from a wheat seed in this SEM, competes with human beings for food. Of human benefit is the blister beetle, *Lytta magister* (right), shown pollinating a California poppy.

Insects and Human Society

Since insects are so abundant, it is not surprising that they affect human society in many ways. A small minority of insect species cause severe problems for people. Boll weevils, corn earworms, and other agricultural pests compete with humans for food by eating crops. Other insects spread diseases. In the tropics female mosquitoes transmit *Plasmodium,* the protozoan that causes malaria. Flies transfer the bacterium *Salmonella typhi,* which causes typhoid fever.

In spite of the problems some insects cause, it would be a serious mistake to think that the world would be better off without them. Insects play many vital roles in the environment. For example, insects pollinate more than two-thirds of the world's flowering plants; they also serve as food for a multitude of fish, birds, and mammals. We tend to think of termites as destructive pests. However, in feeding on decaying wood, they help recycle materials needed to maintain a healthy forest. Honey, silk, and shellac are some products produced by insects. Without insects to pollinate many of our crop plants, our food sources would be greatly diminished.

Section Review

1. What is an *entomologist?*
2. What features distinguish insects from other arthropods?
3. List two characteristics of insects that have helped them move into diverse environments.
4. Give an example of structural variation in insects.
5. How would you characterize the importance of the order Lepidoptera to people? Use Table 33-1 to help you answer.

Answers to Section Review

1. A scientist who studies insects

2. Three pairs of legs, three body parts, one or two pairs of wings in adults of many species, one pair of antennae on the head, abdomen divided into 11 segments

3. Small size, mobility provided by wings and jointed legs

4. Differences in mouthparts

5. Lepidoptera are both beneficial and harmful. Many species pollinate flowers and some produce silk. A few species damage crops or clothing.

33.2 Aspects of Insect Biology

The diversity in the insect world is so great that no typical insect exists. Nevertheless, in this section we will use the grasshopper as a representative example for studying details of structure and function. We will then examine patterns of development and defense that are common to most insect species.

External Structure

The African Goliath beetle grows to more than 10 cm in length, and the Atlas moth has a wingspan of more than 25 cm. However, most insects are far smaller. Among the smallest is the fairy fly, which measures 0.2 mm in length.

The diagram of an adult grasshopper in Figure 33-4 can serve as a model to help you understand the structural components of external anatomy. Like all insects the grasshopper has three body segments. The anterior segment is the head. It contains the brain and bears many of the sensory organs, such as the antennae and compound eyes. The head also has complex mouthparts that are used for gathering food. The middle segment is the thorax, to which the legs and wings are attached. The posterior segment is the abdomen, which is often specialized for reproduction and has structures for digestion, respiration, and excretion.

The thorax consists of three parts: prothorax, mesothorax, and metathorax. The prothorax and mesothorax each have a pair of walking legs that allow the grasshopper to creep along blades of grass. Attached to the metathorax is a pair of jumping legs that enables the grasshopper to leap away from danger and to launch

Section Objectives

- *Summarize the function of each of the external parts of a grasshopper.*
- *Summarize the function of each of the organ systems of a grasshopper.*
- *Describe the processes of incomplete and complete metamorphosis, and explain how they contribute to the success of insects.*
- *Give an example of three types of defense in insects.*

Figure 33-4 The grasshopper's three-part body, paired antennae, paired mandibles, and three pairs of jointed legs are typical of all insect species.

External anatomy of the grasshopper

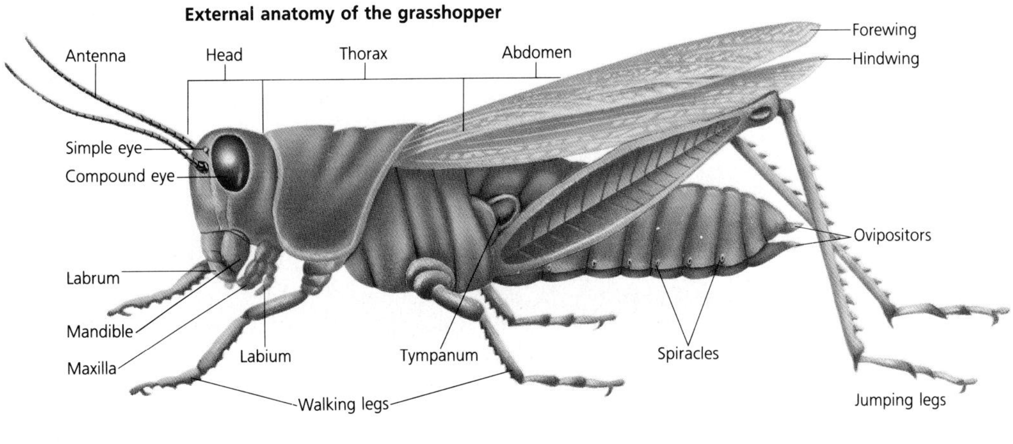

	Crayfish	Grasshopper
locomotion	legs and swimmerets	hopping legs and wings
respiratory system	gills	spiracles and tracheae
excretory system	liquid waste via green glands	solid waste via Malpighian tubules
circulatory system	open	open
nervous system	eye stalks	simple and compound eyes; typanum
reproductive system	modified swimmerets in male	penis in male, ovipositor in female

Graphic Organizer Use this table in Reteaching on p. 502.

Lesson Plan

Section Focus

The grasshopper serves as a good example of insect body structure and function. Its body is organized into three main parts characteristic of all adult insects: head, thorax, and abdomen. Almost all insects undergo either complete or incomplete metamorphosis.

Section Themes

The diversity and success of insects illustrate the theme of **Evolution.** Insects have both adapted to and thrived in some of the most extreme conditions—from harsh climates to chemical pesticides.

Motivating Activity

Show students specimens and photographs of fleas, grasshoppers, and other jumping insects, and display photographs of athletes competing in the long jump. Ask students to estimate the lengths that insects and humans are capable of jumping. Tell students that the world long jump record is 29 feet 2 1/2 inches (8.9 m). Explain that for their size and weight, insects are the strongest jumpers in the world; a grasshopper may leap almost a meter, which is 20 times its length or the equivalent of a person's leaping half the length of a football field.

Teaching Strategies

Interpreting the Visuals Have students observe a live grasshopper in an appropriate environment. Tell students to locate on the live specimen the structures shown in Figure 33-4 on p. 497. Remind students to treat the grasshopper humanely.

- *See* **Overhead Transparency** *T33 and* **Blackline Master** *68.*

Videodiscs

- *1122–1123, Grasshoppers (s)*

Understanding Structures Ask students to recall from the previous section the evolutionary significance of the development of wings in flies. *(It offered them greater scope for success in terrestrial environments.)* Ask students how wings enabled insects to function. *(Insects can move to other locations, search for mates, forage for food, and escape predators.)* Tell students that some insects, such as silverfish, have never had wings and that others, such as fleas, have lost them during the evolutionary process. Ask students why they think that the direction of evolution is from two pairs of wings to only one pair. *(The reduction of two pairs of wings to one pair increased the animal's potential for speed and precision.)*

Interpreting the Visuals Ask students to describe different organ systems of the female grasshopper shown in Figure 33-6 on p. 498. Point out the relationship between the structure of various organs, such as tracheae, and their function, such as oxygen transport. Ask students to explain how each structure has contributed to the successful functioning of insects. *(Answers may include that the tracheal system increases the efficiency of oxygen transport and that multiple hearts help pump blood throughout the body.)*

■ *See* **Blackline Master 69.**

Figure 33-5 This photograph of a grasshopper's head shows the eyes, mouthparts, and base of the antennae (x46).

Figure 33-6 The grasshopper's internal organs are representative of other insect species.

into flight. Spines, hooks, and pads on each foot, or **tarsus,** provide the grasshopper with grip.

The grasshopper has two pairs of wings. A pair of leathery forewings covers and protects the hindwings when the grasshopper isn't flying. Although the forewings can help the grasshopper glide during flight, it is the movement of the hindwings that actually propels the insect through the air. The grasshopper can move its wings because of muscles attached to the inside of its exoskeleton. The forewings are attached to the mesothorax; the hind wings are attached to the metathorax.

Internal Structure

Many structural and physiological adaptations can be observed by examining an insect's organ systems. The grasshopper, shown in Figure 33-6, can serve as a representative example for studying the organ systems of insects.

Digestive and Excretory Systems

Grasshoppers feed on blades of grass, and the jaws of grasshoppers are thus modified for cutting and chewing. The liplike **labium** *(LAY-bee-um)* and **labrum** *(LAY-brum)* help hold the grass in position so that the rough-edged jaws called mandibles can tear off edible bits. Behind the mandibles are the maxillae, a second set of jaws that helps hold and cut the food.

In the mouth food is moistened by saliva from the salivary glands. The moistened food then passes through the esophagus and into the crop for temporary storage. From the crop, food passes into the gizzard, where sharp chitinous plates shred it. The shredded mass then passes into the insect's stomach, called the **midgut.** There the food is bathed in enzymes secreted by pockets

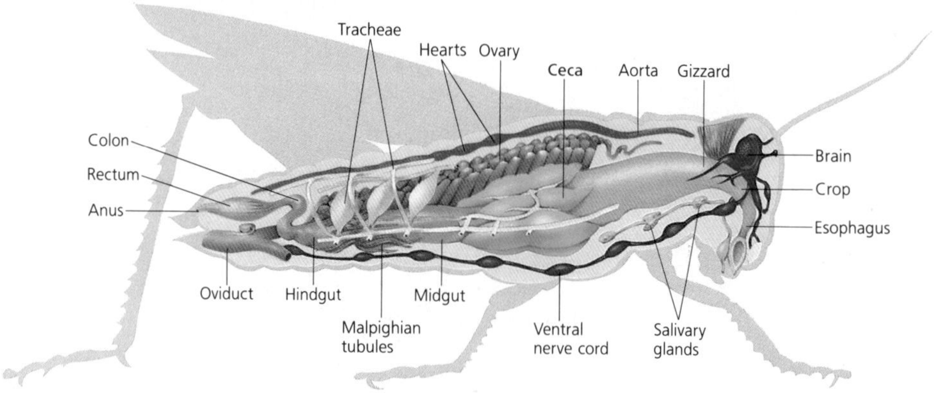

More Information

Insect Flight Movement in insects is controlled by a complex set of muscles that almost entirely fills the thorax. Some insects, such as dragonflies, moths, and butterflies, have only direct flight muscles. Their two pairs of wings are unlinked in flight so that they flap independently. The forewings create a downbeat while the underwings beat upward, creating an X-shaped configuration. These insects can also glide by locking their forewings and underwings.

In addition to direct flight muscles, more highly specialized insects also have indirect flight muscles, a powerful set of muscle bundles attached to the inside wall of the thorax instead of directly to the wing as direct flight muscles are. The thorax changes shape as it is squeezed alternately from top to bottom and side to side by the muscles.

of the stomach called the **gastric ceca** *(SEE-kuh)*. Digested matter then flows through the midgut wall and into the coelom, or body cavity, and is distributed by the circulatory system.

Undigested matter from the midgut travels into the **hindgut,** made up of the colon and the rectum. Meanwhile, wastes from the cells have been picked up by the blood. Malpighian tubules in the hindgut remove chemical wastes from the blood and deposit them in the rectum. All wastes then leave through the anus.

Circulatory System

Digested food and other materials reach the grasshopper's cells through an open circulatory system like that of the crayfish. Blood flows through a large vessel called the **aorta.** Muscular regions of the aorta, often called the grasshopper's hearts, are located in the posterior abdomen. They pump the blood forward through the aorta and into the part of the coelom near the head. The blood then flows back through the coelom toward the abdomen, carrying digested food to the organs. At the same time, the blood transfers cellular wastes to the Malpighian tubules and then completes the circuit back to the aorta through pores called ostia.

Respiratory System

Insects do not breathe with lungs or gills but instead take in air through tiny openings on the abdomen and thorax called spiracles. As muscles expand plates on the grasshopper's abdomen, air flows through the spiracles and enters a network of air tubes called tracheae. Note that in insects oxygen travels directly to body tissues through the tracheae and their smaller branches. In most other animals oxygen is transported by the blood. When the abdomen contracts, waste gases that have diffused out of cells collect in the tracheae. These waste gases are then expelled through the spiracles.

Nervous System

The grasshopper has a complex internal nervous system connected to the external sensory organs. Three simple eyes arranged in a row just above the base of the antennae serve simply to detect light. Two bulging compound eyes, composed of hundreds of six-sided lenses allow the insect to see in several directions at once. They can detect movement but cannot produce sharply focused images. Grasshoppers sense sounds by means of a small, nerve-rich cavity located along the first abdominal segment. This cavity is covered with a sound-sensing membrane called a **tympanum** *(TIM-puh-num)*. Sense organs for both touch and smell are located on the antennae and elsewhere on the body.

If you've ever tried to catch a grasshopper, you've seen the effect of its nervous system in action. The grasshopper's eyes detect your movement. Nerve impulses travel up nerve cords to the nerve ganglia that form the brain. Messages from the ganglia travel rapidly down other nerve cords to the muscles that control

Figure 33-7 A SEM of a diamondback moth shows the individual facets of the compound eyes and the ball-and-socket joint at the base of each antenna (×65).

Describing Functions Explain to students that parthenogenesis, the development of an adult from an unfertilized egg, has been observed in insects, such as aphids and beetles, and in other arthropods. For example, fertilized bee eggs develop into diploid females, and unfertilized bee eggs develop into males that are haploid.

Examining Adaptations Ask students to name specific insect adaptations while you write them on the board. Point out that no other animal has adapted to such extreme living conditions and that insects make relatively small demands on their environment, eat every kind of higher plant, and are able to lie dormant during inhospitable conditions. Ask students what structures or adaptations listed on the board reflect this ability. *(For example, an insect's exoskeleton has a coating of waterproof waxes that retard loss of water through evaporation.)* Ask students what modifications enabled insects to breathe on land. *(The spiracles of most insects have a valve or some other type of closing mechanism to reduce water loss.)* Ask how reproduction is adapted to life on land. *(After mating, winged adults can delay fertilization of eggs because the female stores sperm in a sac and releases them when proper food plants and living conditions are found.)* Ask students how the excretory system of insects contributes to their success. *(By converting nitrogenous wastes into harmless crystals of uric acid, insects can avoid losing water.)*

These contractions rhythmically raise and lower the wings in an elongated figure-eight configuration, while the direct flight muscles control wing tilt. Some insects, such as flies, are distinguished by having hind-wings that operate as miniature gyroscopes that monitor the fly's balance.

Flight speed and wing beat frequency vary. The fastest flying insects, such as the sphinx moth, can fly at 48 km per hour on narrow, fast-beating wings. Light-bodied insects with large wings, such as butterflies, may beat their wings four times per second. Small wings of heavy insects, such as flies and bees, may beat more than 100 times per second. Some insects, such as the migrating monarch butterflies, which travel hundreds of miles at about 10 km per hour, are capable of long, continuous flight.

Making Comparisons Ask students why it is an advantage when discussing insect anatomy to describe a species of insect that is not highly specialized, rather than to make generalizations about all insects. *(Great variety in the external anatomy of insects limits the generalizations that can be made to a very few, such as that insects have three body parts, one pair of antennae, and three pairs of jointed legs.)* Ask students to give examples of the variety of insects' external characteristics. *(Answers may include differences in color, shapes and sizes of wings, body shapes and sizes, and mouthparts.)* Tell students that describing an insect, such as a grasshopper, provides an example for making comparisons with other insects, rather than for making generalizations.

Interpreting the Visuals Before asking students to study Figure 33-8 on p. 500, have them review in Chapter 12, pp. 184–185, the role of homeotic genes in metamorphosis (which involves morphogenesis). Remind students that homeotic genes control development of specific adult structures in the larva (such as the wings shown in Figure 33-8).

Guided Practice

Have students write a short paper comparing incomplete metamorphosis with complete metamorphosis. Tell them to include advantages of complete metamorphosis and provide an explanation of why metamorphosis is an adaptation that contributes to insects' success. Suggest that they consider why natural selection has led to so many insect species that undergo complete metamorphosis and so few that undergo incomplete metamorphosis.

- *See* **Laboratories, *Investigation 33.***

the jumping legs. The legs flex, and in an instant the grasshopper is out of your grasp.

Reproductive System

The reproductive organs of both male and female grasshoppers are located in the abdomen. During mating the male grasshopper deposits sperm into the female's seminal receptacle, a storage pouch that holds the sperm until eggs are released. After release the eggs are fertilized internally. The female grasshopper uses two pairs of pointed organs called **ovipositors** to dig a nest hole in the soil and to deposit the eggs.

Development

All the characteristics we have observed so far are those of the adult grasshopper. However, insects go through a number of stages before they reach their adult forms. Only silverfish and a few other insects start out as smaller versions of adult insects. Most insects undergo distinct changes in both form and size as they develop. This series of developmental changes, called **metamorphosis,** is shown in Figure 33-8. Metamorphosis is the result of the processes of gene expression, described in Chapter 12.

Incomplete Metamorphosis

Grasshoppers, termites, and some other insects go through a pattern of development called incomplete metamorphosis. This process has three stages: egg, nymph, and adult. When the egg hatches, a nymph emerges. A **nymph** is an immature form that looks somewhat like the adult but is smaller, has undeveloped

Incomplete metamorphosis

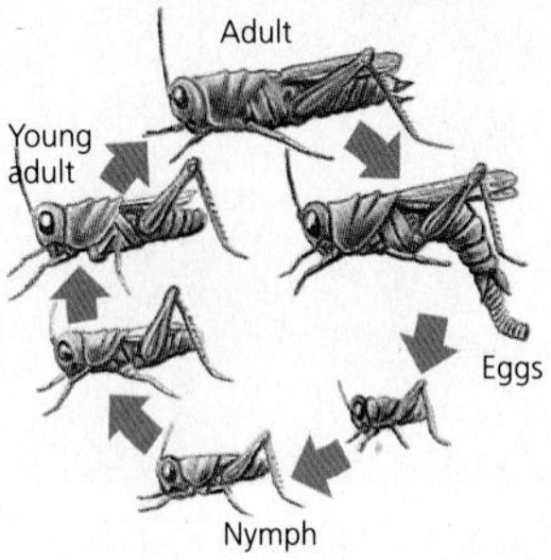

Figure 33-8 In incomplete metamorphosis (above) the nymph resembles the adult form. In complete metamorphosis (below) neither larva nor pupa resembles the adult.

Complete metamorphosis

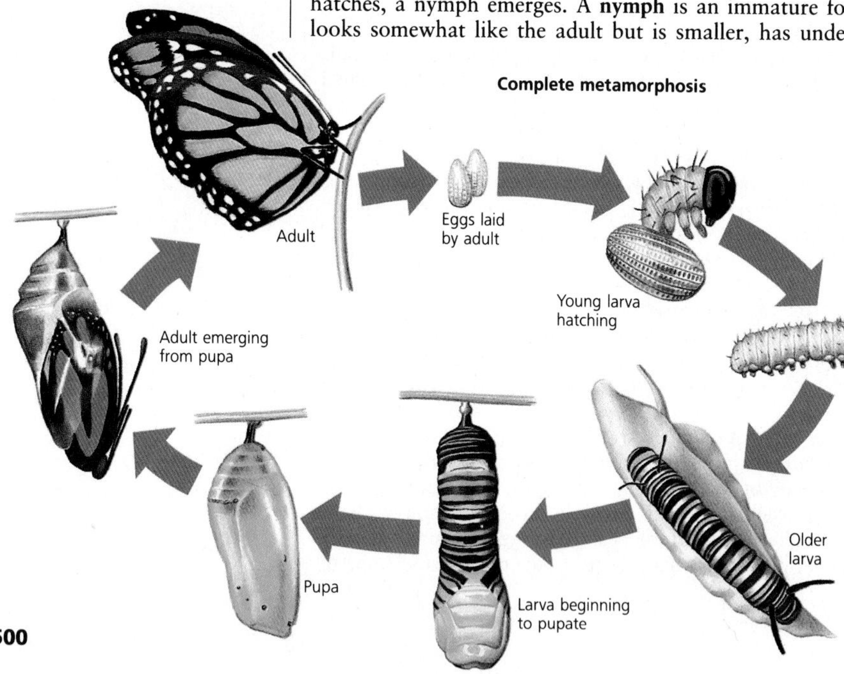

LEP Activity

Show students photographs of different insects in various stages of complete or incomplete metamorphosis. Have each student draw and label the stages as well as identify particular insect features. Then have students write a short paragraph comparing incomplete and complete metamorphosis, using the terms with which they labeled their drawings.

reproductive organs, and lacks wings. The nymph molts several times until it becomes a winged adult that can reproduce.

Complete Metamorphosis

Butterflies, beetles, and most other insects go through complete metamorphosis. Complete metamorphosis includes four distinct stages: egg, larva, pupa, and adult. For example, when a butterfly egg hatches, a segmented larva emerges. The larva, commonly called a caterpillar, looks far more like a worm than an adult butterfly. Unlike a worm, however, a caterpillar has three pairs of jointed legs and several pairs of fleshy legs. A caterpillar devours leaves, grows large, and molts several times. Because caterpillars need a lot of food to grow so rapidly, they can cause much damage to the plants upon which they feed.

Typically when a caterpillar's growth is complete, it finds a sheltered spot and hangs upside down. Its body becomes shorter and thicker. Its exoskeleton splits down the back and falls off. The insect now enters an immobile stage called the **pupa.** Inside the pupa larval tissues are breaking down, and groups of cells called imaginal disks are developing into the tissues of the adult. During this process the pupa is encased in a protective covering, called a **cocoon** in moths and a **chrysalis** in butterflies. When metamorphosis is complete, a sexually mature winged adult emerges.

Hormonal Control of Metamorphosis

The process of metamorphosis is controlled by the sequential expression of genes. These genes cause the production of three hormones: brain hormone, molting hormone (called ecdysone), and juvenile hormone. Brain hormone stimulates a gland in the thorax to release molting hormone. The effect of molting hormone depends on the amount of juvenile hormone in the blood. During larval development the level of juvenile hormone is relatively high, and the release of molting hormone at this stage causes the larva to molt. However, as the insect gets older, the production of juvenile hormone decreases. When the level of juvenile hormone falls low enough, molting hormone triggers the change from larva to pupa. When juvenile hormone is no longer present, molting hormone starts the change from pupa to adult.

Importance of Metamorphosis

Metamorphosis is another adaptation that contributes to the great success of insects. In a life cycle based on complete metamorphosis, different developmental stages of the insect fulfill different functions. For example, a caterpillar is specialized for growth, while an adult butterfly is specialized for dispersal and reproduction. One of the advantages of this specialization is that it eliminates conflict between two activities that require great amounts of energy—growing and reproducing.

Metamorphosis also enhances insect survival in two other ways. First, it eliminates competition between larvae and adults

Figure 33-9 Leaf-feeding gulf fritillary caterpillars, *Agraulis vanillae* (top), do not compete with the adult form (bottom), which feeds on flower nectar.

Independent Practice

■ Have students write answers to the Section Review.

■ Give students pairs of words and have them write sentences that link the words together—for example, nymph and metamorphosis. *(The insects that undergo incomplete metamorphosis produce nymphs that look somewhat like small versions of adult insects.)*

Check Your Understanding

1. Compare defensive adaptations of the grasshopper with those of other insects. *(Grasshoppers have powerful legs to leap away from predators and have protective coloration, while other insects have stingers, pincers, or chemical defenses.)*

2. What might be the advantage of butterfly-pollinated flowers growing on the upper portion of plants? *(Butterflies move by air.)*

3. How is the color of butterflies helpful to them? *(Color plays a role in mating, warning, camouflage, deception, and mimicry.)*

Videodiscs

■ ***Side 4 19464, Butterfly Development Time Lapse (m)***

■ ***Side 4 18824, Mosquito Emergence (m)***

More Information

Insect Wings Wings are outgrowths of the insect's exoskeleton and are not modified limbs as are wings in bats and birds. Wings of many insects are made of a double layer of chitin with a supporting network of hollow veins filled with air or blood.

Most insects fold their wings over the abdomen when at rest. A few, such as the dragonfly (a good example of a primitive winged insect), cannot fold their wings and must keep them outstretched at all times.

Because wings are species constant, they serve as one means of classification. Wings may be thin and membranous as in flies; thin and horny, forming a cover for hindwings as in the frontwings of beetles; covered with hair as in caddis flies; or covered with fine, often highly pigmented scales, as in butterflies and moths.

Answer to Think

Because monarchs emerge first, predators are more likely to encounter them and their unpleasant traits first and so learn to avoid all butterflies with a similar appearance. If viceroys emerged first, the viceroy's mimicry would be less effective.

Reteaching

Have students create a table that compares the crayfish and grasshopper according to the following: locomotion; respiratory, excretory, circulatory, nervous, and reproductive systems. An example of a completed table is shown on p. 497.

■ *See* Section Reviews *worksheet, Section 33.2.*

Enrichment

Have students research and prepare a report on chemical defenses of the insect world. Suggest topics such as the use of formic acid by ant and beetle species and the ability of bombardier beetles to spray a hot, noxious chemical onto their predators.

Closure

Have students compare insect eyes, respiration, and external structures with analogous parts of their own bodies. *(For example, spiracles and trachea vs. human lungs)* Point out that the vastly different survival strategies of insects are every bit as adaptive as our own.

Think

In any given area, monarch butterflies (top) generally emerge as adults earlier in the spring than do viceroy butterflies (bottom). Based on what you know about Batesian mimicry, why do you think it is advantageous for viceroys not to emerge first?

for food and space. For example, a caterpillar eats leafy vegetation, but an adult butterfly feeds on flower nectar. Second, a multistage life cycle helps insects survive harsh weather. Most butterflies spend the winter encased as pupae. Likewise, the eggs of mosquitoes remain unhatched through the winter. The larvae or nymphs of other insects spend the winter under water. Some are even protected from the cold by a chemical in the blood that is similar to the antifreeze used in car radiators.

Defense

Insects have many defensive adaptations that enhance survival. Some adaptations are for aggressive defense. One of the most elaborate is that of the bombardier beetle, which sprays predators with a hot stream of a noxious chemical. The beetle can even rotate an opening on its abdomen to aim the spray at its attacker. A more common defense is the barbed stinger of bees and wasps.

Some adaptations provide a passive defense. The grasshopper's grassy green color is a good example of one form of passive defense—**camouflage,** or the ability to blend into surroundings. Camouflage enhances survival by making it difficult for predators to spot the insect. A remarkable form of camouflage is exhibited by the many species of "stick insects." These creatures look so much like twigs that they often cannot be seen unless they move.

Other insects defend themselves not by hiding but by advertising. Many poisonous or bad-tasting insects have evolved **warning coloration**—bold, bright color patterns that make them clearly recognizable and warn predators away.

In some cases evolution has resulted in several poisonous or dangerous species' having similar patterns of warning coloration. This adaptation, called **Müllerian mimicry,** encourages predators to avoid all of these species. For example, many species of stinging bees and wasps have a similar pattern of black and yellow stripes. In other cases insects that are neither poisonous nor bad-tasting have patterns that fool predators by mimicking the warning coloration of other species. For example, the viceroy butterfly looks much like the unpleasant-tasting monarch. This type of defensive adaptation is called **Batesian mimicry.**

Section Review

1. State the function of each of the following parts of a grasshopper: *labrum, tympanum, ovipositors.*
2. What factor limits the size of an insect?
3. What structure enables a grasshopper to hear? Where is it located?
4. How does complete metamorphosis benefit an insect species?
5. The yellow jacket wasp and the stingless syrphid fly have similar color patterns. How does each of these insects benefit from this coloring? What is the fly's defense called?

Answers to Section Review

1. The labrum helps hold grass within the jaws; the tympanum is a sound-sensing membrane; ovipositors are used by females to lay eggs.
2. The limited ability of the thin exoskeleton to support the body, and the inefficient and fragile respiratory system
3. The tympanum; on the first abdominal segment
4. Complete metamorphosis allows different developmental stages to become specialized for different functions, eliminates competition between larvae and adults for food and space, and increases the likelihood of survival during harsh weather.
5. The yellow jacket has warning coloration. Predators stay away from the fly because they identify it as a harmful insect. The fly displays Batesian mimicry.

33.3 Insect Behavior

Just as most insects go through different developmental stages that are specialized in form and function, some insect species have different kinds of adult individuals that are specialized in form and function. For example, some species of ants, bees, and termites live in complex societies in which some individuals gather food, others protect the society, and still others only breed. This **division of labor** in insect societies creates great interdependence and a heightened need for communication. Even solitary insects such as fleas and fireflies need to communicate at certain critical times—at mating time, for example. These are all behavioral variations in insects. In this section we will look at the social behavior of honeybees and at some ways in which bees and other insects communicate.

Section Objectives

- *Describe the social organization of honeybees and the ways in which they behave.*
- *Name three ways in which insects communicate, and give an example of each.*
- *Summarize Karl von Frisch's discoveries about communication in honeybees.*

Social Behavior in Honeybees

A honeybee hive consists of three distinct forms of individuals: the workers, the queen, and the drones. The workers are the sterile females that make up the vast majority of the hive population, which may reach more than 80,000. The workers do all of the work of the hive except reproduction. The queen is the only fertile female in the hive, and her only function is to reproduce. The drones, or male bees, are needed for mating, but otherwise they are useless to the hive. In fact, their mouthparts are too short to obtain nectar from flowers, so the workers must feed them.

As you read about the complex behavior of honeybees, keep in mind that the bees neither teach nor learn these behaviors. Instead, the behaviors are genetically determined; that is, the insects are acting out instructions stored in their genes and triggered by the substances these genes produce. This genetically controlled behavior is called **instinct** or innate behavior.

The Worker Bees

Worker bees perform many functions at different times during their brief lives, which average about six weeks in length. After making the transition from pupa to adult, workers first feed honey and pollen to the queen, the drones, and the larvae. During this stage the workers are called nurse bees. They secrete a high-protein substance called **royal jelly**, which they feed to the queen and to the youngest larvae.

After about a week as feeders, worker bees stop producing royal jelly and begin to secrete wax, which they use to build and repair the honeycomb. During this stage they may also remove dead bees and wastes from the hive, guard the hive, and fan their wings to circulate fresh air.

The workers spend the last weeks of their lives gathering nectar and pollen. A number of structural adaptations aid them in

Figure 33-10 Worker bees perform the work of the hive, while drones and the queen are involved exclusively with reproduction.

Lesson Plan

Section Focus

This section describes the highly developed social organization of certain insect species. In honeybees, the social structure comprises an elaborate division of labor. Although many solitary insects do communicate, communication is essential to honeybees. Insects communicate by chemicals, sound, movement, and visual signals.

Section Themes

The theme of **Evolution** is evident in the variety of behaviors, from solitary to interdependent, within insect species such as bees, ants, and termites. About 85 percent of bee species are solitary. The rest, including honeybees, have evolved complex interactions well adapted to their survival.

Motivating Activity

Play an audiotape of insect sounds, such as bees buzzing, crickets chirping, and locusts humming. Ask students if they can identify the sounds. Show students an ant farm or provide photographs of an ant colony. Explain that these are examples of social behavior in insects. Ask students to speculate about ways in which communication in human societies compares with insect communication.

Teaching Strategies

Interpreting the Visuals Have students look at Figure 33-10 on p. 503. Ask them why bees benefit from different structures. *(Because they enhance the ability to perform different functions)*

Videodiscs

- ***Side 4 38467, Honeybees (m)***
- ***Side 4 38063, Butterflies (m)***

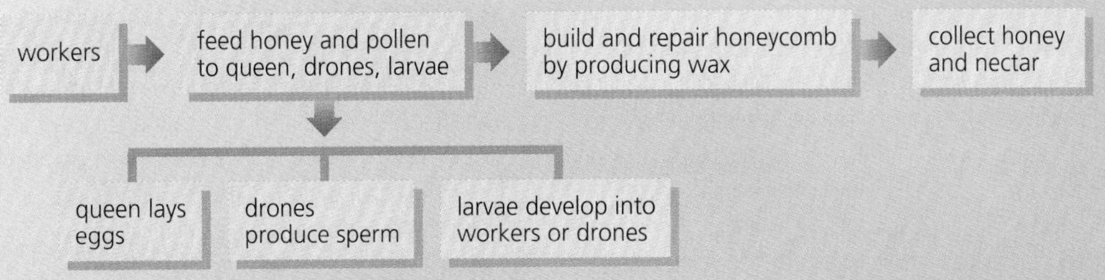

Graphic Organizer Use this sequential diagram in Independent Practice on p. 504.

Observing Organisms Arrange for the class to visit an apiary to observe social behavior of bees. Emphasize the commercial significance of bees to human society. Have students prepare in advance a list of questions about the apiary, such as: How long does a hive last? What happens to hives and bees in winter? How does a hive get started? Who buys bees? ***CAUTION:*** Some people have life-threatening allergies to bee stings. Have all participating students secure parental permission and medical clearance.

Comparing Concepts Ask students what they think is the adaptive significance of insect communication as a social behavior. *(Communication enhances chances for survival by permitting coordination of effort and division of labor.)* What is the difference between innate and learned behavior? *(Innate behavior is genetic; learned behavior is based on experience and can be passed on from one member of a species to another.)*

■ *See* Process Skills, *Chapter 33.*

Guided Practice

Have students design a fictional insect society. Tell them to write Help Wanted ads for the three most important jobs in the society. Have them include the job description and job qualifications in the ad and add a heading. Remind them that these insect jobs must be filled for the mutual benefit of the insect society.

Independent Practice

- Have students write answers to the Section Review.
- Have students prepare a sequential diagram to explain social behavior of honeybees in a hive during the life of one queen. Tell them that the diagram should show activities of workers, drones, and the queen. An example of a completed diagram is shown on p. 503.

Figure 33-11 This magnified image shows worker bees feeding a queen (center).

this work. For example, the design of their mouthparts is highly efficient for lapping up nectar. Their legs have special structures that serve as pollen packers, pollen baskets, and pollen combs. The combs clean the pollen as it is packed. The sterile workers do not use their ovipositors for egg laying. Instead these structures are modified into a stinger that helps the workers protect the hive.

The Queen and the Drones

The queen bee develops from an egg identical with those that develop into the workers. The differences between the queen and the workers result from the continuous diet of royal jelly that the queen is fed throughout her larval development. In addition the queen herself secretes a substance called queen factor that prevents other female larvae from becoming sexually mature.

The queen's role is to reproduce. Although a queen bee may lay as many as a million eggs each year, she mates only during a brief period in her life. A few days after completing metamorphosis into an adult, the queen flies out of the hive and mates in the air with one or more drones. During mating, millions of sperm are deposited in the queen's seminal receptacle, where they are stored for use during the five or more years of her life.

Biology in Process

The Dance Language of the Bees

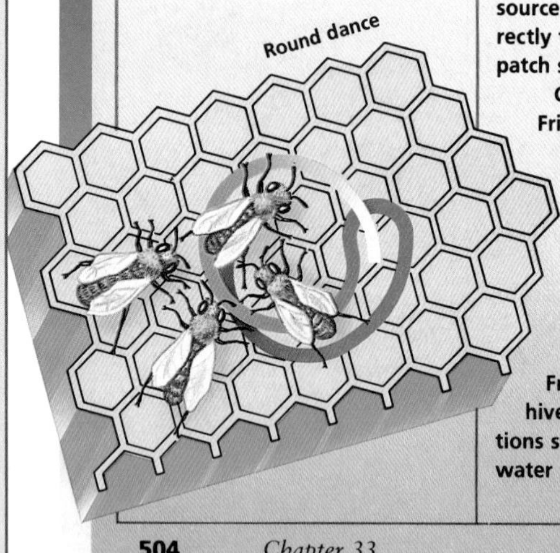

How do bees communicate so well that when one bee returns from a food source, other bees can fly directly to a fragrant flower patch several meters away?

German biologist Karl von Frisch first asked himself this question more than 70 years ago. After 25 years of observation and experimentation, he learned to translate the dance language of the bees.

To observe bees von Frisch built a glass-walled hive and placed feeding stations stocked with sweetened water near the hive. When a bee landed to feed, he dabbed paint on its thorax. This mark allowed him to identify the bee when it returned to the hive.

Again and again, von Frisch observed the painted scout enter the hive, feed several other workers, and then perform a series of dancelike movements on the comb. The scout would circle first to the right and then to the left—a behavior that von Frisch termed the "round dance." Other bees would excitedly follow the scout bee in the dance and place their antennae close to hers. Finally, the other bees would leave and locate the food.

Next von Frisch experi-

More Information

Migrating Monarchs Every September monarch butterflies begin their fall migration from Canada and the northeastern United States. They travel from 32 to 161 km a day toward a small area in the Sierra Madre northwest of Mexico City, Mexico. An estimated 14 billion monarchs cluster so densely in the 800-hectare area that trees 30 m tall look like solid masses of butterflies. Those butterflies that do not get as far south as Mexico spend the winter in California, Florida, and Louisiana hibernating in large swarms in trees. Monarchs always use the same trees, so in some places, such as Pacific Grove, California, butterfly roosts are tourist attractions protected by law.

If the hive becomes overcrowded, the queen leaves with about half the workers to form a new hive. Shortly before this happens or when the queen dies, queen factor disappears from the hive. As a result, workers begin to raise new queens. When a new queen emerges, she produces new queen factor, and in response the workers destroy the other developing queens.

Drones are males that develop from unfertilized eggs. Their sole function is to deliver sperm to the queen. Through the summer the hive population includes a few hundred drones. When the honey supply begins to run low, the workers sting all the drones and clear them from the hive.

Communication

The effect of queen factor is a good example of the most common form of communication among insects—chemical communication. Queen factor is a **pheromone** *(FER-uh-MONE)*, a chemical released by an animal that affects the behavior or development of other animals of the same species. Pheromones play a major role in the behavior patterns of many insects. For example, you may have noticed ants marching along in a tightly defined route. They

Waggle dance

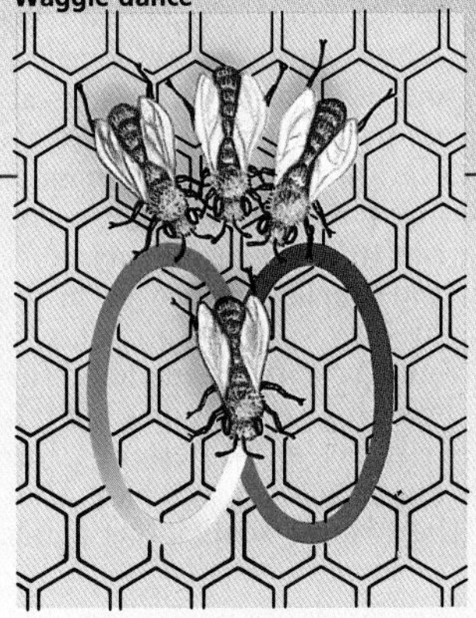

mented by placing four sweetened water samples within 10 m of the hive—one north, one south, one east, and one west. He observed that although a scout might find only one sample, other bees would soon appear at all four. He concluded that the dance did not tell the bees the exact location of the food.

Von Frisch also observed a second dance, which he called the "waggle dance." Performed by pollen-laden bees returning to the hive, this dance consisted of a series of straight runs during which the bees waggled their abdomens from side to side. After each run the bees made a semicircular turn to the right.

At first, von Frisch hypothesized that the round dance was performed by bees returning with sweetened water and the waggle dance was performed by bees returning with pollen. However, experiments with sweetened water placed at various distances from the hive showed that the round dance was performed for food sources near the hive. The waggle dance was performed for food sources more than about 50 m away. Specific movements of the waggle dance gave information about the abundance of the source and its direction and distance from the hive. Direction was shown by the angle of the dance on the comb.

In 1973 von Frisch's work on communication won a Nobel Prize.

- **Why do you think von Frisch decided to conduct experiments with feeding stations at various distances?**

Check Your Understanding

1. Why is it advantageous to have many drones in a hive when only a few get to mate? *(The gene pool is enhanced if only the fittest drones reach the queen for mating.)*

2. How are the antennae of a male mosquito and the tuner in a radio similar and different? *(Both radio tuner and mosquito's antennae can receive a single frequency, but the radio may be changed to another frequency, whereas the mosquito is limited to the frequency emitted by a female of its species.)*

Biology in Process

Using the Feature

The main process skills used in this feature are observing and experimenting. Karl von Frisch observed that when a bee returned to the hive after locating a food source, it performed a series of dancelike movements. By conducting a series of experiments in which he manipulated placement of feeding stations, von Frisch determined that the bees' dance varies according to the distance of the food source from the hive. Point out to students that because two variables are observed together does not in itself establish a relationship between them. Von Frisch at first hypothesized that the type of food—pollen or sweetened water—determined the type of dance performed by the bee. Only through experimentation did he infer that the distance of the food from the hive was the crucial variable.

Answer to the Feature

Von Frisch probably hypothesized that different dances were related to differences in distance to the food and therefore designed the experiments to test this hypothesis.

Cooperative Learning

Insect Communication Assign groups of four students to develop an insect language to communicate where an object is located in the classroom. Each group should decide on signals and sounds (no words or pointing gestures allowed) and what they mean. Next, tell one student in each group to which object in the room he or she should guide the other group members. Have the student demonstrate for the class the group's language. Then ask the rest of the class to describe the language, how it was used to identify the object, and whether the signals were effective.

Section 33.3

Reteaching

Remind students of the evolutionary success of insects. Have them make a table that lists features that demonstrate insects' success. Use column headings: *Structural Variations, Physiological Variations,* and *Behavioral Variations*. Discuss how different variations are interrelated. *(For example, ovipositors of sterile worker bees are modified into stingers used for protecting the hive.)*

■ *See* **Section Reviews** ***worksheet, Section 33.3.***

Enrichment

Have students do library research and write a report that compares the social life of ants with that of termites or that compares the caste system of bees with that of wasps.

Closure

Remind students of problems involving the use of chemical sprays to control harmful insects. Ask students to speculate about how knowledge of insect communication and predator–prey relationships among insects could be harnessed to control insects biologically. Discuss advantages of biological control over application of chemical pesticides.

Videodiscs

■ ***1214–1217, Ants: Types (s)***

Figure 33-12 Ants will follow a pheromone trail left by the ants that have preceded them.

were following a trail of pheromones left by the ants ahead of them. By secreting less than 0.01 μg of a powerful pheromone, female silkworms can attract males from several miles away.

Many insects communicate through sound. Male crickets use sound to attract females and to warn other males away from their territories. They rub a scraper on one forewing against a vein on the other forewing to produce chirping sounds. Each cricket species produces several calls that differ from those of other cricket species. In fact, because many species look similar, entomologists often use the calls to identify the species. Mosquitoes depend on sound, too. Males that are ready to mate home in on the buzzing sounds produced by females. The male senses this buzzing by means of tiny hairs on his antennae, which vibrate only to the frequency emitted by a female of the same species.

Insects may also communicate by tapping, rubbing, or signaling. Fireflies use flashes of light to find a mate. Each species of firefly has its own pattern of flashes. Males emit flashes in flight, and females flash back in response. This behavior allows male fireflies to locate a mate of the proper species. However, they must beware of female fireflies of the genus *Photuris,* which can mimic the flashes of other species. If a male of a different species responds to the flash of a *Photuris* female and attempts to mate, the female devours him. This is surely one of the more unusual behavioral adaptations in the enormously successful world of insects.

Section Review

1. What is a *pheromone?*
2. What determines whether a fertilized honeybee egg will develop into a worker or a queen?
3. How do honeybees behave when a hive is overcrowded?
4. Name some major ways in which insects communicate.
5. Current research indicates that the queen bee mates with drones from another hive rather than her own hive. In what way might this behavior benefit the honeybee society?

Answers to Section Review

1. A chemical produced by an animal that affects the behavior or development of other animals of the same species
2. The type of diet it is fed (royal jelly) and the continuity of this diet
3. The queen leaves and takes about half the workers with her. Then workers in the old hive raise a new queen.
4. Through pheromones, sound, movement, and visual signals
5. Mating with drones from other hives provides a source of genetic diversity; drones from the queen's own hive share all of their genes with her since they develop from unfertilized eggs laid by the queen herself.

Laboratory

External Anatomy of the Wasp

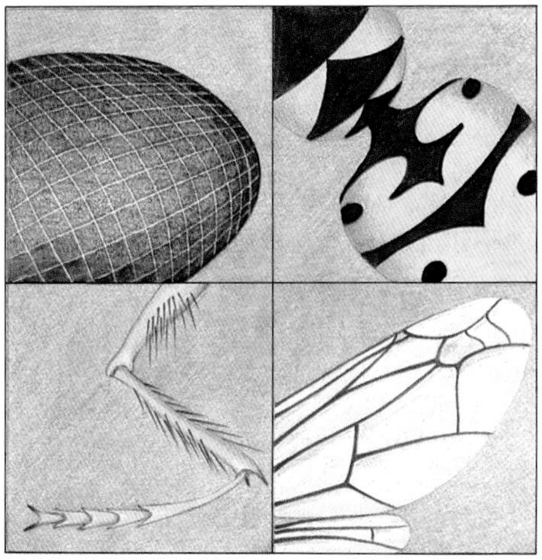

Objective
To examine the external anatomy of a wasp

Process Skills
Inferring, observing

Materials
Forceps, preserved *Polistes* (paper wasp), culture dish, hand lens or dissecting microscope, blunt probe, unlined paper

Humane Alternative
A diagram of a wasp may be used as an alternative to using preserved wasps.

Inquiry

1 The specimen you will work with is a worker wasp. Worker wasps play the same social role as worker bees. Use forceps to rinse the specimen gently but thoroughly with water to remove excess preservative. Try not to touch the wasp since the preservative can be irritating to the skin. Place the wasp in a culture dish.
2 Observe the external features of the wasp through a hand lens or dissecting microscope. Carefully move the wasp with the probe and forceps to observe the head, thorax, abdomen, legs, wings, antennae, compound eyes, and simple eyes.
3 Make a drawing that shows the major external features of the wasp. Begin at the anterior end of the body and slowly work toward the posterior end. Include as much detail in your drawing as necessary to make the features clear.
4 Label the structures listed in step 2. The wasp's most powerful muscles are located in the thorax. Why do you think this is so?
5 Observe the row of tiny openings at each side of the abdomen. These are the spiracles.
6 Observe the structure that protrudes from the last segment of the abdomen. This is the ovipositor. It indicates that the specimen is a female. Include the ovipositor in your drawing, and label it.
7 Using the tip of the probe as a guide, examine the mouth parts of the wasp. Identify the labrum, labium, mandibles, and maxillae. Make separate drawings of the structure of each mouthpart, and give it a label.

Conclusions

1 Compare your drawing of the wasp with the diagram of the grasshopper in Figure 33-3 in your textbook. Based on your observations, describe a typical insect in terms of its body segments, number of legs, number of antennae, and number and types of eyes.
2 What part of your specimen has been modified into a stinger to be used for defense?

Further Inquiry
What are some ways in which the morphology of bees and wasps differs from that of other insect orders? Describe a scientific method for answering this question.

Laboratory

(For an overview of external wasp anatomy and preparatory information related to the laboratory, see p. 491B.)

Inquiry
4. The wings, which need strong muscles to operate efficiently, are attached to the thorax.

Conclusions
1. A typical insect has three body segments: head, thorax, and abdomen. The abdomen is further divided into 11 segments. Insects also have three pairs of jointed legs and two pairs of wings attached to the thorax, paired antennae, one pair of compound eyes, and three simple eyes.
2. The ovipositor

Further Inquiry
Students should suggest that a number of representative insects be looked at to compare them morphologically with bees and wasps.

Chapter 33 Review

Vocabulary

1. Aorta; others are parts of the digestive system.
2. Pheromone; others relate to metamorphosis.
3. Ovipositor; others are involved in digestion.
4. Behavioral variation; others are defenses involving coloration.
5. Nymph; others are body parts.

Review

1. c	6. d
2. a	7. d
3. b	8. a
4. b	9. c
5. a	10. d

11. Small size may allow many species to inhabit the same environment without competing.
12. Different digestive enzymes or any other example involving adaptation of body systems; also different kinds of metamorphosis
13. Three body parts, one pair of antennae, three pairs of jointed legs, and an abdomen with 11 segments
14. By damaging crops, carrying disease, damaging wood in buildings
15. Head, thorax, abdomen
16. In insects, oxygen travels directly to cells through air tubes called tracheae instead of being transported in blood.
17. Camouflage allows insects to hide from predators by blending into surroundings; warning coloration makes insects stand out so that predators associate their appearance with undesirability as food.
18. When levels of juvenile hormone are high, release of molting hormone causes larva to molt. When levels of juvenile hormone drop, molting hormone causes transition to pupa and then to adult.
19. Workers, queen, drones
20. By rubbing a scraper of one forewing against a vein on other forewing; to attract mates and protect territory

Chapter 33 Review

Vocabulary

aorta (499)
Batesian mimicry (502)
behavioral variations (493)
camouflage (502)
chrysalis (501)
cocoon (501)
division of labor (503)
entomologist (494)
gastric ceca (499)
hindgut (499)
instinct (503)
labium (498)
labrum (498)
metamorphosis (500)
midgut (498)
Müllerian mimicry (502)
nymph (500)
ovipositor (500)
pheromone (505)
physiological variations (493)
pupa (501)
royal jelly (503)
structural variations (493)
tarsus (498)
tympanum (499)
warning coloration (502)

For each set of terms below, choose the one that does not belong, and explain why it does not belong.

1. labium, aorta, gastric ceca, labrum
2. pupa, cocoon, pheromone, metamorphosis
3. ovipositor, hindgut, midgut, gastric ceca
4. warning coloration, Batesian mimicry, behavioral variation, camouflage
5. aorta, nymph, tympanum, midgut

Review

1. Insect species are able to adapt to new environments rapidly because individual insects possess (a) jointed legs (b) pheromones (c) short life spans (d) exoskeletons.
2. Differences in mouthparts are an example of (a) structural variations (b) physiological variations (c) behavioral variations (d) metamorphosis.
3. Butterflies and moths belong to the order (a) Orthoptera (b) Lepidoptera (c) Coleoptera (d) Homoptera.
4. An insect's legs and wings are attached to its (a) head (b) thorax (c) abdomen (d) spiracles.
5. The function of the gastric ceca is to (a) secrete digestive enzymes (b) shred food (c) store undigested food (d) remove chemical wastes.
6. The immature form of an insect that undergoes incomplete metamorphosis is a (a) larva (b) pupa (c) caterpillar (d) nymph.
7. Metamorphosis benefits insect species by (a) allowing different developmental stages to fulfill different functions (b) eliminating competition between larvae and adults (c) promoting survival during harsh weather (d) all of the above.
8. Bees perform the round dance to inform other bees of (a) the presence of food near the hive (b) the distance to a food source (c) the direction of a food source (d) all of the above.
9. The substance called queen factor (a) causes larvae to develop into queen bees (b) attracts drones (c) prevents larvae from becoming sexually mature (d) fertilizes eggs.
10. A pheromone is a chemical that (a) regulates metamorphosis (b) digests food (c) regulates the process of cellular respiration in insects (d) affects the behavior or development of other animals of the same species.
11. How has the small size of insects contributed to their success?
12. Give an example of physiological variation in insects.
13. Name the four primary characteristics that entomologists consider when classifying insects.

14. What are three ways that insects cause harm to human society?
15. Name the three main segments of the insect's body.
16. How is the insect's system for transporting oxygen to cells different from the system that is found in most other animals?
17. What is the difference between camouflage and warning coloration?
18. Summarize the role of molting hormone in controlling metamorphosis.
19. What three types of individuals make up a honeybee society?
20. How do crickets produce sounds? What functions do these sounds serve?

Critical Thinking

1. Farmers who use insecticides to control insect pests often find that strains of insects rapidly appear that are resistant to the insecticide. How do these insecticide-resistant strains develop? Why does this happen so quickly among insects?
2. What might you infer about an insect's food source from the fact that the insect has siphoning mouthparts?
3. Study the drawing of the insect on this page. Based on the information in Table 33-1, to which order does this insect belong? What characteristic or characteristics enabled you to classify the insect?
4. In addition to the exoskeleton, another characteristic thought to limit the size of insects is their system of tracheae. Suggest a reason why this means of transporting gases might be a limit to insect size.
5. During their lives worker bees move from first feeding and caring for larvae inside the hive to later gathering nectar and defending the hive. Why do you think this sequence is more advantageous for the hive than the reverse sequence might be? (Hint: Consider the fact that a worker bee has a stinger.)

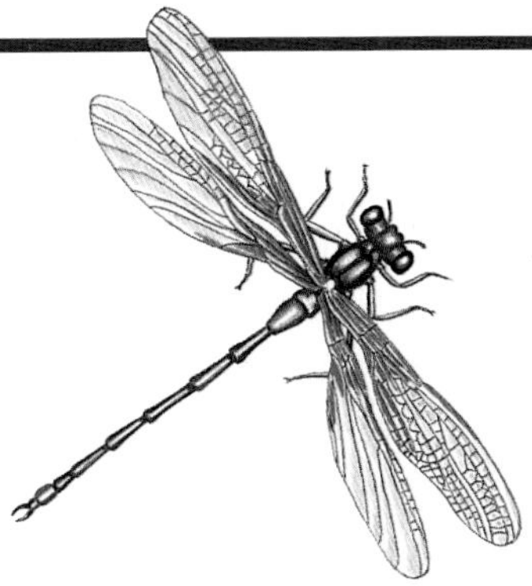

6. What characteristics may have helped insects survive the major climatic changes that led to the extinction of the dinosaurs and many other species about 65 million years ago?

Extension

1. Collect a variety of insects and use a field guide to help you classify your specimens. Share your collection with the class.
2. Read the article by Ivars Peterson entitled "Step in Time" in *Science News*, August 31, 1991, pp. 136–137. Write a report in which you discuss some of the difficulties inherent in the mathematical study of biological oscillators.
3. Read "Caterpillar Call-of-the-Wild Aims at Ants" in *Science News*, June 2, 1990, p. 342. Prepare an oral report in which you explain how certain caterpillars entice ants into a unique mutualistic relationship. How does the relationship benefit both kinds of organisms?
4. Use your school library or public library to research the topic of sociobiology. Prepare a written report on what sociobiologists mean by *altruistic behavior* and how they explain such behavior in insect societies.

Critical Thinking

1. Insects with genes that confer resistance against insecticide survive and reproduce in large numbers; thus they proliferate through natural selection. This process occurs rapidly because insects have short life spans.
2. Siphoning mouthparts suggest that it feeds on liquid food.
3. Odonata; two pairs of long, narrow membranous wings
4. A large organism probably could not transport oxygen quickly and efficiently enough through tracheae to supply all of its cells; instead, the organism would require specialized organs (lungs) for gas exchange.
5. If a worker bee dies from stinging or through an attack by a predator, it has already completed most of its other functions. It would be a greater loss to the hive if death occurred early in the worker's life.

Extension

1. Suggest appropriate methods of collecting; caution students to avoid stinging insects and others that might be harmful.
2. Suggest this article to students with a mathematical bent. Mathematical modeling attempts to explain a phenomenon in mathematical terms. The difficulty has to do with first understanding what is important and what is not. The model that Peskin developed required "special pleading" (leaking) in order to work. His model, however, interested other mathematicians who used it as a starting point.
3. Encourage students to research other examples of the form of symbiosis called mutualism, such as oxpeckers on zebras.
4. Tell students to include a comparison of altruistic behavior in insects and humans. You may wish to suggest that students explore the altruistic behavior of ants through a computer program called SimAnt™.

Chapter 34 Echinoderms

Chapter Overview

Chapter 34 continues the discussion of invertebrates begun in Chapter 29. Section 34.1 examines general characteristics of members of the Phylum Echinodermata and discusses the five classes of echinoderms. Section 34.2 focuses on a representative member of the Class Asteroidea, examining the structures and functions of the sea star.

Chapter Planning Chart

B	S	A	Sections and Subsections	Page	Features	Page	Resources
•	•	•	**34.1 Diversity**				
			Characteristics	511	Biology in Process	512	Videodiscs
			Evolution and Classification	511	Section Review	514	Process Skills: Regeneration
							Section Reviews Worksheet
	•	•	**34.2 Structure and Function**				
			Body Plan	515	Think	516	Videodiscs
			Water-Vascular System	515	Laboratory	517	Blackline Master 70
			Feeding and Digestion	516	Section Review	516	Overhead Transparency T34
			Other Body Systems	516			Laboratories: Live Sea Stars
			Reproduction	516			Section Reviews Worksheet
			End of Chapter Activities				
					Chapter Review	518	Vocabulary Skills
							Chapter Test
							Computer Test Generator

B *The Basic Level curriculum presents the most fundamental knowledge offered in the course.*
S *The Standard Level curriculum is designed for the average student who is able to master most topics.*
A *The Advanced Level curriculum includes suggestions for teaching the most academically able students.*

Cooperative Learning

Group Activity: Echinoderm Classes

- **Group Size:** *3 students*
- **Outcome:** *Students will describe characteristics of one class of echinoderms.*
- **Individual Accountability:** *Each group member will research one aspect of echinoderm structure or function.*
- **Positive Interdependence:** *The group will collaborate in writing and illustrating a report to the class.*

Section 34.2 describes the structure and function of a member of the Class Asteroidea in detail. Have each group use this section as a model in researching and writing a report on a member of one of the other classes of echinoderms: Crinoidea, Ophiuroidea, Echinoidea, or Holothuroidea. Assign each group one class of echinoderm to study, making sure that the whole phylum is well covered. Tell group members to divide the research into *Body Plan, Feeding and Digestion,* and *Reproduction,* with one member being responsible for each topic. Once individual research has been completed, have each group reassemble and prepare a presentation to the class modeled on the one in Section 34.2. Tell students to include both labeled drawings and photos copied from books as well as their written explanation.

Concept Map

The following is one possible solution to the concept mapping activity in Reteaching on p. 514.

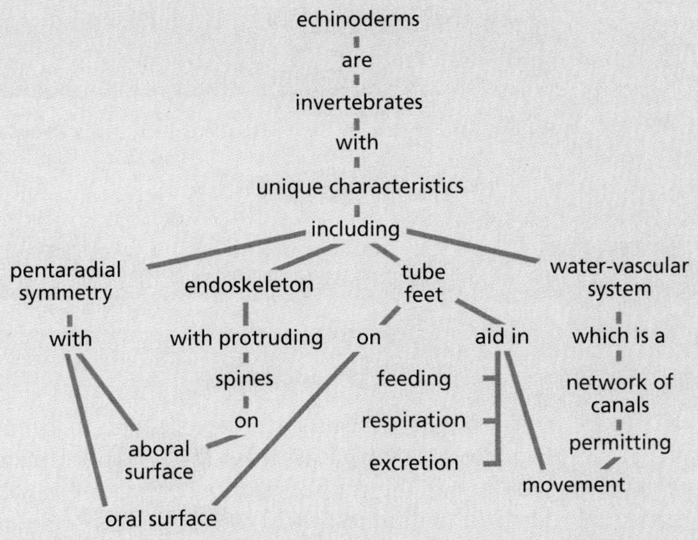

Laboratory Preparation

Overview *(See p. 517.)*

In this lab, students study several representative echinoderms. Either living or preserved specimens may be used. Saltwater aquariums are difficult to maintain but can be a dramatic and effective teaching tool. Students compare similar structures in sea stars, brittle stars, and sea urchins to develop an understanding of echinoderm organization, locomotion, and life habits.

Preparation

Preserved, dried, and live echinoderms can be obtained from biological supply houses. Sea urchin tests are also available. Have students refer to supplementary graphics or textbook illustrations to help them locate structures being observed.

Teaching Tips

Have students reread the chapter and refer to it as they do the investigation. Encourage students to refer to all available specimens, as well as illustrations, if certain structures are difficult to discern. Use of preserved specimens is recommended, although soft structures, such as tube feet and skin gills, are often damaged or do not survive preservation. Observing the specimen under water can often reveal whether such structures survived.

Emphasize the three basic characteristics of echinoderms: spiny skin, radial symmetry, and tube feet. Brittle stars lack skin gills and pedicellariae. Pedicellariae are best observed on the sea urchin. A sea star's pedicellariae, located on a raised ring of skin around the base of each spine and scattered among spines, are best observed on a dried specimen. The sea star's sieve plate is most visible. A sea urchin test clearly shows the animal's symmetry and arrangement of spines and pores through which tube feet protrude.

Discuss habitats of the specimens. All echinoderms are marine animals, the only phylum for which this is true. Sea stars are found in rocky, intertidal zones, brittle stars in deep water farther offshore, and sea urchins on hard sea bottoms. Relate different means of locomotion to these different habitats.

Safety

Students should rinse preserved specimens with water before studying them and should wash their hands thoroughly after finishing the lab. If live animals are used, they should be handled gently.

Chapter 34

Chapter Themes

Evolution Modern classification of organisms is based primarily on evolutionary relationships among organisms. Emphasize the evolutionary divergence of echinoderms from other invertebrates. Make sure that students recognize that fossil and embryological evidence shows that echinoderms are relatively close in evolutionary development to chordates. Point out that the pentaradial symmetry of echinoderms probably developed as an evolutionary adaptation in sessile ancestral forms.

Scale and Structure Section 34.2 highlights the structure of one kind of echinoderm, the sea star. Make sure that students understand how its structures relate to their functions. After they have completed this section, ask students to discuss traits that all echinoderms have in common.

Chapter Motivating Activity

Show students specimens of various kinds of echinoderms, or display photographs from invertebrate zoology texts and nature magazines. Ask them to describe ways in which these animals are similar. *(All are invertebrates, all exhibit some kind of radial symmetry, and none has distinguishable body sections, such as head, thorax, or abdomen.)* Have students compare these invertebrates with those discussed in previous chapters. *(Most other invertebrates have bilateral symmetry.)* Ask students to speculate on how these animals move and obtain food. *(They have tube feet that help them move and obtain food.)*

Chapter 34 *Echinoderms*

Introduction

The spiny-skinned echinoderms are among the oldest phyla of animals on earth. They are very beautiful too, with their bright colors and five-part, or pentaradial, body plans. In this chapter you will learn about the characteristics of sea stars, sea urchins, and other echinoderm species. Scientists suggest that this small group of marine animals may share a common ancestor with the chordates.

Chapter Outline

Chapter Concept

As you read, note the unique structure of the echinoderm, and keep in mind how much echinoderms differ from the other invertebrates you've studied.

Sea star, Galápagos. Inset: Sand dollar, *Encope* sp., Baja, California.

Understanding the Visuals

Ask students to compare the sea star with the sand dollar shown in the photographs on p. 510. How are they alike? *(Each has radial symmetry; both are marine organisms.)* How are they different? *(The sea star has a spiny skin covering and five arms. The sand dollar is disk shaped and has a five-pointed star pattern.)* Point out that the sand dollar's skin has gone and only the hard endoskeleton remains. Encourage students to identify some ways these two echinoderms are different from arthropods. *(Echinoderms have endoskeletons, no body segments, and symmetry based on five radii, while arthropods have exoskeletons, body segments, and bilateral symmetry.)*

34.1 Diversity

Members of the Phylum Echinodermata ("spiny skin") include the sea stars, brittle stars, sand dollars, and sea cucumbers. They inhabit marine environments ranging from shallow coastal waters to ocean trenches over 10,000 m deep. They range in size from 1 cm to 1 m in diameter and often have brilliant coloring.

Echinoderms bear an important evolutionary relationship to vertebrates. Evidence indicates that the echinoderms may share a common ancestor with the lower chordates and hence the vertebrates.

Characteristics

The characteristics of the echinoderms include the following, most of which are not shared by any other invertebrate phylum:

- Most undergo metamorphosis from a free-swimming, bilaterally symmetrical larva to a bottom-dwelling adult with radial symmetry. Most echinoderms have five radii or multiples thereof. Such a symmetry is called **pentaradial symmetry.**
- They have an internal skeleton called an **endoskeleton,** composed of calcium plates, which may include protruding spines.
- They have a **water-vascular system,** which is a network of water-filled canals.
- They have numerous small, movable protrusions called **tube feet** that aid in movement, feeding, respiration, and excretion.
- They have no circulatory, respiratory, or excretory systems.
- They have a nervous system but have no head or brain.
- They have two sexes, and reproduce sexually or asexually.

Evolution and Classification

The fossil record of echinoderms dates back to the Cambrian period, over 500 million years ago. Because echinoderm larvae are bilaterally symmetrical, scientists infer that they evolved from bilaterally symmetrical ancestors. Compare the larva of a hypothetical early echinoderm with the larva of a modern sea star pictured in Figure 34-1.

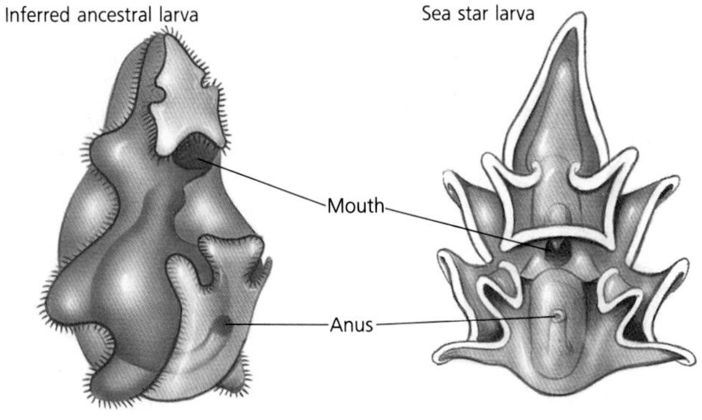

Figure 34-1 Note the similarities and differences between the inferred ancestral larva and the modern larva.

Section Objectives

- *Discuss the origin of echinoderms, and tell why scientists believe that echinoderms may be related to the chordates.*
- *List the characteristics that distinguish echinoderms from other phyla.*
- *Name representative species of each echinoderm class.*
- *Describe the procedure Jacques Loeb followed to determine the cause of parthenogenesis.*

Class	Representative Organisms	General Characteristics
Crinoidea	sea lilies, feather stars	sessile; mouth faces upward
Asteroidea	sea stars	tube feet used in feeding and locomotion
Ophiuroidea	basket stars, brittle stars	live on sea bottom
Echinoidea	sea urchins, sand dollars	grind food with Aristotle's lantern
Holothuroidea	sea cucumbers	armless; soft-bodied

Graphic Organizer Use this table in Guided Practice on p. 513.

Lesson Plan

Section Focus

This section describes characteristics and evolution of members of the Phylum Echinodermata. Students will study examples from each of the five classes of echinoderms.

Section Themes

This section emphasizes the theme of **Evolution.** Because echinoderm larvae have bilateral symmetry, scientists infer that members of this phylum evolved from bilaterally symmetrical ancestors. Radial symmetry may have evolved as an adaptation to a sessile life-style. The theme of **Scale and Structure** unifies the discussion of echinoderm structures and their functions.

Motivating Activity

Demonstrate the concept of symmetry by using a flat-sided mirror and drawings or photographs showing the front view of a human and the upper surface of a sea star. Ask students to observe both images while a volunteer places the flat side of the mirror against the human and turns it in various directions—horizontal, vertical, and diagonal. Then have another volunteer place the mirror against the sea star and turn it in various directions. Ask students to compare their observations. *(The human figure looks correct only when the mirror bisects the vertical center from head to toe. The sea star looks correct whenever the mirror bisects any arm and passes through the center of the animal because its five body parts radiate from the center.)*

Videodiscs

- ***Side 2 39043, Echinoderm Development (m)***
- ***Side 4 26790, Basket Star (m)***

Teaching Strategies

Interpreting the Visuals Have students look at Figure 34-2, p. 512, and then at Figure 1-4, p. 8. Ask to what class these echinoderms belong. *(Crinoidea)* Why are they described as "sessile"? *(Crinoids are attached to rocks or to the sea bottom by a long stalk; they cannot move about.)* Point out that the crinoid in Figure 34-2 exhibits many arms. Ask if this fact seems to contradict characteristics of echinoderms described on p. 511. *(No, because the many arms of crinoids are branches of five main arms.)*

Drawing Conclusions Ask students to consider the fossil record described on pp. 511–512 and form a hypothesis about the evolution of pentaradial symmetry in echinoderms. Have them explain how knowing that echinoderm ancestors were sessile helps us understand why this type of symmetry would be an adaptive advantage. *(If echinoderm ancestors had been unable to move about to capture food, pentaradial symmetry would have an adaptive advantage because such organisms could extend themselves in any direction with equal facility to obtain food.)*

Interpreting the Visuals Ask students to describe any evidence of pentaradial symmetry they see in the photograph in Figure 34-4, p. 514. *(The lines radiating from the top center, or anus, of the organism)* Then, as students look at the labeled drawing, ask them to infer, knowing what sea urchins eat, why the mouth position on the oral, or bottom, surface of the sea urchin is an adaptive advantage. *(The sea urchin obtains food by scraping algae off the surfaces it moves over. Thus, the "intake" opening on the underside of the organism enables it to get food efficiently.)*

Figure 34-2 This adult crinoid of the genus *Comanthina*, found in the Philippines, is sessile.

The fossil record also indicates that the early adult forms of the early echinoderms were probably sessile, not free-living as most modern forms are. Scientists infer that radial symmetry evolved as an adaptation to this sessile existence. Conditions may have later favored free-living species, yet most modern echinoderms have retained radial symmetry. Taxonomists have divided the 6,000 species of echinoderms into five classes: Crinoidea *(kruh-NOID-ee-uh)*, Asteroidea *(uh-STIR-OID-ee-uh)*, Ophiuroidea *(AHF-ee-yur-OID-ee-uh)*, Echinoidea *(ECK-uh-NOID-ee-uh)*, and Holothuroidea *(HAHL-oe-thur-OID-ee-uh)*.

Crinoidea

The Class Crinoidea ("lilylike"), which includes sea lilies and feather stars, most closely resembles the fossils of Cambrian echinoderms. Crinoids are sessile. They have a long stalk that is attached to rocks or to the sea bottom. Feather stars eventually become detached. Unlike that of other echinoderm species, the mouth of crinoids does not face the sea bottom. The five arms that extend from the body branch out to form many more arms—up to 200 in some feather star species. Sticky tube feet located at the end of each arm capture food and serve as a respiratory surface.

Biology in Process

Parthenogenesis in the Eggs of Sea Urchins

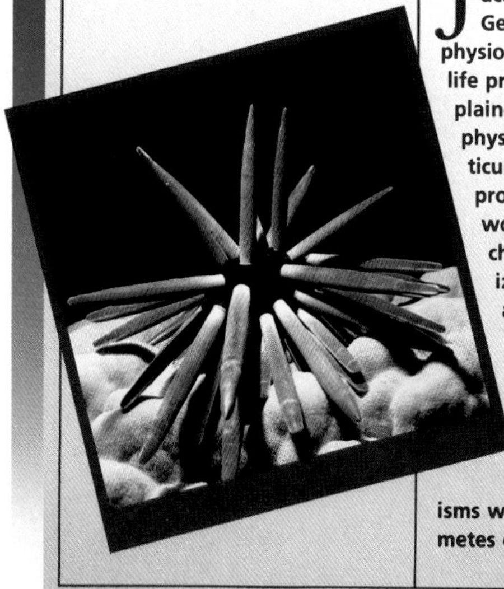

Jacques Loeb (1859–1924), a German-born American physiologist, believed that all life processes could be explained in chemical and physical terms. Loeb was particularly interested in the process of fertilization. He wondered what chemical changes caused a fertilized egg to develop into an embryo.

Loeb knew that brief exposure to sea water could make unfertilized sea urchin eggs begin to divide. Reproduction of organisms without the fusion of gametes of opposite sexes is called parthenogenesis. Loeb hypothesized that the chemical process in parthenogenesis was similar to fertilization by sperm.

To support his hypothesis, Loeb attempted to induce parthenogenesis in the laboratory. He believed that some chemical found in sea water caused parthenogenesis to occur in nature. To test this concept, he placed unfertilized sea urchin eggs into various magnesium solutions for about two hours. He then returned them to ordinary sea water. As he predicted, one of the samples that had been exposed to magnesium began to divide.

LEP Activity

Help students understand the difference between exoskeletons and endoskeletons by providing visual and tactile examples. First, show students skeletal remains of a lobster and small mammal. Ask why one looks like the living animal and the other does not. *(The lobster's skeleton is on the outside and thus even after its soft body parts have decayed, the animal's exterior looks like that of a living animal.)* Explain that the prefix *endo-* means "inside" and the prefix *exo-* means "outside." Then show pictures of various animals, including worms, insects, echinoderms, reptiles, birds, and mammals. For each picture, ask whether the organism has an exoskeleton, an endoskeleton, or no skeleton at all.

Asteroidea

The sea stars, or starfish, belong to the Class Asteroidea ("starlike"). They live all over the world in coastal waters and along rocky shores. They are economically important because they prey on oysters, clams, and other organisms used as food by people. The biology of sea stars is discussed in detail in Section 34.2.

Ophiuroidea

The 2,000 species of basket stars and brittle stars belong to the Class Ophiuroidea ("snakelike"), the largest echinoderm class. Basket stars and brittle stars live primarily on the sea bottom, often beneath stones or in the crevices and holes of coral reefs.

Ophiuroids are distinguished by their long, narrow arms, which allow them to move very quickly. The thin, flexible arms of basket stars resemble a tangle of snakes. Brittle stars, so named because parts of their arms break off readily, can regenerate missing parts. Ophiuroids feed by raking in food with their arms; by gathering food from the ocean bottom with their tube feet; or by trapping suspended particles with their tube feet or with the aid of mucous strands found between their spines.

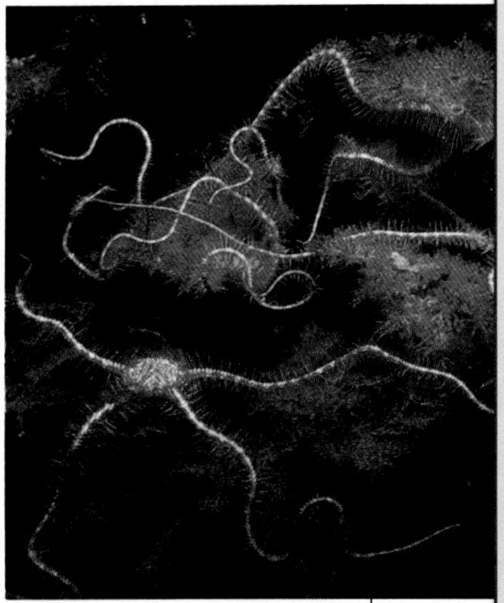

Figure 34-3 Brittle stars, *Ophiuroidea* sp., such as these from the Pacific Ocean, can feed by raking in food with their long, narrow arms.

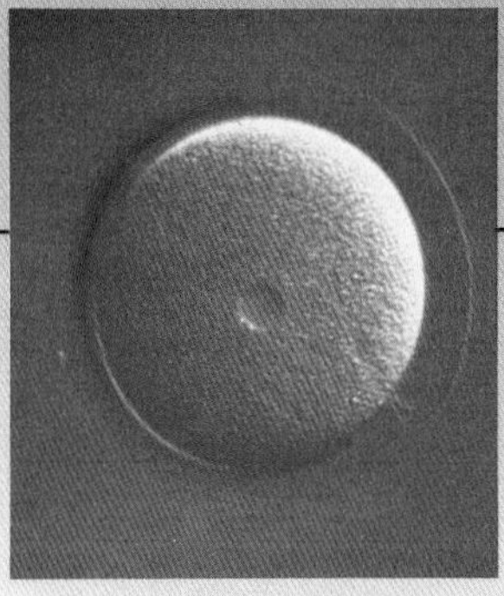

In his next experiments Loeb kept the amount of magnesium in the solution constant and varied the length of time that the eggs were kept in solution. He found that exposures of 100 to 135 minutes gave the best results. However, none of the embryos exposed survived for more than two days. Next he held the exposure time constant and varied the amount of magnesium. He eventually produced virtually normal larvae.

However, was it really magnesium that caused parthenogenesis? Perhaps some other factor was involved. In other experiments Loeb found that other chemicals, such as sodium, potassium, calcium, and even sugar, induced parthenogenesis. So it wasn't the magnesium after all. Loeb determined that parthenogenesis began when the eggs lost a certain amount of water by osmosis. The concentration of the chemical in the solution was the important factor, not the chemical itself.

Loeb then conducted similar experiments with other echinoderms, as well as with chordates. He eventually succeeded in raising frogs to sexual maturity from unfertilized eggs.

Loeb's work paved the way for other scientists to study parthenogenesis. It was later discovered that changes in the egg cell cytoplasm could be caused by many stimuli, including temperature and ultraviolet light. Such changes can induce parthenogenesis.

■ Suggest an experimental procedure Loeb might have used to ensure that cell division was not the result of fertilization by sperm present in the sea water.

Cooperative Learning

Comparing Invertebrates Ask pairs of students to construct a large, poster-sized table to compare various invertebrates they have studied in Unit 7. Row headings of the table could contain representative phyla: *Porifera, Cnidaria, Platyhelminthes, Rotifera, Nematoda, Mollusca, Annelida, Arthropoda,* and *Echinodermata.* Other column headings could include *Representative Organisms, Body Structure, Locomotion, Digestion,* and *Reproduction.* Urge students to include illustrations and as much information as they can. Allow variation in the format of each group's table. Display the tables in the classroom.

Guided Practice

Have students organize a table that includes representative organisms and general characteristics of the five echinoderm classes. Guide them in choosing the most important information to be included. An example of a completed table is shown on p. 511.
■ *See* Process Skills, *Chapter 34.*

Biology in Process

Using the Feature

Ask students to identify the process skills Loeb employed in his investigation. *(He began with a general hypothesis, that all life processes can be explained in chemical and physical terms. He formed a specific hypothesis about egg development based on his general hypothesis, then designed experiments to test this hypothesis.)* Point out to students that Loeb's general hypothesis was not as accepted an idea among scientists a century ago as it is today.

Ask students why sea urchin eggs were a good choice for Loeb's experiments. *(He had observed that exposure to sea water could make unfertilized sea urchin eggs begin to divide.)* Ask them why Loeb was convinced that his final conclusion was valid. *(He had investigated a variety of possibilities by changing the independent variables—amount of solute, nature of solute, length of exposure time.)*

Answer to the Feature

One way in which Loeb could have ensured that cell division was not the result of fertilization would have been to heat sea water to a temperature high enough to kill any sperm present. Then, after the sea water had cooled, he could have introduced unfertilized eggs into this controlled environment.

Section 34.1

Independent Practice

■ Have students write answers to the Section Review.

■ Ask students to compare two classes of echinoderms according to characteristics described in the text.

Check Your Understanding

1. For what functions do echinoderms use their tube feet? *(Movement, feeding, respiration, and excretion)*

2. What is the major difference between echinoderm larvae and adults? (*The larvae have bilateral symmetry, while the adults have pentaradial symmetry.)*

Reteaching

Ask students to make a concept map that describes characteristics of echinoderms. An example of a completed map is shown on p. 509B.

■ *See* Section Reviews *worksheet, Section 34.1.*

Enrichment

Have students use invertebrate zoology texts to research and prepare an illustrated report on development of echinoderms from free-swimming, bilateral larvae to bottom-dwelling, radially symmetrical adults.

Closure

Show photographs of various echinoderms in their natural settings and have students evaluate how specific echinoderm characteristics help these organisms be successful. For example, show a crinoid attached to the sea bottom. *(The sticky tube feet on the multiple-branched arms are an adaptation for this sessile organism to obtain food.)*

Videodiscs

■ ***Side 4 22818, Brittle Star: Larval; Adult (m)***

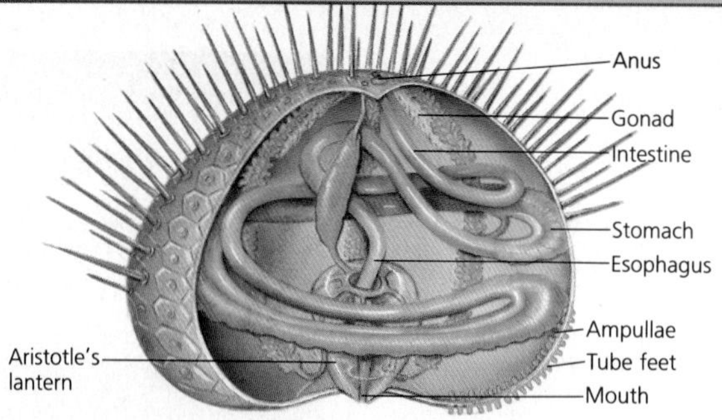

Figure 34-4 Note the spines, tube feet, and rigid endoskeleton of the sea urchin as diagrammed (left) and in the photo (right).

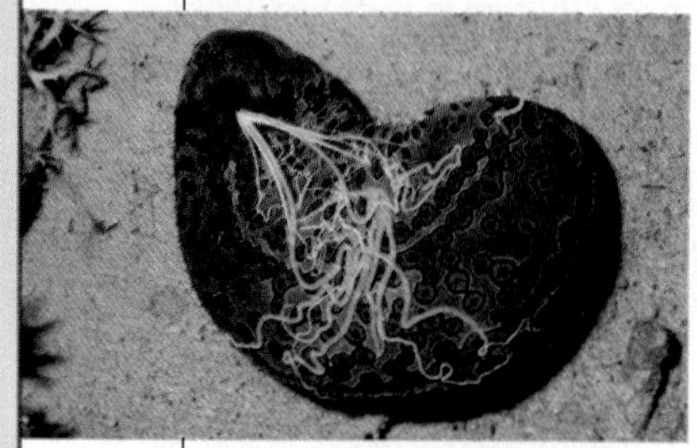

Figure 34-5 This sea cucumber, *Psolus chitonoides*, has ejected its intestines in self-defense.

Echinoidea

About 900 species of sea urchins and sand dollars belong to the Class Echinoidea ("hedgehoglike"). As you can see in Figure 34-4, the internal organs are enclosed within a compact, rigid endoskeleton called a **test.** Most species of echinoids grind their food with a complex jawlike mechanism called **Aristotle's lantern.**

The spherical sea urchins are well adapted to life on hard sea bottoms. These echinoids use their tube feet for locomotion and feed by scraping algae from hard surfaces with teethlike structures that are part of Aristotle's lantern. They have barbs on their long spines and in some species venom that protects sea urchins from predators.

Sand dollars live along seacoasts. As their name implies, they live in sandy areas and have the flat, round shape of a silver dollar, which is an adaptation for shallow burrowing. The short spines of the sand dollar aid in locomotion and burrowing and help clean the surface of the body. Sand dollars use their tube feet to move and to filter food out of the water.

Holothuroidea

The armless sea cucumbers belong to the Class Holothuroidea. Most reside on the sea bottom. Because they do not have a large endoskeleton, their bodies are soft. Tube feet are present on their aboral side. A fringe of tentacles, actually modified tube feet, surrounds the mouth and sweeps up sediment and water. Sea cucumbers then stuff their tentacles into their mouths and clean the food off them.

When threatened, many sea cucumbers eject their internal organs through the anus, a defense mechanism called **evisceration.** They later regenerate their lost parts.

Section Review

1. What is *pentaradial symmetry?*
2. What is the evolutionary significance of echinoderms?
3. How do crinoids differ from other echinoderm classes?
4. Contrast the ways in which sea urchins and sand dollars are adapted to their environment.
5. What characteristics might have enhanced the evolutionary success of the ophiuroids?

Answers to Section Review

1. Five radii or a multiple of five extending from a central body

2. Evidence indicates that echinoderms share a common ancestor with chordates.

3. Crinoids are sessile and the only species in which the mouth does not face the sea bottom.

4. Sea urchins use their tube feet to move and the Aristotle's lantern to scrape food from the sea bottom. The flat, round shape and short spines of sand dollars are adaptations for burrowing in sand.

5. Their great mobility and their ability to obtain food in a variety of ways

34.2 Structure and Function

This discussion of anatomy and behavior will focus on the sea star as a representative echinoderm. The anatomy and behavior of sea stars illustrates the relationship between structure and function in many echinoderms. Also note that the structure and movement of echinoderms is unique among invertebrates.

Body Plan

The sea star's mouth is located on the underside of the body, called the **oral surface.** The top of the body is called the **aboral surface.** While some invertebrates have an external skeleton, a sea star, like all echinoderms, has an endoskeleton—a skeleton found within the body. The sharp, protective spines on the aboral surface form from calcium plates called **ossicles,** which are covered with a thin epidermal layer of cells. Groups of **pedicellariae** surround the spines. Pedicellariae, which resemble tiny forceps, help protect and clean the surface of the body.

Water-Vascular System

While most invertebrates swim, wiggle, or use appendages for movement, sea stars use a water-vascular system. This is a network of canals in which muscle contractions create hydrostatic pressure, which in turn permits movement. Water enters the **sieve plate,** a small opening on the aboral surface. It passes through the madreporite and down the **stone canal.** Use Figure 34-6 to trace the path of water from the **ring canal** encircling the mouth to the five **radial canals** that extend into each arm.

The radial canals carry water to hundreds of paired, hollow tube feet. The upper end of each foot connects to a bulblike sac called an **ampulla.** Muscles in the tube feet contract, forcing water into the ampullae and creating suction, which causes suckers at the tip of the feet to grip the surface. When the ampullae contract, water enters the feet, releasing the suction and causing the feet to

Section Objectives

- *Describe the general body plan of the sea star.*
- *Explain how the water-vascular system aids in movement and feeding.*
- *Describe sexual and asexual reproduction in the sea star.*

Figure 34-6 Trace the path of water in the water-vascular system of the sea star.

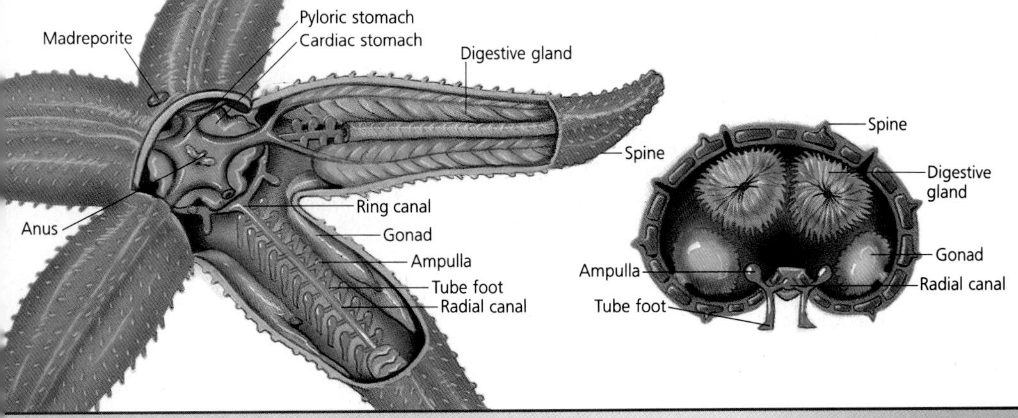

Water-Vascular System

water enters sieve plate → water passes through canal network → water reaches tube feet → muscle contractions create hydrostatic pressure → movement is permitted

Graphic Organizer Use this sequential diagram in Guided Practice on p. 516.

Lesson Plan

Section Focus

This section focuses on the structure and function of a representative echinoderm—the sea star. Students will learn about its body plan, its water-vascular system, and the ways in which it lives and reproduces.

Section Themes

This section emphasizes the theme of **Scale and Structure** by describing how various structures are related to their functions. For example, the sea star uses its tube feet to move and grasp prey.

Motivating Activity

Show students a photograph of a sea star and remind them that it is also called a starfish. How does this name illustrate some problems biologists face? *(First, different names cause confusion in communication. Second, the word* fish *suggests a close evolutionary tie to the vertebrate fish, but no such relationship exists.)* How can these problems be avoided? *(By using scientific names)*

■ *See* Laboratories, *Investigation 34.*

Teaching Strategies

Interpreting the Visuals Ask students to explain how the cross section (on the right) in Figure 34-6, p. 515, relates to the drawing of the sea star's aboral surface. *(The cross section shows the interior of an arm and the detailed structure of tube feet.)*

■ *See* Overhead Transparency *T34 and* Blackline Master *70.*

Videodiscs

■ *1229–1233, Asteroidea: Sea Stars (s)*
■ *1739–1758, Starfish Development (s)*
■ *1759–1785, Sea Urchin Development (s)*

Section 34.2

Guided Practice
Help students create a sequential diagram that shows how the sea star's water-vascular system aids in movement. A sample diagram appears on p. 515.

Independent Practice
■ Have students write answers to the Section Review.
■ Direct students to write a script for a nature film describing a sea star attacking and eating a clam.

Answer to Think
There is a good chance that some eggs will be fertilized even if predators eat many eggs and others are washed away unfertilized.

Check Your Understanding
1. What is unusual about the sea star's digestive system? *(The sea star can extrude its stomach through its mouth, then insert it into a partly opened bivalve.)*
2. How does suction develop at the tip of tube feet? *(Muscle contractions in the tube feet act on the water-vascular system.)*

Reteaching
Ask students to compare the diagram of a sea star in Figure 34-6, p. 515, with that of a sea urchin in Figure 34-4, p. 514. Have them identify similar structures and compare the body plans of the two organisms.
■ *See* Section Reviews *worksheet, Section 34.2.*

Enrichment
Have students research and report on the impact of sea stars on shellfish beds and the economic effects on the seafood industry. Suggest that students use nature and popular science magazines.

Closure
Point out that sea stars are slow-moving organisms that are often easy to see. Ask students to suggest what characteristics help sea stars survive against predators.

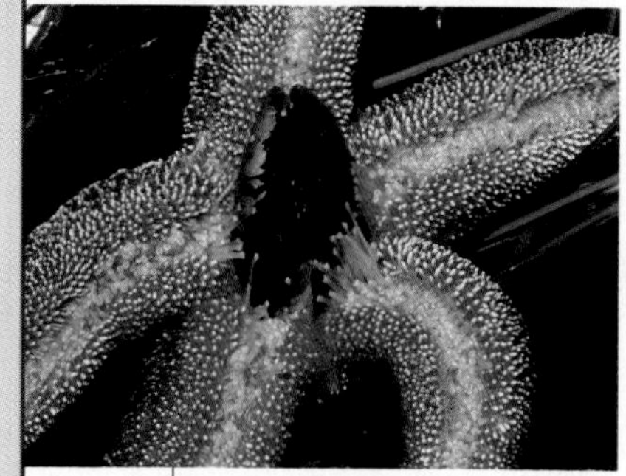

Figure 34-7 This ochre sea star is feeding on a California mussel along the Pacific coast.

Think
Why is it an adaptive advantage for aquatic, externally fertilizing organisms to produce millions of eggs?

extend. These coordinated muscle contractions enable the sea star to climb slippery rocks or to capture prey.

Feeding and Digestion
Sea stars use their tube feet to obtain food—usually mollusks, worms, and other slow-moving animals. The sea star attaches the suckers of its tube feet to both halves of a clamshell and pulls until the shell opens a crack. The sea star then turns its stomach inside out through its mouth and inserts its stomach into the clam.

Enzymes secreted by the sea star's stomach digest the clam's soft parts while they are still in the shell. The sea star then withdraws the stomach, containing the partially digested food, back into its body, where the digestive process is completed.

Other Body Systems
The sea star has no circulatory, excretory, or respiratory systems. Fluid in the coelom bathes the organs and distributes nutrients and oxygen. Gas exchange and waste excretion take place by diffusion through the thin walls of the tube feet and through the **skin gills,** hollow tubes that project from the coelom lining.

The sea star has no head or brain. A **nerve ring** surrounds the mouth and branches off into nerve cords that extend into each arm. Each arm has an eyespot that responds to light and a tentacle that responds to touch. The tube feet also respond to touch.

Reproduction
Each arm of the sea star has two gonads, which produce eggs in females and sperm in males. Fertilization occurs externally. Females produce up to 200 million eggs in one season. Each fertilized egg develops into a bilaterally symmetrical, free-swimming larva called a **bipinnaria.** After about two months the larva settles to the bottom, and metamorphosis begins. During metamorphosis the sea star develops into a pentaradially symmetrical adult.

Sea stars can also reproduce asexually by regenerating lost parts. In fact, a completely new sea star may grow from a segment of an arm as long as part of the central disk is still attached.

Section Review
1. Distinguish between the *oral surface* and the *aboral surface.*
2. Trace the path of water through the water-vascular system.
3. Describe the way a sea star grips and digests a clam.
4. How are gas exchange, distribution of nutrients, and excretion of wastes accomplished in the sea star?
5. Was the former practice of breaking the arms off of sea stars to prevent them from feeding on clams and oysters a good idea?

Answers to Section Review
1. The oral surface is the side where the mouth is; the aboral surface is the opposite side. In sea stars the oral surface faces the sea bottom.
2. Water enters through the sieve plate and then goes through the stone canal, ring canal, radial canals, and tube feet.
3. After opening the shell with its tube feet, the sea star inserts its stomach into the shell, partially digests the clam and then withdraws the stomach and completes digestion in its body.
4. Fluid in the coelom distributes oxygen and nutrients. Excretion and gas exchange take place by diffusion through the tube feet and skin gills.
5. No, because a segment of an arm could regenerate into a new sea star

Laboratory

Comparing Echinoderms

Objective
To compare characteristics of echinoderms

Process Skills
Observing, analyzing data

Materials
Preserved sea star, brittle star, and sea urchin; dissecting pan; dissecting microscope; forceps; sea urchin test

Background

1. List the major characteristics of echinoderms.
2. How does a sea star eat and move?

Inquiry

1. Create a data table in which to record the features you observe in a sea star, brittle star, and sea urchin. Begin with the sea star and then repeat steps 2–9 for the brittle star and the sea urchin. Which feature gives them the name *echinoderm*?
2. Place the first specimen, aboral surface up, in the dissecting pan. Observe and record the specimen's overall appearance.
3. What type of symmetry does the specimen have? Compare your specimen with those of your neighbors. What might account for any differences you observe?
4. Examine the specimen's spines. Describe any pattern you see. Observe one spine under a dissecting microscope. What size, color, and shape is the spine? Is it covered by tissue or exposed? Is it movable or fixed?
5. Are pedicellariae present? What is their location and arrangement? Draw one as it appears under a dissecting microscope.
6. Use the dissecting microscope to look for small skin gills. If any are present, describe their location and structure. How is their structure well suited for gas exchange?
7. Does the specimen have a madreporite, or sieve plate? If so, examine it under the dissecting microscope. Record its location and appearance.
8. Now examine the specimen's oral surface. Find and describe the mouth and its location. Use forceps to gently move aside any soft tissues. What structures are found in or around the mouth?
9. Locate the tube feet. Describe their distribution. How might the structure of the endoskeleton reflect the distribution of tube feet? Using the dissecting microscope, observe and then draw a single tube foot.
10. After perfoming steps 2–9 for all three echinoderms, compare the preserved sea urchin with the sea urchin test. Find the rows of little pores on the test. What might be the pores' function? What might be the function of the small tubercles, or bumps?

Conclusions

1. Review your data table. What four features are common to the three echinoderms you observed?
2. What is a characteristic unique to the sea star? to the brittle star? to the sea urchin?

Further Inquiry
Observe how living sea stars move in a saltwater aquarium. Add some live mussels and observe their feeding behavior.

Laboratory

(For an overview of echinoderms and preparatory information related to the laboratory, see p. 509B.)

Background

1. See list in student text, p. 511.
2. Pries open clams, etc. with its tube feet; extrudes stomach to begin digestion; muscles, water-vascular system, and tube feet permit movement.

Inquiry

1. The specimens' spiny skin
2. Student should describe color, texture, shape, number of arms.
3. Pentaradial. Sea urchin's symmetry is best observed on the test. Missing arms due to injury may affect sea star and brittle star symmetry. Also, differences may be genetic.
4. Several sizes of spines may appear on one specimen. Sea star and brittle star: usually in irregular rows, running the length of the arms; typically short and fixed. Sea urchin: in vertical rows; long and movable.
5. In sea star and sea urchin: scattered among spines; in brittle stars: none
6. Present in sea star, not in brittle star. Gills ring sea urchin's mouth; thin structure and large surface area facilitate gas exchange.
7. Small opening present on the aboral surface of sea star and sea urchin, oral surface of brittle star
8. Mouth in center of oral surface of all three. Sea star's mouth: five pairs of movable spines. Sea urchin's: five teeth connected to plates and muscles. Brittle star jaws: five movable plates.
9. Sea star: rows of sucker-tipped tube feet project from groove on oral surface of each ray. Brittle star: suckerless, tentaclelike tube feet on oral surface. Sea urchin: sucker-tipped tube feet in paired, vertical rows on both surfaces
10. Tube feet protrude through pores. Spines attach at tubercles.

Conclusions

1. Data table: column heads—*Sea Star, Brittle Star,* and *Sea Urchin;* row heads—*General Appearance, Symmetry, Spines, Pedicellariae, Skin Gills, Sieve Plate, Mouth,* and *Tube Feet.* Radial symmetry, spines, sieve plate, and tube feet are four common features.
2. Sea star: groove on its oral surface from which tube feet protrude. Brittle star: arms sharply marked off from central disk; tube feet lack suckers. Sea urchin: globular shape; no arms; movable spines

Further Inquiry

The action of tube feet is very dramatic in living echinoderms. See the *Laboratories* ancillary for directions on setting up a saltwater aquarium.

Vocabulary

1. Evisceration is the defense mechanism employed when a threatened sea cucumber ejects its internal organs through the anus, later regenerating lost parts.
2. The endoskeleton of echinoids is called a test.
3. Pedicellariae are small structures resembling forceps that surround the spines and help protect and clean the sea star's body.
4. Major structures include the sieve plate, stone canal, ring canal, radial canals, tube feet, and ampullae.
5. The bipinnaria is the larval stage of an echinoderm. It is free-living and bilaterally symmetrical.

Review

1. a	**6.** b
2. d	**7.** d
3. c	**8.** b
4. a	**9.** a
5. c	**10.** d

11. Scientists infer that early echinoderms were bilaterally symmetrical because modern echinoderm larvae are bilaterally symmetrical.
12. Echinoderms inhabit marine environments ranging from shallow, coastal waters to deep ocean trenches.
13. The short spines of a sand dollar aid in locomotion and burrowing and help clean the body surface.
14. Sea stars are of particular interest because they prey on some food sources used by humans, such as clams and oysters.
15. The Class Crinoidea is most similar to early echinoderms.
16. A sea cucumber gathers up food with its tentacles, stuffs the tentacles into its mouth, and then cleans off the food.
17. The sea star turns its stomach inside out through its mouth, surrounds the food, and partially digests it. Then it withdraws the stomach and partially digested food into its body, where digestion is completed.
18. Water enters the sea star's body through the sieve plate, a small opening on the aboral surface.
19. According to Loeb's research, embryo development begins when an increase in osmotic pressure causes a loss of water in an egg.
20. During metamorphosis the sea star changes from a bilaterally symmetrical larva into a pentaradially symmetrical adult.

Chapter 34 Review

Vocabulary

aboral surface (515)
ampulla (515)
Aristotle's lantern (514)
bipinnaria (516)
endoskeleton (511)
evisceration (514)
nerve ring (516)
oral surface (515)
ossicle (515)
pedicellaria (515)
pentaradial symmetry (511)
radial canal (515)
ring canal (515)
sieve plate (515)
skin gill (516)
stone canal (515)
test (514)
tube foot (511)
water-vascular system (511)

1. Describe the process of evisceration in the sea cucumber.
2. What term is used for the endoskeleton in echinoids?
3. What are pedicellariae?
4. List the major structures in the water-vascular system.
5. What is a bipinnaria, and what are its major characteristics?

Review

1. Scientists believe that the earliest adult echinoderms were (a) sessile and bilaterally symmetrical (b) free-living and bilaterally symmetrical (c) sessile and radially symmetrical (d) free-living and radially symmetrical.
2. Echinoderms lack all of the following organ systems except (a) a respiratory system (b) an excretory system (c) a circulatory system (d) a digestive system.
3. The echinoderm class that exhibits evisceration is (a) Class Ophiuroidea (b) Class Crinoidea (c) Class Holothuroidea (d) Class Echinoidea.
4. Crinoids superficially resemble (a) lilies (b) silver dollars (c) hedgehogs (d) cucumbers.
5. Aristotle's lantern is a jawlike structure that is characteristic of (a) ophiuroids (b) asteroids (c) echinoids (d) holothuroids.
6. The endoskeleton of the sea star is composed of calcium plates referred to as (a) tests (b) ossicles (c) ampullae (d) sieve plates.
7. The number of eggs that a female sea star can produce in any given season is (a) 20,000 (b) 200,000 (c) 2 million (d) 200 million.
8. Gas exchange and excretion of wastes take place by diffusion through the walls of the (a) ampullae (b) skin gills (c) radial canals (d) test.
9. When the ampullae of the sea star fill with water, the tube feet (a) attach to a surface (b) extend outward (c) fill with water (d) grasp food.
10. Sea stars detect light with (a) the nerve ring (b) tentacles on each arm (c) the tube feet (d) an eyespot on each arm.
11. What evidence has led scientists to believe that early echinoderms exhibited bilateral symmetry?
12. In what type of environment are echinoderms found?
13. What function do the short spines of the sand dollar serve?
14. Why are sea stars of particular interest to humans?
15. Which modern echinoderm class is inferred to be the most similar to the early echinoderms?
16. How does the sea cucumber transport food to its mouth?
17. Summarize the process of digestion in the sea star.
18. Where does water enter the sea star's body?

19. According to Jacques Loeb's research, what critical factor induces parthenogenesis in sea urchin eggs?

20. What happens during the metamorphosis of a sea star?

Critical Thinking

1. Sea cucumbers and sea lilies are relatively sessile animals. However, the larvae of these species are free-swimming. What advantage does a free-swimming larva provide these echinoderms?
2. For many years oyster farmers, who raise oysters for both food and pearls, have been plagued with starfish that invade their oyster beds and kill their oysters. Many oyster farmers have lost their entire crop and have gone out of business. Devise a way for the farmers to rid themselves of the starfish without killing their oysters.
3. Scientists have found many echinoderm fossils from the Cambrian period. However, they have found few fossils of other species that lived during the Cambrian period. What might explain the large number of fossilized starfish, sea urchins, and other echinoderms?

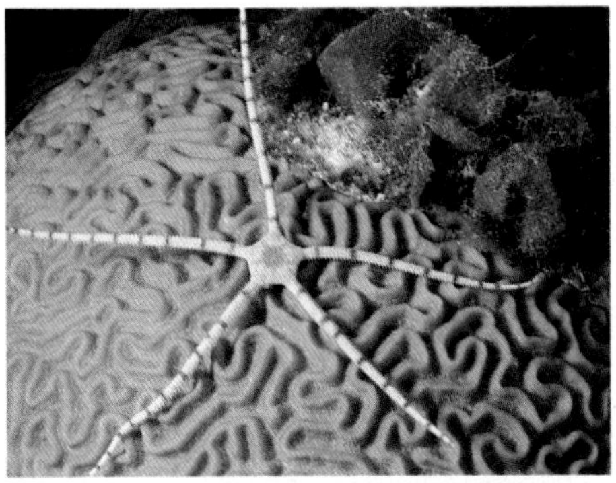

4. Look at this photograph of a brittle star *(Ophiothrix purpurea)* on a coral. Look carefully at the small spines sticking out from its body. Considering that these brittle stars live most of their lives on coral, name two advantages that these spines would provide.

Extension

1. Visit your nearest aquarium or a pet store that carries saltwater fish. Observe living starfish and note their special form of movement and their different colors and shapes.
2. Read the article by S. Hart entitled "Crown-of-Thorns No Johnny-Come-Lately" in *Science News,* August 26, 1989, p. 133. What are the implications of Jull's findings and assertions in terms of the evolution of the Great Barrier Reef ecosystem? What could be proposed as a natural cause of *A. planci* surges?
3. Research this question: Why do basket stars only open at night, and what do they use to protect themselves during the day?
4. Read the article by Glen Martin entitled "Otter Madness" in *Discover,* July 1990, pp. 36–39. Prepare an oral report in which you discuss some environmental consequences of otters' predation on sea urchins in California.
5. Research and write a short paper on the different forms of evisceration among sea cucumbers. Tell how the sea cucumber uses evisceration to escape predators.
6. Research and write a short paper on a species of echinoderms that is not discussed in the preceding chapter. Focus on the particular adaptations that your chosen species shows that enable it to survive in its environment.

Chapter 34 Review

Critical Thinking

1. The free-swimming larva allows sea cucumber and sea lily populations to spread out over large areas of the ocean floor. If the larvae were sessile, all the offspring would be clumped together; the food supply would decrease due to overpopulation, and all the larvae would be easy prey for predators.
2. Students might suggest introducing a natural enemy of the sea star or using a poison that would kill the sea star but not hurt the oyster.
3. Many fossilized echinoderms exist because their hard endoskeletons fossilize easily.
4. The small spines keep space between the hard coral surface and the skin of the brittle star. They also provide protection against predators.

Extension

1. You may want to arrange a field trip to an aquarium so that students can observe sea stars as well as other echinoderms.
2. Jull's findings suggest that surges of the crown-of-thorns sea star may be part of natural periodic fluctuations in the Great Barrier Reef ecosystem that go back 8,000 years. Suggest that students find some other articles with different explanations for the sea star's devastation of live coral.
3. In an adaptation for protection, basket stars curl up their arms, exposing an armored surface during the day. At night they spread their branching arms to filter food particles from the water.
4. Without otters, sea urchins devour kelp beds. With otters' predation of the urchins, kelp beds flourish—as do many species that live in the kelp.
5. Encourage students to use a variety of library resources.
6. Let students share their findings with the class.

Chapter 35 Evolutionary Trends in Invertebrates

Chapter Overview

Chapter 35 discusses the evolutionary trend in invertebrates toward increasing complexity. Section 35.1 examines embryonic and larval development as well as similarities and differences in morphology among invertebrate phyla. Section 35.2 focuses on the increasingly complex internal anatomy in invertebrate phylogeny.

Chapter Planning Chart

B	S	A	Sections and Subsections	Page	Features	Page	Resources
		•	**35.1 Diversity and Phylogeny**				
			Origin	521	Section Review	525	Videodiscs
			Development	521			Blackline Master 71
			Morphology	524			Blackline Master 72
			Phylogeny	524			Blackline Master 73
							Overhead Transparency T35
							Section Reviews Worksheet
		•	**35.2 Internal Anatomy**				
			Digestive Systems	526	Laboratory	529	Videodiscs
			Respiratory Systems	526	Section Review	528	Laboratories: Comparing Invertebrates
			Circulatory Systems	527			Process Skills: Invertebrate Eyes
			Nervous Systems	528			Section Reviews Worksheet
			Excretory Systems	528			
			End of Chapter Activities				
					Chapter Review	530	Vocabulary Skills
							Chapter Test
							Computer Test Generator

B *The Basic Level curriculum presents the most fundamental knowledge offered in the course.*
S *The Standard Level curriculum is designed for the average student who is able to master most topics.*
A *The Advanced Level curriculum includes suggestions for teaching the most academically able students.*

Cooperative Learning

Group Activity: Invertebrate Body Systems

- **Group Size:** *6 students*
- **Outcome:** *Students will compare the complexity of invertebrate body systems.*
- **Individual Accountability:** *Each group member will study one body system and report to the group.*
- **Positive Interdependence:** *Group members will construct one table summarizing their findings.*

Divide the class into groups of six, and instruct each group member to select a different body system to research, including digestive, respiratory, circulatory, nervous, excretory, and reproductive systems. Then have all students who are researching the same body system work together to find information about this system in each of the nine invertebrate phyla covered in Unit 7. Students may want to divide this task so that one student is responsible for researching the body system in one or two phyla. Then students can share their findings. Instruct students to prepare a comparative description and drawing of the system for a representative of each phylum.

After summarizing their information, students should return to their groups and teach one another about different body systems. Group members should discuss advantages of each type of system and record these advantages in a table.

Concept Map

The following is one possible solution to the concept mapping activity in Independent Practice on p. 527.

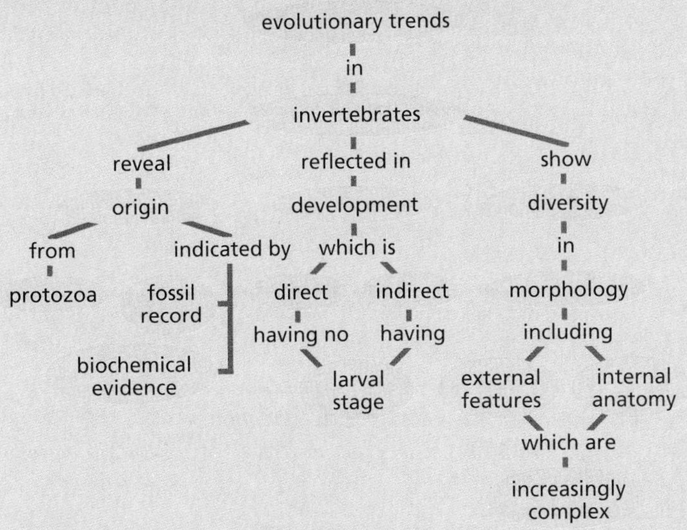

Laboratory Preparation

Overview *(See p. 529.)*

In this lab exercise, students review basic characteristics of invertebrates. Many features used to distinguish among major groups involve characteristics that are difficult to see in adult organisms, for example, whether an animal is a protostome or a deuterostome. However, many external characteristics, such as body symmetry, segmentation, and support, can give clues about the animal's classification. Often the defining characteristic of a phylum, such as spiny skin, is an observable, external characteristic.

Preparation

Live or preserved specimens of the organisms in this lab are available from a biological supply house. If you use live specimens, be certain to have a saltwater aquarium for them.

Teaching Tips

Instruct students to make a data chart in which they record observations. Suggest that students make sketches as they record observations.

After students have made their genus identifications in Conclusions, post the answer key so that they can check their classifications.

As an extension, have students make a dichotomous key for the phyla observed in the lab.

Safety

If any live organisms are used, remind students to handle them in a humane manner. Make sure that students wash their hands after handling specimens.

Chapter 35

Chapter Themes

Evolution Throughout this chapter, emphasize not only the diversity of invertebrates, but also their similarities. Be sure that students realize that scientists compare both internal and external anatomy, patterns of development in embryos and larvae, biochemistry, and fossil remains to determine evolutionary relationships.

Patterns of Change Help students see similarities in development among invertebrate phyla. Make sure that they understand concepts associated with embryo and larva development.

Scale and Structure Emphasize the increasing complexity of internal body systems. Point out adaptive advantages of complex internal systems, as well as those of the less complex systems for simple invertebrates.

Chapter Motivating Activity

Display live or preserved specimens or pictures of various invertebrates. Also display fossils of various invertebrates, or pictures of them. Have students examine modern invertebrates and fossils and then match them. *(They will probably match shelled fossils with mollusks and those with exoskeletons with arthropods, and so on.)* Ask what modern invertebrates seem to be missing from the fossil record. *(Soft-bodied invertebrates)* What kinds of structures were generally fossilized? *(Hard parts, such as shells and exoskeletons)* Ask students whether the history of invertebrate evolution can be based on the fossil record alone. *(No, the fossil record is incomplete.)* Ask students what other evidence scientists might use for establishing the phylogeny of invertebrates. *(Morphology, embryo and larva development, and biochemistry of modern organisms)*

Chapter 35 *Evolutionary Trends in Invertebrates*

Introduction

Invertebrates exist in all shapes and sizes, from the corals to the spiders. This diversity can make it difficult to understand how they are related. However, evolutionary and morphological studies indicate that the systems of invertebrates became increasingly complex as new invertebrate groups evolved.

Chapter Outline

35.1 Diversity and Phylogeny
- *Origin*
- *Development*
- *Morphology*
- *Phylogeny*

35.2 Internal Anatomy
- *Digestive Systems*
- *Respiratory Systems*
- *Circulatory Systems*
- *Nervous Systems*
- *Excretory Systems*
- *Reproductive Systems*

Chapter Concept

As you read, notice the increasing complexity of the evolutionary adaptations in invertebrates.

Soft coral, *Dendronephthya* sp., island of Truk. Inset (top): Spiny orb weaver spider, *Gasteracantha elipsoides*. Inset (bottom): Flatworm, Palau Islands, Micronesia.

Understanding the Visuals

Ask students to explain what the organisms shown in the photographs have in common. *(All are animals without backbones.)* Have students consider the animals' differences. For example, ask them to name the environment of each animal. *(The spider is terrestrial; the others are aquatic.)* Then ask students to describe how each animal is adapted to its environment. *(The spider has legs adapted to walking on webs; the coral has tentacles that capture food; the flatworm is shaped to move easily through water.)*

35.1 Diversity and Phylogeny

Invertebrates first appeared on earth over 800 million years ago, and by the late Precambrian era numerous invertebrates were common. The fossil record from the beginning of the Cambrian period, 500 million years ago, includes members of all the modern invertebrate phyla as well as of some phyla that are now extinct.

Origin

The first invertebrates probably either arose from or shared a common ancestor with protozoa. Biologists have drawn this inference from the fact that both invertebrates and protozoa are heterotrophic and eukaryotic. As you learned in Chapter 29, metazoans, or multicellular organisms, may have developed from colonies of protozoa that lived together. Scientists do not agree on whether the ancestors of metazoans were flagellated or ciliated protozoa. Biochemical evidence indicates that the proteins of some present-day invertebrates are more similar to those of modern flagellates than to those of modern ciliates. However, the cilia of modern invertebrates and protozoa are identical in size, structure, and movement. Some scientists suggest that at least Porifera, the phylum of sponges, shares a common ancestry with certain kinds of colonial flagellated protozoa.

Development

Although fossil evidence does not conclusively indicate the relationships among the invertebrate phyla, comparative studies in development and anatomy show that there are two types of development common to many invertebrates. One is characteristic of the mollusks, arthropods, and annelids while the other type is characteristic of echinoderms.

Early Embryo Development

Two main types of early embryo development occur in invertebrates. The embryos of the mollusks, arthropods, and annelids undergo **spiral cleavage,** in which the cells divide in a spiral arrangement. As the embryo grows, the blastopore develops into a mouth. These organisms are called **protostomes,** meaning "first mouth." The embryos of echinoderms undergo **radial cleavage,** in which the cell divisions are parallel with or at right angles to the polar axis. In echinoderms the blastopore develops into an anus, and a second opening in the embryo becomes the mouth. These organisms are called **deuterostomes,** meaning "second mouth." Compare these types of development in Figures 35-2 and 35-3 on the following pages. The members of the Phylum Chordata are also deuterostomes. Scientists use this evidence in inferring that echinoderms and chordates share a common ancestor.

Section Objectives

- *Summarize the possible origins of invertebrates.*
- *Describe the embryo and larval development of invertebrates.*
- *Summarize invertebrate symmetry, segmentation, and support.*
- *Analyze the organization of the phylogenetic tree of invertebrates.*

Figure 35-1 The cilia of modern invertebrates are similar to those of protozoa, such as these paramecia (×150).

Lesson Plan

Section Focus

This section describes diversity of invertebrates by comparing patterns of development with morphology. Scientists use these comparisons to make inferences about the evolutionary history of invertebrates.

Section Themes

The underlying theme in this section is **Evolution.** Similarities and differences in growth, development, and morphology between some invertebrates and vertebrates give scientists clues to evolutionary relationships among invertebrates.

The theme of **Patterns of Change** is evident in descriptions of embryo and larva development. Invertebrate morphology, which varies with respect to symmetry, segmentation, and support, also shows trends of increasing complexity.

Motivating Activity

Display live or preserved specimens or pictures of invertebrate larva or immature forms with corresponding adult forms. First, have students compare the morphology of invertebrate larva and immature forms, then adult forms. Ask students to consider the importance of differences between larva and immature forms and adult forms. *(They show adaptations to different environments. It is hypothesized that the larva forms exhibit characteristics of the ancestral species from which current species evolved.)*

Videodiscs

- *2026, Fossil Brachiopod (s)*
- *855, Brachiopoda: Deep-Water, Bottom-Living Forms (s)*

Invertebrate Embryo Development

	Examples	Undergo	Cells Specialize by	Coelum Forms by
Protostomes	mollusks, arthropods, annelids	spiral cleavage	determinate cleavage	schizocoely
Deuterostomes	echinoderms	radial cleavage	indeterminate cleavage	enterocoely

Graphic Organizer Use this table in Guided Practice on p. 524.

Teaching Strategies

Identifying Structures Review with students embryo development and structures of the early embryo described in Section 29.1, pp. 438–439. Ask students to describe what a blastula is. *(An early stage of embryo development in which the embryo is generally spherical and hollow.)* Then ask students to explain what occurs during gastrulation. *(The cells at one pole of the blastula begin moving inward, eventually forming a cup-shaped gastrula.)* Finally, ask them to describe a blastopore. *(The depression formed when cells of the blastula move inward)*

Interpreting the Visuals Refer students to cleavage diagrams in Figure 35-2, p. 522 and diagrams of coelom formation in Figure 35-3, p. 523. Have students compare development of protostomes with that of deuterostomes. *(Protostomes undergo spiral cleavage and schizocoely coelom formation; deuterostomes undergo radial cleavage and enterocoely coelom formation.)*
■ *See* **Blackline Masters** *71 and 72.*

Drawing Conclusions Explain that identical twins occur in humans when the developing embryo splits in half before gastrulation. Ask students to conclude whether humans have determinate or indeterminate cleavage. *(Indeterminate; two complete gastrulas form when an early embryo splits in half.)*

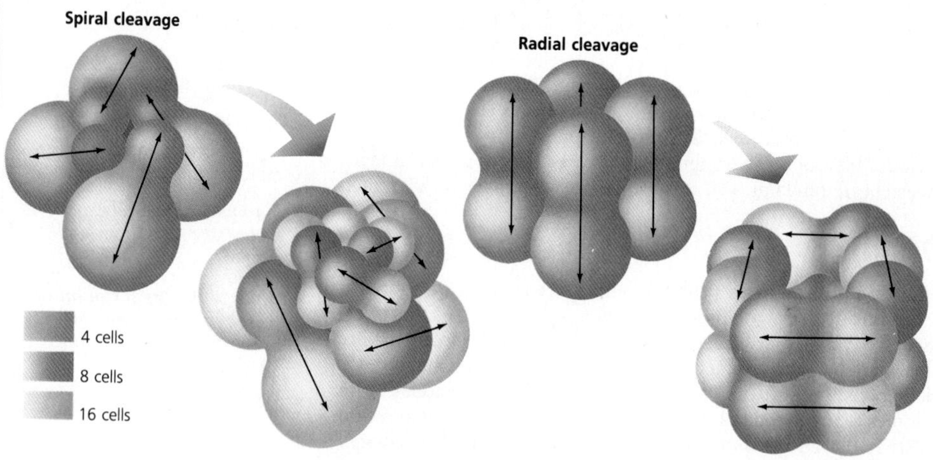

Figure 35-2 Protostomes undergo spiral cleavage during their early embryo development. Deuterostomes undergo radial cleavage during their early embryo development.

Protostomes and deuterostomes also differ in how the cells of the embryo specialize. If the cells of a four-celled protostome embryo are separated, each cell will develop into a quarter of the gastrula. Thus the fate of each cell is determined early in the development of the protostome. This type of specialization is called **determinate cleavage.** In contrast, if the cells of a four-celled deuterostome embryo are separated, each cell will develop into a complete gastrula. This type of development is called **indeterminate cleavage.**

Germ Layers and Coelom Formation

As you learned in Chapter 29, the cells in invertebrate gastrulae are organized into germ layers. Cnidarians have two germ layers, the endoderm and the ectoderm. Platyhelminths were the first invertebrates with a third germ layer, the mesoderm.

The presence of a mesoderm provides a great adaptive advantage to the organism. As well as forming the skeleton, muscles, blood, and blood vessels, the mesoderm forms the lining of the body cavity, called the coelom. The coelom allows movement of the organs within the body and enables the animal to move about more freely. All the organisms with more complex development than that of the platyhelminths have a coelom. During platyhelminth development, although the mesoderm forms various structures, it does not form a coelom.

The way in which the coelom forms in protostomes differs from the way it forms in deuterostomes. In protostomes, cells split off at the junction of the endoderm and ectoderm during gastrulation. Rapid division of these cells forms the mesoderm. This method of mesoderm formation is called **schizocoely,** or "split-body cavity." In deuterostomes, the mesoderm forms when cells

Cooperative Learning

Modeling an Invertebrate Ancestor Have students work in groups of three to make a model, drawing, or diagram of an organism that could have been the ancestor to the first invertebrates. Members of each group should review protozoan morphology, stages in invertebrate life cycles, and invertebrate morphology. After completing their reviews, group members should compile information and look for similarities between protozoans and invertebrates. Ask groups to infer from these similarities the morphology of an invertebrate ancestor. Have groups explain their organism to the class.

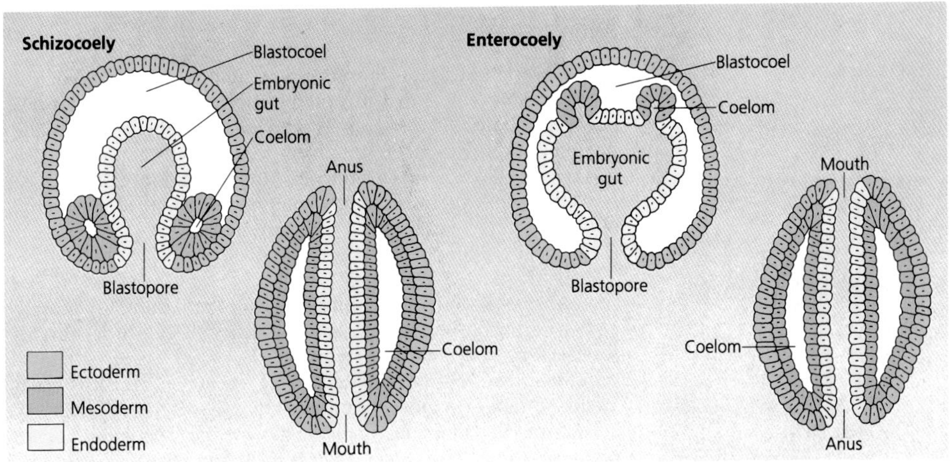

Figure 35-3 The coelom in protostomes arises by schizocoely; the blastopore becomes the mouth. The coelom in deuterostomes arises by enterocoely; the blastopore becomes the anus.

at the top of the gastrula divide. This method of mesoderm formation is called **enterocoely,** meaning "gut-body cavity."

During both enterocoely and schizocoely the coelom becomes a secondary body cavity because the mesodermal cells spread out and the blastocoel disappears. During gastrulation of a roundworm, for instance, the mesoderm lines the body cavity but does not spread out to form a lining on the organs. The body cavity of the roundworm is thus called a pseudocoelom, which means "false-body cavity."

Larva Development

Invertebrates may have indirect or direct development. In **indirect development** the organism has an intermediate larval stage. You learned in Chapter 33 of the adaptive advantages of metamorphosis. In **direct development** the young animal is born or hatched having the same appearance and way of life as the adult; no larval stage occurs. Most invertebrates undergo indirect development, although a few, such as silverfish and grasshoppers, undergo direct development.

An invertebrate that has an aquatic, free-swimming larva often has one of three basic types: planula, trochophore, or bipinnaria. A planula is a free-swimming, ciliated larva with two body layers. Planulae settle to the bottom, where each develops into a colony of polyps. A trochophore is a free-swimming, bilaterally symmetrical larva. The larva of an annelid or a mollusk such as a snail is an example of a trochophore. A bipinnaria is a free-swimming larva that has a distinct pattern of development. The larva of an echinoderm such as a sea star is an example of a bipinnaria. Scientists study the kind of larva an organism has as an aid to classification.

Exploring Careers Invite a university professor familiar with protein analysis to discuss how biochemical evidence is used to propose phylogenetic relationships. Or invite an expert in a particular invertebrate group, such as an entomologist, to explain the basis for classification of these particular invertebrates.

Inferring Relationships Display live or preserved specimens or pictures of an earthworm, hydra, and crayfish. Have students compare symmetry, segmentation, and type of support of the organisms. *(The hydra has radial symmetry and no segmentation; the earthworm and crayfish have bilateral symmetry and segmentation. All have different means of support.)* Ask students to infer which animals are more similar. *(Crayfish and earthworm)* Then ask students to conclude which animals have a closer evolutionary relationship. *(Crayfish and earthworm)*

Interpreting the Visuals Give students copies of Figure 35-5, p. 525. Instruct them to write for each invertebrate phylum the type of (1) embryo and larva development, (2) symmetry, and (3) segmentation.

- *See* **Overhead Transparency** ***T35 and*** **Blackline Master** ***73.***

Videodiscs

- ***2583, Protostome: Schizocoelous (s)***
- ***2584, Deuterostome: Enterocoelous (s)***
- ***Side 4 20156, Snail: Larva and Adult (m)***
- ***Side 4 20892, Octopus: Hatching and Adult (m)***
- ***Side 4 22818, Crab, Brittle Star, and Scallop: Larval and Adult Forms (m)***

More Information

Evolutionary Relationships Although chordates may not appear to have anything in common with invertebrate phyla, echinoderms and hemichordates—a phylum that is composed mainly of marine, wormlike organisms—are closely related to chordates. Members of all three of these phyla are deuterostomes and have coeloms formed by enterocoely. Hemichordates have a larval form almost indistinguishable from echinoderm larvae. In addition, they have gill slits and a dorsal nerve chord like chordates. This evidence suggests that echinoderms, hemichordates, and chordates diverged from a common ancestor.

Section 35.1

Guided Practice

Have students make a table comparing invertebrate embryo development in protostomes and deuterostomes. An example of a completed table is shown on p. 521.

Independent Practice

- Have students write answers to the Section Review.
- Instruct students to choose one invertebrate organism and describe it by type of embryo development and morphology. Have them use the phylogenetic tree in Figure 35-5, p. 525, to determine other invertebrate phyla with which it has a close evolutionary relationship.

Check Your Understanding

1. Why do closely related invertebrates show a large amount of diversity? *(Adaptations of invertebrates to their different environments result in diversity.)*

2. What are the differences between protostomes and deuterostomes? *(Protostome embryos have determinate cleavage and develop spirally; their blastopores develop into the mouth and the coeloms arise by schizocoely. Deuterostome embryos have indeterminate cleavage and develop radially; their blastopores develop into the anus and the coeloms arise by enterocoely.)*

3. What evidence led scientists to infer that annelids, arthropods, and mollusks share a common ancestor? *(All have bilateral symmetry, segmentation, and similar patterns of development.)*

Figure 35-4 Compare segmentation in the polychaete worm (top) and the ghost shrimp, *Callianassa gigas* (bottom). Each unit in the body trunk of the worm is the same, but the segments in the body trunk of the ghost shrimp are fused and specialized.

Morphology

Adult invertebrates show a tremendous amount of morphological diversity, so much so that it is even difficult to see the similarities between a clam and an octopus, which are members of the same phylum. Such diversity results from the different adaptations of invertebrates to their environments. Many variations fall into patterns that indicate invertebrate evolution. As you read, notice the increasing complexity within the patterns.

Symmetry

Invertebrates have radial or bilateral symmetry. Radial symmetry enables drifting invertebrates such as jellyfish or brittle stars to receive stimuli from all directions.

Most invertebrates have bilateral symmetry, which is often an adaptation to a more motile life-style. This type of symmetry allows for cephalization. Cephalization makes it possible for an organism to perceive a new environment and respond before the organism moves into the environment.

Segmentation

Segmentation is the division of the body into repeating units. Segmentation is also called metamerism. Each repeating segment is called a **metameric unit.** In its simplest form, such as that seen in annelids, each unit of the body is basically the same. Within the Phylum Arthropoda there is a trend toward increasing specialization of segments, especially in the adult, and a trend toward fusing segments into larger functional units.

Support

Invertebrates have diverse means of support. The simpler invertebrates, the sponges, secrete spicules that strengthen and support their soft tissue. However, structures such as spicules do not aid in movement. The more complex invertebrates, the coelomates, are supported by the hydrostatic pressure of their fluid-filled coelom. In roundworms, for instance, the coelom also aids in movement by providing hydrostatic pressure against which muscles can contract. Some invertebrates have true exoskeletons. The chitinous coverings of arthropods and the protective shells of some mollusks provide excellent protection, but both limit the size and impede the movement of the organism. The echinoderms are the only invertebrates with an internal skeleton. This endoskeleton allows some echinoderms to move quickly and to grow large.

Phylogeny

Look at Figure 35-5. This reconstruction of probable invertebrate evolution is based on evidence you have just read about, including comparative morphology, patterns of embryo development, study of the fossil record, and comparisons of larva development.

Interdisciplinary Activity

Earth Science Instruct students to make a time line showing some major events in the evolution of invertebrates and other animals. The time line should be divided to accurately reflect earth's history as it is known. Students should include (1) the first appearance of invertebrates, (2) organisms from each of the nine invertebrate phyla studied, (3) vertebrates, and (4) mammals. Students can use Table 15-1, Geologic Time Scale (p. 221), and library resources to find this information.

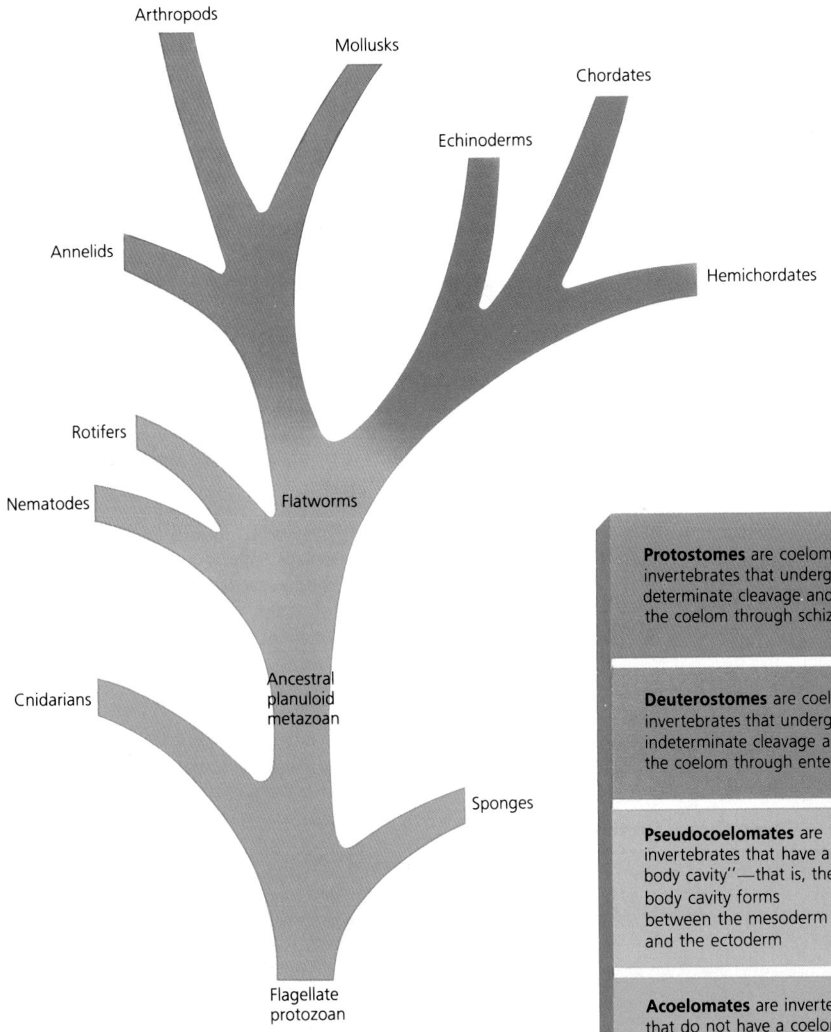

Protostomes are coelomate invertebrates that undergo spiral determinate cleavage and form the coelom through schizocoely.

Deuterostomes are coelomate invertebrates that undergo radial indeterminate cleavage and form the coelom through enterocoely.

Pseudocoelomates are invertebrates that have a "false body cavity"—that is, the body cavity forms between the mesoderm and the ectoderm

Acoelomates are invertebrates that do not have a coelom.

Figure 35-5 This phylogenetic tree shows the probable evolution of invertebrates. Note the evolutionary connection between echinoderms and chordates.

Section Review

1. What is a *metameric unit?*
2. From what group of organisms do scientists suggest that metazoans originated?
3. Give an example of three invertebrate larval forms.
4. State an adaptive advantage that organisms with coeloms have over organisms without coeloms.
5. In what ways might indirect development be an adaptive advantage?

Reteaching

Show students photographs of various invertebrates, including members of each of the nine phyla covered in this unit. For each particular invertebrate, have students describe its symmetry, segmentation, and means of support. *(For example, a sponge is asymmetrical, has no segments, and is supported by spongin or spicules. A sea star is pentaradially symmetrical, has no segments, and has an endoskeleton.)*

■ ***See*** **Section Reviews** ***worksheet, Section 35.1.***

Enrichment

Have students research in popular science magazines the use of protein analysis in determining phylogenetic relationships. Also have them find out how these data have changed what was previously proposed about the evolution of invertebrates. Ask students to cite examples in which protein analysis contributed to those changes.

Closure

Ask students to imagine that a new organism has been found that undergoes radial cleavage and whose coelom is formed through enterocoely. Have students refer to pp. 521–524 and describe other developmental and morphological characteristics they might expect this organism to have. *(It would be a deuterostome and would have indeterminate cleavage, indirect larva development with bipinnaria larva, radial symmetry in adults, and an endoskeleton.)* Ask students to name the phylum to which the organism belongs. *(Echinodermata)*

Videodiscs

■ ***2613–2614, Lobster: Internal and External Structures (s)***

Answers to Section Review

1. A repeating segment in an organism with segmentation

2. Colonies of ciliated or flagellated protozoa

3. Planula—hydrozoa larva; trochophores—snail larva; bipinnaria—sea star larva

4. A coelom enables an organism to move more freely, thus improving its ability to find food and protection.

5. Indirect development produces larvae that do not compete with adults for food. This enables organisms with slow-moving or sessile adult forms to move into new environments, thereby lessening population pressure.

Section 35.2

Lesson Plan

Section Focus

This section discusses how increasing complexity of internal body systems characterizes invertebrate phylogeny. Digestive, respiratory, circulatory, nervous, excretory, and reproductive systems of invertebrates are compared.

Section Themes

This section emphasizes two themes—**Evolution** and **Scale and Structure.** Evolutionary relationships among invertebrates are associated with complexity of structures and functions of their internal body systems.

Motivating Activity

Display diagrams from the other chapters in Unit 7 of the internal anatomy of invertebrate organisms. Pick at least one organism from each invertebrate phylum, such as sponge, hydra, planarian, *Ascaris,* clam, earthworm, crayfish, and sea star. Encourage students to compare internal anatomies of these animals and arrange them in order of increasing complexity. *(The chapters are ordered by increasing complexity of organisms studied.)* Have students review the order of arrangement after completing the section.

■ *See* **Laboratories,** ***Investigation 35.***

Teaching Strategies

Describing Processes Ask students to name some process skills that scientists might use to construct phylogenetic trees. *(Answers include observing, collecting data, organizing data, classifying, inferring, and modeling.)*

Section Objectives

- *Distinguish between types of digestive systems.*
- *Summarize the increase in morphological complexity in respiratory systems.*
- *Identify the different types of circulatory systems.*
- *Identify the increase in complexity in nervous systems.*
- *Identify the different types of excretory systems.*
- *State the adaptive advantages of the different types of reproductive systems.*

35.2 Internal Anatomy

Invertebrate phylogeny is characterized by increasingly complex internal organization. As you read this section, refer to the placement of each group on the phylogenetic tree in Figure 35-5 (p. 525), and compare the systems in Table 35-1.

Digestive Systems

In invertebrates, such as sponges, digestion occurs within individual cells. In those animals with a pseudocoelom or a coelom, the "tube within a tube" body plan makes efficient extracellular digestion possible. Food is broken down within a digestive tract, and nutrients are absorbed by specialized cells that line this region. A distinct digestive system breaks down food and thus provides energy more efficiently.

Some invertebrates, such as *Hydra,* have an **incomplete digestive system,** one opening serving as mouth and anus. Most other invertebrates have a **complete digestive system,** in which food enters through the mouth and passes through the digestive system. Undigested wastes leave through the anus. The cells along the digestive tract are specialized for the various stages of digestion.

Respiratory Systems

As the invertebrates evolved, their respiratory systems became more complex morphologically. This increase in complexity occurred as a response to the presence of protective body coverings

Table 35-1 Invertebrate Systems

	Porifera	Cnidaria	Platyhelminthes	Nematoda
Digestive	Individual cells digest food particles	Enzymes in gastrovascular cavity break down prey	Nutrients are absorbed from the environment	Digestive tract has both mouth and anus
Respiratory	Diffusion	Diffusion	Diffusion	Diffusion
Circulatory	Diffusion	Nutrients absorbed by specialized cells lining body cavity	Diffusion	Gas exchange between cells and fluid-filled cavities
Nervous	None	Nerve net	Cephalized, ladderlike system	Ganglia and nerve rings
Excretory	Wastes carried by amebocytes from cells	Wastes pass through single opening	Specialized excretory cells in free-living species	Ammonia diffuses through body wall
Reproductive	Hermaphroditic but can also regenerate or reproduce asexually	Hermaphroditic, sexual reproduction, asexual budding	Hermaphroditic and asexual	Separate sexes in most species

Body System	Trend
digestive	incomplete system → complete system
circulatory	none → open system → closed system
respiratory	none → gills → tracheae → lungs
nervous	none → nerve net → cephalized → nerve cord

Graphic Organizer Use this table in Guided Practice on p. 527.

and, in some arthropods, as an adaptation to terrestrial life. In all invertebrates gas exchange occurs across a moist membrane. In the simplest respiratory systems the body covering acts as the moist membrane: gas diffuses from cell to cell. In the more complex systems of aquatic mollusks and aquatic arthropods, gas exchange cannot occur through the body covering because a hard protective layer of skin or the outermost layers of tissues are too thick. These animals have specialized structures called gills. In terrestrial invertebrates, which respire through the skin, body surfaces must be kept moist in order to function. The gills in terrestrial arthropods, for example, are modified to prevent desiccation. The spiracles and trachea of insects are two other adaptations for terrestrial life.

Circulatory Systems

Some invertebrates have no circulatory system. In sponges and cnidarians, for example, nutrients and gases are exchanged directly with the environment by diffusion across cell surfaces. In more complex invertebrates, such as roundworms and echinoderms, gas exchange takes place between cells and internal fluid-filled cavities. Arthropods and some mollusks have an open circulatory system, in which blood is pumped by muscularized vessels into the body cavity. The blood is then returned to the vessels from which it was pumped. Annelids have a **closed circulatory system,** in which blood remains within vessels, and nutrient and gas exchange take place between capillaries and cells. The closed circulatory system increases the efficiency of circulation by providing oxygen and nutrients to the cells more quickly.

	Mollusca	Annelida	Arthropoda	Echinodermata
Digestive	Digestive tract has both mouth and anus	Digestive tract has both mouth and anus	Digestive tract has both mouth and anus	Digestive tract has both mouth and anus
Respiratory	Gills or lungs	Diffusion in most species, gills in some	Gills in aquatic species; tracheae in terrestrial species	Diffusion
Circulatory	Open in most mollusks; closed in cephalopods	Closed	Open	Open
Nervous	Various; highly developed in cephalopods	Nerve cord connecting brain with ganglia	Specialized sensory organs	Nerve ring but no head or brain
Excretory	Wastes eliminated by nephridia	Wastes eliminated by nephridia	Wastes eliminated by nephridia	Wastes diffuse out of body
Reproductive	Most species have separate sexes; some species are hermaphroditic	Most species are hermaphroditic; some species have separate sexes.	Separate sexes	Sexual reproduction and asexual regeneration

Interpreting the Visuals Refer students to the photograph of the magnified insect eye in Figure 35-6, p. 528. Tell them that insects' eyes cannot focus. Ask students what they can infer about how its compound eye adapts the moth to its environment. *(It cannot produce sharp images but probably detects motion and pattern.)*

■ ***See*** **Process Skills,** ***Chapter 35.***

Guided Practice

Provide students with diagrams of internal body systems for one organism from each of the eight invertebrate phyla included in Table 35-1, pp. 526–527, such as a sponge, hydra, planarian, hookworm, snail, earthworm, grasshopper, and sea star. For each body system, have students identify the evolutionary trend as one reads from left to right. Ask students to summarize their observations in a table. A portion of a completed table is shown on p. 526 (Graphic Organizer).

Independent Practice

■ Have students write answers to the Section Review.

■ Have students make a concept map summarizing kinds of evidence scientists use to determine evolutionary trends in invertebrates. An example of a completed concept map is shown on p. 519B.

Videodiscs

■ ***2596, Sponges (s)***

■ ***2597, Polyp: Medusa (s)***

■ ***2617, Starfish (s)***

LEP Activity

Have students make a flash card for each of the boldface terms in this chapter. Instruct students to write the term on one side of an index card. When necessary, help them use a dictionary to add the phonetic respelling. On the other side, students should write the definition of the term and list representative invertebrates. For example, mollusks, arthropods, and annelids are protostomes; echinoderms are deuterostomes. Then have student pairs use the flash cards to quiz each other or to study independently.

Check Your Understanding

1. How is a complete digestive system an adaptative advantage? *(Digestion is more efficient because cells along the digestive tract are specialized for different stages.)*
2. How are echinoderms able to survive with respiration by simple diffusion? *(Their spiny skin and endoskeleton alleviate the need for a thick body covering, allowing diffusion to occur.)*

Reteaching

Review Table 35-1, pp. 526–527, with students and ask them to explain terms from the text that are used in the table. For example, ask what *diffusion* means in the context of the respiratory system. *(Oxygen and carbon dioxide pass between moist skin and the environment.)* What is a closed circulatory system? *(One in which blood remains within vessels)* What are nephridia? *(Long tubules through which wastes are eliminated)* What is hermaphroditic reproduction? *(Production of both eggs and sperm by the same organism)*
■ *See* Section Reviews *worksheet, Section 35.2.*

Enrichment

Have students research an invertebrate that was not discussed in the text and prepare a short, illustrated report describing its evolution.

Closure

Provide students with brief descriptions of the systems of "mystery" organisms, and challenge them to determine the possible phylum of each organism, based on your description. For example, ask: What is a segmented, terrestrial invertebrate that respires with tracheae and has compound eyes? *(Arthropod)*

Figure 35-6 How is the highly complex compound eye of the diamondback moth, *Plutellidae lepidoptera*, an adaptation to this organism's environment?

Nervous Systems

As invertebrates evolved, increasingly complex nervous systems enabled the animals to monitor and respond to their environments. Cnidarians, as you read in Chapter 29, have a primitive nervous system, called a nerve net. In bilateral invertebrates there is a trend toward increasing cephalization and the development of more complex sensory organs. In segmented invertebrates, such as the earthworm, large ganglia exist in the head area, though sense organs are not highly developed. In complex invertebrates, such as insects, sense organs are well developed.

Excretory Systems

In simple invertebrates nitrogenous wastes are usually excreted in the form of ammonia gas (NH_3) because it easily diffuses through the cells. In terrestrial invertebrates this poisonous gas would not leave the body quickly enough. Therefore specialized excretory structures filter NH_3 and other wastes from the coelom. These animals convert NH_3 to less toxic substances such as urea or uric acid and excrete these wastes. Another adaptation of the excretory system is the ability to reabsorb water, which is essential for terrestrial animals.

Reproductive Systems

All invertebrates are capable of some form of sexual reproduction, although many may also reproduce asexually. Some invertebrates, such as flatworms and earthworms, are hermaphroditic. Hermaphroditism allows sessile organisms or those that live in less populated areas to reproduce with any other member of their species. However, hermaphroditism requires the organism to expend large amounts of energy to maintain both male and female gonads. It is of adaptive advantage to other invertebrates to develop separate sexes and concomitantly evolve behavior patterns that bring individuals of different sexes together.

Section Review

1. What is the difference between *complete* and *incomplete digestive systems?*
2. What is the adaptive advantage of a closed circulatory system?
3. Why are simple invertebrates able to release their wastes in the form of ammonia, while terrestrial invertebrates must release their wastes in nontoxic forms?
4. What is the adaptive advantage of cephalization?
5. Many evolutionary adaptations in the various invertebrate systems provide the organism with the ability to react and move quickly. What are two advantages speed gives an animal?

Answers to Section Review

1. An incomplete digestive system has one opening that serves as both mouth and anus. A complete digestive system has both mouth and anus.
2. It provides cells with oxygen and nutrients more quickly.
3. The ammonia gas cannot leave the body of terrestrial invertebrates quickly enough.
4. It allows an animal to receive stimuli before moving into a new environment.
5. Speed helps an animal escape from predators and catch food.

Laboratory

Identifying Invertebrates

Objective
To identify representatives of the major invertebrate phyla

Process Skills
Classifying, observing, inferring

Materials
Dissecting microscope; unidentified preserved specimens, including a cnidarian, a flatworm, a roundworm, a mollusk, an annelid, an arthropod, and an echinoderm

Inquiry

1 Perform the following series of observations for each specimen, and answer all of the following questions. Record all of your observations. Use a dissecting microscope where appropriate in order to see characteristics more clearly. If you cannot find evidence of a characteristic you are attempting to observe, write NE—for "no evidence"—after the characteristic in question. Why should you examine the same characteristics in each animal?
2 Before handling any of the specimens, make sure the specimen has been thoroughly rinsed in cool tap water in order to remove preservatives.
3 Can you infer whether the animal is aquatic or terrestrial? What characteristics support your inference?
4 Is the animal asymmetrical, radially symmetrical, or bilaterally symmetrical?
5 Is the animal's body hard or soft? Does it have an endoskeleton or an exoskeleton?
6 Is the organism's body segmented or unsegmented?
7 Is the animal motile or sessile? What might you look for to help you make this inference? When possible, describe the method of movement used by the organism.
8 Observe the external structures of the animal's digestive tract. Does the animal have a mouth and/or an anus?
9 Use external evidence to determine the kind of respiratory system present in the organism. Does the organism have gills or lungs, or does respiration occur through the organism's external surface?
10 Note any evidence of reproductive structures. Is the organism hermaphroditic or a single sex?
11 Review your evidence to determine the phylum to which each animal belongs. Write the name of the phylum after the number of the animal.

Conclusions

1 Identify the animal specimens by genus whenever possible.
2 Name some external characteristics, besides those named in the investigation, that are helpful in classifying these animals.

Further Inquiry
What are some of the advantages and disadvantages of using preserved specimens rather than live animals for this investigation?

Laboratory

(For an overview of invertebrate characteristics and preparatory information related to the laboratory, see p. 519B.)

Inquiry
1. The same characteristics should be examined in each animal so that all are classified according to the same criteria.
3. Presence of legs or wings, and absence of gills, cilia, and flagella can indicate that the animal is terrestrial.
4. Only sponges are asymmetrical. Cnidarians and adult echinoderms have radial symmetry. All other invertebrates, including echinoderm larvae, have bilateral symmetry.
5. Only arthropods have hard bodies; they have exoskeletons. Most mollusks have protective shells.
6. Only annelids and arthropods have segmented bodies.
7. Bilateral symmetry and the presence of legs, wings, cilia, bristles, and flagella often indicate that an organism is motile.
8. Cnidarians and platyhelminthes have only a mouth. Sponges have neither mouth nor anus. All other phyla have both mouth and anus.
9. Mollusks, arthropods, and some annelids have gills or lungs. All other phyla respire by diffusion.
10. Sponges, cnidarians, platyhelminthes, some mollusks, and most

Conclusions
1. Answers will vary according to specimens used.
2. Answers may include bell-shaped body; long, flat body; jointed appendages; external shell; spine-covered body; long, narrow arms; wings; muscular foot; and tube feet.

Further Inquiry
One advantage of using preserved specimens is that they allow students to closely examine the organism without harming themselves. The main disadvantage is that students cannot observe the organism in its habitat, nor can they observe its movement.

Chapter 35 Review

Vocabulary

1. In radial cleavage, cell divisions are parallel with or at right angles to the polar axis. In spiral cleavage, cells divide in a spiral arrangement.
2. In determinate cleavage, the fate of each cell is determined before gastrulation. In indeterminate cleavage, the fate of each cell is determined sometime after gastrulation.
3. A protostome is an organism whose embryo has determinate cleavage and develops spirally; the coelom arises by schizocoely; the blastopore develops into a mouth. A deuterostome is an organism whose embryo has indeterminate cleavage and develops radially; the coelom arises by enterocoely; the blastopore develops into an anus.
4. In direct development the young animal has the same appearance and way of life as the adult. In indirect development the organism has an intermediate larva stage.
5. In an open circulatory system, blood is pumped from vessels into the body cavity, then returned to the vessels. In a closed circulatory system, the blood remains within vessels, and nutrient and gas exchange take place between capillaries and cells.

Review

1. c. **6.** d
2. b **7.** c
3. d **8.** b
4. d **9.** d
5. c **10.** c

11. Over 800 million years ago
12. It allows movement of organs within the body and enables the organism to move about more freely.
13. It allows sessile and drifting invertebrates to receive stimuli from all directions.
14. Food is broken down more completely and more efficiently to provide the organism with energy more quickly.
15. The endoskeleton allows organisms to move easily and grow large.
16. Comparative morphology, patterns of embryo development, study of the fossil record, comparisons of larva development, and biochemical evidence
17. Together they provide an organism with nutrients and oxygen more quickly, allowing the organism to move faster.
18. They cannot excrete toxic ammonia gas quickly enough, and they must conserve water.
19. It allows organisms to monitor and respond to their environments more readily.
20. Hermaphroditism requires an organism to maintain both sets of gonads.

Chapter 35 Review

Vocabulary

closed circulatory system (527)
complete digestive system (526)
determinate cleavage (522)
deuterostomes (521)
direct development (523)
enterocoely (523)
incomplete digestive system (526)
indeterminate cleavage (522)
indirect development (523)
metameric unit (524)
protostomes (521)
radial cleavage (521)
schizocoely (522)
segmentation (524)
spiral cleavage (521)

Distinguish between the terms in each of the following pairs.
1. radial cleavage and spiral cleavage
2. indeterminate cleavage and determinate cleavage
3. protostomes and deuterostomes
4. direct development and indirect development
5. open circulatory system and closed circulatory system

Review

1. Some scientists suggest that colonial flagellated protozoa were the ancestors of metazoans because (a) present-day invertebrate proteins are similar to those of modern ciliates (b) invertebrates are heterotrophic and eukaryotic (c) the cilia of invertebrates and protozoa are identical in size, structure, and movement (d) protozoans clumped together to form colonies.
2. The embryos of protostomes undergo (a) radial cleavage (b) spiral cleavage (c) indeterminate cleavage (d) all of the above.
3. Scientists believe that chordates and echinoderms share a common ancestor because both are (a) protostomes (b) aquatic organisms (c) metazoans (d) deuterostomes.
4. When the cells in a four-celled embryo are separated and each grows into a quarter of a gastrula, the type of cleavage is called (a) spiral (b) radial (c) indeterminate (d) determinate.
5. An adult that has gone through the process of changing from a larva is said to have undergone (a) indeterminate cleavage (b) determinate cleavage (c) indirect development (d) direct development.
6. One of the characteristics of deuterostomes is that the development of their coelom occurs by (a) schizocoely (b) metamerism (c) spiral cleavage (d) enterocoely.
7. One characteristic of invertebrates such as insects is (a) the presence of a pseudocoelom (b) radial cleavage (c) increasing specialization of body segments (d) radial symmetry.
8. In a closed circulatory system (a) blood is pumped through the body cavity (b) blood is contained in blood vessels (c) gases are exchanged with the environment (d) gases are exchanged between cells and the body cavity.
9. Gills arose in invertebrates because (a) gas exchange must occur across a moist membrane (b) terrestrial animals must keep their respiratory surfaces moist in order to breathe (c) invertebrates could not get oxygen readily by diffusion (d) a hard outer shell prevented oxygen gas from diffusing across the skin.
10. Hermaphroditic animals tend to (a) be motile (b) be bilaterally symmetrical (c) be sessile (d) live in highly populated areas.
11. When do scientists believe the first invertebrates appeared on earth?

530 *Chapter 35*

12. What advantage does the mesoderm provide to an organism?
13. What adaptive advantage does radial symmetry provide to less complex invertebrates?
14. What adaptive advantage does a complete digestive system provide to a more complex organism?
15. How is the endoskeleton an adaptive advantage over the exoskeleton?
16. On what evidence do scientists base their construction of the invertebrate phylogenetic tree?
17. How does a closed circulatory system and a complete digestive system allow an organism to increase its motility?
18. Why do terrestrial animals need specialized excretory structures to filter wastes?
19. What adaptive advantage does a complex nervous system provide?
20. Why is hermaphroditism an inefficient use of energy for many invertebrates?

Critical Thinking

1. Many invertebrates are able to regenerate a lost body part. Suggest a reason why some invertebrates are not able to regenerate body parts.
2. Scientists have determined the phylogeny of invertebrates by studying many invertebrate features, as well as invertebrate fossils. From what you know about invertebrates, which ones, do you think, were most likely to fossilize? Why? How might this affect scientists' view of invertebrate evolution?
3. The photo on the right shows bipinnaria larvae of starfish. What adaptations for a free-living life do they show?

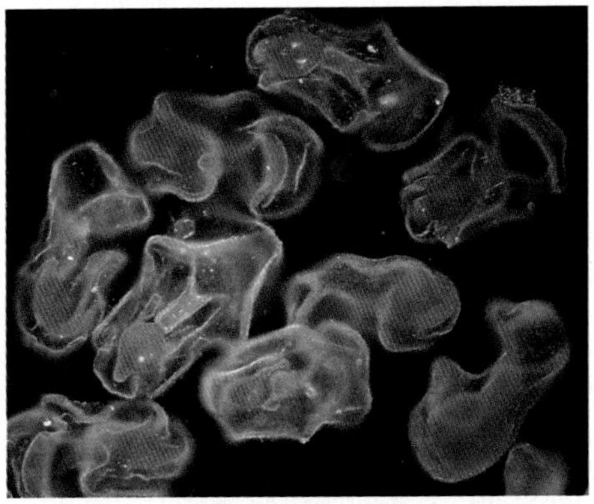

Extension

1. Make a table of the invertebrate phyla that have been discussed in Chapters 29–35. For each phylum list the defining feature of the phylum (e.g., soft bodies for mollusks); the evolutionary adaptations; and the type of reproductive, digestive, excretory, circulatory, and nervous systems.
2. Do research on one type of sessile invertebrate. Find out how sessility can be both an advantage and a disadvantage. Write a short paper in which you report your findings.
3. Read the article by William Stolzenburg entitled "When Life Got Hard" in *Science News*, August 25, 1990, pp. 120–123. What evidence suggests that predation played a primary role in the evolution of animal skeletons? How could the discovery of additional fossil evidence contribute to the story of skeletal origin?
4. Invertebrates are incredibly diverse. Research a type of invertebrate that has not been discussed in Chapters 29–35. Present a short report to your class in which you discuss the phylogeny and evolution of your chosen invertebrate. What characteristics does this organism have that are similar to the characteristics of related invertebrates?

Critical Thinking

1. One reason may be that their body systems are too complex to be successfully regenerated.
2. Invertebrates with hard, outer shells (exoskeletons) and endoskeletons would be most likely to fossilize, since soft bodies are not as readily preserved. Scientists' views of invertebrate evolution might be affected because it would be difficult to get an accurate picture of the evolution of any soft-bodied animals.
3. The bipinnaria larvae possess cilia and a mouth that adapt them to free-living life.

Extension

1. Use Table 35-1, pp. 526–527, as a guide. Students should also include the defining feature of each phylum and specific evolutionary adaptations.
2. Sessility is advantageous because less energy is required to survive since food comes to the organism. It is disadvantageous because the organism cannot escape from predators or move to a new location when food is scarce.
3. Encourage students to follow each line of reasoning of the various researchers and write an essay on how evidence is perceived and weighed in the formulation of a hypothesis.
4. Encourage students to use a variety of library resources for their research.

Discussion

Guide the discussion by posing the following questions.

1. In what ways can application of insecticides promote the development of more resilient pests or increase insect infestation? *(The use of insecticides can result in the development of pest populations having a genetic resistance to the insecticide; insecticides can also kill beneficial insects, such as natural predators of pest insects, and other animals that eat insects, such as birds.)*

2. What are some advantages of applying a combination of methods to control crop pests? *(Encourage students to consider how multiple methods will reduce use of toxic chemicals and inhibit development of resistant varieties of pest insects.)*

3. Why do you think that large quantities of hazardous pesticides have been applied to farmlands and forests? *(People were unaware of the harm done to wildlife and groundwater, while they enjoyed great economic and public health advantages, such as increased crop production and a reduction in insect-borne diseases.)*

4. How do quarantine regulations control the spread of pest insects between countries? *(Students might answer that restricting certain plants and animals at the borders helps keep out unusual varieties of pest insects that could endanger crops, livestock, and human health.)*

5. What role do you think that economics plays in the use of pesticides? *(Possible answers: crops ruined by insects are costly to farmers who produce the food and costly to consumers who buy the food. Lower yields mean higher prices for crops. Pesticide application is also expensive and may harm the environment and human health.)*

Intra-Science

How the Sciences Work Together

The Question in Biology: *Can We Control Insects Safely?*

Farmers worldwide face a dilemma: they can apply pesticides to their crops in hopes of producing rich yields, thereby endangering the environment; or they can withhold added chemicals, risking destruction of food supplies by pests.

Following World War II, farmers began applying pesticides liberally to crops, woods, and waterways to kill insect pests that damage plants and transmit human diseases. In 1962, however, publication of *The Silent Spring*, a book by Rachel Carson, raised public awareness of the dangers of pesticide use, especially the contamination of the environment and the destruction of wildlife.

Pesticides, particularly dichlorodiphenyltrichloroethane (DDT), can persist not only in the soil, but also in every organism of an entire food chain. Birds, such as the bald eagle and the peregrine falcon, either died or encountered problems in producing offspring. DDT caused fragile eggshells; many chicks failed to hatch or were born deformed. DDT also caused a noticeable decline in songbird populations.

Following public protest over the pesticide threat, government officials restricted use of the most toxic pesticides. Scientific studies followed. One study conducted by the Environmental Protection Agency (EPA), an independent agency of the U.S. government, found at least 46 different kinds of pesticides in groundwater in 26 states. Pesticides were also found in the fatty tissues of people who drank the contaminated drinking water or ate foods, such as fruits and vegetables, that contained pesticide residues.

Though pesticides can be misused, their proper use can benefit both farmers and millions of hungry people around the world. Without pesticides, the uncontrolled spread of insects in a field can destroy an entire crop and also seriously affect livestock. Pesticides also help control insect-borne diseases, such as malaria and schistosomiasis, which threaten the lives of millions of people each year. Consequently, various scientists are developing safer ways to fight harmful insects without poisoning the environment, wildlife, or people.

The Connection to Chemistry

Although scientists are developing new insecticides, insects can, in turn, develop resistance to the chemicals. This adaptability of insects often leads to the use of stronger or larger quantities of insecticides. However, chemists hope to develop substances that pest insects will not resist and that will do little or no harm to the environment. To that end, chemists are using natural plant insecticides, such as pyrethrin (a chrysanthemum extract) and rotenone (derived from the root of a Malayan legume). In addition, because only about 1 percent of the 800,000 known insect species are considered pests, chemists are creating insecticides that kill specific pest insects and leave other insects unharmed.

Connections to Other Disciplines

Geography Human populations in different parts of the world are severely affected by insects. Students might investigate how insects affect human health and economy by spreading malaria in sub-Saharan Africa, Chagas disease in Central and South America, or livestock diseases in Australia.

Government Pesticide manufacture has inherent dangers. In 1984 an industrial accident in Bhopal, India, released a toxic gas, methyl isocyanate (an intermediate in the production of the pesticide Sevin), killing and injuring thousands of people. Encourage students interested in investigating the relationships among government, industry, and science to research the safety guidelines and procedures that have resulted directly from the Bhopal disaster.

Chemists are investigating photosynthetic dyes, like the xanthoids, that are poisonous to insects but pose little threat to humans, since the toxic dyes degrade rapidly in sunlight. Biologists and chemists are also working together to develop chemosterilants that inhibit the reproductive capabilities of insects. Releasing sterilized male insects, for example, dramatically reduces the number of fertile offspring produced by pest insects.

- *Why is it preferable to use insecticides that degrade rapidly in the environment?*

The Connection to Biotechnology

Biotechnology is playing an important role in the control of insect populations. Research has focused on various techniques, such as infecting pest insects with fungi that cause insect diseases, using insect pheromones as bait in traps, and releasing a pest insect's natural predators. For example, ladybug beetles have been released in fields of peas to control aphids and other pest insects.

Some genetic engineers are developing crops capable of producing their own pest resistance. Other geneticists are researching the potential for introducing lethal, or "killer," genes into the DNA of many insect species. Biotechnologists are also isolating and growing strains of bacteria, such as

Bacillus thuringiensis, that can be deadly to certain species of insects. (Some strains of *B. thuringiensis* are toxic to mammals.) Researchers have used *B. thuringiensis* successfully to control a variety of pest insects, including the larval stages of mosquitoes, black flies, and Gypsy moths.

- *Why is it important for scientists to be specific in their use of pathogens to kill insects?*

The Connection to Other Sciences

Engineering controls have long been used to eliminate insect breeding grounds, such as stagnant pools of water. Engineers also have developed modern food processing, refrigeration, and dehydration methods to minimize damage from pests after crops have been harvested.

Entomologists and agronomists work in tandem to develop agricultural methods that reduce pest insects while minimizing the need for chemicals. For example, crop rotation, staggered plantings, and carefully timed pesticide applications can sharply reduce the number of pest insects.

- *Why do changes in the normal planting cycle of a particular crop create an unfavorable environment for insects that feed on the crop?*

The Connection to Careers

Architects and rural planners will be needed to design inexpensive housing that is inhospitable to disease-carrying insects, particularly in the economically developing areas of the world. Carpenters, masons, plumbers, and electricians will also be needed to build the new homes. Economists could help policy makers choose economical ways of producing food for a rapidly growing world population. For more information about related careers in the biological sciences, turn to page 842.

6. In what ways do you think that government policy makers can restrict the use of dangerous pesticides? *(Sample answers: by banning the use of certain pesticides, such as DDT; by encouraging farmers to switch to agricultural methods such as crop rotation and staggered plantings; by educating the public on hazards of pesticide use.)*

7. How can insect-borne diseases be controlled without using toxic pesticides? *(Sample answers: engineering controls, such as eliminating insect food supplies or breeding grounds; natural insecticides; and controlling intermediate hosts, for example, rats in the case of rat fleas transmitting the bubonic plague.)*

Answers to

Chemistry Chemicals that degrade rapidly are less likely to remain in the soil, contaminate water supplies, or pollute food chains.

Biotechnology Using nonspecific pathogens to kill insects might destroy not only pest insects but also beneficial insects, such as the honeybee or natural predators of pest insects. Humans might also be affected.

Other Sciences Pest insects often become adapted to the natural life cycle of a particular plant. Changes in the seasonal planting cycle of a crop can disturb the feeding and reproductive patterns of pest insects.

Enrichment

Lyme disease is a recently discovered illness that can occur when a tiny deer tick transmits certain spirochete bacteria to humans and other mammals. Ask students to research the epidemiology of the sudden increase in cases of an arthritis-like disease in Lyme, Connecticut, in 1975. Ask students to investigate how Dr. Allen Steere confirmed the role of the tick and the identity of the bacterial pathogen.

Unit 8 Vertebrates

Chapters

Unit Overview

This unit continues the survey of multicellular organisms with the study of vertebrates, animals with backbones. Chapter 36 describes the ancestral invertebrate chordates and introduces fishes, which include the first true vertebrates. Chapter 37 describes amphibians, which evolved from fishes, and discusses amphibian metamorphosis, which permits amphibians to adapt to both aquatic and terrestrial habitats. Chapter 38 introduces reptiles, the first fully terrestrial vertebrates. Chapter 39 introduces birds and Chapter 40 mammals, both endothermic descendants of reptiles. Chapter 41 surveys evolutionary trends in vertebrates.

Issues in Biology

For many years, scientists have used animals to test the safety and effectiveness of new drugs, medical devices, and surgical procedures. Companies have also used animals to test the safety of new products such as cosmetics. Animals have been used because they serve as efficient models of human body systems. The most commonly used laboratory animals have included rats, mice, rabbits, monkeys, dogs, cats, and pigs. In recent years, however, pressure from groups of people concerned about ethical and humane treatment of animals has caused scientists to seek alternatives to animal testing. Ask students to consider why animal testing might continue to be necessary in the future. Have them list arguments for and against animal testing, including ethical considerations.

Research in Progress

Because most whales are too large to be kept in captivity and because their marine habitat makes studying their natural behavior difficult, many aspects of whale behavior remain mysteries. How and where they migrate, feed, mate, raise young, form groups, and protect themselves are rich subjects for scientific research.

Consequently, scientists are devising new ways to study whales. To follow whale migrations, scientists use tags with tiny transmitters that allow satellite tracking. To explain why North Atlantic right whale populations have not grown despite decades of protection, scientists take tiny skin samples with miniature harpoons. Genetic material from the skin of many whales is compared to determine if the few remaining whales are too closely related to breed successfully.

Interdisciplinary Activity

Technology Throughout history, people have attempted flight by copying shapes and movements of flying vertebrates, usually birds. Only in the last decade, however, has human-powered flight been achieved.

Have students use cardboard, plastic, paper, or other materials to make gliders by copying the shapes of living or extinct flying vertebrates (birds, bats, pterosaurs, *Archaeopteryx*) or gliding vertebrates (flying fish, flying squirrels). Emphasize that several characteristics of flying vertebrates such as wing surface area, center of gravity, lightness, and rigidity should be taken into account in making gliders.

Resources

Chapter	Print: For the Teacher	Print: For the Student	Audiovisual/Software
36	■ Michael Filisky, *The Peterson First Guide to Fishes of North America,* Houghton Mifflin, 1989. ■ P. B. Moyle and J. J. Cech, *Fishes, An Introduction to Ichthyology,* 2nd ed., Prentice-Hall, 1988.	■ Billy Allstetter, "A Fish out of Water," *Discover,* September 1990, 26. ■ Stephen Strauss, "Tree Rings of the Deep," *Technology Review,* August/September 1991, 17–18.	■ *Fish,* revised. Video or film, 14 min. Coronet, 1985. ■ *The Sharks.* Video, 60 min. National Geographic. Distributed by Carolina Biological.
37	■ William E. Duellman and Linda Trueb, *Biology of Amphibians,* McGraw-Hill, 1986. ■ T. R. Halliday and K. Adler, eds., *The Encyclopedia of Reptiles and Amphibians,* Facts on File, 1986.	■ John Horgan, "Bufo Abuse," *Scientific American,* August 1990, 26–27. ■ Kathryn Phillips, "Where Have All the Frogs and Toads Gone?" *BioScience,* June 1990, 422–424.	■ *It's a Frog's Life.* Video, 60 min. Oxford Scientific Films. Distributed by Carolina Biological. ■ *Operation: Frog.* Apple, 64K. Commodore, 64K. Disk. User's handbook. Teaching guide. Scholastic.
38	■ W. Alvarez, F. Asaro, and V. E. Courtillot, "What Caused the Mass Extinction?" *Scientific American,* October 1990, 76–92. ■ John Kricher, *The Peterson First Guide to Dinosaurs,* Houghton Mifflin, 1990.	■ David J. Fishman, "Rex Revealed," *Discover,* January 1991, 43. ■ Carl Zimmer, "Meet the Relatives," *Discover,* January 1990, 56–57.	■ *Sea Turtles: Ancient Nomads.* Video, 60 min. Vestron Video, 1988. ■ *Snakes,* 2nd ed. Film or video, 15 min. Coronet, 1986.
39	■ Christopher M. Perrins and Alex L. A. Middleton, eds., *The Encyclopedia of Birds,* Facts on File, 1985. ■ Joel Carl Welty and Luis Baptista, *The Life of Birds,* 4th ed., Saunders College Publishing, 1988.	■ Tracey Cohen, "Listening to the Birds," *Technology Review,* August/September 1991, 20–22. ■ Ingrid Wickelgren, "Chaos in the Flock," *Discover,* June 1990, 28.	■ *Birds,* revised. Film or video. Teacher's guide. Coronet, 1985. ■ *Flying in Birds.* Film or video, 25 min. Media Guild, 1986.
40	■ R. J. G. Savage, *Mammal Evolution: An Illustrated Guide,* Facts on File, 1986. ■ Terry A. Vaughan, *Mammalogy,* 3rd ed., Saunders College Publishing, 1986.	■ Bruce Bower, "Biographies Etched in Bone," *Science News,* August 18, 1990, 106–107. ■ Elizabeth Procter-Gray, "Kangaroos up a Tree," *Natural History,* January 1990, 60–66.	■ *Search for the Great Apes.* Video, 60 min. National Geographic / Vestron Video, 1989. ■ *Whale Song—Whales and Dolphins of the Pacific.* Video, 37 min. Video Releasing Co., 1989.
41	■ A. S. Romer and T. S. Parson, *The Vertebrate Body,* 6th ed., Saunders College Publishing, 1986. ■ Barbara J. Stahl, *Vertebrate History: Problems in Evolution,* Dover, 1985.	■ Marguerite Holloway, "Sex and Silversides," *Scientific American,* March 1991, 24. ■ Richard Monastersky, "The Lonely Bird," *Science News,* August 17, 1991, 104–105.	■ *Animals with Backbones.* Film, 10 min. Coronet, 1986. ■ *Survey of the Animal Kingdom: The Vertebrates.* 6 filmstrips and cassettes, 30–40 min. each. Teacher's guide. Educational Images, 1986.

Science in Action Video Series

In teaching Unit 8, you may wish to use the videotape *Alternatives to Dissection: The Earthworm and the Frog*, from the Science in Action Video Series. The behavior, internal anatomy, and external anatomy of each animal are shown though photography and animation.

Introducing the Unit

The material about invertebrates in Unit 7 begins the discussion of multicellular animals. To lead students from Unit 7 into the study of vertebrates, ask them the following questions.

1. Given what you know about evolutionary trends in invertebrates, what characteristics do you expect vertebrates to possess? *(Complete digestive systems, closed circulatory systems, cephalization)*

2. To which invertebrate phylum do you expect vertebrates to be most closely related? Why? *(Echinoderms; echinoderms and vertebrates are deuterostomes whose embryos undergo radial cleavage.)*

3. Given what you know about evolutionary trends in invertebrates, what do you expect to be the vertebrate evolutionary trend regarding habitat? *(Vertebrates evolved from aquatic beginnings toward a terrestrial habitat.)*

4. As you begin Unit 8, what questions can you ask about evolutionary trends in vertebrates? *(What was the origin of vertebrates? What is a typical vertebrate body plan? What body systems are typical of vertebrates? What are vertebrate adaptations to various habitats?)*

Unit 8 Vertebrates

Chapters

Tarpon, *Megalops atlanticus*; channel catfish, *Ictalurus punctatus*

"There is grandeur in this view of life . . . that from so simple a beginning endless forms most beautiful and most wonderful have been and are being evolved."
Charles Darwin

What do all of the animals on these two pages have in common? Perhaps the most obvious answer is that they are all vertebrates—that is, animals with backbones. However, all of these animals spend at least part of their life in water. In this unit you will learn that the major trend of vertebrate evolution is toward greater adaptation to life on land. Nevertheless, every class of vertebrates includes some species that are adapted to life in water. Can you name some mammals that live in water?

Sea turtles

Using the Opening Quotation

Have students discuss what Darwin meant by ". . . and are being evolved." *(Evolution is not only a record of how life arrived at its present state but also an ongoing process that works very slowly to adapt organisms to new conditions or habitats. Evolution is happening now, but so slowly that we are usually unaware of it.)* Ask students to discuss whether words such as "grandeur," "beautiful," and "wonderful" sound like the typical language of a scientist. *(Most scientists find aesthetic pleasure as well as intellectual stimulation in science.)*

King penguins, *Aptenodytes patagonica*

UNIT 8

Unit Themes

Evolution Starting from simple cephalochordate ancestors, the vertebrates have evolved seven classes: jawless fishes, cartilaginous fishes, and bony fishes (Chapter 36); amphibians (Chapter 37); reptiles (Chapter 38); birds (Chapter 39); and mammals (Chapter 40). Evolutionary trends among vertebrates have included increasing complexity of body structures and behaviors (Chapter 41).

Scale and Structure Throughout vertebrate evolution, adaptations to new habitats have involved development of new structures. Structural features have included those adapted to water (Chapters 36, 37), to land (Chapters 37, 38, 39, and 40), and to air (Chapter 39).

Stability Some vertebrates have evolved strategies for survival that involve the maintenance of a stable internal environment. Mammals, birds, and possibly some dinosaurs have been endothermic, which ensures a stable internal temperature independent of environmental fluctuations. The viviparity of most mammals also has provided developing embryos with a stable temperature and supply of oxygen and nutrients.

Understanding the Visuals

Ask students how the visuals illustrate the quotation. *(Each animal is "most beautiful and most wonderful" in its own way. They are only three examples of the almost "endless forms" that vertebrate life has taken.)*

Ask students to suggest adaptations that are visible in the visuals. *(Flippers, fins, streamlined shape, waterproof scales, shell, beak, and feathers)* Point out that all three species have adapted to an aquatic habitat, even though they are members of three different vertebrate classes.

Chapter 36 Chordates and Fishes

Chapter Overview

Chapter 36 introduces the Phylum Chordata and the fishes, continuing the discussion of evolutionary trends from the previous chapter. Section 36.1 presents the general characteristics and classification of chordates. Section 36.2 examines the evolutionary history and relationships of fishes. Section 36.3 discusses the structure and function of a representative bony fish.

Chapter Planning Chart

B	S	A	Sections and Subsections	Page	Features	Page	Resources
•	•	•	**36.1 Overview of Chordates**				
			Characteristics	537	Section Review	539	Videodiscs
			Classification	538			Blackline Master 74
							Section Reviews Worksheet
•	•	•	**36.2 Evolution and Classification of Fishes**				
			Adaptations	540	Biology in Process	542	Videodiscs
			Evolution	540	Laboratory	551	Process Skills: The Coelacanth
			Agnatha	541	Section Review	545	Section Reviews Worksheet
			Chondrichthyes	542			
			Osteichthyes	545			
•	•	•	**36.3 Morphology of a Bony Fish**				
			External Anatomy	546	Think	547	Videodiscs
			Internal Anatomy	547	Section Review	550	Blackline Master 75
							Blackline Master 76
							Overhead Transparency T36
							Laboratories: How Fish Breathe
							Section Reviews Worksheet
			End of Chapter Activities				
					Chapter Review	552	Vocabulary Skills
							Chapter Test
							Computer Test Generator

B *The Basic Level curriculum presents the most fundamental knowledge offered in the course.*
S *The Standard Level curriculum is designed for the average student who is able to master most topics.*
A *The Advanced Level curriculum includes suggestions for teaching the most academically able students.*

Cooperative Learning

Group Activity: Fish Types

- **Group Size:** *5 students*
- **Outcome:** *Students compare the major characteristics of fishes in the classes Agnatha and Chondrichthyes, and the three types of Osteichthyes.*
- **Individual Accountability:** *Each student will make a chart of the major characteristics of a single fish group.*
- **Positive Interdependence:** *The group will compare the characteristics of the five fish groups.*

Have one student in each group choose one of the following fish groups: Agnatha, Chondrichthyes, lobe-finned fishes, lungfishes, or ray-finned fishes. Ask each student to make a chart that shows the main distinguishing characteristics, method of feeding, anatomical variations, habitats, and evolutionary significance for his or her fish group. Allow time for library research.

After completing the chart, each student should present the results to the other members of the group. Encourage the group to compare the chart being presented with the charts made by the other group members. For instance, ray-finned fishes exhibit a greater degree of anatomical diversity than other groups. Finally, have the group as a whole discuss not only the differences but the similarities among the fish groups.

Concept Map

The following is one possible solution to the concept mapping activity in Reteaching on p. 539.

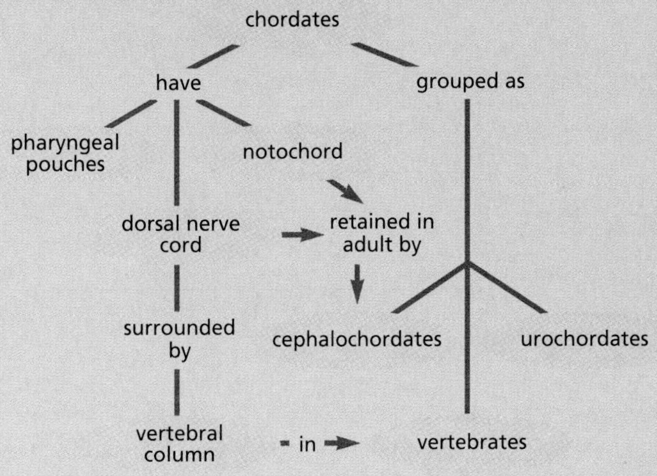

Laboratory Preparation

Overview *(See p. 551.)*

This lab is an excellent review of dichotomous keys, first introduced in the Chapter 18 lab. Because many of the characteristics that define a species are not easily observed in preserved specimens, keys often rely on trivial but distinctive anatomical features. This key will illustrate the kinds of characteristics that are used in the identification of fishes.

Preparation

If the illustration on p. 551 is used, no advance preparation is necessary. Live or preserved specimens may be used instead of the illustrations. Use specimens that vary widely in physical characteristics, as it is sometimes difficult to distinguish among closely related species. Pet stores and many biological supply houses usually stock goldfish (several varieties), tiger bars, catfish, guppies, Siamese fighting fish, tetras, and algae-eaters. Preserved specimens, such as lamprey, skate or ray, dogfish, perch, bowfin, and eel are available from most biological supply houses.

Teaching Tips

If the preserved specimens mentioned above are used, students can construct a dichotomous key as directed in the lab. Have students rinse preserved specimens. If live animals are used, suggest that students use the distinguishing characteristics mentioned in the lab that are appropriate and then add such characteristics as behavior, color, or obvious morphological characteristics. Suggest that students make sketches in order to become familiar with the examples.

Suggest that students make running lists of the characteristics of each example, then compare the lists to indicate the features that may be unique to a particular group.

Point out an example of a feature that may be unique to one particular group of fishes, such as the jawless mouth of the lamprey.

Safety

If you use specimens that have been preserved or fixed in formalin (formaldehyde), be sure to conduct the lab in a well-ventilated room. If live specimens are used, remind students of the proper care and treatment of live animals. Whether live or preserved animals are used, remind students to wash their hands after working with the specimen.

Chapter Themes

Evolution The diverse array of modern invertebrate chordate and fish species derive from simple ancestors. Stress that chordate groups have diverged from earlier species, developing increasingly complex anatomies and ways of life.

Point out that we can witness the present state of this continuing evolution by examining the classification of the Phylum Chordata and especially of the many groups of fishes. The classification of living things is an attempt to schematize their evolutionary relationships.

Scale and Structure Stress the relationships among the anatomical structures of a fish and their functions as they contribute to the fish's survival. Gills, for instance, are well adapted for gas exchange and fins for propulsion and stability.

Chapter Motivating Activity

Ask students to remember fishes they have seen on television nature programs or in books. If a student mentions whales or dolphins, use the opportunity to discuss how fishes differ from mammals. Encourage students to share their experiences with recreational fishing, visiting an aquarium, or keeping tropical fishes as a hobby. Have pairs of students brainstorm about the diversity of fishes. Ask students to think of as many different fishes as possible that represent extremes of size, shape, colors, and ways of life. List students' contributions on the board.

Then ask students to think of as many ways as possible in which all or most fishes are alike. *(Students may name such features as scaly skin, aquatic habitat, and cold blood.)* List these characteristics on the board. Encourage students to examine each feature for exceptions.

Chapter 36 *Chordates and Fishes*

Introduction

Over half of the vertebrates—animals that have backbones—are fishes. This is not surprising, considering that 70 percent of the earth's surface is covered with water. In the last chapter you learned that invertebrates have a wide range of adaptations to different environments. In this chapter you will continue to study adaptations by examining fishes.

Chapter Outline

Chapter Concept

As you read, look for adaptations that have enabled fishes to evolve and thrive in a water environment.

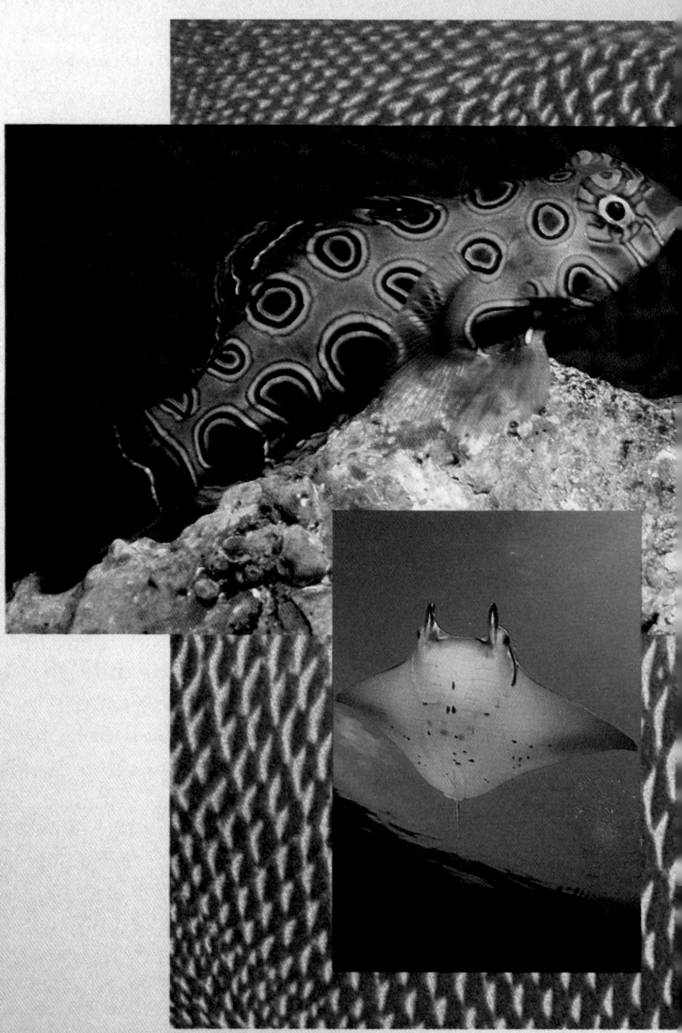

Psychedelic dragonet, *Callionymus* sp., Coral Sea. Inset: Manta ray, *Manta birostris,* Philippines. Background: fish scales.

Understanding the Visuals

Ask students how the shapes of the two fishes in the photos might help each of them survive. Point out that the photos are not to scale; the psychedelic dragonet is only a few inches long while the manta ray can be up to 22 feet wide. *(The stiff pelvic and pectoral fins of the dragonet allow it to rest on coral while the broad, wing-like fins of the manta propel it through the water and allow it to search for plankton on which it feeds.)*

Ask students how the unusual markings of the dragonet might help it survive. *(For example, the rings obscure the position of the eye, confusing predators and, perhaps, disguising the fish as a piece of coral.)* Explain that there can be many valid answers to both questions.

36.1 Overview of Chordates

When you think of a familiar animal, you probably think of a chordate *(KORD-ate)*. The Phylum Chordata includes vertebrates—members of the Subphylum Vertebrata *(vert-uh-BRAHT-uh)*. These are animals with backbones, such as sharks, frogs, crows, dogs, and humans. Chordates also include two other small subphyla of animals without backbones, Urochordata *(yoor-uh-kor-DAHT-uh)* and Cephalochordata *(SEFF-uh-loe-kor-DAHT-uh)*. The name chordate comes from **notochord,** a firm, flexible rod of specialized cells located in the dorsal part of the chordate body. Some chordates retain the notochord all their lives. In most vertebrates, however, the notochord appears only in the embryonic stage. Early in development it is replaced by the **vertebral column,** or backbone.

In Chapter 34 you learned that echinoderms are the closest invertebrate relatives to chordates. Echinoderms and chordates share several characteristics in their embryonic development. Scientists call members of these two phyla deuterostomes. **Deuterostomes** are coelomates whose embryos have radial cleavage, whose anus forms near the blastopore, and whose mesoderm arises from outpocketings of the endoderm. In most invertebrates the mesoderm arises as a separate layer between the endoderm and ectoderm. These characteristics provide strong evidence that echinoderms and chordates may share a common ancestor.

Chordates evolved in water, and their adaptations enabled them to succeed in that environment. Later the same features—an internal skeleton and highly controlled body movements and chemistry—were modified for living on land.

Characteristics

A chordate is an animal that at some stage of its development has a notochord, a dorsal nerve cord, and pharyngeal pouches.

- A notochord is a dorsal rod of specialized cells.
- A **dorsal nerve cord** is a hollow tube just above the notochord.
- **Pharyngeal pouches** are small outpockets of the anterior gut.

In most vertebrates the notochord exists only in the embryo. The notochord is replaced by an **endoskeleton,** an internal skeleton that can support a larger body than can the exoskeleton of an invertebrate. The endoskeleton grows as the animal grows and does not have to be discarded by molting. In vertebrates the dorsal nerve cord develops into a spinal cord with a brain. The brain is connected to a network of complex sensory organs. In lower chordates, fishes, and amphibians, the pharyngeal pouches evolved into filter-feeding structures, which in turn evolved into **gill slits,** which later evolved into gills. In terrestrial vertebrates, pharyngeal pouches evolved into structures in the throat and ear.

Section Objectives

- *List the major characteristics of chordates.*
- *Identify the three chordate subphyla.*
- *Describe the characteristics that distinguish vertebrates from other animals.*
- *Name the seven living vertebrate classes, and give an example of each one.*

Figure 36-1 The adult tunicate, *Clavelina picta,* loses its notochord during metamorphosis and so resembles a filter-feeding invertebrate more than a chordate.

Lesson Plan

Section Focus

This section presents chordates, each of which has a notochord, a dorsal nerve cord, and pharyngeal pouches at some stage of its development.

Section Themes

The theme of **Evolution** is emphasized in the discussion of how evolutionary relationships are determined, especially in the classification of the three chordate subphyla.

Motivating Activity

Ask students to name some animals that either have or lack a head. Refer to cephalization in Section 29.1. *(Insects, spiders, snails, vertebrates have heads; clams, sponges, sea stars, jellyfish lack heads.)* Then ask under what life circumstances having sense organs concentrated at the anterior end confers a survival advantage. *(For an animal that moves, the sense organs enter a new environment first; sessile animals don't need such an arrangement.)* Point out that the tunicate larva swims while the adult is sessile.

Teaching Strategies

Making Generalizations Ask students to name as many kinds of vertebrates as they can and identify characteristics these animals have in common. List on the board the characteristics students agree are shared by all (or nearly all) vertebrates. *(Sample answers: endoskeletons, enclosed brain, central nervous system)*

Videodiscs

- *1256–1264, Urochordata: Sea Squirts (s)*
- *1265–1269, Cephalochordata (s)*
- *Side 4 26902, Fish Swimming (m)*
- *2558–2589, Homologous Forelimbs (s)*

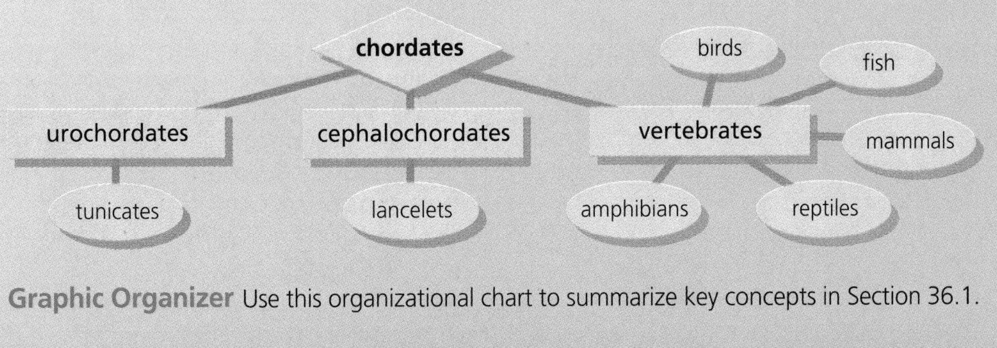

Graphic Organizer Use this organizational chart to summarize key concepts in Section 36.1.

Interpreting the Visuals Guide students step by step through the evolution of the vertebrates in Figure 36-4 on p. 539. Stress that some chordate groups evolved much earlier than others. Point out that the lines indicating time curve down to the right. Using the figure, ask students to determine which vertebrate groups are most closely related based on how recently their evolutionary lines have diverged. *(For instance, both birds and mammals are more closely related to reptiles than to each other; amphibians are more closely related to bony fish than to Chondrichthyes.)*

▪ *See* Blackline Master *74.*

Exploring Relationships Refer to the list, generated in Making Generalizations on p. 537, of the characteristics vertebrates have in common. Based on this list, have the students discuss how they themselves are similar to other vertebrates. *(Humans have a dorsal nerve cord protected by vertebrae, a brain encased in a skull, an axial and appendicular skeleton, and paired limbs.)*

Guided Practice

To help students familiarize themselves with the urochordates, have them study together Figure 36-2 on p. 538. Ask students to infer how the adult tunicate's digestive system might work, based on the structures illustrated. *(Water containing food particles enters through the incurrent siphon and passes through the pharyngeal slits, which filter out the food. The water exits through the excurrent siphon. Food particles trapped in the pharynx fall into the stomach.)*

Classification

Scientists divide the Phylum Chordata into three subphyla: Urochordata, Cephalochordata, and Vertebrata. Members of the first two subphyla live only in the ocean. About 2,000 species of urochordates and about 28 species of cephalochordates exist. Members of Cephalochordata retain the notochord throughout life and so are the closest living relatives of the early animals from which all chordates evolved. The third subphylum, Vertebrata, comprises about 41,000 species. More than 95 percent of all chordates are vertebrates.

Subphylum Urochordata

The hollow, barrel-shaped urochordates are commonly called tunicates because their bodies are protected by a tough covering, or tunic. Tunicates are also called "sea squirts" because they squirt out streams of water when touched. Larvae and some adults swim freely, but most adults, such as the one in Figure 36-2, attach themselves to the sea bottom. They may be solitary or colonial. Tunicates are adapted for filter feeding—straining food particles and taking oxygen gas from water drawn through their bodies by ciliary action. Being anchored and having cilia are adaptations to the filter-feeding way of life. Many such adaptations are examples of convergent evolution that are shared, as you have read, by many filter-feeding invertebrates. Despite their simple body plans tunicates have a notochord and dorsal nerve cord as larvae and gill slits both as larvae and as adults.

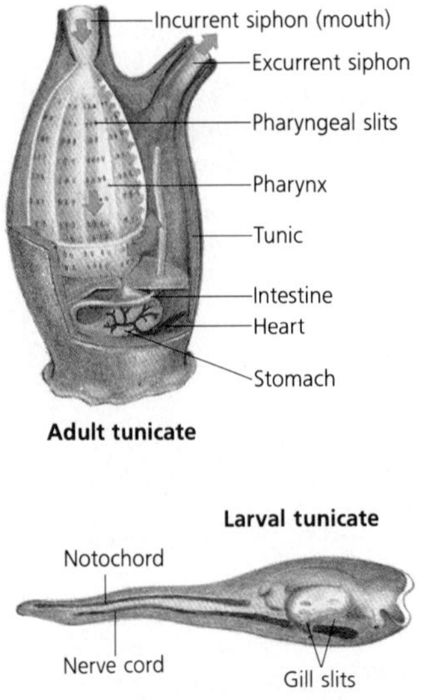

Figure 36-2 Unlike their larval forms most adult tunicates are not free swimming. Only in the larval stage do tunicates exhibit all their chordate features.

Subphylum Cephalochordata

Cephalochordates are marine organisms that live in shallow waters in warm southern regions. They are best represented by a blade-shaped translucent animal called *Branchiostoma (BRANG-kee-AHS-tuh-muh)*. Some people call this organism amphioxus; its common name is lancelet. *Branchiostoma* usually stays buried in sand. Only its head protrudes, allowing it to filter feed on organisms drawn from the water and to breathe through its gill slits. *Branchiostoma's* poorly developed fins force it to swim in a spiral as it moves forward. The lancelet structure shows all three chordate characteristics: notochord, dorsal nerve cord, and gill slits. Locate these structures in Figure 36-3.

Figure 36-3 The lancelet, *Branchiostoma lanceolatum,* retains its chordate characteristics throughout its life.

More Information

Class Appendicularia In this unusual class of urochordates, the adults have retained some of the features of larval tunicates, including a tail stiffened with a notochord. Instead of the larval tadpole shape, however, the body is twisted at right angles to the tail. The tiny appendicularians, only a few millimeters in length, live in the surface plankton of most of the world's oceans. They secrete a "house" made of a fine gelatinous material that traps the tiniest bits of plankton unavailable to most other filter feeders. This structure is shed and replaced every few hours. Although the adult retention of larval features (neoteny) seems a step toward the evolution of cephalochordata, appendicularians actually represent a separate line of development.

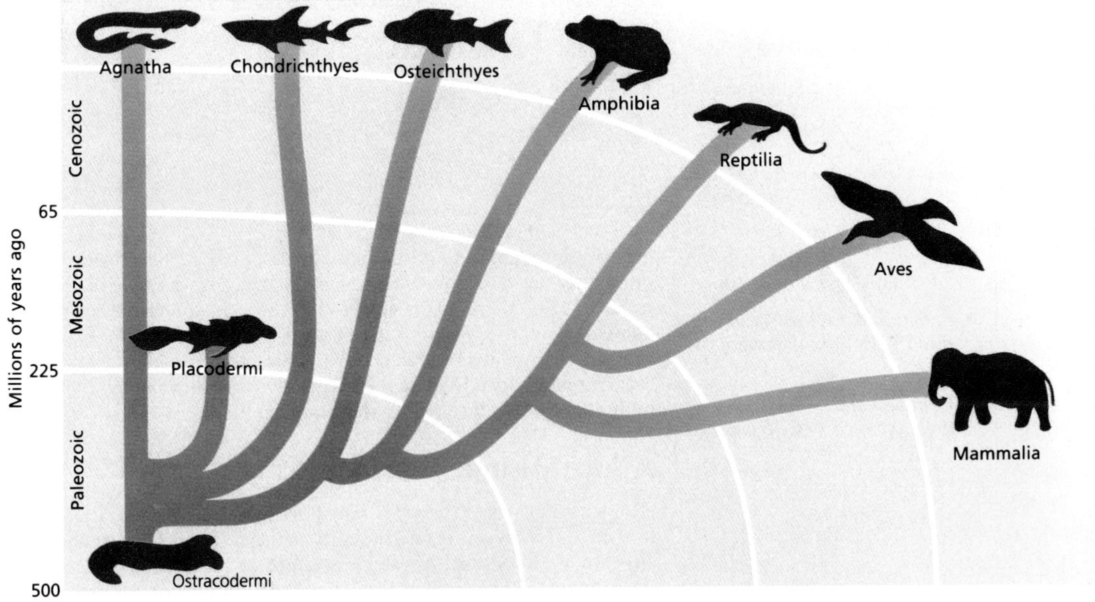

Figure 36-4 The evolution of the vertebrates has led to the seven classes that exist today. The date each class branched from the ancestral tree is the date each class began.

Subphylum Vertebrata

Vertebrates are named for their vertebrae, the bones or cartilage that surround the dorsal nerve cord. Other features characterize vertebrates. Vertebrates have a brain protected by an outer **skull,** or cranium. Their backbone and skull make up the **axial** *(ACK-see-ul)* **skeleton.** Paired limbs or fins are attached to the axial skeleton by girdles of bones or cartilage. The girdles and limbs or fins make up the **appendicular** *(ap-un-DICK-yuh-lur)* **skeleton.** Muscles attached to the skeleton allow movement.

The organs of vertebrates, like those of invertebrates, are organized into ten systems: skeletal, muscular, integumentary, digestive, respiratory, circulatory, excretory, immune, nervous, and reproductive. Each performs a special function. Seven classes of vertebrates exist today. Fossil evidence indicates increasing complexity of body structure corresponding to the order in which the classes evolved. Figure 36-4 shows these relationships.

Section Review

1. How do the notochord and dorsal nerve cord differ?
2. Which invertebrate phylum is developmentally most similar to vertebrates? Explain.
3. Name and give examples of the three chordate subphyla.
4. List four distinguishing features of vertebrates.
5. Name the first living class of vertebrates found in the fossil record. Which is most recent? Refer to Figure 36-4.

Answers to Section Review

1. The notochord is a firm, flexible rod found at some point in the development of all chordates. The dorsal nerve cord is a tube that lies just above the notochord. In vertebrates, the notochord develops into the endoskeleton and the dorsal nerve cord becomes the spinal cord.
2. Echinoderms. Both are deuterostomes.
3. Urochordata, tunicate; Cephalochordata, lancelet; Vertebrata (accept any vertebrate example)
4. Vertebral column, brain enclosed in a skull, axial skeleton, and appendicular skeleton (or paired limbs or fins)
5. Agnatha or jawless fishes; Aves or birds

Independent Practice

- Have students write answers to the Section Review.
- Ask students to list the vertebrate classes in the order in which they are believed to have evolved.

Check Your Understanding

1. In general shape and characteristics, the lancelet resembles what stage of the tunicate? *(Larva)*
2. What type of symmetry do animals that have a notochord exhibit? *(Bilateral symmetry)*
3. What characteristic do urochordates share with some invertebrates? *(Filter feeding)* Of what is this similarity an example? *(Convergent evolution)*

Reteaching

Ask students to make a concept map that presents the major features of chordates. An example of a completed concept map is shown on p. 535B.

- *See* **Section Reviews** ***worksheet, Section 36.1.***

Enrichment

Have students prepare a report on a urochordate or a cephalochordate species. Have them include information on the habitat and special features of the species they have chosen.

Closure

Show students an unlabeled photo of a human embryo. Ask them to determine if it is a chordate or not. *(It is.)* Then ask them whether it is a vertebrate. *(It is.)* Have them explain the basis for their answers. *(The presence of a backbone, paired limbs.)* Then identify the embryo as human.

Videodiscs

- ***2590–2593, Classification; Evolutionary Relationships (s)***
- ***2105–2109, Vertebrate Skeletons (s)***

Lesson Plan

Section Focus

This section describes the phylogeny of fishes, the most numerous of all vertebrates. Fishes are divided into the primitive Class Agnatha, or jawless fishes; Class Chondrichthyes, including sharks, skates, and rays; and the highly diverse Class Osteichthyes, or bony fishes.

Section Themes

The theme of **Evolution** is emphasized in this section. The evolution of the three fish classes from a common ostrocoderm ancestor has given rise to a variety of different shapes and anatomical features. Each adaptation helps the fish survive and reproduce within its habitat: water.

Motivating Activity

Show students pictures of a wide variety of fishes—for example, hagfish, eel, flounder, skate, shark, pufferfish, guppy, catfish, and salmon. Ask students what characteristics each fish has that allows it to be classified as a fish. *(It has fins, seems to have gills; most have scales.)* Stress that fishes are a very diverse group.

Section Objectives

- *List the major adaptations that enable fish to live in water.*
- *Name the three fish classes, and list their distinguishing characteristics.*
- *Describe the feeding behavior of lampreys and hagfish.*
- *Explain how scientists measure the learning potential of sharks.*
- *Compare and contrast the three types of bony fishes.*

36.2 Evolution and Classification of Fishes

The term *fish* encompasses three distinct classes of vertebrates: Agnatha *(AG-nuh-thuh),* jawless fishes; Chondrichthyes *(kahn-DRICK-thee-eez),* sharks, skates, and rays; and Osteichthyes *(AHS-tee-ICK-thee-eez),* bony fishes. Fishes are the most numerous of all vertebrates and the most widespread in their distribution. They are also diverse in size and shape. Fishes range in size from the 13-mm Philippine goby to the 18-m, 14-ton whale shark. Some are solitary, such as the pearl fish that lives in the body cavity of certain invertebrates. Others, such as herring or sardines, form large schools. Despite their diversity fishes have many common adaptations that reflect their aquatic life.

Adaptations

The density of water, which is 800 times the density of air, affects both the body structure and mobility of fishes. Because of its density water offers much greater resistance to movement than air does. To live in water, most fishes have adaptations for buoyancy. One such adaptation consists of the trapping of gas inside their bodies. By controlling the amount of gas in their bodies, fishes regulate their vertical position in the water. Another set of adaptations enables them to swim. A streamlined shape and muscular tail enable fishes to move rapidly through the water. Paired fins allow them to maneuver easily right or left, up or down, and backward or forward. In addition, the mucus that most fishes secrete reduces friction as they swim.

Protective scales on fishes limit chemical exchanges through the skin. Instead, most exchanges between water and blood take place across the membranes of **gills**—the external respiratory organs, usually found on either side of the head. Most fishes have highly developed senses of smell and touch. A prominent adaptation present in all classes except Agnatha is the **lateral line system.** This system consists of a row of sensory structures that run the length of the fish's body on each side and that are connected by nerves to the brain. The lateral line system detects vibrations in the water.

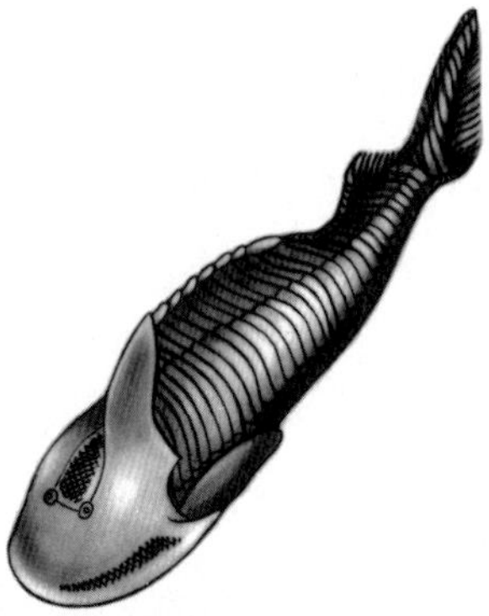

Figure 36-5 Ostracoderms, the earliest vertebrates, lacked jaws and were covered with bony plates.

Evolution

As you see in Figure 36-4, adaptations in fishes are the result of millions of years of evolution by natural selection. The first known vertebrates, small jawless fish placed in the Class Ostracodermi, were covered with heavy bony plates. They first appeared about 540 million years ago. The large bony plates remain today, modified in form, as scales. Comparative morphology shows that

Fish	Distinguishing Characteristics	Method of Feeding	Other Facts
Agnatha Hagfish	jawless, elongated	parasitism, scavenging	hagfish ties self in knot to clean off mucus
Osteichthyes Lobe-finned fish	have paddle-like fins	predators	probable ancestors of higher vertebrates

Graphic Organizer Use this table in Independent Practice on p. 544.

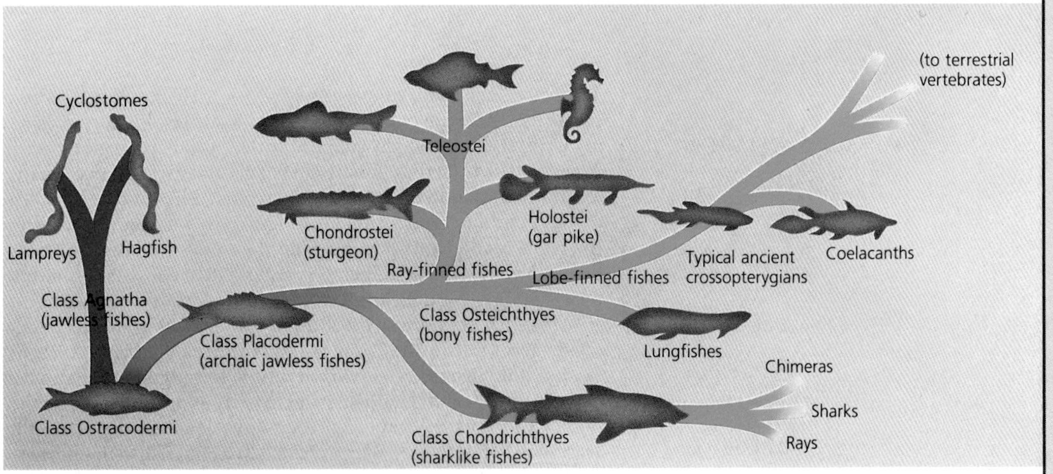

Figure 36-6 The phylogenetic tree of fish begins with jawless fishes. One line of evolution leads to terrestrial vertebrates.

today's jawless fishes, members of the Class Agnatha, are similar to ostracoderms. This indicates that they probably evolved from the ostracoderms. The other two classes—the Chondrichthyes and the Osteichthyes—probably also evolved from ostracoderms, but along a different phylogenetic line, as seen in Figure 36-6. Members of these two classes have jaws that presumably evolved from ostracoderm gills. Relatives of modern jawed, bony and cartilaginous fishes began to appear in the fossil record 400 million years ago.

The fossil record shows that after fishes became abundant, two other adaptations occurred in some species that were central to the evolution of other classes of vertebrates. One was the evolution of a pouch in the posterior portion of the mouth that functioned as a lung. The other was the emergence of fins supported by bony lobes projecting from the body. These adaptations occur today in the lungfish and the lobe-finned fish, two subgroups of bony fishes. The ability to breathe air and to cross land on fins enabled shallow-water species to survive droughts. Comparative morphology indicates that prototype lungs evolved into lungs in land vertebrates and that lobed fins evolved into limbs. These lobe-finned fish were the ancestors of amphibians.

Agnatha

The only existing jawless fishes are the 45 species of lampreys and hagfish that compose the Class Agnatha. *Agnatha* means "jawless." Because of their circular mouths these organisms are often called cyclostomes, meaning "round mouths." The slimy skin of lampreys and hagfish has neither plates nor scales. Both fishes have a notochord that remains throughout life. Each has an eel-like shape, a cartilaginous skeleton, and unpaired fins. Hagfish live only in the oceans. Many lampreys live in fresh water.

Some lampreys are free-living, but most are parasitic. They are adapted for sucking the blood and body fluids of other fish.

Figure 36-7 The disk-shaped mouth of the lamprey, *Lampetra fluviatilis*, is adapted for attachment to prey by suction.

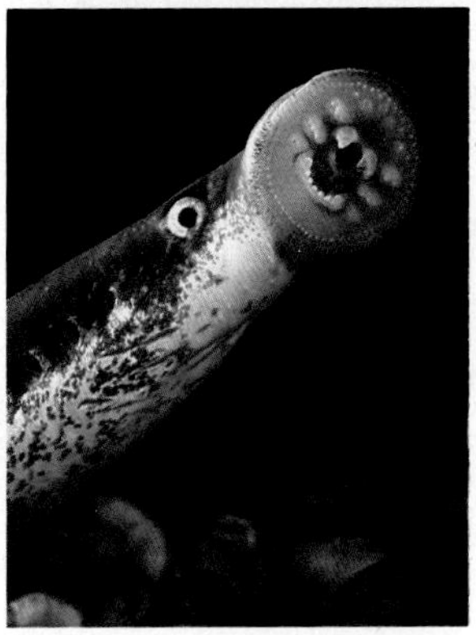

Teaching Strategies

Inferring Relationships Provide students with approximately 12 specimens or pictures representing the three classes of fishes. Have them note how the fishes are alike and how they differ. *(Eels and hagfish are both long and slender, but hagfish have no paired fins; skates and flounders are flat, but flounders lie on their sides; sharks and tuna are streamlined, but sharks have multiple gill slits.)* Ask students to group the fishes by identifying common attributes. Prompt students by asking the following questions: Which fishes should be grouped together? What criteria can be used? How are the groups alike and how do they differ? Have students compare their groupings to the three fish classes. Notice how each group feeds and is adapted to living in the water.

■ *See* Process Skills, *Chapter 36.*

Drawing Conclusions Review with students the major features of each fish class. Ask students to give examples of how these features adapt fishes to their particular ecological niche. *(Lampreys: jawless mouth adapted to parasitism, olfactory bulb adapted to finding prey; Sharks: pectoral fins compensate for downward thrust of tail, sharp teeth for tearing flesh; Lungfishes: lung adapted to drying ponds.)* Remind students that there are many aquatic habitats, such as open ocean, coral reefs, tide pools, lakes, streams, and ponds. This diversity of habitat is reflected in the variety of fish adaptations.

Videodiscs

■ *1270–1273, Agnatha (s)*

Interdisciplinary Activity

Literature Have students read one or more poems about fishes. Several can be found at the ends of chapters in John Hersey's book *Blues* (Knopf, 1987). Recommended poems: "The Fish" by Elizabeth Bishop, "The Lung Fish" by John Ciardi, "Pike" by Ted Hughes, and "The Red Mullet" by Robert Penn Warren. Have students write reports about the poems. Ask the following questions to focus students' thinking. How did the poet use the fish in the poem? How did the fish add to the meaning of the poem? Was the poet's description of the fish biologically accurate? Explain.

Analyzing Adaptations A number of unrelated aquatic animals bear live young rather than laying eggs. These animals include guppies, some sharks, whales and dolphins, and ichthyosaurs (prehistoric marine reptiles resembling dolphins). Have students suggest ways in which bearing live young would be an adaptive advantage. *(It protects the young because they are mobile at birth.)* Have students suggest ways in which egg layers and live bearers may be different. *(Egg layers produce many more young, initially. Female live bearers must devote more energy per offspring.)*

Observing Organisms Plan a visit to a local aquarium so that students may witness the diversity of fishes, observe their behavior, and learn about their habitats. Prior to the trip prepare a list of points to notice, which could include the following questions: Is there a relationship between a fish's shape and the way it moves? What are the functions of the various colors and patterns? In what ways do fishes defend themselves from predators? How many fish groups are represented at the aquarium? Can we find examples of symbiosis between fishes and other organisms?

To locate their prey, lampreys rely on a highly developed sense of smell. A nasal pore on top of the head leads to olfactory sacs rich in nerve endings, which connect with specialized regions of the brain called **olfactory lobes.** The lamprey uses its disk-shaped mouth to attach itself to a fish by suction. Then it tears a hole in the fish with its toothy tongue and secretes a chemical that keeps the fish's blood from clotting. Since lampreys feed on fluids, they do not have a stomach. Their digestive system consists of a mouth, an esophagus, a straight intestine, and associated glands.

Hagfish are bottom dwellers in cold marine waters. They are scavengers of dead and dying fish on the ocean bottom. A hagfish saws a hole in these fish with its toothed tongue and eats them from the inside out. Hagfish are extremely supple and can tie their bodies in knots to evade capture or to clean off the slime they secrete in self-defense. When not feeding, hagfish remain hidden in mud burrows on the ocean floor.

Chondrichthyes

Sharks, skates, and rays belong to the Class Chondrichthyes. Like the Agnatha, Chondrichthyes have skeletons of cartilage, not

Biology in Process

Understanding Sharks

People long feared all sharks without knowing a great deal about them. Scientists studied the anatomy of sharks by dissecting dead ones. Without observing live sharks, scientists were unable to answer some simple questions: How intelligent are sharks? How long do they live? How much food do they need?

Today scientists use a variety of sophisticated methods to collect information about the structure and the behavior of sharks. To study growth rates, researchers measure and tag individual sharks and then release them. When recaught, the sharks are again measured. To determine habitat range, scientists track sharks that have been fitted with transmitters that emit radio signals.

One American biologist, Eugenie Clark, is a world leader in shark study. She was one of the first scientists to construct a shark pen, which enabled her to observe and collect data from live sharks in captivity. In 1958 she conducted the now-classic experiments on the learning abilities of sharks. Up to that time sharks were considered somewhat stupid and poor subjects for the learning experiments that had been conducted on other animals. Clark hypothesized, however, that

Cooperative Learning

Buoyancy Have students work in groups of two or three to perform the following exercise demonstrating how gas trapped internally can help a fish achieve neutral buoyancy. Fill an aquarium or large basin with water. Using a rubber band, attach a series of weights to a Ping-Pong ball. (Weights could be metal washers, coins, modelling clay, and so forth.) Place the weighted ball in the aquarium or basin. Notice whether it floats on top of the water, sinks to the bottom, or floats stationary beneath the surface. The last indicates neutral buoyancy. Keep adjusting the weights until neutral buoyancy is achieved. Weigh all of the materials, including the rubber band and the Ping-Pong ball. Most of this weight reflects the weight of the water displaced by the air in the ball. Have the students bone. Cartilage is a tissue made of cells surrounded by tough, flexible protein structures. Although these cartilaginous fish seem simpler in structure than bony fish, fossil evidence indicates that they probably evolved from bony fish and lost bone over time. Chondrichthyes differ from the Agnatha by having movable jaws and skeletons with paired fins.

Almost all the approximately 275 species of sharks, skates, and rays live in salt water. Most are carnivores that typically use their large olfactory organs and lateral line systems to track prey. The skin of sharks and most rays is covered with **placoid scales**—small, toothlike spines that feel like sandpaper.

Sharks

The voracious predatory habits of some shark species have given them a reputation as killers. Yet fewer than 10 percent of shark species are known to attack humans unprovoked. Whale sharks, for example, are gentle 18-m giants that graze on plankton.

Sharks swim with a side-to-side motion of their asymmetric tail fins. Just behind their heads are paired **pectoral** *(PECK-tuh-rul)* **fins,** which jut out from their bodies like the wings of a plane. These fins compensate for the downward thrust of the tail fin.

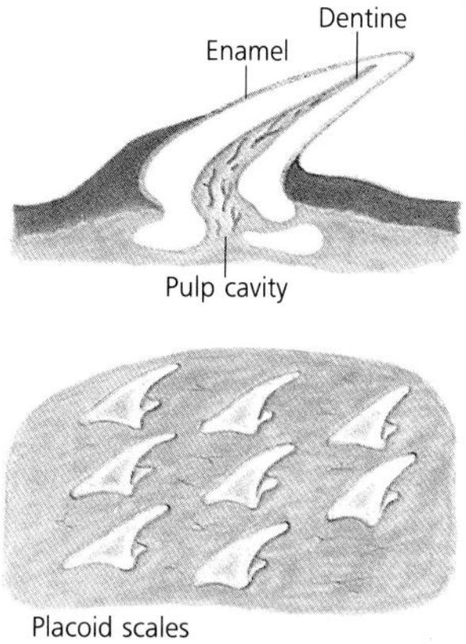

Figure 36-8 What similarities can you note between a shark's tooth (top) and placoid scales (bottom)?

the learning ability of sharks was underrated.

For her study Clark used two adult lemon sharks, which she had captured near the Cape Haze Marine Laboratory, south of Sarasota, Florida. A white target was lowered into the water at feeding time. Pushing on the target caused a bell to ring and also enabled the sharks to get at food lowered into the water on a string. Within a few days the sharks learned that ringing the bell was associated with food.

Clark varied the routine. She threw food out at faster intervals and at greater distances from the target. She altered the volume of the bell sound. Each time the sharks adjusted to the change in routine.

However, Clark learned that sharks had a limited tolerance for change. One day she altered the color of the target to a bright yellow. The male shark started as usual for the target as it was lowered into the water. Then about two feet away from the target he reacted to the change in color and did not hit the target.

■ How would you design an experiment to determine whether the shark reacted to the sudden change in color or whether the reaction was specifically to the color yellow?

discuss their results in class. Ask them how neutral buoyancy is adaptive for a fish. *(A neutrally buoyant fish uses no energy to keep afloat, while a less buoyant fish, such as most sharks, must constantly swim to avoid sinking.)* Also ask students for what types of fish neutral buoyancy would not be a helpful adaptation. *(Fishes, such as flounders or skates, that are adapted to living on the bottom; flounders lack a gas bladder)*

Biology in Process

Using the Feature

The feature focuses on the process skills of observing animal behavior and drawing conclusions about intelligence. Stress that modern scientists study living sharks in the laboratory as well as in their natural habitats.

Explain that radio transmitters and the tag-and-release method are employed to study a wide variety of marine and terrestrial animals. These methods can also be used to gather information about migration patterns of such animals as sea turtles, caribou, and birds.

Stress that much scientific work, such as that done by Eugenie Clark, begins with a hypothesis that may run counter to popular assumptions. Ideally, a scientist should design a research program that will test the hypothesis by trying to knock holes in it. The experimental design should be repeatable so that other scientists can test the hypothesis. Ask students what results would have refuted Dr. Clark's hypothesis that sharks are capable of learning. *(If they had never associated the target or the bell with the food, sharks would not have demonstrated a learning ability.)*

Answer to the Feature

Answers might include using a yellow target from the start and then changing to a white target, but not with the abruptness of Clark's original experiment.

Videodiscs

■ *1274–1282, Chondrichthyes (s)*

Guided Practice

Remind students that convergent evolution is a process by which unrelated species exhibit similar characteristics as they adapt to similar environments. Ask students to suggest examples of convergent evolution in fishes. Stress that students should name the fishes and the characteristics in which they are similar. *(Lampreys and eels: long and slender; rays and flounders: flat; sharks and guppies: live bearers)* Have students suggest the environmental pressures that may have resulted in the similar characteristics. *(Flatness is adaptive to bottom feeding.)* Ask students how a scientist would determine if similar characteristics are the result of convergent evolution or exist because of inheritance from a common ancestor. *(Scientists study the fossil record and living species for evidence of independent evolution of the characteristics. Also scientists compare similar species to see if similar characteristics are achieved in different ways. For example, rays and flounders are flattened along different axes.)*

Independent Practice

- Have students write answers to the Section Review.
- Have students make a table comparing characteristics of each class of fishes. Give students the table on p. 540 as a model, and have them add rows for other classes.

Figure 36-9 The teeth of this sand tiger shark, *Odontaspis taurus,* are pointed inward in a way that keeps prey from escaping by swimming away.

The shark's mouth has 6 to 20 rows of backward-pointing teeth. When a tooth breaks or wears down, a replacement moves forward. One shark may eventually use more than 20,000 teeth. The structure of each species' teeth is adapted to its feeding habits. Sharks that catch primarily large fish have big, triangular teeth with sawlike edges that hook and tear prey. Bottom-feeding species that eat mollusks and crustaceans have flattened teeth that can crush shells. Sharks that eat small fish have long, thin teeth that grasp slippery prey.

The ability of sharks to detect chemicals—that is, their sense of smell—is particularly acute. Paired nostrils on the snout have specialized nerve cells that connect with the olfactory lobes of the brain. Water entering the nostrils is continually monitored for chemicals. Sharks can detect blood from an injured animal as far as 500 m away. Sharks also have a well-developed lateral line system. In most species the sense of sight is less developed than the sense of smell.

Gas exchange requires a continuous passage of water over a shark's gills. Therefore most sharks must swim constantly, pushing water through their mouths, over their gills, and out of their gill slits.

Shark eggs are fertilized internally. During mating the male grasps the female with modified fins called claspers. Sperm runs from the male into the female through grooves in the claspers. The eggs of most species develop within the female's body, and the pups are born alive. A few species lay large yolky eggs right after fertilization.

Rays and Skates

Rays and skates have flattened bodies with winglike, paired pectoral fins and, in some species, whiplike tails. Rays have diamond- or disk-shaped bodies, while most skates have triangular bodies. Most rays and skates are less than 1 m long.

Rays and skates are primarily bottom dwellers and exhibit many adaptations to this life. Their flat shape and speckled or sandy color help to camouflage them on the ocean floor. Because their ventral mouths are often buried in sand, water enters their gills through two openings called spiracles atop their heads. Most feed on mollusks and crustaceans. Their teeth enable rays and skates to crush such prey.

Figure 36-10 The manta ray's coloring provides camouflage from above and below.

More Information

Electroreception Most sharks and a few bony fishes can detect the minute electric currents emitted by the nerves of prey species. In experiments, the dogfish shark can locate a flounder buried in the sediment, even when the prey is concealed beneath an electrically conductive plate. In the same experiment, the dogfish is not attracted to buried chopped fish or to a live flounder covered by an electrically insulating sheet. It will, however, locate and attack buried electrodes with a current similar to that of nerves. The U.S. Navy has developed an antishark screen made of a large polyvinyl bag that provides electric as well as visual and olfactory screening to a wounded swimmer.

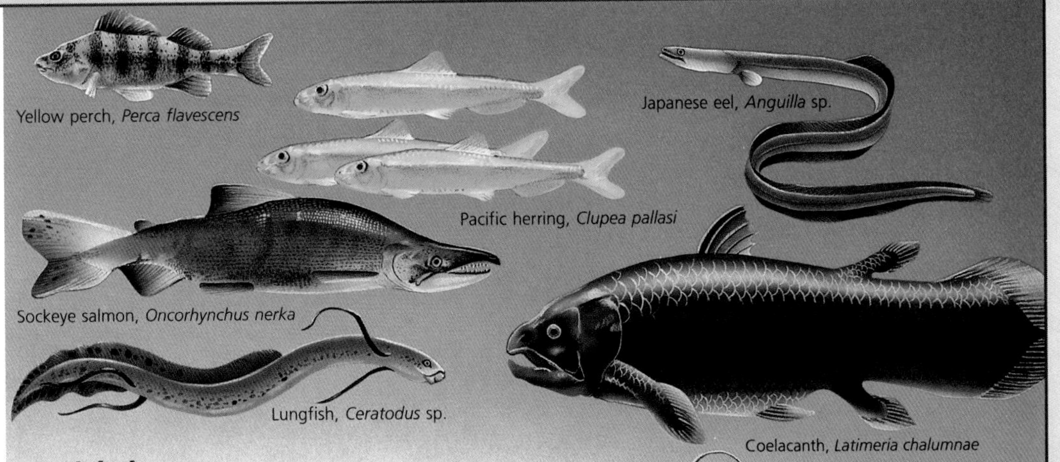

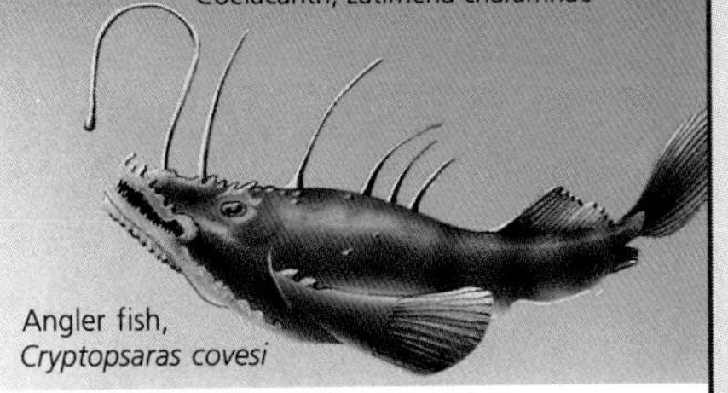

Figure 36-11 The seemingly endless variety of bony fishes reflects their many successful adaptations.

Osteichthyes

Of the 25,000 known species of fishes, about 95 percent are in the Class Osteichthyes—the bony fishes. They make up most of the vertebrate population in fresh water and in salt water. This dominance indicates the success of their adaptations, such as their bony internal skeleton, scaly skin, sense organs, fins, and reproductive patterns. Scientists divide bony fishes into lobe-finned fishes, lungfishes, and ray-finned fishes.

Lobe-finned fishes, or coelacanths *(SEE-luh-KANTHS),* have paddlelike fins with fleshy bases. They were thought to have been extinct for more than 70 million years until South African fishermen caught one in 1938. The genus was named *Latimeria,* after the local museum curator, Mary Latimer, who recognized its biological importance. It is probably related to the ancestors of the first amphibians.

Lungfishes have lungs. **Lungs** are internal respiratory organs where gas exchange takes place between air and the blood. Lungfish also have gills, where gas exchange takes place between water and the blood. Lungfishes live in shallow tropical ponds that dry up in the summer. They burrow into the mud and cover themselves in mucus to stay moist until the pond refills.

Ray-finned fishes have fins that are supported by long bones called rays. They are diverse in appearance, behavior, and habitat. Ray-finned fishes are the most familiar fishes, and include snakelike eels, yellow perch, cave fish, herring, and lantern fish.

Section Review

1. What is the function of a fish's lateral line system?
2. Compare and contrast the three fish classes.
3. How do lampreys feed?
4. Name the three main types of bony fishes, and give a distinguishing feature of each.
5. Horn sharks, which inhabit reef areas, have large molarlike teeth at the back of their jaws and sharp teeth in front. What do you infer that these sharks eat?

Answers to Section Review

1. It detects vibrations in the water.
2. The Agnatha and the Chondrichthyes both have skeletons of cartilage while the Osteichthyes have bony skeletons. Only Chondrichthyes and Osteichthyes have jaws.
3. They use their disk-shaped mouths to attach to another fish by suction and their toothy tongues to tear a hole in the prey. Then they suck the blood and fluids from the prey.
4. Lobe-finned fishes have fins with fleshy bases. Lungfishes have both lungs and gills. Ray-finned fishes have fins supported by long bones or rays.
5. They eat both fish and shellfish. Their molars crush the shellfish. Their sharp teeth catch the fish.

Check Your Understanding

1. How do many fishes adjust their buoyancy? *(By controlling the amount of trapped gas within their bodies)*
2. What fish adaptations led to the evolution of land vertebrates? *(Lungs, and fins supported by bony lobes)*
3. How are shark eggs fertilized? *(Internally; the sperm runs from the male into the female through grooves in the claspers.)*

Reteaching

Provide a list of characteristics that could apply to one or more of the following fish groups: Agnatha, Chondrichthyes, and the three types of Osteichthyes —lobe-finned fishes, lungfishes, and ray-finned fishes. Have the students, working in small groups, assign the characteristics to the correct group or groups. *(For example, slimy, plateless skin is a characteristic of Agnatha.)*

▪ *See* Section Reviews *worksheet, Section 36.2.*

Enrichment

Have students use library references to research the coelacanths and write reports to present to the class. Tell them to examine different aspects of coelacanths, such as evolution, natural history, anatomy, or the circumstances of their rediscovery.

Closure

Ask students to think of reasons why natural selection might have favored the development of such fish characteristics as a backbone, gills, scales, and paired fins. *(Backbone: strength and flexibility; gills: efficient gas exchange; scales: protection; paired fins: mobility)* Have students note evidence that supports their ideas.

Videodiscs

- *Side 4 3305, Manta Ray (m)*
- *Side 4 27168, Ray (m)*

Lesson Plan

Section Focus

This section introduces the anatomy of a bony fish. Even though bony fishes are the most numerous and diverse of the vertebrates, most have some characteristics in common, including a bony skeleton, fins, scaly skin, and details of their systems. Most bony fishes achieve neutral buoyancy by means of a gas bladder.

Section Themes

The theme of **Scale and Structure** is emphasized in this section to show the ways in which the anatomical structures of a typical bony fish are adaptations to its ecological niche. These adaptations include gas bladders, gills, overlapping scales, and fins, among other structures.

Motivating Activity

Ask students who have had experience with fishes, either by visiting an aquarium, diving, keeping tropical fishes as a hobby, fishing, or cooking (or eating) fish to describe some of the behavioral or anatomical features of particular fishes they have observed. *(Bluegills hang in the water in the shadow of the dock, catfish stay on the bottom and have "whiskers," salmon have lots of small bones.)* Have students suggest relationships between structures and function in these features. *(Gas bladders allow bluegills to float motionless in the water; catfish feel for prey with "whiskers"; small bones strengthen the salmon's sleek body.)* Point out that all animal structures have at least one function.

■ *See* **Laboratories,** ***Investigation 36.***

Section Objectives

- *List the characteristics of body structure, fins, and integument of the yellow perch.*
- *Describe the internal anatomy of the yellow perch.*
- *Explain how gills function in respiration.*
- *Describe the spawning behavior of fishes.*

36.3 Morphology of a Bony Fish

The diversity of body shape in bony fishes reflects their varied ways of life. However, all have some characteristics in common. In this section we will examine the morphology of the yellow perch, a representative bony fish. This fish, *Perca flavescens,* grows up to 38 cm long and is common in the Great Lakes and other freshwater lakes of the eastern United States and Canada.

External Anatomy

Look at Figure 36-12 to see how the external appearance of the yellow perch shows several important adaptive features. These include the gill structures, specialized fins, and skin.

Body Structure

The yellow perch, like all bony fishes, has distinct head, trunk, and tail regions. On each side of the head is the **operculum,** a hard plate that opens at the rear and covers and protects the gills. The perch opens its mouth to take in water, and the water passes over the gills, where gases are exchanged. The water leaves through the operculum. Yellow perch have strong muscles along their dorsal backbone that thrust the tail from side to side. They can swim at speeds up to 16 km per hour.

Figure 36-12 The external features of the yellow perch, *Perca flavescens,* are representative of bony fishes. Note the growth rings on the scales shown in the inset. They indicate the fish's approximate age.

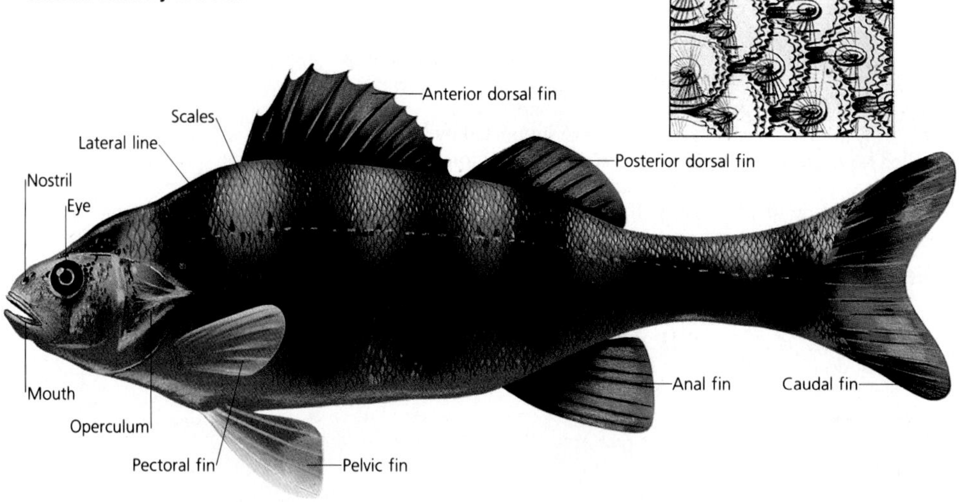

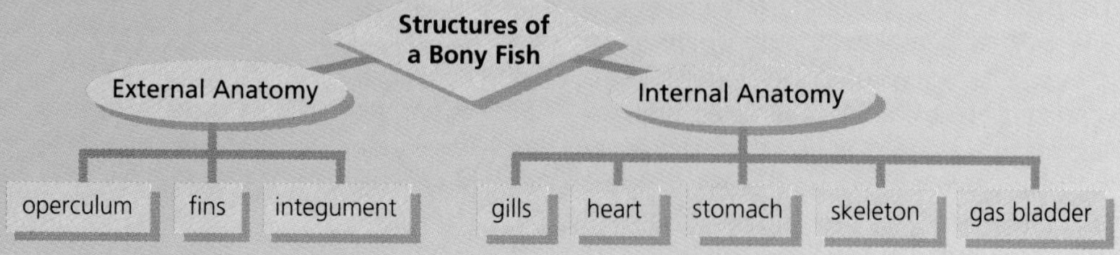

Graphic Organizer Use this organizational chart in Reteaching on p. 550.

Fins

The fins of the yellow perch are adapted for swimming and guiding the fish through the water. Look again at Figure 36-12. The **caudal fin** extends from the tail. It moves from side to side and amplifies the swimming motions. Two **dorsal fins,** one anterior and one posterior, and a ventral **anal fin** help keep the fish upright and moving in a straight line. The paired **pelvic fins** and pectoral fins are more specialized than the fixed fins of sharks. The perch uses these fins to steer, brake, move up and down, and even back up. They also orient the body when at rest.

Fins are thin fan-shaped membranes richly supplied with blood. By raising and lowering its fins, the perch helps regulate its body temperature. The fins are supported by rays or spines. Rays are bony yet flexible, while spines are bony and rigid. In most fish the posterior dorsal fin has rays. The anterior dorsal fin is spiny and is often used in defense. For example, the backward-pointing spines of a perch can pierce the throat of a predator that tries to swallow it from the rear.

Integument

The **integument** *(in-TEG-yoo-munt),* or skin, of the yellow perch is covered with scales. These are thin, round disks of highly modified bone that grow from pockets in the skin. As Figure 36-12 shows, scales overlap like roof shingles, all pointing toward the tail to minimize friction as the fish swims. Scales grow during the entire life of the fish, adjusting their growth pattern to the food supply. The scales grow quickly when food is abundant and slowly when it is scarce. The resulting growth rings give a good approximation of the yellow perch's age.

The skin of bony fishes also contains pigmented **chromatophores** *(kroe-MAT-uh-FORZ)* that create various color patterns as, for example, the bars on the sides of the yellow perch. Many deep-sea fishes are black or have phosphorescent patterns. Others blend in with the ocean bottom by changing color. Flounders, for example, can quickly match the spots of the sand found on the ocean floor.

Internal Anatomy

The yellow perch has the same major organ systems as all other bony fishes. Like other bony fishes, the yellow perch also has an organ called the gas bladder.

The bone of the yellow perch, like that of all vertebrates, is a living tissue in which cells deposit minerals, primarily calcium. Bone can grow, support many times its own weight, and heal if broken. It resists bending or breaking when stressed by muscles or blows. The major parts of the fish skeleton are the skull, spine, and ribs. The spine is made up of many bones, the vertebrae, with cartilage pads in between. This provides both strength and flexi-

Think

The back of the speckled trout shown above makes the fish hard to see by both predator and prey when it lies at the bottom of a pebbly stream. What benefit might the trout derive from its light-colored undersurface?

More Information

Bioluminescence A variety of bony fishes, and some sharks as well, have evolved the ability to generate light within their bodies, a process called bioluminescence. Most often, the light is generated by colonies of luminescent bacteria living within the fish that can oxidize a protein called luciferin with an enzyme called luciferase.

Bioluminescent fishes mostly live deep in the ocean, where virtually no sunlight penetrates. Light is usually concentrated in small organs called photophores. Some fishes use their glow to signal the opposite sex, warn off rivals, or confuse predators. Bioluminescent anglerfishes carry a glowing lure on the end of a "fishing pole," an organ modified from the anterior ray of the dorsal fin.

Teaching Strategies

Analyzing Properties Divide the students into small groups. Provide each group with a different type of bony fish. These could be a fish in an aquarium, fish from a market, or preserved specimens purchased from a biological supply company. Have each group observe and record on a chart several adaptive features, such as the location, shape, and size of the mouth or fins. Ask students to relate these adaptations to the fish's habitat and behavior. Have students compare their fishes with a fish of very different habits and habitat. Ask each group to chart the specific changes in anatomy that would have to occur to make their fishes into that other fish. *(Removing the gas bladder of a perch would be one step in making it more like a flounder.)*

Answer to Think

The light-colored underbelly also serves as a camouflage. It makes the fish hard to see when viewed from below against the light-colored, sunlit water.

Identifying Adaptations Write the following aspects of fish morphology on separate slips of paper: body structure, fins, integument, digestive system, circulatory system, respiratory system, excretory system, nervous system, and reproductive system. Have individual students or pairs of students draw slips from the pile. Give students time to discuss or note ways in which the aspect of fish morphology shows adaptations for a life specifically spent in the water. Have the students present their ideas to the class.

Videodiscs

- *1283–1309, Osteichthyes (s)*
- *Side 4 3461, Puffer Fish (m)*

Interpreting the Visuals Guide students, item-by-item, through the external anatomy of a bony fish (Figure 36-12, p. 546) and the internal anatomy of a bony fish (Figure 36-13, p. 548). Ask students to name the features that are specific adaptations to life in the water. *(Fins, gills, gas bladder)* Ask students to explain how these features adapt the fish to its habitat.

■ *See* Overhead Transparency *T36 and* Blackline Masters *75 and 76.*

Exploring Careers Invite an ichthyologist or ecologist from a local university, aquarium, or government environmental agency (state division of wildlife, fisheries, or environmental protection) to discuss his or her research on adaptations of fishes to their environments. Encourage students to ask the guest speaker about the process of designing and carrying out research.

Guided Practice

Refer students to the small inset of Figure 36-13 on p. 548. Have them trace the circulatory path of the blood starting at the heart and returning to the heart. List the places along the path where gas exchange takes place. *(The gills; the body tissues)*

Figure 36-13 The internal anatomy of a bony fish includes an organ—the gas bladder—unique to this class of vertebrates. The inset shows details of the circulatory system.

bility. The spinal column also partly encloses and protects the spinal cord.

Digestive System

Yellow perch, like many bony fishes, are carnivores. Their jaws are armed with many sharp teeth that point inward to keep smaller fish and other prey from escaping. Strong muscles operate the jaws, which have a hinge that allows the mouth to open wide for capturing large prey. A tongue is anchored, and therefore immobile, in the bottom of the mouth. Lined with nerve cells, it helps detect chemicals in the environment.

Look at Figure 36-13. Food passes from the mouth into the **pharynx,** or throat cavity, and then moves through the tubelike **esophagus** to the stomach. Much digestion takes place in outpockets of the stomach called pyloric ceca *(SEE-kuh)*. The liver and the pancreas, located near the stomach, secrete digestive enzymes such as bile and pancreatic juice that help break down food. The short intestine has fingerlike extensions called villi that extend and increase the surface area for absorption of digested foods. Undigested material leaves through the ventral anus.

Circulatory System

Yellow perch have a highly developed circulatory system that is adapted for rapid swimming and other high-performance

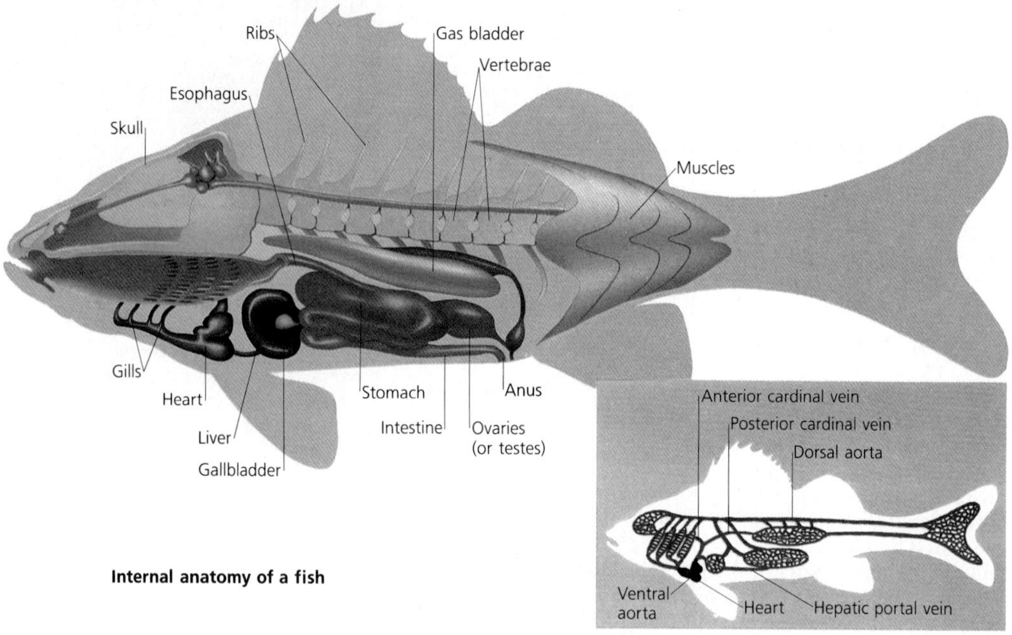

Internal anatomy of a fish

LEP Activity

To help students visualize the relationships between the various aspects of a fish's external and internal anatomy, have them construct a fish model. Ask them to refer to the figures of the perch (both internal and external) in Section 36.3. On a piece of cardboard or construction paper students can draw a general outline of the perch's body. On separate pieces of cardboard they can draw and label diagrams of major aspects of fish morphology (fins, gills, gas bladder, major systems, and an integument to cover).

Have the students cut out the separate diagrams along the outlines. Ask each student or team of students to assemble the pieces into a complete model of a fish. The final assembly step is the placement of the integument. Point out how each aspect of fish morphology is adaptive to life in the water.

activities. Their circulatory system consists of a two-chambered heart, blood vessels, and blood containing red and white blood cells. The **atrium** is the collecting chamber of the heart, and the **ventricle** is the pumping chamber. Follow the circulatory path in Figure 36-13. The heart pumps blood through **arteries** to small, thin-walled vessels called **capillaries** in the gills. There the blood picks up oxygen gas from, and releases carbon dioxide into, the water. The blood tnen moves to the body tissues, where nutrients and wastes are exchanged. The blood returns to the heart through **veins.**

Respiratory and Excretory Systems

The fish's central respiratory organs, the gills, are adapted for gas exchange. Gills consist of four sets of curved pieces of bone on each side of the head. Each gill has a double row of thin projections called gill filaments that are richly supplied with capillaries. The large surface area allows rapid gas exchange. Swimming helps maintain a constant flow of water across the gills. Gill valves prevent particles that enter the mouth from passing over the gills.

Gills also excrete nitrogenous wastes from the body, but that task is carried out primarily by the kidneys. The kidneys filter out dissolved chemical wastes from the blood. The resulting solution, urine, is carried through a system of ducts to the urinary bladder, where it is stored and then expelled.

The gills and kidneys have the vital function of **osmoregulation,** or maintaining homeostasis between salt and water in the body. Salt-water fishes, which take in excess salt from the seawater, have special mechanisms for excreting salt. Yellow perch and other freshwater fish need more salt in their blood than is contained in the surrounding water, so they excrete excess water.

Gas Bladder

Most bony fish, including the yellow perch, have a unique organ, the **gas bladder,** or swim bladder. This thin-walled sac in the abdominal cavity contains a mixture of oxygen, carbon dioxide, and nitrogen obtained from the bloodstream. Comparative morphology suggests that the gas bladder is likely to have evolved from the lungs of lungfish-type ancestors. By regulating the amount of gas in the sac, fish adjust their overall density and thus move up or down in water or hover at a given depth.

Nervous and Sensory System

The nervous system of the yellow perch includes a brain, a spinal cord, and nerves that lead to and from all parts of the body. All fishes have more complex nervous systems than invertebrates do. This increase in complexity makes possible the more varied behavior of fishes.

The brain of the yellow perch consists of five paired lobes. The largest, at the center of the brain, are the two **optic lobes.** They receive nerve impulses from the eyes and other sense organs and signal the muscles to move. The anterior lobes of the brain are

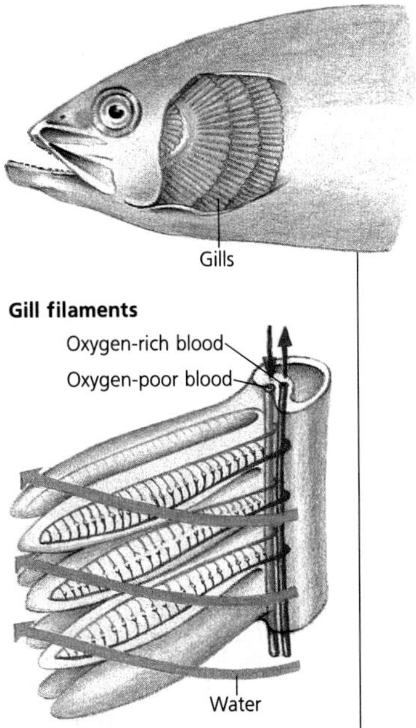

Figure 36-14 The gill filaments provide the organism with a large surface area, thus enabling gas exchange to occur quickly.

Independent Practice

- Have students write answers to the Section Review.
- Give students pairs of fish organs and functions and ask them to write a sentence expressing the relationship between the structures and functions. For example, pair gill filaments and respiration. *(The gill filaments of a fish must have a constant supply of fresh water in order for effective respiration to occur.)*

Check Your Understanding

1. How do the fin spines of the perch protect it? *(The backward-pointing spines can pierce the throat of a predator that tries to swallow it from the rear.)*
2. How are fish scales like the rings of a tree? *(Like a tree's annual rings, the growth rings formed by scales give a good approximation of the fish's age.)*
3. Describe the function of the gas bladder. *(It contains a mixture of gases from the bloodstream. By regulating the amount of gas in the bladder, the fish adjusts its overall density; this causes it to move up or down, or hover at a given depth.)*
4. Give an example of the reproductive or spawning behavior of a fish. *(Answers will vary. Eggs are fertilized within the body of a live-bearing female. In many egg layers, females lay eggs on a surface where the male fertilizes them with sperm. Many species, such as salmon and eels, migrate to spawn.)*

Videodiscs

- *2105–2106, Perch Skeleton (s)*
- *2607, Fish Circulation (s)*
- *Side 2 40663, Fish Development; Heart (m)*
- *Side 2 40427, External Fertilization (m)*

Section 36.3

Reteaching

Have students prepare an organizational chart of external and internal structures or organs of a bony fish. An example of a completed organizational chart is shown on p. 546.

■ *See* Section Reviews *worksheet, Section 36.3.*

Enrichment

Have students read *The Old Man and the Sea* by Ernest Hemingway, *Blues* by John Hersey, or another book of fiction or nonfiction about fishing. Ask them to prepare a report about the book and the issues it raises with regard to humans' relationship to nature.

Closure

Show students a fish fossil. This can be an actual specimen borrowed from a museum or purchased. (Small fish fossils, which are quite common, can be purchased from catalogs.) The fish fossil can also be a photograph from a book about vertebrate paleontology. Ask the students to draw conclusions about the habitat and behavior of the fish, based on its structure. Ask them what inferences they can make about its internal anatomy. Ask them to suggest modern fish to which it may be related, based on its appearance.

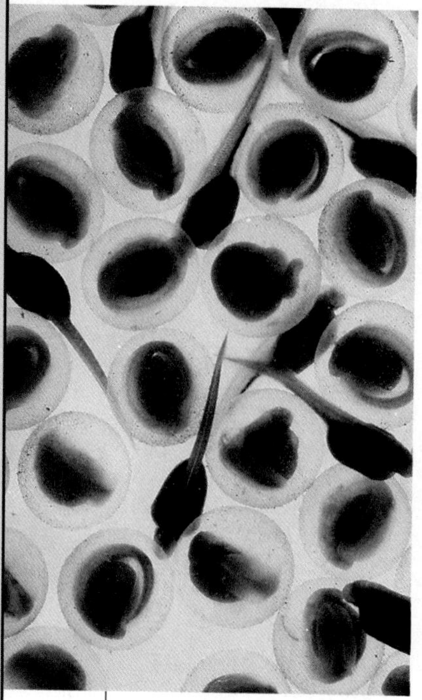

Figure 36-15 Among the many fish that fertilize their eggs externally is the white sturgeon, *Acipenser transmontanus.* Note that several of these white sturgeon eggs are hatching.

the olfactory lobes and the **cerebrum** *(suh-REE-brum),* which respond mainly to smells. Smell is the most important sense in fish. At the posterior of the brain are the **cerebellum** *(SER-uh-BELL-um),* which coordinates the muscles, and the **medulla oblongata** *(muh-DULL-uh ahb-lawn-GAHT-uh),* which regulates the internal organs. The major sense organs are connected directly with the brain via **cranial nerves.**

From the medulla the spinal cord extends the length of the body and carries nerve impulses to and from the brain. **Spinal nerves** connect the spinal cord with the internal organs, muscles, and sense organs. These nerves also carry impulses to the brain from the lateral line system.

Reproduction

The reproductive systems of most bony fishes resemble that of the yellow perch. The sexes are separate. Eggs are produced by ovaries in the female, and sperm is produced by the testes in the male; both are released through an opening just to the rear of the anus. Fertilization of the eggs of yellow perch takes place externally. Young fish hatch from fertilized eggs within a few hours in warm water or after many weeks in cold water. The adaptation of laying large numbers of eggs ensures that at least a few individual yellow perch will survive to become adult fish. Most eggs are not fertilized. Many others die or are eaten. The number of eggs bony fishes lay varies considerably. A brook trout lays from 80 to 5,000 eggs, but an ocean sunfish lays about 3 million.

Some fishes bear live young. The female receives sperm from the male during mating, and fertilization is internal. The female carries the eggs in her body until the young are born. These "livebearers" include fishes common in aquariums, such as guppies, platys, mollies, and swordtails.

Few generalizations can be made about the reproductive, or **spawning,** behavior of bony fish. The female yellow perch lays eggs on the lake bottom, and the male fertilizes them by releasing **milt,** a fluid containing sperm. Some species, such as sticklebacks, build crude nests from plants, sticks, and shells. Many species migrate to warm, protected shallow water to spawn. Freshwater eels from rivers in Europe migrate to the Atlantic to spawn. Adult Atlantic and Pacific salmon migrate back to fresh water to spawn. They use their sense of smell to find the stream where they were hatched. Here they spawn and die.

Section Review

1. Compare the atrium and the ventricle of a perch.
2. How do the caudal, dorsal, and pectoral fins function?
3. How do fish gills function in respiration?
4. Why is laying a large number of eggs adaptive for fish?
5. Bottom-dwelling fish often lack a gas bladder. Explain the adaptive advantage of this modification.

Answers to Section Review

1. The atrium collects blood and the ventricle pumps blood throughout the body.
2. The caudal fin helps move the fish through the water. The dorsal fin keeps the fish from rolling. The pectoral fin aids in steering.
3. Swimming and a pumping action force water across the fish's gills, which are rich in blood vessels. Oxygen and carbon dioxide are exchanged by diffusion.
4. The number is so large because so few of the eggs survive to hatching and few of the young-hatched live to maturity. However, ovoviparous fishes, such as sharks, hatch only a few young each year because those few are well protected within the female.
5. It would be difficult for a bottom-dwelling fish to remain at the bottom if a gas bladder made it buoyant enough to float.

Laboratory

Constructing a Dichotomous Key to Fish Species

Objective
To construct a dichotomous key to fish species using basic fish characteristics

Process Skills
Classifying, communicating

Materials
Pencil and paper

Inquiry
1. A dichotomous key requires a choice between successive pairs of characteristics. Each subject is identified by separating out the one characteristic unique to that subject. Look at the fishes below.
2. Construct a dichotomous key that can be used to identify each species shown. Use the presence or absence of the following characteristics: spiny fins, body flattened from top to bottom, a sucking disk in place of a jaw (if the disk is not shown, assume it is absent), both eyes on the same side (surface) of the head, eyes large relative to head, long thin tail, dorsal fin that covers most of the body. Refer to p. 275 to recall how a dichotomous key should look.

Conclusions
1. Bony fishes belong to the Class Osteichthyes. Most members of that class shown here have spiny fins. Name the members of the Class Osteichthyes pictured here.
2. What additional kinds of information might be helpful in classifying fishes?

Further Inquiry
1. How might you evaluate your key?
2. What are the problems involved in developing an unambiguous dichotomous key?

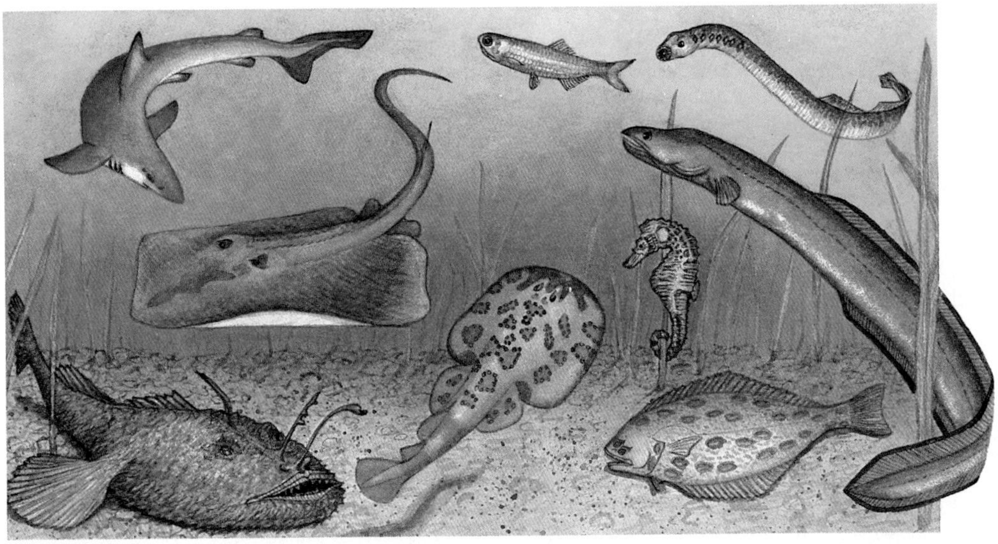

Laboratory

(For an overview of keying fish species and preparatory information related to the laboratory, see p. 535B.)

Inquiry
2. Make sure students demonstrate that their keys utilize characteristics that distinguish major groups of fishes, rather than simply identify the fish pictured.

Conclusions
1. It is not important that students know the exact names, but for your information members of Osteichthyes pictured are: goosefish, Atlantic halibut, bay anchovy, conger eel, and sea horse.
2. Answers will vary but might include information about habitat, feeding habits, and other behaviors.

Further Inquiry
1. Students might answer that they would evaluate their keys by exchanging them with other students or by using them on species other than the ones pictured.
2. Students should identify some of the problems involved in developing an unambiguous key, such as making sure the final selection applies only to one category of objects.

Vocabulary

1. Vertebral column; the others are characteristic of all chordates, while the vertebral column is found only in vertebrates.
2. Operculum; the others are parts of the brain.
3. Milt; the others have to do with the skin.
4. Pharynx; the others have to do with the circulatory system.
5. Gas bladder; the others are features of external anatomy.

Review

1. b
2. a
3. c
4. c
5. a
6. c
7. d
8. c
9. a
10. d

11. Accept any reasonable example. Agnatha, lamprey; Chondrichthyes, shark; Osteichthyes, yellow perch; Amphibia, frog; Reptilia, snake; Aves, falcon; Mammalia, cat.
12. Because the endoskeleton can grow with the body, it does not have to be shed as invertebrate exoskeletons do. The endoskeleton can support a larger body.
13. The appendicular skeleton is made up of the girdles and limbs or fins, while the axial skeleton is made up of a vertebral column and skull.
14. They fit sharks with radio transmitters and record the signals received.
15. Rays and skates have flattened bodies and speckled or sandy colors that help camouflage them against the sandy bottom. The spiracles on top of their heads allow them to take in oxygen while being almost completely buried in the sand. Their strong jaws and teeth allow them to crush bottom-dwelling invertebrates for food.
16. They use gills when there is water in the ponds and lungs during the dry season.
17. The growth rings indicate the age.

Chapter 36 Review

Vocabulary

anal fin (547)
appendicular skeleton (539)
artery (549)
atrium (549)
axial skeleton (539)
capillary (549)
caudal fin (547)
cerebellum (550)
cerebrum (550)
chromatophore (547)
cranial nerve (550)
deuterostome (537)
dorsal fin (547)
dorsal nerve cord (537)
endoskeleton (537)
esophagus (548)
gas bladder (549)
gill (540)
gill slit (537)
integument (547)
lateral line system (540)
lobe-finned fish (545)
lung (545)
lungfish (545)
medulla oblongata (550)
milt (550)
notochord (537)
olfactory lobe (542)
operculum (546)
optic lobe (549)
osmoregulation (549)
pectoral fin (543)
pelvic fin (547)
pharyngeal pouch (537)
pharynx (548)
placoid scale (543)
ray-finned fish (545)
skull (539)
spawning (550)
spinal nerve (550)
vein (549)
ventricle (549)
vertebral column (537)

In each set of terms below, choose the one that does not belong, and explain why.

1. notochord, vertebral column, dorsal nerve cord, gill slits
2. cerebrum, cerebellum, operculum, optic lobe
3. placoid scale, chromatophore, integument, milt
4. pharynx, atrium, ventricle, capillary
5. pectoral fin, gas bladder, operculum, lateral line system

Review

1. Chordates and echinoderms have a similar (a) body plan (b) embryonic development (c) habitat (d) feeding habit.
2. The skull functions to (a) protect the brain (b) anchor the axial skeleton (c) coordinate muscles (d) collect sensory information.
3. The density of water means that fish (a) must be heavy in order to float (b) do not need strong muscles to propel them (c) sink to the bottom when at rest (d) all of the above.
4. The lateral line system (a) keeps fish moving in a straight line (b) initiates migration (c) detects vibrations (d) acts as a camouflage.
5. Lamprey locate prey through a highly developed sense of (a) smell (b) hearing (c) sight (d) touch.
6. Sharks use claspers to (a) increase maneuverability (b) startle other fish (c) hold on to the female while mating (d) hold on to prey while feeding.
7. To move up or down, a fish uses its (a) anal fin (b) dorsal fins (c) caudal fin (d) pelvic fins.
8. The esophagus of a fish (a) creates buoyancy (b) fertilizes eggs (c) carries food from the mouth to the stomach (d) holds wastes moving from the stomach to the anus.
9. A fish's ventricle (a) pumps blood through the body (b) collects blood returning to the heart (c) facilitates gas exchange through diffusion (d) carries oxygen through capillaries.
10. Some fish species (a) build nests for their eggs (b) return to their hatching grounds to spawn (c) lay huge numbers of eggs (d) all of the above.
11. Name the seven living vertebrate classes, and give a representative animal of each.

18. Saltwater fishes excrete excess salt through their gills and kidneys, while freshwater fishes excrete excess water.
19. The blood is pumped by the ventricle through the circulatory system to the gills, where gases are exchanged. The oxygen-rich blood is then circulated among the tissues, where gases are again exchanged, and returns to the atrium.
20. The optic lobe receives messages from the sense organs and signals muscle movement; the olfactory lobe and the cerebrum both deal with the sense of smell; the cerebellum coordinates muscles; and the medulla oblongata regulates the internal organs.

12. Of what advantage is an endoskeleton in comparison with an exoskeleton?
13. Distinguish between the appendicular and axial skeletons.
14. How do researchers determine the habitat range of sharks?
15. Describe adaptations in rays and skates that allow a bottom-dwelling existence.
16. What is the advantage to lungfishes of having both lungs and gills?
17. How can scale pattern show a fish's age?
18. How do saltwater fish and freshwater fish maintain their salt balance?
19. Describe a fish's circulatory system.
20. Describe the function of the five lobes of a fish's brain.

Critical Thinking

1. Neoteny is a phenomenon in which larvae become sexually mature while retaining larval characteristics. The term has been used to explain in part the evolution of vertebrates from ancestral chordates. Use what you know about tunicates to support this hypothesis.
2. The shark has a large corkscrew-shaped structure in its intestine called a spiral valve. How might this organ function in digestion?
3. Many species of fishes that live deep in the ocean where little or no light reaches are luminescent. What might be the advantages of such an adaptation?
4. The four-eye butterfly fish shown here often swims backward. How might the fish's behavior and coloring work to its advantage?
5. Saltwater fish drink more water and produce much less urine than freshwater fish do. How do you account for this?

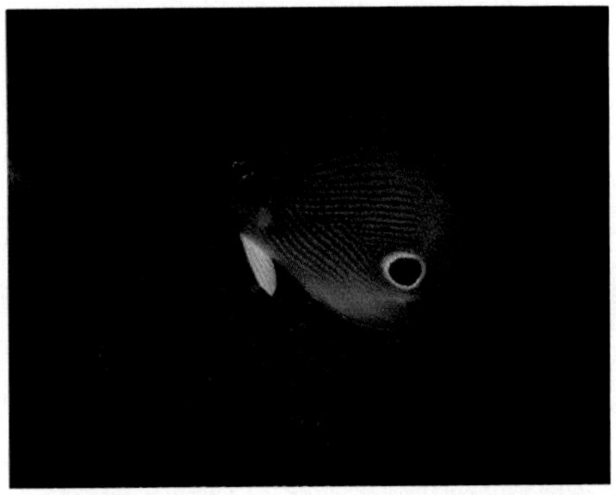

6. Cod and many other ocean fish lay eggs on the surface of the water. The male largemouth bass scoops out a nest in a lake or river bottom and waits for a female to deposit her eggs. What hypothesis would you make regarding the relative number of cod and bass eggs? Why?

Extension

1. The construction of the St. Lawrence Seaway allowed sea lampreys from the Atlantic Ocean to invade the Great Lakes. There they caused extensive damage to lake trout and other commercial fish species. Use your library to find out how the lamprey population was controlled and how successful this effort was. Present your findings to the class.
2. Read the article by Joseph S. Levine entitled "For Fish in Schools Togetherness Is the Only Way to Go" in *Smithsonian,* July 1990, pp. 88–92. Write a report in which you describe and explain the schooling behavior in fishes.
3. Study the anatomy of any fish other than a yellow perch. Identify the operculum, backbone, and each fin. Label the internal parts, and note any structural differences from the yellow perch. What conclusions can you draw about habitat and behavior on the basis of the fish's structure?

Critical Thinking

1. Vertebrates are free moving, while the adult tunicate is sessile. However, the larval tunicate has a tail and can swim. Neoteny suggests that the evolutionary path might be traced back to an ancestral form of tunicate larva that began to reproduce.
2. The corkscrew shape allows for a greater surface area for absorption without an increase in intestine length.
3. Different luminescent displays allow fish of the same species to recognize one another. Also, for some species luminescence acts as a lure, drawing the prey close. It may also frighten off predators.
4. The black dot suggests a false eye, while the real eye is camouflaged. This, together with its habit of swimming backward, might confuse a predator into mistaking the tail for the head, allowing the butterfly fish to escape.
5. Osmosis—the net diffusion of water across a membrane from a less saline solution to a more saline solution—causes saltwater fishes to lose water through gills and membranes. They drink and retain water to maintain homeostasis.
6. The cod eggs far outnumber bass eggs. The more-protected bass eggs have a better chance of being fertilized, and fewer will be eaten by predators.

Extension

1. Suggest that students draw general conclusions about the introduction of exotic species.
2. In some species, schooling has a mating function. In most species, it provides protection from predators.
3. Students can examine figures in a textbook or a fresh or preserved specimen.

Chapter 37 Amphibians

Chapter Overview

Chapter 37 introduces the Class Amphibia, continuing the discussion of vertebrate phylogeny begun in the previous chapter. Section 37.1, an overview of amphibians, examines amphibian evolution, characteristics, and the four amphibian orders. Section 37.2 presents frog anatomy, both external and internal, and Section 37.3 discusses frog reproduction and metamorphosis.

Chapter Planning Chart

B	S	A	Sections and Subsections	Page	Features	Page	Resources
•	•	•	**37.1 Overview of Amphibians**				
			Evolution	555	Biology in Process	556	Videodiscs
			Characteristics	555	Section Review	558	Process Skills: Skin Breathing in Amphibians
			Classification	557			Section Reviews Worksheet
•	•	•	**37.2 Frog Anatomy**				
			External Anatomy	559	Laboratory	567	Videodiscs
			Internal Anatomy	560	Section Review	564	Blackline Master 77
							Blackline Master 78
							Overhead Transparency T37
							Blackline Master 79
							Laboratories: Frogs
							Science in Action Videotape: Alternatives to Dissection
							Section Reviews Worksheet
•	•	•	**37.3 Reproduction in Frogs**				
			Reproductive System	565	Think	566	Videodiscs
			Fertilization	565	Section Review	566	Section Reviews Worksheet
			Metamorphosis	566			
			End of Chapter Activities				
					Chapter Review	568	Vocabulary Skills
							Chapter Test
							Computer Test Generator

B *The Basic Level curriculum presents the most fundamental knowledge offered in the course.*
S *The Standard Level curriculum is designed for the average student who is able to master most topics.*
A *The Advanced Level curriculum includes suggestions for teaching the most academically able students.*

Cooperative Learning

Group Activity: Amphibian Adaptations

- **Group Size:** *4 students*
- **Outcome:** *Students will identify specific amphibian adaptations to their local environment.*
- **Individual Accountability:** *Each student will research a local amphibian.*
- **Positive Interdependence:** *The group will collaborate in writing a television script.*

Have students in the group first choose one local amphibian from a field guide to amphibians. Have group members divide up and research such factors as climate, terrain, the availability of open bodies of water, predators, prey, and cover. Then have each group develop a television nature program script, focusing on the anatomical, physiological, or behavioral features that may be adapted to local conditions. Finally, have volunteers present their scripts to the class.

Stress that local conditions to which amphibians have adapted probably do not include changes made by human activity. Human presence in North America has been too recent to allow much evolutionary response. Human alterations to the environment, however, may have driven away endemic species or attracted exotic ones.

Concept Map

The following is one possible solution to the concept mapping activity in Reteaching on p. 558.

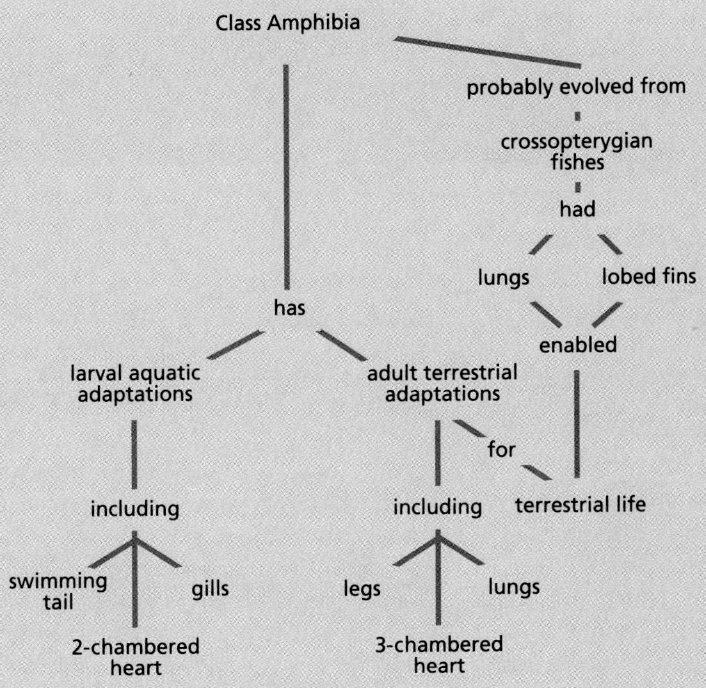

Laboratory Preparation

Overview *(See p. 567.)*

In this lab investigation, students study frog behavior that is mainly reflexive. They consider the adaptive significance of these behaviors. The frog's visual system is highly developed to perceive motion, and movement will cause the frog to jump. The anatomical differences among frog, fish, and salamander locomotion are fundamental, and students can investigate and compare these differences.

Preparation

Feed frogs live crickets or other moving insects for several days before the lab. Set aside frogs that do not feed, as they will not respond to stimuli in the experiment. Do not feed frogs the day of the lab. Since some frogs are more nervous than others, use frogs that respond and feed best, if extras are available.

Teaching Tips

You may want first to demonstrate proper handling techniques or introduce frogs to students in a nonthreatening manner in order to alleviate any fear of frogs.

Frogs that have not been recently fed respond better when presented with food. Do not allow students to overfeed frogs, especially if they are to be used by other classes.

Because frogs will attempt to escape, remind students to be as quiet as possible.

Safety

Remind students of proper treatment and handling of laboratory animals. Remind students to wash their hands after handling live animals.

Release into your local environment only native animals. Consult the *NABT Guidelines for the Use of Live Animals.*

Chapter Themes

Evolution Amphibians probably evolved from one branch of fishes called crossopterygians during the Devonian period. Emphasize that a variety of environmental stresses, including competition for food and space in water, new food sources on land, and periodic drying up of some aquatic habitats, may have contributed to amphibian evolution.

Scale and Structure Highlight the adaptive nature of many amphibian structures to life spent between water and land. Especially stress that larval amphibians are well adapted to life in water, while adults are better suited to terrestrial life.

Patterns of Change Amphibian life history involves the change from aquatic to terrestrial existence that occurs cyclically with each generation. This method of survival, which first enabled vertebrates to invade land, provides modern amphibians with adaptations to a surprising variety of habitats. These include forests, mountains, plains, and even deserts.

Chapter Motivating Activity

Have students brainstorm what changes fishes would have had to make if they had been suddenly forced to start living on land. Explain that this scenario takes place in a science-fiction universe where fishes can think and have access to technology. Direct students to considerations of different organ systems by asking questions such as "How can they move around?" "How do they breathe?" or "How do they keep their eggs moist?"

Chapter 37 Amphibians

Introduction

Between 370 million and 325 million years ago, a major biological event took place: certain species of fish successfully began to live part of their lives on land. In this chapter you will learn about the descendants of these fishes—frogs, salamanders, and other animals that belong to the group we call amphibians. This name, which comes from a Greek term meaning "double life," reflects the fact that amphibians live both on land and in water.

Chapter Outline

Chapter Concept

As you read, note the adaptations of amphibians that enable them to live both on land and in water.

Land eggs of the rain frog, *Eleutherodactylus* sp., Costa Rica (×40). Inset: Central newt, *Notophthalmus viridescens*, Kansas.

Understanding the Visuals

Ask students why there appear to be tiny frogs instead of tadpoles within the eggs of the rain frog in the photograph. *(The rain frog larvae pass through the entire tadpole stage in the egg, then metamorphose into frogs before hatching.)* Ask students what adaptive advantage might be conferred by an accelerated larval stage. Point out that an advantage in one habitat may be unnecessary, or even a disadvantage, in another habitat. *(An accelerated larval stage may be an advantage in an environment where open water is scarce, temporary, or where aquatic predators are especially numerous, but it might be of no advantage where water is plentiful and aquatic predators are relatively rare.)*

37.1 Overview of Amphibians

The fossil record indicates that various fishes were the first vertebrates on earth. In fact, they were the only vertebrates for about 150 million years. As competition for food and space became increasingly intense, natural selection favored animals that could spend at least part of their life on land. These animals evolved into the amphibians.

Section Objectives

- *Summarize the origin of amphibians.*
- *List three conditions of life on land to which amphibians had to adjust.*
- *List the major characteristics of amphibians.*
- *Name the four orders of living amphibians, and give an example of each.*
- *Explain why amphibians may be considered bioindicator species.*

Evolution

Scientists infer that amphibians evolved from lobe-finned fishes called crossopterygians *(KRAW-SAHP-tuh-RIJ-'nz),* pictured in Figure 37-1. The fossils of these fishes show that they had short, limblike fins that they may have used to move about on land. Crossopterygians had no gills but did have internal nostrils and a primitive lung that may have enabled them to respire for short periods of time on land.

On the basis of fossil evidence, biologists conclude that amphibians appeared during the late Devonian period, about 345 million years ago. During the Permian period the evolutionary lines of amphibians diverged, one line leading to reptiles and the other leading to the modern amphibians.

The geologic record includes evidence of a number of environmental pressures and opportunities that could have led to the movement of animals onto land. The Devonian oceans, lakes, rivers, and ponds supported a tremendous number and variety of fishes. Food and space were limited, and the numerous species of fish competed intensely for them. This competition apparently was further increased by periodic droughts that dried up streams, lakes, and tidal beds. In addition primitive land plants and insects, both promising food sources, were beginning to evolve. Yet there is no evidence before this period that vertebrates lived on land, where space and oxygen were plentiful.

Characteristics

For organisms adapted to life in water, the land is a hostile environment. Gills stick together and dry out in the air, preventing the exchange of gases between air and blood. Gravity pulls more strongly on skeletal systems because air is less dense than water. In addition the temperature on land fluctuates between hot and cold much more quickly than it does in water.

Through millions of years of evolution, amphibians adapted to conditions on land. Natural selection favored legs in place of fins, stronger bones and muscles, lungs instead of gills, and keratinized skin that reduced water loss. Species with necks could see and feed more easily, and those with oral glands could moisten the dry plants and insects they ate.

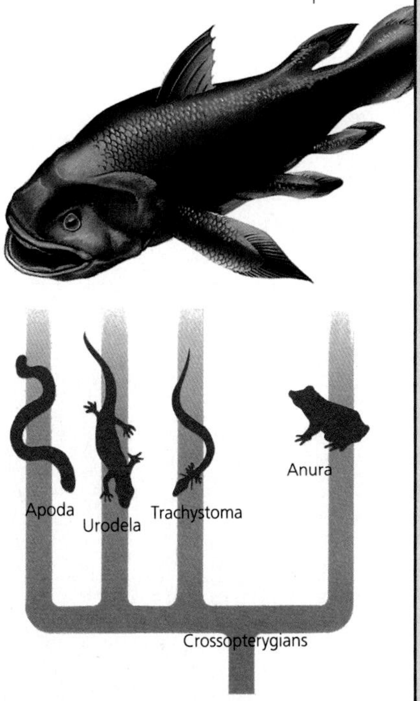

Figure 37-1 The crossopterygian (top) is believed to be the ancestor of modern amphibians. A phylogenetic tree suggesting amphibian origins and relationships appears below it.

Order	Adaptations to Land	Adaptations to Water
Anura (frogs & toads)	▪ legs ▪ lungs ▪ skin glands	▪ external fertilization ▪ larval tail ▪ larval gills
Urodela (salamanders)	▪ legs ▪ lungs ▪ some internal fertilization	▪ external fertilization ▪ larval gills ▪ tail

Graphic Organizer Use this table in Independent Practice on p. 558.

Lesson Plan

Section Focus

This section introduces amphibians, the class of vertebrates that arose during the Devonian period, probably from lobe-finned fishes. The four orders of Class Amphibia are Anura, Urodela, Apoda, and Trachystoma.

Section Themes

This section emphasizes **Evolution.** The four orders of amphibians have diverged from their fish ancestors, adapting to a variety of habitats. This evolution is mirrored in the metamorphosis of most amphibians from aquatic larva into terrestrial adult. Specific amphibian adaptations include respiration by gills in the larval stage, and by lungs, as well as skin, and/or mouth cavity in the adult stage; and a two-chambered larval and three-chambered adult heart.

Motivating Activity

To clear up any initial confusion about what animals are amphibians, show the class pictures (in random order) of a frog, toad, salamander, caecilian, alligator, turtle at the water's edge, marine iguana, mudskipper fish, seal on a beach, person swimming, or any other animals at the boundary between land and water. Pictures can be found in many nature books or magazines. Ask which are amphibians. *(Accept any correct answers. Some students may be confused by turtles. Stress that turtles are reptiles.)* Ask why, if *amphibian* implies living both on land and in water, such animals as seals and alligators are not amphibians. *(Amphibians live and respire exclusively in water as larvae, entering land only after metamorphosis.)*

Teaching Strategies

Interpreting the Visuals After students have read the material about amphibian classification on pp. 557–558, have them turn to the phylogenetic tree, Figure 37-1 on page 555. Ask students why they think that the four amphibian orders are divided into two related groups. *(Division is based on shared features. Apoda, Urodela, and Trachystoma share an elongated body shape. Anura [frogs] have legs that are significantly more developed and lack tails as adults.)*

Drawing Conclusions Have students suggest conditions during which a period of torpor—winter hibernation or summer estivation—might benefit an amphibian. *(Temperatures too high or low for survival, drying up of water source, disappearance of food supply in winter, or dry spells)* Ask students to suggest what characteristics other animals have that enhance survival while avoiding torpor. *(Endothermy, ability to migrate, food storage, independence from water)*

Guided Practice

Ask students to suggest environmental pressures that may have influenced evolution of terrestrial animals from aquatic ancestors. Write suggestions on the board. *(Pressures include increased competition in water, untapped food resources on land, and drought.)*

Amphibians are cold-blooded. Their body temperature rises and falls with that of the surrounding environment. Because of temperature extremes on land, certain protective behaviors arose in amphibians through natural selection. For example, many amphibians enter a state of dormancy, or **torpor,** when conditions are unfavorable. They often bury themselves in mud or leaves, emerging when conditions are better. Such states of inactivity are known as **hibernation** when they occur in winter and **estivation** when they occur in summer.

Amphibians have many prominent characteristics that are adaptations to a life spent both on land and in water:

- They change from an aquatic larval stage to a terrestrial adult form. This transformation is called **metamorphosis.**
- They have moist, smooth, thin skin with no scales.
- Feet, if present, are webbed. The toes lack claws.
- They use gills, lungs, skin, and mouth cavity in respiration.
- Larvae have two-chambered hearts; adults have three-chambered hearts and well-developed circulation.
- Eggs lack multicellular membranes or shells. They are usually laid in water or in a moist environment and fertilized externally.

Biology in Process

The Disappearing Amphibians

In 1959 David Wake, a young biologist, explored Tioga Pass at Yosemite National Park for toads. "We could not help but step upon the mountain yellow-legged frog because it was so abundant it got in the way of us seeing toads." In the late 1980s, Wake, now director of the Museum of Vertebrate Zoology at the University of California, returned to the Yosemite site. This time there was "nothing, no frogs at all," he said. "Something was happening, and I didn't know what."

As Wake talked with other scientists, he realized that many had observed dramatic declines in some of the world's 5,130 amphibian species. For example, Michael Tyler, a biologist at the University of Adelaide, Australia, described how the gastric brooding frog, which swallows its own eggs and regurgitates them as fully formed baby frogs, was abundant in Australian rain forests in 1973 but had disappeared from view by 1981.

Scientists are concerned about these declines because they believe that the two-habitat life cycle of amphibians makes them a bioindicator species that mirrors the health of the environment. Tadpoles, frogs, and salamanders are central to many ecosystems, and

Interdisciplinary Activity

Geography Have students examine a climate map of North America, which can be found in an atlas or on wall charts or transparencies. Ask students to hypothesize where they think that the highest concentrations of amphibian species are found. Also, ask students to predict which regions might have low concentrations of amphibian life. Have students support their predictions.

Provide students with blank maps of North America or have them trace a map from an atlas. Using a field guide to North American amphibians, have students shade ranges of most amphibian species on the blank maps. *(Amphibian ranges are often included in field guides.)* When they have finished, students will have a good idea from the density of their shadings where amphibian species are highly concentrated.

Classification

Biologists have identified about 2,375 living species of amphibians and have classified them into four orders. Frogs and toads make up the Order Anura ("without a tail"). Salamanders and other amphibians with legs and tails make up the Order Urodela ("visible tail"). Wormlike organisms called caecilians *(sih-SIL-yunz)* are part of the Order Apoda ("without legs"). Some aquatic amphibians belong to the Order Trachystoma ("rough mouth").

Anura

Anurans live in environments from deserts and mountains to ponds and puddles. Frogs have smooth, moist skin and short, broad bodies. Their long hind legs make them excellent jumpers. Most frogs live in or near water, though some species live in trees. Toads have dry, bumpy skin, a stocky body, and short legs. True toads belong to the Family Bufonidae, but the term *toad* is commonly used for any anuran that is particularly well adapted to dry environments. Both frogs and toads return to water to reproduce. In nearly all species eggs are fertilized externally. The fertilized eggs hatch into swimming larval forms called **tadpoles.**

Figure 37-2 ***Bufo marinus*** **shows the bumpy skin and stocky body typical of toads.**

their relatively high position in the food chain may magnify these environmental effects. Could the sudden decline or disappearance of amphibians be an early warning signal of serious imbalances in the biosphere?

In 1990 Dr. David Wake convened a two-day conference of biologists sponsored by the National Research Council's Board on Biology to discuss the decline in amphibian populations they had observed and to hypothesize possible causes for the decline.

By the end of the conference, the scientists had agreed to cooperate in a large-scale project of long-term scientific studies. The data collected will quantify the extent of the population decline of amphibians and will determine the actual causes.

Since the conference, a group of 6 biologists have reported their results from a 12-year population survey of three salamander and one frog species. Population sizes fluctuated widely from year to year but correlated with the number of juveniles metamorphosing into adults (p. 557). Drought was often responsible for the failure of juveniles to survive; so widely fluctuating populations may be the result of natural causes rather than human interference with their habitats.

- **Why are amphibians considered a good bioindicator species for environmental degradation?**

Ask students to compare actual amphibian ranges with their predictions. Have students suggest reasons why the predicted and actual concentrations differed, if they did so. Ask if anyone was surprised by the actual results.

In a similar approach, have some students compare concentrations of different orders of amphibians. If different orders are highly concentrated in different regions, ask students to suggest reasons for differences. *(These could include behavioral or physical features, such as internal fertilization or ability to remain in water in arid climates.)*

Biology in Process

Using the Feature

The feature focuses on the process skills of observing, collecting data, hypothesizing, and communicating among scientists. Emphasize to students that much data about amphibian decline are not yet explained by scientific studies. When Dr. Wake and other scientists began to share their observations of declining amphibian populations around the world, they began to realize the scope of decline and the need for further studies. Because amphibians are especially important as a bioindicator species, systematic, large-scale study of amphibian populations around the world could reveal much about our changing biosphere.

Proposed causes of amphibian population decline need to be confirmed or refuted by further studies. Ask students to suggest how they might design a study to test the effects of acid rain on a population of frogs. *(Set up groups of frogs as controls and experimental populations. Introduce simulated "acid rain" into the environment of the experimental group, and take a census of populations in both environments. Count the number of eggs hatching into juveniles and the number of juveniles surviving to adulthood.)*

Answer to the Feature

Amphibians live in two different habitats during their life cycles, and their thin, permeable skins are exposed to a variety of environmental pollutants in air, soil, and water. In addition, amphibians are relatively high in the food chain, and their position magnifies environmental effects.

Videodiscs

- ***1318–1323, Anura (s)***

Independent Practice

■ Have students write answers to the Section Review.
■ Have students prepare a table listing characteristics of the four amphibian orders and showing which are adaptations for life on land or in water. The table on p. 555 is a model for two of the orders.
■ *See* Process Skills, *Chapter 37.*

Check Your Understanding

1. List three differences between the orders Anura and Urodela. *(Members of Urodela have tails, shorter hind legs, and are less able to remain on dry land.)*
2. Name four organs used by amphibians as sites of respiration. *(Gills, lungs, skin, mouth)*

Reteaching

Ask students to make a concept map representing evolution and adaptations of amphibians. An example of a completed concept map is shown on p. 553B.
■ *See* Section Reviews *worksheet, Section 37.1.*

Enrichment

Have students use the library to research unusual amphibians, such as the Surinam toad, which broods eggs in pouches on its back, or the arrow-poison frog.

Closure

Tell students that while atmosphere is 21% oxygen, oxygen in water that is available for breathing is only about 0.5%. A fish must expend up to 20% of its energy on external respiration, while an air breather, such as an amphibian, only uses 1–2%. On the other hand, fishes are less subject to gravity than land animals and use less energy in moving. Ask students to compare the costs and benefits.

Videodiscs

■ *1312–1317, Urodela (s)*
■ *1311, Apoda: Caecilian (s)*

Figure 37-3 Two orders of amphibians are represented by the marbled salamander, *Ambystoma opacum* (left), and the caecilian, *Gymnophis multiplicata* (right).

Urodela

Salamanders, typical members of the Order Urodela, have elongated bodies, long tails, and smooth, moist skin. They range in length from a few centimeters to 1.5 m. Compared to the anurans, salamanders are less able to remain on dry land, although some can live in dry areas by remaining inactive during the day. Many types of salamanders live either in water or in moist places under logs and stones.

Like anurans, many salamanders lay their eggs in water. These eggs hatch into swimming larval forms. Other species can reproduce in damp land environments. Eggs laid on land hatch into miniature adult salamanders. Some salamander species have a type of internal fertilization in which females pick up sperm packets deposited by males.

Apoda and Trachystoma

Caecilians, members of the Order Apoda, compose a highly specialized group of tropical burrowing amphibians. These legless wormlike creatures average 30 cm long, but they can be up to 1.3 m long. They have very small eyes and are often blind. They eat worms and other invertebrates. The caecelian male deposits sperm directly into the female, and the female bears live young.

The Order Trachystoma contains three living species of mud eels, or sirens. Sirens live in the eastern United States and northeastern Mexico. They have minute forelimbs and no hind limbs.

Section Review

1. Distinguish between *hibernation* and *estivation*.
2. What characteristics suggest that crossopterygians are the likely ancestors of amphibians?
3. What environmental conditions may have led to the colonization of land by amphibians?
4. What does the name of each order of amphibians mean?
5. Which amphibian traits are adaptations to land? To water?

Answers to Section Review

1. Hibernation is a state of torpor taking place in winter; estivation is torpor occurring in summer.
2. Their lobed fins may have permitted movement on land. They could have respired through internal nostrils and primitive lungs.
3. Increased competition in water, untapped food resources on land, drought
4. Anura: "tailless"; Urodela: "visible tail"; Apoda: "legless"; Trachystoma: "rough mouth"
5. Land adaptations: moist skin, lungs; water adaptations: webbed feet, gills, uncovered eggs

37.2 Frog Anatomy

The amphibian ancestors that first ventured onto land faced a variety of new and harsh conditions. Those species that survived the new conditions and yet retained some aquatic characteristics gradually evolved into the modern amphibians. The anatomy of the frog reflects these adaptations.

External Anatomy

Close study of the frog's external anatomy reveals remarkable adaptations to its "double life" on land and in water. The frog's powerful hind legs are equally effective in jumping or swimming. On land frogs sit with their hind legs folded against the body, poised to jump at the first sign of danger. Most frogs can make leaps many times their body length. In water muscles working on the bones of the hind legs provide the strength for swimming.

Frog's eyes also work equally well in or out of water. Because the eyes bulge out from the head, the frog can stay submerged while literally "keeping an eye out" for predators. Eyelids that can blink protect the frog's eyes from dust and dehydration. In addition to upper and lower eyelids, a third, transparent eyelid called a **nictitating** *(NICK-tuh-TAY-ting)* **membrane** covers each eyeball and joins the lower eyelid. This membrane keeps each eyeball moist and protects the eye when it is under water. Two nostrils located near the top of the frog's head allow the frog to breathe when all but the top of its head is under water.

Frogs have eardrums, or **tympanic** *(tim-PAN-ick)* **membranes,** which are circular structures located behind each eye. The eardrums function well both in water and in air. A bone called the **columella** *(KAHL-uh-MELL-uh)* transmits sounds from the eardrum to the internal ear. A canal called a **Eustachian** *(yoo-STAY-shun)* **tube** connects each middle ear with the mouth cavity, allowing equalization of air pressure on both sides of the eardrum. Embedded in the skull is the inner ear, a minute system of sacs and canals that helps maintain balance and aids in hearing. Hearing is especially important during the mating season, when the male frog produces a distinctive mating call. The female frog's inner ear is attuned to the frequency of the male frog's call.

Section Objectives

- *List and locate the parts of a frog's external anatomy.*
- *Summarize the digestive process in frogs.*
- *Trace the flow of blood through a frog's heart and lungs.*
- *Describe four ways in which anurans respire.*
- *Name the major parts of a frog's excretory system.*

Figure 37-4 This series of exposures of a frog jumping suggests the power in the muscles of its hind legs.

	Skeletal	Digestive	Circulatory	Respiratory
Adaptations to Water	skull lets eyes and nose be above water	none	larval two-chambered heart	larval gills
Adaptations to Land	strong to support weight	efficient digestion of insects	adult three-chambered heart	adult lungs

Graphic Organizer Use this table in Guided Practice on p. 562.

Lesson Plan

Section Focus

This section explores the external and internal anatomy of the frog. A frog's anatomical features, while retaining some aquatic characteristics, also reflects adaptations of all amphibians to life on land.

Section Themes

This section emphasizes the theme of **Scale and Structure.** By examining structures of a frog's anatomy, we can gain insight into its dual functions in all other amphibians. The frog's external anatomy is well suited to both aquatic and terrestrial life, while its internal anatomy exhibits increasing complexity in response to greater energy requirements of life out of water.

Motivating Activity

Provide students with live frogs (from a biological supply company) or pictures of frogs (from natural history books and magazines). Ask students to suggest, without first looking at the text of Section 37.2, anatomical or physiological features that would be unlikely in a purely aquatic animal. These must be deduced from evidence observed in live frogs or pictures. *(Answers may include eyelids, legs built for leaping, ear membranes for hearing, and so forth. If live frogs are used, answers may include organs for breathing, if this is observed.)* Treat frogs humanely.

Videodiscs

- *Side 4 27650, Frog Locomotion (m)*
- *Side 4 45624, Frog Camouflage (m)*
- *Side 5 16830, Skin (m)*
- *Side 5 23842, Eye (m)*
- *Side 5 28375, Ear (m)*

Teaching Strategies

Comparing Adaptations Have students list features that enable a frog's skin to perform its protective function, as presented on p. 560. Then ask students to list in a second column features of a nonamphibian that perform the same function in either a similar or a different way. *(Sample answers: porcupine quills for protection, patterns of fish scales for protective coloration, chameleon scales that can change color, worm skin moist for respiration)* After students have completed their lists, ask them to share their answers with the class. List the variety of answers on the board.

Interpreting the Visuals Provide a frog skeleton for students to examine as they read the labels in Figure 37-5. If fish and reptile skeletons are available, ask students to compare these to the frog skeleton. *(The frog has a stronger skeleton than the fish and can move its neck. Most reptiles have limbs well adapted for locomotion on land. Frogs have no ribs.)*

■ *See* Blackline Master *77.*

Exploring Careers Invite a herpetologist to discuss his or her work both in the field and in the laboratory. In particular, have the specialist discuss the significance of amphibia to current pharmacological research, such as that involving skin secretions of African clawed frogs.

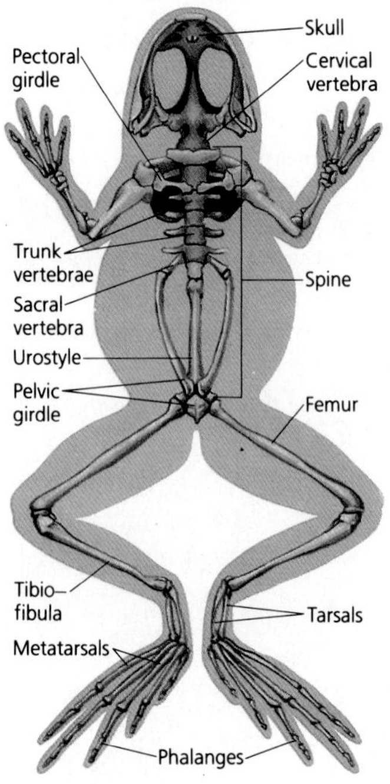

Figure 37-5 This ventral view of the skeletal system of the frog illustrates a number of adaptations for living on land.

The frog's thick, moist skin serves two important functions—respiration and protection. Numerous **mucus glands** supply a lubricant that keeps the skin moist in air, a necessity for respiration through the skin. **Granular glands** secrete foul-tasting or poisonous substances that protect the frog from enemies. A frog's skin also protects against predators by providing protective coloration. Some frogs, such as *Hyla versicolor,* can change color in order to blend with the environment.

Internal Anatomy

The frog's skeletal, digestive, circulatory, respiratory, excretory, and nervous systems reflect adaptations to land and water.

Skeletal System

The structure of early amphibians indicates that selection pressures favored a stronger skeletal system and the evolution of limbs. The frog's spine has nine vertebrae. The cervical vertebra at the anterior end of the spine allows neck movement, an adaptation that helps frogs catch prey. Posterior to this are seven trunk vertebrae, and then a single sacral vertebra that supports the hind legs. A long, slim bone called the urostyle extends from the sacral vertebra. The bones of the pectoral girdle, which form the shoulders, connect to the front legs. They also provide the primary protection to the internal organs, since the frog has no ribs. The pelvic girdle connects to the hind legs.

Digestive System

Most frogs feed on insects, and their digestive system is adapted to their diet. A frog's tongue is an excellent insect catcher. The frog simply flicks out its long sticky tongue, curls it around its prey, and pulls the insect back into its mouth. Then the frog snaps its mouth shut and swallows. Sometimes the frog blinks, pulls its eyes inward, and presses them against the roof of its mouth. This action helps push the food down its throat.

Frogs have two types of teeth that hold on to prey. A row of **maxillary teeth** line the perimeter of the upper jaw. Two patches of **vomerine teeth** project from bones in the roof of the mouth.

Digestion in frogs takes place in the **alimentary canal,** which includes the esophagus, stomach, small intestine, large intestine,

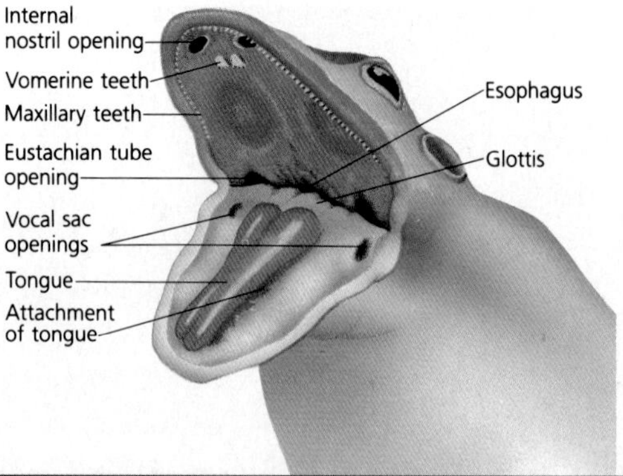

Figure 37-6 The frog's mouth is adapted for catching, holding, and swallowing prey.

Cooperative Learning

Tympanic Membranes Provide the following materials per group: a coffee can with both ends removed, a sheet of latex or rubber large enough to be stretched over one end of the can (may be made by cutting up a large balloon), a small mirror or strip of aluminum foil or reflective Mylar (1 or 2 square inches), strong rubber bands, glue, two support stands with Varigrip or chain clamps, a flashlight. Divide students into small groups or pairs, and have each group make a model of the frog's tympanic membrane that will allow visualization of its sensitivity to sound vibrations.

Have each group stretch the sheet of rubber tightly over one end of the can, securing the sheet with rubber bands. (It will look like a drum.) Then have students glue the reflective material to the center of the and cloaca. The elastic esophagus and stomach allow the frog to swallow large amounts of small vertebrates, insects, and worms. Once food passes through the gullet to the stomach, tiny glands in the stomach walls secrete gastric juices that help break down the food. A muscle called the pyloric sphincter at the lower end of the stomach allows digested food to move into the small intestine.

The upper portion of the small intestine is called the **duodenum** *(DYOO-uh-DEE-num)*. The coiled middle portion of the small intestine is the **ileum** *(ILL-ee-um)*. A fanlike membrane called the **mesentery** holds the small intestine in place. Inside the small intestine nutrients from food broken down in the stomach pass through capillary walls into the blood, which carries them to all parts of the body.

The lower end of the small intestine leads into the large intestine. Here undigestible wastes are collected and pushed by muscle action into a cavity called the **cloaca** *(kloe-AY-kuh)*. Waste from the kidneys and urinary bladder, as well as either eggs or sperm from the sex organs, also passes into the cloaca. Waste materials exit through the **cloacal opening,** or anus.

Other glands and organs aid in the digestion process. The liver produces bile, which is stored in the gallbladder. Bile helps

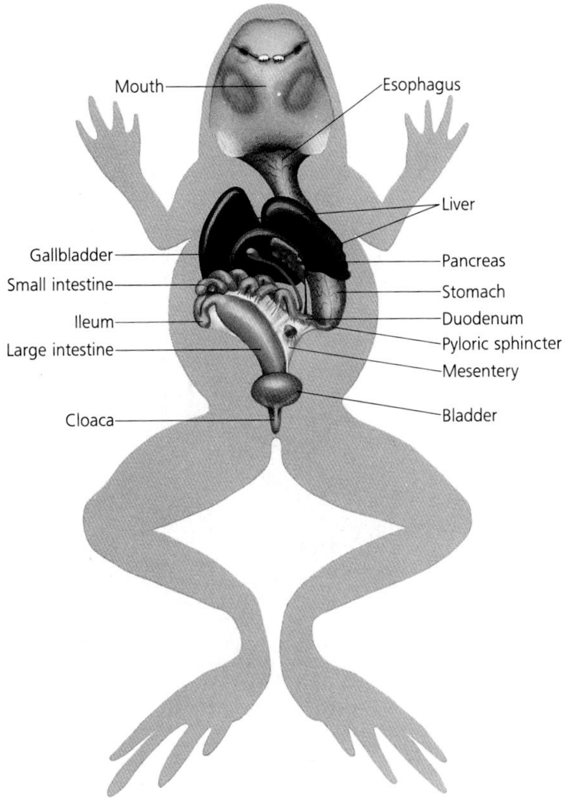

Figure 37-7 The digestive system of the frog, shown here in ventral view, is adapted for eating large amounts of small prey.

Interpreting the Visuals Guide students step-by-step through the digestive system of the frog (Figure 37-7). Stress the role of each organ of the digestive system. Ask students to compare elimination of wastes from the frog's digestive system with what they know of a mammal's. *(A frog has a common opening, the cloaca, for both solid waste and urine, while these functions are separate in mammals.)*

■ ***See* Blackline Master *78 and* Overhead Transparency *T37.***

Observing Organisms Set up an aquarium in the classroom for observing the life cycle of the frog. This activity is best attempted in the spring. Tips on keeping frogs in captivity can be found in *The World of the Frog and the Toad* by George Porter and in other sources. Frog eggs can be purchased from a biological supply company or collected locally in the spring. Consult a field guide to amphibians for information about egg-laying times in the local area. When purchasing eggs, try to obtain those of species that complete the larval stage relatively rapidly, such as wood frogs or spring peepers. Have students note changes in specimens, such as hatching, growth, appearance of limbs, and shrinkage of tail, at regular intervals.

■ ***See* Laboratories, *Investigation 37, Part I.***

Videodiscs

- ***Side 6 47092, Skeletal System (m)***
- ***Side 6 1728, Tongue (m)***
- ***Side 6 2637, Teeth (m)***
- ***Side 6 3767, Digestive System (m)***

stretched rubber sheet and clamp the can and the flashlight to the support stands. When the glue has dried, students are ready for the demonstration.

One student should speak or sing into the open end of the can. Another student will aim the flashlight onto the reflective material so that a reflection appears on an adjacent wall. As the first student varies pitch and volume, the reflection will vibrate accordingly. Adjust light levels in the room as needed.

Ask students in what way the tympanic membrane is an advance over the sensory system of fishes. *(Fishes have only a lateral line system that senses vibration.)* Ask students why they think that frogs lack external ears. *(Primarily for streamlining in water)*

Interpreting the Visuals Have students follow the path of blood flow into and out of the frog's heart according to the arrows in Figure 37-8. Then refer students to Figure 41-5 on p. 623 so they can compare the frog's heart to four-chambered hearts. *(Four-chambered hearts more efficiently separate oxygenated and deoxygenated blood.)*

■ *See* Blackline Master *79.*

Guided Practice

Divide the class into small groups. Have each group prepare a table using as column heads all the frog's body systems *(skeletal, digestive, circulatory, respiratory, excretory, and nervous)*. Have students write "Adaptations to Water" and "Adaptations to Land" as side heads. Ask group members to complete the tables, entering features of each system in appropriate columns. Stress that some features, such as eyes, may be adapted to both habitats. A sample table with answers for four of the systems is shown on p. 559.

■ *See* Laboratories, *Investigation 37, Part II.*

Independent Practice

■ Have students write answers to the Section Review.

■ Have each student draw a diagram of the frog's brain. Ask students to label each part, as described on p. 564. In addition, have each student make a chart listing each part of the brain, its function, and an example of how it may be used by the frog. *(Examples: cerebellum: center of balance and coordination, leaping into the water; cerebrum: voluntary nervous activity, moving toward a prey insect)*

break down fat into tiny globules that can be further digested and absorbed. A gland called the pancreas, located near the stomach, secretes enzymes that enter the small intestine and help break down food into products that can be absorbed by the blood.

The Circulatory System

Land-dwelling animals expend more energy than water dwellers, primarily because they must counteract the greater pull of gravity on land. An adaptation to the greater oxygen needs of land animals is a more efficient circulatory system than the fish's two-chambered heart. The amphibian's three-chambered heart, illustrated in Figure 37-8, partially mixes oxygenated with deoxygenated blood and pumps the blood throughout the body at higher pressure than does the fish's heart.

The three chambers of the heart are the right atrium, the left atrium, and the ventricle. The left atrium receives oxygenated blood from the lungs, and the right atrium receives deoxygenated blood from the body. Both the atria empty into the ventricle, the main pumping chamber of the heart. In the ventricle oxygenated and deoxygenated blood mix partially and are pumped to the lungs and the rest of the body.

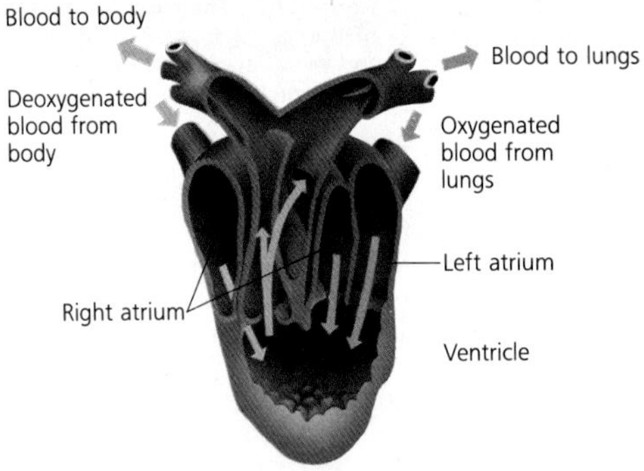

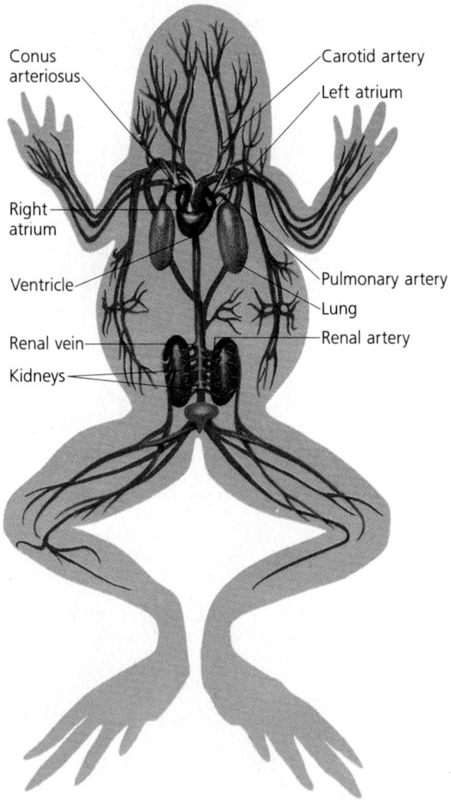

Figure 37-8 The frog's three-chambered heart (above) pumps part of the blood to the lungs and the rest through the entire circulatory system (right). The diagram shows the frog in ventral view.

LEP Activity

Help students understand the internal anatomy of the frog by preteaching important concepts, such as the two-chambered larval heart and three-chambered adult heart. Have students make a chart with two columns. In the left column, have them list names of the major organ systems. Then ask students to join in a word association exercise. As you say the name of each organ system, have students write on their charts words that they associate with it. *(Skeletal: bones, strength; Circulatory: blood, heart; and so forth)* Then have students contribute examples, and add them to the chart on the board.

Figure 37-8 traces the flow of blood through the frog's circulatory system. From the right atrium the blood enters the single ventricle. The ventricle then contracts, pumping some blood to the lungs to receive oxygen and some to the rest of the body. The blood going to the body leaves the ventricle through the **conus arteriosus,** a large vessel that lies against the front side of the heart. This vessel divides into a right and a left **truncus arteriosus,** which immediately branch again into three arches that carry blood to various parts of the body. Deoxygenated blood travels in veins back to the right atrium from the various regions of the body. Oxygenated blood returns from the lungs to the left atrium via the pulmonary veins.

The Respiratory System

Tadpoles respire, or exchange carbon dioxide and oxygen, through gills. Adult frogs lose the gills but can respire in three ways: through the lungs, through the skin, and through the mouth. No other group of animals uses all these methods of respiration.

Respiration through the lungs is called **pulmonary respiration.** A frog breathes by changing the volume and pressure of air in its mouth while either opening or closing its nostrils. Figure 37-9 shows that both inhalation and exhalation are two-step processes, each involving lowering and raising the floor of the mouth. The direction of air flow is controlled by opening or closing the nostrils. Air moves from the throat to the lungs through a slitlike passage called the **glottis.**

Because the frog's lungs are small, **cutaneous respiration,** or respiration through the skin in both air and water, is very important, especially during estivation or hibernation. In the winter a frog may stay buried in the mud at the bottom of a pond for months, respiring only through its skin.

Oxygen can diffuse across the lining of the mouth and into the blood. Frogs use mouth breathing for only a relatively small amount of their respiration.

The Excretory System

Amphibians eliminate two primary types of metabolic waste products—carbon dioxide from respiration and waste compounds from the breakdown of foods. Most of the carbon dioxide is excreted through the frog's skin, although some exits through the lungs.

The kidneys, shown in Figure 37-10 on the following page, are the primary excretory organs and lie on either side of the spine against the dorsal body wall. The kidneys filter nitrogenous wastes from the blood. These wastes, flushed from the body with water, are commonly known as urine. Frog urine flows from the kidney through tiny tubes called urinary ducts to the urinary bladder and from there into the cloaca. Urine and wastes from the digestive system are eliminated through the anus.

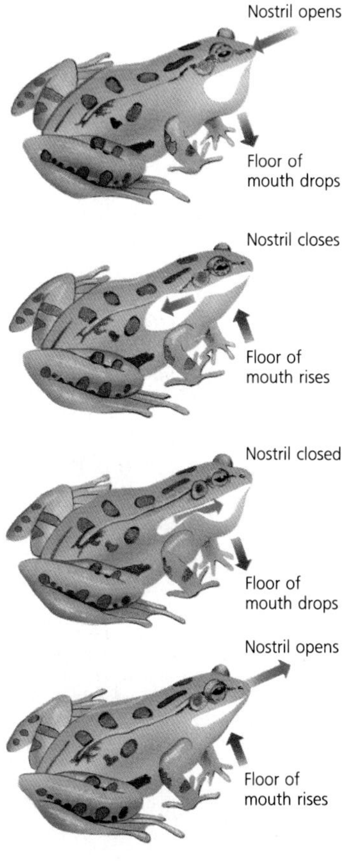

Figure 37-9 These diagrams show the major steps in the process of pulmonary respiration.

Check Your Understanding

1. Describe how a frog's eyes and nostrils are adapted to both aquatic and terrestrial environments. *(Eyelids protect eyes from dehydration on land and are positioned to allow the frog to keep them out of the water when submerged. Nostrils function well for breathing on land and are also positioned to be out of the water when the frog is submerged.)*

2. Where is the cervical vertebra located and what characteristic is an adaptation that helps the frog to catch prey? *(At the anterior end of the spine; allows neck movement)*

3. Describe three ways in which a frog's internal anatomy differs from a fish's. *(Accept all reasonable answers, such as, that the frog has a three-chambered heart instead of two-chambered; its cerebrum is more complex; its skeletal system is adapted to living on land.)*

Videodiscs

- ***Side 5 43257, Circulatory System (m)***
- ***2608, Amphibian Circulatory System (s)***
- ***Side 4 31636, Frog Respiration (m)***
- ***Side 5 37632, Mouth and Lung Respiration (m)***
- ***Side 6 17155, Urinary Tract (m)***

More Information

The Tailed Frog In the swift, cold mountain streams of the Pacific Northwest and southwestern Canada lives the unusual tailed frog, *Ascephus truei*. The male of this species bears a short "tail," which is actually an extension of his cloaca. During mating, the male inserts this organ into the female's cloaca. The tailed frog is one of the few anurans to practice internal fertilization, an adaptation that prevents sperm from being swept away in currents.

Another unusual feature of *A. truei* is that it lacks a voice and tympanic membranes, although it can hear well under water. A voice would be useless to this little frog amid the roar of a mountain torrent.

Reteaching
Ask students what problem a frog that lives primarily in water might face. *(It might absorb too much water through its skin.)* What organ regulates concentration of water in a frog? *(The kidneys)* Would you expect the urine to contain dilute or concentrated amounts of waste products compared with a land frog? *(Dilute)* Why? *(To get rid of excess water)*
■ *See* Section Reviews *worksheet, Section 37.2.*

Enrichment
Have students research and write a short report on how true toads (genus *Bufo*) differ from frogs. Ask students to focus on how toads are better adapted for terrestrial life than frogs.

Closure
Have students compare the external anatomy of frogs with that of fishes, noting which changes have made frogs better adapted to terrestrial life.

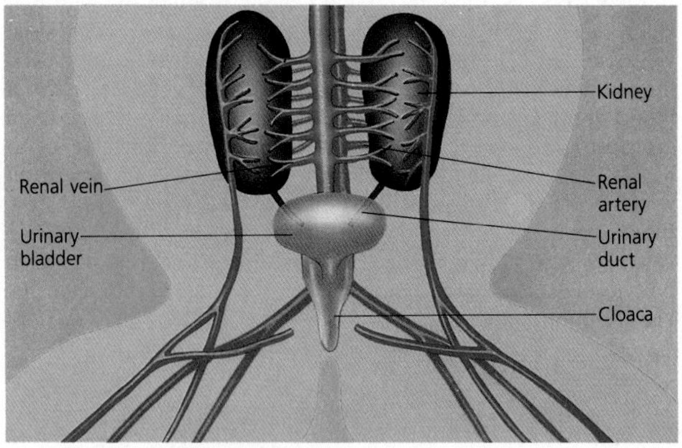

Figure 37-10 The excretory system of the frog, shown here in ventral view, must eliminate excess water when the animal is in water and conserve water when the animal is on land.

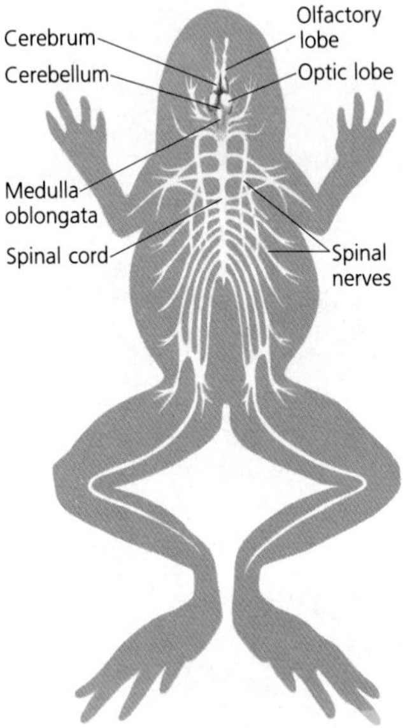

Figure 37-11 The brain of the frog is sufficiently developed to cope with both land and water environments. The diagram shows the frog's nervous system in ventral view.

It is vital that the frog regulate the concentration of water in its body. When the frog is in water, its permeable skin allows the water to enter its body. Frogs that live primarily in water rid themselves of excess water by excreting a large volume of very dilute urine. Frogs that live mainly on land conserve water by producing a small volume of more concentrated urine.

The Nervous System

The frog brain is more complex than the fish brain, enabling the frog to contend with a more varied environment. Use the diagram in Figure 37-11 to find the olfactory lobes, the center of the sense of smell, which lie at the anterior end of the brain. Notice that behind the olfactory lobes are the long lobes of the cerebrum, the area of the brain that controls voluntary nervous activity. The optic lobes, which control vision, lie behind the cerebrum. The cerebellum, a small band of tissue lying at right angles to the long axis of the brain, is the center of balance and coordination. The medulla oblongata lies at the back of the brain and joins the spinal cord. It controls organ functions. Ten pairs of cranial nerves extend out directly from the brain.

The spinal cord transmits signals from all parts of the body to the brain and from the brain back to the body. Encased in protective bony vertebrae, the spinal cord extends down the frog's back. As in fishes, the spinal nerves branch from the spinal cord to various parts of the body.

Section Review

1. In what way is the nictitating membrane useful to frogs?
2. Why do frogs blink when they eat?
3. Trace the flow of blood through the frog's heart.
4. How are wastes eliminated by amphibians?
5. Why would a frog die without mucus glands?

Answers to Section Review
1. It keeps the eyeball moist and protects the eye when the frog is under water.
2. Because they pull their eyes inward to help push food down the throat
3. Blood enters the ventricle from the right and left atria and is then pumped to the lungs and to the rest of the body.
4. Carbon dioxide is eliminated through skin and lungs. Nitrogen compounds are mostly eliminated by kidneys.
5. Skin would dry up and cutaneous respiration would cease; the frog would not live long because the lungs couldn't supply enough oxygen to the body.

37.3 Reproduction in Frogs

The frog's life cycle, like its anatomy, reflects the amphibian's double life. Most frogs have two life stages—an aquatic tadpole stage and a partially terrestrial adult stage. Frog eggs are usually laid in water and hatch into gilled tadpoles that live in water until metamorphosis.

Reproductive System

Because both male and female frogs have internal sex organs, it is difficult to distinguish the sex of a frog during most of the year. However, as the breeding season approaches, the male frog's foreleg muscles and first fingers swell. These swellings help the male maintain his grasp on the female.

The reproductive system of the male frog includes two bean-shaped creamy white or yellowish testes located near the kidneys. During the breeding season, sperm cells develop in the testes and pass through tubes to the kidneys and urinary ducts. During mating sperm leave the body through the cloacal opening.

In female frogs a pair of large, lobed ovaries containing thousands of tiny immature eggs lie near the kidneys. During the breeding season eggs enlarge, mature, and burst through the thin ovarian walls into the body cavity. Cilia move the eggs forward into the funnellike openings of the oviducts. As the eggs pass down the oviducts, they receive protective coats of jellylike material. They remain in structures called ovisacs until ovulation is complete and then leave the body through the cloacal opening.

Fertilization

Most frogs breed once a year. In the first warm days of spring in the temperate zones, frogs emerge from hibernation. They migrate in great numbers to ponds and slow-moving streams. Males establish territories and call to females of their species.

Each species has its own mating call. Air that is driven back and forth between the mouth and the lungs vibrates the vocal cords, producing the frog's croak. Male frogs have vocal sacs that amplify their calls, so they call more loudly than females do.

When a female approaches, the male frog climbs onto her back. He grasps her firmly, just behind the forelegs, in an embrace called **amplexus.** The male will cling to her, sometimes for days, until she lays her eggs. When the female finally releases her eggs into the water, the male frog discharges his sperm over them, and direct external fertilization takes place. The frogs then separate and resume their solitary lives. Within 12 days or so of fertilization, the eggs hatch into tadpoles.

The vast majority of eggs and tadpoles are eaten by predators such as fish, birds, snakes, and turtles. Some species of frogs have

Section Objectives

- *List the parts and functions of the frog's reproductive system.*
- *Summarize the process of fertilization in frogs.*
- *List the stages of metamorphosis in frogs.*

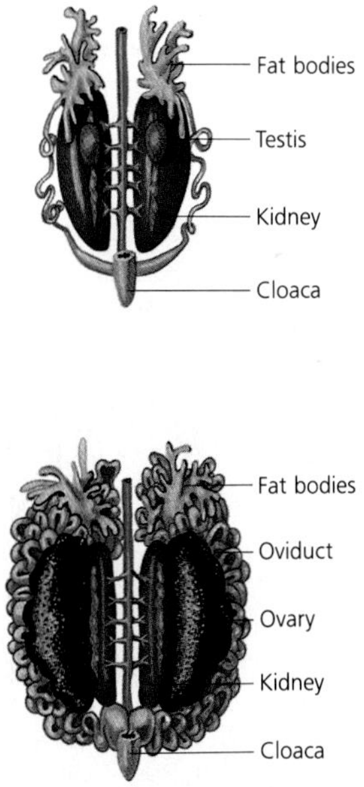

Figure 37-12 In frogs both the male reproductive organs (top) and the female reproductive organs (bottom) are completely internal.

Lesson Plan

Section Focus

This section examines details of the frog's reproduction and development, including anatomy of the reproductive system, physiology of fertilization, and metamorphosis of larva to adult stage.

Section Themes

The theme of **Evolution** applies to the discussion of the frog's reproductive system, which is adapted to achieving fertilization in water, an indication of the frog's phylogenetic relationship to fishes. The life cycle of the frog, characterized by metamorphosis from the aquatic larva to the semiterrestrial adult, exemplifies the theme of **Patterns of Change.**

Motivating Activity

Show students pictures of tadpoles and frogs. Ask students to note differences that may be adaptations to aquatic or terrestrial life. *(Tadpoles: tails; frogs: legs, wide mouths, bulging eyes)*

Teaching Strategies

Drawing a Time Line Have students prepare a circular time line of a frog's life cycle, beginning and ending with release of eggs. Ask students to divide the time line into aquatic and terrestrial stages.

Guided Practice

Have students brainstorm ideas about how frogs could reduce the number of eggs they produce and still insure survival of some of the young. *(Hiding the eggs, parental caring, making eggs unappetizing)*

Videodiscs

- ***Side 2 40823, Frog Development (m)***
- ***2457–2479, Frog Development (s)***

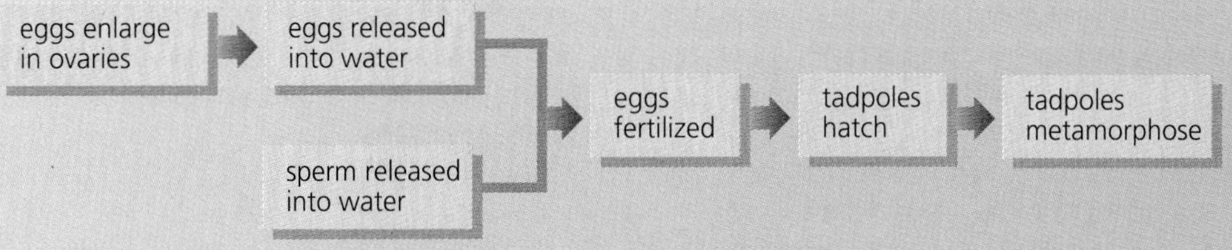

Graphic Organizer Use this sequential diagram in Reteaching on p. 566.

Independent Practice

- Have students write answers to the Section Review.
- Have students write a few paragraphs comparing male and female frogs' reproductive organs. *(Males have internal testes; females, ovaries.)* Ask students to list additional ways in which male and female frogs differ. *(Males call; their foreleg muscles and first fingers swell.)*

Check Your Understanding

1. What is the effect of amplexus? *(To keep the male with the female until she releases her eggs)*
2. List some organs that change during metamorphosis, rather than appearing or disappearing. *(Mouth, gills, heart)*

Answer to Think

Tadpoles with forelegs cannot swim well and are vulnerable. The less time they spend in this transitional state, the more likely they are to survive.

Reteaching

Have groups of students prepare a sequential diagram of events in the frog's reproductive cycle. A sample diagram is shown on p. 565.

- *See* Section Reviews *worksheet, Section 37.3.*

Enrichment

Have students research and write about the small number of frog species that provide some kind of parental care.

Closure

Brainstorm reasons why frog reproduction requires that they live near water. *(Sperm swim to eggs, eggs would desiccate without water, larvae are aquatic.)*

Videodiscs

- ***Side 2 43231, Tadpole Mouthparts and Intestine (m)***

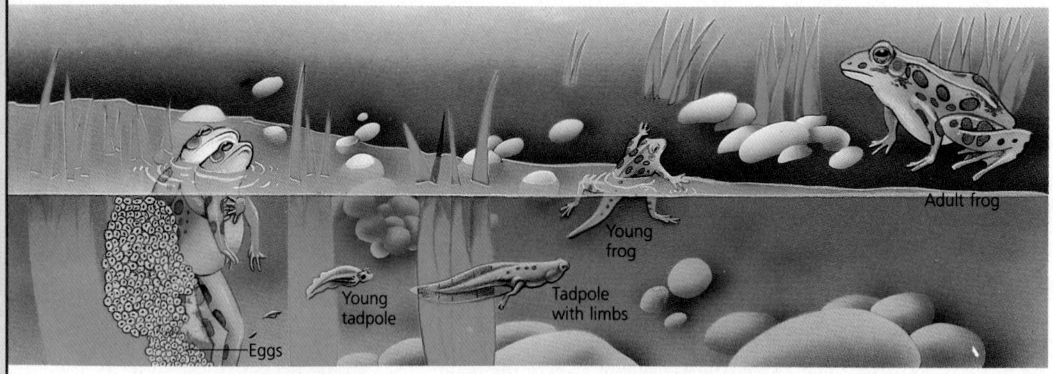

Figure 37-13 External body changes during frog metamorphosis, shown here in diagram form, are paralleled by several internal adaptations to a land environment.

unusual reproductive cycles that may be adaptations to severe predation. In one species, *Pipa dorsalis,* the eggs develop in pouches on the mother's back. In the genus *Rhinoderma* the male "swallows" the eggs, taking them into his vocal sacs. He later releases fully formed froglets by yawning.

Think

Once tadpoles begin to develop forelegs, the process of metamorphosis is completed very quickly, often in only a few hours. Why might a rapid transformation be advantageous?

Metamorphosis

Newly hatched tadpoles live off yolk stored in their bodies. They gradually grow larger and develop three pairs of gills. Like fishes, tadpoles have a two-chambered heart. Eventually, a tadpole's mouth opens, allowing it to feed. Tadpoles can also regenerate injured or lost body parts such as a leg or tail.

A tadpole grows and eventually changes from an aquatic larva into an adult. This process of change is called metamorphosis. Legs grow from the body, and the tail disappears. The mouth broadens, developing teeth and jaws. A saclike bladder in the throat divides into two sacs that become lungs. The heart develops a third chamber. The ability to regenerate disappears.

Biologists have long studied the process of metamorphosis and regeneration to learn what controls such dramatic physical changes. A hormone called thyroxine circulates throughout the bloodstream and stimulates metamorphosis. The cells of the tadpole are genetically programmed to respond to thyroxine at the appropriate stage of development. These developmental processes are important in the adaptation of all amphibians to a life spent both in water and on land.

Section Review

1. What are the *vocal sacs,* and how do they function in mating?
2. What happens to frog eggs in the oviducts?
3. How are frog eggs fertilized?
4. Compare the structures of a tadpole and a mature frog.
5. Why is metamorphosis of adaptive significance to the frog?

Answers to Section Review

1. Structures that amplify the sound of the male's call; to attract a mate
2. The eggs receive a protective coating of jellylike material.
3. The male frog releases sperm over eggs that the female has released into water.
4. Tadpoles have gills, a two-chambered heart, a tail, and the ability to regenerate some lost body parts. Mature frogs have legs, no tail, a three-chambered heart, lungs, teeth, jaws, and do not regenerate.
5. It allows developing frogs to survive in a terrestrial habitat after being protected in water as larvae.

Laboratory

Frog Behavior

Objective
To observe the behavior of a frog

Process Skills
Observing, inferring, hypothesizing

Materials
5-gallon aquarium, live frog, large jar, cardboard box, live cricket or mealworm

Background

1 List and describe the ways a frog breathes.
2 Describe some of a frog's adaptations to its "double life."

Inquiry

1 Fill an aquarium half full with water. Carefully place a frog in the aquarium. How does the frog swim?
2 Frogs have a thin layer of skin called a nictitating membrane that covers their eyes under water. What might be the nictitating membrane's function? How might you observe it without harming the frog?
3 Gently turn the frog on its back. How does it react?
4 Note the color difference between the upper and lower surfaces of the frog's body. How might this be advantageous?
5 Note the location of the nostrils and eyes. How might their position be an adaptation for avoiding predators? What other adaptation allows the frog to breathe even with its nostrils covered?
6 Put the frog in a large jar. When the frog is sitting comfortably on the bottom of the jar, gently tilt the jar along the long axis of the frog's body. Recall that inner ear receptors give the frog information about movement and orientation. Observe the frog's head. Next tilt the jar along the axis running between the frog's ears and observe the frog's behavior. How might this behavior be advantageous? How might this behavior help the frog as it moves?
7 Watch the frog breathe. As the frog inhales, what happens to the throat? What do you think happens to the air?
8 Note the movement of the nostrils. Is the movement of the nostrils always coordinated with the breathing movements? Why might this be advantageous?
9 Place the frog and a cricket or mealworm in a box. Observe the frog's feeding behavior. What are the frog's food-getting adaptations?

Conclusions

1 How does the frog's style of swimming differ from that of a fish?
2 What evidence have you seen that the frog's adaptations have enabled it to inhabit two very different environments?

Further Inquiry
How might you test the reaction of a frog to different colors and movements? Formulate a hypothesis about how these reactions might relate to the feeding habits of frogs.

(For an overview of amphibians and preparatory information related to the laboratory, see p. 553B.)

Background

1. Adult frogs: pulmonary and cutaneous respiration and through gas exchange in the mouth; pulmonary respiration: by changing air pressure and volume in mouth; cutaneous respiration: through skin; mouth: oxygen diffuses across the lining of the mouth into the blood.
2. Strong legs for jumping or swimming; a nictitating membrane keeps eyes moist on land and protected under water; a tympanic membrane allows hearing in air and water; lungs and gills (at different developmental stages)

Inquiry

1. Powerful hind legs and webbed feet push against the water.
2. Protects the eyeball; under water
3. The frog rights itself.
4. Dark, upper surface blends with vegetation, makes frog less visible to predators from above; light, lower surface blends with sky and water, makes frog less visible to predators from below.
5. Allows frog to breathe and see while almost completely hidden under water, making it less visible to predators (and prey); it can respire through gas exchange via mouth and skin.
6. Sense of balance allows it to move accurately, avoid predators, and capture prey.
7. When frog inhales, throat expands, the air goes from nostril, to mouth, to glottis, to the lungs, where O_2 and CO_2 are exchanged.
8. Yes. Air is directed to the lungs and the mouth, for efficient gas exchange.
9. Its long, sticky tongue is adapted for catching insects.

Conclusions

1. The frog uses its legs and webbed feet; fishes use their trunk muscles.
2. A nictitating membrane protects its eyes under water; the ability to breathe in and out of water; a dark, upper body surface and a light, lower surface to camouflage it in two environments, and legs adapted for swimming and jumping

Further Inquiry

One way to investigate this is by testing how the frog responds to different colored paper dots attached to lengths of thread.

Chapter 37 Review

Vocabulary

1. Granular glands secrete foul-tasting or poisonous substances that protect the frog from predators; mucus glands secrete lubricant that keeps skin moist.
2. Maxillary teeth line the perimeter of the upper jaw. Vomerine teeth project from the bones of the roof of the mouth.
3. The duodenum is the upper part of the small intestine; the ileum is the middle portion.
4. The conus arteriosus is the main vessel leaving the ventricle. It branches into the right and left trunci arteriosi, which carry blood throughout the body.
5. Pulmonary respiration is breathing through lungs. Cutaneous respiration is breathing through skin.

Review

1. b	**6.** c
2. c	**7.** d
3. b	**8.** a
4. a	**9.** d
5. c	**10.** a

11. Metamorphosis; thin, smooth, moist skin; webbed feet; respiration through gills, lungs, skin, and/or mouth cavity; larval two-chambered heart, adult three-chambered heart; eggs laid in water or in a moist environment and fertilized externally
12. Frogs have long legs, are good jumpers, and live in or near water. Toads have drier skin than frogs and shorter legs.
13. Because a frog's eyes and nostrils are on top of its head, it can be almost totally submerged and still breathe and see terrestrial predators.
14. It connects the middle ear and mouth cavity, equalizing air pressure on both sides of the tympanic membrane.
15. Cutaneous respiration (through the skin), pulmonary respiration (through the lungs), and mouth breathing
16. Frogs that live mainly in water excrete excess water in a dilute urine. Primarily terrestrial frogs conserve water by producing a small quantity of concentrated urine.
17. To the lungs and rest of the body
18. Through the skin
19. Carbon dioxide and nitrogen compounds
20. Amphibians have a two-stage life cycle and are exposed to a number of environmental hazards. In addition, they have thin, permeable skin and gelatinous eggs. While the exact mechanism for their decline is unknown, such industrially produced factors as acid rain seem likely to be responsible.

Chapter 37 Review

Vocabulary

alimentary canal (560)
amplexus (565)
cloaca (561)
cloacal opening (561)
columella (559)
conus arteriosus (563)
cutaneous respiration (563)
duodenum (561)
estivation (556)
Eustachian tube (559)
glottis (563)
granular gland (560)
hibernation (556)
ileum (561)
maxillary teeth (560)
mesentery (561)
metamorphosis (556)
mucus gland (560)
nictitating membrane (559)
pulmonary respiration (563)
tadpole (557)
torpor (556)
truncus arteriosus (563)
tympanic membrane (559)
vomerine teeth (560)

Explain the difference between each pair of related terms.

1. granular gland, mucus gland
2. maxillary teeth, vomerine teeth
3. duodenum, ileum
4. conus arteriosus, truncus arteriosus
5. pulmonary respiration, cutaneous respiration

Review

1. Amphibians evolved from fishes that could survive (a) salt water (b) dry conditions (c) floods (d) low light.
2. Amphibians must lay eggs in water primarily because the eggs (a) need oxygen from water (b) are not laid in nests (c) do not have multicellular membranes and a shell (d) need protection from predators.
3. Metamorphosis must take place before amphibians are able to (a) swim (b) live on land (c) feed themselves (d) burrow in mud and leaves.
4. The frog's tympanic membranes are (a) eardrums (b) mouth parts (c) eyelids (d) vocal cords.
5. The urostyle is part of the frog's (a) circulatory system (b) lungs (c) spine (d) small intestine.
6. Bile is a fluid that (a) aids in circulation (b) lubricates skin (c) breaks down fats into globules (d) aids in respiration.
7. The frog's ventricle pumps (a) oxygenated blood (b) deoxygenated blood (c) waste products (d) both oxygenated and deoxygenated blood.
8. The spinal cord is (a) a part of the central nervous system (b) the strongest part of the skeletal system (c) the main part of the circulatory system (d) the source of excretion.
9. Most amphibian eggs do not survive because of (a) floods (b) heat (c) disease (d) predators.
10. In the frog brain the center of balance and coordination is the (a) cerebellum (b) medulla oblongata (c) cerebrum (d) olfactory lobes.
11. Name the common characteristics of amphibians.
12. Contrast the characteristics of a frog and a toad.
13. How does the location of the eyes and nostrils of a frog help it avoid enemies and locate prey?
14. In the frog what is the function of the Eustachian tube?
15. Name and describe the three ways in which adult anurans can breathe.
16. Keeping in mind the urine regulatory system of a frog, explain the role that urine plays in allowing the frog to live on both land and water.
17. Where does blood go after it leaves the ventricle?

18. How does a frog breathe during periods of estivation or hibernation?
19. What are the two primary types of metabolic waste products that must be eliminated by amphibians?
20. Explain why amphibians may be considered bioindicator species. What may be some possible causes for their decline in an environment?

Critical Thinking

1. What pattern of evolution would you expect early amphibians to have undergone when they moved from a water environment to a land environment? Explain your answer.
2. Geologists believe that extended droughts occurred during the Devonian period. Keeping in mind the anatomy of the crossopterygians, how would these lobe-finned fishes be adapted for such dry periods?
3. Look at the picture of the tree frog on the right. What adaptations does this frog have that allow it to live in trees?
4. In each species of frog the female's inner ear is attuned to the pitch of the mating call of the male. Why is it important that the ear be so attuned?
5. Frogs feed on insects that are usually alive when the frog swallows them. What adaptation in the frog's anatomy allows the frog to capture live prey?
6. In the brains of amphibians the largest parts are the olfactory lobes and the optic lobes, the centers of smell and sight. The cerebrum, the center of reason and thought, is small. In contrast, the cerebrum in a human brain is about 85 percent of the brain. Why does their brain configuration work well for the life-style and environment of amphibians?

7. Most amphibians lay large numbers of eggs in ponds and then abandon them. The Costa Rican tree frog, however, lays a few large eggs in a depression in the forest floor. Each egg contains all the yolk the developing organism needs for food and houses the frog from its tadpole stage until it is a fully grown frog. Explain these adaptations.

Extension

1. Observe a frog or toad eating a mealworm. Take the mealworm and place it on the end of a toothpick or probe. Holding it in front of the amphibian, watch carefully while the frog eats the worm. Describe what you observe.
2. Research the differences between frogs and toads. Make a comparison chart with headings that include habitat, food, reproduction, mouth parts, skin, feeding, and other aspects of biology and behavior. Include a drawing of a frog and a toad in which you show differences and similarities.
3. Read the article by John Horgan entitled "A Nasty Little Squirt" in *Scientific American,* July 1990, p. 28. Give an oral report in which you discuss how the spraying behavior allows the fire salamander a unique method of self-defense.

Critical Thinking

1. They underwent adaptive radiation. Speciation may have occurred as amphibians, which share a common ancestor, invaded land and adapted to differing habitats and food sources.
2. They could have traveled across land in search of water on lobed fins, breathing air with lungs.
3. Adhesive footpads, countershading, and protective coloration
4. To ensure that a sexually mature female will find a mate of its own species during the reproductive season
5. A well-developed sense of smell and sight, a sticky tongue, and two sets of teeth
6. In their environment, amphibians need keen senses of sight and smell to find food and mates and avoid predators. The reasoning centers of their brains need not be large because amphibians rely on instinct and conditioned reflexes.
7. They do not have a safe aquatic environment for egg laying. The yolk compensates for lack of nutrients other tadpoles find in water. The hole keeps eggs cool and moist. Because eggs are well hidden and likely to survive to hatching, fewer need be laid.

Extension

1. Suggest that students try presenting the mealworm both while moving it about and while keeping it stationary, observing any differences.
2. Point out that only members of the genus *Bufo* are true toads. Some relatively dry land frogs are sometimes called "toads."
3. Encourage students to examine the role of accident in directing the course of experimentation and discovery. Is it likely that Mme. Phisalix-Picot actually experimented with the fire salamander?

Chapter 38 Reptiles

Chapter Overview

Chapter 38 introduces reptiles, descendants of the amphibians discussed in the previous chapter. After a discussion of reptilian adaptations to terrestrial life, Section 38.1 examines the origin and evolution of reptiles. Section 38.2 presents an overview of the four living reptile orders. Finally, Section 38.3 explores the adaptations of snakes for movement, feeding, defense, and reproduction.

Chapter Planning Chart

B	S	A	Sections and Subsections	Page	Features	Page	Resources
•	•	•	**38.1 Evolution of Reptiles**				
			The Amniote Egg	571	Biology in Process	574	Videodiscs
			Other Adaptations to Land	572	Section Review	575	Process Skills: The Extinction of Dinosaurs
			Origin and Evolution	573			Laboratories: Live Reptiles
							Section Reviews Worksheet
•	•	•	**38.2 Modern Reptiles**				
			Rhynchocephalia	576	Laboratory	583	Videodiscs
			Chelonia	576	Section Review	579	Section Reviews Worksheet
			Crocodilia	577			
			Squamata	578			
•	•	•	**38.3 Adaptations of Snakes**				
			Movement	580	Think	582	Videodiscs
			Feeding	580	Section Review	582	Blackline Master 80
			Defense	582			Overhead Transparency T38
			Reproduction	582			Section Reviews Worksheet
			End of Chapter Activities				
					Chapter Review	584	Vocabulary Skills
							Chapter Test
							Computer Test Generator

B *The Basic Level curriculum presents the most fundamental knowledge offered in the course.*
S *The Standard Level curriculum is designed for the average student who is able to master most topics.*
A *The Advanced Level curriculum includes suggestions for teaching the most academically able students.*

Cooperative Learning

Group Activity: Dinosaur Debate

- **Group Size:** *4 students*
- **Outcome:** *Students will describe how paleontologists analyze evidence.*
- **Individual Accountability:** *Each student will research information to contribute to the debate team.*
- **Positive Interdependence:** *The team will participate in a debate, each student contributing evidence to a complete argument.*

Divide each group into two teams to debate among themselves how the dinosaurs became extinct. One team will argue for a sudden extinction due to a catastrophe, such as a meteor's colliding with the earth. The other team will argue for gradual extinction due to changing climates, drifting continents, or other factors. Both students on a team are responsible for researching their team's position. Within each group the two teams will alternate speaking until all four students have had a chance to speak.

Concept Map

The following is one possible solution to the concept mapping activity in Reteaching on p. 574.

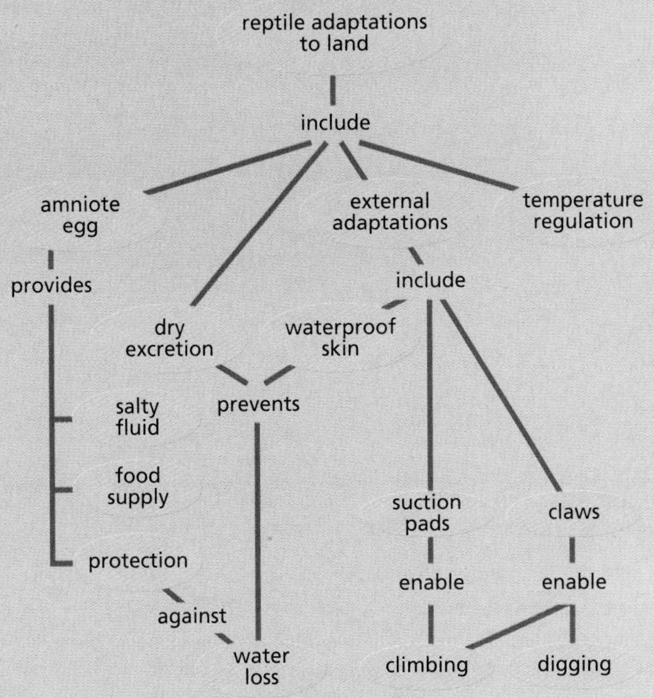

Laboratory Preparation

Overview *(See p. 583.)*

In this laboratory, students will investigate color change in the anole. This color change is usually in response to environmental color brightness or contrast. Color change may be subtle, however. For example, it may be affected by adrenaline if the lizard is frightened or by feeding patterns. Anoles deprived of food for 12 days are usually brown and will turn green after feeding. Very cool temperatures can also produce a change to brown.

Preparation

At least one hour before the lab exercise begins, place the anoles under fluorescent light in two terraria. Place half the anoles in a terrarium lined with black construction paper. These anoles should turn brown. Place the remaining anoles in a terrarium lined with white construction paper. These anoles should turn green. Provide a shallow dish in each terrarium for drinking. Use jars large enough to allow the anoles to settle comfortably on the bottom. Depending on the experimental design students choose, two lab periods may be necessary.

Teaching Tips

Have students carefully read the Technique section before they design their experiment.

Demonstrate to students how to match the color of the anole to the reference construction paper. Stress that each partner on the lab team should agree on the match before continuing.

Ask students to formulate a hypothesis about the adaptive significance of the anole's color-changing trait and design an experiment to test their hypothesis (even one that they cannot carry out at this time). Remind students that the trait will have survival value if it helps the animal find food, avoid predators, find a mate, or insure the survival of its offspring.

Safety

Anoles can run fast and are easily frightened. Remind students to handle anoles with care. If the anole is picked up by the tail, it may break off.

Note that anoles that are no longer needed in the classroom make ideal pets at home.

Chapter Themes

Evolution Tell students that reptiles are thought to have evolved from amphibians as the first vertebrate group not dependent on an aquatic environment. Explain that independence was made possible by a number of terrestrial adaptations, but especially by development of the amniote egg. Through adaptive radiation, 16 orders of reptiles evolved and dominated the land. Point out that several types of reptiles, such as turtles, crocodiles, and the extinct plesiosaurs and ichthyosaurs, readapted successfully to aquatic life.

Scale and Structure Point out to students that because of sophisticated anatomical and physiological features, reptiles have become adapted to a wide variety of habitats. Dinosaurs included the largest land animals ever to have lived. Have students consider the design of the turtle's shell, which has survived nearly unchanged for 200 million years. Point out that snakes, the most recently evolved group of reptiles, have developed various survival-enhancing adaptations, such as long, slim bodies with flexible skeletal and muscular systems and venoms.

Chapter Motivating Activity

Have students brainstorm examples of reptiles from fiction, films, cartoons, myths, and legends. *(Godzilla; the pterodonts in* King Kong; *snakes in "The Speckled Band"—a Sherlock Holmes story; Teenage Mutant Ninja Turtles; The Mock Turtle in* Alice in Wonderland; *alligators in the cartoon strip* Pogo; *dinosaurs battling with cave dwellers in many films)*

Ask the students to suggest how close these depictions are to reality. *(Accept any reasonable answers. Dinosaurs became extinct long before humans evolved.)*

Chapter 38 | *Reptiles*

Introduction

Although amphibians have adapted to life on land, they remain dependent on water for reproduction. The first vertebrates to become totally at home on land were reptiles. In this chapter you will learn about the adaptations that allowed reptiles to dominate the earth for 160 million years and that continue to make them a highly successful group of animals.

Chapter Outline

Chapter Concept

As you read, look for ways in which reptiles are adapted to life on land. Pay special attention to adaptations that prevent drying out of sensitive tissues.

Vine snake, Thailand. Inset: Thorny devil lizard, *Moloch horridus,* Australia.

Understanding the Visuals
Ask students how the vine snake and the thorny devil lizard in the photographs appear to differ. *(Snake: legless, long and slender, sleek, green; lizard: legs, short and broad, thorny, brown and tan)* Ask students how the two pictured reptiles seem to be similar. *(Scales, although difficult to see in the lizard photograph; colors that blend in with the background; both seem alert)* Point out that snakes and lizards, members of the same order, are more closely related to each other than they are to any other living group of reptiles.

38.1 Evolution of Reptiles

About 310 million years ago geological events were reshaping the face of the earth. As new continents emerged, a great diversity of new habitats formed. Plants, amphibians, and insects began to populate these new landmasses, but no vertebrates had yet made a permanent home on land. Onto the dry land came the reptiles—the first vertebrates to make the complete transition to life on land. Two major forces probably helped lead to this transition: (1) an increase in competition for food and space among all the life-forms in aquatic environments and (2) limited competition for the insects and plants that could be used as food on land.

After moving onto land, the reptiles evolved rapidly and dominated the land, seas, and air for 160 million years. Let us begin by taking a look at some of the adaptations that made this evolutionary success possible.

Section Objectives

- *Describe the structure of the amniote egg and explain its importance in the evolution of reptiles.*
- *List three structural characteristics of reptiles that are adaptations to life on land.*
- *Summarize the major developments in the evolution of reptiles.*
- *List three types of evidence that suggest that dinosaurs may have been warm-blooded.*

The Amniote Egg

Studies of the fossil record and comparative anatomy strongly suggest that reptiles evolved from amphibians. Although amphibians can live on land for part of their life cycle, they are forced to return to water to reproduce. With the evolution of reptiles, a new reproductive structure evolved that allowed reproduction on land. This structure is the **amniote egg**, an egg with a protective membrane and a porous shell enclosing the developing embryo. The amniote egg forms a secure, self-contained "nursery" for the developing embryo. In contrast to the naked eggs that amphibians lay in water, the amniote egg provides an internal aquatic environment that enables the embryo to survive the dry environment.

Figure 38-1 shows the complex internal structure of the amniote egg, including its four specialized membranes: amnion, yolk sac, allantois, and chorion. The egg derives its name from the **amnion** *(AM-nee-AHN)*, the thin membrane enclosing the salty fluid in which the embryo floats. The **yolk sac** encloses the yolk, a protein-rich food supply for the developing embryo. The **allantois** *(uh-LAN-tuh-wuss)* stores the nitrogenous wastes produced by the embryo until the egg hatches. The **chorion** *(KOR-ee-AHN)* lines the outer shell and thus encloses the embryo and all the other membranes. It regulates the exchange of oxygen and carbon dioxide between the egg and the outside environment.

The entire amniote egg is surrounded by a leathery shell that may be hard in some species because of the presence of calcium carbonate. The egg is waterproof but allows gases to flow between the environment and the chorion. External fertilization of such an egg would be impossible since the sperm could not penetrate the egg. Instead the male places the sperm inside the female before the shell is formed. This strategy, called **internal fertilization**, makes water transport of sperm unnecessary.

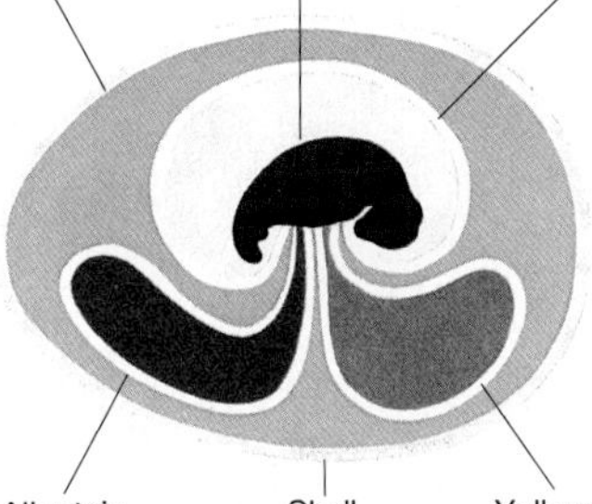

Figure 38-1 The four membranes of the amniote egg surround and protect the embryo and its food supply. The shell permits gases to pass between the egg and the outside environment.

Reptile Adaptations to Land					
amniote egg	waterproof skin	claws and pads	lungs	heart (3 or 4 chambers)	dry nitrogenous waste
Effects					
independent of water	prevents water loss	efficient terrestrial locomotion	no gill-bearing stage	efficient oxygen transport	minimizes water loss

Graphic Organizer Use this table in organizing the topics of Section 38.1.

Lesson Plan

Section Focus

This section introduces the evolution and diversity of reptiles. Reptiles have achieved independence from aquatic life through such adaptations as the amniote egg, waterproof skin, and efficient kidneys that conserve water.

Section Themes

This section emphasizes the theme of **Evolution.** Soon after their evolution from amphibian ancestors, reptiles evolved a wide variety of features and ways of living, adapting to many terrestrial and aquatic habitats.

Motivating Activity

Show students pictures of a wide variety of dinosaurs and modern reptiles. Ask students to propose ways in which dinosaurs may have differed from modern reptiles, based on evidence available in pictures. *(For example, no dinosaur was legless, few modern reptiles are bipedal.)* Point out that not all dinosaurs were enormous. Some grew no larger than a chicken—much smaller than many modern reptiles.

Teaching Strategies

Comparing Groups Have students brainstorm ways reptilian adaptations had to be modified when some reptiles—such as the sea turtles, sea snakes, crocodiles, and the extinct plesiosaurs and ichthyosaurs—became re-adapted to life in water. *(Females must return to land to lay eggs or young must be born alive; limbs would have to adapt to water locomotion)*

Videodiscs

- *2445–2447, Classification: Animalia; Chordata; Reptilia (s)*
- *2619, Amniote Egg (s)*

Observing Organisms Plan a visit to a local zoo so that students can see the diversity of living reptiles, observe their behaviors, and learn about their habitats. Prior to the visit, discuss with students strategies for learning about reptile adaptations. These could include comparing sizes and shapes of scales, noting how colors and patterns are related to natural backgrounds, or observing reptile locomotion. Back in the classroom, have students discuss how well they were able to implement their strategies.

■ *See* **Laboratories,** ***Investigation 38.***

Drawing Conclusions Have students draw generalized diagrams of single circulation (such as found in fishes) and double circulation (as found in amphibians and reptiles). Remind students that with double circulation, deoxygenated blood is first pumped by the heart to the lungs for oxygenation. Then oxygenated blood returns to the heart to be pumped to the body. With single circulation, blood is pumped from the heart to the gills, continues to the body, and finally returns to the heart. Ask students what advantages double circulation might carry. *(More efficient delivery of oxygen to the body)* Point out that the three-chambered heart of amphibians and most reptiles permits a degree of mixing of blood from the lungs and body in the single ventricle. Crocodilians, like birds and mammals, have four-chambered hearts. Ask students why. *(The size and weight of the crocodilians requires a more efficient circulatory system.)*

Figure 38-2 The scaly skin of a snake (top), the claws of a spiny lizard (center), and the suction cup-equipped toes of a gecko are all adaptations for life on land.

Other Adaptations to Land

In addition to the amniote egg and internal fertilization, other adaptations helped make the transition to land possible. These include waterproof skin, modified limbs and body systems, well-developed lungs, and new methods of temperature regulation.

Waterproof Skin

A dry body covering of horny scales or plates protects reptiles. This scaly covering develops as surface cells fill with **keratin,** the same protein that forms human fingernails and bird feathers. These scales prevent water loss and protect reptiles from the wear and tear associated with living in rugged terrestrial environments. In contrast, amphibians have smooth, delicate skin. They can never be far from water or their skin will dry out.

External Structural Adaptations

Reptiles also show structural adaptations for movement on land. The limbs of some reptiles have toes with claws that permit them to climb, dig, and thus move about on a variety of terrains. Other reptiles have toes modified into suction cups that aid in climbing. In the absence of limbs, snakes rely on their scaly skin and highly developed skeletal and muscular systems for movement.

Respiration, Circulation, and Excretion

After they hatch, all reptiles breathe air through lungs, eliminating respiration through gills. Thus in reptiles the tissues involved in gas exchange are all located inside the body, where they can be kept moist in even the driest land environments.

Reptiles have a circulatory system that is more complex than that of amphibians, one that provides more oxygen to the body. Like amphibians, all reptiles have double circulation, and most species have a three-chambered heart. However, a partial division of the ventricle separates the oxygen-poor blood flowing from the body from the oxygen-rich blood returning from the lungs. In alligators and crocodiles the heart has four separate chambers, allowing total separation of oxygenated and deoxygenated blood.

The excretory system of reptiles is also well adapted to life on land. Snakes, lizards, and other land-dwelling reptiles conserve water by excreting nitrogenous wastes in dry or pasty form as crystals of uric acid.

Temperature Regulation

The rate of metabolism in the body of an organism is controlled in part by body temperature. Therefore regulating body temperature is very important. In reptiles, as in fish and amphibians, body temperature is largely determined by the temperature of their surroundings. Animals in which body temperature is determined by the environment are called **ectothermic,** or cold-blooded. Thus reptiles cannot maintain their body temperature as can birds

LEP Activity
Help students understand reptile adaptations to living on land by having students design and make posters. Have them draw pictures of each of the following adaptive features: amniote egg, waterproof skin, external structure, and respiratory, circulatory, and excretory adaptations. Have students provide the name of the adaptation, describe it, and discuss what makes it adaptive. *(Lungs: breathing air; Claws: walking on land)* Have students present their posters to the group or class.

and mammals, which are **endothermic,** or warm-blooded. Reptiles regulate their temperature by their behavior. For example, they may bask in the sun to warm up, thereby increasing their metabolic rate, or they may seek shade to prevent overheating.

Origin and Evolution

From studies of fossils and comparative anatomy, biologists infer that reptiles arose from a group of ancestral reptiles called **cotylosaurs** *(KOT'l-oe-SORZ),* which lived about 310 million years ago. Fossils indicate that these four-legged, sprawling vertebrates resembled small lizards and had teeth well suited to eating insects. In fact, the abundance of insects at the time may have been one reason the cotylosaurs flourished.

During the Permian period (280 million to 225 million years ago), the cotylosaurs began to adapt to other available environments, giving rise to new forms of reptiles. These groups included flying reptiles called pterosaurs, two groups of marine reptiles—the ichthyosaurs and plesiosaurs—and the thecodonts. The dominant land reptiles arose from thecodonts—small, lizardlike carnivores, many of which walked on their hind legs. The thecodonts were the first **archosaurs** ("ruling reptiles"), a group that later included the early crocodiles, the dinosaurs, and the reptiles that evolved into birds. Figure 38-3 shows the probable evolutionary relationships among these and other groups.

Figure 38-3 The phylogenetic tree of reptiles shows animals with a wide array of adaptations diverging from common ancestors.

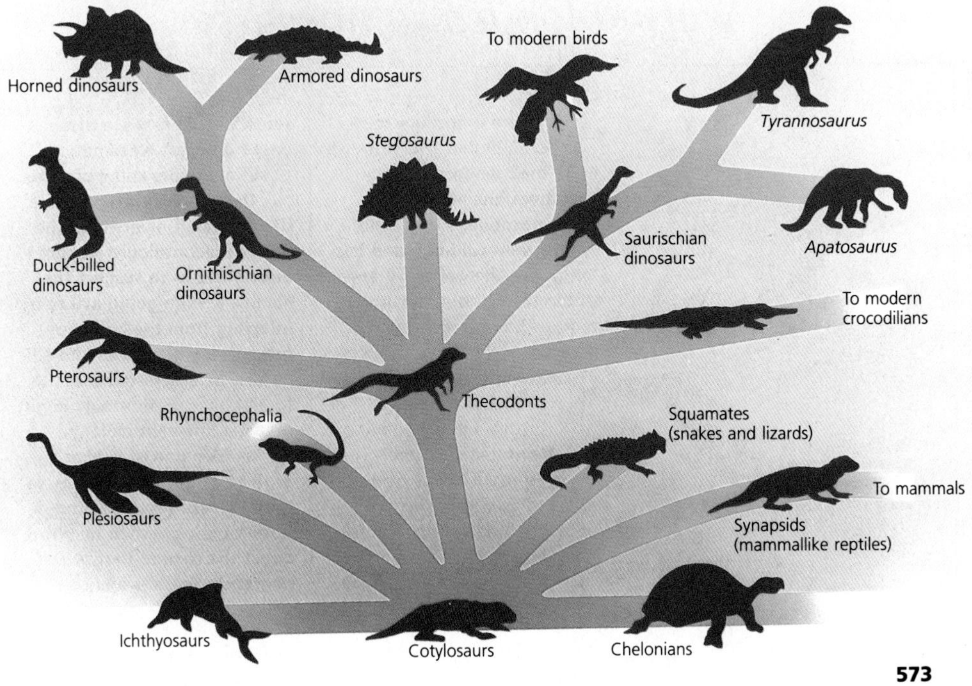

Interpreting the Visuals Have students examine the phylogenetic tree (Figure 38-3, p. 573) and find the branches leading to modern organisms. Suggest that students refer to the text, pp. 573–575, as necessary. Ask them which modern animals are most closely related to dinosaurs. *(Birds are descended from saurischian dinosaurs. Crocodilians share a close common ancestor with dinosaurs, the thecodonts. Mammals and the other modern reptiles are more distantly related to dinosaurs.)* Stress that some scientists might argue for a phylogenetic tree with slightly different relationships. Ask students what evidence might be found in this figure for or against the hypothesis that some dinosaurs were endotherms. *(Their close relationship to birds argues for the hypothesis. The distant relationship of mammals to birds demonstrates that endothermy can arise independently.)*

- *See* Process Skills, *Chapter 38.*

Guided Practice

Use Figure 38-1 on p. 571 to guide students step-by-step through the parts of the amniote egg. Have students make a chart listing the four membranes of the amniote egg and their functions. *(Amnion: encloses the embryo; yolk sac: encloses the embryo's protein-rich food supply; allantois: stores the embryo's nitrogenous wastes; chorion: lines the outer shell)*

Videodiscs

- ***2588–2593, Homologous Forelimbs—Crocodile/Others; Evolutionary Relationships (s)***

Independent Practice

- Have students write answers to the Section Review.
- Have each student write a short essay comparing skins of amphibians and reptiles. Have them relate differences in their adaptive functions.

Check Your Understanding

1. How does the amniote egg allow reptiles to live out of water? *(It contains a food source, a salty fluid, regulates oxygen and carbon dioxide exchange, and has a waterproof shell.)*
2. How is a reptile's circulation different from that of an amphibian? *(Partial separation of oxygen-poor and oxygen-rich blood in the ventricle; crocodilians have four-chambered hearts)*
3. Which modern vertebrate classes have evolved from the first reptiles? *(Modern reptiles, mammals, birds)*

Reteaching

Have students make a concept map showing reptile adaptations to land that are advances over amphibian adaptations. An example of a completed concept map is shown on p. 569B.

- *See* Section Reviews *worksheet, Section 38.1.*

Enrichment

Have students research and write a report on reptiles, such as water moccasins or snapping turtles, that have re-adapted to water. Ask students to include information about terrestrial adaptations that these aquatic reptiles have retained.

Figure 38-4 An artist's rendering of a thecodont, *Euparkeria* sp., reflects scientists' view of what these animals looked like based on fossil remains.

The Mesozoic era (225 million to 65 million years ago) is known as the Age of Reptiles. During that time reptiles—especially the dinosaurs—dominated all other forms of life. Although *dinosaur* means "terrible lizard," many were small. Yet the incredible size of some dinosaurs distinguish the group from all other forms of life. One of the largest dinosaurs, *Brachiosaurus,* measured 23 m long, stood 12 m tall, and weighed more than 77,000 kg. Thus *Brachiosaurus* was as long as a tennis court, as tall as a four-story building, and heavier than ten elephants.

Over 300 genera of dinosaurs have been identified around the world from fossils. These animals were adapted to a wide range of environments and different ways of life. *Brachiosaurus* and such related dinosaurs as *Diplodocus* and *Apatosaurus* (also called *Brontosaurus*) were **herbivores,** or plant eaters, and probably used their long necks to feed on leaves in treetops. *Tyrannosaurus* and other **carnivores,** or meat eaters, walked on their hind legs and used sharp teeth and huge claws to rip apart prey.

Paleontologists who study dinosaurs still have many unanswered questions. Not the least of these questions is why dinosaurs became extinct along with many other forms of animal and plant life 65 million years ago, at the end of the Cretaceous period.

Biology in Process

Warm-blooded Dinosaurs?

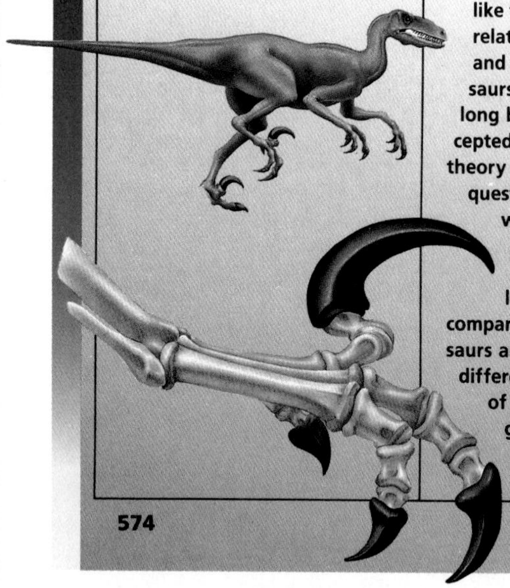

Were dinosaurs cold-blooded and sluggish like their modern reptilian relatives, the alligators and crocodiles? That dinosaurs were cold-blooded has long been the generally accepted theory, but today that theory is being called into question by paleontologists who are reinterpreting the fossil record.

For a long time paleontologists merely compared fossil bones of dinosaurs and classified the many different kinds. In the course of their work, paleontologists made assumptions about the lives of dinosaurs. But these were often based on what was known about alligators and crocodiles.

During his undergraduate days at Yale University in the 1960s, paleontologist Robert T. Bakker began to suspect that his peers were going astray by inferring from the habits of present-day crocodiles and alligators. He suggested that the fossil bones of dinosaurs might reveal a different biology.

In 1969 one of Bakker's professors, John H. Ostrom, set the stage for reconsidering dinosaur biology when he wrote about the clawed foot of *Deinonychus.* Fossil evidence showed that this dinosaur had

574

Cooperative Learning

Etymologies Divide students into small teams. Each will draw up a list of unfamiliar terms in Chapter 38 and research their etymologies. Have each team compile a list of etymologies and then use the roots to brainstorm a list of other words. *(For example,* endotherm *is comprised of the roots* endo- *and* -therm. Endo- *can form endocrine, endoplasm;* -therm *can be used to form thermometer, thermostat.)* When students have finished brainstorming, bring the groups together to share their lists and discuss how knowledge of word roots can help them understand unfamiliar terms.

There are various schools of thought about this mass extinction. Some scientists propose that gradual climatic changes, probably brought about by the drifting of continents into new latitudes, made the earth less hospitable for many forms of Mesozoic life. Other scientists maintain that a catastrophic cosmic event was responsible. Supporters of this theory suggest that a huge asteroid hit the earth, sending so much dust into the atmosphere that the amount of sunlight reaching the earth's surface was greatly reduced. The reduced sunlight caused severe climatic changes that led to the mass extinction.

Section Review

1. Why is the reptile egg called an *amniote egg?*
2. How did the amniote egg help make reptiles completely independent of aquatic environments?
3. Name three adaptations of reptiles for life on land.
4. Name the groups of modern vertebrates that have evolved from archosaurs.
5. In what ways are the adaptations of reptiles to land like the adaptations of vascular plants to land? (See Chapter 25.)

a scythelike claw on its foot, which it may have used to kill prey. Hunters that track and kill require sustained energy to chase down their prey. They need a high metabolism of the sort present only in endothermic animals.

Based on Ostrom's inferences and on other observations, Bakker inferred that some dinosaurs may have been fleet-footed, agile, and warm-blooded. To support his theory, Bakker applied the findings of other research. For example, he used data on bone structure to distinguish between endothermic and ectothermic animals. He found that many dinosaurs had bones similar to those of warm-blooded animals.

Bakker's inference received support from the work of other paleontologists who had uncovered fossil remains of entire dinosaur herds, including eggs (above) and baby dinosaurs. These have provided a way to study the growth rate of dinosaurs. The results show a rapid rate of growth much closer to that of endothermic birds than to that of ectothermic crocodiles.

Despite all the evidence presented, Bakker's findings have by no means been entirely accepted by the paleontological community. Numerous scientists have proposed equally compelling counterarguments to his. Nevertheless, as one paleontologist said of Bakker, "He keeps you thinking," and that is one of his most important contributions to the study of dinosaurs.

■ What processes did Bakker use to test his inference that dinosaurs were warm-blooded?

Answers to Section Review

1. It is named for the amnion, the membrane that encloses the embryo.
2. It provided a protective, watery environment in which the embryo could develop without drying up.
3. Answers may include waterproof skin, feet adapted for land movement, lungs for breathing air, an excretory system for conserving water.
4. Birds and crocodilians evolved from archosaurs.
5. Amniote eggs and internal fertilization eliminate dependence on water for reproduction, as do seeds and pollen grains. Waterproof skin prevents drying up, as does the cuticle. The circulatory system transports materials, as does the vascular system of plants.

Closure

Have students imagine a species of turtle that lives entirely in a cave. What adaptive features of reptiles might have been lost over the years or never developed? *(Accept reasonable answers. For example, the turtle might be blind; its shell might be vestigial.)*

Biology in Process

Using the Feature

The feature focuses on the process skills of observing, hypothesizing, inferring, and communicating. Stress that John Ostrom's study of the clawed foot of *Deinonychus* led to Robert Bakker's inference that some dinosaurs may have had speed and agility, which implies endothermy. Without Ostrom's work, Bakker may not have come to this conclusion.

Bakker began to study the structure of dinosaur bones, comparing them with those of modern animals. Bakker has also looked at the growth rate of some dinosaurs, which can be affected by an animal's mode of temperature regulation.

Emphasize that while scientists prefer to conduct controlled experiments in order to test their hypotheses, in the case of extinct animals, direct experiment is not possible. In such cases, inference is a powerful tool for scientific exploration.

Not all scientists accept Bakker's hypothesis. Ask students to suggest additional evidence that Bakker might seek to test his ideas. *(Rare fossil imprints of dinosaur feathers or fur may be found; also ratios of predators to prey that mirror modern mammals would be important evidence.)*

Answer to the Feature

Observing, hypothesizing, inferring, communicating

Lesson Plan

Section Focus

This section presents the four orders of living reptiles: Rhynchocephalia (represented by a single species, the tuatara), Chelonia (turtles), Crocodilia (crocodiles and alligators), and Squamata (lizards and snakes). Moreover, there are 12 other orders of reptiles that are extinct.

Section Themes

This section emphasizes the theme of **Evolution.** The living orders of reptiles all evolved from a common ancestor and share reptile adaptations to life on land. These include the amniote egg, internal fertilization, a dry body, lungs, a three- or four-chambered heart, and ectothermy.

Motivating Activity

Ask students who have kept reptiles as pets or who have encountered reptiles in their natural habitats to share what they have learned about reptiles from their experiences. Ask if any students have ever eaten snake or turtle meat. Ask them to describe the experience to the class.

Teaching Strategies

Identifying Organisms Show students photographs from nature books and magazines of various reptiles (such as tuataras, alligators, tortoises, iguanas, snakes, sea turtles, geckos) and other classes of animals (toads, salamanders, sea stars, earthworms, bison, perch, robins). Ask students to indicate which animals are reptiles. Have them state the criteria for making their choices. At the end of the activity, have students identify several essential features of reptiles. *(For example, a dry body with scales or plates, limbs with claws)*

Section Objectives

- *List seven characteristics of modern reptiles.*
- *Name the four orders of modern reptiles, and give an example of each.*
- *Describe the basic structure of the turtle shell, and explain how it differs in land-dwelling and water-dwelling species.*
- *Explain how the head structure of crocodilians is related to their feeding behavior.*
- *List three types of defensive adaptations that are common among lizards.*

38.2 Modern Reptiles

Biologists have classified reptiles into 16 orders, of which 12 are extinct. The four surviving orders comprise about 6,000 species. All of these species share traits that you have learned are adaptations to land:

- The amniote egg helps protect the embryo.
- Internal fertilization replaces water transport of sperm.
- A dry body covered by scales or plates prevents water loss.
- Limbs with claws or pads aid movement on land.
- Respiration through lungs eliminates external gills.
- A three-chambered or four-chambered heart helps supply more oxygen to the body.
- Ectothermic temperature regulation controls metabolic rate.

Reptiles occur worldwide except in the coldest regions, where it is impossible for large ectotherms to survive. In recent times, human intervention has had a powerful impact on the number and distribution of reptiles. Many species of turtles, prized for food, have been hunted almost to extinction. Snakes and lizards suffer from needless killings by humans as well as from the effects of pesticides and habitat destruction.

The four living orders of the Class Reptilia are (1) Rhynchocephalia, (2) Chelonia, (3) Crocodilia, and (4) Squamata.

Figure 38-5 The tuatara, often called a "living fossil," has changed little from its prehistoric ancestors, which appeared on earth more than 225 million years ago. Note the crest on the head and back. The name tuatara means "spiny crest."

Rhynchocephalia

The Order Rhynchocephalia *(RING-koe-suh-FAY-lee-uh)* is an ancient one that contains only one living species, *Sphenodon punctatus,* the tuatara. Tuataras inhabit about 20 small islands off the coast of New Zealand. The native Maoris of New Zealand named the tuatara for the conspicuous spiny crest running down its back, which you can see in Figure 38-5. *S. punctatus* resembles a large lizard, growing on the average to about 60 cm long.

An unusual feature of the tuatara is the inconspicuous "third eye" on the top of its head, called a **parietal eye.** Under a thin layer of scales are a lens, retina, and nerves connecting the eye to the brain. The parietal eye seems to function as a thermostat that alerts the tuatara when it has been exposed to too much sun, thus protecting against overheating. Unlike most reptiles, tuataras are most active at low temperatures. They burrow during the day and at night feed on insects, worms, and small animals.

Chelonia

The Order Chelonia consists of about 265 species of turtles and tortoises. The term *tortoise* is generally reserved for the terrestrial Chelonia, such as the giant Galápagos tortoises. Turtles are chelonians that live in water.

Order			
Rynchocepalia	Chelonia	Crocodilia	Squamata
Unique Features			
parietal eye	shell	4-chambered heart	• lower jaw not joined to skull • paired male reproductive organs

Graphic Organizer Use this table in Organizing Characteristics on page 577.

Figure 38-6 The carapace of the sea-dwelling Ridley turtle, *Lepidochelys* sp. (left), is streamlined for efficient swimming. The domed carapace of the Galápagos tortoise, *Geochelone elephantopus* (right), a land dweller, can serve as protection when the head, legs, and tail are withdrawn.

Chelonians have changed little in the last 200 million years. This evolutionary stability may be the result of the continuous benefit of their basic design—a body covered by a shell. In some species the shell is made of hard plates; in other species it is a covering of tough, leathery skin. In either case the shell consists of two basic parts. The **carapace** is the top or dorsal covering. In most species it is fused with the vertebrae and ribs. The **plastron** is the ventral or belly portion.

The shape of the chelonian shell is modified for a variety of ecological demands. Many tortoises have a domed carapace into which they can retract their head, legs, and tail as a means of protection from predators. Water-dwelling turtles have instead a streamlined disk-shaped shell that permits rapid turning in water. When swimming, the marine turtles are the fastest of the reptiles. The forelimbs of marine turtles have evolved into flippers, and freshwater turtles have webbed toes. These adaptations allow for maximum swimming ability both in oceans and in freshwater rivers, lakes, and ponds.

Another adaptation among chelonians is the migratory behavior of the sea and river turtles. Although these animals are adapted for life in water, they must return to land to lay their eggs. For example, Atlantic green turtles migrate from their feeding grounds off the coast of Brazil to Ascension Island in the South Atlantic—a distance of more than 2,000 km. There they lay eggs on the same beaches where they were hatched.

Crocodilia

The Order Crocodilia is composed of about 23 species of large lizard-shaped reptiles. In addition to crocodiles and alligators, the order also includes less familiar animals called caimans (*KAY-*

Organizing Characteristics Have students prepare a table showing the features of each living reptile order that are unique to that order. An example of a completed table is shown on p. 576. Stress that there may be some superficial resemblances between these features and those of some nonreptilian organisms, such as a turtle's shell and the shell of a snail. These are examples of convergent evolution and not evidence of relationship.

Identifying Features Provide students with live or preserved specimens of lizards and tortoises. Have students observe and note characteristics of modern reptiles and explain how each adaptation helps the reptile live on land. *(Waterproof skin minimizes water loss; claws aid terrestrial locomotion.)* Remind students that some reptiles, such as sea turtles and crocodiles, returned to life in the water. Ask students to suggest terrestrial features that they would be likely to find retained in these aquatic reptiles. *(Waterproof skin; eggs laid on land)*

Videodiscs

- *Side 4 3787, Alligator Snapping Turtle (m)*
- *Side 4 4142, Crocodile Maternal Care (m)*
- *Side 4 4398, Sand Lizard (m)*
- *Side 4 27846, Animal Locomotion: Komodo Dragon Lizard (m)*
- *1342–1414, Reptilia: Types; Anatomy; Developments (s)*

Interdisciplinary Activity

Government All species of sea turtles are listed as either threatened or endangered by the U.S. government. Because of this, shrimp fishermen are required to add Turtle Excluder Devices (TEDs) to their nets to prevent sea turtles from becoming entrapped and drowning. Have students write a report on some aspect of TED technology and legislation by using library resources, contacting legislators, or contacting representatives of the shrimping industry or environmental organizations. Stress that there are many differing points of view about what public policy should be regarding endangered species.

Interpreting the Visuals Ask students to make inferences from Figure 38-7 on p. 578 about the feeding behaviors and habitat of each crocodilian species. Emphasize that inferences can include what feeding behavior may *not* be, as well as what it may be. *(The gavial's long snout seems unsuited to crushing, but its many sharp teeth seem well adapted to catching fish. The caiman's short, thick jaws and sharp teeth seem adapted to holding onto strong, struggling prey.)*

Guided Practice
Help students create a chart of differences between land- and water-dwelling reptiles described in the section, such as turtles and tortoises, or various snakes. Have students describe how each difference is an adaptation to the reptile's environment. *(For example: a streamlined carapace in sea turtles versus the hard, domed carapace of some tortoises)*

Independent Practice
- Have students write answers to the Section Review.
- Give students pairs of concepts and ask them to write a sentence expressing the relationship between concepts in each pair. For example, pair ectotherms and metabolism. *(In ectotherms, body temperature, and therefore the rate of metabolism, are determined by environment.)*

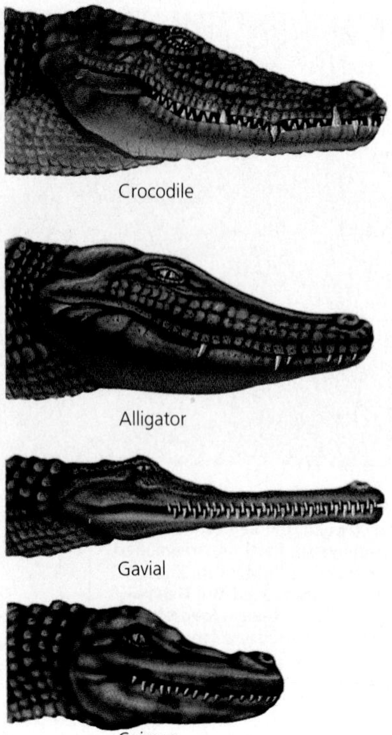

Figure 38-7 The modified snouts of four species of crocodilians reflect their different feeding habits.

munz) and gavials *(GAY-vee-ulz)*. Examination of the fossil record shows that crocodilians are direct descendants of the archosaurs and that many species have remained relatively unchanged for 200 million years.

All crocodilians live in or near water in tropical or subtropical regions of the world. Crocodiles are largely nocturnal animals found in Africa, Asia, and the Americas, including southern Florida. Alligators live in China and the southern United States. Caimans, which closely resemble alligators, are native to Central America but are becoming established in Florida. Gavials are a group of fish-eating crocodilians with an extremely long and slender snout adapted for snaring and eating fish. Gavials live only in India and Burma.

All crocodilians are carnivorous. They generally hunt by stealth, waiting for prey to come near and then attacking aggressively. Many of their anatomical features are adaptations that reflect this feeding behavior. Their eyes are on top of the head; the nostrils, on the top of the snout. This arrangement allows them to see and breathe while lying quietly submerged in water. A valve in the back of the mouth prevents water from entering the air passage when a crocodilian feeds under water.

Parental care is generally lacking in reptiles, though it does occur in some species. In one species of Crocodilia, the Nile crocodile, both parents carry the young in their jaws from the nest to a special nursery area, where they oversee their development. This behavior in a living reptile is interesting in light of new fossil discoveries indicating that certain dinosaurs also probably cared for their young.

Squamata

The Order Squamata consists of about 5,640 species of lizards and snakes. The distinguishing characteristics of this order are an upper jaw that is loosely joined to the skull and the presence of paired reproductive organs in the male. Squamates are more structurally diverse than members of any other order of reptiles. In this section we will look at the different kinds of lizards and see how they have radiated into many habitats. In Section 38.3 we will examine the structure and evolutionary success of the snakes.

Lizards are generally distinguished from snakes by the presence of limbs, although a few species of lizards are limbless. Common lizards include iguanas, horned toads, chameleons, skinks, and geckos. Lizards live on every continent except Antarctica. They have adapted to deserts and tropical forests. Most rely on agility, speed, and camouflage to catch prey and elude predators.

Only two species of lizards are venomous. They are the Gila monster of the southwestern United States and the beaded lizard of western Mexico. Most lizards prey on insects or on other small animals. They do not need to immobilize their prey and therefore have not developed the capacity to produce venom for survival.

More Information
American Alligators Like the beaver, the American alligator alters its habitat. In southern swamps, alligators scour out deep depressions called "gator holes." These holes serve as refuges during seasonal winter droughts that often dry up large areas of the swamp. Fishes, amphibians, turtles, and other aquatic animals survive dry periods by seeking out these winter refuges. The alligator benefits because it feeds on other animals and birds that come in search of fishes. On balance, however, gator holes enable many species to survive droughts in swamps.

Some lizards can blend with their background by changing color. One is *Anolis carolinensis,* a common lizard of North America. Because of this ability, it is commonly called a chameleon, but true chameleons live only in Africa and Madagascar.

Blending with the background is a passive way of remaining inconspicuous. In contrast, many lizards use active displays to fend off enemies. The horned lizards of the southwestern United States, though small, are particularly impressive. They are covered with spiky armor, and when disturbed, they inflate themselves, gape their mouths, hiss, and squirt blood from their eyelids.

Many lizards, including the skinks and geckos, have the ability to lose their tails and then regenerate a new one. From observation, biologists have inferred that this trait, called **autotomy,** is an adaptation that allows the lizard to escape from predators. An unusual form of autotomy occurs in glass lizards, which get their name from the fact that their tails often shatter when grasped by a predator.

Most lizards are small, measuring less than 0.3 m in length. Iguanas can reach 1 m in length, but the largest lizards belong to the monitor family. The largest of all monitors is the Komodo dragon of Indonesia, which reaches 3 m in length and weighs up to 140 kg. Monitors are thought to be related to snakes. Like snakes, they have deeply forked tongues that serve as sense organs. They also consume large prey whole, as do snakes. A monitor lizard uses its tail as a defensive weapon.

Figure 38-8 Among the lizards, a diverse group, can be found the Gila monster, *Heloderma suspectum* (top left), the land iguana, *Conolophus subcristatus* (top right), and the skink (above).

Section Review

1. What is a *parietal eye?* Of what order of reptiles is it a distinguishing characteristic?
2. Describe the structure and function of the chelonian shell.
3. How is the position of a crocodile's eyes and nostrils related to its way of feeding?
4. What are three ways in which lizards defend themselves?
5. What factors do you think might have caused monitors to grow so much larger than other lizards?

Answers to Section Review

1. A third eye on top of the head; Rhynchocephalia
2. It consists of a carapace (top) and plastron (bottom) that together protect the turtle from predators. The carapace is fused to the vertebrae and ribs.
3. Eyes and nostrils on top of the head allow crocodiles to breathe and see while submerged in water.
4. Camouflage, threatening display, autotomy
5. Answers might include lack of competition from mammalian predators and adaptation for feeding on larger prey.

Check Your Understanding

1. Compare adaptations in frogs and crocodilians for hunting by stealth. *(Both have eyes and nostrils on top of the head, and good vision. Crocodilians have a watertight valve in the back of the mouth.)*
2. How are aquatic turtles' shells adapted to life in water? *(The streamlined disk shape permits rapid turning in water.)*
3. What aspect of lizard feeding may explain why so few are venomous? *(They feed on small prey, which do not need to be immobilized.)*

Reteaching

Have students compare respiration and circulation for fishes, amphibians, and reptiles. Ask how amphibian structures represent an evolutionary midpoint between fishes and reptiles. *(Fishes have gills; amphibians have embryonic gills but adult lungs; reptiles have lungs. Fishes have a two-chambered heart, amphibians three chambers, and reptiles three or four chambers.)*
■ *See* Section Reviews *worksheet, Section 38.2.*

Enrichment

Have students research which of the rhynchocephalians, chelonians, and crocodilians are endangered species. Have students contribute to a class discussion of what they might do to prevent extinction of these reptiles.

Closure

Show photographs of different reptiles (sea turtles, tortoises, various lizards, crocodiles) to students. Ask them to evaluate how each animal's structure and behavior is adapted to survival on land or is re-adapted to life in water. Ask what ties aquatic reptiles have to land.

Videodiscs

■ *1353–1363, Alligator; Caiman; Crocodile (s)*

Section 38.3

Lesson Plan

Section Focus

This section describes unique adaptations of snakes for movement, feeding, defense, and reproduction. Snakes have been successful in many different, often inhospitable, environments.

Section Themes

This section emphasizes the theme of **Scale and Structure.** Many of the snake's highly adapted structural features serve to enhance its survival in a variety of habitats. The theme of **Evolution** is also important. Snakes probably evolved from lizards that burrowed underground to escape predators. Their adaptations can best be understood in this context.

Motivating Activity

Show students a photograph of a snake or bring in a live one. Ask students why some people might fear snakes. *(Venom, danger of strangulation)* Use this information as the basis for discussion of whether people's fears of snakes are justified or based on error and exaggeration. *(Most snakes are harmless. Many benefit humans by eating vermin.)*

Teaching Strategies

Identifying Adaptations Have students make a list of internal adaptations of snakes to their way of life. Ask students to share items from the list with the class. *(Venomous fangs, jaws that come unhinged, windpipe that permits breathing while swallowing, ribs, muscles, and scutes adapted for legless locomotion)*

Section Objectives

- *Summarize the evolutionary history of snakes.*
- *Compare the three basic ways in which snakes move.*
- *List three characteristics of snakes that are adaptations to a predatory way of life.*
- *Contrast the two methods by which snakes produce offspring.*

38.3 Adaptations of Snakes

The fossil record of the evolution of snakes is far from complete. However, biologists suggest that snakes probably evolved from lizards that lived above ground during the Cretaceous period. As a way of escaping predators, some may have begun to burrow underground. Natural selection led to changes in these lizards. For example, lizards without legs and those with long and slim bodies survived. These adaptations, which made it easier to move in narrow burrows, have also made snakes highly successful reptiles.

Movement

The graceful undulations of snakes are made possible by their unique anatomy. A snake has a backbone of 100 to 400 vertebrae, each of which has a pair of ribs attached. These bones provide the framework for thousands of muscles. The muscles manipulate not only the skeleton but also the snake's skin, causing this fabric of overlapping scales to extend and contract. This interaction of bones, muscles, and skin enables a snake to move in one of three basic ways: lateral undulation, rectilinear movement, and sidewinding.

Most commonly snakes move by lateral undulation. In this method a snake moves its head to one side, which initiates a wave of muscular contractions along the vertebrae. As this lateral motion moves down its trunk, the snake uses the sides of its body to push off on pebbles, twigs, and small irregularities of the ground. The snake thus moves forward in an S-shaped path.

In rectilinear movement, a snake applies muscular force on its belly, not its sides. The trailing edges of its **scutes,** the scales on its belly, catch on bark or other rough surfaces. The body then relaxes and moves forward, inching along much like a caterpillar.

Some desert-dwelling snakes progress by sidewinding, a method of moving not forward but sideways, as shown in Figure 38-9. Because sand has few surface irregularities, neither lateral nor rectilinear motion is effective in deserts. A sidewinding snake vigorously flings its head to one side. This whiplike motion yanks along the rest of its body. Just as the hindquarters are catching up, the snake thrusts its head sideways again.

Figure 38-9 The whiplike, sidewise movement of some desert-dwelling snakes is an adaptation to a sandy environment.

Feeding

Snakes eat animals, but they have none of the structural adaptations common to other carnivores. They don't hear or see well, and they have no limbs for subduing prey. Their small mouths and tiny teeth cannot rip and grind flesh. Their slim bodies can't even accommodate an elaborate digestive system, as you can see from Figure 38-10. Nonetheless, the evolutionary pressures that shaped them in these ways equipped them well for the predatory life.

Adaptation				
movement	locating prey	killing prey	swallowing & digesting	defense
Features				
▪ lateral undulation ▪ rectilinear movement ▪ sidewinding	▪ Jacobson's organ	▪ venom ▪ constriction ▪ swallowing	▪ unhinged jaw	▪ camouflage ▪ defensive signalling

Graphic Organizer Use this table in Guided Practice on p. 581.

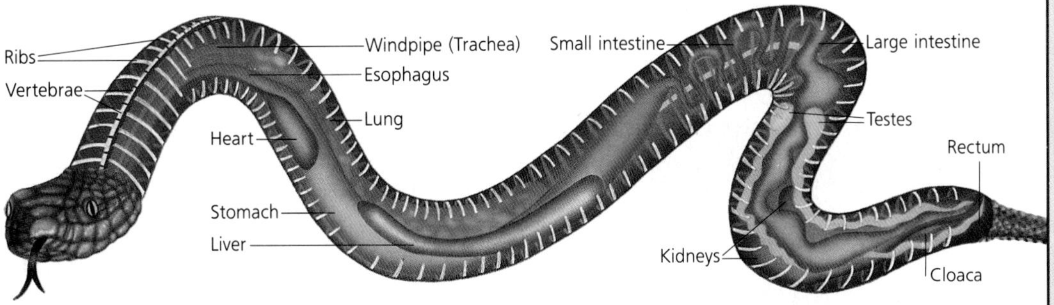

Figure 38-10 Each of a snake's several hundred vertebrae has its own pair of ribs attached. These ribs anchor the many muscles needed to manipulate the long, slender body. How are a snake's organs modified for its body shape?

Locating Prey

Eyesight and hearing do not enhance survival in dark, quiet burrows, and these senses were not highly developed as snakes evolved. Instead, snakes evolved a sense of smell, which they use to locate prey. By flicking its forked tongue, a snake gathers chemicals from the environment. The tongue transfers these chemicals to two pits in the roof of the mouth called **Jacobson's organ.** Nerves in these pits are highly sensitive to chemicals. In this way, a snake stalks prey by following a chemical trail.

Killing Prey

Once snakes locate prey, they usually, if the prey is small, just swallow it whole. Many snakes, however, employ one of two methods for killing: constriction or the injection of venom. Snakes that are constrictors wrap their bodies around prey to squeeze and kill it. This technique is used by boas, pythons, and anacondas—snakes that can consume small pigs and other similar-sized animals.

Some snakes inject their prey with a toxic venom.Three methods have evolved for injecting venom. The rear-fanged snakes, such as the boomslang and twig snakes of Africa, bite the prey and use grooved back teeth to guide the venom into the puncture. Highly venomous cobras and kraits are elapids, which inject poisons through two small front fangs that act like hypodermic needles. The vipers inject venom through large front fangs. When a viper strikes, these hinged fangs swing forward from the roof of the mouth and inject venom more deeply than can the fangs of elapids. Vipers include three groups of North American snakes: rattlesnakes, water moccasins, and copperheads.

Venom is chemically complex. Its different components act in two ways. The **hemotoxins** are proteins that attack the circulatory system, destroying red blood cells and disrupting the clotting power of blood. The **neurotoxins** work on the nervous system. The disruption of nerve pathways is dangerous to respiratory and heart functions. Some venoms contain both types of toxin.

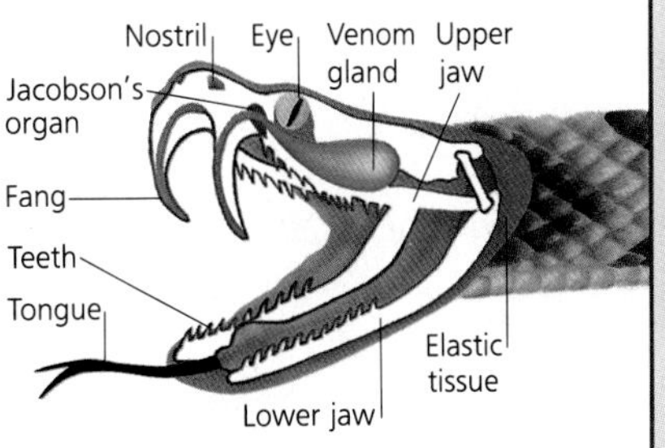

Figure 38-11 Vipers inject venom through two large fangs connected to the venom gland.

Swallowing and Digesting Prey

How do snakes consume such large and bulky prey as birds, fish, rats, and other snakes? Several structural adaptations make this

Interpreting the Visuals Guide students, step-by-step, through the snake's internal anatomy as they refer to Figure 38-10, p. 581. Emphasize that the snake's organs have evolved to fit well within its unusual, slender frame.

- *See* **Overhead Transparency** ***T38 and*** **Blackline Master** ***80.***

Guided Practice

Have students prepare a table of adaptations of snakes for survival. Have students include internal anatomy, structural features, and behavioral adaptations. Use the table on p. 580 as a model.

Independent Practice

- Have students write answers to the Section Review.
- Have students prepare sketches with captions, to illustrate the three different ways in which snakes move. *(Lateral undulation: side-to-side waves; rectilinear movement: muscular force on belly; sidewinding: whiplike, sideways motion)*

Videodiscs

- *Side 4 28122, Animal Locomotion: Yellow-Bellied Sea Snake (m)*
- *1391–1414, Snakes: Types (s)*

More Information

Defense Mechanisms Of the defense mechanisms evolved by snakes, the small hognose snake (60 centimeters long) has developed some of the more unusual ones. Living in sandy areas and woodlands throughout the eastern United States, it seems unremarkable. But when threatened, the hognose snake puts on a display of bluff and sham. First, it inflates its body to appear larger and hisses loudly. Then it lifts its head up to a foot off the ground, spreads a cobra-like hood, and lunges at the intruder. If this fails to frighten the intruder away, the hognose snake will suddenly appear to die. It will collapse upside down in a limp heap with its tongue lolling from its gaping mouth. After the intruder departs, the snake "comes to life" and continues on its way.

Section 38.3

Answer to Think

The skin cannot grow and must be shed as the snake increases in size.

Check Your Understanding

1. Describe how the Jacobson's organ works. *(The tongue transfers chemicals from the environment to this organ where nerves sense chemicals.)*

2. Compare how the two types of toxins in snake venom work. *(Hemotoxins destroy red blood cells and disrupt the clotting ability of blood; neurotoxins disrupt nerve pathways to respiratory and heart functions.)*

3. How do ovoviviparous snakes nourish developing young within their bodies? *(The yolk provides all nourishment.)*

Reteaching

Have students prepare a poster featuring the characteristics of snakes that are adaptations for survival. Have students focus on internal anatomy as well as on structural and behavioral adaptations, including the modification of the snake's elongated body.

■ *See* Section Reviews *worksheet, Section 38.3.*

Enrichment

Have students research and report on venomous snakes found in the area. Ask students to include information about snakes' habitats, behaviors, and the likelihood of a student's being bitten by one. Also have them include ways in which these snakes may be beneficial to the ecosystem and humans.

Closure

Remind students that although ectothermic animals, such as snakes, can maintain a very stable temperature while the sun is out, they must seek shelter at night. Why? *(Lowering of body temperature renders a snake immobile and vulnerable to predators.)*

Think

Based on what you know about the skin of reptiles, why do you think that snakes must periodically shed their skin?

behavior possible. A snake's upper and lower jaws are hinged and move independently. When unhinged, the jaws stretch to allow the mouth to open extremely wide. While holding the prey in its small teeth, the snake places its mouth over the animal and slowly swallows it whole. While swallowing, the snake thrusts its windpipe into the throat. This adaptation lets the snake breathe while swallowing, a process that can take several hours.

The saliva begins to digest food well before it reaches the snake's stomach, which is simply an enlargement at the end of the esophagus. Digestion proceeds slowly in the stomach.

Defense

Just as natural selection resulted in structural adaptations for feeding, it also resulted in a host of modifications for defense. Camouflage, for example, is beneficial for both seeking prey and hiding from predators. Many snakes are green and blend with foliage; others are brown and hide against the bark of trees.

Rather than hiding, some snakes defend themselves by signaling their presence. Some snakes can ward off danger by rapidly changing body shape—expanding a hood, in the case of the cobras. Some snakes hiss; others make mechanical noises, such as the rattling of a rattlesnake.

Reproduction

Most male snakes rely on scent to find females of their own species. Before mating, a male and female snake may glide along side by side, with the male stroking the female with his chin and flicking his tongue over her body. Fertilization is internal.

Most snakes are **oviparous** *(oe-VIP-uh-russ);* that is, the female lays eggs that hatch outside her body. To break out of its shell, the hatchling uses a special tooth, which is lost soon afterward. Other snakes are **ovoviviparous** *(OE-voe-VIE-VIP-uh-russ);* that is, the female carries the eggs in her body throughout development and the young are born live. These eggs have a thin membrane through which water and oxygen pass from the mother. All the nourishment is provided by the yolk. The eggs hatch in the mother's body, and she gives birth to the newly hatched young. All newborns must fend for themselves, relying only on their many specialized adaptations for survival on land.

Section Review

1. Distinguish between oviparous and ovoviviparous snakes.
2. How is a snake's body structure related to its habitat?
3. What are the three main ways in which snakes move?
4. Describe two ways in which snakes subdue their prey.
5. If you observed a snake in the zoo sidewinding, what might you infer about the natural habitat of the snake?

Answers to Section Review

1. Oviparous animals lay eggs; ovoviviparous animals bear young that hatch from eggs internally.
2. The long, legless structure facilitates movement in underground burrows.
3. Lateral undulation, rectilinear movement, sidewinding
4. Injecting venom, constriction, swallowing without killing first
5. That it lived in a desert or other sandy environment

Laboratory

Color Adaptation in the Anole

Objective
To determine what stimulates color change in the Anole

Process Skills
Hypothesizing, experimenting

Materials
Glass-marking pencil, 2 large wide-mouth jars with lids that have air holes in them, 2 live anoles, 6 shades each of brown and green construction paper ranging from light to dark, hand lens

Background

1 What differences in color can you observe among the anoles in the two terraria?
2 Describe some ways in which the ability to change color benefits anoles.

Technique

1 Select two anoles of the same color from the terraria. Anoles will run fast and are easily frightened. Carefully pick them up and place the animals in separate jars. Do not pick up anoles by their tails. Grasp them around the shoulders. Place a lid on each jar.
2 Label one jar, *"Anole No. 1"* and the other jar, *"Anole No. 2."*
3 Place the jar with Anole No. 1 on a piece of construction paper that most closely matches the anole's color. Remove the paper and label it *Original Color of Anole No. 1.* Repeat this for Anole No. 2.
4 Why would it be important at this point, to select a piece of construction paper with a color that most closely matches each anole?

Inquiry

1 Discuss the objective of this laboratory with your lab partners and formulate a hypothesis.
2 Design an experiment to test your hypothesis using the materials provided.
3 What are the independent and dependent variables in your experiment? How will you vary the independent variable? How will you measure changes in the dependent variable?
4 What controls will you include?
5 Before proceeding with your experiment, have it approved by your teacher. Be sure to record all your data.

Conclusions

1 What effect, if any, did changes in the independent variable have on the dependent variable in your experiment?
2 Do your data support your hypothesis? Explain.
3 Can you think of any sources of error in your experiment?
4 Was your experiment a controlled experiment? Explain.

Further Inquiry
Design an experiment that tests the effects of temperature upon anole skin color.

Laboratory

(For an overview of anoles and preparatory information related to the laboratory, see p. 569B.)

Background
1. Anoles in the black-lined terrarium should be brown; anoles in the white-lined terrarium should be green.
2. This ability to change color helps the anole avoid being eaten.

Technique
4. The original color of the anole can be "recorded" by matching it to the colored paper. Once the anole has changed color, and matched to another piece of paper, the color change can be compared between the two pieces of paper. Have available a range of colored paper to include the range and color gradations of the anole.

Inquiry
1. Each lab team should agree upon a testable hypothesis.
2. If students hypothesize that background color stimulates the color change, they should plan experiments that vary background color using colored paper.
3. The independent variable is environmental variation (background color) and the dependent variable is change in anole color. The independent variable can be varied by selecting a range of environmental circumstances (paper of different shades or contrasting color). The dependent variable can be measured subjectively by comparing the anole's color change with the control.
4. An appropriate control would be an anole that remains in its original environment (original color) while an anole of the same color, the experimental animal, is transferred to a new environment (new shade of color).

Conclusions
1. Student answers should clearly describe how each test was conducted and should state results.
2. Students should recognize whether their data support their hypotheses.
3. Variables that affect color in anoles are listed in Overview on p. 569B. Anoles may be reacting to other stimulants than the independent variable selected.
4. Answers will depend upon groups' designs.

Further Inquiry
Set upper and lower limits to the temperature students use in designing this experiment.

Chapter 38 Review

Vocabulary

1. Allantois, amnion, chorion, yolk sac
2. Hemotoxin, Jacobson's organ, neurotoxin
3. *Parietal* is the name of the bone in the skull above which the parietal eye is located.
4. *Hemo* means "blood"; *neuro* means "nerve"; Hemotoxins affect blood, neurotoxins affect nerves.
5. *Ovo* = egg, *vivi* = living, *parous* = bearing young; viviparous

Review

1. a	**6.** c
2. c	**7.** b
3. d	**8.** c
4. b	**9.** d
5. b	**10.** a

11. Desiccation
12. Reptiles have double circulation that partially or completely separates oxygenated from deoxygenated blood.
13. Birds, mammals, and other reptiles
14. Studies of bone structure, predator–prey ratios, and growth rates of dinosaurs suggest that they may have been warm-blooded.
15. The four orders of reptiles are Rhynchocephalia, Chelonia, Crocodilia, and Squamata.
16. Crocodilians generally hunt by stealth, that is by lurking submerged.
17. They use speed to subdue prey.
18. Like snakes, monitor lizards have forked tongues and feed on large prey.
19. Rear-fanged, elapid injection, viper injection
20. Jacobson's organ detects chemicals in air.

Chapter 38 Review

Vocabulary

allantois (571)	chorion (571)	internal fertilization (571)	oviparous (582)
amnion (571)	cotylosaurs (573)	Jacobson's organ (581)	ovoviviparous (582)
amniote egg (571)	ectothermic (573)	keratin (572)	parietal eye (576)
archosaurs (573)	endothermic (573)	neurotoxin (581)	plastron (577)
autotomy (579)	hemotoxin (581)		scutes (580)
carapace (577)	herbivore (574)		yolk sac (571)
carnivore (574)			

1. List the terms for the various parts of the amniote egg.
2. List the terms for the adaptations that help snakes track down and subdue prey.
3. Look up the word *parietal* in a dictionary. Why do you think the tuatara's third eye is called a parietal eye?
4. Look up the meaning of the word parts *hemo-* and *neuro-* in a dictionary. From what you know about the effects of hemotoxin and neurotoxin, explain why they are appropriately named.
5. Look up the origin of the term *ovoviviparous* in a dictionary. What are the meanings of the main parts of this term? What term might you use to describe animals that bear live young that don't hatch from eggs?

Review

1. The membrane that encloses the fluid around a reptile embryo is the (a) amnion (b) yolk sac (c) allantois (d) chorion.
2. The presumed ancestors of all modern reptiles were the (a) archosaurs (b) dinosaurs (c) cotylosaurs (d) tuataras.
3. The most abundant of all modern orders of reptiles is (a) Rhynchocephalia (b) Chelonia (c) Crocodilia (d) Squamata.
4. The two basic parts of a turtle shell are the (a) scutes and amnion (b) carapace and plastron (c) chorion and allantois (d) keratin and scutes.
5. A group of reptiles that does not belong to the Order Crocodilia is (a) alligators (b) tuataras (c) caimans (d) gavials.
6. The ability to lose its tail and grow a new one helps a lizard (a) reduce its need for food (b) hide from predators (c) escape from predators (d) capture prey.
7. Long legless bodies probably arose as an adaptation that helped snakes (a) live in trees (b) move in underground burrows (c) catch prey (d) swallow large animals.
8. Snakes that live in deserts generally move by (a) lateral undulation (b) rectilinear movement (c) sidewinding (d) creeping.
9. To locate prey snakes rely primarily on their sense of (a) eyesight (b) hearing (c) touch (d) smell.
10. Most snakes are oviparous, which means their young (a) hatch from eggs (b) hatch inside the mother and are born alive (c) are born alive without hatching from eggs (d) are cared for by their parents.
11. What problem of life on land was solved by the evolution of the amniote egg?
12. In what major way does circulation of blood in reptiles differ from circulation of blood in amphibians?
13. Which groups of modern vertebrates arose from cotylosaurs?
14. What evidence suggests that dinosaurs may have been warm-blooded?
15. List the four orders of modern reptiles.
16. What method do crocodilians generally use to hunt their prey?
17. How do biologists explain the fact that so few species of lizards are venomous?
18. What characteristics do monitor lizards

share with snakes?

19. Name three ways snakes inject venom.

20. What is the function of Jacobson's organ?

Critical Thinking

1. When a female leatherback turtle comes up on a beach to lay eggs, she first digs a deep hole, lays her eggs, and covers them with sand. Next she crawls about 100 m and digs another hole. This time she lays no eggs but just covers the hole with sand. Suggest a possible explanation for this behavior.
2. Tuataras lived on the two main islands of New Zealand until the 1800s, when British settlers brought in rats, goats, and other mammals. Why do you think the introduction of these mammals made it impossible for tuataras to survive?
3. In 1986 scientists discovered the fossil remains of a dinosaur in Antarctica. From this discovery what might you infer about the climate of Antarctica during the Mesozoic era?
4. Given that reptiles as a class have many adaptations for life on land, how do you account for the fact that some reptiles, such as sea turtles and sea snakes, live in the ocean?
5. Study the graph on this page, which shows the range of body temperatures found in active individuals of some major subgroups of reptiles.

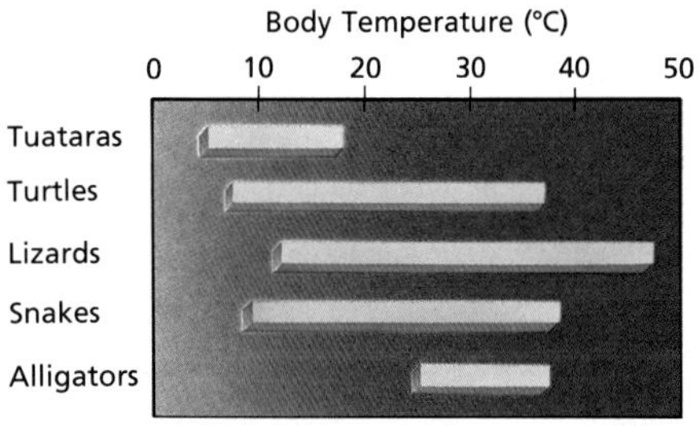

   a. Which two groups show a much narrower range of temperatures than the other groups? How might you account for this? (Hint: Consider the number of different species in each group.)
   b. Which groups do you think are best able to tolerate the temperature extremes found in deserts?
6. Suggest some possible advantages that ovoviviparous reptiles may derive from carrying their eggs inside the body until after they have hatched.
7. Some pain-killing drugs are prepared from snake venom. Which type of toxin do you think is contained in the venom used? Explain your answer.

Extension

1. Read the article by Rick Weiss entitled "Snakebite Succor" in *Science News,* December 8, 1990, pp. 360–362. Describe the problems associated with antivenins and discuss how scientists are working to eradicate those problems.
2. Use your school library or public library to research an endangered species of reptile, such as Kemp's Ridley turtle. Prepare a report describing the conditions that threaten the survival of the species and the efforts being made to save it.
3. Observe the behavior of a small lizard kept in a terrarium. Keep a log of your observations, noting differences in behavior at various times of day and before and after feeding.
4. Research the group of reptiles called amphisbaens. Write a brief report describing the similarites between amphisbaens and earthworms. Be sure to include similarities in both structure and way of life. In what ways are the two groups different?

Critical Thinking

1. Digging empty holes may be a protective behavior that distracts predators.
2. Mammals may have preyed on tuataras or competed more effectively with them for food.
3. Students should infer that the climate of Antarctica was much warmer and at a different latitude during the Mesozoic.
4. Although reptiles are adapted to land, some species have re-adapted to aquatic life to take advantage of more favorable conditions for survival.
5. a. Tuataras and crocodilians show a much narrower temperature range. This difference may be accounted for by the fact that these groups contain few species that are adapted to similar environments. **b.** Snakes and lizards are best able to tolerate desert temperatures.
6. Answers may include protecting eggs from predators or from drying out during development.
7. The venom contains a neurotoxin, which interferes with the perception of pain. Hemotoxins would have no effect on perception of pain.

Extension

1. Encourage students to read Section 44.2 on p. 675 and write a report about the immune system and its response to foreign proteins. Also encourage students to compare problems related to vaccines in general, such as the polio vaccine, with those described in the article.
2. Suggest that students develop ways that individual students or the class as a whole can help save endangered reptile species.
3. Stress that students should note all variables that may effect the lizard, such as movement or sounds, temperature and light, weather.
4. Suggest that students note reptile features that amphisbaens have retained.

Chapter 39 Birds

Chapter Overview

Chapter 39 continues the evolutionary story of vertebrates by introducing the birds, which are descended from the reptiles. Section 39.1 decribes the origin and early evolution of the Class Aves, then briefly presents the ways in which modern birds are classified. Section 39.2 presents the birds' external and internal characteristics, many of which are unique to the class. Finally, Section 39.3 explains how bird eggs are incubated and embryos develop, then describes characteristic bird behaviors such as territoriality and courtship, nest building, and migration.

Chapter Planning Chart

B	S	A	Sections and Subsections	Page	Features	Page	Resources
•	•	•	**39.1 Evolution and Classification**				
			Origin and Early Evolution Classification	587 588	Section Review	588	Videodiscs Section Reviews Worksheet
•	•	•	**39.2 Characteristics of Birds**				
			External Characteristics Internal Characteristics	589 590	Think Laboratory Section Review	592 599 594	Videodiscs Blackline Master 81 Overhead Transparency T39 Blackline Master 82 Laboratories: Bird Beaks and Feet Section Reviews Worksheet
•	•	•	**39.3 Development and Behavior**				
			Incubation and Development Behavior	595 596	Biotechnology Section Review	596 598	Videodiscs Process Skills: Hawk-watching Section Reviews Worksheet
			End of Chapter Activities				
					Chapter Review	600	Vocabulary Skills Chapter Test Computer Test Generator

B *The Basic Level curriculum presents the most fundamental knowledge offered in the course.*
S *The Standard Level curriculum is designed for the average student who is able to master most topics.*
A *The Advanced Level curriculum includes suggestions for teaching the most academically able students.*

Cooperative Learning

Group Activity: Observing Bird Behavior

- **Group Size:** *2–4 students*
- **Outcome:** *Students will hypothesize about how bird behavior enhances the bird's ability to survive.*
- **Individual Accountability:** *Students will separately observe and record bird behavior.*
- **Positive Interdependence:** *Group members will compare observations and consult field guides.*

Have each group of students go to a nearby location to observe birds. This could be a park, vacant lot, cemetery, beach, field, pond, or other site. Provide each group with a field guide to birds of your area and suggest that each student take a small notebook and pencil. Ask each student to record observations of bird behavior, including interaction with members of its own species, behavior directed at other species of birds or other animals, feeding behavior, singing or calling, and all solitary behavior. Explain that the field notes will be used to aid the student's memory of the observations and can include written notes, sketches, and any shorthand method for recording sounds that the student may invent.

After the field observations, have members of the group identify the observed birds (using the field guide) and compare behavioral notes. Ask the group to develop hypotheses to explain the functions of the behavior they have observed. Hypotheses can be compared with information in guides to bird behavior such as the *Stokes Nature Guides.*

Concept Map

The following is one possible solution to the concept mapping activity in Reteaching on p. 594.

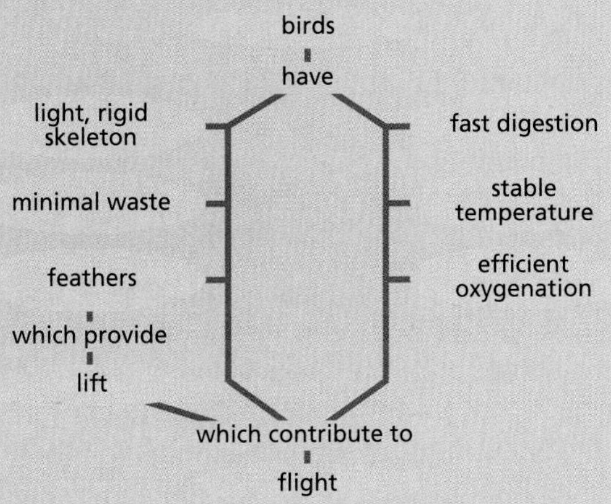

Laboratory Preparation

Overview *(See p. 599.)*

In this lab exercise, students compare the three basic types of bird feathers: quill, contour, and down. Students examine the central shaft and vane macroscopically and the barbs, barbules, and hooks using a microscope. Students compare these structures in the three feather types, speculating on how the structures contribute to the primary function of each type of feather.

Preparation

Prepare slides of contour feathers and slides of down feathers. Whole processed feathers are available from a biological supply house. Feathers can also be collected in the field (pigeon feathers, for instance, can be found on most city streets).

Teaching Tips

Stress that clear, accurate drawings will help students to come to conclusions.

Using the quill feather, demonstrate that the vanes can be separated and then "zipped" back together. Tell students that when vanes become separated in the feathers of living birds, the birds rejoin them by preening with their beaks. Ask students to speculate on why it is to the bird's advantage to have the vanes "zipped up." *(Gaps in the flight feathers offer less air resistance, resulting in less efficient flying.)*

For an analogy to the working of feather hooks, have students examine a piece of Velcro with a hand lens or a low-power microscope. Ask students to draw a diagram of the Velcro.

Safety

Feathers collected from the field may contain disease organisms. If such feathers are used, remind students to wash their hands immediately after handling them.

Chapter Themes

Evolution Although the details of early avian evolution are still a mystery, the unique features of the Class Aves can be traced back to ancestral reptilian precursors. Point out to students that fossil genera, such as *Archaeopteryx*, possess features intermediate between the two classes.

Stability All birds are endotherms, animals that generate and regulate body temperature internally. Emphasize that the maintenance of a constant body temperature independent of environment has enabled birds to inhabit a much wider range of climates than reptiles or amphibians.

Scale and Structure Point out that many of the birds' structural features, both external and internal, are unique to the Class Aves. Stress, however, that these structures vary widely from order to order, providing each bird species with efficient adaptations to a particular way of life.

Chapter Motivating Activity

Show students an object made of or decorated with feathers. Tell them that numerous cultures —African, Polynesian, and Native American—have a rich tradition of feather ornamentation, often for ceremonial purposes.

Now ask students to think of birds that have been used as symbols. *(The eagle, a symbol of nobility and power; the phoenix, a symbol of rebirth; the dove and hawk, symbols of peace and war.)* Point out that people throughout history have venerated birds because of their ability to fly. Ask students how they have come in contact with birds. *(Eating chicken, having a pet canary, maintaining a feeder, and wearing feather jewelry or a down vest.)*

Chapter 39 Birds

Introduction

The ability to fly has enabled birds to inhabit virtually every area of the earth, from the equator to the poles. In this chapter you will learn about the anatomical and physiological adaptations that have made flight in these vertebrates possible.

Chapter Outline

Chapter Concept

As you read, note the characteristics of birds that are adaptations for flight.

Courtship plumage of the northern quetzal, *Pharomachrus mocino*, Central America. Inset (top): Marsh hawk, *Circus cyaneus*, Utah. Inset (bottom): Migrating flock.

Understanding the Visuals

Ask students to compare the plumage of the marsh hawk with the feathers of the northern quetzal and to note differences. *(Color, pattern)* Ask students to suggest reasons why the courtship plumage of the quetzal, a bird of the Central American rain forests, and the feathers of the North American marsh hawk would be different. *(The pattern of the marsh hawk may act as camouflage, disrupting its outline and making it harder for prey to spot. Courtship plumage, on the other hand, makes a bird more visible so that it can attract a potential mate.)* Would the quetzal feathers be well adapted to flying? Explain. *(No, because the branches of the vanes are separated)*

39.1 Evolution and Classification

Birds are vertebrates of the Class Aves. Although birds arose rather late relative to many other vertebrates, they have established themselves all over the earth. No other vertebrate group is so well adapted for life in air, on land, and in water. The evolution of flight and of endothermy, or warm-bloodedness, has enabled birds to survive in virtually every known environment.

Section Objectives

- *List both the avian and the reptilian characteristics of* Archaeopteryx.
- *Summarize the two predominant hypotheses of bird evolution.*
- *Identify the criteria which taxonomists use when they classify birds.*

Figure 39-1 An artist's rendering, based on fossil evidence, suggests the possible appearance of three ancestors of modern birds.

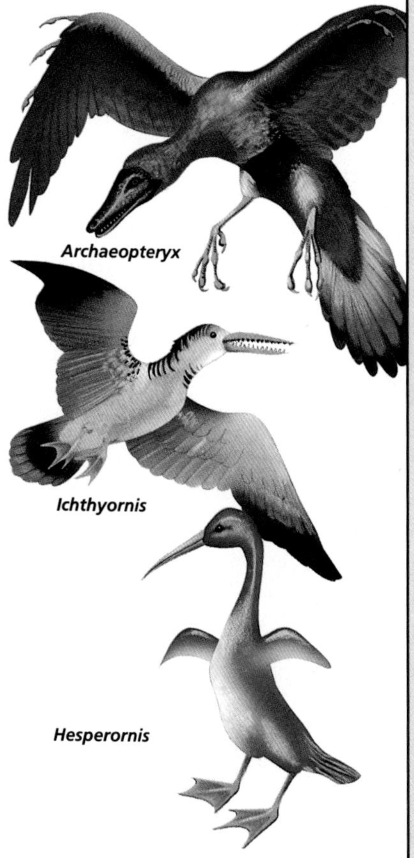

Origin and Early Evolution

Evidence from fossils and from studies of comparative anatomy indicates that birds evolved from reptiles. Because their feathers and their fragile, hollow bones do not preserve well, birds are poorly represented in the fossil record, compared with other vertebrate groups. With so few clues scientists disagree on which particular line of reptiles gave rise to birds. However, they do concur that the fossil genus *Archaeopteryx* ("ancient wing") may represent an evolutionary link between reptiles and birds. The first *Archaeopteryx* fossil, which dates back to the Jurassic period, was discovered in 1861 in the fine limestone sediments of a quarry in southern Germany. Radioisotope dating has verified that the fossil is about 150 million years old.

Archaeopteryx possessed characteristics of both reptiles and birds, as seen in Figure 39-1. Like reptiles it had a large skull with teeth, bones that weren't hollow, claws on its forelimbs, and a long tail. Its strong legs and rounded wings indicate that it glided rather than flew. In contrast, the presence of feathers and of a **furculum** *(FUR-kyuh-lum),* the fused collarbones commonly called a wishbone, suggests that *Archaeopteryx* was birdlike.

What group of reptiles gave rise to *Archaeopteryx*—and thus possibly to all birds? Two hypotheses prevail. One argues that birds arose about 230 million years ago from thecodonts, a group of reptiles discussed in Chapter 38. These reptiles walked on their hind legs like birds. Some, however, may have been tree dwelling. The thecodonts gave rise to a number of subgroups of reptiles. One of these, the pseudosuchians ("false crocodiles"), may have given rise to both dinosaurs and birds. As evidence for this theory scientists note that the pseudosuchian's large collarbone is homologous to the furculum of modern birds.

Another hypothesis states that birds evolved directly from a group of dinosaurs about 150 million years ago. The group, called coelurosaurian theropods, were small predators that walked on their hind legs. Their hips, forelimbs, and hind limbs resembled those of *Archaeopteryx*.

After *Archaeopteryx* the next bird fossils date from about 90 million years ago, in the Cretaceous period. *Hesperornis*, a large,

Lesson Plan

Section Focus

This section presents the evidence that birds evolved from reptiles and traces their early evolution. Taxonomists make use of morphological, behavioral, biochemical, and genetic evidence to classify the 27 orders of living birds.

Section Themes

This section emphasizes the theme of **Evolution.** Even though the exact origin of birds is still conjectural, evidence strongly suggests that they are descended from reptiles. Since their beginnings, birds have evolved into 27 orders adapted to a wide variety of habitats.

Motivating Activity

Direct a brainstorming activity in which students contribute the names of as many birds as possible in ten minutes. Write each name on the board as it is offered. *(Accept all answers that are actually birds.)* When the ten minutes are over, ask students to suggest which birds on the list are likely to be closely related to each other. Have them argue for their suggestions on the basis of appearance, habitat, or feeding habits. Encourage interested students to consult a field guide or ornithology text to compare actual bird classification with the student suggestions.

Teaching Strategies

Supporting Hypotheses Have each student make a chart comparing the two hypotheses of bird origins—from thecodonts or from coelurosaurian theropods. Emphasize that the chart should briefly describe the two hypotheses and compare their supporting evidence.

	Skin Cover	Bones	Mouth Parts	Forelimbs	Collarbones
Reptiles	scales	solid	jaw/teeth	legs/claws	separate
Archaeop.	feathers	solid	jaw/teeth	wings/claws	furculum
Birds	feathers	hollow	beak/no teeth	wings/no claws	furculum

Graphic Organizer Use this table in Guided Practice on p. 588.

Guided Practice
Have students make a table describing major adaptations of reptiles, *Archaeopteryx*, and modern birds. An example of a completed table is shown on p. 587.

Independent Practice
■ Have students write answers to the Section Review.
■ Have students compare the three fossil birds mentioned in this section, concluding which was the earliest and which the most modern, and giving supporting evidence.

Check Your Understanding
1. What are the two reptile groups with rival claims to bird ancestry? *(Thecodonts and coelurosaurian theropods)*
2. Recent technological advances have contributed to avian taxonomy by the analysis of what three features? *(Blood proteins, chromosomes, DNA)*

Reteaching
Have students brainstorm reptile characteristics that may have evolved into bird characteristics. *(Collarbones into furculum, mouth into beak, scales into feathers, forelimbs into wings)*
■ ***See* Section Reviews *worksheet, Section 39.1.***

Enrichment
Have students use the library to research fossil birds such as the *Protoavis* and the teratorns. Have them give short oral reports.

Closure
Ask students to imagine that they have found a vertebrate fossil. How could they determine whether it was a bird? *(Look for a furculum; evidence of hollow bones or feathers)*

Videodiscs

■ ***2588–2593, Homologous Forelimbs: Bird/Other (s)***
■ ***1415–1466, Aves (s)***

Table 39-1 Representative Bird Orders

flightless, diving bird, probably resembled the modern loon but had reptilian teeth. A smaller ternlike bird called *Ichthyornis* had large wings, indicating that it may have been a strong flier. The development of sustained flight may have enabled birds to colonize new areas during the Cretaceous. By about 11 million years ago in the Miocene epoch, most modern genera had evolved.

Classification

Most taxonomists classify the nearly 9,000 species of Class Aves into 27 orders, several of which are described in Table 39-1. To classify birds into orders and families, taxonomists most often use morphological evidence from beaks, feet, plumage, bone structure, and musculature. In recent years taxonomists have also begun to classify birds according to behavior and song. Technological advances in the analysis of blood proteins, chromosomes, and DNA have also contributed to scientists' understanding of avian phylogenetic relationships.

Section Review

1. What is the name for the bone that was present in *Archaeopteryx* and is unique to birds?
2. What characteristics did *Archaeopteryx* share with reptiles?
3. Summarize the two major hypotheses of bird evolution.
4. What were the main characteristics of *Hesperornis* and *Ichthyornis?*
5. Explain the fact that taxonomists commonly base their classification of birds on beaks, feet, and plumage.

Answers to Section Review
1. The furculum or wishbone
2. Claws on forelimbs, solid bones, large skull with teeth, and a long tail
3. One hypothesis claims that birds and dinosaurs both evolved from pseudosuchians, a reptile group that in turn arose from thecodonts. The other claims that birds arose directly from coelurosaurian theropods, a dinosaur group.
4. *Hesperornis* was a large, toothed, flightless diving bird. *Ichthyornis* was a small ternlike bird with large wings.
5. These are the characteristics that show the greatest variation.

39.2 Characteristics of Birds

Birds have many traits in common with other vertebrates, but the aerodynamic requirements of flight have produced a number of unique adaptations. The following characteristics distinguish birds from other vertebrates:

- The body is covered with feathers.
- The bones are thin and hollow.
- In most species the forelimbs function as wings; they are used for flight, not grasping.
- The two hind limbs, with clawed toes, support the body.
- A toothless, horny beak is present.
- Body temperature is generated and regulated internally.
- The four-chambered heart has a single right aortic arch.
- Amniote eggs are encased in hard, calcium-containing shells.
- In most species eggs are incubated in a nest.

External Characteristics

As flight enabled birds to colonize new territories across the earth, they adapted to various terrains, climates, food sources, and other conditions. The variation in the external characteristics of birds reflects these adaptations.

Feathers

Feathers are modified scales that serve two primary functions—providing lift for flight and conserving body heat. Soft, fluffy **down feathers** cover the body of nestling birds and provide an insulating undercoat in adults. **Contour feathers** give adult birds their streamlined shape and provide coloration and additional insulation. **Flight feathers** are specialized contour feathers on the wings and tail. Birds also have hairlike **filoplumes,** or pinfeathers, and dust-filtering **bristles** near the nostrils.

The structure of feathers combines maximum strength with minimum weight. Feathers develop from tiny pits in the skin called **follicles.** A **shaft** emerges from the follicle, and two **vanes,** pictured in Figure 39-2, develop from its opposite sides. At maturity each vane has many branches called **barbs.** The barbs in turn have many projections called **barbules** that are equipped with microscopic hooks. The hooks hold on to each other and give the feather its sturdy but flexible shape.

Feathers need care. In a process called preening, birds use their beaks to rub their feathers with oil secreted by a **preen gland** located at the base of the tail. Just as reptiles shed their skin, birds periodically molt their feathers. The major molt, during which the bird replaces its flight feathers, occurs in the late summer between breeding and migration. Some birds also undergo a spring molt prior to courtship.

Section Objectives

- *Describe the external characteristics of birds.*
- *Identify the major parts of a bird's skeletal system.*
- *List some ways in which a bird's internal organs are adapted for flight.*
- *Describe the mechanism by which birds maintain a constant body temperature.*
- *Explain the importance of the various sense organs to avian life.*

Figure 39-2 The small rectangular area on the drawing of the complete feather is shown in detail in the drawing above.

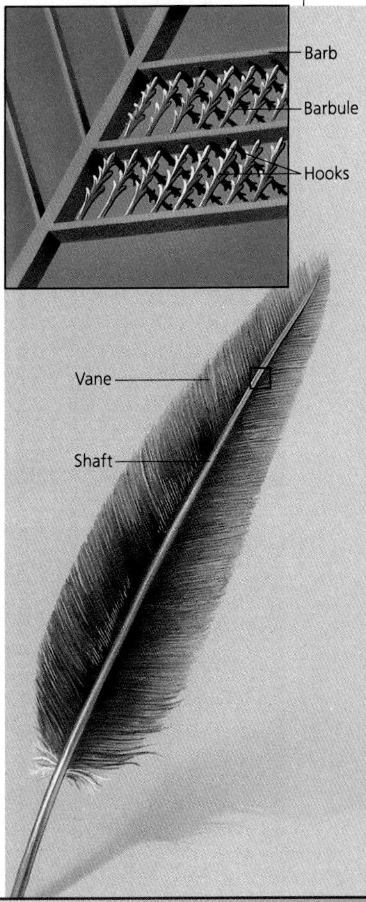

Lesson Plan

Section Focus

This section presents the unique characteristics of birds, many of which are adaptations to flight. These include external features such as feathers, beaks, and feet, and internal features such as skeletal and muscular structure, endothermy, and details of the digestive, excretory, respiratory, circulatory, nervous, and reproductive systems.

Section Themes

This section emphasizes two themes: **Scale and Structure** and **Stability.** Many structural features unique to birds, such as feathers, hollow bones, and air sacs, are adaptations to flight. Bird endothermy introduces a stable internal environment for muscles and other systems.

Motivating Activity

Show students pictures from nature books and magazines of a wide variety of birds. These could include eagles, ostriches, hummingbirds, penguins, woodpeckers, robins, owls, swifts, kiwis, pelicans, gulls, and herons. Ask students to infer each bird's habitat from its appearance. Ask them what criteria led them to their inferences.

Teaching Strategies

Analyzing Adaptations Have students make a table showing how each of the following characteristics adapts birds for flight: endothermy, feathers, air sacs, a four-chambered heart, hollow bones, a reduced reproductive system, and highly efficient digestive and excretory systems. An example of a table completed for five characteristics is shown at the bottom of this page.

Characteristic				
endothermy	feathers	air sacs	4-chambered heart	digestive and excretory systems
Adaptation for Flight				
stable environment for muscles	lifting surface/ smooth contours	efficient respiration/low density/lightness	efficient oxygen delivery	quick elimination of weight of ingested food

Graphic Organizer Use this table with Analyzing Adaptations, at right.

Inferring Functions Show students the same pictures of a wide variety of birds that you used in the Motivating Activity on p. 589. You could also add pictures of oystercatchers, grosbeaks, skimmers, curlews, and mergansers, all of which have unusual beaks. This time, ask the students to suggest each bird's feeding habits based solely on the shape of the beak. Stress that students should infer how the beak is used in feeding. *(Correct answers can be found in bird guides and nature books.)*

■ *See* Laboratorics, *Investigation 39.*

Exploring Careers Invite an ornithologist from a local college, university, museum, zoo, or government agency to speak about various career possibilities for bird specialists. Ask the ornithologist, if possible, to bring specimens or slides to share with the students. Have the speaker focus on ongoing ecological research involving birds or on behavioral studies.

Beaks and Feet

By looking closely at a bird's beak and feet, you can infer many things about where it lives and how it feeds. Hawks and eagles have powerful beaks and clawed talons that help them capture and then rip their prey. Swifts have a tiny beak that opens wide like a catcher's mitt to snare insects in midair. Because many swifts spend most of their lives in flight, their feet are small and adapted for infrequent perching. The feet of flightless birds, on the other hand, are modified for walking and running. Figure 39-3 shows other beak and foot adaptations. In many birds, such as herons and egrets, hormonal changes cause the beak, feet, and legs to turn vivid colors. This is an adaptation that helps attract potential mates.

Internal Characteristics

Like their external features, birds' internal systems reflect many adaptations for the demands of flight. Natural selection has favored a lightweight body, yet the bird's powerful wing muscles give it unusual strength.

Skeleton and Muscles

The avian skeleton combines lightness and strength. The bones are thin and hollow. Compared with a reptile skeleton, many

Figure 39-3 Shown are (clockwise from top left) a black vulture, *Coragyps atratus,* a mountain bluebird, *Sialia currocoides,* a roseate spoonbill, *Ajaia ajaja,* two tufted puffins, *Lunda cirrhata,* and a flock of ostriches, *Struthio* sp. Suggest adaptations for the beaks and feet of each of these birds.

Interdisciplinary Activity

Social Studies Have students use library resources to research the uses and significance of feathers within Native American cultures. This could include uses in clothing and art, ceremonial significance, indications of status within the tribe, or the significance of the species of birds from which feathers are obtained. Suggest that students obtain information about historical tribes or about pre-Columbian civilizations, such as the Peruvian Inca. Have students present short oral reports about their findings. Alternatively, have some students research the use of feathers in Papua, New Guinea, where the feathers of birds of paradise are widely used.

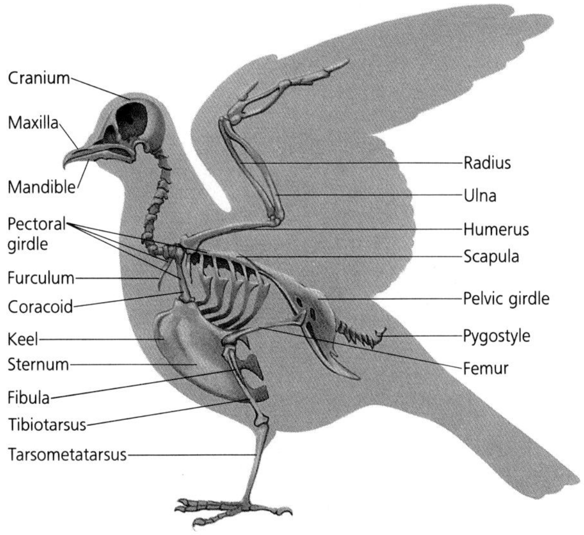

Figure 39-4 The rigid but light avian skeleton is well adapted for flight.

bones are fused, so the avian skeleton is more rigid. The rigid skeleton provides stability during flight. Note in Figure 39-4 the fused bones of the trunk and hip vertebrae and the pectoral and pelvic girdles. These fused bones form a sturdy frame that anchors the powerful breast muscles during flight and supports the leg muscles when the bird is walking or at rest. In some birds, flight muscles account for 50 percent of the body weight.

Also unique to the avian skeleton are the furculum, or wishbone, and the keel-shaped sternum. The sternum supports the large breast muscles. The humerus, ulna, and radius, along with the pectoral girdle and the sternum, support the wing. The pygostyle, the terminal vertebra of the spine, supports the tail feathers, which also play an important role in flight. The tail provides additional lift and aids in steering and braking.

Flight involves a series of complex wing movements, each one using a different set of muscles. On the downstroke each wing cuts forward and downward through the air. The upstroke moves each wing upward and backward. Air flows above and below the wing, creating lift. Muscles in the skin move the feathers, permitting precise flight maneuvers.

Endothermy

Birds are endothermic—that is, they generate and regulate body heat internally. In most birds body temperature ranges from 40° C to 42° C. Endothermy enables birds to inhabit both cold and hot climates. Rapid breathing and the digestion of large quantities of food produce the high metabolic rate necessary to generate heat. Thus birds, unlike reptiles, cannot go for long periods without eating. To help conserve body heat, birds fluff out their feathers for insulation. In aquatic birds a thin layer of fat provides additional insulation.

Interpreting the Visuals Show students the figure of the avian skeleton (Figure 39-4, p. 591), or if possible, display a mounted bird skeleton. Point out that this skeleton is light and rigid. Ask students to suggest how these features are adapted to flight. *(Lightness: less weight to lift; rigidity: stability during flight)* Have students suggest similarities and differences between the avian skeleton and skeletons studied in previous chapters, such as those of the perch, the frog, and the snake. *(Similarities: all have vertebrae and a skull; differences: frogs lack ribs, and perches and snakes lack limb bones.)*

■ *See* **Overhead Transparency** *T39 and* **Blackline Master** *81.*

Drawing Conclusions Ask students whose families have recently had chicken or turkey for dinner to bring in as many whole, clean bones as possible, or bring them in yourself. Ask students to show bones to the class and explain their functions. *(Keel: attachment for flight muscles; wing bones: support for flight structures; furculum: rigidity; pygostyle: support for tail feathers)*

Videodiscs

- ***1445, Plumage in Pheasants (s)***
- ***1462, Feather of Tawny Owl (s)***
- ***Side 4 28334, Animal Locomotion: Hummingbird (m)***
- ***Side 4 28606, Animal Locomotion: Swan Flight (m)***
- ***Side 4 5813, Emperor and Adélie Penguins—Motion and Behavior (m)***

More Information

Wings and Wind Wing shape is just as important as size. The wandering albatross has a wingspan of up to 12 feet. Although one might expect such a bird to have well-developed breast muscles, this is not the case. The wings are very narrow and therefore generate little drag. In fact, the albatross doesn't fly but soars over the ocean. It spreads its wings against the winds at the ocean surface, which causes it to rise. At higher altitudes, where wind speed is stronger, the albatross soars with the wind. It can then glide back down, using its weight and narrow wings to gain momentum, wheel sharply, and execute intricate maneuvers in search of food. Wind is so important that without it the albatross simply stalls out.

Drawing Conclusions Tell students that many birds, such as puffins, petrels, and penguins, swim under water when pursuing fish and other prey, moving their wings much as birds do when they fly in the air. Ask students to suggest ways in which underwater flight may be different from flight in the air. *(Buoyancy in the water reduces the need for lift; greater resistance in water may require more energy.)* Ask students how adaptations to underwater swimming might affect the ability of a bird to fly. *(The wings would probably become narrower and shorter in order to reduce drag. Such wings might not provide lift.)* Point out that the best underwater swimmers, penguins, can no longer fly.

Identifying Adaptations Remind students that no modern bird has teeth. Ask students to point out external and internal adaptation of birds that fill the roles played by teeth in other vertebrates. *(Sharp beaks and talons are used to capture and kill prey, hold food, and manipulate objects. The muscular gizzard crushes food, often with the help of small stones that the bird has swallowed.)*

Answer to Think

Flightlessness may have originated in areas where terrestrial predation was minimal or nonexistent, such as on islands. Flightlessness would have enabled birds to attain greater body size.

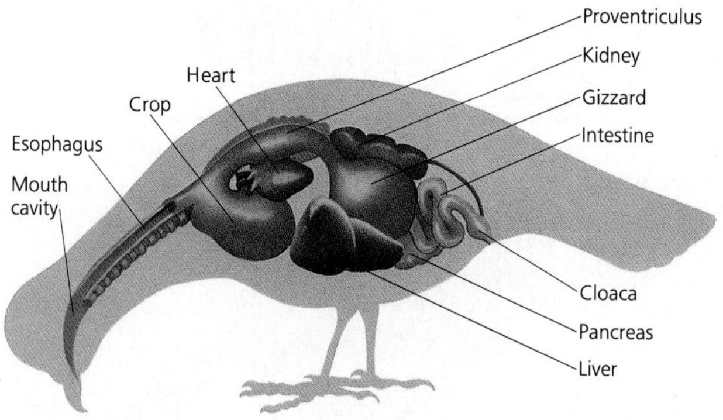

Figure 39-5 A bird's digestive and excretory systems are adapted for the rapid processing of food and metabolic wastes.

Digestive and Excretory Systems

The high energy requirements of flight and of endothermy are met by a quick and efficient digestive system. For instance, a thrush can eat blackberries, digest them, and 45 minutes later excrete the seeds. A magpie can digest a mouse in three hours. In contrast, a snake may require three days to digest a mouse of the same size.

Since birds have neither teeth, nor jaw bones, nor jaw muscles, they are not able to chew their food in their mouths. Instead food passes from the mouth cavity straight to the esophagus. An enlargement of the esophagus called the **crop** stores and moistens food. Food then passes to the two-part stomach, seen in Figure 39-5. In the first chamber, the **proventriculus** *(PRO-ven-TRICK-yuh-luss)*, gastric fluids begin breaking down the food. Food then passes to the **gizzard,** a muscular organ that kneads and crushes the food. The gizzard often contains small stones that the bird has swallowed. These aid in the grinding process. Thus the gizzard performs a function similar to that of teeth and jaws. Food then passes through the pyloric sphincter to the small intestine, also called the duodenum. Here bile and enzymes manufactured in the liver, pancreas, and intestine further break down the food. The digested food nutrients are then absorbed into the bird's bloodstream.

The avian excretory system is also efficient and lightweight. Unlike other vertebrates, most birds do not store liquid waste in a urinary bladder. Instead the two kidneys filter a nitrogenous waste called uric acid from the blood. Highly concentrated uric acid travels by ducts called ureters to the cloaca, where, along with undigested matter from the intestines, it is excreted in a semisolid, usually white mass.

Think

Comparative anatomy studies suggest that flightless birds such as ostriches evolved from flying ancestors. What natural conditions might have favored flightlessness?

Respiratory System

The high metabolic rate of birds requires large amounts of oxygen. Yet some birds migrate thousands of miles at altitudes as high as 7,000 m, where oxygen levels are low. An elaborate and highly efficient respiratory system meets these oxygen needs.

Cooperative Learning

Bird Adaptations Have students work in pairs or small groups to prepare posters or cartoons describing the success of birds for life in the air, on land, and in the water. Stress that students should include both external and internal adaptations for flight. In addition to general bird adaptations, posters can include examples of special bird adaptations to particular habitats, feeding styles, or reproductive strategies. Examples could include peacocks, penguins, hummingbirds, or kiwis. Suggest that each student in a group specialize either in researching, writing text, or finding or making illustrations.

Have each group present its completed poster to the class. Display posters in the classroom.

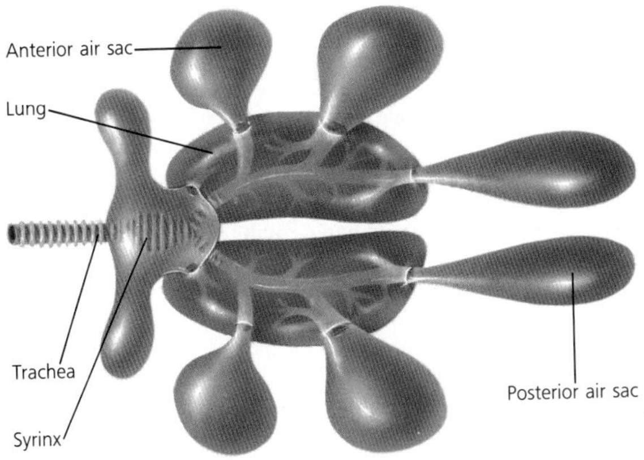

Figure 39-6 Air sacs pass oxygen-rich air to the lungs as the bird exhales carbon dioxide.

Air enters the bird's body through paired nostrils located near the base of the beak. It passes down the trachea past the **syrinx** *(SIR-inks),* or song box, and enters the two primary bronchii. From the bronchii, air moves to the lungs. About 75 percent of the air bypasses the lungs and flows directly to posterior **air sacs,** seen in Figure 39-6. Nine sacs extend out from the lungs, occupying a large portion of the bird's chest and abdominal cavity. These sacs connect with air spaces in the bones, filling the hollow bones with air. Thus the air sacs not only function in respiration but also greatly reduce the bird's density.

When the bird exhales the carbon dioxide-rich air from its lungs, oxygen-rich air is forced out of the posterior air sacs into the lungs via small tubes. The bird thus receives a supply of oxygenated air in its lungs during both inhalation and exhalation. Gas exchange then takes place through capillaries.

Circulatory System

Birds, like some reptiles, have a four-chambered heart. However, in birds the right and left sides of the heart are completely separated. The right side receives deoxygenated blood from the body and pumps it to the lungs. The left side receives oxygenated blood from the lungs and pumps it to the rest of the body. Unlike amphibians and reptiles, birds have a single right aortic arch.

In comparison with reptiles and most other vertebrates, most birds have a rapid heartbeat. The hummingbird's heart beats about 600 times a minute. The active chickadee's heart beats 1,000 times a minute. In contrast, the heart of the larger, less active ostrich averages 70 beats per minute—the same rate as a human heart.

Nervous System

Relative to their size, birds have large brains. The most highly developed areas of the bird's brain are those that control flight-related functions. The cerebellum coordinates movement. The cerebrum controls complex behavior patterns such as navigation,

Guided Practice

Ask students how the bird's digestive and excretory systems are adapted to flight. Remind them that the bird's digestive system (Figure 39-5, p. 592) works much faster than that of reptiles and that the bird's excretory system does not store liquid wastes. *(The fast digestive system and lack of bladder reduce the weight of stored waste and undigested food. Rapid digestion makes energy quickly available to flight muscles.)*

■ *See* Blackline Master *82.*

Independent Practice

■ Have students write answers to the Section Review.

■ Assign students pairs of bird characteristics and ask them to write a sentence that expresses the relationship between each pair—for example, the relationship between preening and vanes. *(In the process of preening, birds repair vanes that may have split.)*

Check Your Understanding

1. Compare the functions of down feathers, contour feathers, and flight feathers. *(Down feathers: insulation; contour feathers: streamlined shape, coloration, insulation; flight feathers: propulsive surface and stability)*

2. How is the bird's keel-shaped sternum a successful adaptation? *(It supports the large breast muscles needed for flight.)*

3. In what ways are the bird's circulatory and respiratory systems well adapted to flight? *(Birds have air sacs that communicate to the lungs and constantly provide oxygenated air. The heart can pump extremely rapidly to remove waste products.)*

Videodiscs

■ *2609, Birds and Mammals: Circulatory System (s)*

Reteaching

Have students create a concept map showing the features and systems of a bird and how they are adapted to flight. An example of a completed concept map is shown on p. 585B.

■ *See* **Section Reviews** *worksheet, Section 39.2.*

Enrichment

Have each student select an endangered bird species from lists found in *The Birdwatcher's Companion,* by Christopher Leahy, or another bird guide or textbook. Have each student give a 5-minute oral report on why the bird is endangered, whether it will be able to survive, and what measures can be taken to protect it.

Closure

Describe a specific environment such as a marsh, seashore, desert, forest, ocean, or polar region. Have students suggest characteristics of a bird that would be adapted to such an environment. Stress that this description should include the bird's physical features, diet, and nesting habits. *(Sample answer: A desert has little rainfall, few leafy plants, and harsh weather conditions. A desert-adapted bird might be sand colored, prey on insects and lizards or eat cactus, sleep during the hot midday, nest in an underground burrow, and have an especially efficient excretory system to prevent water loss.)*

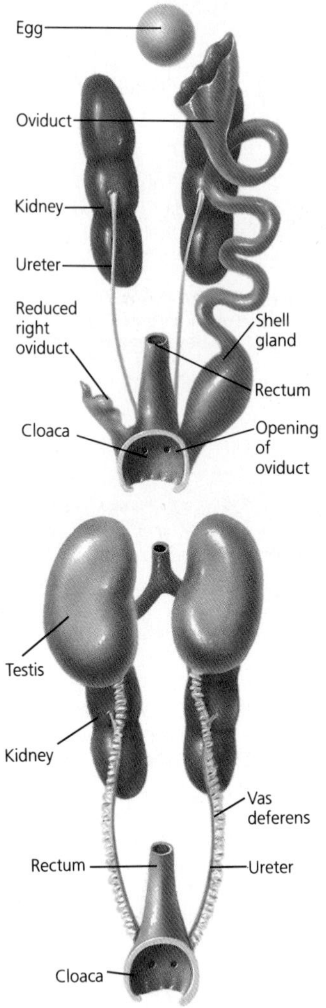

Figure 39-7 The female (top) and male (bottom) reproductive systems of a bird are shown here.

mating, nest building, and care of the young. The optic lobes receive and interpret visual stimuli.

The sense organs are modified for flight and avian life. Keen vision is necessary for taking off, landing, spotting landmarks, hunting, and feeding. Most birds have good color vision that aids them in finding food. In most species the bird's large eyes are located near the sides of its head, giving the bird a wide field of vision. Birds that have eyes located near the front of the head have better binocular vision; they can perceive depth in the area where the visual fields of the two eyes overlap.

Hearing is important to songbirds and also to nocturnal species such as owls, which rely on sounds to help them locate their prey. Look at the cover of this book. Though birds lack external ears, owls possess disk-shaped feathers around their ear openings, or canals, that help direct sounds into the ear. Each ear canal leads to a tympanic membrane, or eardrum. Semicircular canals in the inner ear regulate balance and cue spatial orientation.

Compared with vision and hearing, the sense of smell has less adaptive significance for birds and is often poorly developed except in ducks and flightless birds. The sense of taste helps birds avoid bitter-tasting or toxic foods.

Reproductive System

In the male bird sperm is produced in two testes that lie beneath the kidneys. As you can see from Figure 39-7, sperm passes through small tubes called vasa deferentia into the male's cloaca. During mating the male presses his cloaca to the female's and releases sperm. Most females have a single ovary located on the left side. The ovary releases eggs into a long, funnel-shaped oviduct, where they are fertilized by sperm. Fertilized eggs move down the oviduct, where they receive protective covering and a shell.

An unfertilized egg consists of a nucleus, cytoplasm, and a yolk. When fertilized, the embryo, as shown in Figure 39-7, is suspended in **albumen,** the egg white. This liquid medium is supported by ropelike strands of material called **chalaza** *(kuh-LAY-zuh)* that are attached to the **shell membrane.** The female has a **shell gland** that secretes a protective calcium carbonate shell to surround the egg.

Section Review

1. Distinguish between *vanes, barbs,* and *barbules.*
2. In what ways does the avian skeleton differ from that of other vertebrates?
3. What features of the digestive and excretory systems are adaptations for flight?
4. How do the respiratory and circulatory systems function to meet the bird's high oxygen needs?
5. Why do you think that the sense of smell is not as important to most birds as the senses of sight and hearing?

Answers to Section Review

1. The vanes extend from either side of the shaft and consist of many branches, or barbs. Barbules, in turn, project from the barbs.
2. The bones are hollow and, in many cases, fused. The furculum and keeled sternum are unique to birds.
3. Food is digested and excreted quickly. The gizzard serves a grinding function similar to that of teeth and jaws in reptiles and mammals. Birds have no urinary bladder for storing waste.
4. Air sacs permit oxygenated air to flow through the lungs during both inhalation and exhalation. The heart beats and circulates the blood rapidly.
5. Because birds generally stalk their prey from a great distance and because they hunt in the air where scents would not linger

39.3 Development and Behavior

Although both birds and reptiles lay yolky eggs, birds generally take greater care of their eggs and their young than reptiles do. Most reptiles lay their eggs and immediately abandon them, while most birds invest at least some amount of energy in the care of their young.

Incubation and Development

A female bird usually lays eggs in a nest. Either one or both parents will then **incubate,** or warm, the eggs by sitting on them and covering them with a thickened, featherless patch of skin on the abdomen called a **brood patch.** Some species show other brooding behaviors. The male emperor penguin heats the egg by placing it on his webbed feet and enfolding it with his warm abdomen. In many cuckoo species the female lays the eggs in another species' nest, leaving the incubation and feeding to other birds.

Embryo development begins when the zygote forms a plate of cells on the surface of the yolk. This plate begins to form the tissues and organs of the embryo. A yolk sac membrane grows out of the embryo's developing digestive tract and surrounds the yolk like a net. The membrane produces digestive enzymes that dissolve proteins and lipids in the yolk. Blood vessels in the yolk sac membrane then carry the nutrients to the embryo. As you can see in Figure 39-8, by the time the egg hatches, the embryo has absorbed the yolk.

The allantois, a vascular, netlike sac, also grows from the digestive tract. The allantois attaches to the chorion membrane lining the shell. Together the allantois and chorion function in respiration and help eliminate waste products. Like the reptilian embryo, the avian embryo is enclosed in an amnion, which is filled with amniotic fluid.

When hatching begins, the fully developed embryo makes a star-shaped crack in the shell with the scalelike **egg tooth** on its bill. The chick presses and scrapes the shell until the crack widens enough for the chick to emerge. The egg tooth, having served its purpose, falls off soon after the chick hatches.

Section Objectives

- *Summarize the processes of incubation and embryo development in birds.*
- *Describe the advantages of territorial and courtship behaviors.*
- *Explain how nest building reflects adaptations to a bird's environment.*
- *Identify the cues believed to aid in bird migration.*
- *Explain how computers are used in bird conservation studies.*

Figure 39-8 The drawing below shows internal parts of a newly fertilized egg. The photographs in the bottom row show sequential stages in embryo development.

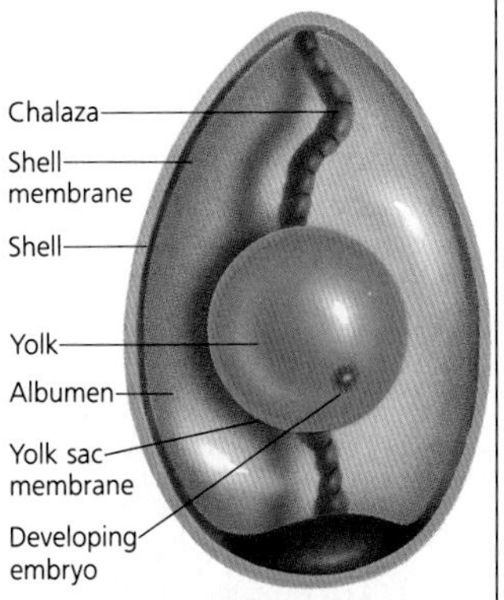

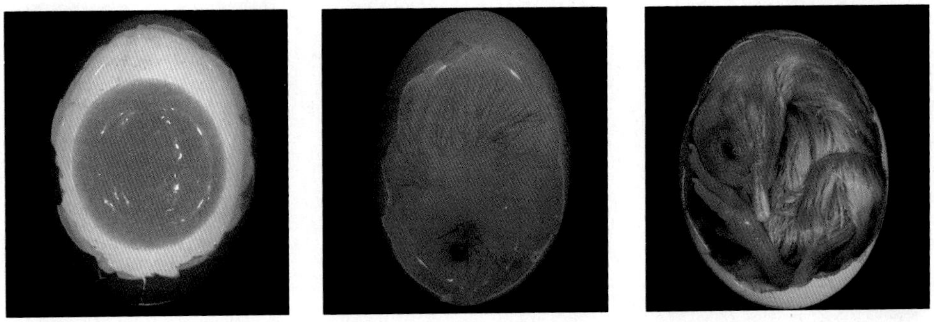

Lesson Plan

Section Focus

This section focuses on bird development, including the incubation of eggs and the development of the embryo, and on bird behavior such as territoriality, courtship, nest building, and migration.

Section Themes

This section emphasizes the theme of **Evolution.** Birds have evolved beyond their reptile ancestors in the care given to their eggs and young and in their elaborate behavioral patterns, which greatly enhance their chances for survival.

Motivating Activity

Show students on a world or Western Hemisphere map that many songbirds thought of as North American migrate to Central and South America in the winter. Ask students if they have seen migrating flocks of birds. Have students describe how these flocks appeared. Ask students to suggest ways in which migrating birds might navigate. *(By following shorelines, by the stars or sun, by wind directions, magnetically)*
■ *See* Process Skills, *Chapter 39.*

Teaching Strategies

Relating Concepts Have each student make a table suggesting how each of the following behavioral features has contributed to the evolutionary success of birds: incubation of eggs, care of young, territoriality, courtship, and nest building. An example of a completed table is shown at the bottom of this page.

Feature				
incubation of eggs	care of young	territoriality	courtship	nest building
Contribution to Evolutionary Success				
stable environment for embryo	ensures survival to maturity	ensures adequate food for young	mate selection	protection of young

Graphic Organizer Use this table with Relating Concepts at right.

Interpreting the Visuals Refer students to the diagram of a newly fertilized bird egg in Figure 39-8 on p. 595. Ask them to compare this diagram with the generic amniote egg in Figure 38-1, p. 571. Ask students to suggest, based on the diagrams and the text on p. 595, where in the bird egg each of the four membranes can be or will be found. *(Chorion: lines the shell; amnion: surrounds the developing embryo; yolk sac: will grow out of the developing embryo's digestive tract and surround the yolk; allantois: will grow out of the developing digestive tract and connect with the chorion.)*

Guided Practice

Provide students with pictures from a bird field guide of familiar species in which the male and female have very different colors and patterns. These could include red-winged blackbirds, mallard ducks, or most warblers. Have students write a short essay on the probable adaptive advantages for this color and pattern difference, which is called sexual dimorphism. *(The male's pattern stands out so that he can defend territories and attract mates; the female's pattern blends with the environment so that she can incubate the eggs in safety.)*

Independent Practice

- Have students write answers to the Section Review.
- Have students write and illustrate a description of the development of a bird embryo from the time of fertilization to the hatching of the chick. Have them include the stages of fertilization, the beginning of zygote growth, the growth of the yolk sac and allantois, and the fully developed chick.

Birds have two contrasting methods for rearing young. Those that lay many eggs and incubate them for long periods hatch **precocial** *(pree-KOE-shul)* young. These birds are active as soon as they are hatched. The mother provides some warmth and protection, but the newly hatched birds can walk, swim, and feed themselves. Ducks, quail, and other ground-nesting species produce precocial offspring. Birds that lay only a few eggs that hatch quickly produce **altricial** *(al-TRIH-shul)* young. These birds hatch blind, naked, and helpless. They depend on both parents for several weeks. The parents keep the young warm and search for food to feed them. The young of woodpeckers, hawks, pigeons, parrots, warblers, and many aquatic birds are altricial.

Behavior

The time and effort birds spend incubating and caring for their young help ensure that most of their offspring will reach maturity. Young birds obviously need protection until they develop the strength to fly and to obtain food. However, the long period of parental care may also enable birds to learn such complex behaviors as courtship, nesting, and migration.

Biotechnology

Conservation of Migratory Birds

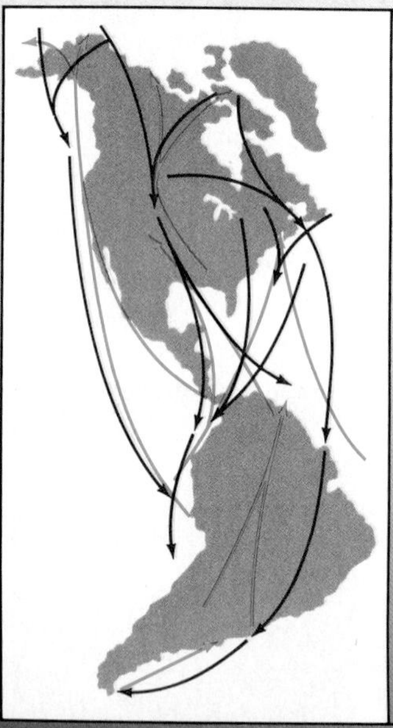

Bird conservation efforts have generally focused on endangered species, but biologists are developing a better understanding of bird behavior, which will enable them to protect species before they become endangered. Advances in computer technology and statistical analysis have made possible large-scale studies that weren't feasible ten years ago.

Computer technology has especially benefited the study of migratory shorebirds, which include sandpipers, plovers, and curlews. Shorebird migrations often extend from the Arctic to Argentina—a round trip exceeding 25,000 km. Conservation efforts for these species obviously require international cooperation among nations throughout the Western Hemisphere.

One such effort is the International Shorebird Survey, a project established in 1974. Conservation groups in North and South America have been collecting data on dozens of shorebird species.

Volunteers record information on bird populations, habitat characteristics, weather conditions, and human activity in their areas. Researchers then use computers to identify relationships among these variables.

LEP Activity

Bring several fertilized chicken eggs to class. These can be purchased at farms or organic food markets. In class, have students carefully break open the eggs in a bowl and identify each of the internal parts of the egg as shown in Figure 39-8 on p. 595. A hand lens or dissecting microscope may be needed to see the early embryo. Then have them write a short report in which they describe and name each of the parts they have seen. If fertilized eggs are unavailable, unfertilized ones will do, although there will be no developing embryo. Even in the unfertilized egg, the "bullseye" dot containing the unfertilized ovum will still be visible. If the eggs are from a farm, incubate them at 37°C for varying lengths of time up to ten days before opening them to show early embryonic development.

Territoriality and Courtship

During the breeding season many male birds establish an area that they defend against other males of their species, a behavior called **territoriality.** The male then attempts to attract a female—or in some species, several females—to share this territory. If the male is successful, no competition will exist for food sources in his territory. An example of this type of behavior is provided by the male red-winged blackbird, which marks his territory by sitting in a prominent location while trilling his song and displaying his red shoulder patches. Once a territory is established, most birds engage in a period of **courtship,** behavior that is designed to attract a mate.

A great deal of variation exists in the courtship behavior of different species of birds. Many males attract females by means of their brightly colored feathers, which they show off in various courtship displays. Some males combine song with flight displays. For example, the brilliant red vermilion flycatcher flies vertically into the air and then dives steeply. He may repeat this courtship behavior for many hours while fluttering his wings and singing a trilling song.

Figure 39-9 During courtship a male great frigate bird, *Fregata minor,* puffs out its red throat pouch.

For example, determining the correlation between two variables such as population and food supply involves plotting data on a two-dimensional graph. However, far more sophisticated computations are required to factor in additional variables such as weather and human intervention.

A high-speed computer can analyze multiple variables far more quickly than a human can. The massive memory capacity of today's computer can easily store the millions of bits of information gathered over the last 15 years.

Statisticians use highly complex methods of trend analysis to interpret the data generated by the computer. As a result researchers now know a great deal about the migratory habits of shorebirds—their velocity, altitude, flight path, and gathering sites. They have also identified significant trends, such as a 70 to 80 percent drop in the population of sanderlings and short-billed dowitchers.

Have natural factors or human intervention caused this population drop? How might construction of a housing development on a prime feeding ground affect a bird population? These and many other questions still face researchers of the International Shorebird Survey. Once they determine the answers, biologists can recommend global strategies to protect shorebird species. Computers will undoubtedly play an important role in the development of these strategies.

Biotechnology

Using the Feature

The feature explains how sophisticated computers are used by bird conservation scientists to analyze data such as population, weather, human activity, food supply, and migration routes of birds.

Stress that by using computers as tools for calculating complex statistical tests based on millions of bits of information collected in the field, scientists can discover patterns that are not apparent any other way. These patterns include population fluctuations, the correlation between changes in bird populations and human activity, and the effects of weather changes on migrations.

In the International Shorebird Survey, biologists, statisticians, meteorologists, and computer scientists use a multidisciplinary approach to make discoveries that none of them could have made alone. Ask students how scientists might go about investigating whether human intervention or natural factors have caused the 70 to 80 percent drop in sanderling populations. *(Data on sanderling population changes, development within sanderling ranges, and changes in weather and other conditions can be analyzed statistically by computer.)*

Videodiscs

- ***Side 4 5371, Ostrich and Young—Behavior (m)***
- ***Side 4 34768, Interaction: Rhinoceros and Birds (m)***
- ***Side 4 4589, Flamingo Feeding (m)***
- ***Side 4 4845, Swan Feeding (m)***

More Information

Chicken Eggs If her eggs are fertilized, a bird will stop laying eggs and brood. Almost all birds will lay eggs even in the absence of fertilization. This is particularly true of fowl. Since the domestication of chickens 6,000 years ago, poultry farmers have developed special breeds as well as methods of using the hen's natural cycle to maximize egg production. In the presence of light, the hen's pineal gland decreases its secretion of the hormone melatonin, thus stimulating mating behavior and egg production. (See Chapter 47, p. 732 of the teacher's edition.) Poultry farmers, therefore, keep hens in coops lighted for up to 14 hours a day all year long, a sort of permanent spring. If they did not, egg production would fluctuate and would stop in the winter.

Check Your Understanding

1. What is the function of the allantois and chorion? *(In the egg they function together in respiration and in helping to eliminate waste products.)*
2. Why is territoriality an important behavior? *(It ensures that a mating pair will have a secure nesting area and access to food.)*
3. What is the adaptive value of migration in birds? *(It allows them to exploit food resources of colder regions in spring and summer, then move to warmer climates during the winter.)*

Reteaching

Ask students to explain how environmental factors might favor the evolution of specific bird behaviors that they have observed, such as caring for young, nest building, territoriality, courtship, and migration. *(Accept any reasonable answer. Variety in types of nests is a particularly interesting subject to discuss.)*

■ *See* Section Reviews *worksheet, Section 39.3.*

Enrichment

Divide students into groups. Have each group select a bird, such as the crow, sparrow, or whooping crane, and research its social behavior for an oral report. The report should describe how the bird builds nests, mates, cares for its young, and migrates. If possible, have students find and report on recent research.

Closure

Ask students whether the following characteristics best describe birds, reptiles, or both: amniote egg *(Both)*, care for young *(Birds and a very few reptiles)*, incubate eggs *(Birds)*, territorial *(Both)*, lay eggs in nests *(Birds and some reptiles)*, migrate *(Birds)*, young hatch ready to feed themselves *(Reptiles and precocial birds)*.

Figure 39-10 Nest builders and the nest materials they use are (clockwise from top left) the hummingbird, mud; the osprey, *Pandion haliaetus*, branches; and the grosbeak weaver, *Amblyospiza albifrons*, grass.

Nest Building

Nests hold eggs, conceal young birds from predators, provide shelter from the elements, and sometimes even serve to attract a mate. Most birds build nests in sheltered, well-hidden spots—from holes in the ground to treetops. Woodpeckers nest in tree holes that they have drilled. Orioles suspend their nests from branches, well beyond the reach of predators. Various swallow species have nesting strategies that result in minimal competition between species. Bank swallows, for example, dig a tunnel in a sand bank, whereas barn swallows build a saucer of mud on the beam of a building.

As a further adaptation to their environment, birds construct their nests of almost any material available. Twigs, grasses, feathers, and mud are the most common materials used.

Migration

Each year thousands of bird species exploit the spring and summer food resources of colder regions. Then, when temperatures drop and the food supply dwindles, these birds migrate to warmer climates. How do birds manage to navigate thousands of miles across varied terrains to the same spot year after year?

Ornithologists—biologists who study birds—know that birds rely on a variety of cues to help them navigate. Some species monitor the position of the stars or the sun. Others rely on topographical landmarks, such as mountains. Magnetic cues, changes in air pressure, and low-frequency sounds may also provide information to migrating birds. The ability of birds to "read" these cues, along with their many adaptations for flight, enables them to migrate to and inhabit virtually any environment.

Section Review

1. Distinguish between *precocial* and *altricial* birds.
2. How do most bird species incubate their eggs?
3. List at least three cues that birds may use for navigation.
4. How do a bird's nest-building habits reflect adaptations to its environment?
5. Why might wrens and cardinals rely on singing to establish territories and attract mates?

Answers to Section Review

1. Precocial birds lay many eggs and have a long incubation period. The chicks are active upon hatching. Altricial birds lay few eggs and have a short incubation period. The chicks hatch naked, blind, and helpless.
2. By warming the eggs under the featherless brood patch on the abdomen
3. Some bird species rely on the position of the stars or sun, topographical landmarks, magnetic field, changes in air pressure, or low-frequency sounds.
4. Birds build nests in almost any safe place—on the ground or in the trees—and use almost any available material.
5. Singing allows them to communicate without exposing themselves to predators.

Laboratory

Structure and Function of Bird Feathers

Objective
To examine the structure and function of the three main types of bird feathers

Process Skills
Observing, inferring, hypothesizing

Materials
1 each of quill, contour, and down feathers; unlined paper; prepared slide of a contour feather; microscope; prepared slide of a down feather

Inquiry

1 Examine a quill feather. Hold the base of the central shaft with one hand and gently bend the tip of the feather with your other hand. Be careful not to break the feather. Next hold the shaft and wave the feather in the air. Record your observations concerning the structure of the quill feather. Relate your observations to its possible function.
2 Examine the vane of the feather. Does the vane appear to be a solid structure? Write a description of its structure. Make a drawing of the quill feather. Label the shaft, vanes, and barbs.
3 Examine a contour feather and a down feather. Make a drawing of the contour feather and the down feather. Label your drawings as before. Do you notice a difference in the structure of the contour and the down feathers?
4 Examine a prepared slide of a contour feather under low power. Note the smaller barbs, called barbules, extending from each of the barbs.
5 How might you observe the region between the barbs? Locate the tiny hooks at the end of each barbule. Note the arrangement of the hooks on adjacent barbs. Why do you think the hooks are so small? Make a labeled drawing of the hooks.
6 Examine the prepared slide of the down feather under low power. Locate the barbs and barbules. Switch your microscope to high power, and make a labeled drawing of the down feather.

Conclusions

1 What is the function of the shaft? What is the function of the vanes and barbs?
2 How do hooks increase the strength and air resistance of a feather?
3 How is the structure of the quill feather related to its function of aiding flight?
4 Why are down feathers more effective at keeping a bird warm than the other two feather types are?

Further Inquiry
Each of the feather types you have examined has a specific structure and function. Review your observations, and try to think of features that account for the efficiency of the three types of feathers.

(For an overview of bird feathers and preparatory information related to the laboratory, see p. 585B.)

Inquiry

1. The quill is the largest and most rigid of the three types of feathers.
2. The vane is made up of many branches.
3. The contour feather is constructed around a strong central shaft and has parallel barbs; the down feather consists of many soft, fluffy barbs.
5. Separate the barbs by disengaging the barbules with a fine needle. If the hooks were large, they could engage with vegetation.
6. Down feathers have neither shafts nor hooks.

Conclusions

1. The shaft supports the vane and makes a feather more rigid. The vanes and barbs form a flat surface that increases the air resistance of a feather.
2. The hooks interlock with the barbs and keep the barbs from being pushed apart by the air.
3. The stiff shaft, broad vanes, and many hooked barbules provide an air-resistant surface that is well suited to flight.
4. Down feathers spread apart easily. The space between the barbs traps air, insulating the bird's body.

Further Inquiry
Students should suggest features that increase rigidity or air resistance.

Vocabulary

1. *Altricial* comes from the Latin word *alere,* meaning "to nourish," and is defined as "helpless when hatched." *Precocial* comes from the Latin word *praecox,* meaning "premature," and is defined as "capable of independent activity at hatching."
2. *Albumen* comes from Latin and means "white material."
3. *Furculum* comes from Latin and means "fork."
4. *Proventriculus* comes from Latin and means "before the stomach or gizzard."
5. *Incubate* comes from Latin and means "to lie on."

Review

1. c
2. a
3. a
4. b
5. d
6. c
7. d
8. a
9. b
10. a

11. Birds are poorly represented in the fossil record because their feathers and hollow bones do not preserve well.
12. Morphological differences in beaks, feet, plumage, bone structure, and musculature; behavior and song; and analysis of blood proteins, chromosomes, and DNA
13. Down feathers, contour feathers, flight feathers, filoplumes, and bristles
14. It kneads and crushes food, often with the help of stones swallowed by the bird. Its function is similar to that of teeth and jaws in mammals.
15. Air sacs increase respiratory efficiency by permitting a continuous flow of oxygenated air through the bird's lungs.
16. Binocular vision enables some birds to perceive depth, which is necessary for capturing prey.
17. The avian heart has a single right aortic arch, unlike the hearts of amphibians and reptiles. Also, in birds the right and left sides of the heart are separated.

Chapter 39 Review

Vocabulary

air sac (593)	chalaza (594)	flight feather (589)	proventriculus (592)
albumen (594)	contour feather (589)	follicle (589)	shaft (589)
altricial (596)	courtship (597)	furculum (587)	shell gland (594)
barb (589)	crop (592)	gizzard (592)	shell membrane (594)
barbule (589)	down feather (589)	incubate (595)	syrinx (593)
bristle (589)	egg tooth (595)	precocial (596)	territoriality (597)
brood patch (595)	filoplume (589)	preen gland (589)	vane (589)

Use a dictionary to find the origin of each of the following terms, and tell why the terms are appropriately named.

1. altricial, precocial
2. albumen
3. furculum
4. proventriculus
5. incubate

Review

1. The first *Archaeopteryx* fossil dates back to the (a) Miocene epoch (b) Cretaceous period (c) Jurassic period (d) Eocene period.
2. The most common basis for classifying birds is (a) morphology (b) flight patterns (c) wingspan (d) color.
3. The major molting in birds usually occurs (a) just after the end of the breeding season (b) just before the beginning of the breeding season (c) just after the fall migration ends (d) just before the first snow of winter.
4. The bone that supports the tail feathers is the (a) pelvic girdle (b) pygostyle (c) ulna (d) furculum.
5. Gas exchange in birds takes place in the (a) anterior air sacs (b) bronchi (c) syrinx (d) capillaries.
6. In order to maintain a constant body temperature, birds cannot go for long periods without (a) resting (b) molting (c) eating (d) nesting.
7. The ropelike substance that supports the embryo and surrounding materials is the (a) allantois (b) albumen (c) amnion (d) chalaza.
8. Some swallows have minimal competition because different species (a) build different types of nests (b) engage in flight display (c) breed at different times of the year (d) migrate at different times of the year.
9. Birds that produce altricial young (a) abandon their newly hatched chicks immediately (b) lay only a few eggs at a time (c) usually build nests on the ground (d) incubate their eggs for a long period of time.
10. A cue that is believed to aid birds in navigation during their annual migrations is (a) the magnetic field (b) weather (c) cloud formations (d) phases of the moon.
11. Why are birds poorly represented in the fossil record?
12. What three criteria are used to classify birds?
13. List the five types of feathers.
14. What function does the gizzard serve in the bird's digestive process?
15. How do air sacs increase respiratory efficiency in birds?
16. Why is binocular vision important to some birds?
17. What features distinguish the avian heart from the heart of amphibians and reptiles?

18. The fully developed embryo uses its egg tooth to crack and scrape the shell until the opening is big enough for it to emerge.
19. Woodpeckers drill holes in trees for nests. Orioles suspend their woven nests from branches. Bank swallows dig tunnels in sand banks. Barn swallows build a saucer of mud on the beam of a building.
20. Computers can analyze multiple variables quickly, and they have the capacity to store large amounts of data.

18. What is the function of the young bird's egg tooth?
19. Describe the nesting habits of three bird species.
20. Name two advantages to using today's high-speed computers in the study of bird populations.

Critical Thinking

1. What factors might account for the fact that birds live in the Arctic but that reptiles do not?
2. Birds are an example of animals exhibiting dimorphism: that is, the sexes differ markedly in appearance. Look at the picture of the bird on the right. From what you have learned in the chapter, is it a male or a female?
3. A large part of the meat (muscles) of the chicken is white, while all the meat of the duck is dark. What difference in the life-styles of the two birds might account for the difference in their muscle texture and color?
4. From studying the circulatory system of birds, you know that the right and left sides of a bird's heart are completely separated. This means that the oxygenated blood is never mixed with the unoxygenated blood. What in the life-style of birds makes this complete separation in the heart necessary?
5. Cowbirds lay their eggs in the nests of other birds. The cowbirds hatch slightly

earlier than the other birds do, and the hatchlings are slightly larger. Why might it be advantageous to the young cowbirds to hatch earlier and to be larger?
6. Several species of hummingbirds are able to see light that is near the ultraviolet range. Insects are also able to see ultraviolet light. Like some insects, hummingbirds are nectar eaters. Why might it be important for a hummingbird to be able to see light that is near the ultraviolet range?

Extension

1. Bird watching is a fascinating and interesting hobby. From your library or bookstore obtain a field guide to the birds in your area, and borrow a pair of binoculars. Take a long walk and try to locate as many birds as you can. Be sure to keep a notebook of the birds you find this year, including species, date, location, and habits.
2. At your grocery buy a whole chicken. Boil and bone the chicken. Lay the bones out as if you were preparing to reconstruct the skeleton. Then identify the bones by referring to Figure 39-4.
3. Read the article by Chris Wille entitled "Mystery of the Missing Migrants" in *Audubon,* May 1990, pp. 80–85. Prepare an oral report in which you discuss the problem of declining migrant bird populations. What difficulties are inherent in migrant bird studies? What are the possible causes of dwindling migrant bird populations?

Critical Thinking

1. Reptiles are ectothermic and cannot survive extreme temperatures. Birds are endothermic and can adapt to some extremes.
2. It is probably a male, since it has brightly colored plumage.
3. The duck is a flying animal, whereas the chicken's wings are often clipped to keep it from flying. Muscles that are used for flight have more blood vessels and are therefore darker.
4. Birds need blood with a high oxygen content because flight muscles require large amounts of oxygen.
5. The cowbird hatchlings will have an edge in growth over the other young. They will be fed first by their foster parents.
6. The hummingbirds are able to see the same nectar guides that insects see in order to find nectar in a flower.

Extension

1. Tell students that their notebook could be the start of a "life list" that serious bird-watchers keep.
2. Suggest that students can do this activity in groups, sharing the expense, the work, and the learning.
3. This article focuses on the question of what constitutes evidence sufficient to call for action. Encourage students to research dwindling bird populations by also reading other books or articles on the subject. Then have them debate conservation proposals based on their interpretation of the evidence presented.

Chapter 40 Mammals

Chapter Overview

Chapter 40 concludes the exploration of the five vertebrate classes with an investigation of the Class Mammalia. After an overview of mammalian origins, evolution, characteristics, and classification in Section 40.1, the chapter examines monotremes and marsupials in Section 40.2 and the characteristics and classification of placental mammals in Section 40.3.

Chapter Planning Chart

B	S	A	Sections and Subsections	Page	Features	Page	Resources
•	•	•	**40.1 Evolution and Characteristics**				
			Origin	603	Laboratory	615	Videodiscs
			Evolution	603	Section Review	605	Blackline Master 83
			Characteristics	604			Overhead Transparency T40
			Classification	605			Section Reviews Worksheet
•	•	•	**40.2 Monotremes and Marsupials**				
			Monotremata	606	Section Review	607	Videodiscs
			Marsupialia	606			Section Reviews Worksheet
•	•	•	**40.3 Placental Mammals**				
			Characteristics	608	Think	609	Videodiscs
			Classification	608	Biology in Process	612	Process Skills: Humpback Whales
					Writing About Biology	614	Laboratories: Mammalian Behavior
					Section Review	613	Section Reviews Worksheet
			End of Chapter Activities				
					Chapter Review	616	Vocabulary Skills
							Chapter Test
							Computer Test Generator

B *The Basic Level curriculum presents the most fundamental knowledge offered in the course.*
S *The Standard Level curriculum is designed for the average student who is able to master most topics.*
A *The Advanced Level curriculum includes suggestions for teaching the most academically able students.*

Cooperative Learning

Group Activity: Mammal Identification Game

- **Group Size:** *Half the class*
- **Outcome:** *Students will identify major characteristics of mammalian orders.*
- **Individual Accountability:** *Each student will contribute information about the mammalian orders to the group.*
- **Positive Interdependence:** *One team of students will challenge the other team with questions about mammals.*

Ask each team to prepare game cards for the Mammal Identification Game. Provide cards made of construction paper, 8" x 10" or larger; colored pencils; glue; and photos or illustrations. Tell each team to make one card for each of the 13 orders of placental mammals described in Chapter 40. On one side of the card, have students glue an illustration or a photograph of a member of the order. On the opposite side, have students write information for each of the following categories: name of the order, habitat, feeding habits, teeth, locomotion, special adaptations, and examples of members.

Members of each team take turns flashing the front of a card at the other team. The student asks for the name of the order and information about one category, such as habitat. The other team has 15 seconds to name the order and supply the information. The teacher will act as judge. For each correct answer, award the team 5 points. If the answer is incorrect, award the other team 5 points. The team with the most points within a given time period is the winner.

Concept Map

The following is one possible solution to the concept mapping activity in Relating Concepts on p. 603.

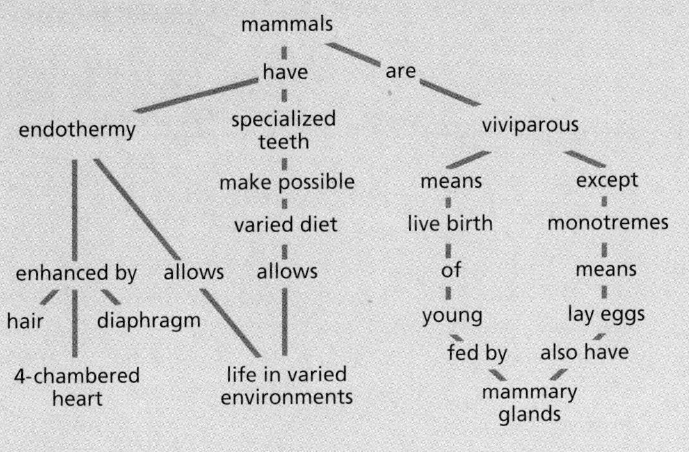

Laboratory Preparation

Overview *(See p. 615.)*

This laboratory lets students observe some differences between mammals and other vertebrates. It also lets them make observations on their own bodies. Depending on availability, a variety of materials can be used to demonstrate specific features and stimulate thought. Students often believe that male and female mammals can be distinguished by the presence of mammary glands. In fact, most nonlactating female mammals show very little mammary development and are not distinguishable from males on this basis. Fetal pigs show that both males and females have undeveloped mammary glands, which continue to be present in mature males.

Preparation

Most materials used in this lab are available from biological supply houses. If real skulls are not available, pictures can be substituted. Provide a variety of mammalian and nonmammalian skulls, skeletons, or pictures.

Teaching Tips

Students are interested in their own bodies. For example, they are often surprised to learn that they have hair on the inner part of their arms.

Point out the relationship between sizes and distribution of mammals' teeth and their diets. Carnivores such as dogs have many canine teeth and few molars. On the other hand, horses, which eat grass, have many large molars. Humans, being omnivores, have both tearing and grinding teeth.

Use this lab to begin a discussion of endothermy. Mammals have many mechanisms that allow them to maintain constant body temperature. One of these is fur, the insulating covering on the skin. Other mechanisms will be discussed in subsequent chapters. For example, spongy lungs, four-chambered heart, and enucleated red blood cells help in getting more oxygen to cells, thereby raising the amount of ATP made and thus permitting a higher metabolic rate.

Safety

Students should handle slides and laboratory specimens with care. They should also wash their hands before and after counting their teeth.

Chapter Themes

Evolution Mammals evolved from reptiles more than 200 million years ago. Explain to students that it was not until after the extinction of dinosaurs, about 65 million years ago, that mammals began to evolve into the present diverse orders.

Scale and Structure Emphasize that because of their sophisticated structures mammals are well adapted to a wide variety of habitats on land, in water, and in air. Mammals exhibit diversity also in their external anatomies, digestive systems, and teeth.

Stability Endothermy, the ability to maintain stable internal body temperature, allows mammals to adapt to many more habitats than their ectothermic reptilian ancestors. Tell students that the viviparity of almost all mammals provides a stable environment, nutrient supply, and oxygen source for the developing embryo. Viviparity also frees adults from incubating eggs in a nest.

Chapter Motivating Activity

Remind students that they studied the classification of animals in Chapter 18. Have students contribute the names of domesticated mammals with which they are familiar. Lead a brainstorming session on what wild animals may be most closely related to these domesticated animals. Ask students to support their surmises based on physical or behavioral similarities. *(For example—cats: tigers, lions; dogs: wolves, foxes; gerbils: rats, mice; horses: zebras; cattle: bison, antelope, deer)*

Chapter 40 | *Mammals*

Introduction

At the end of the Mesozoic era the ruling reptiles, the dinosaurs, became extinct. On the other hand, mammals, which had arisen at about the same time as dinosaurs, survived and adapted to the changing environment. By studying the evolution of mammals and examining their characteristics, you will learn how mammals survived great changes, diversified, and colonized varied habitats.

Chapter Outline

40.1 Evolution and Characteristics
- *Origin*
- *Evolution*
- *Characteristics*
- *Classification*

40.2 Monotremes and Marsupials
- *Monotremata*
- *Marsupialia*

40.3 Placental Mammals
- *Characteristics*
- *Classification*

Chapter Concept

As you read, look for specific adaptations that have made each order of mammals a successful group.

Sperm whale, *Physeter catadon*. Below: Giraffes, *Giraffa camelopardalis*.

Understanding the Visuals

Ask students what differences they can see between sperm whale and giraffe. *(Giraffe: long neck, pointed head, external ears; sperm whale: no neck, blunt head, no external ears)*

Have students speculate on how these features are adaptations to the giraffe's habitat on land and the sperm whale's habitat in the ocean. *(Giraffe: reaches high leaves with long neck, hears approaching predators with external ears; sperm whale: requires compact body to swim, needs no external ears to hear because water carries sound more efficiently than air. See More Information on p. 612, for an explanation of the sperm whale's blunt head.)*

40.1 Evolution and Characteristics

Mammals belong to the Class Mammalia, which includes about 4,000 species. They are the dominant land vertebrates on earth. How did mammals evolve? What led to their success?

Origin

Fossil evidence and evidence from comparative anatomy indicate that mammals evolved from a group of reptiles called **therapsids** *(thuh-RAP-sidz)*. The therapsids arose about 280 million years ago, near the end of the Paleozoic era. Therapsids had both reptilian and mammalian characteristics. Like reptiles, therapsids had a jaw composed of five bones rather than of the single jawbone characteristic of mammals. However, unlike reptiles, the quickest of which ran on two legs, therapsids had mammalian skeletal adaptations that allowed them to be efficient four-footed runners. Unlike reptiles, which you have learned are ectothermic, therapsids were probably endothermic. Like mammals, therapsids had specialized teeth adapted for specialized functions.

The oldest mammalian fossil yet found is from the early Mesozoic era, about 200 million years ago. The jaw, a single bone, is the most obvious mammalian feature. Scientists infer that the mammal was only 10 cm long. Its skeleton was similar to that of a shrew. It had teeth adapted for eating insects. It was probably endothermic, had skin, and was covered with hair.

Evolution

How did early mammals survive competition with the dinosaurs during the Mesozoic era? Fossil skeletons show that early mammals had large eye sockets, evidence that these creatures may have been active at night. By hiding during the day, mammals would have avoided predation by dinosaurs. By feeding on insects, mammals would not have competed with dinosaurs for food.

Though mammals arose near the beginning of the Mesozoic, they were not abundant. Nevertheless, by the end of the Jurassic period, at least five orders of mammals had arisen. Fossils of these mammals are scarce, however, indicating that mammals probably were not as abundant then as they are today.

About 65 million years ago, at the end of the Cretaceous, the dinosaurs became extinct. This opened up new habitats that mammals could exploit without facing competition. Mammals became dominant by the beginning of the Paleocene epoch. By the end of the Eocene epoch, most modern orders of mammals had evolved. The Cenozoic era is named the Age of Mammals because of the emergence and dominance of this vertebrate class.

Section Objectives

- *Summarize the significance of the therapsids in mammalian evolution.*
- *Give a probable reason why mammals survived competition with dinosaurs.*
- *List some characteristics of mammals, and explain how these characteristics enabled mammals to adapt to different environments.*

Figure 40-1 The therapsid, which lived 280 million years ago, was a reptile that also had mammallike characteristics.

Figure 40-2 *Eozostrodon* was a mammal about 10 cm long that lived during the late Triassic period.

Lesson Plan

Section Focus

This section describes the origin and evolution of mammals, which arose from therapsid reptiles more than 200 million years ago. The section also presents major mammalian traits and introduces mammalian classification.

Section Themes

This section emphasizes the themes of **Evolution** and **Stability**. Mammals evolved from their reptilian ancestors, developing many successful adaptations, including endothermy and viviparity. These adaptations permitted mammals to thrive in varied and severe habitats.

Motivating Activity

Show students illustrations and photographs from nature books and magazines of a variety of mammals in their habitats. These could include dolphins, elephants, mice, tigers, anteaters, kangaroos, monkeys, bats, armadillos, deer, seals, beavers, and wolves. Ask students to infer what visible characteristic of each mammal enables it to survive in its habitat. Have students give reasons for their inferences. *(For example, bat wings for flight, dolphin flippers for swimming, tiger stripes for camouflage, armadillo armor for protection)*

Teaching Strategies

Relating Concepts Have each student make a concept map illustrating the adaptive significance of some important mammalian characteristics. An example of a completed concept map is shown on p. 601B.

Videodiscs

- ***1467–1526, Animalia; Mammalia—Examples (s)***

Paleozoic Era	Mesozoic Era		Cenozoic Era
early Permian period	Triassic period	Cretaceous period	Tertiary and Quaternary periods
therapsids arise	oldest mammalian fossils	dinosaur extinction	age of mammals

Graphic Organizer Use this sequential diagram in Organizing Events on p. 604.

Organizing Events Have students draw a sequential diagram illustrating the important stages in mammalian evolution. Have students refer to the Geologic Time Scale on p. 221 for correct eras and periods. An example of a completed diagram is shown on p. 603.

Interpreting the Visuals Have students refer to the phylogenetic tree of mammals on p. 605 (Figure 40-4). Ask students to infer, assuming that positions of branchings correspond to time, which orders are most closely related. *(Proboscidea and Sirenia; Carnivora and Pinnipedia)* Ask students if and why they are surprised by lack of close relationship between some orders. *(Students may have expected closer relationships between Rodentia and Lagomorpha or between Perissodactyla and Artiodactyla.)*

■ *See* **Overhead Transparency** ***T40 and*** **Blackline Master** ***83.***

Guided Practice

Have each student write a short essay comparing mammalian with reptilian or avian adaptations. *(For example, while a mammal has fur to protect it during winter, some birds are able to migrate south.)*

Independent Practice

- Have students write answers to the Section Review.
- Have each student write a short essay describing different types of mammalian teeth and their functions. Have students include a chart of their own teeth, labeled by type.

Characteristics

Mammals have certain characteristics that led to their widespread success in adapting to different environments and gave them survival advantages. Study the list of common traits:

- Mammals are endothermic.
- Mammals have hair.
- The mammalian heart has four chambers.
- Mammals have a muscle, the diaphragm, that aids breathing.
- Mammals have a single lower jawbone, and most species have four different types of teeth.
- Most species are viviparous—females carry their young in the uterus during development and then give birth to live young.
- Females secrete milk from mammary glands to feed newborn young.
- Many mammals have a highly developed brain.

Endothermy is an adaptation that has allowed mammals to be active at any time of the day or night and to colonize many severe environments, from deserts to ice fields. Several mammalian characteristics are adaptations for endothermy. Hair serves as insulation for most mammals. Variations in kinds and amounts of hair reflect adaptations to different environments.

The four-chambered heart and diaphragm are also adaptations for endothermy. Endothermic animals can regulate body temperature in any kind of environment. The **diaphragm** is a sheet of muscle below the rib cage that aids in efficient breathing. The four-chambered heart pumps blood efficiently. These adaptations result in a high metabolic rate, which helps mammals maintain a constant body temperature.

Most mammals have specialized types of teeth, as shown in Figure 40-3. Such teeth allow mammals to exploit a wide variety of food sources. Chisellike **incisors** bite and cut. Pointed **canines** grip, puncture, and tear. **Bicuspids,** teeth with two points, shear and shred. Flattened teeth called **molars** grind and crush. Variations in size and shape of teeth among different mammalian species reflect differences in diet. Different types of teeth are adaptations that allow mammals to use diverse food sources available in a wide range of environments.

Most mammal species are **viviparous**—that is, females carry and nourish the young inside their bodies for a period of time before giving birth to live young. Viviparous mammals can move around without leaving their unborn unprotected.

Newborn mammals are nourished with milk from the mother's milk-secreting glands, or **mammary glands.** Thus young mammals are dependent on the mother for food. In some species the young remain dependent for a long time, during which they mature and learn the behaviors necessary for survival. Such species have well-developed brains. Many also have flexible behavior patterns that allow them to adapt to changes in the environment.

Figure 40-3 Teeth of various shapes enable mammals to grip, tear, shred, and grind food. Thus they can eat a wide variety of foods.

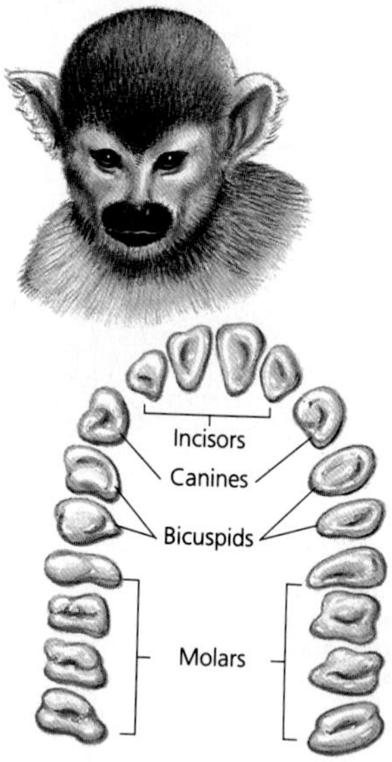

LEP Activity

Have students prepare posters illustrating the following mammalian characteristics: endothermy, hair, teeth, viviparity, and milk production. Posters should be illustrated with pictures from magazines, each one labeled to represent each characteristic. Examples could include a polar bear on ice (endothermy), a woolly sheep (hair), a lion yawning (teeth), a mother ape with her young (viviparity), and piglets suckling (milk). Photographs could include human examples. Display posters in the classroom.

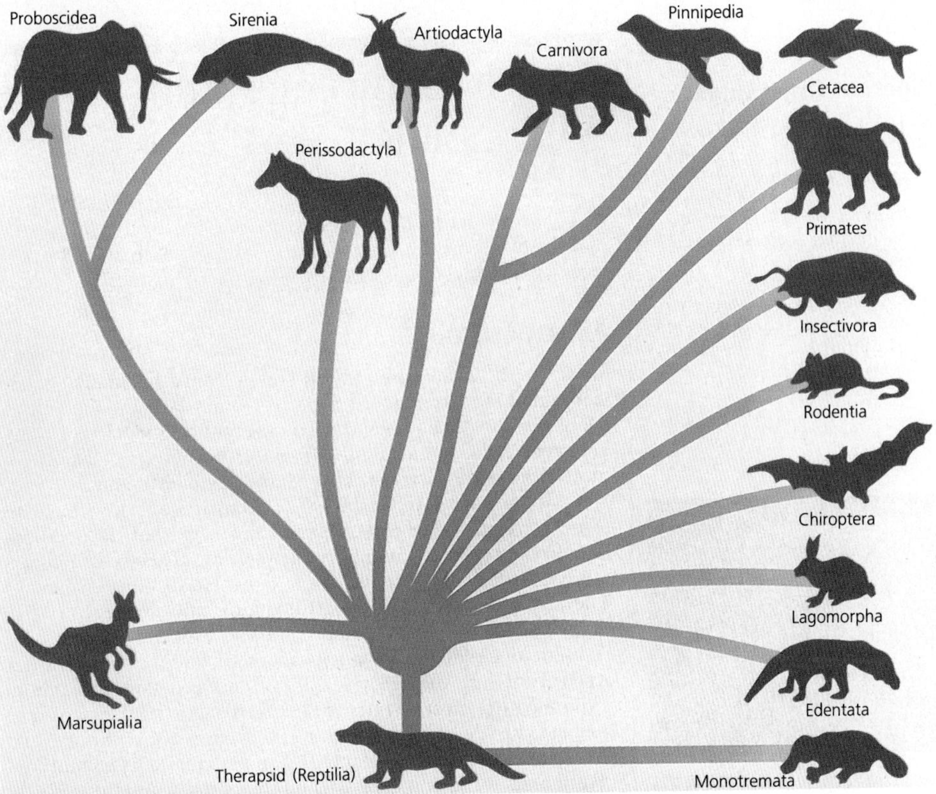

Figure 40-4 The diversity of mammals is a result of evolution since the beginning of the Mesozoic. This phylogenetic tree shows the relationships of the orders discussed in this chapter.

Classification

Mammals share two features that distinguish them from other vertebrates: all have hair, and all produce milk to feed their young. There are 19 orders of modern mammals in the Class Mammalia. Of these, 17 are placental mammals—mammals that nourish unborn young via the placenta. The two remaining orders are Monotremata—egg-laying mammals—and Marsupialia—pouched mammals. As you read Sections 40.2 and 40.3 study the inferred phylogenetic relationships shown in Figure 40-4.

Section Review

1. What type of animal was the therapsid?
2. Describe the oldest mammalian fossil.
3. How did mammals survive competition with the dinosaurs?
4. How have endothermy, specialized teeth, and viviparity aided mammals in adapting to varied environments?
5. What pattern of evolution did the mammals exhibit at the beginning of the Cenozoic era? Explain your answer.

Check Your Understanding

1. How did the extinction of dinosaurs contribute to the evolution of mammals? *(Mammals could exploit new habitats without facing competition.)*

2. What two features distinguish mammals from all other vertebrates? *(Having hair and milk production)*

Reteaching

Have students compare the following traits of mammals and reptiles: temperature regulation, body covering, heart, teeth, mode of reproduction, and feeding of young. How have mammalian traits led to widespread success? *(Mammals: endothermy, hair, 4-chambered heart, specialized teeth, mostly viviparous, lactation, highly developed brain; reptiles: ectothermy, scales, 3- or 4-chambered heart, generalized teeth, ovoviviparity and oviparity, minimal care of young, less developed brain. For list of contributions to mammalian success, see p. 604.)*

■ *See* **Section Reviews** ***worksheet, Section 40.1.***

Enrichment

Provide students with unlabeled mammalian skulls if available or unlabeled pictures of mammalian skulls with teeth showing. Ask students to infer each animal's diet and feeding behavior based on teeth they observe.

Closure

Have students imagine early mammals living at the time of the dinosaurs' extinction. Ask volunteers to tell the class one adaptive trait that would have allowed the mammal to survive. *(For example, keen vision and hearing, nocturnal habits)*

Videodiscs

■ ***2588–2589, Homologous Forelimbs (s)***

■ ***2590–2593, Classification; Evolutionary Relationships (s)***

Answers to Section Review

1. A therapsid was a reptile with certain mammalian characteristics.

2. It was a jaw composed of a single bone with teeth adapted to eating insects.

3. By being active at night and feeding on insects

4. Endothermy has allowed mammals to live in varied environments and be active at all times of the day. Specialized teeth have allowed mammals to exploit a wide variety of food resources. Viviparity has allowed mammals to be mobile while protecting the unborn young.

5. Mammals exhibited adaptive radiation as they evolved into many species, moving into the environments opened up by the extinction of the dinosaurs.

Lesson Plan

Section Focus

This section introduces the Orders Monotremata and Marsupialia. The oviparous monotremes possess some traits in common with reptiles. The marsupials give birth to immature young that complete their development in the mother's pouch.

Section Theme

The theme of **Evolution** is evident in the discussion of many features that monotremes and marsupials may have inherited. Despite their seeming anachronism, modern members of these two orders are well adapted to their habitats.

Motivating Activity

Show students pictures from nature books of platypuses, kangaroos, and opossums. Ask students what they know about or can observe that makes these animals different from more familiar mammals. *(Accept all reasonable answers. Students may know about pouches and egg-laying.)*

Teaching Strategies

Inferring Causes Have students review material in Section 16.3 on speciation due to geographic isolation. Then have students make hypotheses on why Australia is dominated by marsupials. *(Placental mammals had not yet evolved when Australia became isolated; only marsupials lived in Australia then.)*

Guided Practice

Ask students to imagine reptilian and mammalian characteristics combined in one animal. What might such an animal look like? *(Accept any appropriate answer.)* Write answers on the board. Ask students which reptilian characteristics are evident in monotremes. *(Oviparity; cloaca; partial endothermy)*

Section Objectives

- *List examples of both reptilian and mammalian characteristics in monotremes.*
- *Outline the differences in reproduction between monotremes and marsupials.*
- *Describe the circumstances under which marsupials and placentals have undergone convergent evolution.*

40.2 Monotremes and Marsupials

Species in the Orders Monotremata *(MAH-nuh-TREM-uh-tuh)* and Marsupialia *(mahr-SOOP-ee-ALE-ee-uh)* account for only 5 percent of all mammalian species. However, their unusual patterns of reproduction illustrate diversity in mammals.

Monotremata

Species in the Order Monotremata differ from other mammal species in that monotremes are oviparous—they lay eggs. Only three species exist: the duck-billed platypus and two species of spiny anteaters called echidna *(ih-KID-nuh)*. Monotremes live in remote regions of Australia, New Guinea, and Tasmania.

Monotremes have certain characteristics that are similar to those of reptiles. For example, they are oviparous. In addition, monotremes are not completely endothermic. Their body temperature is lower and fluctuates more than that of other mammals. The large intestine, the urinary bladder, and the reproductive organs of monotremes all empty into the cloaca, as in reptiles.

The duck-billed platypus is adapted to life in water. It has waterproof fur, webbed feet, and a flattened tail that aids in swimming. Its most distinctive characteristic is its flat, sensitive, rubbery muzzle, which it uses to grub for worms, shrimp, and other invertebrates in soft mud. The platypus digs channels in river banks for laying eggs. The mother curls around the eggs to protect and incubate them. After hatching, the young lick milk from nippleless glands on the mother's abdomen.

Echidnas, commonly called "spiny anteaters," have a coat of protective spines and a long snout suited for probing into anthills. Echidnas incubate their eggs in a brood pouch on the belly.

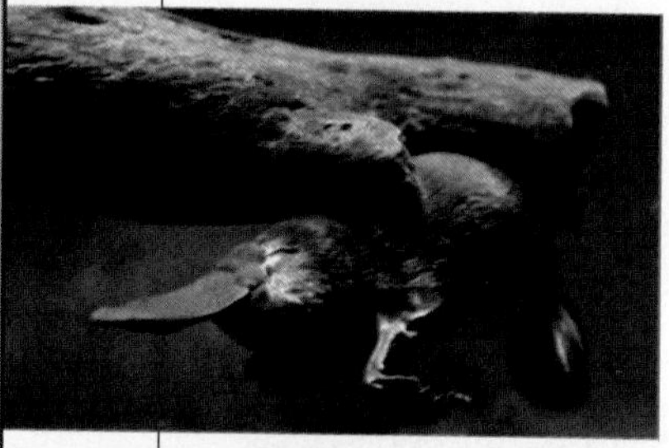

Figure 40-5 Both the platypus, *Ornithorhynchus anatinus* (top), and the echidna, *Tachyglossus aculeatus* (bottom), use their snouts to reach food.

Marsupialia

Species in the Order Marsupialia give birth to tiny, immature young that crawl to a pouch on the mother's belly immediately after they are born. There they attach themselves to milk-secreting nipples, nursing until they are mature enough to survive outside the pouch. About 250 marsupial species exist, inhabiting Australia, New Guinea, Tasmania, and the Americas. North America has only one marsupial species, the common opossum. Most marsupials live in Australia, where they are the dominant mammals.

Why are marsupials the dominant mammals in Australia, whereas placental mammals are the dominant mammals elsewhere? Geologic evidence indicates that 200 million years ago the continents were joined as a single landmass. In time the landmass split up, and the continents drifted apart. When Australia broke

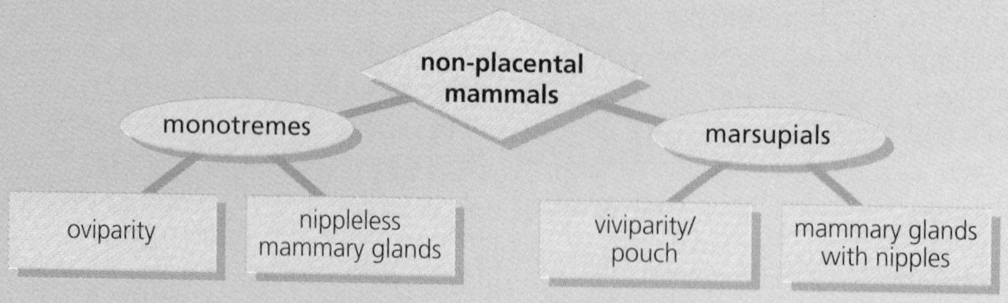

Graphic Organizer Use this organizational chart in Reteaching on p. 607.

Figure 40-6 These paired animals demonstrate the convergent evolution of marsupials and placentals. Although very similar in many ways, they are only distantly related.

off from the larger landmass about 60 million years ago, no placental mammals inhabited that continent. Lacking competition, Australian marsupials underwent adaptive radiation and eventually became adapted to all the environments in Australia. On the other continents placental mammals outcompeted the marsupials for resources, and most marsupial species became extinct.

The marsupial species of Australia resemble familiar placental species. The wombat resembles a groundhog. The glider resembles a flying squirrel, and the cuscus, a monkey. These pairs of animals have adapted to similar environments, use similar food sources, and are similar in body structure and behavior. However, the marsupial and placental pairs are very distantly related. Therefore their similarities are a result of convergent evolution, adaptation to similar environments of different, isolated continents.

Section Review

1. What are some distinguishing features of the echidna?
2. What traits do monotremes share with reptiles? with mammals?
3. What makes marsupial reproduction unique?
4. Why do scientists say that placentals and Australian marsupials have undergone convergent evolution?
5. The pouch of the marsupial mole opens not toward the front of the body but toward the rear. How would such a pouch aid in the survival of this burrowing animal's young?

Independent Practice

- Have students write answers to the Section Review.
- Have students write a short essay about why they think that the platypus has survived into the modern world. Ask them to speculate on whether the platypus could thrive outside Australia.

Check Your Understanding

1. How do newly hatched platypuses feed? *(They lick milk from nippleless glands on the mother's belly.)*
2. Why have most marsupials outside Australia become extinct? *(They could not compete successfully with placental mammals.)*
3. Why do placental mammals lack pouches? *(Their young are born in a more developed form than marsupials, needing less protection.)*

Reteaching

Have students make a chart comparing features of monotremes with those of marsupials. Use the organizational chart on p. 606 as a model.

- ***See* Section Reviews *worksheet, Section 40.2.***

Enrichment

Have students find examples of marsupial species that became extinct, such as *Argyrolagus* and *Thylacosmilus*, and prepare short oral reports.

Closure

Have students brainstorm answers to the following question: What if placental mammals had been present in Australia when it became isolated? *(Most nonplacentals would probably have become extinct.)*

Videodiscs

- ***Side 4 8547, Koala with Young (m)***
- ***1469–1474, Marsupialia (s)***

Answers to Section Review

1. Lays eggs and has protective spines and a long snout for probing anthills
2. Like reptiles, they lay eggs, are partially endothermic, and have a cloaca. Like mammals, they have hair and feed their young with milk.
3. A marsupial gives birth to immature young that crawl into a pouch on the mother's abdomen and attach themselves to milk-secreting nipples; young remain in the pouch until they can survive outside.
4. Placentals and Australian marsupials, though only distantly related, have adapted to similar environments, use similar food resources, and are similar in body structure and behavior.
5. It protects the young from smothering.

Lesson Plan

Section Focus

This section presents placental mammals, which account for about 95 percent of mammalian species. Students will study characteristics of placental mammals and the major orders, which exhibit a wide range of size, habitat, and behaviors.

Section Themes

The themes of **Scale and Structure** and **Evolution** are evident in the great diversity of placental mammals. This diversity is illustrated by the different jaws pictured in Figure 40-7 on pp. 608–609. Each jaw is an adaptation that allows the mammal to exploit a particular ecological niche. All placental mammals, from whales to mice and from bats to apes, are thought to be descended from a single common ancestor, the therapsid, shown in Figure 40-4 on p. 605.

Motivating Activity

Have students brainstorm as many different kinds of placental mammals as possible, and write their contributions on the board. Ask students to organize mammals into groups that seem most closely related. Have students give reasons for their groupings. Record them for later use to see how well they correspond to actual mammalian orders.

Teaching Strategies

Recording Diversity Have students keep a record of every species of placental mammal they see, both domestic and wild, during a week. Ask students to prepare a list of these mammals, grouped according to order. Remind students that humans are placental mammals.

Section Objectives

- *Describe the reproductive features that distinguish placental mammals from monotremes and marsupials.*
- *Name some orders of placental mammals, and give a representative from each.*
- *List some adaptive features of placental mammals for locomotion and feeding.*
- *Summarize Jane Goodall's contributions to the study of wild chimpanzees.*

40.3 Placental Mammals

Monotremes and marsupials are members of orders that are the oddities of the mammal world. Ninety-five percent of all mammal species are placental mammals. You will now study the characteristics of the major orders of placental mammals.

Characteristics

Placental mammals carry unborn young in the uterus until the young can survive in the outside world. In the uterus the young are nourished by the **placenta** *(pluh-SEN-tuh)*, an organ formed from the chorion and allantois. Oxygen and nutrients are transferred from the mother's blood, through the placenta, to the blood of the unborn mammal. The period of time during which mammals develop in the mother's uterus is the **gestation** *(jeh-STAY-shun)* **period.** Gestation periods vary in length from species to species.

Classification

Placental mammals are a diverse group, living on land, in water, and in the air. As you read, notice the adaptations that make members of each order fit their environments. Notice the adaptations for various forms of locomotion and the dietary adaptations, especially teeth, summarized in Figure 40-7. Such adaptations have contributed to the success of placental mammals.

Insectivora

The Order Insectivora *(IN-SECK-TIV-ur-uh)* consists of about 400 species, mainly shrews and moles. Insectivores are usually small animals with a high metabolic rate and are found in North America, Europe, and Asia. Most have long, pointed noses that enable them to grub for insects, worms, and other invertebrates. They have teeth adapted for picking up and piercing the prey.

Insectivora

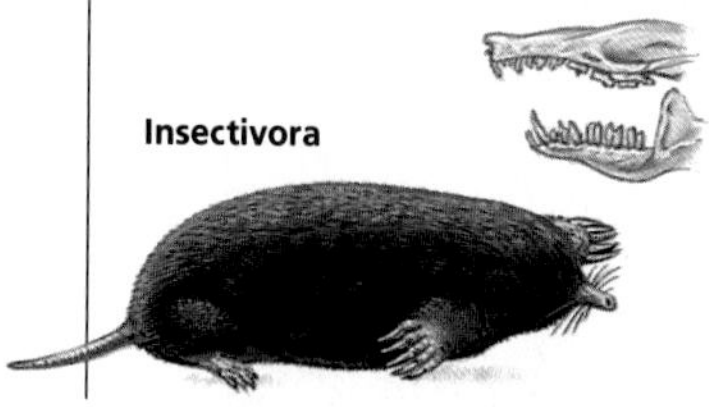

Rodentia

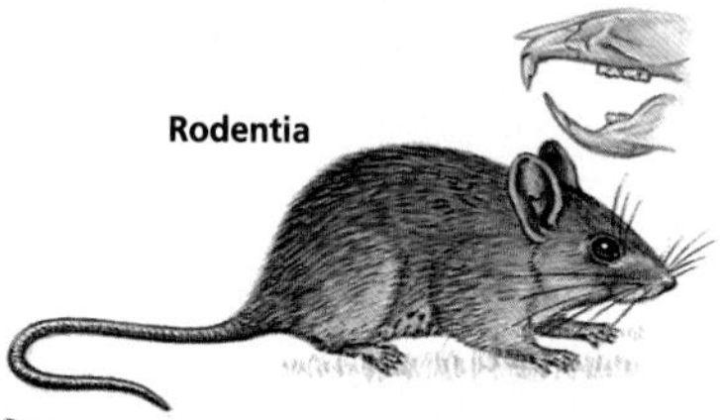

Lagomorpha

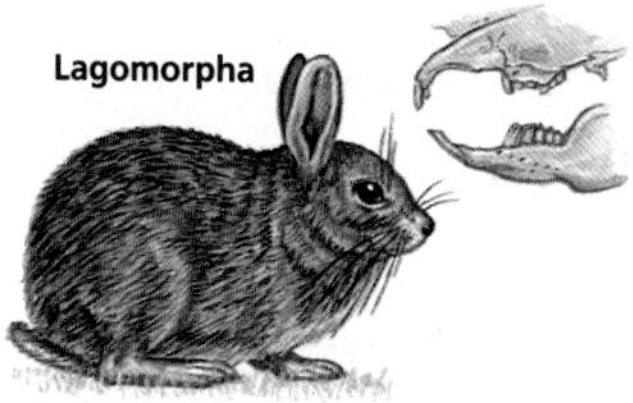

Edentata

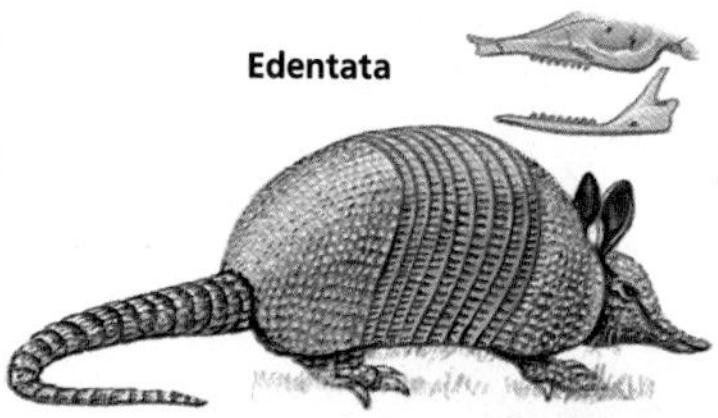

Chiroptera

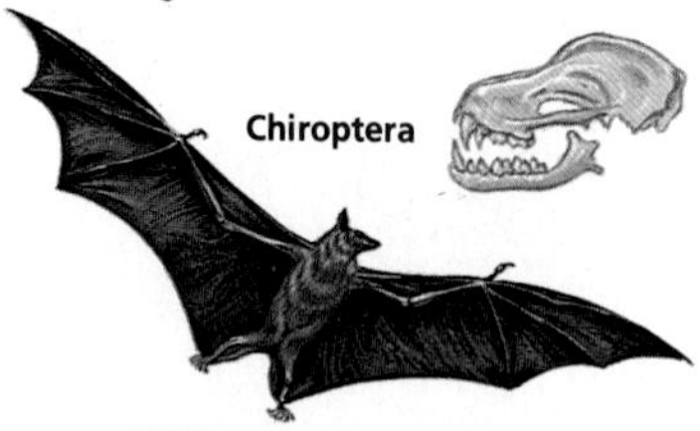

Cetacea

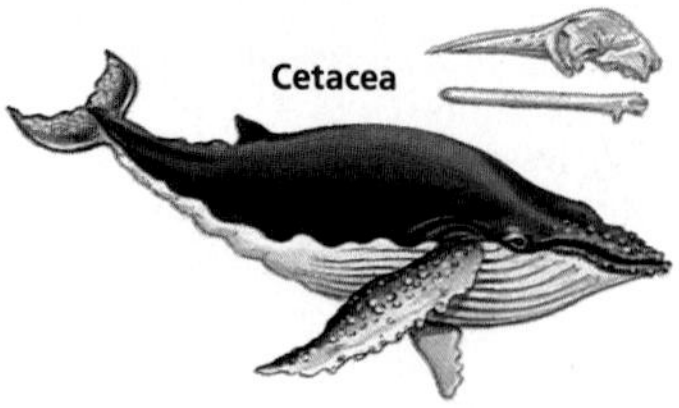

Sirenia

608

	Order
Land	Insectivora, Rodentia, Lagomorpha, Edentata, Carnivora, Artiodactyla, Perissodactyla, Proboscidea
Water	Cetacea, Sirenia, Pinnipedia
Air	Chiroptera

Graphic Organizer Use this table with Identifying Habitats on p. 610.

Insectivores are adapted to life on the ground, in trees, in water, and under ground. Shrews, for example, feed on the ground, sweeping invertebrates into the mouth with clawed paws. Moles, on the other hand, burrow under ground. They have stout limbs for digging, reduced eyes, and no external ears.

Rodentia

Rodentia *(roe-DEN-shuh)* is the largest mammalian order, having over 2,400 species. Rodents flourish on every continent except Antarctica and are adapted to a wide range of habitats. Squirrels, marmots, chipmunks, gophers, muskrats, mice, rats, and porcupines are all rodents. Guinea pigs and capybaras are South American rodents. While most mammals have four incisors in each jaw, rodents have only two. These teeth continue to grow as long as the rodent lives. Rodent incisors are sharp, an adaptation for the rodent's diet of hard seeds, twigs, roots, and bark. As it gnaws, the back surface of the tooth wears away faster than the front surface, maintaining the tooth's chisellike edge.

Lagomorpha

About 70 species make up the Order Lagomorpha *(LAG-uh-MORF-uh)*, which includes rabbits, hares, and small mountain mammals called pikas. Lagomorphs are found worldwide. They differ from rodents in that they have a double row of upper incisors, with two large front teeth backed by two smaller ones. Lagomorph teeth continue to grow throughout the animal's lifetime. Such teeth are an adaptation to the lagomorph's herbivorous diet.

Edentata

The Order Edentata *(EE-DEN-TAHT-uh)* is made up of about 30 living species, including anteaters, armadillos, and sloths. These mammals are found in southern North America, Central America, and South America. The name edentate means "without teeth." However, only anteaters are completely toothless; armadillos and sloths have teeth, though their teeth are peglike and lack enamel.

Think

The animal in the picture is a placental mammal called the pangolin. The seven species of pangolins make up the Order Pholidota. Pangolins eat ants and termites. Like the anteater, an edentate, pangolins lack teeth. What pattern of evolution is exhibited by the pangolins and the anteaters? Explain your answer.

Figure 40-7 **Examine the adaptations for locomotion and eating among the placental mammals.**

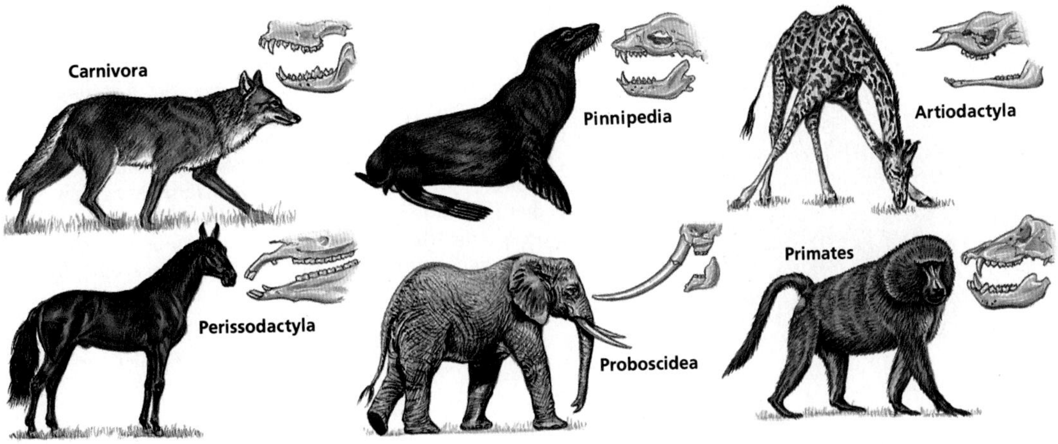

Observing Organisms Organize a field trip to a local zoo to observe placental mammals. Have students compare behaviors of mammals of different orders as well as those of placental mammals with other animals, such as birds and reptiles. Ask students to draw generalizations from these observations.
- *See* **Laboratories, *Investigation 40.***

Interpreting the Visuals After students have read Section 40.3, refer them to Figure 40-7 on pp. 608–609, which illustrates tooth structures and arrangements characteristic of several placental mammal orders. Ask students to predict in detail how teeth illustrated for each order function to process the animal's food and how they are well adapted to the diet of that order. Ask about details of tooth shape, size, and arrangement, including gaps between teeth. *(For example, Perissodactlya incisors may clip off grass, which the tongue then passes back to molars for grinding.)*

Answer to Think

The pangolin and anteater exhibit convergent evolution. Even though they belong to different orders, they exhibit similar characteristics, such as a long snout and loss of teeth.

Cooperative Learning
Mammalian Teeth Divide students into small groups. Have each group make a model, with papier-mâché, modeling clay, or other materials, of tooth structure and arrangement of a particular placental mammal order. Display finished models in the classroom, labeled only with arbitrary numbers. Have all students try to match numbers with correct orders by referring to information in Figure 40-7, pp. 608–609. Stress that the object is not to stump the class but make models so accurate that everyone can get correct answers.

Exploring Relationships Direct a brainstorming session in class about the relationships between humans and other placental mammals. Ask students how humans depend on mammals. *(Food, pets, scientific research, educational specimens, entertainment, and work—horses, oxen, sheep dogs, hunting dogs, guide dogs for the blind, and guard dogs.)* Ask students how these animals depend on humans. *(Wise use of natural resources, humane treatment of working animals, pets, farm animals, and research animals)*

Identifying Habitats Have each student make a table dividing the placental mammal orders into those primarily active on land, in water, or in air. An example of a completed table is shown on p. 608. Challenge students to find examples of species that are exceptions to this division. *(Hippopotami are artiodactyls primarily active in water; sea otters are carnivores and are primarily aquatic.)*

■ *See* Process Skills, *Chapter 40.*

Exploring Careers Have each student use library resources or interviews to research a career that depends in part on placental mammals. (Veterinarian, rancher, animal trainer, dog groomer, mounted police officer, and so forth) Have students prepare short (5 minute) oral reports based on their research.

Figure 40-8 The bony wing structure of this mouse-eared bat, *Myotis myotis,* is evident as the bat swoops in on a cricket.

Edentates have adaptations for an insectivorous diet, including a long, sticky tongue and clawed front paws. Some edentates have adaptations for other diets. Armadillos supplement their insect diet with small reptiles, frogs, mollusks, and dead animal matter. Sloths, on the other hand, are herbivores; their continuously growing teeth are an adaptation for grinding plants.

Chiroptera

The Order Chiroptera *(kie-RAHP-tuh-ruh)* is made up of over 900 species of bats. Bats are the only mammals that are true flyers. They live throughout the world except in polar environments. A bat's wing is a modified front limb in which a skin membrane stretches between extremely long finger bones to the hind limb. The bat's clawed thumb sticks out from the top edge of the wing. Bats use their thumbs for walking, climbing, or grasping.

Most bats are active at night and have a specialized way of navigating and finding food called echolocation. Bats that use **echolocation** emit high-frequency sound waves, which bounce off objects. The frequency of the returning sound waves helps the bat identify the size, distance, and rate of movement of different objects. Bats that use echolocation have small eyes and large ears. They generally feed on insects and have teeth specialized for such a diet. Some tropical bats feed on fruit or flower nectar and do not use echolocation. These bats, sometimes called "flying foxes," have large eyes and a keen sense of smell.

Cetacea and Sirenia

The Order Cetacea *(sih-TAY-shuh)* includes 90 species of whales, dolphins, and porpoises, distributed worldwide. Most cetaceans live in the oceans, but some dolphin species live in freshwater lakes and rivers. Cetaceans have fishlike bodies with forelimbs modified as flippers. They lack hind limbs, but have broad, flat tails that help propel them through the water. Cetaceans breathe through a blowhole at the top of the head.

Figure 40-9 Instead of teeth, the upper jaw of a baleen whale contains two rows of a firm material called baleen. It holds back food as water that the whale has gulped is forced out.

Cetaceans are divided into two groups: toothed whales and baleen whales. Toothed whales include beaked whales, sperm whales, beluga whales, narwhals, killer whales, dolphins, and porpoises. All have from one to over a hundred teeth and prey on fish, squid, seals, and other whales. Baleen whales lack teeth. Instead they have **baleen,** thin plates of fingernaillike material, that hang down from the roof of the mouth. As the baleen whale swims, it opens its mouth and gulps huge quantities of water. Then it closes its mouth and uses its tongue to push the water through the baleen. Shrimp and other small invertebrates that make up its diet remain in the mouth, strained by the baleen.

The Order Sirenia *(sie-REEN-ee-uh)* is made up of four species of manatees and dugongs. These large herbivores inhabit tropical seas, estuaries, and rivers. Their front limbs are flippers, modified for swimming. Like cetaceans, sirenians lack hind limbs but have a flattened tail for propulsion.

Interdisciplinary Activity

Mathematics Have students calculate the answer to the following problem and answer the follow-up questions. The female of a certain field mouse always gives birth to a litter of 8, half of them female. All surviving females achieve sexual maturity and, if mated, give birth at exactly 3 months of age and every 3 months after that until death. (Average life span: 2 years) In order to survive, each field mouse needs 1 square meter of grass.

A pair of adult field mice—a male and a pregnant female—arrive, floating on a log, at a grassy island. The island is about the size of a football field, 91 meters by 49 meters. The day after her arrival, the female gives birth. Because the island has no predators, all of her descendants survive until the island can no longer provide enough space.

Figure 40-10 The lion, *Felis leo* (left), brown bear, *Ursus arctos* (center), and elephant seal, *Mirounga angustirostris* (right), are mainly meat eaters. Note the long canine teeth of the lion, a characteristic of most carnivores.

Carnivora and Pinnipedia

The 250 living species of the Order Carnivora *(kahr-NIV-ur-uh)* are distributed worldwide. Dogs, cats, raccoons, bears, hyenas, and otters are some well-known carnivores. Most of the species mainly eat meat, which explains the name of the order. However, some members of this order, such as bears, feed extensively on plant material as well as meat, so they are called **omnivores** *(AHM-nih-VORZ).*

Carnivores generally have long canine teeth, strong jaws, and clawed toes—for seizing and holding prey. Most have keen senses of sight and smell, which aid in hunting. Skeletal adaptations enable terrestrial carnivores to run quickly.

Members of the Order Pinnipedia *(PIN-uh-PEED-ee-uh)* are water-dwelling carnivores with streamlined bodies for efficient swimming. About 34 species of sea lions, seals, and walruses compose this order.

Artiodactyla and Perissodactyla

Ungulates *(UN-gyuh-luts),* or hoofed mammals, are classified into one of two orders: Artiodactyla *(AHRT-ee-oe-DACK-tuh-luh)* or Perissodactyla *(puh-RISS-uh-DACK-tuh-luh).* Ungulates with an even number of toes make up the Order Artiodactyla. Deer, elk, bison, moose, cows, sheep, goats, pigs, and camels are all artiodactyls. About 150 species belong to the order. Artiodactyls live on every continent except Antarctica. Artiodactyls differ from other ungulates in that they have cloven, or split, hooves. Most are fast runners and use speed as their major defense.

Ungulates with an odd number of toes make up the Order Perissodactyla, which includes about 15 living species. Horses, zebras, rhinoceroses, and tapirs are all perissodactyls. Most species are native to Africa and Asia. However, some tapir species live in Central and South America.

Artiodactyls and perissodactyls are herbivores. Their molars tend to be large and flat, for grinding plant material. Artiodactyls have a storage chamber in the stomach called the **rumen.** Chewed and swallowed plant material is stored in the rumen, where bacteria break down cellulose. This partially digested material, called a cud, is chewed again, swallowed, and passed through the digestive system a second time. This double digestion allows artiodactyls to derive nutrients efficiently from tough grasses.

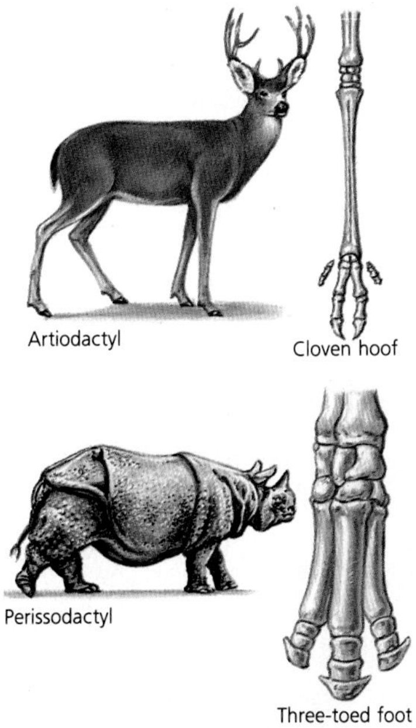

Figure 40-11 Split hooves with an even number of toes are characteristic of artiodactyls, including deer, *Odocoileus* sp. An odd number of toes is characteristic of perissodactyls, such as the rhinoceros, *Diceros bicornis.*

Guided Practice

Have each student prepare a chart describing the method of locomotion of each placental mammal order. *(For example, Chiroptera: flying; Cetacea: swimming; Primates: walking, running, climbing)*

Independent Practice

- Have students write answers to the Section Review.
- Have students use classroom or library resources to write a short essay on one extinct mammal. Examples include recently extinct species, such as the African quagga (a type of zebra/horse), or more ancient mammals, such as the woolly mammoth. Ask students to include information on the probable causes for the mammal's extinction.

Check Your Understanding

1. Distinguish between rodents and lagomorphs. *(Rodents have only two incisors in each jaw. Lagomorphs have two large front teeth backed by two smaller ones.)*
2. Name some adaptations for flight of members of Order Chiroptera. *(Wings modified from front limbs and echolocation to navigate and find prey)*
3. How do bears differ from most other carnivores? *(They are omnivores, feeding on plant material as well as meat.)*

Videodiscs

- *Side 4 9794, Blue Whale (m)*
- *Side 4 12026, Humpback Whale: Maternal Behavior (m)*
- *Side 4 13540, Porpoise: Swimming Ability (m)*
- *1510–1526, Hoofed Mammals (s)*

How many field mice are there after 3 months? After 6 months? After 9 months? After one year? Approximately when can the island no longer support the population of field mice? *(After 3 months: 50; after 6 months: 250; after 9 months: 1,550; after one year: 7,050. The island, which has an area of 4,459 square meters, runs out of space before the end of the first year.)* Discuss with students the importance of predators in a natural system. *(The presence of predators may have kept the field mice population in check.)*

Reteaching

Have each student select an order of placental mammals and create a poster illustrating characteristics of this order. Emphasize that the poster should contain information (either text or graphics) about the order's habitat(s), teeth, feeding habits, and geographic range, and should contain illustrations of as many species from the order as possible.

■ *See* Section Reviews *worksheet, Section 40.3.*

Enrichment

Have each student choose one order of placental mammals for further investigation. Have students use library resources to research and write an essay about the order they choose. Essays should include information about characteristics of the order, diversity within the order, numbers of species, their geographic ranges, and names of representative species.

Closure

Describe a habitat and feeding strategy and ask students to identify order(s) of placental mammals to which these apply. *(Examples: Water, vegetation: Sirenia; plains, grass: Artiodactyla, Perissodactyla, Proboscidia, Rodentia, and Lagomorpha; water, fishes: Cetacea and Pinnipedia)*

Videodiscs

■ *Side 4 29746, Elephant (m)*

Figure 40-12 Elephants are characterized by the presence of a proboscis.

Perissodactyls also have adaptations that help them digest tough plant material. Members of this order have a large, convoluted **cecum** *(SEE-kum)*—a blind sac near the end of the small intestine. Like the rumen of the artiodactyl, the cecum of the perissodactyl contains bacteria that break down cellulose, releasing nutrients that the perissodactyl can digest.

Proboscidea

Members of the Order Proboscidea *(PROE-buh-SID-ee-uh)* are characterized by a boneless trunked nose or proboscis. Only two species of this order exist today—Asian and African elephants. However, species of this order were once quite common. Until 10,000 years ago woolly mammoths roamed many parts of North America.

Elephants are the largest land dwellers alive today. Weighing more than 6 tons, the elephant feeds on plants for 18 hours a day to sustain itself. The elephant uses its proboscis to gather leaves from high branches and to suck up water without lowering its heavy body. It has modified incisors, called tusks, for digging up roots and for stripping bark from branches. It has jagged molars, up to 30 cm long, for grinding plant material.

Biology in Process

Observing Chimpanzees

Evidence from comparative morphology and biochemistry reveals that chimpanzees are our closest living relatives in the animal world. Scientists have found that the DNA of humans and the DNA of chimpanzees are 99 percent equivalent. Biochemical studies have also shown that certain human and chimpanzee proteins, such as cytochrome c, are also 99 percent similar.

Despite our close phylogenetic relationship with chimpanzees, for a long time we knew very little about these primates. Until the 1960s, chimpanzees, which live in the steep mountain forests of Africa, had rarely been scientifically observed in the wild.

In 1960 a young British woman named Jane Goodall moved to East Africa to study wild chimpanzees at the Gombe Stream Reserve in Tanzania. Each day she would hike up the mountains in hopes of observing the chimpanzees. Some days the chimpanzees eluded her completely, and she returned to her camp without having made a single observation. In those early years, even when Goodall was able to sight chimpanzees, they usually ran

More Information

The Spermaceti Organ The blunt front of a sperm whale's head, seen in the photo on p. 602, contains not the brain but the unusual spermaceti *organ.* This huge organ, containing fine oil prized by whalers, contributes to the whale's buoyancy. The whale can alter the oil's density by changing the temperature. It does this by regulating blood flow through the organ's complex network of blood vessels. This adaptation allows the whale to achieve neutral buoyancy at great depth, a feature that conserves energy.

Some scientists suspect that the spermaceti organ may also be used to focus powerful sound waves for long-distance communication or for stunning prey.

Primates

In Chapter 17 you studied characteristics of the Order Primates. The 200 species of living primates are classified as prosimians *(proe-SIM-ee-unz),* including lemurs, tarsiers, and lorises; or anthropoids, including monkeys, apes, and humans. Most primates are omnivores and have teeth specialized for a varied diet. In anthropoids the ratio of brain size to body size is especially large. A complex brain has enabled anthropoids to develop complex behaviors and to live in highly organized social groups.

Section Review

1. What is a *placenta?*
2. List any five orders of placental mammals, and name a representative from each order.
3. What are some dietary adaptations of whales?
4. Distinguish between artiodactyls and perissodactyls.
5. Unlike most mammals of their size, bats usually give birth to only one young at a time. How might small litter size be an adaptive trait in these flying mammals?

away from her or made threatening gestures if she attempted to get close to them.

Despite frustration and hardship Goodall persisted with her work. In time the chimpanzees allowed her to view them from a distance. However, four years passed before the chimpanzees allowed her to make abundant, close-range observations.

For about 30 years Goodall has observed the chimpanzees of Gombe. She has learned that chimpanzees are highly intelligent and intensely social animals. Like humans, each chimpanzee has a distinct personality. Chimpanzees communicate through gestures, postures, facial expressions, and vocalizations.

Although they mainly eat fruit, chimpanzees sometimes hunt for small animals, such as infant baboons, in an organized, cooperative way. They also make and use simple tools, stripping twigs, which they insert into termite nests. They pull out the insect-covered twig and eat the insects.

With these and other observations, Goodall has given us a clearer picture of the life of the chimpanzees. By communicating about her research, she has inspired others to make detailed studies of chimpanzees and other apes in their natural habitats. These studies are helping us gain a better understanding of primates, how they live and how they might have evolved.

▪ What scientific processes are involved in Jane Goodall's research of wild chimpanzees? Explain.

Answers to Section Review

1. A membrane that transfers oxygen and nutrients from the mother's blood to the blood of the unborn mammal
2. Answers will vary. Accept any five of the orders discussed in Section 40.3 and any representative mammal correctly identified.
3. Toothed whales have teeth that allow them to prey on fishes, squid, seals, and other whales. Baleen whales have thin plates of fingernaillike material that strain invertebrates and small fishes from water.
4. Artiodactyls have an even number of toes and a rumen. Perissodactyls have an odd number of toes and a cecum.
5. Small litters are easier to manage when flying.

Biology in Process

Using the Feature

This feature illustrates the importance of observation in scientific research. Through careful and persistent observation, scientist Jane Goodall has learned much about wild chimpanzees, our closest living animal relative.

One benefit of such long-term observations as Goodall's is that slowly developing patterns can emerge. In recent years the Tanzanian chimpanzees have displayed behavior analogous to murder, cannibalism, and war in human societies. One female and her offspring developed the habit of stealing, killing, and eating infants of other females.

In 1973 Goodall discovered that the chimpanzees had split into two separate communities, one in the north of the study area and one in the south. Bands of males from one community were observed invading the other community's territory, attacking and sometimes killing adult chimpanzees.

Point out that observations like Goodall's contribute to the pool of knowledge from which all other scientists devise hypotheses. Ask students whether they think that studying chimpanzee society can tell us anything about human behavior. *(As our closest relatives, chimpanzees may shed light on some human behavioral traits, including violence.)*

Have students read more about Goodall's research on chimpanzees, Dian Fossey's work with mountain gorillas, or Birute Galdika's work with orangutans.

Answer to the Feature

Goodall made long-term observations of wild chimpanzees, carefully recorded data on the chimpanzee population, and communicated with other scientists about her research.

Background

The scene described in the excerpt occurred during Fossey's first trip to Africa, before she had been sponsored by Louis Leakey for her long-term gorilla observations. Even at this early date, the enthusiasm and keen observational ability that would contribute to Fossey's valuable studies were already evident.

Discussion

After students have read the excerpt from *Gorillas in the Mist,* ask them to discuss the following questions.

1. A good observer must use more than just his or her sense of sight. What other senses does Fossey use? How might she use the rest of her senses in her work? *(She describes the smell of gorillas and sounds they make. She could also taste the foods that gorillas eat and feel gorillas' hair.)*

2. Many behavioral patterns that Fossey describes seem very human. What is the danger of making too much of this similarity? *(The similarities may be a coincidence. By attributing human motivation to animals, for example, a researcher may distort his or her observations. An animal must be observed on its own terms.)*

3. Gorillas in this excerpt seem disturbed by the presence of humans. What do you think about human intrusions into the lives of wild animals, even to study their behavior? *(Some students may feel that wild animals should be left in peace, while other students may feel that the benefits of studying animals outweigh the drawbacks.)*

Extension

Have students read about other behavioral studies that have been done on elephants, whales, lions, or wolves. Have students report their findings, including why such studies are important.

Writing About Biology

Gorillas in the Mist

The following account comes from Gorillas in the Mist *by Dian Fossey.*

On my first visit to Kabara in 1963 I was fortunate in meeting Joan and Alan Root, photographers from Kenya who were camped at the meadow while working on a photographic documentary of the mountain gorillas. Both Joan and Alan kindly overlooked the intrusion of a somewhat hobbly and inquisitive American tourist into their secluded mountain workshop and allowed me to accompany them on some of their extraordinary contacts with the . . . gorillas of Kabara. It was only because of their generosity, coupled with the skill of Sanwekwe, a Congolese park guard and tracker, that I was able to contact and photograph the animals during that brief visit. . . .

I shall never forget my first encounter with gorillas. Sound preceded sight. Odor preceded sound in the form of an overwhelming musky-barnyard, humanlike scent. The air was suddenly rent by a high-pitched series of screams followed by the rhythmic rondo of sharp *pok-pok* chestbeats from a great silverback male obscured behind what seemed an impenetrable wall of vegetation. Joan and Alan Root, some ten yards ahead on the forest trail, motioned me to remain still. The three of us froze until the echoes of the screams and chestbeats faded. Only then did we slowly creep forward under the cover of dense shrubbery to about fifty feet from the group. Peeking through the vegetation, we could distinguish an equally curious phalanx of black, leather-countenanced, furry-headed primates peering back at us. Their bright eyes darted nervously from under heavy brows as though trying to identify us as familiar friends or possible foes. Immediately I was struck by the physical magnificence of the huge jet-black bodies blended against the green palette wash of the thick forest foliage.

Most of the females had fled with their infants to the rear of the group, leaving the silverback leader and some younger males in the foreground, standing tense with compressed lips. Occasionally the dominant male would rise to chestbeat in an attempt to intimidate us. The sound reverberated throughout the forest and evoked similar displays, though of lesser magnitude, from gorillas clustered around him. Slowly, Alan set up his movie camera and proceeded to film. The openness of his motions and the sound of the camera piqued curiosity from other group members, who then tried to see us more clearly. As if competing for attention, some animals went through a series of actions that included yawning, symbolic-feeding, branch-breaking, or chestbeating. After each display, the gorillas would look at us quizzically as if trying to determine the effect of their show. It was their individuality combined with the shyness of their behavior that remained the most captivating impression of this first encounter with the greatest of the great apes. I left Kabara with reluctance but with never a doubt that I would, somehow, return to learn more about the gorillas of the misted mountains.

Write

- **Write an informative essay based on Dian Fossey's observations of gorilla behavior.**

From Gorillas in the Mist *by Dian Fossey. Copyright © 1983 by Dian Fossey. Reprinted by permission of Houghton Mifflin Company.*

About the Author

Dian Fossey was an occupational therapist when she traveled to Africa and first saw wild gorillas. There she met renowned scientist Louis Leakey, who sponsored her two decades of research observing mountain gorillas in the country of Rwanda.

Increasingly horrified by the killing of "her" gorillas by poachers, Fossey waged a vigorous campaign against poaching, even capturing and holding suspects. Her crusade and methods alienated some of her colleagues.

On December 27, 1985, Dian Fossey was brutally murdered in her camp. An American colleague, who escaped to the United States, was convicted for her murder, but suspicion has also been cast on poachers and on Rwandan government agents.

Laboratory

Mammalian Characteristics

Objective
To examine characteristics of mammals

Process Skills
Observing, inferring, hypothesizing

Materials
Photographs of male and female fetal pigs, hand lens, microscope slide of mammalian skin, compound microscope, mirror, selection of vertebrate skulls or skeletons

Background
1 What are the characteristics of mammals, and how did they get that name?
2 What is endothermy?

Inquiry
1 Observe pictures of male and female fetal pigs. Are mammary glands present in both? Can you differentiate between the sexes of the pigs on the basis of mammary glands?
2 Use a hand lens to examine several areas of your skin that appear to be hairless. Are these areas actually hairless?
3 Compare the amount of hair on humans to that on the polar bear in the photograph. What role does hair or fur play in enabling mammals to be endotherms?
4 Examine a slide of mammalian skin under low power. Notice the sweat glands. What do you think is their function?
5 Although sweat glands are found only in mammals, some mammals, such as dogs, do not have them. What mechanism for cooling off do dogs have?
6 Using a mirror to look in your mouth, identify the four kinds of mammalian teeth. Count how many of each you have on one side of your lower jaw.
7 Look at the skulls of several mammals. Identify the four kinds of teeth in each skull, and count them as you counted your own. How and why are the four types of teeth different from yours?
8 Look at the skulls of several nonmammalian vertebrates. Describe the teeth in each one and compare them to mammalian teeth.
9 Breathe with your mouth closed. Do you feel a flow of air into your mouth? You have a hard palate (the roof of your mouth), which separates the mouth from the nose.
10 Look again at the different skulls. In which vertebrates do you see a hard palate? What is an advantage of having a hard palate?

Conclusions
1 Name five characteristics you observed that distinguish mammals from other vertebrates.
2 Birds are also endotherms. What structure in birds serves the same role played by the hair of mammals? Explain.

Further Inquiry
Examine the brain cases of the mammalian and nonmammalian skulls and see if you can find a consistent difference in size between mammalian and nonmammalian brains.

Laboratory

(For an overview of mammals and preparatory information related to the laboratory, see p. 601B.)

Background
1. Mammals have fur or hair and mammary glands and bear their young alive. The word *mammal* is derived from *mammary.*
2. Endothermy is the ability to maintain a constant body temperature.

Inquiry
1. Mammary glands are present in male and female fetal pigs. The sexes of mammalian fetuses cannot be differentiated on the basis of mammary glands.
2. No. They have fine hairs.
3. Human hair is shorter, thinner in diameter, and there are fewer hairs. Hair and fur are insulators that hold in body heat produced in cells.
4. Sweat glands help mammals cool off.
5. Dogs pant to lose heat.
6. 2 incisors for biting and cutting; 1 canine for tearing; 2 bicuspids for shearing and shredding; and 3 molars for grinding and crushing. Notice that some students may have only 2 molars, since the third molars ("wisdom teeth") sometimes do not erupt until the late teens, if ever.
7. Students should relate distribution and relative size of teeth to each animal's diet and means of obtaining food.
8. Birds have no teeth. Most other vertebrates do not have highly specialized, differentiated teeth as mammals do.
9. No
10. Only in mammals. One advantage is the ability to chew food while breathing. This means that mammals don't have to swallow food whole and that air can be safely warmed in the nasal passages on its way to the lungs.

Conclusions
1. Presence of fur or hair, mammary glands, sweat glands, specialized teeth, and a hard palate
2. Birds have feathers that insulate their bodies.

Further Inquiry
Examination of pictures of brains of all classes of vertebrates shows students that mammals have the largest cerebrums relative to total cranial size. Even though reptiles and amphibians may have large skulls, the part that holds the brain is very small. Suggest that students explore other characteristics of mammals, such as the presence of large brains with convoluted cerebrums.

Chapter 40 Review

Vocabulary

1. Incisors are for biting and cutting; canines are pointed teeth for gripping, puncturing, and tearing; bicuspids are teeth with two points for shredding and tearing; molars have flattened surfaces for grinding.
2. The rumen is an extra chamber in the stomach; the cecum is a blind sac at the end of the small intestine. Both harbor bacteria that aid in digestion of plant material.
3. The echo of sound waves helps the animal locate and identify objects.
4. Oviparous mammals (monotremes) lay eggs, which hatch outside the body; viviparous mammals bear live young.
5. *Omni-* means "all"; *-vore* comes from the Latin word for "devour"; an omnivore eats both plant and animal material.

Review

1. c	**6.** b
2. b	**7.** c
3. a	**8.** c
4. d	**9.** a
5. d	**10.** b

11. Adaptations for endothermy are body hair, diaphragm, and four-chambered heart.
12. Specialized teeth have enabled mammals to take advantage of diverse food sources available in a wide range of environments.
13. Most mammals are viviparous and all mammals nourish their young with milk from mammary glands.
14. Because of adaptive radiation that occurred after extinction of the dinosaurs
15. All mammals have hair and produce milk to feed their young.
16. They both lay eggs, are not fully endothermic, and have a cloaca into which pass all material from the large intestine, urinary bladder, and reproductive organs.
17. When Australia broke off from the other continents, it had no placental mammals, allowing marsupials to undergo adaptive radiation. Elsewhere, marsupials could not compete with placental mammals.
18. All placental mammals carry their unborn in the uterus. Young are born live and are able to survive outside the mother's body.
19. Chimpanzee communication, eating habits, methods of hunting, and tool use
20. Lagomorphs have a double row of upper incisors, while rodents have only two incisors in each jaw.

Chapter 40 Review

Vocabulary

baleen (610)
bicuspid (604)
canine (604)
cecum (612)
diaphragm (604)
echolocation (610)
gestation period (608)
incisor (604)
mammary gland (604)
molar (604)
omnivore (611)
placenta (608)
rumen (611)
therapsid (603)
ungulate (611)
viviparous (604)

1. List and describe the four types of teeth.
2. Contrast the rumen of the artiodactyl with the cecum of the perissodactyl.
3. Why is echolocation a good name for the type of behavior it describes?
4. Contrast the reproductive behavior of oviparous and viviparous mammals.
5. Find the meaning of the word parts that compose the word *omnivore.* Explain why omnivores are appropriately named.

Review

1. Scientific evidence indicates that therapsids had characteristics of both mammals and (a) amphibians (b) birds (c) reptiles (d) vertebrates.
2. Evidence that early mammals were active at night includes the fossil mammal's (a) single jawbone (b) large eye sockets (c) four-chambered heart (d) mammary glands.
3. After the dinosaurs became extinct, mammal species flourished because (a) many new habitats were suddenly available to them (b) the climate became warmer and wetter (c) the reptiles had undergone adaptive radiation (d) the reptiles had become endothermic.
4. The diaphragm allows mammals to (a) carry the young inside the uterus (b) pump blood efficiently (c) provide nourishment for their young (d) breathe efficiently.
5. Two types of monotremes include the echidna and (a) the edentate (b) the opossum (c) the manatee (d) the duck-billed platypus.
6. Marsupials differ from monotremes in that marsupials (a) lay eggs (b) carry developing young in a pouch (c) nourish unborn young via the placenta (d) nourish their newborns with milk from nippleless glands.
7. Most mammals are (a) monotremes (b) marsupials (c) placentals (d) lagomorphs.
8. The Order Chiroptera is made up of (a) toothless mammals (b) marine mammals (c) flying mammals (d) arboreal mammals.
9. Most members of the Order Carnivora eat (a) meat (b) plants (c) fruits and nuts (c) insects.
10. Artiodactyls and perissodactyls are both (a) carnivores (b) herbivores (c) omnivores (d) insectivores.
11. What are some mammalian adaptations for endothermy?
12. How has the trait of specialized teeth allowed mammals to adapt to a wide range of environments?
13. In what ways do mammals reproduce and raise their young differently from reptiles?
14. Why is the Cenozoic era called the "Age of Mammals"?
15. Name two characteristics common to all mammals.
16. In what ways do monotremes resemble reptiles?
17. Why are marsupials the dominant mammals in Australia and placentals the dominant mammals elsewhere?
18. What features distinguish placental mammals from other types of mammals?

19. What are some behaviors Jane Goodall has observed in her study of the chimpanzees of Gombe Stream Reserve?

20. How do the teeth of rodents differ from those of lagomorphs?

Critical Thinking

1. Some mammal species must care for their young for many years until the young reach maturity and can survive on their own. Section 40.1 indicates how this pattern of rearing young has advantages over the pattern by which reptiles rear their young. List some ways the mammalian pattern might be disadvantageous, compared with the reptilian pattern.
2. Kangaroos are grazing animals that feed on the grasses covering the plains of Australia. Notice that kangaroos live in a similar environment and feed on the same type of plants as deer do. What morphological and behavioral similarities might you expect to find between kangaroos and deer? Consider adaptations for diet, locomotion, and defense.
3. The gestation period of mice is relatively brief, about 21 days. Why might this short gestation period make mice an ideal laboratory animal for experiments dealing with mammalian development and heredity?
4. Sloths are arboreal edentates that spend most of their lives hanging upside down from tree branches in the tropical forests of Central and South America. Most sloths have green algae growing in tiny pits in their hair. What advantage might algae growth in the hair confer to the sloth? What advantage might the green algae gain by colonizing the sloth's fur?

5. The photograph above shows an aardvark, the single species in the mammalian Order Tubulidentata. Like many edentates, aardvarks feed on nesting insects such as termites. Study the picture, and review the characteristics of insectivorous edentates. In what ways do aardvarks and edentates illustrate convergent evolution?

Extension

1. Choose an undomesticated mammal species, and write a report on its classification; habitat; morphology; life cycle; and adaptations for feeding, defense, and reproduction. Discuss its evolution if information is available. You may wish to visit a zoo to observe the mammal. If possible include labeled drawings or photographs of the mammal to illustrate your report.
2. Read the article entitled "Bat Moms" in *Discover*, May 1990, p. 14. Give an oral report in which you explain why the behavior described in the article is a good example of altruism in mammals.
3. Obtain a live mammal, such as a mouse, hamster, or gerbil, from a pet store or your school. Get instructions on the care and feeding of the mammal. Then observe the mammal for several weeks or more if possible. Take notes on its feeding, sleeping, and breeding behavior. Share what you learn with your class.

Critical Thinking

1. Answers will vary, but students should mention one or more of the following disadvantages: adults must protect young; they must gather food for young; the reproductive rate is lower. Accept other answers that students can reasonably justify.
2. Accept any of the following as reasonable expectations: kangaroos may have an extra stomach chamber or a blind sac to aid in digestion; they may have large, flat molars for grinding plant material; they may use speed as defense against predators. Accept any other logical answer.
3. Because mice have such a short gestation period, they can reproduce rapidly; scientists can then study many generations of mice in a short time.
4. Algae help camouflage the sloth as it hangs upside down in a tree; the sloth helps expose the algae to sunlight and protects it from algae-eating animals.
5. Both have a long snout, sticky tongue, and strong claws for breaking into insect nests.

Extension

1. Encourage students to choose a mammal they find personally interesting, as Dian Fossey found gorillas.
2. Students should note examples of a bat's "generosity" from which it has nothing to gain.
3. Emphasize that observations should be as objective as possible: "Animal ate carrot," for example, instead of "Animal seemed to like carrot."

Chapter 41 Evolutionary Trends in Vertebrates

Chapter Overview

Chapter 41 completes the discussion of vertebrates with a survey of vertebrate evolutionary trends. Section 41.1 examines the origins and phylogenetic relationships of vertebrates. Section 41.2 reviews the evolutionary trends in vertebrate embryologic development and in the major organ systems. Section 41.3 briefly presents trends in vertebrate behavior, both individual and social.

Chapter Planning Chart

B	S	A	Sections and Subsections	Page	Features	Page	Resources
		•	**41.1 Origin and Phylogeny**				
			Origin	619	Section Review	620	Videodiscs
			Phylogeny	620			Blackline Master 84
							Overhead Transparency T41
							Section Reviews Worksheet
		•	**41.2 Development and Morphology**				
			Development	621	Laboratory	629	Videodiscs
			Skeletal and Muscular Systems	622	Section Review	626	Blackline Master 85
			Integumentary Systems	623			Process Skills: Vertebrate Limbs
			Circulatory Systems	623			Laboratories: Vertebrate Skeletons
			Respiratory Systems	624			Section Reviews Worksheet
			Digestive Systems	624			
			Excretory Systems	624			
			Nervous Systems	625			
			Reproductive Systems	626			
		•	**41.3 Behavior**				
			Individual Behavior	627	Section Review	628	Videodiscs
			Social Behavior	627			Section Reviews Worksheet
			End of Chapter Activities				
					Chapter Review	630	Vocabulary Skills
							Chapter Test
							Computer Test Generator

B *The Basic Level curriculum presents the most fundamental knowledge offered in the course.*
S *The Standard Level curriculum is designed for the average student who is able to master most topics.*
A *The Advanced Level curriculum includes suggestions for teaching the most academically able students.*

Cooperative Learning

Group Activity: Body Plan Debate

- **Group Size:** *Half the class*
- **Outcome:** *Students will evaluate basic assumptions concerning degree of evolutionary advancement.*
- **Individual Accountability:** *Each student will research and contribute to the predebate brainstorming.*
- **Positive Interdependence:** *The group will decide on a final debate strategy.*

Divide the class in half. Assign each group to research and argue either for or against the statement "Simpler body plans are more 'primitive' than more complex body plans." Suggest that each student research and write notes on the statement. Have them define such terms as *primitive, simple,* and *complex*. After individual research, have each group meet for a brainstorming session at which each student contributes information and insights to developing a group debate strategy. Monitor each group's discussion and ask students questions to check their contribution.

Have each group elect three representatives to speak for the group. Hold a formal debate in class during which the three representatives from each side present rational, analytical arguments and rebuttals. Choose a panel of judges consisting of teachers or others, preferably those with little or no knowledge or expertise in the field of evolutionary biology. Ask the panel to choose the winning team based on thoroughness of analysis in preparation and persuasiveness of argument.

Concept Map

The following is one possible solution to the concept mapping activity in Independent Practice on p. 628.

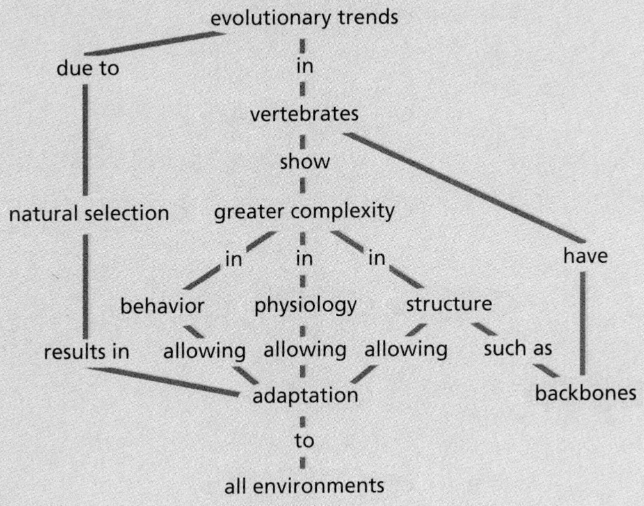

Laboratory Preparation

Overview *(See p. 629.)*

In this lab, students observe vertebrates' adaptations for locomotion in various environments. Students read that the fish moves forward when the body and tail push against the water, generating a propulsive force. The direction in which this force propels the fish is partially determined by its shape. Students will make similar observations of other vertebrates.

Preparation

Suggested vertebrates for this investigation are a goldfish, a newt, an anole, and a garter snake. Many other examples of vertebrates will also be acceptable. If a goldfish is studied, use an ordinary one rather than a complex goldfish with a veil-tail, which cannot use ordinary fish locomotion. Use a covered terrarium to observe the anole (or any other animal likely to escape).

Teaching Tips

Remind students to use objective, behavior-centered language when recording their observations. For instance, ". . . seemed frantic to get out of terrarium" is less specific for the reader than ". . . scratched at the side of terrarium rapidly with front claws for 45 seconds."

Encourage students to use sketches as well as words to record their observations.

Make sure that all students are able to observe both aquarium and terrarium from all angles, including from above. Suggest that students observe animals from as many angles as possible. This will be important in answering Conclusions question 2.

Depending on time constraints, have students take as much time as possible for their observations. Often, animals will not "perform" immediately.

Safety

Remind students to handle animals in a safe and humane manner. If an animal other than those suggested is used, first ensure that there is little likelihood of its biting or injuring students in other ways. Be prepared with antiseptic and bandages, just in case.

Remind students to wash their hands after handling any animal.

Chapter Themes

Evolution From their origins, probably among the cephalochordates, vertebrates include five classes that display various adaptations. Despite their differences, all classes share basic vertebrate characteristics.

Patterns of Change Starting from a fertilized egg, all vertebrates pass through developmental changes while growing to maturity. Emphasize that although all vertebrate classes share aspects of development, different patterns are typical of each class.

Scale and Structure Tell students that vertebrate systems of each class possess structures that are adaptive to a specific way of life. For example, the strong skeletal systems of land mammals withstand gravity well, while birds' hollow bones are advantageous in flight.

Chapter Motivating Activity

To get students to question their assumptions about evolution, use the following nonbiological analogy. Show pictures of a jet and a commuter train. Ask students to consider the issue of evolutionary "improvement" by thinking of these vehicles. *(For example, the jet can transport people quickly over long distances; the train is much slower.)* Point out that jets are a later invention than trains and make use of a much more advanced technology. In this sense, the train is more primitive. Now ask under what circumstances the train is better adapted than the jet. *(For commutes by rail in crowded urban areas)* Tell students that *primitive* does not mean "less adapted." In this chapter the words *primitive* and *modern* describe an animal's place on the phylogenetic tree.

Chapter 41 Evolutionary Trends in Vertebrates

Introduction

Since the evolution of the first vertebrate species, vertebrates have become adapted to nearly every habitat on earth. In the previous five chapters you studied adaptations that characterize the five classes of vertebrates. In this chapter you will study evolutionary trends in vertebrates.

Chapter Outline

Chapter Concept

As you read, look for adaptations of terrestrial vertebrates to their environments.

Hamadryas baboons, *Papio hamadryas*, Africa. Inset: Fossil fish of the genus *Diplomystus*, Wyoming.

Understanding the Visuals

Ask students to suggest characteristics that the fish and the baboons have in common. *(For example, an endoskeleton with a spinal column and bilateral symmetry)* Then ask students what evidence of social behavior they see in the baboon photo. *(Grooming, young clustered together near adults)*

41.1 Origin and Phylogeny

Life on earth began long before the first vertebrates evolved. Fossil evidence indicates that the first prokaryotic cell appeared more than 3.5 billion years ago; the first eukaryotic cell, 2 billion years later; the first primitive vertebrate, another billion years later. Vertebrates have since evolved into a diverse group that consists of the five classes you read about in Chapters 36–40.

Section Objectives

- *Summarize the probable origin of vertebrates.*
- *Describe the major trends in vertebrate evolution.*
- *Explain why adaptations that are simplifications do not necessarily indicate that an organism is phylogenetically more primitive.*

Origin

Where did vertebrates come from? You know from Chapter 36 that vertebrates are a subphylum of the Phylum Chordata and that both chordates and echinoderms are deuterostomes. Deuterostomes are organisms in which, among other things, the embryo divides by radial cleavage. Because chordates and echinoderms share developmental characteristics, scientists infer that they evolved from a common ancestor. Figure 41-1 shows a possible evolutionary pathway leading to vertebrates. Many biologists cite the structural similarities between the organisms shown as evidence that chordates and echinoderms evolved from an echinodermlike organism.

The adult form of lancelets is morphologically similar to the larval form of tunicates. From this similarity scientists infer that the primitive cephalochordates evolved from a larval form of a tunicatelike organism. Scientists also infer that the first vertebrates evolved from primitive cephalochordates. The early vertebrates, however, were distinguished by a backbone.

Figure 41-1 This is one of several possible pathways of vertebrate evolution.

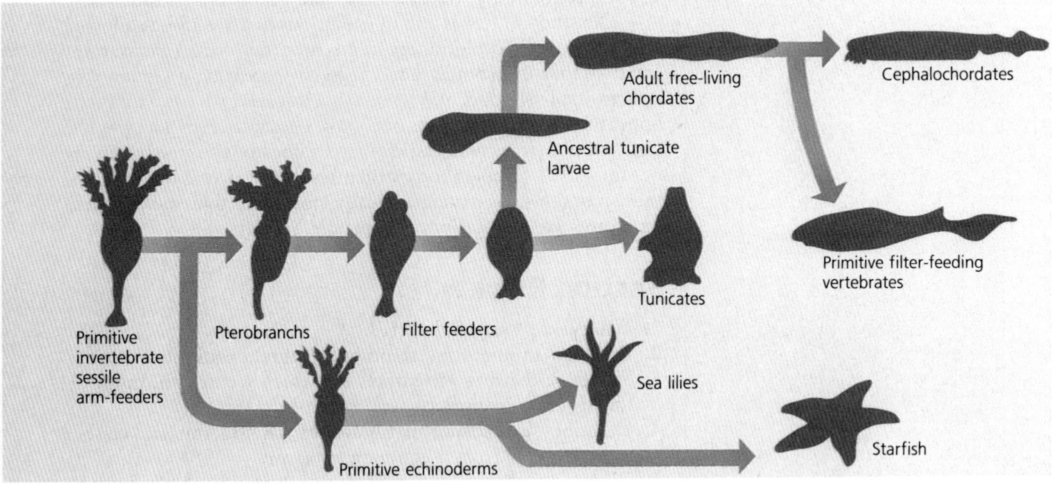

Section 41.1

Lesson Plan

Section Focus

This section presents developmental, morphological, and fossil evidence that scientists use to trace the evolution of vertebrates from their origins among the cephalochordates.

Section Themes

This section emphasizes the theme of **Evolution.** Vertebrates arose and evolved over time in response to pressures and opportunities in their environments. They also became more complex in structure.

Motivating Activity

Bring to class pictures of fossils, or actual fossils if available, of fish, reptiles, and other animals. Challenge students to pick out any organs, organ systems, or other features or characteristics such as symmetry and cephalization that they studied in the previous five chapters. Point out that paleontologists learn about evolution by looking at fossils in just this way and then by comparing changes in them over geologic time.

Teaching Strategies

Interpreting the Visuals Have students write in short paragraphs the evidence scientists use to place each animal on the hypothetical phylogenetic tree in Figure 41-1 on p. 619. *(For example, morphological features that appear to link one species to another)*

- *See* Overhead Transparency *T41 and* Blackline Master *84.*

Videodiscs

- ***2590–2593, Classification System; Evolutionary Relationships (s)***

primitive deuterostomes → tunicates → cephalochordates → vertebrates

Graphic Organizer Use this sequential diagram in Reteaching on p. 620.

Guided Practice
Have students suggest ways that some vertebrates living today are similar to their early ancestors. *(Agnathans are jawless like ostracoderms; insectivores have teeth and a diet similar to early mammals, and so forth.)*

Independent Practice
- Have students write answers to the Section Review.
- Have students use the preceding five chapters to find examples of evolution accompanied by increased complexity in a particular system. *(Amphibian skeleton includes limbs, specialized vertebrae.)*

Check Your Understanding
1. What is the significance for scientists that larval tunicates are similar in form to adult lancelets? *(It indicates that lancelets may have evolved from a tunicate-like larva.)*
2. How has fossil evidence contributed to the reconstruction of vertebrate evolution? *(By providing a link, the ostracoderm, which was a jawless, fishlike vertebrate)*

Reteaching
Have students make a sequential diagram showing the chronological stages in the evolution of primitive vertebrates from a deuterostome ancestor. An example of a completed diagram is shown on p. 619.
- *See* Section Reviews *worksheet, Section 41.1.*

Enrichment
Have students use library resources to write short reports about the early fossil evidence of one vertebrate class, such as the organisms shown in Figure 41-2.

Closure
Have students speculate on future evolutionary trends in vertebrates, giving reasons for their ideas. *(Accept any well-reasoned suggestion.)*

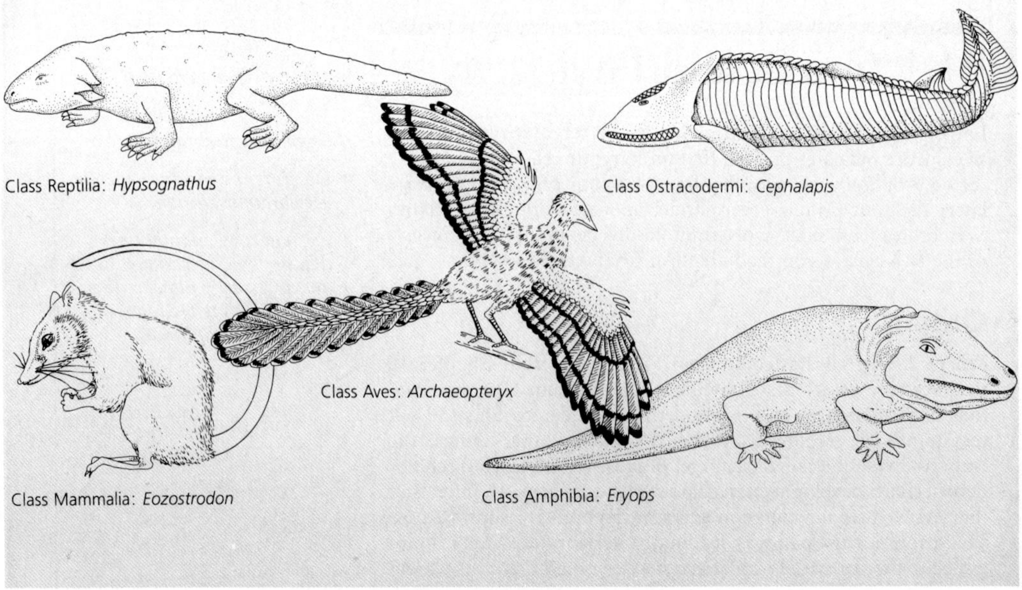

Figure 41-2 Each of these five organisms is the first representative of its class found in the fossil record.

Phylogeny

Using evidence from fossils and comparative anatomy, scientists have reconstructed possible pathways of vertebrate evolution. The first vertebrates were probably filter-feeding organisms. The first vertebrates for which we have indisputable fossil evidence are the ostracoderms, jawless organisms resembling fishes that arose about 540 million years ago in the late Cambrian period.

The study of fossils and of evolutionary patterns has allowed scientists to infer evolutionary trends in vertebrates. An important trend is that vertebrates have become increasingly complex in structure, physiology, and behavior. However, some adaptations appear to be simplifications of complex systems. For example, the limbs of snakes became vestigial, and some bones of the bird wing became fused. Simpler body structures do not necessarily indicate that an organism is phylogenetically more primitive. Rather, these structures are adaptations for specific habitats.

Section Review

1. What is a *phylogenetic tree?*
2. Describe an important trend in vertebrate evolution.
3. What are the first vertebrates for which we have indisputable fossil evidence?
4. Describe the evidence that indicates echinoderms and chordates evolved from a common ancestor.
5. What do you think is the adaptive advantage of fused wing bones in birds?

Answers to Section Review
1. A graphic model of evolutionary history
2. Vertebrates have become increasingly complex in structure, physiology, and behavior.
3. The ostracoderms, jawless organisms that arose in the late Cambrian period
4. Both are deuterostomes and share developmental characteristics. Some larval echinoderms and adult chordates are similar in structure.
5. The fused bones of birds provide a light and rigid structure for flight.

41.2 Development and Morphology

As they have evolved, vertebrates have become more complex in their structure and physiology. As you read about vertebrate adaptations, look for those that are responses to the selective pressures of a terrestrial environment. Also refer to the discussion of structures in the chapters on the five classes.

Section Objectives

- *Describe the major adaptations in embryo development that help vertebrates to live on land.*
- *Explain the way in which adaptations in the skeletal, integumentary, circulatory, and excretory systems made vertebrates better suited to live on land.*
- *List some adaptations in vertebrate reproduction that help ensure the survival of the young.*

Development

The main evolutionary trend in embryo development is an increase in adaptations to the terrestrial environment. For example, the eggs of fishes and amphibians must develop in water, since they dry out quickly when exposed to air. The eggs of reptiles and birds have four embryonic membranes and a leathery or hard shell that enable the embryos to develop on land. Most mammals do not have shells around their eggs. Instead the mammal embryo is protected inside the mother's body until birth.

Figure 41-3 shows the developing embryos of a frog, a bird, and a mammal. In frogs the entire embryo divides repeatedly to give rise to a hollow blastula. The gastrula stage is characterized by more rapid cell divisions at one pole of the embryo than at the other. In birds the early divisions are restricted to one side of the blastula. The cavity in the blastula, or blastocoel, is smaller; and the embryo develops from a much smaller segment of the gastrula. In mammals the embryo develops from a much smaller mass of cells than it does in frogs or birds. The bird embryo tends to have a

Figure 41-3 Compare the development of these three vertebrate embryos. What are the major differences?

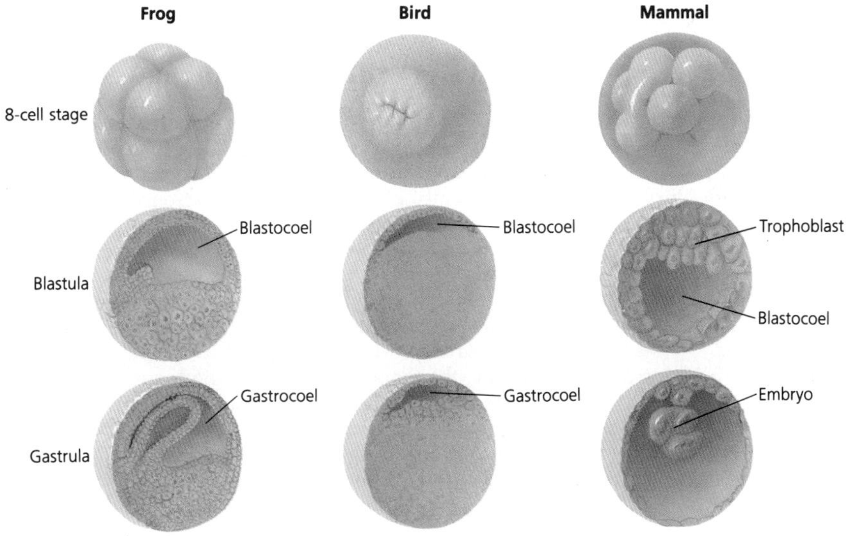

Lesson Plan

Section Focus

This section discusses the major evolutionary trends in vertebrate development and in the skeletal, muscular, integumentary, circulatory, respiratory, digestive, excretory, nervous, and reproductive systems.

Section Themes

This section emphasizes three themes: **Evolution, Patterns of Change,** and **Scale and Structure.** Throughout vertebrate evolution, each system has tended to increase in complexity. Changes that take place from the moment of fertilization through development have also evolved. As animals became more complex, an increasing amount of development took place in the fetus. Each structural change, such as hollow bones in birds, has resulted in systems that are well adapted to the new way of life encountered by the vertebrate class.

Motivating Activity

Provide students with specimens of a fish and a terrestrial mammal. (A goldfish and a hamster are good choices.) If live animals are not available, provide pictures of any fish and any terrestrial mammal from nature books or magazines. Ask students to suggest how each is adapted to living either in water or on land. Ask what characteristics would have to change in order for the fish to live on land. Ask what characteristics would have to change in order for the mammal to live in water. Remind students that cetaceans—whales and dolphins—have readapted to life in water. Ask in what ways dolphins are unlike fishes. *(Lungs, viviparity, endothermy)*

Videodiscs

- ***Side 2 38275, Cleavage in the Fertilized Mouse Egg (m)***

	Fishes	Amphibians	Reptiles	Birds	Mammals
Circ.	2-chambered heart	3-chambered heart	3- or 4-chambered heart	4-chambered heart	4-chambered heart
Integ.	scales	smooth skin	scales and plates	feathers	hair
Resp.	gills	gills, lungs, skin	lungs	lungs, air sacs	lungs

Graphic Organizer Use this table in Cooperative Learning on p. 622.

Teaching Strategies

Making Models Have students use balls of clay, straws, and styrofoam balls to make models of the limb positions of amphibians and mammals. *(The styrofoam ball represents the animal's body, the straws represent the long bones of the limbs, and the clay balls represent the joints and feet.)* Have students experiment with their models, gradually increasing weight on the body to compare the strength and stability of each arrangement. Have students write short reports describing their findings. *(Ideally, the mammalian arrangement, as in Figure 41-4, should be stronger and more stable.)*
■ *See* **Process Skills,** ***Chapter 41,*** ***and*** **Laboratories,** ***Investigation 41.***

Interpreting the Visuals Refer students to Figure 41-3 on p. 621. Have students answer the caption question. Stress that answers can be found in the text and also by inspecting the figure carefully. *(For example, in frogs the dividing embryo becomes a hollow blastula; early division of blastula in birds is restricted to one side; mammalian embryos develop from a smaller mass of cells than do embryos in birds and frogs.)*

Drawing Conclusions In her book *Five Kingdoms,* the biologist and taxonomist Lynn Margulis refers to members of the Class Aves as feathered reptiles. Ask students what they think that this formulation implies. *(Margulis implies that birds are much more closely related to reptiles than was commonly thought. Paleontologists such as Robert Bakker hypothesize that birds are direct descendants of warm-blooded dinosaurs. The classification of these animals remains contested.)*

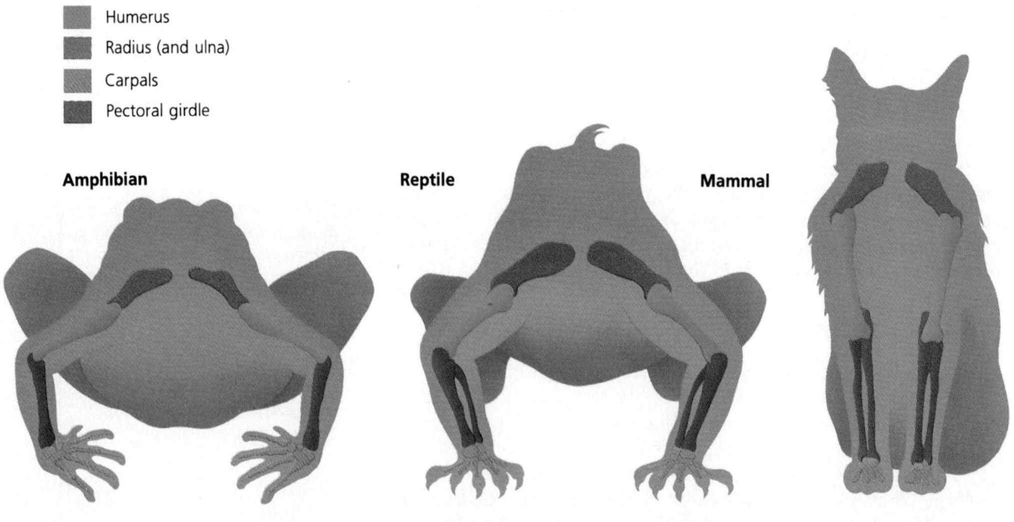

Figure 41-4 Examine the trends in limb position illustrated by these terrestrial vertebrates.

large yolk that provides nourishment. In most mammals, where the embryo is nourished through the placenta, there is no nutritional need for a large yolk.

Another evolutionary trend in vertebrates is the shift from indirect development to direct development. Remember from Chapter 35 that in indirect development the larvae of an organism are different in structure and physiology from the adults. This pattern occurs in the lower chordates and in amphibians. In direct development the young are similar to the adults. This pattern occurs in reptiles, birds, and mammals. This similarity allows the young and the adults to share the same niche and resources—a distinct advantage if those resources are plentiful.

Skeletal and Muscular Systems

As terrestrial vertebrates evolved from aquatic vertebrates, their limbs and associated muscles were modified by natural selection in ways that gave them better support and greater mobility. For example, the limbs of amphibians are positioned away from the body. However, the legs of mammals are positioned directly under their bodies, which allows them to move faster and with a longer stride. Figure 41-4 illustrates this trend. In addition, support and mobility were improved by an increase in the size of the pectoral and pelvic girdles and their accompanying muscles.

Limbs have also become adapted to special environments. For example, the flippers of whales and other marine mammals resemble the fins of fishes. However, an examination of the bone structure of a flipper reveals that it is actually a modification of the mammalian limb. This suggests that marine mammals evolved from land-dwelling mammals that returned to the water.

Cooperative Learning

Evolutionary Trends Have students work in small groups to prepare poster-size tables showing how the skeletal, integumentary, circulatory, respiratory, excretory, nervous, and reproductive systems of each class are adapted to water, land, or both. Along with text, the charts can contain graphics or illustrations. An example of a table completed for three of the systems appears on p. 621.

Integumentary Systems

The major evolutionary trend in vertebrate integumentary systems has been an increased ability of the skin to withstand desiccation. In general, the tough outer coverings of terrestrial vertebrates protect against excessive loss of water from the body, while those of fishes and amphibians are adapted only to moist environments. Integuments also serve other purposes. For example, the scales of a reptile protect it from predators. The smooth skin of an amphibian is a major respiratory organ that allows the exchange of gases. The feathers of birds and the hair of mammals are adaptations that efficiently insulate the body.

Circulatory Systems

As you can see in Figure 41-5, the major evolutionary trend in the vertebrate circulatory system is toward a greater number of chambers in the heart. In general, endotherms such as birds and mammals have higher energy requirements than ectotherms such as fishes and amphibians. As you read in Chapter 37, frogs have only a three-chambered heart. The four-chambered heart of endotherms, however, more efficiently separates oxygenated and deoxygenated blood, thereby helping to provide endotherms with the extra oxygen their high rate of respiration requires.

Figure 41-5 Compare the number and arrangement of chambers in these four representative vertebrate hearts.

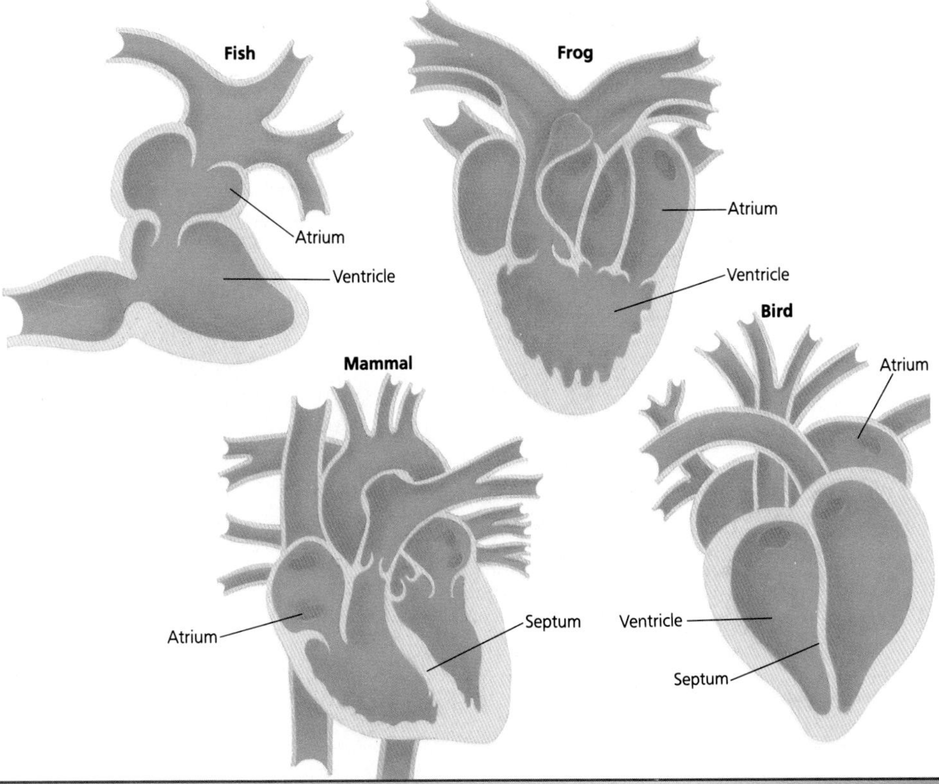

Imagining Features Have students imagine vertebrates that had the integument of other classes. Such animals could include fishes with tortoise shells, elephants with fish scales, or frogs with hair. Ask students to describe the difficulties (or even possible benefits) that such an animal would encounter as a result of its integument. *(For example, the fish would have a hard time swimming.)* Inform students that some vertebrates have evolved integumentary features similar to those of other classes. The "scaly" pangolin, a mammal shown in Chapter 40, p. 609, is such an animal.

Interpreting the Visuals Distribute photocopies of Figure 41-5 on p. 623. Have students color the paths of oxygenated and deoxygenated blood through the figures of the four hearts, using blue pencil to show deoxygenated blood, red pencil for oxygenated blood, and both pencils for mixed blood. Point out that mammal and bird patterns prevent the two bloodstreams from mixing, an efficient method of delivering oxygen in an endotherm; fish and frog patterns are less efficient but also less complex.

- *See* Blackline Master *85.*

Videodiscs

- ***2601–2602, Basic Body Plans (s)***
- ***2607–2609, Circulatory Systems: Fish, Amphibian, Bird, Mammal (s)***

More Information

Taxonomy Prior to Darwin, classification was often accomplished by recourse to preordained plans. For example, in the early 1800s the influential German embryologist Lorenz Oken developed a system of taxonomy based on the number *5*. He chose five because there are five senses, which he ranked by "perfection." All animal forms were placed in categories corresponding to the senses. Thus, he called invertebrates Glossozoa because the tongue was first seen in them; birds were Ophthalmazoa because eyes reached a high level in them. Mammals integrated all senses and were therefore highest of all. From there Oken "deduced" that all nonmammals were simply incomplete mammals.

Comparing Structures Take students on a field trip to a natural history museum. Have them compare skeletal or external structures of one species with those from other species from each of the five vertebrate classes. Species can be either living or extinct. Suggest that students include sketches as well as written observations and insights in their field notebooks. In the classroom, have students write short reports presenting the results of their comparisons. Stress that students should explain how the observed structures are adapted for each animal's habitat. Have students include any features or comparisons that surprised them.

Exploring Careers Have students use library resources or interviews to research one career in which workers deal primarily with animals from only one vertebrate class. *(Dolphin and seal trainer, dog groomer, commercial fisher, snake handler, cattle rancher, ornithologist, poultry processor)* Have students prepare short reports describing the career and knowledge of the particular vertebrate class that each career requires.

Respiratory Systems

The major evolutionary trend in vertebrate respiratory systems is from gills to lungs. The gills of fishes and larval amphibians are efficient in moving water, but would quickly dry out in air. The lungs of amphibians, which also respire through their skin, have far less surface area than those of reptiles. In the larger or more active birds and mammals higher energy demands require a more efficient respiratory system. For example, flying requires a great deal of energy. The air sacs in birds are adaptations that maintain a constant supply of air in the lungs while adding buoyancy.

Digestive Systems

As vertebrates have evolved, the structure of the digestive system has become adapted to many types of environments. The stomach, for example, is modified depending on an organism's diet. In herbivores the digestive system is long and contains storage sacs, called ceca, that hold food while it is digested by bacteria.

Excretory Systems

As vertebrates evolved, the excretory system has become more complex. In most vertebrates two kidneys near the dorsal surface filter wastes from the blood and help regulate the concentration of salts and water in the blood. Figure 41-6 shows modifications in the excretory pathway. Notice that most mammals lack a cloaca. Wastes from their kidneys collect in a urinary bladder and are eliminated through the urethra. In some vertebrates, such as amphibian larvae and fishes, nitrogenous wastes leave the cell as ammonia. Terrestrial vertebrates conserve water when they convert ammonia to the less toxic urea before excretion. They also have kidneys with tubules that reabsorb most of the water that filters from the blood. Birds conserve additional water by eliminating their wastes as uric acid crystals.

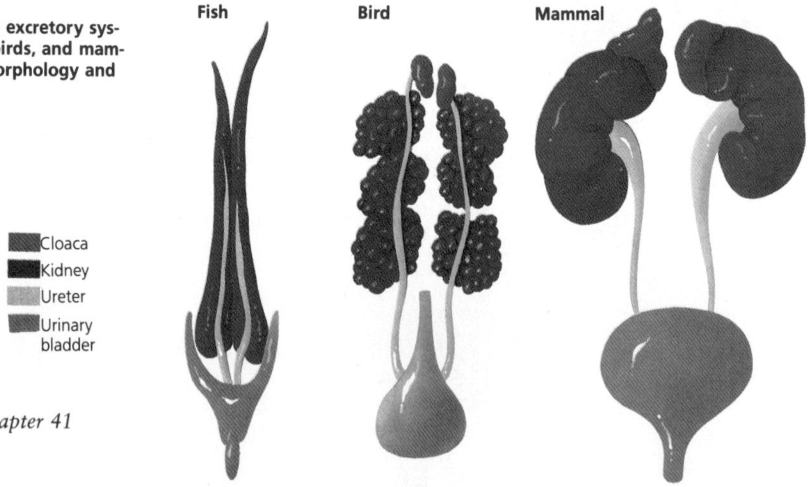

Figure 41-6 The excretory systems of fishes, birds, and mammals differ in morphology and physiology.

Interdisciplinary Activity

Language Arts Have students divide into small groups of four and brainstorm as many clichés as possible that include the name of a vertebrate. If necessary, read students some of the following clichés as examples to get started: dog in the manger, eat crow, snake in the grass, something smells fishy, blind as a bat, wise old owl, timid as a mouse, graceful as a swan.

After the brainstorming, have each group cooperatively write a short (one to two pages) humorous essay or story incorporating as many clichés as possible.

Nervous Systems

The general evolutionary trend in vertebrate nervous systems is toward an increasingly elaborate system, which allows more varied and intricate responses to the environment. Also there is a strong trend toward the concentration of control of most functions in specific centers in the brain, thus allowing for better-coordinated responses. As Figure 41-7 shows, the cerebellum and cerebrum have become larger as vertebrates have evolved. In lower vertebrates the brain stem is the main center of the brain; trunk movements remain mostly reflex actions. In more complex vertebrates the cerebellum plays a greater role than it does in less complex vertebrates in coordinating motor activities. The degree of development of the cerebellum generally corresponds to the intricacy and precision of the movements the organism is able to perform. The highly developed cerebrum in mammals gives them the ability to learn from experience, and humans, in particular, have heightened abilities of foresight and judgment. In general, the size of the optic lobe corresponds to the importance of functioning vision in the organism.

Figure 41-7 Specific areas of the vertebrate brain have grown more complex and have increased in size over evolutionary time.

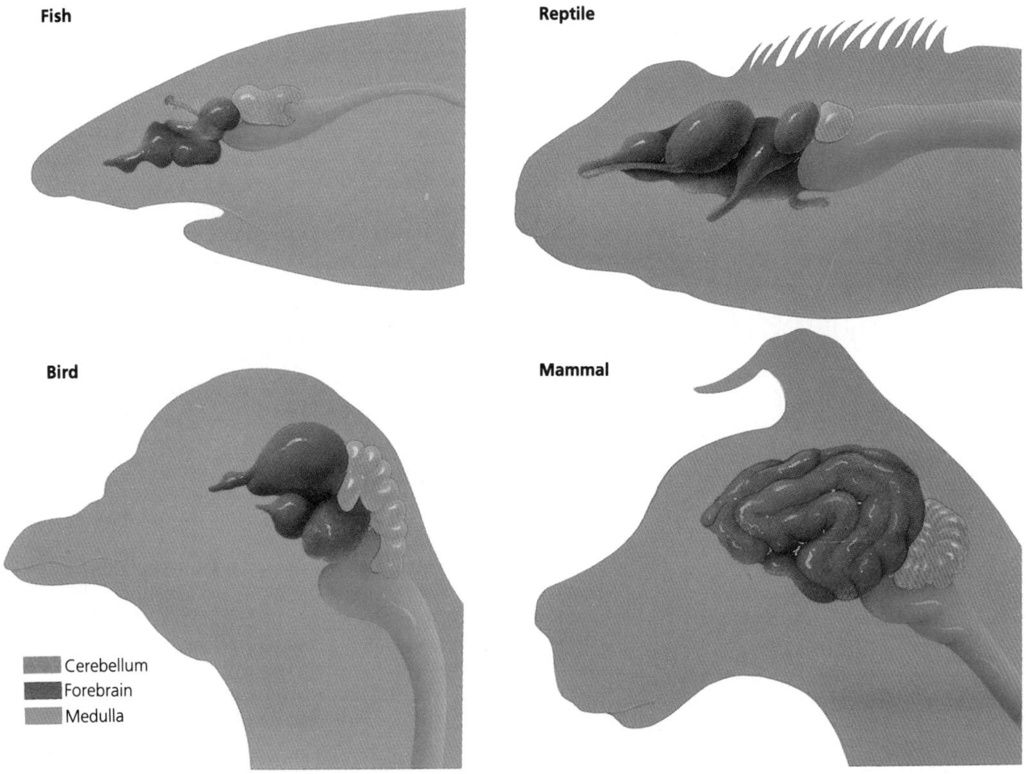

Guided Practice

Have students examine Figure 41-7, noting the increasing complexity of the vertebrate brain. Have students use information from Chapters 36–41 to suggest how changes in relative size of different brain parts was adaptive. *(For example, the bird's cerebellum, the area that coordinates movement, is highly developed—an adaption that enables birds to control flight-related functions.)*

Independent Practice

- Have students write answers to the Section Review.
- For each of the following systems, have students write a description of one adaptation to a terrestrial environment. Have students briefly explain and support their answers. Include skeletal, integumentary, circulatory, respiratory, excretory, nervous, and reproductive systems. *(Sample adaptations include adult amphibian limbs, reptile scales, bird and mammal four-chambered hearts, amniote eggs.)*

Check Your Understanding

1. What would be the effect of a two-chambered heart in a mammal? *(The mammal would be unable to support its metabolic needs.)*

2. What limitations do their bones impose on birds? *(Size and weight; the hollow bones are adaptations of a flying animal.)*

3. Why are reptiles considered more "primitive" than mammals? *(They appear earlier in the phylogenetic tree.)*

LEP Activity

Divide students into six small groups. Have each group examine one of Figures 41-3 through 41-8 and look for evidence of evolutionary trends. Visit each group as they examine the figure, offering guidance and directing attention to relevant features. After students have examined the figure, have each group present its figure to the other groups and explain the evolutionary trends depicted.

Reteaching
Have students focus on an organ system such as the skeletal system. Ask them why an arrangement of legs similar to an amphibian's would not be well adapted to mammals. *(Their placement does not afford sufficient support and mobility.)* Elicit from students that adaptations are the result of natural selection in response to environment over time.
■ *See* Section Reviews *worksheet, Section 41.2.*

Enrichment
Have each student choose an adaptation in a vertebrate system of special interest. *(For example: bat echolocation, pit viper pits, lungfish lungs, peacock tail, poisonous frogs)* Have students use library resources to research and write reports about the feature.

Closure
Provide a detailed description of a vertebrate's body system. Have students identify the vertebrate as aquatic or terrestrial, explaining how they arrived at their answers. *(For example, an excretory system that eliminates wastes as uric acid crystals is characteristic of some land vertebrates because it is an adaptation that conserves water. An integumentary system that functions as a major respiratory organ is characteristic of a primarily aquatic vertebrate because such a process could not occur in air without desiccation.)* Students do not have to state which vertebrate possesses the described system.

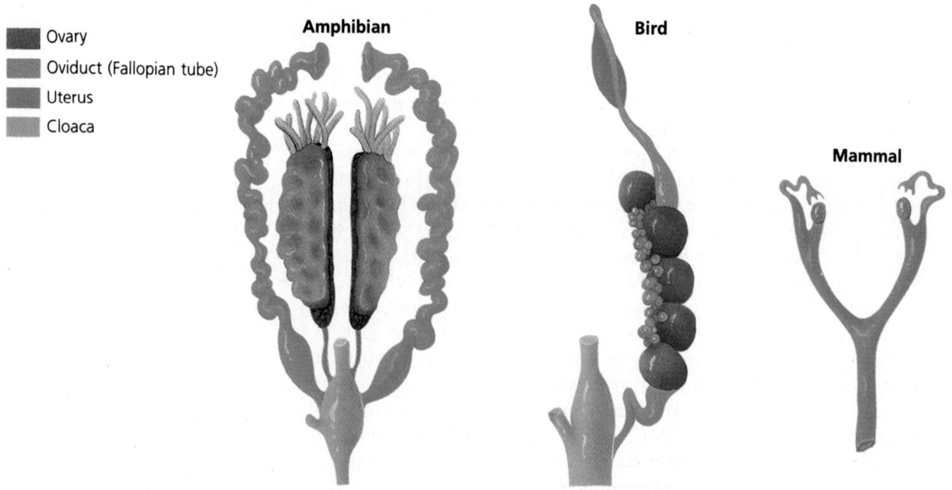

Figure 41-8 Compare the female reproductive systems in these three representative vertebrates.

Reproductive Systems

In vertebrates the evolutionary trend in reproduction is toward internal fertilization and internal development, both of which better ensure the survival of the young. In most fishes and amphibians eggs and sperm are released directly into the water, where fertilization takes place. In reptiles, birds, and mammals the egg and sperm unite within the body of the female, increasing the likelihood that the egg will be fertilized.

In general, the evolutionary trend has been from oviparity to ovoviviparity to viviparity. Many fishes, amphibians, reptiles, and birds are oviparous. Their embryos develop outside the body, protected by jellylike layers, or by a shell, and nourished only by the yolk until they hatch. Some fishes, amphibians, and reptiles are ovoviviparous. Their eggs are nourished only by the yolk but remain inside the female until they hatch. Most mammals are viviparous. Their embryos are nourished in the female through the placenta until the young are born.

Section Review

1. Describe the difference between *indirect development* and *direct development.*
2. Why is there no large yolk in mammal embryos?
3. What is the major evolutionary trend in respiration? Describe one beneficial adaptation in a terrestrial vertebrate.
4. What adaptive advantages are gained in the transition from oviparity to ovoviviparity to viviparity?
5. How might marine mammals, whose ancestors were adapted to land, have become adapted to aquatic conditions?

Answers to Section Review
1. Indirect development: larvae are different in structure from adults; direct development: young are similar to adults.
2. Mammal embryos are nourished through the placenta and do not need a large yolk.
3. Toward lungs with a larger surface area for gas exchange. One example is the air sacs in birds, which maintain a constant supply of air in the lungs.
4. Embryos of ovoviviparous and viviparous animals develop inside the body. Only the yolk provides nourishment in oviparous and ovoviviparous eggs; viviparous mothers nourish embryos continually through the placenta.
5. The adaptations of early marine mammals must have allowed them to successfully exploit the resources of the ocean.

41.3 Behavior

Just as the pressure of natural selection has caused the evolution of increasingly complex structures in vertebrates, that pressure has also caused the evolution of complex behavior. The general trend in vertebrate behavior has been toward more complex, better-integrated behavior that allows more flexible responses to different environmental situations. In higher vertebrates the behavior of both individuals and groups of individuals is increasingly modified through learning.

Section Objectives

- *Describe the major trend in vertebrate behavior.*
- *Explain the process of imprinting.*
- *Describe the apparent adaptive advantage of one example of social behavior.*

Individual Behavior

In many individuals behavior is often predictable. For example, Konrad Lorenz (1903–), an Austrian zoologist, observed that all young geese followed their mother. He hypothesized that this behavior was genetically programmed. To test his hypothesis, he removed a group of recently hatched goslings from their mother. To his surprise, the goslings followed him as if he were the mother. Lorenz also discovered that the goslings would follow a dog, a cat, or a toy train—as long as it was the first moving thing they saw within their first 36 hours of life. Lorenz called this process **imprinting.** Lorenz discovered that after the 36-hour **critical period** imprinting would not occur even if the goslings were placed with the mother.

While the individual is genetically predisposed to learn behaviors that are characteristic of its species, the development of any such behavior requires the proper stimulus. For example, to be able to sing the song of its species, most birds must hear the song first.

Insight learning is a major example of the more complex behavior that is highly developed in anthropoids. **Insight learning** allows individuals to apply what they have learned in one situation to other situations. A few species, most notably humans, are also able to transmit learned behavior symbolically from generation to generation. Changes in behavior that are based on learning are said to be culturally induced.

Figure 41-9 These brown bears, *Ursus arctos,* fishing in the McNeil River of Alaska are exhibiting learned behavior.

Social Behavior

The adaptive interactions among members of the same species are called **social behavior.** In vertebrate societies the organization is not so rigid as that in invertebrate societies. For example, in an ant society most of the individuals are sterile workers; they are chemically induced to assume certain roles and have no ability to reproduce. Nonetheless, vertebrates often form hierarchies, such as the dominance order of male wolves or the hierarchies of females in baboon societies. These hierarchies are adaptations that tend to make those groups stable and orderly.

Lesson Plan

Section Focus

This section presents the evolutionary trend in vertebrate behaviors toward more complexity and better integration.

Section Themes

This section emphasizes **Evolution.** Vertebrates have evolved behavioral adaptations to habitats, such as hierarchy formation and insight learning, analogous to adaptations in body systems.

Motivating Activity

Have students observe behaviors of vertebrates, such as people, pigeons, or squirrels, in or around the school. Ask them to describe examples of individual and social behaviors they observe. *(For example, pigeons courting, squirrels burying nuts, people conversing)* Have students refer to Investigation 40 in *Laboratories.*

Teaching Strategies

Classifying Data Have each student use the library to identify five vertebrate behaviors primarily determined by genetics and five primarily learned. *(For example, genetic behaviors: fishes feeding, lizard breeding display; learned behaviors: chimpanzee "fishing" for termites, most bird songs)*

Guided Practice

Have students use their own experiences (with pets, observing nature) to write short essays about an instance of vertebrate learning they have observed. Have them compare individual and social behavior.

Videodiscs

- ***Side 4 3461, Puffer Fish Defense (m)***
- ***7485, Hippopotamus Males: Fighting (m)***
- ***8547, Koala with Young (m)***

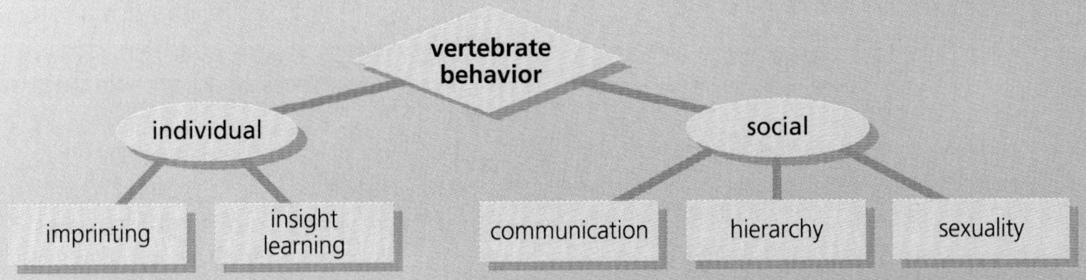

Graphic Organizer Use this organizational chart in Reteaching on p. 628.

Section 41.3

Independent Practice

- Have students write answers to the Section Review.
- Have students make a concept map showing major evolutionary trends in vertebrates. An example of a completed concept map is shown on p. 617B.

Check Your Understanding

1. What is the significance of the critical period in imprinting? *(After this period, imprinting will not occur, even in appropriate situations.)*
2. How do humans transmit learned behavior? *(By teaching less experienced people and by symbolic representation such as written language)*
3. What is the adaptive advantage of the imprinting noted by Lorenz? *(It allows the gosling to bond with its parent.)*

Reteaching

Have students prepare an organizational chart illustrating the ideas in this section. An example of a completed chart appears on p. 627.

- *See* Section Reviews *worksheet, Section 41.3.*

Enrichment

Have students keep a journal of one day's behavior, either their own or that of an imaginary character. Have them include descriptions of behavior and characterize each behavior as individual or social.

Closure

Have students contribute examples of altruistic behavior that they have heard or read about in humans or other animals. *(Bees sacrifice themselves for the hive; people risk their lives to save others or donate an organ to a stranger.)*

Videodiscs

- *Side 4 7229, Giraffes Competing (m)*

Figure 41-10 Elephants, *Loxodonta africana* (left), wrap trunks in an effort to establish dominance. Two factions of macaques, *Macaca fasicularis* (right), vie for leadership of the troop.

In all social behavior communication is necessarily important. Communication is the means by which one individual influences the behavior of others in the group. Among vertebrates there are three basic methods of communication: sound, visual displays, and chemical signals. Again, the trend in communication is toward increasingly complex methods.

Ethologists are scientists who study social communication and hierarchies as well as other kinds of basic social behaviors, such as territoriality, dominance, sexual behavior, and play. They then form hypotheses about the way in which each kind of behavior makes a species adapted to its environment. For example, ethologists may determine the degree of altruism in a society. **Altruistic behavior** is a sacrificing of immediate gratification by an individual that results in an immediate benefit for one or more other individuals. A clear advantage exists for the larger group in such behavior. A bird that gives a warning call to others in a flock that a predator is near, or a porpoise that pushes its injured mate to the surface so it can breathe, improves the chances for survival of members of its species. The individual may be at risk in a particular situation, but in another similar situation might benefit from such behavior by others.

Section Review

1. Define *insight learning.*
2. Describe Konrad Lorenz's experiment with young geese. What does this experiment tell you about instinctual behavior?
3. What are the three basic methods of communication in vertebrates?
4. Describe altruistic behavior.
5. Why is communication so important in social behavior? Why might it be increasingly important in higher vertebrates?

Answers to Section Review

1. Insight learning allows individuals to apply what they have learned in one situation to another situation.
2. Lorenz observed that goslings follow the first moving object they see within their first 36 hours of life, after which time imprinting will no longer occur.
3. Sound, visual displays, and chemical signals
4. Altruistic behavior is the sacrifice of one individual for the benefit of others, conferring a clear reproductive advantage to the group.
5. Communication is the means by which one individual influences the behavior of others in the group. In higher vertebrates, in which behavior is increasingly flexible, communication is especially important to the group and individual.

Laboratory

Comparing Locomotion in Vertebrates

Objective
To relate form of locomotion to body structure in vertebrates

Process Skills
Observing, inferring

Materials
Live fish, salamander, lizard, and snake; large aquarium; large terrarium

Inquiry

1. In the following investigation, record all your observations. First observe a fish by looking down on the fish from a position above. Describe the overall motion of the fish's body. Now observe the fish from the side. Describe the manner in which the fish coordinates its muscles.
2. Place a salamander in an aquarium and observe it from above and then from the side as it swims.
3. Place the salamander in a terrarium and observe the animal as it walks, both from above and from the side. Does the salamander have difficulty walking on land? What impedes its movement?
4. Place a lizard in the terrarium. How does the lizard's movement differ from the movement of the salamander?
5. Place a snake in water and observe it from above as it swims.
6. Remove the snake from the water and place it in the terrarium. Does the snake use its muscles on land the same way it does in water? What does it push against? It is difficult to observe the function of the snake's scales in locomotion. The scales keep the snake from backsliding.
7. Observe the legs of a mammal, in this case, yourself. In addition to the fact that you

walk on two legs, do you notice any structural differences of the legs compared with the legs of other vertebrates?
8. To discover more about the changed position of the limbs in relation to the body in mammals, perform the following exercise: Hold your arms straight out to the sides with your palms facing forward. With the palms still facing forward, bring your thumbs together with your fingers pointing up. Now, with your arms still extended forward, turn your palms so that they face the ground. In performing this exercise, what do you notice about your wrists? Other mammals have this feature on their forelegs.

Conclusions

1. Of the terrestrial vertebrates you examined in this investigation, which resemble the fish in their method of locomotion? In what way?
2. What is the advantage of the placement of a mammal's leg in relationship to the rest of the body?

Further Inquiry
Discuss ways in which this investigation could have been improved.

Laboratory

(For an overview of vertebrate locomotion and preparatory information related to the laboratory, see p. 617B.)

Inquiry

3. The salamander walks with some difficulty on land because its limbs are positioned away from the body, giving it little support. This causes the trunk and tail to drag along the ground, impeding movement.
4. The lizard's limbs are positioned somewhat beneath the body. Unlike the salamander, the lizard can lift its body off the ground, permitting unimpeded movement.
6. Depending on the species of snake used, it will move differently on land from in water. Out of water, the snake has solid land to push against.
7. Human legs are positioned directly beneath the body.
8. The human wrist allows both flexing and rotating.

Conclusions

1. The salamander and snake move on land by undulation, just as the fish moves in water.
2. Legs placed directly under the body can move more efficiently.

Further Inquiry

Encourage students to suggest improvements in choice of vertebrates to study, conditions for making observations (physical space and time available), and questions asked. If possible, have students design a lab that can test research questions of their own.

Vocabulary

1. Ovoviviparous animals, such as some fishes, amphibians, and reptiles, retain embryos within the body, nourishing them only by the yolk. Oviparous animals, such as birds and some reptiles, have eggs that develop outside the body, nourished by the yolk. Viviparous animals, such as most mammals, nourish embryos within the mother's body through the placenta.
2. Animals with direct development can easily share the same resources and ecological niche.
3. Behavior that is based on learning from other members of the species
4. Social communication and hierarchies, as well as basic social behaviors
5. Birds that give warning calls and porpoises that help their injured relatives

Review

1. c
2. a
3. b
4. c
5. c
6. Small filter-feeding organisms that resembled cephalochordates but had a backbone
7. Simpler body structures are often adaptations within more complex systems, which would not necessarily indicate that they were phylogenetically more primitive.
8. Increase in adaptation to terrestrial environment, such as membranes and eggshells that protect the embryo
9. Indirect development occurs in lower chordates and amphibians; direct development occurs in reptiles, birds, and mammals. If resources are plentiful, direct development allows adults and young to share them. If resources are scarce, indirect development prevents competition between adults and young.
10. An increase in size of the pelvic and pectoral girdles and their accompanying muscles
11. The bone structure of the flipper is actually a modification of the mammalian limb.
12. Integuments protect against injury and loss of water and insulate the body.
13. Terrestrial higher vertebrates convert toxic ammonia wastes from their cells into urea. They also have tubules in their kidneys that reabsorb most of the water that they filter from the blood.
14. Control has become concentrated in centers in the brain, allowing better coordination. The highly developed cerebrum of mammals gives them the ability to learn from experience and to have foresight and judgment.
15. Internal fertilization makes successful fertilization more likely. Internal development allows the mother to protect and nourish the developing embryo.

Chapter 41 Review

Vocabulary

altruistic behavior (628) | critical period (627) | ethologist (628) | imprinting (627) | insight learning (627) | social behavior (627)

1. Describe the advantages to organisms of ovoviviparity, oviparity, and viviparity. Give an example of an organism that fits each category.
2. Describe the advantages that direct development gives to organisms.
3. Describe what is meant by culturally induced behavior.
4. What does an ethologist study?
5. Give one example of altruistic behavior among vertebrates.

Review

1. Direct development (a) allows the parent and its young to survive in different environments (b) prevents the parent and its young from competing for the same resources when these are scarce (c) allows the parent and young to share the same niche (d) all of the above.
2. The tough outer skin of vertebrates (a) protects against injury and the excessive loss of water (b) insulates the body (c) allows the absorption of small amounts of water (d) all of the above.
3. Endotherms, which often have four-chambered hearts, (a) have lower energy requirements than ectotherms do (b) have higher energy requirements than ectotherms do (c) do not require extra oxygen (d) require greater numbers of erythrocytes.
4. The evolving behavior in higher vertebrates (a) allows less flexible responses than that in lower vertebrates (b) is dominated by instinctual behavior (c) is increasingly modified through learning (d) none of the above.
5. Culturally determined behavior is based on (a) changes in gene frequencies (b) changes in the environment (c) learning (d) changes in basic human capacities.
6. Describe the probable first vertebrates.
7. Some structural adaptations are actually simplifications. Do such simplifications indicate that an organism should be placed in a more primitive position in the phylogeny? Why or why not?
8. What is the major evolutionary trend in embryo development? Give one example that shows this trend.
9. Describe the vertebrate groups that are characterized by direct and indirect development. List the advantages each group derives from its form of development.
10. Describe the changes in limb structure that gave terrestrial vertebrates greater mobility and support.
11. Explain why the resemblance between the flippers of whales and other marine mammals and the fins of fishes does not indicate that the organisms are closely related.
12. List three ways in which the integuments of terrestrial vertebrates serve as adaptations to a dry environment.
13. Give two examples of adaptations in the excretory system of higher vertebrates, and explain why they are important.
14. Describe two ways in which the nervous system of higher vertebrates has become increasingly complex. Explain why these adaptations are important.
15. Describe the adaptive advantages of internal fertilization and development in higher vertebrates.
16. What kind of behavior dominates in lower vertebrates?
17. Give one example of a hierarchy that exists within a vertebrate society. What is

the function of such hierarchies within vertebrate societies?

18. In vertebrate hierarchies why might a subordinate individual, who might eat last or rarely have an opportunity to reproduce, remain with the group?

19. Give one example of a stimulus that is required if an individual is to learn the behavior characteristic of its species.

20. Explain the conditions under which natural selection might not act against altruistic behavior.

Critical Thinking

1. As you learned in Chapter 38, there are terrestrial and marine turtles. Terrestrial turtles have clawed limbs; marine turtles have paddlelike flippers. How would you go about deciding which organism is probably phylogenetically more primitive?
2. The songs of various species of birds, which are often sung repeatedly by individuals, are clearly distinguishable. What are two possible adaptive advantages of singing distinct songs?
3. There are very few known fossils of birds. Why might this be?
4. Klaus Immelman, a biologist in Germany, did experiments in which he allowed young zebra finch males to be raised by Bengalese finch foster parents. These species are quite different in color and size and do not engage in courtship in nature. Yet when they matured, if given a choice between female Bengalese and female zebra finches, the zebra finch males would court only Bengalese finches. How might you explain this behavior?

5. Examine the photo above. When individual wolves threaten each other, one will usually back down and any fighting will stop. Only rarely will wolves injure other individuals in the pack. What is the adaptive advantage of such behavior?

Extension

1. Read the article by Richard Monastersky entitled "The Lonely Bird" in *Science News,* August 17, 1991, pp. 104–105. Prepare an oral report that includes answers to the following questions: (1) What evidence supports the claim that *Protoavis* is the oldest known fossil bird? (2) How has that claim been challenged? (3) What are some conflicting theories about the origin of birds? (4) How does the discovery of *Protoavis* affect those theories? (5) Why is avian evolution particularly difficult to research?
2. Marine mammals such as whales and porpoises must be able to survive intense pressures when they dive in search of food. Using your library, research and write a report on the adaptations that these marine mammals have evolved that allow them to survive these conditions.
3. Visit a zoo, a farm, or a kennel where you can observe the interactions of individuals of the same species. Observe these interactions for at least a couple of hours. Make a list of the interactions you see and suggest the function of each.

Critical Thinking

1. A study of the bone structure of the limbs of both organisms shows that the flippers of the marine turtles are actually modifications of limbs of terrestrial turtles and that therefore marine turtles are probably descended from terrestrial turtles.
2. To establish the limits of its breeding territory with others of its species and attract mates of its own species
3. Because skeletons of birds are extremely fragile, few of them have been preserved in the fossil record.
4. It demonstrates the lasting effects of the imprinting process.
5. It establishes pack hierarchy while avoiding serious injury, thus ensuring that the group as a whole will survive.

Extension

1. *Protoavis* is a key piece of evidence in the debate over the origin of birds. Emphasize the issue of evidence and interpretation and that the uncertainty over this specimen will spur others to find better-preserved ones.
2. Suggest that students compare the diving abilities of marine mammals with those of humans.
3. Stress that students try not to "read into" the animal behavior by describing it in human terms. Descriptions should be clear and objective records of what the animals did, not what they seemed to be thinking or feeling.

16. Instinctive behavior
17. The pecking order of chickens; to make group interactions stable and orderly
18. Because survival on its own might be far more difficult
19. The song of a bird, which must be heard before it can be repeated
20. When there is a clear advantage to the group in that behavior

Discussion

Guide the discussion by posing the following questions.

1. What are the major factors that have contributed to the decline in salmon populations? *(Commercial overfishing, erosion of deforested soil into streams, industrial pollution, and numerous massive dams.)*

2. Scientists are not sure how salmon find their way from the ocean to their home waters. (Many scientists speculate that salmon navigate to coastal estuaries by sensing the magnetic field of earth and ocean currents. From there they follow the scent to their breeding waters.) Why do you think that salmon, like certain other species of wildlife, return to their birthplace to reproduce? *(Accept reasonable answers. Students may suggest that the salmon return to their home waters for an adequate supply of food for their young.)*

3. Why do scientists place scent chemicals in the water at salmon hatcheries? *(The scent of the water is imprinted in the newly hatched salmon's memory so that as an adult it will follow that scent and return to the hatchery to spawn.)*

4. How may hatchery-raised salmon endanger the species? *(Hatchery-raised salmon have more genetic uniformity than wild salmon. As the number of hatchery-raised salmon increases in the population, the genetic diversity of the species will decrease, leaving the species vulnerable to extinction by one or more diseases. Hatchery-raised salmon are also more likely to be caught by predators.)*

Intra-Science

How the Sciences Work Together

The Question in Biology: *Can We Save the Salmon?*

The behaviors of some vertebrates still amaze many scientists. The annual migration of millions of salmon from the open sea to inland river beds is one example.

Migration varies among species of salmon, but whenever migration occurs, the river mouths, or estuaries, on the Pacific and Atlantic coasts teem with salmon. There they remain until their systems adjust to the change from a saltwater to a freshwater environment. Then the salmon begin their hazardous journeys of up to 3,200 kilometers upstream to the spawning grounds, where about five years earlier they had hatched as translucent fish, called alevins. In their home waters the salmon lay and fertilize their eggs. Then some species of salmon die. Other species complete the journey to and from the open sea about three times before they die. Scientists are not exactly sure how salmon find their way from the ocean to their home waters, but scientists are certain of several dangers threatening the salmon's existence.

In the 1800s salmon were so plentiful that a Smithsonian Institution observer wrote: "Their numbers are beyond calculation and seem to be so great as to challenge human ingenuity to affect them in any way." Human ingenuity, however, has affected the salmon negatively. Scientists estimate that only 20 percent of salmon today are wild, not hatchery bred, and the extinction of three Pacific salmon species may be imminent.

Many factors have contributed to the decline of salmon populations. While overfishing by commercial fleets has been partly responsible, other activities cause most problems. Deforested soil has eroded into streams and has buried salmon nurseries; industrial pollutants have washed into rivers, poisoned the fish, and impeded their navigation; massive dams, built to produce electric power, block the salmon's upstream journey.

Several means of protecting and replenishing salmon, North America's most important food fish, are under way. Each method requires the cooperation of people from a diversity of fields, and each also has its own set of problems.

The Connection to Chemistry

One important method of saving the salmon has been to raise them by the millions in modern hatcheries. Scientists have placed chemicals in hatchery water to give it a scent. When a young salmon hatches, the scent, or chemical makeup, of the water around it is imprinted in the salmon's memory. As an adult, it will look for streams with a chemistry closest to the remembered scent and thus will return from the open sea to spawn at its place of birth, in this case the hatchery.

632

Connections to Other Disciplines

Language Arts The salmon is an important part of the culture of Northwest American Indian peoples. Have students locate and read Indian legends about salmon.

Social Studies Many places in the northwestern United States are named for salmon. Have students find the scientific names of various salmon. Then ask students to examine a map or an atlas of the northwestern United States to locate and list the salmon place names.

History The dams built along the Columbia River system, such as the Bonneville and the Grand Coulee dams, played an important role in the economic development of the Northwest. Have students research the building of one of these dams and its effect on the region.

However, the chemical makeup of rivers and streams is being altered by industrial pollutants dumped daily into many waterways. Scientists suspect that some salmon—both wild and hatchery raised—never find the way back to their spawning waters because of these pollutants.

Another worry for scientists is that while hatcheries help save and replenish salmon, the genetic uniformity of hatchery-raised fish may reduce the genetic diversity of the species. As the number of hatchery-raised salmon increases, scientists fear that in time, as the hatchery-raised salmon and the wild salmon interbreed, the species could become vulnerable to extinction by one or more diseases. In addition hatchery-raised fish, accustomed to being fed every day, are less likely to evade predators and survive to adulthood.

- *How can pollutants in the water affect salmon?*

The Connection to Physics

Even a salmon with its great jumping ability cannot leap over a dam 100 meters high. However, the salmon will keep trying until it dies. To provide a route around high dams, people have built fishways in some places.

One type of fishway, similar to a lock for ships, takes advantage of gravity. Water flows from a high lock into a lower lock where fish have gathered. As the water level in the lower lock rises, so do the fish, which are thus raised from one lock to the next until they reach the level of the river behind the dam.

Ladders, another type of fishway, consist of a series of pools, each about a foot higher than the previous one. The salmon leap up from pool to pool. This type of fishway requires careful control. If the water flows down the steps too quickly, the fish cannot jump against the flow. If the water flows too slowly, the salmon, which always seek the maximum water flow, may not try to leap to the next level.

Fishways help adult fish going upstream, but young salmon, called smolts, headed back to the ocean must still go through large dams. For example, newly hatched smolts migrating down the Columbia River must pass through rapidly spinning turbines in the Bonneville Dam carrying 130,000 gallons of water per second. At every dam, 10 to 15 percent of the young salmon passing through do not survive.

- *How do dams affect natural selection in salmon?*

The Connection to Other Sciences

Restoration of the habitat is another method of trying to save the salmon. In areas that have been overgrazed, botanists plant trees and shrubs along riverbanks to reduce erosion of soil into the river. Fences are built to keep out livestock and preserve breeding areas. As a habitat returns to its natural state, the salmon return. Ichthyologists may attach special screens to irrigation pipes to keep young salmon from being pumped out of a river.

Although habitat restoration increases the numbers of wild salmon, it is a slow process and does not solve the problems the fish encounter during migration.

- *How may reforestation of riverbank habitats help save salmon?*

The Connection to Careers

Thousands of people depend upon salmon for their livelihood. Salmon provide jobs for commercial fishers, cannery workers, truckers, and merchants. Fishways are designed by engineers and built by construction workers. Hatcheries employ biologists, chemists, and support staff. Ecologists and animal physiologists study the life cycle and adaptations of this unique fish. For more information about related careers in the biological sciences, turn to page 842.

5. What would you do to breed a more resilient hatchery-raised salmon? *(Encourage students to consider the need to maintain genetic diversity among salmon and the need for hatchery-raised salmon to compete well with wild salmon.)*

6. Explain why power companies do or do not have a responsibility to conserve or restore the ecosystems they destroy or affect. *(Student responses will vary. Encourage students to supply examples of how local or state power facilities have had positive or negative effects on the environment.)*

Answers to

Chemistry Chemical pollutants in the water may interfere with the salmon's ability to distinguish the scent of its home waters.

Physics During migration, the stronger salmon swim around or over many obstacles, including dams, to reproduce, passing their genes on to a new generation of strong fish. The weaker salmon die before reaching the home breeding waters.

Other Sciences Reforestation of riverbanks would help prevent soil erosion and provide habitats for a variety of wildlife, including the salmon which will swim in cleaner water.

Enrichment

Ichthyologists estimate that fish have existed on earth for about 540 million years. Have small groups of students each create a phylogenetic tree that tracks the ancestry of salmon. During class discussion, have each group present and explain its findings.

Unit 9 Human Biology

Chapters

Unit Overview

This unit concludes the study of vertebrates by examining structures and functions of human organ systems. Chapter 42 introduces the human body plan, describes major types of tissue, and teaches skeletal, muscular, and integumentary systems. In Chapter 43 students will read about the circulatory and respiratory systems. Chapter 44 discusses infectious diseases and explains how the immune system protects the body. Chapter 45 introduces nutrition and the digestive and excretory systems. In Chapter 46 students will read about the nervous system and sense organs. Chapter 47 describes the endocrine and reproductive systems and follows the development of fertilized egg through birth. In Chapter 48 students will read about the effects of tobacco, alcohol, and other drugs.

Issues in Biology

Use your discretion in introducing the following topic for class discussion, and be sensitive to family and community values.

Each year nearly one million American teenage girls become pregnant, and about 500,000 give birth. Most teenage mothers are unmarried, and nearly one-half drop out of school. Ask students to consider some reasons for teen pregnancies and suggest ways to deal with the problem. Ask if there should be more encouragement of abstention from sex or more information on how to avoid pregnancy. Have students debate the pros and cons of a school birth-control clinic.

Research in Progress

Psychoneuroimmunology is a relatively new field of science that investigates the mind's role in helping the immune system fight disease. Scientists have long suspected a relationship between the central nervous system (see Section 46.1) and the immune system (see Section 44.2). For example, a study of people in bereavement suggests that severe depression lowers levels of helper T cells and killer T cells.

Another study examined the influence of stress levels and coping styles on immune systems of people infected with HIV, the AIDS virus (see Section 44.3). The study found that individuals with low stress levels and/or active coping styles—those that involved a coordinated response to a threat—had higher numbers of helper T cells than individuals with high levels of stress and/or passive coping styles.

Interdisciplinary Activity

Technology Since the first kidneys were transplanted about 35 years ago, transplantation of organs has become so successful that demand for suitable tissue has far outpaced supply. Each year more than 23,000 Americans need replacement organs. Most of these organs come from victims of fatal accidents and have to be transplanted within hours. In an effort to quickly match donor organs to potential recipients, a computer data bank has been set up. Have students find out about the United Network for Organ Sharing and methods for matching donor organs.

Resources

Chapter	Print: For the Teacher	Print: For the Student	Audiovisual/Software
42	■ Matt Cartmill, William L. Hylander, and James Shafland, *Human Structure,* Harvard University Press, 1987.	■ Deborah Erickson, "Skin Stand-ins," *Scientific American,* September 1990, 168.	■ *Our Flexible Frame: The Skeletal and Muscular Systems.* Video, 22 min. Rainbow Educational Video, 1989. ■ *The Skeletal System.* Disk. Apple, 48K, Commodore 64. Scholastic.
43	■ John W. Hole, *Human Anatomy and Physiology,* 5th ed., William C. Brown, 1990.	■ R. Cowen, "Cloning the Genes for A and B Blood Types," *Science News,* May 19, 1990, 311.	■ *Breath of Life,* 26 min. Films for the Humanities & Sciences. Distributed by Carolina Biological. ■ *Two Hearts That Beat as One.* Video, 26 min. Films for the Humanities & Sciences. Distributed by Carolina Biological.
44	■ Robert C. Gallo and Gilbert Jay, *The Human Retroviruses,* Academic Press, Inc., 1991. ■ *The Science of AIDS: Readings from* Scientific American, W. H. Freeman, 1989.	■ John Rennie, "Overview: Tolerating Self," *Scientific American,* September 1990, 50–53.	■ *AIDS: Can I Get It?* Video, 48 min. Distributed by Carolina Biological. ■ *The Mechanisms of Defense: Internal Defenses.* Film, 26 min. Films for the Humanities & Sciences, 1985. Distributed by Carolina Biological.
45	■ Nevin S. Scrimshaw, "Iron Deficiency," *Scientific American,* October 1991, 46–52.	■ Larry Husten, "Cholesterol to Go," *Discover,* December 1990, 30–31.	■ *Work of the Kidneys,* 3rd ed. Video, 23 min. Encyclopædia Britannica, 1989.
46	■ Walter J. Freeman, "The Physiology of Perception," *Scientific American,* February 1991, 78–85.	■ Susan Katz Miller, "Picking Up Parkinson's Pieces," *Discover,* May 1991, 22.	■ *The Senses: Skin Deep.* Video, 26 min. Films for the Humanities & Sciences. Distributed by Carolina Biological.
47	■ Anthony W. Norman and Gerald Litwack, *Hormones,* Academic Press, Inc., 1987.	■ Rick Weiss, "Of Pregnancy and Pounds," *Science News,* August 4, 1990, 75.	■ *The Body in Focus.* Disk. Apple 48K. Scholastic. ■ *Diabetes: Beating the Needle.* Film or video, 28 min. Filmmakers (Part of *The Nature of Things* series), 1984.
48	■ Marguerite Holloway, "Rx for Addiction," *Scientific American,* March 1991, 94–103.	■ John Horgan, "When Dad Drinks," *Scientific American,* February 1990, 23.	■ *Drug Free Kids.* Video, 70 min. LCA, A New World Company. Distributed by Carolina Biological. ■ *Hard Facts about Drugs: Alcohol, Marijuana, Cocaine, and Crack.* Video, 22 min. Guidance Associates. Distributed by Carolina Biological.

Introducing the Unit

The coverage of vertebrates in Unit 8 lays the groundwork for understanding the structures and functions of organ systems of the human body. To lead students from Unit 8 into the study of human biology, ask them the following questions.

1. Based on what you have learned about organ systems of vertebrates, what do you think are the 11 major organ systems of the human body? *(Skeletal, muscular, integumentary, circulatory, respiratory, immune, digestive, excretory, nervous, endocrine, and reproductive)*

2. Considering the circulatory system of mammals, try to describe the structure of the human heart. *(It is a four-chambered heart with two atria and two ventricles that keep oxygenated blood separate from deoxygenated blood.)*

3. How do you think that the cerebrum and cerebellum of the human brain compare with these areas of other vertebrates' brains? Why? *(The human cerebrum and cerebellum are more developed than are these areas of other vertebrates' brains because of the complexity of motor and mental abilities of humans.)*

4. How does reproduction in humans differ from reproduction in amphibians? *(In humans, fertilization and development of the embryo is internal, compared with external fertilization and development in most amphibians. Humans give birth generally to only one fully developed child at a time while amphibians lay hundreds of eggs and the young hatch in an undeveloped form.)*

Unit 9 Human Biology

Chapters

"I sing the body electric."
Walt Whitman

The images on the facing page present two contrasting views of parts of the human body—one medieval and artistic, the other modern and technological. However, the highly developed brain shown in the magnetic resonance image is a uniquely human characteristic that underlies all human achievement, including both art and technology. In this unit you will learn many details about the structure and function of the human body. You will also develop a deeper appreciation for such distinctively human characteristics as upright posture, opposable thumbs, stereoscopic vision—and, of course, the human brain. In what ways are these characteristics important to the construction worker and surgeon shown?

Anatomical drawings by Michelangelo (1475–1564); magnetic resonance image of human brain (inset)

Construction worker on skyscraper

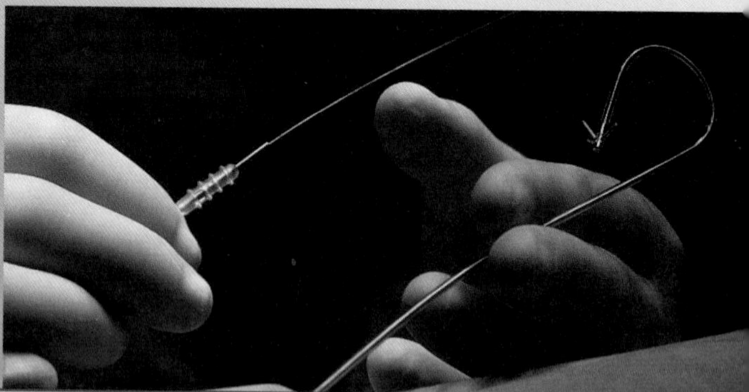

Surgeon's hands

Using the Opening Quotation

Ask students what they think that this quotation means. *(Walt Whitman is celebrating the dynamism and energy of the human body.)* Ask students how they think that this meaning relates to the body. *(It is full of energy that keeps its systems functioning, and these dynamics continue as long as there is life.)* Ask students if they think that electricity plays a role in any of the body's systems. *(Nerve impulses travel throughout the nervous system by the flow of electrochemical energy.)* Point out that the quotation is the title of a poem included in Whitman's *Leaves of Grass*, first published in 1855. Although this was before electricity had become a common source of energy, scientists had discovered some of its basic principles.

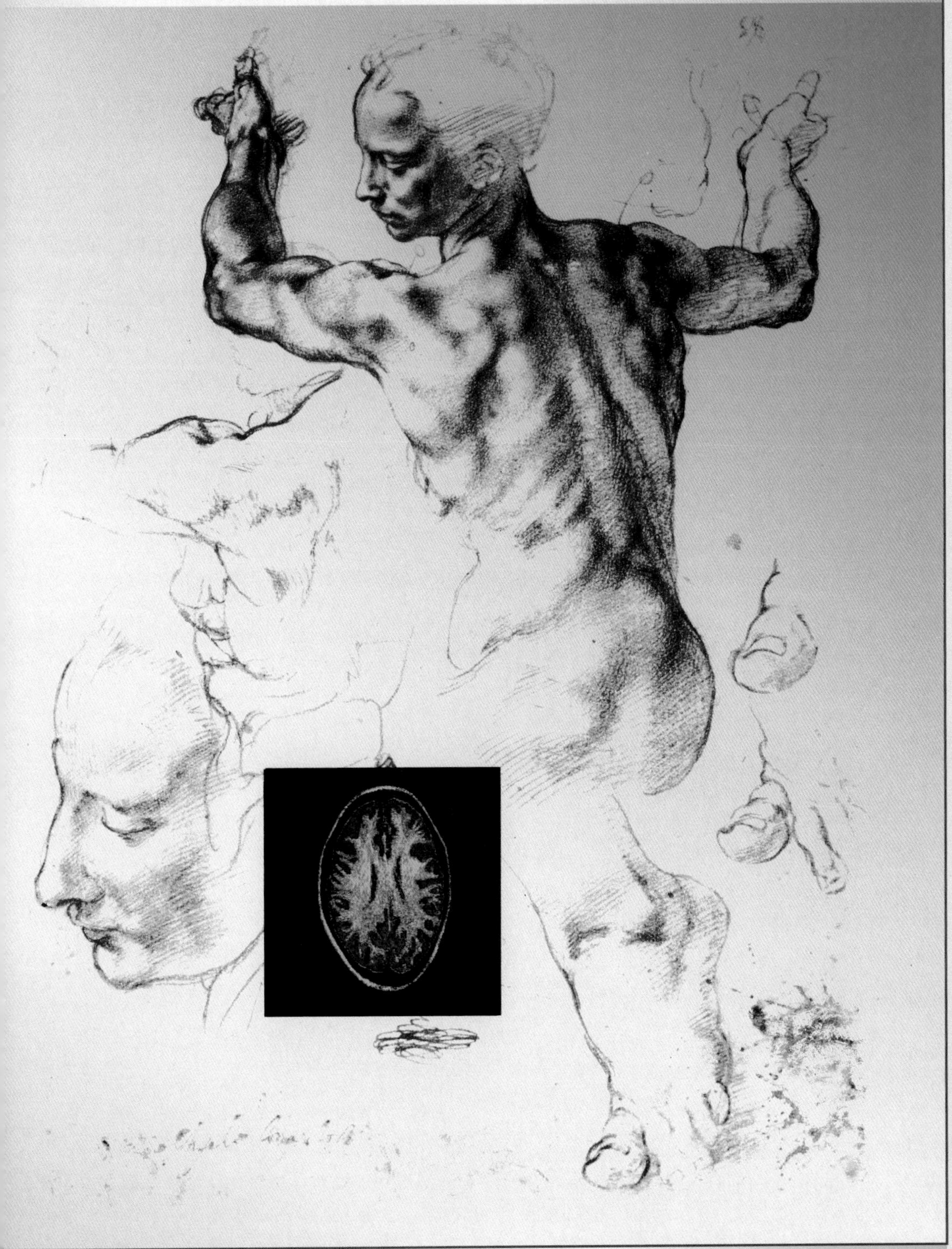

Unit Themes

Energy The study of human organ systems makes clear that the body obtains energy through the digestive system (Chapter 45). Glucose is carried throughout the body by the circulatory system (Chapter 43). The respiratory system maintains oxygen and carbon dioxide exchange necessary for metabolic processes (Chapter 43). Energy produced is then used to keep all of the body systems functioning, including the nervous system, which conducts electrochemical energy throughout the body (Chapter 46).

Scale and Structure The structures of tissue and organs are related to the functions of organ systems. For example, muscles (Chapter 42) are structured so they contract, allowing for movement of the body. In addition, scale of structures is important to their functions, such as the tiny capillaries (Chapter 43) that carry vital nutrients to every individual cell.

Stability Inherent in the functions of most organ systems is homeostasis in the body. This is especially evident in the immune system (Chapter 44), excretory system (Chapter 45), and endocrine system (Chapter 47). Sometimes, drugs (Chapter 48) are used to enhance the body's ability to maintain stability. Abuse of drugs hinders this ability.

Systems and Interactions All body functions are divided among 11 major organ systems. However, no system works independent of others. The nervous and endocrine systems (Chapters 46, 47) play key roles in regulating other systems. Within major organ systems are subsystems, such as the lymphatic system, which is part of the circulatory system.

Understanding the Visuals

Ask students to look at the magnetic resonance image of the human brain on p. 635 and try to describe the perspective of this view. *(It is taken looking at the top of the head and shows the structure of the cerebrum.)* Challenge students to relate the function of the brain to the other visuals shown. *(The brain controls observation and the artistic execution displayed in the drawings; it controls coordination of muscles and ability to make judgments needed by both construction worker and surgeon.)* Point out that the realistic drawings of human anatomy by Michelangelo are among the earliest. Encourage students to contrast what was known about the structure of the human body in the 1500s to what is known about it today.

Chapter 42 Skeletal, Muscular, and Integumentary Systems

Chapter Overview

Chapter 42 begins the study of the organ systems of the human body. Section 42.1 discusses the human body plan and introduces the concepts of tissue, organ, and organ system. Section 42.2 explores the skeletal system, including how bones develop. Section 42.3 examines the muscular system, with an emphasis on how muscles contract. Section 42.4 discusses the integumentary system, which includes the skin.

Chapter Planning Chart

B	S	A	Sections and Subsections	Page	Features	Page	Resources
•	•	•	**42.1 The Human Body Plan**				
			Body Cavities	637	Section Review	639	Videodiscs
			Body Tissues	638			Section Reviews Worksheet
			Organs and Organ Systems	639			
•	•	•	**42.2 Skeletal System**				
			Skeletal Function	640	Biotechnology	642	Videodiscs
			Skeleton and Bone Structure	641	Section Review	644	Blackline Master 86
			Bone Development	642			Overhead Transparency T42
			Joints	643			Section Reviews Worksheet
•	•	•	**42.3 Muscular System**				
			Muscle Types	645	Laboratory	651	Videodiscs
			The Muscle Cell	646	Section Review	648	Blackline Master 87
			How Muscles Contract	647			Process Skills: Muscle Twitch and Sports
			How Muscles Move Bones	648			Laboratories: Muscle Function
							Section Reviews Worksheet
•	•	•	**42.4 Integumentary System**				
			Epidermis	649	Think	650	Videodiscs
			Dermis	649	Section Review	650	Section Reviews Worksheet
			Hair and Nails	650			
			Glands	650			
			End of Chapter Activities				
					Chapter Review	652	Vocabulary Skills
							Chapter Test
							Computer Test Generator

B *The Basic Level curriculum presents the most fundamental knowledge offered in the course.*
S *The Standard Level curriculum is designed for the average student who is able to master most topics.*
A *The Advanced Level curriculum includes suggestions for teaching the most academically able students.*

Cooperative Learning

Group Activity: Muscles and Bones

- **Group Size:** *3–6 students*
- **Outcome:** *Students will describe major muscles, bones, and protective coverings of the body.*
- **Individual Accountability:** *Each student will be responsible for one of three body systems.*
- **Positive Interdependence:** *Group members will work together to prepare a presentation for the class.*

Assign to each group a different area of the human body, such as the head, arm, leg, hand, or foot. Ask each group to investigate the muscular, skeletal, or integumentary systems of their subject to determine the gross composition and function of the parts. Groups should divide their tasks so individuals (or pairs of students) study only one of the three systems each. Students should do the research by using anatomy books, anatomical charts, and other library resources.

After time for the initial research, ask group members to get together to assemble their information and prepare a class presentation. Check that each group knows what or how many bones and muscles make up their body part and that each group is able to describe the integumentary components. The group should also be able to describe the function of the components of their body part.

Concept Map

The following is one possible solution to the concept mapping activity in Reteaching on p. 639.

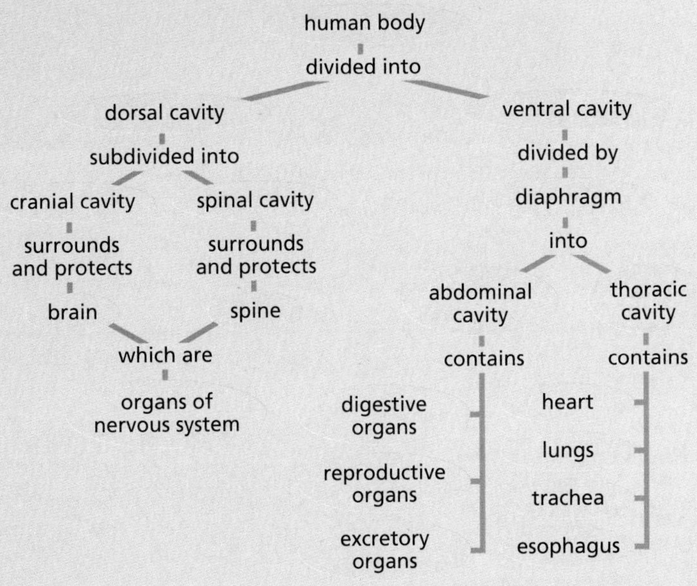

Laboratory Preparation

Overview *(See p. 651.)*

In this laboratory students examine the structure and function of the skeletal and muscular systems of the chicken wing through simple dissection. Students carefully observe the muscles, tendons, ligaments, and bones of the wing. Simple wing movements illustrate the interaction of opposing muscle pairs, tendons, ligaments, and joints. Further dissection reveals the nature of cartilage and its contribution to the smooth action of a typical joint. Based on their observations, students then describe how each of these structures interacts with others to produce movement.

Preparation

Use fresh, raw chicken wings that have been soaked in 70% ethanol and refrigerated overnight to reduce their fat content. Show students where to make the first cut by drawing a dotted line on the wing from the exposed end of the upper wing to the first joint of the wing.

Teaching Tips

This laboratory could be done by pairs of students rather than by individuals.

Demonstrate how to make the first cut with the scissors. Show students what the fascia (or mesentery) is and how to cut it away carefully.

Clarify for students which are the upper and lower portions of the wing. The upper portion is that which was originally attached to the body. The lower portion is between the upper portion and the wing tip.

Make sure that all students have observed muscle movement before cutting the muscles away from the bone. Have students compare the structure of the chicken wing with that of a human arm.

Safety

Remind students to use the scalpels and scissors with care. Ethanol is highly flammable. If the liquid spills, flush the affected areas of the skin immediately with water and wipe up spills.

Chapter Themes

Scale and Structure Central to understanding the human body is the identification of the basic structures of which it is composed: bone, muscle, and skin. Emphasize that these structures define the shape of the body. Point out that learning names of the important muscles and bones is not an end in itself but a way to remember how the body's structures fit together.

Focus on the interplay of structure and function. Emphasize how bones and muscles provide support and work together to allow movement.

Systems and Interactions Although the human body should be understood as an organic whole, the different structures and functions can be classified into 11 organ systems. Emphasize that these organ systems must interact to carry out their functions and that no organ system works in isolation from the others.

Chapter Motivating Activity

Demonstrate to students some simple movement, such as bending and straightening the arm at the elbow. Then ask students to describe what is being moved as well as the mechanics of this motion. Have students focus on the bones, joints, and muscles involved. Ask students to point out which bones are moved, in what direction, and by which muscles. *(The contraction of the muscles of the upper arm moves the bones of the forearm.)* Emphasize how bones and muscles work together to do this movement. Then point out that the elasticity of the skin covering the bones and muscles is essential in allowing for this movement.

Chapter 42 Skeletal, Muscular, and Integumentary Systems

Introduction

The human body is able to make graceful leaps and powerful jumps. The skeleton provides a framework as strong as metal yet far lighter. Muscles provide power and flexibility. The skin protects the body yet keeps it cool. Without the interaction of these systems, the human body would be as graceless as a robot.

Chapter Outline

Chapter Concept

As you read, note how structure is related to function in bones, muscles, and skin.

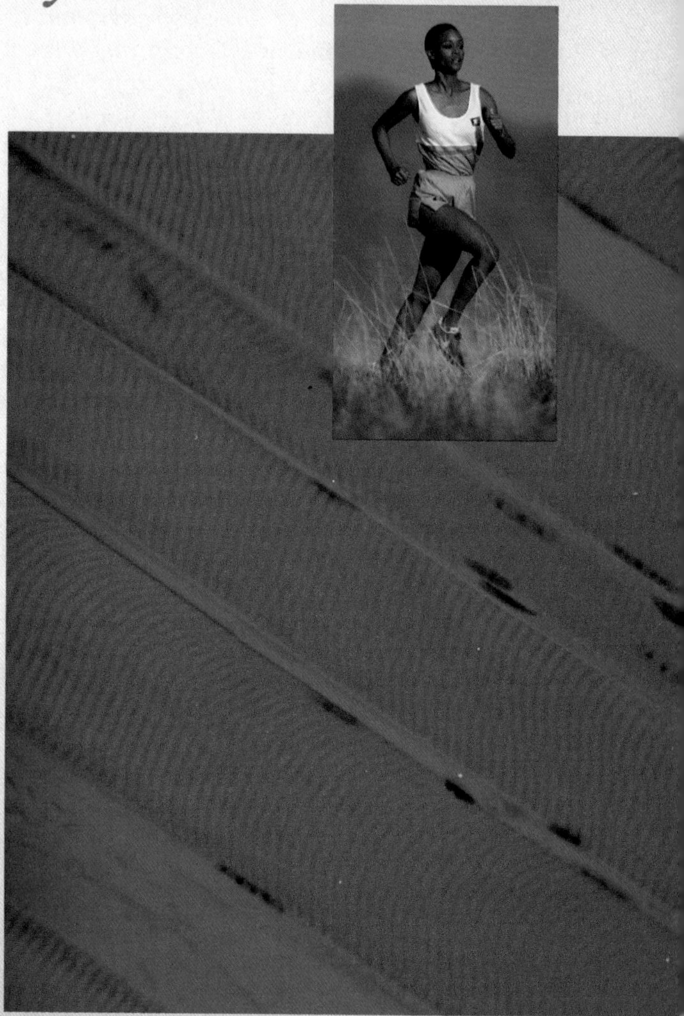

Striated fibers of skeletal muscle. Inset: A runner.

Understanding the Visuals

Have students closely examine the photograph of muscle fibers. Then ask students to explain how the words in the caption describe this photo. *(The photograph shows skeletal muscle, or muscle attached to the skeleton. The long bands that cut across the photo are fibers of the muscle. These fibers are marked by parallel grooves, or striations.)* Ask students how they think that skeletal muscles relate to the runner shown in the inset. *(Skeletal muscles are attached to bones, and the contractions of these muscles allow the runner to run.)*

42.1 The Human Body Plan

The human body begins to take shape in the earliest stages of embryonic development. The cells divide and the embryo takes on the bilaterally symmetrical form that parallels that of the other vertebrates. One unique quality of the human body is the development of the structures into a form that supports an upright body position.

Section Objectives

- *Name the main body cavities, and tell where they are located.*
- *Describe the four types of tissue in the human body.*
- *List the primary organ systems, and describe their functions.*

Body Cavities

The human body can be divided into two main cavities, the **dorsal cavity** and the **ventral cavity.** Each of these cavities, shown in Figure 42-1, contains one or more body organs. The dorsal cavity, which contains the organs of the nervous system, can be further subdivided into the cranial and spinal cavities. The **cranial cavity** surrounds and protects the brain. The **spinal cavity** surrounds and protects the spinal cord.

The ventral cavity is divided into two regions by a wall of muscle called the diaphragm. The upper region, or **thoracic cavity,** contains the heart, lungs, trachea, and esophagus. Notice that the ribs, breastbone, and spine form a frame that protects these organs. The lower region, or **abdominal cavity,** contains the organs of the digestive, reproductive, and excretory systems.

Each body system is made up of many different organs. The organs consist of various tissues, which in turn are made up of groups of similar cells. The organization of all of these components of the body is in part an evolutionary adaptation to the upright posture of humans.

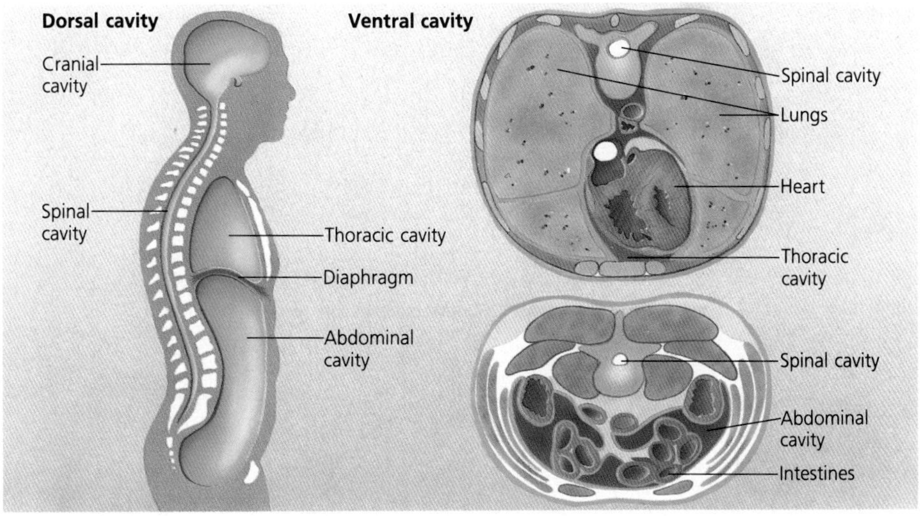

Figure 42-1 The dorsal cavity includes the cranial and spinal cavities. The ventral cavity includes the thoracic and abdominal cavities. Cross sections through the chest (top right) and the abdomen (bottom right) show the position of the organs in the body.

Muscle Tissue	Nerve Tissue	Epithelial Tissue	Connective Tissue
▪ skeletal muscles	▪ brain	▪ skin	▪ bone
▪ heart	▪ spinal cord	▪ organ linings	▪ cartilage
▪ smooth muscle of the digestive organs	▪ sensory organs		▪ tendons
	▪ nerves		▪ fat
			▪ blood
			▪ lymph

Graphic Organizer Use this table in Guided Practice on p. 638.

Lesson Plan

Section Focus

This section describes the two main body cavities and the four types of tissue. Students will learn that tissues make up organs and organs make up organ systems. The human body contains 11 organ systems, which interact to carry out life functions.

Section Themes

The theme of **Systems and Interactions** is evident in the discussion of organ systems. The student will be introduced to the idea that no body system can function in isolation. The theme of **Scale and Structure** is emphasized with the introduction of body organization and tissue types.

Motivating Activity

Introduce this hierarchy to students: organism, organ systems, organ, tissue, cell. Then ask students to think of hierarchies in society, for example, a hierarchy within the local school district. *(School system, high school, grade level, class, student)* Make sure that students understand that separate components at one level of a hierarchy together form the next higher level.

Teaching Strategies

Distinguishing Terms Refer students to Figure 42-1 on p. 637. Point out that *dorsal* means "back" and that *ventral* means "belly." Make sure that students can distinguish between the dorsal and ventral cavities shown in Figure 42-1 and that they understand what a cross section is.

Videodiscs

▪ *2651–2659, Human Body (s)*

Interpreting the Visuals Have students compare the diagram of muscle tissues in Figure 42-2 (top left), p. 638, with the chapter opening photo on p. 636. Then ask what similarities the two illustrations show. *(Both show striated fibers.)* What is clearly shown in the diagram that is not clear in the photo? *(The diagram fibers clearly show nuclei.)* Have students note that cells in each of the four diagrams in Figure 42-2 have nuclei. Ask what the material surrounding the cells in the diagram of connective tissue is called. *(Matrix)*

Identifying Structures The word *tissue* is used in everyday language, although not in the strict sense as defined in this section. Ask students to brainstorm a list of body tissues, as used in the everyday sense. Write these on the board. *(A common list might include muscle, fat, skin, bone, brain, and organ.)* Then ask students to identify each of these tissues as one of the four main types. *(Muscle is made of muscle tissue; fat is connective tissue. Organs, such as skin, bone, and brain cannot be identified by just one type of tissue, since organs are combinations of different tissues.)*

Guided Practice

Have students make a table to organize the text material on tissue types. Use the table on p. 637 as a model. Have students list organs according to their primary tissue type. (Hint: have students consider what the organ does as they determine the proper tissue category.)

Body Tissues

A **tissue** is a group of cells that are similar in structure and function. The human body has four main types of tissue: muscle, nervous, epithelial, and connective tissue, as shown in Figure 42-2.

Muscle tissue is composed of cells that contract. Skeletal muscle tissue moves bones; cardiac muscle tissue, found in the heart, pumps blood through the body; smooth muscle tissue, found in many organs, moves substances through the body.

Nervous tissue consists of cells that transmit messages through the body. Nerve cells respond to changes occurring in all parts of the body. The brain, spinal cord, sensory organs, and nerves are composed of nervous tissue. The nervous system is discussed in Chapter 46.

Epithelial *(EP-uh-THEE-lee-ul)* **tissue** protects, secretes, and absorbs. Epithelial cells bind tightly together, forming a solid sheet that covers, protects, or lines a body part. Examples of epithelial cells include the skin and the cells that line the organs of the body cavity. The cells in each type of epithelial tissue are shaped and arranged so as to perform a particular function. For example, the thin, flat cells that line the inside of the mouth are arranged like tiles on a floor. These cells shield the cells that lie under them.

Connective tissues help support the body. Connective tissues include bone, cartilage, tendons, fat, blood, and lymph. All connective tissues are embedded in or surrounded by a substance called a matrix. The matrix can be solid, semisolid, and in some cases, liquid. Bone cells are surrounded by a hard, crystalline matrix. Cartilage cells, tendon cells, and fat cells are surrounded by a fibrous matrix that is less solid than bone. Various blood cells are suspended in a liquid matrix.

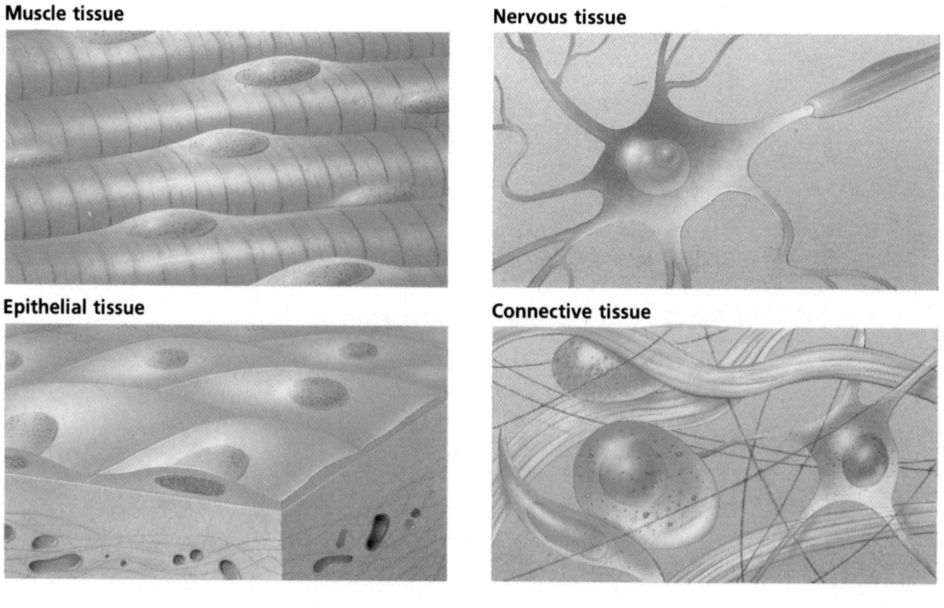

Figure 42-2 These four diagrams show representative cells of the four main types of tissues. The diagram of nervous tissue (upper right) shows one nerve cell.

Cooperative Learning

Organ Systems Have students work in pairs and use Table 42-1 on p. 639 to review the major structures and functions of the 11 organ systems. Suggest that each pair discuss each system and refer to other parts of Unit 9 to clarify any misunderstandings. Then have partners quiz each other about the material. For example, one student might ask the other what system is responsible for regulation of homeostasis. *(Endocrine)* Circulate around the room and randomly ask students questions about the major structures and functions of the organ systems.

Table 42-1 Overview of Organ Systems

System	Major Structures	Functions
Skeletal	Bones	Structure, support, protection
Muscular	Muscles	Structure, support, movement
Integumentary	Skin, hair, nails	Protection, excretion
Circulatory	Heart, blood vessels	Transport
Respiratory	Lungs, air passages	Gas exchange
Immune	Lymph nodes, T and B cells	Defense against disease
Digestive	Stomach, intestines, mouth, esophagus	Digestion, absorption
Excretory	Kidneys, intestines, skin	Removal of waste, reabsorption
Nervous	Brain, spinal cord, nerves	Sense, coordination, control
Endocrine	Glands, hypothalamus	Control, regulation of homeostasis
Reproductive	Gonads	Production of offspring

Organs and Organ Systems

Tissues are arranged into organs. An **organ** consists of different tissues that together carry out a specific function. For example, the heart is an organ in which muscle, nerve, epithelial, and connective tissues work together to move blood through the body. The stomach is an organ in which muscle, nerve, epithelial, and connective tissues work together to digest food.

Usually, a single organ, such as the heart, does not function in isolation. Rather, groups of organs work together in an **organ system.** In the digestive system, for example, the small intestine, stomach, liver, and pancreas all contribute to the process of breaking food down into nutrients that can be used by the cells. You will find a list of the major body organs and organ systems, with their functions, in Table 42-1. As you study the table, think about the ways in which the different organ systems interact in the human body.

Section Review

1. What is the *dorsal cavity?*
2. Name the four different types of tissues found in the body, and give an example of each.
3. Describe the functional differences between nervous tissue and muscle tissue.
4. What is the relationship between an organ and a tissue?
5. When a person is running, what interactions occur among organ systems?

Answers to Section Review

1. The body cavity that contains the organs of the nervous system
2. Muscle tissue: skeletal, cardiac, and smooth muscle; nervous tissue: nerve cells; epithelial tissue: skin and organ linings; connective tissue: bone, cartilage, tendons, fat, blood, and lymph
3. Muscle tissue contracts; nerve tissue transmits messages.
4. An organ consists of different tissues.
5. Answers could include that the circulatory and respiratory systems supply the muscular system with oxygen and nutrients, allowing muscles to move the skeletal system.

Independent Practice

- Have students write answers to the Section Review.
- Have students make a labeled drawing showing the two main body cavities and their subdivisions. Encourage students to vary their drawings from the ones shown on p. 637.

Check Your Understanding

1. Where is the thoracic cavity in relation to the abdominal cavity? *(It lies above the abdominal cavity within the ventral cavity.)*
2. How does the matrix of fat and blood differ? *(The matrix of fat is semisolid, while the matrix of blood is liquid.)*
3. Is skin classified as a tissue or an organ? Explain. *(Skin is an organ because it is composed of different tissues.)*

Reteaching

Ask students to make a concept map showing which human organs are located in each body cavity. An example of a completed concept map is shown on p. 635B.

- *See* Section Reviews *worksheet, Section 42.1.*

Enrichment

Explain to students that a doctor might refer to a "fracture on the lateral surface on the superior end of the tibia" in describing a specific broken leg. Have students use library resources to define the following terms commonly used in describing body structures: *superior, inferior, anterior, ventral, posterior, dorsal, medial, lateral, proximal,* and *distal.*

Closure

Bring to class pictures of a variety of human organs, and ask students to name each organ and the organ system to which it belongs. *(For example: heart, circulatory system)*

Lesson Plan

Section Focus

This section teaches the parts of the skeleton, bone composition and development, and joint articulation. Students will learn the difference between the axial and appendicular skeletons as well as the function of the skeletal system.

Section Themes

The theme of **Systems and Interactions** is central to the section. The bones of the body form a system that supports and protects. The skeletal system is composed of living material that interacts with other body systems, including the muscular, circulatory, and immune systems. The theme of **Patterns of Change** is implicit in the discussion of how bones grow and develop throughout life. Bones are not like steel girders stuck in place; rather, bones are living material that change during a person's life.

Motivating Activity

Many students have experienced some type of injury to the skeletal system, such as a broken bone or an injured joint. Ask students who have had such an injury to share their experiences with the class. Have each student point out the particular bone or joint—naming it, if possible—and explain the cause of the injury and how it was treated. If the injury was to a part of the axial skeleton, ask the student to speculate on what organs might have been injured if there had been no bone for protection.

42.2 Skeletal System

Section Objectives

- *Describe the functions of the skeleton.*
- *List the parts of the skeleton.*
- *Identify the parts of a long bone.*
- *Summarize bone growth.*
- *List the types of joints, and give an example of each.*
- *Explain how arthroscopic surgery differs from other types of surgery.*

The human body contains 206 bones, which are organized into an internal framework called the **skeleton.** Look at Figure 42-3. Examine the variation in size and shape among the bones. Because the human skeleton is an internal structure, biologists refer to it as an **endoskeleton.**

Skeletal Function

The bones that make up the skeleton function in a variety of ways. Bones and groups of bones support the muscles and organs, give shape and structure to the body, and protect delicate internal organs. Notice, for example, that the ribs curve and form a cage that protects the heart and lungs. Similarly some skull bones, together called the cranium, form a protective case for the brain. Bones store calcium and phosphorous, important minerals used by the body in certain vital metabolic processes. In addition, the internal portion of certain bones manufactures blood cells.

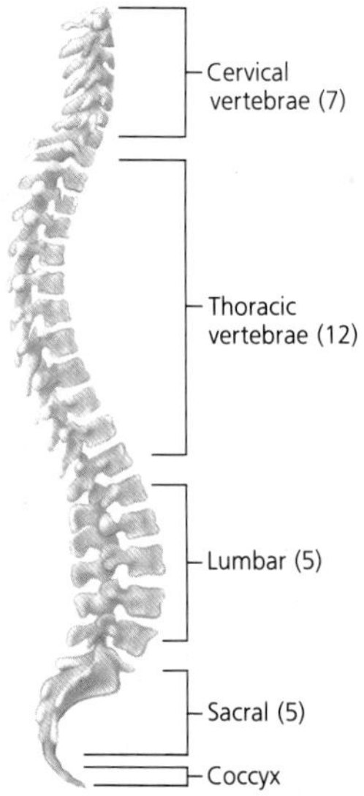

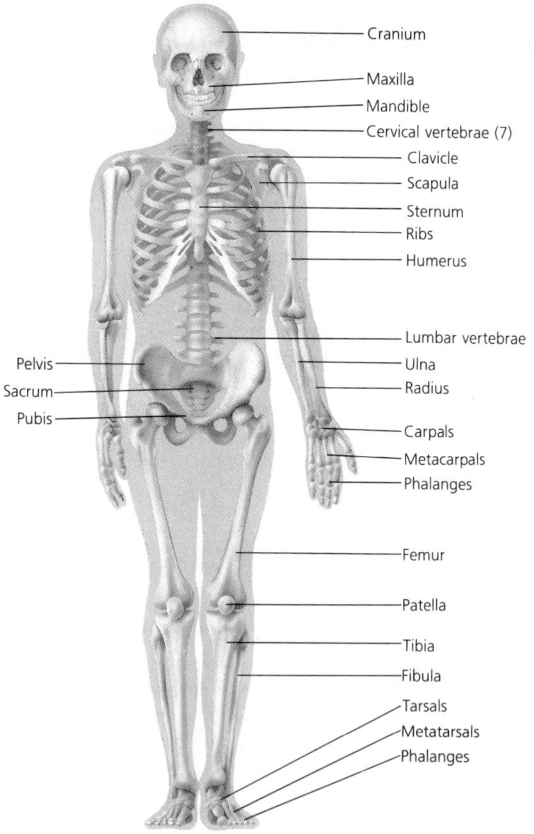

Figure 42-3 Of the 206 bones in the human body 64 are in the hands and arms. How does the size of the bones in the hand adapt the hand for its functions?

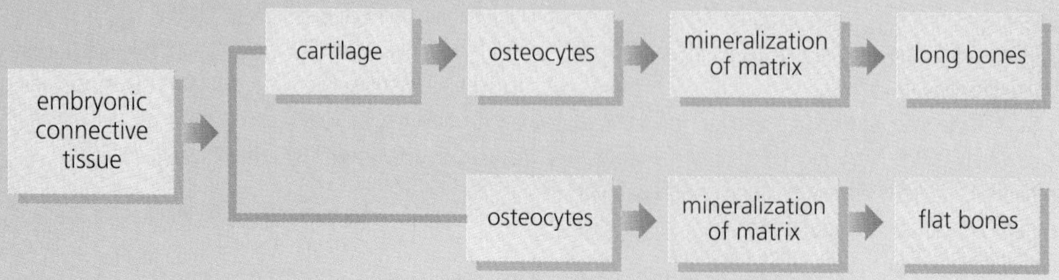

Graphic Organizer Use this sequential diagram in Guided Practice on p. 644.

Skeleton and Bone Structure

The skeleton is composed of two parts—the axial skeleton and the appendicular skeleton. The **axial skeleton,** consisting of about 80 bones, includes the spine, ribs, sacrum, sternum, and cranium. The **appendicular** *(AP-un-DICK-yuh-lur)* **skeleton,** which contains 126 bones, includes the bones of the arms, legs, pelvis, and shoulders. Study these bones in Figure 42-3.

Bones are made up of both organic and inorganic material. Refer to Figure 42-4 to help you understand the internal structure of the long bones of the arms and legs.

The tough outer membrane of the bone is called the **periosteum** *(PER-ee-AHS-tee-um).* This membrane contains a network of blood vessels that supplies living bone cells with O_2 and nutrients and carries away CO_2.

Under the periosteum is a hard material called **compact bone.** In the cross section shown in Figure 42-4 you will notice that compact bone is composed of rings of mineral crystals and protein fibers. Living bone cells called **osteocytes** *(AHS-tee-uh-SITE)* are interspersed throughout these mineral rings. In the center of each ring is a channel called a **Haversian** *(huh-VUR-zhun)* **canal,** which contains nerves and blood vessels. The blood vessels that run through the interconnected Haversian canals nourish the osteocytes. A thick layer of compact bone enables the shaft of the long bone to endure the great amount of stress it receives upon impact with a solid object.

Interior to the compact bone is a network of connective tissue called **spongy bone.** Spongy bone also fills the interior of the knoblike ends of the long bones of the arms and legs. The lacy structure of spongy bone adds strength to the bone without adding much weight. This is an important characteristic, because bones must support the weight of the body and yet be light enough for a person to move easily.

Some bones contain **bone marrow,** which is either red or yellow. Red bone marrow—consisting of blood vessels, fibers, and cells—manufactures erythrocytes and white blood cells. It is found in spongy bone and the ends of long bones, as well as in the ribs, vertebrae, sternum, and pelvis. Yellow bone marrow—consisting mostly of fat cells—serves as an energy reserve. It fills the shafts of the long bones.

Figure 42-4 This cross section shows the internal structure of a long bone. The small box in the cross section is shown in greater detail in the large box.

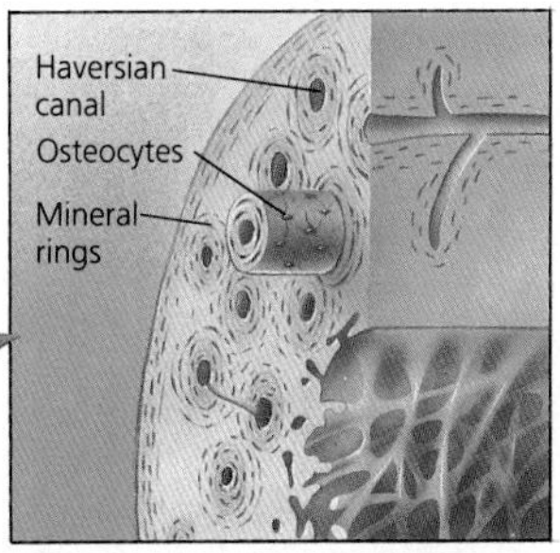

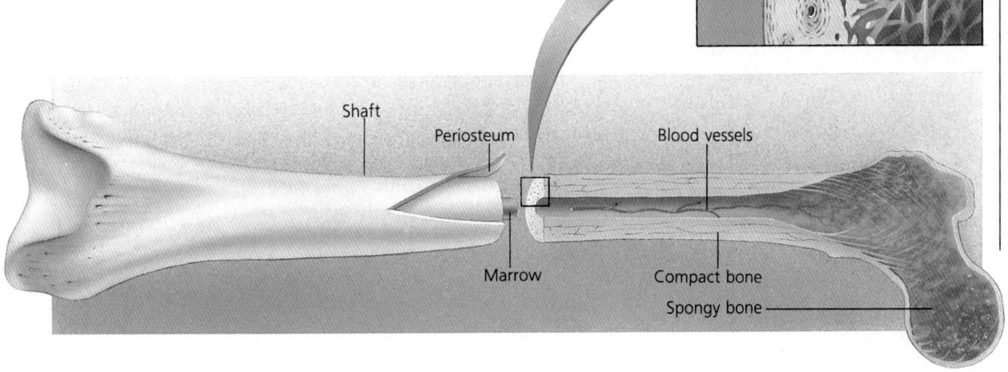

Teaching Strategies

Interpreting the Visuals Use Figure 42-3 on p. 640 to help students learn the names of the major bones. Whenever possible, have students relate the scientific name of a bone to its common name. For example, ask for the scientific name of the jawbone. *(Mandible)* Have students identify whether each bone is part of the axial or the appendicular skeleton. Challenge students to answer the question in the figure caption. *(The small bones in the hand allow for many joints and a full range of motion.)*

■ *See* Overhead Transparency *T42 and* Blackline Master *86.*

Observing Structures Set up several microscope stations and have students observe prepared slides of bone cross sections. Have students make drawings and label them with the terms used in the text. *(For example, Haversian canal, osteocyte)*

Designing an Experiment Emphasize that bones consist of both organic and inorganic materials. Compact bone is solid because calcium and other minerals are deposited in it. Explain that vinegar removes calcium from a bone that is soaked in the solution for several days. Ask students to design an experiment to show that calcium makes bones hard. *(Break an animal bone in half and keep one half as a control. Soak the other half in vinegar or other dilute acid for several days. Then test each for hardness by attempting to bend the bones. The soaked half should be flexible, proving that calcium makes the bone hard.)*

Videodiscs

■ ***2497–2503, Human Skeleton (s)***

■ ***2645–2649, Skeleton; Knee (s)***

■ ***1613–1625, Microscopic Structure of Cartilage, Bone, and Muscles (s)***

LEP Activity

Divide students into groups of three, and have each group construct a cutaway model of a long bone showing the inner anatomy of the bone. The materials each group could use include plastic wrap for periosteum, clay for compact bone, sponge or foam rubber for spongy bone, petroleum jelly for bone marrow, and red string for blood vessels. Have students form the clay first and then add the other materials. Students can work from Figure 42-4 on p. 641 or from an illustration in a reference book. Ask that each group label its model with the proper terms, using toothpick-and-paper flags.

Interpreting the Visuals Refer students to Figure 42-5 and ask what in the X-ray indicates that this is not the hand of an adult. *(The ends of the finger bones are almost transparent, indicating the presence of cartilage rather than bone.)*

Observing Changes Emphasize that bones are living organs that change throughout a person's lifetime. Some of this change is directly observable. Ask students to consider how the bones of an infant differ from those of an adult. *(The infant's bones are soft because they are still composed largely of cartilage.)* Then ask students to consider the bones of older people they know. What differences can they observe between the bones of an older person and a younger adult? *(The joints of an older person may become stiff and knobby, due to arthritis or the aging process.)* Explain why many older women are afflicted with osteoporosis, a condition that makes bones fragile and easily broken. *(Calcium may be leached out of their bones as a result of a reduction in the level of estrogen, a hormone that regulates calcium in the bones.)* Stress that good diet and regular exercise beginning at an early age can help reduce bone deterioration in old age.

Applying Concepts Bring a first-aid manual and a supply of cloth bandages and splints to class. Demonstrate how to wrap injuries to joints and bones. Divide the class into groups and have students practice some of the techniques. If possible, obtain a series of X-rays from a hospital or a physician that show the healing of a broken bone.

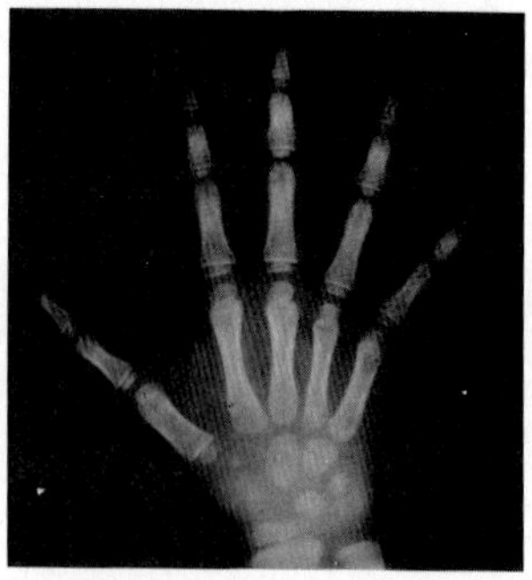

Figure 42-5 A child's fingers grow when bone replaces cartilage in the hand.

Bone Development

Ossification *(AHS-uh-fuh-KAY-shun)* is the process by which bones develop. There are two types of ossification. Long bones first develop as cartilage that is later replaced by bone. Other bones develop directly from embryonic connective tissue.

Cartilage is tough, flexible connective tissue. During the second month of fetal development, the long bones of the skeleton are made up of cartilage. During the third month, osteocytes begin to develop in this cartilage. The osteocytes release minerals that lodge in the spaces between the cartilage cells. Eventually most of the cartilage is replaced by bone. However, some cartilage remains between bones, at the end of the nose, in the external ears, and on the inside of the trachea. It is the cartilage that makes these areas flexible.

A few bones, such as those in the clavicle and in some parts of the skull, develop directly into hard bone from embryonic connective tissue without cartilage forming first. The osteocytes are initially scattered randomly throughout the bone-forming tissue, but soon coalesce into layers and become flat plates of bone. In the skull, suture lines can be seen where the plates meet.

Biotechnology

Arthroscopic Surgery

Today athletes and active people who injure ligaments, tendons, or cartilage are often diagnosed and treated with arthroscopic surgery. In the past joint injuries required extensive surgery and long rehabilitation times, which could mean weeks without training, coaching, or competition.

Advances in biomedical engineering, specifically in fiber-optic technology, instrument design, and miniaturization, all have contributed to the development of arthroscopic procedures. Since arthroscopy requires tiny incisions, often no bigger than a shirt buttonhole, surgeons can often treat an injured area without affecting any adjacent tissues.

Knee surgery is particularly well suited to arthroscopic techniques. Many knee problems are caused by torn cartilage or a piece of tissue that interferes with the motion of the joint, which can become weak and very painful with overtraining, improper body mechanics, or repetitive motion. Young athletes are particularly vulnerable to sports injuries. Good coaching techniques strengthen weak muscles by increasing the repetitions slowly and stressing proper form to minimize injuries. Nevertheless, some injuries do require surgery.

More Information

Fractures Bones start to repair immediately after a fracture because they are so well supplied with blood. During a fracture, blood vessels in the bone itself rupture, forming blood clots. A matrix of proteins and minerals is deposited in and around the clot and begins to harden. This new bone, called callus, bridges the fracture. Because the formation of callus occurs much more rapidly in children than in adults, fractures heal more quickly in children. In addition, a fracture to spongy bone that contains marrow—such as the ends of the femur—generally heals faster than a fracture to bone that does not—such as the middle portion of the femur.

Bones continue to develop after birth. Between early childhood and late adolescence, bone cells replace the cartilage in the fingers, and the fingers grow longer. Growth at the epiphyseal plate on each bone causes the elongation. The **epiphyseal** *(EP-uh-FIZZ-ee-ul)* **plate** is a band of cartilage located near the distal end of a long bone. Cartilage cells within the epiphyseal plate divide and form new cartilage cells. These cells are replaced by bone at the bottom of the epiphyseal plate, allowing the plate to continue to grow at the distal end. Growth continues until the bone has reached its full length and bone has replaced all the cartilage in the epiphyseal plate. At this point, since no further longitudinal growth is possible in the bone, a person has reached full height.

Joints

The place at which two bones meet is called a **joint.** Tough bands of connective tissue called **ligaments** hold the bones of a joint in place. The ligaments also stretch as the bones move. There are three kinds of joints: fixed joints, semimovable joints, and movable joints.

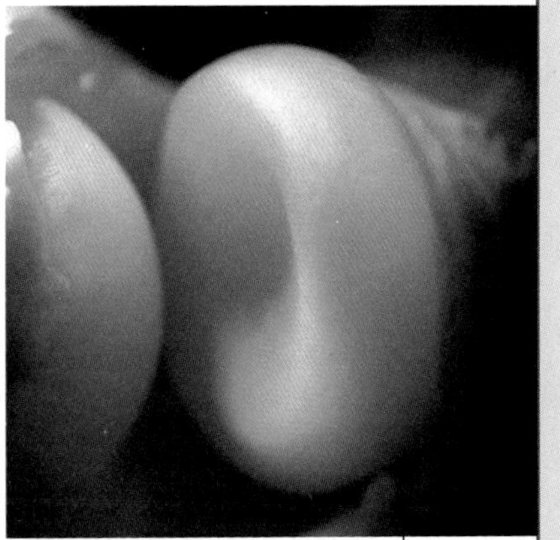

Figure 42-6 The ends of the bones that meet at a movable joint are covered with a layer of smooth cartilage. This joint in the elbow allows rotation of the forearm.

Arthroscopy requires three tiny incisions in the skin, one for the arthroscope to view the injured area, one for a fiber-optic light to illuminate the injured tissues, and one that allows miniaturized surgical instruments to be inserted directly into the joint. In most cases the surgeon has the choice of a direct view through the arthroscope or a video-enhanced image relayed through a miniature video camera built into the scope. Most often the image is relayed to a monitor to allow the surgeon to diagnose the extent of a joint injury and, if possible, complete the correction or repair on the spot.

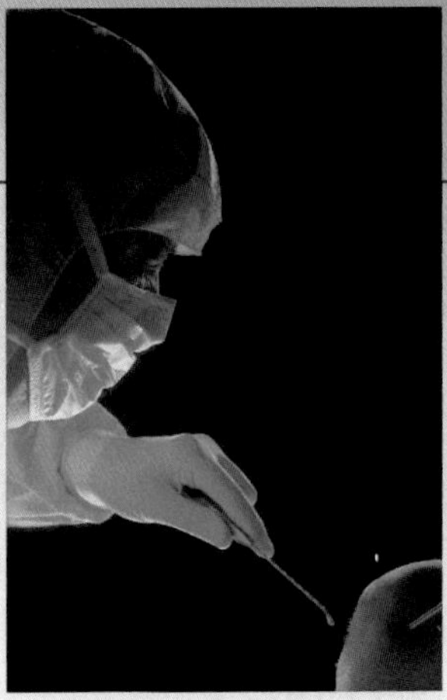

After locating the damaged tissue, the surgeon begins to correct or repair the area. If the problem is a flap of tissue that must be removed, the surgeon uses a tiny cutting instrument to do the work. A special suction tube pulls the pieces out of the working area. Once the work has been completed, the surgeon removes the instruments and closes the incisions with a couple of stitches.

Arthroscopic surgery has many advantages. It can usually be performed on an outpatient basis. A patient can come to the hospital or the clinic in the morning and go home in the afternoon. Most arthroscopic surgery can be done with the use of only a local anesthetic, eliminating the side effects that may occur with general anesthesia. Best of all the recovery time for arthroscopic surgery is short. Rehabilitation and healing times are dramatically reduced.

Cooperative Learning

Movable Joints Have students work in groups of five to study the types of movable joints. Each group member should choose a different one of the five types and find common objects that are similar to this type of movable joint. For example, a door hinge is similar to a hinge joint, and a swivel is like a ball joint. Have the students bring the objects, or pictures of them, to class. Then, each student should demonstrate to the group how the objects are examples of the type of joint. Encourage groups to evaluate the appropriateness of each object.

Identifying Structures While students use Figure 42-7 on p. 644 as a reference, use a model or a chart of the human skeleton, and have students identify the movable joints and classify each as one of the five types. Write the five types of joints on the board, and have students list the specific examples under these headings. *(Under* Ball-and-Socket, *for example, students should be able to name the shoulder and hip joints.)*

Biotechnology

Using the Feature

Clarify for students that the technology described in this feature has been made possible through advances in biomedical engineering, fiber-optic technology, and miniaturization of surgical instruments and video cameras.

Ask students how arthroscopic procedures might offer many advantages to both patient and physician. *(Surgery can often be performed on an outpatient basis with a local anesthetic. Because only small incisions are required, arthroscopic procedures can speed recovery and decrease rehabilitation time.)* Stress that arthroscopy allows a physician to look directly at the joint, while other medical-imaging techniques, such as X-ray or magnetic-resonance imaging (MRI), only offer a two-dimensional picture.

Ask students if they or any other members of their families have had arthroscopic procedures. *(Students may also mention athletes who have undergone arthroscopic repair.)*

Videodiscs

- ***2504–2510, Skeletal Joints (s)***

Section 42.2

Guided Practice
Have students make a sequential diagram that describes the process of bone development, or ossification. Guide students by supplying the major terms. An example of a completed sequential diagram is shown on p. 640.

Independent Practice
- Have students write answers to the Section Review.
- Ask students to sketch and label three of the five types of movable joints in the human body.

Check Your Understanding
1. How are the osteocytes in compact bone nourished? *(By the blood vessels that run through the Haversian canals)*
2. What has happened to the epiphyseal plate when longitudinal growth stops? *(Bone has replaced all the cartilage.)*
3. What is the function of the semimovable joints at the sternum? *(They allow the chest to expand during breathing.)*

Reteaching
Give each student a copy of an unlabeled drawing of the human skeleton. Ask students to label the skeleton with as many applicable terms as they can find in the section.
- ***See* Section Reviews *worksheet, Section 42.2.***

Enrichment
Have students research the fossil record gathered by physical anthropologists to find out how the human skeleton has changed through evolution from its hominid ancestors.

Closure
Using a model of a human skeleton, ask students to identify which bones are involved primarily in support and movement and which function primarily to protect internal organs.

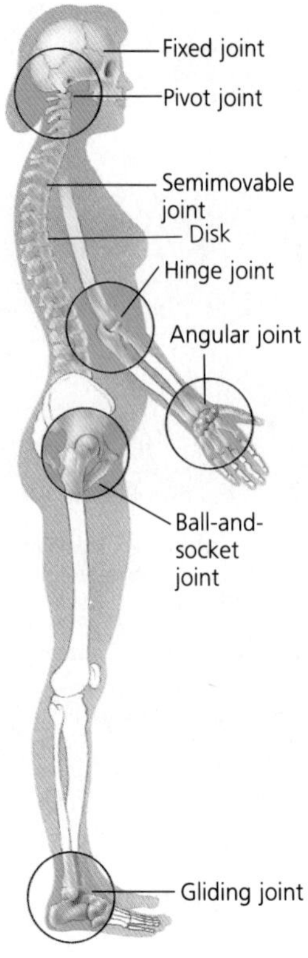

Figure 42-7 In addition to fixed joints and semimovable joints, the human body includes several types of movable joints: hinge, ball-and-socket, pivot, angular, and gliding.

Types of Joints
The bones of the skull meet at fixed joints, the sutures, as shown in Figure 42-7. A small amount of connective tissue remains in the suture and helps absorb any impact on the head and prevent broken bones. The skull bones move very little.

Semimovable joints hold the bones of the vertebral column in place and allow the body to bend and twist. In Figure 42-7 you can see that the bones of the spine are separated by cartilaginous disks. Some ribs are attached to the sternum by long strands of cartilage, allowing the chest to expand during breathing.

The remaining joints shown in Figure 42-7 are examples of movable joints. A hinge joint, such as the elbow, allows bones to move forward and backward. A ball-and-socket joint, such as a hip joint, allows circular motion. A pivot joint, such as the top bones of the vertebral column, allows the head to move from side to side and up and down. Angular joints found in the wrists and ankles allow the hands and feet to make twisting movements. Finally, gliding joints such as those between the small bones of the hand and foot allow the bones to slide against each other.

Functioning of Joints
Joints are often subjected to a great deal of pressure and stress. Connective tissue near the joints secretes synovial fluid, which cushions the bones. This cushioning helps prevent the ends of the bones from wearing away. A fluid-filled sac called a **bursa** is found in the knee and shoulder joints. This sac adds an additional cushion between the bones.

Sometimes all of these protective structures are not enough to prevent injury to a joint. One type of injury, called bursitis, occurs when the bursa becomes inflamed as a result of the overuse of a joint. Bursitis is especially common among athletes. Another type of injury, called a sprain, occurs when the ligaments surrounding the joint are torn.

One of the most mysterious causes of painful and damaged joints is rheumatoid arthritis. Scientists are not sure what causes this type of arthritis. However, they know that in arthritis sufferers the synovial membranes become inflamed and grow thicker. Eventually, fibrous tissues in the joints may become ossified, thus immobilizing the joint and fusing the bones together.

Section Review

1. What is *ossification?*
2. What are three functions of bones?
3. How do bones elongate?
4. Provide operational definitions of hinge joints and ball-and-socket joints.
5. What is the advantage of a cartilaginous skeleton during prenatal development?

Answers to Section Review
1. The process by which bones develop
2. Supporting muscles and organs, giving shape and structure to the body, and protecting organs
3. Cartilage cells at the bottom of the epiphyseal plate are replaced by bone.
4. A hinge joint allows back-and-forth motion; a ball-and-socket joint allows circular motion.
5. A cartilaginous skeleton permits greater flexibility during birth and greater growth potential.

42.3 Muscular System

The bones that make up the supporting framework cannot move alone. It is the muscles that are attached to the bones that cause the body to move. When the body moves, the integration of the various body systems is clearly evident.

Section Objectives

- *Distinguish between the three types of muscles.*
- *Describe a skeletal muscle cell.*
- *Describe muscle contraction and relaxation.*
- *Explain how muscles move bones.*

Muscle Types

A **muscle** is a contractile organ consisting of many cells. The human body contains three types of muscle tissue: skeletal muscle, cardiac muscle, and smooth muscle.

Skeletal muscle is attached to the periosteum of bone, either directly or by a tough connective tissue called a **tendon.** Figure 42-8 shows the different sizes and shapes of human skeletal muscles. Skeletal muscles have **striations,** dark bands located at right angles to the long axis of the muscle. Because their contractions can usually be controlled, skeletal muscles are referred to as voluntary muscles.

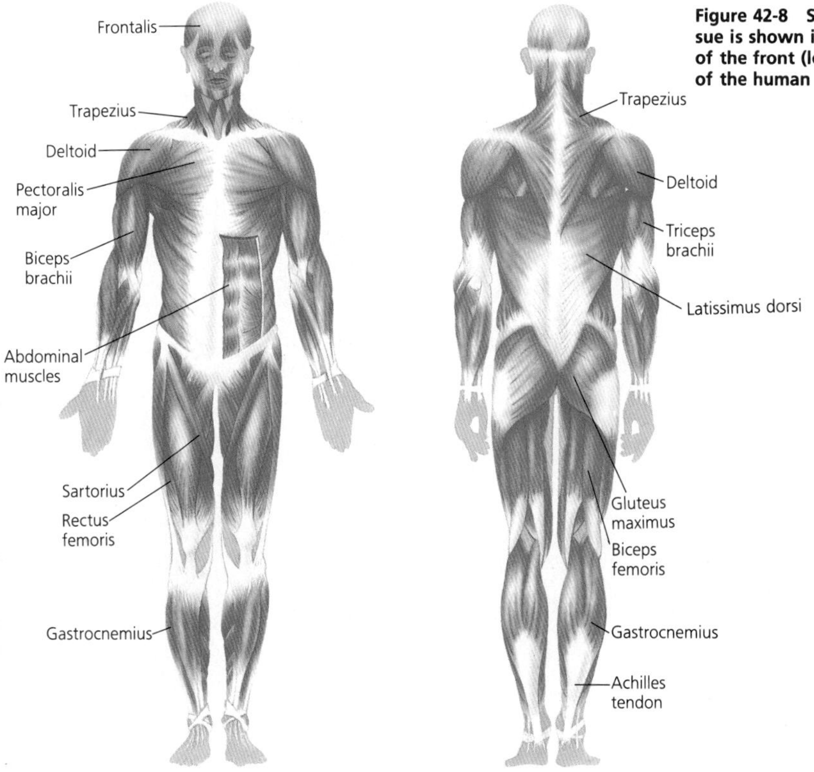

Figure 42-8 Skeletal muscle tissue is shown in these diagrams of the front (left) and back (right) of the human body.

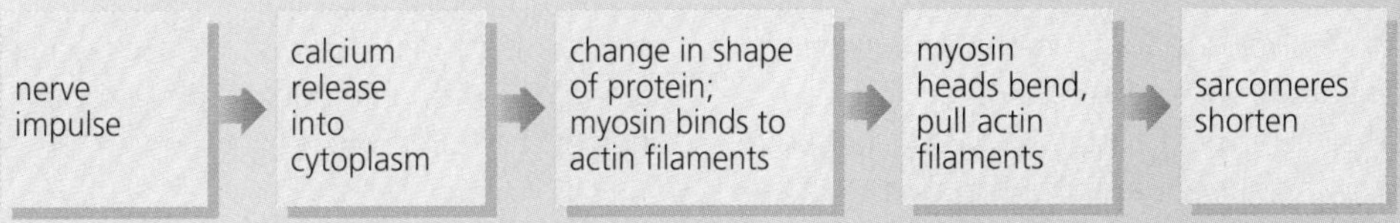

Graphic Organizer Use this sequential diagram in Guided Practice on p. 648.

Lesson Plan

Section Focus

This section covers the three types of muscle—skeletal, cardiac, and smooth—and teaches how muscles contract and relax. Students will learn that most skeletal muscles function in opposing pairs.

Section Themes

The theme of **Systems and Interactions** is inherent in the study of the muscular system. Movement depends on proper function of this entire system, not only of one muscle. The muscular system also interacts with other body systems. For example, the heart muscle pumps blood required by all cells for oxygenation. The theme of **Scale and Structure** is evident in the material focused on specific muscles and their functions.

Motivating Activity

Ask students to make a fist, completely open the hand, and then let the hand relax. Have students repeat the sequence. Then challenge students to identify which muscles contracted and which relaxed to perform these actions. *(The hand is largely controlled by muscles in the forearm.)* Guide the discussion toward the process of these actions. Explain that a thought caused nerves to stimulate the muscles, causing chemical reactions that contracted them. What shape does the hand take when the muscles are most relaxed? *(The fingers curl.)* Point out that straightening the fingers takes as much muscle action as closing them into a fist.

■ *See* **Laboratories,** ***Investigation 42.***

Videodiscs

■ ***Side 2 26461, Muscles: Sliding Filament Theory of Muscle Contraction (m)***

Teaching Strategies

Interpreting the Visuals Use Figure 42-8 on p. 645 to help students learn the scientific names for some of the major muscles of the body. Ask students to find the scientific name of a familiar muscle, such as the chest muscle. *(Pectoralis major)* What are the stomach muscles called? *(Abdominal muscles)* Continue this process until the major muscles have been identified and pronounced.
■ *See* Blackline Master *87.*

Observing Structures Set up several microscope stations, and have students observe prepared slides of skeletal, cardiac, and smooth muscles. Have students make drawings and compare what they see on the slides with the photos in Figures 42-9 and 42-11 on pp. 646 and 647.

Classifying Structures Challenge students to classify muscles in various ways. Ask which of the muscle types are striated and which are not. *(Skeletal and cardiac muscle are striated; smooth muscle is not.)* Which types of muscle are voluntary and which are involuntary? *(Skeletal muscle is voluntary; cardiac and smooth muscle are involuntary.)* Finally, draw a table on the board with headings of the three muscle types. Ask students to name muscles, or locations of muscles, that fall under each heading.

Relating Concepts Visit a local athletic training facility so students can see the types of equipment used in developing the muscular system. Point out that most muscle enlargement occurs when muscle cells increase in size, not through production of new muscle cells. Request that a tour of the facility include an explanation of how different machines and regimens are designed to build different muscles.

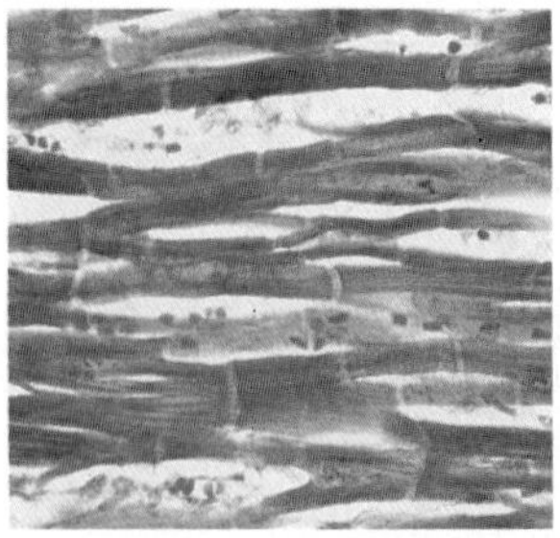

Figure 42-9 In this photograph of a cardiac muscle (×100) the small vertical lines in each muscle fiber are striations.

Figure 42-10 For a muscle to contract, chemical reactions must take place that cause the sarcomere to shorten.

Cardiac muscle, which makes up the walls of the heart, is also striated. Cardiac muscle is stimulated to contract by a special nerve center which sends electrical signals through the cells. Because its movements cannot be controlled, cardiac muscle is called involuntary muscle.

Smooth muscle, which is found in the walls of the stomach, intestines, and blood vessels, does not have striations. It is made up of long spindle-shaped cells that contain a single nucleus. Smooth muscles are involuntary muscles.

The Muscle Cell

Each skeletal muscle cell is called a **muscle fiber.** Each fiber is multinucleate and contains from 1,000 to 2,000 threadlike structures called **myofibrils** *(MIE-oe-FIBE-rulz)*. Each myofibril appears banded. Look at Figure 42-10 and notice the small Z lines in the myofibril. The area betweeen Z lines is called a sarcomere. The **sarcomere** *(SAHR-kuh-mir)* is the functional unit of contraction. The striated appearance of the sarcomere results from the presence of two types of protein filaments, myosin and actin. The

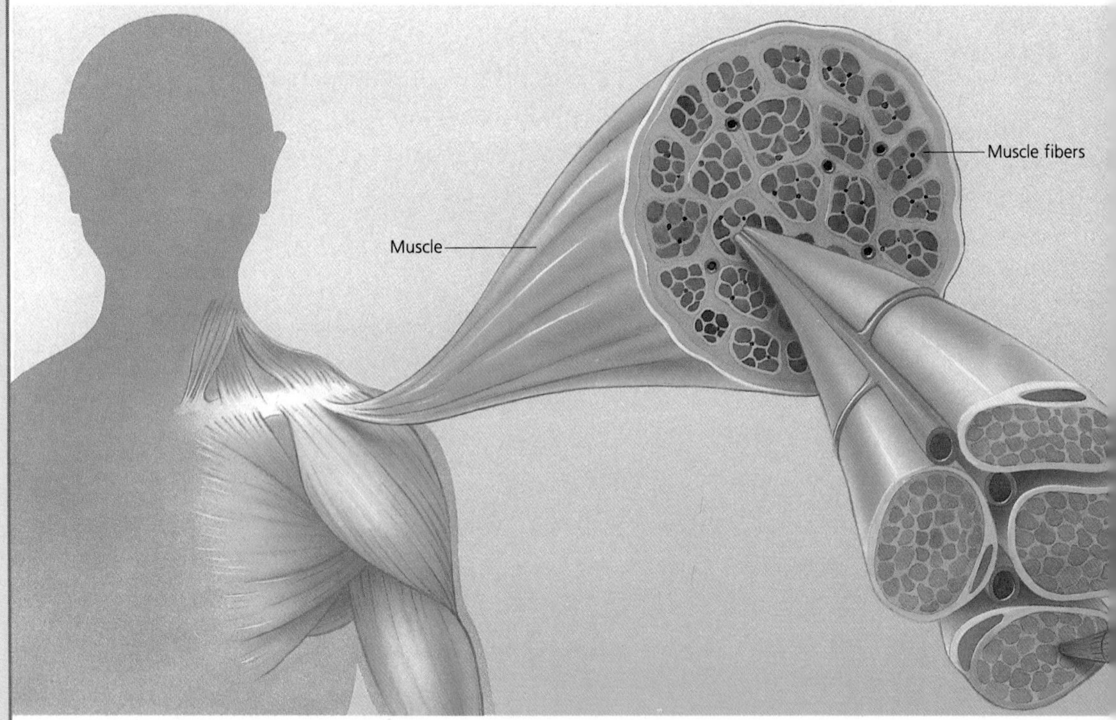

Interdisciplinary Activity

Visual Arts Explain that during the Italian Renaissance, European medicine reclaimed the knowledge of anatomy that had been lost since ancient times. Physicians began to study the ancient authors and to dissect cadavers. Their work greatly impressed Leonardo da Vinci, who came to believe that the study of the anatomy of the muscular system was essential for a painter. His system of anatomical drawing, which included cross-sectional representation, set the standard for centuries. Have students research Leonardo, with an emphasis on his drawings of the human figure.

thicker **myosin** *(MIE-uh-sun)* filaments have lateral extensions called cross-bridges. The cross-bridges are attached to the thinner **actin** filaments that lie beside the myosin filaments. Study the relationship between actin and myosin in Figure 42-10. Notice that the ends of the actin molecule form the Z lines.

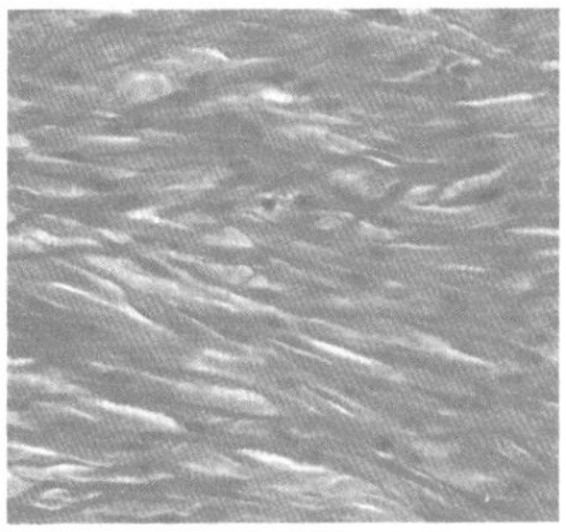

Figure 42-11 Smooth muscles (×100) are involuntary and not striated.

How Muscles Contract

As you read about muscle contractions, refer to Figure 42-10. A contraction begins when a nerve impulse reaches a muscle. The junction of a nerve branch and a muscle is called a motor end plate. A stimulus reaching the motor end plate causes a specialized membrane of the muscle to release calcium into the muscle cytoplasm. Before the nerve stimulates the muscle fiber, myosin cannot bind to actin. The attachment of calcium to muscle proteins causes shape changes in the protein molecules that allow the binding of the myosin heads to the actin filament. The myosin heads then bend inward, pulling the actin filament toward the center of the sarcomere.

The myosin is then released from the actin and uses the energy of ATP to bend the myosin heads back to their original

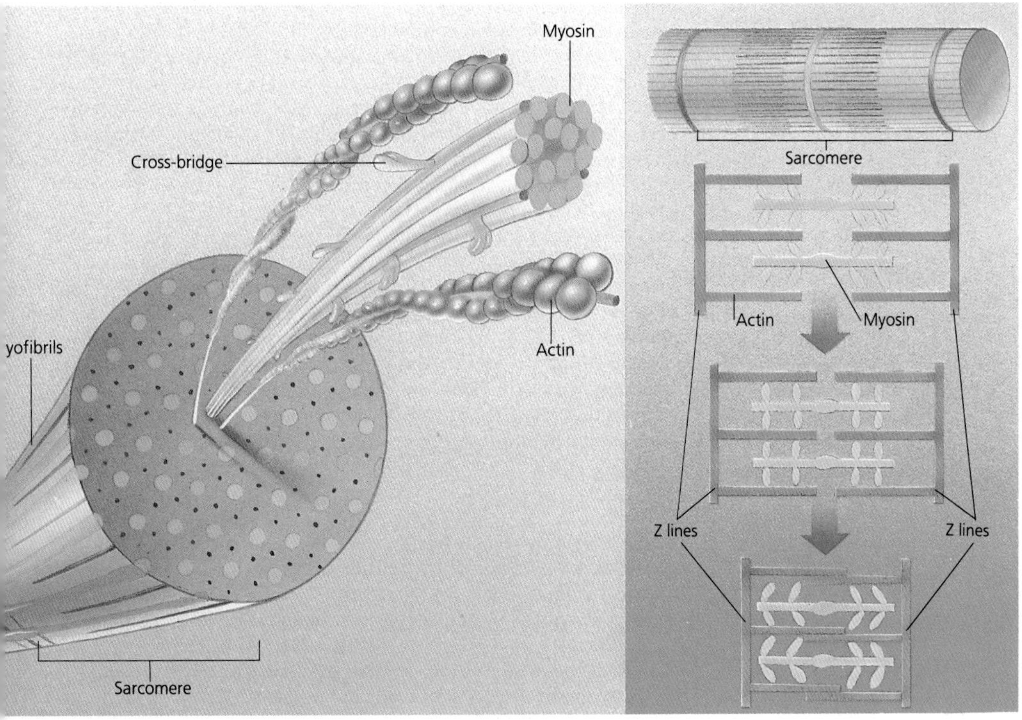

Interpreting the Visuals Help students relate Figure 42-10 on p. 646 to the description in the text. Point out that a muscle fiber is like a rope made of many smaller fibers. Ask students to name these smaller fibers and the units of which they are made. *(Myofibrils; sarcomeres)* What marks the boundaries of sarcomeres? *(Z bands)* Show students that sarcomere fibers contract as myosin filaments pull actin filaments together to make a muscle contract. What events allow myosin filaments to bind with actin filaments and make a sarcomere contract? *(Nerve stimulus reaches muscle, causing calcium and ATP to be released into the muscle cytoplasm; pulling together of actin filaments and thus the Z bands)*
■ ***See* Process Skills, *Chapter 42.***

Identifying Structures Have students study Figure 42-12, p. 648, then demonstrate how the triceps muscle functions as an extensor. *(Bend the elbow to a 90° angle and hold the arm out to the side so it extends from the shoulder while the forearm points down. Then straighten the arm.)* Next, ask students to identify the flexor and extensor muscles of the upper leg. *(Biceps femoris, flexor; rectus femoris, extensor)* How does the biceps brachii function in an opposite way to the biceps femoris? *(They extend over the joint in opposite directions.)*

Drawing Structures Have students make drawings similar to those in Figure 42-12 showing the contraction of these muscles: biceps femoris, rectus femoris, deltoid, and pectoralis major—the flexor, extensor, abductor, and adductor muscles. Have them label their drawings, showing origin and insertion. Explain that they can refer to Figure 42-8 on p. 645 or find diagrams in reference books.

More Information

Anabolic Steroids Anabolic steroids are synthetic drugs that mimic the male hormone testosterone. While it is true that anabolic steroids do build up muscle mass in athletes, the side effects can ultimately be physically devastating. Though prolonged steroid use is hazardous to almost all body systems, the impairment of the cardiovascular system, including disruption of blood clotting, extreme high blood pressure, and atherosclerosis—the deposit of fatty material within the blood vessels—is the most dangerous. (While it is not statistically significant, steroid use may also be implicated in instances of uncontrolled aggression.)

Guided Practice
Have students make a diagram that shows the main events in muscle contraction. Guide students by having them reread the section How Muscles Contract. Use the sequential diagram on p. 645 as a model.

Independent Practice
- Have students write answers to the Section Review.
- Provide students with wide rubber bands, tongue depressors, and tape, and challenge them to make a sample joint and its associated opposing pairs of muscles.

Check Your Understanding
1. Why is smooth muscle called involuntary? *(Its movements can't be consciously controlled.)*
2. What are the lines on striated muscle? *(Z bands, the areas between sarcomeres)*
3. How is a flexor different from an extensor? *(Flexor bends joint; extensor straightens joint)*

Reteaching
Bring pictures of body builders to class and ask students to identify the muscles pictured.
- *See* Section Reviews *worksheet, Section 42.3.*

Enrichment
Have students research sports injuries such as pitcher's arm or pulled hamstring, determining the muscles affected, the cause of the injury, and the treatment. Have students share their findings with the class.

Closure
Name parts of the body and ask students to tell what type of muscle controls each part. For example, ask what type of muscle is found in the esophagus. *(Smooth muscle)*

Have students complete the Laboratory on p. 651 before beginning Section 42.4.

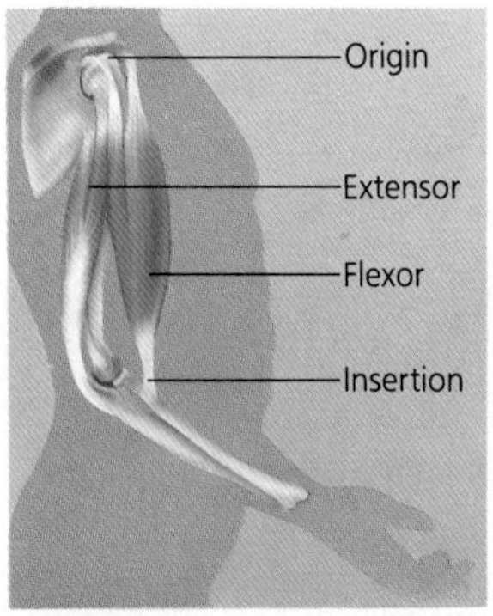

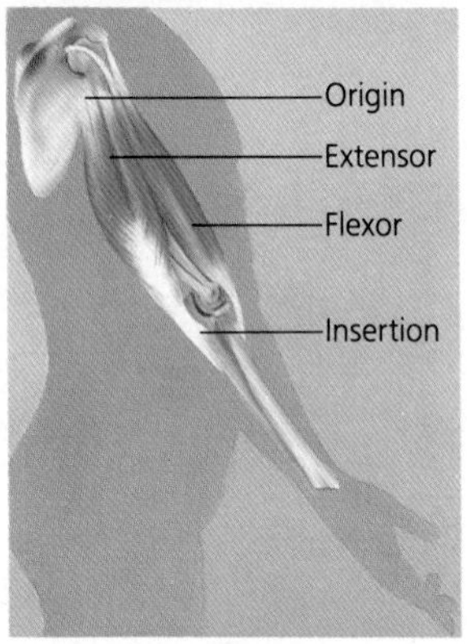

Figure 42-12 When the biceps contracts (top), the elbow bends. When the triceps contracts (bottom), the forearm extends.

position. The process is repeated, with the myosin heads moving down the actin filament and reattaching to a new position. Because actin filaments are attached to the Z lines, the Z lines move closer to each other, and the entire sarcomere contracts. The synchronized shortening of sarcomeres along the full length of a muscle fiber causes the whole fiber, and hence the muscle, to contract. The contraction process continues until calcium and ATP supplies are depleted or nerve stimulation stops.

Experiments have revealed that the relaxing of muscle fibers requires energy also. The energy is used to enable the heads of the cross-bridges to detach themselves and move back to their original positions.

When a single muscle fiber is stimulated, an all-or-none response occurs. This means that the fiber either contracts or it doesn't. No in-between state exists. How, then, can you contract your muscles tightly enough to lift a dumbbell or gently enough to lift a penny? The force of a contraction is determined by the number of fibers stimulated. As more fibers are activated, the force of the contraction increases.

How Muscles Move Bones

When skeletal muscles contract, they pull at the base of a joint. For example, the biceps, the large muscle at the front of the upper arm, is connected by tendons to the forearm at one end and to the shoulder bone at the other. When the biceps contract, the forearm moves while the shoulder remains still. The point of attachment on the moving bone—in this case the forearm—is called the **insertion.** The point of attachment on the stationary bone—in this case the shoulder bone—is the **origin.**

Most skeletal muscles function in opposing pairs. One muscle in a pair moves a body part in one direction, and the other muscle moves it in the opposite direction. Opposing muscles can be grouped into several categories based on their actions. For example, flexors, such as the biceps, bend joints. Extensors, such as the triceps, straighten joints. Abductors, such as the deltoid, move a limb away from the body, as when you raise your arm out to the side. Adductors, such as the pectorals, move a limb toward the body, as when you lower your arm to the side of your body.

Section Review

1. What is a *sarcomere?*
2. What are some functional differences between skeletal and cardiac muscles?
3. What happens within the muscle fibers to cause a muscle to contract?
4. What factor affects the strength of a muscle contraction?
5. How might injury to one of the muscles in a pair affect movement?

Answers to Section Review
1. The functional unit of contraction in a skeletal muscle
2. Skeletal muscle moves bones and is voluntary; cardiac muscle pumps blood and is involuntary.
3. Sarcomeres shorten in synchrony; therefore, muscle fibers contract as does the muscle.
4. The force of a contraction is determined by the number of fibers stimulated.
5. The joint would have unhindered movement in only one direction.

42.4 Integumentary System

The integumentary system, consisting of the skin, hair, and nails, acts as a protective barrier between the body and the outside world. It also functions to retain body fluids, protect against disease, eliminate waste products, and regulate body temperature. As you read the following sections, refer to Figure 42-13.

Section Objectives

- *Describe the functions of the skin.*
- *Distinguish between the different layers of skin.*
- *Identify two glands found in the skin, and describe their functions.*

Epidermis

The skin, which is the largest organ of the human body, is made up of the epidermis and dermis. The **epidermis,** or outer part of the skin, is composed of many layers of cells. The outer layer of cells are dead and are constantly being shed and replaced by new cells from the rapidly dividing inner layers. The cells of the epidermis are filled with a protein, called **keratin,** that gives the skin its rough, leathery texture and its waterproof quality.

Dermis

Dermis, the inner layer of the skin, is composed of living cells and contains nerves, blood, and lymph vessels. The numerous nerves make it possible for the skin to receive many kinds of environmental signals. The blood vessels release heat and help the body maintain a comfortable temperature. The lymph helps the skin fight against infection.

A layer of fat cells lies below the dermis. These cells enable the skin to store food for energy. They also provide protection to the body and insulate it against heat loss.

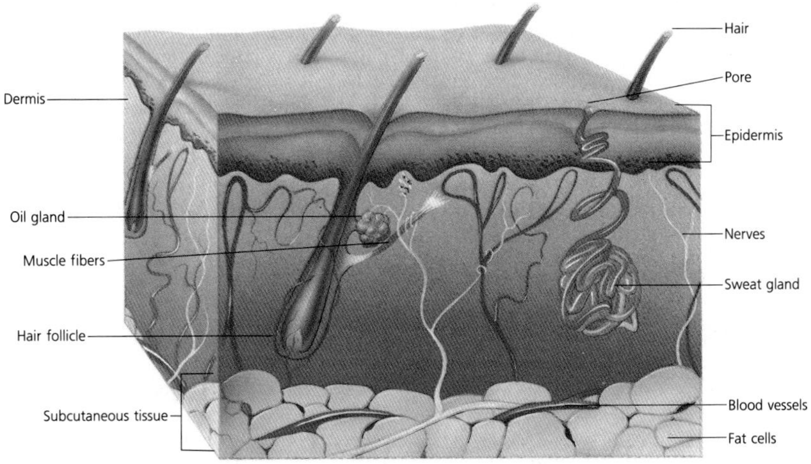

Figure 42-13 Cells in the dermis, the layer of skin beneath the epidermis, are adapted to perform a variety of functions.

Lesson Plan

Section Focus

This section describes the integumentary system and its variety of functions: protection, fluid retention, waste elimination, and temperature regulation. Students will learn about the organ called skin.

Section Themes

The theme of **Systems and Interactions** is evident in the integumentary system's relation to the rest of the body. For example, sweating helps keep body temperature compatible with optimal metabolism and other biochemical functions.

Motivating Activity

Give students hand lenses to examine their skin. What structures do they observe? *(Pores and hairs)* What passes through pores and openings around hairs to the surface? *(Sweat and oil)* How does skin look? *(Rough and leathery)* Challenge students to infer the skin's functions from their observations. *(Protection, fluid retention, waste elimination, temperature regulation)*

Teaching Strategies

Interpreting the Visuals Ask students the functions of the structures labeled on Figure 42-13. For example, ask what the function of an oil gland is. *(Secretes sebum, which helps soften and waterproof the skin)*

Guided Practice

Have students identify the structures such as epidermis, pores, or sweat glands as shown in Figure 42-13. Have them describe each structure's function. *(Epidermis waterproofs the body; pores allow sweat to be excreted; sweat glands help regulate body temperature.)*

Videodiscs

- *2650, Human Skin (s)*

body temperature rises → circulation increases → skin becomes warm and flushed → sweat glands release sweat → water in sweat evaporates; skin is cooled

Graphic Organizer Use this sequential diagram in Independent Practice on p. 650.

Section 42.4

Answer to Think

Putting on a jacket helps the man retain heat and prevents him from losing too much water. This will keep him from becoming chilled and will help his body return to its normal temperature.

Independent Practice

- Have students write answers to the Section Review.
- Have students devise a sequential diagram showing how the skin helps regulate body temperature. An example of a completed diagram is shown on p. 649.

Check Your Understanding

1. What is the dermis composed of? *(Living cells)*
2. What surrounds hair follicles and nourishes the hair root? *(Blood vessels)*
3. What determines skin color? *(The amount of melanin present)*

Reteaching

Some people do not sweat, or they sweat very little. Ask students to consider what such a person should avoid. *(He or she should avoid situations in which overheating might occur, such as hard work on a very hot day.)*

- *See* **Section Reviews** *worksheet, Section 42.4.*

Enrichment

Have students list types of skin cancer and their relationship to overexposure to the sun. Sources may include library research, a dermatologist, or the American Cancer Society.

Closure

Ask students to think about the problems a burn victim would face. Have students focus on how the functions of the skin would be diminished. *(For example, a burn victim's risk of infection increases because the skin no longer serves as a barrier to pathogens.)*

Think

The person in the picture has just completed a strenuous workout. Even though the weather is warm, he is wearing a jacket. What function might the jacket serve in helping the man regulate his body temperature?

Hair and Nails

Hair is produced by cells at the base of the **hair follicles,** deep pockets that extend into the dermis. Blood vessels surrounding the hair follicles nourish the hair root. The shaft of hair that extends beyond the skin consists mostly of keratin and requires no nourishment. Oil secreted by glands in the skin prevents the shaft from drying out and breaking off. Most individual hairs usually grow for several years and then fall out. However hair on the scalp can grow continuously for many years.

Nails, which protect the ends of the fingers and toes, form from cells at the end of a deep fold of epidermis. As new cells form at the base of the nail, the nail grows longer. Like hair, nails are composed primarily of keratin.

Glands

The skin contains exocrine glands, glands that release secretions through ducts. The main exocrine glands of the skin are the **sweat glands** and the **oil glands.**

The skin functions as an excretory organ by releasing excess water, salts, and urea through the sweat glands. By releasing excess water the skin also helps regulate body temperature. When the body temperature rises, the circulation increases, and the skin becomes warm and flushed. The sweat glands then release sweat. As the water in the sweat evaporates the skin is cooled.

The oil glands secrete a substance known as sebum. This substance helps soften the skin and keeps it waterproof. These glands are usually associated with hair follicles. The production of sebum is controlled by hormones.

Among humans there is a great variety in skin color. A pigment called **melanin,** which is produced in the lower layers of the epidermis and which absorbs harmful ultraviolet light, helps determine the color of the skin. If a large amount of melanin is produced, the skin will be dark; if a small amount is produced, the skin will be light. In some individuals exposure to sunlight temporarily increases the production of melanin, thus causing the skin to become darker, called a tan. People with fair skin, which cannot produce much melanin, need to minimize their exposure to the sun to protect against sunburn.

Section Review

1. What is *melanin?*
2. Differentiate between the dermis and the epidermis.
3. How does hair grow?
4. Explain the function of the two types of exocrine glands of the skin.
5. How is the shedding of cells by the skin an adaptive advantage?

Answers to Section Review

1. A pigment produced in the lower epidermis that absorbs ultraviolet rays
2. The dermis, the inner layer of the skin, is composed of living cells and contains nerves, blood, and lymph vessels. The epidermis, the outer layer of the skin, is made up of dead cells that contain keratin.
3. Hair grows from cells at the base of the hair follicles.
4. Sweat glands help rid the body of wastes and maintain body temperature; oil glands help keep skin soft and repel water.
5. Shedding dead skin cells carries pathogens and toxins away from the body and allows cells to move from the dermis to the epidermis as they age.

Laboratory

Observing Muscles and Bones

Objective
To examine the structure and the function of the skeletal and muscular systems of chicken wing

Process Skills
Observing, inferring

Materials
Chicken wing, dissecting pan, scissors, forceps, scalpel, paper towel, unlined paper

Inquiry
1 Place a chicken wing in a dissecting pan. Insert the tip of a scissors under the skin at the exposed end of the upper wing. Keeping the scissors away from the muscle, cut the skin to the first joint of the wing.
2 Use your fingers and a forceps to gently pull the skin away from the muscle. As you pull the skin away you will see a thin, clear layer of tissue, called the fascia. What is the function of the fascia?
3 Use scissors, forceps, and a scalpel to remove the skin completely from the muscles and joints of the wing. Then carefully cut away the fascia. Rinse the wing with water. Blot the muscles dry with a paper towel wherever oil globules remain.
4 Observe the muscles and the tendons of the wing. How does the structure of a tendon relate to its function?
5 Hold the upper portion of the wing while moving the lower portion. Which pair of opposing muscles controls this movement?
6 While holding the lower wing, move the wing tip. Note the movement of the muscles and tendons. Make a detailed drawing that shows all of the muscles and tendons in the wing. Identify on your drawing the pairs of opposing muscles that control the movement of the lower wing and the wing tip.
7 Carefully remove the muscles from the bones. How does the structure of muscle relate to its function?
8 Examine the joints of the wing. Note the ligaments, the tough white tissue that connects two bones. How does the structure of ligament relate to its function? Make a drawing of all the bones and ligaments in the wing.
9 Separate the joints. Examine the shapes of the bone ends and the cartilage that covers the bone ends. How does the structure of cartilage relate to its function?

Conclusions
1 How does tendon tissue differ from muscle tissue? What are the structural or organizational characteristics of these tissues that may account for these differences?
2 How does the structure of a joint enable it to move smoothly?
3 Explain how muscles, tendons, bones, ligaments, and joints combine to allow the back and forth movement of the lower wing.

Further Inquiry
The chicken is not capable of sustained flight. Formulate a hypothesis about how the wing structure of birds that fly differs from the wing structure of flightless birds.

(For an overview of skeletal muscles and bones and preparatory information related to the laboratory, see p. 635B.)

Inquiry

2. Fascia (or mesentery) is connective tissue that binds tissues together.
4. Tendons are tough, stringy connective material suited for binding muscles to bone.
5. The muscles on the upper portion control movement of the lower portion.
6. Muscles on the lower portion control movement in the wing tip.
7. Muscle is material that can contract to move body parts.
8. Ligaments are strips of tough, pliable connective material suited for joining bones together at joints.
9. Cartilage is a tough connective tissue that is more flexible than bone, so it is well suited for areas where bones come together.

Conclusions

1. Tendons are thick, white, fibrous bands; muscle is smooth, pinkish tissue. The tough, fibrous tissue of the tendon resists pulling and tearing during movement. Muscle tissue is softer and more flexible.
2. Ligaments hold the bones together; cartilage prevents rubbing, cushions impact; bone ends fit together smoothly.
3. Opposing muscle pairs act across a joint between a stationary and a movable bone. Ligaments bind bones together and tendons attach muscles to bones.

Further Inquiry

In relation to its body size, a flying bird has longer, lighter wing bones and larger wing muscles than a chicken has.

Vocabulary

1. Matrix is a solid, semisolid, or liquid substance that connective tissue is embedded in or surrounded by.
2. Compact bone is a hard material composed of rings of mineral crystals and protein fibers interspersed with osteocytes. Spongy bone is a lacy network of connective tissue containing bone marrow.
3. A sarcomere is bounded by Z bands, which are attached to actin filaments. Between actin filaments are myosin filaments.
4. Skeletal muscle is striated voluntary muscle attached to bone. Cardiac muscle is striated involuntary muscle that makes up the walls of the heart. Smooth muscle is nonstriated involuntary muscle found in the walls of organs such as the stomach, intestines, and blood vessels.
5. The epidermis is primarily made up of dead cells and is found on the external surface of the skin. The dermis is rich with living cells and is found under the epidermis.

Review

1. c	**6.** b
2. a	**7.** d
3. b	**8.** c
4. c	**9.** a
5. a	**10.** d

11. The abdominal cavity contains the stomach, intestines, reproductive organs, and excretory organs.
12. An organ system contains various organs that work together.
13. The five functions of the skeletal system are: support of muscles and organs, maintenance of shape and structure of the body, protection of organs, storage of minerals, and manufacture of blood cells.
14. The interconnected Haversian canals provide pathways for blood vessels and nerves to reach the osteocytes.
15. The synovial fluid and the bursa prevent the bones of a joint from rubbing together.
16. Skeletal muscle is made up of muscle fibers that consist of myofibrils, which are divided into sarcomeres composed of two types of protein filaments, actin and myosin.
17. Arthroscopic surgery minimizes recovery time because a local anesthesia is used and only a small incision needs to be made.
18. A specialized muscle membrane releases calcium into the muscle cytoplasm.
19. Hair grows from specialized cells at the base of a hair follicle. Oil produced by glands in the skin prevents hair from drying out.
20. To absorb ultraviolet light

Chapter 42 Review

Vocabulary

abdominal cavity (637)
actin (647)
appendicular skeleton (641)
axial skeleton (641)
bone marrow (641)
bursa (644)
cardiac muscle (646)
cartilage (642)
compact bone (641)
connective tissue (638)
cranial cavity (637)
dermis (649)
dorsal cavity (637)
endoskeleton (640)
epidermis (649)
epiphyseal plate (643)
epithelial tissue (638)
hair follicle (650)
Haversian canal (641)
insertion (648)
joint (643)
keratin (649)
ligament (643)
melanin (650)
muscle (645)
muscle fiber (646)
muscle tissue (638)
myofibril (646)
myosin (647)
nervous tissue (638)
oil gland (650)
organ (639)
organ system (639)
origin (648)
ossification (642)
osteocyte (641)
periosteum (641)
sarcomere (646)
skeletal muscle (645)
skeleton (640)
smooth muscle (646)
spinal cavity (637)
spongy bone (641)
striation (645)
sweat gland (650)
tendon (645)
thoracic cavity (637)
tissue (638)
ventral cavity (637)

1. What is the matrix of connective tissue?
2. Distinguish between compact bone and spongy bone.
3. List the components of a sarcomere.
4. Distinguish between skeletal, cardiac, and smooth muscle.
5. What is the difference between the dermis and the epidermis?

Review

1. The thoracic cavity contains the (a) brain (b) intestines (c) respiratory organs (d) spine.
2. The connective tissue is embedded in a substance called its (a) matrix (b) organ (c) cell (d) bone.
3. The periosteum (a) produces erythrocytes (b) covers the bone (c) contains marrow (d) contains Haversian canals.
4. During ossification (a) cartilage replaces bone cells (b) bones become stronger (c) bone replaces cartilage (d) marrow is produced.
5. Hinge joints allow (a) back-and-forth movement (b) circular movement (c) no movement (d) gliding movement.
6. Cardiac muscle is (a) voluntary muscle (b) involuntary muscle (c) a type of smooth muscle (d) found in the lungs.
7. Actin and myosin are (a) found in joints (b) types of cartilage (c) types of muscle cells (d) parts of the sarcomere.
8. Skeletal muscles (a) push and pull bones (b) push bones (c) pull bones (d) cannot be controlled.
9. The outer layer of the epidermis (a) is primarily made up of dead cells (b) contains blood vessels (c) contains nerve cells (d) contains sweat glands.
10. The dermis (a) is primarily made up of dead cells (b) contains keratin (c) is the top layer of the skin (d) contains nerves and blood vessels.
11. What organs are found in the abdominal cavity?
12. What is the relationship between an organ and its organ system?
13. What are the five functions of the skeletal system?
14. Explain the role of the Haversian canals in the bones.
15. What prevents the bones from rubbing together at a joint?
16. Describe the parts of a skeletal muscle.

17. What are some advantages of arthroscopic surgery?
18. What happens when a motor unit is stimulated?
19. How does hair grow? What substance keeps it from drying out? What produces this substance?
20. What is the function of melanin?

Critical Thinking

1. During a normal birth, the baby must pass through the mother's pelvis. The pelvis of the female is much larger in diameter and more oval in shape than that of the male. In addition, the skull bones of a newborn are not completely ossified but are somewhat plastic. Give two reasons why these skeletal properties make birth easier.
2. If young thoroughbred horses are raced too hard and too fast early in life, their leg bones may break. What can you infer about the process of ossification in horses?
3. As you have learned, red bone marrow produces erythrocytes. How are these solids transported to other parts of the body? Use the picture to help you explain your answer.

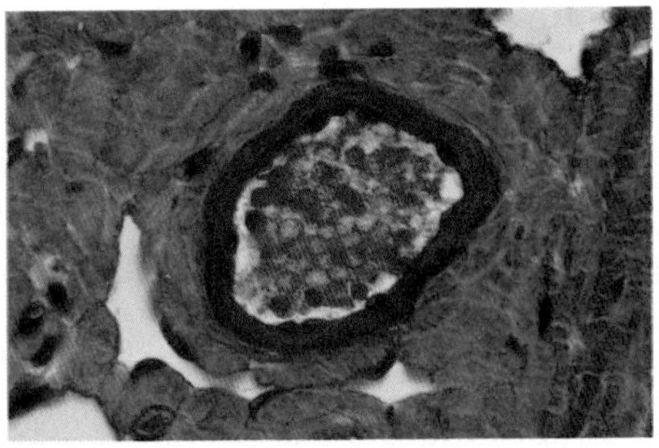

4. Blood vessels have one layer of smooth muscle that encircles the vessel wall. The stomach and small intestine have one layer of circular smooth muscle and one layer of longitudinal smooth muscle. How does this muscle arrangement reflect the function of each structure?
5. In addition to oil, the oil glands of human skin secrete fatty acids that help kill bacteria. Keeping this in mind, why can it actually be unhealthy to wash your skin too much?
6. Both the epithelial cells of the skin and the shingles of a roof are flat and overlapping. How does overlapping help both cells and shingles perform their respective protective functions?

Extension

1. Read the article by Deborah Erickson entitled "Skin Stand-ins" in *Scientific American,* September 1990, p. 168. Describe the different types of dermal substitutes and their possible uses. Focus on why a dermal equivalent is not yet considered to be "artificial skin."
2. Read "Back Track to Fitness" in *Omni,* October 1990, p. 24. Prepare an oral report in which you dicuss the Muscle Fatigue Monitor and its role in physical therapy. How could a company use the MFM to save money?
3. Research and write a report on the effects of a particular exercise on the human body. Choose one exercise, such as running, biking, gymnastics, tennis, or wrestling. What type of skills are necessary for your chosen sport: endurance, strength, speed, fine motor coordination? Do champion athletes in your chosen sport show particular physiological adaptations that enable them to excel? For instance, is a high percentage of their muscle mass in their upper body? Do they have a very low percentage of body fat?

Critical Thinking

1. The larger, oval-shaped pelvis of the mother gives the baby more room to pass through the birth canal. The plasticity of the baby's skull bones allows the head to be compressed when passing through the birth canal.
2. Ossification continues in horses after birth, and thus the bones of young horses are less able to withstand stress than are those of adult horses.
3. They are transported to other parts of the body through the bloodstream, which enters the bones through the Haversian canals.
4. Blood vessels need to constrict in only one way to push blood through the system. The stomach and small intestines constrict in two ways to break up and move food.
5. Too much bathing can remove the fatty acids and thus reduce the skin's natural defense against bacteria.
6. The overlapping helps to eliminate cracks that water or other substances could pass through.

Extension

1. These dermal substitutes do not have enough of the attributes of real skin to be good substitutes for skin grafts. They do not have immune cells or natural coloring, for example.
2. Answer may include savings on workers' compensation and savings from increased productivity (less cheating).
3. Point out to students that although certain body types may be better adapted to certain sports, there have been many instances in which an unlikely-looking person has excelled in a sport.

Chapter 43 Circulatory and Respiratory Systems

Chapter Overview

Chapter 43 describes how the human circulatory and respiratory systems function in transporting nutrients to and wastes from the body's cells. Section 43.1 focuses on the circulatory system, its structure, and its relationship to the lungs and the lymphatic system. Section 43.2 describes blood, its composition, and its function. Section 43.3 discusses the respiratory system, its parts, and its role in supporting body cells.

Chapter Planning Chart

B	S	A	Sections and Subsections	Page	Features	Page	Resources
•	•	•	**43.1 Circulatory System**				
			The Heart	655	Biology in Process	658	Videodiscs
			Blood Vessels	657	Think	660	Blackline Master 88
			Patterns of Circulation	658	Section Review	661	Overhead Transparency T43
			Lymphatic System	661			Blackline Master 89
							Laboratories: Daphnia Heartbeat
							Section Reviews Worksheet
•	•	•	**43.2 Blood**				
			Composition of Blood	662	Section Review	664	Videodiscs
			Blood Types	663			Process Skills: Leukocytes
							Section Reviews Worksheet
•	•	•	**43.3 Respiratory System**				
			The Lungs	665	Laboratory	669	Videodiscs
			Mechanism of Breathing	666	Section Review	668	Laboratories: Pulse and Breathing Rate
			The Passage of Air	667			Section Reviews Worksheet
			Gas Exchange and Transport	667			
			Regulation of Breathing	668			
			End of Chapter Activities				
					Chapter Review	670	Vocabulary Skills
							Chapter Test
							Computer Test Generator

B *The Basic Level curriculum presents the most fundamental knowledge offered in the course.*
S *The Standard Level curriculum is designed for the average student who is able to master most topics.*
A *The Advanced Level curriculum includes suggestions for teaching the most academically able students.*

Cooperative Learning

Group Activity: Comparing Blood Cell Types

- **Group Size:** *3 students*
- **Outcome:** *Students will compare types of blood cells: erythrocytes, leukocytes, and platelets.*
- **Individual Accountability:** *Each student will gather and organize information about one type of blood cell to share with other group members.*
- **Positive Interdependence:** *Individual group members will verify information with a larger "expert" group of students who are studying the same type of cell, and will then share this information with the original three-member group.*

Have each student in a group choose a different kind of cell from the three blood cells described in Section 43.2. Ask students to use library resources to find out more about their particular type of cell. Also set up microscope stations, each with a labeled slide of red cells (erythrocytes), white cells (leukocytes), or platelets. Have all students observe the three kinds of cells.

After students have completed their research, have all students who chose the same type of blood cell meet and share information. Then have the original three-member groups meet and together assemble a chart summarizing the information each member gathered. Encourage students to use illustrations on their charts and to be as creative as possible in their layouts. Have students display their charts in the classroom and refer to them when discussing components of the blood.

Concept Map

The following is one possible solution to the concept mapping activity in Relating Concepts on p. 656.

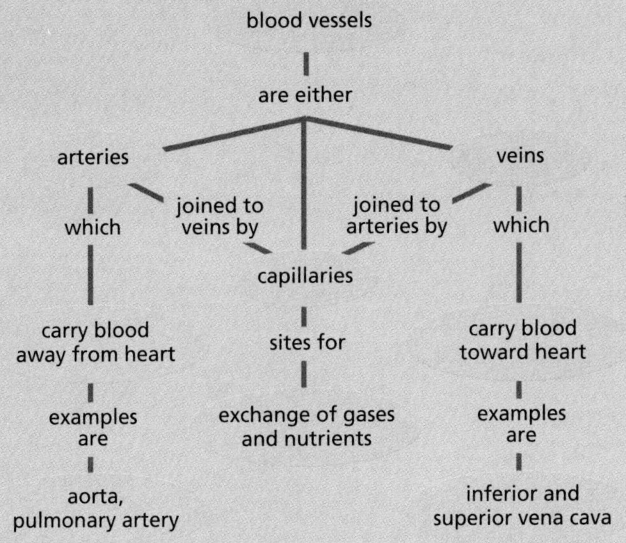

Laboratory Preparation

Overview *(See p. 669.)*

In this lab students measure and learn about breathing rate and tidal volume of the lungs. They form a hypothesis related to the lab objective and then design and set up a controlled experiment to test it. Students collect data and analyze them to determine whether they support the hypothesis.

Preparation

The plastic jugs must be clear or translucent to reveal the water level inside. Have students bring in water or milk jugs. The same jug and rubber tubing may be used for any number of students. The mouthpieces, however, must be discarded after each use. Cut wide plastic drinking straws into short (about 4 cm) lengths for use as mouthpieces. Have a plentiful supply.

Prepare the jugs as described in the Technique section, or have students complete the calibration as their prelab preparation.

Teaching Tips

Have students read the Technique section carefully before they design their experiment.

To relate this laboratory to daily life, explain to students that doctors routinely measure tidal volumes, lung capacities, and breathing rates of hospital patients with lung diseases such as emphysema and asthma. Such measurements are also frequent preoperative tests. Discuss how these tests can show improvement or deterioration in lung function and can suggest the sort of postoperative support a patient might need.

Remind students that lungs are only one part of the cardiopulmonary system. When they think about Further Inquiry, this concept will help them understand why heart rate also increases with exercise.

To get an accurate reading of tidal volume, hold the jug level. Align it with the water surface in the bucket. When they are parallel, the jug is level.

You will have to approve students' experiments before they are performed. Make sure students control for such conditions as time intervals and amount of exercise. Make sure students' breathing returns to normal between trials.

Safety

Caution students with health problems not to perform vigorous exercise. Do not allow them to continue if they feel pain or become dizzy or tired. Caution students to breathe normally between steps to avoid hyperventilation. Wipe up water spills so that no one slips and falls.

Chapter Themes

Systems and Interactions The circulatory and respiratory systems are two of the 11 major organ systems of the human body. Emphasize the interactions between these two systems and between each of these systems and other organ systems.

Energy The energy converted during cell metabolism lets human beings maintain their organ systems, grow, and reproduce. Point out that the body needs energy to maintain the circulatory system and that, in turn, this system transports the raw materials of metabolism to the cells where energy is converted.

Scale and Structure The structures and functions of the human circulatory and respiratory systems are uniquely adapted to keep the complex human organism alive. The structure of the different blood vessels, for example, promotes the function of transport to and from all the cells of the body. The structure of the lungs promotes gas exchange between air and the blood.

Chapter Motivating Activity

Ask students to describe what kinds of physical changes they experience during vigorous exercise. *(The heart beats faster, the number and volume of breaths increases, and the skin flushes and sweats.)* Have students explain why the body responds in these ways. *(The body is trying to speed extra O_2 to the cells and remove CO_2 as well as cool the body.)* Emphasize that human activity is limited by the amount of energy the cells can supply.

Chapter 43 Circulatory and Respiratory Systems

Introduction

A single-celled organism is often bathed in a nutrient- and oxygen-rich fluid. Its survival depends on the exchange of substances through the cell membrane. For humans the process of nutrient and gas exchange is not so simple. The human circulatory and respiratory systems transport substances to and from cells embedded deep within the body.

Chapter Outline

Chapter Concept

As you read, identify ways in which the structures of the circulatory and respiratory systems are related to their functions of transport and exchange of materials.

Inside of human heart. Inset: SEM of bronchial mucous glands (x1,172)

Understanding the Visuals

As students study the photo of the heart, have them speculate on the location from which the photo was taken. *(The camera was looking up from the bottom of the right ventricle.)* Help students locate this area in Figure 43-1 on p. 655.

Explain that the thick bands shown in the photo are papillary muscles and that their threadlike tendons attach to the tricuspid valve. Ask students to infer the tendons' function. *(They hold the valve flaps in position.)*

Have students study the inset photo. What is the function of the mucus glands in the bronchial lining? *(To moisten incoming air and bathe cells in fluid to keep them from drying out)*

43.1 Circulatory System

Human life depends on the distribution of oxygen, hormones, and nutrients to cells in all parts of the body and on the removal of carbon dioxide and other wastes. These tasks are partially carried out by the **circulatory system,** which consists of the heart, an intricate network of blood vessels, and blood. The blood moving through the vessels serves as the transport medium for oxygen, nutrients, and other substances.

The Heart

The **heart** is a muscular organ that pumps blood through the body. About four weeks following fertilization, the fetal heartbeat can be heard as it pumps blood through the developing fetus. The heart continues to beat without interruption more than 2.5 billion times in the average life span. The typical adult heart beats 72 times and pumps about 5.5 L of blood per minute.

The heart rate can change, however, depending on a person's activity level. During strenuous exercise tissues need more oxygen. The heart responds by beating faster and pumping more vigorously. At its maximum rate the heart can reach between 180 and 195 beats per minute and force 17.5 L of blood through its chambers. That's about three times the normal load.

Structure

The heart consists of cardiac muscle, nervous tissue, and connective tissues. The adult heart is about the size of a fist. It lies within the thoracic cavity, behind the sternum and between the two lungs. A tough saclike membrane called the **pericardium** *(PER-uh-KAHR-dee-um)* surrounds the heart and secretes a fluid that reduces friction as the heart beats.

The **septum** divides the heart lengthwise into two sides. The right side pumps blood to the lungs, and the left side pumps blood to the other parts of the body. Each side of the heart is divided into an upper and lower chamber. Each upper chamber is called an **atrium** *(AY-tree-uhm),* and each lower chamber is called a **ventricle** *(VEN-trih-kul).*

In each side of the heart blood flows from the atrium to the ventricle. One-way valves separate these chambers and prevent blood from moving in the wrong direction. The atrioventricular (a-v) valves separate the atria from the ventricles. The a-v valve on the right side is the tricuspid valve, and the a-v valve on the left is the bicuspid valve. Blood also flows out of the ventricles. Two semilunar (s-v) valves separate the ventricles from the large vessels through which blood flows out of the heart. Each of the valves consists of flaps of tissue that open as blood is pumped out of the ventricle. Locate the tricuspid, bicuspid, and semilunar valves in Figure 43-1.

Section Objectives

- *List the different types of vessels found in the circulatory system.*
- *Describe the movement of blood through the heart.*
- *Explain how the sinoatrial and atrioventricular nodes control each heartbeat.*
- *Distinguish between the two primary subsystems of circulation.*
- *Explain how Charles Drew discovered an effective way to preserve blood.*

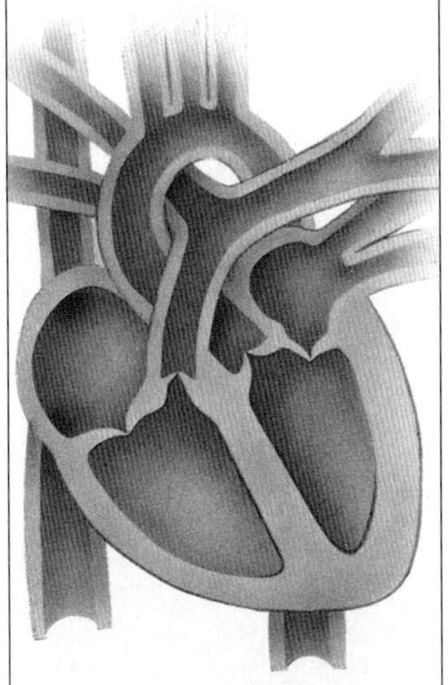

Figure 43-1 Valves control the flow of blood between sections of the heart and from the heart to the rest of the body.

Lesson Plan

Section Focus

This section describes the structures and functions of the circulatory system—heart, blood vessels, and lymphatic system. It also discusses the patterns of blood circulation throughout the body.

Section Themes

The theme of **Scale and Structure** is evident in the discussion of the structure of the heart and blood vessels. Encourage students to relate the structures of these organs to their functions. The theme of **Systems and Interactions** is emphasized in the explanation of the subsystems of the circulatory system, each of which interacts with other body systems. For example, the pulmonary circulation interacts with the respiratory system to such an extent that together they are often referred to as the cardiopulmonary system.

Motivating Activity

Ask a volunteer to have his or her pulse measured for 15 seconds, and have the class calculate this resting pulse rate in beats per minute. Then direct the volunteer first to walk around the room, and then to run in place, each for two minutes. (Note: students with medical excuses from gym class should not volunteer for this.) Measure the pulse rate for 15 seconds after each activity and have the class calculate the two rates in beats per minute. Discuss the connection between pulse rate and activity levels.

Videodiscs

- *2658, Human Heart (s)*

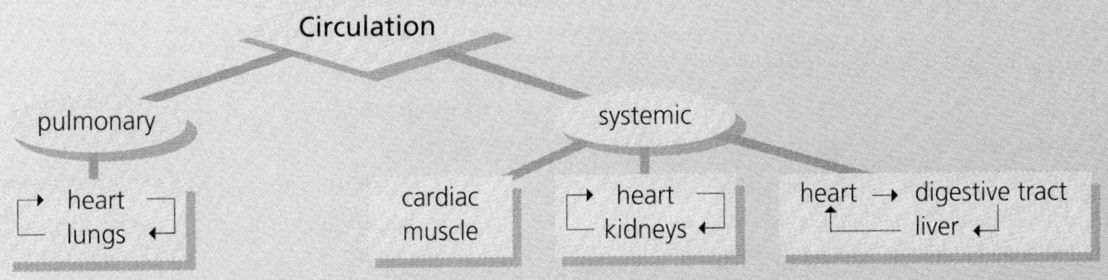

Graphic Organizer Use this organizational chart in Comparing Concepts on p. 658.

Teaching Strategies

Interpreting the Visuals Have students use the text, along with Figure 43-2 on p. 656, to trace the flow of blood through the heart. Ask students what the blue and red colors represent. *(The blue represents deoxygenated blood and the red, oxygenated blood.)* Tell students that deoxygenated blood is not really blue in color but is a darker red than oxygenated blood.

■ *See* **Overhead Transparency *T43 and* Blackline Master *88.***

Relating Concepts Ask students to draw a concept map that illustrates the functions of the different kinds of blood vessels in human organisms. An example of a completed concept map is shown on p. 653B.

Drawing Conclusions Provide a stethoscope and allow students to listen to their heartbeats. Ask them to explain what causes the "lubb dup" sound. *(The "lubb" sound is caused by the closing of the a-v valves while the ventricles contract and force blood through the s-v valves. The "dup" sound is caused by the snapping closed of the s-v valves as blood flows into the ventricles from the atria.)* Help students understand that although the heartbeat is described for convenience as occurring first on the right side and then on the left, the movement of blood occurs on both sides simultaneously.

■ *See* **Laboratories, *Investigation 43.1.***

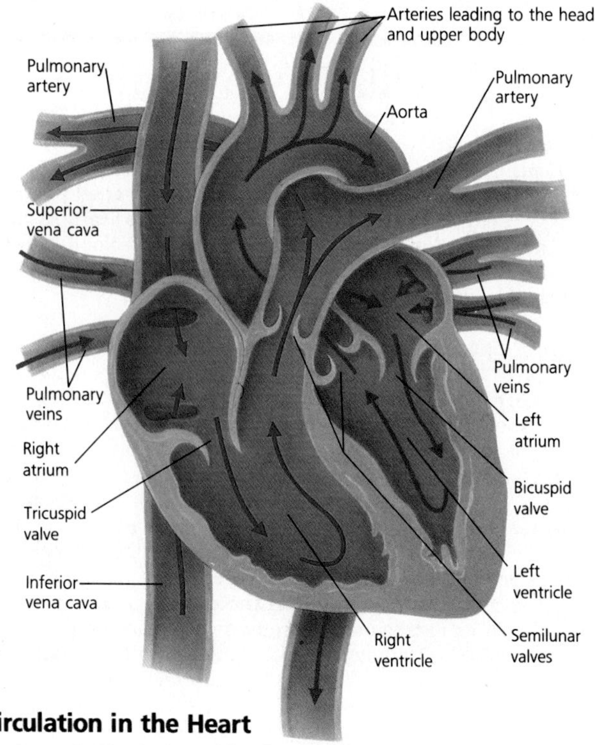

Figure 43-2 Notice the pathway of blood through the heart and the major blood vessels leading to and from the heart.

Circulation in the Heart

As shown in Figure 43-2, blood returning to the heart, which has a high concentration of carbon dioxide and a low concentration of oxygen, enters the right atrium. The atrium pumps it through the tricuspid valve into the right ventricle. The muscles of the right ventricle contract and force the blood through the right semilunar valve and into vessels leading to the lungs. In the lungs, carbon dioxide leaves the circulating blood and oxygen enters it. The oxygenated blood returns to the left atrium of the heart. The oxygenated blood is then pumped through the bicuspid valve into the left ventricle. Strong contractions of the muscles of the left ventricle force the blood through the semilunar valve, into a large blood vessel, and then throughout the body.

Figure 43-3 Each heartbeat starts with a nerve impulse from the sinoatrial node. Within a tenth of a second the impulse reaches the atrioventricular node.

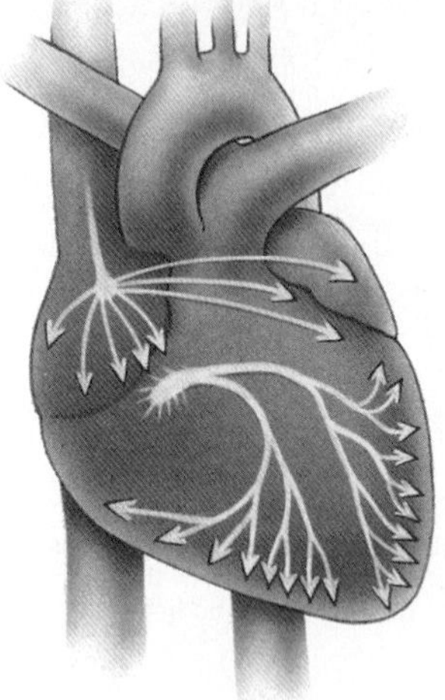

Control of Heartbeat

The heart consists mostly of cardiac muscle, which functions differently from skeletal muscle. Unlike skeletal muscle, in which each cell contracts individually, cardiac muscle cells contract in waves. When the first cell is stimulated, it excites neighboring cells. Those cells in turn stimulate surrounding cells. This chain reaction proceeds until all the cells contract. As the activity spreads, the atria and ventricles contract in synchronous rhythm.

The initial stimulus of this wavelike contraction begins in the **sinoatrial** *(sie-noe-AY-tree-ul)* **node** (s-a node), a region of

Interdisciplinary Activity

Technology Many people with abnormal heart rhythms have been helped by a small electronic device called a pacemaker. Have students research pacemakers and their use in patients with heart disease. Students can find out who invented the pacemaker, what kinds of pacemakers are available, where pacemakers are positioned in the body, and how they are adjusted. Have students find out what types of heart patients are candidates for pacemaker implants. Students can make a drawing of a pacemaker connected to the heart and write an explanation of how it works.

Some students may want to do research in the library, regarding other technologies related to heart disease, such as artificial valves, defibrillators, angioplasty, and artificial hearts. Some of these technologies are specialized cardiac muscle cells located in the right atrium, as shown in Figure 43-3. The s-a node is often called the pacemaker because it regulates the rate of contraction of the entire heart. The s-a node generates an electrical charge that stimulates the atria to contract. About a tenth of a second later the impulse reaches the **atrioventricular** *(AY-tree-oe-ven-TRIK-yuh-lur)* **node** (a-v node), located in the septum between the atria. The a-v node delays the impulse for about a millisecond and then sends it into the ventricles. This electrical charge causes the ventricles to contract, completing the full beat.

The beat just described can also be described as having two phases. In one phase, called **systole,** the ventricles contract and force blood into the arteries. In another phase, called **diastole,** the ventricles relax, and the blood flows in from the atria. The result is the characteristic "lubb dup" we call a heartbeat.

Blood Vessels

Each beat of the heart forces blood through blood vessels. The large, muscular vessels that carry blood away from the heart are called **arteries.** The thick walls of the arteries have three layers, as shown in Figure 43-4: an inner endothelium, a middle layer of smooth muscle, and an outer layer of connective tissue. This structure gives arteries a combination of strength and elasticity that allows them to stretch as blood under high pressure enters them from the heart. You can feel this stretching of arteries as the pulse in your wrist.

When the left ventricle contracts, it forces blood through the left semilunar valve into the body's largest artery, the **aorta.** From the aorta blood travels through a network of smaller arteries, which in turn divide and form even smaller vessels called **arterioles.** The arterioles branch into a fan of tiny vessels called **capillaries,** shown in Figure 43-5. Capillary walls are only one cell thick. Diffusion of gases and nutrients takes place across the thin capillary walls from areas of greater concentration to areas of lesser concentration. If the concentrations of oxygen and nutrients are higher in the blood than in the surrounding cells, these substances will diffuse from the blood into the cells. In this way cells take in oxygen and nutrients and in a similar manner discharge wastes into the blood.

Deoxygenated blood flows through capillaries that merge and form larger vessels called **venules.** Several venules in turn unite to form a **vein,** a large blood vessel that carries blood to the heart. From the lower part of the body the venules transport blood into veins that merge to form the **inferior vena cava** *(VEE-nuh KAY-vuh).* Venules from the upper part of the body merge to form veins, which in turn unite to form the **superior vena cava.** These large veins then carry blood back to the heart.

The walls of veins, which are also composed of three layers, are thinner and less muscular than those of arteries. By the time

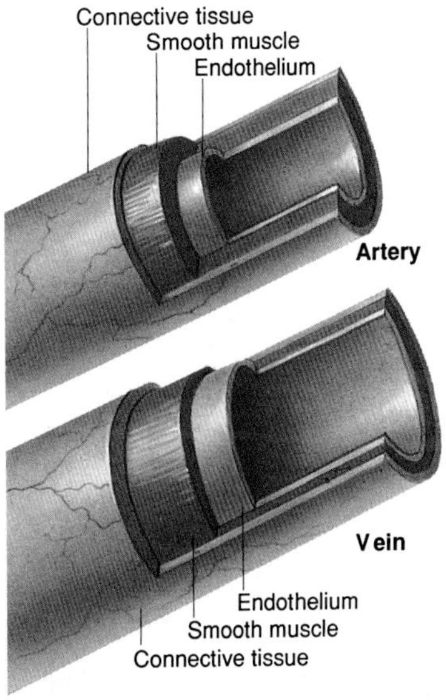

Figure 43-4 The muscle layer of an artery is thicker and stronger than the muscle layer of a vein. Why is this so?

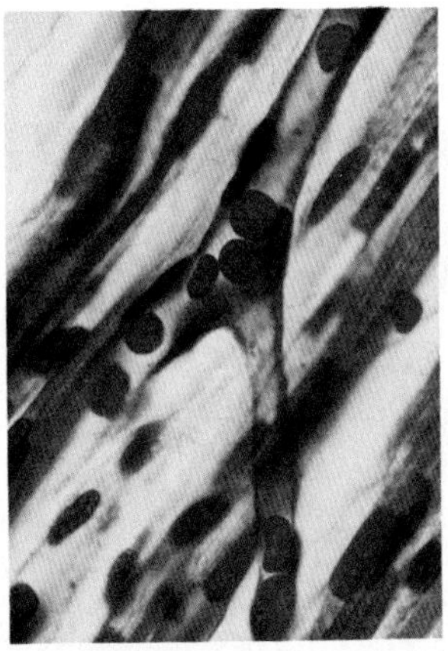

Figure 43-5 Erythrocytes move in single file through the capillaries, as shown in this photo (×1,200).

extremely expensive. Other students may wish to explore economic, legal, or other issues that are connected with the uses of medical technology. Have students share their findings with the class.

Exploring Careers Ask a hematologist to speak to students about diseases of the blood and the ongoing research to find cures. For example, the physician could discuss hemophilia and sickle-cell anemia. Encourage students to write questions in advance for the hematologist to answer.

Comparing Structures Have students study the illustrations in Figure 43-4 and identify how the structure of an artery and vein are alike. *(Both are made of three layers of tissue.)* How are they different? *(Arteries have a thicker layer of smooth muscle than veins have. Veins are valved.)* Have students explain how this difference in structure relates to the difference in function of an artery and a vein. *(The structure of an artery gives it strength and elasticity, allowing it to stretch as blood under pressure from the heart enters it. Blood in a vein is under less pressure, so a vein needs valves to prevent blood from backing up and pooling.)*

Observing an Organism Place a chilled, living goldfish in a watch glass, and cover all but its tail with a wet cloth. Carefully position its tail between two clean slides. Have students use hand lenses or a stereomicroscope to observe the tail, noting arteries and veins. Ask students how they can tell the difference between these two blood vessels. *(The blood cells in the arteries move toward the edges of the fins with each heartbeat; the opposite occurs in the veins.)* Keep the fish cool and wet during this activity.

Videodiscs

- ***Side 2 12259, Blood Flow and Heart Sounds (m)***
- ***Side 2 14805, Living Blood Cells (m)***
- ***Side 2 29869, Heart Muscle (m)***

Inferring Relationships Have students discuss the relationship between blood vessel structure and the function of the heart. Ask students whether the heart could move blood through the hundreds of kilometers of blood vessels if the vessels were rigid and without valves. *(The heart would have to work many times harder to pump blood. The vessel elasticity and the contractions of vessel wall muscles continue the movement of blood begun by the heart. The one-way valves in the veins prevent backflow.)*

Applying Concepts Show students a model or a medical illustration of the inside of a human heart. Ask students to compare the walls of the right and left ventricles and identify which are thicker. *(The left ventricle has walls approximately three times thicker than the right.)* Have students discuss the significance of this difference. *(The left ventricle must be a stronger pump, since it pumps blood throughout the entire body.)*

Comparing Concepts Draw on the board the organizational chart on p. 655 and ask students to compare the paths of the systemic circulation subsystems. Ask students which of the subsystems is markedly different from the others and what the importance of this difference is. *(The hepatic portal circulation is different; in this subsystem, the blood carries the nutrients from the digestive tract to the liver before going to the heart.)* Explain to students that the liver stores carbohydrates and helps to maintain a constant level of glucose in the blood. The liver also detoxifies blood and changes fats and other substances into forms usable by other organs.

blood reaches the veins, it is under much less pressure than it is in the arteries. Thus the veins are not as strong or as flexible as the arteries. Many veins pass through skeletal muscles; during movement these muscles contract, squeezing blood through the veins. Valves prevent the blood from moving backward or downward. These valves, which are usually located above the point at which two veins meet, allow blood to flow in only one direction through the veins. However, when muscle tone is poor, a person's valves may not fully come together, which will then allow some blood to seep backward through the valves.

Patterns of Circulation

The English scientist William Harvey (1578–1657) first showed that the heart and blood vessels formed one continuous, closed system of circulation. To communicate effectively, scientists often say this system is divided into various subsystems. The two primary subsystems of circulation are pulmonary circulation, in which the blood travels between the heart and lungs, and systemic circulation, in which the blood travels between the heart and all other body tissues.

Biology in Process

Charles Drew: Blood Banking Pioneer

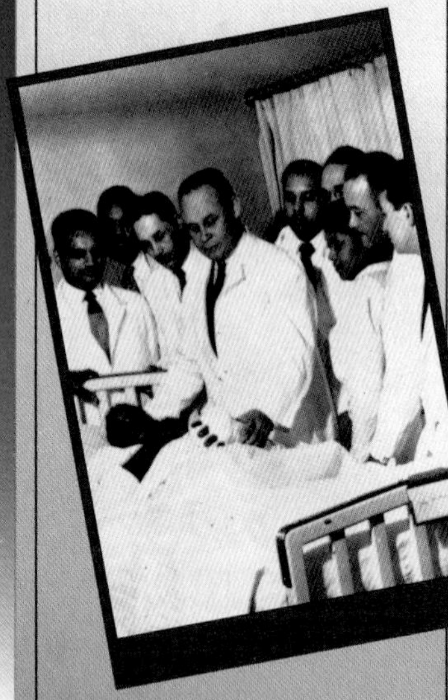

Until 1938 blood transfusions had to be made with the donor present. Few hospitals had any facility for storing blood because it was highly perishable. When a surgical or trauma patient needed blood, a donor had to be found immediately. Charles Drew became interested in this problem while he was a medical student specializing in surgery at McGill University in Montreal, Canada.

The four blood types, A, B, AB, and O, had been identified only a few years earlier. This helped eliminate many difficulties with transfusion, but blood spoilage was still a serious problem. In 1938 Drew, a professor at Howard University Medical School, received a grant to study and work at Columbia University in New York City. He helped set up the blood bank at Columbia's hospital. It soon became the national model.

For more than two years, Drew experimented with a variety of physical and chemical factors in blood, hoping to lengthen the storage time. However, many of the changes left the blood unfit for transfusion.

Also, at Columbia, Drew worked as part of a team investigating surgical shock. Shock often occurs following massive wounds or surgery, and may be

Interdisciplinary Activity

History The views that scientists have held concerning the composition, function, and circulation of blood have changed drastically since ancient times. Have students research some of the predominant theories once held about blood and the circulatory system and the significant discoveries that changed or modified these theories. Some students may want to explore the view of Hippocrates in 400 B.C. that blood was one of the four humors, or fluids, of the body and relate this theory to the practice of bloodletting. Other students, focusing on William Harvey's discoveries, may want to find out about the ways in which scientists of the 1500s and 1600s thought that blood moved through the body.

Pulmonary Circulation

Pulmonary circulation is the movement of blood from the heart to the lungs and back to the heart. Blood from the right ventricle flows through the right semilunar valve into the **pulmonary artery** and then to the lungs. The pulmonary artery is the only artery that carries deoxygenated blood. At the lungs the pulmonary artery divides into two smaller arteries, one leading to each lung. These arteries branch into arterioles and then into capillaries. Blood in the capillaries releases carbon dioxide and absorbs oxygen. Oxygenated blood then flows into venules, which merge into the **pulmonary veins** that lead to the left atrium of the heart. The pulmonary veins are the only veins that carry oxygenated blood.

Systemic Circulation

Systemic circulation is the movement of blood to all parts of the body except the lungs and then back to the heart. Blood from the left ventricle enters systemic circulation through the aorta. Systemic circulation is further divided into several other subsystems. These subsystems are coronary circulation, renal circulation, and hepatic portal circulation.

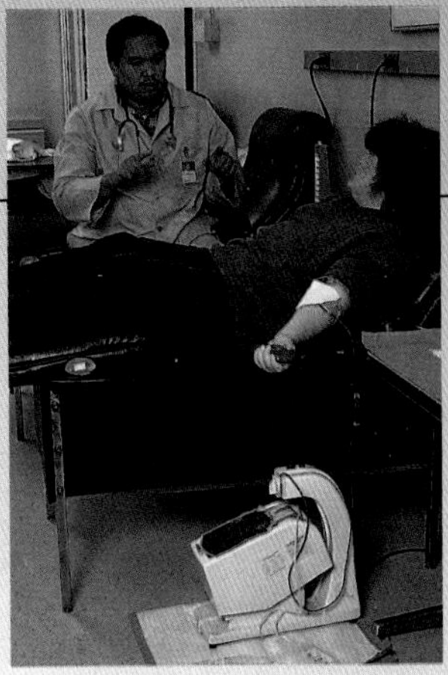

fatal if not treated promptly. Drew recommended giving shock patients just plasma, the portion of the blood without cells. Plasma provided an immediate treatment and could be stored much longer than whole blood. It had no type, so it could be given to anyone. Plasma saved lives and soon became the treatment of choice for surgical shock.

During World War II, Drew was asked to set up blood banks in England. He designed uniform procedures and suggested that plasma be banked instead of whole blood. Many soldiers probably owed their survival to these two simple changes.

When the American Red Cross joined in the effort, they named Drew director of their blood bank project. Although Drew set up a very successful program to collect blood, a storm of controversy erupted. The U.S. armed forces announced that "Negro" blood would not be accepted. Under the armed forces rules, Drew, the very doctor who designed the blood collection program, would be refused as a donor.

Perhaps as a consequence, Drew resigned to return to the Howard University Medical School faculty. His work was rewarded by a full professorship and appointments as chief of surgery, and chief of staff at Freedmen's Hospital. In 1944 he became the first African-American to be appointed an examiner by the American Board of Surgery.

- What advantages does plasma have in the treatment of shock?

Biology in Process

Using the Feature

The feature focuses on the process skills of experimenting and analyzing data. Drew's work shows that experiments often "fail"—in that a solution to a problem is not found.

Analysis of the data, however, taught Drew a great deal about whole blood spoilage. Tell students that during storage the red blood cells broke down as they released potassium ions into the plasma. The potassium ions rose to toxic levels in about a week. Separating red and white cells from plasma resulted in a product that could be safely stored.

Have students respond to the decision of the armed forces not to accept "Negro" blood. Tell them about the outcry in the African American press and the protest letters that came from all over the country. Eventually, the armed forces agreed to accept blood of different races but kept it segregated. Many people believe this segregation of blood caused Drew to resign. Ask students what they would have done in Drew's place. Help them evaluate whether staying or resigning would have been best. *(Staying might have been effective, but leaving to shape the professional development of other African American physicians might have had greater impact on the future of the medical profession.)*

Finally, tell students that Drew died in 1950 after an auto accident in Alabama. He bled to death after three segregated hospitals had refused him treatment solely because of his race.

Answer to the Feature

Plasma can be stored longer than whole blood. Plasma has no type, so it can be given immediately, without the delay of testing for the patient's blood type.

Section 43.1

Relating Structures and Functions Ask students to explain what the term *vascular system* means. *(It is a system of channels that transports fluids through the body.)* Tell students that the circulatory and lymphatic systems are both part of the body's vascular system and are connected, as can be seen in Figure 43-7 on p. 661. However, they have separate structures and functions. Ask students to compare the two systems. *(The heart pumps blood through the circulatory system, and muscles and one-way valves assist the blood in its movement. Lymph is moved by skeletal muscles surrounding the vessels, and one-way valves prevent backflow.)*

■ *See* **Blackline Master** *89.*

Guided Practice

Set up microscope stations with slides of arteries, veins, and capillaries. Have students look at each kind of vessel and make a drawing of each. Guide students in making comparisons based on their observations and the text.

Independent Practice

■ Have students write answers to the Section Review.

■ Give students an unlabeled drawing of a heart similar to Figure 43-2 on p. 656 and a list naming different heart structures. Have students label the drawing, using the terms provided, then allow them to compare their completed drawings with Figure 43-2.

Answer to Think

A heart enlarged by training is capable of stronger contractions, and thus a larger volume of blood can flow from the heart. A slower resting rate means the heart is more efficient. An increased circulation provides more blood—and greater endurance—for the heart.

Figure 43-6 Pulmonary circulation carries blood from the heart to the lungs and back to the heart. Blood circulates through the rest of the body via the systemic system.

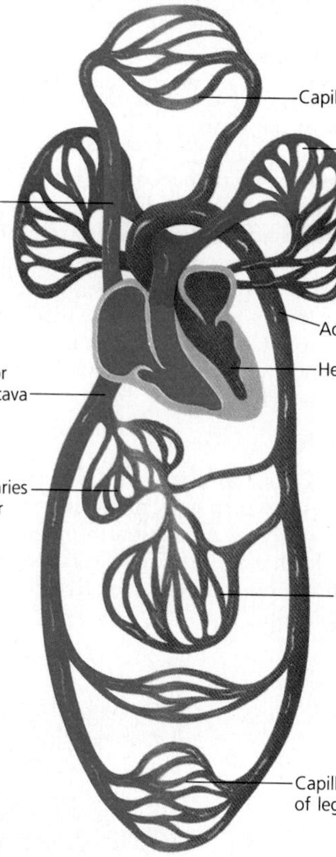

Think

Endurance athletes often have larger hearts, slower resting heart rates, and an increased coronary circulation as a result of endurance training. How would these modifications help the heart deal with the demands placed on it by endurance activities?

Coronary circulation is the subsystem of systemic circulation that supplies blood to the heart itself. Two **coronary arteries** branch off from the aorta and transport blood to arterioles that penetrate the tissue of the heart. The blood then returns to the right atrium through a large vein called the coronary sinus.

With all the blood traveling through the heart, you might think that the heart would have no need for its own arteries. However, heart muscle is thick, and every cell needs oxygen. If, for example, an artery becomes clogged and the blood supply to part of the heart is reduced, muscle cells will die. An artery may become blocked by a blood clot or by atherosclerosis, a disease characterized by the buildup of fatty materials on the walls of the coronary artery. If either blockage totally shuts off the flow of blood to the heart, a heart attack will result.

Renal circulation is the subsystem of systemic circulation that moves blood through the kidneys and back to the heart. Two renal arteries branch from the aorta, one entering each kidney. The kidneys filter nitrogenous wastes from the blood, which then leaves through the renal veins. The renal veins join the inferior vena cava.

Cooperative Learning

Circulatory System Have groups of four students design a trivia game based on the circulatory system. Have two of the students design a gameboard that includes a start, intermediate steps, and a finish. Have the remaining two students create trivia questions and answers. Once students have finished these tasks, have the pairs switch roles so that the gameboard designers can review and add to the questions, and the question developers can add input to the game design. Allow each group to exchange games with another group.

Hepatic portal circulation is a subsystem of systemic circulation that moves blood from the digestive tract directly to the liver. Hepatic portal circulation involves only capillaries and veins. The hepatic portal vein receives nutrient-rich blood from capillaries in the digestive tract. Unlike other veins, the hepatic portal vein then branches into a second set of capillaries in the liver. There, nutrients from the blood move into the liver tissue where they are stored. After unloading most of its nutrients, blood from these "capillaries" leaves the liver through the hepatic vein, which joins the inferior vena cava.

Lymphatic System

Another part of the body's circulatory system is the **lymphatic system,** which is a series of one-way vessels that carry intercellular fluid from the tissues to the bloodstream. The lymphatic and circulatory systems are together often referred to as the body's vascular system.

Some fluid from the blood passes through the capillary walls along with oxygen and nutrients. Some, but not all, of the fluid returns to the blood along with wastes that diffuse through the capillary walls. Some fluid remains in the intercellular spaces. A buildup of this fluid would lead to bloating of the tissues, and so it must be removed. This fluid collects in open-ended vessels of the lymphatic system. Fluid from the blood that has entered the lymph vessels is called **lymph.**

Lymph capillaries transport lymph to lymph vessels and on to two large ducts, the right lymphatic duct and the thoracic duct. The two ducts empty into large veins in the upper chest.

The lymphatic system also plays a role in immunity. Small organs called lymph nodes are located on the lymphatic vessels like beads on a string. Notice in Figure 43-7 that these lymph nodes are concentrated in the neck, armpits, inner elbow, and groin. Nodes filter the lymph as it passes, catching foreign particles, microorganisms, and other tissue debris. They also produce cells called lymphocytes that help fight disease. When a person has an infection, the nodes may become inflamed, becoming swollen and tender to the touch.

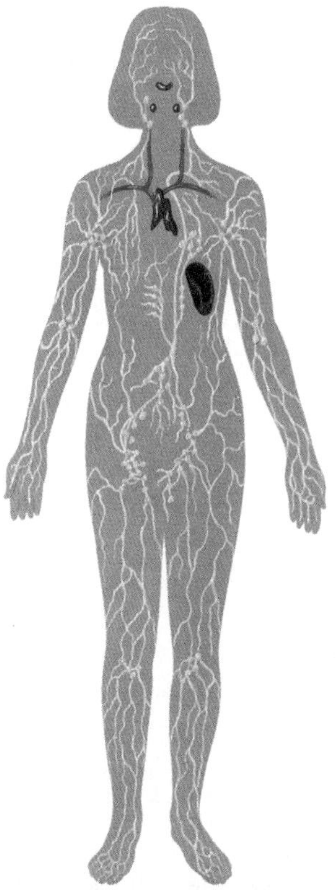

Figure 43-7 The lymphatic system carries fluid that collects in intercellular spaces back into the blood system.

Section Review

1. Distinguish between an *artery* and a *vein.*
2. What prevents blood from moving in the wrong direction in veins?
3. Trace the path that the blood follows in systemic circulation.
4. How would you define the purpose of the entire circulatory system?
5. How does the structure of a capillary enable it to transport substances to cells?

Check Your Understanding

1. What is the path of blood flow through the heart? *(Blood low in O_2 enters the right atrium, is pumped to the right ventricle, and then to the lungs. Blood high in O_2 returns to the left atrium, is pumped to the left ventricle, and then to the body.)*
2. The a-v node delays the impulse sent by the s-a node. What is the effect? *(The ventricles contract a fraction of a second after the atria.)*
3. How does the lymphatic system interact with the circulatory system? *(Fluid from blood leaks into intercellular spaces. It is taken up in the lymphatic system and carried in lymph capillaries to lymph ducts, which empty into veins in the chest.)*

Reteaching

Have students prepare a table. On the left side, list *Pulmonary Artery, Pulmonary Vein, Aorta, Inferior Vena Cava,* and *Superior Vena Cava.* On the top, label two columns: *Flow Direction* and *Concentration of Gases.* Have students complete the table with the appropriate direction (toward/away from) and relative concentrations (high/low, O_2/CO_2) of blood flowing through the listed vessels.
■ *See* **Section Reviews** *worksheet, Section 43.1.*

Enrichment

Have students investigate and report on a cardiac or circulatory disease such as myocardial infarction, arteriosclerosis, or varicose veins. Ask them to find causes of the diseases, the body parts affected, and treatments.

Closure

Divide the class into small groups. Have students discuss the current media focus on diet and exercise in relation to cardiovascular health. Encourage students to develop a list of healthful measures.

Answers to Section Review

1. An artery transports blood away from the heart; a vein returns blood to it.
2. One-way valves close after blood flows through them, allowing blood to flow in only one direction.
3. Blood leaves the left ventricle through the aorta and circulates to all parts of the body except the lungs. It moves through arteries to the head and to three systemic subsystems: the heart, the kidneys, and the digestive tract and liver. Veins return blood to the venae cavae, which enter the right atrium.
4. It distributes oxygen, hormones, and nutrients throughout the body and carries away CO_2 and other wastes.
5. Capillary walls are only one cell thick, allowing easy diffusion of gases and nutrients into surrounding cells.

Section 43.2

Lesson Plan

Section Focus

This section describes the characteristics, composition, and function of the blood components—plasma, erythrocytes, leukocytes, and platelets. Students will also learn about blood typing and compatibility of blood types.

Section Themes

This section illustrates the theme of **Systems and Interactions.** Blood is the connective tissue that allows for gas exchange externally and internally, brings nutrients from the digestive system to every cell, and contains cells that protect body systems from disease.

Motivating Activity

Ask students if they know their blood types. Many people do not know unless they have been in an accident, have undergone surgery, or have donated blood. Why is knowing blood types in such situations important? *(Blood of different types is not compatible, except in the case of type O donors or type AB recipients. Blood transfusions are often necessary in cases of severe blood loss. Blood typing information is important in making a match between donated blood and its recipient.)* Discuss whether students think it is important to donate blood and under what conditions people should not donate.

Section Objectives

- *List the components of blood.*
- *Describe the physical characteristics of the three types of blood solids.*
- *Summarize the process of blood clotting.*
- *Explain what determines the compatibility of blood types for transfusion.*

43.2 Blood

Blood is a liquid connective tissue that forms the transport medium of the circulatory system. The major function of the blood is to transport nutrients and oxygen to the cells and to carry away carbon dioxide and nitrogenous wastes from the cells. Blood also transfers body heat to the body surface and plays a major role in defending the body against disease.

Composition of Blood

Blood is composed of a liquid called plasma and blood solids. Blood solids consist of erythrocytes, also called red blood corpuscles, white blood cells, and platelets. Plasma makes up 55 percent of the blood, and blood solids make up the remaining 45 percent.

Plasma

Plasma is a sticky, straw-colored fluid that is about 90 percent water. Cells receive nourishment from dissolved substances carried in the plasma. These substances—including vitamins, minerals, amino acids, and glucose—are absorbed from the digestive system and transported to the cells. Distribution of these nutrients is essential for the cells to function properly. Plasma also carries hormones and brings wastes from the cells to the kidneys or lungs to be removed from the body.

The various proteins in plasma have important functions. Some of the proteins, such as **fibrinogen,** are essential for the formation of blood clots. Serum albumin plays an integral role in the regulation of osmotic pressure between plasma and blood cells and between plasma and tissues. Other proteins, called serum globulins, include antibodies that help the body fight disease.

Erythrocytes

Red blood corpuscles, or **erythrocytes** *(uh-RITH-ruh-SITES)*, illustrated in Figure 43-8, are vital to the survival of cells in all parts of the body because they transport oxygen. When erythrocytes are formed in the red marrow of bones, an iron-containing protein called **hemoglobin** *(HEE-muh-GLOE-bun)* also forms. Hemoglobin is the molecule that actually transports oxygen and, to a lesser extent, carbon dioxide. During the formation of the corpuscle, its cell nucleus and organelles disintegrate. The mature erythrocyte is therefore merely a membrane sac containing hemoglobin.

Because they lack nuclei, erythrocytes cannot repair themselves and have a limited survival period, usually 120 to 130 days. Of the more than 30 trillion red blood corpuscles circulating throughout the body at one time, 2 million disintegrate every second. The remains of the membranes are removed by the liver and spleen. The iron portion of the hemoglobin molecule is carried in the blood to the marrow, where it is reused for new corpuscles.

Figure 43-8 Each disk-shaped erythrocyte in this SEM is filled with hemoglobin (×2,500).

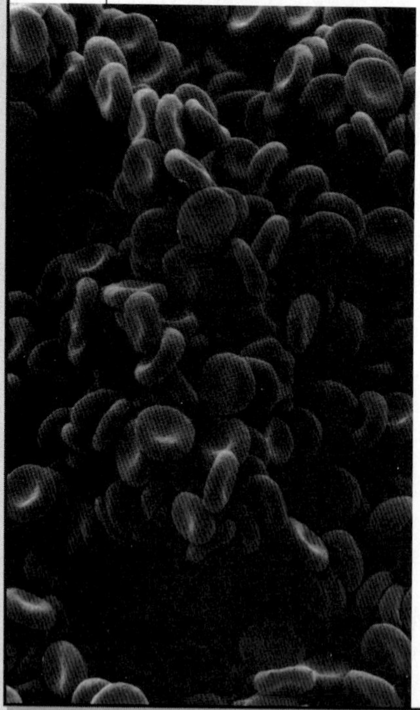

Blood Component	Where Formed	Functions
Plasma	(mostly water)	carries dissolved substances
Erythrocytes	red marrow	carry hemoglobin
Leukocytes	red marrow, lymph nodes, spleen	defend body against disease; some produce antibodies, some engulf invading cells
Platelets	marrow	help form blood clots

Graphic Organizer Use this table in Reteaching on p. 664.

Leukocytes

White blood cells, or **leukocytes** *(LOO-kuh-SITES)*, are cells that help defend the body against disease. They are formed in red marrow, lymph nodes, and the spleen. Leukocytes are larger than erythrocytes and significantly less plentiful. Each cubic millimeter of blood normally contains about 5 million erythrocytes but only 7,000 leukocytes. Notice in Figure 43-9 that a leukocyte may be irregularly shaped and may have a rough outer surface. In contrast with the short-lived erythrocytes, leukocytes may function for years.

Some types of white blood cells are **phagocytes**—that is, cells that engulf invading microorganisms. Other white blood cells produce **antibodies**, proteins that destroy foreign substances. When a person has an infection, the number of white blood cells can increase tenfold.

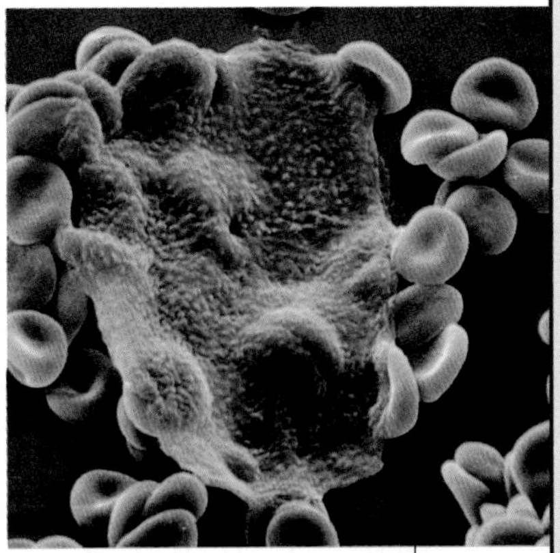

Figure 43-9 One type of phagocyte, called a macrophage, is shown destroying old erythrocytes in this color-enhanced SEM (×2,500).

Platelets

Platelets, also known as thrombocytes, are not whole cells but fragments of very large cells with several nuclei that were formed in the marrow. Platelets lack a nucleus and have a life span of 7 to 11 days. A cubic mm of blood may contain as many as half a million platelets.

Platelets are essential to the formation of a **blood clot,** a mass of interwoven fibers and blood cells that prevents excess loss of blood from a cut. When a blood vessel tears or rips, platelets congregate at the damaged area, stick together, and form a small plug. The vessel constricts, slowing blood flow to the area. Then special clotting factors are released from the platelets. These factors interact with prothrombin, a protein in plasma, to form the enzyme thrombin. This enzyme immediately reacts with the blood protein fibrinogen, causing the fibrinogen to form long sticky threads called **fibrin.** The fibrin forms a net that traps erythrocytes, and the mass of fibrin and erythrocytes hardens into a clot or scab.

Blood Types

The blood carries many chemicals, which have various functions. One group of chemicals, called **antigens,** can stimulate the production of antibodies. Three of the most important human antigens are called A, B, and Rh. The A–B–O system of blood typing is based on the A and B antigens.

A–B–O System

The A–B–O system is a means of classifying blood according to the antigens located on the surface of the erythrocytes. An individual's erythrocytes may carry an A antigen, a B antigen, both A and B antigens, or no antigen at all. These antigen patterns are called A, B, AB, and O, respectively. When A blood is added to B

Teaching Strategies

Interpreting the Visuals Have students examine the erythrocytes and the phagocyte in Figure 43-9, p. 663 and note the difference in size and shape. Ask students how these differences enable each type of cell to carry out its function. *(The shape of the erythrocytes allows greater surface area for gas diffusion, and their small size enables them to squeeze through tiny capillaries. The shape of the phagocyte allows it to engulf other particles, and its size ensures that it can defend the body against a large number of invaders.)* Ask students which type of cell is an indicator of sickle-cell anemia and how might this cellular deformity interfere with the cell's function. Refer to p. 172, Figure 11-9. *(Erythrocytes; diminished cell surface impairs the flow of oxygen; the clumping of cells clogs capillaries)*

- *See* **Process Skills,** *Chapter 43.*

Identifying Structures Provide an illustration of clot formation for students to study. Then ask students to consider a scab on a cut. What is a scab made of? *(Interwoven threads of fibrin and trapped erythrocytes)* What would happen if a scab did not form? *(Bleeding would not stop and death could occur.)*

Videodiscs

- ***Side 2 16313, Blood Platelets and Clotting (m)***
- ***Side 2 18273, Blood Typing and Agglutination (m)***
- ***Side 2 19145, Antibiotics (m)***
- ***Side 2 19769, Antibodies, Lysis, Agglutination, and Phagocytosis (m)***

More Information

Leukocytes Leukocytes have the unique ability to wander through the body and provide protection. There are three types of leukocytes—granulocytes, lymphocytes, and monocytes. All three types can pass through capillary walls and move through the tissue spaces like amebas by extending pseudopodia. In addition to engulfing and digesting bacteria and foreign particles, they are responsible for cleaning up the body's tissue debris, such as old red blood cells, blood clots, or the particles from wound and disease repair. Leukocytes are often destroyed in the process of fighting infection.

Guided Practice

Give characteristics of the various blood components and have students identify the component that matches each characteristic. For example, "transports most of the CO_2" describes plasma.

Independent Practice

- Have students write answers to the Section Review.
- Have students construct a table of the four blood types and include the antigen found on the erythrocyte, the antibodies in the plasma, and compatible blood types. Have students check their table against Table 43-1 on p. 664 in the student text.

Check Your Understanding

1. What can result from an iron deficiency? *(The body may not produce sufficient hemoglobin; tell students that this condition is called anemia.)*
2. What might be a danger of an overabundance of platelets? *(Blood clotting within the circulatory system)*
3. What is blood typing based on? *(Three of the human antigens, A, B, and Rh)*

Reteaching

Have students create a table listing the four main components of blood, where they are formed, and what their main functions are. An example of a completed table is found on p. 662.

- *See* Section Reviews *worksheet, Section 43.2.*

Enrichment

Have students research and report on blood disorders such as hemophilia and leukemia.

Closure

Discuss the importance of blood clotting. Why has the process evolved to include so many steps? Help students conclude that this system allows the body to respond to injury without forming unnecessary clots.

Table 43-1 Blood Types

Type	Genotype	Antigen on the RBC	Antibodies in Plasma	Can Get Blood from	Can Give Blood to
A	I^Ai^O or $^{IA}I^A$	A	Anti-B	O, A	A, AB
B	I^BI^B or I^Bi^O	B	Anti-A	O, B	B, AB
AB	I^AI^B	AB	None	A, B, AB, O	AB
O	i^Oi^O	None	Anti-A, Anti-B	O	A, B, AB, O

blood, the antibodies in the B blood attack the foreign antigens in A blood, and the blood clumps, or agglutinates. In a body the agglutinated blood will block the vessels. For this reason transfusion recipients must receive blood that is compatible with their own. Table 43-1 explains which blood types are compatible.

Rh Factor

The **Rh factor** is another type of blood antigen. Eighty-five percent of the U.S. population is Rh-positive (Rh^+), meaning that they have Rh antigens on their blood cells. A person without Rh antigens in their blood is termed Rh-negative (Rh^-). If Rh^+ blood is put into the body of an Rh^- person, antibodies to the Rh antigen will react with the antigen and agglutination will occur.

Complications arising from Rh incompatibility may occur during pregnancy. When the mother is Rh^- and the father is Rh^+, the child may inherit the dominant Rh^+ allele from the father. Because the blood supply of mother and fetus is separate, only a small amount of the fetus's Rh^+ blood reaches the mother's bloodstream, usually during delivery. However, the mother then develops antibodies to the Rh factor. If a second Rh^+ child is later conceived, serious damage may result when the mother's antibodies attack the child's blood. This condition is called erythroblastosis fetalis. The fetus may die, or if the child is born alive, it may need an immediate transfusion of Rh^+ blood.

In the past several decades these concerns have largely been overcome. Now the Rh^- mother is given anti-Rh antibodies within three days after the birth of her first Rh^+ child. These antibodies destroy the Rh antigens in her blood before her body makes antibodies, eliminating any danger to a second child.

Section Review

1. What is *plasma?*
2. What are the three types of blood solids?
3. What is the final result of the clotting process?
4. Which blood type can be donated to all others? Why?
5. Why should a pregnant woman know her blood type?

Answers to Section Review

1. The liquid part of blood
2. Erythrocytes, leukocytes, and platelets
3. A clot or scab formed of hardened fibrin and erythrocytes
4. Type O^-, because it has no antigens
5. To prevent Rh incompatibility problems; if her blood is Rh^- and her first baby's blood is Rh^+, the mother will form antibodies that could harm a second Rh^+ fetus.

43.3 Respiratory System

You have read how the blood transports oxygen from the lungs to cells and carries carbon dioxide from the cells to the lungs. It is the function of the **respiratory system** to transport gases to and from the circulatory system.

External respiration is the exchange of gases between the atmosphere and the blood. **Internal respiration** is the exchange of gases between the blood and the cells of the body. Cellular respiration is the breakdown of glucose in the cell. In this section we will examine the structures and mechanisms involved in the exchange of gases between cells and the external environment.

Section Objectives

- *Name and describe the organs of the respiratory system.*
- *Summarize the skeletal and muscular changes that occur during breathing.*
- *Explain how the structure of alveoli is related to the function of diffusion of gases.*
- *Describe the physical effects of exercise on the breathing rate.*

The Lungs

The two triangular **lungs** are the sites of gas exchange between the atmosphere and the blood. The right lung has three divisions, or lobes, and is slightly larger than the two-lobed left lung.

The lungs are located inside the thoracic cavity, bounded by the rib cage and the **diaphragm,** a sheet of muscle at the bottom of the thoracic cavity. Lining the entire cavity and encasing the lungs are pleura, double membranes that secrete a mucus that decreases friction from the movement of the lungs during breathing. Figure 43-10 illustrates the organs of the respiratory system.

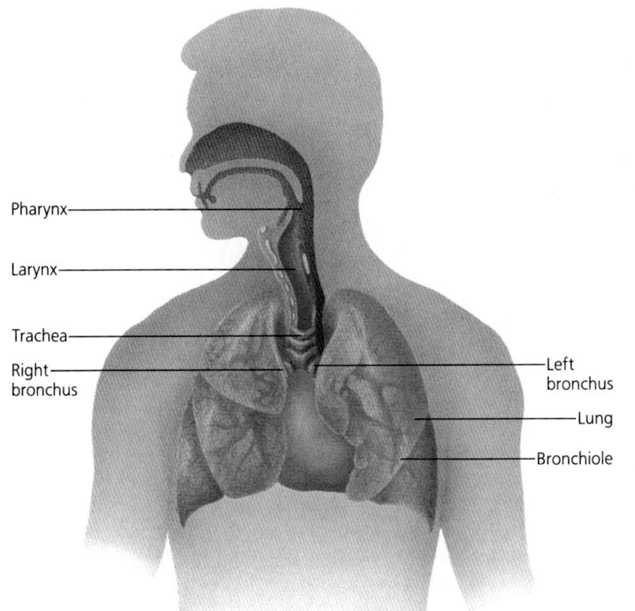

Figure 43-10 Air passes through these main parts of the respiratory system each time a person breathes.

Lesson Plan

Section Focus

This section describes the organs and structures of the respiratory system. Students will also learn about the ways in which the skeletal, muscular, and respiratory systems interact during breathing, as well as the relationship between the circulatory and respiratory systems in O_2 and CO_2 exchange.

Section Themes

The themes of **Systems and Interactions** and **Stability** are brought out in this section. The interactions among the respiratory, circulatory, skeletal, and muscular systems serve to assure stable O_2 and CO_2 concentrations in the blood as well as a steady supply of blood to the cells of the body. The ability to maintain this dynamic equilibrium is a consequence of the feedback mechanisms of the individual systems.

Motivating Activity

Have students count the number of breaths they take in 15 seconds and multiply by 4 for the number of breaths per minute. Ask students to explain why there are differences in breathing rates among members of the class. *(Most people breathe about 16 to 24 times per minute, but rates differ depending on activity level and the resulting need for oxygen. The level of physical conditioning can also affect breathing rates.)*
■ ***See* Laboratories, *Investigation 43.2.***

Videodiscs

■ ***2654–2655, Human Respiratory System (s)***

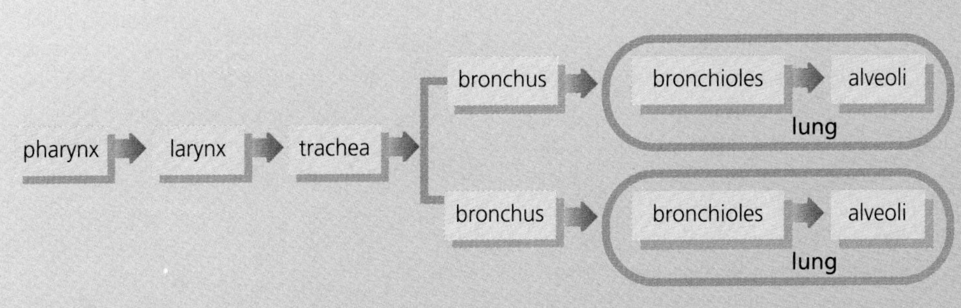

Graphic Organizer Use this sequential diagram in Describing Processes on p. 666.

Teaching Strategies

Interpreting the Visuals Provide an anatomical model of the human respiratory system for students to examine and have them compare the model with Figures 43-10 and 43-11 on pp. 665 and 666. Help students locate the lungs, diaphragm, pharynx, trachea, larynx, and bronchi, and discuss how these structures contribute to the functioning of the respiratory system.

Making a Model Demonstrate to students how the mechanism of breathing works by making a model of a lung and diaphragm. Fasten a small, deflated balloon to a short glass tube, and put the tube through a one-holed stopper. Use the stopper to plug the mouth of a bell jar, allowing the balloon to hang inside the jar. Next, with a rubber band, fasten a thin sheet of rubber to the open end of the jar. Pull the rubber bottom down and let students observe the results. *(The balloon inflates.)* Have them explain why this occurred. *(When the rubber sheet was pulled down, the volume in the jar increased and the air pressure decreased, forcing air into the balloon.)*

Describing Processes On the board, draw the sequential diagram on p. 665. Ask students what the diagram represents. *(The passage of air through the respiratory system)* Encourage students to volunteer to describe one of the structures in the diagram and discuss its function in respiration.

Making Comparisons Demonstrate how the alveoli provide such a great surface area. Use a pad of paper, and have students calculate its surface area. Then arrange the individual sheets side by side and calculate their total surface area.

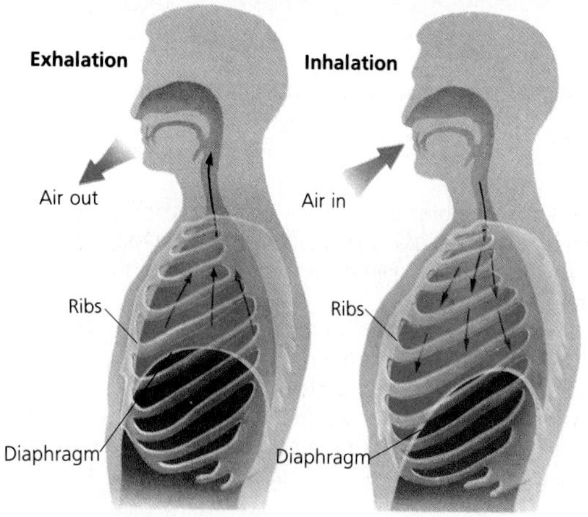

Figure 43-11 Muscles of the diaphragm and the intercostal muscles between the ribs control the movement of the rib cage during breathing.

Mechanism of Breathing

Breathing is the process of inspiring and expiring air. When you breathe, air enters and leaves the lungs. Each phase of breathing involves interactions of the diaphragm, abdomen, and ribs. **Inspiration** is the process of taking air into the lungs. When you take a deep breath, you can feel your chest expand. Your diaphragm flattens as the muscles contract. This pushes down on the abdomen, as shown in Figure 43-11. Muscles in the abdominal wall in turn relax. This action provides room for the flattened diaphragm. At the same time, the intercostal muscles contract, moving the ribs up and outward. This enlarges the chest.

When the diaphragm flattens and the ribs are pushed out, the volume of the thoracic cavity increases. This causes air pressure within the cavity to decrease. The pressure inside the thoracic cavity thus becomes lower than the air outside of the body. As a result air from the atmosphere moves into the lungs and equalizes the pressure.

During **expiration,** the reverse process takes place. As the diaphragm and rib muscles relax, the elastic tissues of the lungs recoil, causing the lungs to deflate. The size of the thoracic cavity then decreases. The air pressure inside the cavity is then greater than the air pressure outside the body. This pressure difference forces air out of the lungs until the pressure is again equalized.

Each of the lungs weighs about 600 g. Together they can hold between 5 and 6 L of gas, the **total lung capacity.** When you breathe, you normally inhale only about 0.5 L instead of the entire 6 L of total lung capacity. Even during deep breathing you can't completely empty your lungs. Through strenuous exercise it is possible to increase the capacity of a single breath to about 4.5 L. The maximum amount of air a person can inhale and exhale is called **vital lung capacity.**

One completed inhalation and exhalation makes up one respiratory cycle. Most people at rest breathe at a rate of 16 to 24 cycles per minute, but rates can vary.

More Information

High Altitude As altitude increases, the gases that make up the atmosphere, including oxygen, become thinner. When people who are used to breathing air fairly close to sea level visit a place at an altitude of 2,000 meters, they sometimes experience shortness of breath, fatigue, nausea, and even blackouts. Then how is it possible for people to live in the Andes at more than 2,500 meters? Over a period of weeks, our bodies are able to compensate for oxygen deprivation by producing more red blood cells, a process called erythropoiesis. Some athletes have trained at high altitudes for certain Olympic events.

The Passage of Air

External respiration begins at the mouth and nose. Air filters through the small hairs of the nose and passes into the nasal cavity located above the roof of the mouth. In the cavity mucous membranes warm and moisten the air, a process that prevents damage to the delicate lung tissue. The walls of the nasal cavity are lined with cilia. These catch inhaled particles and sweep them into the throat, where they are swallowed.

The moistened, filtered air then moves into the **pharynx,** a tube at the back of the nasal cavities and mouth. The pharynx contains passageways for both food and air. When food is swallowed, a flap of cartilage, called the epiglottis, presses down and covers the opening to the air passage. During inhalation the epiglottis is in an upright position, and air passes into a cartilaginous tube called the **trachea,** or windpipe. The trachea is about 10 to 12 cm long and has walls lined with ciliated cells.

The **larynx,** or voice box, is located at the upper end of the trachea. Sounds are produced when air is forced past two ligaments—the vocal cords—that stretch across the larynx. The pitch and volume of sounds varies with the amount of tension on the vocal cords and the amount of air being forced past them.

The trachea branches into two **bronchi** *(BRAHNG-kie),* each of which leads to a lung. Within the lungs, the bronchi branch into smaller and smaller tubes. The walls of the bronchi consist of smooth muscle and cartilage and are lined with cilia and mucus. The smallest tubes, the **bronchioles** *(BRAHNG-kee-OELZ),* are lined with mucus and cilia. Eventually the bronchioles end in clusters of tiny air sacs called **alveoli** *(al-VEE-oe-LIE).* A network of capillaries surrounds each alveolus. It is here that the exchange of gases takes place. Each lung contains nearly 300 million alveoli, each measuring from 0.1 to 0.2 mm in diameter. This results in a total surface area of about 70 m^2 for both lungs.

Figure 43-12 Blood vessels surround the millions of air sacs, or alveoli, in the lungs.

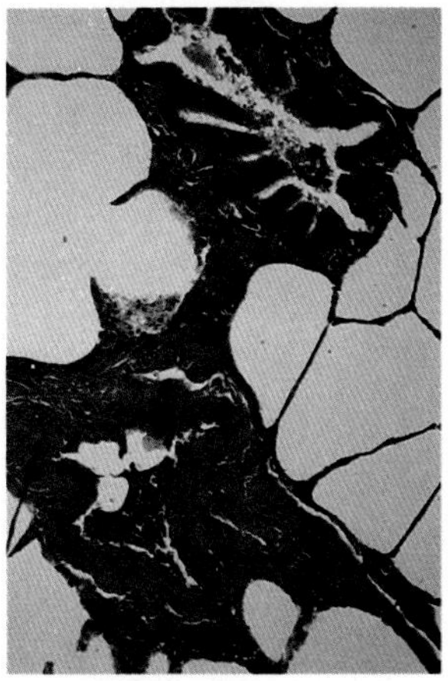

Gas Exchange and Transport

Within the lungs gases are exchanged between the alveoli and the blood in the capillaries. Oxygen moves into the bloodstream, and carbon dioxide moves into the air passages. How does this exchange occur?

Gas Exchange in the Lungs

When air moves into the lungs, oxygen from the air dissolves in the mucus secreted by the lining of the alveoli. The dissolved oxygen then crosses both the thin alveolar membranes and the capillary walls and enters the blood.

What determines the direction in which oxygen and carbon dioxide move? Air moving into the alveoli is rich in oxygen and contains little carbon dioxide. Blood in the capillaries surrounding the alveoli is low in oxygen and contains high levels of carbon

Section 43.3

Applying Concepts Give each student a drinking straw and a test tube half full of limewater. Explain that limewater becomes cloudy when CO_2 is added to it. Ask students to inhale and hold their breath for 2 seconds, then exhale through the straw into the limewater. Have students repeat the process with a fresh test tube, but this time have them hold their breath for 10 seconds before exhaling. How do the results compare? Why? *(The limewater was cloudier the second time because more CO_2 was present. Even while the breath is being held, the cells continue to use O_2 and give off CO_2 in respiration, and the CO_2 builds up in the lungs.)* Point out that much of the CO_2 transported by the blood travels as HCO_3^- dissolved in plasma (as in the equation on p. 668).

Exploring Technologies Take students on a field trip to a hospital or medical school and arrange for a doctor, nurse, or technician to explain how a respirator works and how the iron lung (negative-pressure respirator) worked. Ask the professional to compare the two modes of functioning and then compare each to the functioning of the human lung.

Drawing Conclusions Ask students to describe the Heimlich maneuver. Select a volunteer and gently demonstrate the maneuver on him or her to the class. Have students describe how a piece of food could cause suffocation and how the Heimlich maneuver works. *(If food somehow gets past the epiglottis, it can enter the trachea instead of going down the esophagus, thus cutting off the air supply. The Heimlich maneuver forces air out of the lungs, through the trachea, and thus dislodges the food.)*

Videodiscs

- *2656, Gas Exchange (s)*

LEP Activity

Show students an anatomical model of the respiratory system and provide them with a set of self-sticking labels that name its different structures. Review with students the path that air follows as it enters the respiratory system. As you name the different structures in your description, have students attach the labels to the correct structures on the model.

Guided Practice
Have students inhale and exhale. What do the muscular and skeletal systems do? *(The diaphragm contracts, pushing the abdominal cavity down; abdominal wall muscles relax; intercostal muscles contract, moving the ribs up and out. During expiration, the reverse occurs.)*

Independent Practice
■ Have students write answers to the Section Review.
■ Provide students with a list of terms from this section. Have them define each term without using the text.

Check Your Understanding
1. Why must the chest cavity be airtight for breathing to occur? *(Breathing depends on air pressure differential between the atmosphere and the chest cavity.)*
2. What happens to most of the CO_2 that leaves the cells? *(It is converted to bicarbonate ions, which dissolve in the plasma. CO_2 diffuses from the capillaries into the alveoli and is exhaled.)*
3. What initial effect would high altitude have on breathing? Why? *(Respiratory rate would go up because there is less oxygen.)*

Reteaching
Have students point out on an anatomical model the path air takes as it enters the respiratory system. Help students relate the structures to their functions.
■ *See* Section Reviews *worksheet, Section 43.3.*

Enrichment
Have students research and prepare a report on how the larynx functions in speech. Encourage students to explore the vocal training of singers.

Closure
Have students read the Surgeon General's warnings on smoking and articles on smoking issues. Have them form small groups to discuss the issues.

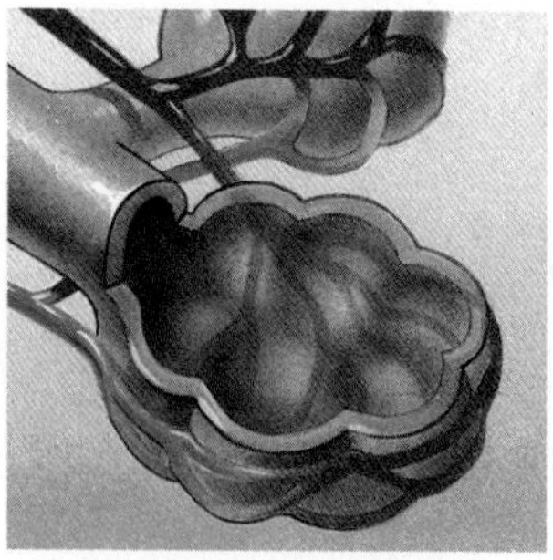

Figure 43-13 Oxygen and CO_2 diffuse through the alveolar membranes and capillary walls.

dioxide. Gases move by diffusion from areas of higher concentration to areas of lower concentration. The differences in concentration cause CO_2 to diffuse from the blood into the alveoli and the oxygen to diffuse from the alveoli into the blood.

Transport and Exchange of Gases
When oxygen diffuses into the blood, only a small amount dissolves in the blood plasma, not enough to nourish the tissues. Hemoglobin makes up the difference. Each hemoglobin molecule can carry up to four molecules of oxygen, which bind with its central iron atom. Hemoglobin transports about 97 percent of the oxygen in the blood. When oxygenated blood reaches tissues, hemoglobin releases O_2. The O_2 diffuses out of the capillaries and into the surrounding cells. Similarly, CO_2 diffuses out of a cell and into the bloodstream. When CO_2 leaves cells and diffuses into the blood, only about 8 percent of the total CO_2 actually dissolves in the blood plasma. About 25 percent binds to hemoglobin. The remaining 67 percent is converted to bicarbonate ions:

$$CO_2 + H_2O \rightarrow H_2CO_3 \rightarrow HCO_3^- + H^+$$

Bicarbonate ions (HCO_3^-) dissolve in plasma. When the blood reaches the lungs, a reverse reaction takes place. CO_2 leaves the capillaries by diffusion and is exhaled into the atmosphere.

Regulation of Breathing
What controls the rate of breathing? Because cells use oxygen for respiration, the rate of oxygen use depends on the activity of the cells, which in turn depends on the activity of the body. For example, cells consume less oxygen when a person is sleeping than when exercising, since a sleeping individual needs less energy to function. **Basal metabolic rate** (BMR) is a measure of the energy required to maintain the body's functions.

As the cells use oxygen in aerobic respiration, they release carbon dioxide into the bloodstream. As metabolism increases, high levels of CO_2 in the bloodstream stimulate nerve cells to send a message to the brain, which in turn sends messages to respiratory muscles to increase the breathing rate. When the CO_2 concentration returns to its normal level, the nerve cells signal the brain to return to a normal breathing rate.

Section Review
1. How do *external* and *internal respiration* differ?
2. Where is air warmed and moistened before it enters the lungs?
3. How is oxygen transported in blood to the cells?
4. How does CO_2 leave the cells?
5. What is the adaptive value of having the organ of gas exchange inside the body?

Answers to Section Review
1. External respiration is the exchange of gases between the atmosphere and the blood. Internal respiration is the exchange of gases between the blood and the cells.
2. In the mouth and nasal cavity
3. Oxygen binds to the hemoglobin in the erythrocytes.
4. CO_2 diffuses through the cell membranes into the blood plasma.
5. The lungs are kept moist, thus allowing an organism to live in a dry environment.

Laboratory

Breathing Rate and Lung Volume

Objective
To determine the effect of exercise on breathing rate and tidal volume

Process Skills
Hypothesizing, experimenting

Materials
250-ml graduated cylinder, water, gallon jug, grease pencil, cellophane tape, rubber tubing, straw mouthpieces, metal or plastic wash basin.

Background
1 Tidal volume is the volume of air you breathe during a single, normal breath. What factors might affect tidal volume?
2 How could breathing rate be measured easily?

Technique
1 Pour 200 mL of water into the empty jug. Mark the water level as *200 mL*. Then pour in another 200 mL of water and mark the level as *400 mL*. Repeat until the jug is calibrated to 3,000 mL. Put tape over the marks to keep them from rubbing off.
2 Fill the jug the rest of the way with water. Then half-fill a basin with water. Cover the jug mouth with your hand and turn the jug upside down into the basin. There should be no air bubble at the top of the jug. Have one student hold the jug steady.
3 Insert a length of soda straw for a mouthpiece into one end of the rubber tubing. Put the other end of the tubing underwater into the jug. Take a normal breath. Now inhale four times through your nose, and exhale through the tube after each inhalation. (When exhaling, hold your nose to direct the air through the tube. Also, make sure that air does not escape around your mouth.)
4 Hold the jug level. Read the volume of air you exhaled in four breaths. Calculate the average tidal volume.

Inquiry
1 Discuss the objective of this laboratory with your partners and develop a hypothesis.
2 Design an experiment to test your hypothesis that uses the setup described in Technique.
3 What are the independent and dependent variables in your experiment? How will you vary the independent variable and measure changes in the dependent variables?
4 What controls will you include?
5 How will you record your results?
6 Obtain your materials and proceed with your experiment after receiving approval from your teacher.

Conclusions
1 Do your data support your hypothesis? Explain your answers.
2 What differences did you detect in your breathing rate and tidal volume after exercise?
3 What were some of the possible sources of error in your experiment?

Further Inquiry
Design an experiment to determine whether exercise affects heart rate in the same way it affects breathing rate and tidal volume.

Laboratory

(For an overview of tidal volume of the lung and preparatory information related to the laboratory, see p. 653B.)

Background
1. Factors that affect tidal volume include genetic makeup, smoking, health problems, and altitude.
2. Answers should describe a method for recording inhalations and exhalations over a fixed period of time.

Inquiry
1. Each laboratory group should agree on a testable hypothesis. For example, one hypothesis might be that breathing rate will increase after exercise by a larger percentage than will tidal volume, or vice versa.
2. Discuss experimental designs with each group of students.
3. The independent variable is exercise; the dependent variables are any measured changes in the tidal volume and breathing rate. At one time the subject will exercise; at another time the subject will not. Changes in the dependent variables will be measured in milliliters or liters (tidal volume) and breaths per unit of time (breathing rate). The controls are the resting tidal volume and resting breathing rate.
4. Both times the subject will use the same jug, which will be refilled with water each time; time intervals will be constant. The control experiment will be measurement of resting tidal volume and resting breathing rate; the experimental will be measurement of tidal volume and breathing rate after exercise.
5. Results may be presented in tables or graphs that are clearly labeled to reflect the hypothesis.

Conclusions
1. Students should recognize whether their data support their hypotheses. Breathing rates and tidal volumes should both increase, breathing rates by a higher percentage.
2. Answers should be supported by data.
3. Individual genetic differences; differences in level of fitness; size, health, and gender; altitude to which a person is acclimatized; error in measuring time and volume or in calculating; letting air escape when exhaling

Further Inquiry
Students can redo the experiment, this time including pulse rate. Remind them of sources of error.

Chapter 43 Review

Vocabulary

1. Systole is the first phase of a heartbeat, in which the ventricles contract; diastole is the second phase, in which the ventricles relax.
2. They are all vessels that transport blood.
3. Total lung capacity is the total amount of air a person's lungs can hold. Vital lung capacity is the maximum amount of air a person can inhale and exhale.
4. They are all contributing factors to the formation of blood clots.
5. Sinoatrial node

Review

1. c
2. d
3. a
4. b
5. a
6. d
7. b
8. b
9. a
10. d
11. Blood enters the right atrium, travels to the right ventricle, goes to the lungs, enters the heart again through the left atrium, goes to the left ventricle, and is pumped out through the aorta.
12. Oxygenated blood leaves the heart through the aorta and travels through the arteries to the arterioles and then to the capillaries, where oxygen and nutrients pass through the capillary walls into the cells.
13. It is the only artery that carries deoxygenated blood.
14. The lymphatic system helps remove excess intercellular fluid and is also part of the immune system.
15. Because they lack nuclei and cannot repair themselves
16. The blood will agglutinate and block the recipient's blood vessels.
17. A Rh$^-$ mother is given anti-Rh antibodies to help prevent Rh incompatibility.
18. During inspiration the diaphragm flattens and the intercostal muscles pull the ribs up and out. During expiration the diaphragm and intercostal muscles relax, lowering the ribs.
19. They are produced by air passing across the vocal cords in the larynx.
20. High levels of CO_2 in the blood

Chapter 43 Review

Vocabulary

alveoli (667)
antibody (663)
antigen (663)
aorta (657)
arteriole (657)
artery (657)
atrioventricular node (657)
atrium (655)
basal metabolic rate (668)
blood clot (663)
bronchi (667)
bronchiole (667)
capillary (657)
circulatory system (655)
coronary artery (660)
coronary circulation (660)
diaphragm (665)
diastole (657)
erythrocyte (662)
expiration (666)
external respiration (665)
fibrin (663)
fibrinogen (662)
heart (655)
hemoglobin (662)
hepatic portal circulation (661)
inferior vena cava (657)
inspiration (666)
internal respiration (665)
larynx (667)
leukocyte (663)
lungs (665)
lymph (661)
lymphatic system (661)
pericardium (655)
phagocyte (663)
pharynx (667)
plasma (662)
platelet (663)
pulmonary artery (659)
pulmonary circulation (659)
pulmonary vein (659)
renal circulation (660)
respiratory system (665)
Rh factor (664)
septum (655)
sinoatrial node (656)
superior vena cava (657)
systemic circulation (659)
systole (657)
total lung capacity (666)
trachea (667)
vein (657)
ventricle (655)
venule (657)
vital lung capacity (666)

1. Distinguish between systole and diastole.
2. What do arteries, capillaries, and veins have in common?
3. What is the difference between total lung capacity and vital lung capacity?
4. Explain the relationship between prothrombin, thrombin, fibrin, and fibrinogen.
5. Identify the structure that regulates the rate of heartbeat.

Review

1. The wall that divides the heart lengthwise is the (a) ventricle (b) pericardium (c) septum (d) atrium.
2. During systole blood moves from the (a) ventricles to the atria (b) atria to the arteries (c) atria to the ventricles (d) ventricles to the arteries.
3. Pulmonary circulation involves movement of the blood to and from the (a) lungs (b) brain (c) liver (d) kidneys.
4. The lymphatic system (a) interacts with the respiratory system (b) helps the body fight infection (c) consists of a series of two-way vessels (d) transports blood from the heart to the lungs.
5. One function of plasma is (a) to carry substances that nourish cells (b) to aid in the formation of blood clots (c) to carry the majority of the oxygen supply of the blood (d) to defend against diseases.
6. The function of fibrin is (a) to transport oxygen (b) to destroy foreign substances (c) to stimulate the production of antibodies (d) to form a blood clot.
7. In the A–B–O system blood is classified according to (a) Rh factor (b) antigens located on the erythrocytes (c) number of erythrocytes (d) ability to clot.

670 *Chapter 43*

8. During internal respiration gases are (a) exchanged between the atmosphere and blood (b) exchanged between blood and the cells (c) produced by the cells (d) warmed and moistened.
9. Gases diffuse (a) from areas of high concentration to areas of low concentration (b) from areas of low concentration to areas of high concentration (c) directly from the cells to the air passages (d) from the alveoli to the cells.
10. Cilia (a) move air molecules (b) moisten the air passages (c) sweep foreign particles into the stomach (d) sweep particles out of the air passages.
11. Describe the movement of blood through the heart.
12. Explain how the blood vessels that carry oxygenated blood to the cells are organized.
13. How is the pulmonary artery unique?
14. What are two major roles of the lymphatic system?
15. Why do erythrocytes have a limited life span?
16. What can happen to the blood of a recipient who receives a type of blood that is incompatible with his or her own?
17. What recent development has reduced the hazards of Rh incompatibility?
18. Describe the movement of the intercostal muscles of the rib cage and the diaphragm during inspiration and expiration.
19. How are human vocal sounds produced?
20. What is one factor that stimulates the brain to increase the breathing rate?

Critical Thinking

1. Anemia is a condition in which the patient has too few erythrocytes. The most common symptom is a lack of energy. Why would anemia have this symptom?
2. Polio is a disease that paralyzes muscles by affecting the nerves that make them move. Before polio vaccine was developed, many people who were stricken by polio died because they could not breathe. From what you know about the respiratory system, why might this happen?
3. Some babies are born with a hole in the septum between the two atria. Look at the drawing of the heart. Keeping in mind what you know about blood flow through the heart, why would this condition be harmful to the baby?

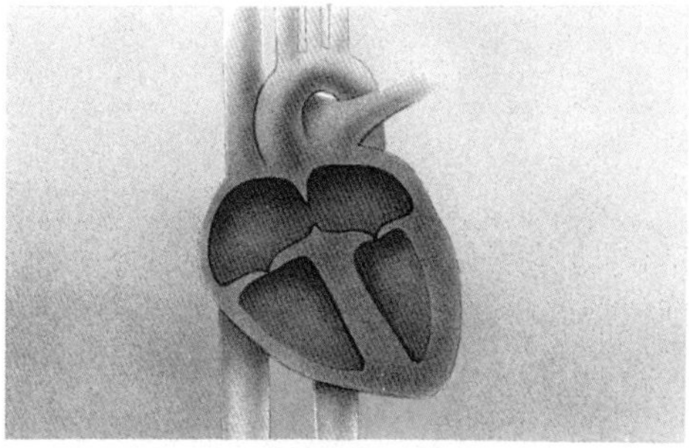

Extension

1. Read "Cloning the Genes for A and B Blood Types" in *Science News,* May 19, 1990, p. 311. Discuss the scientific breakthroughs now possible with the geneticists' findings about A and B blood groups.
2. Using the library, research the Jarvik-7 artificial heart. Write a paper about the operation, the likely candidates for the operation, the number of people who have undergone the operation, and the number of operations that have been successful.
3. Construct a model of the lungs, using any materials available. Some suggestions are clay, sponge, paper, cardboard, or other art supplies. Make sure that all of the parts show: lungs, trachea, and bronchi.

Critical Thinking

1. A shortage of erythrocytes means there is less hemoglobin in the blood to carry oxygen. Less oxygen available for cellular respiration results in a lack of energy.
2. Polio can affect the muscles that control breathing. If these muscles cannot move, the polio victim cannot breathe.
3. The blood on the right side of the heart would mix with blood on the left side. This means that blood high in oxygen would mix with blood high in carbon dioxide and therefore not enough oxygen would get to the body cells.

Extension

1. Students should mention the forensic possibilities and also the potential for helping with immune problems such as epithelial cancers.
2. Have students consider how the artificial heart has worked over time. For example, how long have patients lived after the transplant? What was their quality of life? Would students consider having the surgery under similar circumstances?
3. Some students may want to make two models for comparison: one of a healthy lung and one of a diseased lung, such as a lung damaged by cigarette smoking or lung cancer.

Chapter 44 Infectious Diseases and the Immune System

Chapter Overview

Chapter 44 focuses on how the immune system fights infectious diseases. Section 44.1 describes the types of pathogens that cause infectious diseases and outlines how they are transmitted. Section 44.2 examines the nonspecific and specific defenses of the immune system and explains how immunity to diseases is achieved. Section 44.3 describes the cause, transmission, and prevention of the immune disorder AIDS.

Chapter Planning Chart

B	S	A	Sections and Subsections	Page	Features	Page	Resources
•	•	•	**44.1 Infectious Disease**				
			Koch's Postulates	673	Laboratory	683	Videodiscs
			Pathogens	673	Section Review	674	Blackline Master 90
			Disease Transmission	674			Laboratories: Disease and Immunity Survey
							Section Reviews Worksheet
•	•	•	**44.2 Immune System**				
			Nonspecific Defenses	675	Think	678	Videodiscs
			Specific Defense	676	Biology in Process	678	Blackline Master 91
			Immunity and Immune Disorders	678	Section Review	679	Overhead Transparency T44
							Process Skills: Interferon
							Section Reviews Worksheet
•	•	•	**44.3 AIDS**				
			Cause	680	Writing About Biology	682	Section Reviews Worksheet
			Transmission	680	Section Review	681	
			Viral Action	680			
			Effects of Immune Disruption	681			
			Risk and Prevention	681			
			End of Chapter Activities				
					Chapter Review	684	Vocabulary Skills
							Chapter Test
							Computer Test Generator

B *The Basic Level curriculum presents the most fundamental knowledge offered in the course.*
S *The Standard Level curriculum is designed for the average student who is able to master most topics.*
A *The Advanced Level curriculum includes suggestions for teaching the most academically able students.*

Cooperative Learning

Group Activity: Types of Pathogens

- **Group Size:** *5 students*
- **Outcome:** *Students will compare the five types of pathogens and describe diseases they cause, including their transmission and treatment.*
- **Individual Accountability:** *Each student will research one of the five types of pathogens.*
- **Positive Interdependence:** *The group will make a table summarizing the findings of its members.*

Have each group member choose one type of pathogen. Then instruct all students who chose the same type of pathogen to meet and use their text to review the characteristics of the pathogen. Encourage students to work together to research examples of the pathogen, including how these pathogens are transmitted, what diseases they cause, and how they are treated.

After students complete their research, instruct the original five-member groups to reassemble. Tell each group member to report his or her findings and then have the group members work together to design a table that summarizes their findings. Have a class discussion about pathogens and the diseases they cause and allow students to refer to their tables.

Concept Map

The following is one possible solution to the concept mapping activity in Reteaching on p. 678.

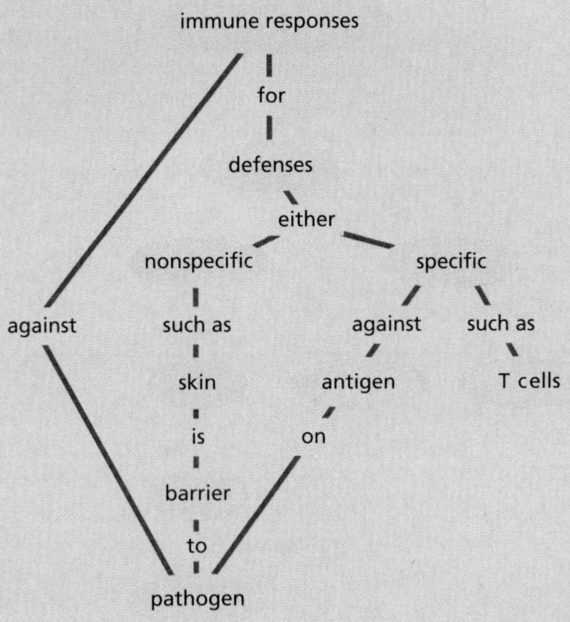

Laboratory Preparation

Overview *(See p. 683.)*

This lab encourages students to think about the many different kinds of organisms that can cause disease and the many ways in which they can do it.

Preparation

Prepared slides of pathogens can be obtained from biological supply houses. Representative organisms have been suggested, but any other pathogens can be used, such as the bacterium that causes pneumonia.

Teaching Tips

Bacteria can be seen as small rods or spirals under high power (×400). If your microscopes have oil immersion lenses, the bacteria can be seen better. Point out that you need such great magnification to see prokaryotic cells, which are small.

Discuss some of the diseases represented in this lab; students are fascinated by them. Botulism is caused by one of the most potent neurotoxins known, produced by *Clostridium botulinum,* a bacterium that grows only under anaerobic conditions (obligate anaerobe). It is found in canned food that has not been properly sterilized. The neurotoxin is fatal because it blocks the signals from the nerves that tell the breathing muscles (diaphragm and intercostal muscles) to move.

Discussion of syphilis and AIDS can lead to a discussion of sexually transmitted diseases. Syphilis is caused by a bacterium that is also an obligate anaerobe and is transmitted only from one moist mucous membrane to another. AIDS is caused by a virus that can lie dormant in cells for many years before causing symptoms. Unfortunately, it can also be transmitted during this dormant period.

Malaria is one of the major health problems worldwide, with millions of people debilitated by the *Plasmodium,* which is transmitted by a mosquito.

Safety

Students should use care in handling glass slides and microscopes.

Chapter Themes

Systems and Interactions The immune system, which responds to an invading pathogen, is an intricate system of defense mechanisms designed to block and destroy any foreign substance entering the body. Emphasize the interactions between the nonspecific and specific defenses of the immune system and how they defend the body against the four mechanisms of pathogen transmission. Point out that the critical health problems created by a deficient immune system can be caused by a viral infection, such as is seen in AIDS patients, or can be the result of genetics, as seen in the "Boy in the Bubble."

Patterns of Change Upon entering the body, pathogens cause it to change. Point out that not only does the immune system act in response to the pathogen, but the pathogen itself affects the body by disrupting the function of cells and tissues and ultimately organs and organ systems.

Stability The immune system is constantly working to maintain a dynamic equilibrium in the human body. Unless disrupted, as in the case of AIDS, the immune system is effective in keeping the body free of infectious disease.

Chapter Motivating Activity

Encourage students to name infectious diseases they have had, such as strep throat or the flu, and list their examples on the board. Ask students to infer why some of them have not had the most often mentioned disease.

Invite students to share their experiences with infectious diseases. Ask them to describe how they felt while they were sick and how the disease was treated. Have them hypothesize about what caused the diseases and how they caught them.

Chapter 44 Infectious Diseases and the Immune System

Introduction

The human body is exposed to a number of agents that cause disease. The immune system adapts and changes to fight off these diseases. In addition, advancements in research techniques have helped scientists understand the normal workings of the immune system, and its disruption by organisms such as the virus that causes AIDS.

Chapter Outline

44.1 Infectious Disease
- *Koch's Postulates*
- *Pathogens*
- *Disease Transmission*

44.2 Immune System
- *Nonspecific Defenses*
- *Specific Defense*
- *Immunity and Immune Disorders*

44.3 AIDS
- *Cause*
- *Transmission*
- *Viral Action*
- *Effects of Immune Disruption*
- *Risk and Prevention*

Chapter Concept

As you read, identify ways to diagnose, prevent, treat, and cure diseases.

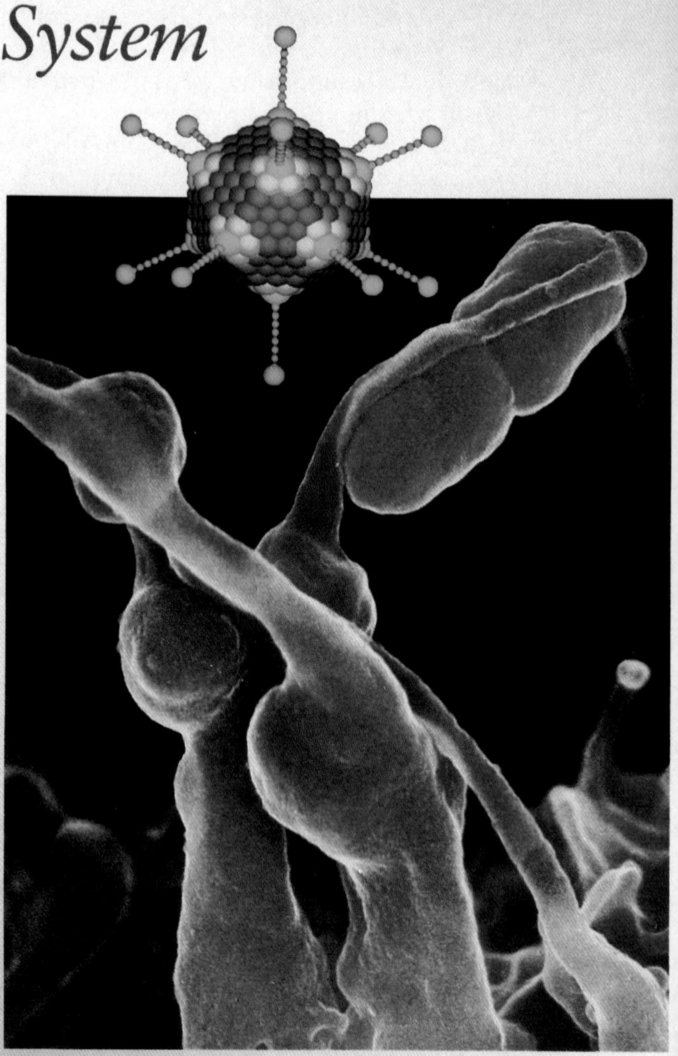

Pseudopodia of a macrophage ensnaring a bacterium that is tinted green (×14,740). Inset: Adenovirus, the virus that causes the common cold.

Understanding the Visuals

Ask students to describe the differences between the bacterium and the adenovirus. *(They differ in shape and composition.)* What do the virus and the bacterium have in common? *(Both have the ability to cause disease.)* Have students point out the macrophage and the bacterium in the photograph. Ask them to recall what a macrophage is and to describe its function. *(A macrophage is one type of white blood cell, or leukocyte. It seeks to destroy disease-causing organisms.)* Ask students to predict the fate of the bacterium. *(It will be ingested by the macrophage.)*

44.1 Infectious Disease

The human body is continuously under attack by disease-causing organisms. An **infectious disease** is one caused by the entrance into the body of an organism and its multiplication there. An infectious disease may spread from host to host. Any agent that causes an infectious disease is called a **pathogen.** The body's immune system fights disease by attacking disease-causing organisms or preventing their entry into the body.

Koch's Postulates

Robert Koch (1843–1910), a German physician, was the first scientist to establish a step-by-step procedure for identifying the pathogen responsible for a given disease. In the 1870s both Koch and Louis Pasteur determined that anthrax, a disease of cattle which can be spread to humans, is caused by a bacterial infection. Koch noticed that cattle with anthrax had swarms of bacteria in their blood. He hypothesized that these bacteria caused anthrax.

To test his hypothesis, Koch isolated these bacteria from the infected host, grew them in a laboratory culture, and then inoculated a healthy cow with the bacteria. The new host then developed anthrax. Koch compared the bacteria from the original host with the bacteria in the new host and found them the same. He concluded that the bacteria caused the disease. The steps that Koch formulated for determining the cause of a given disease, known as **Koch's postulates,** are described in Figure 44-1.

Pathogens

Scientists have used Koch's postulates to identify thousands of pathogens. The most common are bacteria, viruses, protozoa, fungi, and invertebrates. Each type affects the body differently. Table 44-1 on the next page lists common pathogens and diseases.

Many pathogens produce **toxins,** chemical substances harmful to the normal functioning of cells. Among the most powerful toxins are the **neurotoxins,** substances that disrupt the transmission of nerve impulses. For example, the bacterium associated with botulism produces a neurotoxin that causes double vision

Section Objectives

- *Summarize the four steps of Koch's postulates.*
- *Identify five types of pathogens.*
- *Describe four mechanisms of disease transmission.*

Figure 44-1 The bacterium that causes anthrax, *Bacillus anthracis* (left, × 42,268), was identified as a pathogen by means of Koch's postulates (right).

Koch's Postulates

1. Isolate the organism suspected of causing the disease.
2. Grow the organism in laboratory cultures.
3. Inoculate a healthy animal with the cultured organisms. Observe whether the animal contracts the disease.
4. If the animal contracts the disease, isolate the organism that caused it. Compare this organism with the one isolated in step 1.

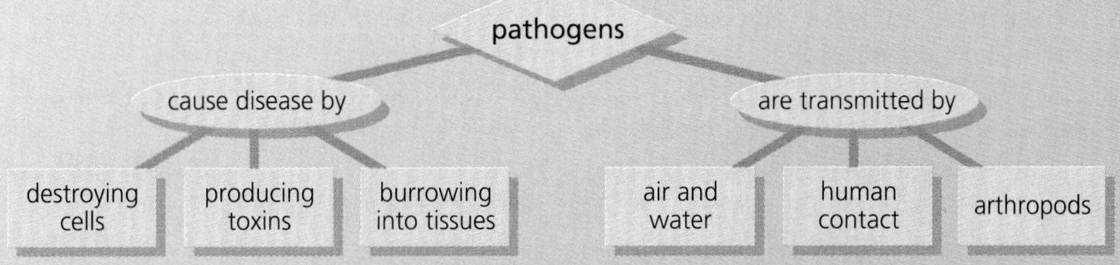

Graphic Organizer Use this organizational chart in Reteaching on p. 674.

Lesson Plan

Section Focus

This section explains how different types of pathogens cause disease and how diseases are transmitted. Students will learn Koch's postulates, the procedure for identifying pathogens.

Section Themes

The theme of **Patterns of Change** is emphasized in this section. By understanding the cyclical changes caused by pathogens, scientists learn to control disease.

Motivating Activity

Tap students' prior knowledge of infectious diseases by asking them what causes a cold. *(A virus)* What do you do to avoid catching a cold? *(Avoid close contact with people with colds, and wash hands frequently.)* Challenge students to draw a conclusion about how the cold virus is transmitted. *(Through saliva of an infected person, from the spray of a sneeze)*

■ ***See* Laboratories, *Investigation 44.***

Teaching Strategies

Describing Scientific Processes

Refer students to the table listing Koch's postulates in Figure 44-1, p. 673. Ask what process skills Koch used to determine the cause of a disease. *(Observing, collecting data, hypothesizing, predicting, experimenting, and analyzing data)*

Guided Practice

Show pictures of various pathogens to students. Ask them to classify the pathogens as one of five types: bacteria, viruses, protozoa, fungi, and invertebrates.

Videodiscs

■ ***Side 1 31819, Bacterial Cells and Membranes (m)***

■ ***2624, Bacteriophage Infection (s)***

■ ***2687, Adenovirus (s)***

Section 44.1

Independent Practice

- Have students write answers to the Section Review.
- Have students choose one disease listed in Table 44-1, p. 674, and research the symptoms of the disease, how it is treated, and how it is prevented.
- *See* Blackline Master *90.*

Check Your Understanding

1. How might a scientist isolate the pathogen that causes strep throat? *(By swabbing the patient's throat, then inoculating a growth medium)*
2. What actions of pathogens cause the symptoms associated with many infectious diseases? *(Pathogens produce toxins, destroy cells, or burrow into tissues as they multiply.)*
3. How can a person avoid getting athlete's foot? *(Use footwear in public places.)*

Reteaching

Have students make an organizational chart that shows the modes of transmission and actions of pathogens. A sample chart is shown on p. 673.

- *See* Section Reviews *worksheet, Section 44.1.*

Enrichment

Before the work done by Pasteur and Koch, prevalent ideas about disease involved such concepts as "spontaneous generation" and "humors." Have students research these concepts and discuss how they hindered the understanding of disease.

Closure

Ask students to list common infectious diseases, how they are spread, and how infection can be prevented. For example, syphilis can be contracted by sexual intercourse, and infection can be prevented by using a condom. Have students summarize general preventive measures to avoid contracting an infectious disease.

Table 44-1 Common Diseases and Their Causes

Disease	Pathogen	Method of Transmission
Athlete's foot	Fungus	Contact with contaminated objects such as shower floors
Common cold	Any of 100 viruses	Close contact with infected person; airborne spread of virus
Hepatitis A	Virus	Person-to-person contact; eating contaminated food and water
Influenza	Any of 100 viruses	Person-to-person contact; contact with contaminated objects
Malaria	Protozoa	Bites from mosquitoes carrying the protozoa; transfusion of infected blood
Measles (rubeola)	Virus	Contact with infected saliva or mucus; airborne spread of virus
Pneumonia	Virus or bacteria	Contact with infected saliva or mucus
Syphilis	Bacterium	Sexual contact

and severe pain. Viruses and certain bacteria also cause diseases by destroying cells. Invertebrates cause diseases by burrowing into tissues, such as muscle or intestinal tissue. They cause pain while interfering with the normal function of the tissues.

Disease Transmission

Pathogenic viruses and microorganisms may spread from host to host. Scientists have identified four main mechanisms of transmission: air, water, human contact, and arthropods.

An organism may be transmitted through air in spores or cysts or in droplets. For example, when a person with a cold sneezes or coughs, droplets, which contain pathogens, are released into the air.

Pathogens may also be transmitted through water. This can occur when wastes containing pathogens are released into water that is then used for other purposes. If a leaky septic tank contaminates a water supply, an entire community can be infected.

An infected person can transmit pathogens directly by touching another person or indirectly by touching some object that is in turn touched by another person.

Pathogens can be transmitted through an arthropod vector. Arthropods such as lice, mosquitoes, ticks, and fleas carry pathogens and transmit them to hosts when penetrating the skin.

Section Review

1. What is an *infectious disease?*
2. How did Koch test his hypothesis about the cause of anthrax?
3. Describe the general effect of a neurotoxin.
4. How are pathogens transmitted by water?
5. How might insects transmit pathogens from water to humans?

Answers to Section Review

1. A disease caused by bacteria, viruses, protozoa, fungi, or invertebrates entering the body and multiplying
2. By isolating the bacteria, growing them in a culture, inoculating a new host, and comparing the bacteria from the new host with the bacteria from the original host
3. Neurotoxins disrupt the transmission of nerve impulses.
4. When wastes containing pathogens are released into water that is then used for other purposes
5. The insects might land on contaminated water, either ingest or pick up the pathogens, then transmit the pathogens to humans by biting them or by landing on food.

44.2 Immune System

The body is able to defend itself against pathogens by means of a complex set of defenses. These defenses make up the body's immune system. The reaction of the body against a foreign substance is called an **immune response.** Both nonspecific and specific defenses exist.

Nonspecific Defenses

Nonspecific defenses are those that act against all disease-causing organisms in the same way regardless of the biological nature of the organism. These defenses include the skin and the mucous membranes of the nose and mouth, which act as mechanical and chemical barriers to pathogens. Other nonspecific defenses are phagocytes, fever, and interferon, all of which act against pathogens that do enter the body.

Skin and Mucous Membranes

The layer of overlapping dead cells on the surface of the skin prevents pathogens from entering the body. A break in the skin may permit pathogens to enter body tissues. Blood clots then form a temporary barrier until new skin seals the wound.

The sweat, oils, and waxes produced by the skin contain chemical substances, such as lactic acid, that are poisonous to many bacteria and fungi. However, not all bacteria are harmful. Large populations of harmless bacteria living on the skin actually aid in protecting the body by inhibiting the growth of pathogens.

Mucous membranes defend the body against pathogens that enter through the mouth and nose. Mucus and tiny hairs in the mouth and nose trap microorganisms. Enzymes in the mucus destroy pathogens. Pathogens that do reach body organs are met with other nonspecific defenses. For example, pathogens that enter the stomach are usually destroyed by digestive acids.

Phagocytes and Fever

An **inflammatory response** is one in which white blood cells gather and engulf the foreign substances and the body temperature rises. These white blood cells are phagocytes. Humans have two types of phagocytes–neutrophils and macrophages. **Neutrophils** *(NYOO-truh-FILLZ)* are small white blood cells with irregular nuclei. Neutrophils ingest small numbers of bacteria. **Macrophages** *(MACK-ruh-FAJ-uz)* are large white blood cells that can engulf hundreds of bacteria. The action of the neutrophils and macrophages is usually accompanied with an increase in body temperature, or **fever.** If the fever is high enough, it can kill pathogens. A fever is not a disease but a symptom. It is a sign that the body is responding to an infection. However, if the infection is severe, fever itself can cause death.

Section Objectives

- *Explain how the skin functions as a defense against disease.*
- *Distinguish between a specific and a nonspecific response.*
- *Describe the actions of B cells and T cells in a primary immune response.*
- *Describe the relationship between vaccination and immunity.*
- *Describe the methods Jonas Salk used to develop a vaccine for the polio virus.*

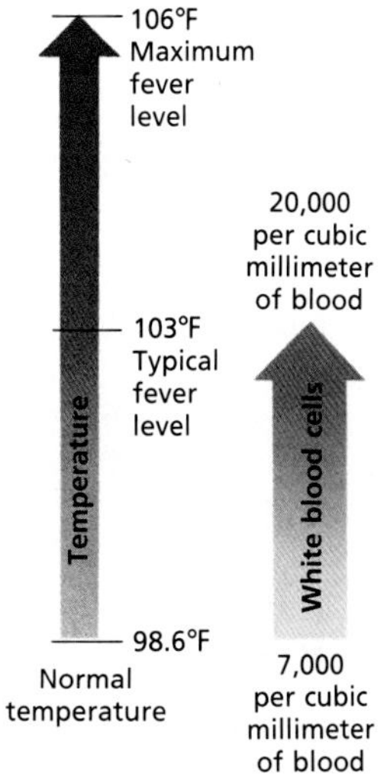

Figure 44-2 The immune response involves both an elevation in temperature and an increase in the number of white blood cells.

Lesson Plan

Section Focus

This section describes both nonspecific and specific defenses of the immune system. Students also study immunity and immune disorders such as allergies.

Section Themes

The theme of **Systems and Interactions** can be illustrated by the interaction between the body's immune system and an antigen. The body has a systematic response that can not only destroy the foreign antigen, but can also keep memory cells for further destruction of the same antigen should it return.

Motivating Activity

Ask students to recall what vaccinations they had before beginning school. Be sensitive to those students who have not been vaccinated for religious or philosophical reasons. *(Most have had polio, diphtheria, tetanus, pertussis or whooping cough, mumps, and rubella vaccinations.)* Then ask students if any have had additional vaccinations for foreign travel. *(Some may have had vaccinations against yellow fever, cholera, hepatitis, and typhoid fever.)* Encourage students to make inferences about the necessity for these additional vaccinations.

Videodiscs

- ***Side 2 18741, Types of Bacteria (m)***
- ***Side 2 19145, Antibodies (m)***

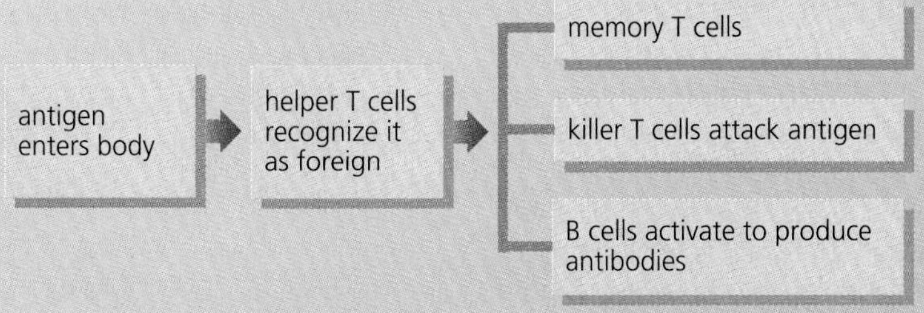

Graphic Organizer Use this sequential diagram in Independent Practice on page 677.

Teaching Strategies

Organizing Information Have students make a chart in which they list the different types of nonspecific defenses and how each defends the body from disease-causing organisms.
■ *See* Process Skills, *Chapter 44.*

Identifying Structures Display a human anatomical model and ask students to identify the openings in the skin that lead into the body. *(Eyes, nose, mouth, ears, reproductive organs, urethra, anus)* Then ask students to name defenses in these body openings that help limit entry of pathogens. *(Mucous membranes, mucus, tiny hairs or cilia, tears, and ear wax)*

Applying Concepts Challenge students to make an analogy between a building's security system and the body's immune system. Ask them to explain the function of both systems. *(To prevent "intruders" from entering)* Then challenge students to compare the function of the security system's components and the analogous components of the immune system. *(Locked doors and windows, skin, and mucous membranes deter "intruders" from entering. Burglar alarms, motion detectors, and fever signal the entrance of "intruders." Armed guards, interferon, phagocytes, B cells, and T cells attack "intruders.")*

Understanding Differences Ask students to think of diseases that are not caused by viruses or other invading organisms. *(Genetically inherited conditions, autoimmune disorders, nutritional deficiencies, hormonal imbalances)*

Interferon

Cells respond to a viral infection by producing a protein called **interferon** *(INT-ur-FIR-ahn),* which inhibits the reproduction of viruses. Interferon triggers the production of an enzyme that enables a cell to recognize a virus as a foreign substance. Interferon thus prevents the virus from reproducing. Interferon affects any type of virus. Through DNA-splicing techniques genetic engineers have made large amounts of human interferon.

Specific Defense

In a specific defense one or more components of the immune system attack a specific pathogen. The immune system identifies specific chemicals on the surface of a pathogen and then targets that pathogen for destruction. Any substance that causes a specific immune response is called an **antigen.**

Specific defenses are of two types, one using cells, and the other using proteins. Both involve **lymphocytes** *(LIM-fuh-SITES),* which are special white blood cells. They exist in two primary forms—T cells and B cells. Their responses to antigens may be primary or secondary.

Primary Response

A **primary immune response** is a specific defense involving both B cells and T cells. **T cells** attack antigens directly. **B cells** produce chemicals that render antigens harmless. Both types of lymphocytes develop in the bone marrow but are named for the place where they differentiate. B cells differentiate in the bone marrow; T cells migrate to the thymus before differentiating.

Figure 44-3 In the primary immune response B cells and T cells act together to destroy the antigen.

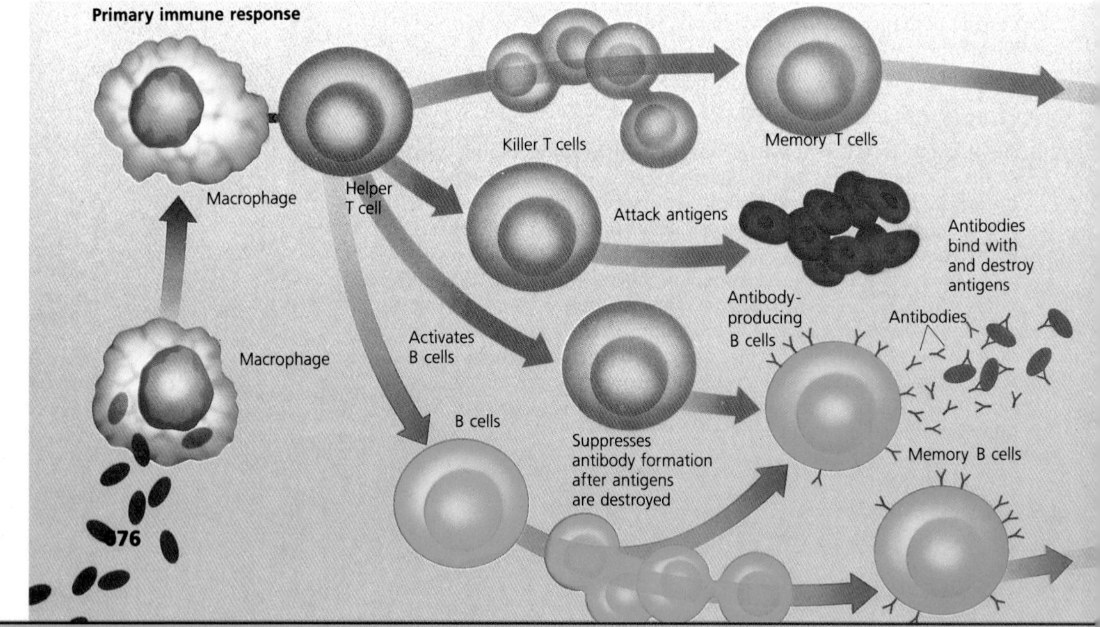

LEP Activity

To help students visually relate the vocabulary terms in this section with the elements of the immune system, have them make posters illustrating nonspecific and specific defenses. Encourage students to show how the two types of defenses work together to deter pathogenic organisms. Make sure that students label their posters using the vocabulary terms. For example, the chemicals, oils, and sweat produced by the skin are all nonspecific defenses. If the invading pathogen gets by them, it will be attacked by specific defenses of the immune system called T cells and B cells.

The response of T cells is a **cell-mediated response.** Figure 44-3 shows this response. Specialized T cells called **helper cells** initiate a cell-mediated response. Each T cell can distinguish the "self" (other lymphocytes) from the "nonself" (foreign substances). When a T cell recognizes a foreign antigen, it rapidly divides to form many cells. Some destroy the antigen. Others, called **memory cells,** stay in the blood. If the same antigen appears again, memory cells recognize and destroy it.

B cells respond by producing antibodies—Y-shaped proteins that bind to and destroy specific antigens. Each B cell synthesizes an antibody that acts only against a particular antigen. When a B cell binds to an invading antigen, the cell is stimulated to divide. Each resulting cell, called a clone, produces the same antibody and thus destroys the same type of pathogen.

Secondary Response

Initially scientists believed that the functions of T cells and B cells were separate. Now they know that the functions of the two types of cells are coordinated. They have discovered that T cells regulate the actions of B cells in the secondary immune response. A **secondary immune response** is the response to a subsequent infection by the same pathogen.

After the pathogen has disappeared from the blood, modified T cells called **suppressor cells** stop the B cells from producing antibodies. Though B cells stop synthesizing antibodies, several clones called memory B cells remain in circulation. As you know, the T cells have also formed memory T cells. Therefore, when the body encounters the same pathogen in the future, the memory T and B cells proliferate quickly and fight the infection before it overwhelms the system.

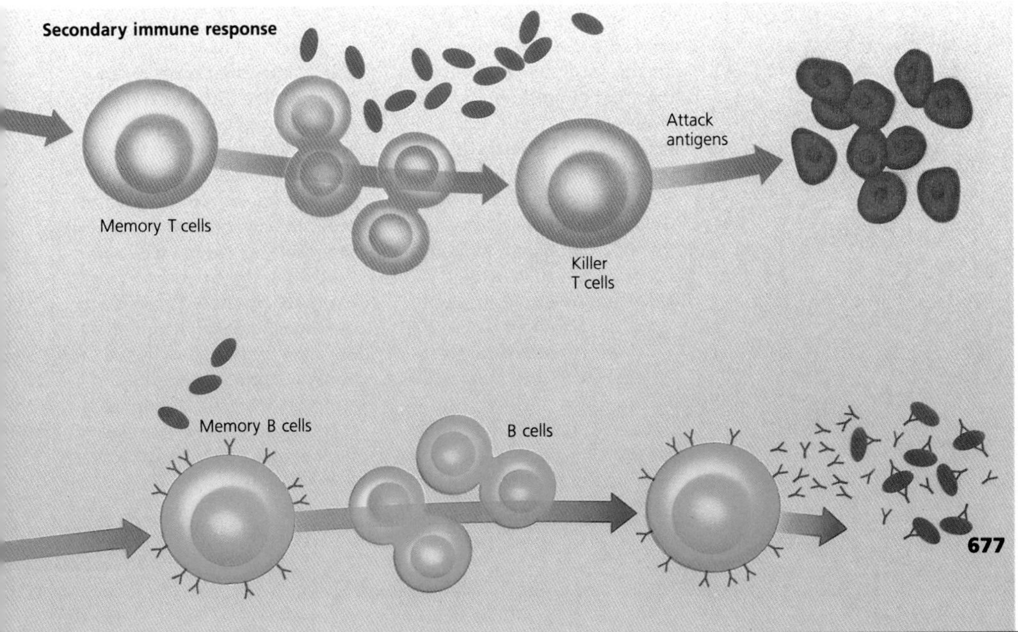

Interpreting the Visuals Take students step-by-step through the primary and secondary immune response of the immune system as diagrammed in Figure 44-3, p. 676. Point out that helper T cells identify pathogens and then send out chemical signals to stimulate production of killer T cells and to trigger B cells to produce antibodies.

■ *See* **Overhead Transparency** ***T44 and*** **Blackline Master** ***91.***

Recognizing Differences Make sure students realize that allergies are not infectious diseases by asking them to contrast an allergen and a pathogen. *(A pathogen multiplies inside the body; an allergen does not.)* Point out that allergies are not contagious and so cannot be spread by sneezing the way some viruses can.

Guided Practice

Tell students to take and record their temperatures just before going to bed and when they get up in the morning. Have them take their temperatures in class, then average all the temperatures taken at a given time. Is there a pattern? *(Temperatures should be lowest in the early morning and highest at night.)* Does the higher temperature at night represent inflammatory response? Formulate a hypothesis. (*The higher body temperature at the end of the day is due to a natural inflammatory response of the immune system.)*

Independent Practice

■ Have students write answers to the Section Review.

■ Copy the sequential diagram on p. 675 on the board. Have students complete the diagram of the primary and secondary immune responses. They may use Figure 44-3, pp. 676–677, as a guide.

Videodiscs

■ ***Side 2 19769, Antibodies: Bacterial Destruction (m)***

Cooperative Learning

Vaccinations Have small groups of students debate the pros and cons of vaccinations. Before students begin their debate, have half of the group members research the risks of vaccinations and the other half research the benefits. Also point out that some people refuse vaccinations on religious or philosophical grounds. Instruct students in their debate to defend the side of the issue that they researched. Then instruct groups to switch roles so students defend the other side of the issue.

Section 44.2

Answer to Think

Pollen grains enter the body through the nose and mouth. Mucus, tiny hairs, and cilia lining the air passages are the first line of defense. If these do not stop the pollen grains, T cells and B cells will attempt to destroy the allergen.

Check Your Understanding

1. What symptoms would lead a doctor to conclude that a patient has an infection? *(A fever and an elevated white blood cell count)*

2. How do T cells regulate B cells? *(They activate B cells in the presence of an antigen and stop B cells from producing antibodies after the antigen has been destroyed.)*

3. Why are vaccines effective against viral infections? *(They provide immunity to specific viruses before the viruses can cause diseases.)*

Reteaching

Ask students to make a concept map that shows the components of the nonspecific and specific defenses of the immune system. An example of a completed concept map is shown on p. 671B.

■ *See* Section Reviews *worksheet, Section 44.2.*

Enrichment

Have students research the difference between active and passive immunity to find out which type of immunity is provided by the vaccines and serums for diseases such as polio, hepatitis, tuberculosis, tetanus, and pneumonia.

Think

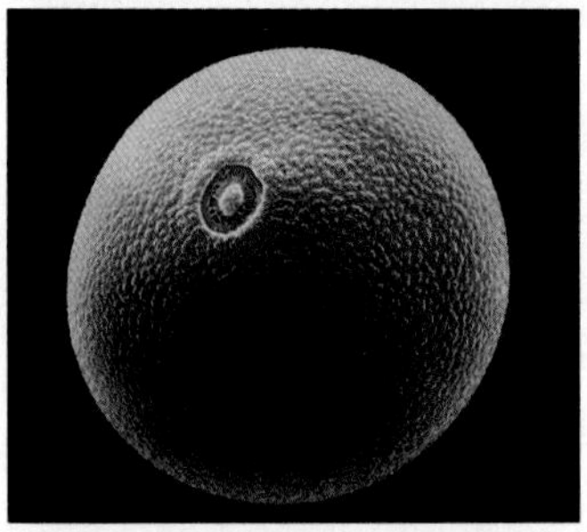

Pictured above is an airborne allergen called a pollen grain. How might such an allergen enter the body? How could the body rid itself of this allergen?

Immunity and Immune Disorders

A person who has a resistance to a specific pathogen is said to have an **immunity** to it. **Natural immunity** is immunity that is present at birth. **Acquired immunity** is developed after birth.

One way of acquiring immunity is through vaccination. In **vaccination** *(VACK-suh-NAY-shun)* an individual is exposed, usually by means of injection, to a killed or weakened form of a pathogen in order to produce immunity to the disease caused by the pathogen.

Antibiotics *(ANT-ih-bie-AHT-icks),* drugs that fight bacterial infection, have made it possible for scientists and physicians to prevent and treat a large number of diseases. Penicillin, one of the best-known antibiotics, was discovered in 1929 by Sir Alexander Fleming (1881–1955), a British bacteriologist.

The immune system is subject to various disorders. Normally suppressor cells prevent B cells from producing antibodies against nonpathogenic substances. In some individuals, however, the lymphocytes react to harmless antigens. These antigens, or **allergens,** include foods, pollen, and substances on animal fur. A reaction to an allergen is called an **allergy.**

Biology in Process

Jonas Salk and the Polio Vaccine

For centuries poliomyelitis affected people in all parts of the world. Polio, which remains incurable, causes symptoms that range from pain and stiffness to paralysis. It can ultimately result in death. The prevalence and severity of poliomyelitis disturbed Dr. Jonas Salk, an American physician. In 1942 Salk began to study polio at the University of Michigan. He concentrated on the cause and physiological effects of polio. Salk identified three polio viruses that all acted in a similar manner. He hypothesized that a polio virus entered the body through the nose or mouth and was carried to the intestines. Through observation and experimentation Salk learned that from the intestines the virus was transmitted to the central nervous system either by nerve fibers or by the blood.

Salk knew from his own previous experiments and from the results of his predecessors that when the virus enters a nerve cell, it alters the function of the cell, causing it to reproduce the virus. The virus can multiply rapidly enough to destroy or kill most adjacent cells. If enough cells are destroyed, the nervous system is affected, and paralysis results.

More Information

Acquired Immunity Immunity can be either active or passive. *Acquired active immunity* occurs after one has been exposed to, or has had, an infectious disease such as chicken pox. It can also occur when dead or weakened pathogens—such as denatured polio virus—are introduced into the body either orally or by injection in a process called vaccination. In active immunity, the body responds to a pathogen by producing antibodies against the disease-causing organism.

Acquired passive immunity is passed to the fetus by antibodies in the mother's blood and to the infant in breast milk. It also occurs when a serum containing antibodies to a disease is injected. Since the body does not produce its own antibodies, the passive immunity wears off.

At the first exposure to an allergen an individual may not have a noticeable reaction. Nevertheless, B cells may synthesize antibodies and develop memory cells. At the second exposure the individual produces a secondary immune response. Antibodies and allergens bind together and cause the release of **histamine** *(HISS-tuh-MEEN)*, a chemical associated with the sneezing, watery and itchy eyes, and wheezing of allergies. Drugs called **antihistamines** help counteract the effect of histamines.

In another type of disorder, **autoimmune disease,** the immune system produces antibodies against cells in the body because it fails to recognize them as self. In some cases, an antigen resembles one of the body's own substances. Antibodies from the immune system may destroy this substance as well as the foreign antigen.

Section Review

1. Define *natural immunity* and *acquired immunity.*
2. Describe three nonspecific responses of the immune system.
3. What is the role of suppressor cells?
4. Describe what happens in an allergic response.
5. How might a doctor treat strep throat, a bacterial infection?

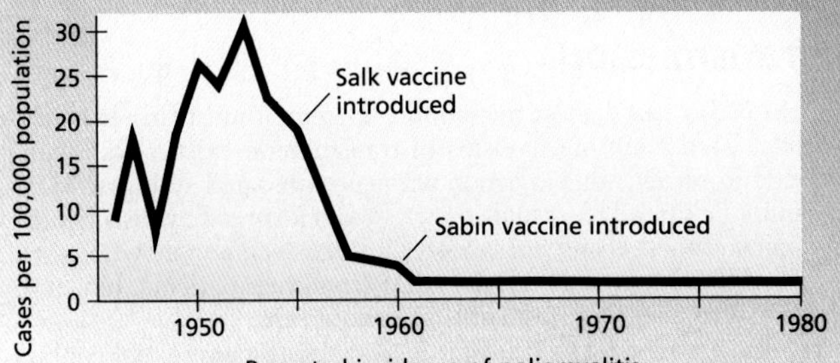

Reported incidence of poliomyelitis in the United States, 1920–1980

After completing his initial investigations Salk had enough information about the virus to begin to develop a vaccine. He researched the work of earlier epidemiologists and incorporated their findings into his plan. Most vaccines are made from actual viruses that have been weakened or killed but can still produce the immune response in a new host. Salk discovered he could kill the three polio viruses by using a formaldehyde solution. Through carefully controlled experimentation Salk produced a vaccine from the treated viruses. The next step was to determine whether the vaccine would work in the human body. He injected himself, his wife, and his three sons. The results were successful.

True success of the vaccines could not be determined by this limited test. Therefore in 1954, with money and personnel from the National Foundation for Infantile Paralysis (later called the March of Dimes Foundation), the Salk vaccine was administered to 1,830,000 American school children. Follow-up studies proved that the vaccine was not only safe but effective. In April 1955 the vaccine was made available to the general population.

Shortly after Salk's initial test, another American physician, Albert Sabin, used further research to develop an oral vaccine. This made the administration of the vaccine easier and less painful.

■ Why was it important for Salk to study prior research?

Answers to Section Review

1. Natural immunity is present at birth; acquired immunity is developed after birth.
2. The skin acts as a physical and chemical barrier to pathogens; mucus, produced by mucous membranes, and tiny hairs trap pathogens entering the mouth or nose; phagocytes, together with fever, destroy pathogens; interferon inhibits reproduction of viruses.
3. Suppressor cells stop B cells from producing antibodies after the pathogen has disappeared from the blood.
4. Antibodies are released in large quantities and bind to the allergen, causing the release of histamines.
5. With an antibiotic

Closure

Poll the class to find out who has allergies or knows someone who does. Encourage students to describe how allergies affect their lives. Ask allergy sufferers how they are being treated for the allergy.

Biology in Process

Using the Feature

The main process skills discussed in this feature are communication and experimentation. Emphasize the importance of communication in science. By studying the findings of other researchers, Jonas Salk was able to save time in developing a polio vaccine by using data that were already collected and methods and techniques that were already proven.

Salk used the process of experimentation to learn about the polio virus and the effectiveness of his vaccine. Point out to students that the school children who received the vaccine were the experimental group. Ask students to identify the control group. *(The general population, which did not receive the vaccination)*

Ask students to discuss some biological facts Salk needed to know before he could develop a vaccine. *(What causes the disease, how the virus acts in the organism, how many pathogens cause poliomyelitis)*

Answer to the Feature

By studying prior research, Salk gained a basis for his own research. He saved time by not having to redo what had already been done, thereby speeding up the development of a polio vaccine.

Lesson Plan

Section Focus

This section describes the cause, transmission, and effects of AIDS, as well as who is at risk and how AIDS is prevented.

Section Themes

This section emphasizes the theme of **Systems and Interactions.** HIV causes AIDS by disrupting the immune system, thereby making the body vulnerable to other pathogens.

Motivating Activity

Ask students to describe how AIDS has affected our society. *(Thousands of people have died. People may be fearful of sexual encounters and wary of using intravenous drugs. People have concerns about receiving blood transfusions, too.)* Ask students whether they believe that physicians or dentists with AIDS should continue practicing and, if so, whether they should tell their patients. *(Allow for students' personal opinions.)* Stress that an effective control against the transmission of AIDS to or from a health professional is proper hygiene (wearing gloves and a mask) and sterilization of instruments.

Teaching Strategies

Discussing the Issues Invite a physician or other healthcare professional to class to discuss the latest information on the HIV virus and AIDS. Ask the speaker to talk about how AIDS has challenged the health care system.

Guided Practice

Ask students to list secondary infections that are commonly fatal to people with AIDS. *(Pneumocystis pneumonia, Kaposi's sarcoma)* Why are these diseases rare in people who do not have AIDS? *(A healthy immune system is able to suppress these diseases.)*

Section Objectives

- *Name the two chief methods of transmitting AIDS.*
- *Describe how HIV affects the immune system.*

44.3 AIDS

The responses of the cell-mediated system and the antibody system keep most diseases from being expressed in the human body. However, disorders of the immune system do occur. One of the most serious disorders is called **AIDS,** which stands for **acquired immune deficiency syndrome.**

Cause

AIDS is a viral disruption of the proper workings of the immune system. The virus that causes the disruption is shown in Figure 44-4. It has been named HIV, which stands for human immunodeficiency virus. It is also called HTLV-III, which stands for human T-cell lymphotrophic virus, and LAV, which stands for lymphadenopathy-associated virus.

The virus is a retrovirus, which means that it contains RNA as its genetic complement. HIV has two strands of RNA that form the template for DNA when acted on by the enzyme reverse transcriptase. The resulting DNA has seven genes that code for the formation of new viruses after infection. As you will see, the virus acts on cells of the immune system.

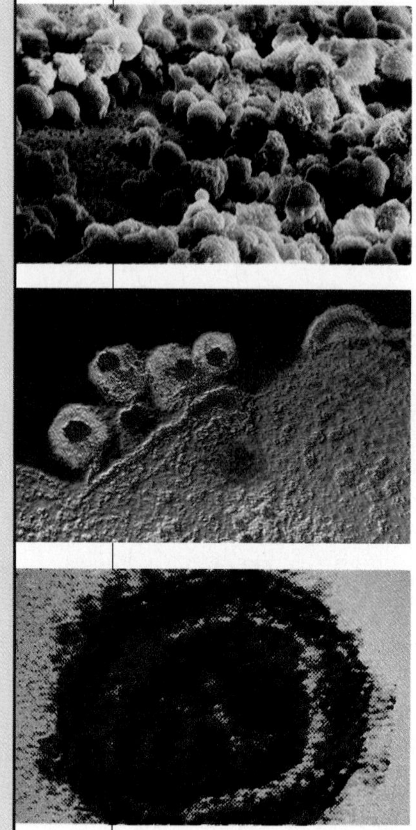

Figure 44-4 These three photos show increasingly greater magnifications of the AIDS virus. The bottom magnification is ×120,000.

Transmission

Before HIV can disrupt the immune system, it must first enter the body. Two main mechanisms of transmission exist: sexual contact and intravenous injection with contaminated syringes. AIDS cannot be spread by casual contact, nor is it spread by insects such as mosquitoes. Using normal precautions even people who work with AIDS patients do not get AIDS from their patients. Infection accompanying blood transfusion is now rare.

The virus may be transmitted during intimate sexual contact involving an exchange of body fluids. Transmission is especially likely when cells along body openings are damaged during sexual acts, thereby allowing the virus to enter the bloodstream directly.

Because the virus is also readily transmitted during intravenous injection with contaminated needles, AIDS is prevalent among users of illegal drugs. Injection of substances under a physician's supervision poses no threat of transmission.

Viral Action

As you read about the mechanisms by which HIV affects the immune system, refer to Figure 44-5. When the virus enters the bloodstream, the immune system recognizes it as an antigen. First the phagocyte engulfs but is unable to destroy the virus. A type of T cell called a T4 cell then attacks the virus, but the virus enters the T4 cells unharmed. At the same time antibodies made by the B

phagocytes attack but do not destroy HIV virus → T4 cells attack HIV; HIV enters T4 cells unharmed → HIV virus reproduces inside T4 cells → new HIV viruses released from T4 cells → more T4 cells infected with HIV and are destroyed

Graphic Organizer Use this sequential diagram in Independent Practice on page 681.

cells also attack the viruses in the blood, but the viruses are unharmed by antibody activity.

The virus may remain dormant in the T4 cells for up to ten years. At some point, however, the virus undergoes a lytic cycle of reproduction and creates many new viruses inside the T4 cells. As these viruses are released, they infect additional T4 cells and eventually destroy the capacity of the T4 cells to fight disease.

Effects of Immune Disruption

Once the T4 cells are destroyed, the immune system cannot fight diseases. People infected with the HIV virus then become susceptible to pathogens to which they normally would be immune. Many people with AIDS have secondary, and usually fatal, infections from *Pneumocystis carinii*, a bacterium that causes pneumonia. Another disease that occurs in an immune-deficient body is a form of cancer called Kaposi's sarcoma. Many other diseases also develop in HIV-infected individuals, diseases that cannot be suppressed and that ultimately lead to death.

Sometimes a full-blown AIDS-related infection is preceded by similar though less virulent diseases. Patients with such diseases are said to have **ARC,** or an **AIDS-related complex.**

Risk and Prevention

AIDS attacks both males and females. At particular risk, as indicated by disease statistics, are intravenous drug users and those homosexual men who engage in unsafe sexual activity. Heterosexual men and women also are susceptible to infection via some forms of intimate sexual contact.

Since AIDS is not spread by casual contact, transmission can be prevented by abstaining from intravenous injection unless under strict supervision of a physician and by abstaining from sexual activity. Any user of injected illegal drugs runs a severe risk of contracting AIDS. Sexual activity carries additional risks for AIDS. According to the Surgeon General of the United States, if sexual activity occurs, the use of condoms will reduce but will not eliminate the threat of transmission.

A blood test that detects antibodies to HIV now exists. The test reveals whether a person has been exposed to the virus.

Section Review

1. What does *AIDS* stand for?
2. Why does AIDS lead to other diseases?
3. Describe the action of the HIV virus after it enters the bloodstream.
4. Why are intravenous drug users at risk for AIDS?
5. How can behavioral changes modify an individual's chance of getting AIDS?

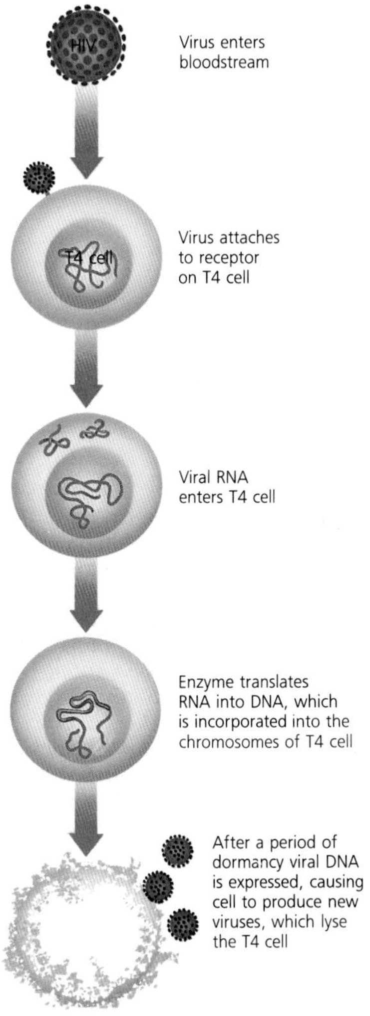

Figure 44-5 After the HIV virus enters the bloodstream, its RNA is translated to DNA, which fuses with T4 cell DNA. For simplicity only one DNA strand has been shown.

Answers to Section Review

1. Acquired immune deficiency syndrome
2. Because HIV disrupts the capacity of the immune system to fight disease
3. HIV is attacked but not destroyed by phagocytes, T4 cells, or antibodies. It enters T4 cells and eventually reproduces inside them, causing the T4 cells to lyse, thereby impairing the function of the immune system.
4. Intravenous drug users who share hypodermic needles with someone infected with HIV can contract AIDS.
5. Abstaining from sexual activity, using condoms, and staying away from intravenous drugs can greatly reduce the danger.

Independent Practice

■ Have students write answers to the Section Review.
■ Ask students to make a sequential diagram of the action of HIV in the human body, using the text and Figure 44-5, p. 681, as a guide. An example of a completed sequential diagram is shown on p. 680.

Check Your Understanding

1. What makes AIDS an immune system disorder? *(HIV colonizes in and destroys the T4 cells with which the body attempts to defend itself.)*
2. Can you contract AIDS if a person infected with HIV sneezes near you? Explain. *(No, HIV can only be transmitted through an exchange of body fluids, such as blood, semen, and vaginal fluid.)*
3. How does a blood test for AIDS help prevent its transmission? *(It identifies carriers of the disease.)*

Reteaching

Review with students the composition of blood (Section 43.2, pp. 662–663). Ask them to identify the type of blood cell that includes T cells and B cells. *(White blood cells)*
■ *See* **Section Reviews** *work-sheet, Section 44.3.*

Enrichment

Have students research the history of AIDS—where it was first identified and in what organism. Have students find out how different populations of people in different countries have been affected.

Closure

Ask students to identify the two surest ways to avoid contracting AIDS. *(By abstaining from intravenous drug use and from sexual activity)*

Background
AIDS has been called the "modern plague" because of its devastating effects and rapid global spread throughout Africa, Europe, Asia, and the Americas. For some years people believed it was a disease of homosexual men. However, with the spread of AIDS to the heterosexual population as well, it has become clear that this notion was largely irrelevant and may have impeded serious AIDS research.

Discussion
After students have read "The AIDS Epidemic," ask them to discuss the following questions.

1. Why does Gallo consider it fortunate that AIDS did not strike in the 1960s? *(Research would have been seriously limited by the lack of even the most basic understanding of retroviruses.)*

2. What are the implications of the two choices that Gallo sets out regarding AIDS research? Which choice should we follow? *(Allow for personal opinion. The first choice can lead to ideas of our mastery of the world, the second to "natural" mechanisms and ecology. Both lead to ethical and political questions.)*

Extension
Point out that this excerpt from Robert Gallo's book places AIDS within a historical context with particular clarity. Have students in partnership research another disease (for example, bubonic plague in fourteenth-century Europe or yellow fever during the building of the Panama Canal) and write a paper about it. Suggest that one partner research the disease itself, while the other looks at its historical setting.

Writing About Biology

The AIDS Epidemic

This excerpt is from Virus Hunting — AIDS, Cancer, and the Human Retrovirus *by Robert Gallo.*

HIV arrived and significantly spread in the United States sometime in the 1970s and was first clinically identified in 1981. I have often been asked what the prospects would have been for quickly identifying this disease's cause had it struck just a decade or two earlier (let us say in the 1960s). . . .

My guess is that if extensive HIV infection had not occurred when it did, nobody in science would have thought to look for a retroviral cause; and if someone had, progress would have been painfully slow. Scientists simply did not believe that retroviruses caused disease in humans, and until the 1970s, no one had worked out the distinctive method by which animal retroviruses replicate. Nor had we developed the techniques necessary to study human retroviruses in the lab or to culture their target T-cells properly. In fact, we didn't even know then that T-cells and their subclasses existed. I suspect the cause would have been discovered, but the time required to do so would have been much greater and our understanding of what to do with that information far less.

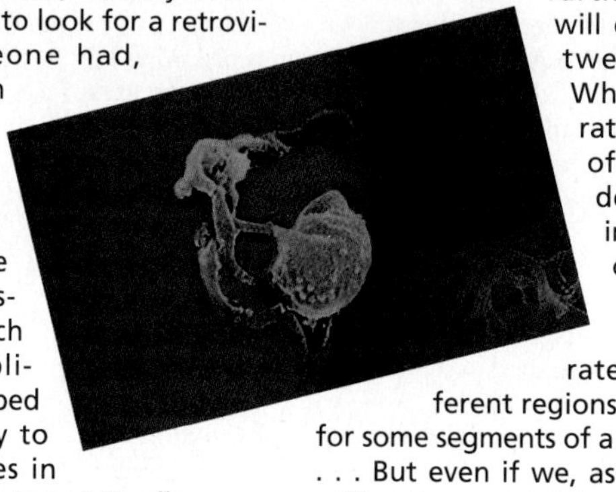

As it was, we were fortunate that by 1980 we already knew enough about animal retroviruses—their genes, their proteins, their "life cycle"—and about human retroviruses as well—and were able to begin work on isolating the virus that caused AIDS and then on developing an effective blood test. Yet it remains sobering to note that even in 1980 there was still no concentration of talent in basic human virology, let alone human retrovirology, to which the worldwide human community could turn for rapid and reliable answers. . . .

Regarding the study of emerging human viral disease, scientists are united in the belief that such work is of scientific urgency. Regarding AIDS, we have two choices. We can set for ourselves the uncompromising goal of not stopping until we conquer this disease, or we can let it follow the path of previous microbes, in which case, even if we do nothing further, some equilibrium will eventually develop between us and the virus. When this happens, the rate of infection will level off on its own and then decline. This may result in a gradual acceptance of a new status quo, one in which there will be "tolerable" rates of infection for different regions of the world, or worse for some segments of a given population.

. . . But even if we, as a society, were finally willing to accept this new situation regarding AIDS, it still does not offer us any comfort regarding the fact that AIDS may be the forerunner of other serious diseases caused by emerging viruses, each representing its own unique challenge. The scientific community is united in its belief that we must focus intensively on emerging viral diseases. I think, given enough information, the public would be also. The only unresolved question is how best to do this.

Write

- **Some experts have suggested that the AIDS epidemic could change the world. Write an essay discussing some of the ways this could happen.**

From Virus Hunting: AIDS, Cancer, and the Human Retrovirus: A Story of Scientific Discovery *(A New Republic Book) by Robert C. Gallo, M.D. Copyright © 1991 by Robert C. Gallo. Reprinted by permission of BasicBooks. A Division of HarperCollins Publisher.*

About the Author
Dr. Robert Gallo heads a laboratory at the National Institutes of Health that has been at the forefront of AIDS research. Originally a cancer researcher (he helped discover the first cancer-causing retrovirus), Gallo suspected that AIDS might also be caused by a retrovirus. This idea led him to switch to AIDS research. His lab subsequently codiscovered the AIDS virus and developed the AIDS blood test. Although his scientific contributions are great, there has been controversy over who first isolated the HIV virus, Gallo or researchers at the Pasteur Institute in France.

Laboratory

Observing Pathogens

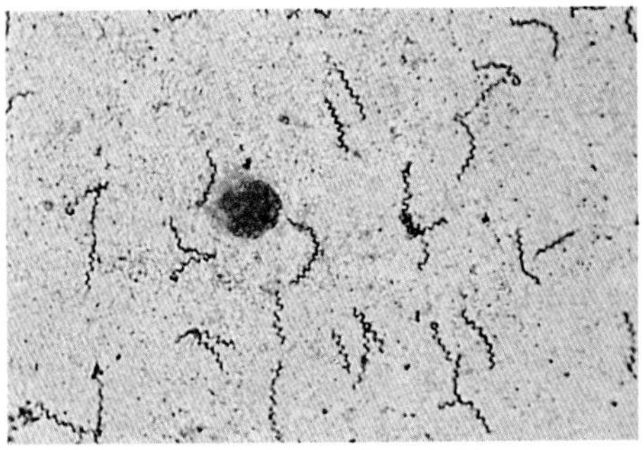

Objective
To study agents that cause disease in humans

Process Skills
Observing, inferring, classifying

Materials
Prepared slides of *Clostridium botulinum*, *Treponema pallidum*, *Histoplasma capsulatum*, red blood cells infected with malarial *Plasmodium*, tapeworm, and *Escherichia coli*; compound microscope

Background
1 What is a pathogen?
2 Name pathogens from four of the five kingdoms. Name pathogens that are not classified into one of the five kingdoms.

Inquiry
1 Using the high power of your microscope, examine a prepared slide of *Clostridium botulinum*, the bacteria that cause botulism. How large are the cells? To which kingdom does *C. botulinum* belong? Why has *C. botulinum* been classified in that kingdom?
2 What shape are the cells of *C. botulinum*?
3 Using the high power of your microscope, examine a prepared slide of *Escherichia coli*, the bacteria that normally lives in the intestines of all humans. How do the size and shape of *E. coli* cells compare with those of *C. botulinum*? Why do you think one of these bacteria is usually harmless and the other causes a deadly disease?
4 Examine a prepared slide of *Treponema pallidum*, the bacteria that causes syphilis. What shape are the cells you see?
5 Examine a prepared slide of red blood cells infected with the malarial *Plasmodium*. What kingdom does this organism belong to? How big are its cells compared with those of *C. botulinum*? Why?
6 *Plasmodium* infects red blood cells. How might this organism cause the classic symptoms of malaria— chronic weakness and fatigue?
7 Using low power, examine a prepared slide of a tapeworm. What kingdom and phylum does this organism belong to? Why was it easy to see on low power? How does a tapeworm cause disease?
8 Examine a prepared slide of *Histoplasma capsulatum*, a fungus that causes lung disease in patients with compromised immune systems. Why are AIDS patients particularly prone to *H. capsulatum*, while it rarely, if ever, infects healthy people?

Conclusions
1 Many viruses are pathogens. Why did you not examine any in this laboratory?
2 Why did you use only prepared slides in this lab?
3 What are the shapes of the three bacteria you observed? What can be learned about pathogens from the study of nonpathogenic bacteria?

Further Inquiry
Examine prepared slides of plant pathogens such as the wheat rust fungus or the powdery mildew of willow.

Laboratory

(For an overview of pathogens and preparatory information related to the laboratory, see p. 671B.)

Background
1. A pathogen is an organism that causes disease.
2. Students should name pathogens from Kingdoms Monera, Protista, Fungi, and Animalia. Examples include *Salmonella, Plasmodium, Candida albicans*, and tapeworm, respectively.

Inquiry
1. *C. botulinum* cells are tiny. Kingdom Monera. All monerans are prokaryotes, lacking a nucleus and membrane-bound organelles.
2. They are rods.
3. *E. coli* are also rod-shaped bacteria. Their appearance is similar to *C. botulinum. C. botulinum* produces a potent neurotoxin that paralyzes the breathing muscles. *E. coli* does not usually produce toxins in the intestines. However, while *E. coli* is the principal bacterial inhabitant of the intestines and does not usually cause disease, some strains of the organism do cause diarrhea. *E. coli* does cause disease in other parts of the body, such as the urinary tract.
4. They are spiral shaped.
5. The malarial *Plasmodium* is a protist. Its eukaryotic cell is larger than a prokaryotic cell.
6. Because red blood cells carry oxygen to the cells. When the plasmodium destroys red blood cells, the production of ATP in muscle cells is inhibited.
7. The tapeworm is an animal in the flatworm (Platyhelminthes) phylum. It is large and multicellular. It lives in the intestines and robs the body of nutrients.
8. This fungus is killed off by a healthy immune system. People with AIDS have lost immune function, so the fungus is able to grow in their lungs.

Conclusions
1. Viruses are too small to be seen with a light microscope.
2. Because of the danger of infection while making slides of living pathogens
3. *C. botulinum* and *E. coli* are rod shaped; *T. pallidum* is spiral. Study of nonpathogenic bacteria allows researchers and students to observe bacteria that are related to pathogens, as well as bacterial structures that are similar to those of pathogens, without danger of infection.

Further Inquiry
Tell students to compare plant pathogens with human or animal pathogens.

Vocabulary

1. Helper cells recognize a foreign antigen and initiate a cell-mediated response. Memory cells stay in the blood to recognize and destroy the antigen if it appears again.
2. Interferon
3. Neutrophils are small white blood cells with irregular nuclei that ingest small numbers of bacteria. Macrophages are large white blood cells that engulf hundreds of bacteria.
4. *Vacca-* means "cow," and the original vaccinations were done by infecting people with cowpox, a disease contracted by cows. *Patho-* means disease, and a pathogen is anything that causes disease.
5. T cells activate B cells to produce antibodies against an antigen and suppress them when the antigen has been destroyed.

Review

1. a
2. d
3. b
4. c
5. d
6. a
7. c
8. d
9. a
10. c

11. Koch's postulates are: isolate the organism, grow the organism, inoculate a new host, and compare the two organisms.
12. The five types of pathogens include bacteria, viruses, protozoa, fungi, and invertebrates.
13. The four main ways in which pathogens are transmitted are through air, water, human contact, and arthropods.
14. In an inflammatory response, neutrophils and macrophages engulf pathogens and the body temperature rises.
15. T cells recognize the antigen as foreign and stimulate B cells to produce antibodies. Both antibodies and killer T cells work together to destroy the antigen.
16. Antibodies destroy specific antigens.

Chapter 44 Review

Vocabulary

acquired immune deficiency syndrome (AIDS) (680)
acquired immunity (678)
AIDS-related complex (ARC) (681)
allergen (678)
allergy (678)
antibiotic (678)
antigen (676)
antihistamine (679)
autoimmune disease (679)
B cell (676)
cell-mediated response (677)
fever (675)
helper cell (677)
histamine (679)
immune response (675)
immunity (678)
infectious disease (673)
inflammatory response (675)
interferon (676)
Koch's postulates (673)
lymphocyte (676)
macrophage (675)
memory cell (677)
natural immunity (678)
neurotoxin (673)
neutrophil (675)
pathogen (673)
primary immune response (676)
secondary immune response (677)
suppressor cell (677)
T cell (676)
toxin (673)
vaccination (678)

1. Define *helper cell* and *memory cell.*
2. Identify the protein that interferes with viral replication.
3. Compare a neutrophil and a macrophage.
4. Using a dictionary, find the meaning of the word part *vacca-* in *vaccination* and *patho-* in *pathogen.* Explain why those terms are appropriately named.
5. Explain the relationship between T cells and B cells.

Review

1. Robert Koch (a) established procedures for identifying the cause of disease (b) identified specific neurotoxins (c) discovered interferon (d) pioneered the process of vaccination.
2. Pathogens can be (a) bacteria (b) viruses (c) invertebrates (d) any of the above.
3. Toxins (a) always affect the brain (b) affect the normal functioning of the cell (c) burrow into tissues (d) usually destroy muscle tissue.
4. Nonspecific defenses include the (a) cell-mediated response (b) primary immune response (c) inflammatory response (d) secondary immune response.
5. Skin acts as a defense against infection by (a) forming a physical barrier to pathogens (b) engulfing and digesting pathogens (c) forming blood clots (d) all of the above.
6. A cell-mediated response involves the (a) recognition of "self" and "nonself" (b) production of interferon (c) general reaction to all pathogens (d) action of cilia lining the air passages.
7. Antibodies are (a) lipids (b) B cells (c) Y-shaped proteins (d) T cells.
8. AIDS is transmitted mainly through (a) blood transfusions with contaminated blood (b) intimate sexual contact that involves the exchange of body fluids (c) intravenous injection with contaminated syringes (d) both b and c
9. Vaccinations (a) prevent diseases (b) cure diseases (c) treat diseases (d) cause diseases.
10. Penicillin (a) causes infections (b) prevents infections (c) cures infections (d) kills viruses.
11. Name the four Koch's postulates.
12. What are five types of pathogens?
13. Name four ways in which pathogens are transmitted.
14. Describe an inflammatory response.

17. Memory cells are specialized T and B cells remaining in the blood after a cell-mediated response. They attack the same antigen if it reenters the body.
18. Jonas Salk developed a vaccine against poliomyelitis.
19. The immune system cannot fight disease, and the infected person becomes susceptible to pathogens that would normally be fought off.
20. The virus may remain dormant for a period ranging from a few months to about ten years.

15. Describe the primary immune response.
16. What function do antibodies serve?
17. What are memory cells, and what is their role in the prevention of disease?
18. What was the result of Jonas Salk's research on poliomyelitis?
19. Explain what occurs in the immune system of a person infected with AIDS once all the T4 cells have been destroyed by the virus.
20. How long can the AIDS virus remain dormant in a person who is carrying it?

Critical Thinking

1. Many people take fever-reducing drugs as soon as their temperature exceeds 98.6° F. Why might it not be a good idea to immediately reduce a fever with drugs?
2. Interferon has been used to treat both cancer and AIDS. Why is interferon used in the treatment of each of these two diseases?
3. Doctors often treat allergies by injecting small amounts of allergen into the blood of the affected person. Why do you think this is an effective treatment?
4. Look at the photo at right of a T cell. T cells attack cancer cells. What causes T cells to launch a primary immune response against cancer?
5. When a person is burned over large areas of the body, the immune system often fails to fight off infections. Why might the immune system fail in these circumstances?

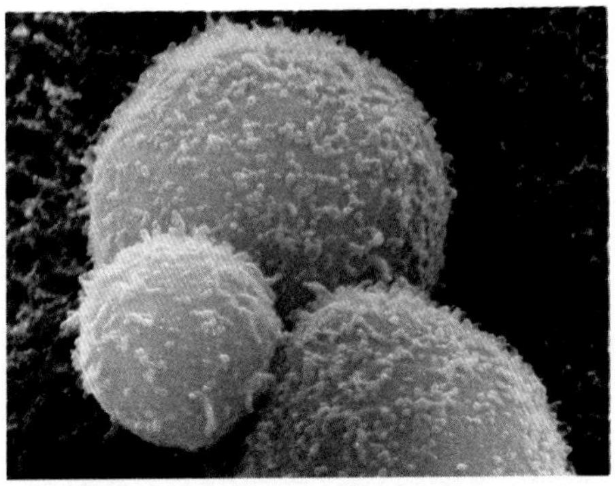

6. Patients are often treated with antibiotics to fight bacterial infections. Repeated exposure to penicillin and other antibiotics has been shown to cause weakness to the immune system. By what mechanism might this weakness occur?

Extension

1. Read the article by B. Bower entitled "Emotional Stress Linked to Common Cold" in *Science News,* June 10, 1990, p. 132. Discuss the methods of the study and its results. What factors other than stress may have had an impact on immunity?
2. Use the *Physicians' Desk Reference* (PDR) at your local library to research the large numbers of specialized antibiotics made by drug companies. Make a large chart on poster board using the following headings: brand name of the drug, generic name of the drug, uses of the drug, company that manufactures the drug, and disease the drug controls.
3. Obtain two cultures of the common bacteria *Escherichia coli.* Place each culture in a petri dish containing nutrient agar. In one dish place a paper disk that has been soaked with ampicillin, a variation of the antibiotic penicillin. Cover both dishes. Label the culture with the ampicillin *Experimental,* and label the one without the ampicillin *Control.* Keep both dishes out of direct sunlight and at room temperature. After two days, open both of the dishes and observe the cultures to see if the bacteria has grown. Record your observations.

Critical Thinking

1. Higher temperature from a fever may kill infectious pathogens; reducing fever makes this defense ineffective.
2. AIDS and some forms of cancer are caused by viruses. Interferon triggers production of an enzyme that enables a cell to recognize the viruses as a foreign substance, thus preventing virus reproduction.
3. The person is gradually desensitized to the allergen by developing a tolerance to it.
4. T cells recognize cancer cells as "nonself." This stimulates them to attack the cancer by launching a cell-mediated response.
5. When skin is destroyed and fluid is lost, many white blood cells and other parts of the immune system are present in smaller amounts. Burn victims have lost the defence that the skin usually provides.
6. When the immune system is repeatedly exposed to antibiotics, it does not develop its own antibodies. Since no memory cells are formed, it has no antibodies against specific antigens that reappear.

Extension

1. Life habits, such as sleep patterns, or alcohol and other drug use, may have had an impact on immunity.
2. Have students choose drugs that treat specific types of diseases or diseases in which they have a special interest.
3. Students can use stock cultures of *Escherichia coli* to inoculate two test tubes filled with liquid (60°C) nutrient agar, then pour the inoculated agar into their petri dishes. Students will observe that the growth of *E. coli* is inhibited in a circle around the ampicillin disk.

Chapter 45 Digestive and Excretory Systems

Chapter Overview

Chapter 45 continues the discussion of human body systems begun in Chapter 42. Section 45.1 examines nutrition, with an emphasis on the six nutrients humans need to grow and function properly. Section 45.2 describes the digestive system and emphasizes how the structure of the organs of the alimentary canal relates to their function. Section 45.3 discusses the kidneys and their role in the excretory system.

Chapter Planning Chart

B	S	A	Sections and Subsections	Page	Features	Page	Resources
•	•	•	**45.1 Nutrients**				
			Carbohydrates	687	Think	688	Videodiscs
			Proteins	688	Biology in Process	692	Laboratories: Nutrition
			Fats	688	Section Review	693	Section Reviews Worksheet
			Vitamins	690			
			Minerals	691			
			Water	692			
•	•	•	**45.2 Digestive System**				
			Mouth	694	Laboratory	703	Videodiscs
			Esophagus	695	Section Review	699	Blackline Master 92
			Stomach	695			Overhead Transparency T45
			Liver	697			Blackline Master 93
			Pancreas	697			Process Skills: Lactose Intolerance
			Small Intestine	698			Laboratories: Starch Digestion
			Large Intestine	699			Section Reviews Worksheet
•	•	•	**45.3 Excretory System**				
			Kidneys	700	Section Review	702	Videodiscs
			Urinary System	702			Section Reviews Worksheet
			End of Chapter Activities				
					Chapter Review	704	Vocabulary Skills
							Chapter Test
							Computer Test Generator

B *The Basic Level curriculum presents the most fundamental knowledge offered in the course.*
S *The Standard Level curriculum is designed for the average student who is able to master most topics.*
A *The Advanced Level curriculum includes suggestions for teaching the most academically able students.*

Cooperative Learning

Group Activity: A Healthy Week's Diet

- **Group Size:** *3 students*
- **Outcome:** *Students will plan a week-long diet that meets nutrient and serving recommendations.*
- **Individual Accountability:** *Each student will develop menus for two days.*
- **Positive Interdependence:** *The group will formulate one day's diet and agree on the week's menu.*

Ask each group to devise a healthy diet for one person for seven days. Have each group divide the week with one day saved for a collaborative effort. Tell students to include menus for breakfast, lunch, dinner, and snacks. Each day's diet should meet recommended nutrient amounts, servings, and Calorie intake. Either provide the recommendations to students, or have them research them in the library. After students work individually, have the group reassemble, assess the individual menus, make changes if necessary, and write the seventh day's menu. Post the menus in the classroom.

As an extension, have groups research and analyze the diet of an ethnic group, then compare diets among various cultures.

Concept Map

The following is one possible solution to the concept mapping activity in Summarizing Concepts on p. 698.

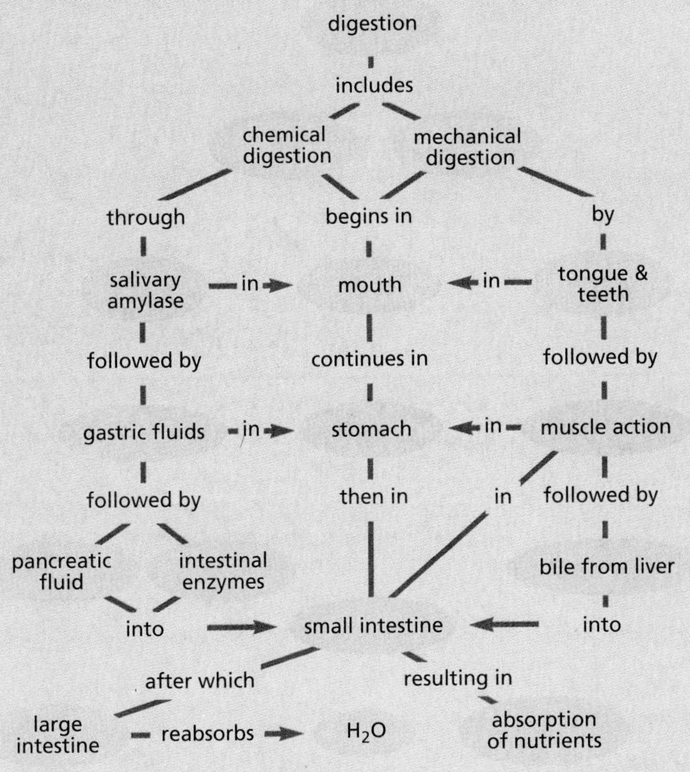

Laboratory Preparation

Overview *(See p. 703.)*

This lab models the digestion of protein in the stomach. Students learn what components must be present in the digestive fluid to cause the breakdown of protein. They observe that each component alone cannot promote digestion and that pepsin requires an acidic environment in which to be chemically active. Students should understand that water is an important part of the digestive mixture.

Preparation

A 0.2% solution of hydrochloric acid can be made by diluting 2 mL of concentrated HCl per liter of distilled water. Use 10 g of sodium bicarbonate per liter of distilled water, and 1 g of pepsin per 100 mL of distilled water. Commercial solutions are also available from science supply companies. Each test tube will hold 10 mL of fluid; calculate the volume you will need for your class size.

Use 10-mL graduated cylinders, if available. Decide on the best way to have students rinse their graduated cylinders when changing solutions.

Teaching Tips

If you wish students to make their observations in 24 hours rather than in 48 hours, provide a 37°C incubator for their test tubes.

This experiment teaches experimental procedures. Pepsin is the independent variable; when it is absent, no digestion occurs. Its activity depends upon a second factor, pH. Water alone and acid alone are controls.

Students with more knowledge of digestion could design their own experiment. They could test, for example, whether an enzyme is active in both acidic and basic conditions. They could compare activity at room temperature and in a refrigerator. Provide extra test tubes so students can test several pairs of variables.

You may wish to connect this lab to gene expression. Synthesis of the protein enzyme pepsin requires the expression of a specific gene. The pepsinogen gene is always active but is more active when the diet is high in protein. Point out to students that different genes are active in different organs—pepsin in the stomach, amylase in the salivary glands and in the pancreas, lipase in the pancreas, and so forth.

Safety

Teach careful handling of acids and bases, even weak ones. Remind students never to eat or drink in a laboratory area. Wash up any spills promptly and thoroughly.

Chapter Themes

Energy The energy intake of an organism fuels its metabolism, growth, and development. Emphasize that the science of nutrition is largely focused on what the human body needs to fulfill its energy requirements as well as provide for building structures and functional enzymes.

Scale and Structure As students learn about the digestive and excretory systems, stress the relationship between structure and function. For example, the stomach's muscle configuration allows it to perform mechanical as well as chemical digestion, whereas the structure of the small intestine is specialized for chemical digestion and absorption.

Systems and Interactions Help students understand that the digestive and excretory systems do not work in isolation but rather work in concert with the other body systems. For example, both interact closely with the circulatory system. Digestion provides the blood with nutrients, and excretion removes wastes from blood.

Chapter Motivating Activity

Survey students informally on what they ate for breakfast. Be sensitive to those students who, for whatever reason, have not had breakfast. Write the foods on the board, and then ask students which of the foods they think are healthy and why. Challenge students to explain what each food provides that the body requires. Assess in this way what students know about basic nutrition.

Then have students compose the "perfect" breakfast—the one that would best provide the body with what it needs. Again, have students give reasons for their choices.

Chapter 45 *Digestive and Excretory Systems*

Introduction

Carrots, fish eggs, hamburgers, blackberries, cow's milk—the human body is able to convert each of these foods into nutrients body cells need to function, grow, and replicate. In this chapter you will learn just how the body does that, as well as how it rids itself of the useless or toxic by-products of cellular activity.

Chapter Outline

45.1 Nutrients
- *Carbohydrates*
- *Proteins*
- *Fats*
- *Vitamins*
- *Minerals*
- *Water*

45.2 Digestive System
- *Mouth*
- *Esophagus*
- *Stomach*
- *Liver*
- *Pancreas*
- *Small Intestine*
- *Large Intestine*

45.3 Excretory System
- *Kidneys*
- *Urinary System*

Chapter Concept

As you read, notice how the structure of each digestive and excretory organ relates to its function.

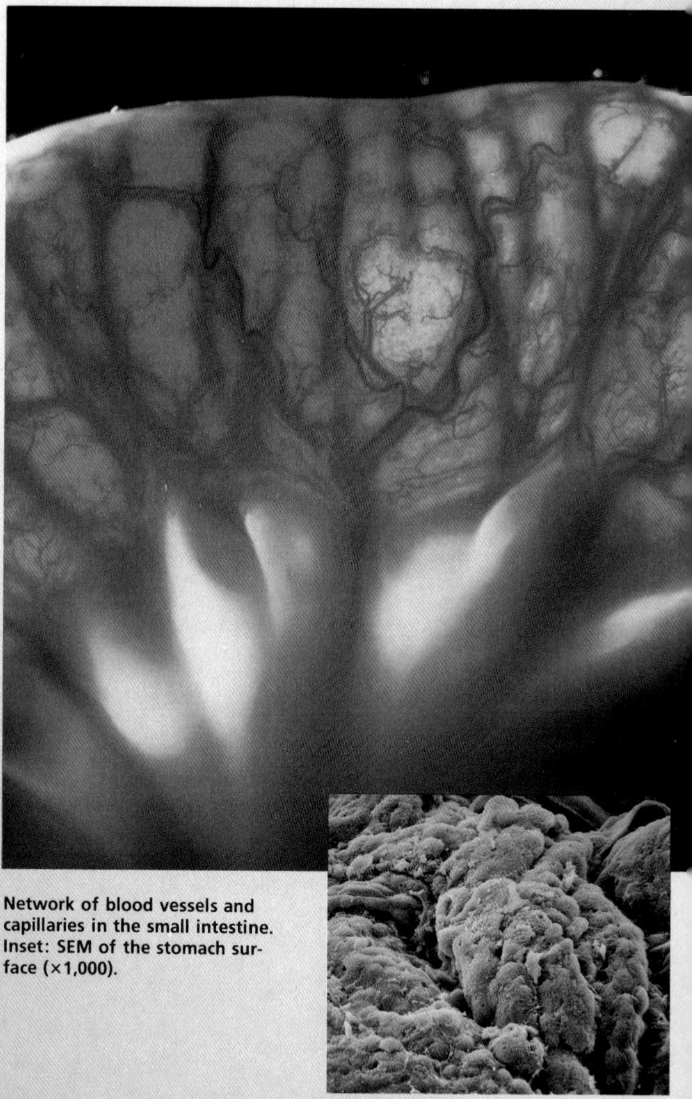

Network of blood vessels and capillaries in the small intestine. Inset: SEM of the stomach surface (×1,000).

Understanding the Visuals

Explain to students that the small intestine is a long, tubelike organ between the stomach and the large intestine. What are the contents of the small intestine? *(Food being digested, digestive enzymes, mucus)* Then ask students what the photo of the small intestine shows about this organ. *(Its lining contains a network of blood vessels.)* Challenge students to explain why this organ contains so many blood vessels. *(To absorb nutrients from digested food into the bloodstream)*

Have students describe the surface of the stomach wall. *(Rough, with bumps and indentations)* Tell students they will soon learn how this structure functions.

45.1 Nutrients

All the different kinds of food in the world are composed of the same six basic ingredients: carbohydrates, proteins, fats, vitamins, minerals, and water. These ingredients, called **nutrients,** are the chemical substances that organisms need in order to grow and function properly. Carbohydrates, proteins, fats, and vitamins are called organic compounds since they contain the elements carbon, hydrogen, and oxygen. Minerals and water are inorganic nutrients since they are not built from these elements.

Few foods contain all the nutrients. In fact most foods contain a concentration of just one or two of them. Nutritionists classify foods with similar nutrients into a single group within a classification system based on four food groups: (1) meat, (2) milk, (3) fruits and vegetables, and (4) bread and cereals.

Carbohydrates, proteins, and fats are involved in specialized functions. However, all of these nutrients can also provide the body with the energy that it needs to maintain itself, to function, and to grow. A **calorie** is the amount of heat required at standard atmospheric pressure to raise the temperature of 1 g of water from 14.5° C to 15.5° C. A kilocalorie is 1,000 calories. Scientists use the term **Calorie,** with a capital C, to express the amount of energy that a particular food provides. A Calorie is the same as a kilocalorie. When you read that a food has 150 Calories, it can also be said to have 150,000 calories. Scientists determine the number of Calories a food contains by measuring the amount of heat a specific quantity of food releases when burned in an instrument called a calorimeter.

Carbohydrates

Carbohydrates are compounds of carbon, hydrogen, and oxygen that provide most of the body's energy when they are broken down in cellular respiration. Although proteins and fats can also supply energy, the body can most easily use the energy provided by carbohydrates. Carbohydrates contain sugars that are converted into the usable energy of ATP. Proteins and fats must be subjected to many more chemical processes before the body can obtain energy from them.

What sugars provide energy? The fructose and the glucose (also known as dextrose) in fruit and honey are simple sugars, **monosaccharides** *(MAHN-uh-SACK-uh-RIDEZ),* that are absorbed directly into the bloodstream. Sucrose (cane sugar), maltose, and lactose (milk sugar) are **disaccharides** *(die-SACK-uh-RIDEZ),* sugars that consist of two monosaccharides that are chemically linked. Disaccharides split into two monosaccharides when water breaks the chemical bond that joins them. This splitting of a molecule through reaction with water is called **hydrolysis** *(hie-DRAHL-uh-suss).*

Section Objectives

- *Define* nutrient, *and distinguish organic from inorganic nutrients.*
- *Describe the molecular structure of carbohydrates, proteins, and fats.*
- *Distinguish between vitamins and minerals, and summarize the functions they perform in the body.*
- *List some of the important functions of water in the body.*
- *Describe the observations Angel Keys made to link diet and heart disease.*

Figure 45-1 This diagram shows the hydrolysis of sucrose, which occurs in the presence of enzymes.

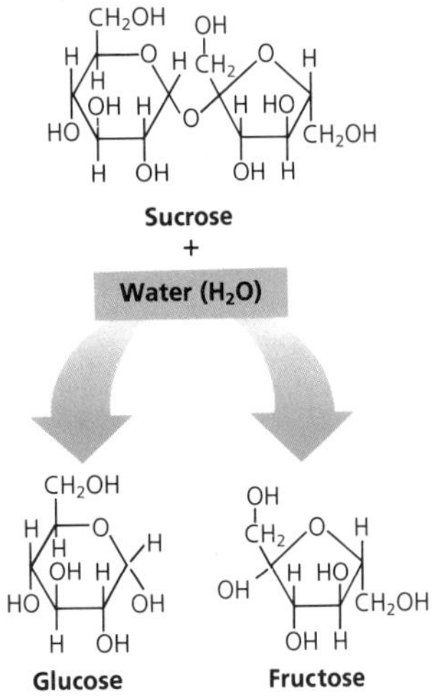

Lesson Plan

Section Focus

This section teaches that nutrients are chemical substances needed by organisms to grow and function properly. Students will learn the composition and function of carbohydrates, proteins, fats, vitamins, minerals, and water, reviewing biochemical concepts first introduced in Chapter 4.

Section Themes

The theme of **Energy** underlies the discussion of three of the four organic nutrients that directly supply the body's energy needs—carbohydrates, proteins, and fats.

The theme of **Scale and Structure** is inherent in the discussion of the chemical structure of the various nutrients. Macromolecules are digested, or hydrolyzed, into their monomer subunits.

Motivating Activity

Bring to class a portion of french fries and a baked potato, or show students a picture of these foods. Have students examine the potato and the french fries carefully and ask them to brainstorm differences between the two foods—preparation, cooking, taste, and nutritional value. *(Unlike the baked potato, french fries are peeled, strip-sliced, fried in oil or fat, and salted.)* Ask students what is the impact of a diet high in oils, fats, and salt—that is, foods processed like french fries. *(Oils and fats increase caloric intake. Saturated fats may increase cholesterol levels. A diet high in salt can cause fluid to be retained in the body. Over a long period of time, high salt intake can contribute to hypertension.)*

Videodiscs

- ***2532–2533, Glucose; Fructose (s)***
- ***2535–2537, Amino Acids (s)***

Sources of Carbohydrates	Sources of Proteins	Sources of Fats
▪ grains	▪ meats	▪ animal fats
▪ vegetables	▪ fish	▪ vegetable oils
▪ fruits	▪ dairy products	
▪ sugars	▪ eggs	
	▪ grains, legumes, seeds	

Graphic Organizer Use this table in Guided Practice on p. 692.

Teaching Strategies

Interpreting the Visuals Have students review pp. 48–54 in Chapter 4. Tell them that *hydrolysis* literally means "breaking with water," a process accomplished in the body with the help of enzymes. Have students study the chemical reaction shown in Figure 45-1 on p. 687. What kind of sugar is sucrose? *(A disaccharide)* Note that the two subunits, or monosaccharides, of the sucrose molecule are linked at the oxygen atom in the middle of the diagram. What happened to the added water molecule during the reaction? *(Each monosaccharide shows an OH group where the bond was. Together, these two groups account for the O of the link and the H_2O of the added water molecule.)* Explain that hydrolysis in digestion breaks down macromolecules and polymers into monomers that can be absorbed into the blood.

Answer to Think

The dieter would get proteins and fats from the eggs but not enough carbohydrates or the proper balance of vitamins. The body would then convert much of its proteins and fats into glucose. The individual's fat stores would diminish, eventually making the person more susceptible to cold and to injury of internal organs. Vitamin and mineral deficiency diseases would also develop.

Identifying Structures Ask students to review the chemical structures of complex carbohydrates, proteins, and fats presented in Chapter 4. Chemically, what are these nutrients? *(Carbohydrates are polymers of monosaccharides. Proteins are chains of amino acids. Fats consist of glycerol and fatty acids.)*

The carbohydrates that require the longest digestion time are polysaccharides. **Polysaccharides** *(PAHL-ih-SACK-uh-RIDEZ)* consist of many simple sugars bonded together. The starch found in rice, corn, and many other grains and vegetables is a polysaccharide made up of long chains of glucose molecules. The body chemically dismantles these long chains into individual glucose units, which can be absorbed by the blood and carried to the tissues.

Many plant foods contain cellulose, a polysaccharide that the body cannot dismantle into its individual component sugars. Cellulose, the substance that forms the walls of plant cells, is nevertheless an extremely important part of the human diet. Although indigestible itself, cellulose provides fiber that aids in digestion.

Think

Many people go on fad diets that consist primarily of selections from one food group. Anyone who follows such a limited diet soon develops a nutrient deficiency. In a diet consisting only of the foods shown above, what nutrients would be lacking? What effects might these deficiencies produce?

Proteins

Proteins are the major structural and functional material of body cells. Proteins from food help the body to grow and to repair tissues. Also, proteins called **enzymes** are organic catalysts in the myriad chemical reactions that take place in the body. You will recall from Chapter 4 that a catalyst is a substance that speeds up a chemical reaction but does not change the end products. Thus enzymes speed up the thousands of different cell reactions.

As you remember from Chapter 4, proteins consist of long chains of amino acids. The human body uses about 20 kinds of amino acids to construct the proteins it needs. The body manufactures many of these amino acids, but it cannot produce all of them in the quantities that it needs. Amino acids that the body produces are termed nonessential amino acids because you do not have to get them from your food. Amino acids that must be obtained from food are called essential amino acids. Ten amino acids are essential to children and teenagers, while only eight are essential to adults. The two additional amino acids children require function in reactions involving growth.

Some foods contain all of the essential amino acids. Most animal proteins—eggs, milk, fish, poultry, beef—contain all the essential amino acids. Most plants, on the other hand, do not. However, eating certain combinations of two or more plant foods can supply all the essential amino acids. Many such combinations exist. Vegetarians who eat no animal products get their proteins by eating two or more plant foods or by combining seeds or grains with legumes. Examine Figure 45-2 to discover just a few of these combinations.

Fats

Fats are organic molecules that the body utilizes to obtain energy and to build cell membranes and other cell parts. The body stores excess fat from the diet in special tissues under the skin and around the kidneys and liver. Excess carbohydrates may be converted into fat for storage.

LEP Activity

Ask students what special foods their family enjoys during holidays or festivals. Then help them identify the nutrients found in each food. For example, a bean and rice dish contains complex carbohydrates and proteins as well as vitamins and minerals. List the dishes and the nutrients they contain on the board. Have students make posters illustrating each dish and the basic nutrients it contains. Guide students in the use of Table 45-1, p. 690, and Table 45-2, p. 691, to analyze the vitamin and mineral content of the foods. Remind students to include water in their surveys of nutrients.

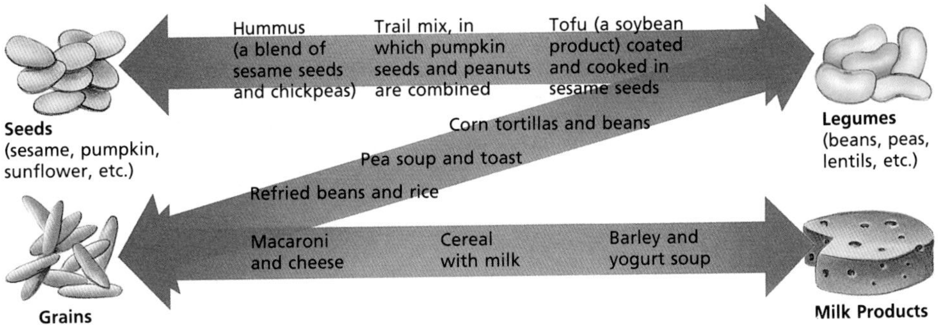

Figure 45-2 Combining legumes with either seeds or grains or combining grains with milk products will furnish all the essential amino acids.

Why does the human body store fat? After all, excessive fat can strain the heart. The answer is that stored fats are actually beneficial unless they are excessive. A light layer of body fat beneath the skin provides insulation in cold weather. Fat surrounding vulnerable organs, such as the kidneys and liver, acts as protective padding. Most important, fat reserves form a backup fuel supply. While you cannot live just off your body fat, the body can use this fat for energy when carbohydrates are unavailable.

Structure of Fats

To use fats, the body must first break down each fat molecule into its parts—glycerol and fatty acids. About 98 percent of the fats in food are **triglycerides** *(trie-GLISS-uh-RIDEZ)*, molecules formed from three molecules of fatty acids and one molecule of glycerol. The glycerol molecule is the same in all fats, but the fatty acids differ in both structure and composition. The body converts some fatty acids into other fatty acids. Which fatty acids the body produces depends upon its needs at the time.

Types of Fats

Scientists classify fats as saturated or unsaturated on the basis of structural differences in their fatty acids. A saturated fatty acid has all its carbon atoms connected by single bonds and thus contains as many hydrogen atoms as possible. An unsaturated fatty acid has at least one double bond between carbon atoms. If there are two or more double bonds, the fatty acid is called polyunsaturated. In general, animal fats are saturated and plant oils are unsaturated. However, some vegetable oils, such as palm oil and coconut oil, are composed primarily of saturated fats.

Scientific studies have indicated that consuming a high level of saturated fats seems to trigger an increase in the production of **cholesterol,** a fatlike molecule in the body. In turn, an elevated blood cholesterol level may lead to the formation of fatty deposits that can clog arteries, hardening them and restricting blood flow. The result of this condition may be heart disease or a stroke.

Drawing Conclusions Ask students if they know anyone who is a vegetarian. Explore the reasons why people choose this kind of diet. *(For religious, ethical, and health reasons)* Ask students what health concerns might lead someone to choose vegetarianism. *(To avoid animal fats, which may cause heart disease)* Finally, turn students' attention to Figure 45-2, and ask why it is necessary for vegetarians to eat foods in combination. *(A single plant food alone does not supply all the essential amino acids.)* Ask why combinations such as corn tortillas and beans are healthy when eaten together. *(Corn is a grain, beans are legumes; grain and legumes combined provide all the essential amino acids.)*

■ *See* **Laboratories, *Investigation 45.1.***

Making Hypotheses Tell students that although almost all medical authorities recommend a low blood cholesterol level, the exact part cholesterol plays in heart attacks is not completely understood. For example, although they have about the same cholesterol level as Americans, the French suffer only a third the number of fatal heart attacks. Ask students why this might be. *(Accept sensible answers, such as life-style or possible chemical factors.)*

Inferring Relationships Explain to students that the body requires a certain level of cholesterol and actually produces it. Then ask what problems an elevated blood cholesterol level may cause. *(The formation of fatty deposits that clog arteries, leading to heart disease or stroke)* Ask what kind of fats seem to increase the body's production of cholesterol. *(Saturated fats)* What kinds of fats and oils are saturated? *(Animal fats, palm and coconut oils)*

More Information

Cholesterol Cholesterol is carried in the bloodstream in two forms, as low-density lipoprotein (LDL) and as high-density lipoprotein (HDL). LDLs carry dietary and newly synthesized cholesterol to various organs of the body, whereas HDLs, because of their structure, seem to carry cholesterol to the liver and allow it to be broken down there. Usually, this system is in balance, with cholesterol being produced and destroyed as needed. However, when there is an excess of LDLs over HDLs—for example, due to high intake of saturated fats—the excess cholesterol may be deposited in the blood vessels. Strenuous exercise seems to increase the blood HDL to LDL ratio, whereas smoking decreases it.

Interpreting Data Ask students questions for which they must use the information in Tables 45-1 and 45-2. For example, ask what vitamins and minerals liver provides. *(Vitamins A, B_{12}, and D and iron salts)* What vitamins and minerals affect nerves in some way? *(Vitamins B_1 and B_3 and sodium salts, calcium salts, magnesium salts, and potassium salts)* Make sure students understand that the terms in parentheses under the vitamin names are alternative names for the vitamins, such as thiamine for vitamin B_1.

Drawing Conclusions Have students name the fat-soluble vitamins. *(Vitamins A, D, E, and K)* What are the water-soluble vitamins? *(Vitamins B_1, B_2, B_3, B_{12}, and C)* Then describe this situation: a health-conscious person notices that a friend is not feeling well. The person advises the friend to take large doses of vitamin C, as well as A from cod-liver oil. The friend is tempted to buy these supplements. Ask students what warning they would give. *(Any excess vitamin C is probably flushed from the body because it is water soluble. Vitamin A, though, will be stored in body fat, because it is fat soluble. High levels of vitamin A are toxic. Therefore, they should warn against taking high doses of vitamin A.)*

Vitamins

Vitamins are complex organic molecules that serve as coenzymes. This means that vitamins activate the enzymes and assist with their function. For example, the presence of vitamin B_1 or thiamine, is essential to the function of two enzymes that catalyze the first step in aerobic respiration. Without thiamine, aerobic respiration cannot proceed. Because vitamins perform such vital functions and generally cannot be synthesized by the body, a daily diet should include the proper amounts of all vitamins.

All vitamins dissolve in either water or fat. The fat-soluble vitamins include vitamins A, D, E, and K. The water-soluble vitamins are vitamins B and C. Fat-soluble vitamins are absorbed and stored like fats. As with fats, your body can amass a reserve of fat-soluble vitamins. However, unpleasant physical symptoms

Table 45-1 Vitamins

Vitamins	Best sources	Essential for	Deficiency diseases and symptoms
Vitamin A (fat soluble)	Fish-liver oils, liver and kidney, green and yellow vegetables, yellow fruit, tomatoes, butter, egg yolk	Growth, health of the eyes, structure and functions of the cells of the skin and mucous membranes	Retarded growth, night blindness, susceptibility to infections, changes in skin, defective tooth formation
Vitamin B_1 (thiamin; water soluble)	Meat, soybeans, milk, whole grain, legumes	Growth; carbohydrate metabolism; functioning of the heart, nerves, muscles	Beriberi: loss of appetite and weight, nerve disorders, faulty digestion
Vitamin B_2 (riboflavin; water soluble)	Meat, fowl, soybeans, milk, green vegetables, eggs, yeast	Growth, health of the skin and mouth, carbohydrate metabolism, functioning of the eyes	Retarded growth, dimness of vision, inflammation of the tongue, premature aging, intolerance to light
Vitamin B_3 (niacin; water soluble)	Meat, fowl, fish, peanut butter, potatoes, whole grain, tomatoes, leafy vegetables	Growth; carbohydrate metabolism; functioning of the stomach, intestines, and the nervous system	Pellagra: smoothness of the tongue, skin eruptions, digestive disturbances, mental disorders
Vitamin B_{12} (water soluble)	Green vegetables, liver	Preventing pernicious anemia	A reduction in number of red blood cells
Vitamin C (ascorbic acid; water soluble)	Fruit (especially citrus), tomatoes, leafy vegetables	Growth, strength of the blood vessels, development of teeth, health of gums	Scurvy: sore gums, hemorrhages around the bones, tendency to bruise easily
Vitamin D (fat soluble)	Fish-liver oil, liver, fortified milk, eggs, irradiated foods	Growth, calcium and phosphorus metabolism, bones and teeth	Rickets: soft bones, poor development of teeth, dental decay
Vitamin E (tocopheral; fat soluble)	Wheat germ oil, leafy vegetables, milk, butter	Normal reproduction	(Undetermined)
Vitamin K (fat soluble)	Green vegetables, soybean oil, tomatoes	Normal clotting of the blood, liver functions	Hemorrhages

Interdisciplinary Activity

Cultural Geography Assign different students to research the typical diet of people in another country. Choices could include Japan, India, Israel, Egypt, Nigeria, Italy, Greece, Germany, Mexico, and Russia. Ask students to investigate how the diet delivers the six nutrients discussed in the section. Also ask groups to compare the diet with a typical American diet in terms of fat intake and cholesterol level. Have students determine what factors might influence the composition of the diet in the various countries.

and even death can result from storing too much of a particular vitamin as well as from having too little. Continual megadoses of vitamin A, for instance, can result in severe nausea and a yellow skin color. The body cannot store the water-soluble vitamins and therefore excretes any surplus amounts.

The only vitamin that the body can synthesize in large quantities is vitamin D. This synthesis begins with the conversion of cholesterol to provitamin D by intestinal enzymes. Provitamin D is stored in the skin, where exposure to the ultraviolet light in sunlight converts it into vitamin D. People who don't spend a lot of time in the sun get their vitamin D from food.

With the exception of vitamin D, human beings must obtain the vitamins they need from food sources and vitamin supplements. For this reason a knowledge of which foods contain which vitamins is important. Study Table 45-1 to learn some of the food sources of the vitamins listed.

Minerals

In the context of nutrition, **minerals** are inorganic substances required for the normal function of the body. Minerals such as calcium, magnesium, and iron are drawn from the soil and become part of plants. Animals that feed on plants, in turn, extract the minerals and incorporate them into their bodies. Table 45-2 lists the primary sources and functions of a few of the minerals most essential to human beings. Iron, for example, is nec-

Table 45-2 Minerals

Minerals	Source	Essential for
Sodium salts	Table salt, vegetables	Blood and other body tissues; nerve action
Calcium salts	Milk, whole-grain cereals, vegetables, meats	Deposition in bones and teeth; heart and nerves
Phosphorus salts	Milk, whole-grain cereals, vegetables, meats	Deposition in bones and teeth; formation of ATP, nucleic acid
Magnesium salts	Vegetables	Muscle and nerve action
Iron salts	Leafy vegetables, liver, meats, raisins, prunes	Formation of red blood corpuscles
Iodine	Seafoods, water, iodized salt	Production of thyroid gland secretion
Potassium salts	Vegetables, citrus fruits, bananas, apricots	Maintain acid–base balance; growth; nerve action

Relating Concepts Ask students what is the predominant mineral in milk. *(Calcium)* Point out that vitamin D is added to milk. Then ask them why. *(Accept any answers that tie vitamin D and calcium together.)* Tell students that vitamin D is needed for the absorption of calcium from the intestines. Explain that rickets, a disease affecting growing bones, and caused by vitamin D deficiency, used to be common in the United States. In the 1930s, the federal government mandated the enrichment of milk with vitamin D. The disease is now virtually unknown here.

Making Calculations Explain to students that the average person loses about 2.3 L of water each day by sweating, in urine, and through respiration. Water is replaced by drinking it or other liquids and by eating foods that contain water, such as fruits and vegetables. To assess their daily water intake, have students record in a notebook the fluids they drink and the water-loaded foods they eat during a day. Tell them that they should estimate in each instance how much water they take in. Have students report their results in the next day's class. *(Most students will find that about half the 2.3 L is replaced by drinking and half by eating.)*

More Information

Recommended Servings Serving recommendations for the "basic four" food groups were first published by the U.S. Department of Agriculture in 1956. Recommended daily servings were: 4 servings of the bread-cereal group; 4 servings of the vegetable-fruit group; 2 servings for adults and 4 servings for teenagers of the milk-cheese group; and 2 servings of the meat-poultry and fish-beans group. New recommendations published in 1991 are arranged in a pyramid: 6–11 servings of the bread-cereal-rice-pasta group; 3–5 servings of vegetables and 2–4 servings of fruit; 2–3 servings of the milk-yogurt-cheese group; and 2–3 servings of the meat-poultry-fish-dried beans group.

Section 45.1

Guided Practice

Have students make a table of the major food sources for carbohydrates, proteins, and fats from the information in their text. Write the column headings on the board. Use the table on p. 687 as a model.

Independent Practice

- Have students write answers to the Section Review.
- Have students keep a diary of everything they eat for lunch for three days. On the fourth day, ask each student to write an evaluation of his or her diet based on the 1991 U.S.D.A. nutritional guidelines. Have students compare the diets of those eating in the school cafeteria with those bringing lunch prepared at home. Tell students to divide mixed foods into approximate servings of their components.

Check Your Understanding

1. Of what advantage to mammals is the ability to store fat? *(It enables them to store energy and it insulates them.)*
2. How are Calories related to the nutritional value of food? *(They are heat units used to measure available energy.)*
3. How are proteins and amino acids related? *(Proteins are made of amino acids.)*

Reteaching

Return to the Chapter Motivating Activity on p. 686. Have students reanalyze their normal breakfast, using the information in this section.

- *See* Section Reviews *worksheet, Section 45.1.*

Enrichment

Have students do library research on vitamin-deficiency diseases, including beriberi, pellagra, scurvy, pernicious anemia, and rickets, then write a report focusing on how cures were discovered.

essary for the formation of red blood corpuscles, while potassium maintains the body's acid–base balance and aids in growth. Both are found in certain fruits and vegetables; iron is also found in meats. Iodine—found in seafoods, water, and iodized salt—is processed and secreted by the thyroid gland. Minerals are excreted through the skin in perspiration as well as through the kidneys in urine.

Water

The importance of water to human life may be inferred from the fact that water accounts for over half of your body weight. Most of the reactions that maintain life can take place only in water. Water makes up over 90 percent of the fluid part of the blood, which carries essential nutrients to all the parts of the body. It is also the medium in which waste products are dissolved and carried away from body tissues.

Water also helps regulate body temperature. It absorbs the heat released in cellular reactions and distributes the heat throughout the body. When the body needs cooling, the problem is solved through perspiration. When this perspiration—a water-

Biology in Process

Diet and Heart Disease

Ancel Keys, the biochemist who developed K-rations for American soldiers, didn't intend to fuel a controversy when he began his research on diet and health. During World War II and the years that followed, he noticed that when food—particularly sugary and fatty foods—was scarce, the rate of death from heart disease and stroke plummeted. This held true even in populations known to have a high incidence of these two killers. Keys wondered if differences in diet might account for the differences in death rates he observed.

Keys began an ambitious investigation. He studied nearly 12,000 healthy men ages 40–59 in seven countries, collecting data on their eating, smoking, physical activity levels, and drinking habits. He collected follow-up data at 5, 10, and 15 years after the study began and looked at long-term survival rates. Keys found that death rates were directly related to the percentage of calories in the diet from saturated fatty acids. By 1986 Keys had gathered enough data from his Seven Countries Study to suggest that aside from differences in weight, fatness, life-style factors, or physical activity—the lower the

Cooperative Learning

Food Labels Have students bring to class food labels with nutritional information. Tell them that on average 1 gram of fat has 9 Calories, 1 gram of protein has 3, and 1 gram of carbohydrate has 4. To convert grams of each into its percentage of total Calories in a serving, multiply the number of grams on the label by 9 for fats, 3 for proteins, and 4 for carbohydrates. Then divide the result by the total number of Calories to get the percentage.

Now, divide students into groups of three, and have them calculate the percentages of Calories of each nutrient for ten labels. Have students in each group pool their information and organize it in a chart. Have groups compare charts.

based substance—evaporates from the skin, heat is drawn away from the body in the process.

Usually the water lost through your skin and kidneys is easily replaced by drinking water, by consuming moist foods, or by inhaling air, since air contains water. If its water supply is not replenished, the body begins to take water from intercellular spaces to perform vital functions within the cells. Eventually the body has to draw water from the cells themselves. As a cell loses water, the cytoplasm becomes more concentrated until finally the cell can no longer function. This condition is referred to as **dehydration** *(DEE-hie-DRAY-shun)*.

Section Review

1. Define *nutrient.*
2. What are two functions performed by proteins?
3. Name three reasons why a certain amount of body fat is beneficial.
4. Why is water a vital nutrient?
5. What do you think would happen to a vegetarian who consumed only water, unpolished rice, and fruits?

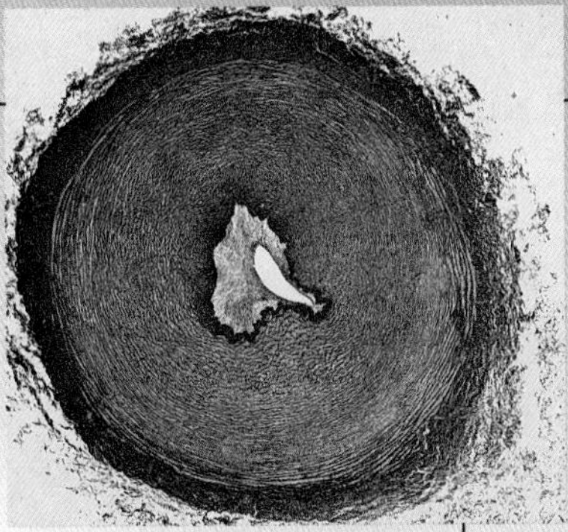

percentage of calories in the diet from saturated fats, the lower the rate of death from heart disease or stroke.

Keys had discovered that if you want to reduce the likelihood of dying from heart disease or stroke, a few simple changes in your diet and life-style could offer a way to dramatically tip the odds in your favor.

Other researchers have focused on the link between dietary fats and the levels of cholesterol in the blood. While cholesterol is a structural part of cell membranes and is needed for the manufacture of bile and hormones, excess cholesterol in the blood collects over time, building into plaques on the inside walls of blood vessels (p. 693). In time these deposits may restrict or stop blood flow, and a heart attack or a stroke will be the most likely result.

Although the controversy about the connection between diet and serum cholesterol is far from settled, what Keys first noticed has essentially been adopted in the newest dietary guidelines from The American Dietetic Association. They suggest: (1) reducing the total percentage of calories from fat in the diet to 30 percent or less per day; (2) increasing the number of servings of fruits, grains, and vegetables; (3) limiting the number of servings of meat, saturated fats, and high-fat dairy products.

■ How did nutritional and epidemiological studies lead scientists to conclude that diets rich in fats contribute to heart disease?

Answers to Section Review

1. A chemical substance that organisms need in order to grow and function properly
2. Proteins help the body grow and repair tissues, and serve as enzymes.
3. Body fat provides insulation, protects organs, and serves as a backup fuel supply.
4. Most reactions that maintain life can take place only in water. Water is the medium in which waste is dissolved and carried away from body tissues and in which nutrients are carried throughout the body. Water also helps regulate body temperature.
5. This vegetarian would suffer from deficiencies of vitamins, minerals, proteins, and fats.

Closure

Pass out copies of the school cafeteria menu for the week. Have students analyze the food's nutritional value and make dietary recommendations if necessary.

Biology in Process

Using the Feature

The feature focuses on the process skills of observing, collecting data, and analyzing. Emphasize to students that a valid epidemiological study requires a large number of subjects in order to achieve statistically significant results.

In the Seven Countries Study, many variables were considered: diet, heredity, weight, fatness, smoking, drinking, and physical activity levels. Each variable must be considered in combination with the other variables. Remind students that although diet is important in preventing heart disease, other factors—including smoking, obesity, lack of exercise, and high blood pressure—also carry significant risks.

You may wish to show "Eat Smart," a video that presents Keys's study and the dietary guidelines that are designed to decrease the risks of heart disease and stroke. The video can be ordered from PBS Video, 4401 Sunset Blvd., Los Angeles, CA 90027, or by calling toll free 1-(800)-328-PBS1.

Answer to the Feature

Analysis of large groups of men over many years indicated that those whose diets were high in fats, particularly saturated fats, were also more likely to die from heart disease or stroke.

Videodiscs

■ 2528, Molecular Structure—Water (s)

Lesson Plan

Section Focus

This section describes the organs and structures of the alimentary canal. Students will learn how the organs of the alimentary canal digest and absorb nutrients.

Section Themes

The theme of **Scale and Structure** is evident in the description of the digestive system organs. The structure of these organs is related to their function. For example, the muscles of the stomach are oriented in three directions to perform mechanical digestion.

The theme of **Patterns of Change** encompasses the change that food undergoes through the process of digestion. The body must change food into a form that can be used to provide energy to the body cells.

Motivating Activity

Begin this demonstration on mechanical digestion the day before teaching the lesson. Use three pieces of hard candy to show the effectiveness of mechanical digestion. Drop one piece of candy into a clear glass of water. With a hammer, break a second piece into small bits and put them all into a second clear glass of water. Keep a third piece of candy as a control. Ask students to predict the results.

The next day at the beginning of class, have students compare the results. *(Although the whole piece of candy has become smaller than the control, the candy in small pieces should have dissolved completely into the water.)* Ask students how breaking up the candy is like mechanical digestion. *(Mechanical digestion in the mouth and stomach breaks food apart and exposes more surface area to digestive enzymes.)*

Section Objectives

- *Define* alimentary canal, *and name the major organs of the digestive system.*
- *Relate the structure of each digestive organ to its function in mechanical digestion.*
- *Identify the source of each major digestive enzyme, and describe the function of the enzyme.*
- *Summarize the process of absorption in both the small and large intestine.*

45.2 Digestive System

Before your body can use the nutrients in the food you consume, the cells must break down the nutrients both physically and chemically. This process of breaking down food into molecules the body can use is called **digestion.** Digestion occurs in the **alimentary canal,** or digestive tract, which begins at the mouth and winds through the body to the anus. Located along the alimentary canal are the stomach and the other organs that aid in digestion. Other digestive organs, such as the liver and pancreas, are not part of the alimentary canal but deliver secretions into the canal through ducts. As you read, locate each of the structures of the digestive system in Figure 45-3.

Mouth

When you take a bite of food, you begin the mechanical phase of digestion. In this phase the body physically breaks down chunks of food into small particles. Mechanical digestion increases the surface area of food on which digestive enzymes can act. Inci-

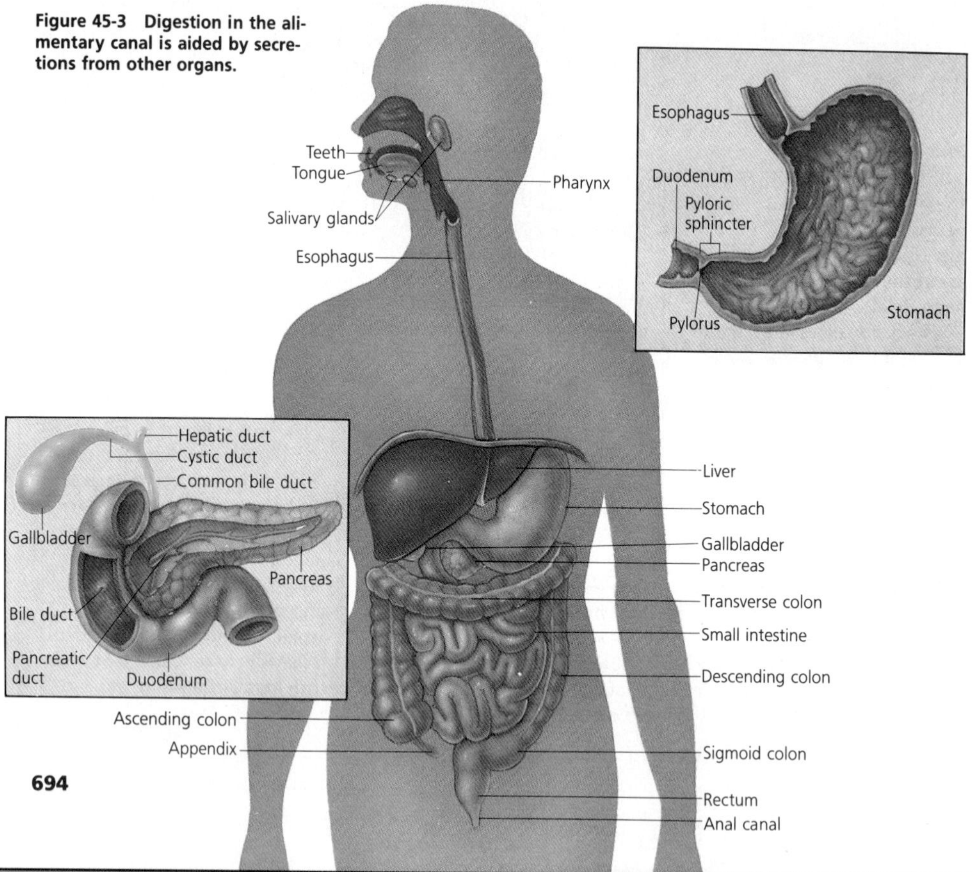

Figure 45-3 Digestion in the alimentary canal is aided by secretions from other organs.

694

mouth → **esophagus** → **stomach** → **small intestine:** duodenum, jejunum, ileum → **large intestine:** caecum, ascending colon, transverse colon, descending colon, sigmoid colon, rectum, anal canal

Graphic Organizer Use this sequential diagram in Reteaching on p. 699.

sors—sharp, flat front teeth—cut the food. Then the broad, flat surfaces of molars, or back teeth, grind it up. The tongue helps keep this food between the chewing surfaces of the upper and lower teeth by manipulating it against the **hard palate,** the bony, membrane-covered roof of the mouth. This is a distinctly different structure from the **soft palate,** the area located just behind the hard palate, made of folded membranes and separating the mouth cavity from the nasal cavity.

While the mechanical phase of digestion is occurring, the chemical phase of digestion is also taking place. Preparations for this phase begin even before the first bite of food is taken. The mouth starts to water—that is, the salivary glands increase their production of **saliva,** a mixture of water, mucus, and a digestive enzyme called salivary amylase. In addition to the many tiny salivary glands located in the lining of the mouth, there are three pairs of larger salivary glands. Locate the three sets of salivary glands in Figure 45-3.

The mucus in the saliva softens and lubricates food and helps hold it together. In addition, the salivary amylase begins the chemical digestion of carbohydrates by breaking down some starch into the disaccharide maltose.

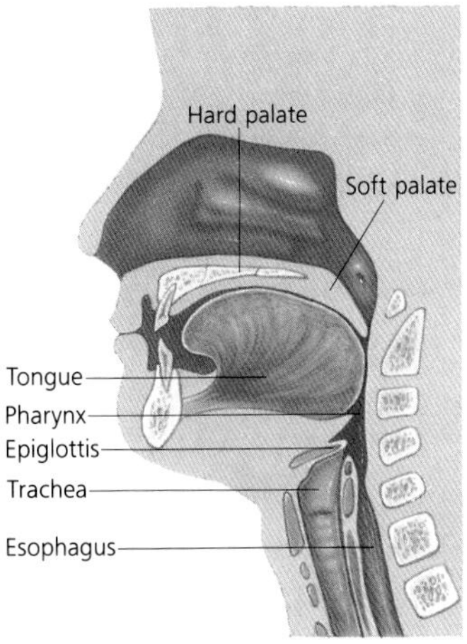

Figure 45-4 The pharynx is the only passage shared by the digestive and respiratory systems. The soft palate and the epiglottis keep the processes of eating and breathing separate in critical areas.

Esophagus

Once food has been thoroughly chewed, moistened, and rolled into a **bolus,** or ball, it is forced by the swallowing action of the tongue into the pharynx. The pharynx *(FER-inks)* is the open area that begins at the back of the mouth and serves as a passageway for both air and food. As Figure 45-4 shows, during swallowing a flap of tissue called the **epiglottis** prevents food from entering the trachea, or windpipe. Instead the bolus passes into the **esophagus,** the approximately 25-cm-long muscular tube that connects the pharynx with the stomach. The esophagus has two muscle layers—a circular layer that wraps around the esophagus and a longitudinal layer that runs the length of the tube. Alternating contractions of these muscle layers push the bolus through the esophagus into the stomach. This series of rhythmic muscular contractions and relaxations is called **peristalsis.**

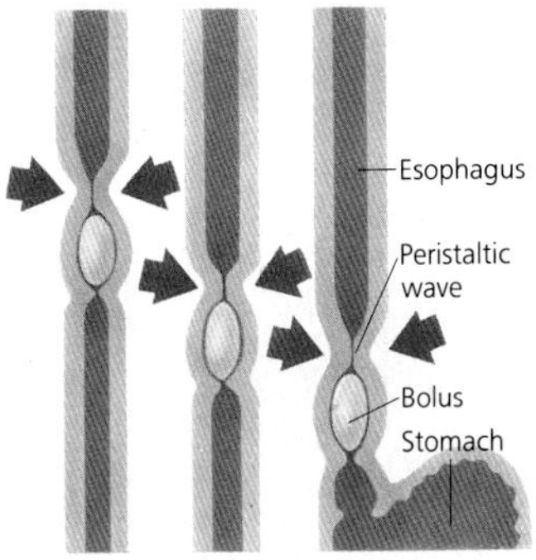

Figure 45-5 A peristaltic wave moves food downward by means of two-way muscular action in the esophagus.

Stomach

The **stomach,** an organ of both mechanical and chemical digestion, is located in the upper left side of the abdominal cavity, just below the diaphragm. It is an elastic bag that is J-shaped when full and that lies in folds when empty. In addition to circular and longitudinal muscles, the walls of the stomach have a third, diagonal layer of muscles. Figure 45-6, shown on the following page, illustrates the arrangement of these muscle layers. Together these muscles can twist the stomach and churn its contents. This churning helps the stomach perform mechanical digestion.

Teaching Strategies

Interpreting the Visuals Refer students to Figure 45-3 on p. 694 for an overview of the digestive system. Point out that the large illustration shows the complete alimentary canal. Ask a student volunteer to name the organs through which food passes, that is, the organs of the alimentary canal. *(Mouth, esophagus, stomach, small intestine, large intestine)* What are the four major and two minor parts of the large intestine? *(Ascending colon, transverse colon, descending colon, sigmoid colon, rectum, anal canal)* Refer students to Figure 45-4 on p. 695 and ask what passage is shared by the digestive and respiratory systems. *(Pharynx)* What structure usually keeps swallowed food from entering the trachea? *(Epiglottis)*

■ ***See* Overhead Transparency *T45 and* Blackline Masters *92 and 93.***

Understanding Concepts Ask students why we do not have bits of egg, meat, and cereals in our bloodstreams. *(Accept any answer that gets to the point of digestion of nutrients.)* Point out that polymers and macromolecules cannot pass through cell membranes and are therefore useless in that form. Now ask how hydrolysis prepares nutrients for absorption. *(It splits the polymers and macromolecules into their component monomers.)* Ask why the villi are so rich in capillaries. *(They absorb the monomers into the bloodstream.)*

Videodiscs

■ ***Side 1 10159, Swallowing and Peristalsis (m)***

■ ***2651–2652, Human Digestive Tract (s)***

LEP Activity

Divide students into small groups and ask each group to make a model of the digestive system. Give each group a large sheet of poster board to use as a base. Explain that the models can have sections drawn on the poster board but most of the model should be three-dimensional. Provide appropriate materials, such as paper and plastic bags, various sizes of tubing, and other common items, to form the digestive organs. Tell students to glue or tape the items to the poster board and label the completed model. Encourage students to present their models in class and describe the functions of the organs.

Making Observations Tell students that iodine tests for the presence of starch and that Tes-tape tests for the simple sugars. Then crumble a soda cracker into a clear glass and mix in two tablespoons of water. Quickly dip a piece of Tes-tape into the mixture, then add three drops of tincture of iodine and have students observe the results. *(The Tes-tape should give a negative or very weak reaction for simple sugars. The cracker should turn a deep blue-black from the iodine.)* Take a second cracker and chew it until it is thoroughly moistened. Place the chewed cracker into a second clear glass, and mix in two tablespoons of water. Repeat the procedure with the Tes-tape and the iodine. Have students compare these results with the first. *(The Tes-tape should indicate the presence of simple sugars; the chewed cracker does not turn as deeply blue-black as the first one did.)* Ask students to explain the difference. *(The enzyme amylase in saliva acted upon the starch in the second cracker, changing some of it into sugar.)* Ask students what kind of digestion has occurred. *(Chemical)*

■ *See* Laboratories, *Investigation 45.2.*

Interpreting the Visuals Have students compare Figure 45-7 with the inset photo on the chapter opener, p. 686. Ask what structure both photos show. *(Gastric pits)* Point out that glands in the epithelial tissue on the inside of the stomach secrete three different substances. Ask students to name them and tell their functions. *(Digestive enzymes, including pepsin, chemically digest food; hydrochloric acid lowers the pH of the stomach; mucus protects the stomach lining.)*

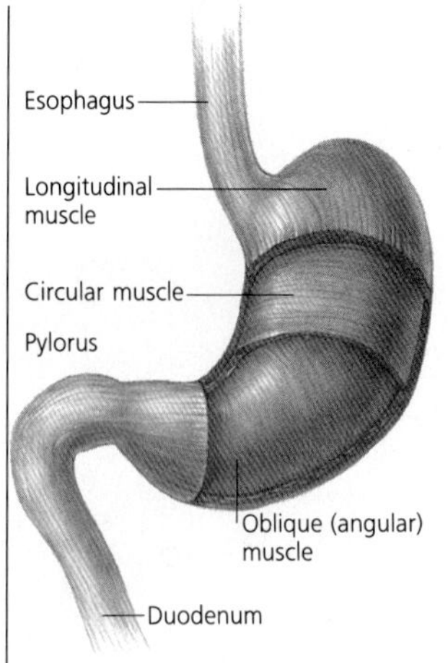

Figure 45-6 Three types of stomach muscles—each oriented in a different direction—permit the stomach to twist and churn, movements that mechanically break up food.

Figure 45-7 This photo shows two of the gastric glands that produce stomach secretions through gastric pits (×400).

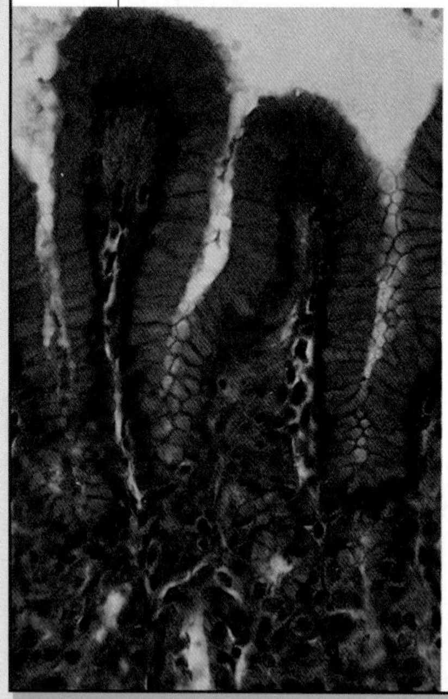

The inner lining of the stomach is a thick, wrinkled mucous membrane dotted with small openings called gastric pits. **Gastric pits** are the open ends of gastric glands that produce the cells that release secretions into the stomach. Some of these glands secrete mucus, others secrete digestive enzymes, and still others secrete hydrochloric acid. The mixture of these secretions forms the acidic **gastric fluid.**

Chemical Digestion

Gastric fluid carries out chemical digestion in the stomach. The chemical breakdown of carbohydrates that started in the mouth is temporarily halted. The stomach begins the chemical digestion of proteins. This process starts as the digestive enzyme pepsin splits complex protein molecules into shorter chains of amino acids called peptides. Pepsin is secreted as an inactive fluid called pepsinogen, which is converted into pepsin at a low pH. The presence of hydrochloric acid within the stomach ensures a low pH. In addition to helping to transform pepsinogen into pepsin, hydrochloric acid dissolves minerals and kills bacteria that enter the stomach along with food.

The mucus secreted in the stomach is vital to the survival of this organ. It forms a coating that protects the lining from hydrochloric acid and prevents pepsin from digesting the proteins that make up the stomach tissue. In some people the mucus coating of the stomach tissue breaks down, allowing digestive enzymes to eat through part of the stomach lining. The sore that results is called an ulcer.

Formation of Chyme

Food enters the stomach when the cardiac sphincter opens. The **cardiac sphincter** is a circular muscle located between the esophagus and the stomach. Once the food is in the stomach, the cardiac spincter closes to prevent the food from regurgitating back into the esophagus. Food usually remains in the stomach for two to three hours. During this time muscle contractions in the stomach walls churn its contents, breaking up food particles and mixing them with gastric fluid. This process forms a mixture called **chyme,** a name that comes from the Greek word meaning "juice." Chyme usually contains fats, sugars, maltose, starches, vitamins, minerals, coagulated milk protein, peptides, and proteins that were not changed by pepsin.

Peristalsis forces chyme out of the stomach and into the small intestine. The **pyloric sphincter,** a circular muscle between the stomach and the small intestine, regulates the flow of chyme. Each time the pyloric sphincter opens, about 5 to 15 mL of chyme moves into the small intestine until finally the stomach is empty.

When chyme enters the small intestine, it mixes with secretions from the liver and pancreas. Before you learn about these secretions, you should know something more about the location, structure, and function of the liver and pancreas.

More Information

Digestive Enzymes Although hydrochloric acid in the stomach starts protein hydrolysis, most of it is accomplished in the duodenum. The pancreas secretes a slightly alkaline fluid that contains a "pre-enzyme" called trypsinogen as well as several other inactive enzymes. An intestinal enzyme, *enterokinase,* converts trypsinogen to trypsin, although trypsin is also able to convert itself. The alkaline pancreatic fluid neutralizes the chyme, providing the optimal pH for trypsin to act on certain peptide bonds that hold together a protein's amino acids. By a complex set of processes, the other "pre-enzymes" are also activated. These enzymes act on different peptide bonds. Hydrolysis of protein is complete when the protein is broken down into its constituent amino acids, which are absorbed by the villi.

Liver

The **liver** is a large organ located to the right of the stomach in the upper right area of the abdominal cavity just below the diaphragm. The liver plays a vital role in the digestion of fats by secreting bile. **Bile** is not a digestive enzyme but an emulsifying agent that breaks fat globules into small droplets, forming a milky emulsion. This process exposes a greater surface area of fats to the action of digestive enzymes and prevents small fat droplets from rejoining into large globules.

The bile secreted by the liver passes from the liver through a Y-shaped duct shown in Figure 45-3. The bile travels down one branch of the Y, the hepatic duct, and then up the other branch, the cystic duct, to the **gallbladder,** a saclike organ that stores and concentrates bile. When chyme is present in the small intestine, the gallbladder releases bile through the common bile duct into the small intestine.

Pancreas

The **pancreas** is an organ that lies behind the stomach, against the back wall of the abdominal cavity. It performs two highly different functions. Chapter 47 discusses its function in regulating the level of glucose in the blood. As part of the digestive system the pancreas secretes pancreatic fluid, which contains digestive enzymes that help complete the breakdown of nutrients in the chyme. This pancreatic fluid enters the small intestine through the pancreatic duct, which joins the common bile duct just before it enters the intestine.

Pancreatic fluid contains sodium bicarbonate, which changes the pH of the chyme from acid to base. Once the pH has changed, the many enzymes in the pancreatic fluid are activated. Pancreatic amylase splits into disaccharides the molecules of starch or glycogen that were not acted upon by salivary amylase. Pancreatic lipase breaks fat into fatty acids and glycerol. Trypsin, chymotrypsin, and carboxypeptidase split proteins into peptides.

Figure 45-8 Chyme entering the small intestine is acted on by pancreatic digestive secretions. At the same time bile from the liver enters by way of the gallbladder to emulsify fats.

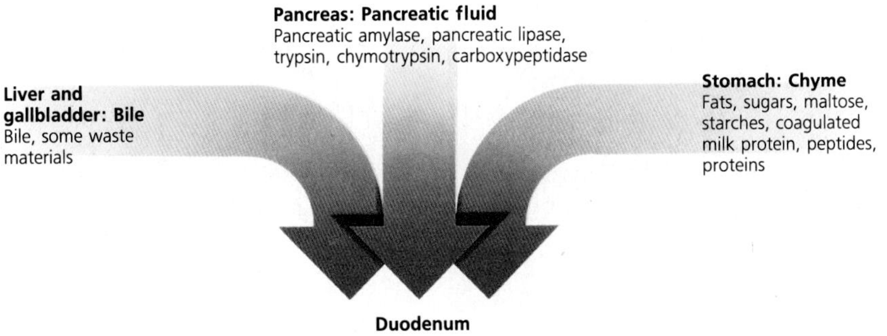

Interpreting the Visuals Ask students which of the arrows in Figure 45-8, p. 697, represents the movement of digested food through the alimentary canal. *(The arrow to the right, showing chyme from the stomach)* What organ does chyme enter as it leaves the stomach? *(Small intestine)* Have students turn back to Figure 45-3, p. 694, and locate the liver, gallbladder, and pancreas. Use a human anatomical model to reinforce the location of these organs. Point out that the duo-denum is the first section of the small intestine. Also point out the hepatic duct, or bile duct, and ask from what organ this duct originates. *(Liver)* Once students have the physical relationships in mind, have them turn back to Figure 45-8. Ask what the arrow to the left represents. *(The common bile duct into the small intestine)* What does the middle arrow represent? *(The pancreatic duct, which delivers enzymes into the duodenum)*

Observing Structures Set up microscope stations around the classroom and have students observe prepared slides of digestive organs, including the stomach, small intestine, liver, and pancreas. Have students make drawings of what they see. Discuss as a class how the structures in the slides relate to function, such as how the distribution of villi of the small intestine relates to nutrient absorption.

Videodiscs

- ***Side 1 28381, Enzyme Structure: Pepsin (m)***
- ***Side 2 11559, The Action of Gastric Juice (m)***

Cooperative Learning

Digestive Organs Divide the class into groups of five, and ask that a member of each group be responsible for one of these sections of the digestive system: (1) mouth; (2) esophagus and stomach; (3) liver, pancreas, and gallbladder; (4) small intestine; and (5) large intestine. Have all members studying the same section meet together to investigate that section's contribution to digestive processes such as hydrolysis. After research time, ask the original groups to reassemble. Have each member teach the other members of the group about his or her section of the digestive system. Move from group to group and randomly ask students questions about digestive organs.

Summarizing Concepts Have students make a concept map that shows how food undergoes mechanical and chemical digestion. An example of a completed map appears on p. 685B.

Identifying Structures Ask students to identify the structures shown in Figure 45-9. *(Villi of the small intestine's inner lining)* How are villi related to the function of the small intestine? *(The major function of the small intestine is to absorb nutrients from the chyme; the villi give the organ more surface area to carry out that function.)* Challenge students to answer the question in the caption of Figure 45-9. *(The processes of diffusion and active transport could be added to illustrate how nutrients are absorbed.)*

Using Models Blow up a long, narrow balloon so that there is a ball of air at one end. Ask a student volunteer to demonstrate how peristalsis works. *(The student should cut off the air flow at one end with the fingers of one hand and push with successive "waves" of movement, using a thumb and forefinger of the other hand.)*

Guided Practice

Have students make a table of the enzymes of the digestive system. Provide them with these column heads: *Enzyme, Organ, Material Digested.*

Small Intestine

If you could stretch the small intestine to its full length, you would find it is nearly 7 m long. The **duodenum** *(DYOO-uh-DEE-num),* the first section of this coiled tube, makes up only the first 25 cm of that length. The **jejunum** *(juh-JOO-num),* the middle section, is about 2.5 m long. The **ileum** *(ILL-ee-um),* which makes up the remaining portion of the small intestine, is approximately 4 m in length.

The secretions from the liver and pancreas enter the duodenum, where they continue the chemical digestion of the chyme. When the secretions from the liver and pancreas along with the chyme enter the duodenum, they trigger intestinal mucous glands to release large quantities of mucus. This mucus protects the intestinal wall from protein-digesting enzymes and the acidic chyme. Glands in the mucous lining of the small intestine release the following enzymes:

- Peptidase completes protein digestion by breaking down peptides into amino acids.
- Maltase, lactase, and sucrase split the disaccharides maltose, lactose, and sucrose into monosaccharides.
- Intestinal lipase splits fats into glycerol and fatty acids.

The end products of digestion—amino acids, monosaccharides, glycerol, and fatty acids—are then absorbed into the circulatory system through blood and lymph vessels in the lining of the small intestine. The structure of this lining provides a huge surface area through which absorption takes place. **Absorption** is the process by which the end products of digestion are transferred into the circulatory system. The highly folded lining is covered with millions of fingerlike projections called **villi.** The cells covering the villi, in turn, have extensions on their cell membranes called **microvilli.** The folds, villi, and microvilli give the small intestine a

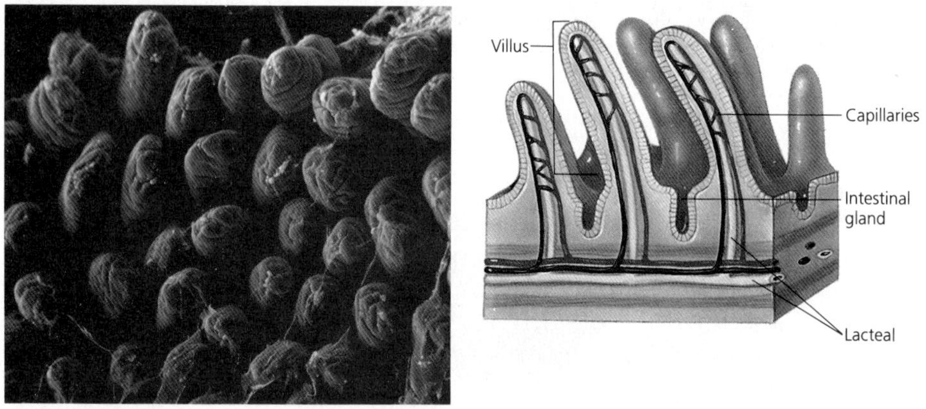

Figure 45-9 Villi, as shown in the SEM (left, ×1,000) and the diagram (right), expand the absorption area of the small intestine. What other processes could be added to the diagram to complete the picture?

Interdisciplinary Activity

Health Stress can cause problems with digestion. A common stress-related ailment is stomach ulcer. Have students research how stress affects the secretion of hydrochloric acid and other digestive juices. Ask students to find out how ulcers are treated and what can happen if an ulcer goes untreated. Encourage students to interview someone who has had an ulcer, if possible.

surface area of about 250 m^2, roughly the size of a tennis court. Nutrients are absorbed through this surface by means of diffusion and active transport.

Inside each villus are capillaries and tiny lymph vessels called **lacteals.** Glycerol and fatty acids enter the lacteals, are carried through the lymph vessels, and eventually reach the bloodstream through lymphatic ducts near the heart. Amino acids and monosaccharides enter the capillaries and are carried to the liver. The liver detoxifies the blood and removes any excess glucose, converting it to glycogen for storage. The filtered blood then carries the nutrients to all parts of the body.

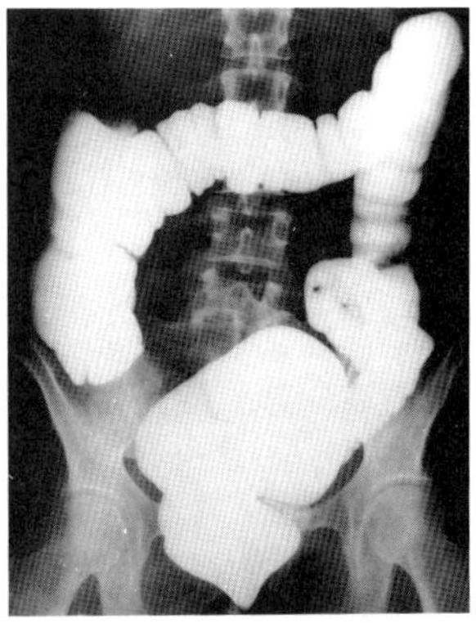

Figure 45-10 This X ray shows the large intestine, or colon. Try to identify the four major parts of the colon in this X ray.

Large Intestine

Once absorption in the small intestine is complete, peristalsis moves the remaining material on to the large intestine. The **large intestine,** or **colon,** is the final organ of digestion. Study Figure 45-3 to identify the four major parts of the colon: ascending colon, transverse colon, descending colon, and sigmoid colon. The rectum and the anal canal that it leads into are the names given to the very short final portions of the large intestine. Find these portions of the large intestine in Figure 45-3.

Most of the absorption of nutrients and water has been completed in the small intestine. About 9 L of water enters the small intestine, but only about 0.5 L of water is present in the material that enters the large intestine. In the large intestine, only minerals and vitamins produced by bacteria that live in the colon, as well as most of the remainder of the water, are absorbed. Slow contractions that occur only three or four times a day move the material in the large intestine toward the rectum and eventually out of the body. As this matter moves through the intestine, the absorption of water solidifies the mass. The solidified material is called **feces.**

As the fecal matter solidifies, mucous secretions of the intestinal wall lubricate the wall to make the passing of the feces less abrasive. Mucus also binds the fecal matter together and neutralizes any acids that are released when bacteria act upon the feces. Such bacteria also aid in the manufacture of vitamin K. The feces are eliminated through the anus.

Section Review

1. What is the *alimentary canal?*
2. Name one structure involved in the mechanical phase of digestion and explain its function in mechanical digestion.
3. What is the function of bile?
4. How is the structure of the small intestine related to the function of absorption?
5. Describe how cellulose aids in digestion. What do you imagine would be the consequence of not eating enough cellulose?

Independent Practice

- Have students write answers to the Section Review.
- Ask students to write a step-by-step description of the changes that various foods of their choice undergo as they move through the alimentary canal.
- *See* Process Skills, *Chapter 45.*

Check Your Understanding

1. What body senses may help initiate digestion? *(Seeing or smelling food often stimulates the secretion of saliva.)*
2. How does hydrochloric acid help enzyme action in the stomach? *(It lowers the stomach's pH, which allows digestive enzymes to work.)*
3. What is the effect of storing protein-digesting enzymes such as pepsin in an inactive form? *(It is less likely that pepsin will digest the stomach tissue itself.)*

Reteaching

Have students make a sequential diagram of the alimentary canal. Use the diagram on p. 694 as a model.

- *See* Section Reviews *worksheet, Section 45.2.*

Enrichment

Have students research how improper diet and poor hygiene result in tooth decay and loss.

Closure

Describe a function of the digestive system to the class and ask for volunteers to explain where and how each function is performed. For example, ask where and how mechanical digestion occurs. *(In the mouth and stomach; by the action of teeth and tongue, and stomach muscles)*

Videodiscs

- *2288, Electron Microscopy: Microvilli (s)*
- *2515–2517, Diffusion Process (s)*

Answers to Section Review

1. The digestive tract, which begins at the mouth and ends at the anus
2. Any of the following: teeth cut and grind food, the tongue keeps food between the teeth, and the stomach churns food.
3. It breaks fat globules into small droplets, exposing a greater surface area of fats to the action of digestive enzymes.
4. By means of folds, villi, and microvilli, the small intestine provides a huge surface area on which absorption can take place.
5. Cellulose aids digestion by drawing water into the large intestine, expanding the intestine walls, and triggering muscle contractions that move the feces out of the body. Insufficient cellulose retards movement of food through the alimentary canal.

Lesson Plan

Section Focus
This section describes the excretory system. Students will learn about the structure and function of the kidneys. They will also find out how metabolic wastes are excreted by the body.

Section Themes
The theme of **Scale and Structure** is paramount in this section. The complex structure of the kidneys allows for filtration, reabsorption, and secretion.

The theme of **Stability** is inherent in the excretory system's crucial role in maintaining homeostasis in the body. This system regulates the balance of water and other substances in the blood.

Motivating Activity
Ask students what generally happens if they eat a lot of salty potato chips or other snacks and drink a lot of liquids, like sodas. *(They get bloated, puffy.)* Tell students that this is a temporary retention of fluid in the body. Ask why this happens. *(The increased salt causes a cellular sodium imbalance. Fluid is retained to maintain osmotic equilibrium.)* Ask what this equilibrium is called. *(Homeostasis)*

Teaching Strategies
Observing Structures Have students examine a cow or pig kidney with hand lenses. After they have examined the exterior of the kidney, cut it in half so they can observe the interior. Help students identify the cortex, medulla, renal pelvis, and renal vein and artery.

Section Objectives
- *Define the term* excretion, *and list the functions of each of the major excretory organs.*
- *Identify the major parts of the kidney.*
- *Relate the structure of a nephron to the functions it performs.*
- *Explain how the processes of filtration, reabsorption, and tubular secretion help maintain homeostasis.*
- *Name the main parts of the urinary system.*

45.3 Excretory System

The body must rid itself of the waste products of cellular activity. This process of removing metabolic wastes, called **excretion,** is just as vital as digestion to maintaining the body's internal environment. Thus the excretory system not only eliminates wastes but also plays a crucial role in maintaining homeostasis by regulating the balance of water and other substances in the blood.

The main waste products that the body must eliminate are, first, carbon dioxide and water from cellular respiration and, second, nitrogenous compounds from the breakdown of proteins. The lungs excrete most of the carbon dioxide and some of the water through respiration. Some water and excess minerals are lost in the form of perspiration. Most water and nitrogenous wastes are eliminated by the kidneys, the main excretory organs of the body.

The most common nitrogenous waste is ammonia, a substance so toxic that it could not remain long in the body without harming cells. The body is protected from ammonia poisoning by the liver, which removes ammonia from the blood and converts it into a less harmful substance called urea. The urea enters the bloodstream and is then removed by the kidneys.

Figure 45-11 The excretory system (left) involves the kidneys. Note the kidney and nephron diagramed at right.

Kidneys

Humans have two **kidneys,** bean-shaped excretory organs each about the size of a clenched fist. The kidneys are located in the small of the back, one behind the stomach and the other behind the liver. The longitudinal section in Figure 45-11 shows the three main parts of the kidney. The **cortex** is the outermost portion of the kidney, which makes up about a third of its tissue mass. The **medulla** is the inner two-thirds of the kidney. The **renal pelvis** is a funnel-shaped structure in the center of the kidney. Also notice in

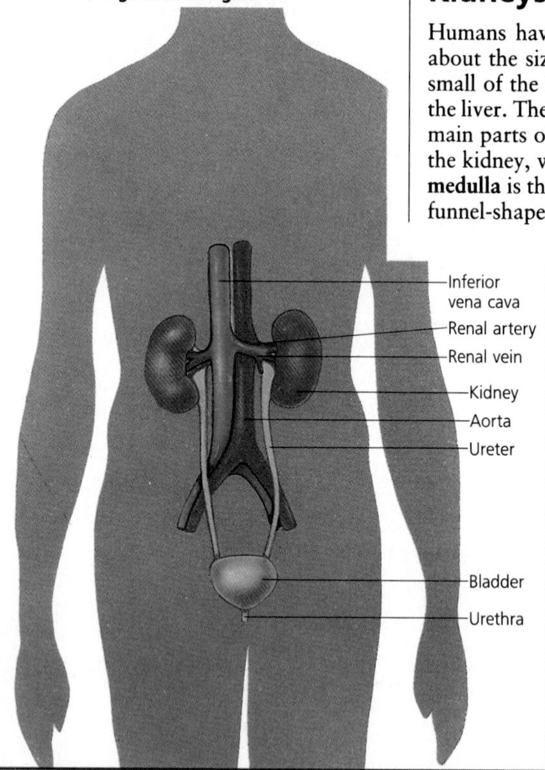

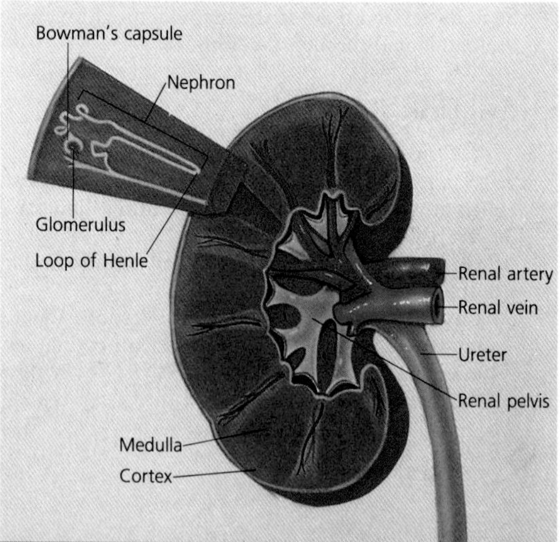

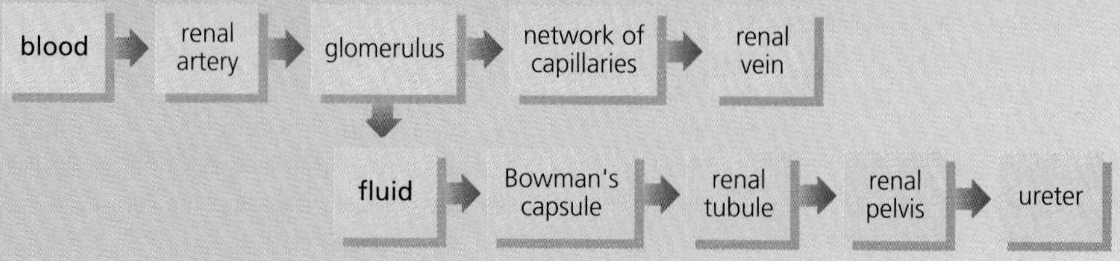

Graphic Organizer Use this sequential diagram in Guided Practice on p. 702.

the figure that blood enters the kidney through a renal artery and leaves through a renal vein.

A complex series of processes in the kidney removes waste from the blood and adjusts its chemical makeup. The substances—toxins, urea, water, and mineral salts—removed from the blood by these processes form an amber-colored liquid called **urine.** The urine flows from the kidneys into the urinary system for storage and eventual elimination from the body.

Nephrons

Take a close look at the structure of the functional unit of the kidney, the **nephron,** shown in Figure 45-12. Each kidney consists of more than a million nephrons. Each nephron has a cup-shaped structure called **Bowman's capsule** that encloses a bed of capillaries. This capillary bed, called a **glomerulus** *(gluh-MER-yuh-luss),* receives blood from the renal artery. High pressure forces fluids from the blood through the capillary walls into Bowman's capsule. The material filtered from the blood then flows through the **renal tubule,** a long tube with permeable walls. Blood remaining in the glomerulus then flows through a network of capillaries that wraps around the renal tubule.

As the blood and fluid flow through a nephron, the composition of both is modified by the exchange of materials among the renal tubule, the capillaries, and the extracellular fluid. Various types of exchange take place in the four different parts of the renal tubule: the proximal convoluted tubule, the loop of Henle, the distal convoluted tubule, and the collecting duct. To understand how the structure of each part of the nephron is related to its function, let's look at the three major processes that take place in the nephron: filtration, reabsorption, and secretion.

Filtration

The process through which materials from the blood are forced out of the glomerulus and into Bowman's capsule is called **filtration.** Pressure forces water, nitrogenous wastes, glucose, and mineral salts through the thin capillary walls. About one-fifth of the fluid portion of the blood filters into the capsule. The rest remains in the capillaries along with proteins and cells, which are too large to pass through the capillary walls. Thus the filtrate—the fluid that enters the nephron—resembles blood plasma without the large protein molecules found in plasma.

Reabsorption and Secretion

The body needs to retain many of the substances that have been removed from the blood by filtration. Thus as the filtrate flows through the renal tubule, these materials return to the blood by passing through the walls of the tubule and entering the surrounding capillaries. This process is called **reabsorption.** Most reabsorption occurs in the proximal convoluted tubule. In this region about 75 percent of the water in the filtrate returns to the capil-

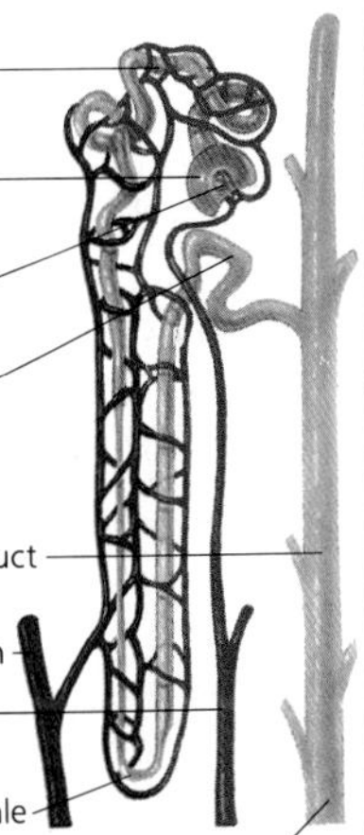

Figure 45-12 A nephron is shown in the diagram (top). A glomerulus is shown in the center of the SEM (below). Surrounding the glomerulus are renal tubules and red blood corpuscles (×250).

Identifying Structures Have students use Figure 45-11 to locate the major organs of the excretory system on a human anatomical model. Point out the renal artery and renal vein and ask how the blood moving through these two vessels differs. *(The blood entering the kidney in the renal artery contains waste products of cellular activity and toxins, which will be filtered out by the kidney before the blood leaves through the renal vein.)* What do the filtered wastes form? *(Urine)* Help students trace the path of urine from the kidneys through the ureter to the urinary bladder and through the urethra.

Interpreting the Visuals Ask students to look at the diagram in Figure 45-12 and notice the different colors. Which color represents blood moving into the nephron from the renal artery? *(Red)* Have students follow the blood up the red blood vessel to the glomerulus. What happens to the blood in the glomerulus? *(Fluid moves out of the blood into the Bowman's capsule.)* Have students turn to Figure 45-13, p. 702, and name the process that occurs in the glomerulus. *(Filtration)* Help students orient the nephron detail shown in Figure 45-13 to the diagram in Figure 45-12. Then ask what the network of capillaries is wrapped around. *(The renal tubule)* What processes occur as the blood moves through these capillaries?*(Reabsorption and secretion)* Where does the blood go after it leaves the nephron? *(Into the renal vein)* Where does the waste fluid, or urine, go after it leaves the renal tubule? *(Into the renal pelvis, then the ureter)*

Videodiscs

- ***Side 2 30353, Kidney: Structure and Function (m)***

More Information

Dialysis Machines More than 100,000 people in the United States suffer from kidney disease. The vast majority of them will undergo *hemodialysis* in order to rid their systems of nitrogenous wastes. A person on dialysis, as the process is commonly known, is hooked up to a stationary machine called a hemodialyzer for about four hours every other day. The machine filters out the wastes through a dialysis membrane and also removes excess fluid from the body. A semipermanent tube called a catheter is implanted in an artery and can be hooked to the hemodialyzer. Blood flows through the catheter to the hemodialyzer, is cleansed, and is then returned to the patient.

Section 45.3

Guided Practice

Help students understand kidney function by guiding them through the making of a sequential diagram. An example of a completed diagram is shown on p. 700.

Independent Practice

- Have students write answers to the Section Review.
- Have students write a description of the pathway ammonia takes once it is formed by the breakdown of cellular proteins. *(It enters the blood from the tissues, is changed into urea in the liver, passes out of the blood in the kidney, and passes out of the body in urine.)*

Check Your Understanding

1. What would happen in the body if the kidneys failed? *(Homeostasis would be undermined; nitrogenous waste would build up in the blood; and fluid would collect in tissues.)*
2. What does fluid go into when it leaves the blood in the glomerulus? *(Bowman's capsule)*

Reteaching

Have students make a table that shows the functions of the organs of the excretory system.

- *See* Section Reviews *worksheet, Section 45.3.*

Enrichment

Ask students to write an essay comparing the natural filtration of the kidney to the synthetic filtration method used in dialysis.

Closure

Tell students that only mammals and birds are able to produce urine more concentrated than the fluids bathing their tissues. Ask them what structure in the kidney allows this concentration to take place. *(The loop of Henle)*

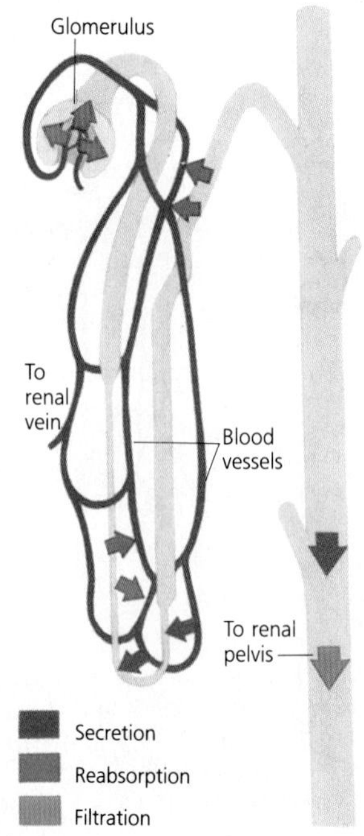

Figure 45-13 Color-coded arrows indicate where in the nephron secretion, reabsorption, and filtration occur.

laries by osmosis. Glucose and minerals such as sodium, potassium, and calcium are returned to the blood by active transport.

Some additional reabsorption occurs in the distal convoluted tubule. Also in this region of the tubule some substances pass from the blood into the filtrate through a process called secretion. The pH of the blood is also adjusted by secreting hydrogen ions into the filtrate. The fluid and wastes that remain in the renal tubule form urine. The urine from several renal tubules flows into a collecting duct.

In the collecting duct urine is further concentrated by the osmosis of water through the wall of the duct into the extracellular fluid. This process allows the body to conserve water. In fact, osmosis in the collecting duct, together with reabsorption in other parts of the tubule, returns to the blood about 99 of every 100 mL of water in the filtrate.

You may have noticed that in tracing the flow of filtrate through the nephron, we skipped over the loop of Henle. The function of the loop of Henle is closely related to that of the collecting duct. Water moves out of the collecting duct because the concentration of sodium chloride (NaCl) is higher in the extracellular fluid of the medulla than it is in the fluid inside the collecting duct. This high concentration of sodium chloride is maintained by the loop of Henle. Cells in the wall of the loop actively transport negatively charged chloride ions from the filtrate into the extracellular fluid. Positively charged sodium ions follow the chloride ions into the fluid through electrical attraction. This ensures that the NaCl concentration of the extracellular fluid remains high and thus promotes the reabsorption of water from the collecting duct. Understanding this relationship between the loop of Henle and the collecting duct will help you understand how these two structures function together to concentrate wastes.

Urinary System

Urine from the collecting ducts flows through the renal pelvis and into a narrow tube called a **ureter.** A ureter leads from each kidney to the **urinary bladder,** a muscular sac that stores urine. Muscular contractions of the bladder force urine out of the body through a tube called the **urethra.**

Section Review

1. What is *excretion?*
2. Name one organ other than the kidney that is involved in excretion, and describe what and how it excretes.
3. What are the structures of the renal tubule?
4. What is the most basic difference between filtration and reabsorption?
5. Given the definition of excretion, why do you think the large intestine is not classified as a major excretory organ?

Answers to Section Review

1. The process of removing metabolic wastes from the body
2. The lungs excrete carbon dioxide and water vapor through respiration; the skin excretes water and excess minerals through perspiration.
3. The proximal convoluted tubule, the loop of Henle, the distal convoluted tubule, and the collecting duct
4. During filtration, the blood loses materials, whereas during reabsorption the blood regains materials.
5. Excretion is the process of removing metabolic wastes; the wastes that pass through the large intestine are generated through the digestion process and are not the result of metabolic processes.

Laboratory

A Model of Human Digestion

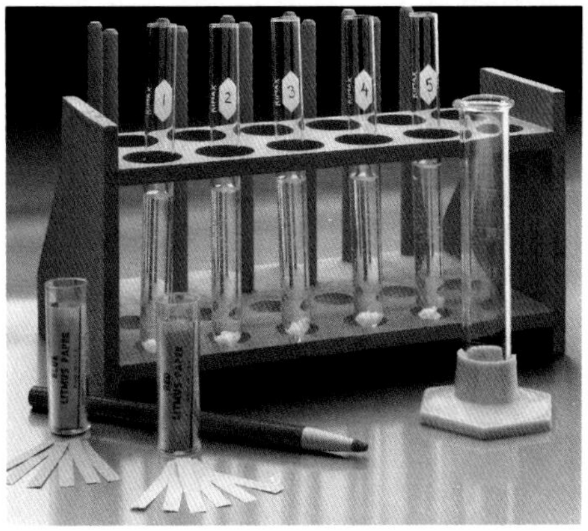

Objective
To test a model of chemical conditions for digestion in the human stomach

Process Skills
Modeling, observing, predicting, inferring

Materials
Glass-marking pencil, 5 test tubes with stoppers, test tube rack, scalpel, cooked egg white, 10-mL graduated cylinder, 1% pepsin solution, 0.2% hydrochloric acid, 1% sodium bicarbonate, distilled water, red and blue litmus paper, notebook paper

Background
1 How is food changed from the chunks you chew with your teeth into the chyme absorbed in your small intestine?
2 What type of organic compound does the enzyme pepsin digest?

Inquiry
1 Number five test tubes *1, 2, 3, 4,* and *5* and place them in the rack.
2 Use a scalpel to cut about 3/4 teaspoon of firm, cooked egg white into fine pieces.
3 Place equal amounts of egg white in each test tube.
4 Use a clean graduated cylinder to add 10 mL of water to test tube 1, 10 mL of pepsin solution to test tube 2, and 10 mL of hydrochloric acid to test tube 3. Measure 5 mL of pepsin solution and 5 mL of sodium bicarbonate solution into test tube 4. Place 5mL of pepsin and 5 mL of hydrochloric acid in test tube 5. Rinse the cylinder between additions so as not to contaminate samples.
5 Stopper and gently shake each test tube. What does the shaking do?
6 Which test tube best models the chemical composition in the human stomach?
7 What information do test tubes 1, 2, and 3 give you? For what do they control?
8 Make a table with four wide columns labelled *Test Tube Number, Contents, pH,* and *Degree of Digestion.* Fill in columns 1 and 2, and save the table for results. Predict which test tube will show the most digestion in 48 hours. Explain your reasoning.
9 Store the test tube rack for 48 hours at room temperature. Post a note of caution so that no one spills the acids or bases.
10 After 48 hours, test each solution for pH with red and blue litmus paper. Record results.
11 In which test tube has the egg white broken down and dissolved most? Record your observations in the table.

Conclusions
1 What conditions caused the greatest digestion of cooked egg white?
2 Comparing test tubes 4 and 5, what can you conclude about the effects of the chemical environment on the activity of pepsin?
3 Would pepsin digest butter? Explain.

Further Inquiry
Design an experiment to test the digestion of carbohydrates such as potato or apple.

(For an overview of digestion of protein and preparatory information related to the laboratory, see p. 685B.)

Background
1. Solid chunks of food are ground by the teeth; digested by enzymes in the mouth, stomach, and small intestine; and dissolved.
2. Pepsin digests protein into peptides.

Inquiry
5. Shaking the test tubes coats all sides of the egg white chunks with solutions.
6. Based on the student text, students should infer that test tube 5, containing pepsin and hydrochloric acid, is the closest model.
7. Neither water, pepsin, nor acid alone would be expected to digest much protein. These test tubes control for the digestive action of each chemical or solution alone.
8. Student predictions depend upon prior study and knowledge. From television programs or commercials, some know that the stomach contains acid. Some will have read that the enzyme pepsin requires acid. Students should predict that test tube 5, containing hydrochloric acid as well as pepsin, will digest the most.
10. Litmus paper should show that test tubes 1 and 2 are neutral, 3 and 5 are acidic, and 4 is basic.
11. Test tube 5 should clearly show the most breakdown of the egg white.

Conclusions
1. Enzyme pepsin plus acid caused the greatest digestion of cooked egg white.
2. Pepsin requires an acidic environment for optimum digestive action.
3. No; however, accept all surmises, since students have no experimental evidence that enzymes are specific. Pancreatic lipase, not pepsin, will digest butter. Pepsin digests only protein.

Further Inquiry
Design an experiment that is parallel to this lab using chopped potato or apple plus saliva or pancreatic extract (as a source for amylases).

Vocabulary

1. *Mineral* names an inorganic nutrient, which does not belong in a group of organic nutrients.
2. *Bolus* names the ball of matter that passes through the alimentary canal, which does not belong with terms naming structures of the canal.
3. *Triglyceride* names a fat molecule, which does not belong in a group of carbohydrate molecules.
4. *Absorption* names a function that occurs in digestive organs, which does not belong with functions performed in the kidneys.
5. *Ileum* names a structure of the small intestine, which does not belong in a listing of the structures of the kidney.

Review

1. c
2. d
3. c
4. b
5. b
6. a
7. c
8. b
9. d
10. c

11. Consuming saturated fats seems to increase production of cholesterol, and an elevated blood cholesterol level is associated with heart disease.
12. Synthesis begins with conversion of cholesterol to provitamin D by intestinal enzymes. Provitamin D, stored in the skin, converts to vitamin D with exposure to the ultraviolet light of the sun.
13. It increases it.
14. Both the pancreas and the liver play major roles in other organ systems. They are the only two digestive organs composed of lobes. They do not lie within the alimentary canal but release secretions into it.
15. The stomach's churning action mixes food with gastric fluid.
16. Ammonia is so toxic that it could not remain long in the body without harming cells. The liver converts ammonia to urea, a less harmful substance.
17. The three main parts of the kidney are the cortex, medulla, and renal pelvis.
18. The excretory processes that maintain homeostasis are filtration, reabsorption, and secretion.
19. Each nephron is made up of a glomerulus, a renal tubule, a Bowman's capsule, and a network of capillaries.
20. The urinary system has two ureters, a urinary bladder, and the urethra.

Chapter 45 Review

Vocabulary

absorption (698)
alimentary canal (694)
bile (697)
bolus (695)
Bowman's capsule (701)
calorie (687)
Calorie (687)
carbohydrate (687)
cardiac sphincter (696)
cholesterol (689)
chyme (696)
colon (699)
cortex (700)
dehydration (693)
digestion (694)
disaccharide (687)
duodenum (697)
enzyme (688)
epiglottis (695)
esophagus (695)
excretion (700)
fat (688)
feces (699)
filtration (701)
gallbladder (697)
gastric fluid (696)
gastric pit (696)
glomerulus (701)
hard palate (695)
hydrolysis (687)
ileum (698)
jejunum (698)
kidney (700)
lacteal (698)
large intestine (699)
liver (697)
medulla (700)
microvilli (698)
mineral (691)
monosaccharide (687)
nephron (701)
nutrient (687)
pancreas (697)
peristalsis (695)
polysaccharide (688)
protein (688)
pyloric sphincter (696)
reabsorption (701)
renal pelvis (700)
renal tubule (701)
saliva (695)
soft palate (695)
stomach (695)
triglyceride (689)
ureter (702)
urethra (702)
urinary bladder (702)
urine (701)
villi (698)
vitamin (690)

For each set of terms below, choose the one that does not belong, and explain why it does not belong.

1. carbohydrate, protein, fat, mineral
2. pharynx, epiglottis, bolus, esophagus
3. monosaccharide, glucose, polysaccharide, triglyceride
4. absorption, filtration, secretion, reabsorption
5. nephron, ileum, glomerulus, renal tubule

Review

1. The primary function of carbohydrates is to (a) break down molecules (b) aid in digestion (c) supply the body with energy (d) regulate the flow of chyme.
2. Cellulose (a) builds body tissue (b) is a monosaccharide (c) is used for energy (d) aids in digestion.
3. Proteins consist of (a) catalysts (b) enzymes (c) amino acids (d) polysaccharides.
4. The body needs vitamins because they (a) supply it with energy (b) serve as coenzymes (c) function as enzymes (d) act as hormones.
5. The best way to prevent dehydration is by (a) inhaling air (b) drinking water (c) not drinking water (d) perspiring.
6. The epiglottis is important because it (a) prevents food from going down the trachea (b) separates the pharynx from the nasal cavity (c) is the passage through which food travels to the stomach (d) regulates the flow of chyme.
7. The gallbladder (a) creates bile (b) stores urine (c) stores, concentrates, and secretes bile (d) is made up of nephrons.
8. During absorption the lacteals absorb (a) glycogen (b) glycerol and fatty acids (c) amino acids and monosaccharides (d) lactose.
9. Organs involved in the excretion process include the (a) kidneys and stomach (b) liver and pancreas (c) nephron and glomerulus (d) kidneys and liver.
10. During secretion in the kidney, substances move from (a) filtrate to blood (b) blood

to blood (c) blood to filtrate (d) filtrate to filtrate.

11. Why can consuming a great deal of saturated fat be harmful?
12. Briefly explain the synthesis of vitamin D in the body.
13. How does a diet high in saturated fats affect the rate of death from heart disease or stroke?
14. In what two ways do the liver and the pancreas differ from other digestive organs?
15. What is the mechanical digestive work performed by the stomach?
16. Why does the body convert ammonia into urea?
17. What are the three main parts of the kidney?
18. What are the excretory processes that maintain homeostasis?
19. What are the structures of a nephron?
20. What are the main structures of the urinary system?

Critical Thinking

1. In some countries many children suffer from a type of malnutrition called kwashiorkor. They have swollen stomachs and become increasingly thin until they die. Even when given rice and water, they still die. What type of nutritional deficiency might they be suffering from?
2. Some people cannot drink milk because they are unable to digest lactose, the sugar in milk. Doctors think this inability involves specific areas of the digestive system. What areas do you think these are?
3. What can happen to a person who gets serious diarrhea? (Hint: Why is it important that the large intestine reabsorb water and not excrete it?)
4. Look at the pictures of the teeth of different animals. What can you tell about the human diet by comparing the teeth of humans with those of the other animals shown here?

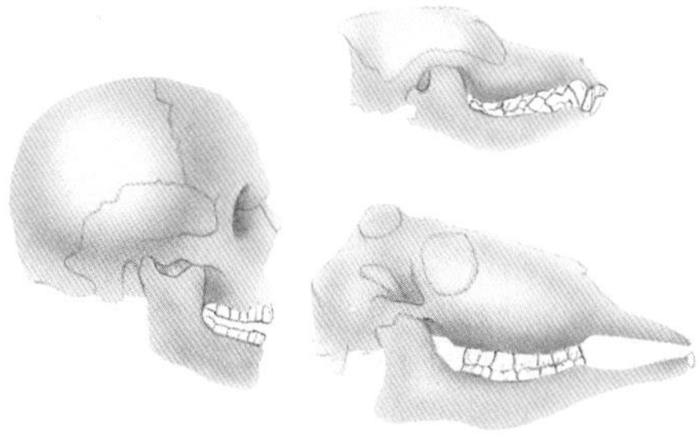

5. When the kidneys stop functioning, urea builds up in the blood and poisons the body. A person whose kidney has failed will eventually die if the urea is not somehow removed. For it to be removed, the patient must be attached to an artificial kidney called a dialysis machine. Suggest a design for the major components of a dialysis machine based on the way a normal kidney works.

Extension

1. Using information from the United States Department of Agriculture on nutrients in food, chart your intake of five nutrients for a week. Compare your intake with the National Academy of Sciences' Recommended Daily Allowances.
2. Look in the *Readers' Guide to Periodical Literature* for articles in which the authors claim that certain diets can help prevent heart attacks and cancer. Write a brief report summarizing a few of these articles.
3. Read "Cholesterol to Go" in *Discover,* December 1990, pp. 30–31. Prepare an oral report in which you explain the roles of LDL and HDL in cholesterol transport. How might Oram's discovery of an HDL receptor lead to breakthrough treatment of coronary artery disease?

Critical Thinking

1. Students should conclude that an important part of the diet is missing. Few plant foods alone provide all the essential amino acids, the building blocks of protein. Eating only rice suggests a lack of an essential amino acid. The correct answer is that kwashiorkor is a protein-deficiency disease.
2. Probably in the small intestine, where lactase breaks down lactose. But students could also say that it might be a problem with reabsorption of this specific sugar.
3. A person with serious diarrhea could die from dehydration, since the large intestine does not have time to reabsorb the water.
4. The sharp teeth of the carnivore are adapted for biting and tearing; the flat teeth of the herbivore are adapted for chewing. The teeth of humans are adapted for both functions.
5. The design should include two hookups to the body, one to take the unfiltered blood away from the body and the other to return the filtered blood to the body. The machine itself should have some mechanism to filter the blood and another to provide fluid balance in the body.

Extension

1. Make sure students use the newest recommendations, which change periodically.
2. Advise students that they may want to use a computer search system to find articles. Many libraries now have these systems.
3. Oram's discovery signals a possibility for a drug that could be developed to act as HDL receptors act. Understanding how HDL and LDL work in the blood can also be used to plan changes in diet and exercise that will prevent the disease.

Chapter 46 Nervous System and Sense Organs

Chapter Overview

Chapter 46 focuses on the body's communication network—the nervous system. Section 46.1 examines the divisions of the nervous system, with an emphasis on the brain. Section 46.2 explores the structure of a neuron and the processes involved in a nerve impulse. Section 46.3 discusses the five types of receptors and examines the organs involved in the senses.

Chapter Planning Chart

B	S	A	Sections and Subsections	Page	Features	Page	Resources
•	•	•	**46.1 Structure**				
			Organization	707	Biotechnology	710	Videodiscs
			Brain	708	Think	712	Blackline Master 94
			Spinal Cord	711	Section Review	712	Overhead Transparency T46
			Peripheral Nervous System	712			Section Reviews Worksheet
	•	•	**46.2 Transmission of Nerve Impulses**				
			Neuron Structure	713	Section Review	717	Videodiscs
			Nerve Impulses	714			Blackline Master 95
			Transmission Across Synapses	716			Section Reviews Worksheet
			Effects of Neurotransmitters	717			
•	•	•	**46.3 The Senses**				
			Receptors and Sense Organs	718	Laboratory	723	Videodiscs
			Vision	718	Section Review	722	Process Skills: Sensory Thresholds
			Hearing and Balance	720			Laboratories: Vision and Hearing
			Taste and Smell	721			Section Reviews Worksheet
			Other Senses	722			
			End of Chapter Activities				
					Chapter Review	724	Vocabulary Skills
							Chapter Test
							Computer Test Generator

B *The Basic Level curriculum presents the most fundamental knowledge offered in the course.*
S *The Standard Level curriculum is designed for the average student who is able to master most topics.*
A *The Advanced Level curriculum includes suggestions for teaching the most academically able students.*

Cooperative Learning

Group Activity: Five Senses

- **Group Size:** *5 students*
- **Outcome:** *Students will understand how the five senses are integrated and how they relate to the central nervous system.*
- **Individual Accountability:** *Each student will investigate one of the senses and teach other group members about it.*
- **Positive Interdependence:** *The group will together design and make a poster that unifies their material on the senses.*

Have each student in every group choose one of the five senses to investigate. Allow time for individual investigation through library research and experimentation. Have students pay attention to neural pathways; structures such as the cochlea and semicircular canals in the ear; and the perception of qualities such as pitch, saltiness, and color. Have each group create a poster that contains information about the senses and how they relate to the central nervous system. Tell students in each group to work together so that all understand and agree upon the material in the poster. Give each group a chance to present its poster to the class.

Concept Map

The following is one possible solution to the concept mapping activity in Independent Practice on p. 712.

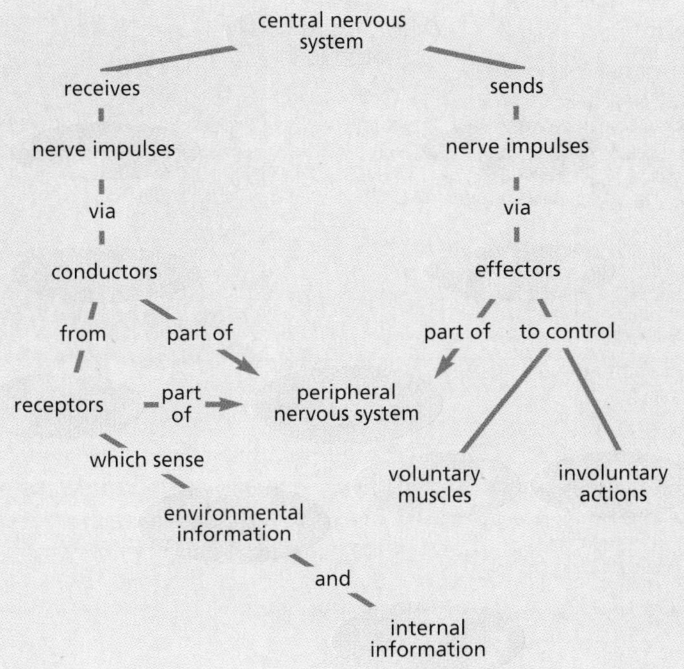

Laboratory Preparation

Overview *(See p. 723.)*

In this lab students map the areas of the tongue that contain specific taste buds for salty, sweet, sour, and bitter tastes. Students conduct the experiment using a double-blind design so that neither the experimenter nor the taster knows the chemical until mapping begins. This technique contributes to the validity of the experiment as an investigation, rather than as a demonstration of the known areas on the tongue. The same experimental design is often used to demonstrate the true efficacy of a drug.

Preparation

To prepare a salty solution, add 10 g sodium chloride to 90 mL water. Label the solution *A*. To prepare a sweet solution, add 5 g sucrose to 95 mL water. Label the solution *B*. To prepare a sour solution, add 33 mL vinegar to 67 mL water. Label the solution C. To prepare a bitter solution, add 0.1 g quinine sulfate to 99.9 mL water. Label the solution *D*. (Quinine sulfate is available from a biological supply house.) For the tasteless solution, use distilled water and label the solution *E*.

Teaching Tips

For Inquiry step 1, suggest to students that their data table should include the column heads *Solution Letter, Tongue Area,* and either the head *Taste Type* or the heads *Sour, Sweet, Bitter, Salty, No Taste*. Under *Tongue Area,* rows are numbered 1 through 5. This is repeated four more times until there are five groups of five, the numbers corresponding to the areas on the tongue. The letter *A* should be recorded under *Solution Letter* opposite the numbers in the first group of five, *B* opposite the number in the second group, and so on for solutions A through E.

Safety

Remind students to dispose of used swabs and paper towels correctly and to use new swabs and paper towels each time they are required.

Chapter Themes

Systems and Interactions The nervous system interacts with and integrates all the other systems of the body as the control system for most body functions. Stress that the organs described in this chapter work together as a system. For example, the brain does not stand alone but functions in concert with other parts of the system, such as the sense organs.

Scale and Structure As students learn about the structures of the nervous system, emphasize the role each plays within the system. Make sure, for example, that students understand the functions of the different parts of the brain.

Energy Help students understand that the nerves function through changes in electrical charge along the cell membranes of neurons.

Chapter Motivating Activity

Ask each student to think of one activity in which he or she engages, such as swimming, painting, playing the piano, or sewing. Lead a brainstorming discussion on all the things the nervous system needs to control and coordinate for students to perform these activities. Help students understand the profound complexity of this system's functions. Encourage students to name not only the obvious movements of the activity *(For example, threading a needle)* but also everything else the system is keeping under control, including internal functions *(For example, heart rate, breathing)*.

Chapter 46 *Nervous System and Sense Organs*

Introduction

Human mental and physical capabilities are controlled by a highly evolved system of cellular communication called the nervous system, within which a carefully organized division of labor allows each part to operate effectively.

Chapter Outline

46.1 Structure
- *Organization*
- *Brain*
- *Spinal Cord*
- *Peripheral Nervous System*

46.2 Transmission of Nerve Impulses
- *Neuron Structure*
- *Nerve Impulses*
- *Transmission across Synapses*
- *Effects of Neurotransmitters*

46.3 The Senses
- *Receptors and Sense Organs*
- *Vision*
- *Hearing and Balance*
- *Taste and Smell*
- *Other Senses*

Chapter Concept

As you read, notice that the nervous system is composed of cells, tissues, and organs.

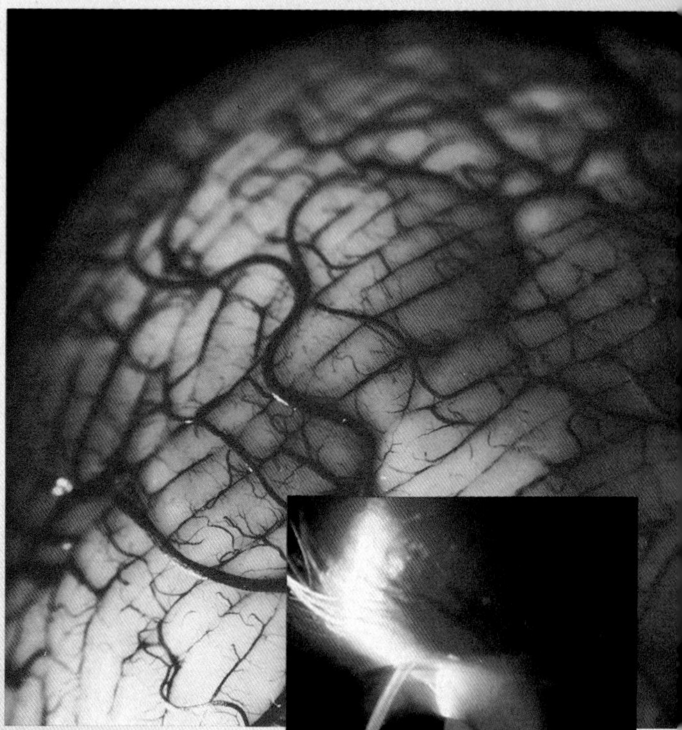
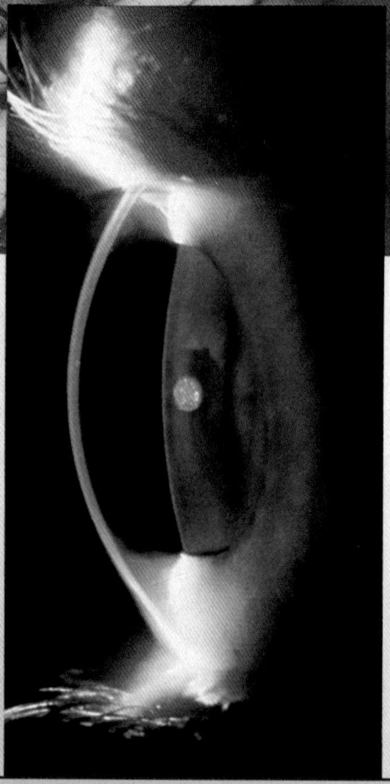

Blood vessels surrounding the human brain. Inset: Side view of a human eye.

Understanding the Visuals

As students look at the picture of the human brain, ask what the prominence of blood vessels implies about this organ. *(The brain is composed of living cells that must be supplied with oxygen and nutrients by the circulatory system.)* Point out that although the brain is usually considered the control center for the body, it depends on the circulatory system. Have students then turn their attention to the picture of the human eye, and ask them how the eye is related to the brain. *(It is a sense receptor that picks up stimuli from the environment and sends them to the brain where they are interpreted.)*

46.1 Structure

The human nervous system enables smooth, efficient communication among all parts of the body. Just as a computer network has interconnected terminals that generate and receive messages in a coordinated effort, so the human nervous system has component parts that process information efficiently.

Organization

The nervous system is composed of cells called **neurons.** Groups of related neurons are organized into **nerves.** Nerves are organized into two major subsystems—the central nervous system and the peripheral nervous system. The brain and the spinal cord make up the **central nervous system.** The spinal cord receives messages from other parts of the body and carries them to the brain, where they are integrated and interpreted. Responses are then transmitted back to the body. The **peripheral nervous system** consists of nerves that radiate out from the brain and spinal cord to the rest of the body. These nerves connect the central nervous system with all parts of the body. A mass of nerve cell bodies outside the central nervous system is called a **ganglion.**

There are three general categories of peripheral nerve cells: receptors, conductors, and effectors. **Receptors** are cells, or groups of cells, that receive information from both internal and external stimuli. **Conductors** are specialized nerve cells that transmit messages from receptors to the central nervous system. **Effectors** are the cells that receive messages from the central nervous system and carry them to an area of the body. Muscles are activated by effectors and contract in response to the signal of an effector. Glands are activated by effectors and secrete hormones in response to the signal of an effector.

Section Objectives

- *Identify the primary divisions of the nervous system.*
- *Describe the function of receptors, conductors, and effectors.*
- *Summarize the functions of the three regions of the brain.*
- *Explain how advances in imaging techniques have helped scientists learn more about the brain.*

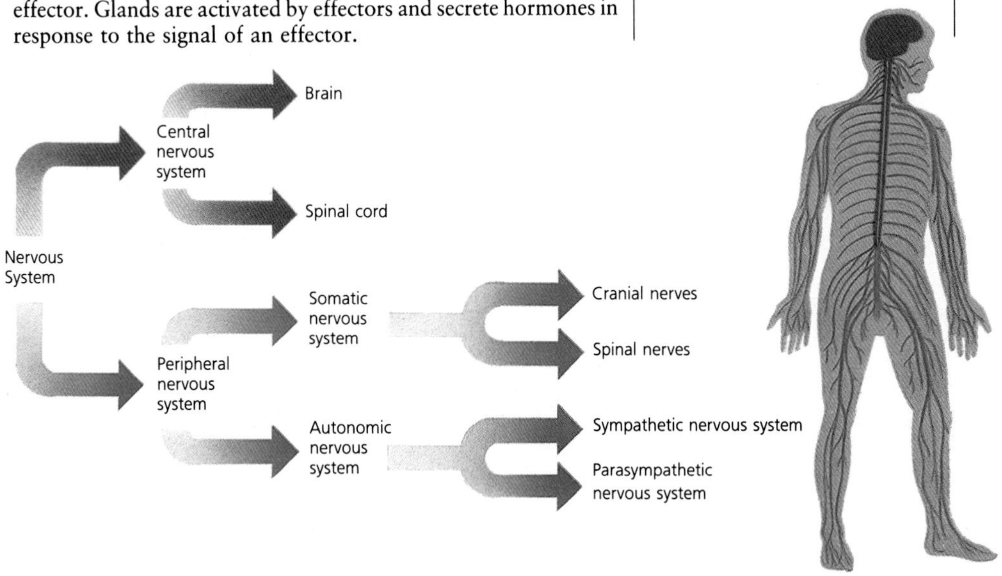

Figure 46-1 The nervous system consists of the central nervous system and the peripheral nervous system.

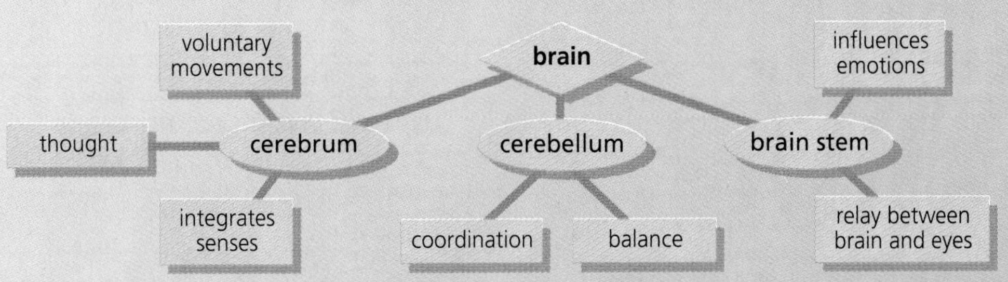

Graphic Organizer Use this organizational chart in Reteaching on p. 712.

Lesson Plan

Section Focus

This section describes the structure of the nervous system. Students will learn to distinguish between the central nervous system and the peripheral nervous system, which includes the somatic and the autonomic nervous systems.

Section Themes

The theme of **Scale and Structure** is evident throughout the section. The nervous system and its major organs are made of nerves, which in turn are groups of neurons. Certain areas of the brain control specific motor and sensory activities.

The theme of **Systems and Interactions** encompasses both the nervous system as a whole and its subsystems. The various parts of the nervous system interact and also communicate with the rest of the body.

Motivating Activity

Ask a student volunteer to sit on a desk or table so his or her legs hang freely. First, show the class the classic knee reflex by tapping just below the kneecap with the side of your hand or the spine of a thin book. Then a minute or so later, without warning, instruct the student to straighten the same leg. Have students note the time difference between the reflex action and the response to the command. Challenge students to explain this difference. *(The second action took longer because it involved thinking on the part of the student.)* Explain that although the two events involved the same result—raising the lower leg—each time it was accomplished through different pathways within the nervous system.

Teaching Strategies

Distinguishing Terms Ask students to name the three types of peripheral nerve cells. *(Receptors, conductors, and effectors)* Point out that many receptors are concentrated in the sense organs and that internal receptors also signal such information as hunger. Ask students to trace the path of an impulse through the receptors, conductors, and effectors. For example, ask students to fold their hands, then have one student describe the path of the impulse. *(Receptors in the ears receive the stimuli; the message is transmitted through conductors to the central nervous system and interpreted by the brain; instructions from the brain move through the central nervous system to the effectors, which activate the muscles to fold the hands.)*

Interpreting the Visuals Ask students what type of symmetry the human body has. *(Bilateral symmetry)* Have students look at the human diagram in Figure 46-1 on p. 707 and describe how the nervous system exhibits bilateral symmetry. *(The central nervous system occupies the center of the body, while the nerves of the peripheral nervous system branch bilaterally from the central nervous system.)*

Then walk students through the flow chart in Figure 46-1, asking a volunteer to describe the significance of each term. Make sure that students understand the reason for each fork in the chart. For example, ask why the peripheral nervous system forks. *(The somatic nervous system controls voluntary movement; the autonomic nervous system controls involuntary movement.)*

■ *See* **Overhead Transparency T46** *and* **Blackline Master 94.**

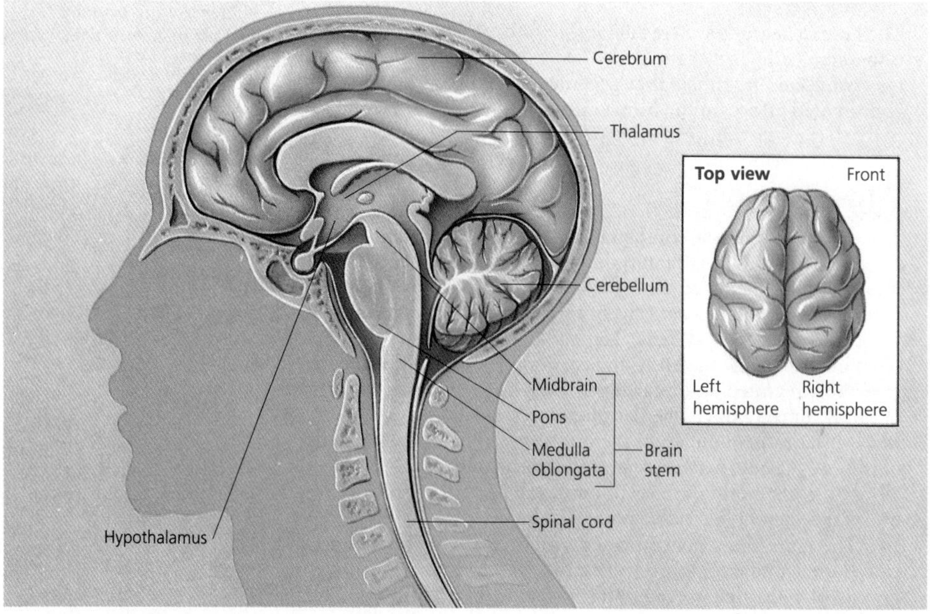

Figure 46-2 A side view of the brain shows its main parts. The top view shows the main sections of the brain, the left and right hemispheres.

Brain

The human **brain** weighs an average of 1.4 kg, or about 2 percent of the total body weight. Nevertheless, the brain contains approximately 100 billion neurons. The network of blood vessels that nourishes the neurons is so dense that 20 percent of the oxygen used by the body at rest is used in the brain. As Figure 46-2 shows, the brain consists of three regions: the cerebrum, the cerebellum, and the brain stem.

Cerebrum

The **cerebrum** *(suh-REE-brum)* is the largest portion of the brain. It is made up of two **cerebral hemispheres.** These are connected by nerves that form a structure called the **corpus callosum.** Deep grooves separate each hemisphere into four lobes: the frontal, parietal, temporal, and occipital lobes.

The highly folded outer layer of the cerebrum is called the **cerebral cortex.** The folds, or convolutions, maximize the surface area of the brain within the limits imposed by the cranium, or skull. Scientists estimate that the cerebral cortex contains nearly 75 percent of the body's total number of neuron cell bodies. The neuron cell bodies in the outer portion of the cerebral cortex are often referred to as gray matter. Beneath the cerebral cortex are large masses of white matter, bundles of nerves that connect the cortex with other parts of the nervous system.

More Information

Human Brain Often the medulla oblongata and the pons are grouped with the cerebellum as the *hindbrain.* The *midbrain* is a second primary division. The third primary division is the *forebrain,* which consists mainly of the cerebrum. Also part of the forebrain are the thalamus and the hypothalamus, which lie deep within the brain. The limbic system of humans and other mammals correlates with the forebrain of animals having more primitive brains, such as reptiles and birds. The development of the large cerebral cortex in humans accounts for the complexity of human thought.

Through experimentation scientists have determined that separate areas of the cerebral cortex control motor and sensory activities. Both hemispheres of the cerebrum control voluntary movement of skeletal muscles, and both intepret sensory stimulation. In general, impulses from and to the right half of the body are processed in the left half of the brain, and vice versa. Some evidence suggests that the right hemisphere controls both verbal and nonverbal artistic abilities and that the left hemisphere controls such skills as reading, writing, and the ability to analyze.

Cerebellum

Just below the occipital lobes of the cerebrum lies the **cerebellum** *(SER-uh-BELL-um)*, a region of the brain that plays a vital role in the coordination of muscle action. The cerebellum receives sensory impulses from muscles, tendons, joints, eyes, and ears. After receiving these impulses the cerebellum sends motor impulses down through the spinal cord to stimulate or inhibit skeletal muscles. The cerebellum also controls balance, an involuntary action, by communicating with sense receptors in the eyes and ears. It relays information regarding body position to appropriate muscles and controls posture by keeping skeletal muscles in a constant state of partial contraction.

Brain Stem

The third major region of the brain, the **brain stem,** connects the cerebrum with the spinal cord. The brain stem relays information to and from the cerebrum and thus plays a role in controlling body actions.

The brain stem has three main sections: the midbrain, the medulla oblongata, and the pons. The **midbrain** controls reflexes such as changing the size of the pupils.

The **medulla oblongata** *(muh-DULL-uh AHB-lawn-GAHT-uh)* is a group of neurons that serves as both a nerve relay station and a control center. Nerve fibers in the medulla oblongata cross over in such a way that impulses from the right side of the body are relayed to the left cerebral hemisphere, and vice versa. Also within the medulla oblongata are centers that control various homeostatic activities, including heart rate, breathing rate, and the flow of blood through the blood vessels.

The **pons** serves as a relay station between the nerves of the cerebrum and those of the cerebellum. It also relays messages between the midbrain and the medulla oblongata.

Two structures near the upper brain stem work with the central nervous system. The **thalamus** directs all incoming sensory impulses except those from smell receptors to the proper region of the cerebral cortex. The hypothalamus, located just below the thalamus, is connected by nerve fibers with the thalamus, cerebral cortex, and parts of the brain stem. The interaction of the hypothalamus and the pituitary gland of the endocrine system help maintain chemical homeostasis in the body.

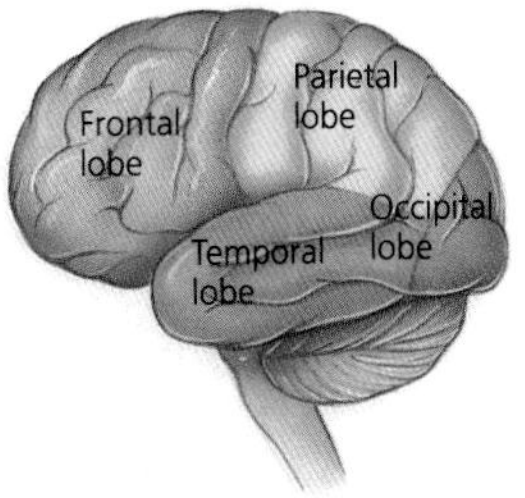

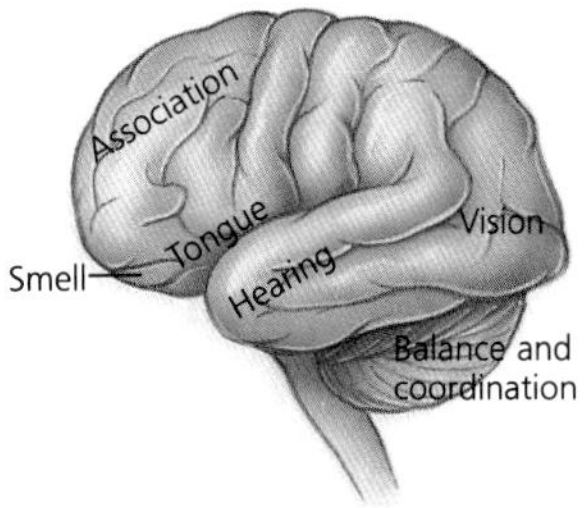

Figure 46-3 Each hemisphere of the brain has four lobes. Note that control of various functions is located in different areas of the brain.

Organizing Terms Write the terms *cell, tissue, organ,* and *organ system* on the board. Ask students to use these terms to organize the various components of the nervous system. *(Cell—neuron; tissue—nerve; organ—brain, spinal cord; organ system—nervous system, central and peripheral)*

Relating Concepts Display an anatomical model of a human brain and have students compare it with the illustration in Figure 46-2 on p. 708. Help students identify the cerebrum, cerebellum, and brain stem on the model. Then have students relate the different parts of the brain to their functions. For example, ask which part of the brain is responsible for controlling homeostasis. *(Medulla oblongata and hypothalamus of the brain stem)*

Drawing Conclusions Have students consider the following case. A man has a stroke that destroys a small part of his brain. The man is barely able to speak a word; yet he can sing the words of a song. Ask students what they conclude about the location of the stroke. *(The right hemisphere, which controls verbal artistic ability, apparently was not affected, since the man can still sing words. The stroke probably affected the language center in the left hemisphere.)*

Videodiscs
- *2664, Brain (s)*

LEP Activity
Pair LEP students with other students and have each group prepare a diagram of the brain. Also have each group make an accompanying chart or diagram to illustrate which parts of the body are controlled by a particular region of the brain—the cerebrum, the cerebellum, and the brain stem. Students should choose one body part and give a brief description of the brain's control over its function. For example, the cerebellum controls skeletal muscles by sending impulses to stimulate or inhibit them. Let students present their diagrams and charts to the class as a basis for a class discussion on the regions of the brain and their functions.

Section 46.1

Identifying Structures Review Chapter 42 by asking students what body cavities contain the central nervous system. *(Cranial cavity and spinal cavity, which together form the dorsal cavity)* What bones primarily form these cavities? *(The cranium and the vertebrae)* Point out that these bones protect the brain and spinal cord. Then ask what other structure protects these organs. *(The meninges)* Have students name its three layers. *(Dura mater, arachnoid layer, and pia mater)* How does cerebrospinal fluid further protect the brain and spinal cord? *(It provides a fluid cushion that protects these organs from shock.)*

Observing Structures Obtain from a butcher a cow or pig brain and a section of spinal cord. Display these organs for students to observe. Explain that the basic structures of these organs are quite similar to the human brain and spinal cord. Encourage students to identify the major regions of the brain and the structures of these regions and of the spinal cord. Section the brain longitudinally through the middle and have students compare it with Figure 46-2, p. 708.

Making Analogies Have students compare the structures of the nervous system to a computer. *(The brain is like a computer memory bank, central processing unit, and software; the nerves are like the circuits; the receptors are like the keys of the keyboard. In both the nervous system and computer, messages travel as impulses.)* Point out that an electrical signal is an analogy for a nerve impulse. Then ask what primary functions of the brain cannot be duplicated by a computer. *(Thinking, reasoning, feeling emotion, and intuiting)*

The thalamus, hypothalamus, and cells deep within the gray matter are connected by a group of neurons that are located near the corpus callosum. Together these make up the **limbic system,** a system that helps regulate the emotions. Research indicates that the limbic system detects changes in the physiological state of the individual and responds by producing feelings, such as fear or anxiety, that may ensure the person's safety.

A network of nerve fibers called the **reticular formation** runs through the brain stem and the thalamus. It acts as a filtering system for incoming sensory impulses. By controlling the numbers of impulses that are sent, the reticular formation enables a person to sleep through the noise of a radio or television but to be awakened by a knock at the door.

Protection

The brain and spinal cord are surrounded by three protective layers called the **meninges** *(muh-NIN-jeez)*. The outer layer, the **dura mater** *(DYOOR-uh MATE-ur)*, consists of connective tissues, blood vessels, and nerves. The dura mater lines the inside of the skull and also forms a tube that surrounds the spinal cord. The middle layer, the **arachnoid layer,** is elastic and weblike. The thin

Biotechnology

New Imaging Techniques

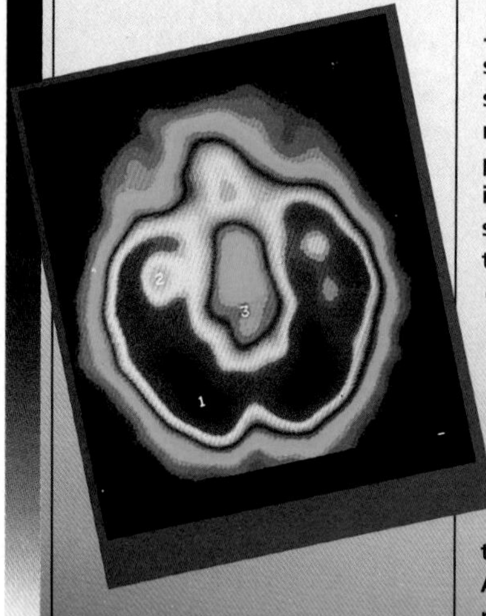

Physicians have always dreamed of being able to see inside the body without surgery. In 1895 the development of X-ray radiography gave physicians a method of capturing images of dense tissues, such as bones. Modern imaging techniques make use of a variety of technologies to achieve an inner view. For example computerized tomography (CT) uses a focused beam of low-dose X-rays to obtain cross-sectional images of structures within the body. CT is able to differentiate tissues of various densities. Another technology, magnetic resonance imaging (MRI), makes use of radio waves emitted by the nuclei of hydrogen atoms activated by a magnetic scanner to create images of soft tissues.

The newest imaging technology uses short-lived radioisotopes to reveal body processes at a cellular and molecular level (p. 710). In 1966 Michael M. Ter-Pogossian and his colleagues at Johns Hopkins Medical Institutions in Baltimore first proposed the use of short-lived radioisotopes in medical research.

In the 1970s Ter-Pogossian and others worked to develop scanners that could detect positrons, positively charged particles emitted when short-lived radioisotopes disintegrate.

More Information

Intelligence For years researchers have been trying to measure intelligence. In the 1800s scientists employed such methods as filling crania with buckshot and then trying to infer intelligence from volume. More recently, the preferred method has involved batteries of test questions. While such IQ tests have their advocates, criticism has focused on the question of whether intelligence is a quantifiable "thing." Critics point out that the measurements one gets from IQ tests are determined by the criteria one uses in setting them up, which suggests that IQ tests are subject to cultural bias. Furthermore, say critics, IQ tests can tell us nothing about a person's physical abilities, creativity, or responses to life.

inner layer, the **pia mater** *(PIE-uh MATE-ur),* contains many nerves and blood vessels. It adheres to the brain and spinal cord. A clear, watery substance called **cerebrospinal fluid** separates the arachnoid layer and the pia mater and provides a fluid cushion that protects the brain and spinal cord from shock. Parts of the skeletal system also protect the central nervous system. The cranium encloses the brain, and the vertebrae surround the spinal cord.

Spinal Cord

The **spinal cord** is a column of nerve tissue that starts in the medulla oblongata and runs down through the vertebral column. It contains an outer sheath of white matter and a rigid inner core of gray matter. Thirty-one pairs of spinal nerves originate in the spinal cord and branch out into both sides of the body. Each spinal nerve consists of a dorsal root and a ventral root. The dorsal root contains **sensory neurons,** nerve cells that carry impulses from receptors to the spinal cord. The ventral root contains **motor neurons,** nerve cells that carry impulses from the spinal cord to the effectors. **Association neurons,** also called interneurons, maintain neural connections within the spinal cord.

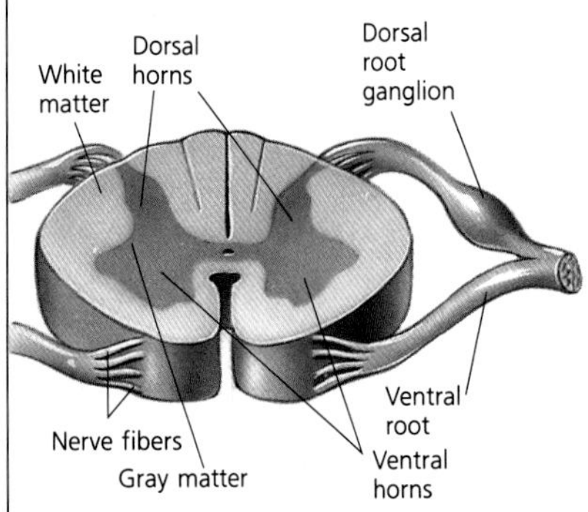

Figure 46-4 An H-shaped section of gray matter lies in the center of the spinal cord. Dorsal and ventral roots connect spinal nerves to the cord.

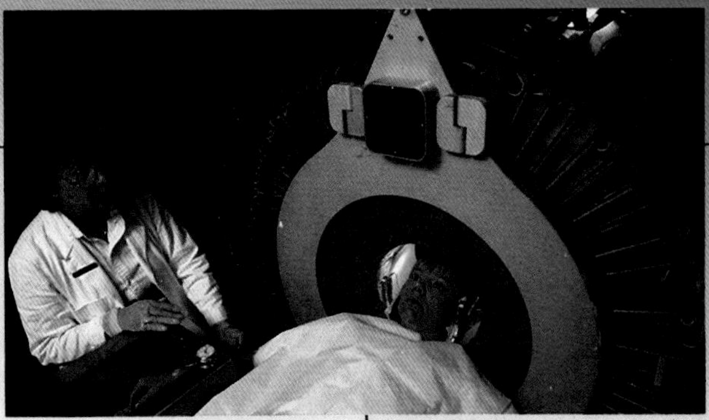

If chemical agents tagged with radioisotopes were injected into the bloodstream, the positron scanning equipment could be used to record the locations where the tagged agents were absorbed into the tissues.

During the 1980s rapid improvements in electronic and computer technology made it possible for biomedical engineers to redesign the scanning equipment. The new design allowed the creation of three-dimensional images from the positron emissions. Today this imaging technology is known as positron emission tomography, or PET.

PET is often used to evaluate brain metabolism (p. 711).

A radioisotope-labeled sugar, such as fluorodeoxyglucose (FDG), given by injection, is rapidly absorbed into areas of the brain that are metabolically active. The positrons emitted by the FDG are tracked by the scanner and translated by computer into bright images that appear on a monitor screen. These images are now being used to map areas of the brain involved in memory, sensation, perception, speech, and information processing.

Neurotransmitters can also be tagged with short-lived radioisotopes. PET scans of the brain uptake of neurotransmitters, such as dopamine and serotonin, are yielding new clues to the physiological and neurochemical basis of many medical and psychiatric disorders.

Interdisciplinary Activity

Government Despite the protective coverings around the brain, that organ can be easily damaged from a blow to the head. One common way in which the brain sustains injury is through motorcycle and bicycle accidents. Explain that the damage from such accidents is often so great that the treatment may last a lifetime and cost more than the injured person can pay. This is one reason many states have passed helmet laws for motorcycle riders. Have students investigate the arguments for and against these laws and write a paper taking a position on the issue, as well as on whether bicycle riders should be required to wear helmets.

Guided Practice

Write the term *nervous system* on the board. Have students name the two major subsystems of the nervous system, then the parts of the central nervous system and the peripheral nervous system. Continue in this way until the diagram in Figure 46-1, p. 707, is duplicated on the board.

Biotechnology

Using the Feature

Tell students that although positron emission tomography (PET) can be used to study many systems within the body, it has found a particular research niche in the study of the brain. In the past most brain chemistry studies were performed on preserved tissue with histological or radioautographic techniques.

PET has been used to investigate many diseases in the brain, including stroke, Alzheimer disease, Parkinson disease, Huntington disease, epilepsy, and many psychiatric disorders. PET is also being used to help us understand the biochemistry of addiction. Emphasize to students that these procedures are being used as tools for clinical diagnosis on living human beings.

Ask students to describe what they think are advantages of having computers to interpret data from imaging techniques such as CT, MRI, and PET. *(Because these methods all rely on information received as bits of data from scanning, the data must be interpreted mathematically before an image can be created. Computers can accomplish these kinds of data interpretation very quickly.)*

Answer to Think

Receptors in the foot detect the sharp object and relay the information to the spinal cord. There an impulse signals muscles to contract and pull the foot away. The impulse also travels to the brain and is comprehended.

Independent Practice

- Have students write answers to the Section Review.
- Have students make a concept map showing the relationships between the central and peripheral nervous systems. An example of a completed concept map appears on p. 705B.

Check Your Understanding

1. Why is the brain so extensively supplied with blood? *(The oxygen requirements of the brain are extremely high.)*
2. What might be the consequence of damage to the cerebellum? *(Loss of balance, the inability to coordinate muscles)*
3. Which part of the central nervous system is not involved in a reflex arc? *(The brain)*

Reteaching

Ask students to make an organizational chart showing the parts of the brain and the functions of each part. An example of a completed chart appears on p. 707.

- *See* Section Reviews *worksheet, Section 46.1.*

Enrichment

Have students investigate and write a report about aphasia or another affective disorder. An excellent source of information is Oliver Sacks's *The Man Who Mistook His Wife for a Hat* (Harper Collins, 1987).

Closure

Discuss with students how the involuntary blink reflex protects the eyes. Demonstrate this reflex by tossing a wad of paper at the eyes of a student standing behind a window.

Think

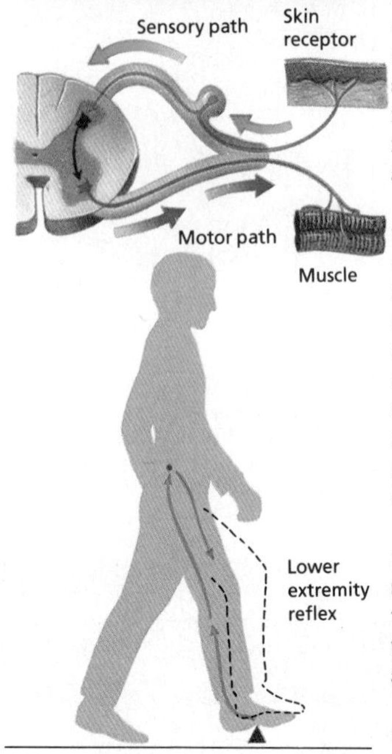

Use the picture above to describe a reflex action. Identify the stimuli, and explain how the nervous system will communicate information about the situation.

Peripheral Nervous System

Communication between the central nervous system and the rest of the body takes place via the branches of the peripheral nervous system. The basic organization of the peripheral nervous system is shown in Figure 46-1. In humans most of the 12 pairs of cranial nerves connect the brain with various parts of the head and upper neck. The 31 pairs of spinal nerves connect the spinal cord with all the remaining parts of the body.

One important function of the peripheral nervous system is the relaying of impulses in **reflex actions**—involuntary and usually self-protective movements. For example, if you touch a hot stove, it is to your distinct adaptive advantage to be able to draw away from the heat automatically without first having to think about the situation. The pathway of such impulses, called a **reflex arc,** involves a minimum of one sensory and one motor neuron. In a reflex arc the spinal cord is responsible for transmitting the response that pulls your hand away. Later, sensory impulses will reach your brain, and you will feel pain or irritation and become aware of what has happened.

The peripheral nervous system is divided into two subsystems—the somatic and the autonomic nervous systems. The **somatic nervous system** consists of nerves that control the voluntary movement of skeletal muscles. The **autonomic nervous system** consists of the nerves that control involuntary actions, such as respiration and heart rate.

The autonomic nervous system can be further divided into the sympathetic and parasympathetic nervous systems. The **sympathetic nervous system** controls the stimulation of internal organs during conditions of high stress or increased activity. The **parasympathetic nervous system** controls internal organs during routine conditions. When a stressful condition arises, the sympathetic nervous system may generate impulses that cause the heart rate and breathing rate to increase. When the situation returns to normal, the parasympathetic nerves signal the organs to revert to routine levels of activity. The alternating actions of these two systems help the body maintain homeostasis.

Section Review

1. Distinguish between *sensory, motor,* and *association neurons.*
2. Distinguish between the structure of the central and peripheral nervous system.
3. How are the brain and spinal cord protected from injury?
4. How do the functions of the cerebrum, cerebellum, and brain stem differ?
5. How might the various parts of the nervous system be related to the increased motor control and higher-level thinking abilities humans possess that less complex animals do not possess?

Answers to Section Review

1. Sensory neurons carry impulses from receptors to the spinal cord; motor neurons carry impulses from the spinal cord to the effectors; association neurons maintain connections inside the spinal cord.
2. The central nervous system consists of the brain and spinal cord; the peripheral nervous system consists of nerves that branch from the central nervous system.
3. By bone, meninges, and cerebrospinal fluid
4. Cerebrum—motor and sensory activities; cerebellum—motor responses and balance; brain stem—relays information to and from the cerebrum and helps control body actions.
5. They allow for more complexity and refinement in response to stimuli.

46.2 Transmission of Nerve Impulses

As you learned in Section 46.1, the structure of the human nervous system is extremely complex. The ability of the nervous system to monitor and respond to the environment depends on the transmission of impulses between cells. This intricate process is effected by the flow of electrochemical energy.

Section Objectives

- *Relate the structure of a neuron to its function.*
- *Summarize the electrical and chemical conditions of a neuron in the resting state.*
- *Describe a nerve impulse.*
- *Describe the role of neurotransmitters in the transmission of impulses across synapses.*

Neuron Structure

Neurons carry electrical signals, called **impulses,** throughout the nervous system. As shown in Figure 46-5, a neuron consists of a nucleated cell body and two kinds of threadlike extensions, dendrites and axons. Most neurons have many dendrites but only one axon. **Dendrites** are branched cell components that receive impulses from other neurons or receptors and carry the impulses to the cell body. The **axon** is an elongated extension that carries impulses away from the cell body. Notice in Figure 46-5 that the end of the axon is divided into fingerlike projections called axon terminals. An electrical impulse travels from the end of a dendrite, through the cell body, down the axon, and into the axon terminals. From there it travels by chemical messenger across the small space between two neurons, called a **synapse,** to the dendrite of another neuron, or to an effector.

In many neurons the axon is surrounded by a layer of cells called **Schwann cells.** These cells form a structure known as the **myelin sheath,** which insulates and protects the axon. The axon is exposed at gaps in the myelin sheath called **nodes of Ranvier** *(RAHN-vee-ay)*.

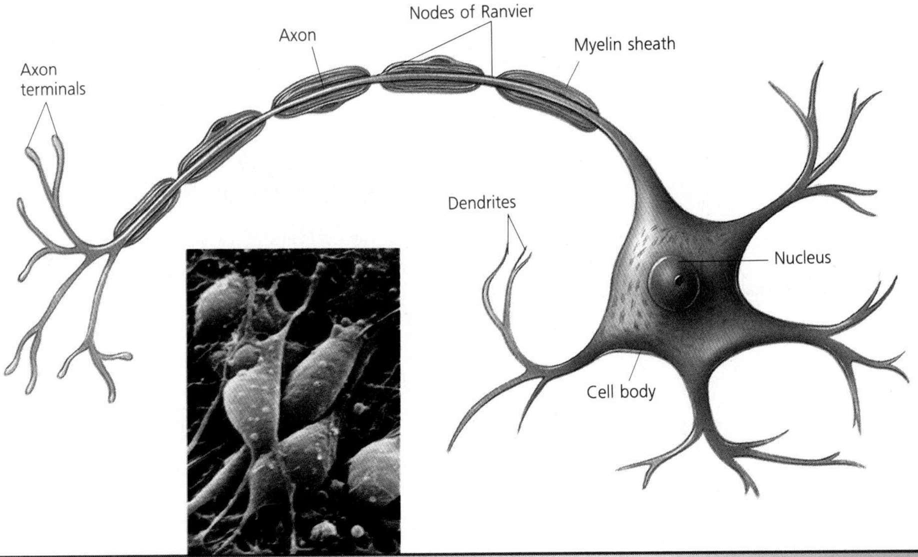

Figure 46-5 Many of the individual parts of a neuron shown in the illustration are visible in the SEM image of a neuron from a human cortex (×890).

resting neuron—Na^+ outside, K^+ inside → stimulated neuron membrane becomes permeable to Na^+ ion → depolarization occurs when Na^+ and K^+ change places → inner membrane surface more negative—creates action potential → action potential reaches synapse, neurotransmitters released

Graphic Organizer Use this sequential diagram in Guided Practice on p. 717.

Lesson Plan

Section Focus

This section describes and relates the structure of a neuron to its function. Students will learn how the activity of neurons depends on electrochemistry, selectively permeable membranes, neurotransmitters, and synapses.

Section Themes

The theme of **Scale and Structure** is evident in the description of a typical neuron, as well as its function in impulse transmission.

The theme of **Energy** is at the base of the description of nerve impulses. All communication throughout the nervous system is produced by the transfer of electrochemical energy.

Motivating Activity

Wire a small lamp to a 6V battery and demonstrate how the lamp lights when the circuit is closed. Ask where the energy to light the lamp comes from. *(From the battery)* Tell students that the potential energy in the battery arises from the separation of positively and negatively charged particles of the chemicals in the battery. Potential energy is also released in a nerve impulse through changes in the permeability of the cell membrane of a neuron to positively charged ions, Na^+ and K^+. Point out that the changes in permeability to the ions proceed along the length of a neuron's membrane in a wavelike fashion. Emphasize that the nerve impulse does not operate like the electrical current, which involves a steady flow of electrons within the circuit's metallic wires.

Videodiscs

- *2082–2085, Giant Multipolar Neurons (s)*
- *2657, Neurons (s)*

Teaching Strategies

Interpreting the Visuals Have students compare the drawing in Figure 46-5 on p. 713 with the inset SEM image. Ask what the bulblike structures in the SEM are. *(Neuron cell bodies)* What are the long extensions attached to these bodies? *(Axons)* Ask what the function of the axon is. *(Carries impulses away from the cell body)* Which structure receives impulses and carries them to the cell body? *(Dendrite)* Ask where a synapse would be if the illustration showed two neurons. *(A synapse is between an axon of one neuron and a dendrite of another.)* Finally, have students trace an impulse from one neuron to another. *(An impulse is received by a dendrite and conducted to the cell body; it travels through the cell body, down the axon, and into the axon terminals; then it crosses a synapse to the dendrite of another neuron.)*

Observing Structures Have students observe prepared slides of neurons. Ask that they look for cell bodies, axons, and dendrites. Have students draw and label what they see and compare their drawings with the neurons shown in Figure 46-5 on p. 713.

Applying Concepts Review with students terms in biochemistry and cell structure from earlier chapters, including *ion, cell membrane, sodium-potassium pump, active transport, diffusion,* and *permeability*. For example, ask what an ion is. *(An atom that carries a positive or negative electrical charge as a result of having gained or lost an electron)*

Nerve Impulses

A nerve impulse is actually a change in the electric charge along the cell membrane of a neuron. This change results because certain ions can move through channels in the membrane, carrying their charges with them. A nerve impulse usually begins at a receptor cell, moves from neuron to neuron, and may eventually cause a gland to secrete a hormone, or cause a muscle to contract.

The Resting State

A neuron that is not conducting an impulse is in a **resting state.** In the resting state the area inside the nerve cell membrane has a much higher concentration of positively charged potassium (K^+) ions and negatively charged organic ions than the fluid outside the neuron does. At the same time the concentration of positively charged sodium (Na^+) ions is much higher outside the cell than inside. These differences are maintained by the selectively permeable cell membrane, which is highly impermeable to Na^+ and organic ions but allows K^+ ions to diffuse freely through it. The movement of ions takes place through a channel in the cell membrane. As shown in Figure 46-6, the differences in ion concentration give the inside of the membrane a negative charge relative to the outside of the membrane. The difference in electric charge, called a potential, is about −70 millivolts (mV). A volt is a measure of the difference in electrical potential. During the resting state the neuron is said to be polarized.

As mentioned, the polarization of the neuron results from the uneven distribution of potassium and sodium ions on the two sides of the membrane. This distribution is achieved both by the selective permeability of the cell membrane and by a mechanism

Figure 46-6 The conduction of a nerve impulse involves a change in electrochemical potential across a nerve cell membrane.

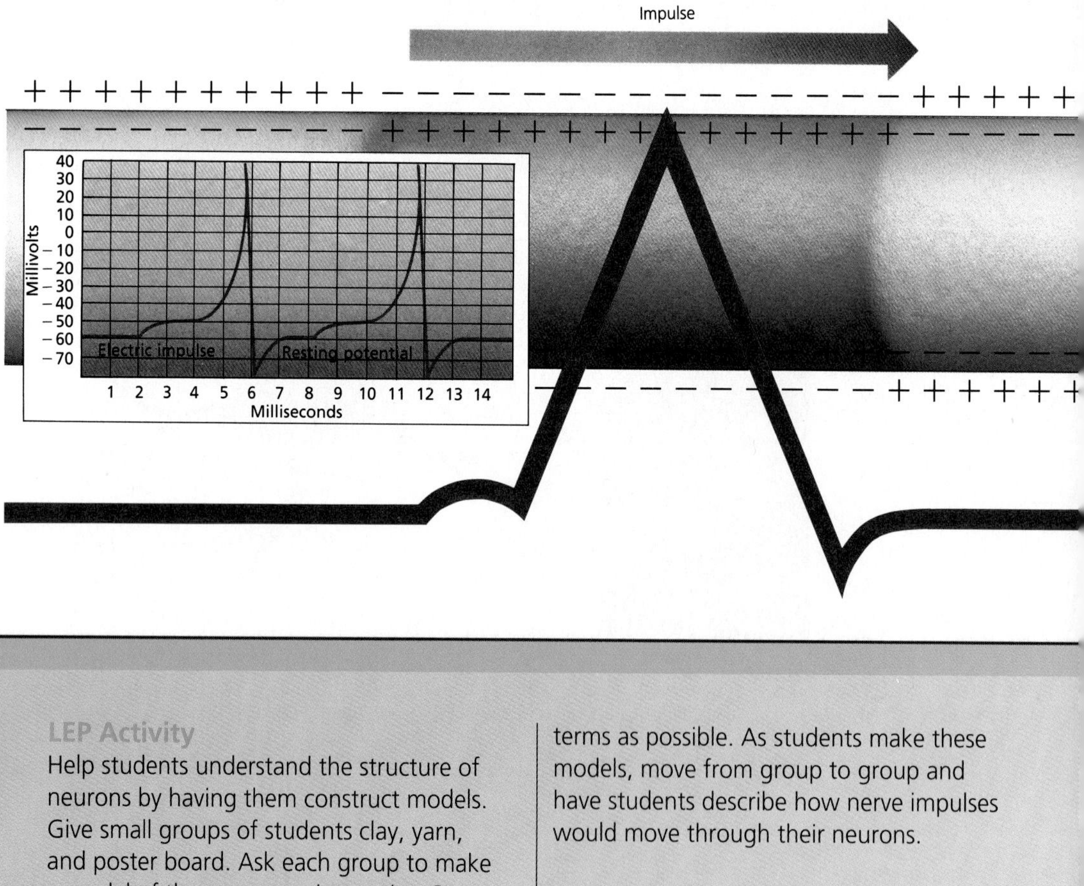

LEP Activity

Help students understand the structure of neurons by having them construct models. Give small groups of students clay, yarn, and poster board. Ask each group to make a model of three neurons in a series. Students can use Figure 46-5 on p. 713 as a basic model. Explain how neurons work together to conduct impulses. Instruct students to label their models with as many terms as possible. As students make these models, move from group to group and have students describe how nerve impulses would move through their neurons.

called the **sodium–potassium pump.** The sodium–potassium pump, described in Chapter 6, moves sodium ions to the outside of the membrane and potassium ions to the inside. The pump is an active transport mechanism powered by the chemical energy of ATP. It moves three sodium ions to the outside of the membrane for every two potassium ions it pumps to the inside. Because potassium can diffuse passively across the membrane, there are more potassium ions on the inside of the membrane than sodium ions on the outside. The result is a resting neuron that has an electrical potential across its membrane.

Impulse Conduction

When a neuron is stimulated, a sudden change occurs in the permeability of the membrane at the point of stimulation. The membrane becomes permeable to Na^+ ions, which then diffuse rapidly from the outside to the inside of the membrane. As a result the inner surface of the membrane becomes more positively charged than the outer surface. This process is called depolarization. When the membrane becomes depolarized, K^+ ions diffuse out of the cell. As the K^+ ions leave the cell, the inner surface of the membrane becomes more negative until the resting potential is reached. This process is called repolarization. A strong depolarization in a small portion of the membrane will disrupt adjacent parts of the membrane. Then, as shown in Figure 46-6, a wave of depolarization and repolarization, called an **action potential** or nerve impulse, will move along the membrane. A weak depolarization will not generate an action potential. Thus, neurons respond to stimulation in an all-or-none fashion.

The presence of a myelin sheath, a structure found primarily in vertebrates, speeds the conduction of an impulse. Exchange of

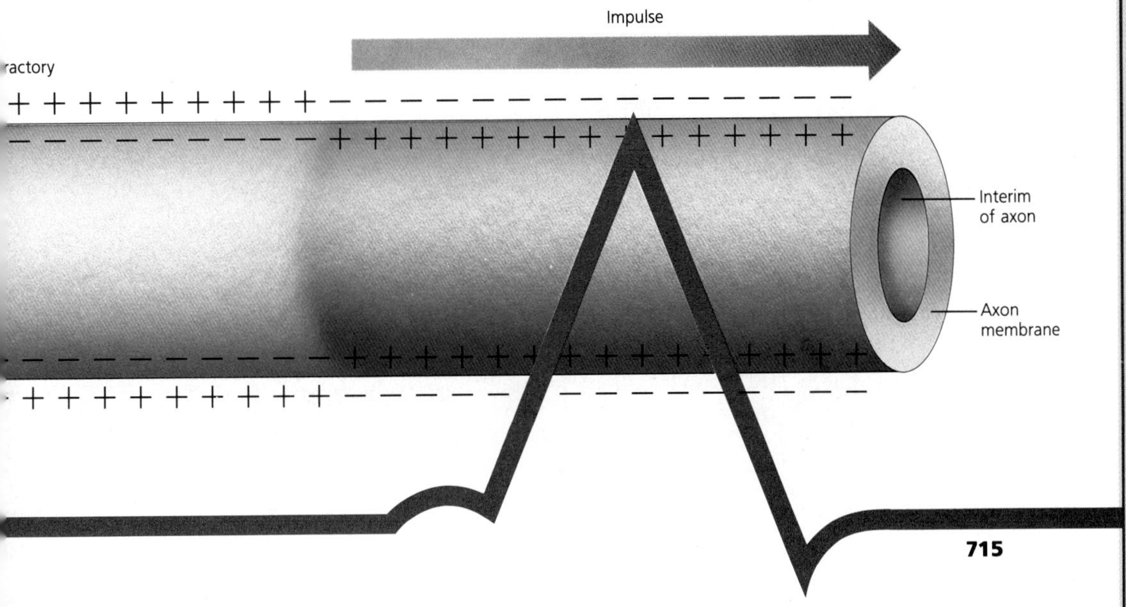

More Information

Nerve Impulses Unlike electricity moving along wires where electrons flow from one ion to another, a nerve impulse depends on ions themselves moving across cell membranes. The stage is set for an impulse by the active transport of the sodium-potassium pump. By transporting sodium ions to the outside, the pump creates an electrical potential. This is potential energy like that of a rock on the top of a hill—the rock fulfills its potential when given a push. The "push" for the sodium ions is the stimulation begun when the neurotransmitter reaches the postsynaptic membrane. The membrane becomes permeable for sodium ions, the ions move through the membrane, and the wave of depolarization moves through the cell.

Inferring Relationships Ask students to describe the distribution of Na^+ and K^+ ions when a neuron is in a resting state. *(There are more Na^+ ions on the outside of the membrane and more K^+ ions on the inside.)* What happens to Na^+ ions when the membrane becomes stimulated? *(Na^+ ions move inside the cell. The inner surface of cell membranes becomes more positively charged than the outer.)* Explain that K^+ ions then move through the membrane to the outside. Point out that the result is an ion distribution that is the opposite of the distribution in the resting state. Then ask what occurs during the refractory period. *(The neuron returns to the resting state.)* Finally, ask students what process accomplishes this reestablishment of polarity. *(The sodium-potassium pump, which moves Na^+ ions to the outside of the membrane and K^+ ions to the inside)*

Interpreting the Visuals Have students look at Figure 46-6 on pp. 714–715 and identify what the long, blue cylinder represents. *(A section of an axon)* Ask which way the impulse proceeds in this diagram. *(From left to right)* What situation is represented at the far left? *(The neuron is in a resting state)* What has occurred to the right of the resting state? *(The membrane has been stimulated, allowing positive Na^+ ions to move through the membrane.)* Ask students how many impulses are moving through this axon. *(Two)* Why is there a gap between the two impulses? *(During the refractory period between impulses, the neuron has returned to the resting state.)*

Videodiscs

- ***Side 2 20738, Neurons and Impulse Conduction (m)***

Interpreting the Visuals Ask students to look again at Figure 46-5 on p. 713 and find axon terminals on the labeled drawing. Then have students look at Figure 46-7 on p. 716 and find the axon terminal. Make sure that students understand that Figure 46-7 shows an enlarged detail of a neuron. Ask them what the bulging part of the axon terminal is called. *(Bouton)* Ask students to define the prefixes *pre-* and *post-*. *("Before" and "after," respectively)* Then ask them to define *presynaptic membrane* and *postsynaptic membrane*. *(The membrane before the synapse and the membrane after the synapse, respectively)* Finally, ask students to describe what the inset illustration shows. *(Neurotransmitters are released because of a nerve impulse from a bouton vesicle; the chemicals move across the synapse and bind with the receptors on a postsynaptic membrane.)*
■ *See* Blackline Master 95.

Drawing Conclusions Explain to students that nerve impulses, or action potentials, can move in any direction along a neuron membrane. Yet the "message" itself only goes in one direction, toward the central nervous system in sensory neurons and away from it in motor neurons. Encourage students to explain this directionality by asking what part of a neuron is able to release a neurotransmitter. *(Axon terminal)* What part of a neuron can receive the chemical message? *(A receptor on a dendrite)* What happens to the chemical once it has been received? *(It is destroyed or reabsorbed.)* Ask then how a synapse serves as a one-way valve for a nerve impulse. *(Neurotransmitters move in only one direction across a synapse.)*

ions cannot take place through the myelin sheath, so depolarization and repolarization occur only at the nodes of Ranvier. The action potential jumps from one node of Ranvier to the next, bypassing the sections of membrane beneath the Schwann cells.

The frequency at which impulses travel along the axon is limited in part by the **refractory period,** the time that follows the passage of a nerve impulse. During the refractory period the neuron is returning to its resting potential and cannot be stimulated. The period of time in which a neuron will not accept an impulse is about 0.0004 of a second.

Transmission Across Synapses

When a nerve impulse travels along the length of an axon, it eventually reaches the axon terminals. The axon terminals lie near an organ, a gland, or the dendrite of another neuron, but do not touch it. The small space between the axon and the next structure is called the synapse.

Impulses are carried across a synapse by chemical messengers called **neurotransmitters,** as shown in Figure 46-7. These chemicals are stored in synaptic vesicles embedded in a **bouton** *(boo-TAHN)*, a bulblike structure at the tip of an axon terminal. The bouton is enclosed by a presynaptic membrane, which lies almost adjacent to the postsynaptic membrane of, for example, the dendrite of another neuron.

When an impulse reaches the presynaptic membrane, Ca^{2+} ions diffuse into the cell. Ca^{2+} ions cause the membranes of the synaptic vesicles to fuse with the presynaptic membrane, thus releasing neurotransmitters into the synapse.

Neurotransmitters travel across the synapse and bind to receptor molecules in the postsynaptic membrane. The interaction of the neurotransmitter and the receptor changes the permeability of the postsynaptic membrane. If an action potential is generated, it travels down the receiving dendrite toward the cell

Figure 46-7 Neurotransmitters released into a synapse carry a nerve impulse to the next neuron.

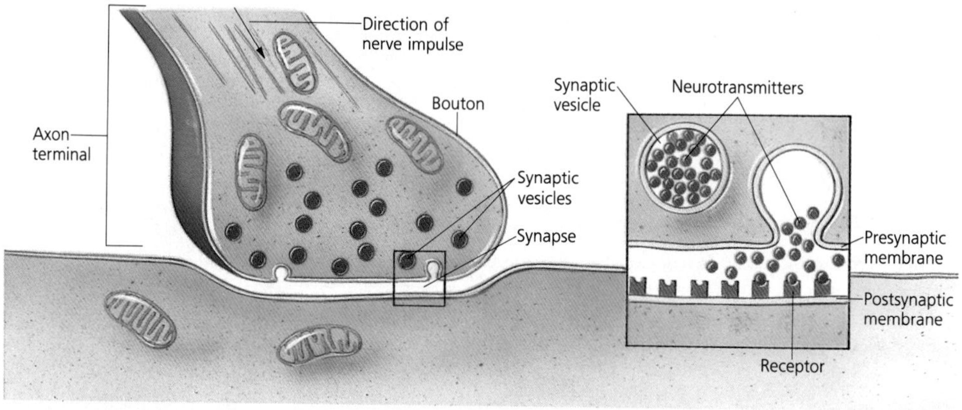

Cooperative Learning
Diseases of the Central Nervous System
Have pairs of students research a disease of the central nervous system, such as poliomyelitis, multiple sclerosis, cerebral palsy, Parkinson syndrome, meningitis, or encephalitis. Instruct students to develop a general description of the disease, and to investigate its cause, symptoms, and treatment. Allow partners to decide how to divide the research responsibilities and how to present their information to the class. Encourage students to prepare diagrams or other visual presentations.

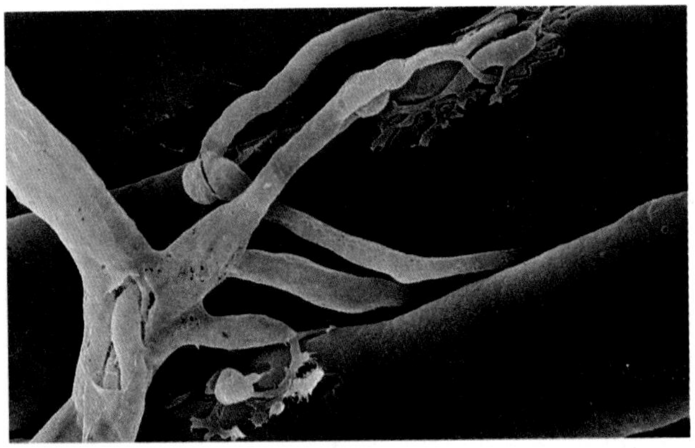

Figure 46-8 SEM of muscle fibers and the neurons that stimulate them (x3,000).

body. After transmission of an impulse, neurotransmitters in the synapse are destroyed by enzymes. It is important for the neurotransmitters to be destroyed so that they will not continue to stimulate the postsynaptic membrane.

Impulses are transmitted along neurons until they reach a muscle or a gland. An example is shown in Figure 46-8. In the muscle or gland the impulse causes the muscle to contract or the gland to release a hormone.

Effects of Neurotransmitters

The approximately 30 different neurotransmitters that have been identified by scientists cause one of two responses. Neurotransmitters either stimulate the action potential in a second cell, as you just learned, or they inhibit it.

Research findings on the effects of neurotransmitters have led investigators to a greater understanding of certain mental and physical disorders. Neurotransmitters have been used in the treatment of such nervous disorders as Parkinson disease. Biochemists have found that low levels of serotonin and norepinephrine, two neurotransmitters found in the brain, may be responsible for serious cases of depression. Doctors have successfully treated such imbalances with a substance that prevents the reabsorption of serotonin and norepinephrine.

Section Review

1. What is a *resting state?*
2. How do impulses travel along myelinated axons?
3. How are impulses transmitted between adjacent neurons?
4. Describe the two possible effects that neurotransmitters may have at a synapse.
5. How might research on the effects of neurotransmitters be useful in the treatment of mental disorders?

Answers to Section Review

1. A state in which a neuron is not conducting an impulse
2. Impulses travel along the membrane until they reach a node of Ranvier, where depolarization occurs and a new action potential is created that jumps across the gap of the myelin sheath.
3. Impulses are conducted across the synapse between neurons by the release of neurotransmitters.
4. Neurotransmitters can either stimulate or inhibit the action potential in a second cell.
5. Psychiatrists may be able to treat some mental disorders by regulating the neurotransmitters in the body.

Guided Practice

Help students make a sequential diagram showing the nerve impulse moving through a neuron. An example of a completed diagram is shown on p. 713. Begin by writing the first stage on the board. Then call on students to supply the subsequent stages.

Independent Practice

- Have students write answers to the Section Review.
- Ask students to describe impulse conduction from a neuron to a muscle or a gland. Make sure that students include the processes that occur at a synapse.

Check Your Understanding

1. What positive ions does the sodium-potassium pump move out of the cell? *(Sodium ions)*
2. What is an action potential? *(A nerve impulse that moves along a neural membrane)*

Reteaching

Have students construct a table listing the parts of a neuron and the functions of each. Tell students that tables should include dendrite, axon, nucleus, nodes of Ranvier, and myelin.

- *See* Section Reviews *worksheet, Section 46.2.*

Enrichment

Have students research and report on the structure and function of different types of cells in the nervous system, such as neuroglia, astrocytes, oligodendroglia, and microglia cells.

Closure

Set up the lamp and 6V battery that you used in the Motivating Activity. Ask students how a battery is different from a neuron. *(Answers will vary but should include the fact that neurons are part of a living system.)*

Lesson Plan

Section Focus

This section shows how the relationship between the sense organs and the central nervous system is important in an organism's adaptation to its environment. Students will learn about the five primary types of sense receptors and about the structures associated with vision, hearing, balance, taste, and smell.

Section Themes

The theme of **Scale and Structure** is evident in the description of the specialized structures in the sense organs. The structure of each sense organ helps it receive stimuli. For example, the structure of the eye aids in gathering light.

The theme of **Systems and Interactions** is inherent in the role of the sense organs. The senses provide the information to the nervous system that allows it to adapt the other systems to the environment. For example, mechanoreceptors in the semicircular canals of the inner ear send impulses to the brain that result in stimulation of skeletal muscles to maintain balance.

Motivating Activity

Have students close their eyes and press lightly on the eyelids until they see an effect. Ask what they see. *(Patterns of colors)* These patterns are called phosphenes. The nerves in the eyes send messages to the brain, which interprets these messages as colors. Point out to students that they are not really "seeing" anything. Then ask what this phenomenon tells them about the sense of sight. *(The eyes receive information, which they send via nerve impulses to the brain, which analyzes and interprets these impulses.)*

Section Objectives

- *Describe a sense receptor, and list the five primary types.*
- *Describe the roles of rods and cones in vision.*
- *Identify the parts of the ear responsible for hearing and for maintaining balance.*
- *Explain the chemical relationship between taste and smell.*

Figure 46-9 The bright red areas in this human brain scan indicate increased activity in those sections of the brain.

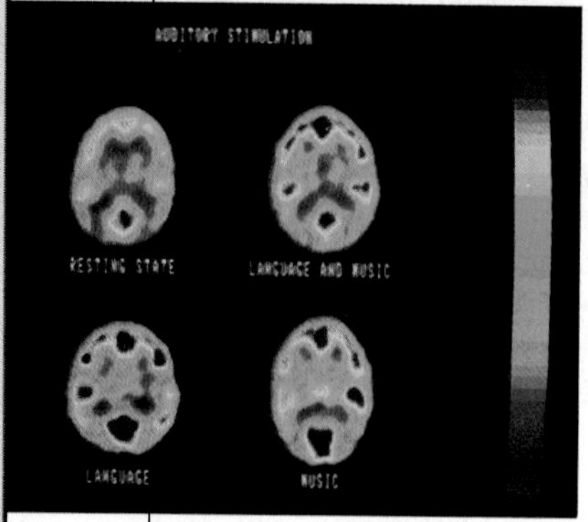

46.3 The Senses

The human environment is filled with both internal and external stimuli. Humans are able to distinguish among the many different types of stimuli by means of a highly developed system of nerves, specialized cells, and organs. The human nervous system is adapted to monitor and respond to a vast range of environmental phenomena.

Receptors and Sense Organs

Receptors are cells that receive information from the environment and then send impulses via conductors to the central nervous system. Receptors may be categorized on the basis of the types of stimuli they respond to:

- Mechanoreceptors detect movement, pressure, or tension.
- Photoreceptors detect variations in light.
- Chemoreceptors detect chemicals.
- Thermoreceptors respond to both internal and external heat and cold.
- Pain receptors respond to tissue damage.

The structure of the receptor cell enables it to interpret the type of energy being generated by a stimulus. The receptor cell then converts that energy into an electrical impulse that is transmitted through the nervous system and is finally interpreted by the brain.

Receptors are the neural components of the **sense organs,** the eyes, ears, nose, mouth, and skin. When a particular sense organ receives stimulation, the receptor converts the stimulus into an electrical impulse that is sent to a specific region of the brain. The impulses generated by the different sense organs are electrically similar, but the region of the brain to which they are directed will vary.

As you learned in Section 46.1, the brain has a specific region for each sense. Thus all impulses received by the auditory region of the temporal lobe are interpreted as sounds whether or not a sound wave was the original source of energy. For example, some people suffer from tinnitus, a sensation of noise such as a ringing or a roaring sound, caused by conditions such as a damaged tympanic membrane.

Vision

The eyes are specialized organs that function by receiving light and transmitting impulses to the visual cortex of the brain. All the structures of the eye act together to focus light on the **retina,** the light-sensitive inner layer of the eye. The **pupil,** an opening in the **iris,** controls the amount of light that enters the eye. The pupil

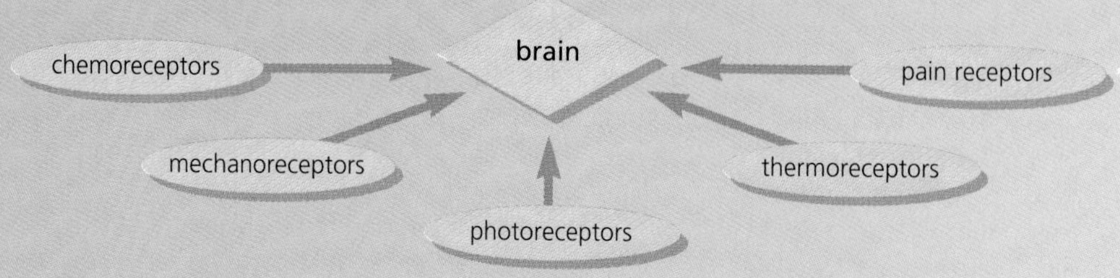

Graphic Organizer Use this diagram in Reteaching on p. 722.

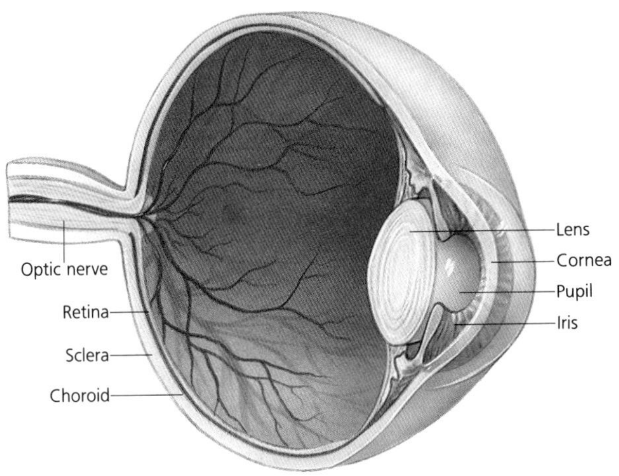

Figure 46-10 Light entering the eye travels through the pupil and lens to the retina, which activates impulses to the optic center of the brain.

becomes larger when light is dim and smaller when it is bright. These involuntary responses are controlled by muscles in the pigmented iris.

After light passes through the pupil, it travels to a convex crystalline structure called the **lens.** Attached to the lens are muscles that adjust its shape to bend the rays of the incoming light. This bending focuses onto the retina the complete image formed by the light.

Lying deep within the retina are rods and cones, photoreceptors that are essential in creating the vast array of visual images you perceive. There are nearly 125 million **rods** in a single retina. These are stimulated by weak light. Rods contain rhodopsin, which is a light-sensitive pigment that allows the rods to respond to weak light. Rods cannot respond to the strong light associated with color, which is why we cannot distinguish colors in dim light. The 7 million **cones** in the retina are stimulated by bright light. The cones initiate the production of sharp images and respond differently to different colors. Humans have three kinds of cones. Each type of cone contains a pigment that absorbs different wavelengths of light. When the impulses from these three kinds of cones are integrated, a person is able to see all the colors in the visible spectrum. Color blindness, which is the inability to distinguish certain colors, is caused by a chemical disorder in the cones.

Each photoreceptor responds to light from a single point in the image and then sends out an electrical signal. Impulses from all of the stimulated photoreceptors travel through nerves to ganglia on the surface of the retina. From the ganglia more than a million nerve fibers form the **optic nerve** and carry impulses to the occipital lobe of the cerebrum, where the impulses are interpreted as vision.

Figure 46-11 Rods and cones in the retina enable humans to see shades of gray and colors. The cells shown in this SEM are magnified 2,500 times.

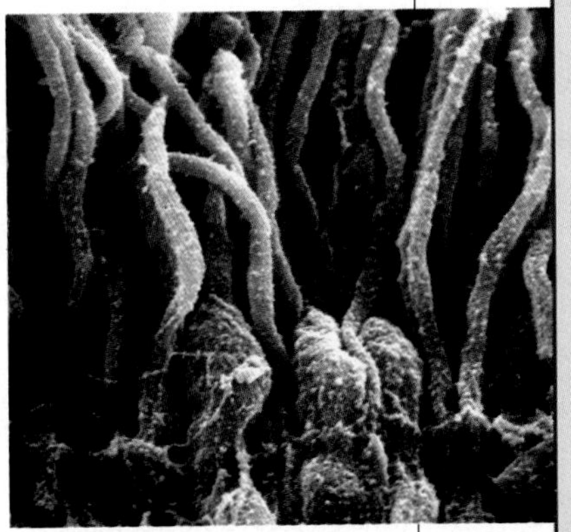

Teaching Strategies

Interpreting the Visuals As students look at Figure 46-10 on p. 719, explain that the cornea is a transparent structure that serves as a covering for the eye. Ask what happens to light after it passes through the cornea. *(It passes through the hole in the iris called the pupil and is focused by the lens onto the retina.)* What are the two kinds of photoreceptors in the retina? *(Rods and cones)* Point out that the veinlike structures shown on the retina are nerve ganglia. Ask what structure sends impulses to the brain from the retina. *(The optic nerve)* Finally, have students turn back to Figure 46-3, p. 709, and locate where in the brain vision is interpreted. *(In the occipital lobe of the cerebrum)*

Observing Structures Give each pair of students a hand lens. Then ask the partners to observe each other's eyes. Ask that they first observe in a well-lit area and then repeat these observations in a dimly lit area. Ask that the students make and label drawings of what they observe. Once all pairs have concluded their observations and drawings, discuss how levels of light affect the eye. *(The pupil narrows in bright light, widens in dim light.)*

Analyzing Properties Ask students to collect examples of optical illusions and to present the examples to the class. Discuss what factors in each example make it difficult for the brain to interpret what the eye sees. *(Wavy lines, color combinations, angles of intersection)*

Videodiscs

- ***2662, Human Eye (s)***
- ***2519–2520, Electromagnetic Spectrum (s)***

More Information

Receptors Receptors can be either specialized endings of sensory neurons or specialized cells associated with sensory neurons. Slight variations in the endings of cells account for their sensitivity to changes in the environment. Yet nothing differentiates the impulses that these receptors send to the brain. Difference results from the fact that, for example, impulses from the eye go to a different area of the brain than impulses from the skin. The brain is able to interpret intensity, of heat for example, because there are many receptors and they have different thresholds at which they are stimulated to produce an impulse. The hotter a stimulus, for example, the more receptors produce impulses.

Interpreting the Visuals As students look at Figure 46-12 on p. 720, have volunteers explain the function associated with each of the labeled parts. Emphasize the transfer of vibrations from the air through the structures of the ear. Ask what part of the ear funnels vibrations. *(External ear)* Where do the vibrations move from there? *(Through the auditory canal)* What happens when the vibrations reach the end of the auditory canal? *(They cause the eardrum to vibrate.)* Continue this process through the ear to the auditory nerve. Finally, have students turn back to Figure 46-3, p. 709, and identify the area of the brain that interprets impulses from the ear. *(An area in the temporal lobe of the cerebrum)* ■ **See Laboratories, *Investigation 46.***

Making Models Bring to class a stringed instrument, such as a guitar. Pluck one of the heavier strings and ask the students to observe the motion of the string. *(It vibrates.)* Then ask students to feel the top of the guitar. Ask what they feel. *(The wood vibrates.)* How does the string make the wood vibrate? *(The vibration of the string causes the air inside the instrument to vibrate, which makes the wood vibrate.)* Point out that students both saw and heard the string vibrate. What structures in the ear vibrated at the same time that the wood vibrated? *(The eardrum, hammer, anvil, stirrup, oval window, and fluid inside the cochlea)*

Exploring Careers Ask someone from a local hearing and speech center to talk to the class about hearing impairment. Ask the speaker to emphasize causes of hearing impairment and technology that can help the hearing impaired.

Hearing and Balance

The ear is specialized for two functions: detecting sound and maintaining balance. Sound, a form of energy consisting of air vibrations, is directed by the outer structures of the ear into the ear, where the vibrations stimulate mechanoreceptors.

Air enters the outer ear through the **auditory canal.** Vibrations in the air passing through the auditory canal cause the **tympanic** *(tim-PAN-ick)* **membrane,** or eardrum, to vibrate. These vibrations are transmitted to the three small bones of the middle ear: the hammer, the anvil, and the stirrup. The stirrup transfers the vibrations to a membrane, called the **oval window,** that separates the middle ear from the inner ear. Air pressure on both sides of the tympanic membrane can be regulated and balanced as air enters the middle ear through the **Eustachian** *(yoo-STAY-shun)* **tube.**

The inner ear contains the **cochlea** *(KOE-klee-uh),* a coiled tube filled with fluid and lined with hair cells. Vibrations of the oval window set up vibrations in the fluid of the cochlea. The movement of this fluid bends the hair cells, stimulating them to produce impulses that travel along the **auditory nerve** to the auditory region of the brain, where they are interpreted as sound. Different pitches stimulate hair cells in different parts of the cochlea. The intensity of a sound is determined by the number of cells stimulated: the more cells that are stimulated, the louder the sound.

Balance is maintained with the help of mechanoreceptors in the three **semicircular canals** of the inner ear. These canals are filled with fluid and lined with hair cells. When the head moves at a different speed or in a different direction, the movement of the fluid stimulates the hair cells. In between the cochlea and the semicircular canals, hair cells are embedded in a gelatinous matrix that has particles of calcium carbonate on its surface. These hair cells detect the direction of gravity. Neurons detect the signal and relay impulses to the cerebellum, where motion and position in space are interpreted.

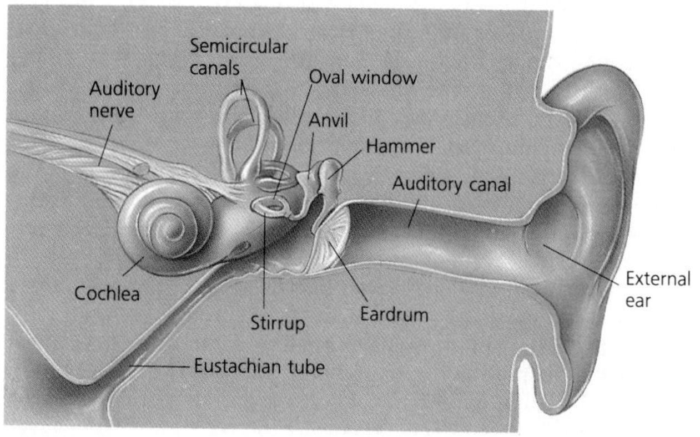

Figure 46-12 Air vibrations entering the ear are transformed into impulses that travel through the ear to the hearing center of the brain. Balance is maintained through the semicircular canals.

Interdisciplinary Activity

Social Studies Although not spoken, American Sign Language (ASL) is a means of communication as rich in nuance as any spoken language. Many deaf people consider ASL their primary means of communication. Tell students that one thing that makes ASL different from spoken languages is the degree to which the communicator's facial expressions and body movements are integral to the process of communication. Divide students into groups of three and provide each group with an ASL manual. Ask that each group translate a verse of a favorite song or a poem into sign and demonstrate the skill to the class.

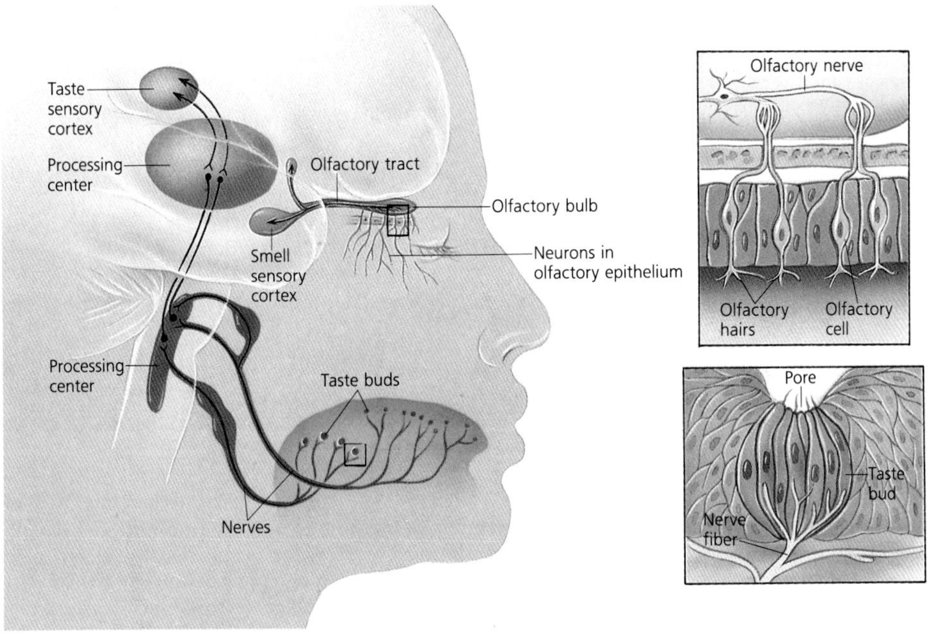

Figure 46-13 Special sensors in the mouth and nasal passages make taste and smell possible. Nerve impulses travel to the appropriate centers of the brain.

Taste and Smell

Specialized chemoreceptors allow humans to perceive variations in tastes and odors. The chemoreceptors for taste are clustered in the **taste buds.** Most of the 10,000 taste buds are embedded between bumps called **papillae** *(puh-PILL-ee)* on the tongue; additional taste buds are found on the roof of the mouth and in the throat.

Chemicals that dissolve in saliva stimulate different kinds of taste. This chemical–saliva mixture enters the taste bud through a small opening and stimulates the nerve endings that line the inner surface. The nerve endings begin an impulse that travels to the cerebrum, where it is interpreted as taste. Humans can taste only salty, sweet, sour, and bitter flavors or combinations of these flavors. Other flavors are perceived by receptors in the nasal passages.

Specialized chemoreceptors called olfactory receptors are located in the olfactory epithelium of the nasal passage, as shown in Figure 46-13. These cells, dendrites of sensory neurons, lie within the mucus lining of the epithelium. Specific olfactory receptors respond to different chemicals. Chemicals as gas or particles enter the nose and dissolve in watery mucus before stimulating the olfactory receptors. These receptors generate impulses that travel through the **olfactory nerve** to the olfactory region of the cerebral cortex, where they are interpreted as odors.

Inferring Relationships Give pairs of students a blindfold and some slices of raw potato and apple. Have one student put on the blindfold while the other directs him or her to the two foods. The blindfolded student should try to identify the foods by tasting, first with nostrils closed and then with nostrils open. Then have the pairs switch roles. When all students have tasted the foods, discuss the results and the importance of smell to taste. Most students will probably do better with nostrils open than closed.

- *See* **Process Skills,** ***Chapter 46.***

Interpreting the Visuals Refer students to Figure 46-13 on p. 721 and ask them to locate the structures on the larger diagram that are shown in detail in the smaller illustrations. *(The taste bud is on the tongue, and the olfactory receptors are in the nasal passage.)* Ask what type of receptor the taste buds and olfactory bulbs are. *(Chemoreceptors)* How do smells and tastes reach the brain? *(Via nerve impulses. Smells reach the brain via the olfactory nerve.)* Ask students to turn back to Figure 46-3 on p. 709, and identify where in the brain smell is interpreted. *(Frontal lobe of the cerebrum)* Explain that the taste center is deep in the cerebrum's parietal lobe.

Identifying Structures Have students review Figure 42-13 on p. 649, and identify the layer of the skin in which the receptors for the sense of touch are located. *(The dermis)* Which type of receptors are these? *(Mechanoreceptors)* Ask students to name the kinds of sensations these receptors sense. *(Touch, pressure, tension, movement, heat, cold, and pain)*

Videodiscs

- ***2663, Ear (s)***

LEP Activity

Help students understand the term *auditory* by exploring derivations and related words. Begin by asking what new terms have the root word *audi-* in them. *(Auditory canal and auditory nerve)* What common word in technology has the same root? *(Audio)* Explain that *audio* is Latin and means "I hear," and that the verb *audire* means "to hear." Ask students to explain what *auditory* means. *(Related to hearing)* What does *auditory nerve* mean? *(The nerve related to hearing)* Then ask students for other words with the same root. *(Audience, audiovisual, audible)* With this example in mind, ask students to explore the root of *visual. (Videre, "to see")*

Section 46.3

Guided Practice

Help students make a table of the sense organs showing the types of receptors found in each organ and the types of stimuli each organ responds to. *(For example, mechanoreceptors in the cochlea respond to vibrations.)*

Independent Practice

- Have students write answers to the Section Review.
- Bring a strong perfume or cologne to class and fan the odor toward the students. Ask students to write a description of how the odor becomes interpreted as a smell.

Check Your Understanding

1. Why would a punctured eardrum result in diminished hearing? *(It would not vibrate effectively.)*

2. Why can humans taste only four basic flavors? *(Because there are only four types of taste buds)*

Reteaching

Have students make a diagram to show how the brain receives internal and external stimuli from the human environment. Use the diagram shown on p. 718 as a model.

- ***See* Section Reviews *worksheet, Section 46.3.***

Enrichment

Have students do research in the library and make drawings showing where light focuses in the case of normal, nearsighted, and farsighted vision. *(On the retina, in front of the retina, and behind the retina, respectively)*

Closure

Ask students to discuss which sense they would give up if they had to give up one. Ask them to tell why.

Videodiscs

- ***2650, Human Skin (s)***

Figure 46-14 Hairs emerge from hair follicles through the dead layers of epithelial cells on the skin. Dendrites on mechanoreceptors at the base of a hair follicle, shown in this SEM, detect movement of the hair and set up nerve impulses (×265).

Other Senses

Mechanoreceptors located throughout the skin make it possible to sense touch, pressure, and tension. In humans, the receptors for touch are concentrated in the face and fingertips. Body hair also plays an important role in the ability to sense touch. Large numbers of mechanoreceptors are found at the base of the hair follicles. The dendrites of these mechanoreceptors detect movement of the hair and relay impulses to the central nervous system. When a stimulus is constant, many receptors stop sending impulses to the brain. For example, when you put on your watch or ring in the morning, you will be aware of its pressure. Soon, however, you "forget" that it's there. Only when the pressure changes in some way will the receptors start sending impulses again.

Two types of specialized thermoreceptors monitor temperature. Cold receptors are most sensitive to temperatures below 20°C. Heat receptors respond to temperatures above 25°C.

Pain receptors are the dendrites of the sensory neurons that are located in the base of the epidermis. Pain receptors are stimulated by mechanical, thermal, electrical, or chemical energy. The type and number of pain receptors vary throughout the body. For example, the hands have a high concentration of pain receptors.

Section Review

1. Distinguish between *chemoreceptors* and *mechanoreceptors.*
2. Explain the role of rods and cones in the perception of images by humans.
3. How are sound vibrations transmitted through the ear?
4. What mechanisms do the sense of taste and the sense of smell have in common?
5. What is the importance of the high concentration of pain receptors in the hands?

Answers to Section Review

1. Chemoreceptors detect chemicals; mechanoreceptors detect movement, pressure, and tension.

2. Rods enable a person to see objects as shades of gray in weak light; cones are stimulated by bright light and can help a person to distinguish colors.

3. Sound vibrations travel through the auditory canal and produce vibrations on the tympanic membrane; from there, the vibrations are transferred through the small bones in the middle ear to the cochlea in the inner ear.

4. Both have chemoreceptors.

5. Humans rely heavily on their hands to gain information and do tasks; the pain receptors serve to protect the hands.

Laboratory

Mapping Tongue Taste Receptors

Objective
To discover the location of various taste receptors on the human tongue

Process Skills
Collecting and interpreting data, hypothesizing, experimenting

Materials
6 paper cups, marking pencil, 5 bottles of prepared solutions labeled A through E, container of tap water, paper towels, 10 sterile cotton swabs

Background
1 Describe and explain the function of a taste receptor.
2 How is saliva important to the sense of taste?
3 What four basic flavors can humans taste?

Inquiry
1 Make a table to record your data. You must be able to record the solution tested, the tongue area tested, as well as the results of each test. Identify the solutions by the letters marked on the containers, and the tongue areas by the numbers shown in the drawing.
2 Use a marking pencil to label five paper cups A through E. Put the sixth cup aside. Fill each of the five labeled paper cups with liquid from the solution bottle having the corresponding letter. Put a container of tap water at your station and fill the unmarked cup with the tap water.
3 Rinse your mouth with the tap water. Blot your tongue with a clean paper towel.
4 Work with a partner. Your partner will put each of the five solutions on your tongue, and you will record your own reactions.

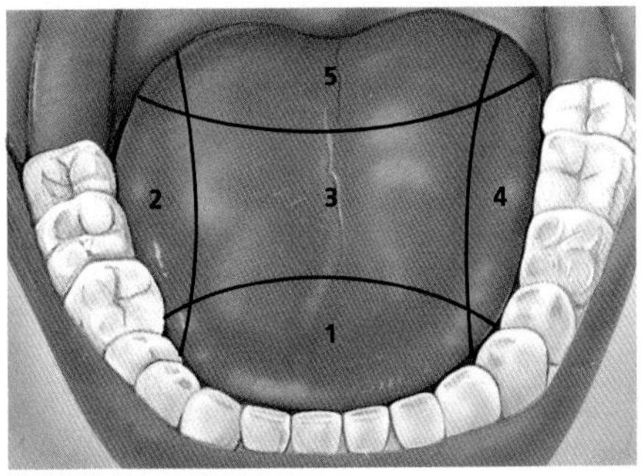

Have your partner dip a sterile cotton swab into solution A and apply the swab to each of the five tongue areas shown. Use a fresh swab for each solution. Why is it important to use a fresh swab each time? After each application, record in your data table the location and type of taste sensation that you experienced. Do not show your results to your partner.
5 Repeat steps 3 and 4 for each remaining solution. Be sure to rinse your mouth and blot your tongue before testing a new solution. Why are these steps important?
6 Trade places with your partner so that he or she can do the procedures listed in steps 3 through 5.
7 Share your information with the class.

Conclusions
1 Identify the tastes of the five liquids.
2 Based on the data that you entered in your table, what area or areas of the tongue are receptive to each taste?
3 Based on your observations, is there evidence that the taste areas overlap? Explain your answer.
4 What are possible sources of error in this experiment?

Further Inquiry
Devise an experiment that tests the relationship between taste and smell.

Laboratory

(For an overview of the sense organs and preparatory information related to the laboratory, see p. 705B.)

Background
1. A taste receptor is a chemoreceptor located in the taste buds. Chemicals dissolved in saliva enter the taste buds and stimulate the nerve endings there. The nerve endings send an impulse to the cerebrum where it is interpreted as taste.
2. The chemicals in a substance must be dissolved in saliva or other fluid before they can reach the taste receptors and be tasted.
3. Sour, sweet, bitter, and salty.

Inquiry
4. Using a clean swab ensures that only one solution is being tested at each test site. Reusing the same swab would mix the solutions so that a tongue area would be tested with more than one type of taste at the same time. Using a clean swab also prevents the spread of disease.
5. Rinsing cleanses the mouth of any residual solution. Drying the tongue prevents the solution from spreading to other test areas. Drying and blotting ensures that only one solution is being tested at a particular test site.

Conclusions
1. The tastes of the liquids in order A through E are salty, sweet, sour, bitter, and tasteless.
2. Salty and sweet are tasted in area 1 and along the front sides of the tongue. Sour is tasted only in areas 2 and 4. Bitter is tasted only in area 5.
3. Yes. There is overlap between salty and sweet and between salty and sour.
4. Forgetting to rinse between tests, touching the wrong area of the tongue, and tasting residual flavors from food, chewing gum or other substances

Further Inquiry
Have students devise an experiment similar to the one just performed, but let the solutions be administered while the nose is held closed.

Vocabulary

1. Central nervous system; other terms relate to the peripheral nervous system.
2. Effector; other terms relate to parts of a neuron.
3. Spinal cord; other terms are regions of the brain.
4. Polarization; other terms refer to the sequence of impulse transmission.
5. Retina; other terms are parts of the ear.

Review

1. d	**6.** c
2. a	**7.** d
3. c	**8.** c
4. c	**9.** d
5. b	**10.** b

11. The cerebrospinal fluid forms a fluid cushion to protect against shock.
12. Receptors respond to stimuli; conductors carry the impulse to the central nervous system; effectors receive impulses from the central nervous system.
13. The right hemisphere controls the left side of the body and is thought to control artistic abilities; the left hemisphere controls the right side of the body and is thought to control reading, writing, and analytical abilities.
14. The midbrain controls reflexes; the pons is primarily a relay station; the medulla oblongata relays impulses from the spinal cord and controls homeostatic activities.
15. The impulse either goes or does not; there is no gradation.
16. Positron emission tomography (PET), magnetic resonance imaging (MRI), and computed tomography (CT)
17. A sense receptor stimulates an impulse in a sensory neuron, which sends that impulse to the spinal cord and eventually to a specific region of the brain.
18. Movement of fluid inside the semicircular canals stimulates mechanoreceptors, which transmit messages to the brain about the position of the body.
19. Tastes are distinguished by different types of taste buds.
20. The movement of body hair stimulates mechanoreceptors at the base of hair follicles to send impulses to the brain.

Chapter 46 Review

Vocabulary

action potential (715)
arachnoid layer (710)
association neuron (711)
auditory canal (720)
auditory nerve (720)
autonomic nervous system (712)
axon (713)
bouton (716)
brain (708)
brain stem (709)
central nervous system (707)
cerebellum (709)
cerebral cortex (708)
cerebral hemisphere (708)
cerebrospinal fluid (711)
cerebrum (708)
cochlea (720)
conductor (707)
cone (719)
corpus callosum (708)
dendrite (713)
dura mater (710)
effector (707)
Eustachian tube (720)
ganglion (707)
impulse (713)
iris (718)
lens (719)
limbic system (710)
medulla oblongata (709)
meninges (710)
midbrain (709)
motor neuron (711)
myelin sheath (713)
nerve (707)
neuron (707)
neurotransmitter (716)
nodes of Ranvier (713)
olfactory nerve (721)
optic nerve (719)
oval window (720)
papilla (721)
parasympathetic nervous system (712)
peripheral nervous system (707)
pia mater (711)
pons (709)
pupil (718)
receptor (707)
reflex actions (712)
reflex arc (712)
refractory period (716)
resting state (714)
reticular formation (710)
retina (718)
rod (719)
Schwann cell (713)
semicircular canal (720)
sense organ (718)
sensory neuron (711)
sodium–potassium pump (715)
somatic nervous system (712)
spinal cord (711)
sympathetic nervous system (712)
synapse (713)
taste bud (721)
thalamus (709)
tympanic membrane (720)

In each set of terms below choose the term that does not belong, and explain why.

1. peripheral nervous system, somatic nervous system, central nervous system, parasympathetic nervous system
2. axon, effector, dendrite, node of Ranvier
3. cerebrum, spinal cord, brain stem, cerebellum
4. polarization, resting state, refractory period, action potential
5. retina, auditory nerve, semicircular canal, Eustachian tube

Review

1. The nervous system consists of (a) the brain and spinal cord (b) 31 pairs of spinal nerves (c) many cranial nerves (d) the central and peripheral nervous systems.
2. The cerebrum (a) controls thinking (b) coordinates muscle action (c) controls balance (d) maintains heart rate.
3. The spinal cord (a) only receives messages (b) only sends messages (c) relays messages to and from the brain (d) interprets messages.
4. In a reflex arc the impulse travels (a) immediately to the brain (b) to the spinal cord and the brain (c) to the spinal cord and out to an effector (d) directly to a sense organ.
5. During the resting state of a neuron (a) the outside is negatively charged (b) the inside is negatively charged (c) both sides are equally charged (d) the inside is positively charged.

6. The speed of an impulse is determined by (a) the length of the axon (b) the diameter of the axon (c) the presence of a myelin sheath (d) both *b* and *c*.
7. Neurotransmitters (a) carry impulses across the synapse (b) inhibit a second cell (c) stimulate a second cell (d) all of the above.
8. Receptor cells (a) carry impulses (b) generate responses (c) respond to stimuli (d) respond only to heat or cold.
9. Photoreceptors are stimulated by (a) air (b) pressure (c) chemicals (d) light.
10. Mechanoreceptors respond to (a) pain (b) pressure (c) temperature (d) all of the above.
11. How does cerebrospinal fluid protect the brain?
12. What is the relationship among receptors, conductors, and effectors?
13. How do the activities of the right cerebral hemisphere differ from the activities of the left cerebral hemisphere?
14. What are the roles of the three sections of the brain stem?
15. How does the term *all-or-none response* relate to impulse transmission?
16. What are two types of macroscopic imaging devices?
17. Describe the basic pathway from a sense receptor to the brain.
18. What is the role of the ear in maintaining balance?
19. How are different tastes distinguished?
20. Why is body hair important to the sense of touch?

Critical Thinking

1. Epilepsy affects one of every 200 Americans. Brain cells normally produce small bursts of impulses in varying patterns. In an epileptic person large numbers of brain cells occasionally send rapid bursts of impulses simultaneously. The individual then may jerk and convulse. From what you know about nerves, how might you explain these symptoms? How might you explain the cessation of the symptoms after a short period of time?
2. For some people too little potassium in the bloodstream is a serious medical problem. Symptoms of this condition include an increased heart rate and headaches. How might you explain these symptoms?

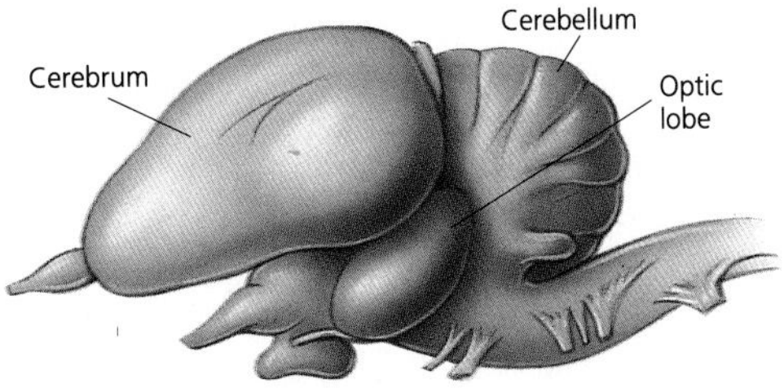

3. Look at the diagram above of the brain of a goose. Using what you know about the human brain, what would you assume the size of the portions of this brain indicate about their relative importance?

Extension

1. Read the article by Susan Katz Miller entitled "Picking Up Parkinson's Pieces" in *Discover,* May 1991, p. 22. Explain how the work of DeLong and his colleagues may lead to a new treatment for Parkinson's disease. Why do you think that monkeys were ideal for DeLong's research?
2. Research the way anesthetics work, and write a report in which you discuss the chemicals used, the effect of the chemicals on the brain, and the effect of body weight and the passage of time on the action of an anesthetic.

Critical Thinking

1. Some of the repeated rapid impulses from the brain reach the muscles and cause intense contractions. Since the impulses are so rapid, the supply of neurotransmitters at the synapses is quickly used up and the impulses cease.
2. Potassium is necessary for the nerves to conduct impulses. If the potassium level is low, the impulses are affected, and they in turn affect the functioning of the brain, muscles, heart, and other organs.
3. Answers will vary. The size of the cerebellum indicates that the movements of the goose are intricate. The relatively small size of the cerebrum indicates a lack of ability to think. The optic lobe of the goose is very large, indicating that eyesight is important.

Extension

1. Student answers should discuss how: the researchers found that halting the overactivity of the subthalamic nucleus could reverse the effects of the disease. Monkeys are genetically similar and can display the same symptoms of Parkinson disease as humans.
2. Encourage students to use library resources. Make sure that students differentiate between general and local anesthetics.

Chapter 47 Endocrine and Reproductive Systems

Chapter Overview

Chapter 47 describes the endocrine and reproductive systems and the interaction between them. Section 47.1 examines the major glands of the endocrine system, the hormones they secrete, and the functions of the hormones. Section 47.2 describes the male and female reproductive systems and the menstrual cycle. Section 47.3 discusses the process of fertilization and the development of the fertilized egg through birth.

Chapter Planning Chart

B	S	A	Sections and Subsections	Page	Features	Page	Resources
•	•	•	**47.1 Endocrine System**				
			Feedback Mechanisms	727	Laboratory	745	Videodiscs
			Endocrine Glands	728	Section Review	734	Blackline Master 96
			Hormones	733			Process Skills: Basal Metabolic Rate
							Section Reviews Worksheet
•	•	•	**47.2 Reproductive System**				
			Male Reproductive System	735	Section Review	738	Videodiscs
			Female Reproductive System	736			Blackline Master 97
			Menstrual Cycle	737			Overhead Transparency T47
							Section Reviews Worksheet
•	•	•	**47.3 Fertilization and Development**				
			Fertilization	739	Biotechnology	740	Videodiscs
			Cleavage and Implantation	740	Think	744	Laboratories: Embryonic Development
			Development	741	Section Review	744	Section Reviews Worksheet
			Birth	744			
			End of Chapter Activities				
					Chapter Review	746	Vocabulary Skills
							Chapter Test
							Computer Test Generator

B *The Basic Level curriculum presents the most fundamental knowledge offered in the course.*
S *The Standard Level curriculum is designed for the average student who is able to master most topics.*
A *The Advanced Level curriculum includes suggestions for teaching the most academically able students.*

Cooperative Learning

Group Activity: Hormonal Regulation of the Reproductive System

- **Group Size:** *4 students*
- **Outcome:** *Students will summarize the hormonal regulation of various reproductive processes.*
- **Individual Accountability:** *Each student will prepare a flow chart.*
- **Positive Interdependence:** *The group will compile their results in a table.*

Have each student in the group choose a different one of the following reproductive processes to research—the menstrual cycle, spermatogenesis, pregnancy, and the onset of puberty. Ask each student to find out the role of hormones in the event he or she chose: what hormones are involved, what their action is, and how they are regulated. Instruct each student to prepare a flow chart and then share his or her findings with the rest of the group. Have members work together to construct one table listing the hormones involved in reproductive processes and their functions.

Concept Map

The following is one possible solution to the concept mapping activity in Organizing Concepts on p. 731.

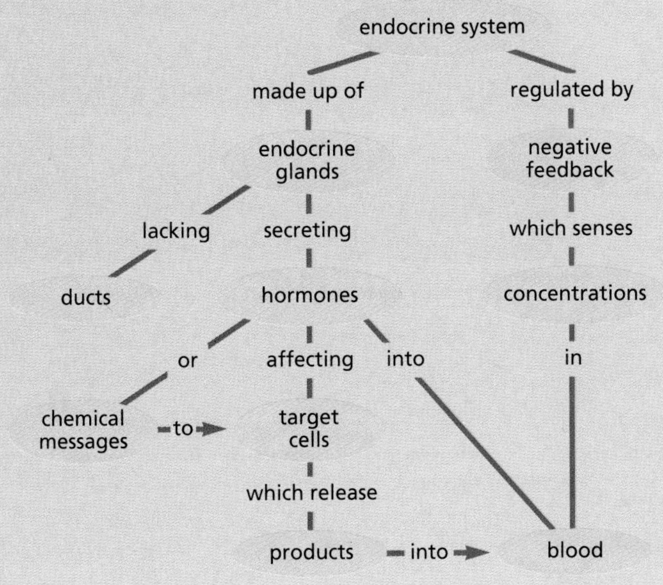

Laboratory Preparation

Overview *(See p. 745.)*

In this lab exercise, students will study the effects of thyroxine on frog metamorphosis. Thyroxine is a hormone that affects many facets of growth, including the transition from gills to lungs, the decrease in tail size, and the growth of limbs. Iodine is a part of the thyroxine molecule, and the presence of more or less iodine will influence the speed of the transformation from tadpole to adult frog. Thyroxine acts by increasing the metabolic rate, thereby increasing the rate of metamorphosis.

Preparation

Check with a biological supply house well in advance of the investigation, since developing tadpoles are not always available.

To prepare thyroxine solution, first dissolve 10 mg crystalline thyroxine in 5 mL of 1% sodium hydroxide solution (which can be prepared by dissolving 0.5 g of NaOH pellets in 50 mL water). Dilute the thyroxine concentrate solution by adding distilled water to make a total volume of 1 L. Keep the solution refrigerated.

If pond water is not available, set out open containers of water the night before the lab session.

The spinach should be canned baby food.

Teaching Tips

Have students read the Technique section carefully before they design their experiment.

This procedure works well when students are divided into groups of three.

Demonstrate to students how to pick up tadpoles with a net and measure them.

A variety of natural factors, in addition to measuring errors, may cause results to vary.

Safety

Remind students to handle tadpoles humanely. Tadpoles should be kept moist and protected from falling on the floor. Note that tadpoles and frogs cannot be released in many areas. See NABT Guidelines for the Use of Live Animals.

Chapter Themes

Systems and Interactions The endocrine system interacts with all other body systems through the action of hormones. Point out how the action of hormones regulates the male and female reproductive systems. Emphasize how most endocrine glands are regulated by negative feedback mechanisms.

Stability Emphasize that the primary role of the endocrine system is to maintain homeostasis. Review examples in which the endocrine system malfunctions and stability is upset.

Patterns of Change The menstrual cycle, embryo and fetal development, and the feedback mechanisms regulating hormone production all represent patterns of change. Emphasize the major phases or stages of each of these changes, making explicit the role of hormones.

Chapter Motivating Activity

Draw a dot on the board and tell students that they were once smaller than the dot. Then show students a series of photographs of a developing fetus (such as the classic series by Lennart Nilsson), and ask them to consider what regulates fetal development in the mother's body. Ask students to consider how the body regulates growth, response to stress, metabolic rate, and gamete production. Encourage students to record their ideas and check them after completing the chapter.

Chapter 47 Endocrine and Reproductive Systems

Introduction

The fetus emerges from the womb and with a gulp of air becomes a breathing human being. During the nine months prior to birth, a single cell grew and changed into an eight-pound baby. In this chapter you will learn how these changes took place. You will also learn how the endocrine system controls the changes that take place as the baby grows.

Chapter Outline

Chapter Concept

As you read, identify the ways that the endocrine system helps maintain homeostasis and ways that it regulates changes in the reproductive systems of males and females.

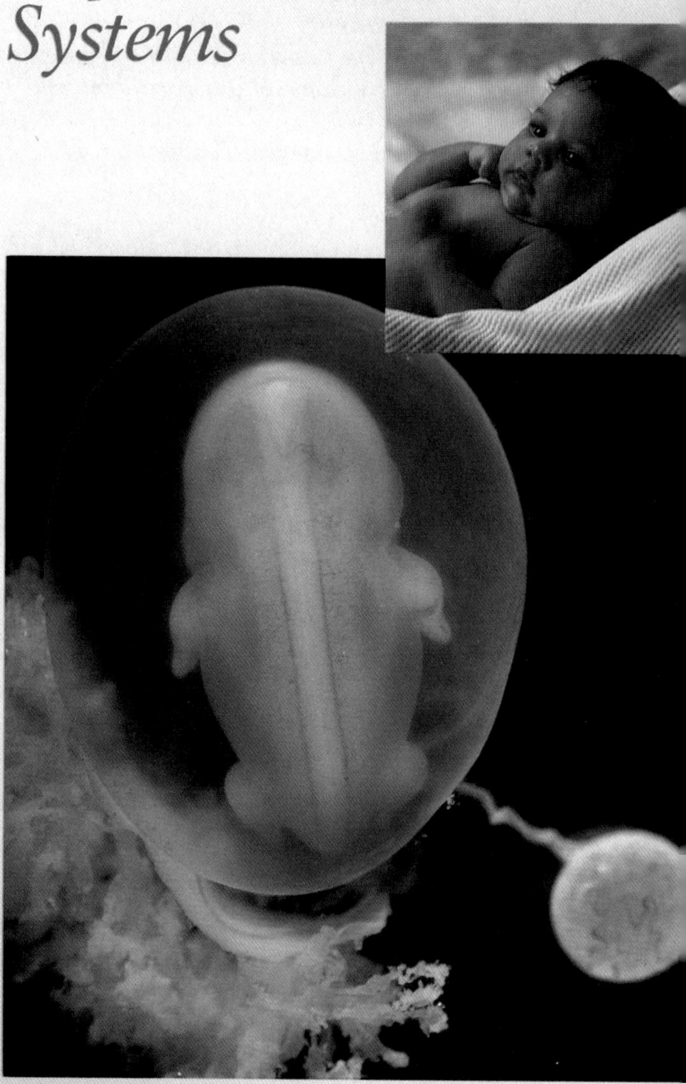

A human embryo at six weeks. Inset: A newborn baby.

Understanding the Visuals

Have students compare the newborn baby in the inset with the six-week-old embryo. Ask students to name body structures they can identify in the embryo. *(Head, arms, legs, spinal cord, blood vessels)* Point out that a six-week embryo is about 1 cm long and newborn infants average 53 cm in length. Ask students to infer the function of the membranes surrounding the embryo. *(They provide nourishment and protection.)* Now ask them what they think the stripe running down the back of the embryo is. *(The developing spinal column)*

47.1 Endocrine System

The endocrine system consists of glands that transmit chemical messages throughout the body. These chemical messages are called **hormones.** Hormones are substances that are produced in one part of the body and specifically influence the activity of cells in another part of the body. The glands secrete tiny amounts of these hormones into the blood. The blood then carries them to every part of the body. However, each hormone affects only specific cells, called **target cells,** that are supplied with receptors for that hormone.

Section Objectives

- *Describe a negative feedback mechanism.*
- *Explain the difference between an exocrine gland and an endocrine gland.*
- *List the major endocrine glands, and describe the function of each.*
- *Describe the chemical action of two types of hormones.*

Feedback Mechanisms

Most endocrine glands have a self-regulating system of checks and balances. This system depends on a **feedback mechanism.** This is a mechanism in which the end product of a series of steps controls the first step in the series. If the end product promotes the first step, the mechanism is called **positive feedback.** If the end product inhibits the first step, the mechanism is called **negative feedback.**

Most endocrine glands have negative feedback mechanisms. To understand how negative feedback works, think of the thermostat that controls the temperature in your home. When the temperature drops below a set level, the thermostat turns on the furnace. The furnace then produces heat, which warms the air. The end product—higher air temperature—is detected by the thermostat, which then turns off the furnace.

Sensing the amount of a product in the blood is the first step in an endocrine feedback mechanism. A gland is then stimulated to secrete a hormone that causes a change in the concentration of this product in the blood. Follow the example of a negative feedback mechanism in Figure 47-1. When the blood glucose level in the body goes up, cells in the pancreas are stimulated and produce insulin. This insulin causes muscles and the liver to absorb glucose and store it in the form of glycogen. The reduced glucose level in the blood causes the cells to stop secreting insulin. As you read about the various endocrine glands, look for examples of how a negative feedback mechanism helps maintain homeostasis in the body.

Figure 47-1 Cells in the pancreas are stimulated to secrete insulin as part of a negative feedback mechanism.

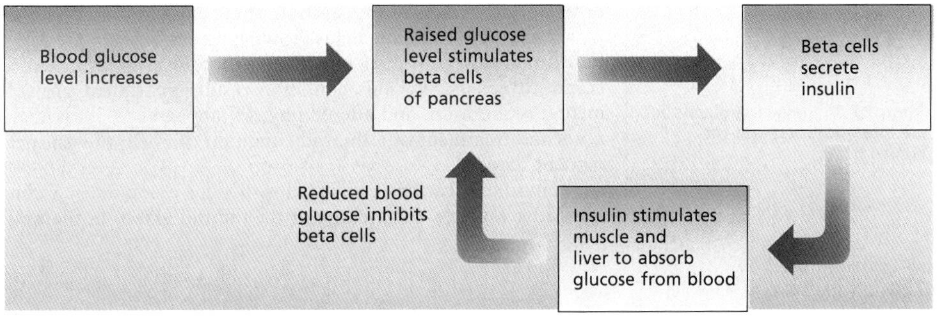

Lesson Plan

Section Focus

This section teaches the locations of the major endocrine glands and the functions of the hormones they secrete. It also describes how hormone production is regulated by feedback mechanisms.

Section Themes

The underlying theme in this section is **Stability.** The primary function of all hormones is to maintain the body's homeostasis. The theme of **Systems and Interactions** is also evident in this section. The interaction of hormones and other molecules in the body affects the activity of all cells.

Motivating Activity

Prior to this activity, have students check and record their pulse. In order to expose students to some mild form of stress, announce a pop quiz that tests their knowledge of the human endocrine system or of the electrochemistry of nerve impulses. Immediately after the quiz, have students again check and record their pulse rates and examine the pupils of each other's eyes to see if they are dilated. Then tell students that the quiz does not count. Later in the class period, have students again check and record their pulse rates and look at the pupils of their eyes. Ask students to account for any differences they observe in the three sets of data. *(In reaction to stress, their pulse rates should increase and their pupils should dilate.)*

Videodiscs

- *2532, Glucose (s)*

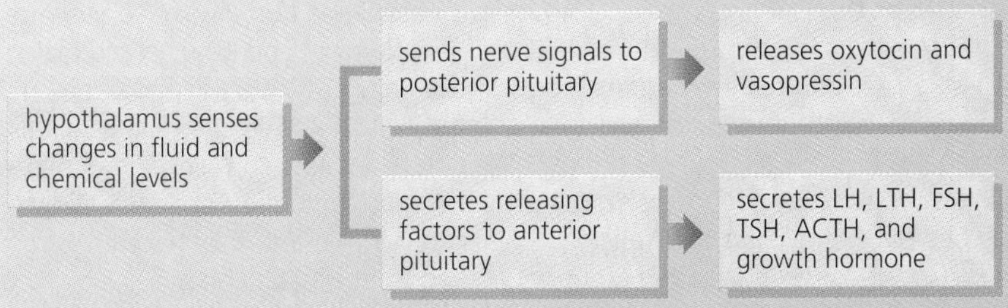

Graphic Organizer Use this sequential diagram in Independent Practice on p. 733.

Teaching Strategies

Applying Concepts Challenge students to speculate on how the body would be affected if insulin were controlled by a positive feedback mechanism. *(One possible answer is that glucose levels would be severely reduced in the bloodstream. Glucose stimulates the production of insulin. In a positive feedback system, the end product—reduced blood glucose—would promote the first step —more insulin secretion.)* Ask students whether this would be an effective method of regulating glucose levels in the bloodstream. *(No; it leaves too little glucose present in the bloodstream.)* Point out that the resulting condition is called hypoglycemia.

Drawing Conclusions Explain to students that thyroxine is produced when levels of thyroxine in the blood are low. Thyroxine production is inhibited when levels of thyroxine in the blood are high. Ask students to explain whether this is an example of positive or negative feedback. *(Negative feedback; thyroxine inhibits its own production.)* What happens if the feedback system does not work correctly? *(Too much or too little hormone is produced, which affects metabolic rate.)*

■ *See* **Process Skills** *Chapter 47.*

Making Generalizations Review the concept of homeostasis (Chapter 6). Ask students how feedback mechanisms help maintain homeostasis in the body. *(A change in the level of a hormone or other substance either stimulates or inhibits the production of a hormone that acts to bring the body chemicals back to equilibrium.)*

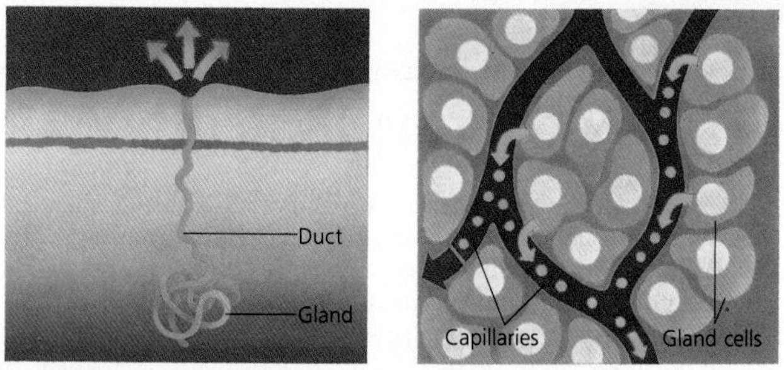

Figure 47-2 Exocrine glands (left) release their secretions through ducts while endocrine glands (right) secrete directly into the blood.

Endocrine Glands

The body has two types of glands. **Exocrine** *(ECK-suh-KRIN)* **glands,** such as sweat glands, are glands with ducts. **Endocrine** *(EN-duh-KRIN)* **glands** have no ducts and secrete directly into the blood. Figure 47-2 shows a comparison of these glands.

Endocrine glands are located throughout the body and include the thyroid, the parathyroids, the adrenals, the pineal, the gonads, and the thymus. In addition, specialized cells also function as endocrine glands. These include the hypothalamus in the brain, the islets of Langerhans in the pancreas, and the digestive glands of the stomach and small intestine. Look for these glands in Figure 47-3 as you read about the hormones they produce.

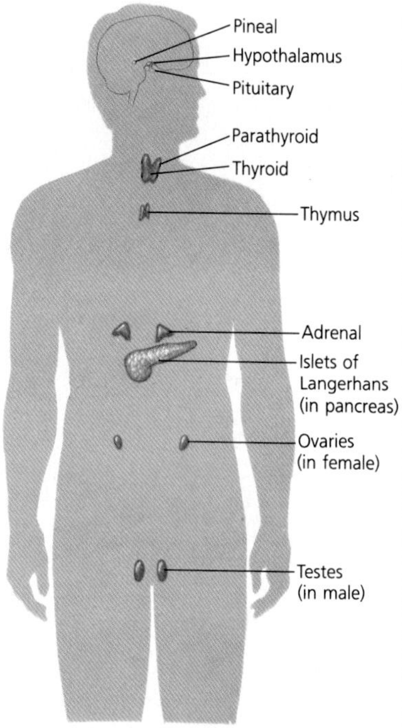

Figure 47-3 Endocrine glands are located throughout the human body.

Thyroid Gland

Notice in Figure 47-4 that the two-lobed **thyroid gland** lies in the neck near the lower part of the larynx. The thyroid gland secretes the hormone thyroxine. Thyroxine plays a vital role in regulating such activities as protein synthesis and ATP production.

If the thyroid gland becomes overactive and produces too much thyroxine, a condition called **hyperthyroidism** can result. People with this condition are physically overactive, their blood pressures are high, their hearts beat faster than normal, and their body temperatures are higher than normal. The secretion of too little thyroxine results in **hypothyroidism,** a condition in which the heart rate and other bodily functions are slower than normal. Victims of hypothyroidism tend to be overweight and often tire easily. Hypothyroidism and hyperthyroidism can be detected by measuring either basal metabolic rate (BMR) or blood thyroxine level. An underactive thyroid can be treated with supplementary thyroxine. An overactive thyroid can be treated with medication or by surgical removal of a section of the thyroid.

In infants, thyroxine helps growing tissues develop properly. If an infant suffers from an underactive thyroid, a condition called cretinism can occur. This condition results in stunted growth, mental retardation, and altered physical appearance. Early diagnosis and treatment of a thyroid condition can help prevent permanent damage.

Thyroxine contains iodine. Insufficient amounts of iodine can cause a goiter, or swelling of the thyroid gland. In the past,

More Information

History The history of science is full of accidental insights prompted by sharp, trained observation. For centuries physicians diagnosed diabetes mellitus by tasting patients' urine. It was known that sugar was excreted into the blood, but the exact mechanism was unknown. In 1889 Johann von Mehring and Oscar Minkowski, two German physicians, stumbled on part of the answer. Von Mehring and Minkowski were interested in the role of the pancreas in producing digestive enzymes, and, as part of their research, they surgically removed the pancreas of a dog. They noticed that the organ attracted an unusual number of ants as it lay on the counter. Alerted, they tested the dog's urine and found that it contained a high concentration of sugar. Subsequently, the dog developed symptoms like those of human

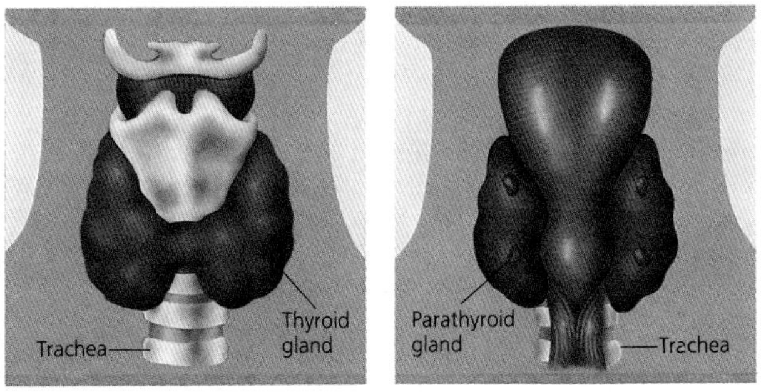

Figure 47-4 The thyroid gland (left) is located in the neck. A dorsal view of the same gland (right) reveals that four parathyroid glands are embedded in the back of the thyroid.

goiters frequently occurred in people living in areas where the soil contained low levels of iodine. Today, the occurrence of goiter is lower as a result of the addition of iodine to water supplies and table salt.

Parathyroid Glands

Four **parathyroid glands** are embedded in the back of the thyroid gland, two in each lobe. These glands secrete parathyroid hormone, which regulates the levels of calcium and phosphate ions in the blood. A proper balance of these two ions is essential for normal bone growth, muscle tone, and nerve activity.

The parathyroid glands regulate calcium and phosphate ion levels through a negative feedback mechanism. Refer back to the diagram of this kind of mechanism in Figure 47-1. When the calcium level in the blood drops, the parathyroids increase their production of parathyroid hormone. This hormone stimulates target cells in the bones to release calcium and phosphate ions into the blood. As the blood level of calcium and phosphate ions rises, the parathyroid glands decrease their hormone production. In this way, the levels of these important ions are kept in balance.

Adrenal Glands

Two **adrenal glands** are located one on top of each kidney. Each adrenal gland has an inner part, or medulla *(muh-DULL-uh)*, and an outer layer, or cortex. The medulla and cortex function as separate endocrine glands.

The medulla of the adrenal gland produces two hormones, adrenaline and noradrenaline, which play an active role in the body's reaction to stress. When a person is in a physically or emotionally stressful situation, the medulla secretes adrenaline and noradrenaline into the bloodstream. These hormones cause the bronchial tubes to enlarge, the pupils of the eyes to dilate, and the heart to beat faster. As the heart beats faster, blood pressure rises, and surface blood vessels constrict. At the same time, more blood is pumped to the muscles, brain, and heart. Intestinal processes slow down, and the liver releases stored sugar, which is oxidized for extra energy. These reactions help provide the additional energy needed during a stressful situation.

The cortex of the adrenal gland produces the hormone cortisol, which regulates certain phases of carbohydrate, fat, and

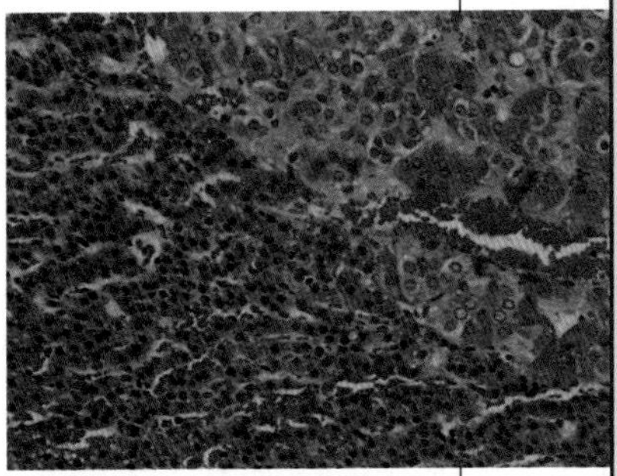

Figure 47-5 This light micrograph of an adrenal gland (×43) shows that the cells of the cortex and the cells of the medulla are morphologically distinct.

Distinguishing Terms Have students use a dictionary to find the meanings of the prefixes *endo-* and *exo-*. (*Endo-* means "internal" and *exo-* means "external.") Ask students to define *endocrine* and *exocrine* glands using the meanings of the prefixes. *(Endocrine glands internally secrete hormones directly into the bloodstream; exocrine glands secrete hormones externally through a duct into another body surface.)*

Interpreting the Visuals Use an anatomical model and Figure 47-3 on p. 728 to reinforce for students the locations of the endocrine glands in the human body. For example, ask students to name the organ of the endocrine system that is near the trachea. *(Thyroid gland)* What gland is attached to the thyroid gland? *(Parathyroid gland)* Ask students to give the location of the hypothalamus and name the endocrine gland that is near it. *(The hypothalamus is located at the base of the brain; the pituitary gland is nearby.)* Continue pointing out the location of each endocrine gland and the body structures nearby.

- *See* Blackline Master *96.*

Videodiscs

- *2653, Human Salivary Glands (s)*
- *2669–2670, Human Reproductive Systems (s)*

diabetes. Von Mehring and Minkowski repeated this surgery on other dogs: all developed the same symptoms. They then performed pancreatic surgery on other dogs, destroying the pancreatic duct without removing the pancreas. None of these dogs developed diabetes, which meant that diabetes was not correlated with the absence of digestive enzyme. By such experimentation, other researchers narrowed the focus of inquiry to the islets of Langerhans. However, it was not until 1921 that insulin was finally isolated through the work of a team of Canadian researchers and a treatment for diabetes could be established.

Inferring Relationships Ask students to study Figure 47-6 on p. 730 and identify the organ shown in the diagram on the left. *(The pituitary gland)* To what part of the brain is the pituitary connected? *(The hypothalamus)* Ask students to describe how the hypothalamus and pituitary are related. *(The hypothalamus secretes releasing factors through blood vessels connected to the anterior lobe of the pituitary; it also sends signals through nerves connected to the posterior lobe of the pituitary. The hypothalamus controls the hormone activity of the pituitary.)* Why is this relationship important to the body? *(The pituitary and hypothalamus form the main link between the endocrine and nervous systems.)*

Applying Concepts Many common phrases relate to the functions of certain endocrine glands. Give students the following sayings and ask them to name the endocrine gland responsible for inducing the behavior. "My heart is racing." *(Adrenal medulla)* "He's growing like a weed." *(Pituitary gland)* "I've got my second wind." *(Adrenal medulla)* "He has a deep voice." *(Gonads)* "She eats and eats and never puts on a pound."*(Thyroid)*

Making Inferences Give students the following scenario. A person undergoing a lie detector test has increased blood pressure, slightly dilated pupils, and an increased heart rate. Ask students to infer which hormones are probably involved in this response. *(Adrenaline and noradrenaline)* Then ask them to name the endocrine gland that produces these hormones. *(The medulla of the adrenal glands)*

protein metabolism. Another hormone, aldosterone, helps maintain the water and salt balance in the body by stimulating the reabsorption of sodium ions by the kidneys.

Gonads

Gonads are gamete-producing organs. The **ovaries** of the female, which produce eggs, and the **testes** of the male, which produce sperm, are gonads. Gonads also produce sex hormones. The ovaries secrete hormones called estrogens *(ESS-truh-jenz)* and progesterone *(proe-JESS-tuh-RONE)*. The testes secrete a group of hormones called **androgens,** the main one being testosterone. Sex hormones are responsible for changes during puberty that result in secondary sex characteristics. In males the voice deepens, the chest broadens, and more hair grows on the body and face. In females the breasts grow and the hips widen. Menstruation also begins. In Section 47.2 you will learn about the hormones and feedback mechanisms that regulate menstruation.

Pituitary Gland and Hypothalamus

The **pituitary gland** is located at the base of the brain. It secretes hormones that control body growth and regulate the activity of the other endocrine glands. The pituitary has an anterior lobe and a posterior lobe. As you can see in Figure 47-6, both lobes are adjacent to the **hypothalamus,** a part of the brain. Nerve cells in the hypothalamus extend into the posterior lobe of the pituitary. The anterior lobe is connected with the hypothalamus by blood vessels. The pituitary and hypothalamus form the main link between the endocrine system and the nervous system.

The hypothalamus secretes hormones called releasing factors into the anterior lobe via the blood vessels. There are six releasing

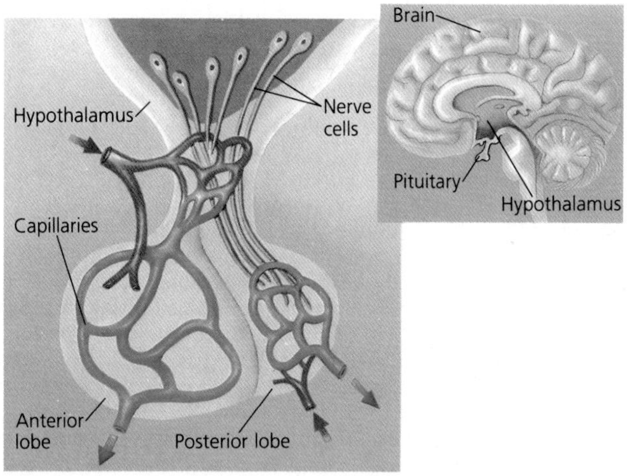

Figure 47-6 The hypothalamus communicates with the pituitary gland by means of both nerve cells and capillaries. The inset shows the location of the pituitary in relation to the brain.

LEP Activity

Have each student prepare a diagram of the human body, showing the location of one of the major endocrine glands. Students can use Figure 47-3 on p. 728 as a guide. In their diagrams, have students label the hormones secreted by the endocrine gland and identify the location of the target tissues. Encourage students to write the names of the endocrine glands and hormones phonetically. Ask students to exchange diagrams and practice pronouncing the names of the endocrine glands and hormones.

factors. Each factor controls the release and therefore the level of one hormone produced in the anterior lobe of the pituitary gland.

One of these hormones is growth hormone, which controls the growth of the body's skeletal and muscular systems. Another is prolactin, which stimulates milk production following the birth of a child. The other four hormones regulate the secretions of other endocrine glands. Refer to Table 47-1 to learn the functions of these hormones.

Table 47-1
Hormones Released by Glands of the Endocrine System

Gland	Hormone	Function of Hormone
Thyroid	Thyroxine	Alter basal metabolic rate
Parathyroids	Parathyroid hormone	Maintain Ca and P levels
Adrenal:		
▪ **Cortex**	Corticoids	Maintain salt-water balance
▪ **Medulla**	Adrenaline, noradrenaline	Initiate responses to stress
Pituitary:		
▪ **Anterior lobe**	Growth hormone	Regulate growth
	LH	Regulate development of sex organs and hormones, control ovulation
	LTH	Control growth of mammary glands, control milk production, maintain corpus luteum
	FSH	Control gamete production
	ACTH	Stimulate adrenal cortex
	TSH	Stimulate production of thyroxine
▪ **Posterior lobe**	Oxytocin	Regulate blood pressure, stimulate smooth muscle contraction, initiate uterine contractions during childbirth, regulate milk production
	Vasopressin	Control reabsorption by kidneys
Islets of Langerhans	Glucagon, insulin	Maintain blood glucose levels
Ovaries	Estrogens	Produce female secondary sex characteristics, affect mature female body functions
	Progesterone	Maintain growth of uterine lining
Testes	Androgens (testosterone)	Produce male secondary sex characteristics
Thymus	Thymosins	Bolster children's immune systems
Digestive glands	Gastrin	Stimulate acid production
	Secretin	Influences digestive activity
Pineal gland	Melatonin	Influences biological cycles

Making Predictions Refer students to Table 47-1 and ask them to predict the outcome if the feedback mechanism failed for each hormone listed. For example, ask students to predict what might happen if the adrenal medulla secreted too much adrenaline. *(The body would be in a constant state of response to stress.)* What would happen to the body if too little growth hormone were secreted? *(The body would not grow to its full potential.)* What would happen if the stomach produced too much hydrochloric acid? *(Stomach ulcers; chronic heartburn)*

Organizing Concepts Divide students into groups of three. Instruct each group to draw a concept map showing how hormones enter the bloodstream and how negative feedback is triggered. Encourage students to write the elements of the concept map on pieces of paper and discuss and rearrange them until they are satisfied that the map accurately reflects the biological process. Have students share their concept maps with those of other groups. An example of a completed concept map is shown on p. 725B.

Videodiscs

▪ ***2664, Brain (s)***

Interdisciplinary Activity

Technology Scientists are able to synthesize many human hormones using recombinant DNA techniques. For example, human insulin and human growth hormone are now produced in this manner. Ask students to choose one of these hormones or another synthetic hormone and find out how it is produced and how it is used for the treatment of hormonal disorders. Encourage students to describe the risks and benefits of using synthetic hormones and ask them to give their opinions about such use.

Making Models Instruct students to use various materials, such as construction paper, pipe cleaners, modeling clay, yarn, and colored markers, to model the interaction of a protein hormone or a lipid hormone and its target cell. Students may use Figure 47-8 on p. 733 or Figure 47-9 on p. 734 as a guide. Ask them to explain why protein hormones cannot enter the target cell like lipid hormones. *(Because of their chemical composition, proteins are unable to simply "dissolve" through the lipid bilayer making up the cell wall.)*

Applying Concepts Review the role of messenger RNA in protein synthesis (Chapter 8, p. 118). Then ask students to describe how lipid hormones initiate protein synthesis in the target cell. *(A lipid hormone binds to a receptor molecule in the cytoplasm, then enters the nucleus and binds to a specific site on the DNA molecule, initiating the production of mRNA. The mRNA moves into the cytoplasm and protein synthesis occurs.)* Finally, ask students to infer the function of the protein produced. *(The protein will initiate a change associated with the action of the hormone.)*

Discussing the Issues Invite an athletic coach from a local university or a physician from a sports medical facility to talk to students about steroid abuse in athletics. The discussion should include information on how steroids affect the body and why scientists warn against their use as a means to enhance athletic ability.

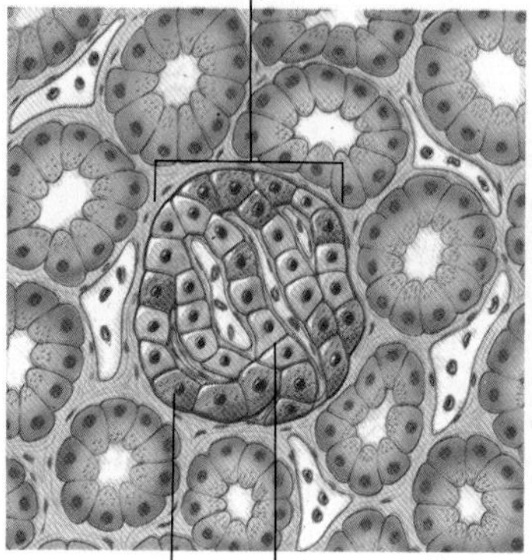

Figure 47-7 The islets of Langerhans play a crucial role in the regulation of blood glucose. The mechanism also involves other hormonal systems.

Cells in the hypothalamus synthesize two hormones—vasopressin and oxytocin—that are released from groups of cells that extend into the posterior pituitary gland. The posterior pituitary gland releases vasopressin when its cell bodies in the hypothalamus detect a low concentration of water in the blood. The increased concentration of vasopressin causes tubules in the kidney to release more water into the blood. As a result, the concentration of water in the blood rises. When hypothalamic cells detect this change, cells in the posterior pituitary no longer release vasopressin. Oxytocin causes the muscles of the uterus to contract during childbirth.

Thymus

The thymus is located under the breastbone, between the lungs. In children the thymus is large, but it diminishes in size as a child grows older. The thymus produces hormones called thymosins that stimulate the development of infection-fighting antibodies and bolster the child's immune system.

Islets of Langerhans

The pancreas primarily is an exocrine gland that produces digestive enzymes and secretes them into the small intestine via ducts. However, special cells in the pancreas called the **islets of Langerhans** function as endocrine glands. These cells, pictured in Figure 47-7, secrete two hormones, insulin and glucagon.

Insulin is a hormone that lowers the blood sugar level by stimulating cells to absorb glucose and by causing the liver and muscles to convert glucose to glycogen. In contrast, glucagon raises the blood sugar level by stimulating the breakdown of glycogen into glucose. In a healthy person the balance between insulin and glucagon maintains normal carbohydrate metabolism.

Without sufficient insulin too much glucose remains in the blood. This condition is called **diabetes mellitus** *(MELL-uh-tuss)*. In the United States more than one million people have one of the two forms of diabetes. Type 1, juvenile-onset diabetes, occurs when cells in the islets of Langerhans secrete little or no insulin. Regular injections of insulin help regulate the imbalance of glucose in the blood. Type 2, maturity-onset diabetes, is milder than Type 1. Persons with Type 2 diabetes may have normal levels of insulin in the blood but cannot use it, probably because their cells have a low number of receptors for insulin molecules. Case studies have revealed that heredity and obesity are contributing factors to occurrence of Type 2 diabetes, which can be treated by a carefully controlled diet. If diabetes is not treated, the victim will starve since his or her cells will not be able to absorb glucose.

Another disorder, called **hypoglycemia,** is the presence of too little glucose in the blood. Excess insulin causes the liver to store sugar that should be delivered to cells and results in an imbalance of blood glucose levels. This imbalance can cause a person to feel tired and dizzy at one time and then nervous and active at another.

More Information

Pineal Gland The pineal gland secretes the hormone melatonin. The production of this hormone increases at night and decreases markedly in the daytime. Interestingly, exposure to light at night interrupts its production. Sparrows that have been injected with melatonin roost in the daytime and their body temperatures drop. Because of such evidence, researchers hypothesize that the pineal gland may control biological cycles by some as-yet-undiscovered mechanism. Moreover, melatonin has been found to inhibit the development of gonads in birds as well as in some mammals. During spring, as the days grow longer, the production of melatonin drops. Thus, the pineal gland may be involved in preparing animals for mating. (See More Information, Chapter 39, p. 597.)

Other Glands

Endocrine glands in the stomach and lining of the small intestine produce hormones that aid digestion. After a person has eaten, cells in the stomach lining secrete gastrin, a hormone that stimulates other stomach cells to produce hydrochloric acid. Cells in the lining of the small intestine produce a hormone called secretin. This hormone affects the pancreas, the stomach, and the liver. Another gland, the pineal, is located in the forebrain. It produces melatonin, a hormone thought to be involved in biorhythms. Melatonin is also believed to influence maturation, perhaps by inhibiting the release of certain sex hormones until puberty.

Hormones

The maintenance of homeostasis and other vital functions performed by endocrine glands involve complex chemical interactions between hormones and other molecules in the body. Hormones differ in their chemical structure but are of two main types, protein hormones and lipid hormones.

Protein Hormones

Most hormones are protein hormones. They are either complete proteins, or polypeptides, amino acids, or amines. The chemical structure of one protein hormone is shown in Figure 47-8. A protein hormone acts by first attaching itself to a receptor on the membrane of a target cell. As you can see in Figure 47-8, the hormone then activates an enzyme in the cell membrane. This enzyme converts ATP molecules inside the cell to cyclic AMP. The cyclic AMP initiates changes within the cell by activating specific enzymes. The hormone adrenaline, for example, causes cyclic AMP to form in liver cells. As a result the cells produce enzymes that transform glycogen into glucose. The protein hormone is therefore called a first messenger; the cyclic AMP is called a second messenger.

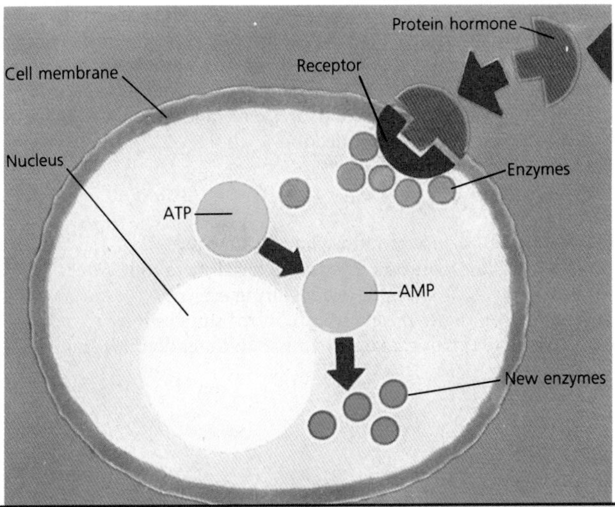

Figure 47-8 Protein hormones, such as oxytocin, shown here in structural form, remain outside the cell but cause changes within by initiating a series of reactions involving enzymes and ATP.

Oxytocin

cys-tyr-ile-glu-asn-cys-pro-leu-gly
S——S

Guided Practice

Using Table 47-1 on p. 731, play "Jeopardy" with students by having them guess which gland produces the hormone that regulates a certain function. Give the answer, and have students come up with the question. For example, if the answer is "This gland regulates blood sugar," the question should be "What is the function of the islets of Langerhans?"

Independent Practice

- Have students write answers to the Section Review.
- Ask students to make a sequential diagram showing how the hypothalamus regulates the pituitary gland. An example of a completed diagram (Graphic Organizer) appears on p. 727.

Check Your Understanding

1. Is the production of vasopressin regulated by a positive or negative feedback mechanism? Explain. *(Negative feedback; the secretion of vasopressin is inhibited when the increased concentration of vasopressin increases the amount of plasma, the fluid part of the blood.)*
2. Compare protein and lipid hormones. *(Protein hormones remain outside target cells but cause changes within them, whereas lipid proteins diffuse through cell membranes before initiating cell changes.)*
3. How do insulin and glucagon regulate blood sugar levels? *(Insulin stimulates cells to absorb glucose and causes the liver and muscles to convert glucose to glycogen; glucagon stimulates the breakdown of glycogen into glucose.)*

Videodiscs

- ***Side 1 3301, Diabetes (m)***
- ***1633–1634, Pancreas with Islets of Langerhans (s)***
- ***2534, ATP (s)***

More Information

Prostaglandins Among their many actions, prostaglandins have been found to dilate or constrict blood vessels, stimulate inflammatory responses, enhance perception of pain, stimulate uterine contractions, and affect the release of hormones such as growth hormone and LH. Now it is known that the effectiveness of aspirin in reducing pain and inflammation is due, in part, to its inhibition of prostaglandin synthesis. It has also been discovered that menstrual cramps are often caused by uterine contractions stimulated by the action of certain prostaglandins.

Reteaching

List randomly on the board the names of all the major endocrine glands as well as a list of disorders associated with them. Then ask students to name the hormones that these glands secrete and match the glands with the disorders. *(For example, the thymus produces thymosins; the associated disorder is a decrease in a child's ability to fight infection.)*

■ *See* Section Reviews *worksheet, Section 47.1.*

Enrichment

Have students research and report on diseases stemming from abnormalities in gland secretion such as pituitary gigantism and dwarfism, acromegaly, Graves' disease, myxedema, and Cushing's syndrome. Ask students to include information about the gland affected, hormone secreted, and effects on the body.

Closure

Divide the class into small groups and assign each group a major endocrine gland. Ask group members to discuss what problems might occur if the gland is overactive or underactive. Have students contribute their conclusions to a class discussion on hyper- and hypoglandular conditions.

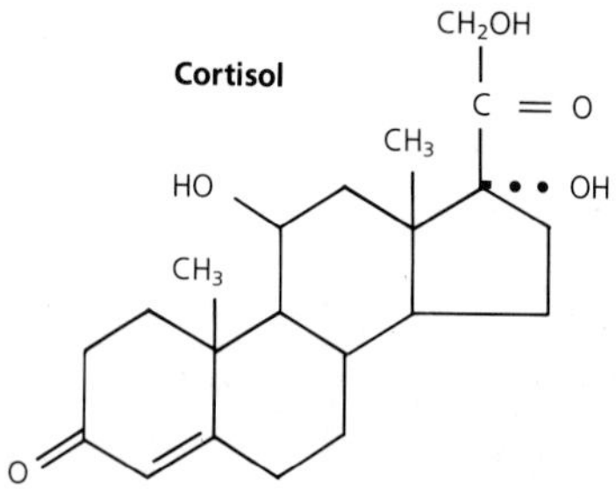

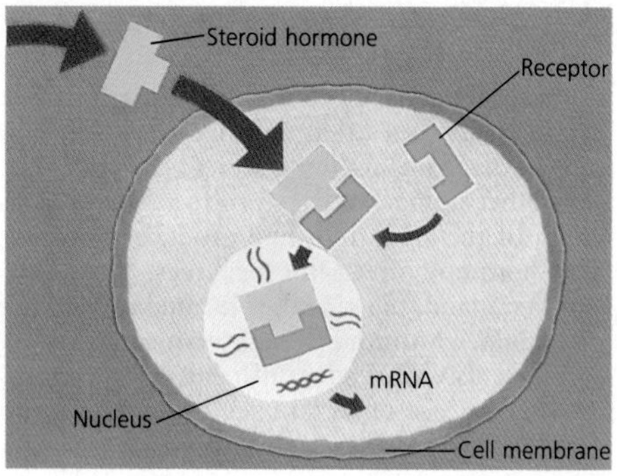

Figure 47-9 Lipid hormones, such as cortisol, shown here in structural form, penetrate the cell wall before initiating cell changes.

Lipid Hormones

A second type of hormone is a lipid hormone or **steroid.** You may have read about steroid abuse among athletes. Certain steroids, specifically ones derived from testosterone, were thought to increase muscle size. Scientists have not found evidence to support this claim. However, they have found that steroid abuse may contribute to liver disease and liver cancer, intestinal bleeding, and sexual dysfunction.

Notice in Figure 47-9 that, unlike protein hormones, steroids diffuse through the cell membrane and enter the cytoplasm. The steroid then binds to a receptor molecule to form a receptor-steroid complex that enters the cell's nucleus. Biologists hypothesize that this action stimulates genes to synthesize messenger RNA. The messenger RNA then moves into the cytoplasm, where it forms proteins that function as enzymes, promoting reactions that bring about the changes associated with the hormone.

Prostaglandins

A special group of lipids, called **prostaglandins,** also function as cell regulators. Unlike lipid and protein hormones, prostaglandins are not produced by specific glands. These powerful substances are produced in small quantities by virtually all cells of the body. They act locally rather than through blood transport. The effects of prostaglandins include relaxation of the smooth muscles of air passages and blood vessels, contraction of the uterine and intestinal walls, regulation of blood pressure, and stimulation of the inflammatory response to infection.

Section Review

1. What are *hormones,* and what do they do?
2. Which gland controls a person's basal metabolic rate?
3. What physical changes occur during stress?
4. How does the hypothalamus control the pituitary gland?
5. How is the hypothalamus similar to an endocrine gland?

Answers to Section Review

1. Hormones are substances produced in organs called glands that specifically influence the activity of cells in another part of the body.
2. The thyroid gland
3. The heart rate increases, blood pressure rises, the bronchial tubes enlarge, breathing quickens, and the pupils dilate.
4. Nerves connect the hypothalamus to the posterior pituitary; secretions from the hypothalamus travel through blood vessels to the anterior pituitary.
5. The hypothalamus has special cells that function like a gland, but it is primarily nerve tissue.

47.2 Reproductive System

Although the gonads play important regulatory roles as part of the endocrine system, their primary function is to produce gametes. The reproductive system in both males and females is composed of a complex set of specialized organs that not only produce gametes but store and release these sex cells in ways that make reproduction possible.

Male Reproductive System

The male reproductive system produces, stores, and releases the male gametes, or **sperm.** Males begin to produce sperm during puberty and continue to do so throughout most of their lives.

Sperm

Notice the shape of the sperm cell in Figure 47-10. This shape reflects the function of sperm—to move and carry genetic information to the egg. The large head region of the sperm contains DNA. The narrow middle part of the cell contains mitochondria that provide the chemical energy that moves the flagellum. The wavelike motion of the flagellum propels the sperm forward.

Male Reproductive Structures

Sperm begin life in two oval-shaped organs called the **testes.** These organs are contained within the **scrotum,** a pouch of skin formed from the lower part of the abdominal wall. The temperature within the scrotum is slightly lower than that inside the abdomen, a condition that promotes the formation and survival of sperm. Tightly coiled tubes called seminiferous *(SEM-uh-NIF-uh-russ)* tubules are located inside the testes. Here special cells divide by meiosis and form sperm. The sperm are released into an elongated sac called the epididymis *(EP-uh-DID-uh-muss),* where they mature and are stored. Maturation takes place within 18 hours.

Sperm leave the epididymis and travel in a duct called the vas deferens *(VASS-DEFF-uh-runz)* into the urethra, a tube within the penis. In the urethra the sperm mix with secretions from the seminal vesicles, the prostate gland, and the small Cowper's gland to form a fluid called **semen.** These secretions nourish and protect the sperm. Semen contains a high concentration of the simple sugar fructose, which sperm metabolize to provide energy for movement. Urine, which is highly acidic, also passes through the urethra and can leave residues that might kill an unprotected sperm cell. However, semen neutralizes the acidity and thus protects the sperm cells. During orgasm the semen is forcefully expelled from the body by strong muscular contractions of the sperm ducts. This process is called ejaculation. The external part of the male reproductive system is the penis. The penis contains the external portions of the urethra. The penis is the organ by

Section Objectives

- *Identify the major parts of the male and female reproductive systems and state the function of each.*
- *List similarities and differences between eggs and sperm.*
- *Summarize the role of hormones in regulating the events of the menstrual cycle.*

Figure 47-10 A sperm cell is essentially a packet of DNA equipped with a flagellum that provides motility and mitochondria that provide the energy for movement.

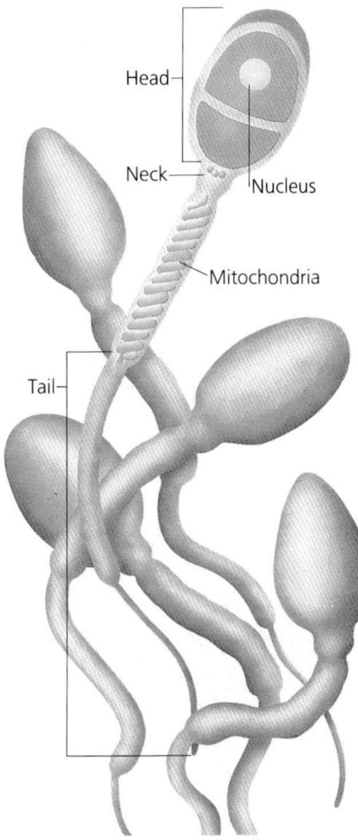

Lesson Plan

Section Focus

This section describes the structures and functions of the male and female reproductive systems, as well as the four phases of the menstrual cycle.

Section Themes

The themes of **Systems and Interactions** and **Patterns of Change** are evident in the explanation of the structures making up the male and female reproductive systems, as well as the menstrual cycle. Whereas most of the male's reproductive system is outside the abdomen, the female's system lies protected within the abdominal cavity. In the four phases of the menstrual cycle, the ovum, or egg, is prepared for fertilization and is discharged if not fertilized.

Motivating Activity

Show students pictures of human eggs and sperm at the same magnification, and ask them to compare the size of eggs and sperm. *(Eggs are much larger.)* Ask students to infer the function of sperm from their shape. *(To transport genetic information to the egg)* Then ask them to infer the function of the egg from its size. *(To provide the initial food supply for the embryo)*

Videodiscs

- ***Side 2 33467, Sperm: Microphotography and Animation (m)***

Female and Male Reproductive Systems

Female	Function	Male	Function
ovaries	▪ produce and store eggs	scrotum	▪ houses testes
Fallopian tubes	▪ carry fertilized eggs to uterus	testes	▪ produce sperm
uterus	▪ houses developing fetus	epididymis	▪ stores sperm
vagina	▪ entry for sperm; birth canal	urethra	▪ site where semen forms
		penis	▪ inserts sperm in female

Graphic Organizer Use this table in Reteaching on p. 738.

Teaching Strategies

Inferring Relationships Review the process of meiosis in Chapter 9 to remind students of how gametes are produced. Ask them to consider the relationship between the relative size of eggs and sperm and the numbers of eggs and sperm produced from the meiotic division of a single cell. *(The single egg cell produced receives all the cytoplasm that would normally be divided among four cells, giving the egg plenty of cytoplasm to accept the sperm nucleus and support the life functions of the fused nuclei.)*

Interpreting the Visuals Refer students to the diagrams of the male and female reproductive systems in Figure 47-11 on p. 736. Ask them to name the parts of each system and describe their functions. Then ask students to describe the production and movement of the sperm and eggs.

■ *See* **Overhead Transparency** *T47 and* **Blackline Master** *97.*

Contrasting Structures Obtain a preserved pig uterus from a biological supply house and display it to the class. Have students refer to Figure 47-11 on p. 736, which shows the structure of a human uterus. Assist students in making structural comparisons between the uteri from the two different species. Explain that swine uteri are bicornuate—the uterus has two "horns" that are folded and are quite long in relation to the short body of the uterus. You may wish to point out that the length of the uterine horns is an anatomic adaptation for producing offspring in litters. If the specimen was obtained from a pregnant pig, have students count the number of embryos present in the uterus.

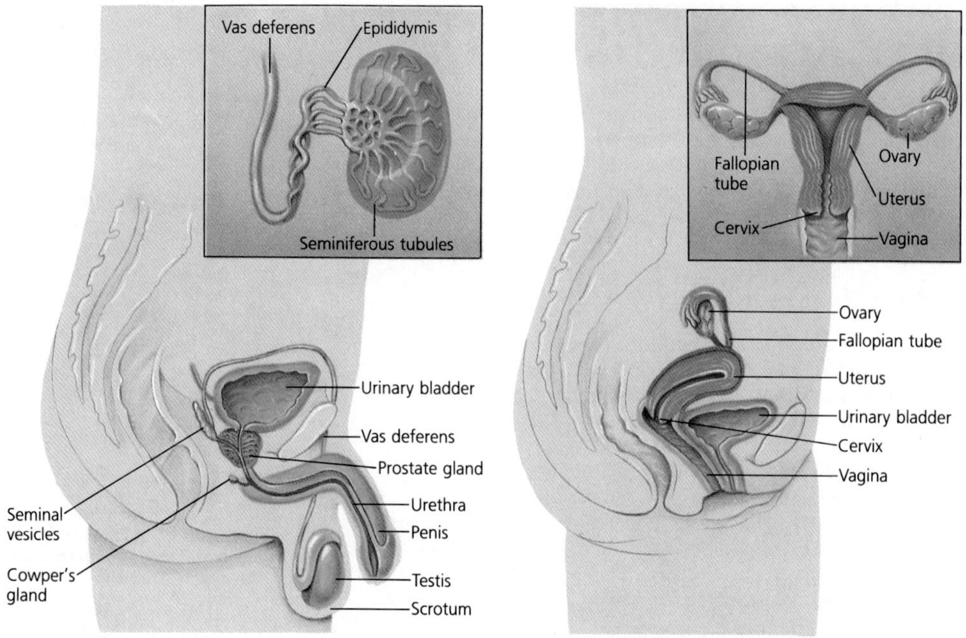

Figure 47-11 The male and female reproductive systems are complex sets of specialized organs. The insets emphasize male and female gonads.

which sperm is introduced into the female. It contains spongy tissue that becomes turgid and erect when filled with blood. The male reproductive system can be seen in Figure 47-11.

Female Reproductive System

The ovaries produce and store eggs, the female gametes. An egg, or **ovum,** is barely visible to the unaided eye, and yet one egg is about 75,000 times larger than a single sperm cell. Each female is born with over 400,000 immature eggs in her ovaries and will not produce any new eggs during her lifetime. In most women only about 400 eggs actually mature. Other structures of the female reproductive system include the Fallopian tubes, the uterus, the cervix, the vagina, and the external genitalia. Females have two **Fallopian tubes,** one located next to each ovary. Each functions to carry eggs from the ovary to the uterus, and each can be the site of fertilization. The **uterus** is a muscular structure that functions to house the developing fetus if fertilization occurs. The lower entrance to the uterus is called the cervix. The vagina is a tube leading from the cervix to the outside of the body. It is the canal that accepts the penis during intercourse and through which the fetus passes during childbirth. The external genitalia include the inner and outer labia and the clitoris. The female reproductive system can be seen in Figure 47-11.

Interdisciplinary Activity

Social Studies Although attitudes toward menstruating women have varied over the centuries from culture to culture, shame and fear have been common themes. One might attribute such customs as the segregation of menstruating women to ignorance of the function of menstruation, but some researchers suggest that male fear of the power of female sexuality plays a more important role. The net effect in many cultures has been to make women mistrustful or dismissive of themselves. Attitudes are changing in the United States (until 1972, TV ads for sanitary products were taboo), but an aura of shame still surrounds the subject. Have students research attitudes toward menstruation at various times in the United States or in other cultures.

Menstrual Cycle

Each month the female reproductive system goes through a series of changes called the **menstrual cycle.** The word *menstrual* comes from the Latin word *mensis,* which means "month." For most women, the menstrual cycle occurs over the course of about 28 days. During this time, an egg matures and is positioned to meet with a sperm cell in the Fallopian tube. If the egg is not fertilized, it is then discharged.

The menstrual cycle has four phases: (1) the follicular phase, (2) ovulation, (3) the luteal phase, and (4) menstruation. As you read about the menstrual cycle, refer to Figure 47-12.

Follicular Phase

The follicular phase begins when the hypothalamus produces a releasing factor. The releasing factor stimulates the anterior lobe of the pituitary gland to release follicle-stimulating hormone, or FSH. FSH is transported via the bloodstream and causes a group of ovarian cells, called a follicle, to form around the egg. Simultaneously, FSH promotes the production of the hormone estrogen, which is released into the bloodstream. Estrogen in turn stimulates the lining of the uterus to thicken. In addition, estrogen causes the pituitary gland to produce luteinizing hormone, or LH. This hormone then causes the maturation of the egg.

Figure 47-12 The four phases of the menstrual cycle occur over about a 28-day span.

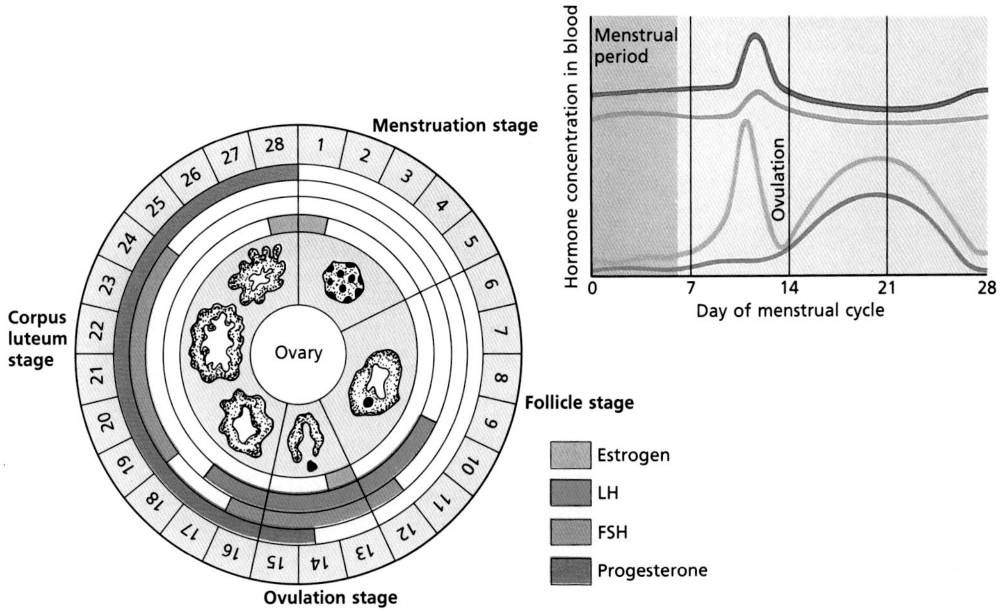

Applying Concepts Birth control pills are composed of varying concentrations of estrogen and progesterone. Ask students to explain how the combination of these hormones effects birth control. *(Estrogen, together with progesterone, inhibits the secretion of FSH; follicles do not form and ovulation cannot occur.)*

Guided Practice

Refer students to Figure 47-12 on p. 737, which illustrates the four phases of the menstrual cycle. Review each phase with students, asking them to describe the actions of the hormones, their concentrations in the blood, and the changes undergone by the egg and the reproductive organs during the cycle. Emphasize how negative feedback regulates the level of hormones.

Independent Practice

- Have students write answers to the Section Review.
- Have students diagram the path of an egg and a sperm through the female and male reproductive systems, respectively. Students should label the parts of the system through which the gametes pass.

Videodiscs

- ***Side 2 35139, Ovulation and Egg Transport (m)***

Cooperative Learning

The Menstrual Cycle Have groups of four students work together to prepare a visual presentation of the menstrual cycle. Instruct group members each to choose a different one of the hormones involved in the menstrual cycle—estrogen, LH, FSH, and progesterone—and determine its action throughout the menstrual cycle and its effect on the egg and other reproductive structures. Have group members discuss their findings and develop a chart or diagram to summarize the action of hormones in the menstrual cycle. Ask each group to present its work to the class.

Section 47.2

Check Your Understanding

1. How do the components of the male reproductive system promote the survival of sperm? *(Sperm is stored in the scrotum at lower than body temperature. Semen contains fructose, which sperm metabolize. It also neutralizes the acidity of urine residue in the urethra.)*

2. During what phase in the menstrual cycle is the egg ready for fertilization? *(During the four days after ovulation, while the egg is in the Fallopian tubes)*

3. Compare the rate at which the male and female reproductive systems produce gametes. *(Sperm are produced continuously; usually only one egg is released each month.)*

Reteaching

Have students design a table in which they list the major parts of the male and female reproductive systems and their functions. Use the table on p. 735 as a model.

■ *See* Section Reviews *worksheet, Section 47.2.*

Enrichment

Have students research and write a report about the causes and effects of premenstrual syndrome (PMS) as well as its treatment or prevention.

Closure

Ask students to summarize the interaction between the endocrine system and the reproductive system. *(Hormones secreted by endocrine glands stimulate the production of eggs and sperm. Sex hormones are also responsible for the changes undergone during puberty as well as for secondary sex characteristics.)*

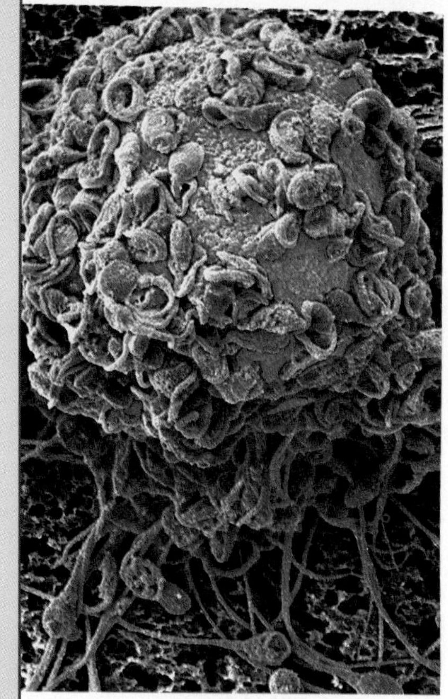

Figure 47-13 This color-enhanced SEM of sperm surrounding an egg (×3,400) shows the relative sizes of the male and female gametes.

Ovulation

When the egg has matured, the follicle moves to the wall of the ovary, ruptures, and releases the ripe egg. This event, called **ovulation,** is the second stage of the menstrual cycle. During ovulation tiny fingerlike projections draw the egg from the ovary into the Fallopian tube. The egg remains in the Fallopian tube for about four days and can be fertilized during this time. Figure 47-13 shows an egg surrounded by sperm. The egg, or zygote if the egg has been fertilized, then moves through the Fallopian tube to the uterus, which is now thick and lined with mucus.

Luteal Phase

During the luteal phase, the ruptured follicle left on the surface of the ovary develops into a new structure called the **corpus luteum.** Another hormone produced by the pituitary, luteotropic hormone (LTH), stimulates the corpus luteum to send out steroid hormones, including estrogen and progesterone, which establish an even thicker lining on the inside wall of the uterus. In addition, the increased levels of these hormones in the blood cause the pituitary gland to stop producing FSH. The uterine lining will enable the uterus to nourish and protect the fertilized egg.

Menstruation

If the egg was fertilized in the Fallopian tube, the resulting embryo attaches to the lining of the uterus. If the egg was not fertilized, it will not attach to the lining. In this case, the corpus luteum stops producing progesterone and the soft tissues of the uterine lining are sloughed off. These tissues along with blood and the unfertilized egg are discharged in the last stage of the cycle, called **menstruation.** They exit through the cervix and the vagina. Following menstruation the cycle begins again.

Most women menstruate until around age 50. At this time, called menopause, menstruation ceases because most of a woman's follicles have either matured and ruptured or they have degenerated. Without follicle cells the ovaries cannot secrete enough estrogen or progesterone to maintain the menstrual cycle. The anterior lobe of the pituitary continues to secrete follicle-stimulating hormone for the remainder of a woman's life.

Section Review

1. What phase of the human life cycle are the *ovum* and *sperm?*
2. Describe the function of semen in reproduction.
3. What happens to the ovum after it leaves the ovary if it has not been fertilized?
4. What are the four phases of the menstrual cycle?
5. What might happen if more than one egg were simultaneously released from the ovaries?

Answers to Section Review

1. The female and male gametes, respectively

2. Semen protects sperm by neutralizing acidic urine residues and nourishes sperm with its high concentration of fructose.

3. The ovum moves from the ovary through the Fallopian tube to the uterus and is then discharged from the body.

4. Follicular phase, ovulation, luteal phase, and menstruation

5. More than one egg might be fertilized, and more than one embryo might develop.

47.3 Fertilization and Development

The primary function of human reproductive systems is to create new individuals. This occurs when the male gamete is successful in reaching and penetrating the female gamete, resulting in the formation of a zygote that develops into a human being.

Section Objectives

- *Describe the process of fertilization.*
- *Summarize the changes that take place during embryo development.*
- *List the three stages of pregnancy and describe characteristics of each stage.*
- *Describe the process of in vitro fertilization.*

Fertilization

Fertilization occurs when a sperm combines with an ovum in a Fallopian tube. Sperm enter the female during the act of sexual intercourse, in which the male places his penis in the female's vagina. Muscular contractions during male orgasm eject semen from the body, through the urethra in the penis, and into the female. Hundreds of millions of sperm cells are released at once.

The egg in the Fallopian tube has a jellylike substance on its outer surface and is surrounded by a layer of cells from the follicle of the ovary. Many sperm may attach and attempt to penetrate these outer layers, but only one sperm will actually enter the egg.

The egg membrane engulfs the head of a single sperm and the sperm nucleus breaks out of the head. Once this has occurred, a membrane forms around the egg and prevents any other sperm from entering. The sperm nucleus then fuses with the egg nucleus.

Each gamete contains 23 chromosomes, the haploid (1N) number. Thus the union of sperm and egg causes the zygote to have 46 chromosomes, the diploid (2N) number. The presence of

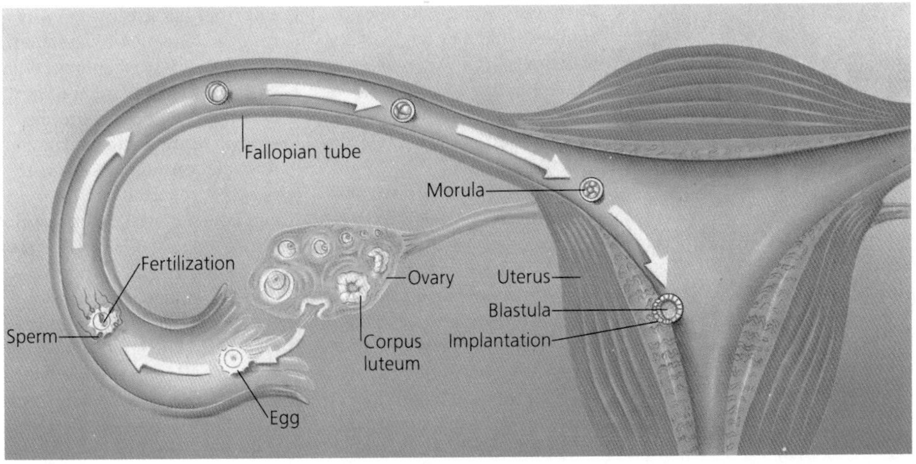

Figure 47-14 Fertilization of the egg takes place in the Fallopian tube, where the egg undergoes its first series of divisions before implantation in the uterus.

- Week 1: fertilization; blastocyte embeds in uterus
- Weeks 2–3: brain, spinal cord, and nervous system form; heartbeat starts
- Weeks 3–5: heart beats rhythmically; eyes, ears, nose form, digestive system, limbs
- Weeks 5–8: digits, external ears, brain waves; embryo moves
- Weeks 8–12: organs established; embryo is 5 cm long

Graphic Organizer Use this sequential diagram in Independent Practice on p. 743.

Lesson Plan

Section Focus

This section describes the process of fertilization and the development of a human embryo and fetus during the three stages of pregnancy.

Section Themes

The themes evident throughout this section are **Systems and Interactions** and **Patterns of Change.** The fusion of the sperm nucleus and the egg nucleus leads to the formation of a zygote. The fertilized egg grows and develops in a set pattern until hormones from the developing fetus and the mother signal the start of the birthing process.

Motivating Activity

Obtain transparencies from a biological supply house of various animal embryos, including humans, at different stages of development, or photocopy them yourself from scientific reference materials. Use an overhead projector to show students side-by-side comparisons of major stages of development from different animal species. Ask students to identify the human embryo. *(At early stages of development this will be difficult, if not impossible.)* Have students consider the similarities between the various species in the early stages of development and the differences between them in the later stages. Then remind students of the embryological evidence of evolution discussed in Chapter 15. Ask them what can be inferred from this evidence. *(Humans and animals share a common ancestry.)*

Videodiscs

■ *2670, Fertilization of the Egg by Sperm (s)*

Teaching Strategies

Interpreting the Visuals Refer students to the diagram of fertilization in Figure 47-14 on p. 739. Review with them the process of fertilization. Ask where fertilization occurs. *(In the Fallopian tubes)* Ask students to infer the importance of the egg becoming impermeable to other sperm once a single sperm has entered it. *(If more than one sperm entered the egg, the fused nuclei would contain more than the diploid number of chromosomes, and the zygote would not be viable.)*

Inferring Ideas Challenge students to infer possible reasons for human infertility based on their careful examination of Figure 47-14 on p. 739. *(Students might mention failure of sperm to move fast or far enough; blockages in Fallopian tubes that prevent the egg and sperm from meeting; low ejaculate sperm count; failure of ovulation to occur; and failure of egg to implant.)*

Identifying Structures Use an anatomical model to help students determine which body tissues develop from which primary germ layer—ectoderm, mesoderm, and endoderm. Point out body tissues and organs, and ask students to identify the germ layer from which each developed. *(For example, skin forms from ectoderm; muscles from mesoderm; lungs from endoderm.)*

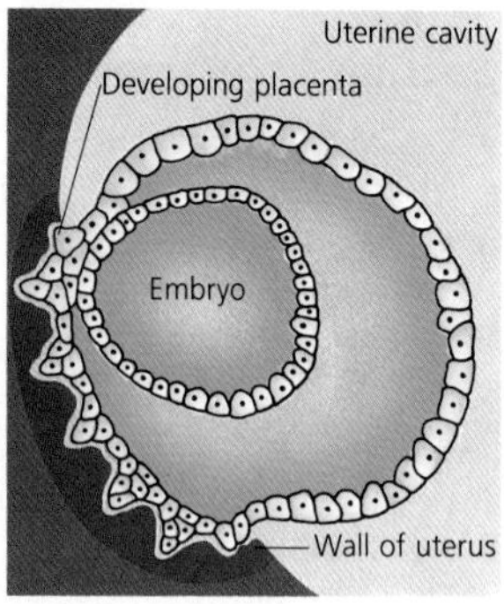

Figure 47-15 The blastocyst, composed of the embryo and the developing placenta, is implanted in the uterine wall.

the diploid set of chromosomes initiates embryo development. You may remember from Chapter 12 that sequential gene expression is very important during development.

Cleavage and Implantation

Immediately following fertilization, a phase known as cleavage occurs in which the zygote goes through many mitotic cell divisions while still in the Fallopian tube. These divisions produce a ball of cells called a morula. As the cells of the morula divide, they release fluid into the center of the sphere. The structure is now called a **blastocyst,** a sphere of cells with a large, fluid-filled cavity at its center. The outer layer of cells of the blastocyst, called the trophoblast, releases an enzyme that breaks down the epithelial tissue of the uterus and enables the blastocyst to embed itself in the thick lining. This process is called implantation.

The embryo will form from a mass of cells on the inner surface of the blastocyst, as shown in Figure 47-15. This inner mass of cells has three **primary germ layers:** the ectoderm, the mesoderm, and the endoderm. These three layers will eventually form all the body organs. The ectoderm forms the skin, the skin glands,

Biotechnology

Infertility and Assisted Conception

For almost three million couples in the United States who want to have children, infertility, or the inability to conceive, is a very real problem. Today the techniques of assisted conception could help a third or more of these infertile couples.

Because there are many causes of infertility, different strategies are used to assist conception. Infertility results from some condition in one or both of the partners. The most commonly used technique to assist conception when the route between the ovaries and uterus is blocked, is called in vitro fertilization. (In vitro means "*in glass.*") The babies that result from this process are often referred to as test-tube babies.

The in vitro technique begins with the administration of fertility agents or hormones to the woman to stimulate ovulation. At ovulation, multiple eggs are released, collected from the ovaries, and fertilized in a petri dish (p. 740). The fertilized eggs are incubated and introduced into the woman's uterus or Fallopian tubes. If the technique is successful, a fertilized egg will implant and complete normal development in the woman's uterus.

Today, ultrasound imaging is used to visualize the egg col-

Cooperative Learning

Contraception Divide the class into small groups and ask each group member to choose one method of contraception and research its effectiveness, its mode of use, mechanism of action, and failure rate. Methods of contraception include birth control pills, condoms, spermicides, IUDs, contraceptive sponges, diaphragms, the rhythm method, and abstinence. Instruct group members to compile their findings in one table to be shared with the rest of the class. Remind students to include appropriate headings in their table.

most cartilage, the nervous system, the pituitary gland, the lining from the mouth to the pharynx, a portion of the lining of the rectum, and the adrenal medulla. The mesoderm forms the connective tissue, the bone, most muscles, the kidneys and their ducts, the gonads and their ducts, the blood and blood vessels, the heart, and the lymph system. The endoderm forms the lining of the alimentary canal from the pharynx to the rectum, the thyroid, the parathyroids, the trachea, the lungs, the bladder, and the liver.

Development

The fertilized egg develops inside the uterus during a nine-month period called **gestation** or **pregnancy.** In the first eight weeks of its development, the organism is referred to as an **embryo.** From eight weeks until birth, it is called a **fetus.** Physicians commonly divide a pregnancy into three equal periods called **trimesters.**

Membranes

Throughout pregnancy the developing child is surrounded and protected by four membranes that develop from the trophoblast. The first of these membranes is called the **chorion** *(KOR-ee-ahn).*

lection procedure. The eggs are collected from the maturing egg follicles through a hollow needle inserted directly into the ovary. This procedure can often be done under a local anesthetic without an incision.

Clinicians are also using new procedures to help men overcome low sperm counts. They are using microsurgical techniques to unite egg and sperm. For example, the jellylike substance that surrounds the egg can be partially cut away, to allow the egg to be fertilized more easily (p. 741). The introduction of a single sperm into an egg—fertilization by microsurgery—offers men with extremely low sperm counts a way to produce biological children.

The newest techniques of assisted conception allow eggs to be introduced into a woman before or after fertilization. In GIFT (gamete intra-Fallopian transfer), egg and sperm are both injected directly into a Fallopian tube, to allow conception to occur where it normally would. In ZIFT (zygote intra-Fallopian transfer), transfer to the woman's Fallopian tube is done after in vitro fertilization.

The chance of the egg's implanting after assisted conception remains about 40–60 percent lower than in natural conceptions. Repeated in vitro procedures, however, improve the chances of pregnancy. As further refinements in assisted conception occur, the percentage of infertile couples able to give birth will probably increase.

Biotechnology

Using the Feature

Tell students that of 100 couples trying to conceive a child, about 84 will be successful within a year. The remaining 16 couples are said to suffer from infertility. Explain that infertility has many causes: (1) low sperm count, (2) problems with sperm production, (3) problems with ovulation, (4) cervical and cervical mucus irregularities, (5) tubal damage, (6) endometriosis, (7) immunologic problems, (8) unexplained causes, or a combination of causes. All of these causes contribute to the total number of couples unable to conceive.

Make sure students understand that for couples who want to have children, a diagnosis of infertility can be emotionally devastating. Ask students why they think that infertile couples might or might not want to try these new reproductive technologies. *(Allow for personal opinion. Some students may suggest adoption as an alternative for infertile couples. Others may suggest that some couples may prefer children that are their biological offspring. Some may mention the desire of a couple to share in the birthing experience.)*

Videodiscs

- ***Side 2 38275, Cleavage in the Fertilized Egg (m)***

More Information

Sperm Counts and Fertility Although the 300 million to 500 million sperm produced in a single ejaculation may seem unnecessarily high, males with lower counts have high failure rates in fertilization. Successful fertilization depends on millions of sperm because they secrete enzymes that break down the barriers to the egg's cell membrane, enabling one sperm to penetrate it. Also, millions of sperm never reach the egg. Some travel to the wrong Fallopian tube. Others never reach the Fallopian tubes; they die or become inactive before leaving the vagina.

Comparing Structures Refer students to Figure 38-1 on p. 571 and ask them to compare the membrane structure of the amniote egg with the membrane structures surrounding the developing child. *(Both have the same four membranes with essentially the same functions.)* Then ask students to contrast the amniote egg and the human embryo. *(The amniote egg is enclosed by a hard shell. The human embryo is enclosed by the placenta inside its mother's body.)*

Comparing Processes Give students the gestation periods of several different mammals. For example, the average length of gestation is 114 days for pigs, 63 days for cats, 425 days for giraffes, 16 days for hamsters, and 645 days for elephants. Ask students to compare the lengths of these gestation periods with that of humans. Encourage them to infer why the length of gestation in animals is so highly variable. *(Larger animals generally require a longer gestation period.)*

Extending the Concept Ask students what the blastocyst is and what happens to it. *(It is the product of mitotic division of the zygote, which embeds in the uterine wall.)* Explain to students that occasionally the blastocyst embeds and develops within the Fallopian tube, a circumstance known as a tubal, or ectopic, pregnancy. Tell students that such a pregnancy is life threatening to the mother and must be terminated.

■ ***See* Laboratories, *Investigation 47.***

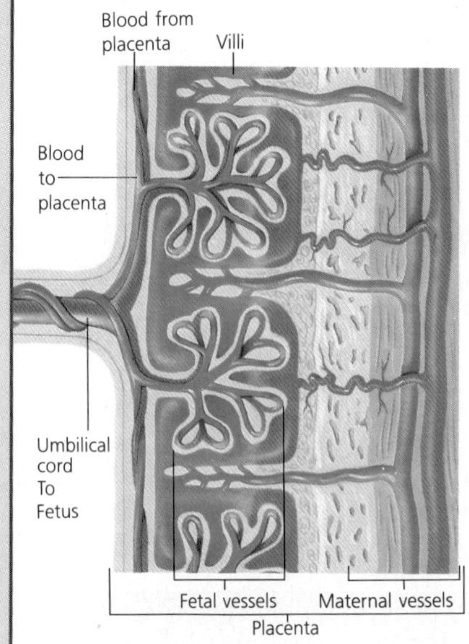

Figure 47-16 Food and oxygen from the mother and waste products from the fetus pass through the placenta, the lifeline between mother and fetus.

This membrane possesses a number of small, fingerlike projections called chorionic villi. Food and oxygen from the mother and waste products from the embryo are exchanged through the membranes of the chorionic villi. The area where the chorionic villi meet the maternal blood supply is called the **placenta.**

A second membrane, called the **amnion,** is a fluid-filled sac that surrounds the developing embryo. This sac is filled with amniotic fluid, which cushions the embryo and keeps it moist.

A third membrane is the **yolk sac.** The yolk sac provides some nourishment during early embryo development.

The fourth membrane surrounding the embryo is the **allantois** *(uh-LAN-tuh-wus).* Along with the chorion, the allantois lengthens to become the **umbilical cord,** a cord that contains arteries and veins that carry blood between the embryo and the placenta.

Cells within the placenta secrete chorionic gonadotropic hormone, which keeps the corpus luteum functioning. The corpus luteum produces estrogen and progesterone, two hormones that maintain the thick lining of the uterus. The high estrogen levels also stop follicle-stimulating hormone and luteinizing hormone production by the pituitary. As a result ovulation and menstruation do not occur during pregnancy.

The placenta, shown in Figure 47-16, is the life-supporting link between mother and fetus. The placenta is also shown in the bottom photograph in the left-hand column of Figure 47-17. Most of what the mother ingests passes into the fluid that surrounds the capillaries in the placenta. These substances can then pass into the capillaries and into the fetal blood supply.

First Trimester

The most dramatic changes in the development of a child take place in its first six to eight weeks. In the first two to three weeks, the human embryo resembles the embryos of other animals. But by the fifth week human features exist.

The brain, spinal cord, and nervous system begin forming in the third week. The heart begins to beat at 21 days and develops a smooth rhythm at 28 days. You can locate the heart as the dark mass in the chest area of the five-week-old embryo in Figure 47-17. By the fifth week eyes, ears, nasal organs, arms, legs, and the digestive system begin to develop. At six weeks the fingers, toes, and the external ears form. Brain waves occur at this time. The embryo also begins to move, although it is so small the mother cannot feel it turning. Figure 47-17 also shows the structures that have developed at six weeks. Compare this photograph with the photograph of the five-week-old embryo to see how quickly the embryo develops.

When the first trimester ends the embryo is only about 5 cm long, but most of its organ systems are established. Throughout its development the embryo, and later the fetus, is sensitive to viruses or toxins that may be passed to it from the mother.

Interdisciplinary Activity

Social Studies Worldwide, prenatal care is highly variable, dependent in part on educational and economic conditions and governmental priorities. Encourage students to choose a particular population and research the quality of prenatal care it receives. Challenge students to determine whether the quantity and quality of prenatal care is adequate and how the care affects the percentage of live births as well as the condition of newborns. Ask students to discuss reasons for inadequate care. Finally, have them propose ways in which prenatal care could be improved.

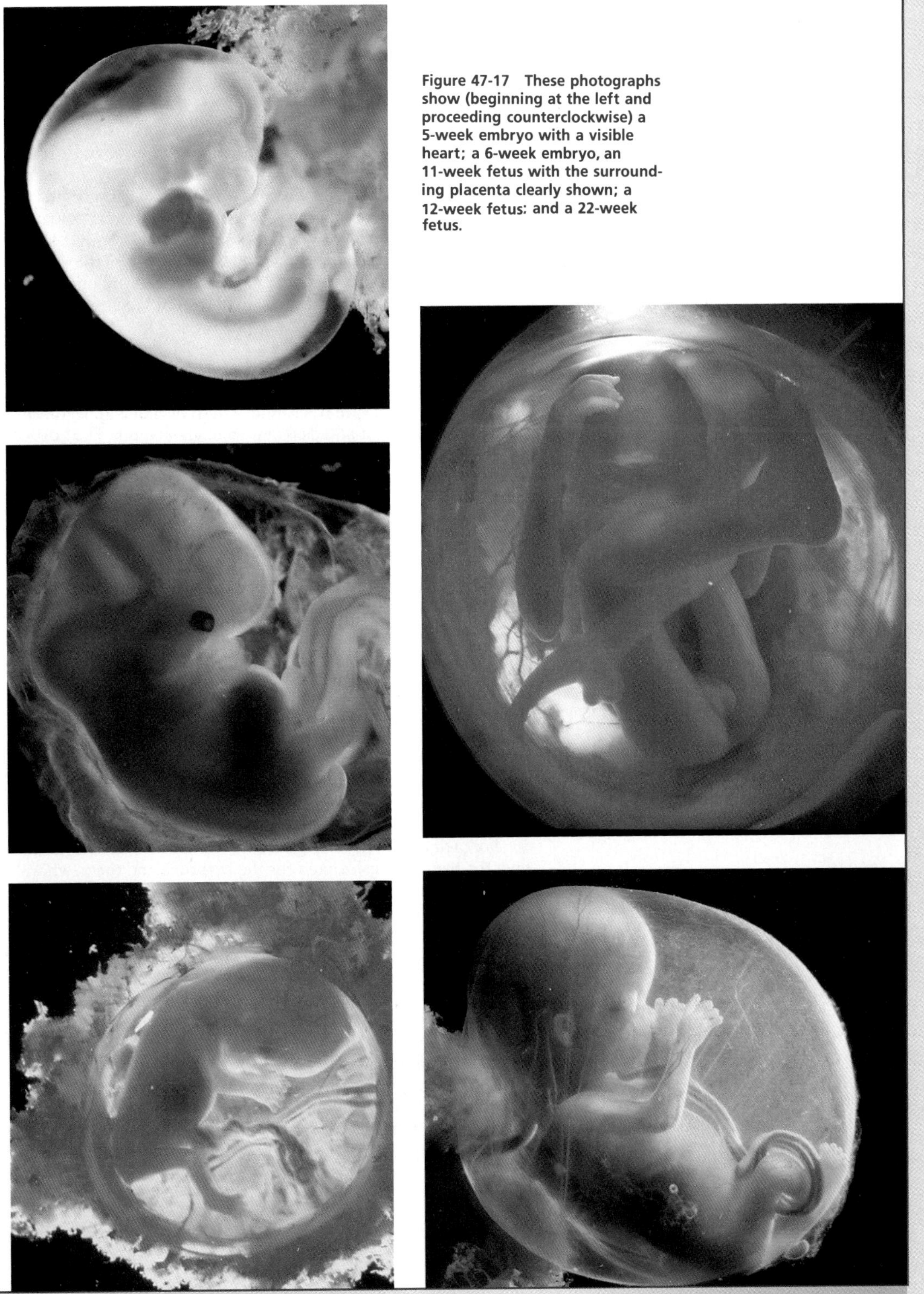

Figure 47-17 These photographs show (beginning at the left and proceeding counterclockwise) a 5-week embryo with a visible heart; a 6-week embryo, an 11-week fetus with the surrounding placenta clearly shown; a 12-week fetus: and a 22-week fetus.

LEP Activity

Have students make flash cards for each vocabulary word in this section. On an index card, instruct students to write the word and its phonetic respelling below it. On the back of the card, have students write the word's definition. Encourage student pairs to use the flash cards to quiz each other on the vocabulary words and their definitions. First, have students show the word to their partners, who must pronounce the word and give its definition. Then have students show the definition.

Discussing the Issues Invite a speaker who can describe some of the popular birthing methods, such as Lamaze and Bradley, as well as Caesarian section. Ask the speaker to provide information on the type of preparation involved and what happens during the actual delivery. The speaker should also discuss the advantages and disadvantages of each method.

Guided Practice

Show students pictures of different stages in human fetal development and ask them to put them in the proper order.

Independent Practice

- Have students write answers to the Section Review.
- Have students make a sequential diagram showing the prominent events that occur during the first trimester of pregnancy. An example of a completed diagram is shown on p. 739.

Check Your Understanding

1. What prevents ovulation from occurring during pregnancy? *(During pregnancy, the corpus luteum continues producing estrogen, which inhibits the pituitary gland from secreting LH and FSH.)*

2. What would happen if the trophoblast did not secrete an enzyme to break down the epidermal tissue of the uterine lining? *(Implantation of the blastocyst would not occur.)*

3. At what stage in fetal development do the brain, spinal cord, and nervous system begin functioning? *(During the first trimester)*

Videodiscs

- *2671, Human Fetus Before Birth (s)*

Answer to Think

Energy for development is used first to develop those organs required for fetal survival. It is advantageous for the lungs to develop later because they are not used until birth.

Reteaching

Divide the class into groups and assign each group to make a poster, illustrating either the process of fertilization, embryo development, or fetal development. Give each group time to display and discuss their poster with the rest of the class.

■ *See* Section Reviews *worksheet, Section 47.3.*

Enrichment

Have students research and report on either fetal alcohol syndrome, cocaine babies, or AIDS babies to find out how they became sick while in the mother's uterus and how their development and lives will be affected after birth.

Closure

Divide the class into groups and have group members discuss how the activities of the mother affect the development of the embryo and fetus. Specifically ask groups to discuss the effects of exercise, diet, smoking, alcohol, and drugs. Encourage groups to summarize their discussion in a list of guidelines for a healthy pregnancy.

Think

In a fetus the lungs are among the last organs to develop. From what you have learned about the conditions surrounding the developing fetus, explain what the advantage is in having the lungs develop later than the other organs.

Second Trimester

In the second trimester the mother's abdomen begins to swell as her uterus enlarges. The fetus' skeleton begins to form and a layer of soft hair grows over its skin. The fetal heartbeat can be heard with the aid of a stethoscope. At this time the fetus also begins to wake and sleep. The mother may now feel the fetus start moving about. The fetus swallows, hiccups, sucks its thumb, and makes a fist. It also kicks its feet and curls its toes. By the end of the second trimester the fetus is about 32 cm long and its eyes are open. The fetus at 12 weeks and 22 weeks can be seen in Figure 47-17.

Third Trimester

In the third trimester the fetus is becoming modified to survive in the outside world. It grows quickly in size and weight, and develops fat deposits that give it a rounded, less wrinkled appearance. The fetus can see light and darkness through its mother's abdominal wall and reacts to music and loud sounds. Ultrasound studies have led some researchers to believe that learning may take place before birth occurs.

Birth

Birth begins about 270 days after the egg has been fertilized by the sperm cell. The pituitary gland of the fetus, prostaglandins in the fetal membranes, and glands within the mother's body all release hormones that initiate childbirth. Oxytocin is secreted in large amounts, causing the smooth muscles of the uterus to contract. The amniotic sac breaks, and the fluid it contains flows out through the vagina. This is called breaking water. The tissues of the normally narrow cervix relax and enlarge, making it easier for the fetus to pass through. During the birth process, strong uterine contractions help push the baby through the cervix, out of the uterus, down the greatly expanded vagina, and out through the external genitalia.

Following birth the umbilical cord is tied and then cut. At this time, the baby's lungs expand for the first time and the newborn begins to breathe on its own. The remains of the placenta and amnion, the **afterbirth,** are then expelled from the mother's body about ten minutes after the birth of the baby.

Section Review

1. Describe the difference between an *embryo* and a *fetus.*
2. Describe a blastocyst.
3. How is the embryo nourished and protected?
4. What are some characteristics of the embryo and fetus in the different stages of pregnancy? Give an operational definition of the beginning of the second trimester.
5. Why is it important for a pregnant woman to follow good health practices?

Answers to Section Review

1. During the first eight weeks of development the organism is an embryo; from eight weeks until birth, it is a fetus.
2. A sphere of cells with a large, fluid-filled cavity at its center
3. Food and oxygen from the mother travel to the embryo through the chorionic villi of the placenta. The amnion moistens and cushions the embryo.
4. First trimester—the organs develop; second trimester—fetal heartbeat is heard; third trimester—fetus grows. The beginning of the second trimester is the point at which the fetus's heartbeat is audible.
5. Many substances entering the mother's blood pass through the placenta to the fetus.

Laboratory

Effects of Thyroxine on Frog Metamorphosis

Objective
To determine the effect of thyroxine on the development of tadpoles

Process Skills
Hypothesizing, experimenting

Materials
Glass-marking pencil, 8 1/4-inch culture dishes, pond water, 50-mL graduated cylinder, 0.01% thyroxine stock solution, strained spinach, graph paper marked in 1-mm squares, petri dish, small fish net, tadpoles with hind legs just beginning to show, three different colored pencils

Background
1 What cellular activities are influenced by thyroxine?
2 What effect does the hormone thyroxine have on growth and development?

Technique
1 Add 2.5 L of pond water to a culture dish.
2 Determine the size of a tadpole by placing a sheet of graph paper, ruled side up, underneath a petri dish. Catch a tadpole with a fish net and place the tadpole in the petri dish. Measure the tail length and body length of the tadpole in millimeters by counting the number of squares it covers on the graph paper. Record your measurements in a table. Place the tadpole in the culture dish.
3 Repeat step 2 with two more tadpoles. Feed the tadpoles 1 mL of spinach every other day. Be careful not to overfeed. Change the water every four days.
4 Measure the tadpoles twice a week for 3 weeks. Record your data. Calculate the average growth per week for the three tadpoles. Why is it better to use three tadpoles in this procedure?

Inquiry
1 Discuss the objective of this laboratory with your partner and formulate a hypothesis.
2 Design an experiment to test your hypothesis using the steps described in the Technique section above.
3 What are the independent and dependent variables in your experiment? How will you vary the independent variable? How will you measure changes in the dependent variable?
4 What advantage, if any, would there be to using tadpoles about the same size?
5 What type of controls will you set up?
6 Use a table to record your measurements. Use graph paper to plot the average growth per week for each group of tadpoles. Why plot the average growth for each group of tadpoles instead of the growth of each tadpole?
7 Proceed with your experiment once your design is approved by your teacher.

Conclusions
1 What effect did changes in the independent variable have on the dependent variable?
2 Do your data support your hypothesis? Explain.
3 How do average body length and tail length change during metamorphosis?

Further Inquiry
Iodine is needed to produce thyroxine. Design an experiment that shows the effect of adding iodine to tadpole water.

Laboratory

(For an overview of thyroxine and preparatory information related to the laboratory, see p. 725B.)

Background
1. Protein synthesis and ATP production
2. Thyroxine helps growing tissues develop properly.

Technique
4. Calculating an average of the measurements for three tadpoles compensates for slight differences in data measurement and variations among tadpoles.

Inquiry
3. The independent variable is the concentration of thyroxine in the beaker; the dependent variable is the rate of growth of the tadpoles. The independent variable can be varied by adding different quantities of thyroxine to separate beakers. The changes in the dependent variable will be reflected in changes in size and appearance of the tadpoles.
4. If all tadpoles start at about the same size, differences in growth will be easier to compare and plot on a graph.
5. The control can be set up in the same manner as the tests, with no thyroxine added to the culture dish. The rate of change in the tadpoles should be slower, indicating the rate of normal metamorphosis.
6. Plotting the average growth compensates for slight differences in data measurement and variations among tadpoles. Average measurements for tadpoles in each concentration of thyroxine should be graphed separately.

Conclusions
1. The rate of metamorphosis should be directly related to the concentration of thyroxine used.
2. Students should recognize whether their data support their hypothesis.
3. The body length increases, and the tail length decreases.

Further Inquiry
Students can design and conduct an experiment similar to the one completed, using iodine in place of thyroxine. They should offer hypotheses concerning the results.

Chapter 47 Review

Vocabulary

1. Uterus; others are glands.
2. Semen; others are hormones.
3. Hypothalamus; others are organs in the male reproductive system.
4. Prostate; others are organs in the female reproductive system.
5. Placenta; others are stages of development.

Review

1. b	**6.** d
2. a	**7.** c
3. c	**8.** b
4. d	**9.** b
5. a	**10.** b

11. Exocrine glands release their secretions through ducts, and endocrine glands release their secretions directly into the blood.
12. Steroid hormones pass through the cell membrane and bind with a special receptor. The receptor-steroid complex enters the nucleus, where it stimulates genes to synthesize messenger RNA.
13. The thyroid gland
14. Possible answers include the islets of Langerhans secreting insulin, the parathyroid glands secreting parathyroid hormone, and the posterior lobe of the pituitary gland secreting vasopressin.
15. Sperm have a large, rounded head that contains a nucleus, a narrow middle that contains mitochondria, and a tail or flagellum that moves the sperm.
16. In the ovaries.
17. Unfertilized eggs are discharged from the uterus during menstruation.
18. In vitro fertilization is fertilization that takes place in the laboratory in a glass dish; it is a technique for helping couples who have fertility problems.
19. Food and oxygen from the mother are passed to the fetus through the placenta.
20. The cervix relaxes and enlarges.

Chapter 47 Review

Vocabulary

adrenal gland (729)
afterbirth (744)
allantois (742)
amnion (742)
androgen (730)
blastocyst (740)
chorion (741)
corpus luteum (738)
diabetes mellitus (732)
embryo (741)
endocrine gland (728)
exocrine gland (728)
Fallopian tube (736)
feedback mechanism (727)
fertilization (739)
fetus (741)
gestation (741)
gonads (730)
hormone (727)
hyperthyroidism (728)
hypoglycemia (732)
hypothalamus (730)
hypothyroidism (728)
insulin (732)
islets of Langerhans (732)
menstrual cycle (737)
menstruation (738)
negative feedback (727)
ovary (730)
ovulation (738)
ovum (736)
parathyroid gland (729)
pituitary gland (730)
placenta (742)
positive feedback (727)
pregnancy (741)
primary germ layer (740)
prostaglandins (734)
scrotum (735)
semen (735)
sperm (735)
steroid (734)
target cells (727)
testes (730)
thyroid gland (728)
trimester (741)
umbilical cord (742)
uterus (736)
yolk sac (742)

For each set of terms below, choose the one that does not belong and explain why it does not belong.

1. adrenal, pituitary, uterus, parathyroid
2. estrogen, insulin, corticoid, semen
3. vas deferens, hypothalamus, scrotum, urethra
4. prostate, vagina, uterus, cervix
5. embryo, placenta, blastocyst, fetus

Review

1. The endocrine system (a) affects only the nervous system (b) helps maintain homeostasis (c) affects only the reproductive system (d) primarily utilizes a positive feedback mechanism.
2. In a negative feedback system the (a) end product inhibits the first step (b) end product inhibits the last step (c) end product stimulates the first step (d) end product stimulates the last step.
3. Steroid hormones (a) attach to a receptor on the cell membrane (b) convert ATP to cyclic AMP (c) diffuse through the cell membrane (d) increase muscle size.
4. The correct pathway of sperm is (a) testes to vas deferens to epididymis (b) epididymis to urethra to vas deferens (c) urethra to vas deferens to testes (d) testes to epididymis to vas deferens.
5. The correct pathway of an ovum is (a) ovary to Fallopian tube to uterus (b) Fallopian tube to ovary to urethra (c) uterus to ovary to Fallopian tube (d) ovary to Fallopian tube to urethra.
6. Fertilization takes place in the (a) vagina (b) cervix (c) uterus (d) Fallopian tubes.
7. During menstruation (a) the egg moves into the Fallopian tube (b) the corpus luteum develops (c) the uterine lining is discharged (d) the egg matures.
8. For fertilization to occur (a) many sperm must penetrate the egg (b) only one sperm must penetrate the egg (c) many eggs must be released (d) the uterus must be enlarged.
9. By the end of the first trimester (a) the fetus can suck its thumb (b) all of the organs have begun to form (c) the fetus uses

its lungs to breathe (d) the brain is fully developed.

10. The placenta is (a) the site of yolk development (b) the site of nutrient and gas exchange between the mother and the fetus (c) a structure that protects against injury (d) the tip of the uterus.
11. Explain the difference between an exocrine gland and an endocrine gland.
12. Describe the interaction between a steroid and its receptor cell.
13. Which gland regulates basal metabolism?
14. Give an example of a biological negative feedback mechanism.
15. Describe the structure of a sperm cell.
16. Where are ova produced?
17. What happens to an egg if it is released but is not fertilized?
18. What is in vitro fertilization?
19. How does the developing fetus receive nourishment?
20. What changes does the cervix undergo during childbirth?

Critical Thinking

1. A number of years ago a widely used treatment for tonsillitis, an inflammation of the tonsils, was to expose the neck area to X rays to shrink the tonsils. Explain why this procedure was later suspected of being dangerous and was therefore discontinued.
2. Using the concept of a negative feedback mechanism, explain how a hormone imbalance might occur and how the imbalance could be treated.
3. Why might damage to the pituitary gland be considered far more serious than damage to one of the other endocrine glands?
4. What do you think might happen if more than one sperm was able to penetrate the egg membrane?
5. Why do you think that doctors recommend that pregnant women drink milk?
6. What is the fetus doing in the photograph at right? Suggest an adaptive advantage for this activity.

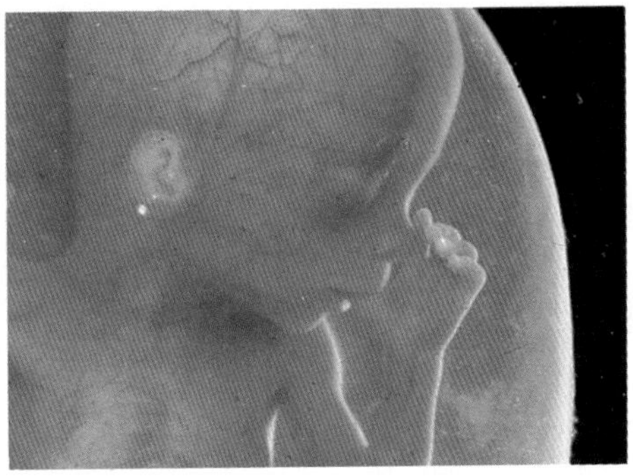

7. About 20 years ago a large number of women who took a tranquilizer called thalidomide early in pregnancy gave birth to babies with serious limb defects. Other mothers who took the drug later on in pregnancy had normal children. What does this tell you about the sequence of development of the fetus?

Extension

1. Research some of the physical and hormonal causes of infertility. Write a report describing the conditions, and explain how medical science is helping overcome infertility.
2. Read "Of Pregnancy and Pounds" in *Science News*, August 4, 1990, p. 75. What evidence suggests that standard limits for acceptable weight gain during pregnancy may be overly conservative?
3. Steroids can be used to treat certain illnesses. Using the Physician's Desk Reference (PDR), list the names and uses of the specific steroids.

Critical Thinking

1. The thyroid gland is located near the tonsils. The X-ray exposure was suspected of causing thyroid cancer many years later in those people treated for tonsillitis.
2. If a gland does not secrete enough of a hormone, a blood hormone deficiency would result. Supplemental hormones could help control such a problem. An excess of a hormone may be treated by a supplement of its antagonist, although it is sometimes necessary to remove the gland.
3. The pituitary regulates the activity of other glands. It forms the main link between the endocrine and nervous systems.
4. The development of the embryo depends on a diploid set of chromosomes—one haploid set from a sperm and one from the egg. A third set could prevent normal development.
5. A fetus needs calcium to develop bones.
6. The fetus is sucking its thumb; this helps develop the sucking response needed after birth.
7. Limbs develop during the early stages of pregnancy.

Extension

1. Encourage students to focus on only one type of infertility.
2. Student answers may include: higher weight gains have been associated with healthy pregnancies; higher weight gains may encourage fetal growth.
3. You might ask students to limit their lists to five to ten different steroids.

Chapter 48 Tobacco, Alcohol, and Other Drugs

Chapter Overview

Chapter 48 teaches students about the physical and behavioral effects of tobacco, alcohol, and other drugs. Section 48.1 examines tobacco and its effects on the body. Section 48.2 explains the immediate effects of alcohol on the body and the results of long-term use. Section 48.3 distinguishes between drugs used for medical purposes and drugs used for recreational purposes, and describes the short- and long-term effects of illegal drugs.

Chapter Planning Chart

B	S	A	Sections and Subsections	Page	Features	Page	Resources
•	•	•	**48.1 Tobacco**				
			Effects of Tobacco	749	Section Review	750	Videodiscs
			Tobacco and Disease	749	Laboratory	757	Blackline Master 98
							Overhead Transparency T48
							Process Skills: Cigarette Smoking
							Section Reviews Worksheet
•	•	•	**48.2 Alcohol**				
			Effects of Alcohol	751	Section Review	752	Videodiscs
			Alcohol and Disease	752			Laboratories: Reaction Times
							Section Reviews Worksheet
•	•	•	**48.3 Other Drugs**				
			Medical Uses of Drugs	753	Think	754	Blackline Master 99
			Drug Addiction	754	Biology in Process	754	Section Reviews Worksheet
			Illegal Drugs	755	Section Review	756	
			End of Chapter Activities				
					Chapter Review	758	Vocabulary Skills
							Chapter Test
							Computer Test Generator

B *The Basic Level curriculum presents the most fundamental knowledge offered in the course.*
S *The Standard Level curriculum is designed for the average student who is able to master most topics.*
A *The Advanced Level curriculum includes suggestions for teaching the most academically able students.*

Cooperative Learning

Group Activity: Effects of Drugs on Society

- **Group Size:** *4 students*
- **Outcome:** *Students will analyze the risks and social costs of drug use.*
- **Individual Accountability:** *Each student will search a newspaper for information relating to using drugs.*
- **Positive Interdependence:** *Group members will construct a visual display of their findings.*

Distribute several issues of the local newspaper to each group of students. Have students look through the papers for articles relating to drug use—whether of tobacco, coffee, alcohol, or illegal drugs. The articles may include drug arrests/trials, laws concerning drugs, drug-related accidents or deaths, drug treatments, or community programs against drugs. Have students cut out articles they find and then work together to organize them according to a common theme.

After they have organized their articles, tell students to create a visual display reflecting their findings. For example, students may want to create a graph or chart reflecting the risks that use of a particular drug poses to the local community, or the costs associated with controlling drug use. Then have groups compare their results in a class discussion.

Concept Map

The following is one possible solution to the concept mapping activity in Organizing Concepts on p. 754.

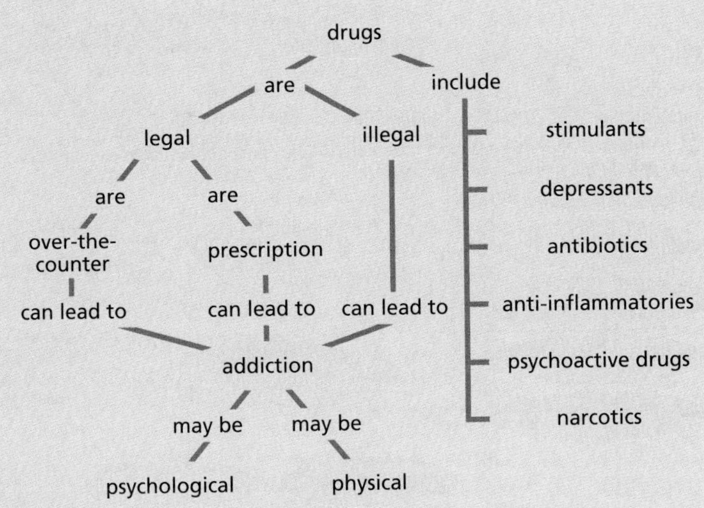

Laboratory Preparation

Overview *(See p. 757.)*

This lab concentrates on the tars in cigarette smoke. Substances in the tars cause genetic changes that can lead to lung cancer. The apparatus simulates how smoke coats the respiratory system of a smoker. You may wish to expand the experiment to include a comparison of filtered and nonfiltered cigarettes or of low-tar and regular brands.

Preparation

Because of the fragility of the glass and the legal liability involved should a tube break in a student's hand and cause severe cuts, it is advisable to prepare the tubing-cork system for the smoking machines beforehand. Students should have little trouble assembling the rest of the smoking machine themselves.

Prepare a tubing-cork system for each team. Carefully bore a hole through the cork that has a slightly larger diameter than the glass tubing. **CAUTION:** Handle the glass tubing with care, as it can break and cause cuts. Protect your hands with a cloth towel. Lubricate a 15-cm length of glass tubing with a few drops of glycerine. Then slide the glass tubing about halfway through the hole in the cork.

Purchase the cigarettes yourself. To accept cigarettes offered by students, even for experimental purposes, might be seen as encouraging students' smoking.

Teaching Tips

If a student objects to being in a room with cigarette smoke, you will need to make suitable arrangements.

Explain the limited nature of this experiment to the students. It will not tell them anything specific about the actual effects of smoke on living tissue. For example, the Further Inquiry section will lead students to conclude, correctly, that smoke will mix with the mucus. However, smoke also stimulates the body to increase mucus production as a way of soothing the air passages. Because the cilia are inhibited by smoke, the lungs and bronchial passages cannot clean out the mucus, which is an excellent culture medium for bacteria.

Safety

To keep cigarette smoke in the classroom to a minimum, open windows, run an exhaust fan, or use a fume hood. Make sure students put the rubber tubing onto the glass tubing cautiously to avoid cuts. Have glycerine handy for stubborn or dried tubing.

Chapter Themes

Systems and Interactions The balanced interaction among the many organs and systems of the human body is necessary for survival. Drugs are often used to enhance or restore systemic functions. Review with students the ways in which the circulatory and respiratory systems interact, and discuss how drug use can disturb this interaction. Emphasize the danger of interfering with these systems.

Stability As students learn about the short- and long-term effects of tobacco, alcohol, and other drugs on the body, discuss the various ways in which the body's homeostasis is affected. For example, blood levels of oxygen and carbon dioxide are affected by tobacco smoke. Help students understand how specific drugs affect the normal functions of the body's systems.

Chapter Motivating Activity

Have the class discuss some of the reasons that might influence someone to use drugs—a desire to escape from problems, or a desire to belong to the group. Be sensitive to students who may use drugs or who know someone who does. Have the class collaborate on a list of harmful effects of drugs. Students should understand that using drugs can have serious repercussions to their health and welfare regardless of the reason that drugs are used.

Chapter 48 Tobacco, Alcohol, and Other Drugs

Introduction

The human body is the product of many organ systems working together as a functional organism. Its health depends on the performance level of each organ system. Medical science has developed many different kinds of drugs that greatly improve the body's ability to overcome illness and maintain health. However, the use of tobacco and alcohol and the misuse of other drugs can interfere with normal body functions and cause irreversible damage. In this chapter you will learn how drugs interfere with normal body functions.

Chapter Outline

48.1 Tobacco
- *Effects of Tobacco*
- *Tobacco and Disease*

48.2 Alcohol
- *Effects of Alcohol*
- *Alcohol and Disease*

48.3 Other Drugs
- *Medical Uses of Drugs*
- *Drug Addiction*
- *Illegal Drugs*

Chapter Concept

As you read, try to identify ways each substance interferes with the body's ability to function properly.

Drug research in a modern laboratory. Inset: Leaf of marijuana, *Cannabis sativa*.

Understanding the Visuals

Have students consider why drug research and testing are so important. *(Scientists are always looking for new treatments for diseases and disorders. Drug research is undertaken to determine a drug's efficacy, as well as its possible side effects.)*

Direct students' attention to the marijuana leaf. Explain that there are different kinds of marijuana, all of which vary slightly in appearance and structure. Ask students why it is important for researchers to study marijuana. *(To determine its makeup and its effects on the body, and to evaluate possible medical usefulness; for example, dronabinol [a derivative of cannabis] is registered for use as a treatment for the nausea and vomiting experienced by people undergoing chemotherapy.)*

48.1 Tobacco

A **drug** is any chemical taken into the body that alters the normal processes of either the mind or the body. Tobacco and alcohol are drugs, as are cocaine, marijuana, and nicotine.

Tobacco comes from *Nicotiana tabacum,* a tall, leafy plant of the Solanaceae, the nightshade family. After being dried and crushed, tobacco leaves are smoked in cigarettes, cigars, and pipes. Tobacco is also snuffed or chewed. Scientific experiments have repeatedly shown that tobacco can have severe effects on the body. Each year an estimated 350,000 Americans die from tobacco-related diseases. These deaths are mostly the result of the more than 2,000 potentially toxic chemical compounds produced when tobacco is burned. The most potent of these compounds are nicotine and tar.

Nicotine, the major drug found in tobacco, is a **stimulant,** a drug that increases the activity of the central nervous system. Nicotine can cause **addiction**—the user can become dependent on the presence of the drug and thus find it difficult to do without. **Tar,** a complex mixture of chemicals and smoke particles, settles into the lungs. The result is a reduction in breathing capacity and increased susceptibility to infections.

Effects of Tobacco

When tobacco smoke is inhaled, nicotine is absorbed into the bloodstream through the lining of the mouth and through the lungs. It is transported to the brain in 7.5 seconds. Effects on the circulatory system include an increase in blood pressure, an increase in heart rate by up to 33 beats a minute, a decrease in oxygen supply to body tissues, and a decrease in circulation to the hands and feet.

Tar and other particles in smoke paralyze the cilia that line the air passages. Normally cilia move particles out of the air passages and protect them from disease-causing microorganisms. Tar irritates the nose, throat, trachea, and bronchial tubes, causing sore throats and coughing. Figure 48-2 on the following page illustrates other effects of smoking.

Tobacco and Disease

Scientific studies have shown that smokers are more susceptible than nonsmokers to many kinds of diseases and may also have a shorter life expectancy. Nearly 90 percent of all lung cancer deaths can be attributed to smoking, and approximately 25 percent of all heart attacks are associated with the use of tobacco.

Many smokers are highly susceptible to **chronic bronchitis,** an inflammation of the bronchi and bronchioles, and **emphysema,** a degenerative lung disease. Emphysema results from the rupture

Section Objectives

- *Identify two harmful chemicals produced when tobacco is burned.*
- *Describe the physical effects of inhaling tobacco smoke.*
- *List three diseases that can result from smoking or chewing tobacco.*
- *Explain what can happen to the fetus if a pregnant woman smokes.*

Figure 48-1 Cancer can transform a healthy lung (top) into a diseased lung (bottom).

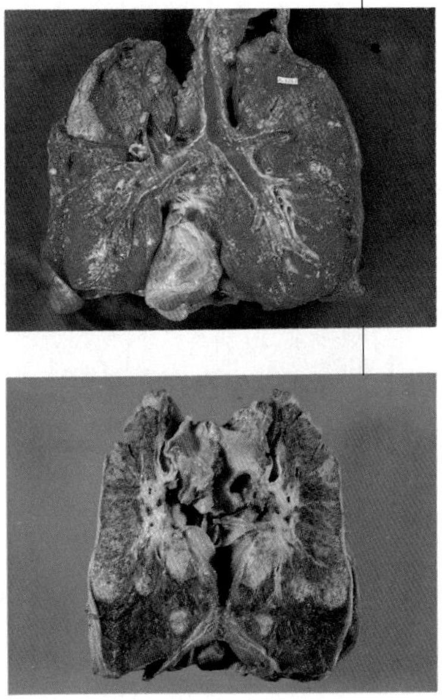

System	Organ	Risk
respiratory	air passages lungs	paralyzed cilia, upper respiratory disease emphysema, cancer
circulatory	blood vessels heart	constriction, decreased circulation hypertension, rate disturbances, heart attacks
digestive	mouth; stomach	laryngeal and oral cancer; ulcers

Graphic Organizer Use this table in Reteaching on p. 750.

Lesson Plan

Section Focus

This section describes the chemical composition of tobacco and its short- and long-term effects on the body. Students will also learn about the effects of sidestream smoke and the effects of tobacco smoke on fetuses.

Section Themes

This section emphasizes the theme of **Systems and Interactions.** Tobacco use causes lung cancer and other damage to the lungs and has been implicated in heart disease, oral and laryngeal cancers, low birthweight in newborns, and damage to numerous other organs and organ systems.

Motivating Activity

Ask students why people smoke in spite of the well-known risks. Encourage students to speak from their personal experience or about the experiences of friends and relatives. Ask students whether they think it is reasonable for the family of a long-term smoker who has died of lung disease to sue tobacco companies. *(This question can start a discussion about free will, what addiction really means, whether companies should market addictive products, and the cumulative effects of advertising. Accept all constructive responses.)*

Teaching Strategies

Drawing Conclusions Remind students that nicotine is a highly addictive substance. Ask them how a smoker of filtered cigarettes might compensate for decreased nicotine content. *(Typically, filtered cigarette smokers smoke more cigarettes.)*

- *See* **Process Skills,** *Chapter 48.*

Videodiscs

- ***2654–2655, Human Respiration; Gas Exchange (s)***

Section 48.1

Guided Practice
Using Figure 48-2 on p. 750 as a guide, name one by one the systems or organs especially affected by smoking. Have students describe what the risk is to each system or organ.
■ *See* **Overhead Transparency** ***T48 and*** **Blackline Master** ***98.***

Independent Practice
■ Have students write answers to the Section Review.
■ Distribute cigarette ads to students. Have them decide how the ad makes smoking seem attractive. Encourage them to modify the ads to show the dangers of smoking.

Check Your Understanding
1. How does smoke affect the respiratory system? *(Paralyzes cilia, irritates airways, coats and destroys alveoli)*
2. Name two effects of smoking on a fetus. *(Lower birthweight, higher mortality rate)*
3. Why is sidestream smoke dangerous? *(Nonsmokers inhale unfiltered smoke.)*

Reteaching
Ask students to make a table listing the systems and organs affected by smoking and the associated health risks. A sample table completed for three systems is shown on p. 749.
■ *See* **Section Reviews** ***worksheet, Section 48.1.***

Enrichment
Have students research and write about Edward Bernays's 1929 campaign to get women to smoke. Have them compare it with current ads aimed at women.

Closure
Divide students into small groups and have groups take sides and debate the issue of whether to ban smoking from work and public places.

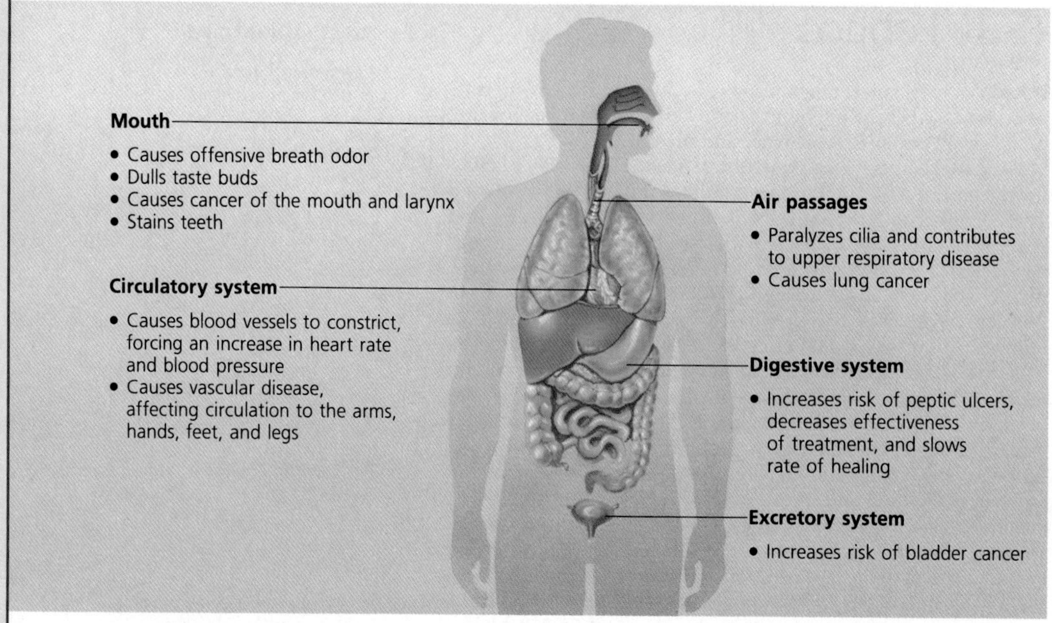

Figure 48-2 The health risks brought on by smoking extend to many parts of the body.

Table 48-1
Tobacco Use Statistics

- The average smoker will spend $10,000–20,000 on cigarettes during a lifetime
- Average life span decreases by 5½ years if one pack a day is smoked, 7 years if two packs a day are smoked
- 25,000 injuries and $313,000 in property damages per year result from fires caused by smoking

of the alveoli, the air sacs where gas exchange occurs. Users of smokeless tobacco have a higher rate of lip, gum, and mouth cancer than those who do not use smokeless tobacco.

Nonsmokers who are around smokers also have increased health risks. Tobacco smoke flowing from cigarettes or exhaled by a smoker is called **sidestream smoke.** Laboratory experiments have shown that sidestream smoke puts anyone who inhales it at risk for the same diseases as those who smoke.

The consequences of smoking during pregnancy are profound. Pregnant women who smoke are twice as likely as nonsmoking mothers to suffer miscarriages. Their babies are often much smaller and less robust than other babies and are twice as likely to die in the first few months of life. The long-term risks for children whose mothers smoke during pregnancy include heart disease.

Section Review

1. What is *emphysema?*
2. In what ways does nicotine affect the body?
3. How does tar contribute to a smoker's increased susceptibility to colds and infection?
4. What are some diseases caused by smoking tobacco?
5. Why might it be harmful for a pregnant woman to work in an office that does not have smoking restrictions?

Answers to Section Review
1. A degenerative lung disease characterized by ruptured alveoli
2. It increases the activity of the central nervous system, causes an increase in heart rate and blood pressure, and decreases circulation to the hands and feet.
3. It paralyzes the cilia that move disease-causing microorganisms out of the body, and it irritates the air passages.
4. Lung cancer, heart disease, chronic bronchitis, emphysema, and others
5. She may be exposed to an excessive amount of sidestream smoke, and thus her baby would be at risk for the same problems that could result if the mother herself smoked.

48.2 Alcohol

Ethanol (C_2H_5OH) is the drug found in beer, wine, liquor, and certain other beverages. Ethanol is produced by **alcoholic fermentation,** the anaerobic action of yeast on the sugars found in fruits or grains. Ethanol is a **depressant,** a drug that decreases the activity of the central nervous system and lowers the level of activity of many body functions. **Alcoholism** is the disease of being addicted to ethanol.

Section Objectives

- *Define* alcohol.
- *Summarize how alcohol affects the body.*
- *Describe long-term results of excessive alcohol consumption.*

Effects of Alcohol

Following consumption, alcohol is immediately absorbed from the stomach and intestines into the bloodstream and then transported to the brain and other body organs. When alcohol diffuses into the tissues of the liver, it is oxidized by the cells, resulting in a series of physiological changes. First, oxidation produces heat, which increases blood temperature. This stimulates the brain to increase circulation to the skin, resulting in a decrease in blood flow to the internal organs.

When alcohol enters the control centers of the brain, coordination is impaired, speech may become slurred, and reaction time is greatly slowed. Changes in other body organs include increased perspiration as a response to the rise in blood temperature at the skin surface. Water in the kidneys is reabsorbed to compensate for the loss of water through the skin. As a result nitrogenous wastes collect in the kidneys, interfering with the normal filtration and secretion processes. Drinking alcohol removes water from the body, resulting in general dehydration.

The severity of these effects depends largely on **blood alcohol concentration** (BAC), a measurement of the amount of alcohol in the blood. Table 48-2 relates weight and consumption to impairment

Table 48-2 Blood Alcohol Level and Its Effects

Drinks in One Hour	Body Weight in Pounds								Influence
	100	120	140	160	180	200	220	240	
1	.04	.03	.03	.02	.02	.02	.02	.02	Possibly
2	.06	.06	.05	.05	.04	.04	.03	.03	Impaired
3	.11	.09	.08	.07	.06	.06	.05	.05	
4	.15	.12	.11	.09	.08	.08	.07	.06	Impaired
5	.19	.16	.13	.12	.11	.09	.09	.08	
6	.23	.19	.16	.14	.13	.11	.10	.09	
7	.26	.22	.19	.16	.15	.13	.12	.11	Legally
8	.30	.25	.21	.19	.17	.15	.14	.13	Impaired

Subtract .015% for each hour of drinking. One drink is 1 oz. of 80 proof liquor at 40% alcohol, 12 oz. of beer at 4.5%, or 4 oz. of wine at 12% alcohol.

Organ	Short-term Effects	Long-term Effects
brain	loss of coordination, slowed reaction time	—
liver	oxidation of alcohol	fatty liver, hepatitis, cirrhosis
skin	increased perspiration	—
kidneys	interference with normal function	—
stomach	stimulates secretion of gastric juices	gastritis, ulcers
heart	—	high blood pressure, heart disease

Graphic Organizer Use this table in Guided Practice on p. 752.

Lesson Plan

Section Focus

This section describes the chemical composition of ethyl alcohol, its immediate effects on the body, and diseases that may result from its long-term abuse.

Section Themes

The theme of **Systems and Interactions** is emphasized in this section. After alcohol is consumed, the body's organs and systems interact to rid the body of the drug and to regain stability.

Motivating Activity

Bring in a newspaper from a Monday or the day after a holiday weekend. Show students the stories about accidents that occurred in which use of alcohol was implicated. Ask how drinking can become so dangerous. *(Judgment and reaction time are impaired.)* Have students offer their opinions on the legal controls on drinking, such as controls on drinking age or on amount consumed.

Teaching Strategies

Applying Concepts Have students study Table 48-2. Ask them if it is possible to know the specific amount of alcohol one can consume and still remain unimpaired. *(No; other factors affect the BAC besides body weight. Also, reaction times can be affected before a drinker is considered legally impaired.)* With this in mind, ask students why a designated driver is so important. *(A sober driver is less likely to have an accident.)*
■ ***See* Laboratories, *Investigation 48.***

Videodiscs

- ***2651–2652, Human Digestive Tract (s)***
- ***2659, Human Kidney (s)***
- ***Side 2 12259, Blood Flow (m)***

Section 48.2

Guided Practice

Have students construct a table on short- and long-term effects of overconsumption of alcohol on the various body organs, using the information in Section 48.2. An example of a completed table is shown on p. 751.

Independent Practice

■ Have students write answers to the Section Review.

■ Tell students that alcohol is the most commonly abused drug in the United States. Have them write an explanation of why they think this is so and have them suggest at least one way to reduce alcohol abuse.

Check Your Understanding

1. What effects does a depressant such as ethanol have? *(Impairs muscle control, speech, and higher brain functions)*

2. How is alcohol passed to a fetus? *(Through the placenta)*

3. How does alcohol cause cirrhosis? *(By altering the function of liver cells)*

Reteaching

Ask students why alcohol is considered a drug. *(It alters processes of both mind and body.)* Then have students write their own definition of alcohol. *(Alcohol is any beverage containing ethanol, a central nervous system depressant.)*

■ *See* **Section Reviews** ***worksheet, Section 48.2.***

Enrichment

Have students research the history of Mothers Against Drunk Driving and Students Against Drunk Driving. Encourage them to focus on these groups' activities that are aimed at reducing alcohol abuse.

Closure

Invite a speaker from Alcoholics Anonymous to talk about the difference between alcohol use and alcohol abuse and about how AA deals with alcoholism.

Table 48-3
Alcohol Use Statistics

Alcohol contributes to:
▪ Over 50% of all suicides
▪ 70% of all murders
▪ 50% of all arrests
▪ Nearly 50% of all fatal crashes involving young people
▪ Over 50% of all fire-related deaths
▪ Over 50% of all drownings
750,000 teens are alcoholics.

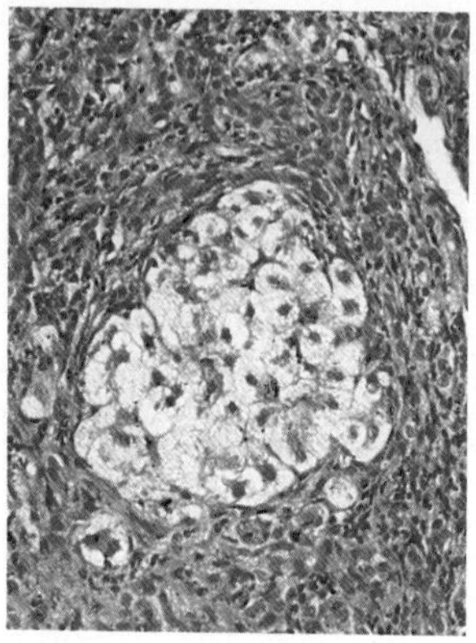

Figure 48-3 Alcohol abuse can cause cirrhosis, a disease in which scar tissue, like that shown in center, replaces normal liver cells.

changes that occur as BAC levels increase. The BAC can be estimated from a breath test, which measures alcoholic vapors given off by the lungs. The amount of alcohol consumed is not the only factor determining BAC. Rate of consumption, ability to metabolize alcohol, body weight, and amount of food in the stomach are other factors that affect BAC.

The effects of alcohol are compounded when it is used with other drugs. Aspirin taken while drinking can cause the lining of the stomach to bleed. Alcohol combined with another depressant can slow body functions to a dangerous level and result in death.

Alcohol and Disease

Long-term use of alcohol damages the body. People who consume alcohol in large amounts and over long periods of time may be more likely than nonusers to suffer from high blood pressure and some forms of heart disease. Excessive alcohol use can irritate the lining of the stomach, a condition called **gastritis,** and eventually can lead to stomach ulcers. In some individuals, alcohol takes the place of nutritious foods, causing metabolic disorders.

Chronic alcohol use forces the liver to use alcohol as an energy source instead of relying on fatty acids. Eventually liver cells are unable to function properly and they accumulate fat deposits. As a result the liver begins to swell, causing **fatty liver,** a condition that occurs in 75 percent of all alcoholics. If the drinker abstains from alcohol, the liver can usually return to normal functioning. If drinking continues, the drinker may develop alcoholic hepatitis, an inflammation of the liver, or even **cirrhosis** *(suh-ROE-suss),* a condition in which normal liver tissues are replaced by scar tissue, as shown in Figure 48-3. Cirrhosis results in severe impairment of liver function and can be fatal.

Children born to women who drink during pregnancy may suffer from **fetal alcohol syndrome** (FAS), a condition that can cause physical and mental disabilities in newborn babies. Immediate effects of FAS are low birthweight, below-average length, cleft palate, general weakness, and heart defects. The long-term effects include lack of coordination, slow growth, and learning difficulties due to mental retardation, weak attention span, and hyperactivity.

Section Review

1. What is *blood alcohol concentration?*
2. What happens when alcohol is oxidized by the liver cells?
3. What are some typical behaviors of a person who has a BAC of 0.15 percent?
4. What are some of the effects of fetal alcohol syndrome?
5. Would a person be able to safely drive a car after two drinks in one hour? Explain your answer.

Answers to Section Review

1. A measure of the amount of alcohol in the blood

2. Heat is produced, raising blood temperature and stimulating the brain to increase circulation to the skin, which decreases blood flow to other body organs.

3. Slurred speech, blurred vision, and lack of motor control

4. Low birthweight, below-average birth length, cleft palate, general weakness, heart defects, lack of coordination, slow growth, and learning difficulties

5. No; some impairment to reaction time and coordination would be likely.

48.3 Other Drugs

In Sections 48.1 and 48.2 you learned that nicotine and alcohol act on the central nervous system. Other types of drugs also act on the central nervous system. **Psychoactive drugs** are chemical compounds that change sensory perception and thought processes. **Narcotics** are those drugs made from opium that suppress the cerebral cortex. Because of their highly addictive nature, narcotics can be obtained legally only with a prescription from a doctor. Table 48-4 describes the effects of various drugs.

Section Objectives

- *Distinguish among the four major types of drugs.*
- *List one example of each type of drug, and describe how it affects the body.*
- *Explain the difference between physical and psychological addiction.*
- *Identify a role that dopamine plays in the neurochemistry of addiction.*

Medical Uses of Drugs

Some drugs are administered for medical purposes. These drugs are used to improve health. **Prescription drugs** are those that can be obtained only on written orders from a doctor. The doctor specifies the dosage and length of time the medication must be taken and monitors the effects of the drug on the patient.

Table 48-4 Short-Term and Long-Term Effects of Drugs

Drug	Dependence Potential	Short-term Effects	Long-term Effects
Stimulants			
Caffeine	Probable	Increased heart rate, increased blood pressure	Irregular heartbeat, high blood pressure, headaches, stomach disorders, nervousness; for cocaine, paranoia and death
Amphetamines	High		
Cocaine	High		
Depressants			
Barbiturates	High	Drowsiness, decreased coordination	Depression, emotional instability, hallucinations, death
Tranquilizers	High		
Methaqualone	High		
Phencyclidine hydrochloride (PCP)	Probable	Illusions, poor time–space perception, violent behavior	
Psychoactive drugs			
Lysergic acid diethylamide (LSD)	Probable	Hallucinations	Psychosis
Cannabis sativa (marijuana)	Probable	Short-term memory loss, disorientation	Lung damage, loss of motivation
Narcotics			
Heroin	High	Drowsiness, respiratory depression, nausea, constricted pupils	Convulsions, coma, death
Codeine	High		
Morphine	High		
Inhalants			
Model glue	High	Disorientation, confusion, memory loss	Hallucinations; permanent damage to brain, kidneys, liver, and bone marrow; death
Correction fluid	High		
Aerosol spray	High		

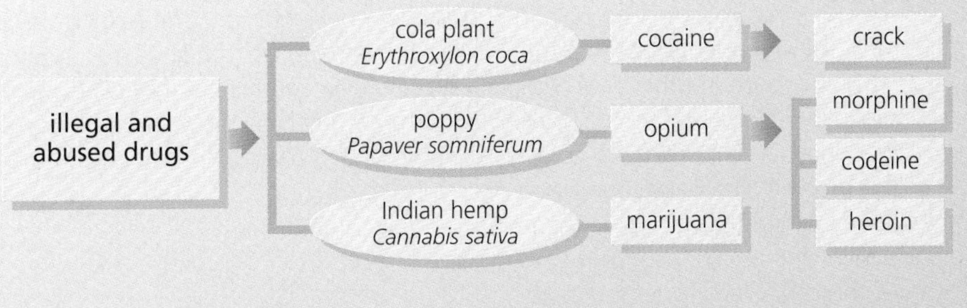

Graphic Organizer Use this organizational chart in Reteaching on p. 756.

Lesson Plan

Section Focus

This section describes the medical use of prescription and over-the-counter (OTC) drugs. Illegal psychoactive and narcotic drugs are also discussed. Students will learn about addiction as well as short-term and long-term effects of drug abuse.

Section Themes

This section points to the theme of **Stability.** Doctors prescribe drugs in particular dosages to restore stability to organs and systems that are impaired or are functioning improperly. Drug abuse destroys stability.

Motivating Activity

Pass around the class empty packages of over-the-counter drugs. Have students read the labels to discover what the drugs are meant to do, what special instructions are given, and what possible side effects are listed. In what ways could such medicines be abused? *(By exceeding the dosage or ignoring warnings and precautions)* Emphasize that even OTC drugs can be abused.

Teaching Strategies

Interpreting the Visuals Call on a student to name the drugs listed under "Stimulants" in Table 48-4 on p. 753. Ask in what foods caffeine is found. *(Coffee, tea, colas, chocolate)* What are amphetamines? *(Stimulants sometimes used by dieters)* What is another form of cocaine? *(Crack)* Have students note the dependence potential and short- and long-term effects of stimulants. Then, ask students to infer why these drugs are legal *(caffeine)*, prescription *(amphetamines)*, and illegal *(cocaine)*. Continue discussing the other groups of drugs in a similar way.

- *See* **Blackline Master 99.**

Discussing Issues Have students consider some of the public programs aimed at keeping people from abusing drugs. Ask them to describe any advertisements or commercials they have seen that deal with the subject. To whom are these programs directed? *(Probably to people considering trying drugs)* Have students consider the reasons why such media programs would not help those already addicted. *(People addicted to drugs cannot just decide to quit based on negative advertising. They need medical help and counseling to quit.)*

Organizing Concepts Have students create a concept map showing legal and illegal drugs and how they can be abused. An example of a completed concept map is shown on p. 747B.

Answer to Think

Transdermal administration allows the drug to be absorbed into the system more quickly than does oral administration and is less painful than injection. Also, since motion sickness often results in vomiting, antinausea medication taken orally may never have the chance to take effect.

Guided Practice

Review the types of drugs and their effects by naming a drug effect and having students name the type of drug that causes it. For example, ask students what drugs slow down the processes of the body. *(Depressants and narcotics)*

Think

One method of administering drugs is transdermally, by a patch placed on the skin that releases a continual supply of the medication. For example, antinausea medication, often used by persons susceptible to motion sickness, can be administered in this way. What do you think are the advantages of such a method?

Some drugs can be purchased without a prescription. These are called **over-the-counter drugs.** The labels on these drugs contain information regarding correct usage. Over-the-counter drugs are safe when taken in the recommended dosage but can be dangerous if too much is taken. As an example, more than 100 children in the United States die each year from accidental overdoses of aspirin.

Both prescription and over-the-counter drugs can be administered in a variety of ways. The most common way is orally, in pill or liquid form. Oral drugs are absorbed by the small intestine and then enter the bloodstream. Drugs can also be injected directly into the bloodstream or into muscle tissue. Other methods of administration effective in certain circumstances include placing the drug under the tongue, inhaling the drug, or placing the drug into the rectum in the form of a suppository.

Drug Addiction

When taken correctly, both prescription and over-the-counter drugs can be beneficial. However, if a drug is taken for longer than the recommended time, a patient may develop an addiction

Biology in Process

The Neurochemistry of Addiction

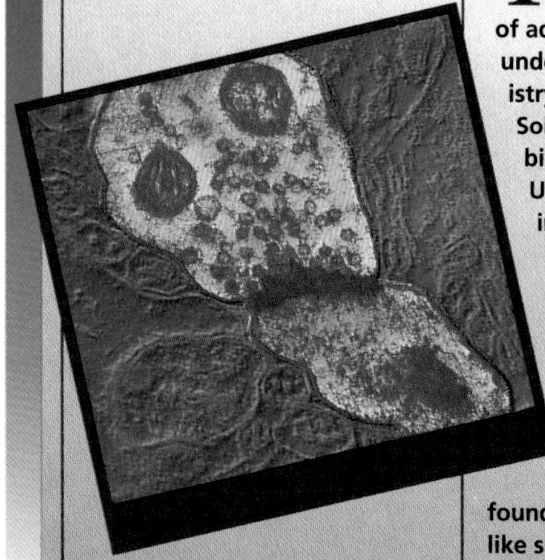

The key to understanding the biological foundation of addiction most likely lies in understanding the neurochemistry of the brain. In the 1970s Solomon H. Snyder, a neurobiologist at Johns Hopkins University, found receptors in the brain for opiates. He inferred that the brain also had opiumlike substances that could bind to these receptors. When Snyder and his colleagues designed an experiment to test this hypothesis, they looked for and found naturally occurring opiate-like substances in brain tissue and called them endorphins.

Endorphins create pleasurable sensations and block pain at receptor sites within the brain, especially within the limbic system (p. 755). The limbic system is an area of the brain that controls the emotions, hunger, thirst, and instinctual responses. Endorphins are responsible for many well-known but little understood neurochemical phenomena, including deep relaxation and "runner's high."

The discovery that receptors deep inside the brain produce pleasure raises new questions about the medical and psychological models of addiction. For example, Edythe D. London, chief of the neurophar-

Interdisciplinary Activity

Social Studies Have students research the prevalence of drug abuse in other countries, such as England, Switzerland, Canada, Mexico, and India. Encourage students to compare the drug problems in these countries with those of the United States. Have them address the following questions: What types of drugs are abused? What societal factors predispose to drug use? How does the government deal with the problem? Have students share their findings, focusing on successful programs in other countries. Might any of these programs be successful in the United States?

to it. An emotional dependence on a drug is called a **psychological addiction.** Changes in body chemistry that result in a demand for a steady supply of a drug create a **physical addiction.** These two types of addictions often occur together.

When physical addiction causes the body to become less responsive to the drug, the user is said to have developed a **tolerance.** The user's body needs increasingly large amounts of the drug to maintain the feelings previously achieved with a smaller dose. If the drug supply is cut off, the addict will go through **withdrawal,** the physical and mental reactions to the lack of the drug. The symptoms of withdrawal vary, depending on the drug being used and duration of use. Symptoms may include nausea, headache, insomnia, breathing difficulties, depression, mental instability, and seizure. Addicts undergoing withdrawal are often hospitalized so that their responses can be monitored.

Illegal Drugs

Some drugs listed in Table 48-4 are illegal. Any use of these illegal drugs is considered drug abuse. Marijuana, which comes from the flowers, leaves, and seeds of *Cannabis sativa*—the Indian hemp

macy lab at the Addiction Research Center of the National Institute on Drug Abuse, has used PET scans to establish that the brains of cocaine addicts have fewer dopamine receptors than those of the nonaddicted controls.

After a neurotransmitter carries a signal across a synapse (p. 754), it is normally carried back into the neuron by a reuptake protein. Neurochemists, however, have noted increased dopamine levels in the limbic system of the brains of alcoholics. As long as dopamine molecules are attached to receptors, pleasurable sensations can continue across the synapse.

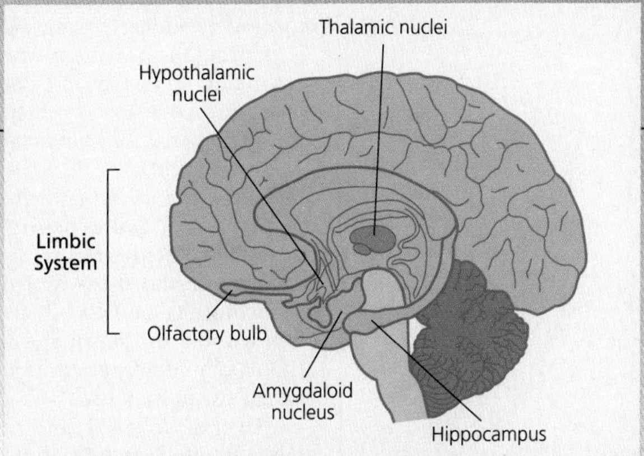

Although researchers are developing drugs to block the neurochemical effects of addictive substances, none of the drugs now being investigated will eliminate addiction. Addiction involves changes in behavior as well as in neurochemistry. Recovery from addiction requires changes in attitude and behavior rather than breakthroughs in neurochemistry. Participation in Alcoholics and Narcotics Anonymous remains the most effective solution available to people who want to recover.

- **How did Snyder infer the existence of endorphins?**

Biology in Process

Using the Feature

The feature focuses on the process skills of inferring, hypothesizing, and experimenting. Explain to students that many potentially addictive substances, including opiates, cocaine, and marijuana, have now been linked to specific receptors in the brain. For pictures of PET scans, refer students to the Biotechnology feature in Chapter 46 (pp. 710–711).

Solomon H. Snyder hypothesized that there may be more than one receptor for each potentially addictive substance. For example, one receptor might block pain, as when cocaine is used for topical anesthesia; another receptor might stimulate pleasure and could lead to cocaine addiction.

Refer students to the text on the limbic system on p. 710. Ask why research on addiction has focused on the limbic system. *(It seems to be the area of the brain responsible for sensation and control of feelings. An addict is out of control. Any agent that could affect the brain at this basic level might be able to block pain, alter perception, and change the quality of sensation, or produce a "high," and thus potentially be abused.)*

Answer to the Feature

The existence of receptors for opiates indicated that the brain might also have opiatelike substances that could bind to these receptors.

LEP Activity

Help students understand the emotional and physical effects of drug abuse by discussing the term *addiction*. Explain that the word *addict* comes from the Latin *addictus*, which means "to deliver over." In an obsolete use of the word, *addict* meant "delivered to another as a slave." Have students discuss ways in which addicts are enslaved by drugs. *(They spend all their money on drugs, sometimes committing crimes to get the money; they are unhappy without the drug; they feel that they cannot survive without the drug; fear of the symptoms of withdrawal often convinces addicts not to quit.)*

Independent Practice

■ Have students write answers to the Section Review.

■ Have students refer to Table 48-4 on p. 753. For each group of drugs, ask students to identify what normal body processes are altered by using the drugs. *(For example, stimulants increase the activity of the nervous system and alter the normal processes of the circulatory system.)*

Check Your Understanding

1. How do physical and psychological addiction differ? *(Physical addiction is caused by changes in the body's chemistry; psychological addiction can be a craving or emotional dependence.)*

2. What physiological condition is suggested by withdrawal symptoms? Explain your answer. *(Physical addiction; the body is reacting to the absence of a drug.)*

Reteaching

Have students create a chart organizing the illegal drugs discussed in the text and the plants from which the drugs come. An example of a completed chart is shown on p. 753 (Graphic Organizer).

■ *See* Section Reviews *worksheet, Section 48.3.*

Enrichment

Have students research the history of marijuana use and its therapeutic value as a medicine. Ask students to present their findings and opinions to the class.

Closure

Have students discuss how drugs have affected the community in which they live. Encourage them to suggest ways to help rid their community of drug abuse.

Figure 48-4 Three plants that are the source of dangerous drugs are (left to right) the Indian hemp plant, *Cannabis sativa,* the opium poppy, *Papaver somniferum,* and the coca plant, *Erythroxylon coca.*

plant—is a psychoactive drug. The active ingredient in marijuana is Δ9-tetrahydrocannabinol, or THC. When smoked, or when heated and eaten, marijuana acts on the nervous system, producing feelings of disorientation in time and space. Continuous use of marijuana can lead to psychological addiction and to a suppressed activity level, often referred to as **amotivational syndrome.**

Opium comes from the fruit of the poppy, *Papaver somniferum.* Morphine and codeine, two types of prescription painkillers, are both made from opium. Heroin, considered one of the most highly addictive drugs, is a compound made from morphine.

Cocaine is a white powder extracted from the leaves of the coca plant, *Erythroxylon coca.* It is a powerful stimulant that raises heart rate, blood pressure, and body temperature. Cocaine acts by changing the chemistry of nerve synapses in the brain. It is extremely addictive, both psychologically and physically. Prolonged use can cause hallucinations, psychosis, and death. Inhaling cocaine also causes damage to the nasal septum. Recently new and highly addictive forms of cocaine such as crack have emerged.

One of the most dangerous depressants is phencyclidine hydrochloride, or PCP. PCP is sometimes added to marijuana, often without the marijuana user being aware of its presence. Use of PCP can cause paranoid and violent behavior. PCP has been banned for human use.

Alcohol, tobacco, and other drugs have great potential for abuse. While drugs are often necessary for proper medical care, their abuse can cause serious physical and mental problems.

Section Review

1. What are *prescription drugs?*
2. What can happen if a person takes a prescription drug for longer than the recommended time?
3. What are some differences among various types of drugs?
4. Name three methods of administering drugs.
5. Why might a person use more than one drug at a time?

Answers to Section Review

1. Drugs that can be bought only on a doctor's orders

2. The person can become addicted to the drug or experience harmful side effects.

3. Drugs differ in the ways they affect people physically and mentally and in their potential for becoming habit-forming.

4. Orally, by injection, by inhalation, by suppository, or transdermally

5. To counteract or enhance the effect of another drug; to treat different health problems

Laboratory

Effects of Cigarette Smoke

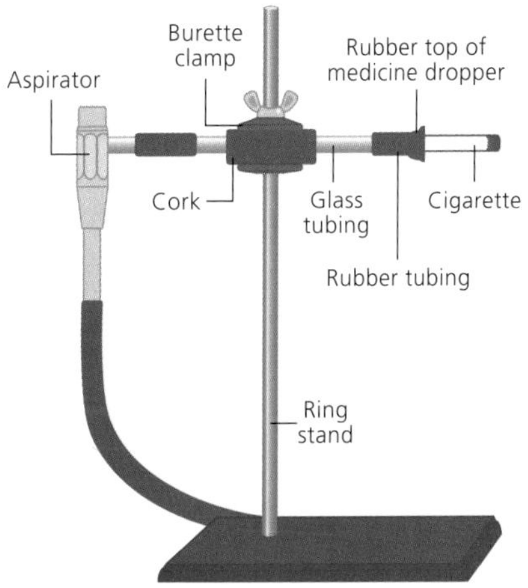

Objective
To use a model that simulates the collection of substances along the air passages as a result of smoking

Process Skills
Modeling, observing, inferring

Materials
Rubber bulb from medicine dropper, scissors, tubing-cork system, rubber tubing, aspirator, burette clamp, ring stand, cigarettes, matches

Background
1 Identify substances normally found in cigarette smoke that may be harmful to the body.
2 List the respiratory structures through which inhaled air passes.

Inquiry
1 Cut the bulb end off the top of the dropper bulb and use it as a holder for the cigarette. What body part does this holder simulate?
2 Use a short piece of rubber tubing to connect the cut end of the holder to one end of the glass tubing. What body part does this section simulate?
3 Connect a 20-cm length of rubber tubing to the aspirator. Use a second short length of tubing to connect the aspirator to the open end of the glass tubing. What will happen in the system when the aspirator is started?
4 Use a burette clamp to hold the apparatus by the cork at an appropriate level on the ring stand.
5 Place a cigarette in the rubber holder. Light the cigarette, and use the rubber tubing connected to the aspirator to draw air through the system. How is this model different from the way a person appears to inhale and exhale cigarette smoke?
6 Use the apparatus to "smoke" two or three cigarettes. What appears on the inside surface of the glass tubing as the cigarettes are smoked?
7 Gently touch the glass tubing. How has its temperature changed since beginning the investigation?
8 Disconnect the glass tubing and smell the open end. Describe the scent.

Conclusions
1 What evidence from your experiment indicates that substances in cigarette smoke coat the air passages?
2 What effect might these substances have on the cilia that line human respiratory passages?
3 What substances in cigarette smoke did the model not detect?
4 How could a scientist determine what chemicals are present in cigarette smoke?

Further Inquiry
Design an experiment to determine whether particulate matter of the smoke affects the mucus in the respiratory system. Consider what you might use to simulate mucus.

Laboratory

(For an overview of cigarette smoke and preparatory information related to the laboratory, see p. 747B.)

Background
1. Nicotine, tars, carbon monoxide, carbon dioxide
2. Air passes through the nostrils, is warmed by the nasal passages, passes down the trachea and into the bronchi. Next, air passes through a branching network of bronchioles and finally reaches the alveoli, where gas exchange takes place.

Inquiry
1. The holder represents the lips.
2. This section represents the respiratory passages.
3. The smoke from the cigarette will be drawn through the apparatus.
5. A smoker draws on a cigarette intermittently, rather than in one long, continuous inhalation; also, a smoker exhales the same smoke through the same respiratory passages, which the apparatus does not do.
6. Brown-black substances collect on the inner surface of the glass tubing.
7. The tube's temperature has increased.
8. The tube smells like a very strong cigarette or a smoker's breath.

Conclusions
1. The gases condense into a brown-black coating on the inside of the glass.
2. Answers will vary but should suggest that the tar inhibits the normal functioning of cilia and thus the ability of the respiratory system to cleanse itself.
3. Gases, such as carbon monoxide
4. By removing the substances from the glass and performing chemical fractionalization tests; by analyzing the gases collected in the apparatus

Further Inquiry
Students may suggest coating the inside of a glass tube with a water-based gel such as K-Y to simulate mucus and then repeating the investigation to see whether particulates are trapped in the gel.

Chapter 48 Review

Vocabulary

1. They are two harmful compounds found in tobacco.
2. Emphysema, chronic bronchitis, lung cancer
3. Psychoactive drugs, narcotics, stimulants, and depressants
4. BAC is a measurement of the level of alcohol in the bloodstream; rate of consumption, ability to metabolize alcohol, body weight, and amount of food in the stomach are factors affecting BAC.
5. A person who has become addicted to a drug may develop a tolerance, causing the drug to have less effect. If the person tries to quit using the drug or cannot get the drug, he or she will have withdrawal symptoms.

Review

1. b	**6.** d
2. c	**7.** a
3. a	**8.** b
4. b	**9.** d
5. c	**10.** c

11. Nicotine is absorbed through the lining of the mouth and through the lungs.
12. Sidestream smoke can cause the same effects as smoking.
13. The mother is twice as likely to suffer a miscarriage; babies are smaller and less robust and are twice as likely to die in the first few months; babies also have a high risk of developing heart disease.
14. Excessive use of alcohol causes the cells of the liver to use alcohol as an energy source, and eventually they are unable to function properly. The result is accumulation of fat deposits that may lead to fatty liver and cirrhosis.
15. Coordination is impaired, speech may become slurred, and reaction time is greatly slowed.

Chapter 48 Review

Vocabulary

addiction (749)
alcoholism (751)
alcoholic fermentation (751)
amotivational syndrome (756)
blood alcohol concentration (751)
chronic bronchitis (749)
cirrhosis (752)
depressant (751)
drug (749)
ethanol (751)
emphysema (749)
fatty liver (752)
fetal alcohol syndrome (752)
gastritis (752)
narcotic (753)
nicotine (749)
over-the-counter drug (754)
physical addiction (755)
prescription drug (753)
psychoactive drug (753)
psychological addiction (755)
sidestream smoke (750)
stimulant (749)
tar (749)
tolerance (755)
withdrawal (755)

1. How are nicotine and tar related?
2. Identify two respiratory diseases caused by smoking.
3. List the four major types of drugs.
4. What is *blood alcohol concentration,* and what are some factors affecting it?
5. Describe the relationship between addiction, tolerance, and withdrawal.

Review

1. Nicotine is a (a) psychoactive drug (b) stimulant (c) narcotic (d) depressant.
2. Tar (a) causes an increase in heart rate (b) is a stimulant (c) paralyzes cilia (d) is transported by the brain.
3. Emphysema is (a) a degenerative lung disease (b) a form of cancer (c) an inflammation of the kidneys (d) a result of chewing tobacco.
4. Alcohol is a (a) stimulant (b) depressant (c) narcotic (d) psychoactive drug.
5. BAC specifically measures (a) the rate at which a person has been drinking (b) a person's genetic ability to metabolize alcohol (c) the amount of alcohol in a person's blood (d) the time at which a person was drinking.
6. Fetal alcohol syndrome can cause (a) low birthweight (b) heart defects (c) learning difficulties (d) all of the above.
7. Aspirin is one kind of (a) over-the-counter drug (b) illegal drug (c) depressant (d) psychoactive drug.
8. Psychological addiction (a) occurs when the body becomes dependent on a substance (b) is an emotional dependence on a drug (c) occurs after tolerance to a drug has developed (d) is caused only by illegal drugs.
9. Depressants include (a) cocaine (b) tar (c) nicotine (d) alcohol.
10. Narcotics cause (a) increased heart rate (b) increased alertness (c) decreased alertness (d) lung damage.
11. How is nicotine absorbed into the bloodstream?
12. Describe the harmful effects of sidestream smoke.
13. What are some of the harmful effects of smoking during pregnancy?
14. Describe the specific effects of alcohol on the cells of the liver.
15. In what ways are mental capabilities diminished as BAC increases?
16. What are some potential effects of long-term, excessive alcohol use?
17. What is the relationship between fatty liver and cirrhosis?
18. What are psychoactive drugs?
19. Describe a role that dopamine plays in alcohol addiction.
20. Describe the harmful effects of cocaine.

16. Heart disease, gastritis, ulcers, high blood pressure, metabolic disorders, fatty liver, cirrhosis, and alcoholism
17. Alcohol abuse can lead to fatty liver, which if untreated can eventually result in cirrhosis.
18. Chemical compounds that alter sensory perceptions and thought processes
19. Alcohol blocks dopamine reuptake, allowing pleasurable sensations to continue across a synapse.
20. Cocaine can cause addiction, hallucinations, psychosis, and death.

Critical Thinking

1. Caffeine is a stimulant commonly found in coffee, tea, cola drinks, and cocoa. Authorities say that people who consume 500 mg or more of caffeine per day may suffer harmful effects. Look at the chart on the right, which shows the milligrams of caffeine contained in given amounts of various beverages and chocolates. Estimate your daily caffeine intake, listing sources and the times of day you ingest it. Is your caffeine intake too high?
2. Alcohol is known to be a depressant. How do you explain the fact that consumption of alcohol sometimes results in a carefree attitude and a feeling of elation?
3. Methadone, a synthetic narcotic drug, is often used in the treatment of heroin addiction. Methadone blocks the body's craving for heroin. Based on your knowledge of the nervous system, suggest a mechanism by which this is possible.
4. Aspirin is one of the most commonly used drugs. Look into some of the positive and negative effects of aspirin and write a short paragraph about your findings.
5. If a pregnant woman smokes cigarettes or takes drugs, the fetus can be affected. Explain how nicotine and drugs get into the bloodstream of the unborn child.
6. In Europe in the 1960s many pregnant women took the drug thalidomide. Although tests were conducted using laboratory animals, many children were born with severe deformities to women who had taken thalidomide. In the United States this drug was not available, because it had not undergone the lengthy testing required for approval. Discuss the advantages and disadvantages of requiring a long testing period.

Amounts of Caffeine in Some Beverages and Foods (in milligrams)

Coffee (5 oz.)	
Brewed, drip method	60–180
Brewed, percolator	40–170
Instant	30–120
Decaffeinated, brewed	2–5
Decaffeinated, instant	1–5
Tea (5 oz.)	
Brewed, major U.S. brands	20–90
Brewed, imported brands	25–110
Iced (12 oz.)	67–76
Instant	25–50
Chocolate and cocoa	
Cocoa (5 oz.)	2–20
Chocolate milk (8 oz.)	2–7
Milk chocolate (1 oz.)	1–15
Semisweet chocolate (1 oz.)	5–35
Chocolate flavored syrup (1 oz.)	4
Soft drinks (12 oz.)	
Cola drinks and cola–fruit drinks	30–46
Other soft drinks	52–58

Extension

1. Read "Opium, Cocaine and Marijuana in American History" in *Scientific American,* July 1991, pp. 40–47. How does an examination of America's relation to drugs in history shed light on our current reaction to drug use?
2. In the local library or a doctor's office ask to see the *Physicians' Desk Reference.* This book shows all the prescription drugs made by drug companies in the United States. Make a chart of ten different drugs. Headings should include name of the drug, generic name, drug manufacturer, uses, dosage, and side effects.
3. Both private groups and local and federal government agencies can give you information about preventing addiction. Send for information about the Say No to Drugs campaign and about Students Against Drunk Driving (SADD).

Critical Thinking

1. Answers will vary; students should list the sources of the caffeine they consume and estimate the total milligrams of caffeine they ingest in a typical day.
2. Among the early effects of alcohol are increased feelings of relaxation and lightheadedness. People in this stage of intoxication may appear carefree and happy.
3. Methadone probably mimics heroin's interference with normal nerve transmission.
4. Answers will vary, but students might include the fact that aspirin in some cases causes intestinal bleeding and that an overdose of aspirin can be fatal. Students might also say that aspirin is sometimes very helpful in treating diseases such as heart conditions and arthritis.
5. The nicotine and drugs enter the fetus's bloodstream through the placenta.
6. Answers will vary, but students should see that drug testing is important and that the FDA in the United States tries to be thorough. However, the long testing period becomes difficult when drugs used successfully in other countries are unavailable to people in the United States who need them.

Extension

1. Students should list examples to show they understand the pendulum nature of public opinion on drug use.
2. Encourage students to begin their search with prescription drugs with which they are familiar. You may want to discuss with students the advantages and disadvantages of using generic drugs.
3. Have students look in the Yellow Pages under "Alcoholism" and "Drug Abuse" to find other organizations through which they can find information.

Discussion

Guide the discussion by posing the following questions.

1. Explain whether poor or uninsured sick people should receive a new organ. If you think yes, who should pay? *(Encourage students to consider how medical expenses would be paid for the poor. If students say that poor people should be denied organs, ask them how they would explain their opinion to a dying poor person. If time permits, have students role-play this situation.)*

2. A team of researchers has created an artificial pancreas that uses cells from animals. What ethical issues do you see in the manufacture of this artificial organ? *(Some students may say it is unethical to use animals in medicine. Others may say people should try to relieve all human pain.)*

3. The sale of organs is illegal in many countries, including Canada and the United States. However, in some countries, such as India, people can sell their organs. Explain why people should or should not have the right to sell their organs. *(Some students will say that people have a right to control what they do with their bodies. Others may express religious beliefs that condemn the sale or use of organs in unusual ways.)*

4. In the United States the sale of blood is permitted, but the sale of organs is illegal. Explain why this policy is or is not reasonable. *(Encourage students to consider both sides of the issue. Some doctors think that organ donors should benefit financially from the transplant process, since the recipient benefits greatly by receiving the organ. Moral, religious, or other ethical convictions can influence policymakers and other citizens.)*

Intra-Science

How the Sciences Work Together

The Question in Biology: *Can We Replace Damaged Organs?*

Advances in medical science have made organ transplants possible but not without our encountering new problems and asking more questions. Therefore, doctors and patients must weigh risks and benefits before a medical team can transplant an organ.

People have different types of tissues, just as they have different types of blood. To achieve a successful transplant, doctors must minimize the chances of organ-tissue rejection, which is less likely to occur if the tissues of the donor's organ are a good match with the recipient's tissues. Since human tissue has 32 kinds of antigens, doctors look among prospective donors for a good match with a recipient's antigens, knowing that a recipient's immune system will attack any foreign antigens. As a result, the organ will be rejected because the recipient's T cells will attack the donor organ, causing blood clots and other complications. Just as a patient with type A blood must receive blood of a compatible type, a transplant recipient must receive an organ that is compatible.

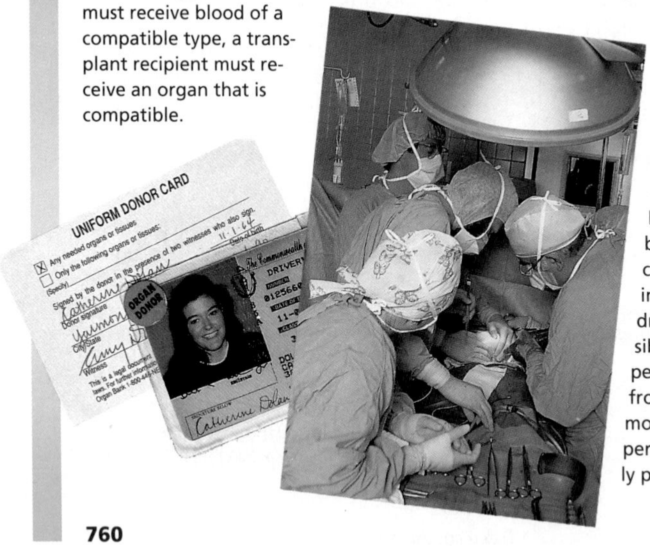

The first successful organ transplant occurred in 1954, when a team of doctors at Boston's Peter Bent Brigham Hospital removed a kidney from one identical twin and implanted it in the other twin. Organ transplants between twins have a high success rate. Because identical twins have identical genotypes, they have identical tissues and antigens. Most transplant patients, however, do not have a twin and face a lifelong threat of rejecting a donor organ. If an organ transplant is made between a child and a parent, a sibling, or another close relative, it has a better chance of success than a transplant between two unrelated persons.

Since the first successful organ transplant in 1954, doctors have learned to transplant hearts, lungs, livers, pancreases, skin, corneas of the eye, bone marrow, and even nerves. Whereas humans have two kidneys, they have only one heart and only one liver. Such a vital organ must come from a recently deceased individual and must also match the recipient's tissue type. For the past several years, the demand for various transplantable organs has remained about five times higher than the annual supply of about 4,000 donor organs.

The Connection to Chemistry

In many cases the patient's declining health does not allow time to find the best possible tissue and antigen match. To counteract organ rejection, doctors use immunosuppressant drugs. Cyclosporine, a drug that has made heart transplants possible, was first used in 1972. FK 506, an experimental immunosuppressant derived from a fungus, blocks the immune response more effectively than cyclosporine. Early experiments have shown that FK 506 effectively prevents some autoimmune diseases.

Connections to Other Disciplines

History Students should research the early years of transplant surgery and project where the technology might be 25 years from now. Encourage students to give a rationale for their projections.

Ethics Some people object to prolonging life through such means as organ transplants. Students may wish to interview their family doctor or school nurse to learn how medical professionals deal with the medical and social ethics of procuring and transplanting organs.

Sometimes a donor organ becomes available on short notice immediately after a fatal accident. Yet it may be several hours before the surgical team and the recipient are notified and ready. Consequently, the organ must be preserved until it can be transplanted. To protect the usefulness of donor organs, chemists have created a new fluid that helps preserve organs. In experiments on donor livers, for example, those stored in the new fluid remained viable almost twice as long as livers stored in other fluids. Some livers remained viable for up to 24 hours before deterioration began.

■ *What advantages will organ preservatives give transplant teams and recipients waiting for organs?*

The Connection to Engineering

Some scientists hope that artificial organs will eliminate the need for tissue typing and dispel the fear of organ rejection altogether. Today, however, some artificial organs can still cause serious problems. For example, blood cells stick to the plastics in some artificial hearts, causing dangerous blood clots. In the artificial lung, called an intravascular oxygenator (IVOX), having an anticoagulant coating on the ventilating fibers has proved essential to preventing blood clots. Researchers are also investigating how lining artificial organs with cells like those inside blood vessels might prevent clotting.

Medical engineers have a different problem with artificial joints. Human bone does not bond well with the metal, usually titanium, used in artificial joints. Medical engineers have tried coating titanium joints with calcium and apatite compounds. The results have been encouraging. So far, the calcium-coated implants have proved to be about 25 percent stronger than their noncoated counterparts; and the apatite-coated devices have bonded well to bone.

■ *Describe some properties that researchers might find useful in materials for artificial organs.*

The Connection to Other Sciences

After a successful transplant, a recipient may feel uncomfortable or guilty about having another person's heart or liver, especially if the organ came from someone who died tragically. Some people believe that such feelings can provoke organ rejection. To help patients cope with their feelings, mental health professionals have become members of the transplant team, though they may never enter the operating room. These psychological technicians help organ recipients and their families deal with their fears and anxieties; they also help a donor's family cope with the stress of donating a loved one's organs.

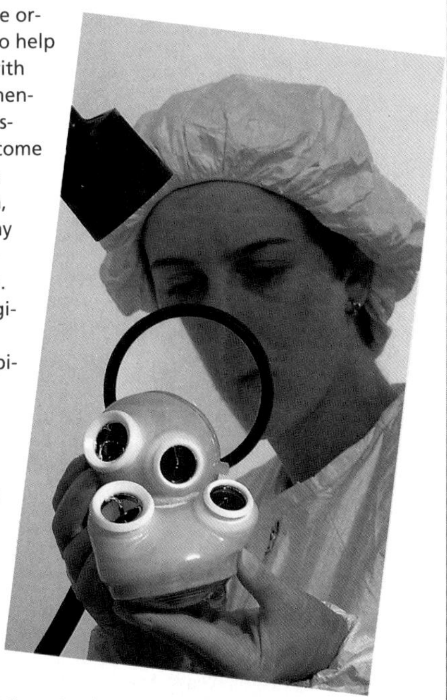

■ *What help could a physical therapist give someone who has received an artificial limb?*

The Connection to Careers

Operating rooms will need more skilled specialists as the number of organ transplants increases. Surgeons, operating room and intensive care nurses, anesthesiologists, and medical technologists are all vital to a successful transplant. Pharmacologists and chemists are needed to seek new drugs to decrease the chances of rejection, with the help of laboratory technicians. Biomedical engineers, computer programmers, and physical therapists may work together to design more lifelike artificial organs and limbs. For more information about related careers in the biological sciences, turn to page 842.

Intra-Science

5. Should parents have the right to donate the tissues or the organs of one child, even to save the life of another child? *(Student responses will vary. Ask students to consider that parents in California did conceive and give birth to a daughter to provide an older daughter with the supply of bone marrow needed to treat her fatal disease. In the past the U.S. Supreme Court has ruled that no one may be forced to donate; however, parents can and must consent for their child to donate.)*

Answers to

Chemistry By increasing the length of time an organ can survive outside a body, the preserving fluids will allow more time to transport the organ greater distances or will allow more time for transplant recipients to arrive at a transplant center.

Engineering As students offer suggestions, encourage them to describe how their materials would be used for artificial organs. Students may suggest a variety of material properties, including being nonsticky, porous, flexible, or having some other property, depending on its use in the body. Tell students that researchers are investigating calcium ceramics, hydrogels, and compounds synthesized from monomers that have mechanical properties and porosity similar to living tissues.

Other Sciences The physical therapist can help the recipient of an artificial limb adjust to the loss of a natural limb and to using the artificial limb.

Enrichment

By signing a Uniform Donor Card, people can pledge to donate any or all of their organs for use after their death. In many states, a donor's card appears on the back of the driver's license. Ask students to write a brief essay explaining why they would or would not consent to donate their organs. Some students may be willing to read their essays to the class.

Unit 10 Ecology

Chapters

Unit Overview

Unit 10 covers how individual organisms interact with one another and the world around them. Chapter 49 discusses the biosphere and properties of different terrestrial and aquatic biomes. Chapter 50 describes the flow of energy and nutrients in food chains. Chapter 51 discusses symbiotic relationships, rhythmic patterns, and ecological succession. Chapter 52 describes factors influencing population size, including discussion of the size of the human population. Chapter 53 concludes the unit by discussing renewable and nonrenewable natural resources, and human efforts to avoid their harmful or wasteful use.

Issues in Biology

Many scientists consider the preservation of species diversity the most important problem facing people today. As human populations increase, wildlife habitats such as tropical rain forests are being destroyed. Some scientists fear that as many as one-fourth of the species on earth today could become extinct in the next 50 years. This would represent a tremendous loss of potential knowledge and resources. Many species might even become extinct before they can be studied for possible use in medicine or agriculture. Therefore, scientists are hoping that biological diversity can be maintained by increasing protected wildlife areas and preserving selected species in artificial environments such as zoos, botanical gardens, DNA banks, or seed banks. Ask students to discuss some advantages and disadvantages of zoos and of the other preservation methods.

Research in Progress

In a society concerned about its environment, photovoltaic cells seem an ideal source of electric power because they produce electricity from sunlight with no pollution, noise, or moving parts. Researchers are attempting to diversify applications of photovoltaic power by creating flexible, solar-powered cells that are thin, lightweight, and inexpensive. These devices are made from amorphous silicon applied to flexible, plastic backings. Until now, however, amorphous silicon cells have proved to be less efficient and durable than rigid silicon cells, but researchers are working to solve these problems. Since photovoltaic systems require little maintenance and no water, they are suitable for use in remote, arid regions. Someday, solar-powered camping tents, sails, clothing, and even airplanes could become available.

Interdisciplinary Activity

Government Many environmental problems facing us today require the help of government regulations. Protection of endangered species and their habitats, preservation of the ozone layer, pollution control, and development of a long-term energy strategy are a few prevailing problems. Suggest that students research a local, state, national, or international law or policy that supports a governmental agency such as the National Park Service, the Environmental Protection Agency, or a local conservation commission. Have students present a brief description of the legislation, history, and functions of the agency and give their opinions of the agency's usefulness. Require evidence to support opinions.

Resources

Chapter	Print: For the Teacher	Print: For the Student	Audiovisual/Software
49	■ R. S. D. Barnes and R. N. Hughes, *Introduction to Marine Ecology*, 2nd ed., Blackwell Scientific, 1988. ■ L. B. Holm-Nielsen, I. C. Nielsen, and H. Balsley, *Tropical Forests*, Academic Press Ltd., 1989.	■ Anna Maria Gillis, "The New Forestry," *BioScience*, September 1990, 558–562. ■ Richard Monastersky, "The Fall of the Forest," *Science News*, July 21, 1990, 40–41.	■ *Atlantic Realm: Into the Abyss*. Video, 60 min. Films, Inc., 1989. ■ *Atlantic Realm: Ocean of Light*. Video, 50 min. Films, Inc., 1989. ■ *Biomes: Grassland* (*Biomes* series). Video, 12 min. Coronet, 1989.
50	■ Sir Edmund Hillary, ed., *Ecology 2000: The Changing Face of Earth*, Beaufort Books, 1984. ■ Jean H. Sibbald, *Homes in the Sea: From the Shore to the Deep*, Dillon, 1986.	■ Robert Holland, "The Quandary of Leaves," *Audubon*, November 1990, 96–99. ■ Stephen Strauss, "Climbing the Food Chain," *Technology Review*, July 1990, 17–18.	■ *Equatorial River: The Amazon*. Video, 23 min. Bullfrog Films, 1987. ■ *The Flowing Oasis* (*Essence of Life* series, part 1). Video, 55 min. PBS/KD Enterprises, 1987.
51	■ Sue Binkley, *The Clockwork Sparrow: Time, Clocks and Calendars in Biological Organisms*, Prentice-Hall, 1990.	■ Robert Adams, "Smithsonian Horizons," *Smithsonian*, February 1990, 12. ■ Timothy M. Beardsley, "The Sea Turtle's Tale," *Scientific American*, August 1990, 32.	■ *Balance: A Predator-Prey Simulation*. Apple II, 48K. IBM PC, 64K. Disk. Diversified Educational Enterprises. ■ *The Islands: Watery Outposts of Australia*. Video, 25 min. Centre, 1986. ■ *Whale Rescue (Nova)*. Video, 52 min. WGBH/Coronet, 1988.
52	■ Norman Arnheim, Tom White, and William E. Rainey, "Application of PCR: Organismal and Population Biology," *BioScience*, March 1990, 174–182. ■ David Attenborough, *The Living Planet*, Little, Brown and Co., 1986.	■ John Nielsen, "What Ever Happened to the Population Bomb?" *National Wildlife*, April/May 1990, 28.	■ *Animal Populations: Nature's Checks and Balances*. Film or video, 22 min. Teacher's guide. Encyclopædia Britannica, 1983. ■ *Population Growth*. Apple II, 48K. Includes diskette with backup and 150-page text. COMPress. Carolina Biological.
53	■ Philip D. Jones and Tom M. L. Wigley, "Global Warming Trends," *Scientific American*, August 1990, 84–91. ■ Robert Repetto, ed., *The Global Possible: Resources, Development, and the New Century*, Yale University Press, 1986.	■ Art Kleiner, "Oily Wastes and Wants," *Discover*, May 1991, 30. ■ Peter Steinhart, "Innocent Victims of a Toxic World," *National Wildlife*, February/March 1990, 21–27.	■ *Can Polar Bears Tread Water?* (Protecting the Global Environment) Video, 60 min. Cinema Guild, 1989. ■ *The Price of Progress* (Narrated by Bob Geldof). Video, 54 min. Bullfrog Films, 1987.

Introducing the Unit

In Unit 9, students learned about individual human beings. Unit 10 shows how people and other organisms interact with each other and their environment. Introduce the unit by asking the following questions.

1. In what ways do organisms interact with each other? *(Sample answers: They eat each other; they compete for food and other resources, such as nesting sites; animals disperse plant seeds; bacteria and fungi decompose dead organisms.)*

2. How are organisms dependent on nonliving factors in the environment? *(Sample answers: They need air, water, soil, minerals, sunshine, a reasonable climate, and an ozone layer.)*

3. Suggest different kinds of environments on earth that organisms have adapted to. *(Sample answers: There are aquatic and terrestrial environments; some are hot, others are cold; some are wet, others are dry; some environments have rich soil, others are poor in nutrients.)*

4. How do organisms other than humans change the environment? *(Sample answers: All the oxygen in the atmosphere results from producers; topsoil is the result of decomposition; roots of plants keep soil from eroding; lakes tend to fill in as organisms grow in them and then die.)*

5. How are people changing the earth? *(We are using up resources very rapidly, destroying habitats, and creating many pollutants. We also have increased the earth's carrying capacity.)*

Unit 10 Ecology

Chapters

"No part of life can be considered apart from any other; there is no such thing as an organism without an environment." *Lewis Mumford*

You've probably never thought of a layer of moisture on moss as an environment, but it is in fact an environment in which tiny invertebrates called tardigrades make their home. The relationships between organisms and their environments make up the subject matter of ecology. Ecologists may choose to study tiny microenvironments like the surface of a moss leaf or larger environments like the volcanic craters where the silversword plant grows. The largest environment of all is the biosphere, the thin layer of the earth's surface where all organisms live.

Tardigrade, *Echiniscus spiniger*

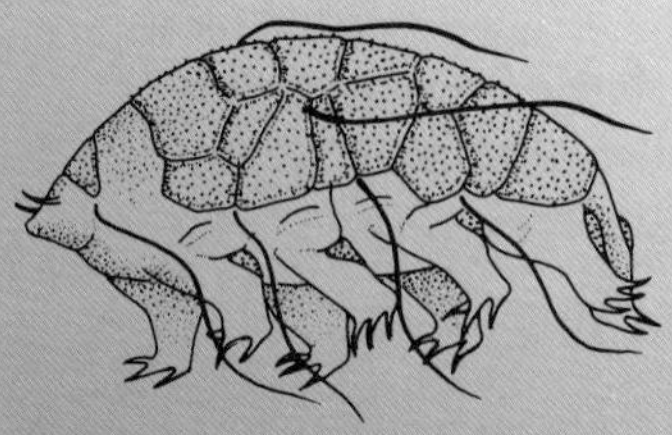

Dewdrops on moss, *Polytrichum hirsutum*

762

Using the Opening Quotation

Ask students to express what they think that the Mumford quotation means. If necessary, help students infer that the interrelationships among organisms and their environments form an ecological unit. In this unit students will recognize how organisms depend on one another and on the resources of their environment. Ask students to identify some life-sustaining relationships they have with their environment. *(Students should describe some necessities of life—oxygen, food, shelter, clothing, warmth— and their sources.)* Ask students what harmful effects are results of our relationships with our environment. *(Students will offer a variety of ways in which people destroy or pollute various environments.)*

Silversword plant, *Argyroxiphium sandwicense*, in Hawaii

The biosphere from space

Unit Themes

Energy Organisms ultimately obtain energy from the sun. Plants harness this energy by making sugars and other carbohydrates in photosynthesis. Energy stored by plants is then transferred to other organisms through food chains.

Patterns of Change Changes are always occurring in the environment. Nutrients such as water, nitrogen, carbon, and oxygen are always being recycled. The process of succession occurs as organisms modify their environments, often making them more favorable for other types of organisms.

Stability Stability is maintained as long as earth remains hospitable to life. After an area undergoes succession, it remains basically unchanged until there is a major environmental disruption. Populations of organisms fluctuate but can reach a stable carrying capacity for long periods of time.

Systems and Interactions Organisms are always interacting with one another and with the abiotic factors of their environments. Organisms feed upon one another and use one another for nesting places. They are constantly using the abiotic factors of the environments and changing them. Plants change the atmosphere by producing oxygen while at the same time plants use carbon dioxide in the atmosphere. The amount of rainfall and temperature in an area determines how much and what type of vegetation will grow there.

Understanding the Visuals

Astronauts commented that from space there are no political boundaries, only a fragile planet covered with water and land. Ask students to consider how the photograph of the biosphere relates to the quotation and to the concept that all life is interdependent. Ask students to name the area of the earth visible in the photograph. *(Africa and the Middle East, with the Indian Ocean and Asia to the east)* Ask students how big they think that the moss is *(a few centimeters).* Tell them that the silversword is one of many organisms unique to Hawaii. Ask students why they think that there are so many organisms found on Hawaii and nowhere else. *(Hawaii is surrounded by the Pacific Ocean; new species evolved there that did not disperse elsewhere.)*

Chapter 49 The Biosphere and Biomes

Chapter Overview

Chapter 49 discusses biomes and the factors in each biome that determine which kinds of organisms will live there. Section 49.1 defines biotic (living) and abiotic (nonliving) factors in the biosphere and describes the interactions between them. Section 49.2 describes the major terrestrial biomes and Section 49.3 the aquatic biomes of the earth.

Chapter Planning Chart

B	S	A	Sections and Subsections	Page	Features	Page	Resources
•	•	•	**49.1 Ecological Units**				
			The Biosphere	765	Section Review	766	Videodiscs
			Ecosystems	765			Laboratories: Brine Shrimp
							Section Reviews Worksheet
•	•	•	**49.2 Terrestrial Biomes**				
			Polar Biomes	767	Think	768	Videodiscs
			Tundra	768	Biotechnology	770	Blackline Master 100
			Coniferous Forest	769	Section Review	773	Overhead Transparency T49
			Deciduous Forest	770			Blackline Master 101
			Grassland	771			Process Skills: Biomes
			Desert	772			Section Reviews Worksheet
			Rain Forests	772			
•	•	•	**49.3 Aquatic Biomes**				
			Marine Biome	774	Laboratory	777	Videodiscs
			Freshwater Biome	776	Section Review	776	Section Reviews Worksheet
			End of Chapter Activities				
					Chapter Review	778	Vocabulary Skills
							Chapter Test
							Computer Test Generator

B *The Basic Level curriculum presents the most fundamental knowledge offered in the course.*
S *The Standard Level curriculum is designed for the average student who is able to master most topics.*
A *The Advanced Level curriculum includes suggestions for teaching the most academically able students.*

Cooperative Learning

Group Activity: Marine Biomes

- **Group Size:** *3 students*
- **Outcome:** *Students will be able to describe the biotic and abiotic factors in each zone of the marine biome and how these factors influence the organisms living there.*
- **Individual Accountability:** *Each student will research a different aspect of one zone of the marine biome.*
- **Positive Interdependence:** *The group will discuss how all the factors in each zone interact.*

Assign each group one of the following zones: intertidal zone, neritic zone, benthic zone, estuaries, oceanic zone (including the photic and aphotic parts of the oceanic zone, but not the benthic zone). Refer them to Section 49.3. Have one student in the group list the abiotic factors of the zone. Have another student list the organisms that live there. Additional organisms may be found in an encyclopedia. Have a third student color a blackline map of North America to show where the zone occurs along the Pacific, Atlantic, or Gulf coasts of the United States.

After they complete their individual assignments, ask members of the group to pool their information and discuss the interrelationships between the biotic and abiotic factors. Encourage students to see the interaction between organisms and their zone as evolutionary adaptations. Have a volunteer from each group present the group's zone to the class. Encourage class discussion in order to present a whole picture of the marine biome.

Concept Map

The following is one possible solution to the concept mapping activity in Reteaching on p. 776.

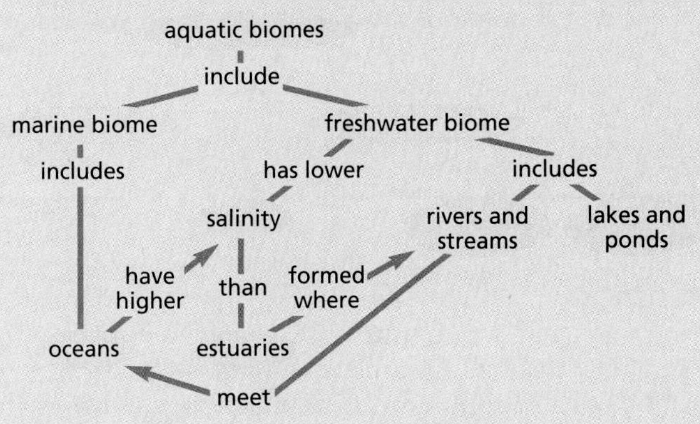

Laboratory Preparation

Overview *(See p. 777.)*

In this lab students relate the activity of *Elodea* to changes in its environment. Students use a simple chemical test to obtain a quantitative indication of the oxygen content of the environment. Then they use the data to draw conclusions about the effect of *Elodea* on its environment and speculate on how the organisms can produce effects that are both beneficial and harmful to other community members.

Preparation

Twenty-four hours before this procedure, prepare two bottles of *Elodea* for each team of students. For each team, put two sprigs of *Elodea* and 100 mL water in a 180-mL widemouth bottle. Seal the bottle, label it A, and put it under a lighted 200- to 300-watt light bulb. Repeat the process, labeling the second bottle B. Put bottle B in total darkness.

To prepare a 25% manganese sulfate solution, add 350 g manganese sulfate to 1,050 mL distilled water. To prepare a 40% potassium hydroxide–potassium iodide solution, add 500 g potassium hydroxide to 1 L distilled water, and then add 150 g potassium iodide. To prepare a 0.003% sodium thiosulfate solution, add 3.1 g sodium thiosulfate to 1 L distilled water.

Teaching Tips

Have students read the laboratory carefully before they begin.

For Inquiry step 7, the medicine droppers should have the same size openings as the bulb pipettes. Droppers may differ in their delivery rate; they may deliver anywhere from 20 to 30 drops per mL. Data indicating a very low oxygen level in bottle *A* may be due to drop size.

The water temperature also influences the oxygen level. Make sure the bottles are kept at about the same temperature.

Safety

Safety goggles must be worn at all times during this lab. All chemicals used are harmful to skin and clothing. Sulfuric acid is a strong corrosive. If it is spilled on clothing, remove clothing at once, and if it is spilled on skin, immediately flush the area with water. Avoid breathing the fumes. Remind students to use a bulb pipette when working with acids.

Chapter Themes

Systems and Interactions Organisms are constantly interacting with their environment. Emphasize that living things must get all they need from their environment.

Ask students why different kinds of organisms grow in different habitats. Have them give examples of how particular organisms are adapted for their particular environment. For example, grasses grow in parts of the West where there is not enough rain to support trees.

Stability As long as an environment is undisturbed for a long period of time, the organisms living there are unlikely to change dramatically. Ask students what they think would happen if climatic changes occurred that, for example, brought more rain to the grasslands. *(The grass would, over a period of time, be replaced by trees.)* Point out to students that such climatic changes have occurred in the past.

Chapter Motivating Activity

Display pictures from reference books, or slides of two different biomes such as a desert and a tropical rain forest. Try to include the biome where you live. Have students describe the kinds of organisms they see in the pictures. Then have them describe what it would be like to be standing there. (How hot, cold, wet, or dry would it be? Would the soil be rich or poor?) Finally, have students brainstorm ways in which the organisms they see are adapted to the conditions they have described, and list their ideas on the board.

Chapter 49 *The Biosphere and Biomes*

Introduction

From the highest mountain peak to the deepest ocean trench, nearly every part of the earth supports some form of life. Much of the diversity of living things reflects adaptations to the earth's varying climate and geography. In this chapter you will learn about the major distribution patterns of plant and animal life found throughout the biosphere—that area of the earth where life exists.

Chapter Outline

Chapter Concept

As you read, note how plants and animals are adapted to the various climatic and geographic conditions found on the earth.

Tree opuntias, *Opuntia* sp., Arizona. Inset: The marine biome.

Understanding the Visuals

Have students use the two photographs to contrast desert and marine biomes. Ask them to name several factors in each biome to which organisms would have to adapt. *(A hot, dry, terrestrial environment in the desert, salt water in the ocean)* Ask them how the organisms they see in the desert are adapted to this environment. *(The plants are not leafy and thus have very little surface area, enabling them to conserve water. They have spines that prevent animals from eating them.)* Ask students to speculate about what adaptations organisms in the marine environment might have. *(They need to get oxygen from water, so the animals probably have gills.)*

49.1 Ecological Units

No organism—no rhinoceros, duck, oak tree, or bacterium—exists alone. Each is part of an intricately linked system of living and nonliving elements. The study of the relationship between organisms and their environment is called **ecology.** Ecologists study not only how organisms act together but also how they are adapted to their environments. Adaptation, which results from evolution by natural selection, is a factor that unifies the structure, physiology, and behavior of all organisms throughout the biosphere.

Section Objectives

- *Define the term* biosphere.
- *Distinguish between populations, communities, and ecosystems.*
- *Name the types of abiotic factors in an ecosystem.*
- *Name three types of interactions among biotic factors in an environment.*
- *List some ways biotic and abiotic factors in an environment interact.*

The Biosphere

The **biosphere** is that area of the earth where life exists. Insects and spores of microorganisms and plants have been found 8 km high in the atmosphere. Other organisms such as sea urchins and brittle stars live 8 km below the surface of the ocean. Almost all life, however, exists on or within a few meters of the earth's surface. The biosphere is so thin that if the earth were the size of a basketball, the biosphere would be much thinner than this page.

Ecologists learn about the biosphere by studying smaller and simpler ecological units within it. These simpler levels serve as models for the larger, more complex biosphere. In Sections 49.2 and 49.3 you will learn about large ecological units of the biosphere called biomes. A smaller ecological unit is a **population,** all the members of a species that live in the same area and make up a breeding group. For example, the moose on Isle Royale, a national park in Lake Superior, constitute a population. They interact with each other and with other species on the island, including the timber wolves that kill and eat moose. The moose population, the wolf population, and all the other living things on the island form a community. A **community** includes all the populations in an area.

Figure 49-1 Moose are just one of the many populations that interact to make up the Isle Royale community.

Ecosystems

Ecologists also study ecosystems. An **ecosystem** is an ecological unit that includes all the interacting parts of an environment in an area. A lake, a prairie, and a cave are all examples of ecosystems. The nonliving components of an ecosystem are called **abiotic** *(ay-bie-AHT-ick)* **factors,** and the living components are called **biotic** *(bie-AHT-ick)* **factors.**

Abiotic Factors

Abiotic factors in an ecosystem include sunlight, precipitation, temperature, the slope and drainage of the land, and the chemistry of soils and of the atmosphere. These physical factors interact with one another. For example, a season of heavy rains can cause

Lesson Plan

Section Focus

This section defines the basic terms of ecology—biosphere, populations, communities, and ecosystems. It discusses the relationships among abiotic factors (rainfall, sunlight, temperature, physical characteristics of the land, and types of soil) and biotic factors (plants, animals, and other organisms).

Section Themes

This section emphasizes the theme of **Systems and Interactions** through discussion of the interactions between the biotic and abiotic factors of the environment.

Motivating Activity

Bring in a selection of desert plants or pictures of a desert. Ask students what they think the main abiotic factor is in the desert. *(Very little water)* Have students discuss ways in which desert plants are adapted to this lack of water. *(Reduced surface area reduces water loss by evaporation, large root systems capture the available water, succulent leaves store water, thick cuticle reduces evaporation.)*

Teaching Strategies

Applying Concepts Have students name as many abiotic factors as they can. Then have them explain how biotic factors interact with the named abiotic factors and with each other. *(Sample answers: in tropical rain forests where there is plenty of sun, trees don't lose their leaves; in the tundra where only the top of the ground thaws in the spring, the plants have shallow roots and grow low to the ground.)*

Videodiscs

- ***Side 4 31833, Associations and Interactions (m)***

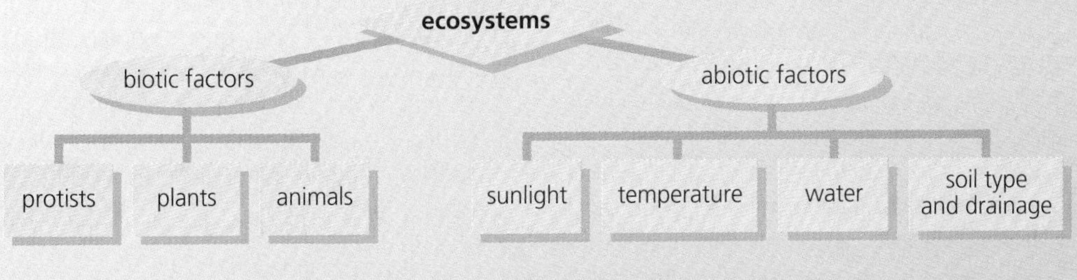

Graphic Organizer Use this organizational chart in Reteaching on p. 766.

Guided Practice

Ask students to list the environmental factors in the ecosystem that is represented in Figure 49-1, p. 765, and to classify each item as biotic or abiotic. *(Abiotic: lake and level land. Biotic: moose, grass, and trees)*

■ *See* **Laboratories,** ***Investigation 49.***

Independent Practice

■ Have students write answers to the Section Review.

■ Ask students to compare symbiosis and predation. *(Symbiosis is a close relationship between two species. Predation is one organism killing another for food.)*

Check Your Understanding

1. Name one abiotic factor and describe how it influences plant life. *(The more rain an area gets, the more trees and plant life can be sustained.)*

2. How are animals dependent on a soil type? *(Plants eaten by animals can only grow in specific soils.)*

Reteaching

Ask students to make an organizational chart that compares biotic and abiotic factors. Use the completed chart shown on p. 765 as a model.

■ *See* **Section Reviews** ***worksheet, Section 49.1.***

Enrichment

Divide students into small groups. Have students in each group research and make a map of abiotic factors in their state. Ask them to include rainfall, temperature, and soil types.

Closure

Have students write a paragraph describing their ecosystem. Ask them to predict some of the effects of drastically altering one factor in the ecosystem. *(In coastal areas, if the level of the ocean rose, low-lying land would be flooded.)*

Figure 49-2 Surtsey, an island off the coast of Iceland, emerged from the ocean in 1963. Built of lava from volcanic eruptions, it continued to grow until the eruptions ceased four years later.

a river to flood its banks, depositing sediments on nearby land. When the flood recedes, the sediments will have changed the soil composition. Other interactions of abiotic factors can produce more dramatic results. A river can completely change course, or, as Figure 49-2 illustrates, volcanic activity can suddenly create a mountain or an island.

Biotic Factors

Biotic factors in an ecosystem include plants, animals, protists, and all other living organisms. Like abiotic factors, biotic factors also interact in many ways. All organisms compete for food, water, space, and other resources. One type of competition occurs between members of the same species, and another type of competition occurs between different species. For example, two different species in the same community may eat the same plants.

Two other forms of interaction of biotic factors are predation and symbiosis. In **predation** one animal, the predator, kills and eats another animal, the prey. In the Isle Royale community wolves are the predators and moose are the prey. **Symbiosis** *(SIM-BIE-OE-suss)* is a close relationship between two organisms of different species. Usually at least one of the species benefits from the relationship. Chapter 51 will provide a more detailed discussion of predation and of the various types of symbiosis.

Abiotic and Biotic Interactions

Abiotic and biotic factors in ecosystems also interact with each other. For example, climate and soil conditions determine which plants will live in a certain area. Plant life in turn affects the distribution of animals. For example, the grass that grows in Siberia must withstand that region's cold, dry climate. The teeth and digestive system of the saiga antelope are adapted for eating this grass. In contrast, deer that reside in the wetter forests of the eastern United States are adapted for browsing on the leaves of the trees that are found there.

Living organisms also affect abiotic factors. For example, plants replenish oxygen in the atmosphere by the process of photosynthesis. The interaction of biotic and abiotic factors results in the great diversity of ecosystems in the biosphere.

Section Review

1. What is the *biosphere?*
2. What is an ecosystem? Name two abiotic and two biotic factors in an ecosystem.
3. Name and describe two types of interactions among biotic factors in an environment.
4. What major factor determines the kinds of animals that live in an ecosystem?
5. What do you think would happen to other animals on Isle Royale if the moose disappeared?

Answers to Section Review

1. The area of the earth where life exists
2. All the biotic and abiotic factors in an area. Abiotic—rainfall, temperature, sunlight; biotic—all organisms
3. Answers may include competition, which is a contest among organisms for food or water; predation, which involves one species feeding on another; and symbiosis, which is a close relationship between two organisms of different species, which usually benefits at least one of the species.
4. The kinds of plants that grow there
5. Either the wolves would die out from lack of food or they would need to find other species to prey on.

49.2 Terrestrial Biomes

Abiotic factors such as temperature, rainfall, and soil determine which organisms will thrive in a certain area. A **biome** is a large area identified by the presence of characteristic plants and animals. Biomes are commonly identified by their dominant plant life—for example, hardwood trees are the dominant form of plant life in the deciduous forest biome.

Because abiotic factors change gradually, biomes seldom have distinct boundaries, but Figure 49-3 shows an approximate distribution of the world's biomes. As climate varies over the earth's surface, deserts tend to grade into grasslands, and cold-climate forests grade into warmer-climate forests. Ecologists separate biomes into two very broad classifications: terrestrial biomes, or those on land, and aquatic biomes, or those of water. Table 49-1 on the following page lists the major land biomes and their average temperature and rainfall. Organisms that live in a biome are adapted to the environment of the biome. As you read, pay attention to these adaptations.

Polar Biomes

The biomes found at the earth's coldest extremes are the **polar biomes.** They surround the North and South poles. Similar conditions exist on the tops of the highest mountains. The poles receive almost no precipitation, so although ice is abundant, fresh water is scarce. The sun barely rises in the winter months, and fierce winds sweep over the land. Despite the harsh conditions, however, life does exist in the polar biomes.

Section Objectives

- *Describe the major terrestrial biomes.*
- *Give examples of the adaptation of plants in a biome.*
- *Give examples of the adaptation of animals in a biome.*
- *Describe ways in which ecologists use the LANDSAT satellite.*

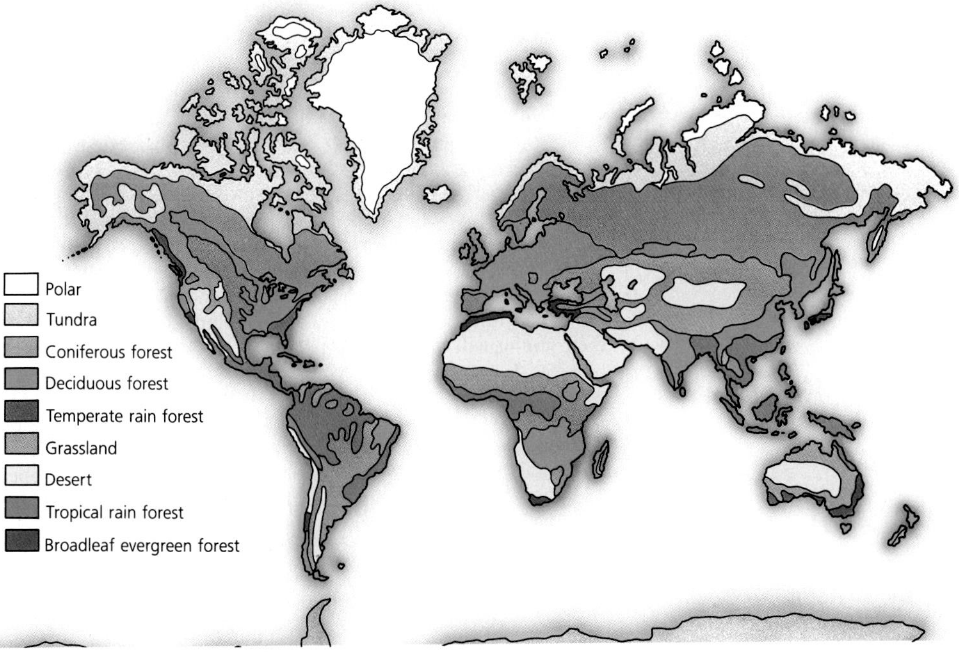

Figure 49-3 The biomes of the world occur in approximately the areas shown. Note the inclusion of the broadleaf evergreen forest.

Lesson Plan

Section Focus

This section describes the major terrestrial biomes. It discusses the abiotic factors in each one (rainfall, temperature, soil type) and describes how these influence the kinds of organisms that live there.

Section Themes

This section emphasizes the theme of **Systems and Interactions.** The organisms living in each biome are adapted to the physical conditions of the biome and are themselves considered biotic factors.

Motivating Activity

Ask students to find their own location on the map in Figure 49-3. Ask them to identify the biome in which they live and what they think its main forms of vegetation are. Make a list on the board of the vegetation in your area. Ask students to estimate the average annual rainfall for your location, as well as the annual temperature range. Then read the description of your biome from Table 49-1, p. 768, and compare it with the student's description of the biome.

Videodiscs

- ***Side 4 45808, Ptarmigan in Timberline Zone (m)***
- ***641, Bryophyta: Moss (s)***

Biome	Quiz question
desert	What biome is characterized by sandy soil and succulent plants?
temperate rain forest	What biome has nutrient-rich soil and over 200 cm of precipitation yearly?

Graphic Organizer Use this table in Independent Practice on p. 772.

Teaching Strategies

Interpreting the Visuals Using Figure 49-3 on p. 767 and Table 49-1 on p. 768 as guides, ask students to take an imaginary trip from east to west across the United States. Ask them what kinds of plants they would expect to find along the way. *(You would expect to find deciduous trees—maples, beeches, and oaks—in the East; grasses in the high plains; pines, firs, and spruces in the coniferous forest of the mountain states; cactuses in the desert; and conifers, including redwoods, in the Far West.)* Then ask students why they think the vegetation changes across the country. *(The changes mainly reflect the amount of rainfall. The eastern deciduous forests get a lot of rain; the high plains grasslands have less rain and the desert has still less. The coniferous forests in the mountain states have moderate rainfall, but these states are elevated several thousand feet, making the average temperature colder than in most of the East.)*

- *See* Overhead Transparency *T49 and* Blackline Masters *100 and 101.*
- *See* Process Skills, *Chapter 49.*

Answer to Think

More animals migrate to the Arctic and thus take with them more seeds from other biomes. Also, the closer proximity of the Arctic to land means that seeds can be carried to the Arctic by winds and that animals can more easily enter and leave the Arctic environment.

Table 49-1 Terrestrial Biome Characteristics

Biome	Average Yearly Temperature Range	Average Yearly Precipitation	Soil	Vegetation
Polar	−40°C–4°C	< 10 cm	Sparse, very low in nutrients, frozen much of year	Mosses, lichens, small flowering plants along coast
Tundra	−26°C–4°C	< 25 cm	Thin, moist topsoil over permafrost; nutrient-poor; slightly acidic	Mosses, lichens, dwarf woody plants
Coniferous forest	−10°C–14°C	35–75 cm	Low in nutrients, highly acidic	Needle-leafed evergreen trees
Deciduous forest	6°C–28°C	75–125 cm	Moist, moderate nutrient levels	Broad-leafed deciduous trees and shrubs
Grassland	0°C–25°C	25–75 cm	Very rich in nutrients, deep layer of topsoil	Dense, tall grasses in moist areas; short clumped grasses in drier areas
Desert	24°C–34°C	< 25 cm	Dry, sandy, nutrient-poor	Succulent plants; scattered grasses and sagebrush
Tropical rain forest	25°C–27°C	200–400 cm	Thin, moist, low in nutrients	Broadleaf evergreen trees and shrubs
Temperate rain forest	10°C–20°C	200–400 cm	Moist, nutrient-rich, highly acidic	Giant needle-leafed evergreen trees

Think

Could there be reasons, other than the warmer temperatures, that explain why more organisms have adapted to life in the Arctic than to life in the Antarctic? Consider the effect of geographic position on each of the two areas.

In the Arctic polar biome an ice cap lies over the Arctic Ocean, where the heat coming from the ocean waters keeps the ice no thicker than 5 to 30 m. During the summer months, when temperatures can rise to 25° C, some of the ice melts, revealing scattered patches of soil. More than 100 species of flowering plants, along with mosses and lichens, live here. Animals such as gulls, walruses, and polar bears also inhabit the Arctic coast.

In the Antarctic polar biome an ice cap lies over a large landmass; therefore the ice cap is not warmed by water's latent heat. Only a few species of lichens and mosses live along the coast. Three types of flowering plants also grow on the rocky tip of the Antarctic peninsula. Only bacteria and some small insects inhabit the vast Antarctic interior. Seals, whales, and penguins are found on or near the Antarctic coast. Penguins breed in winter so that their young will hatch in the spring.

Tundra

The **tundra,** a treeless biome blanketed by snow in the winter, forms a continuous belt across northern North America, Europe, and Asia. Tundralike areas also exist on mountains above the tree line, the highest point at which trees can grow. **Permafrost,** a per-

Interdisciplinary Activity

Social Studies Ask students to go to the library and find out what the vegetation in their area was before the land was settled and developed. This is especially appropriate for students living in a city. Many students may not know that there used to be forests or plains where now there are skyscrapers. Students can also research when the native vegetation was cut down. They might consult books and/or people who have been living in the area a long time or whose grandparents settled the area. *(Answers would depend on when the area was settled. Students might hear some interesting stories from "old-timers" who remember when there were cornfields where there are now shopping malls. Students might want to find out what grew on the land before it was developed for agriculture.)* Ask them manently frozen layer of ground over 500 m thick, characterizes the northern tundra. Even the surface soil above the permafrost remains frozen for all but eight weeks of the year.

In the brief summer the tundra landscape explodes with life, becoming a patchwork of ponds, bogs, and soggy soil. Tundra plants, which are short and often woody, appear, as do swarms of mosquitos and blackflies. Ducks, geese, and predatory birds arrive in great numbers. By mid-September the cold returns.

Figure 49-4 shows some adaptations of plants and animals to the cold, snowy tundra environment. Dwarf willows are only about 0.3 m tall, an adaptation to the cold winds that sweep across the tundra. The large size of caribou creates a low surface to volume ratio that helps prevent heat loss. Caribou are also swift runners with great stamina, adaptations that allow them to avoid predators and migrate long distances.

Figure 49-4 Dwarf willows, *Salix* sp., and blueberries, *Vaccinium* sp., appear during the brief summer on the tundra of Alaska (top). Caribou, *Rangifer tarandus,* (bottom), are adapted to tundra life.

Coniferous Forest

The **coniferous forest** is a biome that is dominated by conifers, cone-bearing evergreen trees such as pines, firs, spruces, and cedars. In the northern hemisphere this biome lies south of the tundra. Plants are adapted for long, cold winters; short summers; nutrient-poor soil; and frequent droughts. Their waxy needles remain on the trees all winter. The shape of their needles is an adaptation that reduces water loss. In addition, their stomata are recessed in the body of the leaf, which helps conserve water.

Typical mammals of this biome include moose, bears, and lynx. Many of these animals rely on stored body fat during the cold months. Although some animals reside in the forest year round, others migrate to warmer climates in the fall and return in the spring. Most invertebrate species hibernate six to eight months of the year, taking advantage of the insulating snow cover.

Large tracts of coniferous forest cover northern parts of Europe, Asia, and North America. Ecologists subdivide the coniferous forest in North America into three areas:

- The taiga *(TIE-guh)*, the northernmost band, occupies northern Canada and Alaska. The widely spaced trees include spruce and balsam fir, whose cone-shaped crowns shed heavy snows.
- The coniferous belt is found south of the taiga and extends across much of Canada as well as northern parts of the United States. Ecologists call this the "spruce-moose" belt, named for two prominent resident species.
- The southern pine forests cover much of the southeastern United States. In addition to conifers, oaks and other broadleaf trees are found in this more temperate zone. In areas with frequent forest fires, southern pines dominate. The pitchy bark of these trees scorches but does not burn, protecting the cells in the sapwood beneath it. Fires clear the land. Pine seedlings that germinate after a fire grow well on the unshaded land.

what abiotic factors that exist today contributed to the vegetation once found in their area. *(Factors such as average temperature and rainfall have not changed significantly in the last few hundred years.)* Students can also research the kinds of animals that used to live where they live now. *(Some interesting examples would be the bison of the high plains and the wild turkeys in the East and Midwest.)*

Inferring Relationships Tell students that caribou are reindeer that migrate to the tundra in the summer and return to the coniferous forest for the winter. Ask students to speculate as to why the caribou migrate. *(In summer, the tundra vegetation supplies food. In winter, the coniferous forest offers protection and food.)*

Interpreting the Visuals Again using Figure 49-3, p. 767, and Table 49-1, p. 768, ask students how climate changes as one goes from south to north in the northern hemisphere. Then have students take an imaginary trip from Central America to northern Canada. Ask them which biomes they would be passing through. *(They would go from tropical rain forests to deciduous forests to coniferous forests to tundra.)* Ask them what abiotic factor would permit forests in all these biomes except the tundra. *(All the other biomes get a lot of rainfall; seasonal amounts of sunlight are also a factor.)* Then ask them what kinds of trees live in each forest. *(The tropical rain forest has a lot of broad-leaved trees that do not lose their leaves. The deciduous forest has trees such as oaks, beeches, and maples, which have broad leaves that fall in autumn. The coniferous forest has pines, firs, spruces, cedars, and larches, which have thin, needlelike leaves. With the exception of the larches, these trees do not shed their leaves.)*

Videodiscs

- *2346, Coniferophyta (s)*
- *Side 3 9886, Pine Life Cycle (m)*

Interpreting the Visuals Direct students' attention to Figure 49-5, p. 771. Explain that the apical meristem is the growing part of the plant. In this grass, the apical meristem is underground and therefore can survive fires. Point out to students that this accounts, in part, for the rebounding of vegetation in Yellowstone National Park after the widespread forest fires of the summer of 1988.

Guided Practice
Read aloud the vegetation lists from Table 49-1, p. 768. Have students write down which biome would contain each kind of vegetation named and why that vegetation is an adaptation to the abiotic factors of that biome. *(For the tundra, students might say that mosses, lichens, and dwarf woody plants are all adapted to land that has only a thin, nutrient-poor layer of soil above the permafrost by having a shallow root system and growing close to the ground.)*

Deciduous Forest

The **deciduous forest** is a biome characterized by the presence of trees that lose their leaves in the fall. Deciduous forests stretch across the eastern United States, much of Europe, and parts of Asia, South America, Africa, and Australia. These regions have pronounced seasons, with precipitation evenly distributed throughout the year. The moderate rainfall and rich soil in this biome support vast numbers of plant and animal species.

Deciduous trees have broad, thin leaves with large surface area that permits maximum light absorption. Dominant species include birches, beeches, maples, oaks, hickories, sycamores, elms, willows, and cottonwoods. White-tailed deer, foxes, raccoons, and squirrels are typical mammals. Black bears live in some less populated regions. Some animals of the deciduous forest biome hibernate during the cold winters. Others, like hundreds of bird species such as warblers, spend the warm months in the deciduous forest and migrate to warmer climates for the winter. About one-fourth of the bird species that live in the deciduous forest, including the cardinal and bluejay, remain in the forest throughout the winter.

Biotechnology

Remote-Sensing Satellites

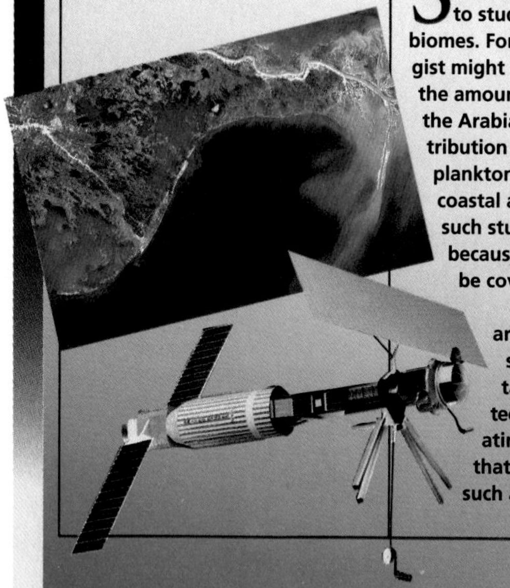

Sometimes ecologists want to study huge parts of biomes. For example, an ecologist might want to determine the amount of vegetation in the Arabian Desert or the distribution of photosynthetic plankton along a large coastal area. Until recently such studies were difficult because of the vast area to be covered.

Today ecologists are studying large ecosystems in great detail. Remote-sensing technology is now operating aboard satellites that are geostationary, such as GOES, and earth-orbiting satellites, such as LANDSAT, SPOT, and AVHRR. Until recently satellites (p. 770) were able only to differentiate between forests of hardwood and coniferous trees. Refinements in the technology today allow scientists to distinguish between red maples and sugar maples within a single hardwood forest. Satellites monitor detailed ecological information that could not otherwise be obtained.

Although the data from remote-sensing devices provide images that look somewhat like high-altitude photographs, the images are usually not actual photographs of the earth's

LEP Activity
Have students create a diorama depicting a biome. Divide the class into eight groups and assign one terrestrial biome to each group. Have students use either shoe boxes or larger cardboard boxes. They may use the inside back of the box to depict vegetation and the inside bottom to secure stand-up models of other inhabitants of the biome. Suggest that they use magazine pictures or their own drawings. On the outside top of the box, have students sketch a map of the world, showing where their biome occurs. On the other side of the box, have them list the abiotic factors of the biome and its plants and animals.

Grassland

The **grassland** is a biome dominated by grasses. This biome covers about one-fourth of the land surface of the earth. Grassland areas vary greatly in their temperature range. They occur at about the same latitude as deciduous forests but do not receive enough rainfall to support trees. Grasslands are known by various names in different regions of the world—prairie in North America, steppes in Asia, pampas in South America, and veldt in South Africa. The savanna is a grassland with scattered trees found in tropical and subtropical areas.

Some grasslands produce much food and support large numbers of animals. Dominant grazing mammals include bison and antelope in North America; antelope, elephants, and giraffes in Africa; and kangaroos in Australia. In South America the rhea, a huge flightless bird similar to the ostrich, is a major grazing animal. Billions of grass-eating insects also inhabit this biome, including numerous species of grasshoppers. Grasses can survive not only the grazing of animals but also the occasional fires that sweep across the plains. Note in Figure 49-5 that most of the growth in a grass plant occurs underground, safe from damage.

Figure 49-5 Because the growing part of a grass plant is underground, the plant can survive prairie fires.

surface. They are digitally-enhanced images of various kinds of electromagnetic radiation (EMR) from ultraviolet light, visible light, infrared light, and microwave radiation.

Plants, water, soil, rocks, and other materials absorb, emit, or reflect characteristic kinds of EMR. Remote-sensing devices measure these variations in EMR.

The EMR recorded by geostationary and earth-orbiting sensors is converted to digital form and transmitted back to receiving stations on the earth and stored on various media. Computers process the data to produce enhanced images, such as the ones on these two pages. Usually scientists instruct the computer to highlight the variations in EMR with bright colors. Although the images do not always represent the actual colors our eyes would see, they do make comparisons easier.

Moreover, an ecologist can overlay images taken at different times to study changes in a biome over time. For example, an ecologist might compare an image of a rain forest taken on January 15 with one from the following April 15. The ecologist can then determine how much of the forest was cleared during that period.

In recent years scientists have used this remote-sensing technology to estimate the amounts of photosynthetic plankton in portions of the Pacific Ocean. Others assess the extent of suspected air pollution damage in large areas of a forest, and still others find ecosystems suitable for grizzly bears in the Rocky Mountains.

Biotechnology

Using the Feature

Point out to students that the technology described in the feature on remote sensing has improved so dramatically in recent years that it can now be used to distinguish among species of trees within a single type of forest. Ecologists use these images to observe the changes in the characteristics of large areas of the earth.

Discuss with students how these images can be used for measuring the amount and kind of vegetation in the Arabian Desert or for locating a suitable habitat for grizzly bears. Help students understand how important it is for scientists to be able to compare images from the same area at different times in order to spot changes occurring in the biosphere. Refer students to the Intra-Science feature, "Will Earth's Forests Vanish?" on pp. 58–59.

Tell students that recent improvements in satellite-imaging technology make it possible for scientists to spot changes in an area to a resolution of 10 meters. Point out that by comparison, some of the older earth-orbiting satellites were only able to monitor such changes to a resolution of 100 meters.

Ask students to think about other possible applications of remote-sensing technology. *(Students may mention the use of satellite images for making topographic and other maps, and for military intelligence and weapons guidance, as during Operation Desert Storm.)*

Videodiscs

- ***713,* Quercus—*Oak (s)***
- ***714,* Gramineae—*Grass Inflorescence (s)***
- ***2455, Velvet Monkey with Young (s)***

More Information

Climatology On mountains of very high elevation, the higher one climbs the more the environment resembles that of northerly biomes. For example, a climb in some South American mountains can reveal tropical forest, deciduous forest, coniferous forest, and tundra biomes by turn. This is because the average temperature drops as one climbs. This drop in temperature, and precipitation, affects the vegetation.

Parts of some of the mountain states (Wyoming, Colorado, Montana) are coniferous forest even though they are at the same longitude as the deciduous forests farther east. Why? Because they are several thousand feet above sea level.

Independent Practice

■ Have students write answers to the Section Review.

■ The goal of this exercise is to have students create a game show quiz about terrestrial biomes. Ask students to make a two-column table. In one column have them list the terrestrial biomes: polar, tundra, coniferous forest, deciduous forest, temperate rain forest, grassland, desert, and tropical rain forest. In the other column have them write questions, each of which is answered by the name of the biome next to it. Finally, have each student quiz a partner. A model of a partly completed quiz table is shown on p. 767.

Check Your Understanding

1. How would you expect plants to be adapted to the tundra, where roots cannot penetrate the permafrost? *(Plants are small, low to the ground, and have shallow roots.)*

2. Name one way animals are adapted to the food shortage of the coniferous forest in wintertime. *(They hibernate, migrate, or rely on stored body fat.)*

3. Describe briefly what happens to the vegetation in temperate climates as rainfall decreases. Name the biomes involved. *(As rainfall decreases, the plants are smaller and fewer. Biomes change from deciduous forest to grassland to desert.)*

Figure 49-6 Organisms well adapted to desert life are (left to right) the black-tailed jackrabbit, *Lepus insularis,* the saguaro cactus, *Cereus gigantea,* and the Kalahari ground squirrel, *Paraxerus* sp. Jackrabbits spend the hottest hours of the day in cool, underground burrows.

Figure 49-7 What are the conditions to which trees that form a rain forest canopy must adapt?

Desert

Deserts are dry areas where rainfall averages less than 25 cm per year. Rain may fall on Africa's Sahara Desert only once every few years. Yet most deserts are not barren, and most harbor many species of plants and animals. Many deserts are not hot year round. In the desert of Idaho and northern Nevada, winter temperatures often plunge below freezing.

Organisms are adapted to the desert climates. Some desert plants absorb water through deep root systems, while cactuses and other succulents have shallow, diffuse roots. The saguaro cactus of Arizona and Mexico stores water and carries out photosynthesis in thickened stems and branches. A single saguaro can take up and store as much as a ton of water. A thick, waxy cuticle covering the stem helps prevent water loss. The leaves of the saguaro have evolved into sharp protective spines, seen in Figure 49-6, an adaptation that protects against thirsty predators.

Within days or even hours of the infrequent rains, a desert becomes awash with color. Plants have little time to exploit the sudden moisture for photosynthesis and cell growth. Thus they are adapted to quick growth, flowering, and seed production.

Like plants, desert animals are also adapted to their environment. The camel absorbs water from food and produces dung so dry that it can be used to fuel a fire hours after it is excreted. Many desert animals also show behavioral or physiological adaptations. For instance, the Kalahari ground squirrel uses its bushy tail as an umbrella, holding it over its body for shade.

Rain Forests

There are two types of rain forest biomes—the tropical rain forest and the temperate rain forest. The **tropical rain forest** biome is found near the equator where rainfall and sunlight abound. These rain forests may get as much rain in a month as some grasslands do in a year. One small area may support 100 species of plants, all of which compete for sunlight. Thus evolution has resulted in a distinct stratification of vegetation in rain forests, as shown in Figure 49-7. The tallest trees, which reach heights of 30 to 45 m,

Cooperative Learning

Illustrated Maps Divide the class into eight groups and assign one of the major terrestrial biomes to each group. Have students collect data from an atlas or encyclopedia on climate and land forms, along with pictures or drawings that show representative adaptations of plants and animals to each biome. Have students in each group draw a large map of the world and place pictures of the plants and animals in each biome on the appropriate parts of the map. Have each group give a brief oral report to the entire class with their map displayed.

form the canopy. Lower levels of growth make up the understory. The bottom vegetative layer is the forest floor, also called the ground layer. Though you may think of the tropical rain forest as an impenetrable jungle, much of the forest floor is surprisingly cool and free of vegetation since little sunlight reaches it. The very dense growth known as jungle is actually a specific kind of community found only along riverbanks where sunlight breaks through to the forest floor.

Animal life is also rich and diverse, with hundreds of thousands of insect species; colorful birds such as parrots and toucans; apes, monkeys, and predatory cats in South America; and the clouded leopard in Asia. Animals of the tropical rain forest inhabit various levels of the forest. Some are adapted to tree-dwelling life. Primates, for example, use their hands and tail to grasp branches and vines. Stereoscopic vision improves their ability to judge distances. Some animals, such as the flying lizard, glide from tree to tree. Brilliant plumage helps distinguish a tropical bird from its thousands of competitors.

Moderate temperatures and high humidity characterize the **temperate rain forest.** This biome extends along the west coast of North America from central California to southern Alaska. Plant life includes conifers such as the redwood and the Sitka spruce. Unlike mammals of the tropical rain forest, deer, elk, rodents, and most other temperate rain forest species live on the ground.

Figure 49-8 Three organisms found in tropical rain forests are (clockwise from top left) a tropical butterfly, *Marpesia iole,* of Costa Rica; the gibbon, *Hylobates* sp., of southeast Asia; and the scarab beetle, *Scarabaeidae* sp., of Papua New Guinea.

Section Review

1. Define *terrestrial biome,* and name the major ones.
2. Why is life in the Arctic more abundant than life in the Antarctic?
3. Name three dominant tree species in the coniferous forest biome and three in the deciduous forest biome.
4. List at least two animals that live in each of these biomes: desert, grassland, and tundra.
5. Why do most tropical rain forest animals live in the trees?

Reteaching

Make a list of the terrestrial biomes on the board. For each biome, have students name the most important abiotic factors and describe the resulting plant and animal life in the biome. *(For example, in a grassland biome, students might list moderate temperature, low rainfall, and rich soil, with dense tall grasses in moist areas and short clumped grasses in drier areas.)*

■ ***See* Section Reviews *worksheet, Section 49.2.***

Enrichment

Have students research and make a map of vegetation types in their state, using the maps they made in the Enrichment activity of Section 49.1. Ask them to note which abiotic factor is most closely related to the vegetation they report.

Closure

Have each student list a plant and an animal from each of three terrestrial biomes and describe how those organisms are adapted for life in that biome. *(Polar—mosses, polar bears. Mosses do not have roots, so they can live on frozen soil. Polar bears are white—camouflaged—and are good swimmers, so they can eat the food in the ocean and reproduce on land. Coniferous forest—pines, moose, bears, lynxes. The pines have thin needles, which conserve water. Animals living here store large amounts of food as fat and use it during the winter. Many of them hibernate. Deciduous forest—maples, deer, foxes. Trees have broad leaves for maximum surface area. Animals often hibernate or migrate for the winter. Grassland—grasses, bison, antelopes. Grasses live with less water. Grazing animals eat grass. Desert—Cactuses, camels. Both plant and animal use and store water very efficiently.)*

Answers to Section Review

1. A large land area of the biosphere with distinct biotic patterns; polar, tundra, coniferous forest, deciduous forest, grassland, desert, tropical rain forest, and temperate rain forest

2. The Arctic ice cap is heated by underlying water and melts in places in the summer.

3. Coniferous—spruces, pines, firs, cedars. Deciduous—birches, beeches, maples, oaks, hickories, sycamores, elms, cottonwoods

4. Answers can include: desert—kangaroo rat, camel; grassland—cattle, grasshopper, antelope; tundra—mosquito, caribou, owl.

5. More food sources, such as leaves and insects, are available in the canopy.

Lesson Plan

Section Focus

This section discusses the two major aquatic biomes, the marine biome and the freshwater biome. It describes the three areas of the marine biome—oceanic, intertidal, and estuarine—and the two areas of the freshwater biome—lakes and ponds (still water), and rivers and streams (moving water).

Section Themes

This section emphasizes the theme of **Systems and Interactions.** As in terrestrial biomes, organisms in aquatic biomes must interact with the abiotic factors in their environment.

Motivating Activity

Have students look at photographs of aquatic organisms. You can use Figures 49-11 and 49-12 on pp. 775–776, and the photograph of the shark on p. 543. Ask them how these organisms are adapted to an aquatic life. *(The sea stars have skin gills that can obtain oxygen from water and tube feet that can cling to rocks; the water lilies have leaves on the water surface, so they can photosynthesize; the shark has gills to obtain oxygen from water and a streamlined body suitable for swimming.)* Why couldn't these organisms live on land? *(They would dry out and not be able to obtain oxygen.)*

Teaching Strategies

Discussing Issues Ask students why, if the Atlantic Ocean is almost 5,000 km wide, it has been important to the New England fishing industry to limit foreign fishing in the 320 km (200-mile zone) closest to the coast. (*This is where most of the fish are—in the neritic zone.)*

Section Objectives

- *Name three areas of the marine biome, and list their characteristics.*
- *Give examples of adaptations of organisms to the marine biome.*
- *Name two freshwater biomes, and describe how they differ.*

49.3 Aquatic Biomes

Aquatic biomes occupy the majority of the earth's surface. As with land biomes, organisms are evolutionarily adapted to the various abiotic and biotic factors. For example, algae are adapted to the intensity of sunlight that penetrates the water and determines the rate of photosynthesis. As you read look for the adaptations that enable organisms to live in aquatic biomes.

Marine Biome

The **marine biome** is the earth's ocean and its associated areas. Ecologists have subdivided marine biomes into three areas: ocean, intertidal zones, and estuaries.

Ocean

The ocean covers about 70 percent of the earth and has an average depth of 3.7 km. In some places the ocean is 11.5 km, about 7 miles, deep. The water contains about 3.5 percent salt, mostly NaCl, a fact that profoundly affects the biology of organisms living there. Ecologists divide the ocean into two zones: the open ocean, or **pelagic zone,** and the ocean bottom, or **benthic zone.** As shown in Figure 49-9, the ocean is further divided into the **photic zone,** where light penetrates, and the **aphotic zone,** where no light penetrates. The photic zone extends to a depth of about 200 m; photosynthesis occurs most efficiently above this depth.

The pelagic zone is divided into two subareas. The first subarea, the **neritic zone,** extends over the continental shelf. Since light penetrates these waters and strong currents, called upwellings, carry minerals from the ocean bottom, the neritic zone supports the greatest amount of marine life. These waters are rich in plankton—the protozoa, algae, and invertebrates on which larger animals feed. Numerous fish, squid, sea turtles and other animals live in these waters.

Figure 49-9 The various zones of the ocean support different forms of life.

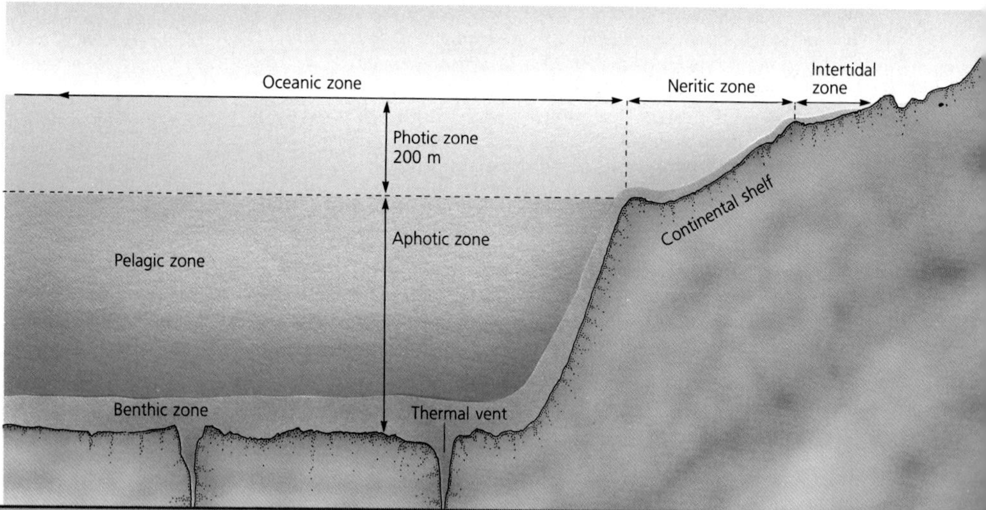

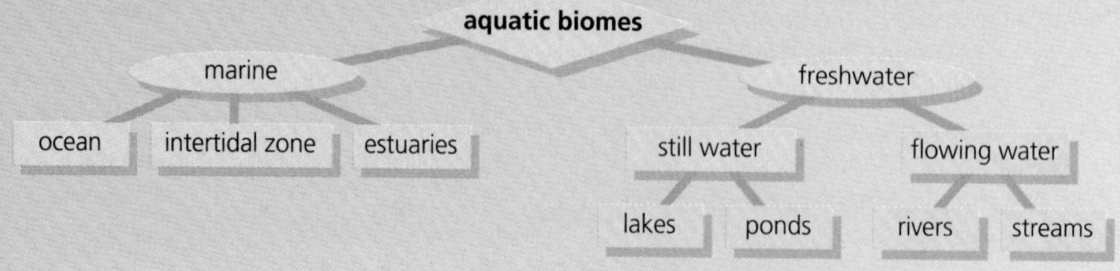

Graphic Organizer Use this organizational chart in Guided Practice on p. 775.

The second subarea, the **oceanic zone,** the deep water of the open sea, is less populated. Even in photic areas, mineral levels are too low to support much life. Animals of the oceanic zone feed primarily on sinking plankton and dead organisms.

Organisms living below 2,000 m are called abyssal organisms and are some of the strangest on earth. Deep-sea fish have slow metabolic rates and reduced skeletal systems that are adaptations to near-freezing temperatures and tremendous pressure. Their large jaws and teeth and expandable stomach can accommodate the rare prey that they can catch at these depths. Even more unusual organisms inhabit thermal vent communities. Near these areas seawater and sulfur gases seep through vents in the earth's crust. These hot springs, rich in minerals and often exceeding 700° C, support about 200 species of bacteria in the surrounding area. The bacteria are chemosynthetic—that is, they manufacture food with chemical energy, rather than light energy. Most convert sulfur compounds to useable energy. An assortment of unique clams, crabs, and worms feed on these bacteria.

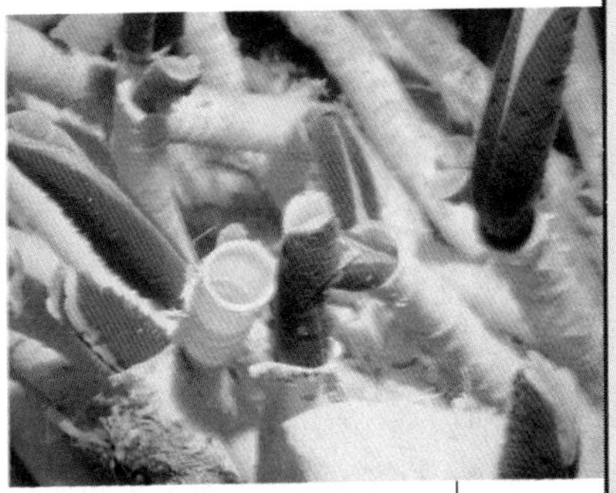

Figure 49-10 These Galápagos rift tube worms are part of a thermal vent community. The photo appears washed out because, at a depth of 2,000 m, it had to be taken with artificial light.

Intertidal Zones

Along ocean shores, the tides produce a rhythmic rise and fall of water in an area called the **intertidal zone.** Organisms in this zone are adapted to periodic exposure to air. Crabs prevent dehydration by burrowing into sand or mud. Clams, mussels, and oysters filter plankton from the water during high tide, then retreat into their shells at low tide. At low tide, shorebirds descend on the beaches to snatch this abundant food. One bird, the oystercatcher, uses its long beak to pry open clam shells.

These animals are also adapted to the force of waves crashing onto the shore. Sea anemones cling to rocks with a muscular disk. Sea stars gain footing with the aid of tube feet. The streamlined shape of most chitons and bivalves helps protect these mollusks from the pounding waves.

Figure 49-11 Sea stars have adaptations for life in the intertidal zone.

Estuaries

An **estuary** is a biome found throughout the world where freshwater rivers and streams flow into the sea. Examples of estuarine communities include bays, mud flats, and salt marshes. The shallow waters ensure plenty of light, and rivers deposit large amounts of mineral nutrients. However, the interplay between fresh and salt water causes great variation in temperature and salinity. In addition, like the intertidal zone, much of the estuary is exposed to the air during low tide.

Estuarine life is adapted to frequent change. For example, some mangrove trees have special glands on their leaves that eliminate excess salt water taken up by the roots. Soft-shell clams lie buried in mud, with only their long siphons protruding above the surface. The siphon filters plankton from the water at high tide and also detects predators at low tide, contracting whenever it senses danger.

Interpreting the Visuals Have students study Figure 49-9 on p. 774, which shows the zones of the ocean. Point out to them that the pelagic zone includes both the oceanic zone and the neritic zone, but not the benthic zone. Ask them where they would expect to find the most life and why. *(The neritic and intertidal zones have the most life because these have the most light for photosynthesis and the most minerals.)*

Analyzing Properties Ask students to compare the abiotic factors of the two kinds of freshwater biomes. *(Water in lakes and ponds is still. Lakes and ponds, which are fed by the moving water of rivers and streams, vary in turbidity and amounts of nutrients. Gradients are a major abiotic factor in moving water.)* Point out that the more agitated water is, the more oxygenated it is. Tell students that fresh water shows thermoclines, layers of varied temperature and oxygenation.

Exploring Careers Invite an oceanographer to talk about the different life forms in different oceanic zones, including coastal areas. Alternatively, invite an aquaculturist to talk about growing and harvesting fish in an "artificial" freshwater biome.

Guided Practice

Copy the organizational chart on p. 774 onto the board. Have students give the main characteristics of each area of the marine and freshwater biomes.

Videodiscs

- *Side 3 31821, Coelenterata: Jellyfish (m)*
- *Side 3 33785, Seafan (m)*
- *Side 3 41933, Starfish and Scallop (m)*
- *Side 4 34994, Ghost Crab and Land Crab (m)*
- *579–582, Seashore Algae (s)*

LEP Activity

Have students build either a marine or a freshwater aquarium. Discuss with them the importance of having both plants and animals in the aquarium and having the aquarium properly aerated. Have students get information from the library or from pet shops on fish that would be suitable for their aquarium. Supplies are available from biological supply houses or pet stores.

Independent Practice

- Have students write answers to the Section Review.
- Have students copy Figure 49-9, p. 774, on paper. Have them indicate where the most photosynthesis will occur, where the most minerals are, and where the most organisms will be. *(Photosynthesis will occur near the surface, at the top of the photic zone and in the intertidal zone. Minerals and organisms will be concentrated in the neritic and intertidal zones.)*

Check Your Understanding

1. Why do organisms in intertidal zones need protection against drying out? *(At low tide they are not covered with water.)*
2. What changes must organisms in estuaries be adapted to? *(Temperature and salinity)*
3. What is the difference between the two freshwater biomes? *(Rivers and streams flow; lakes and ponds do not.)*

Reteaching

Have students draw a concept map relating key concepts from this section. A sample concept map is shown on p. 763B.

- *See* Section Reviews *worksheet, Section 49.3.*

Enrichment

Have students study and report on the adaptations that such animals as fishes, whales, and seals have for life in salt water.

Closure

Name a biome or zone and then name a plant or animal that does not reside there. (For example: freshwater biome, sea stars) Have students give one reason why the organism could not survive there and give the correct biome for that organism. *(Sea stars, which live in the intertidal zone, could not live in fresh water because they couldn't find shellfish to eat. Sea stars belong in the marine biome.)*

Freshwater Biome

Low levels of dissolved salts characterize the **freshwater biome.** The salt content of fresh water is about 0.005 percent, compared with 3.5 percent in oceans. The freshwater biome includes bodies of water as huge as Lake Superior and as small as a half-acre pond. They include clear mountain streams in the Himalayas or the Rockies and slow, turbid rivers like the lower Mississippi or the Mekong River of southeast Asia.

Lakes and Ponds

Ecologists divide lakes and ponds into two categories. **Eutrophic lakes** are rich in organic matter and vegetation, making the waters relatively murky. The giant water lily pictured in Figure 49-12 is growing in a shallow, eutrophic pond. **Oligotrophic lakes** contain little organic matter. The water is much clearer, and the bottom is usually sandy or rocky.

Fishes inhabit both eutrophic and oligotrophic lakes. Carp and catfish are typical of murky eutrophic waters. Largemouth bass and pike survive in more moderately eutrophic waters. Lake trout are found in oligotrophic lakes. Freshwater lakes and ponds also support mammals such as the otter and muskrat, and birds such as ducks and loons.

Figure 49-12 The Amazon water lily, *Victoria amazonica,* is adapted to life in shallow, eutrophic ponds.

Rivers and Streams

A river is a body of water that flows down a gradient, or slope, toward its mouth. A river can be as short as a few kilometers or as long as the Nile, which runs from east Africa to the Mediterranean, a distance of 6,738 km.

Gradient is a key abiotic factor in a river. Water flows swiftly down steep gradients, and organisms here are adapted to withstand powerful currents. These include the larvae of caddis flies and the nymphs of mayflies, stoneflies, and dobson flies, which cling to the rocky bottom. Brook trout and other fishes are strong enough to face upstream while feeding on drifting invertebrates. Slow-moving rivers and their backwaters are richer in nutrients than fast waters are and therefore support a greater diversity of life. Rooted plants and the fishes that feed on them are adapted to the weak currents.

Section Review

1. Distinguish between the *photic* and *aphotic zones.*
2. Identify and describe the three parts of the marine biome.
3. How do organisms survive the breaking of waves in an intertidal zone?
4. List two ways that the gradient of a river limits the types of organisms that live in the river.
5. What might happen to organisms living in a fast-moving river if a dam is built on the river?

Answers To Section Review

1. The photic zone is the ocean region into which light penetrates. The aphotic zone is the region into which no light penetrates.
2. Oceans are large, deep bodies of salt water. Intertidal zones are coastal areas that are periodically covered and uncovered by tidal waters. Estuaries are areas where fresh water and salt water mix as streams and rivers meet the sea.
3. By attaching themselves to rocks and shells
4. The gradient affects current strength and nutrient availability.
5. A dam can slow a river, change its volume, or change its mineral content. Any of these changes could kill organisms that cannot adapt.

Laboratory

Organisms and the Environment

Objective
To examine how organisms alter abiotic factors

Process Skills
Predicting, measuring, experimenting

Materials
Safety goggles; lab aprons; 2 bottles of *Elodea* in water, labeled A and B; 1-mL and 2-mL bulb pipettes; 25% manganous sulfate solution; 40% potassium hydroxide–potassium iodide solution; 2 medicine droppers; concentrated sulfuric acid; 0.003% sodium thiosulfate solution

Background
1 What gas is made by photosynthesis?
2 How can an organism affect its environment?

Inquiry
1 You will test to determine the concentration of oxygen in two water samples. Dissolved oxygen reacts with the chemicals to produce iodine. The amount of iodine is proportional to the amount of oxygen present. What would a small amount of iodine indicate?
2 Bottle A has been in the light for 24 hours. Bottle B has been in the dark for 24 hours. Which bottle do you predict contains more dissolved oxygen?
3 Uncap each bottle and carefully remove the *Elodea.* Do not agitate the water. Gently shake each sprig over the bottle to keep as much water in the bottle as possible. Why should you not agitate the water?
4 Wear safety goggles and a lab apron for the rest of the lab. Use a 1-mL pipette to add 0.5 mL of manganous sulfate solution to each bottle. Rinse the pipette. Use a 2-mL pipette to add 1.5 mL of potassium hydroxide–potassium iodide solution to each bottle. Rinse the pipette. Cap the bottles. Swirl them to mix the solutions.
5 Uncap each bottle and use the 1-mL pipette to add 0.5 mL of sulfuric acid to each bottle. What happens? Color indicates the presence of iodine. CAUTION: Handle sulfuric acid very carefully. It can cause severe chemical burns.
6 The relative amount of iodine in the water can be measured by using sodium thiosulfate. The more iodine in the sample, the more thiosulfate solution you will have to add before the sample becomes colorless. To which bottle will you have to add the most sodium thiosulfate?
7 Use a clean dropper to add sodium thiosulfate solution to each bottle. How many drops are needed to make each sample colorless? Based on your results, which bottle contains more dissolved oxygen?

Conclusions
1 Why does the oxygen content of the two samples differ? Explain.
2 How do the samples of *Elodea* differ in the way they affect the environment?
3 Why must one bottle be kept in the dark and one in the light?

Further Inquiry
What might be the effect of a pollutant on the environment in the bottles? Devise a test.

Laboratory

(For an overview of Elodea and preparatory information related to the laboratory, see p. 763B.)

Background
1. Oxygen is produced during photosynthesis.
2. An organism can affect its environment by adversely affecting other organisms; or, its presence may be beneficial to one or more different species, contributing to a population increase that could result in depletion of resources to the detri ment of both the biotic and abiotic factors in the environment.

Inquiry
1. A small amount of iodine indicates a small amount of dissolved oxygen.
2. Bottle A probably contains more oxygen because the *Elodea* in it has been photosynthesizing in the light.
3. The water should not be agitated so it does not become aerated with oxygen from the air.
4. The solution should turn a brown color.
6. Predictions will vary, but bottle A should need to have the most thiosulfate solution added to it.
7. The number of drops will vary, depending on dropper delivery rate. Students should infer that bottle A has more dissolved oxygen.

Conclusions
1. Bottle A contains more oxygen because the *Elodea* in it has been photosynthesizing.
2. The *Elodea* in bottle A provides more oxygen, which can support other organisms; this represents a change in the abiotic factors.
3. Each bottle acts as a control for the other, allowing comparisons to be made in oxygen production in both light and dark environments.

Further Inquiry
Students should suggest a water pollutant and hypothesize about its effect on photosynthesis. The hypothesis may be tested by adding the pollutant to the water in bottles A and B and then repeating the experiment using only bottle A.

Vocabulary

1. A population is all the members of a species living in the same area. A community is made up of all the populations in one area.
2. Abiotic factors are the nonliving parts of an environment such as sunlight and rainfall.
3. Symbiosis means the interdependence of organisms of two different species; predation involves one species eating another.
4. The pelagic zone is the open ocean, and the benthic zone is the ocean bottom.
5. *Eu-* means "good," *oligo-* means "few," and *-troph* means "nourishment." Thus, eutrophic lakes are rich in nutrients; oligotrophic lakes have few nutrients.

Review

1. b	**6.** c
2. c	**7.** b
3. c	**8.** a
4. d	**9.** d
5. a	**10.** b

11. Answers will vary but may include the following: an island or a mountain that is created by a volcano, a river that changes course.
12. Antarctic ice is over land; Arctic ice is over water. The latent heat of the water melts the ice from below, making the Arctic ice thinner.
13. Grasses are highly efficient at converting solar energy to food energy.
14. They can quickly utilize moisture, which is available only for a short time.
15. Temperatures in the temperate rain forest are more moderate than those in the tropical rain forest. Most trees of the temperate rain forest are conifers, and most animals live on the ground.

Chapter 49 Review

Vocabulary

abiotic factor (765)
aphotic zone (774)
benthic zone (774)
biome (767)
biosphere (765)
biotic factor (765)
community (765)
coniferous forest (769)
deciduous forest (770)
desert (772)
ecology (765)
ecosystem (765)
estuary (775)
eutrophic lake (776)
freshwater biome (776)
grassland (771)
intertidal zone (775)
marine biome (774)
neritic zone (774)
oceanic zone (775)
oligotrophic lake (776)
pelagic zone (774)
permafrost (768)
photic zone (774)
polar biome (767)
population (765)
predation (766)
symbiosis (766)
temperate rain forest (773)
tropical rain forest (772)
tundra (768)

1. What is a population, and how does the concept of population relate to that of community?
2. What are some abiotic factors that influence an ecosystem?
3. What is the difference between symbiosis and predation?
4. Distinguish between the pelagic and benthic zones of the ocean.
5. Use a dictionary to find the meaning of the word parts *eu-*, *oligo*, and *-troph*. Explain why eutrophic and oligotrophic lakes are appropriately named.

Review

1. An ecosystem includes (a) all the members of one species (b) the living and nonliving factors in an environment (c) all parts of the earth where life exists (d) all members of a species in the same area.
2. Abiotic factors in an ecosystem can include (a) plants (b) animals (c) sunlight (d) microorganisms.
3. Permafrost is (a) a glacier (b) Arctic ice (c) permanently frozen ground (d) ground that thaws in the spring.
4. The neritic zone is in the (a) tundra (b) tropical rain forest (c) intertidal zone (d) ocean.
5. Organisms in the deserts must be adapted to low levels of (a) water (b) food (c) heat (d) salt.
6. An estuary is an area where (a) deserts become grasslands (b) coniferous forests meet deciduous forests (c) salt water meets fresh water (d) rain forests become grasslands.
7. Eutrophic lakes are (a) clear (b) murky (c) swift (d) small.
8. Adaptations of life in a river are primarily determined by (a) gradient (b) salinity (c) plankton (d) predation.
9. Plants and animals become adapted to life in particular biomes through a process of (a) symbiosis (b) competition (c) growth (d) evolution by natural selection.
10. Ecologists use remote-sensing technology to measure (a) heat waves (b) variations in EMR waves (c) variations in climate (d) changes in rainfall.
11. Give an example of a relatively permanent physical change that is caused by abiotic factors.
12. Why is the ice in the Antarctic thicker than the ice in the Arctic?
13. Why can some grasslands support a large amount of animal life?
14. What is the advantage of a short life cycle for desert plants?
15. How does the temperate rain forest differ from the tropical rain forest?
16. What are some adaptations of animals in the tropical rain forest to tree dwelling?

16. Some adaptations of animals to tree-dwelling life are: the ability to grasp vines and branches with hands or tail, stereoscopic vision, and the ability to fly or glide.
17. The three areas of the pelagic zone are the neritic zone, oceanic zone, and abyssal zone.
18. Plankton are the organisms that drift freely in open waters.
19. Sulfur is the source of energy in thermal vent communities.
20. Answers will vary but can include carp, catfish, largemouth bass, and pike.

17. What are the three subareas of the pelagic zone?
18. What are the organisms that drift freely in open waters?
19. What is the source of energy in the thermal vent communities?
20. Name two types of fish that can live in eutrophic water.

Critical Thinking

1. Examine the graph at the right. From what you know about the biomes of the world, which biome do you think this graph represents? List the reasons for your answer.
2. Deciduous forests once covered a large portion of eastern North America. However, humans have cleared much of these forests to make way for cities and towns. How do you think this shrinking area has affected plants and animals in the remaining forests?
3. Although plants of the coniferous forest and desert biomes seem to have little in common, both contend with dry conditions and a brief growing season. Compare the ways in which conifers and succulent plants are adapted to these conditions.
4. What are the significant abiotic factors in the thermal vent communities? How do they determine the types of life found there?
5. The plant *Artemisia gerardi* has diffuse roots and will continue to grow even if subjected to periodic fire and drought. What kind of animal do you think would feed on this plant?
6. Estuaries serve as breeding sites for thousands of species of marine animals. What characteristics of this biome would make estuaries advantageous areas for fishes, mollusks, crustaceans, and other aquatic animals to reproduce? What might be some disadvantages of reproducing in estuarine areas?

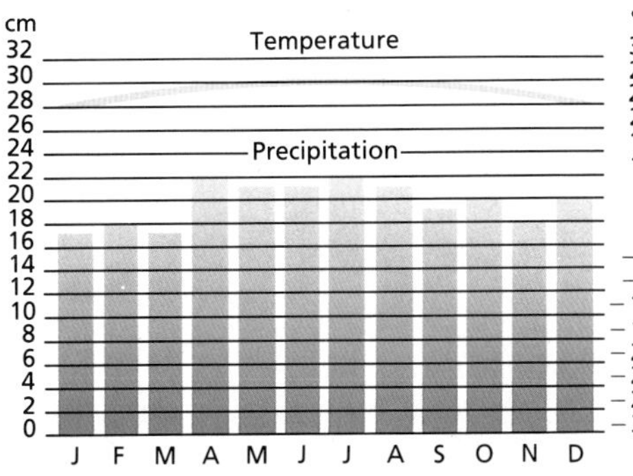

Extension

1. Read the article by Anna Maria Gillis entitled "The New Forestry" in *BioScience,* September 1990, pp. 558–562. Explain how "new forestry" attempts to resolve conflicts between foresters and environmentalists.
2. Research the changes in the environment surrounding Mount St. Helens after the eruptions in 1980. Write a report on the efforts of ecologists to restore the area.
3. Visit a biological community in your area. Choose a lake, pond, seashore, marsh, forest, park, or even an abandoned railroad track. Draw a selective sample of plants you see there and try to identify them from books in the library.
4. Pick a small community—a tree, lawn, window sill, or part of your back yard. With string, mark off a 1-foot-square area and count carefully the plants and animals found within this area. Note the number of species found, and identify as many as you can. Compare your findings with those of others in the class.

Critical Thinking

1. Tropical rain forest biome, since the amount of rainfall is high and the temperature is warm
2. Many of the animals died off as their food supply dwindled. Those that survived would have experienced a decreased reproduction rate until a new balance was reached between plant and animal populations.
3. Both conifers and succulents have reduced leaves. Conifers have needles with sunken stomata and a waxy coating that prevents water loss. Some succulents, such as cactuses, have spines rather than true leaves, and photosynthesis takes place in the large stem, which also has a waxy protective covering.
4. Abiotic factors include the heat generated from the earth's crust, the lack of light, and the abundant supply of minerals. These allow bacteria to thrive without being able to photosynthesize. A variety of marine animals can then live off these bacteria.
5. Animals that graze on grassland would eat this type of plant.
6. Nutrient levels are much higher in estuaries than in the open ocean. Estuaries are also less stable environments and many predators live there.

Extension

1. Answers should include reference to instances in which the new forestry benefits both foresters and environmentalists.
2. Ask students where similar disruptions might have occurred in the past, such as at Krakatoa.
3. Encourage students to appreciate the diversity of ecosystems that can be found in a very small area.
4. Encourage students to use hand lenses to observe insects and other small organisms in their area.

Chapter 50 Ecosystems: Structure

Chapter Overview

Chapter 50 introduces ecosystems, their structure, and the factors that determine the structure. Section 50.1 discusses the habitats, niches, and trophic levels of organisms in an ecosystem. Section 50.2 describes the energy transfers between organisms in the form of food chains and food webs. Section 50.3 describes three biogeochemical cycles: the water cycle, the nitrogen cycle, and the oxygen–carbon cycle.

Chapter Planning Chart

B	S	A	Sections and Subsections	Page	Features	Page	Resources
•	•	•	**50.1 The Structure of Ecosystems**				
			Habitat	781	Think	783	Videodiscs
			Niche	781	Laboratory	793	Laboratories: Ecosystem in a Jar
			Trophic Levels	782	Section Review	784	Section Reviews Worksheet
•	•	•	**50.2 Energy Flow**				
			Food Chains	785	Section Review	787	Blackline Master 102
			Food Webs	786			Overhead Transparency T50
			Ecological Pyramids	786			Process Skills: Pyramids
							Section Reviews Worksheet
	•	•	**50.3 Biogeochemical Cycles**				
			Water Cycle	788	Biology in Process	788	Videodiscs
			Nitrogen Cycle	789	Writing About Biology	792	Blackline Master 103
			Oxygen–Carbon Cycle	790	Section Review	791	Blackline Master 104
							Section Reviews Worksheet
			End of Chapter Activities				
					Chapter Review	794	Vocabulary Skills
							Chapter Test
							Computer Test Generator

B *The Basic Level curriculum presents the most fundamental knowledge offered in the course.*
S *The Standard Level curriculum is designed for the average student who is able to master most topics.*
A *The Advanced Level curriculum includes suggestions for teaching the most academically able students.*

Cooperative Learning

Group Activity: Biogeochemical Cycles

- **Group Size:** *3 students*
- **Outcome:** *Students will learn about each of the three major biogeochemical cycles.*
- **Individual Accountability:** *Each student will describe the characteristics of one biogeochemical cycle.*
- **Positive Interdependence:** *The group will verify the conclusions of group members and compare results.*

Tell students to supplement their text with library resources. Have one student in each group study the water cycle. Have a second student study the nitrogen cycle. Have the third student study the oxygen–carbon cycle. Ask each student to describe with words and diagrams how the element(s) in his or her cycle is used as a nutrient by living organisms. Tell students to name the reservoir of their nutrient—where most of it is stored in the biosphere. *(The reservoir for water is the oceans; for nitrogen, the nitrogen gas in the atmosphere; for oxygen, the oxygen gas in the atmosphere and dissolved in water; for carbon, fossil fuels and inorganic carbonates.)* They should then trace the path of their nutrient from the reservoir into an organism, and then from that organism back into the reservoir. Each student should explain his or her cycle to the other group members. The group should then go over each cycle together and discuss the importance of each one.

Concept Map

The following is one possible solution to the concept mapping activity in Guided Practice on p. 790.

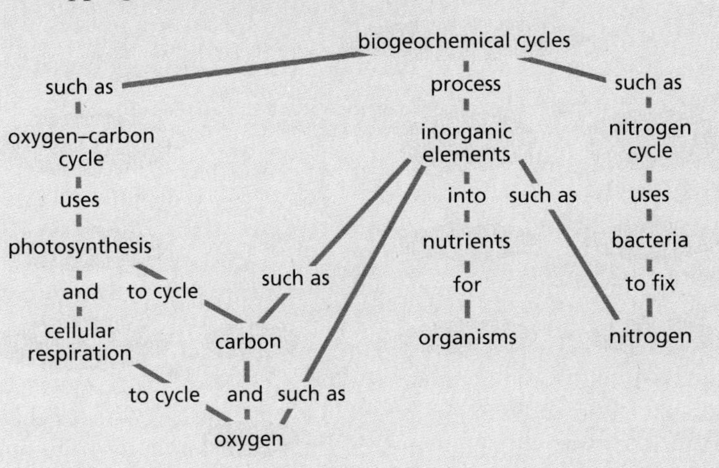

Laboratory Preparation

Overview *(See p. 793.)*

This lab gives students the opportunity to examine pond water. They should find a wide variety of organisms.

Preparation

If a pond is not available, biological supply houses offer pond water culture kits. Otherwise, collect pond water with plants and other organic debris in buckets from any nearby pond or swamp. Pond water is best kept in clear glass aquariums or in bowls loosely covered with plastic wrap to prevent evaporation while letting light in.

Use a guide or key to familiarize yourself with the more common pond organisms. Green organisms are usually either plants or green algae; golden brown organisms are diatoms; colorless, motile organisms are probably protozoa such as ameba or paramecia.

Teaching Tips

Remind students of the process of photosynthesis and the types of organisms capable of carrying out that process. Also remind them of the different types of chlorophyll.

Go over the concepts of trophic levels, food chains, and food webs. Emphasize that a food chain always starts with a producer and that about 85 percent of the mass and energy is lost at each trophic level. This is why most food chains have no more than three or four trophic levels and why large predators, often at the third or fourth level, are endangered—many are threatened by lack of food. Students may be disappointed that there are not more protozoa. Again, this is because there are fewer consumers than producers in an ecosystem.

Have a set of pictures to help students identify the organisms they find. *Microbiological Applications,* by Harold J. Benson, has excellent diagrams of green algae and diatoms. Many other keys are also suitable.

This lab is a good chance to discuss diatoms—the most abundant aquatic producers on earth. Students will usually find many diatoms in their pond water. Remind students of *phytoplankton* and *zooplankton*—various species of microscopic (usually), free-floating aquatic organisms. Phytoplankton are producers, and zooplankton are consumers.

If the pond water culture is observed for several weeks (Further Inquiry), it can be used to introduce the process known as *succession,* discussed in Chapter 51.

Safety

Students should be careful handling glass slides and coverslips and should wash their hands thoroughly after finishing the lab.

Chapter Themes

Energy This chapter emphasizes the flow of energy through individuals in an ecosystem. Make clear to students that energy cannot be recycled. The energy of most ecosystems comes from the sun and is converted from radiant energy to chemical energy by photosynthesis. It is then transferred from one organism to another through a food chain. Tell students that at each trophic level of a food chain, about 85 percent of the energy is used or "lost," so only 15 percent is available for transfer to the next higher level.

Patterns of Change This theme is manifest in the biogeochemical cycles, which show how nutrients are recycled in an ecosystem. Emphasize to students that, unlike energy, nutrients are recycled through decomposition.

Systems and Interactions This chapter discusses the interactions between organisms within an ecosystem as well as between organisms and the abiotic elements of their environment.

Chapter Motivating Activity

Ask students to name some of the inhabitants of their biome. List the organisms on the board, eliciting both plant and animal examples. Tell students that all organisms in a biome are organized according to what they eat and who eats whom. Ask students what plants "eat." *(Students should recall photosynthesis.)* Then introduce them to the concept of producers, consumers, and decomposers. *(Plants, algae, and some bacteria are producers, animals and protozoa are consumers, and fungi and some bacteria are decomposers.)* Then ask them how the organisms listed relate to each other.

Chapter 50 Ecosystems: Structure

Introduction

The biotic and abiotic factors of an ecosystem interact in highly complex ways. The transfer of energy and nutrients is the basis for many of these interactions. By analyzing the flow of energy and the cycling of nutrients through ecosystems, ecologists can gain a better understanding of ecosystem structure.

Chapter Outline

50.1 The Structure of Ecosystems
- *Habitat*
- *Niche*
- *Trophic Levels*

50.2 Energy Flow
- *Food Chains*
- *Food Webs*
- *Ecological Pyramids*

50.3 Biogeochemical Cycles
- *Water Cycle*
- *Nitrogen Cycle*
- *Oxygen–Carbon Cycle*

Chapter Concept

As you read, note the way energy relationships determine the structure of ecosystems.

Comet Geyser in Yellowstone National Park, Wyoming. Inset: Bald eagle, *Haliaeetus leucocephalus*.

Understanding the Visuals

Point out to students that the water coming from the geyser is boiling. Ask them what kind of organisms they think live in such an environment. *(Bacteria and algae live in hot springs near the geysers.)* Ask students what they know about where the bald eagle lives and what kind of food it eats. *(It nests high in trees, is a bird of prey, eats small mammals.)* Tell students that bacteria and eagles live in different levels of the ecosystem. Explain that while the bacterium's habitat may be very different from the bald eagle's, each organism has a niche in the same ecosystem.

50.1 The Structure of Ecosystems

You learned in Chapter 49 that an ecosystem is a unit of the biosphere consisting of interacting biotic and abiotic factors. A single forest—its climate, soil, trees, shrubs, bacteria, invertebrates, and vertebrates—makes up one ecosystem. A lake beside the forest and a meadow beyond the lake are also distinct ecosystems. Each organism in an ecosystem has a specific role. Three important aspects of the ecology of an organism are its habitat, its niche, and its trophic level.

Habitat

To understand an organism's role in the structure of an ecosystem, ecologists often begin by studying the organism's **habitat**—the physical area in which an organism lives. They will study the climate, topography, soil and water chemistry, and plant and animal life of the habitat. An organism's habitat may include many different kinds of areas. The habitat of the bald eagle, for example, may include both the deciduous forests and the prairies of central Wisconsin. The mouse's habitat may include a forest, a garden, and the walls of a house. The monarch butterfly's habitat may be the forests of the Great Lakes region during the warm months and the forests of Mexico during the winter.

A drastic change in the abiotic or biotic factors of a habitat that affects one organism can have an effect on the whole ecosystem. For instance, as Figure 50-1 shows, dumping chemicals into a pond changes the water chemistry, which may disturb the biotic and abiotic interactions of the plants and animals in the pond. Cutting down a patch of forest may result in the death of the animals that live there. In Brazil, for example, the tropical forest along the Atlantic coast once covered an area as large as Texas and New Mexico combined. Today only 2 percent of the forest habitat remains, the rest having been cleared to make way for cities, towns, and farms. As a result of the destruction of their habitat, 14 of the 21 species and subspecies of monkeys that live there are now considered endangered species.

Niche

A **niche** is the way of life of a species. An organism's niche includes its habitat, feeding habits, reproductive behavior, and all other aspects of its biology.

Consider the niche of the North American beaver. Beavers live in coniferous and deciduous forest habitats in the Northern Hemisphere. A beaver cuts down trees and builds dams that create temporary ponds. It eats plants. It reproduces. It adds nutrients to

Section Objectives

- *Distinguish between habitat and niche.*
- *Describe the function of producers in an ecosystem.*
- *Name the types of consumers, and describe the feeding habits of each.*
- *Explain how decomposers make nutrients available to the ecosystem.*

Figure 50-1 Dumping phosphorus into this pond has resulted in a bloom of algae that seriously affects the lives of other organisms in the pond.

Lesson Plan

Section Focus

This section describes the structure of an ecosystem and defines the roles that organisms play within an ecosystem.

Section Themes

This section emphasizes the theme of **Systems and Interactions** in its review of the habitats and niches within ecosystems. The theme of **Patterns of Change** is expressed in discussions of the flow of energy and the cycling of nutrients at different trophic levels in ecosystems.

Motivating Activity

Display a picture of a rabbit. Ask students to describe the diet of such an herbivore. *(Grass or other plants)* Then ask what the rabbit gets from the plants it eats. *(Matter and energy)* Ask if anything eats the rabbit. *(Snakes, birds of prey)* Define grass as producer, the rabbit as primary consumer, and the snake as secondary consumer.

Teaching Strategies

Inferring Relationships To help students distinguish habitat from niche, use a common organism such as a squirrel as an example. Point out that the squirrel's habitat is deciduous forests or urban parks and its niche in that habitat is, in brief, to eat acorns, bury nuts, and build nests. Ask students to describe the habitat, niche, and trophic level of a North American beaver. *(Habitat: Coniferous and deciduous forests in the Northern Hemisphere. Niche: cuts down trees to build dams, creating temporary ponds; eats plants; is host to ticks and mites, and so on. Trophic level: primary consumer)*

Videodiscs

- ***Side 4 34994, Territorial Relationships (m)***

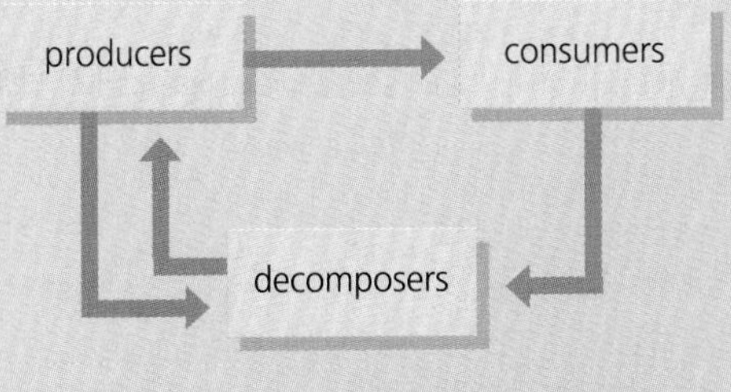

Graphic Organizer Use this diagram in Reteaching on p. 784.

Applying Concepts Ask students to read the definitions of producers, consumers, and decomposers. Then ask them to brainstorm various organisms that might reasonably be found at a zoo. Be sure that students include plants and trees in that list. Ask them to classify each organism as a producer, consumer, or decomposer. *(The plants will be producers, the animals will be consumers, and the fungi will be decomposers.)* Ask them which of the consumers are primary and which are secondary. *(Plant eaters are primary consumers; those that eat animals are secondary consumers.)* Ask them whether each consumer is an herbivore *(Deer, eat only plants)*, a carnivore *(Lions, eat only animals)*, or an omnivore *(Grizzly bears, eat both plants and animals)*.

■ ***See*** **Laboratories, *Investigation 50.***

Interpreting the Visuals Ask students what information about the blue-gray gnatcatcher is given on the graph but not portrayed in the photograph (Figure 50-2, p. 782). *(The graph tells you the size of the captured insects—average 4 mm—and where they are captured—between 3 and 5 m above the ground.)*

Then refer students to Figure 50-3 on p. 783. Ask them what this graph shows. *(It shows the difference in primary productivity of various ecosystems.)* Ask them to define primary productivity. *(The rate at which solar energy is converted to and stored as organic compounds)* Ask students to speculate on why the different biomes have different net primary productivities. *(Biomes with the most plants per square meter and the most sunlight—tropical rain forest and marine coast—would be highest in productivity.)*

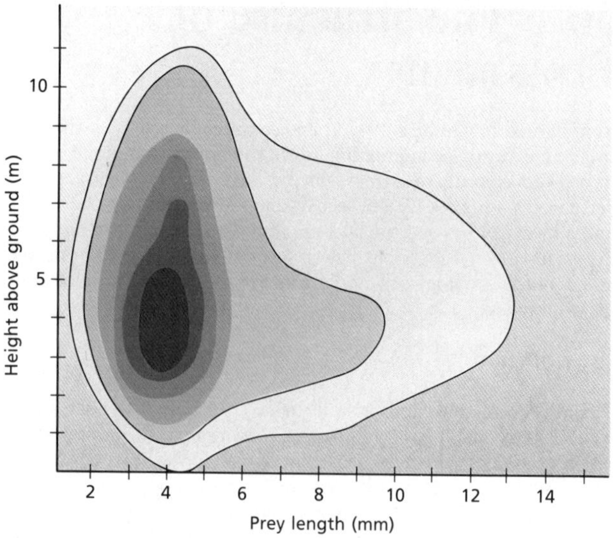

Figure 50-2 The contour lines on the graph show the frequency of capture of prey in trees by the blue-gray gnatcatcher. Prey—mostly insects—are most often captured between 3 and 5 m above ground. Prey averaging about 4 mm in length are the most frequently captured.

the environment not only by pulling plants into the water but by excreting waste products. It is also host to a number of tick and mite parasites. The male beaver establishes a territory and defends it against other males. These and many more features of the biology of a beaver make up its niche.

An organism's niche can be quantified. For instance, the graph in Figure 50-2 illustrates just two characteristics of the niche of the blue-gray gnatcatcher, a type of warbler that lives on insects. Hundreds of similar graphs would be needed to fully quantify its niche.

Trophic Levels

To understand the role of an organism in an ecosystem, ecologists must study the energy flow among the organisms of the ecosystem. Energy enters an ecosystem primarily from the sun. Energy flows between organisms when one organism eats another. The relationship between what an organism eats and what it is eaten by defines its **trophic level,** its feeding level, in an ecosystem.

Producers

Autotrophic organisms, which include plants, algae, and photosynthetic and chemosynthetic bacteria, manufacture their own food, using solar or chemical energy. Because autotrophs manufacture all the organic nutrients for an ecosystem, they are called **primary producers.** In a tropical rain forest, for example, tall trees produce most of the nutrients. In a midwestern prairie or an African veldt grasses produce most of the nutrients. In aquatic ecosystems species of phytoplankton, such as diatoms and dinoflagellates, are the major producers.

LEP Activity

Have students develop a bulletin board displaying photographs of producers, consumers, or decomposers. Have them use magazines to obtain pictures of many different organisms including, if possible, protists and bacteria. Have them mount each picture on construction paper and under each picture print the name of the organism and label it a producer, consumer, or decomposer.

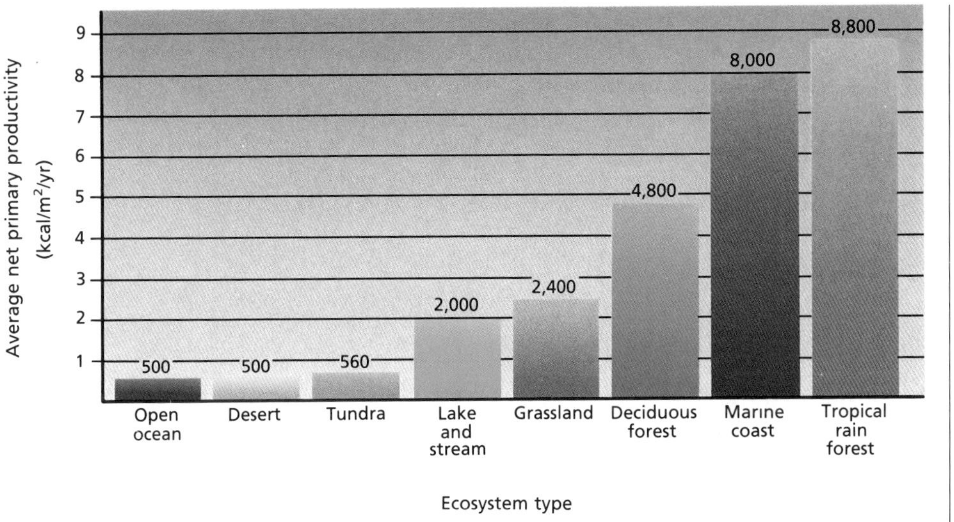

Figure 50-3 The amount of energy stored by plants after respiration has taken place is greatest in tropical rain forests and least in deserts and open oceans.

The rate at which solar energy is converted into organic compounds is called the **primary productivity** of the ecosystem. Primary productivity is usually expressed as the rate at which energy is stored as organic matter. The units are kilocalories per square meter per year (kcal/m^2/yr). **Gross primary productivity** is the total amount of energy produced, including the energy used by the plants for their own respiration. **Net primary productivity** is the rate at which plants store energy that is not used in plant respiration. Over time net primary productivity would show up as plant material that can be used as food by animals.

Figure 50-3 shows that the primary productivity of different ecosystems can vary greatly. For example, productivity in a tropical rain forest exceeds that of the same area of tundra by 16 times. Although rain forests occupy only 5 percent of the earth's surface, they account for almost 30 percent of its productivity.

Consumers

Animals, protozoa, and fungi are heterotrophs. Unlike autotrophs, heterotrophs cannot manufacture their own food. Instead they obtain energy from the chemical bonds in the nutrients they eat. Ecologists call heterotrophs **consumers.** They often call any organism that eats a producer a **primary consumer.** A **secondary consumer** is an organism that eats a primary consumer.

Consumers are also classified according to the type of food they eat. **Herbivores** obtain their nutrients by eating primary producers. The grass-eating antelope is an herbivore. So are the minute zooplankton that feed on phytoplankton floating in ocean or lake waters. **Carnivores** obtain nutrients by eating other consumers. Lions, eagles, cobras, and preying mantises are all carni-

Think

What adaptations does this sparrow hawk, *Falco sparverius*, have for carnivory?

Guided Practice

Tell students to imagine an ecosystem with no decomposers. Ask them to predict the consequences. *(Dead tissues and wastes would not break down. Autotrophs would exhaust the soil's chemical nutrients. Eventually life in the ecosystem would cease.)*

Independent Practice

- Have students write answers to the Section Review.
- Have students select a biome from Chapter 49 and list five or six organisms in that biome. Ask them to describe the trophic level of each organism as accurately as possible and then describe in detail the habitats and niches of two organisms.

Check Your Understanding

1. If you said a cockroach lives in dark places such as the spaces under cabinets, would you be describing its habitat or its niche? *(Habitat—the physical area in which it lives)*

2. List two components of the niche of the bald eagle. *(It eats rodents; it reproduces in nests in high trees.)*

3. Slime molds are found in dark, moist areas where they break down decaying wood. Are they producers, consumers, or decomposers? *(Decomposers)*

Answer to Think

The sparrow hawk's adaptations include grasping talons, acute vision, and a beak modified for tearing flesh.

Interdisciplinary Activity

Public Policy Have students contact a park ranger for a nearby park, or a member of the Audubon Society, Sierra Club, National Wildlife Federation, the local health department, or other environmentally oriented organization. Have the student find out about habitat conflicts, especially about whether there are any local habitat conflicts such as rats or raccoons in urban areas, deterioration of song bird habitat, or proliferation of a specific plant. Ask each student to report on the conflict, its causes, and its probable outcome.

Reteaching
Copy the diagram from p. 781 onto the board. Emphasize that the arrows indicate the flow of matter. Ask students to describe the relationships shown between producers, consumers, and decomposers. *(Consumers eat producers; decomposers break down both producers and consumers; producers get their minerals and inorganic nutrients from the products of decomposition. So consumers get their matter from producers; decomposers get their matter from both producers and consumers; producers get their matter from decomposers.)* Point out that a diagram of energy flow would be different. Ask students to describe the differences. *(Producers get their energy from the sun, whereas consumers get their energy from producers, and decomposers get their energy from producers and consumers. Energy is "lost" at each stage.)* ■ *See* Section Reviews *worksheet, Section 50.1.*

Enrichment
Contact the World Wildlife Fund for a list of endangered species. Have students choose a species and report on how encroachment on its habitat is threatening its survival. Have them address the question of who or what is benefiting from the habitat that is being yielded.

Closure
Select one biome from Chapter 49. Have students name three or four producers, consumers, and decomposers found in that biome. Ask students to describe as many interrelationships among the various organisms as they can.

Figure 50-4 A white-backed vulture, *Gyps africanus,* a scavenger, feeds on a dead giraffe at Masai Mara, Kenya.

Figure 50-5 The bracket fungus, *Polyporus versicolor,* is a decomposer that breaks down dead tissue in tree trunks and wooden structures.

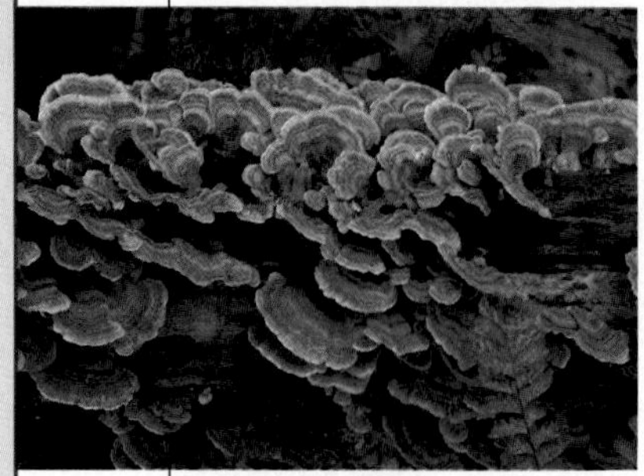

vores. **Omnivores** obtain nutrients by eating both primary producers and consumers. Grizzly bears, whose diet ranges from berries to salmon, are omnivores. Biologically humans are also omnivores. Whenever one organism eats another, energy in the form of the chemical bonds of nutrients is transferred from one organism to another.

Scavengers are consumers that feed on organisms that have recently died. Vultures and crows, which eat animal remains, are scavengers. Notice the vulture's head in Figure 50-4. It has a heavy, powerful beak that is adapted for tearing flesh. Its lack of head feathers is an adaptation that reduces the possibility that its feathers might be infected by bacteria as it sticks its face into decaying meat.

Decomposers
When leaves fall off trees or when animals die, they are acted upon by decomposers. **Decomposers,** such as bracket fungi shown in Figure 50-5, are organisms that break down dead tissues and wastes into nitrogen, carbon, phosphorus, and other elements and compounds. Autotrophs then extract these materials from the soil and use them to manufacture food. Thus the process of decomposition recycles chemical nutrients, making them available to the producers once again. This cycle is repeated over and over in the same ecosystem.

Section Review
1. Distinguish between a habitat and a niche.
2. Why are primary producers an essential component of an ecosystem?
3. Give three examples of a primary consumer and three examples of a secondary consumer.
4. What is the function of a decomposer?
5. What abiotic factors might account for differences in net primary productivity in ecosystems?

Answers to Section Review
1. A habitat is the physical area in which an organism lives; a niche is the way of life of a species in an ecosystem.
2. They produce all the organic nutrients for an ecosystem.
3. Sample answers: Zooplankton, caterpillars, antelopes, and other herbivores are primary consumers. Carnivores such as lions and cobras, and scavengers such as vultures, are secondary consumers.
4. To break down dead tissue and wastes, thus returning nutrients to the soil.
5. Levels of water, oxygen, carbon dioxide, and light

50.2 Energy Flow

Although energy flows in various patterns through an ecosystem, the total energy of one trophic level of an ecosystem never flows to the next level. In this section, you will see that the lower trophic levels of an ecosystem always contain more total energy than do the higher trophic levels.

Section Objectives

- *Describe the flow of energy through a food chain.*
- *Explain how food chains interact to form a food web.*
- *Identify the three types of ecological pyramids and explain what they measure.*

Food Chains

A **food chain** is the specific sequence in which organisms obtain energy in an ecosystem. In a freshwater ecosystem, for example, a food chain may begin with a primary producer, such as an autotrophic alga, which is eaten by a primary consumer, such as a tiny insect nymph. A fish then eats the insect nymph. An otter eats the fish. When the otter dies, bacteria feed on the carcass, releasing nutrients back into the ecosystem. Then other algae use the nutrients and energy from the sun to make food. As a result of this series of interactions a specific sequence of production and consumption exists in the ecosystem.

Figure 50-6 shows a food chain in a grassland ecosystem. The food chain begins with the autotrophic grass, which is the primary producer. The chain continues with the primary consumer of the grass—an herbivorous zebra. Then the chain continues with a carnivorous lion and a scavenging vulture. Again bacteria perform the final job of decomposing carcasses, dead leaves, and wastes into basic nutrients.

Food chains usually have only four or five levels. In the example above, the vulture may seem to be the highest-level consumer. However, most large animals are hosts for thousands of parasites of many different species. These parasites, such as ticks, insects, mites, worms, and lice, can be fifth- or sixth-level consumers. If they have their own parasites, and those parasites also have parasites, a food chain can consist of as many as eight or nine trophic levels.

As shown in Figure 50-6, energy flows through a food chain. However, only a portion of the energy available to organisms at each level of the food chain is stored. Only this stored energy is available to organisms at the next trophic level. For example, a plant converts only about 1 to 5 percent of the solar energy that falls on it. The rest is reflected off the plant, used in the life processes of the plant, or lost in the form of heat. In addition, a zebra that then feeds on this plant stores only about 10 to 20 percent of the energy it receives from the plant. In turn, a lion that eats the zebra stores only a small percentage of the energy it gets. On the average an organism stores only about 15 percent of the energy available to it from the trophic level beneath it. Thus the amount of energy available to the higher trophic levels is much smaller than the amount available to lower levels.

Figure 50-6 The food chain in a grassland ecosystem begins with grass (a producer) and ends with scavengers.

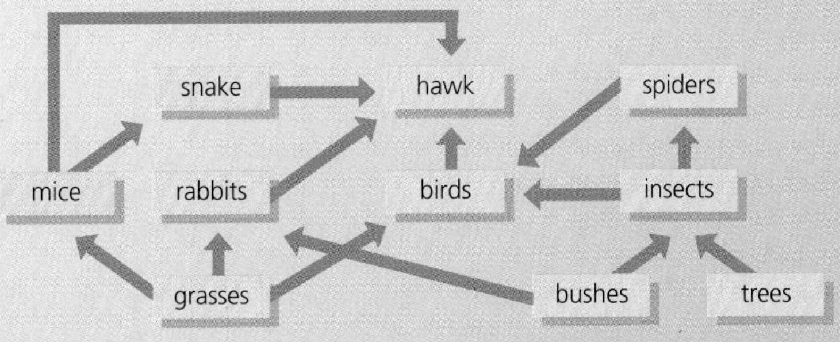

Graphic Organizer Use this food web in the Guided Practice on p. 786.

Lesson Plan

Section Focus

This section describes how energy flows through the various levels of an ecosystem. It shows how ecological pyramids compare energy or biomass at each trophic level.

Section Themes

This section emphasizes the theme of **Energy**. It describes how energy flows through the organisms in an ecosystem from producer to primary consumer to secondary consumer to scavenger to decomposer.

Motivating Activity

Ask students what they ate at their last meal. List the foods on the board. Ask where they think the energy in their food came from. *(Calories in organic compounds)* Tell them that the energy in their food ultimately comes from the sun. Using the list, show students the source of energy. *(Bread came from wheat, which is a plant; eggs came from a chicken, which ate grain; bacon came from a pig, which ate corn and other grains; cereals are made from plants; fruits come from plants; milk came from a cow, which ate grass.)*

Teaching Strategies

Interpreting the Visuals Point out that Figure 50-6, p. 785, is a simplified picture of real life. For a truly straight food chain of energy flow (as pictured here), the scavenger (vulture) should be eating a secondary consumer—that is, the dead lion and not the dead zebra. In real life, however, vultures eat both dead lions and dead zebras since a lion doesn't eat all of its kill. To introduce food webs, ask students to diagram this relationship. *(They should show two arrows from the zebra, one to the lion and one to the vulture.)*

Applying Concepts Explain that only about 15 percent of the energy in any trophic level is available to the next level. Have students calculate how many grams of organisms would be at each trophic level if there were 1 million grams of producers. *(Primary consumers—150,000 grams; secondary consumers—22,500 grams; scavengers—3,375 grams)*

■ *See* Process Skills, *Chapter 50.*

Interpreting the Visuals Have students examine Figure 50-7. Ask what impact the elimination of a particular species would have. *(A temporary increase in the food it ate and a temporary decrease in the animal that ate* it*)* Ask students from where the decomposers receive their energy. *(From the other organisms in the food web)* Have students add arrows to a copy of this figure to show the energy flow to the decomposers.

■ *See* Overhead Transparency *T50 and* Blackline Master *102.*

Guided Practice

Using the food web (Graphic Organizer) on p. 785, write the names of the organisms on the board and ask students which organism is eaten by another; draw the connections they suggest with arrows. Ask which organisms are consumers, producers, and decomposers. *(Producers—grasses, bushes, trees; consumers—mice, rabbits, birds, hawks, spiders, insects)* Ask what they need to add to complete the food web. *(Decomposers)*

Independent Practice

■ Have students write answers to the Section Review.

■ Have students draw an imaginary but realistic food chain for the energy pyramid in Figure 50-10, p. 787. *(Sample answer: algae, zooplankton, minnows, trout)*

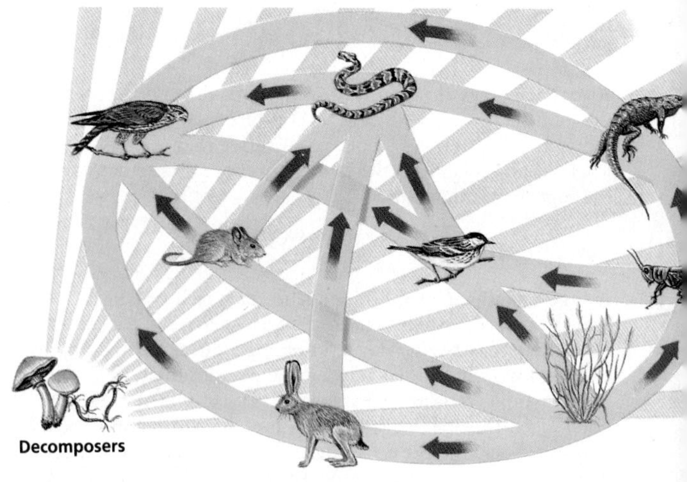

Figure 50-7 The illustration shows the relationships between a variety of producers, consumers, and decomposers in a grassland food web.

Food Webs

Feeding relationships and energy flow among species in an ecosystem are actually too complex to be represented by a single food chain. Many consumers eat more than one type of food. In addition, more than one species of consumer may feed on the same organism. Thus in nature many food chains interlink and overlap within a single ecosystem. Both otters and eagles, for example, may eat the same species of fish. A diagram of the feeding relationships among all the organisms in a single ecosystem would look much like a web. For this reason, the interrelated food chains in an ecosystem are called a **food web.** Figure 50-7 shows a simplified food web.

Figure 50-8 A numbers pyramid for an acre of bluegrass shows that 1 million primary producers are needed to support one tertiary consumer. What might that consumer be?

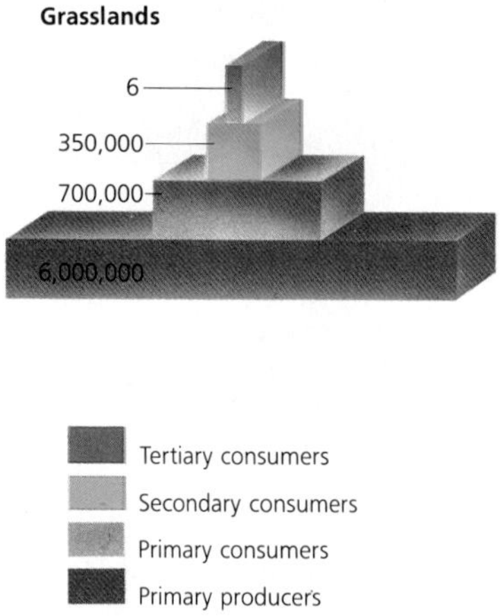

Ecological Pyramids

To simplify the complexities of an ecosystem, ecologists often graph the relationships in an ecosystem as a pyramid, with the primary-producer trophic level at the base and the consumer levels above it. Common pyramid models include numbers pyramids, biomass pyramids, and energy pyramids.

Numbers Pyramids

Numbers pyramids compare the number of individuals at each trophic level. Figure 50-8 shows a numbers pyramid for an acre of bluegrass. Ecologists determined that 5,842,424 primary producers, 707,624 primary consumers, and 354,904 secondary consumers, such as ants, spiders, and predatory beetles, existed in the acre of bluegrass. At the top of the pyramid there were three birds and three moles.

Cooperative Learning

Food Webs Divide the class into groups of four. Assign each group one of the terrestrial or aquatic biomes discussed in Chapter 49. Have each student in the group develop several possible food chains using organisms found in that biome. Then have the four students in the group combine their food chains into a food web for the biome. Have each group write out its food web and present it to the class or put it on the bulletin board. *(Example of a food chain in a river: algae to zooplankton to minnows to trout. In a food web, the zooplankton would be eaten by insects, and the minnows would eat insect larvae and be eaten by birds and larger fish.)*

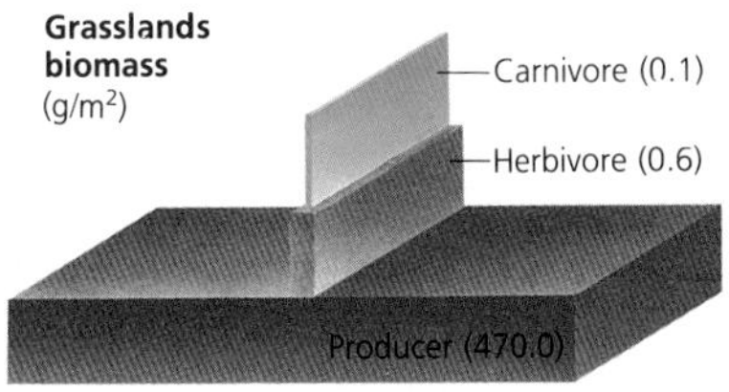

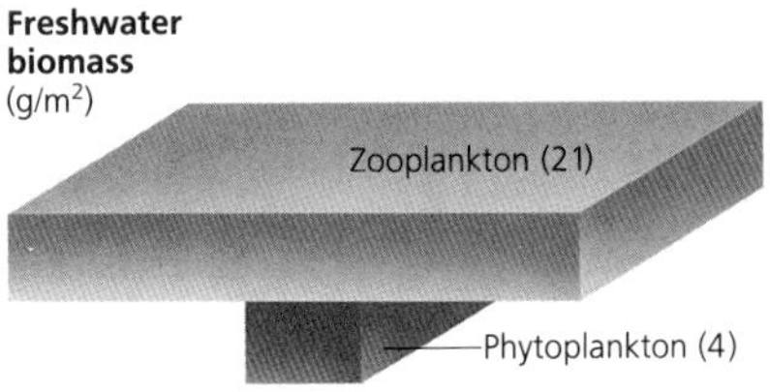

Figure 50-9 The biomass pyramids for a grassland and a freshwater biome are different. Why might this be so?

Numbers pyramids often reveal that organisms at the base of the pyramid are the most numerous. In some cases, however, a numbers pyramid can seem inverted. An inversion seems to exist when an organism that occurs in the greatest number does not fall at the bottom of the pyramid. For example, in a forest ecosystem a single large producer, such as an oak tree, may support thousands of caterpillars and hundreds of secondary consumers, such as spiders and birds.

Biomass Pyramids

Biomass pyramids compare the amount of biomass at each trophic level. **Biomass** is the total dry weight of the organisms in the ecosystem. Figure 50-9 shows the biomass pyramid for a grassland area. Note that in the grassland ecosystem the biomass of the primary producers is over 783 times greater than that of the primary consumers. In contrast, phytoplankton in a marine ecosystem have less than one-fifth the biomass of the zooplankton they support.

Energy Pyramids

Energy pyramids compare the total amount of energy, measured in kilocalories, in each trophic level. Unlike numbers pyramids and biomass pyramids, energy pyramids are never inverted, because energy is always lost from one trophic level to the next higher. Figure 50-10 shows an energy pyramid for a river in Florida. Note that as energy flows through the food chain, there is a dramatic drop in the amount of energy each trophic level retains.

Figure 50-10 The illustration shows an energy pyramid for a river ecosystem. Note that energy levels are expressed in thousands of kilocalories per square centimeter per year.

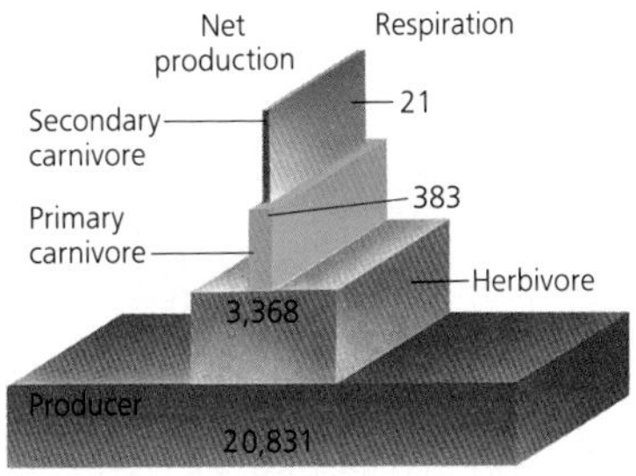

Section Review

1. How does a *food chain* differ from a *food web?*
2. What percentage of the available solar energy is stored by producers and what percentage is stored by consumers?
3. Distinguish between numbers, biomass, and energy pyramids.
4. Why are energy pyramids never inverted?
5. Suppose that a set of ecological pyramids for an ecosystem reveals that producers have extremely high biomass and productivity. What type of ecosystem might these pyramids represent?

Check Your Understanding

1. Put the following organisms in the correct sequence for a food chain: mouse, owl, grass. *(Grass, mouse, owl)*
2. How would you incorporate a rabbit and a snake into the food chain in question 1 to make a food web? *(The rabbit would eat the grass, the snake would eat the mouse and rabbit, and the owl would eat the mouse, snake, and rabbit.)*
3. How would you incorporate decomposers into the above food web? *(The decomposers would break down all the organisms in the web.)*

Reteaching

Have students study Figure 50-7, p. 786, and list as many food chains within the food web as possible. Emphasize that the arrows in the web indicate the direction of energy flow. For each chain, ask them which way the energy is flowing. *(Some examples of food chains are: grass–rabbit–hawk; grass–mouse–hawk; grass–bird–snake; grass–rabbit–snake; grass–grasshopper–lizard–hawk; grass–grasshopper–lizard–snake–hawk. Energy flows from the grass to the primary consumer, then to the secondary consumer, tertiary consumer, and quarternary consumer.)*
■ *See* **Section Reviews** *worksheet, Section 50.2.*

Enrichment

Suggest that students read *Diet for a Small Planet*, by Frances M. Lappé. Ask students to write an essay explaining Lappé's reasons for choosing to be a primary versus a secondary consumer.

Closure

Help students to diagram on the board a food web for common local organisms. Ask them to consider the possible consequences of disrupting a food web—for example, through human activity or a natural catastrophe.

Answers to Section Review

1. A food chain is a specific sequence of energy transfer; a food web is an interlinked network of food chains.
2. Producers store 1 to 5 percent of available solar energy; consumers store 10 to 20 percent of energy received from producers.
3. Numbers pyramids show numbers of organisms; biomass pyramids show the dry weight of the organisms; energy pyramids show energy production for each trophic level.
4. Because energy is always lost from one trophic level to the next higher
5. It is probably a rain forest because of the very high biomass and productivity.

Lesson Plan

Section Focus
This section describes three of the major biogeochemical cycles: the water cycle, the nitrogen cycle, and the oxygen–carbon cycle. These are the processes by which nutrients are recycled from one organism to another. Students will learn that although energy cannot be recycled, nutrients are always being recycled.

Section Themes
This section emphasizes the theme of **Patterns of Change**. It discusses the three cycles—water, nitrogen, and oxygen–carbon—by which nutrients are recycled through the biosphere.

Motivating Activity
Pour a glass of water and ask students where they think it came from. *(Possible answers: reservoirs, wells, rivers)* Then water a plant with the water and ask students what they think will happen to the water. *(Some will be used for photosynthesis, but most will be transpired back into the atmosphere.)* Ask students to trace the path of the water from the time the plant took it up until it is returned to the reservoir. *(Plants eliminate some water in the process of transpiration. Other water retained by plants is ingested by consumers. Animals [including humans] eliminate water in respiration, perspiration, and excretion. Lakes, oceans, and rivers eliminate water through evaporation. The atmosphere eventually becomes saturated and precipitates the water back to the earth.)*

Section Objectives

- *Trace the cycle of water between the earth and the atmosphere.*
- *Summarize the major steps in the nitrogen cycle.*
- *Explain how oxygen and carbon are cycled through an ecosystem.*
- *Describe the role of vegetation in nutrient cycling in a forest.*

50.3 Biogeochemical Cycles

The process by which inorganic materials move from the atmosphere or soil into living organisms and back again is called a **biogeochemical cycle.** Some materials, including nitrogen, water, oxygen, and carbon, reach ecosystems via the atmosphere. Rocks and soil particles contain other important elements, such as calcium and phosphorus, which are usually chemically bound as mineral salts. The weathering of rocks and soil by precipitation releases these minerals. In addition, every time you breathe, there is a good chance that you are taking in oxygen once breathed by a dinosaur. Your teeth probably contain calcium that was once part of a long-extinct invertebrate.

Water Cycle

Chemical reactions and mineral transport within most organisms cannot occur without water. Plants absorb water through their roots and eliminate water through their stomata. Animals drink water or obtain it from their food. They return water to the bio-

Biology in Process

Nutrient Cycling and Deforestation

What effect do trees have on nutrient cycling in a forest? How does their removal affect the nutrient balance in the ecosystem? Through long-term studies Cornell University ecologist Gene Likens and other scientists have attempted to answer these questions.

Since 1963 these scientists have studied nutrient cycling and the effects of deforestation in the Hubbard Brook Experimental Forest in New Hampshire. Because solid granite bedrock lies under the thin soil of the area, water cannot seep into the bedrock. Water leaves this ecosystem only through evaporation and transpiration or by flowing out through one of six small creeks in the forest.

Likens and his colleagues obtained runoff samples by building metal V-shaped weirs across the creeks. All water flowing out of the valleys had to flow over one of the weirs. To measure the water entering the ecosystem, they set up rain and snow collectors.

Next they measured the nutrient levels of the precipitation; the creek water; and the plants, animals, and soil in the forest. Interpreting the massive amount of data provided a picture of nutrient uptake, recycling, and retention.

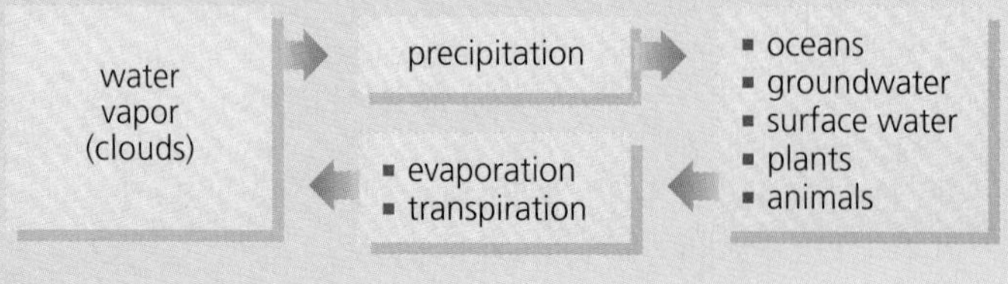

Graphic Organizer Use this diagram in Independent Practice on p. 791.

sphere when they exhale, perspire, or excrete. Of the nearly 1.5 billion km^3 of water on the earth, less than 1 percent is available to land organisms.

Water that sustains life on land cycles constantly between the air and the earth. Most of this cycling takes place through evaporation, transpiration, and precipitation. Evaporation occurs when solar energy causes water to move from the earth into the atmosphere. Plants also release water into the atmosphere during transpiration. The amount of water the atmosphere can hold depends on such abiotic factors as temperature and air pressure. Once the atmosphere becomes saturated with water, precipitation occurs in the form of rain, snow, sleet, hail, or fog.

Nitrogen Cycle

Plants and animals use nitrogen to build nucleic acids, structural proteins, and enzymes. Nitrogen gas makes up about 78 percent of the atmosphere. However, most living things cannot use atmospheric nitrogen (N_2). They must rely instead on nitrogen compounds found in soils, such as the nitrites (NO_2^-) and nitrates (NO_2^-). The process that converts nitrogen gas into compounds

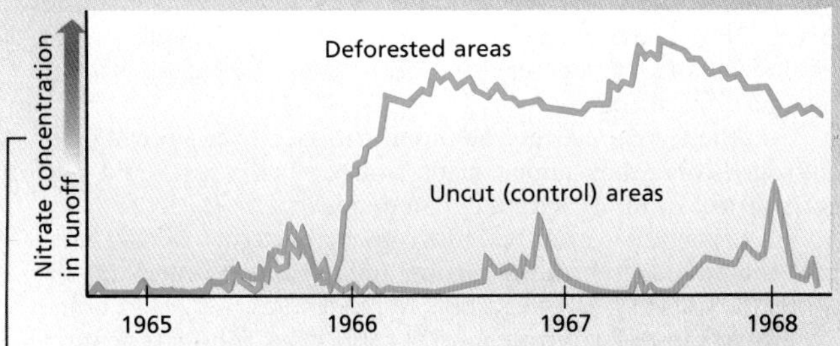

The ecologists discovered that the ecosystem retained most of its own nutrients. In other words, the amount of nutrients held in the ecosystem far exceeded the amount that entered or exited. For example, plants recycled almost all of the inorganic nutrients from decomposed leaves and twigs. In addition, they found that the amount of nutrients flowing out of the ecosystem nearly equaled the amount deposited from the atmosphere.

Once Likens and his colleagues determined the efficiency of nutrient cycling in the forest, they designed experiments to test the effects of deforestation. They cut down all the trees and shrubs in one of the six valleys and then collected data on nutrient runoff.

The flow of water from the creek immediately increased by 40 percent. More important, nutrients began to flow out of the ecosystem at a dramatically increased rate. In fact, loss of nitrates increased by more than 60 times after deforestation. Clearly vegetation plays a key role in maintaining nutrient levels in the ecosystem.

In further experiments the scientists tried to find ways to prevent nutrient runoff. They proved that by leaving intermittent strips of trees, the nutrient loss was greatly reduced. By writing their findings in books and journals, the scientists communicated to foresters the advantages of reducing the rate of deforestation.

■ What process did Likens and his colleagues use to determine how trees affect nutrient cycling in a forest ecosystem?

Biology in Process

Using the Feature

The main process skills used in this feature are collecting and interpreting data, experimenting, and communicating. The collection of massive amounts of data on precipitation, runoff, and nutrient levels provided information not only about the role of vegetation in an ecosystem, but also about the possible effects of human intervention. Note that Gene Likens and his colleagues used experiments to devise solutions to the problem of nutrient runoff, not merely to identify the problem. Also point out the significance of communicating such information to the public. Tell students that Likens is currently researching the effects of acid rain on forests, another ecological problem of great concern to humans.

Have students speculate on the long-term effects of deforestation. *(Soils would become poor in nutrients; water runoff would cause topsoil erosion.)* Ask them what long-term effect they think reforestation (tree planting) projects would have. *(Initially, the forest would grow more slowly because the soil has been depleted, but eventually, as trees became established, they would once again begin to concentrate water and nutrients.)*

Answer to the Feature

They first studied the nutrient levels in all parts of the ecosystem and then removed trees from one part of the forest and studied the impact of deforestation on nutrient levels.

Videodiscs

■ ***Side 3 26888, Stomatal Opening (m)***

More Information

Nutrient Reservoirs The reservoir for a nutrient is the place on earth where it is most abundant and accessible to its consumers in the biogeochemical cycle. The reservoir for water is the ocean. The reservoir for nitrogen is the atmosphere. The reservoir for oxygen is the oxygen that is dissolved in water and the oxygen of the atmosphere. The reservoir for carbon is limestone and fossil fuels. The path of a nutrient can be traced through the living and nonliving parts of the biosphere, beginning at the reservoir.

Teaching Strategies

Interpreting the Visuals Tell students that nitrogen is vital to the productivity of an ecosystem; it is used to make important proteins and enzymes. Explain that the abundant nitrogen in the atmosphere is not in a usable form for most organisms. Ask students to look at Figure 50-11 and list three sources of nitrogen. *(Dead plants and animals, animal wastes, and the atmosphere)* Tell students that bacteria are involved in each of the four processes that make the nitrogen cycle. Ask them to name the four processes. *(Nitrogen fixation, nitrification, ammonification, denitrification)* Ask which process involves the release of nitrogen back into the atmosphere. *(Denitrification)*

Have students look at Figure 50-13 on p. 791, the oxygen–carbon cycle. Have them identify all the ways in which atmospheric carbon dioxide is absorbed and released. *(Absorption: photosynthesis by algae and green plants; release: cellular respiration by animals and decomposers and by all heterotrophs; combustion of fossil fuels)*

Review photosynthesis and respiration as necessary (Sections 7.2 and 7.3). Point out that oxygen molecules are released to the atmosphere when water molecules are split during photosynthesis. Also, when oxygen is used in aerobic respiration, water is released.

■ *See* **Blackline Masters** ***103 and 104.***

Guided Practice

Ask students to make a concept map showing at least two of the three biogeochemical cycles (water, nitrogen, oxygen–carbon) and the purpose of these kinds of cycles. An example of a completed concept map is shown on p. 779B.

Figure 50-11 Since only a few microorganisms can fix atmospheric nitrogen, the movement of nitrogen through an ecosystem is more like that of a mineral than a gas.

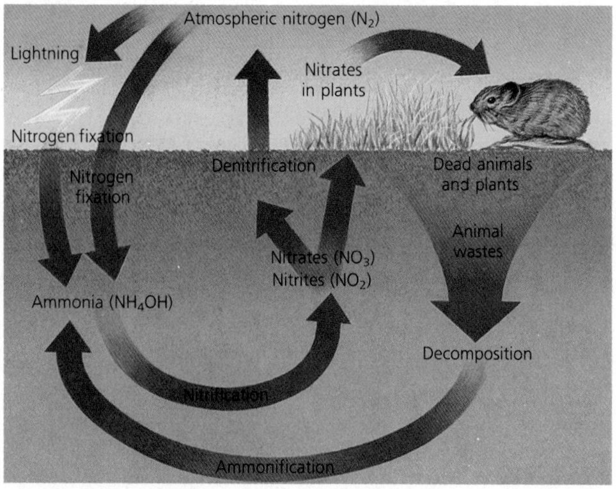

Figure 50-12 Nodules containing *Rhizobium japonicum,* nitrogen-fixing bacteria, adhere to a red alder plant. Bacteria like these convert nitrogen into ammonium compounds.

that plants and animals can use is called the nitrogen cycle. The cycle includes four major processes: nitrogen fixation, ammonification, nitrification, and denitrification.

During **nitrogen fixation** bacteria such as *Rhizobium japonicum* convert nitrogen gas (N_2) into ammonium compounds (NH_4OH). These bacteria live on the roots of legumes, which include alfalfa, clover, peas, and beans. Some blue-green bacteria can also fix nitrogen.

In the second process, **ammonification,** bacteria break down nitrogen-containing amino acids from animal wastes and dead organisms, forming ammonia compounds.

During **nitrification,** chemosynthetic bacteria oxidize ammonia compounds to produce nitrites and nitrates. Nitrates can also enter the soil from other sources. The enormous energy in a bolt of lightning can cause nitrate ions to form from atmospheric nitrogen. The erosion of nitrate-rich rocks also creates nitrates. Plants use the nitrites and nitrates to form amino acids.

In the final process, **denitrification,** anaerobic bacteria break down nitrates, releasing nitrogen gas back into the atmosphere. The process of converting atmospheric nitrogen into nitrites and nitrates requires much energy and so occurs slowly. As a result nitrogen availability often limits the productivity of an ecosystem. The nitrogen cycle is illustrated in Figure 50-11.

Oxygen–Carbon Cycle

During photosynthesis plants use carbon dioxide (CO_2) along with water and solar energy to make glucose and release oxygen. Both plants and animals use oxygen to break down glucose during cellular respiration. The by-products of respiration are carbon

Interdisciplinary Activity

Government Have students use the library to research the greenhouse effect. (The greenhouse effect is an increase in global temperature caused by an increase in the concentration of CO_2 in the atmosphere from the burning of fossil fuels.) Tell students that there is significant controversy about whether we are experiencing the greenhouse effect. Ask them to find out what changes in our environmental policy are being considered regarding the greenhouse effect. Have students contact both environmental organizations and legislators and attempt to discover the nature of the controversy.

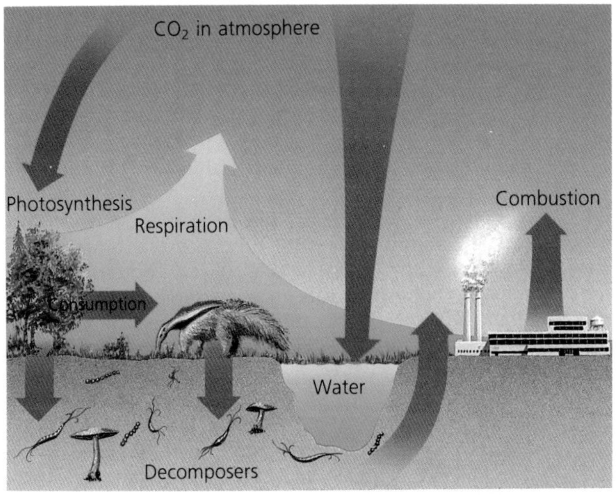

Figure 50-13 The processes of photosynthesis and respiration cause the balanced cycling of oxygen and carbon through an ecosystem.

dioxide and water. Together photosynthesis and cellular respiration form the basis of the oxygen–carbon cycle. Decomposers also contribute to the cycle by releasing carbon dioxide back into the atmosphere when they break down organic compounds. Figure 50-13 traces the path of oxygen and carbon through an ecosystem.

The processes of photosynthesis and respiration generally balance each other. In other words, the levels of oxygen and carbon dioxide remain fairly constant. However, since about 1850 humans have increased their consumption of fossil fuels. These fuels, principally petroleum products and coal, come from the stored carbon compounds found in the transformed remains of prehistoric plants and animals. The combustion of fossil fuels and the destruction of the world's rain forests have created a slow but steady increase in atmospheric carbon dioxide levels. The increase in levels of CO_2 in the atmosphere may have adverse environmental effects, as this causes an increase in the ability of the atmosphere to trap heat. This trapped heat may cause temperatures around the world to gradually rise, a phenomenon called the **greenhouse effect.** This kind of long-term disruption of the natural cycling of nutrients can change the habitat of many species.

Section Review

1. What is the *greenhouse effect?*
2. Trace the cycling of water between air and earth.
3. List the two main processes of the oxygen–carbon cycle.
4. How has the increased consumption of fossil fuels affected the oxygen–carbon cycle?
5. What abiotic factors might affect the rate of nitrogen cycling?

Answers to Section Review

1. The trapping of heat within the atmosphere due to an increase in levels of carbon dioxide
2. Water enters the atmosphere through evaporation and transpiration. It returns to the earth as precipitation.
3. Photosynthesis and respiration
4. It has increased the level of carbon dioxide.
5. Water and oxygen levels, temperature, and soil chemistry can affect the activity of bacteria and therefore the rate of nitrogen cycling. Erosion of nitrate-rich rocks and lightning create soil nitrates.

Independent Practice

■ Have students write answers to the Section Review.
■ Have students diagram the water cycle. An example of a completed diagram is shown on p. 788.

Check Your Understanding

1. How does deforestation harm ecosystems? *(Soil erosion)*
2. What important function do nitrogen-fixing bacteria serve? *(Convert N_2 into ammonium compounds plants can use)*

Reteaching

Have students list types of bacteria crucial for the nitrogen cycle. *(Nitrogen-fixing bacteria; decomposing bacteria; chemosynthetic bacteria)* Then ask them to identify the role of bacteria in the oxygen–carbon cycle. *(Bacteria act as decomposers that release carbon through breakdown of organic compounds.)*
■ ***See* Section Reviews *worksheet, Section 50.3.***

Enrichment

Have students read through a newspaper for one week looking for stories related to biogeochemical cycles *(Recycling initiatives, hazardous waste day, power plant construction)*. Have them write a report showing how the structure of their ecosystem is being affected.

Closure

Go through the three cycles and discuss how we participate in the ecological balance of the planet. *(Water is used in everything from industry to agriculture. Extensive farming depletes the soil of nitrogen faster than the nitrogen cycle can replace it.)*

Videodiscs

■ *2514, Water Cycle (s)*
■ *2571, Water and Mineral Uptake in Roots (s)*
■ *2576, Carbon Dioxide and Water Movement in Leaves (s)*

Background

The Arctic is one of the places on this planet most inhospitable to life. And yet life persists there too. *Arctic Dreams* was written by a man who spent many months living in the Arctic and observing the unique characteristics of life there.

Discussion

After students have read the excerpt from *Arctic Dreams*, ask them to discuss the following questions.

1. Plants need warmth and water in order to photosynthesize. How are these essentials limited in the Arctic? *(It is warm only very close to the ground because the earth absorbs heat from the sun and re-radiates it. Higher above the ground, the wind cools the air. Water is limited because there is very little rainfall and most of the ground is frozen, so the soil cannot hold a lot of water.)*

2. How are the trees in the Arctic adapted to obtain warmth and water? *(They are very short, growing close to the ground. They grow very slowly.)*

Extension

Point out that the intimate knowledge of the arctic landscape shown by the author is the result of his having lived there and observed life there for a long time. Have students select a single tundra plant and write a report on how it is adapted to the arctic climate.

Writing About Biology

Arctic Dreams

This excerpt is from the first chapter of Barry Lopez's prize-winning book, Arctic Dreams.

The far northern trees, like the animals, constitute a very few species—willows growing in valleys where they are protected from the wind and a dwarf form of birch. Along the tree line itself, the only successful strategists are species in the pine and birch families. Their numbers thin out over a span of several miles, with trees persisting farther north in isolated patches where there is a fortuitous conjunction of perennially calm air, moisture, and soil nutrients. Islands of trees in the tundra ocean.

The growth of trees in the Arctic is constrained by several factors. Lack of light for photosynthesis of course is one; but warmth is another. A tree, like an animal, needs heat to carry on its life processes. Solar radiation provides this warmth, but in the Arctic there is a strong correlation between this warmth and closeness to the ground. In summer there may be a difference of as much as 15° F in the first foot or so of air, because of the cooling effect of the wind above and the ability of dark soils to intensify solar radiation. To balance their heat budgets for growth and survival, trees must hug the ground—so they are short. Willows, a resourceful family to begin with, sometimes grow tall, but it is only where some feature of the land stills the drying and cooling wind.

Lack of water is another factor constraining the development of trees. No more moisture falls on the arctic tundra in a year than falls on the Mojave Desert; and it is available to arctic plants in the single form in which they can use it—liquid water—only during the summer.

Permafrost, the permanently frozen soil that underlies the tundra, presents arctic trees with still other difficulties. Though they can penetrate this rocklike substance with their roots, deep roots, which let trees stand tall in a windy landscape, and which can draw water from deep aquifers, serve no purpose in the Arctic. It's too cold to stand tall, and liquid water is to be found only in the first few inches of soil, for only this upper layer of the ground melts in the summer. (Ironically, since the permafrost beneath remains impervious, in those few weeks when water *is* available to them, arctic trees must sometimes cope with boglike conditions.)

Trees in the Arctic have an aura of implacable endurance about them. A cross-section of the bole of a Richardson willow no thicker than your finger may reveal 200 annual growth rings beneath the magnifying glass. Much of the tundra, of course, appears to be treeless when, in many places, it is actually covered with trees—a thick matting of short, ancient willows and birches. You realize suddenly that you are wandering around on *top* of a forest.

Write

- **The trees of the Arctic tundra are so tiny that in relation to them a human seems like a giant. In the tropics, however, enormous trees, ferns, and other plants dwarf any person. Using Barry Lopez's observations as a basis for reasoning, write an explanation for the tremendous size—and variety—of plants in the tropics.**

Barry Lopez, excerpted from Arctic Dreams. *Copyright © 1986 Barry Holstun Lopez. Reprinted with the permission of Charles Scribner's Sons, an imprint of Macmillan Publishing Company.*

About the Author

Barry Lopez has written many books and magazine articles on subjects dealing with nature. For this book, he traveled widely in the Arctic with native residents, biologists, archaeologists, and landscape painters. His writings reflect the personal observations he makes during his travels. He is a contributing editor to *Harper's* and *North American Review*.

Laboratory

Producers and Consumers

Objective
To identify the producers and consumers in a pond water ecosystem

Process Skills
Observing, classifying, inferring

Materials
Fresh pond water, eyedroppers, slides, coverslips, microscope, keys to freshwater organisms

Background

1 What is a producer? A consumer? Give some examples of each.
2 In most ecosystems, would you expect to find, by mass, more producers or consumers? Why?

Inquiry

1 Using an eyedropper, take a sample from the part of the pond water having the most organic debris, and place one drop on your slide. Why do you want a lot of organic debris? Cover the slide with a coverslip.
2 Examine your slide under low power. After you find an organism, observe it at high power. Draw each organism you find, recording as many details as possible.
3 Identify as many organisms as possible, using your text and any guides or keys your teacher may have. Identify each organism by name, kingdom, and phylum. Is it a producer or consumer? To what kingdoms might a green organism belong?
4 Search for small green or golden brown organisms with intricate patterns. These are probably diatoms, the most abundant aquatic producers. What gives them their colors?
5 Look carefully for colorless protists that move around. How do they differ from diatoms? How do the protists move?
6 Search for a nematode or insect larva. How do they differ from the protists?

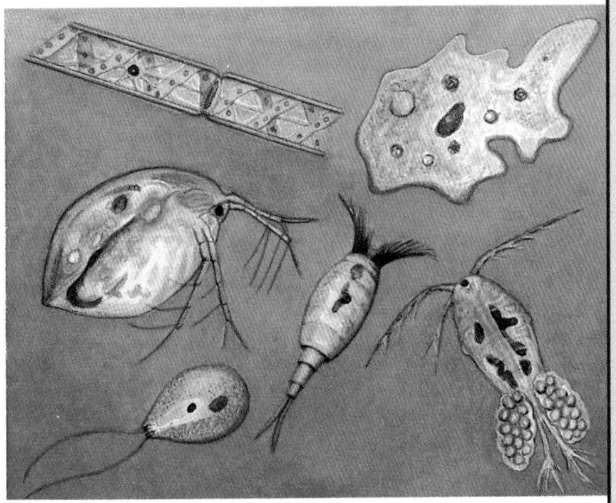

7 If you have time, make slides using different parts of the pond water. Examine each slide for new producers and consumers.
8 Construct a food chain using the organisms you found in your sample. If you found enough organisms, construct a food web. Identify the producers and consumers in your food chain or food web. Are the consumers primary or secondary. Explain why.

Conclusions

1 If you were taking samples from a 200-foot deep pond, where would you expect to find the most organisms? Why? How is this different from your sample of pond water?
2 How were you able to tell the difference between producers and consumers?
3 How does an organism's mobility relate to whether it is a producer or a consumer? Explain.

Further Inquiry
Continue observing your pond water over a period of several weeks or months. Are some organisms becoming more abundant while others are dying out?

(For an overview of pond water cultures and preparatory information related to the laboratory, see p. 779B.)

Background

1. A producer is an autotroph, an organism that makes its own food. Examples include plants, algae, and photosynthetic and chemosynthetic bacteria. A consumer is a heterotroph, an organism that gets its energy from what it eats. Examples include animals and protozoa.
2. You would probably find more producers. Many producers are needed to support a few consumers.

Inquiry

1. Most of the organisms are in the organic debris.
3. Most of the green and golden brown organisms are producers, usually diatoms. The colorless ones are consumers. A green organism could belong to Kingdoms Monera, Protista, or Plantae.
4. Several types of chlorophyll give the diatoms their colors.
5. Protists are usually unicellular, heterotrophic, have no protective outer covering, and have eyespots. They move by pseudopodia, cilia, or flagella.
6. They are multicellular and are usually larger than protists.
8. A food chain might have a diatom or a green alga as the producer, a protist as the primary consumer, and a nematode or insect larva as both primary and secondary consumer since they will eat both producers and consumers. Both food chains and food webs always begin with producers.

Conclusions

1. Most organisms are at the surface of a pond since light does not penetrate deeply in a pond. Producers need light to carry on photosynthesis. In a small aquarium, light penetrates fully to the bottom.
2. Producers had green or golden brown photosynthetic pigments.
3. With the exception of some protists, producers do not move, whereas many consumers do move.

Further Inquiry

Pond water, if covered loosely to prevent evaporation, keeps for months. During this time, some organisms die while others become more abundant.

Chapter 50 Review

Vocabulary

1. Gross primary productivity is the total energy production for an ecosystem; net primary productivity is gross productivity minus the energy plants use for respiration.
2. Both carnivores and scavengers are flesh-eaters, but scavengers feed only on carrion.
3. Primary consumers eat producers; secondary consumers eat primary consumers.
4. Primary producers manufacture energy for the ecosystem; decomposers return nutrients to the ecosystem by breaking down dead tissues.
5. In nitrification, nitrates are formed from the oxidation of ammonia. In denitrification, nitrites and nitrates are broken down into atmospheric nitrogen.

Review

1. d	**6.** c
2. d	**7.** b
3. a	**8.** d
4. b	**9.** c
5. a	**10.** c

11. The major producers in a prairie, a tropical rain forest, and a lake are grasses, leaves in the canopy, and phytoplankton, respectively.
12. An herbivore feeds on primary producers; a carnivore feeds on consumers; and an omnivore feeds on producers and consumers.
13. The vulture's adaptations for scavenging include a powerful beak for tearing flesh and a lack of head feathers that might foster bacterial infections.
14. The energy not stored by primary producers is either reflected, used for the life processes of plants, or lost in the form of heat.
15. Because of the interrelatedness of habitat, niche, and food webs
16. Because in a forest ecosystem a few trees may support thousands of consumers
17. The biomass or dry weight of organisms in an ecosystem
18. Photosynthesis and respiration
19. Energy flows through an ecosystem in one direction, with some loss at each trophic level. Nutrients are recycled through an ecosystem.
20. Nitrification, lightning energy, or the erosion of nitrate-rich rocks

Chapter 50 Review

Vocabulary

ammonification (790)	food chain (785)	net primary productivity (783)	primary producer (782)
biogeochemical cycle (788)	food web (786)	niche (781)	primary productivity (783)
biomass (787)	greenhouse effect (791)	nitrification (790)	scavenger (784)
carnivore (783)	gross primary productivity (783)	nitrogen fixation (790)	secondary consumer (783)
consumer (783)	habitat (781)	omnivore (784)	trophic level (782)
decomposer (784)	herbivore (783)	primary consumer (783)	
denitrification (790)			

Explain the difference between the terms in each of the following sets.

1. gross primary productivity, net primary productivity
2. carnivore, scavenger
3. primary consumer, secondary consumer
4. primary producer, decomposer
5. nitrification, denitrification

Review

1. The physical area in which an organism lives is its (a) trophic level (b) niche (c) ecosystem (d) habitat.
2. An organism's niche in an ecosystem does not include its (a) feeding habits (b) reproductive behavior (c) habitat (d) biomass.
3. The major producers found in aquatic ecosystems are (a) phytoplankton (b) chemosynthetic bacteria (c) aquatic plants (d) zooplankton.
4. Decomposers benefit an ecosystem by (a) manufacturing energy (b) returning nutrients to the soil (c) controlling the population (d) removing toxic substances.
5. The greatest amount of energy in an ecosystem is available to (a) producers (b) primary consumers (c) secondary consumers (d) decomposers.
6. If you measure the biomass of an ecosystem, you are measuring the (a) amount of energy produced (b) amount of nutrients (c) dry weight of organisms (d) dry weight of all organic material.
7. The percentage of the earth's water supply that is available to land organisms is (a) more than 50 percent (b) less than 1 percent (c) 10 percent (d) 5 percent.
8. The combustion of fossil fuels has increased atmospheric levels of (a) nitrates (b) carbon monoxide (c) ammonium compounds (d) carbon dioxide.
9. Most plants obtain their nitrogen from (a) ammonium compounds (b) nitrogen gas (c) nitrites and nitrates (d) ammonia.
10. The removal of trees from the Hubbard Brook Experimental Forest resulted in (a) several resident animal species' becoming endangered (b) severe flooding in the valleys (c) increased nutrient runoff (d) higher nutrient levels in the soil.
11. Name the major primary producers in a prairie, a tropical rain forest, and a lake.
12. Distinguish between an herbivore, a carnivore, and an omnivore.
13. How is a vulture adapted to scavenging?
14. What happens to the solar energy not stored by primary producers?
15. Why do changes in an environment often have far-reaching effects?
16. Why might a numbers pyramid appear inverted?

17. What do biomass pyramids measure?
18. Name the two major processes involved in the oxygen–carbon cycle.
19. How does the transfer of energy in an ecosystem differ from the transfer of nutrients?
20. Describe three ways in which nitrates become available to an ecosystem.

Critical Thinking

1. Human beings, raccoons, and bears are omnivores. What adaptive advantage might this give them?
2. During the 1970s, shark-killing expeditions became a fad. Why are sharks important in the food chain of the ocean, and what do you suppose might happen to other fishes if large numbers of sharks disappeared?
3. When insecticides are sprayed on fields or forests, residues of the insecticide show up in the bodies of the organisms living in these habitats. The most concentrated residues usually show up in the bodies of organisms on the highest trophic levels of the food chain. Why do you think this is so?
4. If an organism's habitat is destroyed, how do you suppose this would affect an individual within the species? How might this affect the species as a whole if the damage is widespread?

5. Explain why farmers often grow alfalfa, soybeans, or other legume crops in a field after they have grown corn.
6. Which organisms in the picture above are consumers? What other organisms would you guess are part of their food chain?

Extension

1. Build your own ecosystem in an aquarium or a terrarium. Be sure to include a representative consumer, producer, scavenger, and decomposer.
2. Study an ecosystem near your home or school. Make a list of all the consumers, producers, scavengers, and decomposers you observe. Draw an ecological pyramid that includes them all.
3. Read the article by Stephen Strauss entitled "Climbing the Food Chain" in *Technology Review,* July 1990, pp. 17–18. Explain how isotopic tracking of plant atoms allows scientists to trace the path of a food chain. What lines of research are possible with the use of this technique?
4. Use your library to research the ecosystem that exists around the floating and free-living plankton in the ocean. Draw the plankton types you learn about, and make a diagram of the food chain that begins with them.
5. Some scientists believe that the growing amount of carbon dioxide in the atmosphere will cause the greenhouse effect, resulting in rising world-wide temperatures. Other scientists argue that other kinds of pollution are creating large amounts of dust and other particles in the atmosphere. This pollution, they argue, will counteract the greenhouse effect. Use your library to research both of these theories, and make a list of the arguments on both sides.

Critical Thinking

1. An omnivore can choose from many types of food. If its environment changes, it may choose another type of food.
2. Sharks eat many smaller fishes. An increase in smaller fishes would either be followed by an increase in the numbers of another of their predators or by the smaller fishes overconsuming their own food supply.
3. Insecticides are sprayed on plants that can be eaten by a primary consumer. The insecticide residues are often bound up inside the organism's cells. These residues are then concentrated as they bind to the cells of successive consumers.
4. An individual might move to a new ecosystem or might change the type of food it ate. Those members of the species who could adapt to the new conditions would carry on the species.
5. Farmers grow alfalfa or soybeans because these plants fix nitrogen, thus replenishing the nitrogen the corn has used.
6. The consumers are the birds and seals. They both consume fishes, which consume other fishes or algae and plankton.

Extension

1. Suggest that students build a terrarium or aquarium to include organisms from one ecosystem such as a bog or a desert.
2. Ask students to draw a food web including these organisms.
3. Answers should include the distinctive fingerprint left by plant atoms. Research may include anthropology, paleontology, and animal behavior.
4. Encourage students to compare this plankton-based food chain with a food web that would exist in a pond.
5. Help students evaluate conflicting arguments. Ask them to determine whether there is any evidence that global warming is already occurring.

Chapter 51 Ecosystems: Relationships

Chapter Overview

Chapter 51 discusses relationships within ecosystems. Some of the relationships are between organisms; others are between organisms and their environment. Section 51.1 discusses types of relationships among organisms: competition, predation, and symbiosis. Section 51.2 discusses rhythmic biological patterns: circadian rhythms, annual rhythms, migratory rhythms, and tidal rhythms. Section 51.3 discusses succession, the gradual sequential replacement of populations in an area.

Chapter Planning Chart

B	S	A	Sections and Subsections	Page	Features	Page	Resources
	•	•	**51.1 Biotic Relationships**				
			Competition	797	Laboratory	807	Videodiscs
			Predation	798	Section Review	799	Blackline Master 105
			Symbiosis	798			Process Skills: Complex Relationships in an Ecosystem
							Laboratories: Owl Pellet
							Section Reviews Worksheet
		•	**51.2 Rhythmic Patterns**				
			Circadian Rhythms	800	Think	801	Videodiscs
			Annual Rhythms	801	Section Review	802	Section Reviews Worksheet
			Migratory Rhythms	801			
			Tidal Rhythms	802			
		•	**51.3 Succession**				
			Primary Succession	804	Biology in Process	804	Videodiscs
			Secondary Succession	805	Section Review	806	Blackline Master 106
			Succession in Lakes	806			Overhead Transparency T51
							Section Reviews Worksheet
			End of Chapter Activities				
					Chapter Review	808	Vocabulary Skills
							Chapter Test
							Computer Test Generator

B *The Basic Level curriculum presents the most fundamental knowledge offered in the course.*
S *The Standard Level curriculum is designed for the average student who is able to master most topics.*
A *The Advanced Level curriculum includes suggestions for teaching the most academically able students.*

Cooperative Learning

Group Activity: Symbiosis

- **Group Size:** *3 students*
- **Outcome:** *Students will compare the three kinds of symbiosis discussed in the chapter: parasitism, commensalism, and mutualism.*
- **Individual Accountability:** *Each student will describe one kind of symbiosis and give an example.*
- **Positive Interdependence:** *The group will compare different kinds of symbiosis.*

Have one student in each group do library research on parasitism. Have a second student in each group research commensalism. Have the third student research mutualism. Then ask each student to write a brief report on the type of symbiosis he or she is studying and include an example of two pairs of organisms that exhibit that kind of symbiosis. Ask them to explain how the symbiosis is advantageous to either or both of the participants.

After completing their individual reports, students should explain their results to the other students in the group. The group should then prepare a table comparing the three kinds of symbiosis.

Concept Map

The following is one possible solution to the concept mapping activity in Reteaching on p. 802.

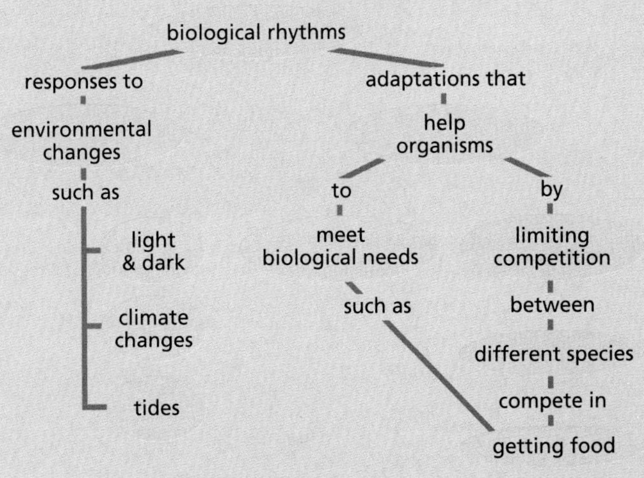

Laboratory Preparation

Overview *(See p. 807.)*

This lab introduces students to two key concepts. One is nitrogen fixation; nitrogen is the major limiting nutrient in most soils. Without nitrogen-fixing bacteria, the lack of available nitrogen for plant growth would noticeably change vegetation worldwide. The second concept is symbiosis; symbiosis is important for nitrogen fixation in legumes and is also responsible for the formation of coral reefs. In addition, scientists hypothesize that symbiosis among ancient unicellular organisms was responsible for the presence of chloroplasts and mitochondria in plant cells, and the presence of mitochondria in animal cells.

Preparation

Rhizobium and legume seeds are available from a biological supply house. Noninfected plants, used as a control, must be grown from sterile seeds in sterile soil. Label the plants *Infected* and *Noninfected* so that students can select one of each.

Teaching Tips

Point out to students that once a *Rhizobium* bacterium is committed to fixing nitrogen, nearly all its other genes are turned off, so it can no longer reproduce. Therefore, new *Rhizobium* have to come from bacteria that are not actually fixing nitrogen. Nitrogen fixation is an extremely energy-intensive process.

Point out that a single family of bacteria (which includes *Rhizobium*) contains the only organisms on earth able to utilize the nitrogen gas in the atmosphere. Without them no nitrogen would be available to other organisms, and there would be no life on earth.

Safety

Remind students to handle the scalpels with care.

Chapter Themes

Patterns of Change Organisms respond to rhythmic changes in the environment—such as seasonal changes—by rhythmic changes of their own. Emphasize that biological rhythms are adaptations that help provide biological stability.

Systems and Interactions Organisms interact with one another and with the environment. Help students appreciate that the goal of meeting biological needs underlies all interactions.

Stability The result of succession is a stable climax community. Point out to students that stability in an ecosystem can take millennia to develop but can be destroyed in a short time.

Chapter Motivating Activity

Show students a tree branch or rock that has a lichen on it, or a photograph of a lichen. Explain that a lichen consists of an alga and a fungus living in very close association with each other. Ask students how they think these two organisms affect each other. *(Sample answer: both organisms benefit since the alga can photosynthesize for the fungus and the fungus can hold water efficiently for the alga.)* Ask students if they can think of other examples of two species living in close association. *(Sample answer: heartworms in dogs or ticks on deer)* Ask them if both parties always benefit from these close associations. *(Encourage diverse student answers. They should be able to think of cases, such as the heartworm in dogs, where one benefits and the other is harmed. In other cases one benefits and the other is neither harmed nor helped.)*

Chapter 51 Ecosystems: Relationships

Introduction

You have seen that energy and nutrients flow through an ecosystem in predictable patterns. Similarly, individuals and populations in an ecosystem interact in predictable ways. In this chapter you will learn about the major types of interactions among organisms and about some of the ways in which organisms respond to and alter their environment.

Chapter Outline

51.1 Biotic Relationships
- *Competition*
- *Predation*
- *Symbiosis*

51.2 Rhythmic Patterns
- *Circadian Rhythms*
- *Annual Rhythms*
- *Migratory Rhythms*
- *Tidal Rhythms*

51.3 Succession
- *Primary Succession*
- *Secondary Succession*
- *Succession in Lakes*

Chapter Concept

As you read, look for predictable patterns in the ways organisms live together, respond to rhythmic changes in the physical environment, and alter the environmental conditions in an ecosystem.

Grunion, *Leuresthes tenuis*, depositing eggs, southern California. Inset: Sea stacks at low tide, Tillamook Bay, northern coast of Oregon.

Understanding the Visuals

The picture of the grunion depositing eggs illustrates how organisms use the resources of their environment to survive. Ask students if they think grunions compete with each other for places to lay their eggs. *(They do. This illustrates intraspecific competition.)* Point out that biotic relationships center on access to resources such as food, water, sunlight, and space or territory.

Ask students how the picture of the stacks would look at high tide. *(Much of the rock would be under water.)* Ask them to speculate on the kinds of adaptations that organisms living on the rock would need. *(They would have to be able to survive the dry times at low tide and meet their requirements from the water at higher tides.)*

51.1 Biotic Relationships

All relationships among organisms are called **biotic relationships.** In studying food webs in Chapter 50, you learned about one type of biotic relationship. In this section we will take a look at other major biotic relationships, including competition, predation, and symbiosis.

Competition

One of the primary ways that organisms interact is through competition. **Competition** is the use or defense of a resource by one individual that reduces the availability of that resource to other individuals. For example, a brook trout may compete for habitat by defending an area directly around a fallen log. When other fish attempt to move into this territory, the brook trout fights to hold it. If the trout is successful, it retains access to food and space. Fish that do not gain this prime habitat may be less successful in the struggle to survive and reproduce.

Biologists recognize two main types of competition—intraspecific and interspecific competition. **Intraspecific competition** occurs between organisms of the same species. **Interspecific competition** occurs between organisms of different species.

Intraspecific Competition

Intraspecific competition is very keen because members of the same species require the same food, space, and mates. For example, in many mammalian species, such as the musk-ox and baboon, the males fight for the social status that will allow them to mate. Beech trees likewise compete for access to nutrients and water in the soil and for the sunlight needed for photosynthesis.

In a population the individuals best adapted to survive will pass their genetic material on to offspring at a greater rate than less fit competitors. Thus intraspecific competition, a constant process in nature, is one of the driving forces of evolution.

Interspecific Competition

Interspecific competition is often less intense than intraspecific competition because individuals of different species do not compete for exactly the same kinds of food, space, or mates. However, when two species do compete for a certain natural resource, one will succeed in obtaining it, and the other will not. This was demonstrated in an experiment conducted in the 1930s by Soviet ecologist G. F. Gause. Gause used two species of paramecia that compete intensely for one kind of food. Figure 51-1 shows the results of Gause's experiments. Note that each species grew well in a separate culture, but when Gause placed the two species in the same culture, the population of *Paramecium caudatum* always died, and the population of *P. aurelia* always survived.

Section Objectives

- *Define* competition, *and distinguish between intraspecific and interspecific competition.*
- *State the competitive exclusion principle.*
- *Describe the importance of predator–prey relationships in an ecosystem.*
- *Identify the three types of symbiosis, and give an example of each.*

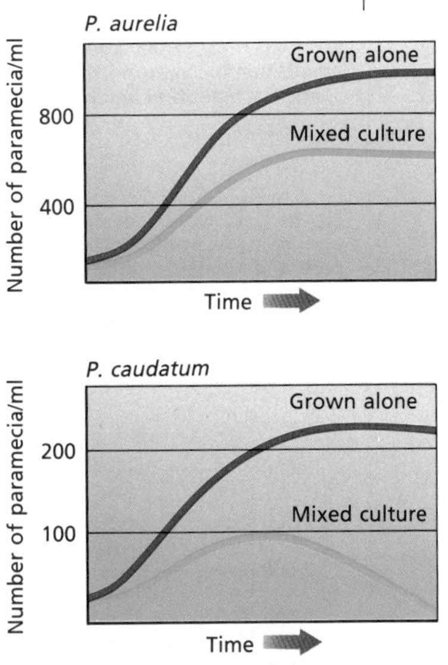

Figure 51-1 Note that both species of paramecia thrived when they were grown separately but that *P. caudatum* always died when the two species were mixed.

Symbiotic Relationship	Species A	Species B
parasitism	+	–
commensalism	+	neutral
mutualism	+	+

Graphic Organizer Use this table in Reteaching on p. 799.

Lesson Plan

Section Focus

This section discusses competition both within and between species. It describes the competitive exclusion principle and the three main forms of symbiosis: parasitism, commensalism, and mutualism.

Section Themes

This section emphasizes the theme of **Systems and Interactions.** It discusses how organisms in an ecosystem interact with each other and explores the diversity of these interactions, from predation to symbiosis.

Motivating Activity

Show students a picture of a wolf chasing a rabbit. Ask them what their reaction is. Then ask what would happen if the wolf never caught a rabbit or any other prey. *(There would be too many rabbits. The rabbits would overeat the plants, and when there weren't enough plants, some rabbits would starve.)* Ask students if they think that predation (that is, wolf eating rabbit) is a necessary part of an ecosystem, and have them justify their answers. *(Predators control a prey population.)*

Teaching Strategies

Applying Concepts Ask students why they think two species cannot occupy the same niche. *(If one is even slightly more successful, it would eventually replace the other.)* Then ask them to think of all the possible things that could happen in such a competition. *(The three possible outcomes are: one species becomes extinct; the two species diverge, and both survive in different niches; both species survive in the same niche, but in different places, such as on opposite sides of a river or mountain.)*

Interpreting the Visuals Discuss the three warblers illustrated in Figure 51-2. Ask students which outcome of Gause's exclusion principle they represent. *(The second outcome—the warblers have diverged so that each occupies a different niche.)* Direct students' attention to Figure 51-3. Ask them to explain the relationship between the predators and prey. *(The number of prey rises first, followed by a rise in the number of predators, then a decrease in the number of prey, then a decrease in the number of predators. When the number of prey goes up, there is more food for the predators, they eat more of the prey, then food is scarce, so the number of predators goes down.)*

■ *See* Blackline Master *105.*
■ *See* Laboratories, *Investigation 51 and* Process Skills, *Chapter 51.*

Guided Practice

Describe some symbiotic relationships and ask students whether the symbiosis is parasitism, commensalism, or mutualism. Some examples are: birds nesting in a tree *(Commensalism)*; bacteria growing in the human intestines *(Mutualism)*; a tapeworm growing in the intestine of a dog and consuming a lot of its food *(Parasitism)*.

Independent Practice

- Have students write answers to the Section Review.
- Have students identify the kind of symbiosis in each part of Figure 51-4, p. 799, and explain the relationship of the organisms. *(The mistletoe grows at the expense of the mesquite tree—parasitism; the shrimp is sheltered by the sea cucumber without harming it—commensalism; the algae camouflage the clam, and the clam provides an anchor for the algae—mutualism.)*

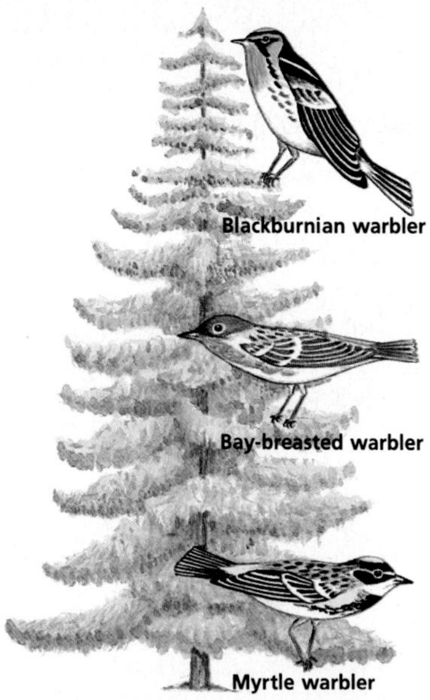

Figure 51-2 These species of warblers have adapted so that each species eats primarily at a different level of the tree. This adaptation has reduced the interspecific competition among them.

Gause's work and similar experiments by other scientists established that when two or more species compete for the very same resource, all but one will eventually fail as a competitor. In other words, two competitors cannot coexist on the same limiting resource. Biologists call this idea the **competitive exclusion principle.** Figure 51-2 illustrates one instance of adaptation of habits that reduces competition. The three species of warblers shown eat similar types of food and can occupy the same forest, but they differ in their feeding patterns. Each species feeds at a different height in the trees. Such behavioral adaptations greatly reduce—but do not entirely eliminate—the competition for food.

Predation

Another kind of biotic relationship is predation, in which one organism feeds upon another. In any ecosystem the relative numbers of predators and prey vary from year to year. Over time, however, a biological balance is established. This pattern is shown in Figure 51-3, which charts the numbers of predator mites, *Typhlodromus,* and prey mites, *Eotetranychus,* during an experiment over an eight-month period.

Predators and prey are part of the food web of an ecosystem. Therefore a change in the number of either affects the entire ecosystem. In some areas, for example, sheep are preyed upon by coyotes. However, coyotes also prey on other animals, such as jackrabbits. Therefore if ranchers kill coyotes to protect their sheep, a few more sheep may survive, but the number of jackrabbits in the area may rise, allowing them to compete with the sheep for food and other necessary resources.

Symbiosis

Symbiosis is a biological relationship in which two dissimilar organisms live together in a close association. Biologists distinguish three main types of symbiosis: parasitism, commensalism, and mutualism.

Figure 51-3 Notice the cycles of predation: As predators eat the prey, the number of predators increases and the number of prey decreases. As the food supply drops, the number of predators decreases and the number of prey increases.

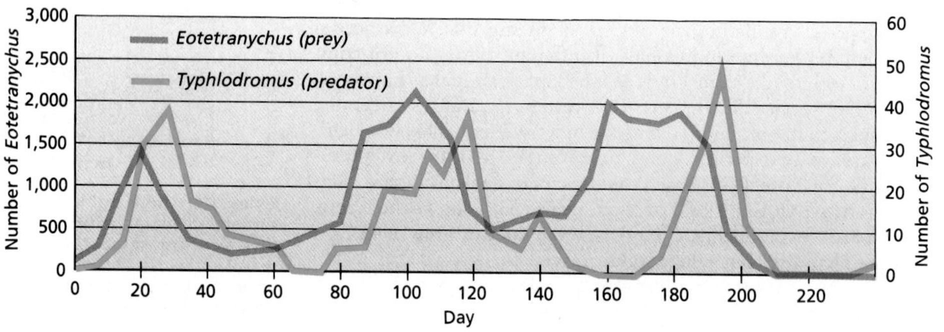

LEP Activity

Have students prepare a bulletin board display illustrating the three kinds of symbiosis. Have each student select one kind of symbiosis (parasitism, commensalism, mutualism) and use the library to find an example of two pairs of organisms living this way. Ask students to either photocopy pictures from nature magazines or make an illustration showing the relationship between the two organisms in each pair. Have them mount their pictures on oak tag or construction paper, using magic marker to label the organisms and the kind of symbiosis they show.

Parasitism

Parasitism is a close, long-term symbiotic relationship in which one organism obtains its nutrition from another organism. The organism receiving the benefits is a **parasite.** The organism providing them is a **host.** For example, the parasitic worms in the digestive tract of a white-tailed deer survive by consuming some of the deer host's own partially digested food. In time the parasite's food consumption may be enough to deprive the deer of nutrition. This deprivation weakens the host, making it less fit to survive. In Figure 51-4 you can see the effects of mistletoe parasitizing a mesquite tree.

Commensalism

Commensalism is a form of symbiosis in which one organism benefits and the other neither benefits nor suffers harm. **Epiphytes** *(EP-uh-FITES),* plants that grow on other plants, are examples. Among these are the orchid species that grow high in the trees of tropical forests. The trees provide the orchids with the support to grow and allow them to capture more sunlight than they would on the forest floor. The trees are not harmed, since the orchids neither feed on their tissues nor prevent significant amounts of sunlight from reaching their leaves. Figure 51-4 shows another commensal relationship, between shrimp and a sea cucumber.

Mutualism

Mutualism is a form of symbiosis in which both organisms benefit from living together. For example, the enzymatic action of bacteria that live in the digestive tracts of cattle enables the cattle to digest grasses. By breaking down the cellulose in the grasses, the bacteria make it possible for the cattle to use the nutrients the grasses contain. At the same time the bacteria take in nutrients for themselves—but not enough to harm the host. Both organisms therefore benefit from this close association. The clam and the algae shown in Figure 51-4 have a similar relationship. While the clam provides the algae with a place to anchor, the algae camouflage the clam, thus providing protection.

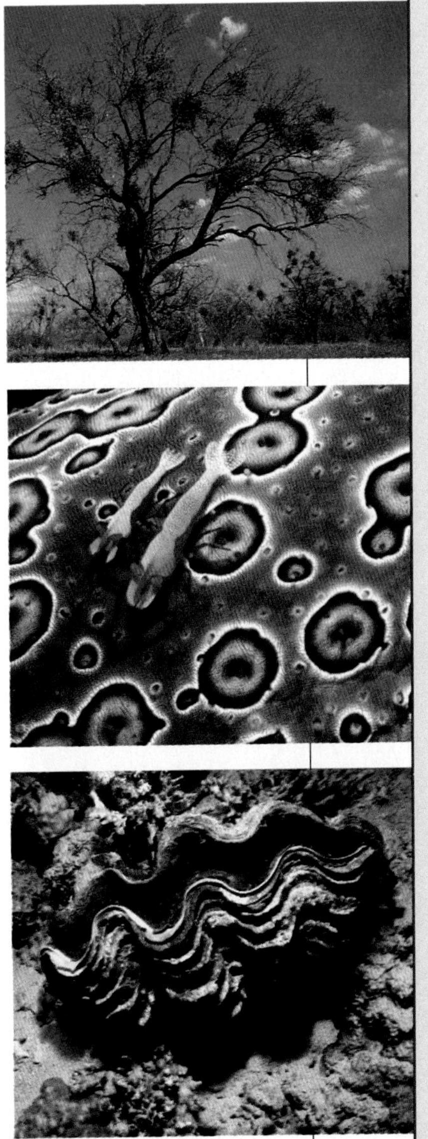

Figure 51-4 Various symbiotic relationships are shown here: parasitism (top), a mistletoe, *Phoradendron tomentosum,* in a mesquite tree, *Prosopis glandulosa;* commensalism (center), a shrimp and sea cucumber, *Periclimenes imperator;* and mutualism (bottom), a clam and algae.

Section Review

1. Define *intraspecific competition,* and explain how it differs from *interspecific competition.*
2. State the competitive exclusion principle, and give one example of how it works.
3. Briefly describe one example of a parasitic relationship. Be sure to identify and define both the parasite and the host.
4. How does commensalism differ from mutualism?
5. In what way does predation result in homeostasis in the ecosystem?

Check Your Understanding

1. Why are predators important in an ecosystem? *(They keep the prey population in check.)*
2. If two deer are fighting for the same territory, is this interspecific or intraspecific competition? *(Intraspecific)*
3. Compare parasitism and predation. *(In both relationships, one organism obtains its nutrition from another organism. A predator kills its prey outright, whereas a parasite has a long-term relationship with its host—the latter may be weakened.)*

Reteaching

Copy the table on p. 797 on the board. Have students give one example of each kind of symbiosis and explain why their examples fit each category.
- *See* Section Reviews *worksheet, Section 51.1.*

Enrichment

Have students research and report on the coevolution of an example of mutualism (such as aphids and ants, or ants and acacia trees) or parasitism (such as the *Myxoma* virus and the European rabbit).

Closure

Tell students that scientists hypothesize that the mitochondria in our cells are descendants of specialized bacteria. Ask students what kind of biotic relationship might have led to this situation. *(Mutualism)* Have them list the interspecific types of biotic relationships and explain the role each plays in the ecosystem. *(Competition, predation, symbiosis; all serve to help organisms meet biological needs.)*

Videodiscs

- ***Side 4 34768, Associations and Interactions (m)***

Answers to Section Review

1. Competition between organisms of the same species is intraspecific; between different species it is interspecific.
2. The principle holds that two interspecific competitors cannot coexist. Gause's experiments with paramecia demonstrated that these two competing species could not survive in the same culture.
3. Parasitic roundworms may live and feed in the digestive tract of a host such as a deer, depriving the host of nutrients and causing it to weaken. Only the parasite benefits from the relationship.
4. In commensalism only one organism benefits; in mutualism both benefit.
5. Predation establishes a long-term balance in numbers between predator and prey.

Section 51.2

Lesson Plan

Section Focus

This section discusses various rhythmic patterns that characterize the lives of organisms: circadian, annual, migratory, and tidal.

Section Themes

This section emphasizes two themes: **Patterns of Change** and **Stability.** It shows how rhythmic patterns of change are adaptations that help organisms to maintain stability in changing environments.

Motivating Activity

Ask students to imagine themselves in a room with no windows and no clock. The room is always lighted and food is always available. They have a blindfold, so they can sleep whenever they want. Ask them how they would organize their time under such circumstances. *(Encourage diverse answers.)* Tell students that experiments such as this have been done and that, on the average, people regulate their lives with a slightly longer than 24-hour periodicity. This is known as a circadian rhythm. One hypothesis on why circadian rhythms evolved holds that the rhythms enable animals to anticipate and prepare for daily events, thus increasing the animals' efficiency and conserving their energy.

Teaching Strategies

Applying Concepts Ask students to name animals that hibernate. *(Bats, squirrels, hamsters)* Point out that bears do not hibernate. Bears' metabolism and activity slow down, but their body temperature does not fall significantly. Ask why hibernation might be a suitable adaptation for some animals. *(It enables them to survive the cold and the scarcity of food during winter. By lowering their metabolism and body temperature, these animals can live entirely off stored fat.)*

Section Objectives

- *Define* circadian rhythms, annual rhythms, migration, *and* tidal rhythms.
- *Explain the adaptive advantages of rhythmic patterns.*
- *Distinguish hibernation from estivation.*

51.2 Rhythmic Patterns

Living things interact not only with other organisms but also with their physical environment. In this section we will examine biological rhythms, the periodic responses of organisms to periodic changes in their physical environment. For example, many organisms, such as dogs and humans, are **diurnal** *(die-URN-'l)*—that is, they are active mainly during the day. Other organisms, such as raccoons and owls, are **nocturnal**—that is, they are active mainly at night. This daily alternation between periods of activity and inactivity is just one of many rhythmic patterns.

Rhythmic patterns are adaptations that often limit competition, facilitate food gathering, or help organisms respond to changes in climate. Rhythmic patterns also allow different species to occupy the same habitat but to utilize its resources at different times. For example, when the owl hunts by night and the hawk by day, competition for the same food, mice, is limited.

Circadian Rhythms

When the physiological or behavioral pattern of an organism occurs in cycles of about 24 hours, the pattern is called a **circadian rhythm.** If, for example, an animal sleeps during the day and is active during the night it follows a circadian rhythm. Likewise, a plant whose flower petals open during the day and close at night exhibits a circadian rhythm.

Scientists have investigated whether human circadian rhythms are controlled by sunlight, by other physical factors, or by some internal physiological mechanism. Human subjects placed in darkened rooms maintain regular circadian rhythms of between 22 and 26 hours. Scientists therefore suggest that while these rhythms can be affected by social needs or by cycles of daylight, they are controlled by some internal timing mechanism, referred to as a **biological clock.** Many organisms seem to respond to a biological clock. The exact nature of this internal control is unknown, but it may involve fluctuating levels of hormones.

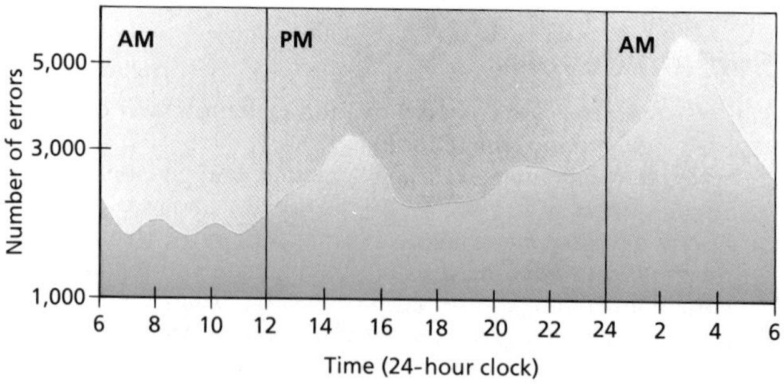

Figure 51-5 In a test of circadian rhythms in humans assigned to eight-hour shifts, highest efficiency occurred between 7 A.M. and 11 A.M. and lowest efficiency at 3 A.M.

Kind of Rhythm	Length of Cycle
circadian	24 hours
annual	1 year
migratory	seasonal
tidal	roughly 12 hours

Graphic Organizer Use this table in Guided Practice on p. 801.

Annual Rhythms

A physiological or behavioral pattern that recurs in yearly cycles is called an **annual rhythm.** The reproductive cycles of many plants and animals, for example, are annual rhythms. Female bears give birth during the winter in the protection of the den. Ducks nest and lay eggs in the spring and summer, which allows the young to grow strong enough to survive migration in autumn. Many plants also reproduce in the spring, allowing the next generation to grow and set seeds before the next cycle of cold weather.

Hibernation, a state of severely reduced physiological activity occurring during the winter, is another kind of annual rhythm. This adaptation allows an otherwise active creature to survive during the months when temperatures are extremely cold and food is scarce. When the woodchuck nestles into its protected den as winter approaches, its metabolism, breathing rate, and heartbeat slow. This sleeplike state can be maintained with the use of very little energy.

Estivation *(ES-tuh-VAY-shun)* is an annual rhythm characterized by severely reduced physiological activity during the summer. Animals such as toads and box turtles bury themselves in cool mud and estivate during the hot summer when ponds dry up. Estivation can last for days, weeks, or even months.

Think

How might you determine whether the degree of cold and the availability of food would trigger the hibernation of an organism during the winter?

Migratory Rhythms

Many species of animals move from one community or biome to another with the change of seasons. Such seasonal movement is a kind of rhythm called **migration.** Migration is a behavioral adaptation that allows animals to exploit the nutrients, climatic conditions, and habitats that are available only seasonally. In summer the northern tundra biome becomes a complex of ponds and wetlands. Dozens of species of waterfowl migrate north to the tundra, where they find a rich supply of vegetation and invertebrates to eat and space in which to hatch and rear their young. The birds then migrate south in the fall to avoid the Arctic winter, which is too cold and dry to support much life. The arctic tern may make the longest journey of any migratory species. Every year it flies 36,000 miles between the North Atlantic, where it breeds, and the Antarctic.

Birds are not the only animals that migrate. Reindeer migrate between the northern taiga and the tundra. Monarch butterflies migrate between the mountains of Mexico and the northern United States and parts of Canada. Many kinds of whales migrate between polar seas, where they feed during the summer, and tropical waters, where they mate and raise young during the winter.

Mountain-dwelling animals may migrate vertically. For example, the bighorn sheep and elk that live in the Rocky Mountains move up the slopes with the onset of summer and descend into the valleys again in winter.

Figure 51-6 A mountain goat, *Oreamnos americanus*, migrates vertically with the change in seasons.

Answer to Think

A study of the habitat of an organism—the temperature range and availability of food—and the dates of hibernation could help you determine the conditions that would trigger the hibernation of an organism. Experiments involving the variation of the temperature in zoos might also yield clues.

Applying Concepts Ask students how they think migrations and hibernations are different solutions to the same problem. *(Both are ways of coping with adverse climatic conditions. Migrating animals move to where conditions are better. Hibernating animals lower their metabolism and reduce their need for food.)* Ask students how birds benefit by laying their eggs in the spring. *(The young will be grown by winter and be ready to migrate.)*

Guided Practice

Copy the table on p. 800 onto the board. Ask students to write down and explain one example of each of the four kinds of rhythms.

Independent Practice

- Have students write the answers to the Section Review.
- Give students a list of animals displaying rhythmic patterns. Have them write down the function served by the rhythm. Some examples are: barnacles *(Close up during low tide to remain moist)*; caribou *(Migrate to tundra in summer for food, to coniferous forest in winter for shelter)*; squirrels *(Hibernate in winter, thus reducing food requirements and conserving energy)*; bats *(Conserve energy by sleeping during the day, hunt at night when there is less competition for food, and also hibernate)*.

Videodiscs

- ***Side 4 8843, Bat Flight (m)***

Cooperative Learning

Biological Rhythms Divide the class into groups of four students. Have one student in each group study circadian rhythms, another study annual rhythms, another study migratory rhythms, and the fourth study tidal rhythms. Ask each student to select one organism displaying the rhythm to be studied, read about it in the library, and write a report describing the rhythm and the role it plays in the organism's life. Have students report about their organism to the rest of the group. Have each group discuss how each type of biological rhythm is an adaptation to a rhythmic change in the environment.

Section 51.2

Check Your Understanding

1. With what adverse conditions do animals with tidal rhythms need to cope? *(Drying out at low tide)*

2. How does a vertically migrating animal benefit by moving to the valleys in the winter? *(Winter in the valleys is less severe than on the mountain.)*

3. Why is it advantageous for a moth-pollinated flower to be most fragrant at night? *(Moths are active at night; the flowers conserve energy by producing scents only at night.)*

Reteaching

Ask students to draw a concept map showing what conditions biological rhythms respond to and how they are adaptive. An example of a completed concept map is shown on p. 795B.

■ *See* Section Reviews *worksheet, Section 51.2.*

Enrichment

Have students research the role of the pineal gland in circadian rhythms. Ask them how these rhythms can be disrupted. *(By jet lag, occupational demands, and going without sleep too long)* Have students present oral reports to the class.

Closure

Ask each student to name a single organism that exhibits a rhythmic pattern. Ask the student to describe the details of what the organism does. *(Students may draw a migration map.)* Have the student explain the adaptive advantage of the rhythm and identify the type of rhythmic pattern. *(Sample answer: a migration might be a way of escaping a cold winter)*

Videodiscs

■ ***Side 4 34994, Ghost Crab and Land Crab: Territorial Relationships (m)***

Figure 51-7 Starfish and sea urchins are two types of organisms that can live in deep water at high tide and shallow water at low tide.

Tidal Rhythms

The position of the sun and moon causes tides. When cyclical changes in the physiology or behavior of an organism correspond to the rise and fall of the sea, the cycles are **tidal rhythms.** As you read in Chapter 49, organisms that live in ecosystems along coastlines have adapted to the rhythms of the tides. During low tide small fishes and crustaceans may find protection in tidal pools, and clams seal in moisture by clamping their shells shut.

Barnacles are examples of organisms with a tidal rhythm. Barnacles, crustaceans that are sessile, are adapted to tidal conditions. They secrete a substance that glues their shells to rocks or to the shells of other animals. Opposite the end where it is attached, the barnacle shell is open. When the tide is low, the barnacle is exposed to air. The barnacle then pulls deep into its shell to prevent its body from becoming desiccated. When the tide is high, the barnacle extends itself out of its shell and feeds by filtering microorganisms and small invertebrates from the water.

Regular tides also affect organisms that live in the open ocean. Many fish feed in tidal pools at high tide and leave the pools as the tide recedes.

Section Review

1. Define *circadian rhythms.*
2. What are three adaptive advantages of rhythmic patterns or cycles?
3. Compare and contrast hibernation and estivation.
4. Briefly describe the adaptation of a barnacle to the movement of tides.
5. The lack of a regular human reproductive pattern is an exception to the usual seasonal cycle of many animals. What advantage might humans gain by not having an annual reproductive rhythm?

Answers to Section Review

1. A circadian rhythm is a daily pattern in an organism's physiology or behavior.
2. They limit competition, facilitate food gathering, and help an organism adjust to climatic changes.
3. Both are states of severely reduced physiological activity, but hibernation occurs during winter and estivation during summer.
4. During low tide barnacles retreat into their shells to prevent dessication. During high tide they extend themselves from the shell and feed.
5. Answers will vary but should reflect an understanding that an organism capable of reproducing at any time of year may have a selective advantage over organisms tied to an annual pattern.

51.3 Succession

Just as biologists can often predict the periodic responses of organisms, they can also often predict specific patterns of change in plant and animal populations. The gradual, sequential replacement of populations in an area is called **succession.**

Figure 51-8 illustrates the process of succession. The grasses shown are the **pioneer species,** or the first species to colonize a new habitat. All the pioneer species in an area make up a pioneer community. Each set of species in the community changes the environment in ways that ultimately make it unfavorable for the survival and reproduction of those species. Yet these changes allow other species to survive and reproduce. As a result the pioneer community will be replaced by a new community, which will later be replaced by another. Each intermediate community that arises through this process is called a **seral** *(SIR-ul)* **community.** The repeated replacement of seral communities eventually leads to the establishment of a **climax community,** a community that will remain stable as long as the area is undisturbed. What plants dominate the climax community in Figure 51-8?

The soil, climate, and other abiotic factors in a region determine the organisms that will make up a climax community. The forest in Figure 51-8 is a typical climax community in temperate areas of the eastern United States.

Section Objectives

- *Define* primary *and* secondary succession, *and give an example of each.*
- *Distinguish between seral and climax communities.*
- *Describe the succession process in lakes.*
- *Summarize the evidence that Cowles used to develop his model of succession in sand dunes.*

Figure 51-8 From a pioneer community of grasses, this area has progressed to a climax community. Two seral communities preceded the climax community.

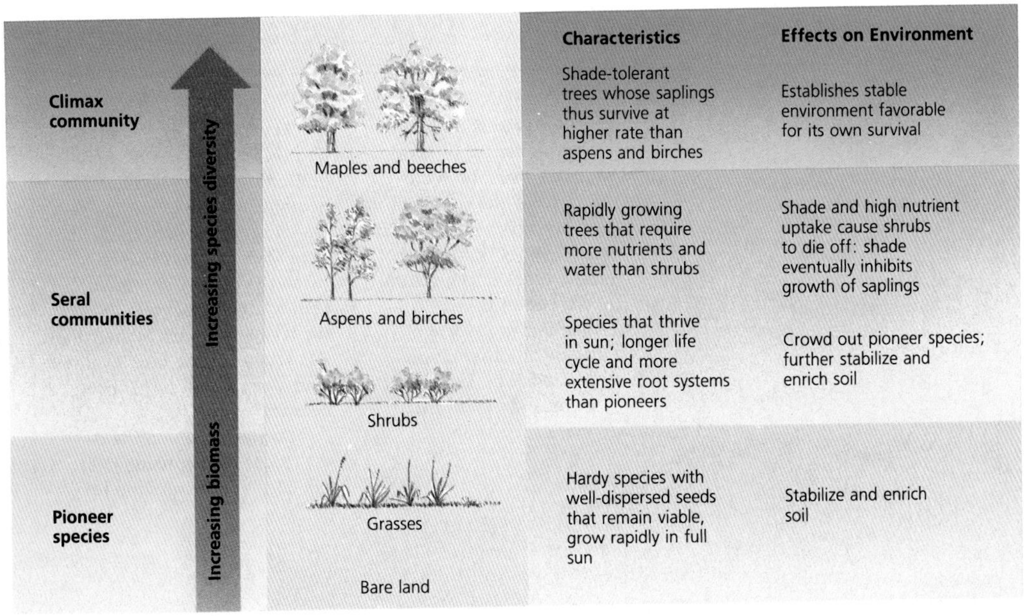

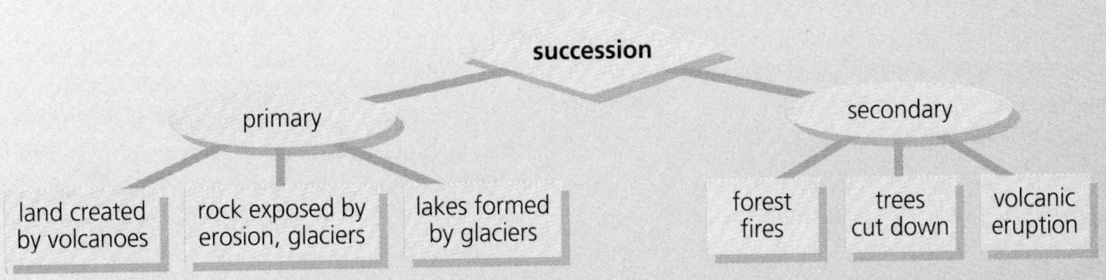

Graphic Organizer Use this organizational chart in Reteaching on p. 806.

Lesson Plan

Section Focus

This section describes succession, a process that occurs either when new habitats are established or when old ones are destroyed. Students are probably already familiar with some examples of succession (if, for example, they have seen vacant lots change).

Section Themes

This section emphasizes two themes: **Patterns of Change** and **Systems and Interactions.** Habitats change as organisms change their environment, ultimately making it less suitable for themselves and more suitable for other species. Such change is the result of interactions between organisms and their environment.

Motivating Activity

Show students pictures of Mt. St. Helens before and immediately after it erupted. Ask them what they think Mt. St. Helens looks like now. (*Answers will vary. Encourage a diversity of viewpoints.*) Then show students a picture of Mt. St. Helens a few years after the eruption, when vegetation is evident. Ask what they think happened. *(Using the nutrients left behind by the volcano, new vegetation grew from seeds dispersed from nearby areas.)* Ask students to speculate on what Mt. St. Helens might look like 100 years from now.

Teaching Strategies

Interpreting the Visuals Take students step-by-step through Figure 51-8, p. 803. Ask them what factors will determine the makeup of a climax community. *(Soil, climate, amount of sunlight, and so forth.)*

■ *See* **Overhead Transparency** *T51 and* **Blackline Master** *106.*

Applying Concepts Ask students what happens to an empty lot over a period of years if it is left alone. *(It becomes overgrown with "weeds." Eventually shrubs and trees will grow.)* Ask them if this is an example of primary or secondary succession. *(Secondary succession since most empty lots were once cleared of their original vegetation)*

Inferring Relationships Display photos or an actual sample of a rock covered with lichen or moss. Ask students what the moss or lichen would be called. *(Pioneer species)* Ask them why lichens can colonize bare rock. *(They don't have roots, but they can attach strongly to the rock and photosynthesize.)* Have them predict what would grow on the rock after the lichens and mosses. *(Vascular plants, grasses, bushes, and trees; they would use the soil built up by the lichens and mosses.)*

Guided Practice

Ask students to study Figure 51-9, p. 806, which shows succession in a lake. Have them write down what they think this area looked like 1,000 years ago. *(It was a larger body of water with less vegetation.)* Ask them to write down their predictions as to how this area will change over the next 500 years. *(More vegetation will grow; the lake will become richer in nutrients. It will eventually be replaced by a meadow with grasses, then shrubs, then the trees that will form a climax community.)*

Primary Succession

Primary succession is the sequential replacement of populations in an area that has not previously supported life, such as bare rock or a sand dune. The transformation of a barren environment into a climax community may require a thousand years or more.

When glaciers last retreated from eastern Canada about 12,000 years ago, they left a huge stretch of barren bedrock from which all the soil had been scraped. This geologic formation, called the Canadian Shield, was inhospitable to plants and to most animals.

Repeated freezing and thawing broke this rock into smaller pieces. In time lichens colonized the barren rock. Acids in the lichens and mildly acidic rain leached out nutrient minerals from the rock. Eventually the **necromass,** or dead organic matter, from the lichens and minerals from the rock began to form a thin layer of soil in which a few herbaceous plants could grow. These plants then died, building the thickness of the soil. Soon shrubs could grow and then trees. Today much of the Canadian Shield is dense with pine, balsam, and spruce trees whose roots cling to soil that in some areas is still only a few inches deep.

Biology in Process

Developing a Model of Succession

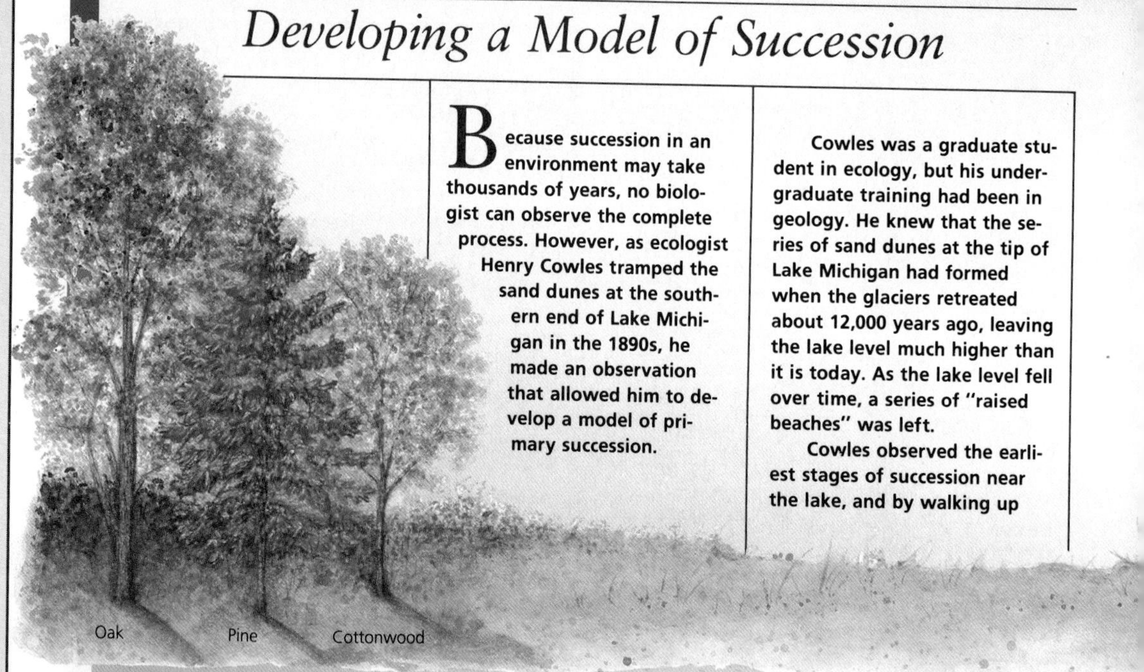

Because succession in an environment may take thousands of years, no biologist can observe the complete process. However, as ecologist Henry Cowles tramped the sand dunes at the southern end of Lake Michigan in the 1890s, he made an observation that allowed him to develop a model of primary succession.

Cowles was a graduate student in ecology, but his undergraduate training had been in geology. He knew that the series of sand dunes at the tip of Lake Michigan had formed when the glaciers retreated about 12,000 years ago, leaving the lake level much higher than it is today. As the lake level fell over time, a series of "raised beaches" was left.

Cowles observed the earliest stages of succession near the lake, and by walking up

Interdisciplinary Activity

Government In 1988 a forest fire lasting several months burned down half of Yellowstone National Park. For many years, the policy of the National Park Service was to put out all fires in national parks. As a result, many dead trees were left standing in parks. After the policy was changed to a "let burn" policy, the 1988 fire resulted. Ask students to research the reasons for the original policy and why it was changed to the "let burn" policy. *(Most forest fires are caused by lightning. If the parks were left in their natural state, these fires would burn uncontrolled.)* Have students describe what has happened in Yellowstone since the fire. *(There is vigorous new growth of vegetation.)* Ask them to write a report giving and defending their opinion as to which policy the National Park Service should follow.

In the Galápagos Islands ecologists have gained further insights into primary succession. These relatively new islands were created by volcanic eruptions about 2.5 million years ago. Rainfall gradually weathered the volcanic rock into tiny mineral particles. Ecologists assume that marine organisms and sea birds were among the first life-forms to reach the islands. Bird droppings, called guano, provided a habitat for bacterial spores deposited by the wind. In time other organisms arrived, blown by winds or carried on ocean currents. Some of these organisms thrived and established new communities. As more new species arrived, new seral communities formed, and the process of primary succession continued.

Secondary Succession

Secondary succession is the sequential replacement of populations in disrupted habitats that have not been totally stripped of soil and vegetation. The disruption may stem from a natural disaster, such as a forest fire or volcanic eruption, or from human activity, such as farming, logging, or mining. After a forest fire, for example, succession might follow the pattern shown in Figure 51-8.

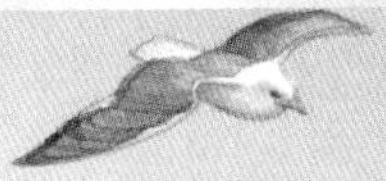

through the dunes he "went backward" in successional time. Since the soil was the same and the climate had changed little, he had a natural laboratory.

As Cowles moved away from the bare sand of the shore, he found the following sequence of plant communities: marram grass; other grasses; sand cherry, willow, and cottonwood; jack pine and white pine; and black oak. Cowles hypothesized that this sequence formed the pattern of succession in the dune ecosystem.

Further studies by Cowles and others helped build this model of succession. Marram grass is adapted as a pioneer plant on dunes; its long, horizontal stems spread quickly and form a network that anchors the sand. Then the marram dies out as later colonists move in. The extensive roots of all of these plants make the dune stable.

Carbon dating of these dunes revealed that about 100 years after the first deciduous trees appeared, pines began to grow. Another 100 to 150 years later the first black oaks, the climax tree species, arrived and shaded out the pines.

In 1899 Cowles speculated that the succession process on the dunes might continue until beech and maple forests overtook the black oaks. Subsequent studies by other scientists suggest that the acid dune soil will probably not allow the growth of beech–maple forests. This hypothesis is supported by the fact that even the dunes farthest from the lake are still dominated by black oaks.

- **How did Cowles's knowledge of geology help him interpret his observations?**

Independent Practice

- Have students write answers to the Section Review.
- Ask students to walk around the neighborhood near their homes or school and record observations of a process of succession. *(The neighborhood where they live might have been a farm 50 or 100 years ago; there might be small ponds or swamps that are being filled in with organic matter.)*

Biology in Process

Using the Feature

The main process skills illustrated in this feature are observing, inferring, and modeling. The feature describes how Henry Cowles developed a model of succession in a dune ecosystem. He inferred that as the level of the lake dropped over the last 12,000 years, new levels of land were exposed and colonized. Thus communities nearest the lake's edge (most recently exposed) would exhibit the earliest stages of succession and those farthest from the edge of the lake (exposed the longest) would exhibit the latest stages. Refer students to the illustration on pp. 804–805 to clarify the order of succession discussed in the feature.

Answer to the Feature

From geology Cowles learned about sand dunes and the water level of Lake Michigan. Thus he was able to infer that the series of dunes were a record of the process of succession in the dune ecosystem.

Videodiscs

- ***592, Lichen on Rock (s)***
- ***Side 3 9886, Pine Life Cycle (m)***

LEP Activity

Take students on a field trip to a lakeshore, dune, field, pine forest, or other seral community. Ask them to identify different species of plants and look for evidence of succession. Have them observe what other types of organisms beside plants are present. You may wish to suggest that they take photographs or make sketches of such evidence to display in class. Have them try to identify as many species as possible as members of either pioneer, seral, or climax communities. Ask them to write a report summarizing their findings.

Section 51.3

Check Your Understanding

1. Compare primary succession and secondary succession. *(Primary succession occurs in new habitats; secondary succession occurs in habitats that have been disturbed.)*
2. What causes eutrophication in lakes? *(The accumulation of organic matter from the organisms living in the lake)*
3. Compare a seral and a climax community. *(A seral community will eventually be replaced by a climax community. A climax community will remain stable unless the environment changes.)*

Reteaching

Ask students to make an organizational chart comparing the situations in which primary succesion and secondary succession occur. Use the chart on p. 803 as a model.

■ *See* Section Reviews *worksheet, Section 51.3.*

Enrichment

Have students read about the formation of the Galápagos Islands and the process of succession that has occurred there. Have them discuss where the organisms living there came from and how they have evolved over the years.

Closure

Remind students that an uninterrupted process of succession leads to a stable community. During succession the pioneer and seral organisms change the environment in ways that are unfavorable to themselves. Ask students where the human community fits into the model of succession. *(The human community is not stable in terms of population growth; our net effect on the environment is negative.)*

Videodiscs

■ *728–729, Dandelion (s)*
■ *Side 3 3302, A Drop of Fresh Water (m)*

Figure 51-9 This lake is gradually being filled by vegetation.

Old field succession is the replacement of populations in abandoned farm fields. It commonly takes about 100 years to produce a stable community of trees, such as beech and maple, in an old field. Secondary succession in an abandoned field in the eastern United States begins with annual grasses, mustards, and dandelions. The succession proceeds with perennial grasses and shrubs, continues with trees such as aspens and dogwoods, and ends with a climax deciduous forest of beech and maples.

In many areas environmental conditions are such that a true climax community never forms. For example, the natural climax community in many grassland biomes would be a forest, but periodic fires prevent forests from developing. These grasslands are called fire-controlled climax communities.

Succession in Lakes

Lakes undergo succession that slowly transforms them from crystal clear bodies of water into dry land. A tiny prairie pond may be transformed into dry land in a few dozen years. Changes in the largest lakes take place over millions of years.

The process of lake succession, shown in Figure 51-9, involves eutrophication. **Eutrophication** *(yoo-TROE-fuh-KAY-shun)* is the increase in nutrients in an environment. Early in its existence a lake may be so low in nutrients that relatively few organisms can survive in it. Such a lake is termed **oligotrophic.** As nutrients such as nitrogen and phosphorus flow into the lake from surrounding land and from the atmosphere, the biomass in the lake gradually increases and the lake becomes murkier. Meanwhile, sediment accumulates around the roots of the cattails and rushes that have begun growing along the shore of the lake. Also, an increasing number of aquatic arthropods and fish begin to populate the lake.

In time the accumulated soil from the surrounding watershed along with the necromass begins to fill in the lake. The lake has then gone from an oligotrophic condition to a **eutrophic** condition, one in which there are many nutrients. Eventually the lake may become so full of rich sediment that it becomes a marsh, then a swamp, and finally dry land—which may then proceed through successional stages to become a dense forest.

Section Review

1. Define *succession.*
2. How do seral and climax communities differ?
3. Give one example of secondary succession. Be sure to indicate the disturbance that preceded it, and identify the pioneer species.
4. Briefly describe the eutrophication of a lake.
5. How is interspecific competition related to the process of succession?

Answers to Section Review

1. Succession is the gradual, sequential replacement of populations in a habitat.
2. Seral communities are part of the evolution of a habitat, leading to the establishment of a stable climax community.
3. Sample answer: a forest fire is followed by pioneer weed species, succeeded by sun-loving shrubs, then by aspen, birch, cottonwood, then shade-tolerant maple and beech.
4. Nutrients from the land and atmosphere flow into the lake; sediment accumulates around plants near the shore; aquatic arthropods and fish increase; soil and necromass begin filling the lake.
5. As the environment changes, different species become more effective in competing for the same resources and so displace species from the previous seral community.

(For an overview of nitrogen fixation and preparatory information related to the laboratory, see p. 795B.)

Inquiry

2. The bacteria and the legume have a mutualistic relationship. The bacteria supply fixed nitrogen to the plant, and the plant supplies carbohydrates for the bacteria to use as food.

5. The nodules that are not fixing nitrogen might contain *Rhizobium* that are actively reproducing. Once *Rhizobium* begins to fix nitrogen, it can no longer reproduce. For the species to continue, there must be some *Rhizobium* that are not fixing nitrogen so there will be some reproducing bacteria.

Laboratory

Nitrogen Fixation in Root Nodules

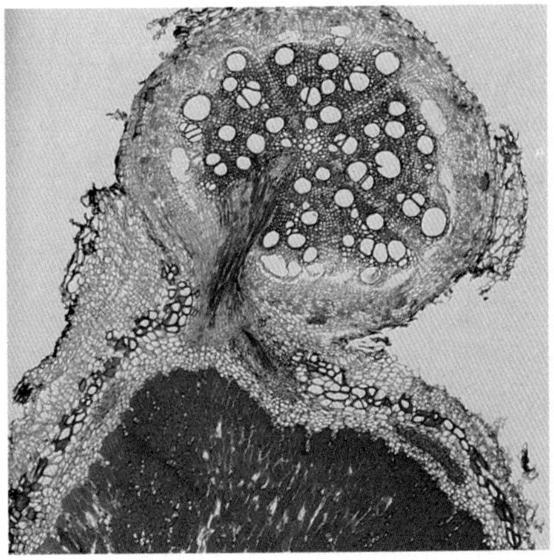

Objective
To examine the structure and function of root nodules in legumes

Process Skills
Observing, inferring

Materials
Living alfalfa, bean, or other leguminous plant infected with symbiotic *Rhizobium;* the same type of plant without *Rhizobium* infection; scalpel; microscope; prepared slide of cross-section of legume nodules

Inquiry

1. Carefully dig a plant from the pot labeled *Noninfected.* Shake free any soil that clings to the roots. Examine the root system closely. Set the plant aside.
2. Dig a plant from the pot labeled *Infected,* and repeat step 1. Locate a root nodule on the root system as shown in the photo at the right (×20). Inside the nodules are cells filled with *Rhizobium* bacteria. The bacteria fix atmospheric nitrogen (N_2) by converting it into ammonia compounds (NH_4OH). Excess ammonia is expelled into the soil and plant tissue surrounding the nodules. Given the need of all green plants for nitrogen, how would you describe the relationship between the bacteria and the legume?
3. Using a scalpel, carefully cut open one of the root nodules.
4. Examine the inside of the nodule carefully. What color is it? If the infecting strain of *Rhizobium* is able to fix nitrogen in this species of legume, the inside of the nodule will be pink. If the strain cannot fix nitrogen, the inside will be green. The pink color indicates the presence of a plant protein necessary for the fixation of nitrogen.
5. Use the scalpel to cut through several other nodules. Are you able to find both types of nodules on the roots of the same plant? Does the fact that some of the nodules are not effective at fixing nitrogen mean that they do not function in the relationship between the bacteria and the legume? What role might the uninfected nodules play?
6. Use a microscope to examine prepared slides of sections of root nodules. Use low power to locate an area you wish to view, and then switch to high power. Determine whether all the cells are infected with bacteria.

Conclusions

1. If you were to grow legumes without root nodules to use as experimental controls, why should you plant the seeds in sterile soil?
2. Why would a farmer want to plant legumes in a particular field one year and a nonlegume crop the next?

Further Inquiry
In the course of this investigation you have discovered how legumes benefit from this relationship. Devise an experiment that shows whether *Rhizobium* also benefits.

Conclusions

1. Nonsterile soil might contain *Rhizobium* that could infect the young plants.
2. When the legumes were harvested, some usable nitrogen would be left in the soil.

Further Inquiry

Students may attempt to grow *Rhizobium* in a culture without a legume nodule. If the *Rhizobium* bacteria fail to grow without the legume, this would be evidence that their relationship is mutually beneficial.

Chapter 51 Review

Vocabulary

annual rhythm (801)
biological clock (800)
biotic relationships (797)
circadian rhythm (800)
climax community (803)
commensalism (799)
competition (797)
competitive exclusion principle (798)
diurnal (800)
epiphyte (799)
estivation (801)
eutrophic (806)
eutrophication (806)
hibernation (801)
host (799)
interspecific competition (797)
intraspecific competition (797)
migration (801)
mutualism (799)
necromass (804)
nocturnal (800)
old field succession (806)
oligotrophic (806)
parasite (799)
parasitism (799)
pioneer species (803)
primary succession (804)
secondary succession (805)
seral community (803)
succession (803)
tidal rhythm (802)

Use a dictionary to find the origin of each of the terms below. Explain how the root meaning of each underlined part relates to the meaning of the term.

1. circadian
2. commensalism
3. eutrophication
4. necromass
5. hibernation

Review

1. Intraspecific competition may occur between (a) musk-oxen and baboons (b) red-winged blackbirds and beech trees (c) two baboons (d) starlings and blue-jays.
2. Competition, predation, and symbiosis are all types of (a) parasitic relationships (b) mutualistic relationships (c) biotic relationships (d) annual rhythms.
3. Epiphytes are (a) a type of orchid (b) plants that grow on other plants (c) insects that live high up on trees (d) bacteria that live in the digestive tract of grazing animals.
4. Estivation (a) occurs during months when conditions are favorable for the organism's physiology (b) occurs during the winter (c) always lasts for months (d) occurs during the summer.
5. Seasonal movement is known as (a) hibernation (b) migration (c) estivation (d) succession.
6. Regular tidal rhythms (a) only affect organisms in tidal pools (b) do not affect organisms that do not live in the intertidal zone (c) may affect organisms that don't live in the intertidal zone (d) affect all organisms.
7. Primary succession is the sequential replacement of populations starting (a) on bare rock (b) in a disrupted habitat (c) after a forest fire (d) only on dry land.
8. The biological community on the Galápagos Islands is the result of (a) primary succession (b) secondary succession (c) eutrophication (d) old field succession.
9. Henry Cowles developed his model of succession by (a) experimenting with paramecia (b) studying the fossil record (c) observing sand dune communities (d) using computers.
10. Old field succession (a) is a type of primary succession (b) results in a fire-controlled climax community (c) begins with pioneer tree species (d) is a type of secondary succession.

Vocabulary

1. *Dian* comes from the Latin *dies,* which means "day." Combined with *circa* it forms a word meaning "about one day."
2. *Mensal* comes from *mensa,* the Latin word for "table." *Commensalism* refers to a relationship between organisms in which each obtains food from the same place, or "at the same table."
3. *Eutroph* comes from the Greek *eutrophos,* which means "well nourished"; eutrophication is the process by which a lake becomes nutrient-rich.
4. *Necro* comes from the Greek *nekros,* which means "dead body." *Necromass* refers to material from dead organisms.
5. *Hiber* comes from a word for "winter"; *hibernation* refers to a state of dormancy during winter.

Review

1. c **6.** c
2. c **7.** a
3. b **8.** a
4. d **9.** c
5. b **10.** d

11. Gause used two species of paramecia (*Paramecium caudatum* and *P. aurelia*) that competed for the same food. He placed them in separate cultures and found that each grew well. Then he combined them in one culture and found that only *P. aurelia* survived.
12. These three do not feed in the same place on a tree. Blackburnian warblers feed in the canopy, bay-breasted warblers in the middle layers of the tree, and myrtle warblers near the ground.
13. In both relationships one organism feeds on another. However, a predator catches and kills its prey; a parasite lives within the organism it feeds on and can only feed if the host organism remains alive.
14. A diurnal animal is most active during the day, and a nocturnal animal is most active at night.
15. To discover whether physical factors such as daylight control human circadian rhythms or whether the rhythms are controlled by something else, scientists placed human subjects in darkened rooms and noted their circadian rhythms.
16. It refers to an undefined internal timing mechanism in organisms.
17. Migration gives organisms an advantage in exploiting nutrients, climatic conditions, and habitats available only seasonally.
18. The interactions of pioneer species with the environment change the microenvironment to one that is ultimately unfavorable to the growth of seedlings

11. Briefly describe the experiment that led G. F. Gause to establish the competitive exclusion principle.
12. Explain how three species of warblers that consume similar types of food can occupy the same forest without violating Gause's principle.
13. Compare and contrast predation and parasitism.
14. What is the difference between a diurnal animal and a nocturnal one?
15. Describe one study in which scientists studied circadian rhythms in humans. What was the purpose of the study?
16. What does the term *biological clock* mean?
17. Name three adaptive advantages of migratory behavior.
18. Explain what occurs so that an undisturbed community of pioneer species does not remain stable.
19. How does necromass aid in succession?
20. What was the pioneer species in the area known as the Canadian Shield?

Critical Thinking

1. A number of birds and animals reach adult size long before they begin mating and reproducing. What competitive advantages might the delay in reproduction give individuals?
2. In any community of animals, including humans, disease will claim a certain number of the population. How might disease affect competition? In your answer be sure to consider both intraspecific and interspecific competition.
3. Normally, snowy owls hunt lemmings in the Arctic. However, about every four years the owls move south to hunt in southern Canada and the northern United States. How would you explain the migratory rhythm of the owls?
4. Men and women who work on a police force or in a fire department are often required to work nights. Some of them find it very difficult to adjust to this irregular schedule. How might you explain their difficulty?

5. Look at the photo above. Ferns, asters, and fireweeds were some of the first species to grow out of the ash from the eruption of Mt. St. Helens in Washington. Why might this type of plant have emerged first? What general kinds of plants might follow?

Extension

1. Keep a log of your waking and sleeping hours for one week. Compare your data with those of other students. Notice any variations, and consider what they might say about human circadian rhythms.
2. Read the article by Timothy M. Beardsley entitled "The Sea Turtle's Tale" in *Scientific American,* August 1990, p. 32. Give an oral report on the unique migration patterns of the sea turtle.
3. Write a report on the migration of the monarch butterfly. Draw a map of the migration route and destinations, and include the time required for the butterfly to make its trip.

of the pioneer species but favorable to the growth of other species.

19. Necromass becomes soil, which can fill in lakes and support terrestrial plants.

20. Lichens were the pioneer species.

Critical Thinking

1. Answers may vary. The delay may give the individual time to gain the strength and status to compete with older adults of its own species and become expert at feeding itself and therefore its future young. Also, the delay may give the individual time to become expert at protecting its territory and therefore its future mate against competitors of its own species, and at protecting its young against predators. The more adept the individual has become when it reproduces, the more likely that the species will survive.

2. Disease kills the weakest individuals. This reduces the species population and lessens intraspecific competition. In the long term, the culling of the weak strengthens the species in interspecific competition.

3. The owls must move south when the lemmings are scarce—every fourth year on average.

4. Because people have different circadian rhythms, some adjust better to night work.

5. Herbaceous plants, which can seed themselves and which grow quickly in the fertile volcanic dust, would appear first, probably followed by shrubs and, much later, pines. (Scientists estimate that it may take 40 years to rebuild the food chain, even with the help of the U.S. Forest Service.)

Extension

1. Ask students if any of their circadian rhythms were upset by an unusual event, such as staying up all night. If so, ask what effect this had on their sleep pattern afterward.

2. Reports should refer to a turtle's two tools for navigation: the "wave compass" and the "magnetic compass."

3. Ask students why it is advantageous to the monarch butterfly to migrate.

Chapter 52 Populations

Chapter Overview

Chapter 52 focuses on populations and factors that affect their size. Section 52.1 discusses general aspects of population growth and density-dependent and density-independent factors that limit population size. Section 52.2 discusses human populations and the unique factors that affect them.

Chapter Planning Chart

B	S	A	Sections and Subsections	Page	Features	Page	Resources
	•	•	**52.1 Population Growth**				
			Biotic Potential	811	Biology in Process	812	Videodiscs
			Growth Curves	812	Think	814	Blackline Master 107
			Limits to Growth	814	Laboratory	817	Overhead Transparency T52
					Section Review	814	Blackline Master 108
							Process Skills: Population Size
							Laboratories: Population Sampling
							Section Reviews Worksheet
	•	•	**52.2 Human Populations**				
			Human Population Growth	815	Section Review	816	Videodiscs
			Human Population Structures	815			Blackline Master 109
							Section Reviews Worksheet
			End of Chapter Activities				
					Chapter Review	818	Vocabulary Skills
							Chapter Test
							Computer Test Generator

B *The Basic Level curriculum presents the most fundamental knowledge offered in the course.*
S *The Standard Level curriculum is designed for the average student who is able to master most topics.*
A *The Advanced Level curriculum includes suggestions for teaching the most academically able students.*

Cooperative Learning

Group Activity: Life Expectancy in the United States

- **Group Size:** *4 students*
- **Outcome:** *Students will compare life expectancy with mortality in the United States since 1900.*
- **Individual Accountability:** *Each group member will prepare one graph.*
- **Positive Interdependence:** *The group will discuss the significance of each graph and how it relates to life expectancy.*

Obtain data on life expectancy and death rates from different causes in the United States since 1900. This is available in *Historical Statistics of the United States, Colonial Times to 1970,* published by the Bureau of the Census. Have the first student in each group graph life expectancy in the United States since 1900 (every five years is sufficient). Ask the second student to graph number of deaths due to tuberculosis. The third student graphs number of deaths due to pneumonia and influenza, and the fourth student graphs number of deaths due to cardiovascular disease. Ask group members to compare the graphs and discuss their significance. *(Life expectancy since 1900 has increased from about 47 years to over 70. Deaths due to tuberculosis, pneumonia, and influenza, which kill younger people, have decreased greatly but may be showing some recent increases. Deaths due to cardiovascular disease, which kills older people, have increased.)*

Concept Map

The following is one possible solution to the concept mapping activity in Reteaching on p. 814.

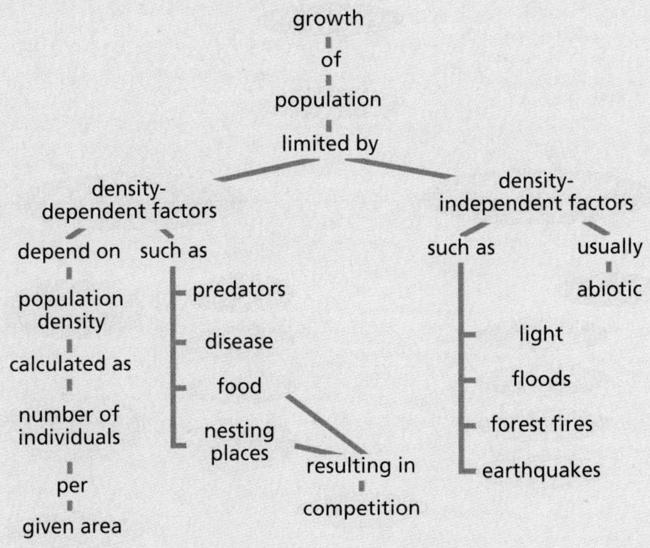

Laboratory Preparation

Overview *(See p. 817.)*

In this laboratory students will inquire about the effect of temperature on population growth in a *Tetrahymena* community. *Tetrahymena* is a small ciliate often used for food in protist cultures. It is appropriate for this lab because it is easy to grow and count. *Tetrahymena* grows rapidly and uniformly as it moves through the medium. Students should understand how to calculate population numbers from diluted samples. Variables that may affect population growth, such as temperature, pH, or salinity, produce better data than do agents that may kill all the organisms.

Preparation

Tetrahymena can be ordered from a biological supply house. Provide semi-logarithmic graph paper.

Both culture and culture medium must be sterile. To prepare *Tetrahymena* medium, add 5 g proteose peptone, 5 g tryptone, and 0.2 g K_2HPO_4 to 1 L of distilled water. Adjust the pH to 7.2 before autoclaving the mixture.

Find three locations that approximate room temperature, 10°C above room temperature, and 10°C below. If possible, use an incubator. Do not set any cultures in sunlight. This investigation requires five sessions.

Teaching Tips

Remind students to read the Technique section before designing their inquiry.

For sterilization in steps 2 through 4, students should flame the top edge of the culture container—pass it through the flame of an alcohol lamp—after removing the stopper or top. They should also flame the pipette and the edge of the culture tube before replacing the stopper.

You may wish to review serial dilution techniques with students. Remind them that if they dilute 1 drop of *Tetrahymena* with 9 drops of water, they have made a 1:10 dilution. The dilution factor is 10, so students must multiply the number of *Tetrahymena* counted times 10 to determine the population per drop.

Safety

Remind students to use caution with the alcohol lamp. Freshly sterilized equipment is very hot and can cause burns if touched. Have cold water and first aid cream available. Long hair should be tied back.

Chapter Themes

Patterns of Change This chapter shows how rates of population growth fluctuate predictably as populations encounter limitations such as lack of food and nesting places. Point out that these same populations can predictably flourish if sufficient resources are available.

Stability Make sure that students understand that under constant environmental conditions, populations can level off to a carrying capacity, which is the population size a given environment can support over a long period of time.

Chapter Motivating Activity
Ask students to imagine a single bacterium. If it reproduced once an hour, ask students to guess how many bacteria there would be after one day. *(Most students will guess numbers such as 24 or 48.)* Then ask them to calculate the actual number. You may wish to help them set up a chart that lists hours on the left and number of bacteria on the right. After one hour, there will be 2 bacteria, after two hours there will be 4, and after three hours there will be 8. *(The actual number after 24 hours is 2^{24}, or 16,777,216.)* Students will be surprised at how large this number is. Then ask them if bacteria can grow this quickly, why don't they take over the world? *(Because they run out of food, dry out, get eaten, or drown in their wastes.)* Point out that larger organisms also can potentially reproduce in tremendous numbers but that their population size is also limited by similar factors.

Chapter 52 Populations

Introduction

Cheetahs and lupines are members of populations. Although lupines are thriving, cheetahs are endangered. Environmental conditions and human interference have reduced the number of cheetahs to a dangerously low level. The methods used to save such organisms from extinction depend on knowledge of the biology of populations, the subject of this chapter.

Chapter Outline

Chapter Concept

As you read, notice how mathematical models are used to examine variations in the growth of populations.

Cheetahs, *Acinonyx jubatus*, central Africa. Inset: Lupines, *Lupinus* sp.

Understanding the Visuals
Although cheetahs are powerful predators with few if any enemies, their populations are declining. Ask students to speculate why this might be so. *(Their habitats are being destroyed, which reduces the amount of available food.)*

Tell students that lupines thrive in swampy areas and along river banks. However, lupines can spread so quickly that they encroach on other plant species, often crowding them out. Ask students to speculate on possible deleterious effects of the spread of such a species. *(Lupines disrupt the ecosystem and might replace plant species upon which animals rely.)*

52.1 Population Growth

A population is a group of individuals of the same species that live in the same area. An increase in a population is called **population growth.** The **population growth rate** is the change in the number of individuals in a population over time. This rate is determined by using the following formula:

$$\text{Population growth rate} = \frac{\text{change in number of individuals}}{\text{time}}$$

A population may grow at such a great rate that available resources become insufficient to support all its members. It was Charles Darwin's observation of this and related phenomena that led him to form his theory of evolution by natural selection. Darwin's theory was that when natural resources were limited, the best adapted members of a given population would survive and the least adapted would perish. Keeping this theory in mind as you read about population growth will help you understand the factors that may affect it.

Biotic Potential

The **biotic potential** of a population is the rate at which a population will grow if all individuals survive and reproduce at maximum capacity. Biotic potential can be reached when organisms capable of reproducing are put into an ideal environment, one with unlimited resources and space and without such hazards as disease and predators.

The high reproductive capability of the common housefly, *Musca domestica,* can be used as an example of how biotic potential can be achieved. One housefly produces 120 eggs in one year. How many houseflies can be produced in seven generations? If each fly lives only one generation, if half the eggs of each generation are female, and if each female produces 120 eggs a total of 5,598,720,000,000 flies will result. Table 52-1 shows the number of flies that will be produced in each of the seven generations if biotic potential is achieved.

In nature populations rarely achieve their biotic potential for any sustained period. Eventually the number of individuals declines because of shortage of food, shortage of space, predation, or accumulation of waste. For example, forest managers often introduce trout into lakes that contain no large fish. Because the trout have no competition for food or space, their population grows rapidly—but only for a while. The number of fish soon becomes so great that intraspecific competition for food and space ensues. This competition results in a decline in the number of trout. Once a balance is reached between the number of individuals and the amount of resources available, this decline ceases, and the population becomes stable.

Section Objectives

- *Define* biotic potential.
- *Differentiate between J-shaped and S-shaped growth curves, and explain the phases of population growth they illustrate.*
- *Distinguish between density-dependent and density-independent factors, and explain how each may limit population growth.*
- *State Edward Wilson and R. H. MacArthur's hypothesis pertaining to island biogeography.*

Table 52-1 Biotic Potential of the Housefly

Generation	Population
1	120
2	7,200
3	432,000
4	25,920,000
5	1,555,200,000
6	93,312,000,000
7	5,598,720,000,000

Phase	What Happens	Why
Lag	Little increase in numbers of organisms	Organisms are adjusting to the environment; few reproducing organisms exist.
Exponential	Organisms are reproducing at maximum rate	There is plenty of food and space; minimal competition. Population keeps doubling.
Carrying Capacity	Population size remains constant	Number of births equals number of deaths. Ecosystem is stable and at capacity for support.

Graphic Organizer Use this table in Guided Practice on p. 813.

Lesson Plan

Section Focus

This section describes the dynamics of population growth. It defines biotic potential as maximum rate of growth of a population. It discusses growth curves and limiting factors that keep populations at the carrying capacity of their environment.

Section Themes

This section emphasizes two themes: **Patterns of Change** and **Stability**. Students will learn factors that affect population dynamics and how populations level off and stabilize.

Motivating Activity

Show students a photograph of a dense penguin colony. Ask what they think limits the size of the population. *(Competition for nesting sites and food)*

Teaching Strategies

Applying Concepts Ask students to suggest reasons why the population of a local organism, such as mosquitos, might change. *(Sample answers: Mosquito populations vary with warmth and moisture. Fleas are more numerous in a summer following a warm winter. Newly introduced plants such as lupine can spread under favorable conditions and crowd out other plants.)*

■ *See* Laboratories, *Investigation 52 and* Process Skills, *Chapter 52.*

Interpreting the Visuals Have students look at Table 52-1 on p. 811. Tell them that if a single pair of houseflies reached their full biotic potential, they would produce 25 million descendants in only two months, enough to fill a large closet.

Videodiscs

■ *Side 4 7861, Elephants: Feeding (m)*

■ *Side 4 7485, Hippopotamus Competition (m)*

Interpreting the Visuals Ask students to study the J-shaped curve in Figure 52-1 and identify both the lag phase and exponential phase. Ask them what they think is happening during the lag phase. *(The sunfish are getting acclimated to their new environment and are beginning to reproduce.)* Tell students that in the exponential phase the number of sunfish is doubling with a constant doubling time—that is, population increases rapidly as a function of time. Ask students whether the exponential phase can continue forever and to explain why or why not. *(It cannot because the sunfish will run out of food, places to lay their eggs, and so forth.)*
■ *See* Overhead Transparency *T52 and* Blackline Master *107.*

Inferring Relationships Ask students to picture a meadow with mice that are eaten by snakes. Ask students what they think would happen to the mouse population if all the snakes were killed. *(The mice would enter a period of exponential growth. Their numbers would increase greatly and would probably level off when they started running out of food.)* Emphasize that because populations in an ecosystem interact, change in one can cause change in another.

Interpreting the Visuals Ask students to study Figure 52-2 on p. 813. Ask them how it differs from Figure 52-1. *(After the exponential phase of growth, population levels off.)* Tell students that the carrying capacity of the environment is a population size that the environment can support indefinitely. Ask them what they think determines carrying capacity. *(The amount of food, nesting sites, predators, and so forth)*
■ *See* Blackline Master *108.*

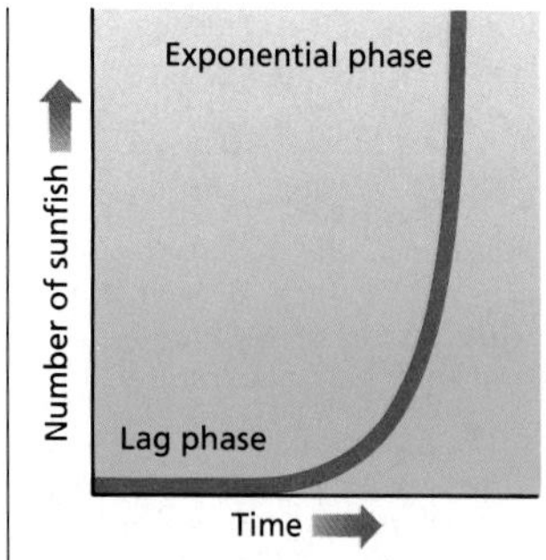

Figure 52-1 Population growth can be charted on a J-shaped curve. It shows that population grows slowly during the early lag phase and then very rapidly during the exponential phase.

Growth Curves

A useful tool for studying the patterns of population growth is the growth curve. A **growth curve** is a graph showing the number of individuals in a population over time. The **J-shaped curve** is a growth curve that tracks two phases of population growth—the lag phase and the exponential phase.

During the **lag phase,** little or no increase occurs in a population. For example, when only one male and female sunfish are introduced into a fertile pond, the sunfish population increases slowly because only one female is producing young. However, as more females are born and in turn reproduce, the rate of population growth increases. If there is enough food and space for the sunfish to thrive, the population will eventually increase at an exponential rate.

During the **exponential phase** a population increases so rapidly that the number of individuals doubles in a specific time interval and keeps doubling in increasingly shorter periods of time. Carefully study the J-shaped curve in Figure 52-1. Note the difference in the rate of growth of the sunfish population during the lag phase and the exponential phase.

Biology in Process

Island Biogeography

Can the number of plant and animal populations on an island be predicted from the size of the island or its distance from the mainland? In the late 1960s ecologists collected and compared data on the number of species that had survived on each of the many islands of the New Guinea shelf. These islands at one time had each been populated by the same mix of species. Over time they had been subject to virtually the same density-independent factors. But the islands were of different size and distance from the mainland. The ecologists discovered a direct relationship between the size of an island and the number of species surviving on that island. They found that the smaller the island was, the fewer species it had.

This result led ecologists Edward Wilson and R. H. MacArthur to hypothesize that the number of species that could be supported on an island reached an equilibrium and that this number was affected by both the size of the island and its distance from the mainland. Wilson and Daniel Simberloff then devised an experiment to test the validity of the hypothesis.

Interdisciplinary Activity

Government Have students research the population growth in selected countries around the world. Where is population growing most rapidly? Is population growth leveling off in any countries? *(Population growth is most rapid in poorer countries; in many developed countries it is leveling off.)* Have students write a report describing population trends around the world.

An **S-shaped curve** is a growth curve that depicts the period of relative stability in a population that occurs after its lag and exponential phases. This curve therefore gives an indication of the carrying capacity of the ecosystem. The **carrying capacity** is the maximum number of individuals that the ecosystem is capable of supporting. The S-shaped curve in Figure 52-2 reveals that the number of sunfish in the pond usually did not exceed 100. Thus for the sunfish population in the example the carrying capacity of the pond is about 100. Notice that the J-shaped curve is the lower part of the S-shaped curve.

When the environment is stable, the maximum number of individuals in a population fluctuates near the carrying capacity of the environment. If the environment becomes unstable, the fluctuations become more radical. For example, high in the Rocky Mountains the size of the butterfly population is usually stable, although it may vary somewhat with available food and space. However, freak snowstorms sometimes cause a sudden drop in the number of individuals. Nevertheless, because the number of butterflies is then well under the carrying capacity of the ecosystem, the population usually increases quickly until it again approaches the carrying capacity.

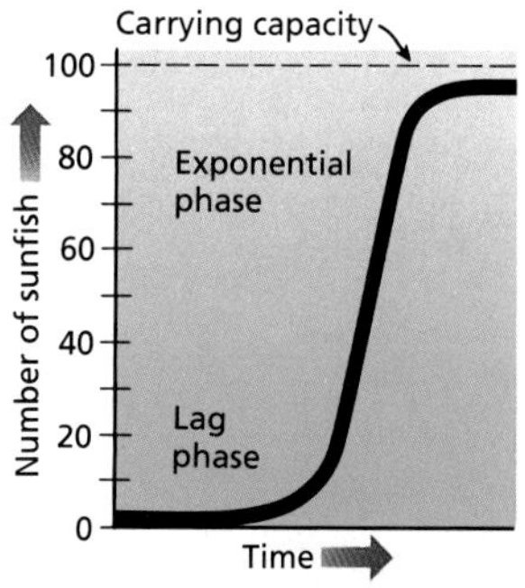

Figure 52-2 An S-shaped curve shows that population growth levels off after the exponential phase. The top of this curve indicates the carrying capacity of an ecosystem.

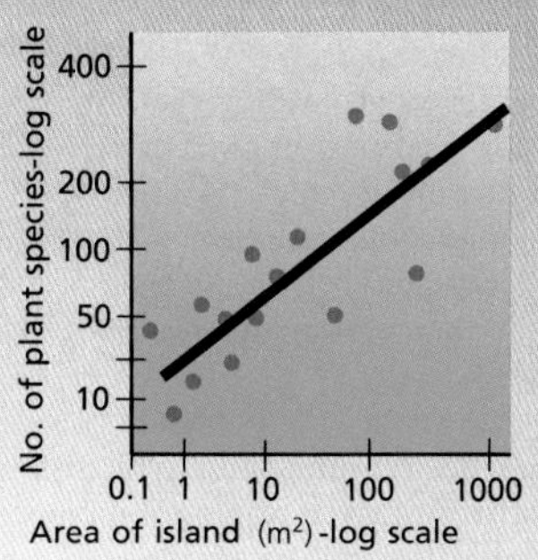

They examined arthropod communities on six tiny mangrove islands off the coast of Florida. First, they collected data on the kind and number of arthropod populations on each island. Then, using scaffolding and plastic sheets, Wilson and Simberloff erected a tent over each island. Next they sprayed the islands with pesticides that killed off all the invertebrates. Finally they removed the tents and observed the recolonization. After a period of six months the same number of species—although not always the same species—had repopulated the islands. Continued observations revealed that after reaching an equilibrium the diversity in species remained constant, thus supporting the hypothesis.

More recently biologist William Newmark observed that in wilderness areas and in continental national parks, similar patterns existed. Although these habitats were not islands in the literal sense—they were not enclosed by water—they were surrounded by cities, highways, and ranches. Even the scent of humans could create an islandlike environment. Newmark therefore predicted that if these areas were truly islandlike, then Wilson and MacArthur's "island effect" would hold true for them too. Newmark discovered that the number of mammal species in wilderness preserves did in fact decline as barriers encroached on them. His findings suggest that the island effect holds true for these areas.

- **What aspect of Wilson and MacArthur's hypothesis was not tested in the experiment designed by Wilson and Simberloff?**

Guided Practice

Copy the first two columns of the table (Graphic Organizer) at the bottom of p. 811 onto the board but leave the last column blank. Ask students to explain why the events of each phase are occurring and fill in the third column.

Independent Practice

- Have students write answers to the Section Review.
- Distribute U.S. census figures for the last 50 years. Have students plot the numbers, describe the curve, and make inferences about U.S. population trends.

Biology in Process

Using the Feature

The main process skills used in this feature are observing, collecting data, hypothesizing, experimenting, and analyzing data. To test the hypothesis that size of an island affects the number of species on the island, Wilson and Simberloff collected data on arthropod populations on a group of islands, removed the populations, and observed recolonization. Results of their experiments supported the hypothesis and led to further predictions that the "island effect" would apply to areas isolated by barriers other than water.

Answer to the Feature

Whether the distance of the island from the mainland was a factor was not tested.

LEP Activity

Have students construct an exponential curve based on the housefly population figures in Table 52-1 on p. 811. Tell students to draw a graph and label the *x* axis "generation," the *y* axis "fly population." Have students mark the *y* axis in increments of 5 billion and mark the *x* axis with points for six generations. Ask students where the lag phase is *(the flat part of the curve)* and where the exponential phase is *(the steep part of the curve)*. Ask students what happened between the lag phase and the exponential phase. Ask students to speculate on what it would mean if the curve were to level off. *(That the population is no longer growing)*

Answer to Think

Since this park is, in effect, an island, the number of species it can support will decline until equilibrium is reached. This number would be affected by the size of the park and its distance from other wildlife areas. Density-dependent factors would also have an effect.

Check Your Understanding

1. Distinguish between biotic potential and carrying capacity. *(Biotic potential is the maximum rate of population growth. Carrying capacity is the number an ecosystem can support.)*

2. Explain why a killing frost is a density-independent limitation. *(It kills organisms without regard for how many there are.)*

Reteaching

Ask students to draw a concept map that shows how density-dependent factors and density-independent factors limit a population. An example of a completed concept map is shown on p. 809B.

■ *See* Section Reviews *worksheet, Section 52.1.*

Enrichment

Have students get their town's census figures for the last 50 years, plot the numbers, and describe the curve that emerges. Have students research local newspaper archives to find reasons for population changes.

Closure

Ask students why the cheetah pictured on p. 810 is not reaching its biotic potential. *(Habitat destruction, not enough food, not enough den sites, limited gene pool)* Have students suggest solutions. *(Setting up national parks or reservations)*

Think

Study this aerial photo of Central Park in New York City. From what you have learned about island biogeography, what change might you foresee in the diversity of insect species in the park?

Limits to Growth

Ecologists label factors that can limit population growth as density-dependent or density-independent. Here the word *density* refers to **population density,** the number of individuals in a population in a given area at a given time. For example, if a sunfish pond holds 1,000 m^3 of water, 100 sunfish represent a population density of one fish per 10 m^3, as shown in the following formula:

$$\text{Population density} = \frac{100 \text{ sunfish}}{1{,}000 \text{ m}^3 \text{ of water}} = \frac{1 \text{ sunfish}}{10 \text{ m}^3 \text{ of water}}$$

Density-dependent Factors

Density-dependent factors are factors that affect populations in different ways depending on population density. For example, when 20 sunfish are put in a pond with 1,000 m^3 of water, population density is one fish per 50 m^3 of water, and food is abundant. As the population density increases, less food is available to each individual. This results in intense competition for food and the elimination of some sunfish. Thus the availability of food is a density-dependent factor that controls population size. Other common density-dependent factors may include the availability of space and light, parasitic infections, and disease.

The number of predators in an ecosystem may also be a density-dependent factor. Usually a predator population increases after the prey population has increased. So the increased number of predators prevents another increase in the number of prey.

Abiotic factors may be density-dependent. For example, if the food in our sunfish pond were unlimited, the population might increase until a shortage of oxygen resulted. The availability of oxygen would then be a density-dependent factor. However, it is one that will affect population size only when density is high.

Density-independent Factors

Density-independent factors are factors that affect populations regardless of population density. These factors, which are usually abiotic, include changes in weather, temperature, and humidity; variations in the amount of sunlight; and the amount of available energy. For example, a population may be entirely wiped out by a forest fire or decimated by an earthquake or a flood.

Section Review

1. Define *biotic potential.*
2. In what ways do J-shaped and S-shaped growth curves differ?
3. What is the carrying capacity of an ecosystem?
4. What is the difference between density-dependent and density-independent factors? How are they similar?
5. How might parasitic infections and diseases be density-dependent factors?

Answers to Section Review

1. The rate at which a population would grow if all individuals reproduced at maximum capacity

2. J-shaped curves illustrate only lag and exponential phases of population growth; S-shaped curves track these and the following carrying capacity period.

3. The maximum number of individuals of a species that the ecosystem can support

4. Density-dependent factors are related to the density of the population, whereas density-independent factors are not. Both may affect population size.

5. Poor sanitation and hygiene prevalent in dense populations increase the likelihood of contact between parasites and other organisms.

52.2 Human Populations

Early humans foraged for the plants they ate and hunted for the animals they used for food and clothing. Later they learned to cultivate crops and to tame wild animals. Plants and animals that are adapted or trained to live in a human environment are referred to as **domesticated.** By domesticating plants and animals people were often able to increase their food supply, even to create surpluses that could be stored. Domestication gave people a more reliable and constant supply of food, which was one important factor in determining human population size.

Section Objectives

- *Explain how the domestication of plants and animals has affected human population growth.*
- *Summarize the growth that has taken place in the human population since people learned to domesticate plants and animals.*
- *Compare and contrast three different models of human populations.*

Human Population Growth

From about 6000 B.C. until about A.D. 1800, the number of people in the world increased steadily. This increase, however, was relatively slow. Then in the middle of the eighteenth century the population began to increase dramatically. This exponential growth rate can be largely explained by the increase in food production, the rise of industry, and advances in medicine. In the field of medicine alone, the development of immunology, the discovery of anesthetics, and the introduction of antiseptic surgery increased human life expectancy in many parts of the world. Look at Figure 52-3 to see how the world population has grown since the 1600s and how the population is projected to grow from the present to the year 2000.

In the year 1650 there were about 500 million people in the world; today, according to United Nations estimates, there are over 5 billion people. The human population is increasing by approximately 70 million per year. This growth rate may eventually be limited by the same density-dependent factors that limit the growth of other populations—the availability of natural resources.

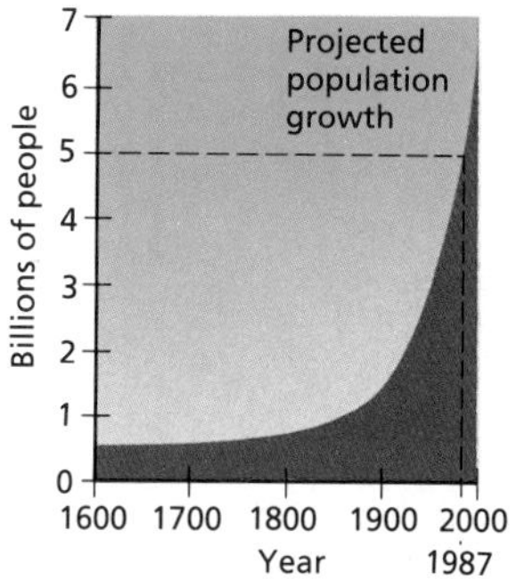

Figure 52-3 This growth curve shows how large the human population is expected to be by the year 2000. What phase is the human population in currently?

Human Population Structures

The growth rate for a human population in a given area is dependent on a number of factors. To make predictions about population growth, population biologists must consider the composition of a population. The following hypothetical example, although oversimplified, will illustrate the point: Suppose that you want to predict the growth patterns for three small villages, all with the same number of people. One is made up of families with children, parents, and grandparents—a population of mixed age and sex. The second is made up solely of children. The third is made up only of elderly people. If you considered only external limits to growth, such as the availability of food and the potential for natural disasters, you would conclude that each of the three populations had the same potential for growth.

first humans
100,000 years ago
→
first agriculture
10,000 years ago
→
industrialization
150 years ago

Graphic Organizer Use this sequential diagram in Guided Practice on p. 816.

Lesson Plan

Section Focus

This section discusses the two main events that have caused human population growth. The first event was the development of agriculture and the domestication of animals about 10,000 years ago. The second event was industrialization and advances in medicine, beginning in the 1800s.

Section Themes

This section emphasizes the theme of **Patterns of Change.** It shows how changes in food supply and medical care have caused tremendous human population growth.

Motivating Activity

Ask students to imagine what they would eat if there were no agriculture or animal husbandry. *(They would eat whatever they could find—edible plants, wild animals.)* Ask them whether this kind of food supply could support today's human population. *(No. The so-called hunter and gatherer system can reliably support only a small population.)* Point out to students that much of their food today is grown on farms.

Teaching Strategies

Interpreting the Visuals Copy the graph in Figure 52-3 on p. 815 onto the board. Ask students what has happened to the human population in the last 400 years. *(It has increased greatly.)* Ask them to suggest reasons why this has happened. *(Improvements in the standard of living—medicine, food supply, technology)* Tell students that in 1900, life expectancy in the United States was under 50 years.

Guided Practice
Copy on the board the sequential diagram on p. 815. Ask students to discuss how each change permitted an increase in human population.

Independent Practice
- Have students write answers to the Section Review.
- Have students study Figure 52-4 on p. 816. Ask them which of the countries has the greater growth potential and why. *(Country B—it has more young people.)*
- *See* **Blackline Master** *109.*

Check Your Understanding
1. How does agriculture support an increased population? *(It provides the means to control and increase food supply.)*
2. What factors supported an exponential increase in the world population? *(Agriculture, medicine, industry)*

Reteaching
Help students answer the in-text questions on p. 816. *(Country A: village 1, which would probably grow steadily; Country B: villiage 2, which would not grow for a time, then would increase quickly)*
- *See* **Section Reviews** *worksheet, Section 52.2.*

Enrichment
Assign a different country to each student, choosing a variety of developed and developing nations. Have students research its population growth, project future growth, and construct a growth curve.

Closure
Ask students to speculate on the consequences of continued increase in human population. *(Food shortages, other resources shortages, increase in pollution)*

Videodiscs
- *1581–1582, Laboratory Apparatus: Colony Counter (s)*

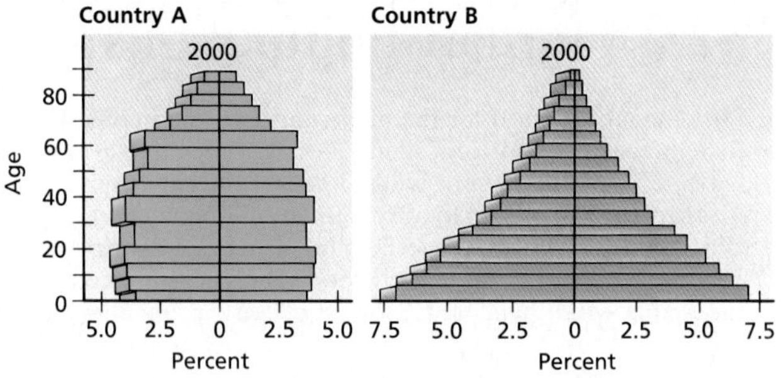

Figure 52-4 These population pyramids, showing distribution of population by age, indicate that Country B has a much greater growth potential than Country A has.

In fact, the actual growth patterns for the three villages would differ dramatically. If no density-dependent or density-independent factors limited population growth, you could reasonably make the following assumptions: (1) The first population, a balanced one, could be expected to grow steadily. (2) The second population, consisting of members still too young to reproduce, would not grow at all for a time. Then, once the children reached reproductive maturity, the population would increase rapidly. (3) The third population, which consists entirely of members past their reproductive age, would decline until it reached zero.

Having learned something about the patterns of population growth after analyzing this hypothetical case, you can now make some rough predictions about growth patterns in actual populations. Study Figure 52-4, which shows the population structures of two countries. To which hypothetical village populations can you compare these actual populations? What predictions can you make about changes in the two populations in the course of the next 20 years?

Section Review

1. Define *domesticated,* and list the benefits that people have derived by domesticating plants and animals.
2. To predict accurately the growth pattern of a population, what must you examine in addition to the external limits to growth? Why?
3. In what way would the initial growth pattern of a village consisting solely of children be similar to that of the growth pattern of a village consisting solely of elderly people? In what way would the growth patterns of these two villages then differ?
4. Explain why a population with a pyramidlike structure grows steadily.
5. Although population growth in some nations has slowed to nearly a standstill, the world population is still increasing at an exponential rate. What might account for this rapid population growth?

Answers to Section Review
1. Adapted to being raised by humans; by domesticating plants and animals, people increased their food supply and their ability to survive.
2. You must study the composition of this population; the reproductive capacity of its members will affect its growth.
3. At first, neither would grow; then the population in the village of children would eventually increase, and the population in the village of elderly would decline.
4. In each succeeding year more individuals are entering the reproductive phase of development.
5. Population in some areas is growing exponentially.

Laboratory

Studying Population Growth

Objective
To study how temperature affects population growth in a protist community

Process Skills
Hypothesizing, experimenting

Materials
Tetrahymena culture, test tube rack, pasteur pipette with bulb, alcohol lamp, tongs, microscope slides, microscope, medicine dropper, test tubes 10 × 75 mm, *Tetrahymena* medium in a screwcap culture tube, thermometers, graph paper

Background
1 In studies of population growth, what are density-dependent factors? What are density-independent factors?

Technique
1 Place a tube of *Tetrahymena* culture in a test tube rack.
2 Use the following technique to make an accurate count of the *Tetrahymena* population. Obtain a pipette. Light an alcohol lamp. Follow your teacher's instructions for using the lamp to sterilize the pipette and for maintaining sterile technique. Use tongs to hold the pipette while it cools. When cooled place a bulb on the end of the pipette. Use the pipette to gently stir the culture. Withdraw some culture and place a drop of it on a microscope slide. Why stir the culture?
3 Observe the *Tetrahymena* under low power of a microscope. If there are more than 100 organisms in the drop, dilute a drop of culture with 9 drops of water in a test tube (10 × 75 mm). What is the dilution factor?
4 Mix the contents of the tube gently. Place a drop of diluted culture on a glass slide and count the number of organisms. If there are more than 10 protozoa in the drop, dilute a drop of the diluted culture using the procedure in step 3 above until fewer than 10 protozoa are counted in a drop.
5 Multiply the number of protozoa counted by the dilution factor to estimate the number of *Tetrahymena* in a drop of culture. Record your results in a table.
6 Repeat steps 2 through 5 four times. Calculate the average of the five samples. Use this figure as the population per drop of culture. Why should multiple counts be made? What is the advantage of using an average?
7 Using sterile technique as instructed by your teacher, add one drop of the original culture to a fresh culture medium tube.
8 Using the procedure above, estimate the *Tetrahymena* population over the following four days.

Inquiry
1 Discuss the objective of this laboratory with your partner and formulate a hypothesis.
2 Design an experiment that will test your hypothesis using the method outlined in the Technique section.
3 What are the independent and dependent variables in your experiment? How will you vary the independent variable? How will you measure changes in the dependent variable?
4 What controls will you include?
5 What method of reporting your data will most clearly determine if your hypothesis is supported?
6 Proceed with your experiment once your design is approved by your teacher.

Conclusions
1 What effect did changes in the independent variable have on the dependent variable?
2 Do the data support your hypothesis? Explain.
3 Were density-dependent or density-independent factors most influential on the outcome of your experiment? Explain.

Further Inquiry
Ask your teacher for the ingredients used to prepare the culture medium for *Tetrahymena*. Design an experiment to find out which ingredient is the most essential for optimum growth of *Tetrahymena*.

Laboratory

(For an overview of population growth of Tetrahymena *and preparatory information related to the laboratory, see p. 809B.)*

Background
1. Density-dependent factors affect populations in different ways depending on population density. Density-independent factors affect populations regardless of population density.

Technique
2. Stirring the culture ensures an even distribution of *Tetrahymena* in the culture.
3. The dilution factor is 10.
4. If a 1:10 dilution is made in step 3, the dilution factor is 100.
6. Making five counts will remove variation due to differences in sampling technique and random variation among samples. Taking an average will give a mean value of the data obtained.

Inquiry
1. Each lab group should agree on a testable hypothesis.
3. The independent variable is temperature. The temperature used should be 10°C above and below room temperature. The dependent variable is the rate of growth of the *Tetrahymena* population. A daily count of the number of protozoa in the cultures, according to the given technique, will indicate the population's response to changes in the temperature variable.
4. A culture should be maintained at room temperature as a control to determine the normal rate of increase in a population.
5. Students should use a graph. The number of protozoa in the population should be plotted on the *y* axis and days should be plotted on the *x* axis.

Conclusions
1. As the temperature rises, the number of protozoa should increase.
2. Students should state whether their data support their hypothesis.
3. The density-independent factor, the temperature, should be the most influential. A single drop of original culture in a fresh culture tube eliminates overcrowding as an influence.

Further Inquiry
Students should design an experiment similar to the one just performed, but this time vary the amounts (or presence) of each ingredient in the culture. If they use one of the temperatures in the completed investigation, they can use the previous results as the control.

Vocabulary

1. Population growth is an increase in the number of individuals in a given species in a given area over time. The increase over a specified time is the population growth rate.
2. Population growth rate is the rate at which the population is actually growing. Biotic potential is the maximum rate at which a population could possibly grow.
3. The lag phase of population growth may precede the exponential phase and differs from it in that it is a slow period of growth. In the exponential phase, the population size doubles repeatedly.
4. The carrying capacity of an ecosystem is the approximate number of individuals in a given population that the ecosystem can support. This capacity can be inferred by studying an S-shaped curve of this population's growth.
5. Population density is the number of individuals in a given population in relation to the amount of space. Density-dependent factors affect the growth of a population only when this population reaches a critical density.

Review

1. d **6.** c
2. a **7.** b
3. c **8.** d
4. a **9.** d
5. d **10.** b

11. $\frac{\text{change in number of individuals}}{\text{time}}$
12. Population growth can occur at rates so great that after a while not enough resources exist to support all the members of this population.
13. Shortage of food, shortage of space, and accumulation of wastes
14. The initial phase in population growth for any population that begins with so few individuals that an increase in numbers can occur only very slowly
15. You could determine when this population reached a period of relative stability.
16. The butterfly population is subject to density-independent factors such as snowstorms and car windshields unless it grows to a critical level where it exceeds the ecosystem's carrying capacity.
17. $\frac{\text{number of individuals}}{\text{area}}$
18. Availability of oxygen. The food supply of a population of sunfish becomes so plentiful that the population increases until shortage of oxygen results.

Chapter 52 Review

Vocabulary

biotic potential (811)	density-independent factors (814)	growth curve (812)	population growth (811)
carrying capacity (813)	domesticated (815)	J-shaped curve (812)	population growth rate (811)
density-dependent factors (814)	exponential phase (812)	lag phase (812)	S-shaped curve (813)
		population density (814)	

Explain the difference between the terms in each of the following sets.

1. population growth, population growth rate
2. population growth rate, biotic potential
3. lag phase, exponential phase
4. S-shaped curve, carrying capacity
5. population density, density-dependent factors

Review

1. Population growth (a) is a group of individuals of the same species living in the same place (b) is an estimated change in the number of individuals in a given population over a specific period of time (c) will never occur at so great a rate that the members of the population will be unable to exist on the available resources (d) can occur at so great a rate that existing resources cannot support all the members of the population.
2. The biotic potential of a population is its maximum rate of growth (a) if all individuals survive and reproduce at maximum capacity (b) if all individuals survive and reproduce (c) if most individuals survive and some of these reproduce at their maximum capacity (d) if a balance is reached between the number of individuals in the population and the amount of resources available to them.
3. The biotic potential of a population existing in nature is (a) always achieved (b) usually achieved (c) rarely achieved (d) never achieved.
4. The maximum number of individuals in a population located in a stable environment tends to (a) fluctuate near the carrying capacity of the environment (b) fluctuate radically (c) be about 100 (d) be limited by density-independent factors.
5. Availability of space, susceptibility to disease, and number of predators are all (a) abiotic factors (b) density-independent factors (c) factors that provoke greater intraspecific competition (d) density-dependent factors.
6. A predator population usually (a) decreases after the density of the prey population increases (b) increases after the density of the prey population decreases (c) increases after the density of the prey population increases (d) is not at all affected by changes in the density of the prey population.
7. Abiotic factors are (a) never density dependent (b) sometimes density dependent (c) never density independent (d) only density independent.
8. A volcanic eruption is an example of (a) something that would be charted on an S-shaped curve (b) a density-dependent factor (c) something that would be charted on a J-shaped curve (d) a density-independent factor.
9. The following are not domesticated: (a) plants cultivated in plots (b) animals

bred in pens (c) herbs growing in window boxes (d) herbs growing in the forest.

10. In the year 1650, the human population (a) began growing at an exponential rate (b) numbered about 500 million (c) began increasing by approximately 70 million annually (d) numbered about 5 billion.
11. What formula is used to determine the growth rate of a population?
12. What observation helped Charles Darwin to form his theory of evolution by natural selection?
13. Name three common factors that in nature can lead to the decline in the number of individuals in a given population.
14. What is a lag phase, and when does this phase occur?
15. How would you determine the carrying capacity of the ecosystem of a given species?
16. What factors may cause the number of individuals in the Rocky Mountain butterfly population to fluctuate over time?
17. What formula would you use to determine population density?
18. Give one example of an abiotic factor that could be density dependent, and explain how it might be so.
19. What factors made the New Guinea shelf an ideal place to determine whether the number of populations on an island was related to the size of the island?
20. What basic data would you need in order to accurately predict the growth pattern of a given population?

Critical Thinking

1. Humans have tried to control insects with insecticides, such as DDT. Although DDT was effective for the first ten years it was used, eventually the insect population began to increase again. What do you think caused DDT to lose its effectiveness?
2. At right is a map showing the populations of pinnipeds—seals and sea lions—around the world. From examining this map what can you infer about density-dependent factors that affect these populations?

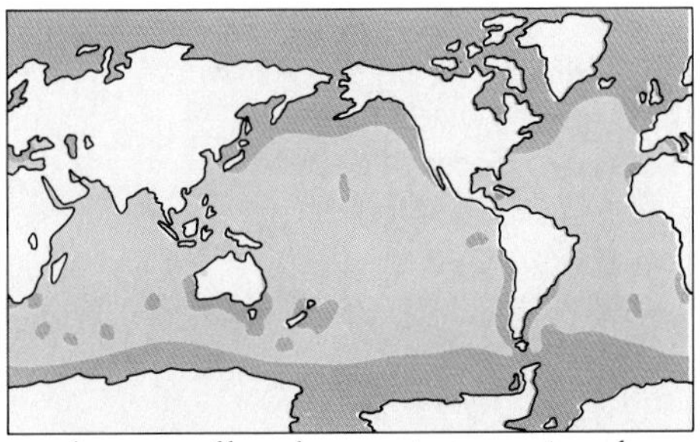

3. Since humans have more power to alter their environment than other animals do, they can affect the carrying capacity of their ecosystems. How do humans increase or decrease the carrying capacity of their local areas?

Extension

1. Read "The Numbers Game" in *Discover*, April 1990, pp. 42–49. Prepare an oral report in which you discuss both sides of the debate over human population growth. How has the debate influenced government policies and family planning?
2. Research and report on how the U.S. census is conducted. Examine the 1980 census for statistics on age, births and deaths, and marriages and divorces.
3. Using Table 52-1, graph paper, and a scientific calculator, make a logarithmic plot of fly population growth. Enter each value of fly population in the calculator and press the "log" key. Plot the result on the y axis. Plot the generation numbers on the x axis. Assume that the population for generation "0" is 1. Describe the graph that you plotted. Predict the population of the eighth generation using the graph.

19. It was an ideal site because each of these islands had been populated at one time by the same mix of species.
20. The structure of the population—the ages and sexes of its members; and information on density-dependent factors such as availability of food

Critical Thinking

1. DDT became ineffective as the insect population gradually developed resistance to the insecticide. Although initially most insects treated were killed by DDT, a small number were resistant to it and survived. They reproduced and passed DDT resistance to some of their offspring. This cycle continued until virtually the entire insect population was unaffected by DDT.
2. You can infer that pinnipeds feed along the coastlines where they live and are affected by availability of food and by predators there. If the pinniped population gets too large, there will not be enough fish to feed on. Pinnipeds are prey to killer whales and other predators, which reduce the size of the pinniped population.
3. Humans kill animals directly by hunting and indirectly by destroying habitats. Humans can increase the carrying capacity by land-use planning efforts geared toward habitat recognition.

Extension

1. Students can mention a variety of influences but should recognize that the subject is far from closed.
2. Further references published by the Bureau of the Census are the *Statistical Abstracts of the United States,* published annually, and *Historical Statistics of the United States, Colonial Times to 1970.* Both of these books contain a wealth of information about life expectancy, causes of death, and other matters related to the population of the United States.
3. Semi-logarithmic graph paper is useful for this assignment. Encourage students to think about factors that limit the population of houseflies and other organisms as well.

Chapter 53 Protecting Life

Chapter Overview

Chapter 53 concludes the unit on ecology. Section 53.1 discusses natural resources and distinguishes between renewable resources, which can be replenished, and nonrenewable resources, which cannot. Section 53.2 discusses different kinds and sources of pollution as well as undesirable changes in an ecosystem and offers suggestions for minimizing pollution.

Chapter Planning Chart

B	S	A	Sections and Subsections	Page	Features	Page	Resources
•	•	•	**53.1 Natural Resources**				
			Renewable Resources	821	Biotechnology	822	Videodiscs
			Nonrenewable Resources	823	Section Review	824	Blackline Master 110
							Overhead Transparency T53
							Section Reviews Worksheet
•	•	•	**53.2 Pollution**				
			Primary and Secondary Pollutants	825	Think	826	Videodiscs
			Sources of Pollution	826	Laboratory	827	Process Skills: The Ozone Hole
					Section Review	826	Laboratories: Effects of Acid Rain
							Section Reviews Worksheet
			End of Chapter Activities				
					Chapter Review	828	Vocabulary Skills
							Chapter Test
							Computer Test Generator

B *The Basic Level curriculum presents the most fundamental knowledge offered in the course.*
S *The Standard Level curriculum is designed for the average student who is able to master most topics.*
A *The Advanced Level curriculum includes suggestions for teaching the most academically able students.*

Cooperative Learning

Group Activity: Possible Energy Sources

- **Group Size:** *4 students*
- **Outcome:** *Students will compare advantages and disadvantages of different energy sources.*
- **Individual Accountability:** *Each group member will research and report on one energy source.*
- **Positive Interdependence:** *The group will develop a policy for energy generation for the next 1,000 years.*

Have one student in each group research solar energy, another research fossil fuels (oil and coal), a third research biomass (gasohol), and a fourth research nuclear energy. Tell each student to find out what available technology there is for generating energy from the assigned source, what risks are associated with this technology, how friendly the technology is to the environment, and how expensive will be the energy produced. Then have group members compare notes. Ask the group to develop a strategy and prediction for what would keep safe energy available for the next 1,000 years. Require students to cite their sources of information and state what biases, if any, these sources show. Ask students to explain if and how energy conservation would be relevant to their findings.

Concept Map

The following is one possible solution to the concept mapping activity in Contrasting Terms on p. 822.

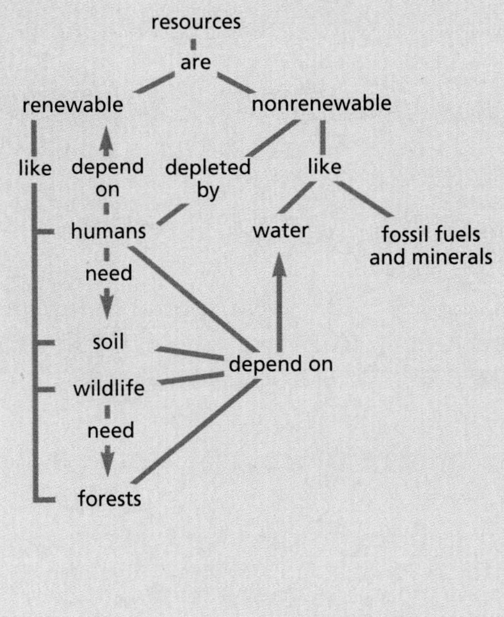

Laboratory Preparation

Overview *(See p. 827.)*

This laboratory shows students how a technique can be used to measure the effect of a pollutant. You may wish to have students do small, independent projects using this technique. This can prompt them to think about how variations in technique can be used to answer different questions.

Preparation

Paramecium culture is available from biological supply houses and pond water. If pond water is not available for use in the lab, leave tap water standing more than 24 hours. You will need 50 mL of each. Bend 12-cm lengths of glass tubing into the shape of a broad **U**.

Teaching Tips

Have students read the Technique section carefully before they design their experiment.

This lab can lead to discussion of what a pollutant is and what effect pollutants have on organisms. Ask students to infer what would happen to a pond that became warmer. Point out that a population can respond positively or negatively to a pollutant by increasing or decreasing in population. In a real-life ecosystem this population response will occur during a longer period of time.

Ask students to speculate on how an increase or decrease in a *Paramecium* population might affect organisms higher on the food chain that eat paramecia or organisms lower on the food chain that are eaten by paramecia. Students should understand that even small changes in an ecosystem can produce "ripple" effects.

Suggest in Inquiry step 4 controls for light, atmospheric conditions, gravity, and possible paramecium reaction to the corks.

In Inquiry step 6, the tubing could be divided into three sections, Cold, Moderate, and Hot. Cold would include tubing from the cork in the ice water up to the first bend. Moderate would be the section between the bends. Hot would be the section from the cork in the hot water up to the second bend.

Safety

Students should use care when handling glass apparatus. They should wash their hands after finishing the lab.

Chapter Themes

Energy This chapter emphasizes the use of natural resources to support life. Make certain that students understand that these natural resources can be depleted if they are not used with care.

Stability The stability of the ecosystem is manifest in the interconnectedness of many resources. Point out to students that the balance of nature can be disrupted or maintained by the actions of humans.

Chapter Motivating Activity

Prepare two trays of soil, one with only bare soil and the other containing a healthy crop of grass. (Buy sod, or plant grass seed two to three weeks in advance.) Tip the trays as you pour equal amounts of water over the soil. Collect the runoff water. Let the soil particles settle. Ask students to compare the amounts of soil that have washed away from the trays. *(More soil will have washed away from the tray without the grass.)* Ask students what implications this demonstration has for soil preservation. *(Bare soil is vulnerable to erosion. It is important to keep some kind of vegetation on soil, even in fallow seasons.)*

Tell students that erosion can occur not only on farm fields but also in development projects, especially where large tracts of land have been cleared for extended periods of time. Point out to students that erosion is not only "bad" for topsoil but that it can also alter rivers, streams, or other bodies of water, wherever the topsoil is "dumped."

Chapter 53 Protecting Life

Introduction

As the human population continues to increase, so does its need for natural resources such as soil, timber, water, and fuels for energy. However, as part of our responsibility to future generations, we must both conserve our natural resources and reduce pollution of the environment. In this chapter you will learn about the impact human society has had on such natural resources as wildlife, water, fossil fuels, and minerals. You will also see the efforts people are making to conserve these valuable resources.

Chapter Outline

53.1 Natural Resources
- *Renewable Resources*
- *Nonrenewable Resources*

53.2 Pollution
- *Primary and Secondary Pollutants*
- *Sources of Pollution*

Chapter Concept

As you read, note the ways in which people are using their knowledge of biology in an effort to find ways to protect natural resources.

Giant mirrors of a solar power plant in Daggett, California. Inset: Ponderosa pine seedlings in Klamath Falls nursery, Oregon.

Using the Visuals

Use the photo of the solar power plant as a springboard for discussion of renewable energy. Tell students that fossil fuels such as oil are nonrenewable resources. Remind students that heavy use of these fuels has been blamed for the greenhouse effect (Chapter 50). Ask students to name some alternative sources of energy *(Sun, wind, the atom)* and discuss how they can replace fossil fuels. *(Solar power plants, windmills, and nuclear power plants generate electricity.)*

Ask students to brainstorm reasons for cultivating tree seedlings such as those from the ponderosa pine. Point out that seedlings can be used to replenish forests, protect watersheds, and prevent wind and water erosion.

53.1 Natural Resources

Natural resources are the raw materials—biotic and abiotic—that support life on earth. Human society, with its increasing population and its industrial way of life, consumes the greatest proportion of available resources. This consumption leads to depletion of resources, which can occur by direct destruction, such as the burning of fuels, by displacement, or by pollution of resources and the environment.

Renewable Resources

Renewable resources are those materials that can be regrown or replenished. However, the increasing human population is consuming renewable resources faster than they can be replaced. An example of a renewable resource is a forest. Although its trees are cut for timber and firewood the forest, if properly managed, can be reforested and reharvested. Wildlife and soil are also potentially renewable resources.

Forests

Forests are biological communities dominated by trees and composed of hundreds of species of organisms. The increasing need for wood to produce paper, fuel, building materials, and furniture has led to the **deforestation,** or clearing, of vast regions of forested land. **Reforestation** is the process of nurturing new growths of trees on sites formerly occupied by forests, thereby preventing soil erosion and maintaining moisture in the ground.

Wildlife

Wildlife refers to all the plants and animals indigenous to a community. As you have learned in Chapter 50, all species in a community interact in a complex system of food chains and food webs. The destruction of any one species can have an impact on many other organisms in the community. Preventing the loss of species through conservation and wildlife management is an important area of scientific concern.

The primary threat to wildlife is habitat destruction. **Endangered species** are those plants and animals that are currently at risk of extinction in their native habitats. **Threatened species** are those plants and animals that are likely to become endangered in the near future.

The U.S. government has passed laws, most importantly the Endangered Species Act of 1973, that define endangered species and establish regulations for their protection and conservation. In addition, nearly 100 nations have signed a treaty—C.I.T.E.S., an acronym for Convention on the International Trade in Endangered Species—that outlaws the trade of endangered species and their products across international borders.

Section Objectives

- *List three types of renewable resources and three types of nonrenewable resources.*
- *Describe some efforts being made to preserve habitats and wildlife.*
- *Describe three methods of increasing soil fertility.*
- *List some technological advances that can help conserve fossil fuels and minerals.*
- *Describe the benefits of municipal composting and materials recycling facilities.*

Figure 53-1 The manatee, *Trichesus* sp., is one animal whose survival as a species is in jeopardy because of human interference.

Resource	Depleted By	Sustained By
forests	timber industry, fire, agriculture	reforestation, land use planning
wildlife	deforestation, urban sprawl	land use planning, including reserves
soil	development, agriculture, erosion	contour plowing, land use planning

Graphic Organizer Use this table in Applying Concepts at right.

Lesson Plan

Section Focus

This section discusses natural resources as the raw materials that support life on earth. It distinguishes between renewable resources, which can be replenished, and nonrenewable resources, which cannot.

Section Themes

This section emphasizes the theme of **Stability**. The ecosystem depends on a variety of resources in a complicated and interconnected web. Water, for instance, on which all life depends, is a nonrenewable resource.

Motivating Activity

Bring in a photograph of a plant or an animal from an endangered species list, such as the spotted owl. Make this an opportunity to weigh costs and benefits of saving the endangered spotted owl or of saving an endangered lumber industry. Tell students that timbering was halted in areas of the Pacific Northwest that were also the habitat of the spotted owl and that many workers were laid off as a result.

Ask students if they think that it is important to have laws that protect endangered species. *(Student answers will vary. Encourage an open discussion.)*

Teaching Strategies

Applying Concepts Copy on the board only the column heads from the table to the left. Ask students to describe what can deplete forests, wildlife, and soil. Tell students that another way to think of taking care of resources is to sustain them. Ask students how these resources might be sustained. Write students' answers in the columns.

Videodiscs

- ***Side 4 7861, Elephants (m)***
- ***Side 4 9794, Blue Whale (m)***

Exploring Technology Arrange for the class to visit a power plant in your area, if possible one that uses a renewable source of energy such as hydroelectric, solar, or geothermal. If such a trip is not feasible, arrange a field trip to a recycling facility, preparing in advance for students a list of questions to answer or details to notice.

Contrasting Terms Ask students to draw a concept map identifying resources as renewable or nonrenewable. Ask where they would put humans on the map. An example of a completed concept map is shown on p. 819B.

Interpreting the Visuals Ask students what they think that Table 53-1, p. 823, suggests about an affluent society today. *(That it consumes large quantities of resources to produce goods)* Ask students to speculate on whether there are areas of the United States where one would not build an auto manufacturing plant. *(The desert; automobile production consumes large amounts of water)* Tell students that the wealth of an industrialized society is often built on nonrenewable resources.

■*See* **Overhead Transparency** *T53 and* **Blackline Master** *110.*

Guided Practice

Put two headings on the board—*Renewable Resources* and *Nonrenewable Resources.* Have students list specific resources under each heading. *(Sample answers: lumber, natural rubber, soil, water, oil, coal, copper)* Have students list products that are made from these resources. *(Sample answers: oil—plastic containers; lumber—paper products)* Ask students how each of the products or the resources is conserved or recycled. Identify those that come from areas near or somewhat near their community.

Soil

Soil is constantly formed as rocks break down and as dead organic matter accumulates. Soil is a mixture of rock fragments, minerals, and animal and plant matter. Soil retains water, which thus supports plant and animal life and controls flooding. **Humus,** the organic component of the soil that helps it retain most of its moisture and nutrients, is composed primarily of plant remains. A single acre of **topsoil,** the uppermost layer of soil, can hold up to 11 tons of worms, insects, bacteria, fungi, and other organisms.

Each year erosion carries away 2.7 billion tons of soil from U.S. farmlands. **Erosion** is the loss of soil resulting from the effects of abiotic factors such as wind and water. This eroded soil enters streams and pollutes the water. To prevent erosion caused by wind, farmers may plant grasses or other vegetation on otherwise bare fields, add plant wastes and manure to depleted soil, put up windbreaks or shelter belts of trees, or build irrigation ditches. To limit erosion caused by water, several techniques are used. **Contour plowing—**plowing that follows the contour of a slope rather than going up and down—and **terracing—**carving a series of steps along a hillside—help to lessen erosion by water.

Biotechnology

Integrated Waste Management

Gardeners throughout the ages have recycled vegetable matter, manure, and soil—through the process of composting—into a valuable resource called humus. Given time and plenty of exposure to air and water, organic materials left to rot will be broken down by bacteria and fungi into humus—a rich mixture that can enrich the soil, increase its moisture retention, and supply valuable nutrients to plants.

Composting on a larger scale offers a method of solid waste disposal that could save our eroding farmlands and help solve the problem of where to put our garbage. Large-scale composting can be done by piling waste in long rows and watering and turning it periodically to expose the material to oxygen. In the United States, only 10 cities have composting plants operating, but more than 200 composting plants are operating in Europe.

Humus created by composting solid waste could one day replace the expensive chemical fertilizers that pollute lakes and groundwater. But to be effective as a method of disposing of municipal waste, composting must be combined with source reduction and recycling, in an approach known as integrated waste

Cooperative Learning

Public Service Ads Divide the class into groups of three or four students, and assign each group a renewable or a nonrenewable resource. Have each group write a script and perform an informative and persuasive 60-second commercial on protection of their resource. Tell students to consider conservation and recycling as possible concepts for their skits. Have students perform them in class. If desirable, videotape them and show them to other classes or during a school assembly.

Nonrenewable Resources

Nonrenewable resources are those that cannot be replaced or replenished by nature or people. As a result, they require special management and attention. Among the most important nonrenewable resources are fresh water, fossil fuels, and minerals.

Water

The biosphere contains a fixed amount of water, of which only 3 percent is fresh water available for human consumption. Because fresh water is unevenly distributed over the earth, some highly populated areas may soon face severe water shortages.

Communities can conserve water by managing its flow in their **watershed**—the area of land that drains into a river. Creating water reservoirs by building dams also conserves water and prevents flooding. However, this practice may endanger species that live behind the dam by inundating their habitat and may harm species downstream by decreasing their supply of fresh water. Finding ways to use less water and to distribute it more efficiently is crucial. The data in Table 53-1 will give you an idea of how much water is required to produce food and other items.

Table 53-1 Water Required to Produce Consumer Goods

Consumer Good	Gallons of Water
One egg	40
One pound of flour	75
Loaf of bread	150
Sunday newspaper	280
One pound of beef	2,500
Automobile	100,000

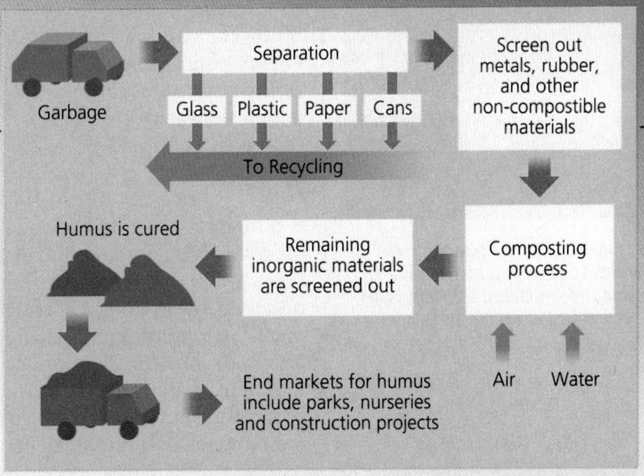

management. The need for reducing waste at its source is gaining recognition from industry. Many products no longer come with excess packaging, and others, such as paper goods and disposable diapers, can be made out of recycled materials. Some states already demand that packaging must be at least partially made of recycled materials.

Materials recovery facilities (MRFs) can provide an integrated approach to waste management. In Massachusetts an MRF is already serving 91 communities. The plant processes 240 tons of glass, aluminium, paper, and plastics each day. Usable materials are sorted, separated, and cleaned before being shipped for recycling. The remaining materials are then incinerated or sent to another site for composting. The MRF literally sells its trash to paper mills, glass and plastic container manufacturers, and metal fabricators.

MRFs are an attractive alternative. Participating cities and towns in Massachusetts save about $3 million dollars per year on waste disposal costs and divert 50,000 tons of trash each year that would otherwise have to be burned or buried.

Independent Practice

- Have students write answers to the Section Review.
- Ask students to list the natural resources they consume in a week. Have students list how each resource can be conserved, renewed, or recycled. *(For example, paper is made from trees; paper can be recycled and trees replanted.)*

Biotechnology

Using the Feature

Ask students to identify the low technology and high technology described in the feature. *(Low tech: composting. High tech: a materials recovery facility [MRF])* Explain to students that these technologies can be used together for an integrated approach to waste management. Recyclables can be separated at an MRF in a presorting process or at a composting facility. Extensive source separation and preprocessing are necessary to make an MRF efficient. However, the Massachusetts facility has found that citizens who use it provide cleaner trash because they want to recycle.

Encourage students to think of advantages and disadvantages of composting. *(Advantages—It can convert organic wastes in 28 to 80 days. Its byproduct, humus, can be sold. Disadvantages—Composting can be smelly and requires presorting and the removal of toxic wastes.)* Ask students how they would deal with these drawbacks. *(Possible answers: enclosed facilities; special plant exhaust design and equipment)*

Videodiscs

- ***2514, The Water Cycle (s)***

Interdisciplinary Activity

Government Tell students that ecological policy in the United States is developed at the state and federal levels as a result of legislation. Each law once in place has a reauthorization period when it is reviewed and changed. Assign students one of the federal environmental laws and have them research what it protects or conserves. Ask students to research various lobbies that have tried to influence reauthorization of the law and what their concerns were. Have students contact their legislators as part of their research.

Check Your Understanding

1. What could happen to soil if you "clear cut" a forest? *(The soil could erode.)*

2. Why is habitat destruction a threat to wildlife? *(It deprives them of food and nesting places.)*

Reteaching

Tell students that gasohol is a mixture of a renewable resource (alcohol made through the fermentation of corn) and a nonrenewable resource, gasoline. Ask students how production of gasohol can reduce the demand for a nonrenewable resource. *(Less gasoline is used per gallon.)* Ask them to suggest other ways to reduce the use of fossil fuels. *(Photovoltaic cells use solar energy to generate electricity, heat water, power cars; windmills use wind energy to generate electricity; conservation)*

■ *See* Section Reviews *worksheet, 53.1.*

Enrichment

Have students contact the state parks and wildlife office for a list of endangered and threatened species with habitats in their state. Ask them to choose a plant or animal and write a report that includes information about the species' habitat, niche, how it is threatened, and what is being done to help it recover. Ask students to determine what impact recovery measures have on local residents or on the economy. *(Example: Temporarily closing a beach to protect the nesting area of the piping plover)*

Closure

Ask students to discuss the dual roles of conservation and use of renewable energy sources in meeting our energy needs in the next century.

Videodiscs

■ *2529, Methane (s)*
■ *2531, Butane (s)*

Figure 53-2 Steam rises above the wells and pipes of a geothermal installation in Wairakei, New Zealand.

Figure 53-3 This quarry, from which rock formed from lava is removed, in Oahu, Hawaii, is an example of strip mining.

Fossil Fuels

Fossil fuels are the result of the incomplete decay of prehistoric plants and animals that lived during the Carboniferous period, about 300 million years ago. Fossil fuels include coal, oil, and natural gas. We use fossil fuels for about 95 percent of our energy needs. Fossil fuels are used to heat homes, propel cars, and produce electricity. Researchers have developed ways to use alternative energy sources to conserve the limited supply of fossil fuels. Both private homes and major utility companies now take advantage of solar energy, using photovoltaic cells to capture it. Other utility companies around the world are using **geothermal energy,** which is heat from beneath the earth, to generate electricity, as shown in Figure 53-2.

Minerals

A **mineral** is an inorganic solid formed in the earth. Minerals such as iron, silver, aluminum, zinc, and copper are important components of many materials that humans use. Most minerals are obtained by mining, a process that often disrupts the environment. **Strip mining,** in which layers of earth are removed to gain access to minerals, is more economical than mining ores in tunnels, but it damages the land. Treating and containing runoff, controlling emissions released into the air, and revegetating strip-mined areas can minimize environmental damage.

Section Review

1. Distinguish between *renewable* and *nonrenewable resources.*
2. What steps have been taken to protect endangered species?
3. Name three farming practices that lessen soil erosion.
4. Summarize efforts being made by scientists and the public to conserve fossil fuels.
5. Since fossil fuels are formed from decaying organic matter, why are these fuels considered a nonrenewable resource?

Answers to Section Review

1. Renewable resources can be replaced; nonrenewable resources cannot.

2. Endangered species have been identified and regulations established to ensure protection and conservation.

3. Answers may include contour plowing, terracing, irrigating, growing plants on bare soil, and creating windbreaks or shelter belts.

4. Scientists have developed technology to use alternative energy sources. The public has reduced its energy use.

5. Because it takes hundreds of thousands of years to form fossil fuels, they are being used up faster than they can be replaced.

53.2 Pollution

Pollution is an undesirable change in the physical, chemical, or biological characteristics of an ecosystem. One source of pollution is the accumulation of impurities, called pollutants, in the environment. Some pollutants, such as organic garbage, are **biodegradable**—subject to decay by microorganisms. Those pollutants that cannot be decomposed by microorganisms are **nonbiodegradable.** Pollutants are also classified as either primary or secondary pollutants.

Section Objectives

- *List several primary pollutants and their sources.*
- *Identify the sources of ozone and acid rain, and describe the effects of these pollutants on the environment.*
- *Describe industrial, agricultural, and domestic sources of pollution.*

Primary and Secondary Pollutants

Pollutants emitted directly into the atmosphere are called **primary pollutants.** Some primary pollutants are injurious to humans. For example, carbon monoxide (CO), a component of automobile exhaust, combines quickly with hemoglobin and interferes with the ability of the blood to transport oxygen. In addition, **particulates,** the tiny solid particles found in smoke, can irritate the respiratory system and lead to chronic lung diseases. Other primary pollutants include lead, sulfur dioxide, and hydrocarbons.

Secondary pollutants result from some effect acting on primary pollutants. Sunlight catalyzes a series of chemical reactions in the mixture of primary pollutants in the atmosphere. The product of these reactions is **photochemical smog.** Photochemical smog damages the photosynthetic tissues of plants. Nitrogen oxides, primary pollutants produced as by-products of combustion in furnaces and engines, also react with sunlight and chemicals to form **ozone,** another secondary pollutant.

Conditions that exist in the upper atmosphere are the catalyst for a different series of chemical reactions. Under these conditions primary pollutants such as chlorines and fluorines destroy the natural ozone layer that protects the earth from harmful ultraviolet radiation.

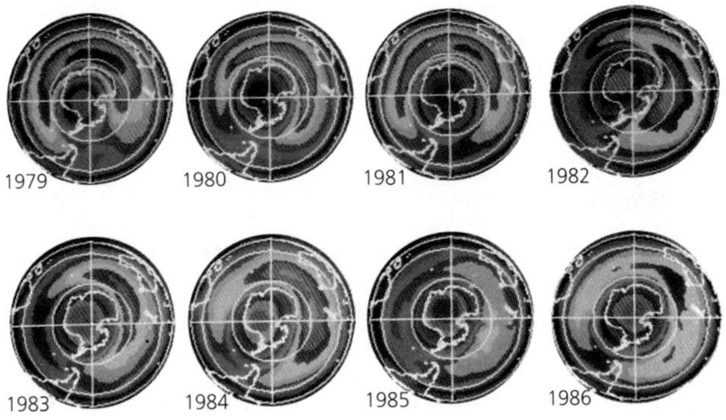

Figure 53-4 These computer-generated images show changes in the ozone level over the South Pole from 1979 to 1986. The dark purple indicates a very low ozone level. In 1987 the ozone level decreased again.

	Sources of Pollution
Industrial	chemical wastes from factories
Agricultural	pesticides, fertilizers, animal wastes
Domestic	solid wastes, including sewage

Graphic Organizer Use this table in Guided Practice at right.

Lesson Plan

Section Focus

This section discusses primary and secondary pollutants and their three major sources: industry, agriculture, and domestic uses.

Section Themes

This section emphasizes the theme of **Systems and Interactions.** It shows how humans cause pollution, a problem that threatens the system on which all life depends.

Motivating Activity

Tell students to assume that a family of four generates three 30-gallon (114-L) bags of garbage a week. Ask them how much garbage this would be per year *(90 × 52 = 4,680 gallons).* Ask them how much garbage their community produces every year. Ask how recycling programs and conservation can reduce this amount.

Teaching Strategies

Interpreting the Visuals Ask students to look at Figure 53-4 and describe what happened to ozone levels over the South Pole from 1979 to 1986. *(The geographic area of decreased ozone increased.)* Point out that the ozone layer in the upper atmosphere screens out UV light. Ask what could happen to people in Chile and Australia where holes have been discovered in the ozone layer. *(Increase in skin cancers and eye disease)*

- *See* **Process Skills,** *Chapter 53.*

Guided Practice

Copy the table to the left onto the board, leaving the *Sources of Pollution* column blank. Ask students to fill it in.

Videodiscs

- *2654–2655, Human Respiratory System (s)*

Answer to Think

It could result in high levels of pesticides in humans. Ways to reduce the risk include developing nonbioaccumulative pesticides, developing pest-resistant crops, or changing pesticide use practices.

Independent Practice

- Have students write answers to the Section Review.
- Ask students to discuss how lead released by autos can be an example of biological magnification. *(Lead is washed into streams and enters the food chain.)*

Check Your Understanding

1. Compare a primary with a secondary pollutant. *(Primary pollutants are released directly into the atmosphere. Secondary pollutants result from something acting on a primary pollutant.)*
2. What organisms are most harmed by biological magnification? *(Those at the top of the food chain)*

Reteaching

Have students keep a record of all the pollutants they encounter in one day and the sources of these pollutants. *(Sample answers: automobile exhaust, cigarette smoke, litter)* Brainstorm ways to reduce the pollutants.
- *See* Section Reviews *worksheet, Section 53.2.*

Enrichment

Ask students to find out how solid waste is disposed of in their city or town. Have them prepare a report describing the waste stream, any problems with volume of waste, any proposals for handling these problems and any recycling efforts.

Closure

Have students list sources of pollution. Ask how they might change their habits based on what they have learned Ask what other changes they would like to see.

Think

The figures show how pesticide levels increase at each level of a food chain. How might such biological magnification affect humans? How might scientists direct their research in order to solve the problem?

Host	Concentration (parts per million)
Water	0.000003
Plankton	0.04
Small fish	0.05
Large fish	2
Fish-eating bird	25

Acid rain is precipitation with below-normal pH, the result of industrial pollution and automobile exhaust emitted into the atmosphere. Sulfur dioxide and nitrogen oxide found in these pollutants combine with water vapor to form acids. The accumulation of acid rain lowers the natural pH of lakes and ponds, often killing the organisms that live there.

Sources of Pollution

To control pollution we must understand its sources. Major national efforts are under way to monitor and control industrial, agricultural, and domestic sources of pollution.

Industrial Sources

Industries cause pollution by creating chemical wastes in factories and processing plants and then either releasing them into the air or water or storing them incorrectly. Some industries produce **hazardous wastes** that are toxic, radioactive, explosive, or otherwise dangerous to humans and the environment. Wastes such as industrial cleaning chemicals and waste oils used to be placed in steel barrels and buried. However, over time the barrels have corroded, allowing the wastes to leak out. Today regulations require the safe disposal of hazardous wastes. Still, hundreds of these former hazardous waste sites must be cleaned up.

Agricultural Sources

Many North American and European farmers rely on manufactured chemicals called **pesticides** to control insects and other pests. However, pesticides can soak into the soil and flow into streams, where they enter the food chain. **Biological magnification** is the process in which hazardous wastes become increasingly concentrated in successive levels of the food chain.

Domestic Sources

The United States accumulates more than 130 metric tons of solid wastes per year. Over 70 percent comes from residences. Sewage is another form of domestic waste. To prevent sewage from flowing into rivers and lakes and tainting the water supply, cities and other municipalities have developed sewage treatment facilities to purify and recycle water.

Section Review

1. Explain the difference between *biodegradable* and *nonbiodegradable* substances.
2. What purpose does the ozone layer serve?
3. Describe how photochemical smog is produced.
4. Describe the process of biological magnification.
5. Why do areas far from sites of industrial pollution experience the effects of acid rain?

Answers to Section Review

1. Biodegradable substances can be broken down by microorganisms; nonbiodegradable substances cannot.
2. The ozone layer protects the earth from ultraviolet light.
3. Sunlight catalyzes a series of chemical reactions in a mixture of primary pollutants in the atmosphere, which forms photochemical smog.
4. Biological magnification occurs when hazardous wastes enter the food chain and become increasingly concentrated at higher levels of the ecosystem.
5. Because pollutants are carried for hundreds of miles by the wind before returning to earth in the form of precipitation

Laboratory

Effects of Thermal Pollution

Objective
To model the effects of thermal pollution on living organisms

Process Skills
Hypothesizing experimenting, inferring

Materials
2 400-mL beakers, ice, thermometer, 12 cm of U–shaped glass tubing, corks to fit both ends of the tubing, 125-mL beaker, pond water, *Paramecium* culture, dissecting microscope

Background
Some power plants use water from rivers as a coolant. After the water is used, it is much hotter than the temperature of the river water.

1 What is a pollutant?
2 Why can heat be considered a pollutant?

Technique

1 Fill a 400-mL beaker with ice water. Make sure that ice remains in the beaker for the entire experiment. Fill another 400-mL beaker with 60°C tap water.
2 Cork one end of a piece of U-shaped glass tubing.
3 In a 125-mL beaker, gently swirl 50 mL of pond water and 50 mL of *Paramecium* culture. What is the purpose of the swirling? Pour the mixture into the glass tubing, leaving just enough room for a cork. Cork the open end.
4 Use the tubing, the ice water, the hot water, and the dissecting microscope to observe any response of the paramecia to their environment. What is the approximate temperature range?

Inquiry

1 Discuss the objective of this laboratory with your partners and develop a hypothesis.
2 Design an experiment to test your hypothesis using the setup described in Technique.
3 What are your independent and dependent variables? How will you vary the independent variable? How will you measure changes in the dependent variable?
4 What controls will you include?
5 Why are the length of time and the temperature range important factors?
6 How will you record your results?
7 Get *Parmamecium* culture and proceed with your experiment after receiving approval from your teacher.

Conclusions

1 Do your data support your hypothesis? Explain.
2 What might have been some sources of error in your experiment?
3 Was there evidence that the paramecia preferred a certain temperature?
4 Might a pollutant cause an *increase* in the number of organisms? Explain.

Further Inquiry
Develop a hypothesis as to how acid rain affects *Paramecium* and design an experiment to test your hypothesis.

(For an overview of pollutants and preparatory information related to the laboratory, see p. 819B.)

Background
1. Something that causes an undesirable change in an ecosystem
2. Heat can cause undesirable changes, for example, when hot water runs into rivers.

Technique
1. Use the thermometer.
3. To make the initial paramecium distribution random. Note: fill the tubing completely.
4. About 0°C to 60°C

Inquiry
1. Remind students that paramecia exhibit avoidance behavior in response to potentially harmful situations.
2. Discuss experimental designs with each group. Be sure that students understand that one end of the tubing must be placed in the ice water, the other in the hot water.
3. The independent variable is the temperature, varied through the use of ice and hot water. The distribution of paramecia is the dependent variable. To measure changes, compare initial distribution with distribution after temperature range exposure.
4. An identical setup but excluding exposure to temperature extremes. The setup should include two beakers of room temperature water.
5. The paramecia need time to respond to their environment. Advise students to wait at least 15 minutes before removing the tubing. The temperatures used must not injure or kill the organisms.
6. By marking sections in the tubing and by counting the number of paramecia per section before and after the experiment. Results could be shown in a table or a graph.

Conclusions
1. Students should recognize this.
2. Jarring the tube, unhealthy paramecia, using temperatures that do not affect the organisms or temperatures that harm them, inaccurate counting, giving the paramecia insufficient time to respond
3. Data should support answers. Paramecia prefer moderate temperature and congregate in the center of the tubing.
4. Yes. An increase in temperature can promote algae growth as can nutrient pollution from sewage or fertilizer runoff.

Further Inquiry
Have students adapt the techniques for *Tetrahymena* on p. 817. Students can also study seed germination. See *Laboratories,* Investigation 53.

Chapter 53 Review

Vocabulary

1. Contour plowing means plowing across a field rather than up and down; terracing involves building a series of steps down a slope.
2. Deforestation is the clearing of forested land; reforestation is the growing of new trees on deforested land.
3. A primary pollutant is an impurity emitted directly into the environment; when it combines with other substances and undergoes a chemical reaction, it becomes a secondary pollutant.
4. Ozone is a pollutant that forms when nitrogen oxides react with other chemicals and sunlight. It is one component of photochemical smog.
5. An endangered species is at risk of extinction; a threatened species is likely to be endangered in the near future.

Review

1. a **6.** a
2. c **7.** d
3. b **8.** b
4. d **9.** b
5. b **10.** c

11. It involves nurturing new trees on sites that have been deforested, preventing soil erosion, and maintaining ground moisture.
12. It defined what species were endangered and established regulations for their protection and conservation.
13. Soil is formed from the breakdown of rocks and the accumulation of dead organic matter.
14. A watershed consists of all the land that drains into a river.
15. Strip mining is an economical method of obtaining minerals. However, it also disrupts the environment when the soil is removed.
16. Geothermal energy is obtained from hot water beneath the earth.
17. The three sources of pollution are industrial, agricultural, and domestic.
18. Inhaled particulates can irritate the lining of the lungs and eventually lead to chronic lung disease.
19. Organic materials are "disposed of" by turning them into useful soil and reducing the amount of garbage.
20. If pesticides are absorbed into the soil and get into the water supply, they can poison fish and various other aquatic animals.

Chapter 53 Review

Vocabulary

acid rain (826)
biodegradable (825)
biological magnification (826)
contour plowing (822)
deforestation (821)
endangered species (821)
erosion (822)
fossil fuel (824)
geothermal energy (824)
hazardous waste (826)
humus (822)
mineral (824)
natural resource (821)
nonbiodegradable (825)
nonrenewable resource (823)
ozone (825)
particulate (825)
pesticide (826)
photochemical smog (825)
pollution (825)
primary pollutant (825)
reforestation (821)
renewable resource (821)
secondary pollutant (825)
strip mining (824)
terracing (822)
threatened species (821)
topsoil (822)
watershed (823)
wildlife (821)

Distinguish between the terms in each of the following pairs.

1. contour plowing, terracing
2. deforestation, reforestation
3. primary pollutant, secondary pollutant
4. ozone, photochemical smog
5. endangered species, threatened species

Review

1. The primary cause of species endangerment is (a) disappearing habitat (b) biological magnification (c) acid rain (d) exposure to hazardous waste.
2. Erosion is the loss of soil that results from (a) recycling (b) reforestation (c) abiotic factors (d) contour plowing.
3. Renewable resources include all of the following except (a) wildlife (b) minerals (c) soil (d) forests.
4. The organic part of the soil that helps it to retain most of its moisture and nutrients is called (a) topsoil (b) organic fertilizers (c) watershed (d) humus.
5. All of these are fossil fuels except (a) oil (b) lead (c) coal (d) natural gas.
6. Energy sources such as solar energy and geothermal energy may help reduce consumption of (a) fossil fuels (b) minerals (c) electricity (d) water.
7. Carbon monoxide restricts the oxygen supply of the body by (a) irritating the lining of the lungs (b) accumulating in blood-forming organs (c) causing lung disease (d) combining with hemoglobin.
8. The major component of photochemical smog is (a) acid rain (b) ozone (c) particulates (d) sulfur dioxide.
9. Acid rain is a (a) primary pollutant (b) secondary pollutant (c) by-product of ozone (d) particulate.
10. The primary source of trash that is burned to produce energy in a trash-to-resource incinerator, such as the one currently being used in Dade County, Florida, is (a) plastic (b) chemicals (c) paper (d) metal.
11. Explain the process of reforestation.
12. What steps were taken in the Endangered Species Act of 1973 to protect species in danger of extinction?
13. How is soil formed?
14. What is a watershed?
15. Describe the advantages and disadvantages of strip mining.
16. What is the source of geothermal energy?
17. Name the three sources of environmental pollution.
18. Describe what effects the inhaling of particulates has on the body.

19. How does municipal composting contribute to the success of integrated waste management?

20. How can pesticides harm organisms other than the pests they are intended to kill?

Critical Thinking

1. Carbon monoxide is an air pollutant that combines with hemoglobin in a person's blood. Why is carbon monoxide such a dangerous pollutant to human beings and animals?
2. Through conservation and wildlife management the United States and other nations are making efforts to prevent the loss of species. What are some ways that this prevention can be achieved?
3. Humus is made up of decomposed organic substances. It is the component of soil that helps it retain moisture and nutrients. Why does desert soil have such a low percentage of humus? How could humans compensate for the lack of humus in desert climates in order to spur plant growth?
4. DDT was effectively used to kill crop-eating insects for a number of years before its use was banned by the United States in 1973. DDT was considered unsafe after it was linked to defects in other species such as birds. Some people were even found to have a low concentration of DDT in their bodies. How might a pesticide such as DDT be present in species other than insects?

5. The accumulation of acid rain, produced by industrial pollution and automobile exhaust, can damage or even kill off many plants and animals. The photo above shows a situation that contributes to the production of acid rain. What methods could be used to reduce the pollutants that cause acid rain?

Extension

1. Read the article by Peter Steinhart entitled "Innocent Victims of a Toxic World" in *National Wildlife*, February/March 1990, pp. 21–27. Prepare an oral report in which you include answers to these questions: (1) How is the chemical assault on wildlife apparent throughout the country? (2) Why are PCBs and DDT still a problem even though they were banned in the 1970s? (3) Why are the use and disposal of synthetic chemicals so difficult to regulate? (4) What are possible solutions to this complex problem?
2. If you live near a zoo, ask the director if the zoo is participating in the breeding of endangered species of animals. Find out which methods are most successful in producing offspring when the animal is not breeding in its natural habitat.
3. Contact your state department of natural resources to find out what animals and plants in your state are on the endangered species list. Pick one and make a poster showing what it looks like, its location in the state, and what efforts are being made to protect it.

Critical Thinking

1. If enough carbon monoxide binds with hemoglobin, the blood cannot carry sufficient oxygen for respiration, and the organism suffocates.
2. Hunting can be limited. Specimens of endangered species can be bred in captivity and their offspring returned to the natural habitat to repopulate it. If industrial development is unavoidable, displaced species could be relocated to a similar habitat.
3. In deserts where plant life is sparse, there is little decomposed plant material available to form humus. Humans could apply fertilizer to supply plants with nutrients and moisture normally provided by humus in less arid climates.
4. The pesticide is accumulated in insects and is passed on to predators higher in the food chain. It could have spread to humans who ate fish that had consumed insects that had been sprayed with pesticide.
5. Filters on smokestacks reduce the amount of sulfur dioxide and nitrogen oxide released into the air; less acid rain is formed. Catalytic converters on cars change exhaust fumes into harmless products.

Extension

1. Reports should note the deformities or illnesses in contaminated wildlife, the bioaccumulative nature of PCBs and DDT, the high cost of regulation that reduces effectiveness, and various solutions—from reducing pesticide use to changing industrial processes.
2. You can also ask students to research those zoos that have programs to breed endangered species of animals.
3. If some of these organisms exist locally, you might take students on a field trip to observe and photograph them.

Discussion

Guide the discussion by posing the following questions.

1. In addition to preventing temperature increases, what other positive environmental effects can result from reduced emissions of greenhouse gases? *(Answers will vary. Emphasize to students that controlling emissions of gaseous pollutants can benefit public health and reduce acid rain.)*

2. The United States is the largest emitter of carbon dioxide from fossil fuel use. In what ways can the government encourage control of emissions? *(Encourage students to consider the government's ability to ban certain chemicals, induce reduction of emissions through financial penalties, and offer tax benefits for the research and application of alternative sources of energy.)*

3. Environmental changes affect species of organisms differently; how do you think that global warming might affect certain animals, such as giraffes on the Serengeti, penguins in Antarctica, or trout in Scotland? *(Help students consider the effects of desertification on the giraffes' environment, changes in temperature and the planktonic food chain that ultimately feeds penguins, and sensitivity of trout reproduction to increases in water temperature.)*

4. What natural events can contribute to global warming and with what effects? *(Answers might include lightning that forms ozone and can spark forest fires, volcanoes that spew gases into the atmosphere, or herds of large animals that consume vegetation in an area, contributing to desertification.)*

Intra-Science

How the Sciences Work Together

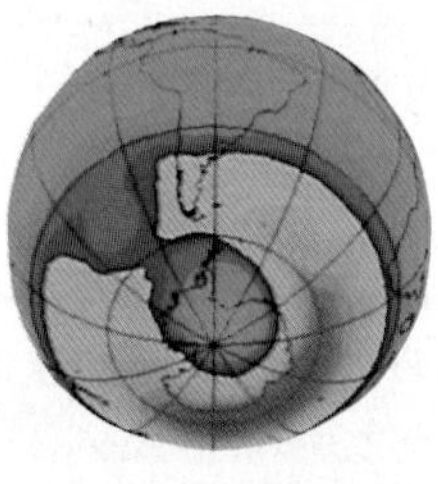

The Question in Biology: *Can We Save Our Atmosphere?*

A global experiment is occurring in the earth's atmosphere. Tons of gaseous pollutants are trapping heat in our air, just as windows trap heat in a greenhouse. Scientists hypothesize that as more and more gaseous pollutants pour into the atmosphere, the earth's climates will become warmer and warmer.

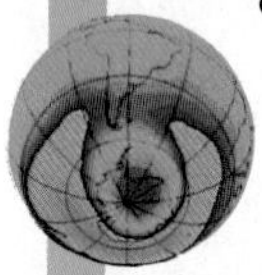

Earth is a warm, temperate planet because the troposphere, the atmospheric layer closest to the earth's surface, retains heat energy caused by sunlight. It is this warmth that makes life possible on the earth. The troposphere also releases excess heat. However, when tons of carbon dioxide, ozone, and nitrogen oxides pollute the atmosphere, the troposphere retains more heat. Industrial and auto emissions are a major source of these gaseous pollutants, called greenhouse gases. However, deforestation is now responsible for about 30 percent of the buildup of carbon dioxide in our atmosphere, and its contribution is expanding.

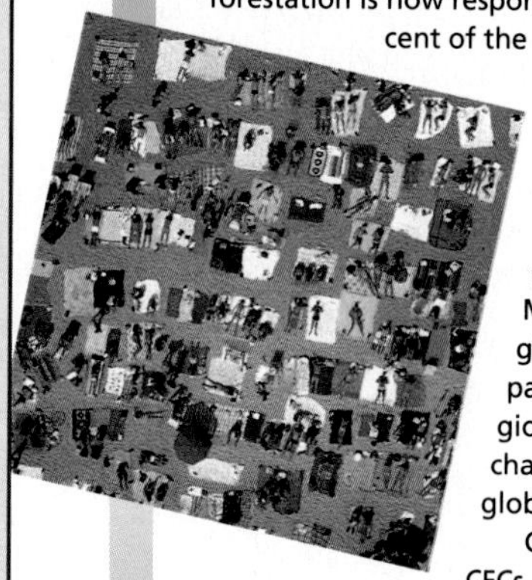

The buildup of carbon dioxide is the main cause of global warming. Meteorologists predict global changes in weather patterns, larger tropical regions, and other ecological changes resulting from global warming.

Chlorofluorocarbons, or CFCs, are also a major threat to our atmosphere. When these chemicals rise into the atmosphere, they release chlorine molecules that destroy the earth's protective ozone layer. The ozone layer shields the earth from the sun's harmful rays. Medical doctors predict that skin cancers and cataracts can increase as more of the sun's harmful rays penetrate the earth's thinning ozone shield.

CFCs are released into our air everyday. They are often used as a coolant in automobile air conditioners, and in various manufacturing processes. As a result they are often part of auto and industrial emissions released daily. CFCs are also found in some plastic foam cups and dinnerware.

Hoping to combat ozone depletion, scientists, economists, and leaders from many nations have gathered to plan strategies to eliminate CFCs and other threats to the ozone layer. "Even as CFCs are being eliminated, chlorine already emitted will continue to destroy ozone for decades," said atmospheric scientist Dr. Michael Oppenheimer of the Environmental Defense Fund. "The ozone layer will not recover in our lifetime. So we must phase out CFCs as quickly as possible. . . ."

Unfortunately world leaders cannot agree on how to end harmful emissions while preserving national economies. Yet policy makers and scientists do agree on one point: no one can spend the years or decades it will take to gather conclusive evidence as to the long-range effects of human activities on the ozone layer or on global warming. By then it might be too late to halt a global disaster.

The Connection to Computer Science

Fortunately, with the aid of computers, scientists can analyze years of temperature data from worldwide sources—ocean temperatures from ship logs and land temperatures from monitoring stations around the world. However, temperature changes do not always reflect global warming. When heat from urban areas causes false readings, computer scientists can adjust the temperature data for these areas and construct fairly accurate models of climates in change.

830

Connection to Other Disciplines

Geography Environmental changes have occurred throughout the world due to human impact. Encourage students to research such changes and show them on maps of the world. Some examples are the gradual desertification in Africa's Sahel over the last century or the extensive destruction of rain forests in Central or South America during the same period.

Literature Some classical science fiction authors wrote about imaginary technologies that were later actually developed; for example, Jules Verne wrote about submarines in the book *Twenty Thousand Leagues Under the Sea* long before modern submarines were constructed. Ask students to explore and report on works of modern science fiction in which imaginary technology is used to solve environmental problems.

Other scientists can then use the computer models as a base for the data they accumulate. For example, geophysicists have drilled boreholes to examine rocks and sediments throughout the world to estimate temperature fluctuations as long ago as the last Ice Age. Scientists can then compare this information to determine how drastically climates are changing.

■ *How are computer models valuable tools in making predictions about global warming?*

The Connection to Chemistry

Chemists can analyze reactions taking place between greenhouse gases and atmospheric components. They can then construct mathematical models based on a number of factors: number of different gases; sources or types of emissions; or movement of gases at different atmospheric levels. Chemists can then estimate from these models how reducing emissions of one gas will affect the atmospheric concentrations of others.

Chemists are also working to develop substitute chemicals for fossil fuels and for the CFCs used in coolants. Chemists have found CFC substitutes that break down before reaching the stratosphere, saving the ozone from destruction. However, some of these new chemicals may have cancer-causing properties, so safer substitutes must be found.

■ *Why is it important to investigate the chemical interactions of different greenhouse gases in the atmosphere?*

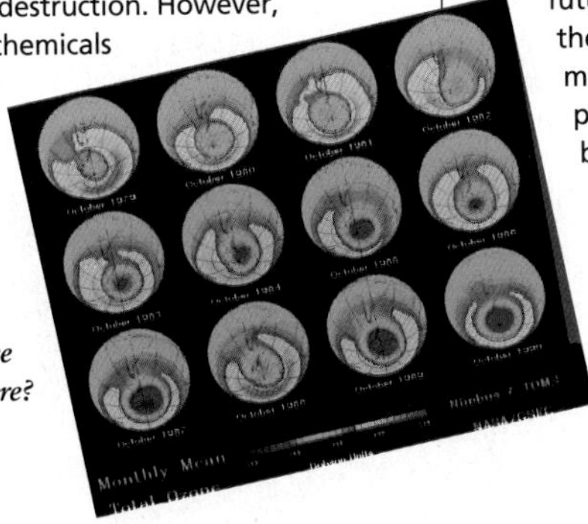

The Connection to Other Sciences

Interdisciplinary approaches are vital to understanding global warming and ozone depletion. Biogeochemists continue to study and track the release of CO_2 into the atmosphere during biomass burning, such as deforestation. Oceanographers are investigating the role that marine plankton play in the carbon dioxide cycle. Auto engineers are designing electric car engines that will not pollute the air and coolant systems that do not use CFCs.

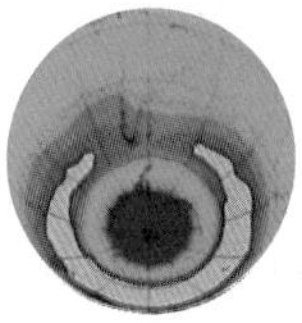

■ *Why does finding solutions to ozone depletion require the efforts of a variety of scientists?*

The Connection to Careers

Computer scientists, chemists, biologists, climatologists, and geologists are needed to accumulate data and construct models used to predict future trends in global warming. In addition the effects of atmospheric pollution on human health—such as increased respiratory problems and skin cancers—are already being observed by medical experts. More medical researchers and health care specialists will be needed to develop new treatments and to provide better health care. For more information about related careers in the biological sciences, turn to page 842.

Enrichment

A geologist found ice crystals in fossils of plants that had lived in Wyoming 65 million years ago. At that time, North America had a subtropical climate. The ice crystals in the fossil plant tissue were evidence of an unseasonal freeze. Scientists speculate that this "winter" may have resulted from an extraterrestrial object that crashed into the earth and created a worldwide cloud. Ask students to research a major volcanic eruption or meteor impact. Have them describe how these events might have affected earth's climates and organisms.

5. In what ways do you think that each person can contribute to controlling emissions of greenhouse gases? *(Possible answers include recycling, bicycling or walking more, and supporting organizations and businesses that work to reduce emissions of greenhouse gases.)*

6. If atmospheric pollution is not controlled, how might people avoid health problems? *(Sample answers: sensitive or asthmatic people will have to stay in controlled atmospheres; people will have to use suntan lotion or cover their skin, and use dark glasses in sunlight; outdoor events may have to be held later in the day.)*

7. Harmful ultraviolet radiation kills phytoplankton, which absorb large amounts of carbon dioxide from the air. What effect would a wider hole in the ozone layer have on atmospheric gases? *(The ozone hole lets harmful ultraviolet light reach the earth; this could kill large numbers of plankton, thus increasing carbon dioxide in the atmosphere.)*

Answers to

Computer Science Computer modeling can quickly combine data from many sources and depict or predict past, present, or future events.

Chemistry Using the results of investigations of chemical interactions, economists and world leaders can choose cost-effective controls to reduce emission of greenhouse gases.

Other Sciences Ozone depletion is a complex process that involves the interactions of various activities affecting the earth. Point out to students the following examples: biota interact with atmospheric chemicals; chemical emissions affect climate, climate affects living organisms; sunlight affects living and nonliving matter.

Toward the 21st Century

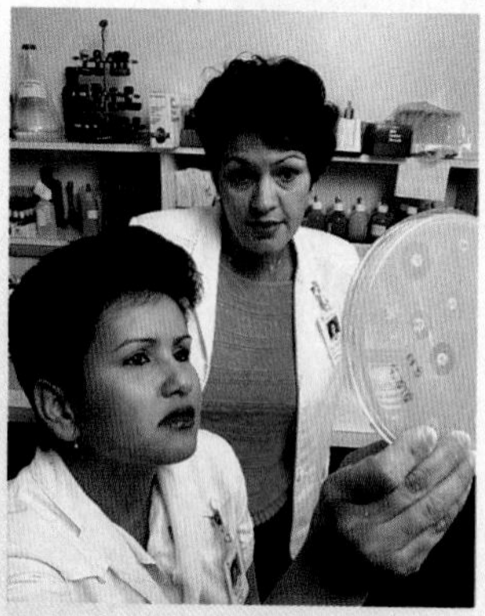

Take just a moment to flip through Modern Biology. *You will spot many pictures and diagrams that recall the biological principles you have studied. The unifying concepts of evolution, genetics, biochemistry, and cell structure that underlie the amazing diversity of organisms; the complex web of ecological relationships that tie living things to one another; the means by which this great diversity of life evolved and is still evolving—these are the concepts we hope this course has taught you.*

You have learned many scientific processes, skills, and techniques. Most important, you have learned to think logically, to approach problems in a scientific way. As you face your adulthood in the next century, remember these lessons. You will be better equipped to seek solutions to the problems that confront you.

The biological sciences are in the midst of a golden age of discovery. Each year promises greater insights into virtually every facet of biological study. Some of you may become physical scientists, biologists, and physicians and will share in the discoveries that lie ahead. All of you will be asked to make decisions based on your understanding of the life sciences.

So far genetic engineering has given us drugs to treat heart attacks and diabetes, and genetic engineers are working to create microbes that will improve crop yields and degrade environmental pollutants. Yet many thoughtful people fear the unforeseen consequences of

832

creating new life-forms and releasing them into our environment. The question of regulating this technology will also confront us in the years ahead. As tomorrow's voters, you will need your knowledge of biology in order to understand such issues.

The world's rain forests are being destroyed at an alarming rate. With their demise comes the potential extinction of thousands—perhaps millions—of species, some not yet known to biologists. Can these irreplaceable ecosystems be saved? This, too, is a complex question, one that pits the economic growth of developing nations against the ecological well-being of the earth.

Finally, on a personal level, we hope you will recall this course as you observe the ebb and flow of life around you. When you view the splendor of a coniferous forest or the grandeur of a tallgrass prairie, when you plant a garden, or perhaps witness the miracle of the birth of your own children, we hope you will reflect on what you have learned. Your knowledge of biology will make your observations meaningful as you survey the beauty and complexity of our world.

A Five-Kingdom System for the Classification of Organisms

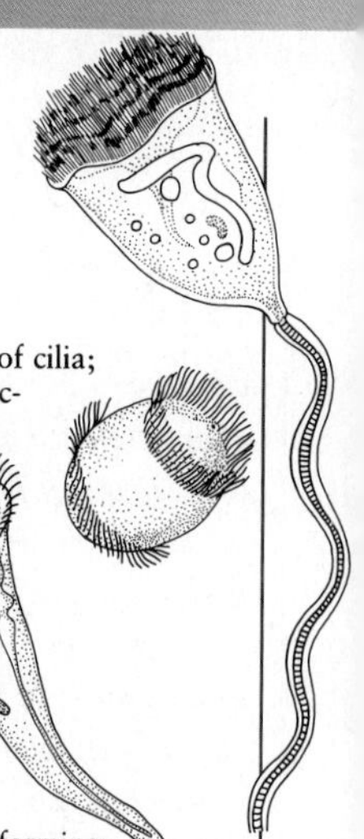

Kingdom Monera

Unicellular, sometimes forming groups or filaments; prokaryotic (lacking nuclear membrane and organelles with membranes); nutrition mainly by absorption, but some are photosynthetic or chemosynthetic; cell wall a polysaccharide with polypeptide cross-links; reproduction usually by fission or budding, but some may exchange genetic material.

Phylum Archaebacteria: Anaerobic bacteria adapted to harsh environments; differ in terms of biochemistry from all other organisms: methanogens, extreme halophiles, thermoacidophiles.

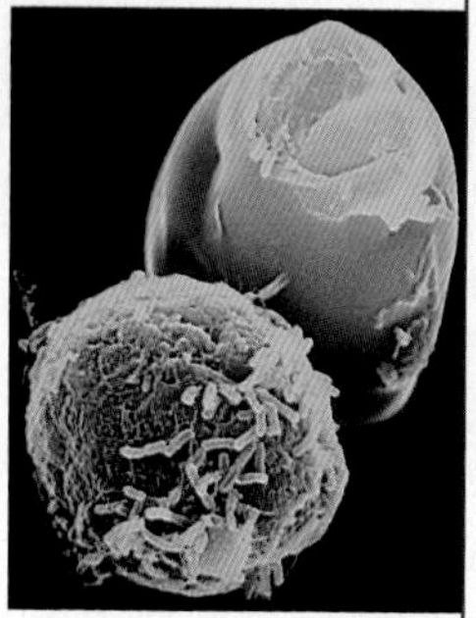

Phylum Schizophyta: Mostly parasitic or saprophytic organisms; cells lacking an organized nucleus, with nucleoproteins in contact with cytoplasm; reproduction by fission, certain forms producing endospores: bacteria, rickettsias, actinomycetes, spirochetes.

Phylum Cyanophyta: Cells containing chlorophyll and other pigments not localized in plastids; cells lacking an organized nucleus, with nucleoproteins in contact with cytoplasm; reproduction by fission and spores: blue-green algae (*Nostoc, Anabaena, Gloecapsa, Oscillatoria*).

Phylum Prochlorophyta: Unicellular, nonmotile, and spherical; photosynthetic bacteria, resembling chloroplasts of green algae and plants; symbiotic; containing chlorophyll b in addition to a; seven strains, all of the same genus: *Prochloron*.

Kingdom Protista

Unicellular, colonial, and multicellular organisms with eukaryotic cells (cells with an organized nucleus and organelles with membranes); protists lack specialized tissue and include both heterotrophic and autotrophic forms.

Phylum Sarcodina: Move by means of pseudopodia; pellicle lacking; some with shells; reproduction principally by fission; freshwater and marine: *Ameba, Foraminifera, Radiolaria.*

Phylum Ciliophora: Move by means of cilia; pellicle present; many forms with macronucleus and micronucleus: ciliates (*Paramecium, Vorticella, Stentor*).

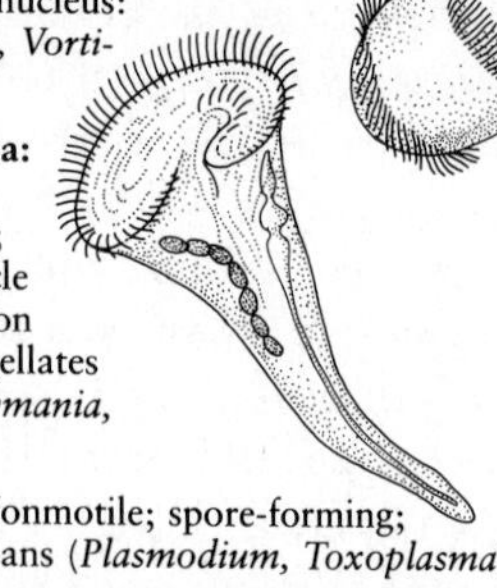

Phylum Zoomastigina: Move by means of one or more flagella; some parasitic; pellicle usually present; fission longitudinal: zooflagellates (*Trypanosoma, Leishmania, Giardia*).

Phylum Sporozoa: Nonmotile; spore-forming; all parasitic: sporozoans (*Plasmodium, Toxoplasma*).

Phylum Myxomycota: Slime molds with multinucleate amebalike feeding stage (plasmodium); reproductive stage forms sporangia, producing many spores; some spores may act as gametes: plasmodial slime molds (*Physarum*).

Phylum Chytridiomycota: Primarily unicellular organisms whose gametes and zoospores have a single, posterior flagellum; mostly aquatic; parasitic and saprophytic forms; chytrids.

Phylum Acrasiomycota: Slime molds with a one-celled amebalike feeding stage (myxameba) with a single nucleus; forms a mass of discrete cells (pseudoplasmodium) that form fruiting structures producing spores: cellular slime molds (*Dictyostelium*).

Phylum Oomycota: Branched filaments with many nuclei; mostly aquatic; reproduce asexually by means of motile zoospores; also reproduce sexually: water molds (*Saprolegnia*).

Phylum Chlorophyta: Cells containing chlorophyll a and b and other pigments localized in plastids; food stored as starch; unicellular, colonial, and filamentous forms; motile, free-floating, and sessile: green algae (*Spyrogyra, Oedogonium, Ulva, Chlamydomonas, Volvox, Chlorella,* desmids).

Phylum Phaeophyta: Cells containing chlorophyll a and c usually masked by fucoxanthine; food stored as oil and complex carbohydrates; multicellular; nonmotile; plant body usually large, complex, and sessile; mostly marine; motile

834

zoospores and gametes: brown algae (*Fucus, Sargassum, Laminaria, Postelsia*).

Phylum Rhodophyta: Cells containing chlorophyll a and d usually masked by phycobilins; some unicellular, most filamentous; carbohydrates stored as a type of starch; cell walls with cellulose and polysaccharides outside of walls; some epiphytic or parasitic; no motile cells in life cycle; some with stiff thalli (coralline algae): red algae.

Phylum Chrysophyta: Cells containing chlorophyll a and c and other pigments localized in plastids; cells often yellow-green, golden-brown, or brown; food stored as oil and complex carbohydrates; cell walls often with silicon; unicellular, colonial, and filamentous; motile and free-floating: golden-brown algae: diatoms.

Phylum Pyrrophyta: Cells containing chlorophyll a and c and other pigments localized in plastids; cells often yellow-green or golden-brown; food stored as starch or oil; unicellular flagellates with two flagella, one lateral and one longitudinal; mostly marine organisms: dinoflagellates (*Noctiluca, Gonyaulax*).

Phylum Euglenophyta: Unicellular autotrophic or secondarily heterotrophic organisms with chlorophyll a and b in chloroplasts; motile by means of a single flagellum; water content controlled with contractile vacuole; no cell wall; mostly freshwater; asexual reproduction by fission.

Kingdom Fungi

Eukaryotic heterotrophs with nutrition by absorption; most with a continuous filamentous body with many nuclei; cross walls may form at some time in the life cycle; some unicellular forms; cell walls made of chitin; reproduction asexual (by means of spore production, budding, or fragmentation) or sexual.

Division Zygomycota: Terrestrial saprophytes; hyphae lack cross walls: bread molds (*Rhizopus, Pilobolus*).

Division Ascomycota: Terrestrial, marine, and freshwater species; hyphae with perforated cross walls; sexual reproduction by formation of haploid ascospores in an ascus; asexual reproduction by means of conidia or budding; one unicellular form, the yeasts; red bread mold, wilt fungi, powdery mildews, ergot, morels, truffles, yeasts.

Division Basidiomycota: Mycelium with cross walls; sexual reproduction by means of basidiospores borne on basidia following meiosis: mushrooms, bracket fungi, rusts, smuts.

Division Deuteromycota: Fungi Imperfecti (fungi whose sexual phase is not known); asexual reproduction by means of conidia: *Aspergillus,* some *Penicillium,* athlete's foot fungus.

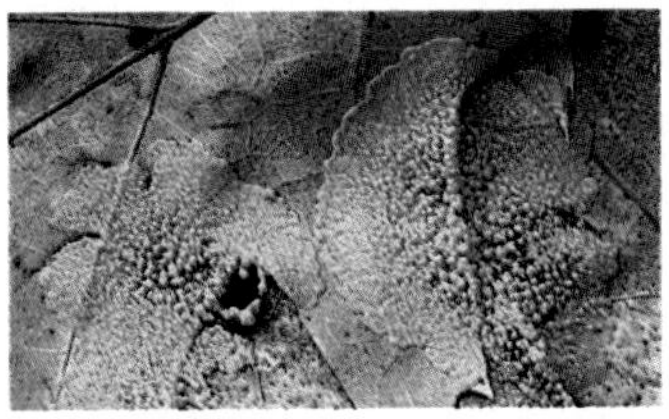

Kingdom Plantae

Multicellular, eukaryotic, autotrophic organisms having tissues and organs, cell walls containing cellulose; chlorophyll a and b present and localized in plastids; food stored as starch; sex organs multicellular.

Division Bryophyta: Multicellular green plants living on land, usually in moist situations; vascular tissues lacking; alternation of generations with the gametophyte the dominant generation; motile sperm.

Class Hepaticae: Gametophyte leafy or thalloid, usually prostrate: liverworts (*Marchantia*).

Class Anthocerotae: Gametophyte thalloid, sporophyte elongated and cylindrical: hornworts (*Anthoceros*).

Class Musci: Gametophyte usually an erect leafy shoot, sporophyte inconspicuous and parasitic on the gametophyte: mosses (*Polytrichium, Sphagnum*).

Division Psilophyta: Vascular seedless fern allies; no roots or leaves; produce sporangia on the ends of short branches; tropical and subtropical: whisk ferns of the genus *Psilotum.*

Division Lycophyta: Vascular plants; sporophyte dominant; trailing or erect with simple leaves; spores produced in a strobilus; gametophyte underground: club mosses (*Lycopodium, Selaginella, Isoetes*).

Division Sphenophyta: Vascular plants; sporophyte dominant; stems containing silica, hollow and jointed; leaves tiny scales, in whorls at stem joints; fertile stems with strobili: horsetails (*Equisetum*).

835

Division Pterophyta: Vascular plants; sporophyte generation dominant with leafy fronds; creeping rhizome; gametophyte a free-living prothallus; motile sperm: ferns and tree ferns.

Division Cycadophyta: Palmlike plants; male and female cones on different trees; seeds naked: cycads, sago palms.

Division Ginkgophyta: Pollen in conelike structure; seeds naked; one living species: *Ginkgo biloba.*

Division Gnetophyta: Specialized gymnosperms; seeds naked; desert species with xylem like that in angiosperms; few species: *Welwitschia, Ephedra, Gnetum.*

Division Coniferophyta: Gymnosperms with sex organs in cones; leaves as needles or scales; most evergreen; seeds naked: pines, spruces, firs, larches, yews.

Division Anthophyta: Flowering plants; sex organs in whorls in flowers; seeds enclosed in ovary that ripens into a fruit.

Class Monocotyledoneae: Embryo has one cotyledon; flower parts in threes; leaf veins parallel; vascular bundles scattered through stem tissue; grasses, sedges, lilies, irises, palms, grasses.

Class Dicotyledoneae: Embryo has two cotyledons; flower parts in fours or fives; leaves with netlike veins; vascular bundles in orderly arrangement in stems: roses, maples, elms.

Kingdom Animalia

Multicellular, eukaryotic, heterotrophic organisms; nutrition mainly by ingestion; specialized tissues and many have complex organ systems; no cell walls; reproduction mostly by sexual means; tissues often considerably reorganized during embryonic development.

Phylum Porifera: Body wall consists of two cell layers, penetrated by numerous pores; "skeleton" formed by siliceous or calcareous spicules or horny spongin; sessile marine and freshwater animals: sponges.

Class Calcarea: Simple sponges of shallow waters; calcareous spicules: *Grantia.*

Class Hexactinella: Deep-water sponges; siliceous spicules: Venus's flower basket.

Class Demospongiae: Large sponges; spongin or a combination of spongin and siliceous material; freshwater and marine: bath sponge, finger sponge.

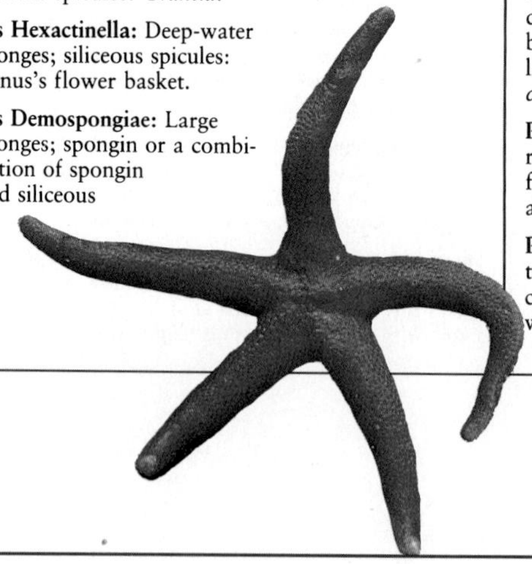

Class Sclerospongiae: Spongin and siliceous and calcareous spicules.

Phylum Cnidaria (also called Coelenterata): Usually free-swimming; baglike body of two cell layers with a noncellular substance between them; gastrovascular cavity with one opening leading to the outside; many with tentacles and all with stinging capsules; solitary or colonial forms; marine and freshwater: hydroids, jellyfish, corals.

Class Hydrozoa: Solitary or colonial; freshwater and marine; reproduction by asexual buds and gametes; alternation of generations in many: *Hydra, Physalia.*

Class Scyphozoa: Exclusively marine; most have mesentaries; polyp stage usually absent: jellyfish.

Class Anthozoa: Marine forms; solitary or colonial; numerous tentacles: sea anemones, corals, sea fans.

Phylum Ctenophora: Marine forms resembling jellyfish; hermaphroditic; definite digestive system with anal pore; biradially symmetrical: comb jellies.

Phylum Platyhelminthes: Body flat and ribbonlike, without true segments; acoelomates; no skeletal, circulatory, or respiratory systems; head provided with sense organs; nervous system composed of two longitudinal nerve cords: flatworms.

Class Turbellaria: Mostly free-living aquatic or terrestrial forms; many with cilia on the epidermis: planarians.

Class Trematoda: Parasitic forms with mouth at anterior end; intestine present; no cilia on adults: human blood flukes (*Schistosoma*), sheep liver fluke.

Class Cestoda: Parasitic forms; body a series of proglottids; intestine lacking; hooked scolex: tapeworms.

Phylum Rotifera: Crown of cilia on anterior end; pseudocoelomates; chitinlike jaws and well-developed digestive system; body usually cylindrical: rotifers.

Phylum Nematoda: Body slender and elongated; pseudocoelomates; unsegmented body wall in three layers; body cavity present; bilaterally symmetrical; free-living and parasitic forms: roundworms (*Ascaris, Trichinella*, pinworm, hookworm, vinegar eel).

Phylum Nematomorpha: Body slender and elongated, resembling a hair; larvae parasitic in insects, adults free-living in fresh water; mouth often lacking in adults: horsehair worms.

Phylum Acanthocephala: Body elongated, digestive tract lacking; anterior proboscis armed with many recurved hooks; parasitic in vertebrates: spiny-headed worms.

836

Phylum Bryozoa: Microscopic organisms forming branching colonies; row of ciliated tentacles at anterior end; usually marine: bryozoans (sea mosses).

Phylum Brachiopoda: Body enclosed in dorsal and ventral shells; two spirally coiled arms within shell bearing a row of ciliated tentacles; simple circulatory system; marine; mostly fossil forms: brachiopods.

Phylum Mollusca: Coelomates; undergo spiral cleavage in early stages of development; body in three parts; all organ systems present; mantle, secreting a shell in many genera; rasplike radula; trochophore and veliger larvae; terrestrial, freshwater, marine: clams, snails, octopuses.

Class Gastropoda: Stomach-footed, with or without single coiled shell; head, distinct eyes, and tentacles present: snail, slug, whelk.

Class Bivalvia (also called Pelecypoda): Hatchet-footed with bivalve shell; gills in mantle cavity; head, eyes, and tentacles lacking: clam, oyster, scallop.

Class Cephalopoda: Head-footed; foot modified into grasping tentacles; marine animals: squid, octopus, chambered nautilus.

Class Polyplacophora: Elongated body and reduced head, without tentacles; many forms with a shell composed of eight plates: chiton.

Class Scaphopoda: Body elongated and enclosed in a tubular shell, open at both ends; gills lacking; marine: tooth shells.

Phylum Annelida: Segmented coelomate worms; all organ systems present; bristles or setae on most; spiral cleavage in early development stages: segmented worms.

Class Polychaeta: Fleshy outgrowths, or parapodia, extending from segments; marine; many bristles: sandworm.

Class Oligochaeta: Head not well developed; few bristles; terrestrial and freshwater forms: earthworm, *Tubifex.*

Class Hirudinea: Body flattened from top to bottom; no bristles on body; suckers at both ends; mostly freshwater forms, but may occur as terrestrial or marine organisms: leeches.

Phylum Arthropoda: Segmented bodies, the segments bearing jointed appendages; all organ systems, including ventral nervous system and open circulatory system; chitinous exoskeleton; aerial, terrestrial, and aquatic forms: arthropods.

Subphylum Chelicerata: Distinguished by absence of antennae and presence of chelicerae; nearly all are land-dwellers.

Class Arachnida: Head and thorax usually fused into a cephalothorax; antennae lacking; four pairs of legs; book lungs and trachea for respiration: spiders, scorpions, ticks, mites.

Subphylum Crustacea: Antennae, mandibles, and branched appendages.

Class Crustacea: Head and thorax joined in a cephalothorax; usually five pairs of legs; two pairs of antennae; mostly aquatic; gills for respiration; many with calcareous deposits in exoskeleton: crayfish, lobster, crab, shrimp, water flea, sowbug, barnacle.

Subphylum Uniramia: Antennae, mandibles, and unbranched appendages.

Class Chilopoda: Body flattened and consisting of 15 to 170 or more segments; one pair of legs attached to each segment; maxillipeds developed into poison claws: centipedes.

Class Diplopoda: Body more or less cylindrical and composed of 25 to 100 or more segments; most segments bearing two pairs of legs: millipedes.

Class Insecta: Head, thorax, and abdomen separate; three pairs of legs; one pair of antennae; usually two pairs of wings; trachea for respiration: insects.

Order Thysanura: Silverfishes.

Order Ephemeroptera: Mayflies.

Order Odonata: Dragonflies, damsel flies.

Order Orthoptera: Grasshoppers, cockroaches, walking stick, mantis, crickets.

Order Isoptera: Termites.

Order Dermaptera: Earwigs.

Order Mallophaga: Chicken lice.

Order Anoplura: Human body louse.

Order Hemiptera: True bugs, water bug, water strider, water boatman, back swimmer, bedbug, squash bug, stinkbug.

Order Homoptera: Cicada, aphids, leaf hopper, tree hopper, scale insects.

Order Neuroptera: Dobson fly (hellgrammite), aphis lion, lacewing.

837

Order Coleoptera: Beetles, ladybugs, firefly, boll weevil.

Order Lepidoptera: Butterflies, moths, skippers.

Order Diptera: Housefly, bot fly, blowfly, midge, mosquitoes, crane fly, gall gnat.

Order Siphonaptera: Fleas.

Order Hymenoptera: Bees, ants, wasps, hornets, ichneumon fly.

Phylum Echinodermata: Pentaradially symmetrical; adults covered with spiny or calcareous plates; most forms with tube feet for locomotion; radial cleavage in early development; digestive tract and nervous system; endoskeleton; marine: echinoderms.

Class Crinoidea: Five branched rays and pinnules; tube feet without suckers; most forms with stalk; many fossil forms: sea lily, feather star.

Class Asteroidea: Body usually with five rays and double rows of tube feet in each ray; eyespots: starfish.

Class Ophiuroidea: Usually with five slender arms or rays: brittle stars, basket stars.

Class Echinoidea: Body spherical, oval, or disk-shaped; rays lacking; tube feet with suckers: sea urchin, sand dollar.

Class Holothuroidea: Elongated, thickened body with tentacles around the mouth; no rays or spines: sea cucumber.

Phylum Hemichordata: Wormlike chordates; body in three regions with a proboscis, collar, and trunk: acorn worm (tongue worm).

Phylum Chordata: Notochord present at some time, disappearing early in many forms and replaced by vertebral column; paired gill slits temporary or permanent; dorsal nerve cord.
Subphylum Urochordata: Saclike covering or tunic in adult; marine; free-swimming or attached: sea squirts and other tunicates.
Subphylum Cephalochordata: Fishlike with a permanent notochord: lancelet (*Branchiostoma*).
Subphylum Vertebrata: Chordates in which most of the notochord is replaced by a spinal column composed of vertebrae and encasing the dorsal nerve cord: vertebrates.

Class Ostracodermi: Extinct; jawless primitive vertebrates; marine; protective scales: ostracoderms.

Class Agnatha: Freshwater or marine eellike forms without true jaws, scales, or paired fins; cartilaginous skeleton: lamprey, hagfish.

Class Chondrichthyes: Fishes with true jaws and paired fins; gills present but not free and opening through gill slits; no air bladder; cartilaginous skeleton: sharks, rays, skates.

Class Osteichthyes: Freshwater and marine fishes with gills free and attached to gill arch; one gill opening on each side of body; true jaws and paired fins; bony skeleton: bony fishes.

Class Amphibia: Freshwater or terrestrial forms; gills present at some stage; skin slimy and lacking protective outgrowths; limbs without claws; three-chambered heart in adults; numerous eggs, usually laid in water and externally fertilized; metamorphosis: amphibians.

Order Apoda: Wormlike; tail short or lacking; no limbs or limb girdles: caecilians.

Order Urodela: Body elongated and with a tail throughout life; most forms with two pairs of limbs: salamanders, newts.

Order Anura: Body short; tailless in adult stage; two pairs of limbs, the hind limbs adapted for leaping; gills in larval stage, lungs in adult stage: frogs, toads, tree frogs.

Order Trachystoma: Aquatic, eellike, tiny forelimbs and no hindlimbs; three species: sirens, mud eels.

Class Reptilia: Terrestrial or semiaquatic vertebrates; breathing by lungs at all stages; body covered by scales or plates; toes with claws, amniote eggs provided with a leathery, protective shell; fertilization internal: reptiles.

Order Rhynchocephalia: Tuatara (*Sphenodon*).

Order Chelonia: Turtles and tortoises.

Order Crocodilia: Alligators, crocodiles, gavials, caimans.

Order Squamata: Lizards and snakes.

Class Aves: Body covered with feathers; forelimbs modified into wings; four-chambered heart; warm-blooded; amniote egg: birds.

Order Gaviiformes: Loons: common loon.

838

Order Pelecaniformes: Tropical birds: white pelican, brown pelican, cormorants.

Order Ciconiiformes: Long-legged wading birds: herons, bitterns, ibises, spoonbill.

Order Anseriformes: Short-legged gooselike birds: ducks, geese, swans.

Order Falconiformes: Large birds of prey: hawks, falcons, eagles, kites, vultures, buzzards.

Order Galliformes: Fowllike birds: pheasant, turkey, quails, partridges, grouse, ptarmigans.

Order Gruiformes: Cranelike birds: cranes, coots, gallinules, rails, limpkin.

Order Charadriiformes: Shore birds: snipes, sandpipers, plovers, gulls, terns, auks, puffins.

Order Columbiformes: Pigeons and doves: mourning dove, white-winged dove.

Order Psittaciformes: Parrots and parrotlike birds: parrots, parakeets, macaws.

Order Cuculiformes: Cuckoos: cuckoo, roadrunner.

Order Strigiformes: Nocturnal birds of prey: owls.

Order Caprimulgiformes: Goatsuckers: whippoorwill, chuck-will's widow, nighthawk.

Order Apodiformes: Swifts: chimney swift, hummingbirds.

Order Coraciiformes: Fishing birds: kingfishers.

Order Piciformes: Woodpeckers: woodpeckers, sapsuckers, flickers.

Order Passeriformes: Perching birds: robin, bluebird, sparrows, warblers, thrushes.

Class Mammalia: Hair on at least part of body; young nourished with milk secreted by mammary glands; warm-blooded; four-chambered heart; lung breathing; many with highly developed cerebrum and cerebellum.

Order Monotremata: Egg-laying mammals: duckbilled platypus, spiny anteater.

Order Marsupialia: Pouched mammals: opossum, kangaroo, koala.

Order Insectivora: Insect-eating mammals: moles, shrews.

Order Chiroptera: Flying or hand-winged mammals: bats.

Order Edentata: Mammals that are toothless or have peglike teeth: armadillo, sloth, great anteater.

Order Pholidota: Anteaterlike mammals that have scalelike skin: pangolins.

Order Rodentia: Gnawing mammals: squirrels, woodchucks, mice, rats, muskrats.

Order Lagomorpha: Harelike mammals: rabbits, hares, pika.

Order Cetacea: Marine mammals: whales, porpoises, dolphins.

Order Sirenia: Aquatic mammals: sea cow.

Order Proboscidea: Trunk-nosed mammals: elephant, fossil mammoth, fossil mastodon.

Order Carnivora: Flesh-eating mammals: bears, weasels, mink, otters, skunks, lions.

Order Pinnipedia: Flesh-eating marine mammals: seals, sea lions, walruses.

Order Perissodactyla: Odd-toed hoofed mammals: tapir, rhinoceroses, horses.

Order Artiodactyla: Even-toed hoofed mammals: hippopotamuses, camels, llamas, deer, giraffes, cattle, sheep, goats.

Order Primates: Erect mammals: monkeys, lemurs, gibbon, orangutan, gorilla, human.

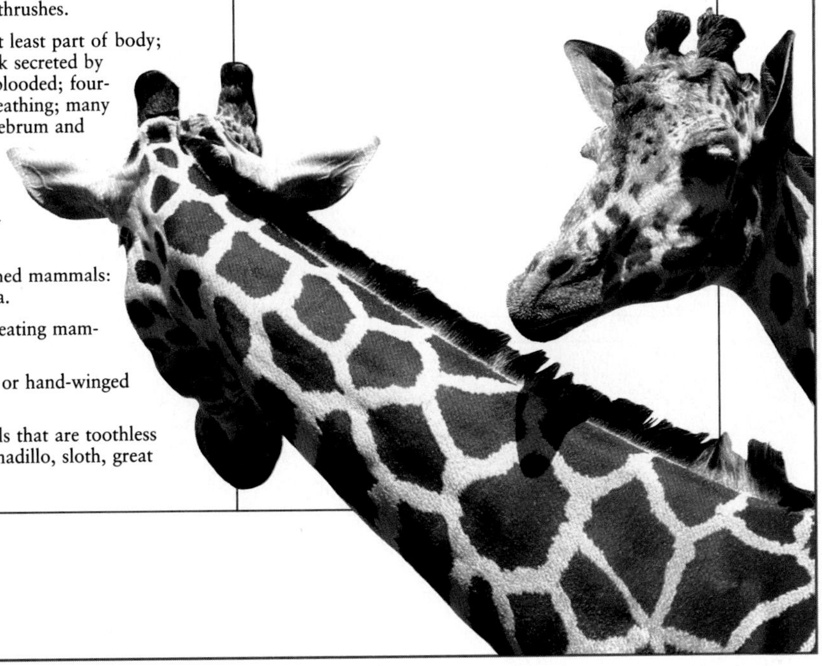

Measurement

All measurements in this book are expressed in metric units. Scientists throughout the world use the metric system, and you will always use metric units when you make measurements in the laboratory. The official name of the measurement system is the Système International d'Unités, or International System of Measurements. It is usually referred to simply as SI.

The metric system is a decimal system—that is, all relationships between units of measurement are based on powers of 10. Most units have a prefix that indicates the relationship of that unit to the base unit. For example, a meter equals 100 centimeters or 1,000 millimeters. The lists below show the most commonly used prefixes as well as the main units used for each type of measurement.

Metric Prefixes

Prefix	Symbol	Factor of Base Unit
giga	G	1,000,000,000
mega	M	1,000,000
kilo	k	1,000
hecto	h	100
deka	da	10
deci	d	0.1
centi	c	0.01
milli	m	0.001
micro	μ	0.000001
nano	n	0.000000001

Temperature

In the metric system temperature is measured on the Celsius (C) scale. On the Celsius scale, 0° is the freezing point of water, and 100° is the boiling point of water. Thus 1° C equals 0.01 of the difference between the freezing point and boiling point of water. You can use the scale shown to convert between the Celsius scale and the Fahrenheit scale, which is used in the United States.

Area

square kilometer (km^2)	= 100 hectares
1 hectare (ha)	= 10,000 square meters
1 square meter (m^2)	= 10,000 square centimeters
1 square centimeter (cm^2)	= 100 square millimeters

Mass

1 kilogram (kg)	= 1,000 grams
1 gram (g)	= derived from kg (base unit of mass)
1 milligram (mg)	= 0.001 gram
1 microgram (μg)	= 0.000001 gram

Liquid Volume

1 kiloliter (kL)	= 1,000 liters
1 liter (L)	= base unit of liquid volume
1 milliliter (mL)	= 0.001 liter

Note: When measuring liquid volume in a graduated cylinder, be sure to read the measurement at the bottom of the meniscus, or curve.

Length

1 kilometer (km)	= 1,000 meters
1 meter (m)	= base unit of length
1 centimeter (cm)	= 0.01 meter
1 millimeter (mm)	= 0.001 meter
1 micrometer (μm)	= 0.000001 meter
1 nanometer (nm)	= 0.000000001 meter

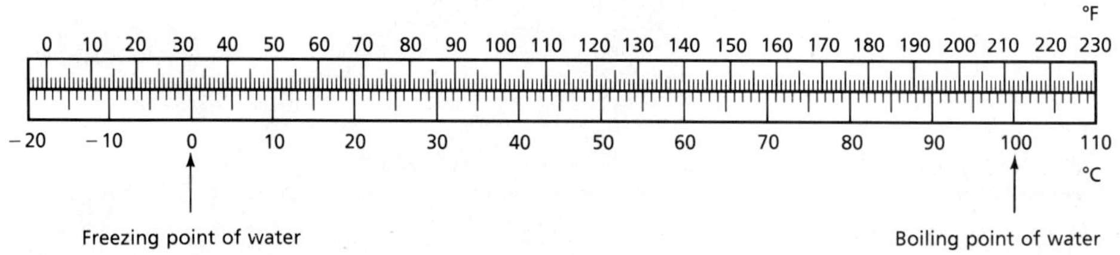

840

Safety

You will avoid accidents in the biology laboratory by following directions, handling materials carefully, and taking your work seriously. Before you begin working, be sure that you are familiar with safety procedures and know the location of fire-fighting equipment and first aid supplies. Be aware of your classmates' safety as well as your own. Never attempt any laboratory procedure without an instructor's direction, and never work in the laboratory by yourself.

Read the text that follows to familiarize yourself with the safety symbols used in your text and the guidelines that you should follow when you see these symbols.

Electrical Safety

Watch for loose plugs or worn electric cords. Be sure that cords are not placed where they could cause a fall. Do not use electrical equipment near water or with wet hands.

Chemical Safety

Use poisonous chemicals with extreme caution. Two harmless chemicals may become poisonous when combined. Never mix chemicals without teacher direction. Never put chemicals in your mouth and avoid chemical contact with eyes or skin.

Caustic Substances

Use extreme care when handling caustic substances such as hydrochloric acid. These substances can injure the skin. If your skin comes in contact with a caustic substance, flush thoroughly with water and notify your teacher immediately.

Water Safety

When working near water, always work with a partner or adult. Always wear a life jacket. Do not work near water during stormy weather.

Eye Safety

Wear approved safety goggles when working near an open flame or handling chemicals. If any chemical gets into your eyes, flush it out thoroughly with water and notify your instructor immediately.

Fire Safety

Keep combustible materials away from sources of fire. Shield any open flame with asbestos-protected screen.

Clothing Protection

Wear a laboratory apron in the classroom. Confine loose clothing.

Glassware Safety

Handle glassware carefully. Never attempt to clean up broken glass. Notify your teacher immediately.

Hand Safety

Dissect specimens in dissecting pans—never in your hand. Never use chipped or cracked glassware. Wear gloves when working with an open flame or with caustic chemicals.

Hygienic Care

Always wash your hands after the lab. Keep hands away from your face and mouth. Use sterile technique when transferring bacteria or other microorganisms between cultures or to a microscope slide. Do not open a petri dish to observe or count bacterial colonies.

Animal Safety

Wear leather or thick gloves when handling laboratory animals, especially rodents. When working in the field, be aware of poisonous or dangerous animals in the area. Do not touch or approach wild animals.

Explosion Danger

Many chemicals are explosive when combined, and some will explode when jarred, heated, or exposed to air. When heating chemicals, always point the test tube away from people.

Proper Waste Disposal

Clean up the laboratory after you finish. Follow your teacher's directions for waste disposal, especially for chemicals and microbes. Place broken glass in a special container.

Heating Safety

Use proper procedures when lighting Bunsen burners. Heat flasks or beakers on a ring stand with a wire gauze between glass and flame. Use only heat-resistant glassware for heating materials or storing hot liquids. Turn off hot plates and open flames when not in use.

Gas Precaution

Do not inhale fumes directly. When instructed to smell a substance, wave fumes toward your nose and inhale gently. Use flammable liquids only in small amounts and in a well-ventilated room or under a fume hood. Always use a fume hood with toxic or flammable fumes. Do not breathe the pure gases such as hydrogen, argan, helium, nitrogen, or high concentrations of carbon dioxide.

Plant Safety

Some plants cause ill effects when touched or eaten. Use a good field guide when collecting specimens; never eat any part of an unknown plant.

Animal Care

You are both legally and ethically required to treat all animals in as humane a way as possible.

841

Careers

The following career listing provides the names and addresses of organizations that can supply information on a broad range of careers in biology. The listing presents possible careers in areas related both to the contents of the units and to the subjects discussed in the Intra-Science features. Keep in mind that almost any interest or talent can be developed and used in a career in the biological sciences.

Research and Communication

Science Writer and Editor
National Association of Science Writers and Editors
P.O. Box 294
Greenlawn, NY 11740

Biomedical Researcher
Federation of American Societies for Experimental Biology
9650 Rockville Pike
Bethesda, MD 20814

Biophysicist
Biophysical Society
9650 Rockville Pike
Bethesda, MD 20814

Exobiologist
Planetary Biology Branch
Code SSX
NASA Ames Research Center
Moffett Field, CA 94035

Scientific Illustrator
Association of Medical Illustrators
2692 Hugeunot Springs Road
Midlothian, VA 23113

Cell Biology

Cellular Physiologist
American Physiological Society
9650 Rockville Pike
Bethesda, MD 20814

Photobiologist
American Society for Photobiology
8000 Westpark Drive
Suite 400
Lean, VA 22101

Genetics

Medical Geneticist
Genetics Society of America
9650 Rockville Pike
Bethesda, MD 20814

Agrigeneticist, Crop Breeder, Cell Biologist, Plant Physiologist, Turf Scientist, Soil Physics, Soil Chemist, Soil Microbiologist and Chemist, Fertilizer Technologist
American Society of Agronomy
677 South Segoe Road
Madison, WI 53711

Diagnostic Medical Sonographer
Society of Diagnostic Medical Sonographers
12225 Greenville Avenue
Suite 434
Dallas, TX 75243

Evolutionary Biology

Botanist
Dr. Robert H. Essman
Publications Manager
Botanical Society of America
Department of Genetics
Ohio State University
1735 Neil Avenue
Columbus, OH 43210

Physical Anthropology
American Association of Physical Anthropologists
Department of Anthropology
State University of New York at Buffalo
365 MFAC
Buffalo, NY 14261

Microbiology

Virologist
American Society for Microbiology
1325 Massachusetts Ave., N.W.
Washington, DC 20005

Nurse Epidemiologist

Director
Epidemiology Program Office, MS CO8
Center for Disease Control
Atlanta, GA 30333

Agriculture

Farm Manager
American Society of Farm Managers and Rural Appraisers
950 S. Cherry Street
Suite 106
Denver, CO 80222

Seed Analyst
Association of Official Seed Analysts
Illinois Department of Agriculture
Seed Lab, c/o Jom Lair
801 Sangamon Avenue
Springfield, IL 62794-9281

American Phytopathological Society
3340 Pilot Knob Road
St. Paul, MN 55121

Invertebrate Zoology

Parasitologist
American Society of Parasitologists
1041 New Hampshire Street
Lawrence, KS 66044

Marine Biologist
American Society of Limnology and Oceanography
Virginia Institute of Marine Science
The College of William and Mary
Gloucester Point, VA 48109

Entomological Inspector
Entomological Society of America
9301 Annapolis Road
Lanham, MD 20706

Vertebrate Zoology

Zoology Professor
American Society of Zoologists
Box 2739
California Lutheran University
Thousand Oaks, CA 91360

Wildlife Manager
U.S. Department of Interior
Fish and Wildlife Service
Division of Personnel Management
Mail Stop 100 Arlington Square
Washington, D.C. 20240

Health and Medical

Biomedical Engineer
Biomedical Engineering Society
P.O. Box 2399
Culver City, CA 90231

Fitness Instructor/Physical Education Teacher
VGM Career Horizons
4255 W. Touhy Avenue
Lincolnwood, IL 60646

Pharmacologist
American Society for Pharmacology and Experimental Therapeutics
9650 Rockville Pike
Bethesda, MD 20814

Environmental Protection

Sanitation Inspector
National Sanitation Foundation
P.O. Box 1468
3475 Plymouth Road
Ann Arbor, MI 48105

Public Health Microbiologist
American Society for Microbiology
1325 Massachusetts Ave., N.W.
Washington, DC 20005

842

Glossary

The phonetic respellings throughout this text are based on the pronunciations given in *Webster's Ninth New Collegiate Dictionary* and *Webster's Third New International Dictionary*. Primary stress is indicated by capital letters; secondary stress, by small capitals. Vowels are respelled according to the following system:

Webster's Symbol	Respelling	Note
ā	ay	At end of syllable
	a-e	When consonant follows
a	a	
ar	ar	
ä	ah	At end of syllable
	ah	When consonant follows
är	ahr	
aù	ou	
ē	ee	
e	eh	At end of syllable
	e	When consonant follows
er	er	
a(ə)r	air	
ī	ie	At end of syllable
	i-e	When consonant follows
i	ih	At end of syllable
	i	When consonant follows
ir	ir	
ō	oe	At end of syllable
	o-e	When consonant follows
ȯ	aw	Except when *r* follows
ȯr	or	
ȯi	oi	
ü	oo	
ù	ooh	
yü	yoo	
ə	uh	At end of syllable
	u	When consonant follows
ər	ur	
ə (schwa)	uh	For indefinite sound at end of syllable
	’	When schwa is elided

A

abdomen a posterior segment of an animal that usually houses the organs of digestion and excretion (483)

abdominal cavity the posterior portion of the human ventral cavity (637)

abiotic factor any nonliving component of an ecosystem (765)

aboral surface the surface opposite the mouth on a sea star (515)

abscisic acid a hormone in plants that plays a role in regulation of both the growth of buds and the germination of seeds (424)

abscission zone the area at the base of a leaf petiole where the leaf breaks off from the stem (428)

absorption in excretion, the movement of wastes from the bloodstream to the excretory system (698)

acid rain precipitation with below-normal pH, often the result of industrial pollution and automobile exhaust (826)

acid solution a solution containing more hydronium ions than hydroxide ions; also called acid (40)

acoelomate an animal with no coelom, or body cavity (453)

acquired immune deficiency syndrome (AIDS) a group of diseases caused by a viral disruption in the immune system (680)

acquired immunity disease protection gained after birth (678)

actin one of the two protein filaments in a muscle cell that function in contraction (647)

actinomycotes members of a class of bacteria characterized as rod-shaped monerans that form branched filaments (291)

action potential a wave of depolarization that moves down through the neural membrane (715)

activation energy the amount of energy required for a chemical reaction to get started and to continue on its own (42)

active transport the movement of any substance across a cell membrane with the use of energy from ATP (84)

adaptation an inherited trait that increases an organism's chance of survival in a particular environment (6, 230)

adaptive radiation an evolutionary pattern in which many species evolve from a single ancestral species (231)

addiction a dependency on the presence of a drug (749)

adenine a nitrogen base that is a component of a nucleotide and ATP (113)

adenosine diphosphate (ADP) the molecule adenosine with two phosphate groups attached (94)

adenosine triphosphate (ATP) storage molecule for energy that is composed of the molecule adenosine with three phosphate groups attached (94)

adrenal gland an endocrine gland located on the top of a kidney (729)

aerobic respiration the breakdown of pyruvic acid with the use of oxygen (103)

afterbirth the remains of the placenta and the amnion, expelled from the mother's body following birth (744)

agroforestry the planting of trees and crops to maintain a forest, prevent erosion, and shield young crops (355)

AIDS-related complex (ARC) a group of diseases similar to but less virulent than those of AIDS (681)

air sac in birds, a section that stores air, functions in respiration, and reduces density (593)

albumen the proteinaceous portion of an egg; the egg white (594)

alcoholic fermentation the process by which pyruvic acid is converted to ethyl alcohol; the anaerobic action of yeast on the sugars found in fruits and grains (105, 751)

843

alcoholism the disease of addiction to ethanol (751)
algal bloom a population explosion of algae that colors the environment (327)
alimentary canal the digestive tract (560, 694)
allantois in amniote eggs, the membranous sac that contains many blood vessels; in humans, a membrane surrounding the embryo that becomes the umbilical cord (571, 742)
allele an alternative form of a gene (152)
allele frequency the percentage of an allele in a gene pool (240)
allergen a usually harmless antigen in the environment (678)
allergy a reaction to an allergen (678)
alternation of generations a sexual life cycle in plants and algae involving two or more phases (368)
altricial referring to birds that, when hatched, are immature and in need of parental care (596)
altruistic behavior the sacrifice of immediate gratification by one individual that results in a benefit for another individual (628)
alveolus one of the air sacs found in the lungs (667)
amebocyte an amebalike cell in a sponge that moves through the body cells, supplying nutrients and removing wastes (442)
ameboid movement movement by means of pseudopodia involving a cytoplasmic gel–sol conversion (311)
Ames test a procedure used to identify carcinogenic substances (164)
amino acid one of 20 monomers that form proteins (52)
ammonification the process in the nitrogen cycle in which ammonia compounds form (790)
amniocentesis a procedure used in fetal diagnosis in which cells are removed from the amniotic fluid (176)
amnion one of four membranes of an amniote egg (571, 742)
amniote egg the four-membrane egg of a terrestrial vertebrate (571)
amotivational syndrome a suppressed activity level caused by habitual use of marijuana (756)
amplexus the mating embrace of frogs (565)
ampulla a bulblike sac in an echinoderm that functions in movement (515)
anaerobic respiration the breakdown of pyruvic acid using oxygen as a reactant (104)
anal fin medial fin near the anus of a fish (547)
anal pore an opening where protozoan wastes are eliminated (313)
analyzing data the process of determining whether data are reliable (20)
anaphase a stage of mitosis and meiosis in which the chromosomes separate (133)
anatomy a branch of morphology that deals with the internal structure of organisms (8)
androgen a hormone secreted by the testes that controls secondary sex characteristics (730)
angiosperm a flowering plant (367)
annual rhythm a pattern of activity of organisms that occurs about once a year (801)
annual ring a yearly growth ring in a woody plant (389)
antenna an appendage of some invertebrates specialized for touch and taste (484)
antennule an antennalike appendage with receptors for touch, taste, and equilibrium (484)
anterior the front end of a bilaterally symmetrical organism (437)
anther the microsporangium of an angiosperm in which pollen grains are produced (406)
antheridium in plants and algae, a reproductive structure that produces flagellated sperm by mitosis (330, 401)
anthropoid a subgroup of primates including monkeys, apes, and humans (256)
antibiotic a chemical produced by microorganisms that is capable of inhibiting the growth of some bacteria (304, 678)
antibody a blood protein produced by B cells that destroys antigens (663)
anticodon a region of tRNA consisting of three bases complementary to the codon of mRNA (121)
antigen a substance that stimulates the production of antibodies (174, 663, 676)
antihistamine a drug that counteracts histamines (679)
anus the posterior opening of the alimentary canal (458)
aorta the largest artery in the body (499, 657)
aortic arch in invertebrates, a tube that links the dorsal and ventral blood vessels (473)
aphotic zone the ocean layer that receives no light (774)
apical meristem the growing region at the tips of stems and roots in plants (382)
apical dominance a plant growth pattern in which branches near the shoot tip are shorter than branches farther from the shoot tip (422)
appendage any complex part or organ extending from the body (479)
appendicular skeleton in vertebrates, the bones extending from the axial skeleton (539, 641)
applied genetics the science of manipulating heredity characteristics to improve or create specific traits in offspring (191)
aqueous solution a solution in which water is the solvent (38)
arachnoid layer the middle layer of the meninges (710)
archaebacterium a type of bacterium that has physiological adaptations to extreme environments (296)
archegonium in plants, a reproductive structure that produces a single egg by mitosis (402)
archosaurs a group of reptiles that gave rise to crocodiles, dinosaurs, and those reptiles that evolved into birds (573)
Aristotle's lantern a jawlike feeding mechanism in Echinoidea (514)
arteriole a small artery (657)
artery a vessel that carries blood from the heart (549, 657)
artificial propagation in plants, asexual reproduction manipulated by humans (416)
ascocarp the reproductive body of an ascomycete (339)
ascogonium an egg-producing structure in Ascomycetes (339)
ascospore one of eight haploid cells in an ascus (339)
ascus a sac that forms on the surface of an ascocarp (339)
asexual reproduction the production of offspring that does not involve the union of gametes (7, 138)
association neuron a cell that maintains neural connections within the spinal cord (711)
aster a centriole with its radiating fibers that is active during cell division (132)
atom the fundamental unit of matter (33)
atomic number the number of protons in an atom (34)
atrioventricular node a group of nerves in the heart that functions in establishing the heartbeat (657)
atrium the anterior chamber of the heart (549, 655)
auditory canal the tube through which air enters the ear (720)
auditory nerve the nerve along which impulses from the cochlea travel to the auditory region of the brain (720)
autoimmune disease a disorder in which the immune system produces antibodies against the organism's own cells (679)
autonomic nervous system a part of the peripheral nervous system that controls involuntary actions (712)
autosome a chromosome that is not a sex chromosome (165)

844

autotomy the ability of an organism to regenerate body parts (579)
autotroph an organism that uses energy, such as light, to synthesize organic molecules from inorganic substances (9, 93, 301)
auxin a plant hormone that regulates cell elongation (421)
avoidance behavior a reaction away from danger (313)
axial skeleton the backbone, skull, and associated bones of vertebrates (539, 641)
axon in a neuron, an elongated extension that carries impulses away from the cell body (713)

B

bacteriophage a virus that infects bacteria (288)
baleen the bony plates that function to filter food from water in some whales (610)
barb a branch of a vane in the feather of a bird (589)
barbule a branch of a barb in the feather of a bird (589)
bark the protective layer of cells produced by a cambium in woody plants (389)
basal metabolic rate the energy expended by the body when resting (668)
base solution a solution containing more hydroxide ions than hydronium ions (40)
basidiocarp the productive body of a basidiomycete (338)
basidiospore a cell resulting from meiosis that is found at the end of a basidium (338)
basidium a specialized club-shaped reproductive structure that forms on the gills of mushrooms (338)
Batesian mimicry a defensive adaptation in which a nonpoisonous organism has the appearance of a poisonous species (502)
B cell a lymphocyte that produces antibodies in response to antigens (676)
behavior a set of responses to a stimulus (11)
behavioral variations differences in responses among closely related organisms (493)
bell curve a graph in the shape of a bell that usually describes the normal range of a trait (240)
benign tumor an abnormal but nonthreatening cell mass (186)
benthic zone the ocean bottom (774)
bicuspid a tooth with two points used to shred food (604)
bilateral symmetry a type of symmetry in which the left and right sides mirror each other (437)
bile a yellowish fluid secreted by the liver that functions as an emulsifier (697)
binary fission an asexual, mitotic division of unicellular organisms that produces identical offspring (302)
binomial nomenclature a system of naming organisms that uses the genus name plus a specific epithet (267)
biochemical pathway a complex series of reactions that performs a specific function (94)
biodegradable referring to any pollutant that is subject to decay by organisms (825)
bioethics the application of ethics in biology (10)
biogenesis the theory that living organisms come only from other living organisms (207)
biogeochemical cycle the process by which materials necessary for organisms are circulated through the environment (788)
biological clock an internal timing mechanism that controls endogenous rhythms (800)
biological magnification the process by which hazardous wastes are concentrated as a result of feeding in a food chain (826)
biological species concept the idea that organisms can be classified by their ability to breed with one another (238)
biology the science of life (5)
bioluminescence the ability of an organism to produce light by means of a chemical reaction (327)
biomass the dry weight of an organism (787)
biome a geographic area characterized by specific kinds of plants and animals (767)
biosphere the area on and around the earth where life exists (765)
biosystematics a form of taxonomy that examines reproductive compatibility and gene flow (271)
biotic factor a living component of an ecosystem (765)
biotic potential the rate at which a population grows if all members survive and reproduce at maximum capacity (811)
biotic relationships the interactions among organisms (797)
bipedalism the ability to walk upright on two legs (256)
bipinnaria the larva of echinoderms (516)
blade the broad, flat portion of a typical leaf (324, 394)
blastocyst a mass of cells that will become the organs of a new human being (740)
blastopore a depression formed when cells of the blastula move inward (438)
blastula a hollow ball of cells formed when a zygote undergoes repeated cycles of cell division (184, 438)
blood alcohol concentration (BAC) a measurement of the amount of alcohol in a person's blood (751)
blood clot a structure caused by the entrapment of red blood cells in fibrin (663)
bloom a population explosion of a species (298)
blue-green bacterium a photosynthetic moneran classified into Phylum Cyanophyta (297)
bolting the rapid lengthening of internodes caused by gibberellic acid (424)
bolus a ball of thoroughly chewed and moistened food in the digestive tract (695)
bone marrow the soft tissue in the center and ends of long bones where blood cells are produced (641)
book lung a structure in the abdomen of an arachnid where gases are exchanged between air and the blood (487)
bouton the swollen tip of an axon terminal (716)
Bowman's capsule a cup-shaped structure of the nephron of a kidney that encloses the glomerulus and where absorption takes place (701)
brain the anterior end of the central nervous system; in vertebrates, the cerebrum, the cerebellum, and the brain stem (708)
brain stem the ventral region below the brain that connects the brain to the spinal cord (709)
bristle a hairlike structure (589)
bronchus one of the two branches of the trachea that enter the lungs (667)
bronchiole a small tube that branches from the bronchi within the lungs (667)
brood patch in birds, a patch of the parent's skin used to cover eggs (595)
bundle sheath the parenchyma cells around a vein in a leaf (395)
bursa a fluid-filled sac that aids lubrication in some joints (644)

C

C_4 pathway a carbon-fixing process in which carbon dioxide is bound to a compound to form a four-carbon (C_4) intermediate (102)
calorie the amount of heat required to raise the temperature of 1 g of water 1° C (687)

845

Calorie one kilocalorie; the unit used to measure the amount of energy a particular food provides (687)
CAM crassulacean acid metabolism, a process in which some plants store CO_2 at night as crassulacean acid and release CO_2 during the day for use in the Calvin cycle (102)
camouflage the characteristic of blending with the surroundings (502)
cancer the uncontrolled growth of cells (186)
canine a pointed tooth used to grip and tear (604)
cap the flattened, top portion of a mushroom (338)
capillarity the ability of a liquid to move upward against the force of gravity by molecular attraction to a surrounding surface (47)
capillary the smallest vessel in the blood vessel network (549, 657)
capsid the protein covering that encases a virus (283)
capsule in mosses, a sporangium that produces spores; in bacteria, a protective layer of slime around the cell wall (300, 369)
carageenan a substance found in the cell walls of red algae that is used commercially as a smoothing agent (325)
carapace the dorsal part of a turtle shell (577)
carbohydrate an organic compound composed of carbon, hydrogen, and oxygen in which the hydrogen-to-oxygen ratio is two to one (49, 687)
carbon fixation the formation of organic compounds from inorganic compounds through carbon-carbon bonding (98)
carcinogen a cancer-causing substance (186)
carcinoma a malignant tumor that grows in tissues (186)
cardiac muscle the involuntary muscle of the heart (646)
cardiac sphincter a circular muscle located between the esophagus and the stomach (696)
carnivore a consumer that eats other consumers (574, 783)
carpel the ovule-containing reproductive structure of flowering plants (406)
carrier a person heterozygous for a trait, the recessive gene of which causes a disease (171)
carrier molecule a protein that functions in transport of molecules across a membrane (84)
carrying capacity the maximum number of individuals of a species that an ecosystem is capable of supporting (813)
cartilage a strong, flexible connective tissue (642)
Casparian strip a narrow band of suberin belting each cell of the endodermis in a root (384)
cast a type of fossil formed when sediments fill in the cavity left by a decomposed organism (219)
caudal fin in fishes, a fin extending from the tail that moves from side to side and amplifies the swimming motions (547)
cecum a blind sac usually found in the digestive system (612)
cell a membrane-bound structure that is the basic unit of life (63)
cell culture a population of identical cells grown in the laboratory (27)
cell cycle the events of cell division; includes interphase, mitosis, and cytokinesis (131)
cell differentiation the change in morphology or physiology of a cell in relation to its neighboring cells (184)
cell division the formation of cells from a parent cell (12)
cell enlargement an increase in cell size (12)
cell-mediated response the immune response involving a T-cell attack on an antigen (677)
cell membrane the outer bilipid boundary of a cell (66)
cell plate a membrane that divides the daughter cells following mitosis of a plant cell (135)
cell theory the theory that all living things are made up of cells, that cells are the basic units of organisms, and that cells come only from existing cells (64)
cell wall an extracellular, strengthening component of a plant cell (72)
central nervous system the brain and the spinal cord (707)
centric diatom a member of Chrysophyta algae with circular valves (326)
centrifugation a technique used to separate cell parts by type by spinning fractionated cells at high speeds (28)
centriole a rod-shaped structure that appears during mitosis and is responsible for spindle formation and movement (132)
centromere the structure formed when chromatids join (129)
cephalization a concentration of nerve tissue and sensory organs at the anterior end of an organism (438)
cephalothorax a body part formed by the fusion of the head with the thorax (483)
cereal any species of the grass family whose grain is eaten (353)
cerebellum a posterior portion of the brain that controls movement and muscle coordination (550, 709)
cerebral cortex the folded outer layer of the cerebrum that controls motor and sensory activities (708)
cerebral hemisphere one of two halves of the cerebrum (708)
cerebrospinal fluid a watery substance that provides a cushion that protects the brain and spinal cord (711)
cerebrum the anterior portion of the brain where higher brain functions occur (550, 708)
chalaza the ropelike strands that support the albumen in a fertilized egg (594)
chelicera a pincerlike mouthpart of some arthropods (482)
cheliped in arthropods, a claw used to capture food and to provide defense (484)
chemical equation an equation showing the products and reactants of a chemical reaction (42)
chemical reaction the process of breaking chemical bonds, forming new bonds, or both (42)
chemiosmosis the diffusion of chemicals through a membrane down a chemical gradient (98)
chemoautotroph an organism that synthesizes inorganic compounds by using chemicals instead of sunlight (301)
chemotropism plant growth in response to a chemical (428)
chitin a carbohydrate that forms part of the arthropod exoskeleton (479)
chloroplast a plastid containing chlorophyll; the site of photosynthesis (74)
cholesterol a type of steroid; a lipid (689)
chorion the outer membrane surrounding an embryo (571, 741)
chorion villi sampling a procedure involving the analysis of the chorion villi to diagnose fetal genotypes (176)
chromatid one of two identical parts of a chromosome (129)
chromatin the DNA and proteins in the nucleus of a nondividing cell (72)
chromatography a method of separating components of a chemical based on their varying rates of movement up a piece of paper or down a column of beads (28)
chromatophore skin pigmentation that creates color patterns; a pigment cell that allows organisms to blend with their surroundings (470, 547)
chromoplast a type of plastid that synthesizes and stores pigments to trap sunlight for energy (74)
chromosome DNA in a coiled, rod-shaped form that occurs during cell division (72)
chromosome map a diagram of allele positions on a particular chromosome (167)
chronic bronchitis an inflammation of the bronchi and bronchioles (749)
chrysalis the outer covering of a butterfly pupa (501)

846

chyme the mixture formed in the stomach from digested food particles and gastric fluid (696)
cilia a structure made up of microtubules, extending out from a cell, and aiding movement (71, 312)
circadian rhythm a pattern of behavior that is about one day in length (800)
circulatory system the system that distributes oxygen and nutrients to cells in all parts of the body (655)
cirrhosis a condition in which normal tissues are replaced by scar tissue (752)
class in taxonomy, a group of similar orders (267)
classifying the grouping of objects, organisms, or phenomena into a new or established organizational scheme (19)
climax community a community of organisms that will remain stable in an area as long as the area is undisturbed (803)
clitellum a noticeable swelling around the sex organs of an earthworm during reproduction (474)
cloaca a cavity holding undigested wastes (561)
cloacal opening the site where waste materials and eggs leave the body (561)
clone an offspring produced by asexual production (415)
closed circulatory system a system in which blood is contained within vessels (470)
cnidarian a member of the Phylum Cnidaria (444)
cnidocyte the stinging cells of cnidarians (444)
coacervate a cell-like droplet formed from dissimilar substances (210)
cochlea a coiled tube in the inner ear filled with fluid and lined with hair cells (720)
cocoon the covering of an insect during its pupal stage; a chrysalis (501)
codominance the condition of two alleles of the same gene neither of which totally masks the other (157)
codon a group of three sequential nitrogen bases of an mRNA molecule (120)
coelenterate another name for members of the Phylum Cnidaria (444)
coelom a body cavity formed from the mesoderm (453)
coenocytic referring to filaments without internal cross walls (336)
coevolution the joint change of interacting species (232)
cohesion the bonding of water molecules to each other (48)
colchicine a chemical that prohibits the formation of the cell plate during plant cell division (193)
coleoptile in plants, a cylindrical sheath that protects the shoot during germination (411)
coleorhiza in plants, a sheath that protects the embryonic root (411)
collar cell a cell lining the inside of sponges that circulates water; also called a choanocyte (441)
collecting data the gathering and recording of specific information based on observations (18)
collenchyma plant tissue made up of elongated cells with unevenly thickened, flexible walls (381)
colloid a mixture in which particles do not settle out over time (39)
colon the large intestine (699)
colonial organism a group of unicellular organisms that live together in closely connected groups (76)
columella a bone that transmits sounds from the eardrum to the middle ear (559)
commensalism a form of symbiosis in which one organism benefits and the other neither benefits nor is harmed (799)
common name an everyday name given to an organism (267)
communicating the process of sharing information (22)
community all the populations in one area (765)
compact bone the layer of bone just beneath the periosteum that gives the bone its strength (541)
companion cell a specialized plant cell that helps control the movement of sugars through sieve tubes (381)
competition the use or defense of a resource by an organism that reduces availability of that resource to others (797)
competitive exclusion principle the extinction of all but one species when two or more species occupy the same niche (798)
complete digestive system a system in which food enters via the mouth and passes sequentially through the system to the anus (526)
compound two or more elements that are chemically joined (35)
compound eye an eye with many lenses (485)
compound leaf a type of leaf in which the blade is divided into leaflets (394)
concentration a measurement of the amount of solute dissolved in a fixed amount of solvent (38)
concentration gradient the difference in concentration of a substance across space (81)
condensation reaction a chemical reaction, also called dehydration synthesis, in which water is produced (48)
conductor a specialized nerve cell that transmits messages to the central nervous system (707)
cone a photoreceptor within the retina that can produce sharp images and distinguish colors (719)
conidiophore the specialized branch where conidia form (340)
conidium a spore produced during asexual reproduction in ascomycetes (340)
coniferous forest a biome dominated by evergreens (769)
conjugation a form of reproduction in which genetic information moves from a cell of one filament to a cell of an adjoining filament (302)
connective tissue the most common type of human body tissue, which supports and holds body structures together (638)
consumer a heterotroph that obtains energy from chemical bonds in nutrients it eats (783)
contour feather a feather that provides coloration, insulation, and a streamlined shape to adult birds (589)
contour plowing forming rows for farming perpendicular to a slope (822)
contractile vacuole an organelle in microorganisms that excretes water (83, 312)
controlled breeding the manipulation of heredity by selecting parents with specific phenotype traits (191)
controlled experiment a comparison of a control group or phase with an experimental group or phase (20)
conus arteriosus the vessel in front of a frog's heart (563)
convergent evolution the process by which unrelated species become more similar as they adapt to the same kind of environment (231)
cork a layer of bark that functions for protection (382)
cork cambium the lateral meristem of a plant; produces cork (382)
coronary artery a vessel supplying blood to the heart (660)
coronary circulation the systemic subsystem that supplies blood to the heart (660)
corpus callosum the structure formed by nerve fibers connecting the cerebral hemispheres of the brain (708)
corpus luteum the structure that forms from the ruptured follicle in the ovary at ovulation (738)
cortex in plants, a mature ground tissue located just inside the epidermis; in animals, the outermost portion of an organ (384, 700)

847

cotyledon a seed leaf (375)
cotylasaurs a group of ancestral reptiles resembling small lizards that lived about 300 million years ago (573)
courtship behavior used to attract a mate (597)
covalent bond a bond that forms when two atoms share one or more pairs of electrons (37)
coxal glands in some spiders, organs that remove wastes and discharge them at the base of the legs (487)
cranial capacity the size of the brain case (256)
cranial cavity the area in which the brain rests (637)
cranial nerves nerves between the major sense organs and the brain (550)
critical length the length of daylight above or below which plant species will flower (427)
critical period the period when imprinting may occur (627)
crop in earthworms, a structure that stores soil; in birds, a structure that stores food (472, 592)
crossing-over the exchange of genes by homologous chromosomes during meiosis (137)
cross-pollination a reproductive process in which pollen from one plant is transferred to the stigma of another plant (148, 408)
cutaneous respiration in frogs, the exchange of gasses through the skin (563)
cuticle in plants, a waxy covering that prevents desiccation; in parasites, a nonliving layer that protects them from the host's digestive and immune systems (365, 454)
cyst a dormant cell with a protective outer wall (312, 456)
cytokinesis the division of the cytoplasm of a parent cell into two daughter cells (131)
cytokinins plant hormones that promote cell division (423)
cytolysis the intake by a cell of so much water that it bursts (83)
cytoplasm the jellylike fluid of a cell interior (66)
cytoplasmic streaming the circular motion of the cytoplasm (67, 311)
cytosine a nitrogen base; a pyrimidine of DNA and RNA (113)
cytoskeleton the framework of a cell (70)

D

day-neutral plant a plant unaffected by the daylight length (427)
deciduous forest a biome characterized by trees that lose their leaves in the autumn (770)
decomposer an organism that uses nutrients from dead plants and animals (784)
deforestation the clearing of forested regions (359, 821)
dehydration the condition resulting from excessive water loss (693)
deletion a mutation in which a segment of DNA breaks off of a chromosome (163)
dendrite an extension of a neuron that receives impulses from other neurons and carries the impulses to the cell body (713)
denitrification a final step in the nitrogen cycle, during which nitrogen gas is returned into the atmosphere (790)
density-dependent factors variables related to the density of a population that affect population size (814)
density-independent factors variables that affect population size regardless of population density (814)
deoxyribonucleic acid (DNA) a double-helix-shaped nucleic acid (7, 54)
deoxyribose a five-carbon sugar molecule found in DNA (113)
dependent variable the responding variable in an experiment (20)
depressant a drug that decreases the activity of the central nervous system and slows many body functions (751)
dermal tissue system one type of plant tissue system, which forms the outer covering of plants (382)
dermis the layer of skin beneath the epidermis (649)
desert an area where rainfall averages less than 25 cm per year (772)
determinate cleavage a process in which each cell develops into a specific part of the gastrula (522)
deuterostome an organism in which the blastopore develops into the anus and the coelom arises by enterocoely and whose embryo has indeterminate cleavage and develops radially (521, 537)
development the process by which an organism grows (7)
diabetes mellitus a disorder of glucose metabolism caused by insufficient insulin (732)
diaphragm a thoracic cavity muscle used in breathing (604, 665)
diastole a phase in the heartbeat when the ventricles relax and the blood flows in from the atria (657)
diatomaceous earth a layer of material formed of the rigid shells of dead diatoms (326)
dichotomous key a written set of choices that leads to the name of an organism (269)
dicot an angiosperm with two cotyledons, net venation, and flower parts in fours or fives (375)
diffusion the process by which molecules move from an area of greater concentration to an area of lesser concentration (81)
digestion breaking down food into usable molecules (694)
digitalis a medicine used in the treatment of heart disease (356)
dihybrid cross a cross between individuals that involves the pairing of contrasting traits (157)
dipeptide a formation from two amino acids bonded together by means of a condensation reaction (53)
diploid a cell that contains both chromosomes of a homologous pair (130)
direct development a process by which a young animal is born in a smaller form of the adult (523)
directional selection a type of natural selection in which the distribution of a trait is shifted toward one of the extremes (245)
disaccharide a double sugar formed from two monosaccharides (50, 687)
disruptive selection natural selection in which individuals with an extreme form of a trait have an advantage (245)
diurnal referring to organisms that are awake and active mainly during the day (800)
divergent evolution the process of two or more related species becoming more and more dissimilar (231)
division a grouping of similar classes of plants (268)
division of labor specialization in form and function in a cell, colony, organism, or society (503)
domesticated adapted for human use (815)
dominant referring to an allele that masks the presence of another allele for the same characteristic (150)
dormancy a state of decreased metabolism (413)
dorsal the top of a bilaterally symmetrical animal (537)
dorsal cavity the cavity containing the organs of the nervous system (637)
dorsal fin the median dorsal fin or fins of a fish (547)
dorsal nerve cord a neural tube dorsal to the notochord (537)
double fertilization in plants, the process in which two types of cell fusion take place in the embryo sac (410)
double helix spiral-shape characteristic of the DNA molecule (114)
down feather soft, fluffy feathers that cover the body of nesting birds (589)

848

Down syndrome a disorder caused by an extra twenty-third chromosome (175)
drug any chemical taken into the body that alters the normal processes of either the mind or the body (749)
duodenum the first section of the small intestine (561, 697)
dura mater the outer layer of the meninges (710)

E

echolocation a method of navigation similar to sonar in which the sound produced bounces off an object (610)
ecology the study of the relationship between organisms and their environments (10, 765)
ecosystem all the biotic and abiotic components of an environment (765)
ectoderm one of the three germ layers of the gastrula (439)
ectoplasm the region in the cytoplasm located directly inside the cell membranes (311)
ectothermic cold blooded; referring to an animal whose body temperature is determined by the environment (573)
effector peripheral nerve cell that responds to messages from the central nervous system (707)
egg tooth scalelike tooth on a bird embryo used to crack the surrounding egg (595)
electron a particle with a negative electric charge that orbits the nucleus (33)
electron transport chain the passage of electrons from a high energy level to a lower energy level by electron carriers (98)
electrophoresis a procedure that separates large molecules by acting on differences in their size and electric charge (28, 284)
element a substance that ordinarily cannot be broken down chemically to form simpler kinds of matter (34)
embryo an organism in its early stages of development (438, 741)
embryo sac in plants, the megagametophyte containing seven cells and eight nuclei (407)
emphysema a degenerative lung disease (749)
endangered species those plants and animals that are currently at risk of extinction (821)
endocrine gland a ductless gland that secretes substances directly into the blood (728)
endocytosis the process by which a cell engulfs and surrounds large substances (87)
endoderm one of the three germ layers; found in the innermost layer of the gastrula (439)
endodermis in plants, a specialized layer of cells that regulates substances entering the center of the root (384)
endoplasm the region in the cytoplasm found in the interior of the cell (311)
endoplasmic reticulum a membrane system in the cytoplasm (68)
endoskeleton an internal skeleton; in humans, the 206 bones that are the body framework (511, 537, 640)
endosperm a tissue in angiosperms that provides food for the developing embryo (409)
endospore a dormant cell enclosed by a tough coating, often found in bacteria (300)
endosymbiosis the theory that prokaryotic intracellular parasites evolved into various cell organelles (214, 309)
endothermic warm blooded; referring to an animal that generates its own body heat (573)
endothermic reaction a chemical reaction that involves a net consumption of energy (42)
endotoxin a substance that causes a poison reaction; a lipopolysaccharide compound that makes up part of the cell wall of Gram-negative bacteria (303)
energy the ability to do work (41)
enhancer a region adjacent to a eukaryotic gene that must be activated if the gene is to be expressed (182)
enterocoely the method of mesoderm formation in deuterostomes in which the coelom forms in folded mesoderm (523)
entomologist a scientist who studies insects (494)
enzyme a protein that acts as a catalyst in intermediary metabolism (53, 688)
epicotyl in plant embryos, the region above the cotyledons (411)
epidermis in plants, the outer layer of cells; in animals, the outer layer of skin that encloses the body in a continuous sheet (382, 649)
epiglottis a flap of tissue that covers the trachea (695)
epiphyseal plate a band of cartilage located between the shaft and the end of a long bone (643)
epiphyte a plant that grows on other plants (799)
epithelial tissue tissue composed of cells that create a solid sheet that covers a body part (638)
equilibrium a state that exists when the concentration of a substance is the same throughout a space (81)
erosion the loss of soil that is caused by wind or water (822)
erythrocyte a red blood corpuscle (662)
esophagus the tube connecting the mouth and the pharynx to the stomach (472, 548, 695)
estivation an annual rhythm characterized by reduced activity during the summer (556, 801)
estuary an aquatic biome found where freshwater streams and rivers flow into the sea (775)
ethanol the type of alcohol found in beer, wine, and liquor (751)
ethics the study of what is morally good and bad (10)
ethologist a scientist who studies social behaviors (628)
ethylene C_2H_2; a gaseous hormone produced by various parts of plants and released into the air (424)
eubacterium a bacterium in the Class Eubacteria (297)
euchromatin the uncoiled form of chromatin (182)
eukaryote a cell that contains a nucleus and membrane-bound organelles (65)
Eustachian tube a canal that connects the middle ear to the mouth cavity (559, 720)
eutrophication the increase of nutrients in an environment (806)
eutrophic lake a lake or pond rich in organic matter (776, 806)
evisceration the ejection of internal organs (514)
evolution the theory that species change over time (6, 219)
excretion the process of removing metabolic wastes (700)
excurrent siphon a hollow tube through which water exits the mantle cavity of a clam (468)
exocrine gland a gland that secretes substances through a duct (728)
exocytosis the process by which wastes are packaged in vesicles and leave the cell (88)
exon a segment of DNA and mRNA that is not excised and that functions in protein synthesis (183)
exoskeleton a hard external covering of some invertebrates that provides protection and support (479)
exothermic reaction a reaction that has a net release of energy (42)
exotoxin a protein secreted by pathogenic bacteria (303)
experimenting the process of testing a hypothesis by gathering data under controlled conditions (20)
expiration the process in which air is forced out of the lungs (666)

849

exponential phase a period of population growth in which the population keeps doubling in increasingly shorter time periods (812)
external respiration the exchange of gases between the atmosphere and the blood (665)
extinct the state of a species when it no longer exists (249)
extreme halophile an archaebacterium that lives only in areas of high salt concentration (296)
eyespot a localized region of pigment in some invertebrates that detects changes in the quantity and quality of light (310)

F

facilitated diffusion a passive form of carrier transport (85)
facultative anaerobe an organism that can metabolize with or without oxygen (301)
Fallopian tube a tube that carries eggs from the ovary to the uterus (736)
family in taxonomy, a group of similar genera (267)
famine a food shortage that exists over a wide area over a long period (355)
fat a triglyceride that is solid at room temperature (51, 688)
fatty acid a monomer that is part of most lipids (51)
fatty liver a swelling of the liver due to excessive alcohol use (752)
feces waste materials that pass through the anus or cloacal opening (699)
feedback mechanism a mechanism in which the end product of a process controls the first step in the process (727)
fermentation the breakdown of pyruvic acid without the use of oxygen (104)
fertilization the fusion of gametes (739)
fetal alcohol syndrome a condition affecting some of the children born to women who drink alcohol during pregnancy (752)
fetoscopy a visual, observational procedure for diagnosing disorders in a fetus (176)
fetus referring to the embryo from the end of the eighth week until birth (741)
fever an increase in body temperature in response to the presence of pathogens (675)
fiber a type of sclerenchyma cell in which the wall is long and thin (381)
fibrin the long sticky threads that function in blood clotting (663)
fibrinogen a blood protein essential for the formation of blood clots (662)
fibrous root one of many small roots that spread out near the top of the soil (383)
fiddlehead a coiled fern leaf (373)
filament in flowers, the structure that supports the anther; part of a stamen (406)
filoplume the hairlike pinfeathers near the nostrils of birds (589)
filter feeding the method by which a sessile organism screens food out of the water (442)
filtration the process in the kidney in which materials from the blood are forced out of the glomerulus and absorbed by the cells of Bowman's capsule (701)
first filial, or F_1, generation the offspring of cross-pollinated P_1 generation plants (148)
flagellum a hairlike structure made up of microtubules that function for motility (71, 313)
flame cells in platyhelminths, cells that enclose a tuft of cilia and function in excretion (455)
flight feather a specialized contour feather on the wing or tail of a bird (589)
fluid mosaic model a model of cell membrane structure representing the dynamic nature of lipids and proteins (67)
follicle a pit in the skin in which hair or a feather develops (589)
food chain the specific feeding sequence in which organisms obtain energy in an ecosystem (785)
food vacuole the portion of a cell membrane surrounding the food during phagocytosis (312)
food web the interrelated food chains in an ecosystem (786)
foot an organ in a mollusk used for locomotion (466)
fossil the remains or traces of a once-living organism (209)
fossil fuel fuel formed from the incomplete decay of prehistoric plants and animals (824)
fractionation a technique that breaks up cells and releases cell components (28)
frameshift mutation a specific type of point mutation in which the genetic code is read out of sequence (164)
freshwater biome an aquatic biome characterized by low levels of dissolved salts (776)
frond the mature leaf of a fern (373)
fruit a mature plant ovary; a modified flower part that encloses a seed or seeds (355)
Fungi Imperfecti a group of about 25,000 species of fungi whose sexual phase has not been discovered (341)
furculum the keel-shaped sternum unique to avian skeletons (587)

G

gallbladder the saclike organ connected to the liver that produces bile (697)
gamete a sexual reproductive cell (138)
gametophyte in plants and algae, a multicellular structure that produces gametes (330, 368)
ganglion a mass of nerve cell bodies (455, 707)
gas bladder an organ in fish that provides buoyancy and prevents sinking (549)
gastric cecum one of the pockets in the stomach that secretes enzymes (499)
gastric fluid a liquid secreted by gastric glands (696)
gastric pit the open end of gastric glands through which secretions are released (696)
gastritis an irritation of the stomach lining (752)
gastrovascular cavity the hollow gut of some lower invertebrates (445)
gastrula a cup-shaped embryo formed as the blastula folds inward (184, 438)
gated channel a protein-lined passage making cell membranes permeable to certain large molecules (86)
gel a colloid in a semisolid state (39)
gemmule an asexual reproductive structure of amebocytes surrounded by organic material and spicules (442)
gene a short segment of DNA that contains coding for a polypeptide or protein (7, 123, 152)
gene cloning the process by which a gene is replicated (196)
gene expression the transcription of DNA into RNA and then into proteins (181)
gene flow the movement of genes into or out of a population (242)
gene pool all the genes for all the traits in a population (240)
gene sequencing a process that determines the exact order of bases in a fragment of DNA (196)
gene splicing the process by which a gene from one organism is placed into the DNA of another organism (195)
generative cell in a pollen grain, the cell that forms two sperm (407)

850

genetic code the system that contains information needed by the cell for proper functioning (120)
genetic counseling the process of informing a couple about genetic problems that have the potential to affect their offspring (176)
genetic drift a shift in allele frequencies in a population due to random events or chance (243)
genetic engineering a form of applied genetics in which scientists directly manipulate genes (194)
genetic equilibrium the condition in which allele frequencies in a population do not change from generation to generation (241)
genetic marker a short section of DNA that indicates the presence of an allele that codes for a trait (173)
genetic recombination the process that results in chromosomes being rearranged in many different ways (138)
genetic screening an examination of a person's genetic makeup (175)
genotype the genetic makeup of an organism (153, 240)
genus in taxonomy, a group of similar species (267)
geographic isolation the physical separation of populations (247)
geothermal energy the heat originating beneath the earth (824)
germ cell mutation a change in the DNA of a sex cell (163)
germ layer a specific layer of cells in an embryo from which specific organ systems are derived (439)
gestation period length of pregnancy (608, 741)
gibberellin a plant hormone that, among other actions, stimulates bolting and cessation of dormancy (423)
gill in mushrooms, the radiating rows on the underside of the cap; in animals, an organ specialized for the exchange of gases with water (338, 466, 540)
gill slits the openings in the throat region of a fish that lead to the gill chambers (537)
gizzard a muscular organ in birds that crushes food; a digestive structure in earthworms in which thick, muscular walls grind soil to release organic matter (472, 592)
glomerulus a cluster of capillaries that receives blood from the renal artery and that is enclosed in Bowman's capsule (701)
glottis a structure at the end of the passage from an organism's throat to its lungs (563)
glycocalyx a covering in some prokaryotes that functions to stick the organism to a surface (300)
glycolysis the breakdown of glucose to pyruvic acid (103)
glycoprotein a molecule of protein with attached sugar chains (285)
Golgi apparatus an organelle of a cell that functions in secretion (68)
gonads the organs that produce gametes and some sex hormones (730)
G_1 phase the first period of interphase, in which the cell doubles in size (132)
G_2 phase the final period of interphase, in which the cell undergoes rapid growth that prepares it for mitosis (132)
grafting a technique in which a portion of one plant is inserted into and grows with the root or shoot of another (416)
Gram-negative bacterium a bacterium that stains pink with Gram stain and that usually has an outer covering on its cell wall (297)
Gram-positive bacterium a bacterium that stains purple with Gram stain and that usually lacks an outer covering on its cell wall (297)
Gram stain a series of dyes that turn either purple or pink according to the chemistry of a bacterial cell wall (297)
grana stacks of thylakoids in a chloroplast (96)
granular gland an organ in frogs that secretes foul-tasting or poisonous substances (560)
grassland a biome dominated by grasses (771)
gravitropism a plant growth response to gravity (425)
green gland an excretory organ in crayfish that removes wastes from the blood and helps retain salts (484)
greenhouse effect a condition of increased heat due to reflection of sunlight back to earth from the atmosphere (791)
Green Revolution a change in worldwide food production implemented by improving productivity (355)
gross primary productivity the total amount of energy produced in an ecosystem (783)
ground system one type of plant tissue system made up of parenchyma, collenchyma, and sclerenchyma (381)
growth curve in populations, a graph of the number of individuals in a population over time (812)
guanine a nitrogen base; one component of a nucleotide (113)
guard cell one of two cells bordering a stoma, each of which has flexible cell walls that allow it to bend (396)
gullet the structure that forms food vacuoles that circulate throughout the cytoplasm of the paramecium (312)
gymnosperm a seed plant whose seeds are not enclosed by an ovary (367)

H

habitat the physical area in which an organism lives (781)
hair follicle a structure in the skin that produces hair (650)
half-life the period of time in which half of a radioactive substance decays (220)
haploid a cell that has only one chromosome of each homologous pair (130)
hard palate the bony roof of the mouth (695)
Hardy-Weinberg principle a theory that states the conditions necessary for gene frequencies to remain stable across generations (241)
Haversian canal a channel containing nerves and blood vessels making up compact bone (641)
hazardous waste industrially produced material that is toxic, radioactive, explosive, or otherwise dangerous (826)
head the anterior end of a cephalized animal (466)
heart a muscular organ that pumps blood (655)
helper cell a T cell that plays a role in the cell-mediated immune response (677)
hemocoel the blood-filled space or body cavity in the tissues of some invertebrates (467)
hemoglobin an iron-containing protein in blood (622)
hemophilia a trait in which the blood lacks a protein that is essential for clotting (175)
hemotoxin a component in snake venom that destroys red blood cells and disrupts the clotting of blood (581)
hepatic portal circulation the system of blood movement through the digestive tract and liver (661)
herbaceous plant an annual plant that is nonwoody (382)
herbivore a consumer that eats primary producers (574, 783)
heredity the transmission of traits from parents to their offspring (147)
hermaphrodite any individual that produces both eggs and sperm (443)
heterochromatin the chromatin that contains inactive genes not currently being transcribed into RNA (182)
heterocyst a cell of cyanophytes that fixes atmospheric nitrogen (298)
heterokaryotic referring to a hypha with nuclei from genetically different mating strains coexisting within it (336)

851

heterospory a phenomenon in which two types of spores are produced by an individual plant (403)
heterotroph an organism that cannot make its own food (9, 93, 301)
heterozygous referring to a gene pair in which the two alleles do not code for the same trait (153)
hibernation a state of severely reduced physiological activity occurring during the winter (556, 801)
hilum a scar along the edge of a plant seed marking where the seed was attached to the ovary wall (411)
hindgut the colon and the rectum of some invertebrates (499)
histamine a chemical associated with the sneezing and wheezing of allergies (679)
histone a special protein molecule that DNA wraps around during chromosome formation (129)
holdfast the part of an algal thallus that anchors it to a rock (324)
homeostasis the biological balance between a cell or an organism and its environment (81)
homeotic gene a gene that controls the development of a specific adult structure (185)
hominid a subgroup of primates that includes human beings and their immediate ancestors (258)
homokaryotic referring to a hypha with genetically similar nuclei (336)
homologous chromosome one of two members of a pair of morphologically similar chromosomes (130)
homologous structures structures that are embryologically similar (223)
homospory a phenomenon in which all spores look alike and produce similar gametophytes (402)
homozygous referring to a gene pair in which the two alleles code for the same trait (153)
hormone a substance produced in one part of an organism that specifically influences the activity of cells in another part of the organism (421, 727)
host an organism that supports a parasite (454, 799)
humus the organic component of the soil (822)
Huntington disease a human genetic disorder caused by a dominant allele (172)
hybrid the offspring of two dissimilar organisms (192, 238)
hybridization a type of controlled breeding in which two different but related species are crossed (192)
hybrid vigor the quality displayed by hybrids that grow faster and are healthier than their parents (192)
hydrogen bond a chemical bond in which atoms share a hydrogen nucleus (114)
hydrolysis the splitting of a molecule through reaction with water (48, 687)
hydrophilic referring to the molecular attraction to water (51)
hydrophobic referring to the molecular repulsion to water (51)
hydrotropism a plant growth response to water (426)
hyperthyroidism a condition that results when too much thyroxine is secreted by the thyroid gland (728)
hypertonic the condition when the concentration of solute molecules is higher outside than inside a cell (83)
hypha the vegetative filament of a fungus (336)
hypocotyl a stemlike area in plants between the cotyledons and radicle (411)
hypoglycemia a condition caused by a lack of glucose in the blood (732)
hypothalamus the structure located below the thalamus (709)
hypothesis a statement that can be tested experimentally (19)
hypothesizing the process of forming testable statements about observable phenomena (19)
hypothyroidism a condition in which too little thyroxine is secreted by the thyroid gland (728)
hypotonic the condition when the concentration of solute molecules is lower outside than inside a cell (83)

I

icosahedron a polyhedron or a capsid of a virus with 20 triangular faces (284)
ileum the middle portion of the small intestine (561, 698)
imaginal disk the specific tissue area in the pupal stage that leads to a specific structure in the adult stage (185)
immune response a reaction of the body against a foreign substance (675)
immunity a resistance to a specific pathogen (678)
imprint a type of fossil in which a thin film of carbon remains after the organism has decayed (219)
imprinting the behavior process that causes young animals to follow the first moving thing seen after birth (627)
impulse an electrical signal carried by neurons (713)
inbreeding a type of breeding based on the idea that individuals with similar phenotypes also will have similar genotypes (192)
incisor the chisellike tooth used for biting and cutting (604)
incomplete digestive system in invertebrates, a system in which one opening serves as both mouth and anus (526)
incubate the process of warming eggs before they are hatched (595)
incurrent siphon a hollow tube through which water enters the mantle cavity of a clam (468)
independent variable an experimentally manipulated variable (20)
indeterminate cleavage a process in which each embryonic cell will develop into a complete gastrula (522)
indirect development in invertebrates, morphogenesis with an intermediate larval stage (523)
indoleacetic acid (IAA) an auxin produced in actively growing regions of plants (421)
inducer the molecule that binds to repressor molecules and induces gene expression (182)
infectious disease a transmittable disease (673)
inferior vena cava the large vein carrying blood from the lower part of the body (657)
inferring the process of drawing conclusions on the basis of facts or premises instead of direct perception (21)
inflammatory response a response in which white blood cells engulf foreign substances and body temperature rises (675)
inheritance the acquisition of traits by offspring (7, 147)
inorganic compound a compound generally derived from nonliving things (47)
insertion the attachment point of a tendon to a moving bone (648)
insight learning the ability of individuals to apply what they learn in one situation to other situations (627)
inspiration the process of taking air into the lungs (666)
instinct genetically controlled behavior (503)
insulin a hormone that lowers the blood sugar level (732)
integument in plants, one or two outer layers of the ovule; in animals, the outer covering (407, 547)
interferon a protein produced by the body that inhibits the reproduction of viruses (194, 676)
intermediary metabolism a series of chemical reactions in which energy is released slowly (42)
internal fertilization the method of fertilization by which sperm fuses with an egg inside the female's body (571)
internal respiration the exchange of gases between the blood and the cells of the body (665)

852

interphase a period of cell growth and development that precedes mitosis (131)
interspecific competition competition between organisms of different species (797)
intertidal zone a biome along ocean shorelines that is repeatedly covered and uncovered by seawater (775)
intraspecific competition competition between organisms of the same species (797)
intron a DNA segment producing an RNA segment that is excised before it codes for a protein (183)
inversion a mutation that occurs when a chromosome piece breaks off and reattaches in reverse orientation (163)
invertebrate an animal without a backbone (437)
ion an atom or a compound with a net electrical charge (36)
ionic bond a bond formed by electrical attraction between two oppositely charged ions (36)
iris the structure of the eye that controls the amount of light entering the eye (718)
islets of Langerhans the special cells in the pancreas that secrete two hormones—insulin and glucagon (732)
isomer one of two or more compounds that differ in structure but not in molecular composition (50)
isotonic the condition when the concentrations of solute molecules inside and outside a cell are equal (83)
isotope an atom of an element that has a different number of neutrons than other atoms of that element (34)

J

Jacobson's organ the two pits in the mouth of a snake that contain nerves which are extremely sensitive to odors (581)
jejunum the middle section of the small intestine (698)
joint the place where two bones meet (643)
J-shaped curve a growth curve that describes the lag phase and the exponential phase of population growth (812)

K

karotype a picture of an individual's chromosomes (175)
keratin a protein substance that forms hair, bird feathers, human fingernails, and the horny scales of reptiles (572, 649)
kidney an excretory organ in which wastes are filtered from the blood (700)
kinetic energy the energy of motion (41)
kinetochore fiber a fiber extending from a centriole to a centromere during mitosis (132)
kingdom in taxonomy, a group of similar phyla or divisions (267)
Koch's postulates the steps that Koch formulated for determining the cause of a given disease (673)
Krebs cycle a series of biochemical reactions that release carbon dioxide and hydrogen ions and result in the formation of ATP (106)

L

labium a liplike structure (498)
labrum a structure forming the roof of the mouth in insects (498)
lac operon DNA segment on the chromosome of the *E. coli* bacterium that codes for polypeptides that cleave lactose (181)
lacteal a tiny lymph vessel (698)
lactic acid fermentation the process by which pyruvic acid is converted to lactic acid (104)
lag phase a period of little increase in the number of individuals in a population (812)
laminarin a type of polysaccharide with glucose units linked differently from those in starch (324)
large intestine the organ of digestion in which water is reabsorbed (699)
larva an immature, morphologically distinct form of an organism (443)
larynx the voice box that houses the vocal cords (667)
lateral line system a row of sensory structures that run the length of the body of a fish (540)
lateral meristem a growing region that increases the circumference of a plant (382)
law a general statement that describes a wide variety of phenomena (23)
leaf plant organ often specialized for capturing sunlight (381)
legume a member of the pea family (354)
lens a convex crystalline structure in the eye (719)
leucoplast a plastid in plants that stores food (74)
leukemia a disease characterized by the abnormal growth of immature white blood cells (186)
leukocyte a white blood cell (663)
lichen a symbiotic association between fungi and green algae (342)
ligament a connective tissue in a joint (643)
light-dependent reactions the set of reactions that convert solar energy to chemical energy (97)
light-independent reactions the set of reactions that produce organic compounds, using the chemical energy produced during the light-dependent reactions (99)
limbic system a group of neurons in the brain that helps regulate the emotions (710)
linkage group the group of genes, located on the same chromosome, that are usually inherited together (166)
lipid a fat, an oil, a wax, or a steroid made up of carbon, hydrogen, and oxygen (50)
liver a large organ that aids digestion (697)
lobe-finned fish a fish having paddlelike fins with fleshy bases (545)
long-day plant a plant that flowers when exposed to day lengths longer than the plant's critical length (427)
lung the respiratory organ where gas exchange occurs (545, 665)
lungfish a fish having both lungs and gills (545)
lymph the fluid of the lymphatic system (661)
lymphatic system a series of one-way vessels that carries intercellular fluid from tissues to the bloodstream (661)
lymphocyte a type of white blood cell occurring in two primary forms—T cells and B cells (676)
lymphoma a tumor in the tissues that form blood cells (186)
lysis the disintegration of an infected cell (289)
lysogenic cycle the life cycle of a temperate virus (289)
lysosome an organelle containing digestive enzymes, existing primarily in animal cells (70)
lytic cycle the basic reproductive process of viruses (288)

M

macromolecule a large molecule, often a polymer (48)
macronucleus in paramecia, the larger of the two types of nuclei (312)
macronutrient an element used by plant cells in relatively large amounts (386)
macrophage a large white blood cell that can engulf hundreds of bacteria (675)
magnification the increase in an object's apparent size (25)
malignant tumor a cancerous mass of cells (186)
Malpighian tubule the main excretory organ of some invertebrates (487)

853

mammary gland one of the milk-secreting glands of mammals (604)
mandible a movable mouthpart that usually functions in chewing (482)
mantle the epidermal layer of mollusks (466)
mantle cavity a space between the mantle and the visceral mass in mollusks (466)
map unit a unit in chromosome mapping equal to a 1 percent occurrence of crossing-over (168)
marine biome the earth's oceans (774)
mass the quantity of matter of an object (33)
mass number the sum of the protons and the neutrons in an atom (34)
mass selection the process of choosing a few individuals to act as parents from a larger pool of individuals (191)
mastax a muscular organ that chops up food in rotifers (460)
matter anything that occupies space and has mass (33)
maxilla a structure located behind the mandibles that helps hold and cut food (484)
maxillary teeth the teeth in the upper jaw (560)
maxilliped a specialized appendage used to hold food (484)
measuring the process of determining the characteristics of an object or a group in quantitative units (18)
medulla the innermost portion of an organ (700)
medulla oblongata in fish, the posterior brain lobes that regulate the internal organs; in humans, a part of the brain stem (550, 709)
medusa a bell-shaped stage in the life cycle of a cnidarian (444)
megaspore a spore produced by meiosis in a megasporangium (404)
meiosis the process of nuclear division that reduces the number of chromosomes in a cell by half (136)
meiosis I a division during meiosis in which the homologous chromosomes are separated into separate cells (136)
meiosis II a division during meiosis in which the chromatids are segregated into separate cells (136)
melanin a substance that determines skin color and protects the body from overexposure to sun (650)
memory cell a specialized white blood cell that remains in the blood after an antigen has been destroyed (677)
meninges the three protective layers that surround the brain and spinal cord (710)
menstrual cycle the monthly changes in the female reproductive system (737)
menstruation the release of uterine lining, blood, and unfertilized egg at the end of the menstrual cycle (738)
meristem the growing region in plants (382)
mesentery a fanlike membrane that holds the digestive organs in place (561)
mesoderm a layer of cells in the gastrula that gives rise to muscles and to interior body linings (439)
mesoglea in cnidarians, the jellylike material located between the endoderm and the ectoderm (445)
mesophyll in leaves, the tissue where photosynthesis occurs (395)
messenger RNA (mRNA) the type of RNA that carries genetic information from the nucleus to the ribosomes (118)
metameric unit a repeating part in a segmented body (524)
metamerism segmentation (471)
metamorphosis the changes through which an immature organism passes into adulthood (500, 556)
metaphase the second phase of mitosis, during which all the chromosomes move to the cell's equator (133)
metastasis the breaking away of cells from a malignant tumor to cause new tumors (186)
metazoan a multicellular organism (438)
methanogen a bacterium that produces methane during anaerobic respiration (296)
microfilament a fine protein threadlike organelle (70)
microfossil a microscopic fossil (209)
micronucleus in paramecia, the smaller of the two nuclei, involved in sexual reproduction (312)
micronutrient an element used by plants in relatively small amounts (386)
micropyle in plants, a small opening at one end of the ovule through which pollen enters (407)
microscope an instrument that can form an enlarged image of an object (25)
microsphere a type of microscopic droplet closely resembling a living cell (210)
microspore a spore produced by meiosis in a microsporangium (404)
microtubule a long, slender tube-shaped proteinaceous organelle (70)
microvillus one of the extensions of membranes covering the villi (698)
midbrain the section of the brain stem controlling reflexes (709)
middle lamella the thin, gluelike layer containing pectin that forms in plant cell division where the new cells meet (73)
midgut the stomachlike region of some invertebrates (498)
migration the movement of individual organisms into or out of a population, community, or biome (242, 801)
milt in fish, a fluid containing sperm (550)
mineral an inorganic solid formed in the earth (691, 824)
mitochondrion the organelle that is the site of aerobic respiration in cells (69)
mitosis the division of the cell nucleus (131)
mixed cropping the simultaneous planting of different crops in one field (355)
mixture a combination of two or more substances in which each substance retains its original chemical properties (38)
modeling the construction of a representation of a process or phenomenon (22)
molar a flattened tooth used to grind and crush (604)
mold a type of fossil formed from an impression of the shape or tracks of an organism (219)
molecule a group of atoms held together by covalent bonds (37)
molting the process of shedding an exoskeleton (480)
monocot an angiosperm with a single cotyledon, parallel veins, and flower parts in multiples (375)
monohybrid cross a cross between individuals that involves one pair of contrasting traits (154)
monomer a repeated, single-molecule unit in a polymer (48)
monosaccharide a simple six-carbon sugar such as fructose or glucose (49, 687)
monosomy a condition resulting from nondisjunction during meiosis (175)
morphogenesis the change in form of an organism resulting from cell differentiation (184)
morphological species concept the idea that organisms can be classified by differences in their appearance (237)
morphology the internal and external appearance of an organism (8, 237)
motor neuron a nerve cell in a ventral root that carries impulses from the spinal cord to the effectors (711)
mouth pore the structure at the oral groove into which the paramecium sweeps food (312)
mucus gland an organ that supplies a lubricant to keep the skin moist (560)

854

Müllerian mimicry the adaptation among several poisonous or bad-tasting species of similar patterns of coloration (502)
multicellular gametangium one of the multicellular structures that form gametes in plants (365)
multicellular organism a living thing that consists of more than one cell (7, 63)
multiple alleles three or more contrasting genes that control a trait (153)
muscle a contractile organ consisting of many cells (645)
muscle fiber a skeletal muscle cell that runs the length of the muscle and contains many nuclei (646)
muscle tissue the body tissue that enables movement (638)
mutagen an environmental factor that damages DNA (164)
mutation a change in DNA (163, 242)
mutualism a form of symbiosis in which both organisms benefit from living together (342, 799)
mycelium a mat of interwoven hyphae (336)
mycorrhiza a symbiotic association between fungi and plant roots (342)
myelin sheath a cellular covering that protects an axon (713)
myofibril a contracting thread in a skeletal muscle (646)
myosin the thick protein filament of a sarcomere (647)
myriapod the common name for centipedes and millipedes (488)
myxameba a uninucleate cell that is the feeding stage of a slime mold (343)

N

narcotic a drug derived from opium (753)
nastic movement a type of plant movement that is independent of the direction of the stimuli (426)
natural immunity an immunity that is present at birth (678)
natural resource a raw material that supports life (821)
natural selection the process by which organisms with favorable variations survive and reproduce at higher rates than those without such variations (230)
necromass dead organic matter in soil (804)
nectar in flowers, a nourishing solution of sugars and amino acids (408)
negative feedback a process in which an end product inhibits the first step of the system (727)
nematocyst a coiled stinger in cnidarians (445)
nephridium a long tubule through which some invertebrates eliminate wastes (473)
nephron the functional unit of the kidney (701)
neritic zone the ocean subarea over the continental shelf (774)
nerve a strand of nerve cells through which impulses travel (707)
nerve ring a nerve surrounding the mouth of a sea star (516)
nervous tissue a type of human body tissue that conducts electrical impulses (638)
net primary productivity the rate at which plants store energy that is not used in plant respiration (783)
neuron a cell that carries electrical signals (707)
neurotoxin a component in snake venom that disrupts the transmission of nerve impulses (581, 673)
neurotransmitter a chemical messenger that carries a nerve impulse from cell to cell (716)
neutron a subatomic particle with no electric charge (33)
neutrophil a small white blood cell with an irregular nucleus (675)
niche the way of life of a species (781)
nicotine the stimulant found in tobacco (749)
nictitating membrane a third membrane that can cover the eyeball (559)
nitrification the process in the nitrogen cycle by which nitrites and nitrates are produced (790)
nitrogen fixation the process by which gaseous nitrogen in the air is converted into nitrates and nitrites (301, 790)
nocturnal referring to organisms that are primarily active by night (800)
nodes of Ranvier gaps in the myelin sheath (713)
nonbiodegradable referring to a pollutant that cannot be decomposed (825)
nondisjunction a mutation caused when a replicated chromosome pair fails to separate during cell division (164)
nonrenewable resource a natural resource that is unreplaceable (823)
nonvascular plant a plant that lacks vascular tissue, and true roots, stems, and leaves (367)
notochord a firm, flexible rod found in the dorsal part of chordates (537)
nuclear envelope the double membrane of lipids and proteins that surrounds the nucleus of a cell (72)
nucleic acid an organic molecule, DNA or RNA, that stores and carries important information for cell function (54)
nucleolus the structure found in most nuclei in which ribosomes are synthesized and partially assembled (72)
nucleosome the histone complex around which DNA wraps itself when coiling into heterochromatin (182)
nucleotide a monomer of DNA and RNA, consisting of a nitrogen base, a sugar, and a phosphate group (54, 113)
nucleus in atoms, the core of protons and neutrons; in eukaryotic cells, the organelle that contains most of the DNA (33, 65)
nutrient a chemical substance an organism needs to grow and function properly (687)
nymph an immature form of some invertebrates (500)

O

objective lens in a microscope, the lens closest to the specimen (25)
obligate aerobe an organism that requires oxygen (301)
obligate anaerobe an organism that lives in the absence of oxygen and dies when exposed to it (301)
obligate intracellular parasite a parasite that requires a host cell in order to reproduce (283)
observing the use of one or more of the five senses to perceive objects or events (18)
oceanic zone one of two subareas of the pelagic zone (775)
ocular lens in a microscope, the lens in the eyepiece (25)
oil a triglyceride that is liquid at room temperature (51)
oil gland a skin gland that secretes sebum (650)
old field succession the replacement of populations in abandoned farm fields (806)
olfactory lobe the brain region that interprets smell (542)
olfactory nerve the nerve that carries impulses from olfactory receptors in the nasal passage to the brain (721)
oligosaccharin a plant hormone that regulates growth and may fight disease (424)
oligotrophic lake a lake that is very low in nutrients (776)
omnivore an animal that eats both plants and animals (611, 784)
oncogene a cancer-causing gene (186)
oogonium a unicellular gametangium that produces eggs (330)
oospore a thick-walled, diploid structure that develops from a zygote (344)
ootid a cell that develops into an egg (138)
open circulatory system a system in which the blood does not circulate entirely within vessels (467)

855

operational definitions definitions that are limited to repeatable and observable phenomena (22)
operator one of three segments of the operon that controls expressions of a gene (181)
operculum in fish, a hard plate attached to each side of the head that covers gills and is open at the rear (546)
operon the operator and the structural genes on a DNA segment (181)
opposable thumb a thumb that can be positioned opposite the other fingers (256)
optic lobe one of the paired brain lobes that receives nerve impulses from the eyes (549)
optic nerve the nerve that carries impulses from the retina to the occipital lobe of the cerebrum (719)
oral groove a funnellike structure lined with cilia, used by ciliates for feeding (312)
oral surface the underside of a sea star, opposite the aboral surface (515)
order in taxonomy, a group of similar families (267)
organ several types of tissues that together perform a bodily function (75, 639)
organelle cell component that performs a special function (65)
organic compound a compound that is derived from living things and contains carbon (47)
organism a living thing (5)
organizing data the process of placing observations and measurements in some kind of logical order (18)
organ system a group of organs that interact to perform a set of related tasks (76, 639)
origin attachment point of a tendon to a stationary bone (648)
osculum an opening at the top of sponges (441)
osmoregulation maintaining homeostasis between salt and water in the body (549)
osmosis the diffusion of water (82)
ossicle a protective spine on a sea star (515)
ossification process by which cartilage is converted to bone (642)
osteocyte a living bone cell (641)
oval window a membrane that separates the middle ear from the inner ear (720)
ovary in plants, the base of the pistil; an egg-producing organ (406, 446, 730)
over-the-counter drug a drug that can be obtained without a prescription (754)
oviparous referring to organisms that produce eggs that hatch outside the body (582)
ovipositor a pointed organ in some female invertebrates that digs a nest hole and deposits eggs (500)
ovoviviparous referring to organisms that produce eggs that hatch inside the body (582)
ovulation the second stage of the menstrual cycle, in which the follicle ruptures and releases the ripe egg (738)
ovule the megasporangium of a flowering plant (404)
ovum a female gamete or an egg (736)
ozone a secondary pollutant formed when primary pollutants react with sunlight and chemicals (825)

P

paleoanthropologist scientist who studies human evolution (255)
palisade parenchyma in leaves, a type of mesophyll directly below the upper epidermis, where most photosynthesis occurs (395)
pancreas the organ that lies behind the stomach against the back wall of the abdominal cavity (697)
papilla one of the bumps, mostly on the tongue, between which most of the taste buds are embedded (721)
parapodium one of the fleshy appendages of annelids (471)
parasite an organism that obtains its nutrition at the expense of another (454, 799)
parasitism a symbiotic relationship in which one organism obtains its nutrition at the expense of another (799)
parasympathetic nervous system the part of the autonomic nervous system that controls internal organs (712)
parathyroid gland a gland that secretes hormones that regulate calcium and phosphate ions in the blood (729)
parenchyma the living tissue of the ground system consisting of cells with thin cell walls (381)
parental, or P_1, generation a strain obtained through self-pollination (148)
parietal eye a third eye on the top of the head, characteristic of the tuatara (576)
particulate a particle found in smoke (825)
passive transport the movement of any substance across a cell membrane without the use of cell energy (84)
pathogen an organism that causes a disease (303, 673)
pectoral fin a fin located on the side of a fish body just behind the head (543)
pedicellarium in sea stars, a structure surrounding the spine (515)
pedigree a record that shows how a trait is inherited over several generations (171)
pedipalp in arachnids, an appendage that aids in chewing (486)
pelagic zone the open ocean (774)
pellicle a rigid protein covering of some unicellular organisms (312)
pelvic fin in fish, one of the paired fins positioned in the ventral, posterior portion of the body (547)
pennate diatom a type of golden-brown algae with long, rectangular valves (326)
pentaradial symmetry an organism with radii in multiples of five (511)
peptide bond a covalent bond between a nitrogen atom and a carbon atom (53)
pericardium the tough saclike membrane that surrounds the heart (655)
pericycle the outermost cylinder of cells in the central vascular area (384)
periosteum the tough outer membrane of a bone; the point where tendons attach muscles to bones (641)
peripheral nervous system the network of nerves that connects the central nervous system with all parts of the body (712)
peristalsis a series of rhythmic muscular contractions (695)
permafrost a permanently frozen layer of ground (768)
permeable referring to a membrane through which molecules can pass (82)
pesticide a chemical used to control insects (826)
petal the showy part of a flower (405)
petiole in leaves, the structure that attaches blade and stem (394)
phagocyte a white blood cell that engulfs foreign cells (663)
phagocytosis the engulfing of food by a cell (88, 312)
pharyngeal pouch a small outpocket of the anterior gut in a chordate (537)
pharynx the open area at the back of the mouth; in planarians, a muscular tube that extends out of the mouth; in earthworms, a structure through which soil is pumped into the gut (455, 548, 667)
phenotype the external appearance of an organism (153, 240)
pheromone a chemical released by an animal that affects the behavior of other animals of the same species (505)

856

phloem in plants, the specialized tissue in the vascular system that transports dissolved sugars (371)
phosphorylation the transfer of a phosphate group from one molecule to another molecule with the transfer of energy (95)
photic zone the layer of the ocean that receives light (774)
photoautotroph an organism that uses sunlight as an energy source (301)
photochemical smog the product of sunlight catalyzing a series of chemical reactions among pollutants (825)
photoperiodism a plant response to changes in day length (427)
photosynthesis the series of reactions that convert radiant energy to the chemical energy stored in the bonds of organic compounds, usually carbohydrates (93)
photosystem in plants, a unit of several hundred chlorophyll molecules and associated carrier molecules (97)
phototropism plant growth in response to light (425)
pH scale a scale for measuring the relative concentrations of hydronium ions and hydroxide ions in a solution (40)
phylogenetic tree a visual model of the inferred evolutionary relationships among organisms (271)
phylogeny evolutionary history (6, 269)
phylum in taxonomy, a group of similar classes (267)
physical addiction the changes in body chemistry that result in a demand for a steady supply of a drug (755)
physiological variations differences in the way systems function (493)
phytochrome a pigment in plants that helps monitor changes in day length (427)
phytoplankton a photosynthetic microorganism (321)
pia mater the inner layer of the meninges (711)
pilus an appendage bacteria use to attach to objects (300)
pinocytosis the movement into cells of solutes or fluids (88)
pioneer species the first species to colonize a new habitat (803)
pistil a plant structure formed of fused carpels (406)
pit a thin, porous area of a cell wall (381)
pith the plant tissue located in the center of the stem (388)
pituitary gland a gland that secretes hormones to control body growth and to regulate the activity of the other endocrine glands (730)
placenta the organ that nourishes the unborn young of placental mammals (608, 742)
placoid scale a toothlike spine found on a shark (543)
plant ecology the study of the interaction of plants and the environment (359)
plant growth regulator a hormone that affects growth (421)
planula a free-swimming, ciliated larva (447)
plasma the liquid component of blood (662)
plasmid a single ring of DNA in bacteria (195, 300)
plasmodium the multinucleate cytoplasm of a slime mold surrounded by a membrane that moves as a mass (344)
plasmolysis the shrinking or wilting of a cell from low turgor pressure (83)
plastid an organelle in which food or pigments are stored (72)
plastron the ventral portion of a turtle shell (577)
platelet a partial cell needed to form blood clots (663)
plumule in plants, the structure composed of the epicotyl plus any embryonic leaves (411)
point mutation the change of a single nitrogen base within a codon or larger segments of DNA (164)
polar biome the areas that surround the earth's poles (767)
polar body a cell formed during meiosis that receives little or no cytoplasm and eventually disintegrates (138)
polar compound a compound with one side having a negative charge and the other side a positive charge (47)
polar fiber a type of spindle fiber that extends across the cell from centriole to centriole (132)
polar nucleus in plants, a nucleus that migrates to the center of the cell during embryo sac formation (407)
pollen grain the microgametophyte of seed plants (404)
pollen tube a structure that grows from a pollen grain, down which the sperm travels to the eggs (404)
pollination the transfer of pollen from an anther to a stigma of a flower of the same species (148, 408)
pollution an undesirable change in an ecosystem (825)
polygenic trait a trait controlled by multiple genes (173)
polymer a compound consisting of repeated linked monomers (48)
polyp the vase-shaped stage in the life cycle of a cnidarian (444)
polypeptide a long chain of several amino acids (53)
polyploidy a condition in which cells contain multiple, complete sets of chromosomes (193)
polysaccharide a complex carbohydrate composed of three or more monosaccharides (50, 688)
pons a part of the brain stem (709)
population all the members of a species that live in the same area and make up a breeding group (239, 765)
population density the number of individuals in a population in a given area at a specific time (814)
population growth an increase in the number of individuals in a population (811)
population growth rate the change in the number of individuals in a population over time (811)
population sampling a small number of individuals chosen to represent an entire population (170)
positive feedback a process in which an end product regulates the first step of the system (727)
posterior the hind end of an organism (437)
potential energy stored energy or energy of position (41)
precocial referring to birds that, when hatched, are physically active and mature (596)
predation a form of interaction in which one animal kills and eats another (766)
predicting the process of stating in advance the result that will be obtained from testing a hypothesis (19)
preen gland the oil-secreting gland of a bird (589)
pregnancy the phenomenon of carrying an embryo internally (741)
prescription drug a drug that can be obtained only on written orders from a doctor (753)
pressure-flow hypothesis an explanation of the movement of sugars in the phloem of plants (389)
primary consumer any organism that eats a producer (783)
primary germ layer any of three layers of the inner mass of cells on the inner surface of the blastocyst (740)
primary growth the tissue produced by apical meristems in plants (382)
primary immune response a specific defense involving both B cells and T cells (676)
primary mycelium a heterokaryotic mass of hyphae (338)
primary pollutant a pollutant emitted directly into the ecosystem (825)
primary producer an autotrophic organism (782)
primary productivity rate at which solar or chemical energy is converted into organic compounds in an ecosystem (783)
primary root the first root to grow out of a seed (383)
primary succession the process of sequential replacement of populations in an area that has not previously supported life (804)
primate a member of Primates, the mammalian order that includes humans (255)

857

principle of dominance and recessiveness the principle that one factor in a pair may mask the other factor (150)
principle of independent assortment the principle that each pair of factors is distributed independently (151)
principle of segregation the principle that each pair of factors separates during gamete formation (151)
prion a glycoprotein particle implicated in diseases with long incubation periods (287)
probability the likelihood that a given event will occur by chance (154)
proglottid one of the square body sections produced by tapeworms (457)
prokaryote a cell without a nucleus (65)
promoter one of three segments of an operon that regulates the production of a metabolizing enzyme (181)
prophage an intracellular bacteriophage that is harmless to the host cell (290)
prophase the first stage of mitosis (132)
prostaglandin a lipid that functions as a cell regulator (734)
protein an organic compound composed of one or more chains of polypeptides, which in turn are formed from amino acids (52, 688)
protein synthesis the formation of proteins using information coded on DNA and carried out by RNA (120)
proton a subatomic particle with a positive charge (33)
protonema an early stage of gametophyte development in mosses that resembles a slender thread (402)
protostome an organism in which the blastopore develops into the mouth and the coelom arises by schizocoely and whose embryo has determinate cleavage and develops spirally (521)
proventriculus the first of two chambers in the stomach of a bird (592)
pseudocoelom a body type characterized by a cavity between the mesoderm and the ectoderm (453)
pseudoplasmodium a group of cells that act together as a unit to form a sporangium (343)
pseudopodium a cytoplasmic extension that functions in movement (311)
psychoactive drug a chemical compound that changes sensory perception and thought processes (753)
psychological addiction an emotional dependency on a drug (755)
pulmonary artery the artery that carries deoxygenated blood from the heart to the lungs (659)
pulmonary circulation the movement of blood between the heart and the lungs (659)
pulmonary respiration a type of respiration involving lungs in which air is inhaled and exhaled by changing the volume and pressure of air in the mouth (563)
pulmonary vein the vein that carries oxygenated blood from the lungs to the heart (659)
punctuated equilibrium a theory that speciation may occur during brief periods of rapid genetic change (249)
Punnett square a method used to establish the probabilities of the results of a genetic cross (154)
pupa an inactive stage in metamorphosis of some invertebrates (501)
pupil an opening in the iris that allows light to enter (718)
pure referring to a strain that always produces offspring with a certain trait (147)
purine an organic molecule that has a double ring of carbon and nitrogen atoms (113)
pyloric sphincter the valve that separates the stomach from the small intestine (698)
pyrenoid an organelle that synthesizes and stores starch (321)
pyrimidine an organic molecule that has a single ring of carbon and nitrogen atoms (113)

Q

quinine a drug used to treat malaria (356)

R

radial canal a canal in a sea star arm, part of the water-vascular system (515)
radial cleavage in deuterostomes, the division of cells in a parallel position with or at right angles to the polar axis (521)
radial symmetry an arrangement of body parts in which many planes can divide the organism into similar halves (437)
radicle in plants, the embryonic root (411)
radioisotope an isotope with unstable nuclei (35)
radula a rough, tonguelike structure used in feeding by many mollusks (467)
ray a tissue that transports food across the xylem (389)
ray-finned fish a fish with fins supported by bones (545)
reabsorption a process in the kidney by which materials return to the blood from the nephron (701)
receptacle the swollen tip of a branch that is the base of a flower (405)
receptor a nerve cell that receives information from both internal and external stimuli (707)
receptor site the area of a cell membrane where antigen attachment takes place (288)
recessive referring to an allele that is masked by the presence of another allele for the same characteristic (150)
recombinant DNA a DNA segment from at least two different organisms (194)
red tide discoloration of sections of the ocean caused by algal bloom (327)
reflex actions involuntary movements caused by external stimuli (712)
reflex arc the pathway of reflex impulses (712)
reforestation the process of nurturing new growths of trees on sites formerly occupied by forests (821)
refractory period the time following passage of a nerve impulse, during which the neuron cannot be stimulated (716)
regeneration the regrowth of missing parts (443)
regulator gene a gene that controls the production of a genetic repressor molecule (181)
renal circulation a subsystem of systemic circulation that involves the movement of blood through the kidneys (660)
renal pelvis the central structure of the kidney (700)
renal tubule a long tube with permeable walls in a nephron (701)
renewable resource a natural material that can be replenished (821)
replication the process of copying a DNA molecule (115)
repressor a protein that inhibits an operator and thus stops gene expression (182)
reproductive isolation the inability of formerly interbreeding organisms to produce offspring (248)
resolution the power of a microscope to show detail (25)
respiration the processes that release chemical energy from food molecules for use by the cell (93)
respiratory system the system of organs that functions to transport gases to and from the circulatory system (665)
response a reaction to a stimulus (11)
resting state the state in which a neuron is polarized (714)
restriction enzyme a protein that cuts a DNA molecule into distinct pieces (194)

858

reticular formation a network of nerve fibers running through the brain stem and the thalamus (710)
retina the light-sensitive inner layer of the eye (718)
retrovirus a virus that contains RNA and reverse transcriptase (286)
reverse transcriptase an enzyme that makes DNA from RNA (286)
Rh factor a type of antigen found in blood that may cause complications during some pregnancies (664)
rhizoid a rootlike structure attaching a gametophyte to soil, rock, or tree bark (337, 369)
rhizome the underground stem of a fern sporophyte (373)
ribonucleic acid (RNA) a single-stranded nucleic acid distinguished from DNA by containing ribose and uracil (54)
ribose the five-carbon sugar in RNA (118)
ribosomal RNA (rRNA) the type of RNA found in a ribosome (118)
ribosome an organelle that functions in the synthesis of proteins (67)
rickettsia a small Gram-negative moneran (297)
ring canal a channel encircling the mouth of a sea star, part of the water-vascular system (515)
rod a photoreceptor that detects light as gray shades (719)
root the organ that anchors a plant, absorbs water and minerals, and stores food made during photosynthesis (381)
root cap a shield covering the apical meristem (384)
root crop a plant grown for the nutrients it stores in its roots or modified underground stems (394)
root hair an extension of the epidermal cells (384)
royal jelly a high-protein substance secreted by worker bees and fed to the queen and the youngest larvae (503)
rumen the storage chamber in the stomach of artiodactyls (611)

S

salicylic acid the chief ingredient of aspirin, originally obtained from willow tree bark (356)
saliva a mixture of water, mucus, and a digestive enzyme called salivary amylase (695)
saprophyte an organism that feeds on dead organic material (301)
sarcoma a tumor growing in bone or muscle tissue (186)
sarcomere a dark band that runs from side to side down each myofibril (646)
scanning electron microscope an electron microscope that scans the surface of an object with a beam of electrons (26)
scavenger a consumer that eats organisms that have recently died (784)
schistosomiasis a disease caused by a parasitic blood fluke of the genus *Schistosoma* (456)
schizocoely the method of mesoderm formation in protostomes (522)
Schwann cell a cell that forms part of the myelin sheath of nerves (713)
scientific method a procedure that is a logical combination of scientific processes used to solve a problem (23)
scientific name the two-word Latin name of a species, always italicized (268)
scientific sampling a technique in which a small sample can be used to represent an entire population (28)
sclerenchyma the tissue of the ground system that supports and strengthens the plant (381)
scolex the head of a tapeworm (457)
scrotum a pouch of skin that encloses the testes (735)
scutes the scales on the belly of a snake (580)
secondary consumer an organism that eats a primary consumer (783)
secondary growth the tissue produced by lateral meristems of plants (382)
secondary immune response the response to a subsequent infection by the same pathogen (677)
secondary mycelium the result when mating strains of homokaryotic septate hyphae fuse (338)
secondary pollutant a chemical that results from some process acting on primary pollutants (825)
secondary succession the sequential replacement of populations in a disrupted habitat (805)
second filial, or F_2, generation the offspring of a self-pollinated F_1 generation (148)
seed a plant embryo enclosed in a protective coat (373)
seed coat the protective structure of a plant seed (411)
segmentation a division of a body into units (524)
selectively permeable membrane a cell membrane that keeps out some molecules but allows others to pass (66, 82)
self-pollination the transfer of pollen from one flower to another flower on the same plant (147, 408)
semen a fluid formed from sperm and various secretions (735)
semicircular canal a structure in the inner ear that helps maintain balance (720)
seminal receptacle a structure that contains sperm until the sperm is released (474)
sense organ an organ that monitors external stimuli (718)
sensory neuron a spinal nerve cell of a dorsal root that carries impulses from receptors to the spinal cord (711)
sepal a modified leaf that protects a young flower (405)
septum a perforated cross wall dividing hyphae into cells; a thick wall that divides the heart lengthwise (336, 655)
seral community the intermediate community that arises through the process of succession (803)
serology the study of blood serums (284)
sessile referring to an organism that attaches firmly to surfaces and does not move (441)
seta one of the external bristles on annelids (471)
sex chromosome a chromosome that determines sex (165)
sex-influenced trait a trait that is influenced by the presence of male or female sex hormones (175)
sex-linked trait a trait that is determined by alleles on the sex chromosome (166)
sexual reproduction the production of offspring from the combination of genetic material (7, 138)
sexual selection the preferential choice of a mate based on the presence of a specific trait (246)
shaft the center of a bird feather (589)
shell gland a gland in female birds that secretes a protective calcium carbonate shell to surround an egg (594)
shell membrane the interior of an egg shell (594)
short-day plant a plant that flowers when exposed to day lengths shorter than the plant's critical length (427)
sickle-cell disease a disease resulting from abnormal hemoglobin (171)
sidestream smoke tobacco smoke flowing from cigarettes or exhaled by a smoker (750)
sieve plate a region at the end of a sieve tube member through which compounds move from cell to cell (381, 515)
sieve tube member the conducting cell of angiosperm phloem (381)
simple leaf a leaf with only one blade (394)
sink the place where a plant stores or uses sugars (389)
sinoatrial node the nerve tissue in the right atrium that regulates the contraction rate of the heart (656)

859

skeletal muscle voluntary muscle, attached to bones by tendons, that moves parts of the body (645)
skeleton the internal framework of the human body (640)
skin gill a hollow tube through which diffusion takes place in sea stars (516)
skull the protective structure for the brain in vertebrates (539)
smooth muscle an involuntary muscle (646)
social behavior the adaptive interactions among members of the same species (627)
sodium–potassium pump an active transport mechanism that moves ions in order to achieve polarization (85, 715)
soft palate a soft area made of folded membranes that separates the mouth cavity from the nasal cavity (695)
sol a colloid in a liquid state (39)
solute a substance dissolved in a solution (38)
solution a mixture in which one or more substances are uniformly dissolved in another substance (38)
solvent the substance in which a solute is dissolved (38)
somatic mutation a mutation that occurs in a body cell (163)
somatic nervous system the part of the peripheral nervous system that controls skeletal muscles (712)
sorus a cluster of sporangia in ferns (403)
source the place where sugars are made in a plant (389)
spawning the egg-laying behavior of some bony fishes (550)
specialization the adaptation of a cell for a particular function (438)
speciation the formation of a new species (247)
species a group of organisms that look alike and are capable of producing fertile offspring in the natural environment (237)
sperm a motile gamete (735)
S phase the second period of interphase (132)
spherical symmetry the arrangement of body parts in the shape of a globe or sphere (437)
spicule a tiny, hard particle shaped like a spike or a star that forms the skeleton of some sponges (442)
spinal cavity the area that surrounds and protects the spinal cord (637)
spinal cord a column of nerve tissue running through the vertebral column (711)
spinal nerve in fish, a nerve connection between the spinal cord and an organ or a muscle (550)
spindle fiber one of the microtubules of protein that develop during the middle period of prophase in mitosis and that aid in chromosome movement (70)
spinneret the structure through which fluid from the silk gland of spiders passes (487)
spiracle an opening that functions in respiration in spiders and grasshoppers (487)
spiral cleavage in protostomes, the division of cells in a spiral arrangement (521)
spirochete a spiral-shaped bacterium (297)
spongin the network of protein fibers making up the simple skeleton of some sponges (442)
spongy bone the lacy network of connective tissue in the center of a bone (641)
spongy parenchyma a type of mesophyll that allows oxygen and carbon dioxide to diffuse into and out of a leaf (395)
spontaneous generation the development of living organisms from nonliving material (205)
sporangiophore an upright hypha in some fungi that produces sporangia (337)
sporangium a spore-bearing sac in plants and algae (330, 368)
spore a resistant reproductive cell of some organisms (366)
sporophyte the diploid generation of land plants that produces spores (330, 368)
springwood secondary xylem with cells that are wide and thin walled (389)
S-shaped curve a growth curve that depicts stable, lag, and exponential phases (823)
stabilizing selection a type of natural selection in which the average form of a trait causes an organism to have an advantage in survival and reproduction (244)
stalk a stem or stemlike structure (338)
stamen the structure in the flower of plants that produces pollen (406)
stem an organ of plants with the primary functions of support, transport, and storage (381)
steroid a lipid in which the molecule is composed of four carbon rings (51, 735)
stigma the tip of a style in plants (406)
stimulant a drug that increases the activity of the central nervous system (749)
stipe the stemlike region of a thallus (324)
stolon the horizontal hypha of some fungi (337)
stomach an organ that prepares food for absorption by both physical and chemical activity (695)
stone canal part of the water-vascular system in sea stars (515)
strain the term used to denote all organisms pure for a specific trait (147)
striation a dark band of skeletal muscle that functions in contraction (645)
strip mining a type of mining in which layers of earth are removed to gain access to minerals (824)
strobilus a conelike structure of sporangia-bearing leaves (372)
stroma in plants, the protein-rich solution that surrounds the grana (96)
structural gene one of three segments of an operon that controls the production of an enzyme (181)
structural variation a difference in morphology (493)
style a stalklike structure of a pistil (406)
substrate the reactant in a chemical reaction (54)
succession the predictable, sequential replacement of populations in an ecosystem (803)
summerwood secondary xylem cells that are small and thick walled and that are produced in hot dry summers (389)
superior vena cava the large vein carrying blood from the upper part of the body (657)
suppressor cell a modified T cell that prevents further antibody production after infection (677)
suspension a mixture in which particles spread through a liquid or gas but settle out over time (38)
sweat gland a skin gland that excretes water (650)
swimmeret an organ in crustaceans that creates water currents and functions in reproduction (484)
symbiosis the relationship between different species living in close association with one another (766)
symmetry an arrangement of body parts around a point or central axis (437)
sympathetic nervous system the part of the autonomic nervous system that controls internal organs during conditions of high stress or increased activity (712)
synapse the space between the axon terminals of one neuron and an organ or the dendrite of another neuron (713)
synapsis the pairing of homologous chromosomes during meiosis (136)
syrinx the vocal organ of birds (593)
systemic circulation the movement of blood between the heart and all parts of the body except the lungs (659)
systole the phase of the heartbeat in which the ventricles contract and force blood into the arteries (657)

860

T

tadpole the swimming larva of toads or frogs (557)
taproot the organ that results when the primary root grows downward and becomes the largest root (383)
tar a mixture of chemicals and particles from tobacco (749)
target cells the specific cells affected by a hormone (727)
target tissue an area that is affected by hormones, triggering a physiological response (421)
tarsus the end of the leglike appendages of some invertebrates having spines, hooks, and pads (498)
taste bud a structure in which chemoreceptors for taste are clustered (721)
taxonomy the science of grouping organisms according to their presumed relationships (267)
T cell a lymphocyte that attacks antigens (676)
tegument the tough covering that protects some invertebrates (454)
telophase the final stage of mitosis (133)
telson a flat triangular section at the posterior tip of the seventh segment of the abdomen in crayfish (487)
temperate referring to a virus that does not cause disease for some time after it enters an organism (283)
temperate rain forest rain forest biome characterized by moderate temperatures and high humidity (773)
tendon a tough, solid band of connective tissue that supports and connects body parts (645)
tentacle an appendage with which an organism captures and paralyzes prey (444)
terracing a method of plowing that carves a series of steps out of hillsides in order to limit erosion by water (822)
territoriality the establishment of an area by one organism that it defends against others of the species (597)
test a compact, rigid endoskeleton that is found in some invertebrates (514)
testcross the crossing of an individual of unknown genotype with a homozygous recessive individual (156)
testes the gamete-producing organs of a male (446, 730)
tetrad the grouping of two homologous chromosomes during meiosis (136)
thalamus the structure that directs incoming sensory impulses to the proper region of the cerebral cortex (709)
thallus the body of an alga (321)
theory the most probable explanation for a large set of data (23)
therapsid the reptile group from which mammals evolved (603)
thermoacidophile an archaebacterium that lives only in hot, acid places (296)
thigmotropism plant growth in response to contact with a solid object (425)
thoracic cavity the upper ventral cavity of the human body, containing the heart, lungs, and esophagus (637)
threatened species those plants and animals that are likely to become endangered in the near future (821)
thylakoids flattened, membranous sacs inside plant chloroplasts; site of light absorption (96)
thymine a nitrogen base, one component of a nucleotide (113)
thyroid gland the endocrine gland that secretes thyroxine (728)
tidal rhythm a period of activity that corresponds to the rise and fall of ocean tides (802)
tissue in most multicellular organisms, a group of similar cells that carry out a common function (75, 381, 638)
tissue culture the growing of living cells in a controlled medium (283)
tolerance a lessening response to a drug as a result of physical addiction (755)
topsoil the uppermost layer of soil (822)
torpor a state of dormancy (556)
torsion the process in gastropods that allows an animal to protect its head when threatened (467)
total lung capacity the amount of gas that the lungs are able to hold (666)
toxin a chemical substance that is harmful to the normal functioning of cells (303, 673)
trachea in insects, one of a network of air tubes; the tube that connects the pharynx to the lungs (487, 667)
tracheid a long, thick wall with tapering ends, forming part of the xylem tissue of plants (381)
transcription the process in which RNA is made from DNA (118)
transduction the process in which a virus carries genetic material from one cell to another (290)
transfer RNA (tRNA) the type of RNA that carries amino acids in the cytoplasm to the ribosomes (118)
translation the process of converting the genetic code in RNA into the amino acid sequence that makes up a protein (121)
translocation a mutation in which a broken piece of chromosome attaches to a nonhomologous chromosome (163)
transmission electron microscope a microscope that transmits a beam of electrons through a thinly sliced specimen (26)
transpiration the evaporation of water through stomata (386)
transpiration–cohesion theory the theory that water may move up a plant because it is a cohesive fluid (391)
trichinosis the disease caused by the round worm genus *Trichinella* (460)
triglyceride a lipid made of three fatty acid molecules and one glycerol molecule (51, 689)
trimester one of three divisions of pregnancy (741)
trisomy a condition resulting from nondisjunction during meiosis (175)
trochophore a type of larva of mollusks and annelids (465)
trophic level a feeding level in an ecosystem (782)
tropical rain forest a biome near the equator with large amounts of rain and sunlight (772)
tropism plant movement toward or away from an environmental stimulus (425)
truncus arteriosus a vessel in a frog's heart that emerges from the conus arteriosus (563)
trypanosomiasis any of the various forms of sleeping sickness (314)
tube cell the cell of a pollen grain (407)
tube foot a small protrusion on an echinoderm arm that functions in movement (511)
tumor an abnormal mass of cells (186)
tundra a biome of low-growing vegetation that forms a continuous belt across North America, Europe, and Asia (768)
turgor pressure water pressure within a cell (83)
tympanic membrane the eardrum (559, 720)
tympanum a sound-sensing membrane in a grasshopper (499)

U

ultrasound a procedure using sound waves to diagnose genetic disorders in a fetus (176)
umbilical cord the cord that connects the placenta and the body of the unborn mammal (742)
ungulate a hoofed mammal (611)
unicellular gametangium a single-celled gamete holder (321)
unicellular organism a living thing composed of one cell (7, 63)
uracil a nitrogen base found in RNA (118)
ureter a narrow tube through which urine flows from the renal pelvis to the urinary bladder (702)

861

urethra the tube through which urine flows from the urinary bladder out of the body (702)
urinary bladder a muscular sac that stores urine (702)
urine a liquid containing wastes that have been removed from the blood (701)
uropod an anterior flipper that propels some crustaceans through water (484)
uterus in flukes, a tube that shelters eggs until they are released; a structure that houses a developing fetus (456, 736)

V

vaccination inoculation with a pathogen to produce immunity to a disease (678)
vacuole a fluid-filled cavity found in plant cells (72)
valve one half of a diatom wall (326)
vane the projection on either side of a bird's feather (589)
vascular bundle a strand of vascular tissue formed near the apical meristem that lies embedded in the cortex (388)
vascular cambium the lateral meristem in a plant that produces additional vascular tissue (382)
vascular cylinder the innermost part of a root, containing xylem and phloem (384)
vascular plant a plant that has xylem and phloem (367)
vascular system the system that includes the xylem and phloem tissues of plants (381)
vascular tissue the tissue that transports water and food from one part of a plant to another (365)
vegetative propagation asexual reproduction in plants (415)
vein a vessel carrying blood to the heart (549, 657)
venation the arrangement of veins in a leaf (394)
ventral the bottom surface of a bilaterally symmetrical organism (437)
ventral cavity the cavity containing the thoracic and abdominal cavities (637)
ventricle the lower chamber or chambers of the heart (549, 655)
venule a small vessel in the network of veins (657)
vernalization the requirement that some seeds or spores be exposed to cold before germination (428)
vertebral column the backbone (537)
vessel element an elongated, water-conducting plant cell wall with slanting ends and holes through which water can pass (381)
vestigial organ a functionless structure that may be homologous to useful structures in other species (223)
villus one of the small projections lining the small intestine (698)
viroid a short, single strand of RNA that causes disease (286)
virulent referring to a disease-causing agent (283)
virus a biological particle composed of genetic material and protein that is not usually considered to be a living organism (283)
visceral mass the interior of an organism, containing the organs of digestion, excretion, and reproduction (466)
vital lung capacity the maximum amount of air a person can inhale or exhale (666)
vitamin a complex organic compound that serves as a cofactor for enzymes (690)
viviparous referring to organisms that carry and nourish the young inside the body before birth (604)
vomerine teeth the teeth in frogs used to hold prey (560)

W

warning coloration in poisonous or bad-tasting organisms, bold bright color patterns that warn predators of possible danger (502)
watershed the area of land that drains into a river (823)
water-vascular system a network of water-filled canals in echinoderms (511)
wax a type of lipid (51)
weed a plant that grows quickly in disturbed areas (415)
wildlife all the organisms indigenous to a natural community (821)
withdrawal a reaction to the lack of a drug (755)
woody plant a perennial plant adapted for growth year after year, such as a tree (382)

X

xylem the vascular tissue in plants that transfers water and minerals from the roots to the leaves (371)

Y

yolk sac in amniote eggs, the membrane that encloses the yolk and supplies the embryo with food (571, 742)

Z

zooplankton unicellular, heterotrophic organisms that drift in water (310)
zoospore a flagellated spore (328)
zygospore the protective structure that results when the wall surrounding a zygote thickens (328)
zygote the cell that results from the fusion of gametes (438)

862

Index

Page references to illustrations are printed in boldface type.

A

863

864

C

865

D

868

H

869

I

J

K

L

870

871

872

P

873

Q

R

874

875

876

T

U

V

877

W

X

Y

Z

878

Credits

Illustrations

Ligature 169, 173, 185, 195, 200, 201, 261 (chart), 303, 421, 423, 424, 427, 429, 459, 489, 755, 757, 823 **Precision Graphics** 6, 18, 21 (b), 34, 48, 50, 51, 52, 53, 54 (b), 83, 93, 94 (t), 94 (b), 96, 98, 99 (t), 102, 129, 131, 137 (t), 138, 146, 147, 149, 152, 164, 168, 171, 175, 197, 199, 207, 208, 209, 210, 212, 219, 222, 228, 239, 240, 241, 243, 245, 249, 251, 253, 259 (chart), 262, 263, 274, 293, 368, 376, 391 (t), 423, 439, 451, 482, 493-494, 493 (t), 497, 498, 500, 503, 504, 505, 509, 525, 539, 541, 543, 545, 546, 548, 555, 560, 561, 562, 563, 564, 565, 566, 573, 574, 585, 587, 588, 591, 592, 596, 605, 619, 681, 687, 689, 697, 727, 737, 779, 782, 783, 786 (b), 787, 789, 797, 798 (b), 800, 803 (graphics), 812, 813, 815, 816, 819 **Nadine B. Sokol** 13, 21 (t), 43, 154, 233, 705, 723 **George V. Kelvin, Science Graphics** 33, 35, 37, 39, 114, 115, 119, 121, 122, 123, 124, 146, 150, 155, 156, 157, 158, 181, 282, 284-285, 288, 289, 290, 676-677, 679 **Douglas Schneider** 22, 24, 236, 270, 331, 358, 363, 391 (b), 440, 456 (sheep), 461, 551, 793, 804-805 **Cecile Duray-Bito** 2, 60, 67 (br), 144, 202, 235, 257, 261 (skulls), 280, 350, 422, 435, 453, 454, 456, 457, 460, 465, 466, 467, 469, 473, 507, 534, 538, 540, 549, 620, 762, 772, 798 (t), 803 (trees) **Sarah Woodward** 220, 224, 364, 401, 402, 403, 405, 406, 407, 409, 410, 411, 412, 414, 416, 419, 437, 438, 441, 443, 445, 446, 447 **Harry Whitver** 22 (arrows), 25, 27, 95, 99 (b), 101, 103, 104, 106, 107, 108, 790 **Joe LeMonnier** 40, 47, 49, 54 (t), 87, 163, 165, 166, 167, 179, 183, 185, 195, 196, 217, 221, 300, 302, 311, 312, 313, 341, 353, 354, 522, 523, 529, 714-715, 767, 771, 774 **Stansbury, Ronsaville, Wood, Inc.** 66, 67 (t), 68, 69 (t & b), 70, 73, 75, 219, 223, 225, 366, 367, 374, 381, 382, 387, 389, 392, 394, 396, 571, 578, 581, 728 (t), 729, 733, 734, 735, 740 **Cynthia Turner Alexander** 80, 81, 84, 85, 88, 132, 133, 134, 135, 136, 137 (b), 237, 471, 589 **Andrew Grivas** 97, 105, 327, 328, 329, 330, 333, 336, 338, 339, 511, 514, 515, 593, 594, 595, 728 (b), 730, 732, 736, 739, 750 **Howard S. Friedman** 259 (figures), 603, 604, 607, 608-609-611, 785, 786 (t), 791 **Scott Thorn Barrows** 316, 694, 695, 696, 698, 700, 701, 702 **Walter Stuart** 479, 484, 485, 487, 655, 656 (b), 657, 668, 671 **Floyd E. Hosmer** 621, 622, 623, 624, 625, 626, 656 (t), 660, 661, 665, 666 **Keith Kasnot** 637, 638, 640, 641, 644, 645, 646-647, 648, 649 **Robert Margulies** 707, 708, 709, 711, 712, 713, 716, 719, 720, 721, 725

Photographs

AA—Animals, Animals; PR—Photo Researchers

Front and back covers Ron Kimball; **i** Raymond A. Mendez, AA; **ii** Henry Ausloos, AA; **iii** Lou Jones, (tl); **2** Carl Roessler, FPG (b); **3** C. Allen Morgan (l); G.C. Kelley (b); **4** Jeff Gnass, West Stock (b); Dan McCoy/Rainbow (t); **5** Bob Gossington, Bruce Coleman; Gerry Ellis, Manhattan Views (l); **7** CNRI Science Library, PR (r); P.A. McTurk, PR (l); **8** Culver Pictures (b); Jeffrey Rotman (t); **9** William Hopkins (b); **10** G. Zysler, Peter Arnold; **11** Gerald Corsi, Tom Stack and Assoc. (r); Kjell Sandved, Bruce Coleman (l); **12** Root Resources, Hillstrom Stock Photography (r); C.B. & D.W. Frith, Bruce Coleman (l); **15** Kevin Schafer, Tom Stack and Assoc. (c); **16** David Scharf (b); Henley and Savage, Click/Chicago (t); **17** Steve Mangold; **18** Richard/Mary Magruder (r); Luiz Claudio Marigo, Peter Arnold (l); **19** Ruth Dixon; **20** David Cavagnaro; **23** Fred Whitehead, AA; **25** Michael Abbey, PR; **26** Jerry Burgess, PR (tl); Lawrence Berkeley Laboratory/Science Photo Library, PR (bl); **28** Sinclair Stammers/Science Photo Library, PR; **29** Dan McCoy, Rainbow; **31** Tony Brain, PR (t); Tony Brain, PR (b); **32** John Shaw, Tom Stack and Assoc. (t); M.I. Walker, PR (b); **34** Culver Pictures; **35** Ulrich's Fossil Gallery/William Ferguson; **36** John Colwell, Grant Heilman; **38** Runk/Schoenberger, Grant Heilman; **39** Biology Media, PR; **41** Gary Milburn, Tom Stack and Assoc. (l); Doug Wilson, The Stock Solution (r); **42** Omikron/Science Source, PR (l); **45** D.R. Specker, Earth Scenes; **46** M.I. Walker, PR; **47** William Hopkins; **50** Fred Whitehead, AA; **52** Arthur Lesk, PR; **55** Runk/Schoenberger, Grant Heilman (tl); Runk/ Schoenberger, Grant Heilman (br); Runk/Schoenberger, Grant Heilman (tr); Runk/Schoenberger, Grant Heilman (bl); **57** D. Kirkland, Image Bank; **58** Bryan Parsley, Tony Stone Worldwide (bl); M & A Doolittle, Rainbow; **59** Jacques Jangoux, Peter Arnold, Inc. (tr); Science VU, Visuals Unlimited (cl); Danny Lehman, Tony Stone Worldwide (br); **60** Michael Abbey, PR; **61** The Incredible Machine/Nat'l. Geo. Soc., Lennart Nilsson (t); Jerome Pickett-Heaps, PR (b); **62** Biophoto Assoc./Science Source, PR (in); The Incredible Machine/Nat'l. Geo. Soc., Lennart Nilsson; **63** Michael Abbey, PR (t); P. Dayanandan, PR (br); Kitty Kohout, Root Resources (bl); **64** Komura/D.W. Fawcett (l); David Scharf (c); PR (r); **65** Lee Simon, PR (b); Ann Smith/Science Source, PR (t); **68** Don Fawcett, PR; **69** Bob Bolendern, PR (b); K.R. Porter, PR (t); **71** Gopal Murti, PR (t); Susan Mullally Clark, Wakeforest University (c); **72** K. Hausmann, Peter Arnold; **74** Biophoto Assoc., PR; **76** Peter Parks, AA; **77** Runk/Schoenberger, Grant Heilman (tl); Runk/Schoenberger, Grant Heilman (tr); **79** P. Manfred, Peter Arnold (l); Walter Dawn (r); **80** Omikron, PR; **82** Lester Bergman & Assoc. (t); Lester Bergman & Assoc. (b); **86** Robert Knauf, PR; **89** William Hopkins; **91** D.W. Fawcett, PR; **92** Jeremy Burgess, PR (inb); Keith Porter, PR (int); Frederick Atwood; **94** Stephen Krasemann, Alaska Photo/Aperture (t); **97** Jeremy Burgess/Sci. Photo Libr, PR; **100** E.R. Degginger; **101** George Gersier, PR; **112** Dan McCoy, Rainbow (b); Tom Rooker, Rainbow (t); **116** Science Source, PR; **117** UPI/Bettmann Newsphotos; **118** Omikron, PR; **120** Michael Abbey, PR (t); Jeffrey Rotman (b); **125** Dan McCoy, Rainbow; **128** CNRI/Science Photo Library, PR (t); Dan McCoy, Rainbow (b); **130** Biophoto Assoc., PR (l); **133** Lester Bergman & Assoc. (l); Lester Bergman & Assoc. (c); Lester Bergman & Assoc. (c); Lester Bergman & Assoc. (r); **134** Biophoto Assoc./Science Source, PR; **135** D. Fawcett, PR; **139** Runk/Schoenberger, Grant Heilman (l); Runk/Schoenberger, Grant Heilman (c); Runk/Schoenberger, Grant Heilman (r); **141** M.I. Walker, PR; **142** Dan McCoy, Rainbow (cl); Tony Stone Worldwide (bl); **143** Hank Morgan, Rainbow (tr); Catherine Twomey, Anatomy Works (bl); **144** David Cavagnaro; **145** Biophoto Assoc./Science Source, PR; **146** Fiona Sunquist, Tom Stack and Assoc.; **150** Biophoto Assoc./Science Source, PR; **151** Dan McCoy, Rainbow; **153** Karl Maslowski, PR (l); Karl Maslowski, PR (r); **159** Runk/Schoenberger, Grant Heilman; **162** The Incredible Machine/Nat'l Geo. Soc., Lennart Nilsson, (t); R. Knanft, PR (b); **172** R. Roseman, Custom Medical Stock Photo (t); Dan McCoy, Rainbow (b); **174** L. Rhodes, Click/Chicago (c); L. Rhodes, Click/Chicago (r); **176** Diana Rasche; **177** William Hopkins; **180** Louis Quitt, PR (t); John Gerlack, Tom Stack and Assoc. (b); **182** Don Fawcett, PR; **183** Gerald Corsi, Tom Stack and Assoc. (r); Robert Simpson, Tom Stack and Assoc. (l); E.R. Degginger (in); David Dennis, Tom Stack and Assoc. (int); **184** D.C. Lowe, Medichrome; **187** E.R. Degginger; **189** David Scharf (t); David Scharf (b); **190** Gopal Murti, PR (t); Grant Heilman (b); **191** Runk/ Schoenberger, Grant Heilman (l); Luther Burbank Home & Gardens (r); Grant Heilman (c); **192** B. Ullman, Taurus Photos; **193** William Ferguson; **194** Glen H. Doran, Windover Archaeological Research Project (bl); **200** R. Langridge, Dan McCoy, Rainbow (bl); **201** Ansell Horn, Phototake. NYC (tc); **200, 201** Rivera Collection, Superstock (bc); **202** Ulrich's Fossil Gallery/William Ferguson; **203** Edward Ross (t); Edward Ross (b); **206** Photofile (t); California Institute Tech., Palomar Observatory (b); **211** Michael Abbey, PR (t); S.M. Awramik, University of California, Santa Barbara (b); **213** D.W. Deamer; **214** Lee Simon, PR (b); Omikron, PR (t); **215** Omikron, PR (r); Biophoto, PR (l); **216** Richard Kokar, AA (b); Rod Planck, Tom Stack and Assoc. (t); **218** Tui DeRoy, Bruce Coleman; Julia Cameron, The Bettmann Archive (t); **223** Hans Pfletschinger, Peter Arnold (t); Christy Volpe, Marilyn Gartman (b); **226** T. Pritchett, Mary Evans Picture Library; **228** Heather Angel, Biofotos; **230** Mark Kelley, Alaska Photo/Aperture (b); Breck Kent (t); **231** C. Allan Morgan, Peter Arnold (r); Kevin Schafer, Peter Arnold (l); **232** Mickey Gibson, AA (l); Patti Murray, AA (r); **233** Schlowsky Photography; **236** Charles Mauzy, Alaska Photo/Aperture; **238** William Hopkins; **242** D. & J. Heaton, Click/Chicago (t); D. & J. Heaton, Click/Chicago (b); **243** Tui DeRoy, Bruce Coleman; **244** E.R. Degginger; **246** John Chellman, AA; **247** Peter Sanchez, Death Valley National Monument (int); Peter Rowlands, Death Valley National Monument (inb); Peter Rowlands/Bessken, Death Valley National Monument (b); Tim Coonan, Death Valley National Monument (t); **248** Zig Leszczynski, AA (b); Zig Leszczynski, AA (t); **250** Stephen Krasemann, Alaska Photo/Aperture (l); Tim Clark (r); **254** Enrico Ferorelli, DOT (b); C. Allan Morgan (t); **255** Michael Diek, AA; **256** Nancy Adams, Tom Stack and Assoc. (b); Co Rentmeester, Image Bank (t); **258** Steve Ward, Anthro-Photo File; **259** John Reader; **260** Alan Walker, National Museum of Kenya (b); E.R. Degginger (t); **265** John Chellman, AA; **266** Patti Murray, AA (c); E.R. Degginger, AA (r); Sea Studios, Peter Arnold(t); Roger Archibald, AA (l); **267** Zig Leszczynski, AA; **268** Dee Wilder; **269** Johnny Johnson, Alaska Photo/Aperture (b); J. & M. Ibbotson, Alaska Photo/Aperture(t); **271** Science Photo Library, PR; **272** John Edmond/M.I.T./Courtesy Woods Hole Oceanographic Institute; **273** Corale Brierly, Visuals Unlimited (c); **275** E.R. Degginger; **277** Eric Grave, PR; **278** Tony Stone Worldwide (cl); **279** Ray Nelson, Phototake. NYC (tr); Dan McCoy, Rainbow (cr); T.J. Florian, Rainbow (br); **278, 279** Craig Wells, Tony Stone Worldwide (bc); **280** F.E. Unverhau, AA; **281** CNRI/Science Photo Library, PR; **282** Science Photo Library, PR; **286** T.O. Diener, United States Department of Agriculture (t); Historical Pictures Service (b); **287** Science Photo Library, PR; **288** Science Photo Library, PR; **289** Lee Simon, PR; **291** Larry Lefever, Grant Heilman; Grant Heilman (in); **294** Jeremy Burgess, PR (t); Science Photo Library, PR (b); **295** Tony Brain, PR (l); David Scharf (r); Science Photo Library, PR (c); **296** William Ferguson; **297** Science Photo Library, PR (c); Michael Abbey, PR (b); Science Photo Library, PR (r); Tony Brain, PR (l); **298** T.E. Adams, Click/Chicago (l); Biophoto, PR (c); T.E. Adams, Click/Chicago (r); **299** CNRI/Science Photo Library, Custom Medical Stock; **300** Science Photo Library, PR; **301** USDA, PR; **302** Dudley Foster/Woods Hole Oceanographic Institute (t); Rod Catanach/Woods Hole Oceanographic Institute (b); **305** Eric Grave, Phototake. NYC; **307** Manfred Kage, Peter Arnold; **308** Michael Abbey, PR (r); Manfred Kage, Peter Arnold (l); **309** Michael Abbey, PR; **310** E. McArdle, Custom Medical Stock Photo (r); Center for Disease Control (c); E.R. Degginger (t); E.R. Degginger (l); **314** Tim Sheperd, Oxford Scientific Films; **315** Gary J. James, Biological Photoservice; **317** Eric Grave, Phototake. NYC; **319** Eric Grave, PR; **320** Biophoto Assoc., PR (r); Howard Hall, Tom Stack and Assoc. (l); **321** M.I. Walker, PR; **323** Biophoto Assoc., PR (b); M.I. Walker/Science Source, PR (l); Phil Degginger, E.R. Degginger (r); **324** Tom Stack, Tom Stack and Assoc. (t); Tom Smoyer, Harbor Branch Foundation (b); **325** E.R. Degginger (t); Ralph A. Lewin, Oxford Scientific Films (cl); **326** Biophoto Assoc., PR (l); Biophoto Assoc., PR (r); M.I. Walker, PR (t); **329** Dan McCoy, Rainbow; **334** Ed Reschia, Peter Arnold (t); Michael Fogden, AA (b); **335** C.C. Lockwood, AA; **336** Steve Solum, West Stock; **339** J.L. Lepore, PR; **340** Jeremy Burgess, PR (t); J. Forsdyke, PR (b); **342** G.R. Roberts (b); Biophoto Assoc., PR (t); **343** J.T. Bonner, Princeton University Press; **344** Rod Planck, Tom Stack and Assoc. (t); Kim Taylor, Bruce Coleman (b); Biophoto Assoc., PR (c); **345** E.R. Degginger; **347** Ray Simons, PR; **348** Custom Medical Stock (tr); Jon Feingersh, Tom Stack and Assoc. (bc); **349** Robert Llewellyn, Superstock (tr); Robert E. Daemmrich, Tony Stone Worldwide (bl); **350** David Muench; **351** Kerry Givens, Tom Stack and Assoc. (t), Chuck Place (b); **352** Dan McCoy, Rainbow (t); Martin Rogers, Click/Chicago (b); **354** Photri, Marilyn Gartman (b); Herta Newton, Click/Chicago (t); **355** Odyssey Productions, Robert Frerck (c); G.R. Roberts (t); **356** Chuck O'Rear, Click/Chicago (b); William Hopkins (t); **357** Earle Luby, Superstock; **359** G.R. Roberts (b); Richard LaVal, AA (l); **360** James Carmichael, Nature Photographics (l); E.R. Degginger (r); Marcia Griffen, AA (c); **361** Schlowsky (tr); **364** Chuck Place; **365** Linda Graham; **366** Harlan Banks; **367** Breck Kent, AA; **369** Fred Bavendam; **370** Heather Angel, Biofotos (l); E.R. Degginger (r); **371** Peter Zika (c); Heather Angel, Biofotos (l); G.R. Roberts (r); **372** Peter Zika (tc); Heather Angel, Biofotos (l); William Ferguson (tr); **373** William Ferguson (b); William Ferguson (t); **374** Michael Fogden, AA; **375** Matt Brown, West Stock; **377** Runk/Schoenberger, Grant Heilman (l); Runk/Schoenberger, Grant Heilman (t); Barry Runk/Grant Heilman (r); Schlowsky (b); **379** Pamela Zilly, Image Bank; **380** Dan McCoy, Rainbow (b); Chuck Place (t); **383** Walter Chandoha (tl); Dan McCoy, Rainbow (b); Brian Parker, Tom Stack and Assoc. (tc); Thomas Hovland, Grant Heilman (tr); **384** Runk/Rannels, Grant Heilman (t); Runk/Schoenberger, Grant Heilman (b); **385** George Whiteley, PR (r); Omikron, PR (t); Manfred Kage, Peter Arnold (l); **387** Walter Chandoha (b); Walter Chandoha (l); Frank Ledermann, Manhattan Views (t); **388** P. Dayanandan, PR (tr); John Shaw, Bruce Coleman (b); E.R. Degginger (tl); **389** Bruce Iverson; **390** Science Photo Library, PR; **393** C. Allan Morgan (c); John Colwell, Grant Heilman (bl); Ruth Dixon (r); **394** Walter

879

Chandoha (t); Runk/Schoenberger, Grant Heilman (b); **395** Runk/Schoenberger, Grant Heilman; **396** Jeremy Burgess, PR; **397** Stephen Downer, Oxford Scientific Films; **399** David Muench; **400** Rod Planck, Tom Stack and Assoc. (t); Edward Ross (b); W. Eberhart, Click/Chicago (c); **403** Heather Angel, Biofotos; **404** W. Geiersperger, Click/Chicago; **405** Raymond Barnes, Click/Chicago (b); Wally Eberhart, Click/Chicago (l); **407** David Phillips, Taurus Photos (c); David Phillips, Taurus Photos (t); **408** Heather Angel, Biofotos; **413** Lois Moulton, Click/Chicago; **415** Kitty Kohout, Root Resources; **417** Barry L. Runk, Grant Heilman (tl); Runk/Schoenberger, Grant Heilman (tr); **420** Kenneth Hayden, Click/Chicago (l); Joe Devenney, Image Bank (t); John Sims, Click/Chicago (c); Willard Clay, Click/Chicago (r); **422** Runk/Schoenberger, Grant Heilman; **425** Terry Domico, AA; **426** Zig Leszczynski, AA (l); Randy Moore, Flora and Fauna Stock Photos (t); **428** Bill Ross, West Light (l); Grant Heilman (r); **431** Phil Degginger, Click/Chicago; **432** Leonard Lee Rue III, PR (cl); Ian Murphy, Tony Stone Worldwide (br); **433** Hank Morgan, Rainbow (tr); Runk/Schoenberger, Grant Heilman (cr); **434** Michael Fogden, AA (r); Lynn Funkhouser (l); **436** Zig Leszczynski, AA (l); Brian Parker, Tom Stack and Assoc. (r); **442** Al Grotell (l); David Hall, Image Bank (r); **444** David Hall, Image Bank (b); Carl Roessler (t); **446** Heather Angel, Biofotos; **448** F. Stuart Westmore, Tom Stack and Assoc.; **449** Oxford Scientific, AA; **452** CNRI/Science Library, PR (b); Sea Studios, Peter Arnold (t); **454** Carl Roessler; **455** T.E. Adams, Click/Chicago; **458** Martin Rogers, Click/Chicago; **459** E.R. Degginger; **463** E.R. Degginger; **464** Robert Holland, Marilyn Gartman (b); Alex Kerstitch (t); **467** Jeff Foott (t); Don Fawcett, PR (b); **468** Mr./Mrs. M.B. Proudfit; **470** Steinhart Aquarium, PR (c); Carl Roessler, AA (t); **472** Jim Stevenson, PR; **473** Michael Markin, Bruce Coleman; **474** Sea Studios, Peter Arnold; **475** Brian Parker, Tom Stack and Assoc.; **477** W. Gregory Brown, AA; **478** W. Curtsinger, PR (l); Jim Shives, Alaska Photos/Aperture (c); Tom McHugh, PR (t); James Carmichael, Nature Photographics (b); **480** Tom McHugh, PR (b); James Rowan, Marilyn Gartman (t); **481** Schlowsky (c); William Hopkins (r); **483** Oxford Scientific, AA (l); Bill Curtsinger, PR (c); J.P. Jackson, PR (r); **486** Tom McHugh, PR (l); George Dodge, Tom Stack and Assoc. (c); Jeremy Burgess, PR (r); **487** Rod Planck, PR; **488** C. Perkins, AA (t); Oxford Scientific, AA (c); **491** K. Preston-Mofham, AA; **492** Donald Specker, Animals, Animals/Earth Scenes (t); William Ferguson (c); **493** Science Photo Library, PR (b); Biophoto Assoc., PR (t); **496** D. Wilder, PR (r); David Scharf, PR (l); **498** Richard LaVal, AA; **499** David Scharf; **501** Charles Palek, AA (t); Patti Murray, AA (b); **502** Rod Planck, Tom Stack and Assoc. (b); Patti Murray, AA (t); **504** Edward Ross; **506** Rudolf Freund, PR; **510** L. Rhodes, AA (t); Carl Roessler (b); **512** Carl Roessler, Tom Stack and Assoc. (t); Jeffrey Rotman (b); **513** Carl Roessler (b); Charles Seaborn, Odyssey Productions (t); G. Schatten, PR (r); G. Schatten, PR (l); **514** Steve Lissau, Rainbow (c); Carl Roessler (r); **516** Thomas Kitchin, Tom Stack and Assoc.; **517** Peter Parks, Oxford Scientific Films; **519** Dave Woodward, Tom Stack and Assoc.; **520** Rod Planck, Tom Stack and Assoc. (r); Jeffrey Rotman (b); Carl Roessler (t); **521** Michael Abbey, PR; **524** Jeff Foott (c); Robert Holland (t); **528** David Scharf; **529** Lynn Stone, AA (b); Jeff Foott (t); Carl Roessler, AA (in); **531** E.R. Degginger; **532** Grant Heilman (tr); Andy Sacks, Tony Stone Worldwide (cl); **533** Michael S. Thompson, Comstock, Inc. (tr); Grant Heilman (bl); **534** C. Place, Image Bank; **535** Art Wolfe, Image Bank; **536** Alex Kerstitch (int); Carl Roessler, FPG (inb); Dave Woodward, Tom Stack and Assoc.; **537** Dave Woodward, Tom Stack and Assoc.; **538** G. Bernard/Oxford Scientific/Animals, Animals/Earth Scenes; **541** Heather Angel, Biofotos; **542** Gretchen Allen, Mote Marine Foundation; **543** Steinhart Aquarium/Tom McHugh, PR (br); **544** Jeffrey Rotman (t); Carl Roessler, Tom Stack and Assoc. (b); **547** Hans Reinhard, Bruce Coleman; **550** Terry Domico, West Stock; **553** Lynn Funkhouser; **554** Joseph Collins, PR (t); Michael Fogden, AA (b); **556** Tom & Pat Leeson, PR; **557** George I. Bernard, Oxford Scientific Films; Zig Leszczynski, AA (t); **558** Michael Fogden, AA (tl); Zig Leszczynski, AA (b); **559** Stephen Dalton, AA; **566** Oxford Scientific, AA; **567** Zig Leszczynski, AA; **569** George Porter, PR; **570** Breck Kent (t); David Dennis, Tom Stack and Assoc. (b); **572** Zig Leszczynski, AA (c); Henry Aysloos, AA (b); Zig Leszczynski, AA (t); **575** E.R. Degginger; **576** Heather Angel, Biofotos; **577** Ann Duncan, Tom Stack and Assoc. (l); Breck Kent (r); **579** C. Allan Morgan (l); J. Robinson, AA (c); Carl Roessler (r); **580** Anthony Bannister, AA; **582** Zig Leszczynski, AA; **583** Runk/Schoenberger, Grant Heilman; **586** David Cavagnaro (c); Robert Perron, Nawrocki Stock Photo (b); R.J. Erwin, DPI (t); **590** William Boehm, West Stock (br); Ralph Hunt Williams, West Stock (c); Nicholas Devore III/Photographers/Aspen (bl); James Carmichael, Image Bank (r); Stan Osolinski, FPG (l); **595** Bo Jarner, Marilyn Gartman (c); Bo Jarner, Marilyn Gartman (r); Bo Jarner, Marilyn Gartman (l); **597** Jeff Foott, Tom Stack and Assoc. (b); Richard Kolar, AA (t); **598** Anthony Mercieca, Root Resources (tl); Terry Murphy, AA (b); Pete/Alice Bengeyfield, The Stock Solution; **599** Stephen Dalton, PR (t), David Cavagnaro (b); **601** G.C. Kelley; **602** Zig Leszczynski, AA (b); Paulo Curto, Image Bank (t); **606** Robert Frerck, Odyssey Productions (t); Hans/Judy Beste, AA; **609** Hans/Judy Beste, AA; **610** Stephen Dalton, AA (t); Bill Byrne (b); **611** Michael Dick, AA (l); Jack Swenson, Tom Stack and Assoc. (r); Art Wolfe, Image Bank (c); **612** Alfred Thomas, AA (t); Jenny Garst, Tom Stack and Assoc. (b); **613** Rick Browne, Stock, Boston; **614** Nicholas Devore, Bruce Coleman (r); K. & K. Ammann, Bruce Coleman (l); **615** Fred Whitehead, AA (r); David Fritts, AA; **617** Gary Milburn, Tom Stack and Assoc.; **618** Tom McHugh, PR; Breck Kent (in); **627** Art Wolfe, Image Bank; **628** Zig Leszczynski, AA (r); Anthony Bannister, AA (l); **629** Bill Frantz, Click/Chicago; **631** Zig Leszczynski, AA; **632** Tony Stone Worldwide (tr); Kevin Beebe, Custom Medical Stock (cl); Jeff Foott, Tom Stack and Assoc. (br); **633** Rodger Jackman, Oxford Scientific Films (tr); Lou Jacobs, Jr., Grant Heilman (bl); **634** Gary Gladstone, Image Bank (r); Michael Radigan, The Stock Market (l); **635** Shostal Assoc. (t); NY Hospital, Peter Arnold (in); **636** Michael Abbey, PR (b); Team Russell, Click/Chicago (t); **642** David Madison (b); Martin Rotker, Taurus Photos (t); **643** The Incredible Machine/Nat'l. Geo. Soc., Lennart Nilsson (t); Art Stein, PR (b); **646** Michael Abbey, PR; **647** Terry Kirk, Tom Stack and Assoc.; **650** Sipa-Press, Focus West; **651** Townsend Dickinson, PR; **653** Ed Reschica, Peter Arnold; **654** The Incredible Machine/Nat'l. Geo. Soc., Lennart Nilsson (t); Tony Brain, PR (b); **657** The Incredible Machine/Nat'l. Geo. Soc., Lennart Nilsson; **658** Schomburg Center for Research in Black Culture, NYPL, Astor, Lenox and Tilden Foundation; **659** Yoav Levy, Phototake. NYC; **662** David Scharf; **663** Manfred Kage, Peter Arnold; **667** Manfred Kage, Peter Arnold; **669** Dan McCoy, Rainbow; **672** NCI/Science Source, PR (t); The Incredible Machine/Nat'l. Geo. Soc., Lennart Nilsson (b); **673** CNRI/Science Photo Library, PR; **678** Jeremy Burgess, PR (c); UPI/Bettmann Newsphotos (b); **680** Luc Montagnier, PR (c); CDC/ Science Source, PR (t); Alfred Pasieka, Taurus Photos; **682** CDC/Science Photo Library, PR; **683** CNRI, Phototake. NYC; **685** A. Liepins, PR; **686** Manfred Kage, Peter Arnold (b); The Incredible Machine/Nat'l. Geo. Soc., Lennart Nilsson (t); **688** William Hopkins; **692** Steven Mark, Needham, Envision; **693** Alfred Pasieka, Peter Arnold Inc.; **696** Ed Reschke, Peter Arnold; **698** Biophoto Assoc./Science Source, PR; **699** Lester Bergman & Assoc.; **701** Biophoto Assoc., PR; **703** William Hopkins; **706** The Incredible Machine/Nat'l. Geo. Soc., Lennart Nilsson (b); The Incredible Machine/Nat'l. Geo. Soc., Lennart Nilsson (l); **710** Philippe Plailly/Science Photo Library, PR; **711** Hank Morgan/Science Source, PR; **713** Science Photo Library, PR; **717** Don Fawcett, PR; **718** Dan McCoy, Rainbow; **719** Ralph Eagle, PR; **722** David Scharf; **726** Ed Lettau, FPG (t); A Child Is Born- Dell Pub. Co., Lennart Nilsson (b); **729** Biophoto Assoc., PR; **738** David Scharf; **740** Hank Morgan, Rainbow; **741** Hank Morgan, Rainbow; **743** The Incredible Machine/Nat'l. Geo. Soc., Lennart Nilsson (tr); A Child Is Born-Dell Pub. Co., Lennart Nilsson (tl), Behold Man-Little Brown & Co., Lennart Nilsson (bl); The Incredible Machine/Nat'l. Geo. Soc., Lennart Nilsson (br); Behold Man-Little Brown & Co., Lennart Nilsson (cl), **745** Runk/Schoenberger, Grant Heilman; **747** A Child Is Born-Dell Pub. Co., Lennart Nilsson; **748** Breck Kent, AA (b); Gary Gladstone, Image Bank(t); **749** Martin Rotker, Taurus Photos (c); Martin Rotker, Taurus Photos (b); **752** F. Skvara, Peter Arnold; **754** CNRI/Science Photo Library, PR; **756** Michel Viard, Peter Arnold (r); W.H. Hodge, Peter Arnold (c), W.H. Hodge, Peter Arnold (l); **760** Hank Morgan, Rainbow (c); Schlowsky (bl); **761** Dan McCoy, Rainbow (cr); Hank Morgan, Rainbow (bl); **762** Keith Murakaml, Tom Stack and Assoc. (t); NASA (b); **764** Jeff Gnass (t); Ed Robinson, Tom Stack and Assoc. (b); **765** Leonard Rue, Click/Chicago; **766** Harold Simon, Tom Stack and Assoc.; **769** Leonard Rue, AA (b); Nancy Simmerman, Click/Chicago (t); **770** John Shelton (t); Jet Propulsion Laboratory (b); **771** E.R. Degginger; **772** K.G. Preston-Mafham, Animals, Animals/Earth Scenes (r); G.C. Kelley, Tom Stack and Assoc. (l); C. Allan Morgan (c); **773** William Ferguson (br); Co Rentmeester, Image Bank (tr); James Carmichael, Nature Photographics (l); **775** Dudley Foster, Woods Hole Oceanographic Institute (t); Art Wolfe, Alaska Photo/Aperture (b); **776** Sheryl McNee, Tom Stack and Assoc.; **777** E.R. Degginger, AA; **780** Gary Ladd (t); R. Armstrong, AA(b); **781** Chuck Place; **782** Ron Austing, PR; **783** Anthony Mercierk, Root Resources; **784** Peter Katsaros, PR (l); Zig Leszczynski, AA (t); **788** United States Department of Agriculture; **790** G.R. Roberts; **792** Kenneth Fink, Bruce Coleman; **795** Mickey Gibson, AA; **796** Anthony Mircieca, Hillstrom Stock Photography (t); D.C. Lowe, Alaska Photo/Aperture (b); **799** John Shaw, Tom Stack and Assoc. (t); Jeffrey Rotman (b); Charles Seaborn, Odyssey Productions (c); **801** Tim Sharp, Earth Images; **802** Art Wolfe, Alaska Photo/Aperture; **806** William Ferguson; **807** E.R. Degginger; **809** Gary Braasch, Alaska Photo/Aperture, **810** Leonard Nadel, After Image; Russ Kinne, COMSTOCK (b); **812** Leonard Nadel, After Image; **814** Richard Laird, FPG; **820** Phil Degginger, E.R. Degginger (t); Earl Roberge, PR (b); **821** F. Gohier, PR; **822** E.R. Degginger, Bruce Coleman, Inc.; **824** William Ferguson (t); Greg Vaughn, Tom Stack and Assoc. (c); **825** NASA; **827** Bohdan Hrynewych, Southern Light; **829** Doug Wechsler, AA; **830** Joe Viesti, Viesti Assoc. (bl); **831** Grant Heilman (tl); Tony Stone Worldwide (tc); Hank Morgan, Rainbow (tr); **830-831** Goddard Space Flight Center, NASA (c); **832** David Scharf (b); Lou Jones (c); David York, Medichrome, The Stock Shop (t); **833** David Austen, Click/Chicago (l); Chip Isenhart, Tom Stack and Assoc. (br); Behold Man-Little Brown & Co., Lennart Nilsson(tr); Herbert Wagner, Phototake (cr).

880